Safety Symbols

These symbols appear in laboratory activities to alert you to possible dangers and to remind you to work carefully.

Safety Goggles Always wear safety goggles to protect your eyes during any activity involving chemicals, flames or heating, or the possibility of flying objects, particles, or substances.

Lab Apron Wear a laboratory apron to protect your skin and clothing from injury.

Breakage Handle breakable materials such as thermometers and glassware with care. Do not touch broken glass.

Heat-Resistant Gloves Use an oven mitt or other hand protection when handling hot materials. Heating plates, hot water, and glassware can cause burns. Never touch hot objects with your bare hands.

Plastic Gloves Wear disposable plastic gloves to protect yourself from contact with chemicals or organisms that could be harmful. Keep your hands away from your face, and dispose of the gloves according to your teacher's instructions at the end of the activity.

Heating Use a clamp or tongs to hold hot objects. Do not touch hot objects with your bare hands.

Sharp Object Scissors, scalpels, pins, and knives are sharp. They can cut or puncture your skin. Always direct sharp edges and points away from yourself and others. Use sharp instruments only as directed.

Electric Shock Avoid the possibility of electric shock. Never use electrical equipment around water or when the equipment or your hands are wet. Be sure cords are untangled and cannot trip anyone. Disconnect equipment when it is not in use.

Corrosive Chemical This symbol indicates the presence of an acid or other corrosive chemical. Avoid getting the chemical on your skin or clothing or in your eyes. Do not inhale the vapors. Wash your hands when you are finished with the activity.

Poison Do not let any poisonous chemical get on your skin, and do not inhale its vapor. Wash your hands when you are finished with the activity.

Physical Safety This activity involves physical activity. Use caution to avoid injuring yourself or others. Follow instructions from your teacher. Alert your teacher if there is any reason that you should not participate in the activity.

Animal Safety Treat live animals with care to avoid injuring the animals or yourself. Working with animal parts or preserved animals may also require caution. Wash your hands when you are finished with the activity.

Plant Safety Handle plants only as your teacher directs. If you are allergic to any plants used in an activity, tell your teacher before the activity begins. Avoid touching poisonous plants and plants with thorns.

Flames Tie back loose hair and clothing, and put on safety goggles before working with fire. Follow instructions from your teacher about lighting and extinguishing flames.

No Flames Flammable materials may be present. Make sure there are no flames, sparks, or exposed sources of heat present.

Fumes Poisonous or unpleasant vapors may be produced. Work in a ventilated area. Avoid inhaling a vapor directly. Test an odor only when directed to do so by your teacher, using a wafting motion to direct the vapor toward your nose.

Disposal Chemicals and other materials used in the activity must be disposed of safely. Follow the instructions from your teacher.

Hand Washing Wash your hands thoroughly when finished with the activity. Use antibacterial soap and warm water. Lather both sides of your hands and between your fingers. Rinse well.

General Safety Awareness You may see this symbol when none of the symbols described earlier applies. In this case, follow the specific instructions provided. You may also see this symbol when you are asked to design your own experiment. Do not start your experiment until your teacher has approved your plan.

NEW YORK

Prentice Hall

Biology

NEW YORK STATE

Kenneth R. Miller, Ph.D.
Professor of Biology
Brown University
Providence, Rhode Island

Joseph Levine, Ph.D.
Science Writer and Producer
Concord, Massachusetts

PEARSON
Prentice Hall
Upper Saddle River, New Jersey
Needham, Massachusetts

Thomas

Prentice Hall Biology

Print Components

New York Student Edition
New York Teacher's Edition
New York Progress Monitoring Assessments
New York Standardized Test Preparation Workbook
New York Teaching and Planning Guide

Laboratory Manual A
Laboratory Manual A, Annotated Teacher's Edition
Laboratory Manual B
Laboratory Manual B, Annotated Teacher's Edition
Teaching Resources
Reading and Study Workbook A
Reading and Study Workbook A, Annotated Teacher's Edition
Adapted Reading and Study Workbook B
Adapted Reading and Study Workbook B, Annotated Teacher's Edition
Chapter Tests: Levels A and B Includes Unit Tests and Final Exams (also available in Spanish)
Computer Test Bank
Biotechnology Manual
Laboratory Assessment With Scoring Guide
Issues and Decision Making
BioDetectives: Investigations in Forensics
Probeware Lab Manual
Teacher's ELL Handbook
Lesson Plans

Technology

Transparencies Plus
Transparencies
Presentation Pro CD-ROM
Biology iText CD-ROM
Biology iText Web Site
BioDetectives Videotapes
Prentice Hall *Biology* Web Site
TeacherExpress™ CD-ROM
Computer Test Bank CD-ROM
Animated Biological Concepts Videotapes (also available in Spanish)
Lab Simulations CD-ROM
Virtual Labs CD-ROM

Credits begin on page 1144, which constitutes an extension of this copyright page.

ISBN 0-13-126051-0
4 5 6 7 8 9 10 09 08 07 06

About the Authors

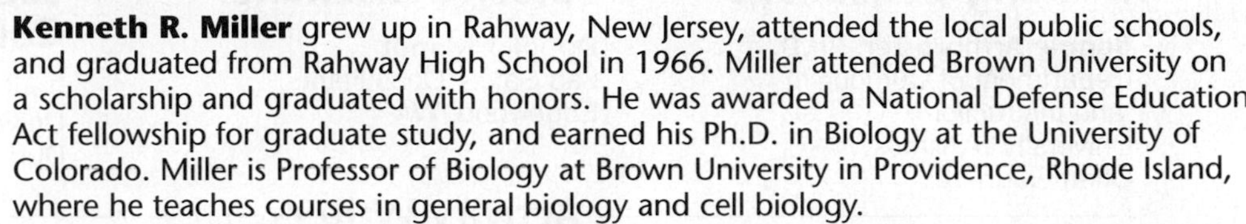

Kenneth R. Miller grew up in Rahway, New Jersey, attended the local public schools, and graduated from Rahway High School in 1966. Miller attended Brown University on a scholarship and graduated with honors. He was awarded a National Defense Education Act fellowship for graduate study, and earned his Ph.D. in Biology at the University of Colorado. Miller is Professor of Biology at Brown University in Providence, Rhode Island, where he teaches courses in general biology and cell biology.

Miller's research specialty is the structure of biological membranes. He has published more than 70 research papers in journals such as *CELL, Nature,* and *Scientific American*. In 1999, he wrote the popular trade book *Finding Darwin's God*.

Miller lives with his wife, Jody, on a small farm in Rehoboth, Massachusetts. He is the father of two daughters, one of whom is a wildlife biologist. He swims competitively in the masters' swimming program and umpires high school and collegiate softball.

Joseph S. Levine was born in Mount Vernon, New York, where he attended public schools. He earned a B.S. in Biology at Tufts University, a master's degree from the Boston University Marine Program, and a Ph.D. at Harvard University. His research has been published in scientific journals ranging from *Science* to *Scientific American*, and in several academic books. He taught introductory biology, marine ecology, and neurobiology for six years at Boston College.

After receiving a Macy Fellowship in Science Broadcast Journalism at WGBH-TV, Levine dedicated himself to improving public understanding of science. His popular scientific writing has appeared in five trade books and in magazines such as *Smithsonian, GEO,* and *Natural History*. He has produced science features for National Public Radio and has designed exhibit programs for state aquarium projects in Texas, New Jersey, and Florida.

Since 1987, Levine has served as scientific advisor at WGBH, where he worked on *NOVA* programs and on projects including the film *Cocos: Island of Sharks* and the series *The Secret of Life*. Most recently, he served as Science Editor for *The Evolution Project*.

Levine and his family live in Concord, Massachusetts, a short distance from Thoreau's Walden Pond.

New York Writers

John Bartsch

Bartsch, a biology teacher for 34 years, has been a consultant to the New York State Education Department for the development of The Living Environment Core Curriculum, and currently works with their Office of State Assessment.

Mary Colvard

Colvard is an award-winning New York high school biology educator and has served on a number of State and National panels. Currently she is a consultant to the New York State Education Department, and served as a member of the writing team for The Living Environment Core Curriculum.

Consultants

Reading Consultant

Bonnie Armbruster, Ph.D.
Department of Curriculum and Instruction
University of Illinois
Champaign, IL

Safety Consultant

Douglas Mandt
Lab Safety Consultant
Edgewood, WA

Lab Activity Consultant

Paul C. Johnson
University of New Hampshire
Durham, NH

Activity Writers

Kathy Laney
Hicksville HS
Hicksville, OH

Neo/SCI
Rochester, NY

Patsye Peebles
Louisiana State University Lab School
Baton Rouge, LA

Herbert L. Saxon, Ed.D.
Ball State University
Muncie, IN

Content Reviewers

J. David Archibald, Ph.D.
Professor of Biology
Curator of Mammals
San Diego State University
San Diego, CA

David M. Armstrong
Professor
Environmental, Population, and Organismic Biology
University of Colorado
Boulder, CO

Katharine Atkinson
Associate Professor of Cell Biology
Department of Cell Biology and Neuroscience
University of California
Riverside, CA

David L. Brautigan
Director, Center for Cell Signaling
Professor, Microbiology and Medicine (Endocrinology)
University of Virginia
Charlottesville, VA

Elizabeth Coolidge-Stolz, MD
Medical Writer
North Reading, MA

Dr. Darleen A. DeMason
Botany and Plant Sciences
University of California, Riverside
Riverside, CA

Elizabeth De Stasio
Raymond H. Herzog
Professor of Science and Associate Professor of Biology
Lawrence University
Appleton, WI

Betsey Dyer
Professor of Biology
Wheaton College
Norton, MA

Milton Fingerman
Professor of Biology
Department of Ecology and Evolutionary Biology
Tulane University
New Orleans, LA

Katherine Glew
Assistant Professor
University of Puget Sound
Tacoma, WA

Deborah L. Gumucio, Ph.D.
Associate Professor
Department of Cell and Developmental Biology
University of Michigan Medical School
Ann Arbor, MI

Paul R. Haberstroh, Ph.D.
Assistant Professor of Chemical Oceanography
Department of Marine Science
University of Hawaii at Hilo
Hilo, HI

Evan B. Hazard, Ph.D.
Professor Emeritus of Biology
Bemidji State University
Bemidji, MN

Donald C. Jackson
Professor of Physiology
Brown University
Providence, RI

Jeremiah N. Jarrett
Assistant Professor
Department of Biological Sciences
Central Connecticut State University
New Britain, CT

Kirk Johnson
Curator of Paleontology
Denver Museum of Nature and Science
Denver, CO

Ted Johnson, Ph.D.
Professor of Biology
St. Olaf College
Northfield, MN

Joe Leverich, Ph.D.
Professor
Biology Department
St. Louis University
St. Louis, MO

Martin K. Nickels, Ph.D.
Professor of Physical Anthropology
Illinois State University
Normal, IL

Gerald P. Sanders, Sr.
Biology Publishing Consultant
Former Biology Instructor at Grossmont College
El Cajon, CA

Ronald L. Sass, Ph.D.
Professor of Biology, Chemistry, and Education
Department of Ecology and Evolutionary Biology
Rice University
Houston, TX

David Scholnick
Assistant Professor
Eckerd College
St. Petersburg, FL

Dr. Dilbagh Singh
Professor of Biology
Blackburn College
Carlinville, IL

Bruce A. Wilcox
Affiliate Faculty
University of Hawaii
Kailua, HI

Alan C. Yen
Research Fellow
Harvard University
Cambridge, MA

Bruce A. Young
Professor of Biology
Department of Biology
Lafayette College
Easton, PA

Edward J. Zalisko
Professor of Biology
Illinois Professor of the Year, 2000
Blackburn College
Carlinville, IL

High School Reviewers and Contributing Writers

Dr. William C. Alexander
So. Carolina Governor's School for Science and Mathematics
Hartsville, SC

Myron E. Blosser
Harrisonburg High School
Harrisonburg, VA

James Boal
Natrona County High School
Casper, WY

Jan Bowersox
Nathan Hale High School
Seattle, WA

LouEllen Parker Brademan
Potomac Senior High School
Dumfries, VA

Heidi Busa
Marcellus High School
Marcellus, NY

Dr. Charles E. Campbell
Burbank High School
Burbank, CA

Robert Campbell
Wilson Classical High School
Long Beach, CA

Beverly Cea
Grimsley High School
Greensboro, NC

Bob Culler
Avon Lake High School
Avon Lake, OH

Don Morris Curry
Silverado High School
Las Vegas, NV

Liz Dann
Phoenix Country Day School
Paradise Valley, AZ

Bob Demmink
East Kentwood High School
Kentwood, MI

Eloise Farmer
Torrington High School
Torrington, CT

Dale Faughn
Caldwell County High School
Princeton, KY

Steve Ferguson
Lee's Summit High School
Lee's Summit, MO

Diedre Galvin
Ridgewood High School
Ridgewood, NJ

Dennis Glasgow
Little Rock School District
Little Rock, AR

Ruth Gleicher
Niles West High School
Skokie, IL

John E. Gonzales
Temescal Canyon High School
Lake Elsinore, CA

Betsy Halpern
South Eugene High School
Eugene, OR

Dick Jordan
Timberline High School
Boise, ID

Marion LaFemina
Ridgewood High School
Ridgewood, NJ

Janice Lagatol
Fort Lee High School
Fort Lee, NJ

Leon Lange
Fort Campbell High School
Fort Campbell, KY

Michael I. Lopatka
Edgewater High School
Orlando, FL

Sue Madden
Chippewa Valley High School
Clinton Township, MI

Lora L. Marschall
Nathan Hale High School
Tulsa, OK

Gregory W. McCurdy
Salem High School
Salem, IN

Lynne M. McElhaney
LeFlore High School
Mobile, AL

Tamsen Knowlton Meyer
Boulder High School
Boulder, CO

Francis K. Mustapha
Snider High School
Fort Wayne, IN

Duane Nichols
Alhambra High School
Alhambra, CA

Joe E. Nunley, Jr.
Riverdale High School
Murfreesboro, TN

Richard K. Orgeron
Carencro High School
Lafayette, LA

Charlotte M. Parnell
Lakeside High School
Hot Springs, AR

Wendy Peterson
Velva High School
Velva, ND

Amelia Quillen
Smyrna High School
Smyrna, DE

Tracy Rader
Fulton Jr. High School
Indianapolis, IN

Debbie Richards
Bryan High School
Bryan, TX

Kathey A. Roberts
Lakeside High School
Hot Springs, AR

Dr. Thomas P. Rooney
Father Judge High School
Philadelphia, PA

Linda S. Samuels
Dana Hall School
Wellesley, MA

Jorge E. Sanchez
Green Valley High School
Henderson, NV

Sheila Smith
Terry High School
Terry, MS

Bob Sprang
Mitchell Public High School
Mitchell, SD

Tracy Swedlund
Medford Area Senior High
Medford, WI

Frank Tworek
Omaha North High School
Omaha, NE

Brenda Waldon
Clayton County Public Schools
Morrow, GA

Adam Weiss
Essex High School
Essex Junction, VT

Audra J. Williams
Sprayberry High School
Marietta, GA

Activity Testers

Diane Clark
Monticello High School
Charlottesville, VA

Lucy M. Fern
Ridgewood High School
Ridgewood, NJ

Laine Gurley, Ph.D.
Rolling Meadows High School
Rolling Meadows, IL

Patricia Anne Johnson
Ridgewood High School
Ridgewood, NJ

Wade Mercer
Fairhill School
Dallas, TX

Dwight Taylor
Goldenview Middle School
Anchorage, AK

Contents

UNIT 3 Cells 166–259

UNIT 4 Genetics 260–365

UNIT 5 Evolution 366–467

UNIT 10 The Human Body 888–1059

Labs and Activities

Inquiry Activity

Opportunities for exploration and inquiry before reading

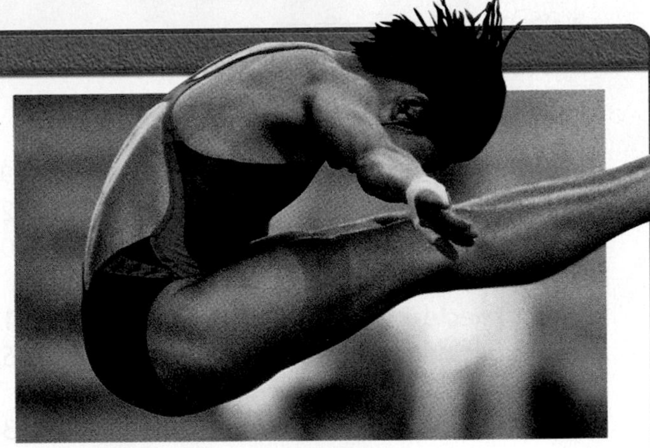

Quick Lab

Activities that reinforce key biological concepts

Real-World Lab

Labs that demonstrate everyday applications of biological concepts

Design an Experiment

Labs that build key science skills

Exploration

Labs that provide in-depth exploration of biological concepts

Analyzing Data

Activities that provide students opportunities to interpret data and draw conclusions

Problem Solving

Activities that build critical-thinking skills

Biology and History

Time lines that place biology in a historical context

Features

Features that relate content to current issues

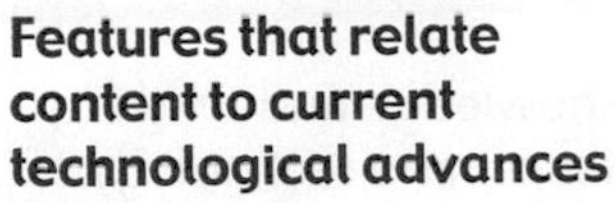

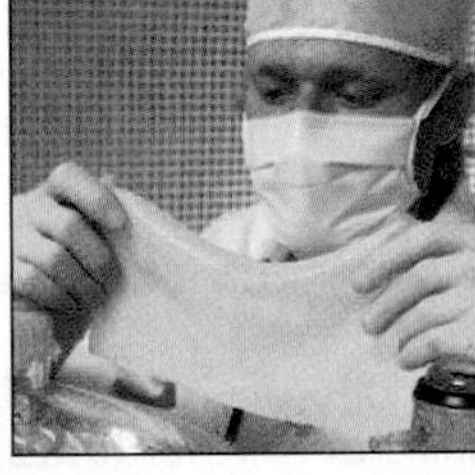

Features that relate content to current technological advances

Go Online *active art*

Careers in Biology

Features that relate biology to actual occupations

New York State Living Environment Core Curriculum

The state of New York has established standards describing science knowledge and skills you will learn this year. At first glance, learning all this information may seem overwhelming. In the following pages, however, we provide examples of how this book will help you gain the knowledge and skills you need to be successful. Listed below are the seven learning standards for mathematics, science, and technology that your curriculum is based on. Standards 2, 6, and 7 address the interconnectedness between biology, math, and other science disciplines. Your book will cover these three standards by teaching how current technologies affect biology, and by providing real-world examples of how biology, math, chemistry, and other disciplines are used. Standards 1 and 4 outline the inquiry skills and biology content that you are expected to learn. You will find a review of these two standards in depth in the following pages.

To check your mastery of your new skills and knowledge, you may use the Preparing for the Living Environment Exam section at the end of each chapter. Also, don't forget to make use of our Take It to the Net feature located at: **www.phschool.com**

Learning Standards for Mathematics, Science, and Technology

STANDARD 1
Students will use mathematical analysis, scientific inquiry, and engineering design, as appropriate, to pose questions, seek answers, and develop solutions.

STANDARD 2
Students will access, generate, process, and transfer information using appropriate technologies.

STANDARD 3
Students will understand mathematics and become mathematically confident by communicating and reasoning mathematically, by applying mathematics in real-world settings, and by solving problems through the integrated study of number systems, geometry, algebra, data analysis, probability, and trigonometry.

STANDARD 4
Students will understand and apply scientific concepts, principles, and theories pertaining to the physical setting and living environment and recognize the historical development of ideas in science.

STANDARD 5
Students will apply technological knowledge and skills to design, construct, use, and evaluate products and systems to satisfy human and environmental needs.

STANDARD 6
Students will understand the relationships and common themes that connect mathematics, science, and technology and apply the themes to these and other areas of learning.

STANDARD 7
Students will apply the knowledge and thinking skills of mathematics, science, and technology to address real-life problems and make informed decisions.

Standard 1, Key Ideas and Performance Indicators

STANDARD 1

Students will use mathematical analysis, scientific inquiry, and engineering designs, as appropriate, to pose questions, seek answers, and develop solutions.

Key Idea 1

The central purpose of scientific inquiry is to develop explanations of natural phenomena in a continuing and creative process.

1.1 Elaborate on basic scientific and personal explanations of natural phenomena, and develop extended visual models and mathematical formulations to represent one's thinking.

Example: You will build a model of the food chain to explain why pesticides accumulate in certain animals. (Chapter 6)

1.2 Hone ideas through reasoning, library research, and discussion with others, including experts.

Example: You will discuss controversial topics challenging biologists today, such as the safety of herbal drugs. (Chapter 25)

1.3 Work toward reconciling competing explanations; clarify points of agreement and disagreement.

Example: You will discover that all scientific explanations are tentative and subject to change or improvement. (Section 15–2)

1.4 Coordinate explanations at different levels of scale, points of focus, and degrees of complexity and specificity, and recognize the need for such alternative representations of the natural world.

Example: You will learn how a theory develops and becomes well accepted. (Section 1–1)

Key Idea 2

Beyond the use of reasoning and consensus, scientific inquiry involves the testing of proposed explanations involving the use of conventional techniques and procedures and usually requiring considerable ingenuity.

2.1 Devise ways of making observations to test proposed explanations.

Example: You will design an experiment to determine the effects of temperature on enzyme activity. (Chapter 2)

2.2 Refine research ideas through library investigations, including electronic information retrieval and reviews of the literature, and through peer feedback obtained from review and discussion.

Example: You will visit the Prentice Hall Web site (www.phschool.com) for extended learning opportunities. (each chapter)

2.3 Develop and present proposals including formal hypotheses to test explanations; i.e., predict what should be observed under specific conditions if the explanation is true.

Example: You will develop a hypothesis on how a lack of light effects photosynthesis. (Chapter 8)

2.4 Carry out a research plan for testing explanations, including selecting and developing techniques, acquiring and building apparatus, and recording observations as necessary.

Example: You will design an experiment to investigate homeostasis in fishes and amphibians. (Chapter 30)

Key Idea 3

The observations made while testing explanations, when analyzed using conventional and invented methods, provide new insights into natural phenomena.

3.1 Use various methods of representing and organizing observations (e.g. diagrams, tables, charts, graphs, equations, matrices) and insightfully interpret the organized data.

Example: You will build a chart that allows you to examine how hydra respond to stimuli. (Chapter 26)

New York State Living Environment Core Curriculum

Standard 1, Key Ideas and Performance Indicators (cont'd.)

3.2 Apply statistical analysis techniques when appropriate to test if chance alone explains the results.

Example: You will study the ban on CFCs and determine whether the ban has helped the environment. (Section 6–4)

3.3 Assess correspondence between the predicted result contained in the hypothesis and actual result, and reach a conclusion as to whether the explanation on which the prediction was based is supported.

Example: You will learn how to test whether a hypothesis is true or false. (Chapter 1)

3.4 Based on the results of the test and through public discussion, revise the explanation and contemplate additional research.

Example: You will learn that claims should be questioned if fact and opinion are intermingled. (Chapter 25)

3.5 Develop a written report for public scrutiny that describes the proposed explanation, including a literature review, the research carried out, its results, and suggestions for further research.

Example: You will write lab reports detailing your discoveries. (Chapter 18)

Standard 4, Key Ideas and Performance Indicators

STANDARD 4: Students will understand and apply scientific concepts, principles, and theories pertaining to the physical setting and living environment and recognize the historical development of ideas in science.

Key Idea 1

Living things are both similar to and different from each other and from nonliving things.

1.1 Explain how diversity of populations within ecosystems relates to the stability of ecosystems.

Example: You will learn that an ecosystem is shaped by weather and climate, as well as by its interacting species. (Section 4–1)

1.2 Describe and explain the structures and functions of the human body at different organizational levels (e.g. systems, tissues, cells, organelles.)

Example 1: You will examine the human body's complex systems in depth. (Chapters 35–40)

Example 2: You will delve into great detail about the reproductive, digestive, circulatory, nervous systems, and more. (Chapters 35–40)

1.3 Explain how a one-celled organism is able to function despite lacking the levels of organization present in more complex organisms.

Example: You will learn how a cell moves material through its membrane by active transport. (Section 7–3)

Key Idea 2

Organisms inherit genetic information in a variety of ways that result in continuity of structure and function between parents and offspring.

2.1 Explain how the structure and replication of genetic material result in offspring that resemble their parents.

Example: You will build a model of cell division to better understand heredity. (Section 11–4)

2.2 Explain how the technology of genetic engineering allows humans to alter genetic makeup of organisms.

Example 1: You will study bacteria cell transformation. (Section 13–3)

Example 2: You will learn how selective breeding is used to obtain desirable traits in certain animals. (Section 13–1)

Standard 4, Key Ideas and Performance Indicators (cont'd.)

Key Idea 3

The observations made while testing explanations, when analyzed using conventional and invented methods, provide new insights into natural phenomena.

3.1 Explain the mechanisms and patterns of evolution.

Example: You will build a model civilization to understand how changes in the environment affect survival. (Section 15–3)

Key Idea 4

The continuity of life is sustained through reproduction and development.

4.1 Explain how organisms, including humans, reproduce their own kind.

Example: You will investigate the human reproductive system. (Section 39–3)

Key Idea 5

Organisms maintain a dynamic equilibrium that sustains life.

5.1 Explain the basic biochemical processes in living organisms and their importance in maintaining dynamic equilibrium.

Example: You will learn how a cell's membrane regulates what enters and leaves the cell. (Section 7–3)

5.2 Explain disease as a failure of homeostasis.

Example: You will learn how the human body's immune system functions. (Chapter 40)

5.3 Relate processes at the system level to the cellular level in order to explain dynamic equilibrium in multicelled organisms.

Example: You will examine how kidneys help maintain a chemical balance inside the human body. (Section 38–3)

Key Idea 6

Plants and animals depend on each other and their physical environment.

6.1 Explain factors that limit growth of individuals and populations.

Example: You will study how human population has changed through the years. (Section 5–3)

6.2 Explain the importance of preserving diversity of species and habitats

Example: You will learn strategies for conservation. (Section 6–3)

6.3 Explain how the living and nonliving environments change over time and respond to disturbances.

Example: You will learn how geology effects evolution. (Section 16–3)

Key Idea 7

Human decisions and activities have had a profound impact on the physical and living environment.

7.1 Describe the range of interrelationships of humans with the living and nonliving environment.

Example: You will conduct an experiment to understand the effects of acid rain. (Section 6–4)

7.2 Explain the impact of technological development and growth in the human population on the living and nonliving environment.

Example: You will learn how antibiotics have affected human health. (Section 19–2)

7.3 Explain how individual choices and societal actions can contribute to improving the environment.

Example: You will learn the importance of renewable resources. (Section 6–2)

UNIT 1

The Nature of Life

Chapters

▶ The ocean floor off the coast of New Guinea is home to many forms of life. Small fish called basslets swim gracefully among the rocks and coral, while yellow feather star crinoids grow out of plate corals.

From the Author

What is science? Most scientists would say, "Science is a way of knowing." This means that science involves a particular way of observing and explaining the natural world. Scientists test and retest their ideas and hypotheses and question one another's results. Why do they do that? Because science emphasizes how the world works, and nothing is taken for granted. It's tough to do, but that's how science works.

What discoveries lie ahead?

- How will individuals, businesses, and governments respond to new information about humanity's complex effects on the living world?
- How will studies of life's smallest systems (molecules) help us understand the largest biological systems (ecosystems and the biosphere)?

Go Online
PHSchool.com

For: Latest discoveries
Visit: PHSchool.com
Web Code: cbe-1000

CHAPTER 1

The Science of Biology

Researchers paired this wood ant and microchip to show their relative sizes. A scanning electron microscope was used to make this image, which has been artificially colored.

Inquiry Activity

Can your procedure be replicated?

Procedure

1. Behind a screen, assemble 10 blocks into an unusual structure. Write directions that others can use to replicate that structure without seeing it.
2. Exchange directions with another team. Replicate the team's structure by using its directions.
3. Compare each replicated and original structure. Identify which parts of the directions were clear and accurate, and which were unclear or misleading.

Think About It

1. **Evaluating and Revising** How could you have written better directions?
2. **Inferring** Why is it important that scientists write procedures that can be replicated?

1–1 What Is Science?

1-S1.1 Historical development of science
1-S1.1 Development of scientific explanations
1-S1.2 Judging reliability/relevance
1-S1.3 Scientific explanations
1-S1.4 Theories supported by many individuals
1-S1.3-S1.5 Experiments

One ancient evening, lost in the mists of time, someone looked into the sky and wondered for the first time: What are those lights? Where did plants and animals come from? How did I come to be? Since then, humans have tried to answer those questions. At first, the answers our ancestors came up with involved tales of magic or legends like the one that accounted for the eye-like markings on the peacock's tail in **Figure 1–1.** Then, slowly, humans began to explore the natural world using a scientific approach.

What Science Is and Is Not

What does it mean to say that an approach to a problem is scientific? **The goal of science is to investigate and understand the natural world, to explain events in the natural world, and to use those explanations to make useful predictions.**

Science has several features that make it different from other human endeavors. First, science deals only with the natural world. Second, scientists collect and organize information in a careful, orderly way, looking for patterns and connections between events. Third, scientists propose explanations that can be tested by examining evidence. In other words, **science** is an organized way of using evidence to learn about the natural world. The word *science* also refers to the body of knowledge that scientists have built up after years of using this process.

Guide for Reading

Key Concept
- What is the goal of science?

Vocabulary
science
observation
data
inference
hypothesis

Reading Strategy: Making Comparisons As you read, list steps that scientists use to solve problems. After you read, compare the methods you use to solve problems with those used by scientists.

◀ **Figure 1–1** Male peacocks have markings on their tails that resemble giant eyes. According to an ancient Greek myth, the peacock's "eyes" once belonged to Argus, a giant with 100 eyes. An angry goddess had Argus killed, but she transferred the giant's eyes to the tail of the peacock.

▲ **Figure 1–2** **The goal of science is to investigate and understand nature.** The first step in this process is making observations. This researcher is observing the behavior of a manatee in Florida.

Thinking Like a Scientist

Suppose a car won't start. Is the car out of gas? A glance at the fuel gauge tests that idea. Perhaps the battery is dead. An auto mechanic can use an instrument to test that idea. To figure out what is wrong with the car, people perform tests and observe the results of the tests.

This familiar activity uses the approach scientists take in research. Scientific thinking usually begins with **observation,** the process of gathering information about events or processes in a careful, orderly way. Observation generally involves using the senses, particularly sight and hearing. The information gathered from observations is called **data.**

There are two main categories of data. Quantitative data are expressed as numbers, obtained by counting or measuring. The researcher in **Figure 1–2,** for example, might note that the manatee "has one scar on its back." Qualitative data are descriptive and involve characteristics that can't usually be counted. The researcher might make the qualitative observations that "the scar appears old" and "the animal seems healthy and alert."

Scientists may use data to make inferences. An **inference** is a logical interpretation based on prior knowledge or experience. The researcher in **Figure 1–3,** for example, is testing water in a reservoir. Because she cannot test *all* the water, she collects water samples from several different parts of the reservoir. If all the samples are clean enough to drink, she may infer that all the water is safe to drink.

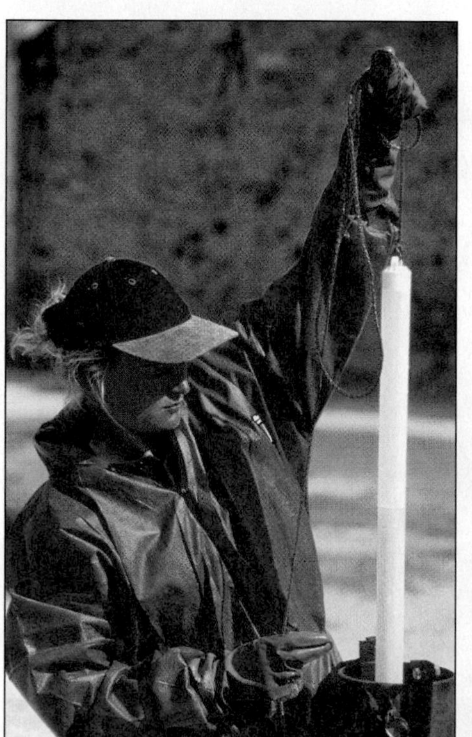

◀ **Figure 1–3** Researchers testing water for lead pollution cannot test every drop, so they check small amounts, called samples. **Inferring** ***How might a local community use such scientific information?***

Explaining and Interpreting Evidence

Scientists try to explain events in the natural world by interpreting evidence logically and analytically. Suppose, for example, that many people contract an unknown disease after attending a public event. Public health researchers will use scientific methods to try to determine how those people became ill.

After initial observations, the researchers will propose one or more hypotheses. A **hypothesis** is a proposed scientific explanation for a set of observations. Scientists generate hypotheses using prior knowledge, or what they already know; logical inference; and informed, creative imagination. For the unknown disease, there might be several competing hypotheses, such as these: (1) The disease was spread from person to person by contact. (2) The disease was spread through insect bites. (3) The disease was spread through air, water, or food.

Scientific hypotheses must be proposed in a way that enables them to be tested. Some hypotheses are tested by performing controlled experiments, as you will learn in the next section. Other hypotheses are tested by gathering more data. In the case of the mystery illness, data would be collected by studying the location of the event; by examining air, water, and food people were exposed to; and by questioning people about their actions before falling ill. Some hypotheses would be ruled out. Others might be supported and eventually confirmed.

Researchers working on complex questions often collaborate in teams like the one in **Figure 1–4.** These groups have regular meetings at which they analyze, review, and critique each other's data and hypotheses. This review process helps ensure that their conclusions are valid. To be valid, a conclusion must be based on logical interpretation of reliable data. To learn about sources of error in scientific investigations, see Appendix A.

How do scientists develop hypotheses?

For: Articles on the nature of science
Visit: PHSchool.com
Web Code: cbe-1011

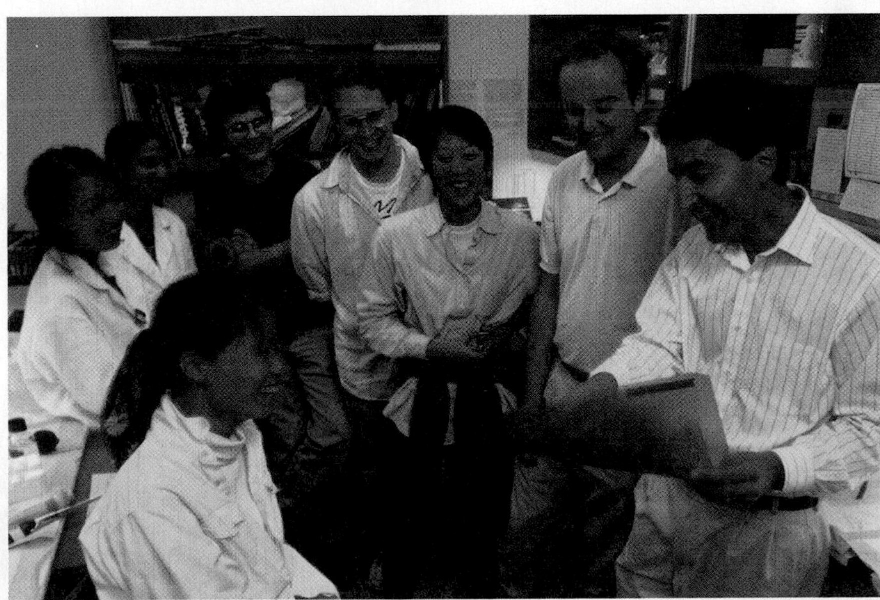

◀ **Figure 1–4** Researchers often collaborate by working in teams, combining imagination and logic to develop and test hypotheses. **Applying Concepts** *How do scientists decide whether to accept or reject a hypothesis?*

Science as a Way of Knowing

This book contains lots of facts, but don't think biological science is a set of truths that never change. Instead, science is a way of knowing. This means that rather than unchanging knowledge, science is an ongoing *process*—a process that involves asking questions, observing, making inferences, and testing hypotheses. You can learn more about these and other science skills in Appendix A.

Because of new tools, techniques, and discoveries, such as the discovery shown in **Figure 1–5,** scientific understanding is always changing. Research can have a profound impact on scientific thought. For example, the discovery of cells revolutionized understanding of the structure of living things. Without doubt, some things you learn from this book will soon be revised because of new information. But this doesn't mean that science has failed. On the contrary, it means that science continues to succeed in advancing understanding.

Good scientists are skeptics, which means that they question both existing ideas and new hypotheses. Scientists continually evaluate the strengths and weaknesses of hypotheses. Scientists must be open-minded and consider new hypotheses if data demand it. And despite the power of science, it has definite limits. For example, science cannot help you decide whether a painting is beautiful or whether school sports teams should be limited to only the best athletes.

The scientific way of knowing includes the view that the whole physical universe is a system, or a collection of parts and processes that interact. In the universe, basic natural laws govern all events and objects, large or small. The physical universe consists of many smaller systems. Biologists focus on living systems, which range from invisibly small to the size of our entire planet.

▼ **Figure 1–5** In 1991, hikers in the Italian Alps discovered a well-preserved corpse that was about 5000 years old. Scientists might have asked how the corpse could be so well preserved, but they already knew the answer. Sub-zero temperatures keep the organisms that cause decomposition from doing their job. **Asking Questions** *What are some other scientific questions that might be asked about this discovery?*

Science and Human Values

Because of new knowledge gained through research, scientists continually revise and re-evaluate their ideas. The importance of science, however, reaches far beyond the scientific world. Today, scientists contribute information to discussions about health and disease, and about the relationship between human beings and the living and nonliving environment.

Make a list of things that you need to understand to protect your life and the lives of others close to you. Chances are that your list will include drugs and alcohol, smoking and lung disease, AIDS, cancer, and heart disease. Other questions focus on public health and the environment. How can we best use antibiotics to make sure that those "wonder drugs" keep working for a long time? How much of the information in your genes should you be able to keep private? Should communities produce electricity using fossil fuels, nuclear power, or hydroelectric dams? How should chemical wastes be disposed of? Who should be responsible for their disposal?

All of these questions involve scientific information. For that reason, an understanding of science and the scientific approach is essential to making intelligent decisions about them. None of these questions, however, can be answered by science alone. They involve the society in which we live and the economy that provides jobs, food, and shelter. They may require us to consider laws and moral principles. In our society, scientists alone do not make final decisions—they make recommendations. Who makes the decisions? We, the citizens of our democracy do—when we vote to express our opinions to elected officials. That is why it is more important than ever that everyone understand what science is, what it can do, and what it cannot do.

▲ **Figure 1–6** Scientific research has an impact on many aspects of our lives. These racers are raising money to help support research directed at preventing and treating cancer. **Applying Concepts** *Identify three ways in which science affects your life.*

1–1 Section Assessment

1. **Key Concept** What does science study?
2. What does it mean to describe a scientist as skeptical? Why is skepticism considered a valuable quality in a scientist?
3. What is the main difference between qualitative and quantitative observations?
4. What is a scientific hypothesis? In what two ways can a hypothesis be tested?
5. Is a scientific hypothesis accepted if there is no way to demonstrate that the hypothesis is wrong? Explain your answer.
6. **Critical Thinking Making Judgments** Suppose a community proposes a law to require the wearing of seatbelts in all moving vehicles. How could scientific research have an impact on the decision?

Thinking Visually

Making a Table
List the five main senses—vision, hearing, smell, taste, and touch—and give an example of an observation that you have made using each sense. Then, add at least one inference that could be made based on each observation.

1–2 How Scientists Work

1-S1.1 Historical development of science
1-S1.1 Development of scientific explanations
1-S1.2 Judging reliability/relevance
1-S1.3 Scientific explanations
1-S1.4 Theories supported by many individuals
1-S1.3-S1.5 Experiments
4-5.2 Biological research helps with diseases

Guide for Reading

Key Concepts
- How do scientists test hypotheses?
- How does a scientific theory develop?

Vocabulary
spontaneous generation
controlled experiment
manipulated variable
responding variable
theory

Reading Strategy: Outlining As you read, make an outline of the main steps in a controlled experiment.

▼ **Figure 1–7** About 2000 years ago, a Roman poet wrote these directions for producing bees. **Inferring** *Why do you think reasonable individuals once accepted the ideas behind this recipe?*

Recipe for Bees

1. Kill a bull during the first thaw of winter.
2. Build a shed.
3. Place the dead bull on branches and herbs inside the shed.
4. Wait for summer. The decaying body of the bull will produce bees.

Have you ever noticed what happens to food that is left in an open trash can for a few days in summer? Creatures that look like worms appear on the discarded food. These creatures are called maggots. For thousands of years people have been observing maggots on food that is not protected. The maggots seem to suddenly appear out of nowhere. Where do they come from?

Designing an Experiment

People's ideas about where some living things come from have changed over the centuries. Exploring this change can help show how science works. Remember that what might seem obvious today was not so obvious thousands of years ago.

About 2300 years ago, the Greek philosopher Aristotle made extensive observations of the natural world. He tried to explain his observations through reasoning. During and after his lifetime, people thought that living things followed a set of natural rules that were different from those for nonliving things. They also thought that special "vital" forces brought some living things into being from nonliving material. These ideas, exemplified by the directions in **Figure 1–7,** persisted for many centuries. About 400 years ago, some people began to challenge these established ideas. They also began to use experiments to answer their questions about life.

Asking a Question For many years, observations seemed to indicate that some living things could just suddenly appear: Maggots showed up on meat; mice were found on grain; and beetles turned up on cow dung. People wondered how these events happened. They were, in their own everyday way, identifying a problem to be solved by asking a question: How do new living things, or organisms, come into being?

Forming a Hypothesis For centuries, people accepted the prevailing explanation for the sudden appearance of some organisms, that some life somehow "arose" from nonliving matter. The maggots arose from the meat, the mice from the grain, and the beetles from the dung. Scholars of the day even gave a name to the idea that life could arise from nonliving matter—**spontaneous generation.** In today's terms, the idea of spontaneous generation can be considered a hypothesis.

In 1668, Francesco Redi, an Italian physician, proposed a different hypothesis for the appearance of maggots. Redi had observed that these organisms appeared on meat a few days after flies were present. He considered it likely that the flies laid eggs too small for people to see. Thus, Redi was proposing a new hypothesis—flies produce maggots. Redi's next step was to test his hypothesis.

Setting Up a Controlled Experiment In science, testing a hypothesis often involves designing an experiment. The factors in an experiment that can change are called variables. Examples of variables include equipment used, type of material, amount of material, temperature, light, and time.

Suppose you want to know whether an increase in water, light, or fertilizer can speed up plant growth. If you change all three variables at once, you will not be able to tell which variable is responsible for the observed results. **Whenever possible, a hypothesis should be tested by an experiment in which only one variable is changed at a time. All other variables should be kept unchanged, or controlled.** This type of experiment is called a **controlled experiment.** The variable that is deliberately changed is called the **manipulated variable.** The variable that is observed and that changes in response to the manipulated variable is called the **responding variable.**

Based on his hypothesis, Redi made a prediction that keeping flies away from meat would prevent the appearance of maggots. To test this hypothesis, he planned the experiment shown in **Figure 1–8.** Notice that Redi controlled all variables except one—whether or not there was gauze over each jar. The gauze was important because it kept flies off the meat.

 *What was the responding variable in Redi's experiment?*

For: Redi's Experiment activity
Visit: PHSchool.com
Web Code: cbp-1012

▼ **Figure 1–8** **In a controlled experiment, only one variable is tested at a time.** Redi designed an experiment to determine what caused the sudden appearance of maggots. In his experiment, the manipulated variable was the presence or absence of the gauze covering. The results of this experiment helped disprove the hypothesis of spontaneous generation.

Redi's Experiment on Spontaneous Generation

OBSERVATIONS: Flies land on meat that is left uncovered. Later, maggots appear on the meat.

HYPOTHESIS: Flies produce maggots.

PROCEDURE

Controlled Variables: jars, type of meat, location, temperature, time

Manipulated Variable: gauze covering that keeps flies away from meat

Responding Variable: whether maggots appear

Uncovered jars

Maggots appear.

Several days pass.

Covered jars

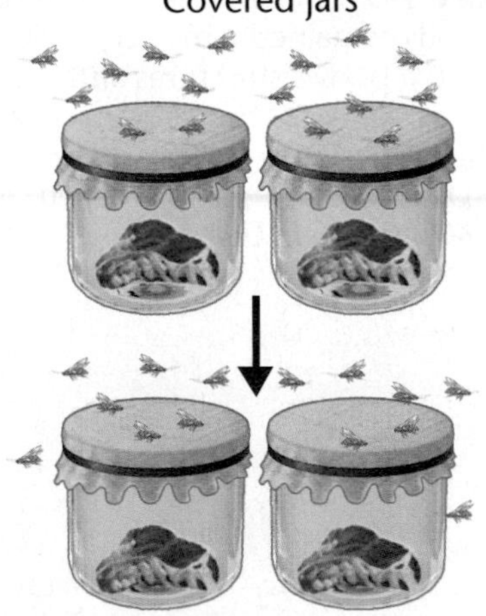

No maggots appear.

CONCLUSION: Maggots form only when flies come in contact with meat. Spontaneous generation of maggots did not occur.

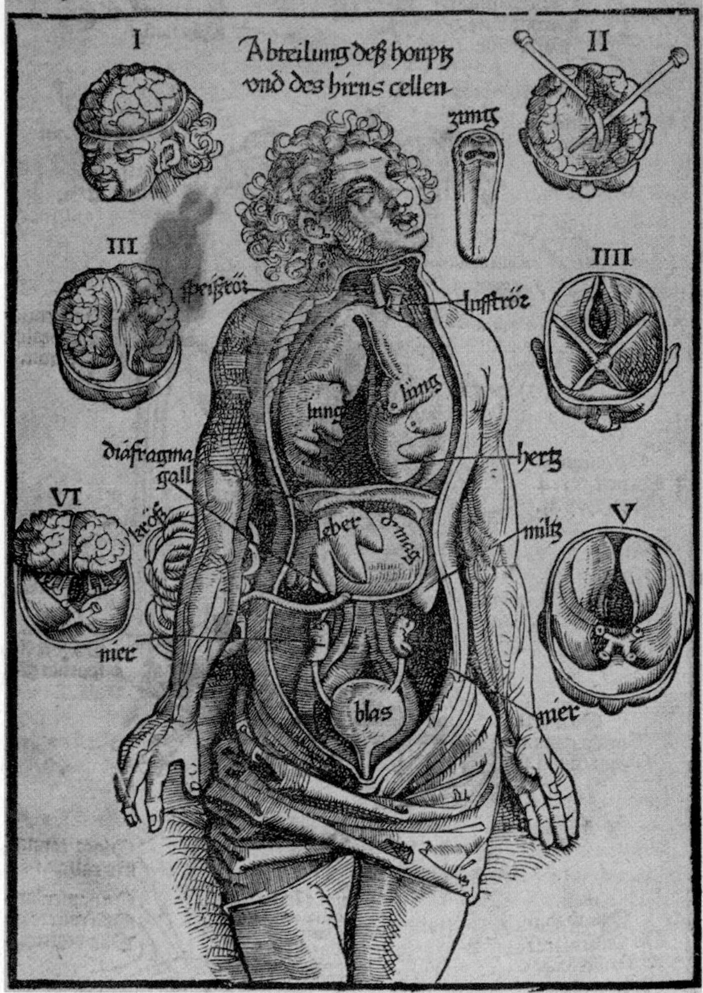

▲ **Figure 1–9** For centuries, the workings of the human body remained a mystery. Gradually, scientists observed the body's structures and recorded their work in drawings like this. This diagram dates back to fifteenth-century Austria. **Comparing and Contrasting** *How does this drawing compare with the modern illustrations in Unit 10?*

Recording and Analyzing Results Scientists usually keep written records of their observations, or data. In the past, data were usually recorded by hand, often in notebooks or personal journals. Sometimes, drawings such as **Figure 1–9** recorded certain kinds of observations more completely and accurately than a verbal description could. Today, researchers may record their work on computers. Online storage often makes it easier for researchers to review the data at any time and, if necessary, offer a new explanation for the data. Scientists know that Redi recorded his data because copies of his work were available to later generations of scientists. His investigation showed that maggots appeared on the meat in the control jars. No maggots appeared in the jars covered with gauze.

Drawing a Conclusion Scientists use the data from an experiment to evaluate the hypothesis and draw a valid conclusion. That is, they use the evidence to determine whether the hypothesis was supported or refuted. Redi's results supported his hypothesis. He therefore concluded that the maggots were indeed produced by flies.

As scientists look for explanations for specific observations, they assume that the patterns in nature are consistent. Thus, Redi's results could be viewed not only as an explanation about maggots and flies but also as a refutation of the hypothesis of spontaneous generation.

CHECKPOINT *What did Redi conclude?*

Repeating Investigations

A key assumption in science is that experimental results can be reproduced because nature behaves in a consistent manner. When one particular variable is manipulated in a given set of variables, the result should always be the same. In keeping with this assumption, scientists expect to test one another's investigations. Thus, communicating a description of an experiment is an essential part of science. Today's researchers often publish a report of their work in a scientific journal. Other scientists review the experimental procedures to make sure that the design was without flaws. They often repeat experiments to be sure that the results match those already obtained. In Redi's day, scientific journals were not common, but he communicated his conclusion in a book that included a description of his investigation and its results.

Needham's Test of Redi's Findings Some later tests of Redi's work were influenced by an unexpected discovery. About the time Redi was carrying out his experiment, Anton van Leeuwenhoek (LAY-vun-hook) of the Netherlands discovered a world of tiny moving objects in rainwater, pond water, and dust. Inferring that these objects were alive, he called them "animalcules," or tiny animals. He made drawings of his observations and shared them with other scientists. For the next 200 years or so, scientists could not agree on whether the animalcules were alive or how they came to exist.

In the mid-1700s, John Needham, an English scientist, used an experiment involving animalcules to attack Redi's work. Needham claimed that spontaneous generation could occur under the right conditions. To prove his claim, he sealed a bottle of gravy and heated it. He claimed that the heat had killed any living things that might be in the gravy. After several days, he examined the contents of the bottle and found it swarming with activity. "These little animals," he inferred, "can only have come from juice of the gravy."

Spallanzani's Test of Redi's Findings
An Italian scholar, Lazzaro Spallanzani, read about Redi's and Needham's work. Spallanzani thought that Needham had not heated his samples enough and decided to improve upon Needham's experiment. **Figure 1–10** shows that Spallanzani boiled two containers of gravy, assuming that the boiling would kill any tiny living things, or microorganisms, that were present. He sealed one jar immediately and left the other jar open. After a few days, the gravy in the open jar was teeming with microorganisms. The sealed jar remained free of microorganisms.

Spallanzani concluded that nonliving gravy did not produce living things. The microorganisms in the unsealed jar were offspring of microorganisms that had entered the jar through the air. This experiment and Redi's work supported the hypothesis that new organisms are produced only by existing organisms.

CHECKPOINT *How did Spallanzani's investigative procedures improve upon Needham's work?*

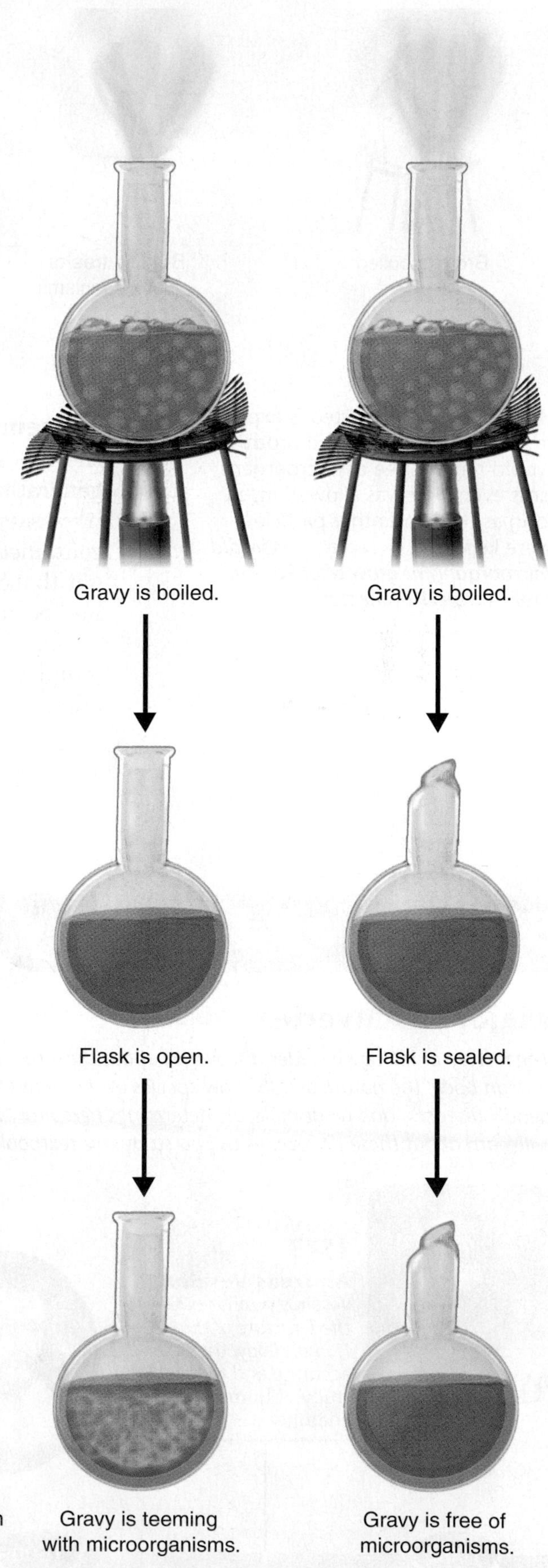
Gravy is boiled.
Gravy is boiled.
Flask is open.
Flask is sealed.
Gravy is teeming with microorganisms.
Gravy is free of microorganisms.

▶ **Figure 1–10** Spallanzani's experiment showed that microorganisms will not grow in boiled gravy that has been sealed but will grow in boiled gravy that is left open to the air. **Interpreting Graphics** *What variable was controlled in this experiment?*

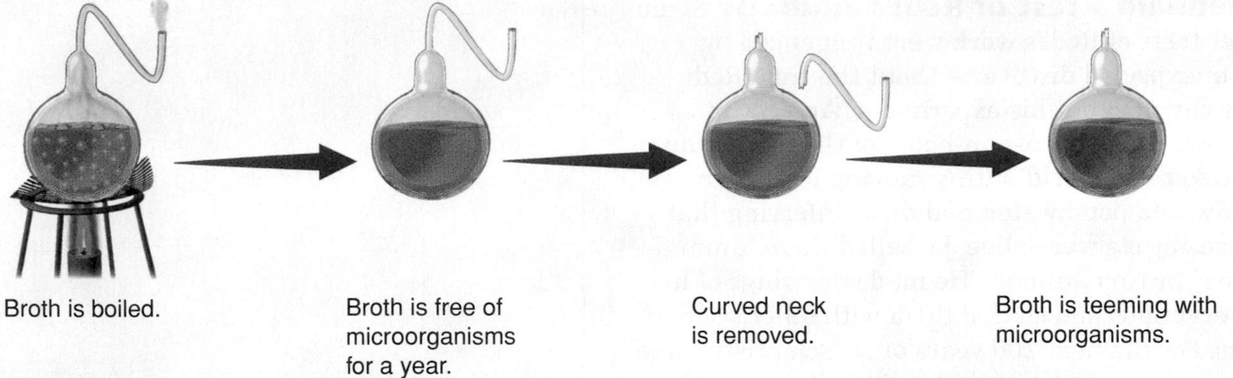
Broth is boiled.
Broth is free of microorganisms for a year.
Curved neck is removed.
Broth is teeming with microorganisms.

▲ **Figure 1–11** Pasteur's experiment showed that boiled broth would remain free of microorganisms even if air was allowed in, as long as dust and other particles were kept out. **Inferring** *Why did microorganisms grow after Pasteur broke the neck of the flask?*

Pasteur's Test of Spontaneous Generation Well into the 1800s, some scientists continued to support the spontaneous generation hypothesis. Some of them argued that air was a necessary factor in the process of generating life because air contained the "life force" needed to produce new life. They pointed out that Spallanzani's experiment was not a fair test because air had been excluded from the sealed jar.

In 1864, an ingenious French scientist, Louis Pasteur, found a way to settle the argument. He designed a flask that had a long curved neck, as shown in **Figure 1–11.** The flask remained

Biology and History

Major Discoveries

The history of biology includes discoveries about the structure of the human body, the nature of cells, how species evolve, ways to fight deadly diseases, and what molecule determines hereditary traits. You will learn about these discoveries as you study this textbook.

1543
Andreas Vesalius
Vesalius publishes *On the Structure of the Human Body,* the first accurate and detailed study of human anatomy.

1628
William Harvey
Harvey is the first scholar to describe the circulation of blood. He shows how blood pumped through blood vessels returns to the heart and is recirculated.

1673
Anton van Leeuwenhoek
Van Leeuwenhoek perfects the simple microscope and observes cells and microorganisms.

1500 1600 1700

open to the air, but microorganisms from the air did not make their way through the neck into the flask. Pasteur showed that as long as the broth was protected from microorganisms, it remained free of living things. About a year after the experiment began, Pasteur broke the neck of the flask, and the broth quickly became filled with microorganisms. His work convinced other scientists that the hypothesis of spontaneous generation was not correct. In other words, Pasteur showed that all living things come from other living things. This change in thinking represented a major shift in the way scientists viewed living things.

CHECKPOINT *What improvement did Pasteur make to Redi's experiment?*

The Impact of Pasteur's Work During his lifetime, Pasteur made many discoveries related to microorganisms. His research had an impact on society as well as on scientific thought. He saved the French wine industry, which was troubled by unexplained souring of wine, and the silk industry, which was endangered by a silkworm disease. Moreover, he began to uncover the very nature of infectious diseases, showing that they were the result of microorganisms entering the bodies of the victims. Pasteur is considered one of biology's most remarkable problem solvers.

Writing in Science

Find out more about one of these discoveries. Research the person or people who made the discovery and how they did it. Write a one-page report describing the contribution of the scientists.

1859
Charles Darwin
Darwin publishes *On the Origin of Species,* stating that all forms of life have evolved into their present state over the course of millions of years.

1881
Louis Pasteur
Pasteur develops the first vaccine against anthrax, a deadly bacterial disease.

1953
James Watson and Francis Crick
Watson and Crick determine the structure of DNA.

1800 1900 2000

▲ **Figure 1–12** In animal field studies, such as the observation of wild elephants, scientists usually try to work without making the animals aware that humans are present. **Comparing and Contrasting** *How do animal field studies differ from controlled experiments?*

When Experiments Are Not Possible

It is not always possible to do an experiment to test a hypothesis. For example, to learn how animals in the wild interact with others in their group, researchers carry out field studies. It is necessary to observe the animals without disturbing them, as shown in **Figure 1–12.** Ethical considerations prevent certain experiments, such as determining the effect on people of a chemical suspected of causing cancer. In such cases, medical researchers may choose volunteers who have already been exposed to the chemical. For comparison, they would study a group of people who have not been exposed to the chemical.

When researchers design such alternative investigations, they try to maintain the rigorous thinking associated with a controlled experiment. They often study large groups of subjects so that small differences do not produce misleading results. They try to identify as many relevant variables as possible so that most variables are controlled. For example, in a study of a cancer-causing chemical, they might exclude volunteers who have other serious health problems. By exerting great care in planning these kinds of investigations, scientists can discover reliable patterns that add to scientific knowledge.

Why are controlled experiments sometimes impossible?

How a Theory Develops

As evidence from numerous investigations builds up, a particular hypothesis may become so well supported that scientists consider it a **theory.** That is what happened with the hypothesis that new organisms come from existing organisms. This idea is now considered one of the major ideas in science. It is called biogenesis, meaning "generating from life."

You may have heard the word *theory* used in everyday conversations as people discuss ideas. Someone might say, "Oh, that's just a theory," to criticize an idea that is not supported by evidence. **In science, the word *theory* applies to a well-tested explanation that unifies a broad range of observations.** A theory enables scientists to make accurate predictions about new situations.

For: Links on experimenting
Visit: www.SciLinks.org
Web Code: cbn-1012

Figure 1–13 **A theory is a well-tested explanation that unifies a broad range of observations.** The theories of plate tectonics and evolution help explain why marsupials such as the koala (top) and kangaroo (below) can be found only in Australia and some nearby islands.

Sometimes, more than one theory is needed to explain a particular circumstance. For example, why are the marsupial mammals in **Figure 1–13** found only in Australia and some nearby islands? An answer lies with the theories of plate tectonics and evolution. Millions of years ago, when marsupials were evolving, Australia, Antarctica, and South America were joined as a single landmass. That landmass began to break apart, and Australia became a separate continent. Its marsupials were thus separated from other kinds of mammals, and they evolved as a unique group. You will study the theory of evolution in Unit 5.

A useful theory may become the dominant view among the majority of scientists, but no theory is considered absolute truth. Scientists analyze, review, and critique the strengths and weaknesses of theories. As new evidence is uncovered, a theory may be revised or replaced by a more useful explanation. Sometimes, scientists resist a new way of looking at nature, but over time new evidence determines which ideas survive and which are replaced. Thus, science is characterized by both continuity and change.

1–2 Section Assessment

1. **Key Concept** Why is Redi's experiment on spontaneous generation considered a controlled experiment?
2. **Key Concept** How does a scientific theory compare with a scientific hypothesis?
3. How do scientists today usually communicate their results and conclusions?
4. How did the design of Pasteur's flask help him successfully refute the hypothesis of spontaneous generation?
5. **Critical Thinking Making Judgments** Evaluate the impact of Pasteur's research on both scientific thought and society. What was the effect of Pasteur's investigations on scientists' ideas and people's lives?

Writing in Science

Critique a Hypothesis
Write a paragraph in which you analyze, review, and critique the spontaneous generation hypothesis. *Hint:* In preparation, ask yourself questions such as these: What observations did the hypothesis account for? Why did it seem logical at that time? What evidence was overlooked or ignored?

1–3 Studying Life

1-S1.1 Values and application of knowledge
4-1.1 Ecosystems and population interactions
4-1.2 Human systems and homeostasis
4-2.1 Heredity and sexual and asexual reproduction
4-3.1 Evolution from earlier species
4-5.1 Photosynthesis
4-5.2 Maintaining homeostasis
LS, 1-S1.2 Observations, hypotheses, assessing information

Guide for Reading

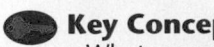

Key Concepts

- What are some characteristics of living things?
- How can life be studied at different levels?

Vocabulary

biology
cell
sexual reproduction
asexual reproduction
metabolism
stimulus
homeostasis
evolution

Reading Strategy: Summarizing As you read, make a list of the properties of living things. Write one sentence describing each property.

Beneath the sparkling waves near a South Pacific island, divers carry cameras and underwater notepads as they crisscross a coral reef. Outside an Antarctic research station, a lone figure searches the ice around her for signs of life. In a high-security facility in Atlanta, a man dressed like an astronaut passes through a double airlock into a sterile laboratory. Sweltering in the heat and humidity of sub-Saharan Africa, volunteers collect blood samples from women and children with AIDS. What do these people have in common? They are all biologists.

The word *biology* means the study of life. (The Greek word *bios* means "life," and *-logy* means "study of.") **Biology** is the science that seeks to understand the living world. A biologist is someone who uses scientific methods to study living things. The work of biologists can be quite varied, because organisms are complex and vary so greatly.

Characteristics of Living Things

Are the firefly and the fire in **Figure 1–14** alive? They are both giving off energy. Describing what makes something alive is not easy. No single characteristic is enough to describe a living thing. Also, some nonliving things share one or more traits with living things. Mechanical toys, automobiles, and clouds move around, for example, whereas mushrooms and trees live their lives in one spot. Other things, such as viruses, exist at the border between organisms and nonliving things. (You'll read more about viruses in Chapter 19.)

Despite these difficulties, it is possible to describe what most living things have in common. **Living things share the following characteristics:**

- **Living things are made up of units called cells.**
- **Living things reproduce.**
- **Living things are based on a universal genetic code.**
- **Living things grow and develop.**
- **Living things obtain and use materials and energy.**
- **Living things respond to their environment.**
- **Living things maintain a stable internal environment.**
- **Taken as a group, living things change over time.**

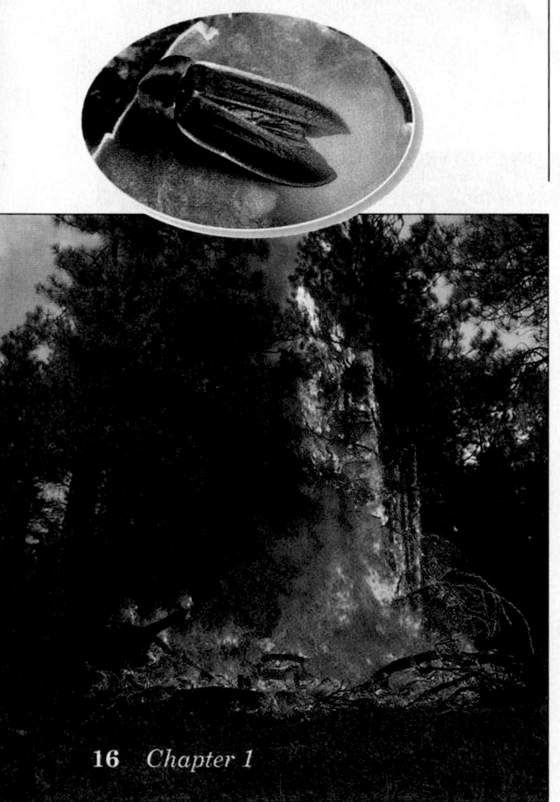

Figure 1–14 A Colorado firefly beetle (top) has all of the characteristics of living things. Even though fire (bottom) uses materials and can grow as living things do, fire is not alive because it does not have other characteristics of living things. **Applying Concepts** *What characteristics of living things are missing from a fire?*

Made Up of Cells Living things, or organisms, are made up of small, self-contained units called cells. A **cell** is a collection of living matter enclosed by a barrier that separates the cell from its surroundings. Cells are the smallest units of an organism that can be considered alive. Cells can grow, respond to their surroundings, and reproduce. Despite their small size, cells are complex and highly organized.

Many living things consist of only a single cell and are therefore called unicellular organisms. (The Latin prefix *uni-* means "one," so *unicellular* means "single-celled.") Many of the microorganisms involved in Spallanzani's and Pasteur's experiments were unicellular organisms.

The organisms you are most familiar with—for example, animals and plants—are multicellular. You can see one type of multicellular organism in **Figure 1–15.** (The Latin prefix *multi-* means "many." Thus, *multicellular* means "many-celled.") Multicellular organisms contain hundreds, thousands, or even trillions of cells. The cells in these organisms are often remarkably diverse, existing in a variety of sizes and shapes. In some multicellular organisms, each type of cell is specialized to perform a different function. The human body alone is made up of at least 85 different cell types. You will learn more about cells in Chapter 7.

▲ **Figure 1–15** **Living things are made of cells.** Cats and most other familiar organisms are made of many cells. The inset shows cells from a cat's stomach (magnification: 500×).

Reproduction All organisms produce new organisms through a process called reproduction. There are two basic kinds of reproduction: sexual and asexual. The vast majority of multicellular organisms—from maple trees to birds and humans—reproduce sexually. In **sexual reproduction,** cells from two different parents unite to produce the first cell of the new organism. In **asexual reproduction,** the new organism has a single parent. In some forms of asexual reproduction, a single-celled organism divides in half to form two new organisms. In the type of asexual reproduction shown in **Figure 1–16,** a portion of an organism splits off to form a new organism.

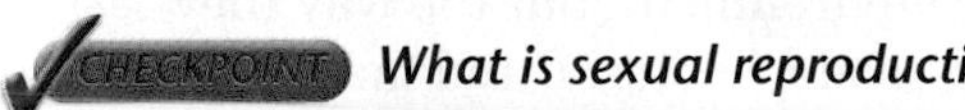

What is sexual reproduction?

Based on a Genetic Code Offspring usually resemble their parents. With asexual reproduction, offspring and their parents have the same traits. With sexual reproduction, offspring differ from their parents in some ways. However, there are limits to these differences. Flies produce flies, dogs produce dogs, and seeds from maple trees produce maple trees.

Explaining how organisms inherit traits is one of the greatest achievements of modern biology. Biologists now know that the directions for inheritance are carried by a molecule called deoxyribonucleic acid, or DNA. This genetic code, with a few minor variations, determines the inherited traits of every organism on Earth. You will learn how this is possible in Unit 4.

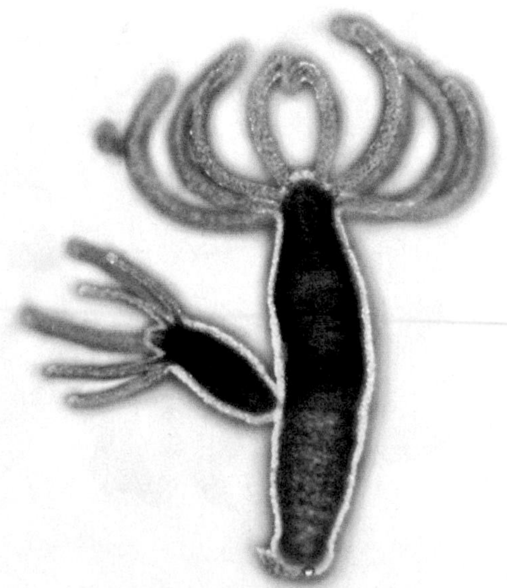

▲ **Figure 1–16** **All living things reproduce.** Here, one hydra is being formed from another through a type of asexual reproduction called budding. Shortly, the new organism will break away from the parent and live independently.

Figure 1–17 **All living things grow and develop.** These photographs show how a spicebush swallowtail butterfly develops from an egg into a caterpillar (larva), a pupa, and, finally, an adult butterfly.

Growth and Development All living things grow during at least part of their lives. For some single-celled organisms, such as bacteria, growth is mostly a simple increase in size. Multicellular organisms, however, typically go through a process called development. During development, a single fertilized egg cell divides again and again to produce the many cells of mature organisms. As those cells divide, they change in shape and structure to form cells such as liver cells, brain cells, and muscle cells. This process is called differentiation, because it forms cells that look different from one another and perform different functions.

For many organisms, development includes periods of rapid and dramatic change, as shown in **Figure 1–17.** In fact, although you will not sprout wings, your body is currently experiencing one of the most intense spurts of growth and development of your entire life!

Need for Materials and Energy Think of what an organism needs as it grows and develops. Just as a building grows taller because workers use energy to assemble new materials, an organism uses energy and a constant supply of materials to grow, develop, and reproduce. Organisms also need materials and energy just to stay alive. The combination of chemical reactions through which an organism builds up or breaks down materials as it carries out its life processes is called **metabolism.**

All organisms take in selected materials that they need from their surroundings, or environment, but the way they obtain energy varies. Plants, some bacteria, and most algae obtain their energy directly from sunlight. Through a process called photosynthesis, these organisms convert light into a form of energy that is stored in certain molecules. That stored energy is ready to be used when needed.

Most other organisms rely on the energy stored during photosynthesis. Some organisms, such as grasshoppers and sheep, obtain their energy by eating plants and other photosynthesizing organisms. Other organisms, such as birds and wolves, get energy by eating the grasshoppers or sheep. The chameleon in **Figure 1–18** gets the materials it needs by eating insects and other small animals. And some organisms, called decomposers, obtain energy from the remains of organisms that have died.

CHECKPOINT *What is metabolism?*

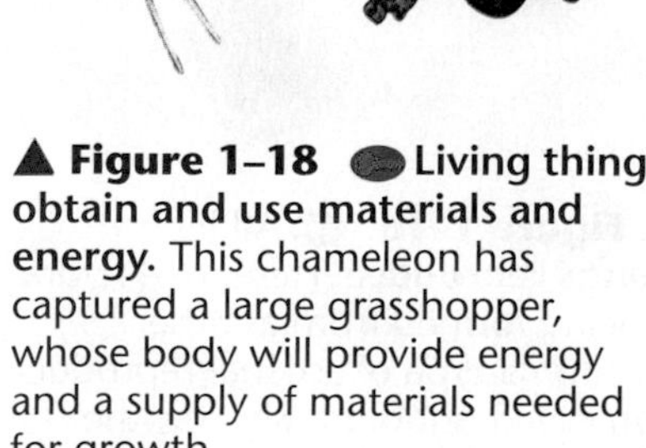

▲ **Figure 1–18** **Living things obtain and use materials and energy.** This chameleon has captured a large grasshopper, whose body will provide energy and a supply of materials needed for growth.

Response to the Environment Organisms detect and respond to stimuli from their environment. A **stimulus** is a signal to which an organism responds. External stimuli, which come from the environment outside an organism, include factors such as light and temperature. For example, when there is sufficient water and the ground is warm enough, a plant seed responds by germinating. The roots respond to gravity and grow down into the soil. The new leaves and stems grow toward light. In contrast, internal stimuli come from within an organism. The level of the sugar glucose in your blood is an example of an internal stimulus. If this level becomes low enough, your body responds by making you feel hungry.

Maintaining Internal Balance Even though conditions in the external environment may vary widely, most organisms must keep internal conditions, such as temperature and water content, fairly constant to survive. The process by which they do this is called **homeostasis** (hoh-mee-oh-STAY-sis). Homeostasis often involves internal feedback mechanisms that work in much the same way as a thermostat. Just as a thermostat in your home turns on the heat when room temperature drops below a certain point, you have an internal "thermostat" that makes your body shiver if your internal temperature drops too low. The muscle action involved in shivering produces heat, thus warming your body. In contrast, if you get too hot, your biological thermostat turns on "air conditioning" by causing you to sweat. Sweating helps to remove excess heat from your skin. When birds get cold, they hunch down and adjust their feathers to provide maximum insulation, as shown in **Figure 1–19.** Often internal stimuli help maintain homeostasis. For example, when your body needs more water to maintain homeostasis, internal stimuli make you feel thirsty.

▲ **Figure 1–19** **Living things maintain an internal stability.** Despite the cold temperatures of this robin's environment, its body temperature remains fairly constant, partly because its feathers provide a layer of insulation and partly because of the body heat it produces.

Quick Lab

What are the characteristics of living things?

Materials hand lens, unknown objects (dry), same objects soaked in water

Procedure 

1. Examine the dry unknown object your teacher provides. Record your observations.
2. **Predicting** In step 3, you will observe the same kind of object after it has been soaked in water. Write a prediction describing what you expect to see.
3. Examine one of the objects that has been soaking in water for a period of time. Record your observations. Wash your hands when you have finished.

Analyze and Conclude

1. **Evaluating** Was the prediction you made in step 2 correct? Explain your answer.
2. **Inferring** Were the objects you observed in step 1 living or nonliving? Were the objects you observed in step 3 living or nonliving? Use the observations you made as supporting evidence for your answers.
3. **Formulating Hypotheses** Suggest one or more ways to explain the differences between the dry and wet objects.

Figure 1–20 **Taken as a group, all living things change over time.** If you suddenly moved most plants to this Namibian desert (left), they would be killed by the heat and lack of water. But a few types of plants have become adapted to these hot and dry conditions, surviving periods of drought to grow and flower after a rainfall (right).

Evolution Although individual organisms experience many changes during their lives, the basic traits they inherited from their parents usually do not change. As a group, however, any given kind of organism can evolve, or change over time.

Over a few generations, the changes in a group may not seem significant. But over hundreds of thousands or even millions of years, the changes can be dramatic. The ability of certain plants, such as those in **Figure 1–20,** to survive periods without water is one example. Another example concerns fishes. Scientists study deposits containing the remains of animals that lived long ago to learn about the evolution of organisms. From the study of very early deposits, scientists know that at one time there were no fishes in Earth's waters. Yet, in more recent deposits, the remains of fishes and other animals with backbones are abundant. The ability of a group of organisms to change over time is invaluable for survival in a world that is always changing. You will read about the processes of **evolution** in Unit 5.

Branches of Biology

Living things come in an astonishing variety of shapes, sizes, and habits. Living systems also range in size from groups of molecules that make up structures inside cells to the collections of organisms that make up the biosphere. No single biologist could study all this diversity, so biology is divided into different fields. Some fields are based on the types of organisms being studied. Zoologists study animals. Botanists study plants. Other fields study life from a particular perspective. For example, paleontologists study ancient life.

Some fields focus on the study of living systems at different levels of organization, as shown in **Figure 1–21.** **Some of the levels at which life can be studied include molecules, cells, organisms, populations of a single kind of organism, communities of different organisms in an area, and the biosphere. At all these levels, smaller living systems are found within larger systems.** Molecular biologists and cell biologists study some of the smallest living systems. Population biologists and ecologists study some of the largest systems in nature. Studies at all these levels make important contributions to the quality of human life.

Levels of Organization

Level	Description	Example
Biosphere	The part of Earth that contains all ecosystems	 Biosphere
Ecosystem	Community and its nonliving surroundings	 Hawk, snake, bison, prairie dog, grass, stream, rocks, air
Community	Populations that live together in a defined area	 Hawk, snake, bison, prairie dog, grass
Population	Group of organisms of one type that live in the same area	 Bison herd
Organism	Individual living thing	 Bison
Groups of Cells	Tissues, organs, and organ systems	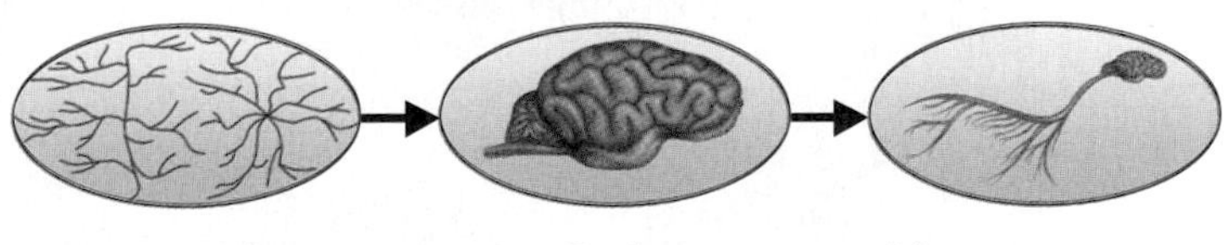 Nervous tissue → Brain → Nervous system
Cells	Smallest functional unit of life	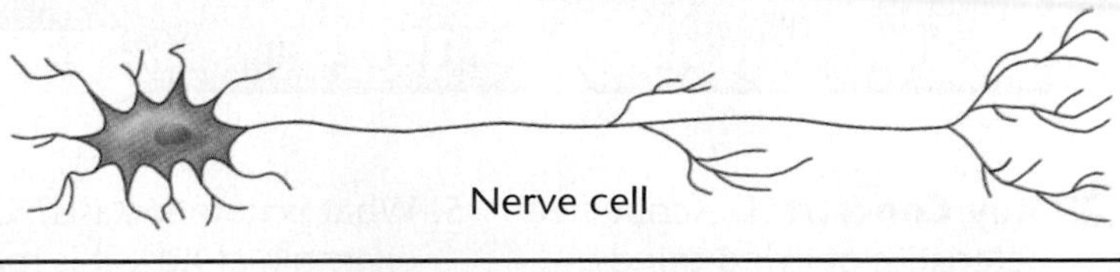 Nerve cell
Molecules	Groups of atoms; smallest unit of most chemical compounds	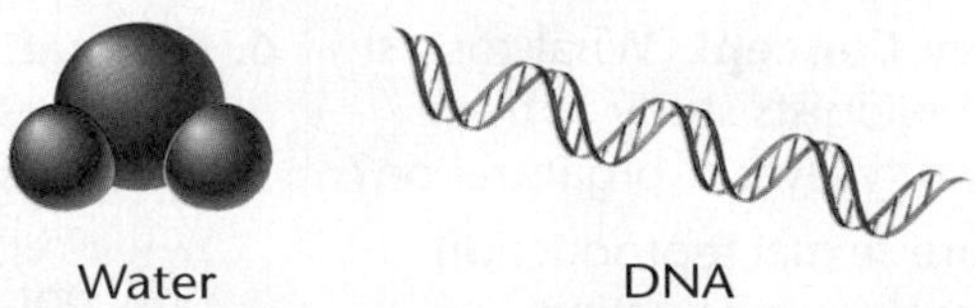 Water; DNA

Figure 1–21 Living things may be studied on many different levels. The largest and most complex level is the biosphere. The smallest level is the molecules that make up living things.

▲ **Figure 1–22** Progress in biology has meant huge improvements in health not just for you and your family but, in some societies, for pets as well. **Predicting** *How do you expect advances in biology to change health care during your lifetime?*

Biology in Everyday Life

As you begin studying biology, you may be thinking of it as just another course, with a textbook to read plus labs, homework, and tests. It's also a *science* course, so you may worry that it will be too difficult. But you will see that more than any other area of study, biology touches your life every day. In fact, it's hard to think of anything you do that isn't affected by it. It helps you understand and appreciate every other form of life, from pets such as the dog in **Figure 1–22** to dinosaurs no longer present on Earth. It provides information about the food you need and the methods for sustaining the world's food supplies. It describes the conditions of good health and the behaviors and diseases that can harm you. It is used to diagnose and treat medical problems. It identifies environmental factors that might threaten you, such as disposal of wastes from human activities. More than any other science, biology helps you understand what affects the quality of your life.

Biologists do not make the decisions about most matters affecting human society or the natural world; citizens and governments do. In just a few years, you will be able to exercise the rights of a voting citizen, influencing public policy by the ballots you cast and the messages you send public officials. With others, you will make decisions based on many factors, including customs, values, ethical standards, and scientific knowledge. Biology can provide decision makers with useful information and analytical skills. It can help them envision the possible effects of their decisions. Biology can help people understand that humans are capable of predicting and trying to control their future and that of the planet.

1–3 Section Assessment

1. **Key Concept** Describe five characteristics of living things.
2. **Key Concept** What topics might biologists study at the community level of organization?
3. Compare sexual reproduction and asexual reproduction.
4. What biological process includes chemical reactions that break down materials?
5. What is homeostasis? Give an example of how it is maintained.
6. **Critical Thinking Applying Concepts** Suppose you feel hungry, so you reach for a peach you see in a fruit bowl. Explain how both external and internal stimuli are involved in your action.

Connecting Concepts

Making Observations
List some observations that could be made to determine whether an object that is not moving is living or nonliving. Refer to Section 1–1 to help yourself recall what an observation is.

When Scientists Have a Conflict of Interest

Scientists are expected to be completely honest about their investigations. Doctors are expected to place the welfare of their patients first. Yet, conflicts of interest can often threaten the credibility of a researcher. A conflict of interest exists when a person's work can be influenced by personal factors such as financial gain, fame, future work, or favoritism. For example, suppose scientists have received funds to test a potential anti-cancer drug. If experiments show that the drug is not very effective, the researchers may be tempted to conceal the results in order to avoid losing their funding.

The Viewpoints

Regulation Is Necessary

Some scientists argue that, because the public must be able to trust the work of science, some rules are essential for preserving scientific integrity. Every profession should regulate its members, and every science publication should have strict rules about avoiding conflicts of interest. In any published work, announcements of potential conflicts should be required. In some cases, scientists should avoid or be forbidden to do work that involves personal gain in addition to the usual payment for doing the work. Some form of government regulation may be needed.

Regulation Is Unnecessary

Other scientists insist that conflict-of-interest regulations are unnecessary for the majority of researchers, who are honest and objective about their work. It is unfair to assume that a researcher's discoveries would be different because of the nature of the financial support for the research. In fact, without the opportunity for scientists to get additional funding for successful work, many new drugs or new techniques would never have been developed. So it is important that scientists be allowed to investigate any topic, even those in which they have the opportunity for personal gain.

Research and Decide

1. **Analyzing the Viewpoints** To make an informed decision, learn more about this issue by consulting library or Internet sources. Then answer the following question: How might the views about a possible conflict of interest differ among a group of scientists, the company employing a scientist, and people seeking information from a scientist?
2. **Forming Your Opinion** How should this problem of possible conflicts of interest be decided? Include information or reasoning that answers people with the opposite view.
3. **Role-Playing** Suppose doctors who own a company developing a new medicine want their patients to help test the medicine. Let one person represent a doctor, a second person a patient, and a third person a medical reporter asking: Should the patients take part in the tests?

For: Links from the authors
Visit: PHSchool.com
Web Code: cbe-1013

1–4 Tools and Procedures

1-S3.1 Interpreting data leads to further hypotheses and explanations
1-S3.2 Test experimental data using statistical analysis
LS- Analyzing results and formulating conclusions

Guide for Reading

Key Concepts
- What measurement system do most scientists use?
- How are light microscopes and electron microscopes similar? How are they different?

Vocabulary
metric system
microscope
compound light microscope
electron microscope
cell culture
cell fractionation

Reading Strategy: Using Graphic Organizers As you read, create a table that lists the equipment and techniques discussed in this section. List one example of what biologists can accomplish using each piece of equipment or procedure.

For: Links on microscopes
Visit: www.SciLinks.org
Web Code: cbn-1014

Imagine being one of the first people to see living things through a magnifying glass. How surprised you would have been to discover a whole new realm of life! Could there still be other types of life that remain undiscovered today because the right tools are not available?

Scientists select and use equipment, which sometimes includes technology such as computers, for their investigations. Electronic balances measure the mass of objects with great precision. Microscopes and telescopes make it possible to observe objects that are very small or very far away. With powerful computers, scientists can store and analyze vast collections of data. Biologists have even devised procedures that help them unlock the information stored in the DNA of different organisms.

A Common Measurement System

Because researchers need to replicate each other's experiments and most experiments involve measurements, scientists need a common system of measurement. **Most scientists use the metric system when collecting data and performing experiments.** The **metric system** is a decimal system of measurement whose units are based on certain physical standards and are scaled on multiples of 10. A revised version of the original metric system is called the International System of Units, or SI. The abbreviation SI comes from the French *Le Système International d'Unités.*

Because the metric system is based on multiples of 10, it is easy to use. Notice in **Figure 1–23** how the basic unit of length, the meter, can be multiplied or divided to measure objects and distances much larger or smaller than a meter. The same process can be used when measuring volume and mass. You can learn more about the metric system in Appendix C.

Common Metric Units

Length	Mass
1 meter (m) = 100 centimeters (cm) 1 meter = 1000 millimeters (mm) 1000 meters = 1 kilometer (km)	1 kilogram (kg) = 1000 grams (g) 1 gram = 1000 milligrams (mg) 1000 kilograms = 1 metric ton (t)
Volume	**Temperature**
1 liter (L) = 1000 milliliters (mL) 1 liter = 1000 cubic centimeters (cm^3)	0°C = freezing point of water 100°C = boiling point of water

▶ **Figure 1–23** **Scientists usually use the metric system in their work.** This system is easy to use because it is based on multiples

Water Released and Absorbed by Tree

Time	Absorbed by Roots (g/h)	Released by Leaves (g/h)
8 AM	1	2
10 AM	1	5
12 PM	4	12
2 PM	6	17
4 PM	9	16
6 PM	14	10
8 PM	10	3

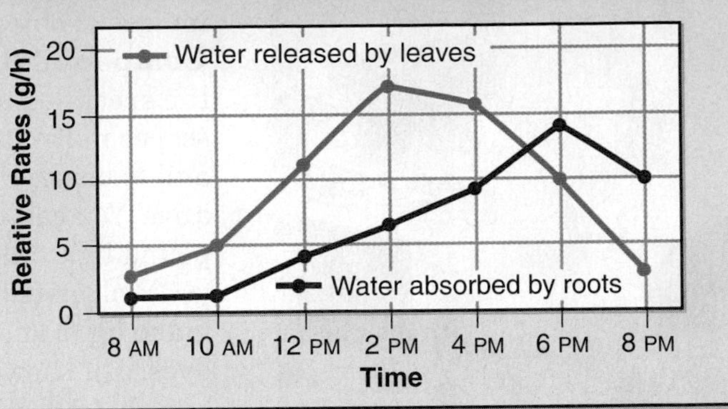

▲ **Figure 1–24** One way to record data from an experiment is by using a data table. Then, the data may be plotted on a graph to make it easier to interpret. **Using Tables and Graphs** ***At what time of day is the rate of water released by leaves equal to the rate of water absorbed by roots?***

Analyzing Biological Data

When scientists collect data, they are often trying to find out whether certain factors changed or remained the same. Often, the simplest way to do that is to record the data in a table and then make a graph. Although you may be able to detect a pattern of change from a data table like the one in **Figure 1–24,** a graph of the data can make a pattern much easier to recognize and understand.

The amount of data produced by biologists today is so huge that no individual can look at more than a tiny fraction of it. To make sense of the data, biologists often turn to computers. For example, computers help determine the structure of molecules. They also allow biologists to search through a DNA molecule, find significant regions of the molecule, and discover how organisms are affected by those regions. At the opposite end of the scale, computers are essential to gathering data by satellite, analyzing the data, and presenting the results. Analyses of satellite data are used to make predictions about complex phenomena such as global climate changes.

How can a graph help biologists analyze data?

Microscopes

When people think of scientific equipment, one of the first tools that comes to mind is the microscope. **Microscopes,** such as the light microscope in **Figure 1–25,** are devices that produce magnified images of structures that are too small to see with the unaided eye. **Light microscopes produce magnified images by focusing visible light rays. Electron microscopes produce magnified images by focusing beams of electrons.** Since the first microscope was invented, microscope manufacturers have had to deal with two problems: What is the instrument's magnification—that is, how much larger can it make an object appear compared to the object's real size? And how sharp an image can the instrument produce?

▲ **Figure 1–25** **Light microscopes produce magnified images by focusing visible light rays.**

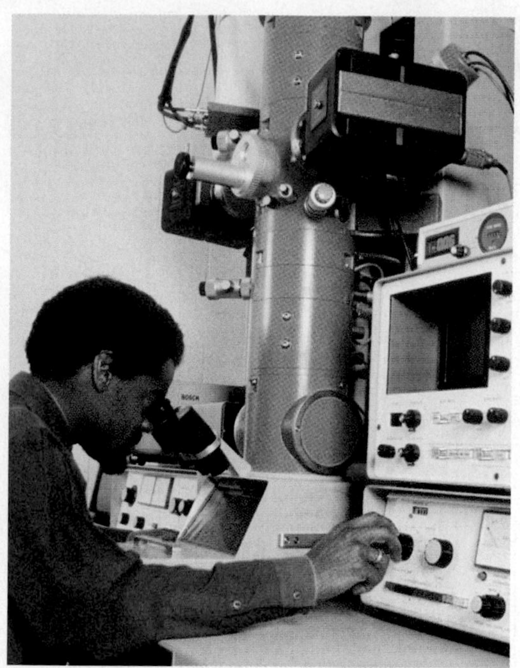

▲ **Figure 1–26** This scientist is using an electron microscope to make observations. **Electron microscopes produce images by focusing beams of electrons.**

Light Microscopes The most commonly used microscope is the light microscope. Light microscopes can produce clear images of objects at a magnification of about 1000 times. **Compound light microscopes** allow light to pass through the specimen and use two lenses to form an image. Light microscopes make it possible to study dead organisms and their parts, and to observe some tiny organisms and cells while they are still alive. You can refer to Appendix D to learn how to use a compound light microscope.

Biologists have developed techniques and procedures to make light microscopes more useful. Chemical stains, also called dyes, can show specific structures in the cell. Fluorescent dyes have been combined with video cameras and computer processing to produce moving three-dimensional images of processes such as cell movement.

Electron Microscopes All microscopes are limited in what they reveal, and light microscopes cannot produce clear images of objects smaller than 0.2 micrometers, or about one-fiftieth the diameter of a typical cell. To study even smaller objects, scientists use electron microscopes. **Electron microscopes,** such as the one shown in **Figure 1–26,** use beams of electrons, rather than light, to produce images. The best electron microscopes can produce images almost 1000 times more detailed than light microscopes can.

Biologists use two main types of electron microscopes. Transmission electron microscopes (TEMs) shine a beam of electrons through a thin specimen. Scanning electron microscopes (SEMs) scan a narrow beam of electrons back and forth across the surface of a specimen. TEMs can reveal a wealth of detail inside the cell. SEMs produce realistic, and often dramatic, three-dimensional images of the surfaces of objects. Because electron microscopes require a vacuum to operate, samples for both TEM and SEM work must be preserved and dehydrated before they are placed inside the microscope. This means that living cells cannot be observed with electron microscopes, only with the light microscope. **Figure 1–27** shows images taken with a light microscope, a transmission electron microscope, and a scanning electron microscope.

▼ **Figure 1–27** Observe the images of pollen grains as seen with a light microscope (left), transmission electron microscope (center), and scanning electron microscope (right). **Interpreting Graphics** ***In which image can you see the most detail on the pollen grain's surface?***

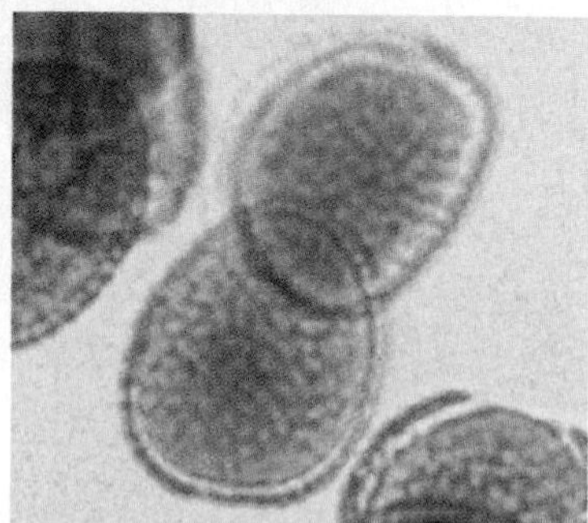

(magnification: about 400×)

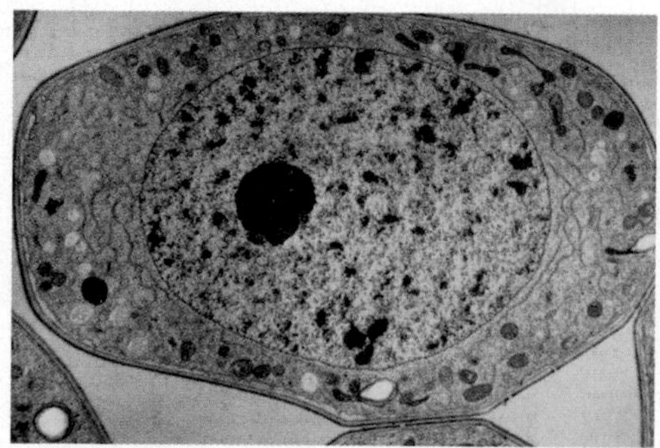

(magnification: about 2200×)

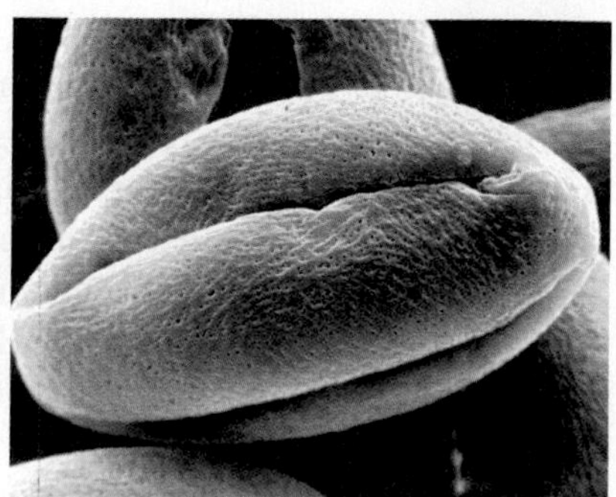

(magnification: about 1000×)

Analyzing Data

Bacterial Reproduction

Bacteria are tiny microorganisms that can reproduce by dividing into two. The graph shows the results of an experiment on the effect of temperature on bacterial reproduction. At the beginning, three populations of bacteria, all of the same type, were of equal size. Each population was kept at a different temperature for 4 days.

1. **Classifying** What variable did the researcher change during this experiment?
2. **Inferring** What do the shapes of the curves tell you about the changes in population size?
3. **Calculating** For the bacteria kept at 15°C, how did population size change during the experiment?
4. **Drawing Conclusions** What effect did the different temperatures have on the growth of the bacterial populations?

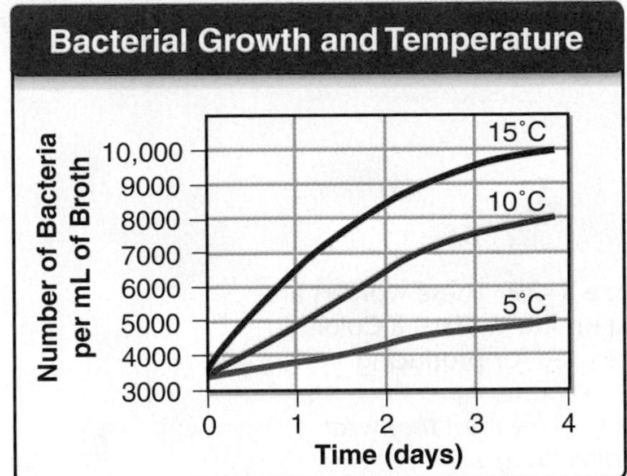

5. **Predicting** Suppose some bacteria used in this experiment were kept at a temperature of 100°C (the temperature of boiling water). Would you expect the population sizes to increase even faster than at 15°C? Explain your reasoning.

Laboratory Techniques

Biologists use a variety of techniques to study cells. Two common laboratory techniques are cell culturing and cell fractionation.

Cell Cultures To obtain enough material to study, biologists like the one in **Figure 1–28** sometimes place a single cell into a dish containing a nutrient solution. The cell is able to reproduce so that a group of cells, called a **cell culture,** develops from the single original cell. Cell cultures can be used to test cell responses under controlled conditions, to study interactions between cells, and to select specific cells for further study.

Cell Fractionation Suppose you want to study just one part of a cell. How could you separate that one part from the rest of the cell? Biologists often use a technique known as **cell fractionation** to separate the different cell parts. First, the cells are broken into pieces in a special blender. Then, the broken cell bits are added to a liquid and placed in a tube. The tube is inserted into a centrifuge, which is an instrument that can spin the tube. Spinning causes the cell parts to separate, with the most dense parts settling near the bottom of the tube. A biologist can then remove the specific part of the cell to be studied by selecting the appropriate layer.

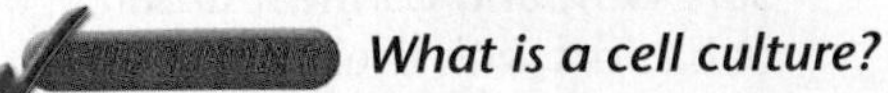
What is a cell culture?

▼ **Figure 1–28** This researcher is transferring bacteria to a solid that contains nutrients, which will enable the bacteria to reproduce. **Comparing and Contrasting** *How do the results of a cell culture differ from the products of cell fractionation?*

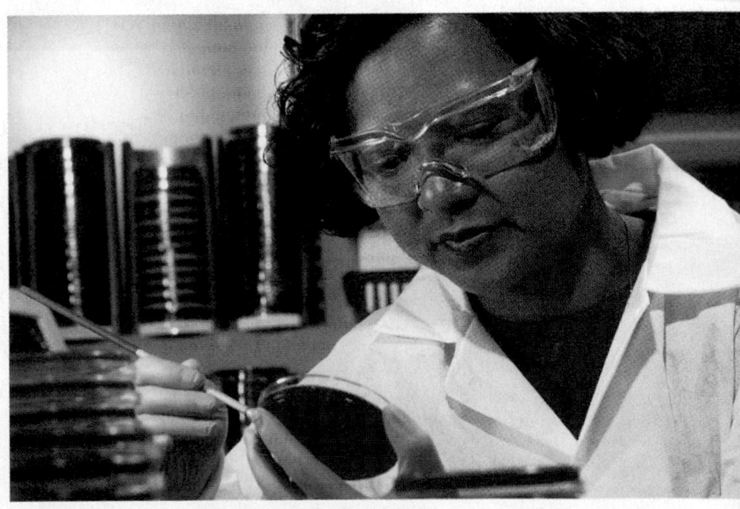

Using a Compound Microscope

In this investigation, you will use a compound microscope to determine the positions and sizes of objects. Before you begin, read the safety rules described in Appendix B. Then, read Appendix D to learn how to use a microscope.

Problem

What kinds of information can a compound microscope provide?

Materials

- compound microscope
- microscope slide
- newspaper or other small-print text
- scissors
- dropper pipette
- coverslips
- prepared slide of crossed fibers
- transparent 15-cm plastic ruler
- prepared slide of root or stem
- prepared slide of bacteria

Skills

Observing, Measuring, Calculating

Procedure  

1. Use scissors to cut out a square of printed text approximately 1 cm wide. Place the paper square on a microscope slide. **CAUTION:** *Be careful when handling sharp instruments.*
2. Use a dropper pipette to place a drop of water on the paper square. Add a coverslip. Place the slide on the stage of a compound microscope. Use the stage clips to hold the slide in place.
3. Use the low-power objective to bring the letters on the paper square into focus. Slowly move the slide in different directions along the stage. Record how the image changes. **CAUTION:** *Handle the microscope carefully.*
4. Observe a prepared slide of crossed fibers through the low-power objective. Use the fine adjustment to focus up and down through the area where the fibers cross. Record the order of the fibers, from top to bottom.
5. Observe a transparent ruler through the low-power objective. Use the ruler to measure in millimeters the diameter of your field of view as precisely as you can. Record this distance and the magnification of the low-power objective.
6. Calculate and record the diameter of the field of view through the other objectives. For example, if a 4× objective has a field of 2 mm (2000 micrometers), then a 10× objective will have a field of $(4 \div 10) \times 2 \text{ mm} = 0.8 \text{ mm}$ (800 micrometers).
7. Examine a prepared slide of a plant stem or root at low and high powers. The small round shapes you see are cells. Use the field diameters you calculated in step 6 to estimate and record the size of a typical plant cell. For example, if 4 cells fit across an 800-micrometer field, then each cell is 200 micrometers long.
8. Repeat step 7 with a prepared slide of bacteria.

Analyze and Conclude

1. **Applying Concepts** What are the advantages of using the high-power objective? What are the disadvantages?
2. **Inferring** Some plant diseases are caused by bacteria. Could a bacterium injure a plant by surrounding a plant cell and consuming it? By entering a plant cell? Explain your answer.
3. **Drawing Conclusions** In what ways did the microscope alter the image in step 3? How did moving the slide affect the image?
4. **Drawing Conclusions** In what order were the fibers arranged on the slide you observed in step 4?

Go Further

Measuring With your teacher's permission, use the microscope to observe one of your hairs and estimate its width.

Chapter 1 Study Guide

1-1 What Is Science?

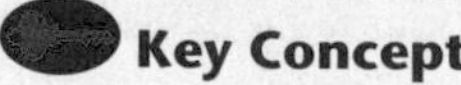

Key Concept

- The goal of science is to investigate and understand the natural world, to explain events in the natural world, and to use those explanations to make useful predictions.

Vocabulary
science, p. 3 • observation, p. 4 • data, p. 4
inference, p. 4 • hypothesis, p. 5

1-2 How Scientists Work

Key Concepts

- Whenever possible, a hypothesis should be tested by an experiment in which only one variable is changed at a time. All other variables should be kept unchanged, or controlled.
- In science, the word *theory* applies to a well-tested explanation that unifies a broad range of observations.

Vocabulary
spontaneous generation, p. 8
controlled experiment, p. 9
manipulated variable, p. 9
responding variable, p. 9 • theory, p. 14

1-3 Studying Life

Key Concepts

- Living things share characteristics including cellular organization, reproduction, a universal genetic code, growth and development, use of materials and energy, response to their environment, maintaining an internal stability, and, as a group, change over time.
- Some of the levels at which life can be studied include molecules, cells, organisms, populations of a single kind of organism, communities of populations living in the same area, and the biosphere. At all these levels, smaller living systems are found within larger systems.

Vocabulary
biology, p. 16 • cell, p. 17
sexual reproduction, p. 17
asexual reproduction, p. 17
metabolism, p. 18 • stimulus, p. 19
homeostasis, p. 19
evolution, p. 20

1-4 Tools and Procedures

Key Concepts

- Most scientists use the metric system when collecting data and performing experiments.
- Light microscopes produce magnified images by focusing visible light rays. Electron microscopes produce magnified images by focusing beams of electrons.

Vocabulary
metric system, p. 24
microscope, p. 25
compound light microscope, p. 26
electron microscope, p. 26
cell culture, p. 27
cell fractionation, p. 27

Thinking Visually

Make a concept map that shows some ways scientists think and work. You can start with the partial concept map shown below or create your own. Recalling how scientists investigated spontaneous generation may help you identify important ideas to include.

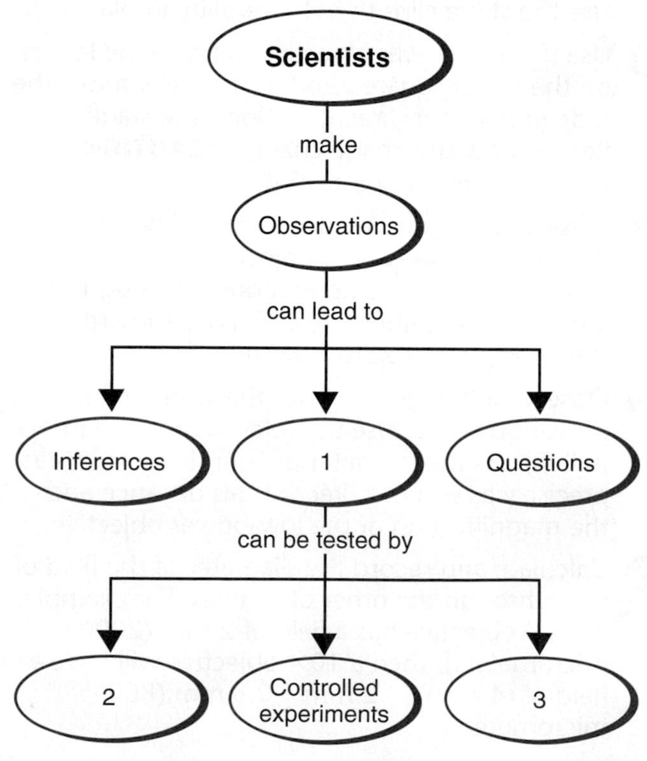

Preparing for the Living Environment Exam

Blue questions emphasize Regents Exam content

Chapter 1

Part A

Multiple Choice

For each statement or question, select the number of the word or expression that, of those given, best completes the statement or answers the question.

1 Which statement about the image shown below is *not* an observation?

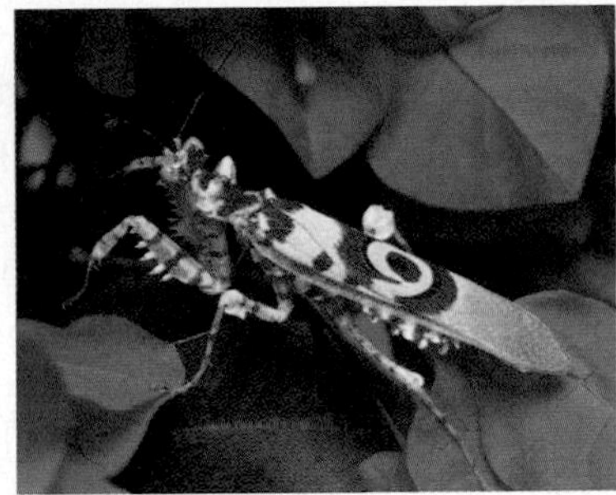

(1) The insect has three legs on the left side.
(2) The insect has a pattern on its back.
(3) The insect's pattern shows that it is poisonous.
(4) The insect is green, white, and black.

2 The statement "the worm is 2 cm long" is a(an)
(1) quantitative observation
(2) qualitative observation
(3) inference
(4) hypothesis

3 An inference is
(1) the same as an observation
(2) a logical interpretation of an observation
(3) a statement involving numbers
(4) the best way to avoid bias

4 To be useful in science, a hypothesis must be
(1) measurable (3) testable
(2) observable (4) correct

5 The term *spontaneous generation* means that
(1) living things can arise from nonliving matter
(2) living things arise from other living things
(3) a maggot is part of the life cycle of a fly
(4) living things evolve over time

6 Which statement about a controlled experiment is true?
(1) All the variables must be kept the same.
(2) Only one variable is changed at a time.
(3) Scientists always use controlled experiments.
(4) Controlled experiments cannot be performed on living things.

7 A scientific theory is
(1) another word for hypothesis
(2) a well-tested explanation that unifies a broad range of observations
(3) the same as the conclusion of an experiment
(4) established when the conclusions of two separate experiments are the same

8 The process in which two cells from different parents unite to produce the first cell of a new organism is called
(1) homeostasis
(2) development
(3) asexual reproduction
(4) sexual reproduction

9 Which process is used by organisms to keep their internal conditions relatively stable?
(1) metabolism
(2) reproduction
(3) evolution
(4) homeostasis

10 An instrument that produces images by focusing light rays is called a(an)
(1) light microscope
(2) transmission electron microscope
(3) scanning electron microscope
(4) electronic balance

For questions 11 and 12, complete each analogy by selecting the correct number. In analogies, A : B :: C : means "A is to B as C is to __?__."

11 Sexual reproduction : two parents :: asexual reproduction :
(1) two parents
(2) two cells
(3) one parent
(4) one cell

12 One gram : 1000 milligrams :: one meter :
(1) 1000 millimeters
(2) 1 millimeter
(3) 1000 meters
(4) 1 milliliter

Test-Taking Tip Before taking a standardized test, it helps to become familiar with the format of the test, including the different question types. One helpful method is to complete practice tests, such as this one.

Preparing for the Living Environment Exam

Part B

Multiple Choice and Extended Response
For those questions that ask you to select a response, choose the one that best completes the statement or answers the question. For all others follow the directions given.

Base your answers to questions 13 and 14 on the information and graph below and on your knowledge of biology.

A researcher investigated two groups of fruit flies. Population A was kept in a 0.5-L container. Population B was kept in a 1-L container.

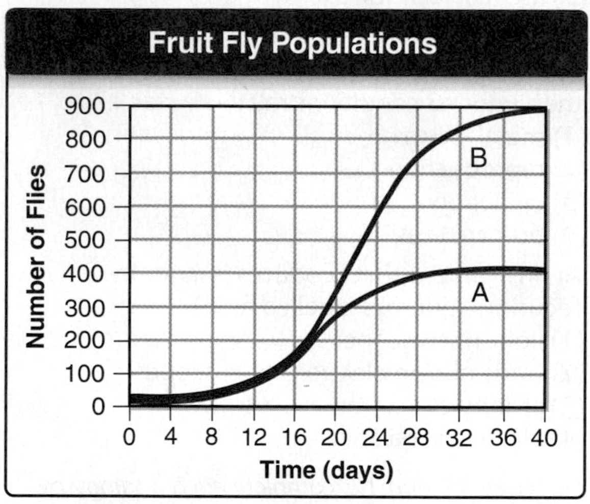

13 The manipulated (independent) variable was the
(1) number of flies
(2) number of groups studied
(3) time in days
(4) size of the containers

14 Which is a scientific inference based on the contents of the graph?
(1) The flies in Population B were healthier than those in Population A.
(2) A fly population with more available space will grow larger than a population with less space.
(3) In 40 more days, the sizes of both populations would decrease at the same rate.
(4) The pattern shown in this graph is true only for fruit flies.

---

15 In a controlled experiment, there is one variable that is changed at a time. This is the manipulated (independent) variable. The experimental data can then show a difference between the way the experimental and control groups responded. The variable that is measured during the experiment is referred to as the responding (dependent) variable. Identify both the manipulated (independent) variable and the responding (dependent) variable in Redi's experiment and in Spallanzani's experiment. (*Hint:* Refer to pages 9 and 11.)

16 A scientist does an experiment and draws a conclusion. How does this conclusion differ from a theory?

17 Explain how a graph of data can be more informative than a table of the same data.

18 An animal has a mass of 1.5 kilograms. Identify one specific scientific instrument that could be used to determine the mass of the animal.

19 Explain why a valid conclusion about the effect of one variable in an investigation cannot be drawn when there are several variables in the experiment.

Part C

Extended Response
Answer the questions or follow the directions given.

20 A controlled experiment typically includes a hypothesis, one manipulated (independent) variable, observations, and inferences.
a State one purpose for stating a hypothesis before conducting an experiment.
b Explain how a hypothesis that is not supported by experimental data can be helpful to a scientist.
c Explain why it is important that scientists test only one independent variable in a controlled experiment.
d State one way an observation about an object differs from an inference about that object.

Base your answer to questions 21 and 22 on the information below and on your knowledge of biology.

A scientist adds an equal quantity of a new fertilizer he is testing to each of the pots in which 50 tomato plants are growing. He then measures the growth of the plants over a 3-week period, records his results, and draws a conclusion about the benefit of the new fertilizer.

21 Is this a controlled experiment? Support your answer with an explanation.

NEW YORK LIVING ENVIRONMENT

22 Explain why it was important to use 50 plants rather than one plant for the experiment.

23 Explain why publishing the design and results of an experiment is considered an essential part of science.

Base your answers to questions 24 and 25 on the graphs below.

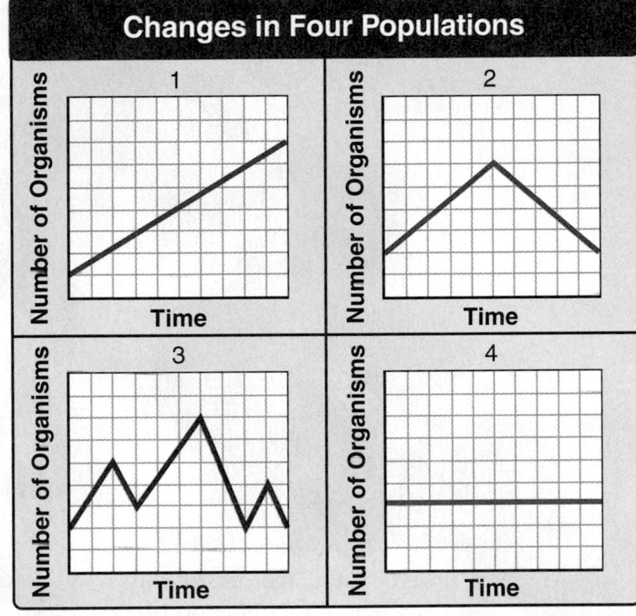

24 Write a separate statement to summarize the population change indicated for *each* of the four populations represented.

25 Graphs that represent two entirely different situations can have the same appearance. Select one of the four graphs from question 24 and explain how the shape of the graph you choose could apply to something other than population change.

26 Describe a controlled experiment that could be carried out to test the hypothesis that mosquitoes are attracted to people wearing light-colored clothing. In your description, be sure to:

- identify the manipulated (independent) variable
- identify the responding (dependent) variable
- describe what the control group for this experiment will consist of
- state what data must be collected during the experiment

27 A drug company has developed a new antibiotic that is effective against a strain of *Staphylococcus aureus* that has become resistant to most of the currently available antibiotics. The new antibiotic has been tested successfully on animals and will soon be tested on humans. The company claims that results so far indicate that the antibiotic could be a cure for what have often been lethal *Staphylococcus* infections.

In conducting the research on human subjects, several questions need to be answered. Summarize some of the important aspects of the research on humans. In your summary, be sure to explain

- how the experimental and control groups will be treated differently
- why it would be important to use a large number of people in this research
- how the researcher will be able to conclude that the new antibiotic is effective in curing *Staphylococcus* infections in humans

For: An interactive self-test
Visit: PHSchool.com
Web Code: cba-1010

CHAPTER 2

The Chemistry of Life

The beautiful feathers of this great egret are made up of protein. Proteins are one of the main groups of carbon compounds found in living things.

Inquiry Activity

Do large and small molecules behave exactly alike?

Procedure   

1. Label six test tubes as follows: tofu, soy sauce, butter, soap, starch, and sugar. Place a tiny amount of each sample in the appropriate test tube.
2. Half-fill each test tube with water. Stopper the test tubes. Shake each test tube for 2 minutes. Record your observations of each test tube.

Think About It

1. **Observing** Which substances dissolved easily in water?
2. **Drawing Conclusions** Tofu, starch, and butter consist mostly of large molecules (protein, starch, and fat, respectively). Soy sauce, sugar, and soap contain smaller molecules that are related to the large molecules. Are the larger molecules more or less soluble than the smaller molecules?

2–1 The Nature of Matter

4-1.2 Cells use small molecules as building blocks
4-1.2 Organic and inorganic molecules react
LS- Make observations
LS- Formulate conclusions

Life depends on chemistry. When you eat food or inhale oxygen, your body uses these materials in chemical reactions that keep you alive. Just as buildings are made from bricks, steel, glass, and wood, living things are made from chemical compounds. If the first task of an architect is to understand building materials, then the first job of a biologist is to understand the chemistry of life.

Guide for Reading

Key Concepts

- What three subatomic particles make up atoms?
- How are all of the isotopes of an element similar?
- What are the two main types of chemical bonds?

Vocabulary

atom
nucleus
electron
element
isotope
compound
ionic bond
ion
covalent bond
molecule
van der Waals forces

Reading Strategy: Using Prior Knowledge Before you read, write down what you already know about atoms, elements, and compounds. As you read, note the main new concepts you learn.

Atoms

The study of chemistry begins with the basic unit of matter, the **atom.** The Greek word *atomos,* which means "unable to be cut," was first used to refer to matter by the Greek philosopher Democritus nearly 2500 years ago. Democritus asked a simple question: If you take an object like a stick of chalk and break it in half, are both halves still chalk? The answer, of course, is yes. But what happens if you go on? Suppose you break it in half again and again and again. Can you continue to divide without limit, or does there come a point at which you cannot divide the fragment of chalk without changing it into something else? Democritus thought that there had to be a limit. He called the smallest fragment the atom, a name scientists still use today.

Atoms are incredibly small. Placed side by side, 100 million atoms would make a row only about 1 centimeter long—about the width of your little finger! Despite its extremely small size, an atom contains subatomic particles that are even smaller.

Figure 2–1 shows the subatomic particles in a helium atom. **The subatomic particles that make up atoms are protons, neutrons, and electrons.** Protons and neutrons have about the same mass. However, protons are positively charged particles (+) and neutrons carry no charge. Their name is a reminder that they are neutral particles. Strong forces bind protons and neutrons together to form the **nucleus,** which is at the center of the atom.

The **electron** is a negatively charged particle (–) with 1/1840 the mass of a proton. Electrons are in constant motion in the space surrounding the nucleus. They are attracted to the positively charged nucleus but remain outside the nucleus because of the energy of their motion. Because atoms have equal numbers of electrons and protons, and because these subatomic particles have equal but opposite charges, atoms are neutral.

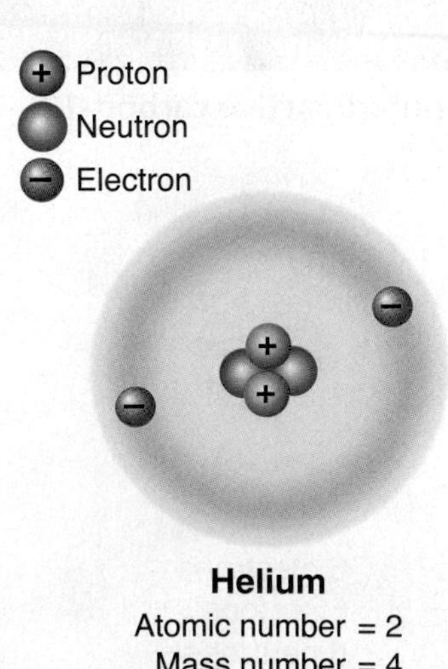

▶ **Figure 2–1 Helium atoms contain protons, neutrons, and electrons.** The positively charged protons and uncharged neutrons are bound together in the dense nucleus, while the negatively charged electrons move in the space

Elements and Isotopes

A chemical **element** is a pure substance that consists entirely of one type of atom. More than 100 elements are known, but only about two dozen are commonly found in living organisms. Elements are represented by a one- or two-letter symbol. C, for example, stands for carbon, H for hydrogen, and Na for sodium. The number of protons in an atom of an element is the element's atomic number. Carbon's atomic number is 6, meaning that each atom of carbon has six protons and, consequently, six electrons. See Appendix G, The Periodic Table, which shows the elements.

Isotopes Atoms of an element can have different numbers of neutrons. For example, some atoms of carbon have six neutrons, some have seven, and a few have eight. Atoms of the same element that differ in the number of neutrons they contain are known as **isotopes.** The sum of the protons and neutrons in the nucleus of an atom is called its mass number. Isotopes are identified by their mass numbers. **Figure 2–2** shows the subatomic composition of carbon-12, carbon-13, and carbon-14 atoms. The weighted average of the masses of an element's isotopes is called its atomic mass. "Weighted" means that the abundance of each isotope in nature is considered when the average is calculated. **Because they have the same number of electrons, all isotopes of an element have the same chemical properties.**

Radioactive Isotopes Some isotopes are radioactive, meaning that their nuclei are unstable and break down at a constant rate over time. The radiation these isotopes give off can be dangerous, but radioactive isotopes have a number of important scientific and practical uses.

Geologists can determine the ages of rocks and fossils by analyzing the isotopes found in them. Radiation from certain isotopes can be used to treat cancer and to kill bacteria that cause food to spoil. Radioactive isotopes can also be used as labels or "tracers" to follow the movements of substances within organisms.

▼ **Figure 2–2** **Because they have the same number of electrons, these isotopes of carbon have the same chemical properties.** The difference among the isotopes is the number of neutrons in their nuclei.

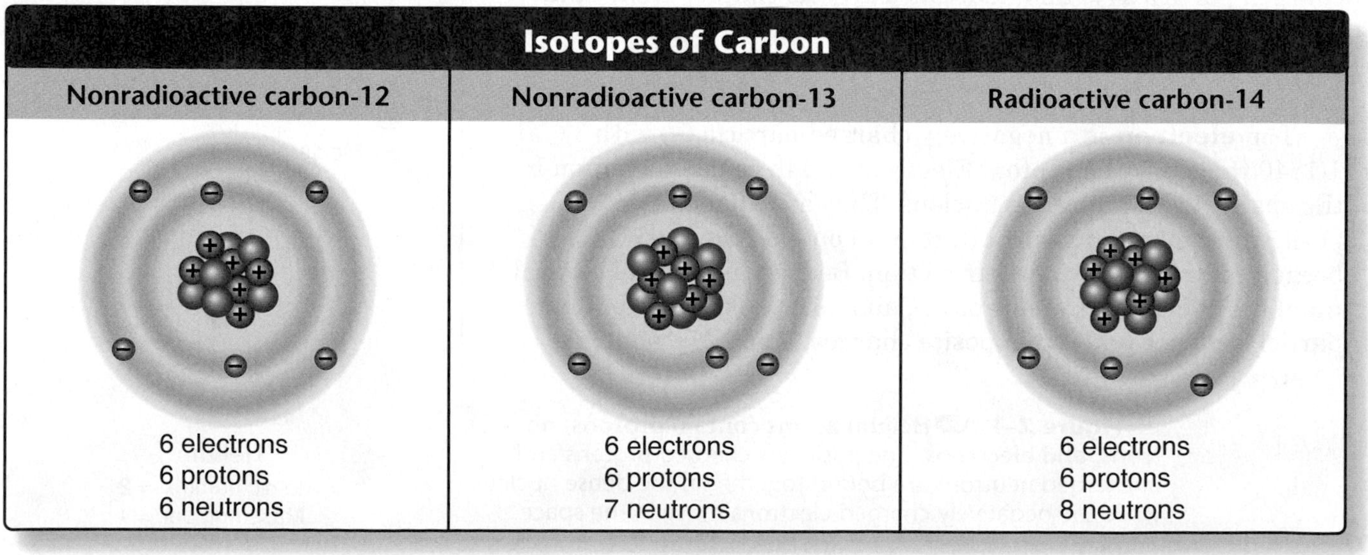

Isotopes of Carbon

Nonradioactive carbon-12	Nonradioactive carbon-13	Radioactive carbon-14
6 electrons 6 protons 6 neutrons	6 electrons 6 protons 7 neutrons	6 electrons 6 protons 8 neutrons

Careers in Biology

Forensic Scientist

Job Description: work as a forensic scientist for local, state, or federal investigative agencies in order to conduct scientific forensic examinations in criminal investigations

Education: a bachelor's degree in science—biology, physics, chemistry, metallurgy; some states require several years of forensic laboratory experience

Skills: analytical, logical, computer literate, detail oriented, able to take meticulous notes and to prepare evidence for presentation in court as well as to testify as an expert witness

Highlights: have the opportunity to use logic and science to solve unique or unusual problems in criminal investigations and to work collaboratively with other scientists

To find out more about forensic science, view the segment "History's Mystery: An Introduction to Forensic Science," on Videotape One.

For: Career links
Visit: PHSchool.com
Web Code: cbb-1021

Chemical Compounds

In nature, most elements are found combined with other elements in compounds. A chemical **compound** is a substance formed by the chemical combination of two or more elements in definite proportions. Scientists show the composition of compounds by a kind of shorthand known as a chemical formula. Water, which contains two atoms of hydrogen for each atom of oxygen, has the chemical formula H_2O. The formula for table salt, NaCl, indicates that the elements from which table salt forms—sodium and chlorine—combine in a 1 : 1 ratio.

The physical and chemical properties of a compound are usually very different from those of the elements from which it is formed. For example, hydrogen and oxygen, which are gases at room temperature, can combine explosively and form liquid water. Sodium is a silver-colored metal that is soft enough to cut with a knife. It reacts explosively with cold water. Chlorine is very reactive, too. It is a poisonous, greenish gas that was used to kill many soldiers in World War I. Sodium and chlorine combine to form sodium chloride (NaCl), or table salt. Sodium chloride is a white solid that dissolves easily in water. As you know, sodium chloride is not poisonous. In fact, it is essential for the survival of most living things.

What information is contained in a chemical formula?

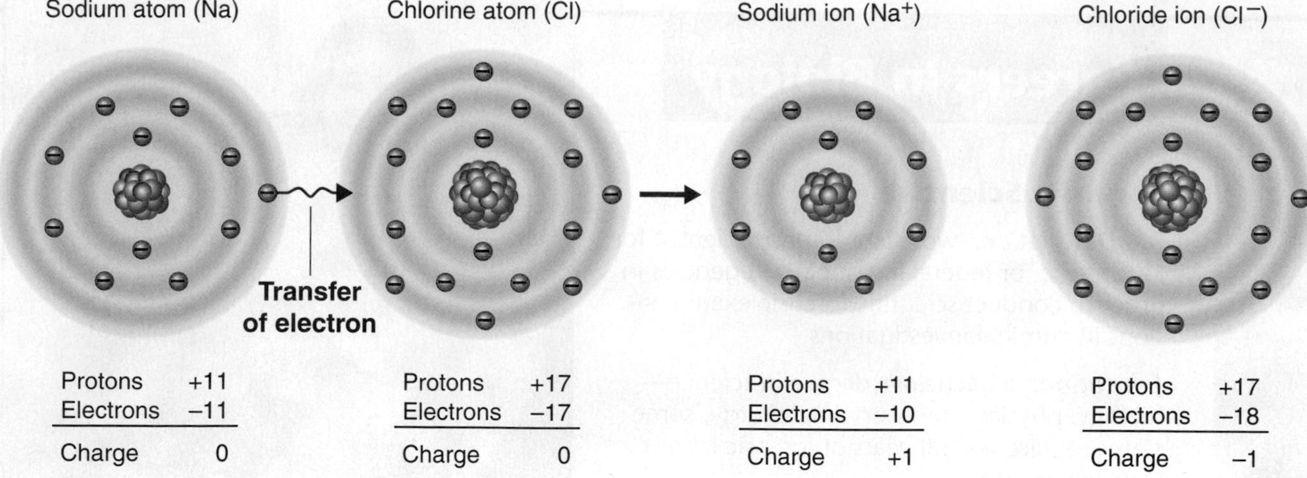

▲ **Figure 2–3** **The chemical bond in which electrons are transferred from one atom to another is called an ionic bond.** The compound sodium chloride forms when sodium loses its valence electron to chlorine.

Chemical Bonds

The atoms in compounds are held together by chemical bonds. Much of chemistry is devoted to understanding how and when chemical bonds form. Bond formation involves the electrons that surround each atomic nucleus. The electrons that are available to form bonds are called valence electrons. **The main types of chemical bonds are ionic bonds and covalent bonds.**

Ionic Bonds An **ionic bond** is formed when one or more electrons are transferred from one atom to another. Recall that atoms are electrically neutral because they have equal numbers of protons and electrons. An atom that loses electrons has a positive charge. An atom that gains electrons has a negative charge. These positively and negatively charged atoms are known as **ions.**

Figure 2–3 shows how ionic bonds form between sodium and chlorine in table salt. A sodium atom easily loses its one valence electron and becomes a sodium ion (Na^+). A chlorine atom easily gains an electron and becomes a chloride ion (Cl^-). In a salt crystal, there are trillions of sodium and chloride ions. These oppositely charged ions have a strong attraction. The attraction between oppositely charged ions is an ionic bond.

Covalent Bonds Sometimes electrons are shared by atoms instead of being transferred. What does it mean to "share" electrons? It means that the moving electrons actually travel in the orbitals of both atoms. A **covalent bond** forms when electrons are shared between atoms. When the atoms share two electrons, the bond is called a single covalent bond. Sometimes the atoms share four electrons and form a double bond. In a few cases, atoms can share six electrons and form a triple bond.

The structure that results when atoms are joined together by covalent bonds is called a molecule. The **molecule** is the smallest unit of most compounds. The diagram of a water molecule in **Figure 2–4** shows that each hydrogen atom forms a single covalent bond with the oxygen atom.

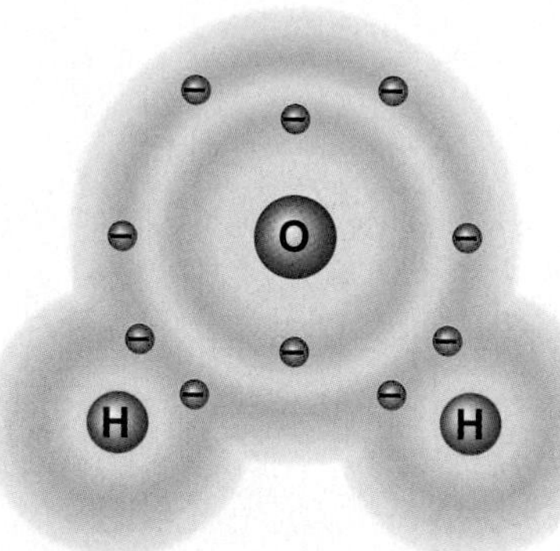

▲ **Figure 2–4** **The chemical bond in which electrons are shared between atoms is called a covalent bond.** In a water molecule, each hydrogen atom shares two electrons with the oxygen atom.

Van der Waals Forces Because of their structures, atoms of different elements do not all have the same ability to attract electrons. Some atoms have a stronger attraction for electrons than do other atoms. Therefore, when the atoms in a covalent bond share electrons, the sharing is not always equal. Even when the sharing is equal, the rapid movement of electrons can create regions on a molecule that have a tiny positive or negative charge.

When molecules are close together, a slight attraction can develop between the oppositely charged regions of nearby molecules. Chemists call such intermolecular forces of attraction **van der Waals forces,** after the scientist who discovered them. Although van der Waals forces are not as strong as ionic bonds or covalent bonds, they can hold molecules together, especially when the molecules are large.

People who keep geckos as pets have already seen van der Waals forces in action. These remarkable little lizards can climb up vertical surfaces, even smooth glass walls, and then hang on by a single toe despite the pull of gravity. How do they do it? No, they do not have some sort of glue on their feet and they don't have suction cups.

A gecko foot like the one shown in **Figure 2–5** is covered by as many as half a million tiny hairlike projections. Each projection is further divided into hundreds of tiny, flat-surfaced fibers. This design allows the gecko's foot to come in contact with an extremely large area of the wall at the molecular level. Van der Waals forces form between molecules on the surface of the gecko's foot and molecules on the surface of the wall. The combined strength of all the van der Waals forces allows the gecko to balance the pull of gravity. When the gecko needs to move its foot, it peels the foot off at an angle and reattaches it at another location on the wall.

▼ **Figure 2–5** Van der Waals forces help geckos to grip smooth, vertical surfaces. **Applying Concepts** *Which product(s) might be developed based on van der Waals forces? Explain.*

2–1 Section Assessment

1. **Key Concept** Describe the structure of an atom.
2. **Key Concept** Why do all isotopes of an element have the same chemical properties? In what way do isotopes of an element differ?
3. **Key Concept** What is a covalent bond? An ionic bond?
4. What is a compound? How are compounds related to molecules?
5. How do van der Waals forces hold molecules together?
6. **Critical Thinking Comparing and Contrasting** How are ionic bonds and van der Waals forces similar? How are they different?

Writing in Science

Writing an Article

Write an article for your school newspaper on forensic science as a career. Assume that you have already interviewed a forensic scientist who works for a law enforcement agency. The article should be about 500 words long. *Hint:* Consider the interests of your readers.

Working Safely in Biology

Scientists working in a laboratory or in the field like those in **Figure 1–29** are trained to use safe procedures when carrying out investigations. Laboratory work may involve flames or heating elements, electricity, chemicals, hot liquids, sharp instruments, and breakable glassware. Laboratory or field work may involve contact with living or dead organisms—not just the plants, animals, and other living things you can see but other organisms you cannot see without a microscope.

Whenever you work in your biology laboratory, it's important for you to follow safe practices as well. Before performing any activity in this course, study the safety rules in Appendix B. Before you start any activity, read all the steps, and make sure that you understand the entire procedure, including any safety precautions that must be followed.

The single most important rule for your safety is simple: Always follow your teacher's instructions and the textbook directions exactly. If you are in doubt about any part of an activity, always ask your teacher for an explanation. And, because you may be in contact with organisms you cannot see, it is essential that you wash your hands thoroughly after every scientific activity. Remember, you are responsible for your own safety and that of your teacher and classmates. If you are handling live animals, you are responsible for their safety as well.

▼ **Figure 1–29** These workers are cleaning up Rocky Flats, a Colorado site once used for producing nuclear weapons. **Applying Concepts** *Why must they wear heavy protective gear?*

1–4 Section Assessment

1. **Key Concept** Why do scientists use a common system of measurement?
2. **Key Concept** What is the difference in the way light microscopes and electron microscopes produce images?
3. What types of objects can be studied with a light microscope? What types can be studied with an electron microscope?
4. Describe the technique and purpose of cell fractionation.
5. **Critical Thinking Applying Concepts** It has been said that many great discoveries lie in wait for the tools needed to make them. What does this statement mean to you? If possible, include an example in your answer.

You & Your Community

Safety Poster
After reading the safety guidelines in Appendix B, prepare a poster on lab safety to display in your school in which you describe at least five safety rules. You might organize your poster or brochure in two columns labeled *Dangerous Way* and *Safe Way,* and contrast unsafe behaviors with their safe alternatives.

2–2 Properties of Water

4-1.2 Organic and inorganic molecules react
LS- Analyze results
LS- Use of indicators

Guide for Reading

Key Concepts
- Why are water molecules polar?
- What are acidic solutions? What are basic solutions?

Vocabulary
cohesion
adhesion
mixture
solution
solute
solvent
suspension
pH scale
acid
base
buffer

Reading Strategy: Using Visuals Before you read, preview **Figure 2–7** and **Figure 2–9.** As you read, note how these two figures are related.

After several days in space, one of the first astronauts to travel to the moon looked back longingly at Earth and marveled at its distant beauty. If there are other beings who have seen Earth, he said, they must surely call it "the blue planet." The astronaut was referring to the blue appearance of the water in the oceans, which cover three fourths of Earth's surface. Water is also the single most abundant compound in most living things.

Water is one of the few compounds that is a liquid at the temperatures found over much of Earth's surface. Unlike most substances, water expands as it freezes. Thus, ice is less dense than liquid water, which explains why ice floats on the surface of lakes and rivers. If the ice sank to the bottom, the situation would be disastrous for fish and plant life in regions with cold winters, to say nothing of the sport of ice skating!

The Water Molecule

Like all molecules, a water molecule (H_2O) is neutral. The positive charges on its 10 protons balance out the negative charges on its 10 electrons. However, there is more to the story.

Polarity With 8 protons in its nucleus, an oxygen atom has a much stronger attraction for electrons than does the hydrogen atom with a single proton in its nucleus. Thus, at any moment, there is a greater probability of finding the shared electrons near the oxygen atom than near the hydrogen atom. Because the water molecule has a bent shape, as shown in **Figure 2–6,** the oxygen atom is on one end of the molecule and the hydrogen atoms are on the other. As a result, the oxygen end of the molecule has a slight negative charge and the hydrogen end of the molecule has a slight positive charge.

A molecule in which the charges are unevenly distributed is called a polar molecule because the molecule is like a magnet with poles. **A water molecule is polar because there is an uneven distribution of electrons between the oxygen and hydrogen atoms.** The negative pole is near the oxygen atom and the positive pole is between the hydrogen atoms.

◀ **Figure 2–6** **The unequal sharing of electrons causes the water molecule to be polar.** The hydrogen end of the molecule is slightly positive and the oxygen end is slightly negative.

Hydrogen Bonds Because of their partial positive and negative charges, polar molecules such as water can attract each other, as shown in **Figure 2–7.** The charges on a polar molecule are written in parentheses, (–) or (+), to show that they are weaker than the charges on ions such as Na^+ and Cl^-. The attraction between the hydrogen atom on one water molecule and the oxygen atom on another water molecule is an example of a hydrogen bond. Hydrogen bonds are not as strong as covalent or ionic bonds, but water's ability to form multiple hydrogen bonds is responsible for many of its special properties.

A single water molecule may be involved in as many as four hydrogen bonds at the same time. The ability of water to form multiple hydrogen bonds is responsible for many of water's properties. **Cohesion** is an attraction between molecules of the same substance. Because of hydrogen bonding, water is extremely cohesive. Water's cohesion causes molecules on the surface of water to be drawn inward, which is why drops of water form beads on a smooth surface. Cohesion also explains why some insects and spiders can walk on a pond's surface, as shown in **Figure 2–8.**

Adhesion is an attraction between molecules of different substances. Have you ever been told to read the volume in a graduated cylinder at eye level? The surface of the water in the graduated cylinder dips slightly in the center because the adhesion between water molecules and glass molecules is stronger than the cohesion between water molecules. Adhesion between water and glass also causes water to rise in a narrow tube against the force of gravity. This effect is called capillary action. Capillary action is one of the forces that draw water out of the roots of a plant and up into its stems and leaves. Cohesion holds the column of water together as it rises.

How are cohesion and adhesion similar? Different?

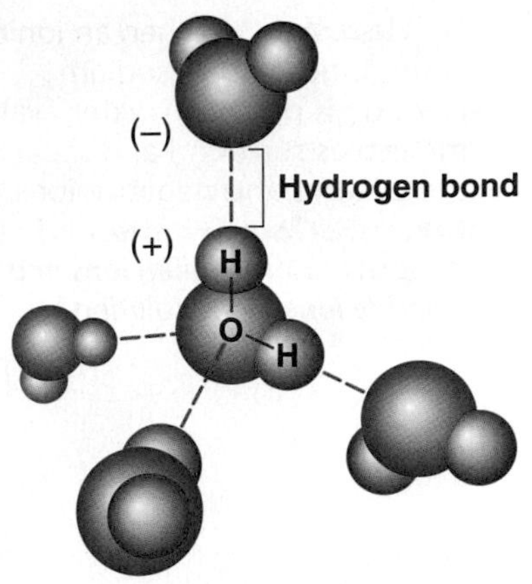

▲ **Figure 2–7** The illustration shows the hydrogen bonds that form between water molecules. **Applying Concepts** *Why are water molecules attracted to one another?*

Solutions and Suspensions

Water is not always pure—it is often found as part of a mixture. A **mixture** is a material composed of two or more elements or compounds that are physically mixed together but not chemically combined. Salt and pepper stirred together constitute a mixture. So do sugar and sand. Earth's atmosphere is a mixture of gases. Living things are in part composed of mixtures involving water. Two types of mixtures that can be made with water are solutions and suspensions.

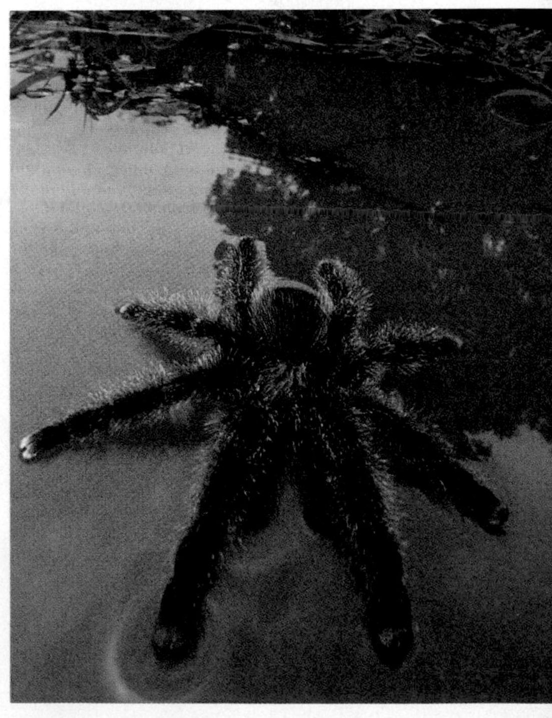

▶ **Figure 2–8** Cohesion is responsible for enabling this tarantula to rest on the water's surface. The strong attraction between water molecules produces a force sometimes called "surface tension," which can support very light objects, including this spider. **Observing** *How does the tarantula's physical structure help it to stay afloat?*

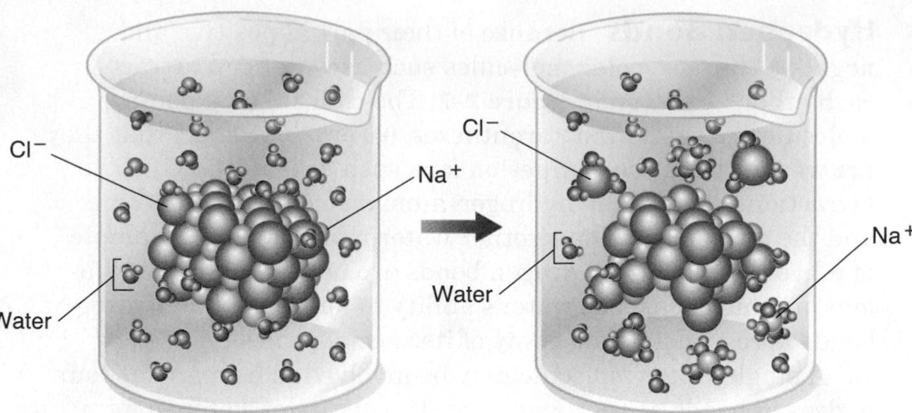

▶ **Figure 2–9** When an ionic compound such as sodium chloride is placed in water, water molecules surround and separate the positive and negative ions. **Interpreting Graphics** *What happens to the sodium ions and chloride ions in the solution?*

Quick Lab

Are foods acidic or basic?

Materials pH paper, samples of food, paper towel, scalpel, dropper pipette

Procedure   

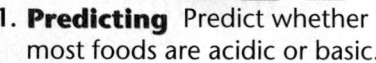

1. **Predicting** Predict whether most foods are acidic or basic.
2. If using a pH probe, see your teacher for instructions.
3. Tear off a small piece of pH paper for each sample you will test. Place these pieces on a paper towel.
4. Construct a data table in which you will record the name and pH of each food sample.
5. Use a scalpel to cut a piece off each solid. **CAUTION:** *Be careful not to cut yourself. Do not eat the food.* Touch the cut surface of each sample to a square of pH paper. Use a dropper pipette to place a drop of any liquid sample on a square of pH paper. Record the pH of each sample in your data table.

Analyze and Conclude

1. **Analyzing Data** Were most of the samples acidic or basic?
2. **Evaluating** Was your prediction correct?

Solutions If a crystal of table salt is placed in a glass of warm water, sodium and chloride ions on the surface of the crystal are attracted to the polar water molecules. Ions break away from the crystal and are surrounded by water molecules, as illustrated in **Figure 2–9.** The ions gradually become dispersed in the water, forming a type of mixture called a solution. All the components of a **solution** are evenly distributed throughout the solution. In a saltwater solution, table salt is the **solute**—the substance that is dissolved. Water is the **solvent**—the substance in which the solute dissolves. Water's polarity gives it the ability to dissolve both ionic compounds and other polar molecules, such as sugar. Without exaggeration, water is the greatest solvent on Earth.

Suspensions Some materials do not dissolve when placed in water but separate into pieces so small that they do not settle out. The movement of water molecules keeps the small particles suspended. Such mixtures of water and nondissolved material are known as **suspensions.** Some of the most important biological fluids are both solutions and suspensions. The blood that circulates through your body is mostly water, which contains many dissolved compounds. However, blood also contains cells and other undissolved particles that remain in suspension as the blood moves through the body.

Acids, Bases, and pH

A water molecule can react to form ions. This reaction can be summarized by a chemical equation in which double arrows are used to show that the reaction can occur in either direction.

$$H_2O \rightleftharpoons H^+ + OH^-$$

$$\text{water} \rightleftharpoons \text{hydrogen ion} + \text{hydroxide ion}$$

How often does this happen? In pure water, about 1 water molecule in 550 million reacts and forms ions. Because the number of positive hydrogen ions produced is equal to the number of negative hydroxide ions produced, water is neutral.

The pH scale Chemists devised a measurement system called the **pH scale** to indicate the concentration of H^+ ions in solution. As **Figure 2–10** shows, the pH scale ranges from 0 to 14. At a pH of 7, the concentration of H^+ ions and OH^- ions is equal. Pure water has a pH of 7. Solutions with a pH below 7 are called acidic because they have more H^+ ions than OH^- ions. The lower the pH, the greater the acidity. Solutions with a pH above 7 are called basic because they have more OH^- ions than H^+ ions. The higher the pH, the more basic the solution. Each step on the pH scale represents a factor of 10. For example, a liter of a solution with a pH of 4 has 10 times as many H^+ ions as a liter of a solution with a pH of 5.

Acids Where do all those extra H^+ ions in a low-pH solution come from? They come from acids. An **acid** is any compound that forms H^+ ions in solution. **Acidic solutions contain higher concentrations of H^+ ions than pure water and have pH values below 7.** Strong acids tend to have pH values that range from 1 to 3. The hydrochloric acid produced by the stomach to help digest food is a strong acid.

Bases A **base** is a compound that produces hydroxide ions (OH^- ions) in solution. **Basic, or alkaline, solutions contain lower concentrations of H^+ ions than pure water and have pH values above 7.** Strong bases, such as lye, tend to have pH values ranging from 11 to 14.

Buffers The pH of the fluids within most cells in the human body must generally be kept between 6.5 and 7.5. If the pH is lower or higher, it will affect the chemical reactions that take place within the cells. Thus, controlling pH is important for maintaining homeostasis. One of the ways that the body controls pH is through dissolved compounds called buffers. **Buffers** are weak acids or bases that can react with strong acids or bases to prevent sharp, sudden changes in pH.

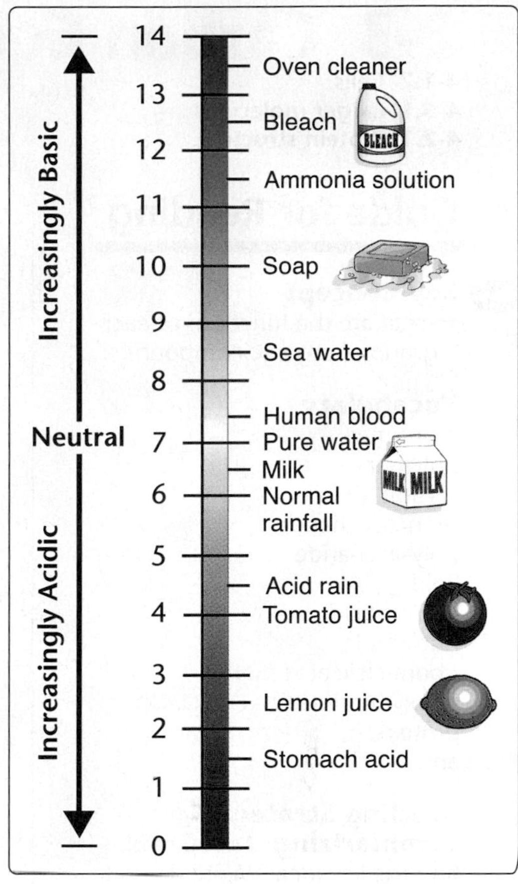

▲ **Figure 2–10** **The concentration of H^+ ions determines whether solutions are acidic or basic.** The most acidic material on this pH scale is stomach acid. The most basic material on this scale is oven cleaner.

2–2 Section Assessment

1. **Key Concept** Use the structure of a water molecule to explain why it is polar.
2. **Key Concept** Compare acidic and basic solutions in terms of their H^+ ion and OH^- ion concentrations.
3. What is the difference between a solution and a suspension?
4. What does pH measure?
5. **Critical Thinking Predicting** The strong acid hydrogen fluoride (HF) can be dissolved in pure water. Will the pH of the solution be greater or less than 7?

Thinking Visually

Creating a Concept Map

Draw a concept map on the properties of water. Include the following terms in your concept map: hydrogen bonds, polarity, cohesion, adhesion, capillary action, and solvent.

2–3 Carbon Compounds

4-1.2 Cells
4-5.1 Larger molecules
4-2.1 Protein structure
4-2.1 Proteins are responsible for much of the work of cells
4-5.1 Energy stored in chemical bonds

Guide for Reading

Key Concept
- What are the functions of each group of organic compounds?

Vocabulary
monomer
polymer
carbohydrate
monosaccharide
polysaccharide
lipid
nucleic acid
nucleotide
ribonucleic acid (RNA)
deoxyribonucleic acid (DNA)
protein
amino acid

Reading Strategy: Summarizing As you read, find the key ideas. Write down a few key words from each main idea. Then, use the key words in your summary. Reread your summary, keeping only the most important ideas.

Until the early 1800s, many chemists thought that compounds created by organisms—organic compounds—were distinctly different from compounds in nonliving things. In 1828, a German chemist was able to synthesize the organic compound urea from a mineral called ammonium cyanate. Chemists soon realized that the principles governing the chemistry of nonliving things could be applied to living things. Scientists still use the term *organic chemistry,* but now it describes something a little different. Today, organic chemistry is the study of all compounds that contain bonds between carbon atoms.

The Chemistry of Carbon

Is carbon so interesting that a whole branch of chemistry should be set aside just to study carbon compounds? It is indeed, for two reasons. First, carbon atoms have four valence electrons. Each electron can join with an electron from another atom to form a strong covalent bond. Carbon can bond with many elements, including hydrogen, oxygen, phosphorus, sulfur, and nitrogen.

Even more important, a carbon atom can bond to other carbon atoms, which gives carbon the ability to form chains that are almost unlimited in length. These carbon-carbon bonds can be single, double, or triple covalent bonds. Chains of carbon atoms can even close upon themselves to form rings, as shown in **Figure 2–11.** Carbon has the ability to form millions of different large and complex structures. No other element even comes close to matching carbon's versatility.

▼ **Figure 2–11** Carbon can form single, double, or triple bonds with other carbon atoms. Each line between atoms in a molecular drawing represents one covalent bond. **Observing** *How many covalent bonds are there between the carbon atoms in acetylene?*

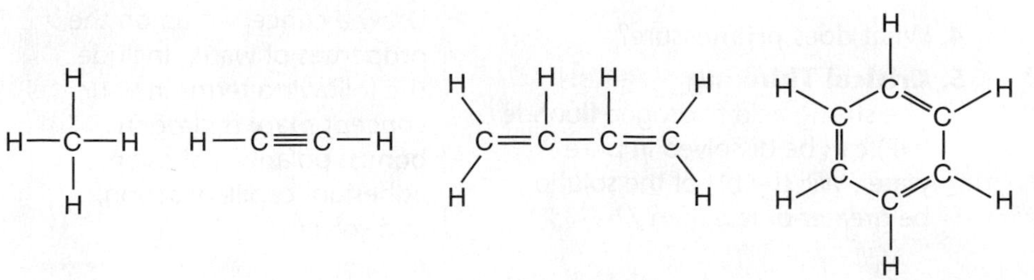

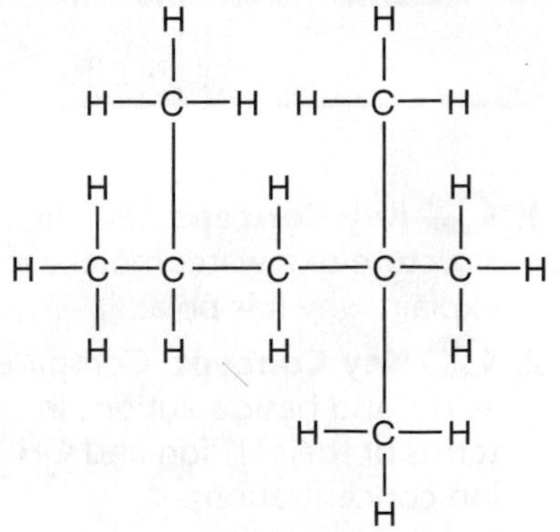

Methane
Acetylene
Butadiene
Benzene
Isooctane

Macromolecules

Many of the molecules in living cells are so large that they are known as macromolecules, which means "giant molecules." Macromolecules are made from thousands or even hundreds of thousands of smaller molecules.

Macromolecules are formed by a process known as polymerization (pah-lih-mur-ih-ZAY-shun), in which large compounds are built by joining smaller ones together. The smaller units, or **monomers,** join together to form **polymers.** The monomers in a polymer may be identical, like the links on a metal watch band; or the monomers may be different, like the beads in a multicolored necklace. **Figure 2–12** illustrates the formation of a polymer from more than one type of monomer.

It would be difficult to study the millions of organic compounds if they were not classified into groups. **Four groups of organic compounds found in living things are carbohydrates, lipids, nucleic acids, and proteins.** Sometimes these organic compounds are referred to as biomolecules. As you read about these molecules, compare their structures and functions.

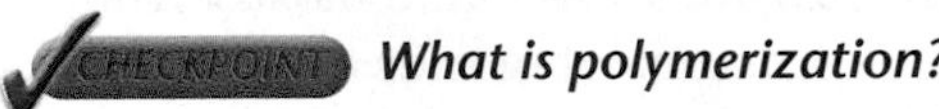

What is polymerization?

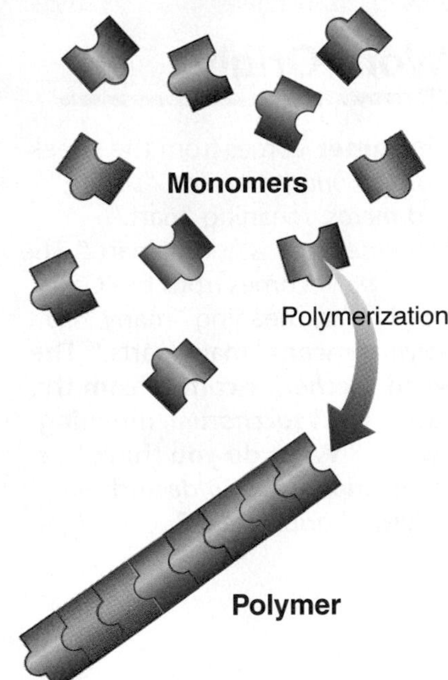

▲ **Figure 2–12** When small molecules called monomers join together, they form polymers, or large molecules. **Using Analogies** ***How are monomers similar to links in a chain?***

Carbohydrates

Carbohydrates are compounds made up of carbon, hydrogen, and oxygen atoms, usually in a ratio of 1 : 2 : 1. **Living things use carbohydrates as their main source of energy. Plants and some animals also use carbohydrates for structural purposes.** The breakdown of sugars, such as glucose, supplies immediate energy for all cell activities. Living things store extra sugar as complex carbohydrates known as starches. As shown in **Figure 2–13,** the monomers in starch polymers are sugar molecules.

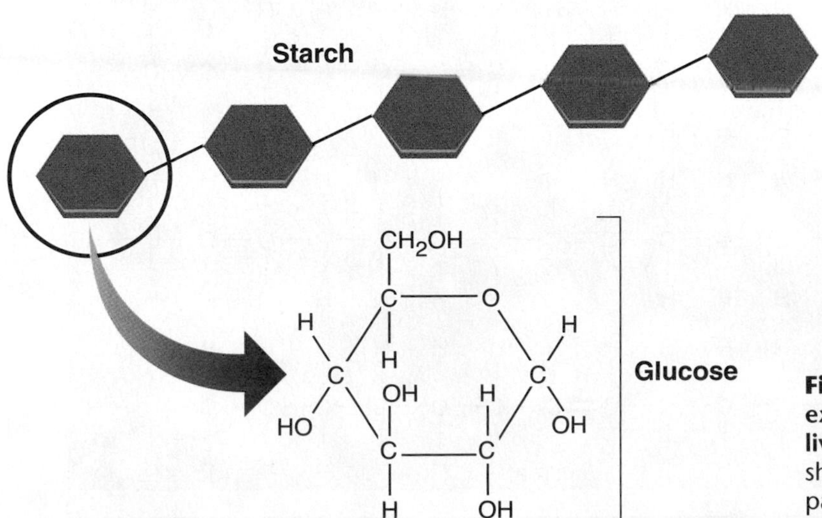

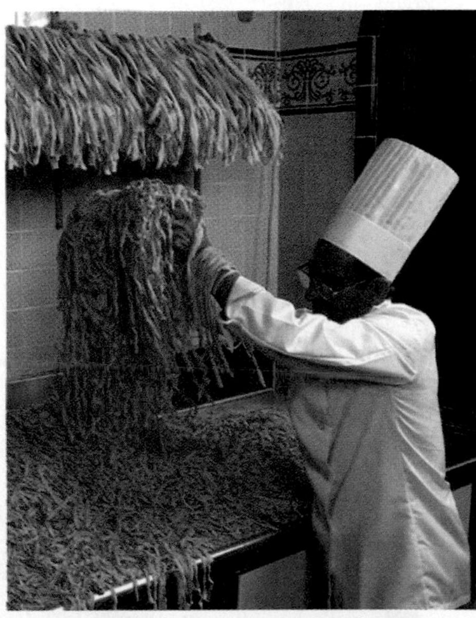

Figure 2–13 **Starches and sugars are examples of carbohydrates that are used by living things as a source of energy.** The chef shown here is drying pasta, which is made principally of starch. Starches form when sugars join together in a long chain.

Word Origins

Monomer comes from the Greek words *monos,* meaning "single," and *meros,* meaning "part." *Monomer* means "single part." The prefix *poly-* comes from the Greek word *polus,* meaning "many," so *polymer* means "many parts." **The word *saccharide* comes from the Latin word *saccharum,* meaning "sugar." What do you think the terms *monosaccharide* and *polysaccharide* mean?**

Single sugar molecules are also called **monosaccharides** (mahn-oh-SAK-uh-rydz). Besides glucose, monosaccharides include galactose, which is a component of milk, and fructose, which is found in many fruits.

The large macromolecules formed from monosaccharides are known as **polysaccharides.** Many animals store excess sugar in a polysaccharide called glycogen, or animal starch. When the level of glucose in your blood runs low, glycogen is released from your liver. The glycogen stored in your muscles supplies the energy for muscle contraction and, thus, for movement.

Plants use a slightly different polysaccharide, called plant starch, to store excess sugar. Plants also make another important polysaccharide called cellulose. Tough, flexible cellulose fibers give plants much of their strength and rigidity. Cellulose is the major component of both wood and paper, so you are actually looking at cellulose as you read these words!

Lipids

Lipids are a large and varied group of biological molecules that are generally not soluble in water. **Lipids** are made mostly from carbon and hydrogen atoms. The common categories of lipids are fats, oils, and waxes. **Lipids can be used to store energy. Some lipids are important parts of biological membranes and waterproof coverings.** Steroids are lipids as well. Many steroids serve as chemical messengers.

Many lipids are formed when a glycerol molecule combines with compounds called fatty acids, as shown in **Figure 2–14.** If each carbon atom in a lipid's fatty acid chains is joined to another carbon atom by a single bond, the lipid is said to be saturated. The term *saturated* is used because the fatty acids contain the maximum possible number of hydrogen atoms.

▼ Figure 2–14 Lipids are used to store energy. Lipid molecules are made up of fatty acids and glycerol. Liquid lipids, such as olive oil, contain mainly unsaturated fatty acids.

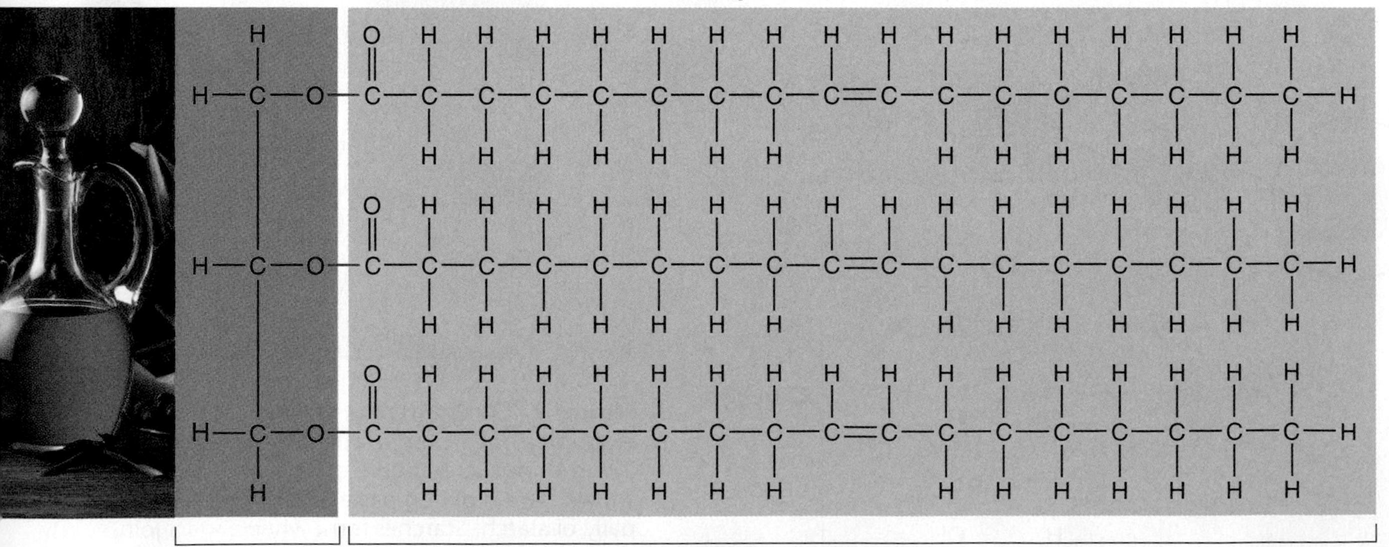

If there is at least one carbon-carbon double bond in a fatty acid, the fatty acid is said to be unsaturated. Lipids whose fatty acids contain more than one double bond are said to be polyunsaturated. If the terms *saturated* and *polyunsaturated* seem familiar, you have probably seen them on food package labels. Lipids such as olive oil, which contains unsaturated fatty acids, tend to be liquid at room temperature. Cooking oils, such as corn oil, sesame oil, canola oil, and peanut oil, contain polyunsaturated lipids.

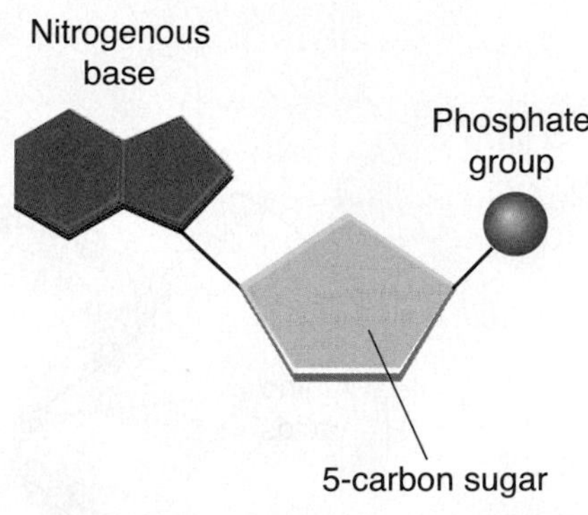

▲ **Figure 2–15 Nucleic acids store and transmit genetic information.** The monomers that make up a nucleic acid are nucleotides. Each nucleotide has a 5-carbon sugar, a phosphate group, and a nitrogenous base.

Nucleic Acids

Nucleic acids are macromolecules containing hydrogen, oxygen, nitrogen, carbon, and phosphorus. Nucleic acids are polymers assembled from individual monomers known as nucleotides. **Nucleotides** consist of three parts: a 5-carbon sugar, a phosphate group, and a nitrogenous base, as shown in **Figure 2–15.** Individual nucleotides can be joined by covalent bonds to form a polynucleotide, or nucleic acid.

Nucleic acids store and transmit hereditary, or genetic, information. There are two kinds of nucleic acids: **ribonucleic acid (RNA)** and **deoxyribonucleic acid (DNA).** As their names indicate, RNA contains the sugar ribose and DNA contains the sugar deoxyribose.

What are the three parts of a nucleotide?

Proteins

Proteins are macromolecules that contain nitrogen as well as carbon, hydrogen, and oxygen. Proteins are polymers of molecules called **amino acids.** Amino acids are compounds with an amino group ($-NH_2$) on one end and a carboxyl group ($-COOH$) on the other end.

Figure 2–16 shows one reason why proteins are among the most diverse macromolecules. More than 20 different amino acids are found in nature. All amino acids are identical in the regions where they may be joined together by covalent bonds. This uniformity allows any amino acid to be joined to any other amino acid—by bonding an amino group to a carboxyl group.

Amino Acids

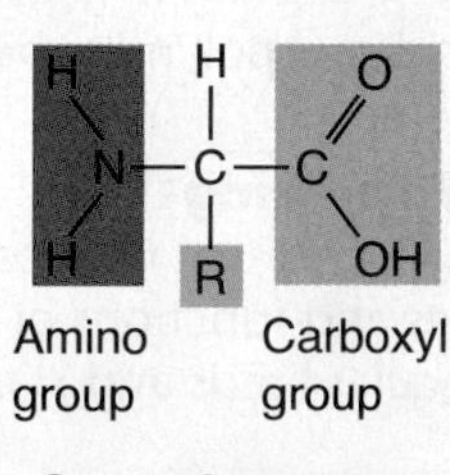

General structure

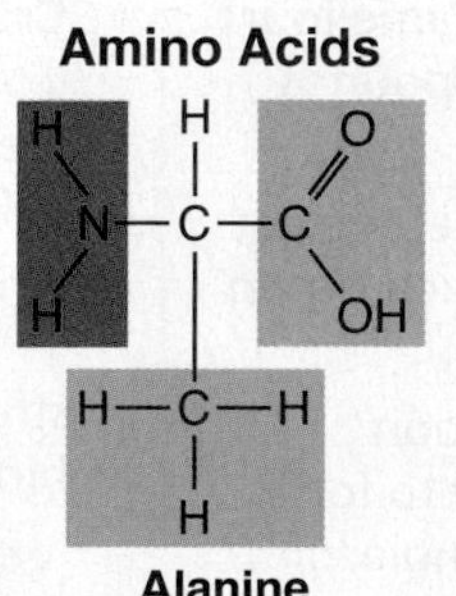

Alanine

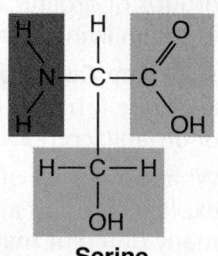

Serine

▶ **Figure 2–16** Amino acids are the monomers of proteins. All amino acids have an amino group at one end and a carboxyl group at the other end. What distinguishes one amino acid from another is the R-group section of the molecule. **Comparing and Contrasting** *How are proteins and carbohydrates similar? How are they different?*

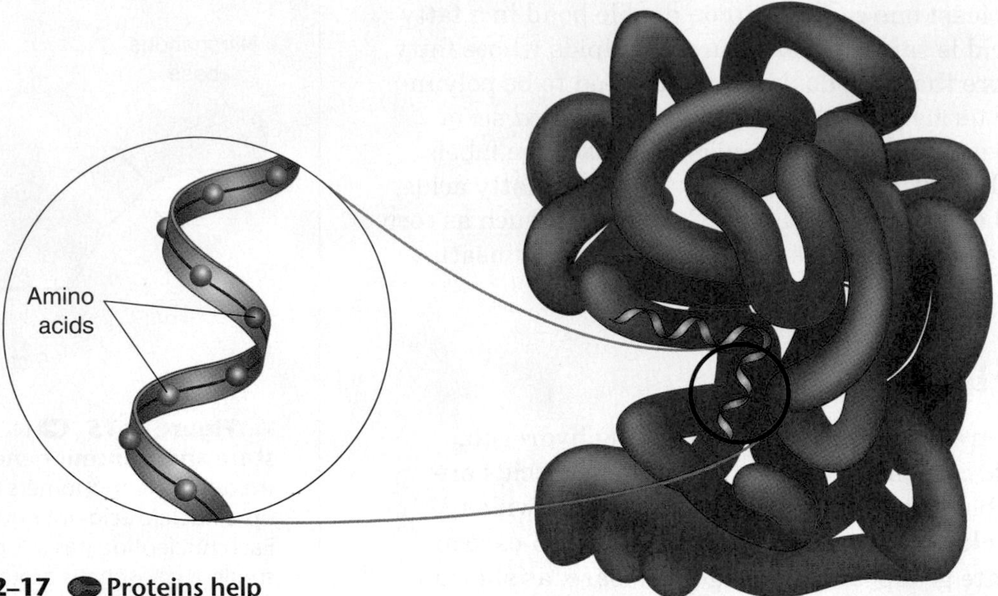

▲ **Figure 2–17 Proteins help to carry out chemical reactions, transport small molecules in and out of cells, and fight diseases.** Proteins are made up of chains of amino acids folded into complex structures.

The portion of each amino acid that is different is a side chain called an R-group. Some R-groups are acidic and some are basic. Some are polar and some are nonpolar. Some contain carbon rings. The instructions for arranging amino acids into many different proteins are stored in DNA. Each protein has a specific role. **Some proteins control the rate of reactions and regulate cell processes. Some are used to form bones and muscles. Others transport substances into or out of cells or help to fight disease.**

Proteins can have up to four levels of organization. The first level is the sequence of amino acids in a protein chain. Second, the amino acids within a chain can be twisted or folded. Third, the chain itself is folded. If a protein has more than one chain, each chain has a specific arrangement in space as shown by the red and blue structures in **Figure 2–17.** Van der Waals forces and hydrogen bonds help maintain a protein's shape. In the next section, you will learn why a protein's shape is so important.

Go Online
SCIENCE NEWS®
For: Articles on organic chemistry
Visit: PHSchool.com
Web Code: cbe-1023

2–3 Section Assessment

1. **Key Concept** Name four groups of organic compounds found in living things.
2. **Key Concept** Describe at least one function of each group of organic compounds.
3. What properties of carbon explain carbon's ability to form many different macromolecules?
4. **Critical Thinking Applying Concepts** Explain why proteins are considered polymers but lipids are not.
5. **Critical Thinking Comparing and Contrasting** Compare the structures and functions of the biomolecules lipids and starches.

Connecting Concepts

Levels of Organization
Use what you learned about levels of organization in Section 1–3 to discuss the levels of organization in macromolecules. Begin your discussion with the smallest structure.

2–4 Chemical Reactions and Enzymes

1-S3.1 Interpreting data
4-5.1 Photosynthesis connects solar energy with life
4-5.1 Enzymes are affected by pH and temperature
4-5.1 Enzymes

Living things, as you have seen, are made up of chemical compounds—some simple and some complex. But chemistry isn't just what life is made of—chemistry is also what life does. Everything that happens in an organism—its growth, its interaction with the environment, its reproduction, and even its movement—is based on chemical reactions.

Guide for Reading

Key Concepts
- What happens to chemical bonds during chemical reactions?
- How do energy changes affect whether a chemical reaction will occur?
- Why are enzymes important to living things?

Vocabulary
chemical reaction
reactant
product
activation energy
catalyst
enzyme
substrate

Reading Strategy: Building Vocabulary After you read, write a phrase or sentence in your own words to define or describe each highlighted, boldface term.

Chemical Reactions

A **chemical reaction** is a process that changes, or transforms, one set of chemicals into another. An important scientific principle is that mass and energy are conserved during chemical transformations. This is also true for chemical reactions that occur in living organisms. Some chemical reactions occur slowly, such as the combination of iron and oxygen to form an iron oxide called rust, shown in **Figure 2–18.** Other reactions occur quickly. The elements or compounds that enter into a chemical reaction are known as **reactants.** The elements or compounds produced by a chemical reaction are known as **products.**  **Chemical reactions always involve changes in the chemical bonds that join atoms in compounds.**

One example of an important chemical reaction that occurs in your body involves carbon dioxide. Your cells constantly produce carbon dioxide as a normal part of their activity. This carbon dioxide is carried to your lungs through the bloodstream, and then is eliminated as you exhale. However, carbon dioxide is not very soluble in water. The bloodstream could not possibly dissolve enough carbon dioxide to carry it away from your tissues were it not for a chemical reaction. As it enters the blood, carbon dioxide reacts with water to produce a highly soluble compound called carbonic acid, H_2CO_3.

$$CO_2 + H_2O \longrightarrow H_2CO_3$$

The reaction shown above enables the bloodstream to carry carbon dioxide to the lungs. In the lungs, the reaction is reversed.

$$H_2CO_3 \longrightarrow CO_2 + H_2O$$

This reverse reaction produces carbon dioxide gas, which is released as you exhale.

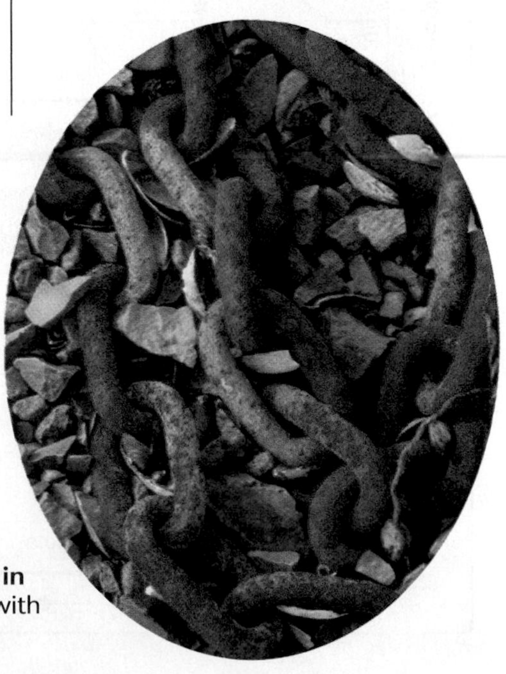

▶ **Figure 2–18** **Chemical reactions always involve changes in chemical bonds.** The iron in these chain links gradually combined with

Energy in Reactions

Energy is released or absorbed whenever chemical bonds form or are broken. Because chemical reactions involve breaking and forming bonds, they involve changes in energy.

Energy Changes Some chemical reactions release energy, and other reactions absorb energy. Energy changes are one of the most important factors in determining whether a chemical reaction will occur. **Chemical reactions that release energy often occur spontaneously. Chemical reactions that absorb energy will not occur without a source of energy.** An example of an energy-releasing reaction is hydrogen gas burning, or reacting, with oxygen to produce water vapor.

$$2H_2 + O_2 \longrightarrow 2H_2O$$

The energy is released in the form of heat, and sometimes—when hydrogen gas explodes—light and sound.

The reverse reaction, in which water is changed into hydrogen and oxygen gas, absorbs so much energy that it generally doesn't occur by itself. In fact, the only practical way to reverse the reaction is to pass an electrical current through water to decompose water into hydrogen gas and oxygen gas. Thus, in one direction the reaction produces energy, and in the other direction the reaction requires energy.

In order to stay alive, organisms need to carry out reactions that require energy. Because matter and energy are conserved in chemical reactions, every organism must have a source of energy to carry out chemical reactions. Plants get that energy by trapping and storing the energy from sunlight in energy-rich compounds. Animals get their energy when they consume plants or other animals. Humans release the energy needed to grow tall, to breathe, to think, and even to dream through the chemical reactions that occur when humans metabolize, or break down, digested food.

Activation Energy Even chemical reactions that release energy do not always occur spontaneously. That's a good thing because if they did, the pages of this book might burst into flames. The cellulose in paper burns in the presence of oxygen and releases heat and light. However, the cellulose will burn only if you light it with a match, which supplies enough energy to get the reaction started. Chemists call the energy that is needed to get a reaction started the **activation energy.** As **Figure 2–19** shows, activation energy is a factor in whether the overall chemical reaction releases energy or absorbs energy.

CHECKPOINT ***What is activation energy?***

▼ **Figure 2–19 Chemical reactions that release energy often occur spontaneously. Chemical reactions that absorb energy will occur only with a source of energy.** The peak of each graph represents the energy needed for the reaction to go forward. The difference between this required energy and the energy of the reactants is the activation energy.

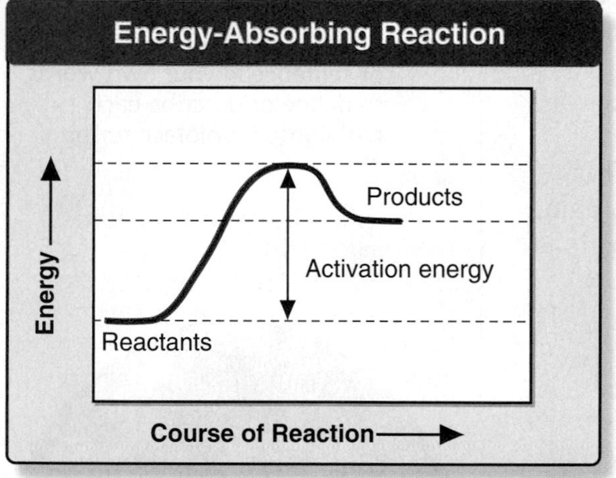

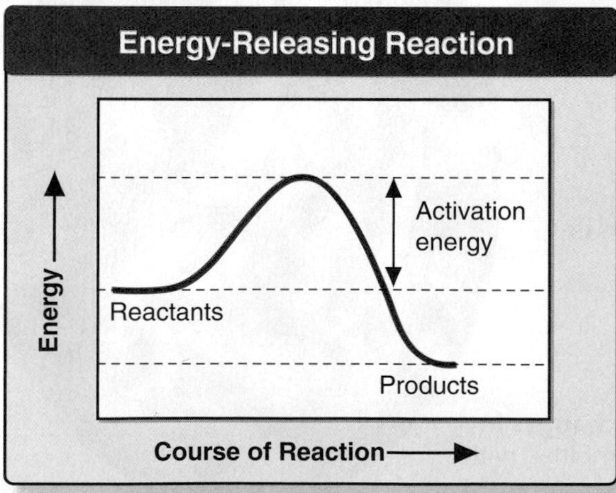

Analyzing Data

How Does pH Affect an Enzyme?

Catalase is an enzyme that helps decompose the toxic hydrogen peroxide that is produced during normal cell activities. The products of this reaction are water and oxygen gas. The pressure of the oxygen gas in a closed container increases as oxygen is produced. Any increase in the rate of the reaction will cause an increase in the pressure of the oxygen.

The purple line on the graph represents the normal rate of the reaction in a water solution of hydrogen peroxide and catalase. The red line represents the rate of reaction when an acid is added to the solution. The blue line represents the rate of reaction when a base is added to the solution.

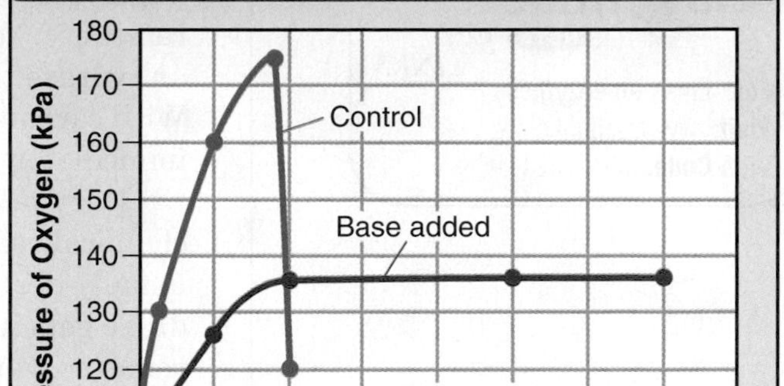

1. **Applying Concepts** What variable is plotted on the *x*-axis? What variable is plotted on the *y*-axis?
2. **Interpreting Graphics** How did the rate of reaction change over time in the control reaction?
3. **Inferring** Suggest an explanation for the change in the control reaction at about 40 seconds.
4. **Drawing Conclusions** What effect do acids and bases have on the enzyme catalase?
5. **Drawing Conclusions** Would it be valid to conclude that if a base were added, the rate of the reaction would slow down? Explain.
6. **Going Further** Predict what would happen if vinegar were added to a water solution of hydrogen peroxide and catalase.

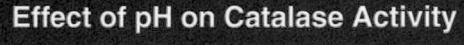

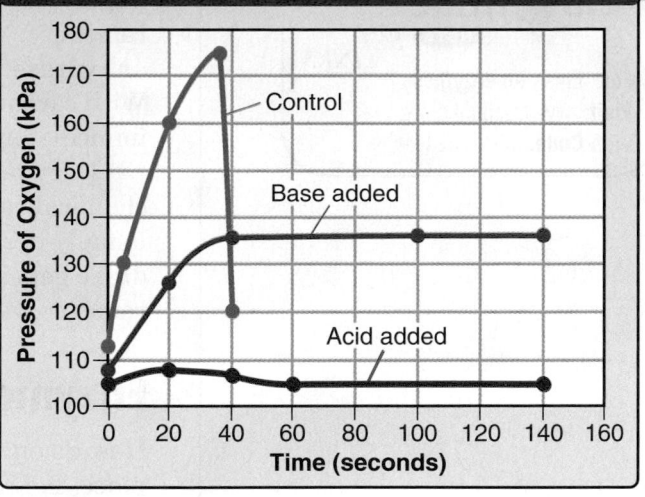

Enzymes

Some chemical reactions that make life possible are too slow or have activation energies that are too high to make them practical for living tissue. These chemical reactions are made possible by a process that would make any chemist proud—cells make catalysts. A **catalyst** is a substance that speeds up the rate of a chemical reaction. Catalysts work by lowering a reaction's activation energy.

Enzymes are proteins that act as biological catalysts. **Enzymes speed up chemical reactions that take place in cells.** Like other catalysts, enzymes act by lowering the activation energies, as illustrated by the graph in **Figure 2–20.** Lowering the activation energy has a dramatic effect on how quickly the reaction is completed. How big an effect does it have? Consider the reaction in which carbon dioxide combines with water to produce carbonic acid.

$$CO_2 + H_2O \longrightarrow H_2CO_3$$

▼ **Figure 2–20** **Enzymes speed up chemical reactions that take place in cells.** Notice how the addition of an enzyme lowers the activation energy in this reaction. This action speeds up the reaction.

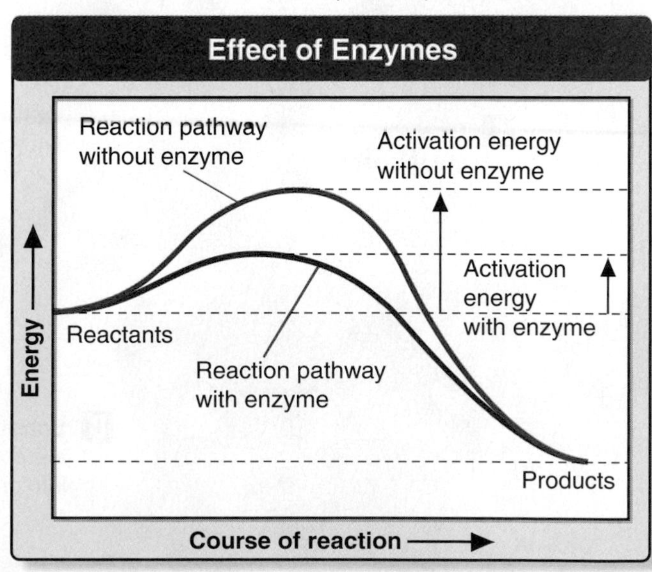

Left to itself, this reaction is so slow that carbon dioxide might build up in the body faster than the bloodstream could remove it. Your bloodstream contains an enzyme called carbonic anhydrase that speeds up the reaction by a factor of 10 million. With carbonic anhydrase on the job, the reaction takes place immediately and carbon dioxide is removed from the blood quickly.

Enzymes are very specific, generally catalyzing only one chemical reaction. For this reason, part of an enzyme's name is usually derived from the reaction it catalyzes. Carbonic anhydrase gets its name because it catalyzes the reaction that removes water from carbonic acid.

Enzyme Action

How do enzymes do their jobs? For a chemical reaction to take place, the reactants must collide with enough energy so that existing bonds will be broken and new bonds will be formed. If the reactants do not have enough energy, they will be unchanged after the collision.

The Enzyme-Substrate Complex Enzymes provide a site where reactants can be brought together to react. Such a site reduces the energy needed for reaction. The reactants of enzyme-catalyzed reactions are known as **substrates.**

▼ **Figure 2–21** The enzyme hexokinase converts the substrates glucose and ATP into glucose-6-phosphate and ADP. **Predicting** *What happens to the hexokinase after the products are released?*

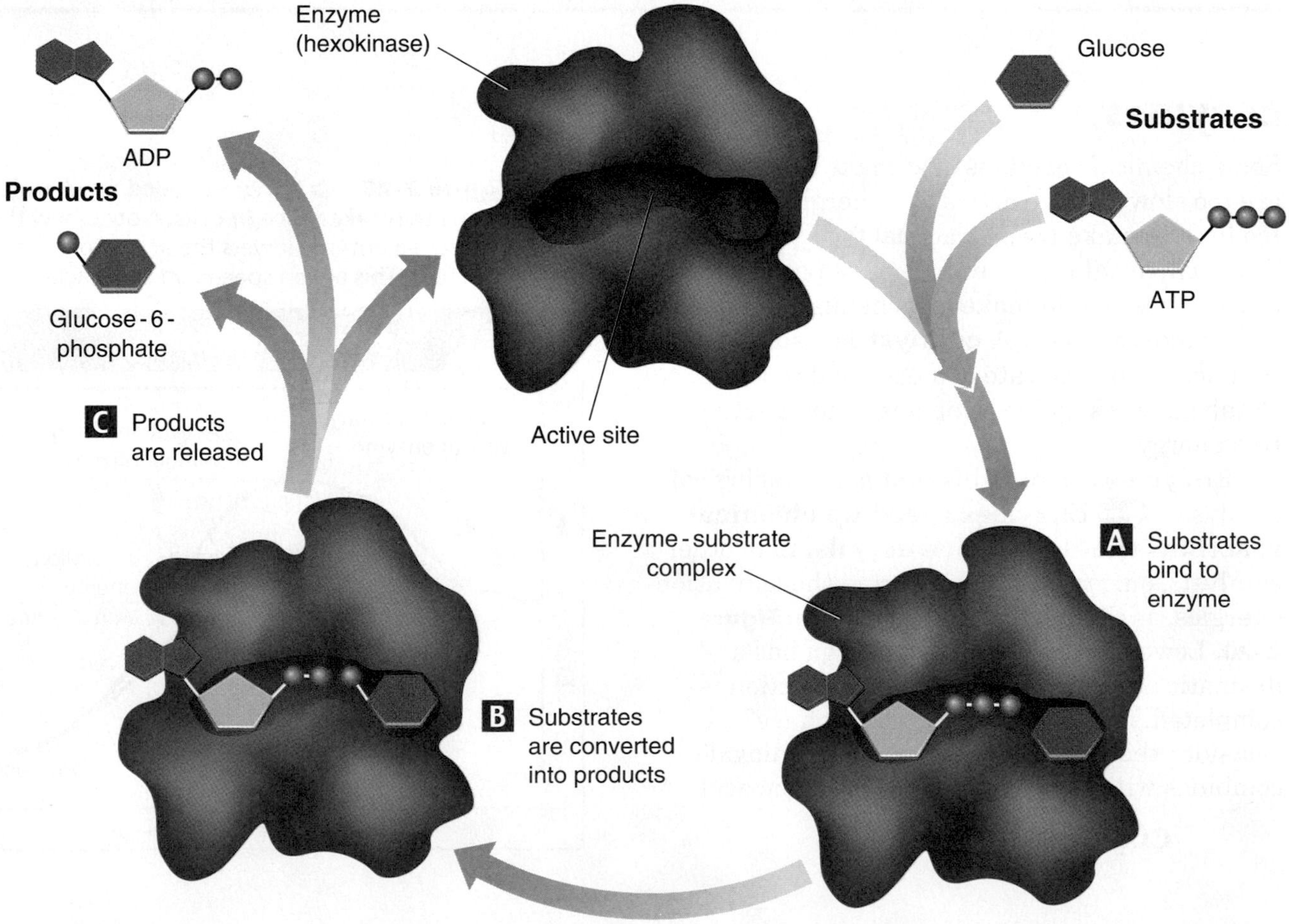

Enzyme (hexokinase)
Glucose
Substrates
ADP
Products
ATP
Glucose-6-phosphate
Active site
C Products are released
Enzyme-substrate complex
A Substrates bind to enzyme
B Substrates are converted into products

Figure 2–21 provides an example of an enzyme-catalyzed reaction. The enzyme is hexokinase. The substrates are glucose and ATP. During the reaction, a phosphate group is transferred from ATP to the glucose molecule. Recall that each protein has a specific, complex shape. The substrates bind to a site on the enzyme called the active site. The active site and the substrates have complementary shapes. The fit is so precise that the active site and substrates are often compared to a lock and key.

Figure 2–22 shows a substrate fitting into an active site on an enzyme. The enzyme and substrate are bound together by intermolecular forces and form an enzyme-substrate complex. They remain bound together until the reaction is done. Once the reaction is over, the products of the reaction are released and the enzyme is free to start the process again.

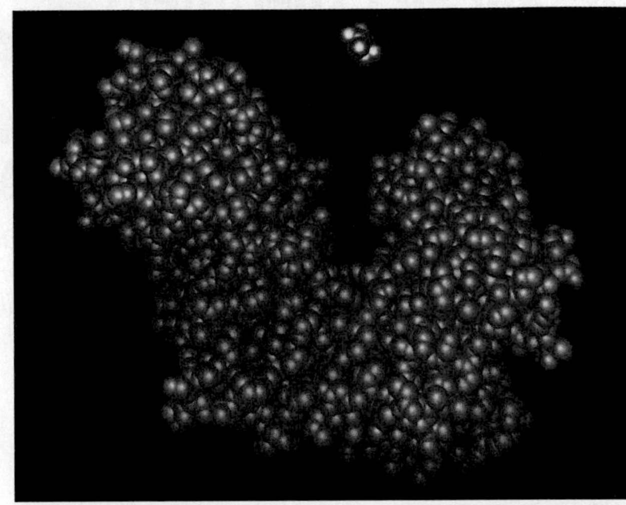

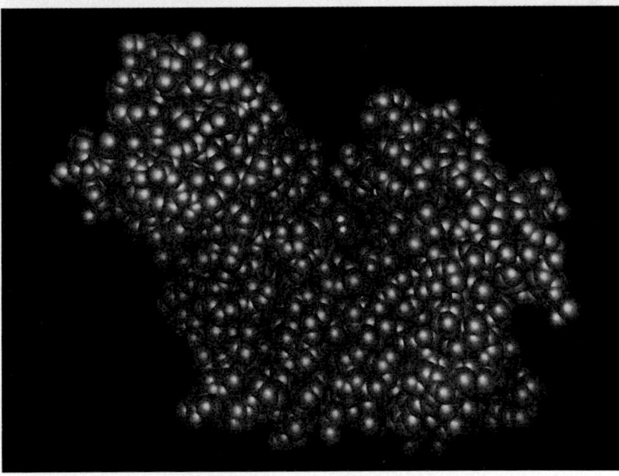

▲ **Figure 2–22** This space-filling model shows how a substrate binds to an active site on an enzyme. **Interpreting Graphics** *What happens after the substrate binds to the enzyme?*

Regulation of Enzyme Activity Because they are catalysts for reactions, enzymes can be affected by any variable that influences a chemical reaction. Enzymes, including those that help digest food, work best at certain pH values. Many enzymes are affected by changes in temperature. Not surprisingly, those enzymes produced by human cells generally work best at temperatures close to 37°C, the normal temperature of the human body.

Cells can regulate the activities of enzymes in a variety of ways. Most cells contain proteins that help to turn key enzymes "on" or "off" at critical stages in the life of the cell. Enzymes play essential roles in regulating chemical pathways, making materials that cells need, releasing energy, and transferring information.

2–4 Section Assessment

1. **Key Concept** What happens to chemical bonds during chemical reactions?
2. **Key Concept** Describe the role of energy in chemical reactions.
3. **Key Concept** What are enzymes, and how are they important to living things?
4. Describe how enzymes work, including the role of the enzyme-substrate complex.
5. **Critical Thinking Applying Concepts** A change in pH can change the shape of a protein. How might a change in pH affect the function of an enzyme such as hexokinase? (*Hint:* Think about the analogy of the lock and key.)

Sharpen Your Skills

Modeling

Make a model that demonstrates how an active site and a substrate are like a lock and a key. Give a brief talk in which you refer to your model as you explain how enzymes work.

Design an Experiment

Investigating the Effect of Temperature on Enzyme Activity

Almost all chemical reactions that occur in living organisms are catalyzed by enzymes. Many factors in a cell's environment affect the action of an enzyme. In this investigation, you will design an experiment to determine the effect of temperature on an enzyme-catalyzed reaction.

Problem How does temperature affect the rate of an enzyme-catalyzed reaction?

Materials

- raw liver
- petri dish
- dropper pipette
- 1% hydrogen peroxide solution
- liver puree
- 25-mL graduated cylinder
- five 50-mL beakers
- filter-paper disks
- forceps
- glass-marking pencil
- ice bath
- 3 thermometers
- warm water bath
- clock or watch with second hand
- paper towel

Skills Formulating Hypotheses, Predicting

Design Your Experiment    

Part A: Observe the Catalase Reaction

1. Put on your apron, gloves, and safety goggles. Use forceps to place a small piece of raw liver in an open petri dish. Use a dropper pipette to put a drop of hydrogen peroxide solution on the liver. **CAUTION:** *Hydrogen peroxide can be irritating to skin and eyes. If you spill any on yourself or your clothes, wash it off immediately and tell your teacher.* Observe what happens. Liver contains the enzyme catalase, which breaks down hydrogen peroxide (H_2O_2) to water (H_2O) and oxygen gas (O_2). When hydrogen peroxide, which is formed in cells, is broken down by catalase, bubbles of oxygen gas are released.
2. With your teacher's guidance, select the proper equipment and technology to measure catalase activity—either a filter-paper disk or an oxygen probe. If using an oxygen probe, see your teacher for instructions.
3. To measure the activity of catalase, use a graduated cylinder to place 25 mL of hydrogen peroxide solution in a 50-mL beaker.

4. Use forceps to dip a filter-paper disk in liver puree. Place the filter-paper disk on a paper towel for 4 seconds to remove any excess liquid.
5. Use the forceps to place the filter-paper disk at the bottom of the beaker of hydrogen peroxide solution. Observe the filter-paper disk and record the number of seconds it takes to float to the top of the liquid.

Part B: Design an Experiment

6 **Formulating Hypotheses** Use your observations and knowledge to develop a hypothesis. Develop a hypothesis about how temperature will affect the rate at which catalase breaks down hydrogen peroxide. Record your hypothesis.

7 **Designing Experiments** Design an experiment to test your hypothesis. Your experimental plan should include a prediction of the result based on your hypothesis, and any appropriate controls and replications (repetitions). Be sure to identify all manipulated, responding, and controlled variables in your experimental plan. Include any necessary safety precautions and safety equipment in your plan.

8 As you plan your investigative procedures, refer to the Lab Tips box on this page for information on demonstrating safe practices, making wise choices in the use of materials, and selecting equipment and technology.

9 Construct a data table in which to record the results of your experiment. Perform your experiment only after you have obtained your teacher's approval of your plan.

10 Make a graph of the results of your experiment. Plot temperature on the *x*-axis and the variable by which you measured catalase activity on the *y*-axis. With your teacher's guidance, select the proper equipment and technology to use—either graph paper or a graphing calculator.

Analyze and Conclude

1. **Inferring** How does the time required for a catalase-soaked filter-paper disk to float reflect the amount of catalase activity in the solution?
2. **Inferring** How did temperature affect catalase activity? Was your prediction confirmed?
3. **Drawing Conclusions** Many mammals, including cattle and pigs, have body temperatures close to 37°C. Does your graph indicate that catalase is most active close to that temperature? How might mammals benefit from that relationship?
4. **Evaluating** Identify and discuss possible sources of error in your procedure.
5. **SAFETY** Explain how you demonstrated safe practices when using hydrogen peroxide.

Lab Tips

Demonstrate Safe Practices

Consider what safety precautions you will need to take. Review the Science Safety Rules and Safety Symbols on pages 1066–1068. In your experimental plan, include any needed safety precautions. For example, if you will be using an irritating chemical, you should wear an apron, goggles, and plastic gloves. Review your plan with your teacher and get it approved before beginning your experiment.

Make Wise Choices in the Use of Materials

Consider how you will use materials wisely. For example, how can you use a reusable container rather than a disposable one? For materials that cannot be reused in the lab, consider whether they can be recycled. If a material cannot be recycled, determine whether any precautions for disposal must be taken to prevent soil or water contamination. Make sure your teacher has approved your material-use plan before beginning your experiment.

Select Equipment and Technology

Consider what equipment and technology you might need to use. If Probeware can be used to collect data, consider whether doing so will improve precision.

Evaluate Your Experimental Design

Follow scientific procedures, including those described in Appendix A. Identify and define the manipulated, responding, and controlled variables. Identify and discuss possible sources of error. Write needed operational definitions.

Go Further

Designing Experiments Catalase is also found in potatoes. Design an experiment using potato puree instead of liver puree to determine the temperature at which potato catalase is most active.

Chapter 2 Study Guide

2–1 The Nature of Matter

Key Concepts

- The subatomic particles that make up atoms are protons, neutrons, and electrons.
- Because they have the same number of electrons, all isotopes of an element have the same chemical properties.
- The main types of chemical bonds are covalent bonds and ionic bonds.

Vocabulary

atom, p. 35 • nucleus, p. 35 • electron, p. 35
element, p. 36 • isotope, p. 36
compound, p. 37 • ionic bond, p. 38
ion, p. 38 • covalent bond, p. 38
molecule, p. 38 • van der Waals forces, p. 39

2–2 Properties of Water

Key Concepts

- A water molecule is polar because there is an uneven distribution of electrons between the oxygen and hydrogen atoms.
- Acidic solutions contain higher concentrations of H^+ ions than pure water and have pH values below 7.
- Basic, or alkaline, solutions contain lower concentrations of H^+ ions than pure water and have pH values above 7.

Vocabulary

cohesion, p. 41 • adhesion, p. 41 • mixture, p. 41
solution, p. 42 • solute, p. 42 • solvent, p. 42
suspension, p. 42 • pH scale, p. 43 • acid, p. 43
base, p. 43 • buffer, p. 43

2–3 Carbon Compounds

Key Concepts

- Four groups of organic compounds found in living things are carbohydrates, lipids, nucleic acids, and proteins.
- Living things use carbohydrates as their main source of energy. Plants and some animals also use carbohydrates for structural purposes.
- Lipids can be used to store energy. Some lipids are important parts of biological membranes and waterproof coverings.
- Nucleic acids store and transmit hereditary, or genetic, information.
- Some proteins control the rate of reactions and regulate cell processes. Some proteins build tissues such as bone and muscle. Others transport materials or help to fight disease.

Vocabulary

monomer, p. 45 • polymer, p. 45
carbohydrate, p. 45 • monosaccharide, p. 46
polysaccharide, p. 46 • lipid, p. 46
nucleic acid, p. 47 • nucleotide, p. 47
ribonucleic acid (RNA), p. 47
deoxyribonucleic acid (DNA), p. 47
protein, p. 47 • amino acid, p. 47

2–4 Chemical Reactions and Enzymes

Key Concepts

- Chemical reactions always involve changes in the chemical bonds that join atoms in compounds.
- Chemical reactions that release energy often occur spontaneously. Chemical reactions that absorb energy will not occur without a source of energy.
- Enzymes speed up chemical reactions that take place in cells.

Vocabulary

chemical reaction, p. 49 • reactant, p. 49
product, p. 49 • activation energy, p. 50
catalyst, p. 51 • enzyme, p. 51 • substrate, p. 52

Thinking Visually

Create a table in which you compare the structures and functions of the following biomolecules: carbohydrates, lipids, proteins, and nucleic acids.

Preparing for the Living Environment Exam

Blue questions emphasize Regents Exam content

Chapter 2

Part A

Multiple Choice

For each statement or question, select the number of the word or expression that, of those given, best completes the statement or answers the question.

1 Two or more different elements are chemically combined in definite proportions in any
(1) symbol (3) element
(2) isotope (4) compound

2 A covalent bond is formed by the
(1) transfer of electrons
(2) sharing of electrons
(3) gaining of electrons
(4) losing of electrons

3 Examples of large, complex molecules formed by joining together many smaller molecules include
(1) proteins and amino acids
(2) carbohydrates and sugars
(3) DNA and proteins
(4) mitochondria and vacuoles

4 Which formula represents an amino acid?

```
     H   H   H   OH  H   H
     |   |   |   |   |   |
  H--C---C---C---C---C---C==O
     |   |   |   |   |
A    OH  OH  OH  H   OH
```

```
       H                          H
       |                          |
    H--C--OH                   H--C--OH
       |                          |
       C------O                   C------O
    H /|       \  H            H /|       \  OH
     / H        \ |             / H        \ |
    C            C             C            C
    |\ OH     H /  \         / |\ OH     H /|
  HO  \ |     |/    \       /     \ |    |/  H
       C------C      \  O  /       C------C
       |      |       \ | /        |      |
B      H      OH        O          H      OH
```

```
     H  H  O
     |  |  ||
  H--N--C--C--OH
        |
     H--C--H
        |
C       H
```

```
     H   H   OH  OH  H   H
     |   |   |   |   |   |
  H--C---C---C---C---C---C==O
     |   |   |   |   |
D    OH  OH  H   H   OH
```

(1) formula A (3) formula C
(2) formula B (4) formula D

5 When you shake sugar and sand together in a test tube, you cause them to form a
(1) compound (3) solution
(2) mixture (4) suspension

6 Proteins are organic molecules formed from
(1) fats (3) amino acids
(2) carbohydrates (4) simple sugars

7 A protein that acts as a biological catalyst is a(an)
(1) enzyme (3) hormone
(2) fat (4) simple sugar

8 In humans, carbon dioxide and water quickly combine to form carbonic acid in the presence of a particular enzyme. Most likely, this same enzyme
(1) helps in the breakdown of acidic foods in the stomach
(2) is not involved in other types of reactions because enzymes are specific
(3) is involved in other reactions where the temperature and pH are the same
(4) helps in the synthesis of sugars during photosynthesis

9 Which is *not* an organic molecule found in living organisms?
(1) protein (3) sugar
(2) water (4) carbohydrate

10 Which combination of particle and charge is correct?
(1) proton: positively charged
(2) electron: positively charged
(3) neutron: negatively charged
(4) electron: no charge

11 In which way do isotopes of the same element differ?
(1) in number of neutrons, only
(2) in number of protons, only
(3) in number of protons and in mass
(4) in number of neutrons and in mass

Test-Taking Tip As you briefly scan the questions, mark those that may require pure guesswork on your part and save them for last. (Do not write in this book.) Use whatever time you have left for those questions to eliminate as many answers as possible through reasoning.

Preparing for the Living Environment Exam

Part B

Multiple Choice and Extended Response

For those questions that ask you to select a response, choose the one that best completes the statement or answers the question. For all others follow the directions given.

For questions 12 through 14, select the best choice among those listed below. A choice may be used once, more than once, or not at all.

A Cohesion
B Adhesion
C Catalysts
D Reactants
E Products

12 An attraction between different substances

13 Lowers a chemical reaction's activation energy

14 The elements or compounds that enter into a chemical reaction

---

15 State the relationship between an enzyme and a catalyst.

16 State *two* factors that may influence enzyme activity.

17 State what substance could be added to a solution to decrease the pH. Support your answer with an explanation.

18 State why it is important that energy-releasing reactions take place in living organisms.

19 The bar graph below shows the total amount of product from a chemical reaction performed at three different temperatures. The same enzyme was involved in each case.

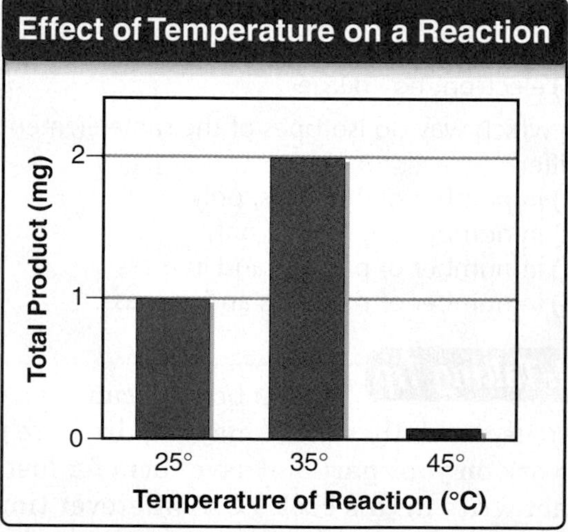

- Compare the activity of this enzyme at the three temperatures.
- State one likely explanation for the activity shown at 45°C.

Base your answers to questions 20 through 22 on the information and graph below and on your knowledge of biology.

The enzyme catalase speeds up the chemical reaction that changes hydrogen peroxide into oxygen and water. The amount of oxygen given off is an indication of the rate of the reaction.

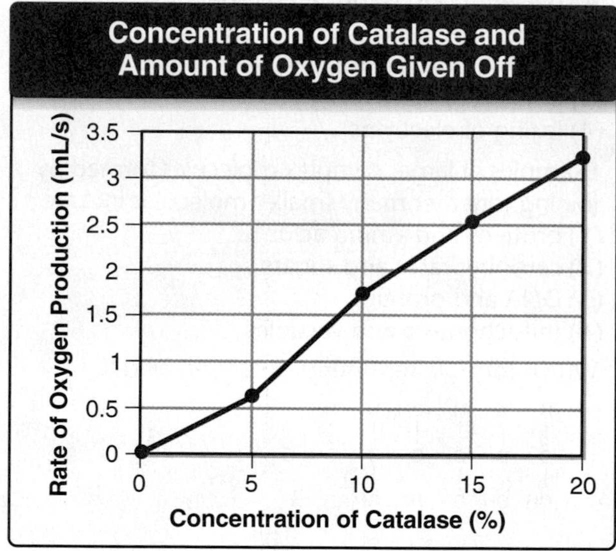

20 Based on the graph, state the relationship between enzyme concentration and reaction rate.

21 Which concentration of catalase will produce the fastest reaction rate?
(1) 0%
(2) 10%
(3) 15%
(4) 20%

22 Catalase is found in a variety of human body tissues. State one way the graph would be different if the pH of the hydrogen peroxide and catalase was reduced from pH 7.1 to a pH of 5.2. Support your answer with an explanation.

---

23 *a* State one way that acids and bases differ, other than by their pH values.

b Describe how the pH value can be used to identify an acid, a base, and a neutral solution.

Part C

Extended Response

Answer the questions or follow the directions given.

Base your answers to questions 24 and 25 on the reading passage below and on your knowledge of biology.

Molecular Modeling

The way a molecule behaves chemically, along with its physical characteristics, provides information about the numbers and kinds of atoms making it up. For centuries chemists and biologists have been working to find out more about chemical bonds and molecular structure.

Molecular modeling allows scientists to build and visualize molecules. With this information, scientists have the ability to design new and more potent drugs to use in the fight against various diseases. For example, based on experimental evidence, researchers proposed that the outer protein shell of most viruses is composed of small, repeating subunits. They thought these subunits were packed together in such a way that all sides of a virus are provided with an identical environment. Through the use of modern electron microscopes and molecular modeling, these ideas have been confirmed. Learning more about the structure of viruses may make it easier to combat viral diseases.

Molecular modeling has become important in designing medications and in learning more about biological structures. Recently, the structural arrangement and bonding patterns of several proteins important in the process of photosynthesis were discovered. Scientists will be able to use this knowledge to develop systems that can carry out artificial photosynthesis.

24 Molecular modeling involves the use of
(1) potent drugs that can modify proteins
(2) modeling clay and other materials to construct representations of viruses
(3) high-speed computers in learning more about the shape of molecules
(4) powerful computers to carry out photosynthesis in space

25 State *two* ways molecular modeling can improve our lives.

Base your answers to questions 26 and 27 on the information below and on your knowledge of biology.

Often a model referred to as a "lock and key" model is used to describe the way an enzyme works.

26 Explain why comparing the way a key and a lock work together is a good analogy for explaining how an enzyme works.

27 State one way this lock-and-key analogy is *not* perfect.

28 The most abundant organic compounds in living things are classified into four groups. Lipids and nucleic acids are two of the groups. Identify the *two* other large groups of organic compounds and state *two* ways each of the two groups is important to the normal functioning of living organisms.

29 A student conducted an experiment to determine whether pH can affect the rate at which an enzyme found in yeast cells breaks down hydrogen peroxide. In the investigation, yeast, hydrogen peroxide, and several solutions at various pH values were used. Describe the essential parts of this experiment.

- State one likely hypothesis that would be tested in this investigation.
- Identify what the manipulated (independent) and responding (dependent) variables were for this investigation.
- Identify one specific variable that must be kept the same for *all* of the setups.

For: An interactive self-test
Visit: PHSchool.com
Web Code: cba-1020

UNIT

2 Ecology

Chapters

▶ Like all living things, alligators such as this one are involved in interactions with other living things (trees and vines) and with their physical surroundings (water, air, and climate).

From the Author

There's a swamp behind my house. You may think "Swamp? Ugh!" But I'm glad it's there. Whenever I walk through it, I see something new—a rare bird, a mushroom, or a fragrant flower. I go there to learn and enjoy. But that swamp is important in another way. Roughly a third of my town is swamp, marsh, river, stream, or pond. That's part of the reason why the residents often have water in their wells when other towns run dry. This is a mini ecology lesson: Natural habitats aren't just pretty—they support life, as well.

What discoveries lie ahead?

- Can our society learn how to produce the food and energy we need while preserving the environment?
- How will the introduction of new species affect native plants and animals?

Go Online
PHSchool.com

For: Latest discoveries
Visit: PHSchool.com
Web Code: cbe-2000

CHAPTER 3 The Biosphere

A tawny owl prepares to seize a mouse. The mouse is carrying a berry in its mouth as it runs along a fallen, moss-covered tree trunk. The owl, the mouse, the tree trunk, and the moss are all members of this forest ecosystem.

Inquiry Activity

How do organisms affect one another's survival?

Procedure

1. Make a list of all the types of organisms, including plants, humans, insects, and so on, that you have seen near your home or school.
2. Make a diagram that shows how the organisms on your list interact with one another.

Think About It

1. **Classifying** Which organisms on your list provide energy or nutrients to the others?
2. **Predicting** What would you expect to happen if all the plants on your diagram died? Explain your answer.
3. **Asking Questions** Why is it difficult to make accurate predictions about changes in communities of organisms?

3–1 What Is Ecology?

1-S1.1 Science combines what is known with new evidence
1-S1.2 Inquiry
4-1.1 Populations and food webs—concepts and terminology
4-1.1 Ecosystems
4-1.1 Interactions in ecosystems

Guide for Reading

Key Concepts
- What different levels of organization do ecologists study?
- What methods are used to study ecology?

Vocabulary
ecology
biosphere
species
population
community
ecosystem
biome

Reading Strategy: Asking Questions Before you read, rewrite the headings in this section as *how, what,* or *why* questions about ecology. Then, as you read, write brief answers to your questions.

"Floods hit Texas!" "Wildfires char three states!" "Drought withers Florida!" Such news often flashes across television screens, newspapers, and the Internet. We are fascinated and frightened by these natural events, but there are other stories, as well. Some tell of projects to restore wetlands in southern Florida and along the Mississippi River for the purpose of controlling floods and droughts. Others report on improvements in air and water quality as a result of changes in the gasoline that we put in our cars. Like all organisms, we interact with our environment. To understand these interactions better and to learn how to control them, we turn to the science called ecology.

Interactions and Interdependence

Ecology (ee-KAHL-uh-jee) is the scientific study of interactions among organisms and between organisms and their environment, or surroundings. The word *ecology* was coined in 1866 by the German biologist Ernst Haeckel. Haeckel based this term on the Greek word *oikos,* meaning house, which is also the root of the word *economy.* Haeckel saw the living world as a household with an economy in which each organism plays a role.

Nature's "houses" come in many sizes—from single cells to the entire planet. The largest of these houses is called the biosphere. The **biosphere** contains the combined portions of the planet in which all of life exists, including land, water, and air, or atmosphere. It extends from about 8 kilometers above Earth's surface to as far as 11 kilometers below the surface of the ocean.

Interactions within the biosphere produce a web of interdependence between organisms and the environment in which they live. Whether it occurs on top of a glacier, in a forest like the one in **Figure 3–1,** or deep within an ocean trench, the interdependence of life on Earth contributes to an ever-changing, or dynamic, biosphere.

▶ **Figure 3–1** Organisms and their environment are interdependent. This giant land snail could not survive without plants and algae to eat, and the plants and algae could not grow unless bacteria and other organisms helped recycle nutrients in the water and soil. **Classifying** *List the organisms that you see in the photograph. Then, list the nonliving parts of the environment with which the organisms interact.*

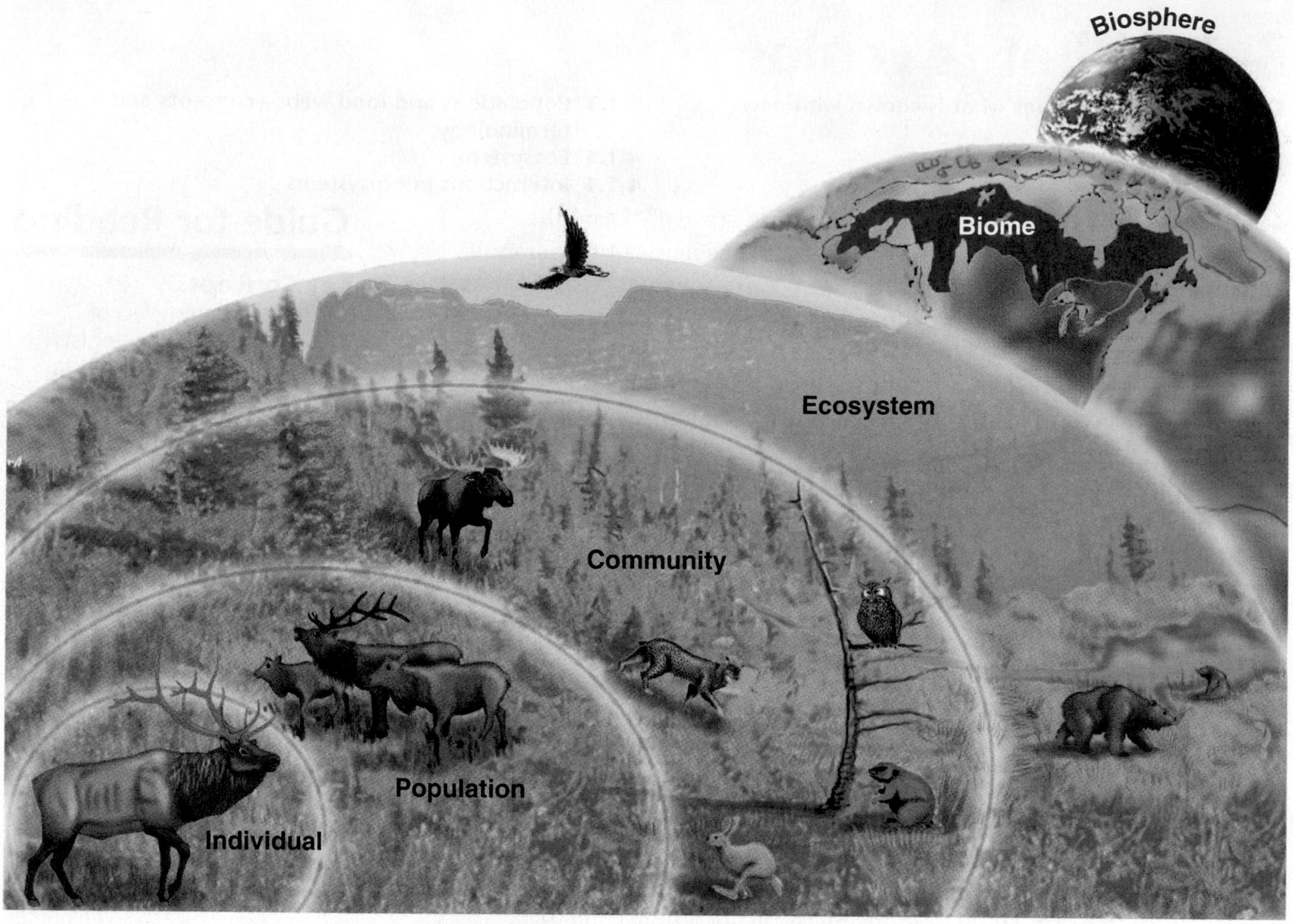

▲ **Figure 3–2** **The study of ecology ranges from the study of an individual organism to populations, communities, ecosystems, biomes—and, finally, to the entire biosphere.** The information that ecologists gain at each level contributes to our understanding of natural systems.

Levels of Organization

To understand relationships within the biosphere, ecologists ask questions about events and organisms that range in complexity from a single individual to the entire biosphere. The many levels of organization that ecologists study are shown in **Figure 3–2.**

Some ecologists study interactions between a particular kind of organism and its surroundings. Such studies focus on the species level. A **species** is a group of organisms so similar to one another that they can breed and produce fertile offspring. Other ecologists study **populations,** or groups of individuals that belong to the same species and live in the same area. Still other ecologists study **communities,** or assemblages of different populations that live together in a defined area.

Ecologists may study a particular ecosystem. An **ecosystem** is a collection of all the organisms that live in a particular place, together with their nonliving, or physical, environment. Larger systems called biomes are also studied by teams of ecologists. A **biome** is a group of ecosystems that have the same climate and similar dominant communities. The highest level of organization that ecologists study is the entire biosphere itself.

What is an ecosystem?

Ecological Methods

Ecologists use a wide range of tools and techniques to study the living world. Some, like the scientists in **Figure 3–3,** use binoculars and field guides to assess changes in plant and wildlife communities. Others use studies of DNA to identify bacteria in the mud of coastal marshes. Still others use radio tags to track migrating wildlife or use data gathered by satellites.

Regardless of the tools they use, scientists conduct modern ecological research using three basic approaches: observing, experimenting, and modeling. All of these approaches rely on the application of scientific methods to guide ecological inquiry.

Observing Observing is often the first step in asking ecological questions. Some observations are simple: What species live here? How many individuals of each species are there? Other observations are more complex and may form the first step in designing experiments and models.

Experimenting Experiments can be used to test hypotheses. An ecologist may set up an artificial environment in a laboratory to imitate and manipulate conditions that organisms would encounter in the natural world. Other experiments are conducted within natural ecosystems.

Modeling Many ecological phenomena occur over long periods of time or on such large spatial scales that they are difficult to study. Ecologists make models to gain insight into complex phenomena such as the effects of global warming on ecosystems. Many ecological models consist of mathematical formulas based on data collected through observation and experimentation. The predictions made by ecological models are often tested by further observations and experiments.

▲ **Figure 3–3** **The three fundamental approaches to ecological research involve observing, experimenting, and modeling.** These ecologists are studying a rain forest ecosystem in Sri Lanka. They are using field observations to collect data on vines and other plants.

3–1 Section Assessment

1. **Key Concept** List the six different levels of organization that ecologists study, in order from smallest to largest.
2. **Key Concept** Describe the three basic methods of ecological research.
3. Identify two ways in which you interact every day with each of the three parts of the biosphere—land, water, and air.
4. **Critical Thinking Applying Concepts** Suppose you wanted to know if the water in a certain stream is safe to drink. Which ecological method(s) would you choose, and why?
5. **Critical Thinking Applying Concepts** Give an example of an ecological phenomenon that could be studied by modeling. Explain why modeling would be useful.

Thinking Visually

Creating a Table

Refer to **Figure 3–2,** which shows the various levels of organization that ecologists study. In a table, provide examples of the ecological levels where you live—individuals, populations, communities, and ecosystems—that could be studied by ecologists. *Hint:* You may wish to use library resources or the Internet.

TECHNOLOGY & SOCIETY

Exploring Ecology From Space

Modern research in global ecology would not be possible if all its tools were earthbound. Studies on a planetary scale require enormous data-gathering networks. Through a process called remote sensing, satellites extend the range of information that ecologists can collect within the biosphere.

Remote-sensing satellites are fitted with optical sensors that can scan several bands of the electromagnetic spectrum and convert those bands into electrical signals. The signals are run through a computer and converted into digital values, which are used to construct an image.

Remote sensing provides detailed images of essentially every square meter of Earth's surface. How else could scientists view all the world's lakes and oceans to see where concentrations of algae are the highest? Or view areas of destroyed forests in places like the Amazon Basin or northern Russia?

Global Change

The false-color image below was assembled from data gathered by NASA's Sea-viewing Wide Field-of-view Sensor (SeaWiFS) Project. The project's goal is to study factors that affect global change and to assess the oceans' role in the global carbon cycle, as well as other chemical cycles. The different ocean colors indicate varying concentrations of microscopic algae. Blue represents the least amount of algae, and red represents the highest amount. On land, the dark green areas have the most vegetation, and gold land areas have the least.

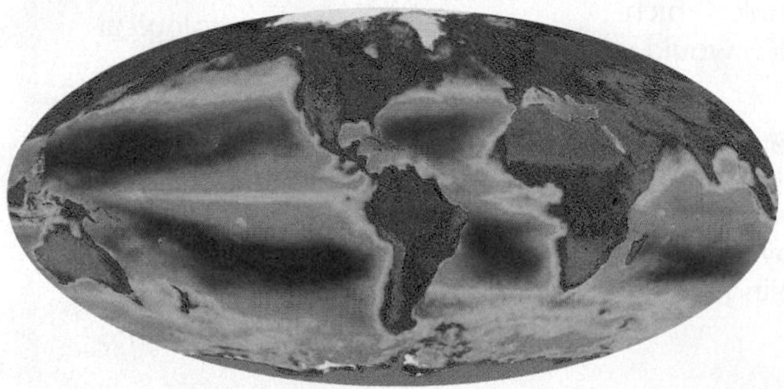

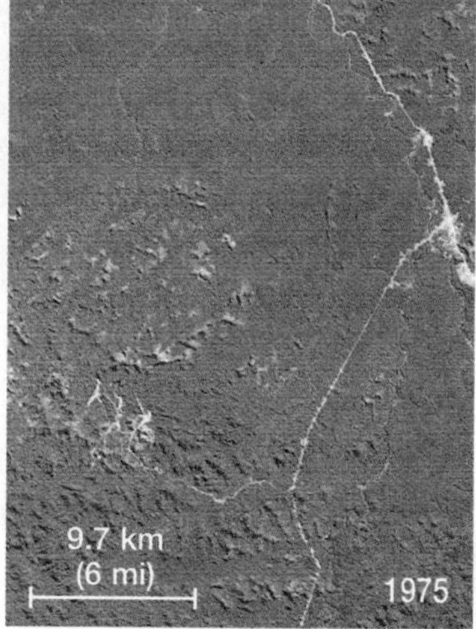

Rain Forest Destruction

Satellite images that show the presence or absence of vegetation are useful in studying the effects of human activity on natural ecosystems. The two images above, taken 26 years apart, show the same tract of land in a Brazilian rain forest. Red areas show undisturbed forest, and whitish areas show places where trees have been cut and cleared. Note the "fishbone" pattern of vegetation clearing. This pattern occurs because cutting of forests typically begins along existing roads and rivers and then spreads out as new roads and paths are cut.

Data in images such as these, especially when taken over time, help ecologists estimate the rate at which rain forests are being cut down. These data are also valuable in discussing the effects of development with local governments.

Research and Decide

Use library or Internet resources to learn more about the use of satellites in ecological studies. Decide how ecologists and local governments might use the data in their discussion.

For: Links from the authors
Visit: PHSchool.com
Web Code: cbe-2031

3–2 Energy Flow

4-1.1 Ecosystems
4-5.1 Photosynthesis
4-6.1 Solar energy flow
4-6.1 Atoms and molecules cycle

At the core of every organism's interaction with the environment is its need for energy to power life's processes. Consider, for example, the energy that ants use to carry objects many times their size or the energy that birds use to migrate thousands of miles. Think about the energy that you need to get out of bed in the morning! The flow of energy through an ecosystem is one of the most important factors that determines the system's capacity to sustain life.

Guide for Reading

 **Key Concepts**
- Where does the energy for life processes come from?
- How does energy flow through living systems?
- How efficient is the transfer of energy among organisms in an ecosystem?

Vocabulary
autotroph • producer
photosynthesis
chemosynthesis • heterotroph
consumer • herbivore
carnivore • omnivore
detritivore • decomposer
food chain • food web
trophic level
ecological pyramid • biomass

Reading Strategy: Building Vocabulary As you read, make notes about the meaning of each term in the list above and how it relates to energy flow in the biosphere. Then, draw a concept map to show the relationships among these terms.

Producers

Without a constant input of energy, living systems cannot function. **Sunlight is the main energy source for life on Earth.** Of all the sun's energy that reaches Earth's surface, only a small amount—less than 1 percent—is used by living things. This seemingly small amount is enough to produce as much as 3.5 kilograms of living tissue per square meter a year in some tropical forests.

In a few ecosystems, some organisms obtain energy from a source other than sunlight. **Some types of organisms rely on the energy stored in inorganic chemical compounds.** For instance, mineral water that flows underground or boils out of hot springs and undersea vents is loaded with chemical energy.

Only plants, some algae, and certain bacteria can capture energy from sunlight or chemicals and use that energy to produce food. These organisms are called **autotrophs.** Autotrophs use energy from the environment to fuel the assembly of simple inorganic compounds into complex organic molecules. These organic molecules combine and recombine to produce living tissue. Because they make their own food, autotrophs, like the kelp in **Figure 3–4**, are also called **producers.** Both types of producers—those that capture energy from sunlight and those that capture chemical energy—are essential to the flow of energy through the biosphere.

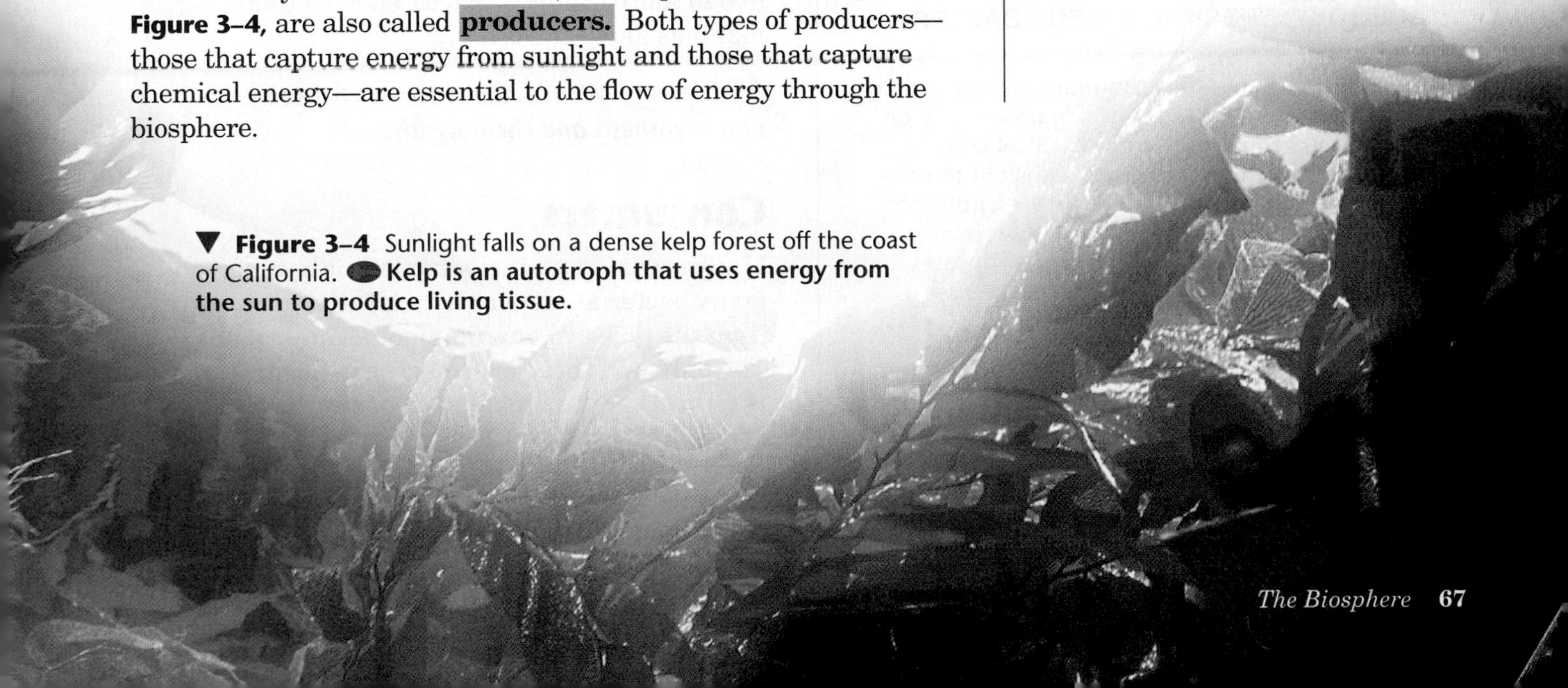

▼ **Figure 3–4** Sunlight falls on a dense kelp forest off the coast of California. **Kelp is an autotroph that uses energy from the sun to produce living tissue.**

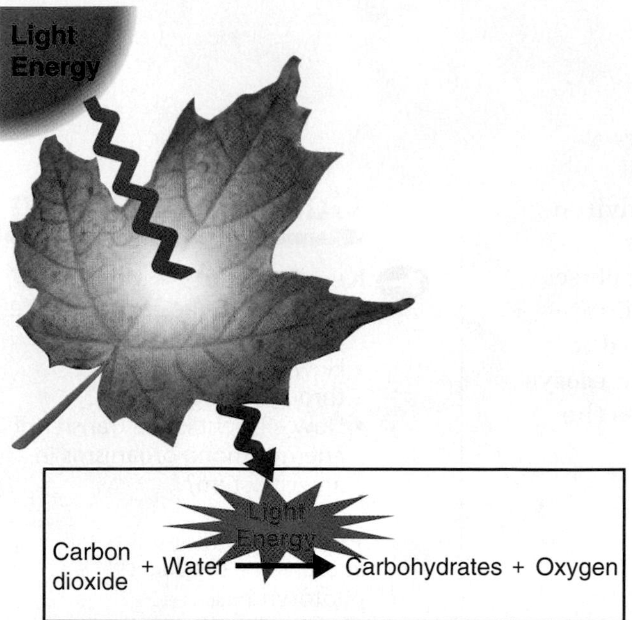

PHOTOSYNTHESIS IN PLANTS

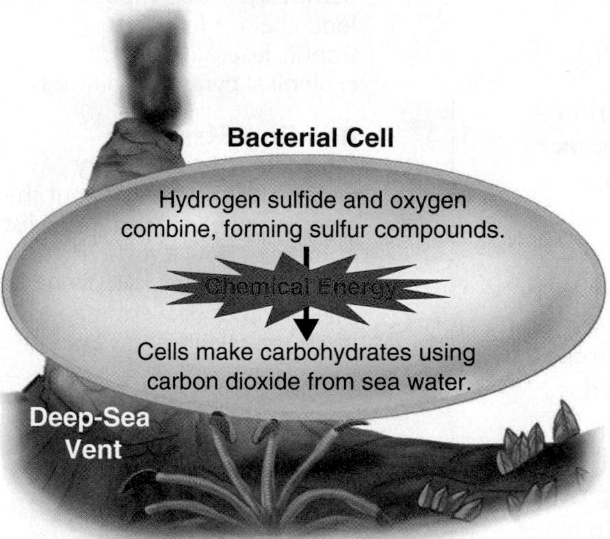

CHEMOSYNTHESIS IN SULFUR BACTERIA

Figure 3–5 **Sunlight is the main energy source for life on Earth. Some types of organisms rely on the energy stored in inorganic chemical compounds.** Plants use the energy from sunlight to carry out the process of photosynthesis. Other autotrophs, such as sulfur bacteria, use the energy stored in chemical bonds for chemosynthesis. In both cases, energy-rich carbohydrates are produced.

Energy From the Sun The best-known autotrophs are those that harness solar energy through a process known as photosynthesis. During **photosynthesis,** these autotrophs use light energy to power chemical reactions that convert carbon dioxide and water into oxygen and energy-rich carbohydrates such as sugars and starches. This process, shown in **Figure 3–5** (top), is responsible for adding oxygen to—and removing carbon dioxide from—Earth's atmosphere. In fact, were it not for photosynthetic autotrophs, the air would not contain enough oxygen for you to breathe!

On land, plants are the main autotrophs. In freshwater ecosystems and in the sunlit upper layers of the ocean, algae are the main autotrophs. Photosynthetic bacteria, the most common of which are the cyanobacteria (sy-an-oh-bak-TEER-ee-uh), are important in certain wet ecosystems such as tidal flats and salt marshes.

Life Without Light Although plants are the most visible and best-known autotrophs, some autotrophs can produce food in the absence of light. Such autotrophs rely on energy within the chemical bonds of inorganic molecules such as hydrogen sulfide. When organisms use chemical energy to produce carbohydrates, the process is called **chemosynthesis** (kee-moh-SIN-thuh-sis), as shown in **Figure 3–5** (bottom). This process is performed by several types of bacteria. Surprisingly, these bacteria represent a large proportion of living autotrophs. Some chemosynthetic bacteria live in very remote places on Earth, such as volcanic vents on the deep-ocean floor and hot springs in Yellowstone Park. Others live in more common places, such as tidal marshes along the coast.

CHECKPOINT ***What is the difference between photosynthesis and chemosynthesis?***

Consumers

Many organisms—including animals, fungi, and many bacteria—cannot harness energy directly from the physical environment as autotrophs do. The only way these organisms can acquire energy is from other organisms. Organisms that rely on other organisms for their energy and food supply are called **heterotrophs** (HET-ur-oh-trohfs). Heterotrophs are also called **consumers.**

There are many different types of heterotrophs. **Herbivores** obtain energy by eating only plants. Some herbivores are cows, caterpillars, and deer. **Carnivores,** including snakes, dogs, and owls, eat animals. Humans, bears, crows, and other **omnivores** eat both plants and animals. **Detritivores,** (dee-TRYT-uh-vawrz), such as mites, earthworms, snails, and crabs, feed on plant and animal remains and other dead matter, collectively called detritus. Another important group of heterotrophs, called **decomposers,** breaks down organic matter. Bacteria and fungi, such as the one in **Figure 3–6,** are decomposers.

▲ **Figure 3–6** This fungus, growing on the forest floor, is a decomposer that obtains nutrients by breaking down dead and decaying plants and animals. It is called a coral fungus because of its color and shape. **Classifying** ***Is the fungus a producer or a consumer?***

Feeding Relationships

What happens to the energy in an ecosystem when one organism eats another? That energy moves along a one-way path. **Energy flows through an ecosystem in one direction, from the sun or inorganic compounds to autotrophs (producers) and then to various heterotrophs (consumers).** The relationships between producers and consumers connect organisms into feeding networks based on who eats whom.

Food Chains The energy stored by producers can be passed through an ecosystem along a **food chain,** a series of steps in which organisms transfer energy by eating and being eaten. For example, in a prairie ecosystem, a food chain might consist of a producer, such as grass, that is fed upon by a herbivore, such as a grazing antelope. The herbivore is in turn fed upon by a carnivore, such as a coyote. In this situation, the carnivore is only two steps removed from the producer.

In some marine food chains, such as the one in **Figure 3–7,** the producers are microscopic algae that are eaten by very small organisms called zooplankton (zoh-oh-PLANK-tun). The zooplankton, in turn, are eaten by small fish, such as herring. The herring are eaten by squid, which are ultimately eaten by large fish, such as sharks. In this food chain, the top carnivore is four steps removed from the producer.

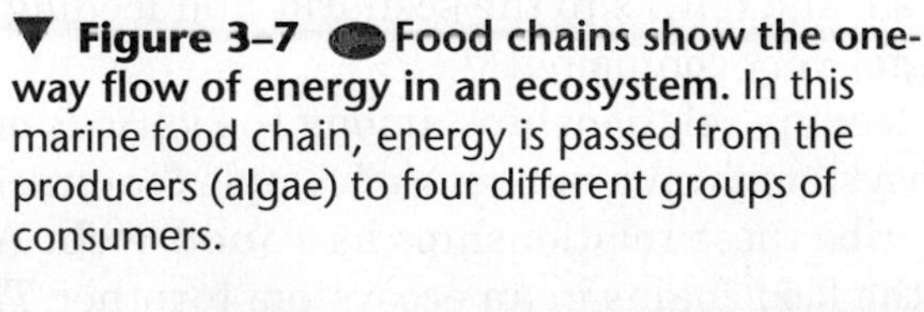

▼ **Figure 3–7** **Food chains show the one-way flow of energy in an ecosystem.** In this marine food chain, energy is passed from the producers (algae) to four different groups of consumers.

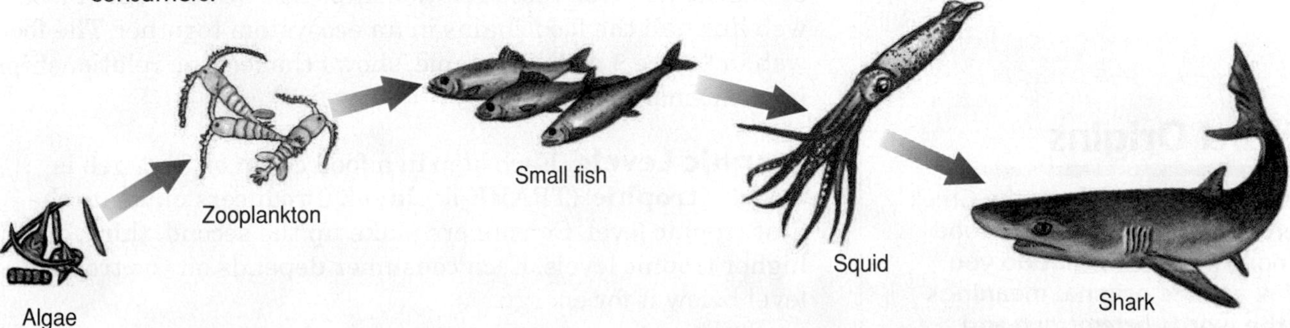

Quick Lab

How is a food chain organized?

Materials 2 wide-mouth jars, 2 pieces of flexible screening, 2 rubber bands, 2 bean seedlings in small pots or paper cups, pea aphids, ladybird beetles

Procedure 

1. Place a potted bean seedling in each of the two jars.
2. Add 20 aphids to one jar and cover the jar with screening to prevent the aphids from escaping. Use a rubber band to attach the screening to the jar.
3. Add 20 aphids and 4 ladybird beetles to the second jar. Cover the second jar as you did the first one.
4. **Formulating Hypotheses** Record your hypothesis about how the presence of the ladybird beetles will affect the survival of the aphids and the bean seedling. Also, record your prediction of what will happen to the organisms in each jar during the next week.
5. Place both jars in a sunny location. Observe the jars each day for one week and record your observations each day. Water the seedlings as needed.

Analyze and Conclude

1. **Observing** What happened to the aphids and the seedling in the jar without the ladybird beetles? In the jar with the ladybird beetles? How can you explain this difference?
2. **Classifying** Identify each organism in the jars as a producer or a consumer.

Food Webs In most ecosystems, feeding relationships are more complex than can be shown in a food chain. Consider, for example, the relationships in a salt marsh. Although some producers—including marsh grass and other salt-tolerant plants—are eaten by water birds, grasshoppers, and other herbivores, most producers complete their life cycles, then die and decompose. Decomposers convert the dead plant matter to detritus, which is eaten by detritivores, such as sandhoppers. The detritivores are in turn eaten by smelt and other small fish. Some of those consumers will also eat detritus directly. Add mice, larger fish, and hawks to the scenario, and feeding relationships can get very confusing!

When the feeding relationships among the various organisms in an ecosystem form a network of complex interactions, ecologists describe these relationships as a **food web.** A food web links all the food chains in an ecosystem together. The food web in **Figure 3–8,** for example, shows the feeding relationships in a salt-marsh community.

Trophic Levels Each step in a food chain or food web is called a **trophic** (TRAHF-ik) **level.** Producers make up the first trophic level. Consumers make up the second, third, or higher trophic levels. Each consumer depends on the trophic level below it for energy.

What is a food web?

Word Origins

Trophic originates from the Greek word *trophe,* which means "food or nourishment." **What do you think are the original meanings of the words *heterotroph* and *autotroph?***

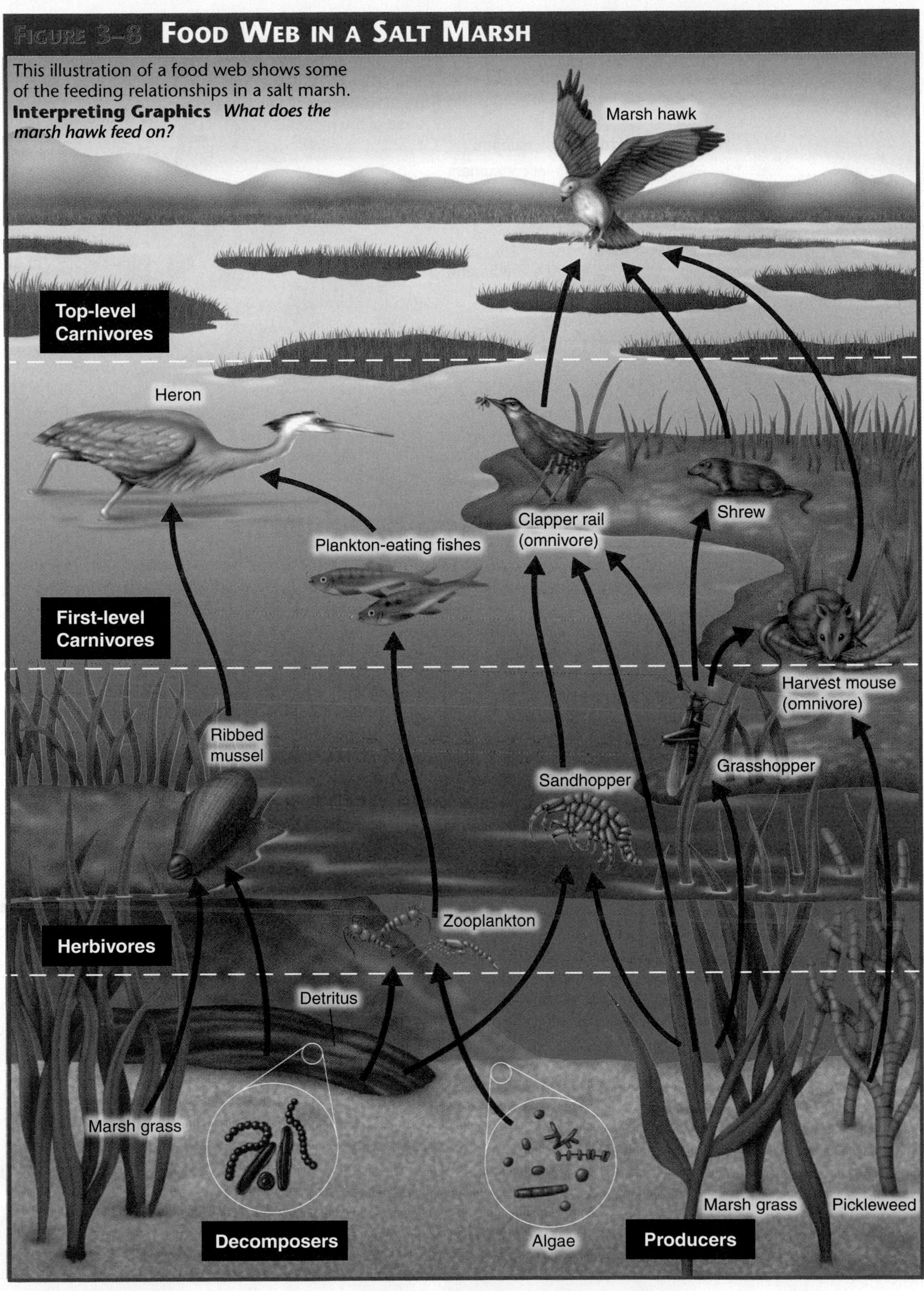
Figure 3–8 Food Web in a Salt Marsh
This illustration of a food web shows some of the feeding relationships in a salt marsh. **Interpreting Graphics** *What does the marsh hawk feed on?*
Marsh hawk
Top-level Carnivores
Heron
Clapper rail (omnivore)
Shrew
Plankton-eating fishes
First-level Carnivores
Harvest mouse (omnivore)
Ribbed mussel
Sandhopper
Grasshopper
Zooplankton
Herbivores
Detritus
Marsh grass
Marsh grass
Pickleweed
Decomposers
Algae
Producers

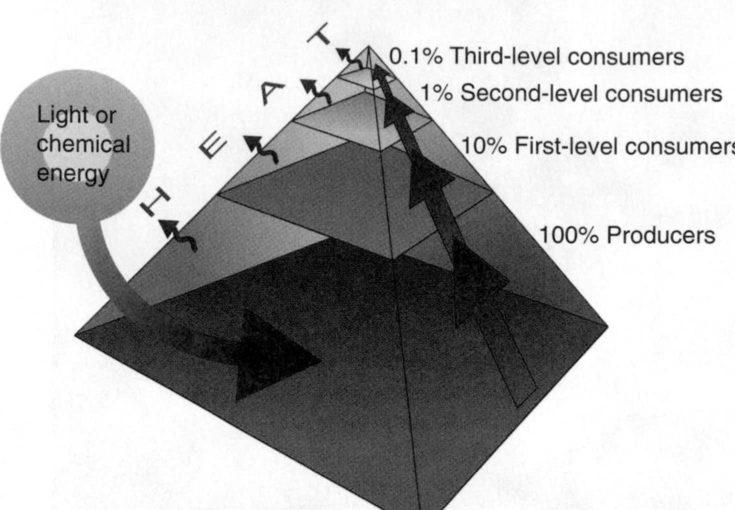

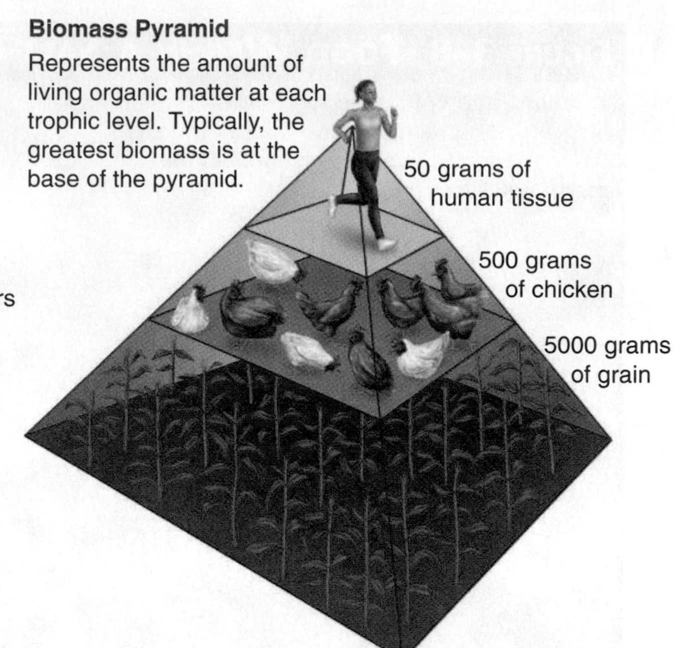

Biomass Pyramid
Represents the amount of living organic matter at each trophic level. Typically, the greatest biomass is at the base of the pyramid.
50 grams of human tissue
500 grams of chicken
5000 grams of grain

Ecological Pyramids

The amount of energy or matter in an ecosystem can be represented by an ecological pyramid. An **ecological pyramid** is a diagram that shows the relative amounts of energy or matter contained within each trophic level in a food chain or food web. Ecologists recognize three different types of ecological pyramids: energy pyramids, biomass pyramids, and pyramids of numbers. **Figure 3–9** shows an example of each type.

Energy Pyramid Theoretically, there is no limit to the number of trophic levels that a food chain can support. But there is one hitch. Only part of the energy that is stored in one trophic level is passed on to the next level. This is because organisms use much of the energy that they consume for life processes, such as respiration, movement, and reproduction. Some of the remaining energy is released into the environment as heat. **Only about 10 percent of the energy available within one trophic level is transferred to organisms at the next trophic level.** For instance, one tenth of the solar energy captured by grasses ends up stored in the tissues of cows and other grazers. Only one tenth of that energy—10 percent of 10 percent, or 1 percent total—is transferred to the humans that eat the cows. Thus, the more levels that exist between a producer and a top-level consumer in an ecosystem, the less energy that remains from the original amount.

Biomass Pyramid The total amount of living tissue within a given trophic level is called **biomass.** Biomass is usually expressed in terms of grams of organic matter per unit area. A biomass pyramid represents the amount of potential food available for each trophic level in an ecosystem.

For: Links on energy pyramids
Visit: www.SciLinks.org
Web Code: cbn-2032

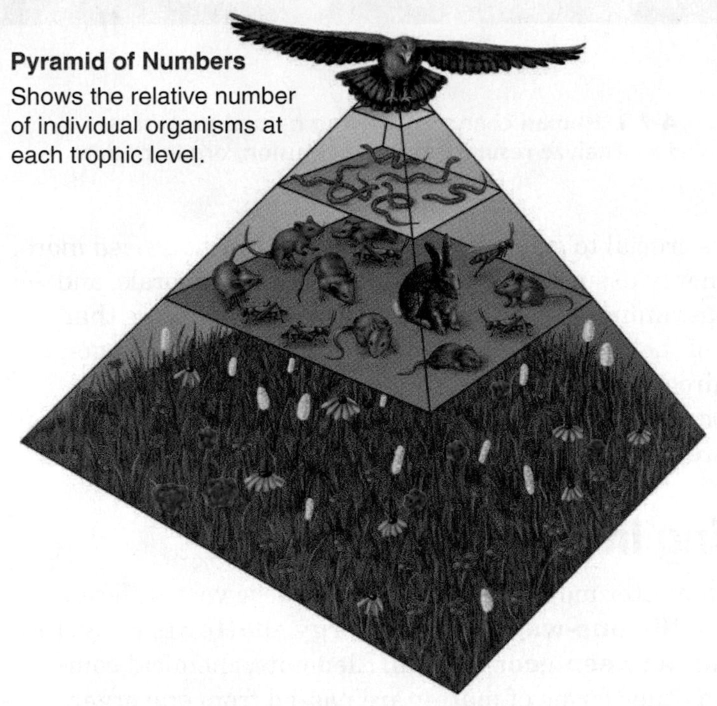

Pyramid of Numbers
Shows the relative number of individual organisms at each trophic level.

Figure 3–9 Ecological pyramids show the decreasing amounts of energy, living tissue, or number of organisms at successive feeding levels. The pyramid is divided into sections that represent each trophic level. **Because each trophic level harvests only about one tenth of the energy from the level below, it can support only about one tenth the amount of living tissue.**

Pyramid of Numbers Ecological pyramids can also be based on the numbers of individual organisms at each trophic level. For some ecosystems, such as the meadow shown in **Figure 3–9** above, the shape of the pyramid of numbers is the same as that of the energy and biomass pyramids. This, however, is not always the case. In most forests, for example, there are fewer producers than there are consumers. A single tree has a large amount of energy and biomass, but it is only one organism. Many insects live in the tree, but they have less energy and biomass. Thus, a pyramid of numbers for a forest ecosystem would not resemble a typical pyramid at all!

3–2 Section Assessment

1. **Key Concept** What are the two main forms of energy that power living systems?
2. **Key Concept** Briefly describe the flow of energy among organisms in an ecosystem.
3. **Key Concept** What proportion of energy is transferred from one trophic level to the next in an ecosystem?
4. Explain the relationships in this food chain: omnivore, herbivore, and autotroph.
5. **Critical Thinking Calculating** Draw an energy pyramid for a five-step food chain. If 100 percent of the energy is available at the first trophic level, what percentage of the total energy is available at the highest trophic level?

Writing in Science

Descriptive Writing

Refer to **Figure 3–8,** which shows a food web in a salt marsh. Choose one of the food chains within this web. Then, write a paragraph describing the feeding relationships among the organisms in the food chain. *Hint:* Use the terms *producers, consumers,* and *decomposers* in your description.

3–3 Cycles of Matter

1-S1.1 Values are essential in applying knowledge
1-S3.1 Interpreting data leads to new hypotheses
4-1.1 Ecosystems are shaped by physical conditions
4-6.1 The carrying capacity of an environment
4-7.1 Human changes affecting natural processes
LS- Analyze results, form a conclusion, organize data

Guide for Reading

Key Concepts
- How does matter move among the living and nonliving parts of an ecosystem?
- How are nutrients important in living systems?

Vocabulary
biogeochemical cycle
evaporation
transpiration
nutrient
nitrogen fixation
denitrification
primary productivity
limiting nutrient
algal bloom

Reading Strategy: Using Visuals Before you read, preview the cycles shown in **Figures 3–11, 3–13, 3–14,** and **3–15.** Notice how each diagram is similar to or different from the others. As you read, take notes on how each chemical moves through the biosphere.

Energy is crucial to an ecosystem. But all organisms need more than energy to survive. They also need water, minerals, and other life-sustaining compounds. In most organisms, more than 95 percent of the body is made up of just four elements: oxygen, carbon, hydrogen, and nitrogen. Although these four elements are common on Earth, organisms cannot use them unless the elements are in a chemical form that cells can take up.

Recycling in the Biosphere

Energy and matter move through the biosphere very differently. **Unlike the one-way flow of energy, matter is recycled within and between ecosystems.** Elements, chemical compounds, and other forms of matter are passed from one organism to another and from one part of the biosphere to another through **biogeochemical cycles.** As the long word suggests, biogeochemical cycles connect *bio*logical, *geo*logical, and *chemi*cal aspects of the biosphere.

Matter can cycle through the biosphere because biological systems do not use up matter, they transform it. The matter is assembled into living tissue or passed out of the body as waste products. Imagine, for a moment, that you are a carbon atom in a molecule of carbon dioxide floating in the air of a wetland like the one in **Figure 3–10.** The leaf of a blueberry bush absorbs you during photosynthesis. You become part of a carbohydrate molecule and are used to make fruit. The fruit is eaten by a caribou, and within a few hours, you are passed out of the animal's body. You are soon swallowed by a dung beetle, then combined into the body tissue of a hungry shrew, which is then eaten by an owl. Finally, you are released into the atmosphere once again when the owl exhales. Then, the cycle starts again.

Simply put, biogeochemical cycles pass the same molecules around again and again within the biosphere. Just think—with every breath you take, you inhale hundreds of thousands of oxygen atoms that might have been inhaled by dinosaurs millions of years ago!

▼ **Figure 3–10 Matter moves through an ecosystem in biogeochemical cycles.** In this Alaskan wetland, matter is recycled through the air, the shrubs, the pond, and the caribou—as it is used, transformed, moved, and reused.

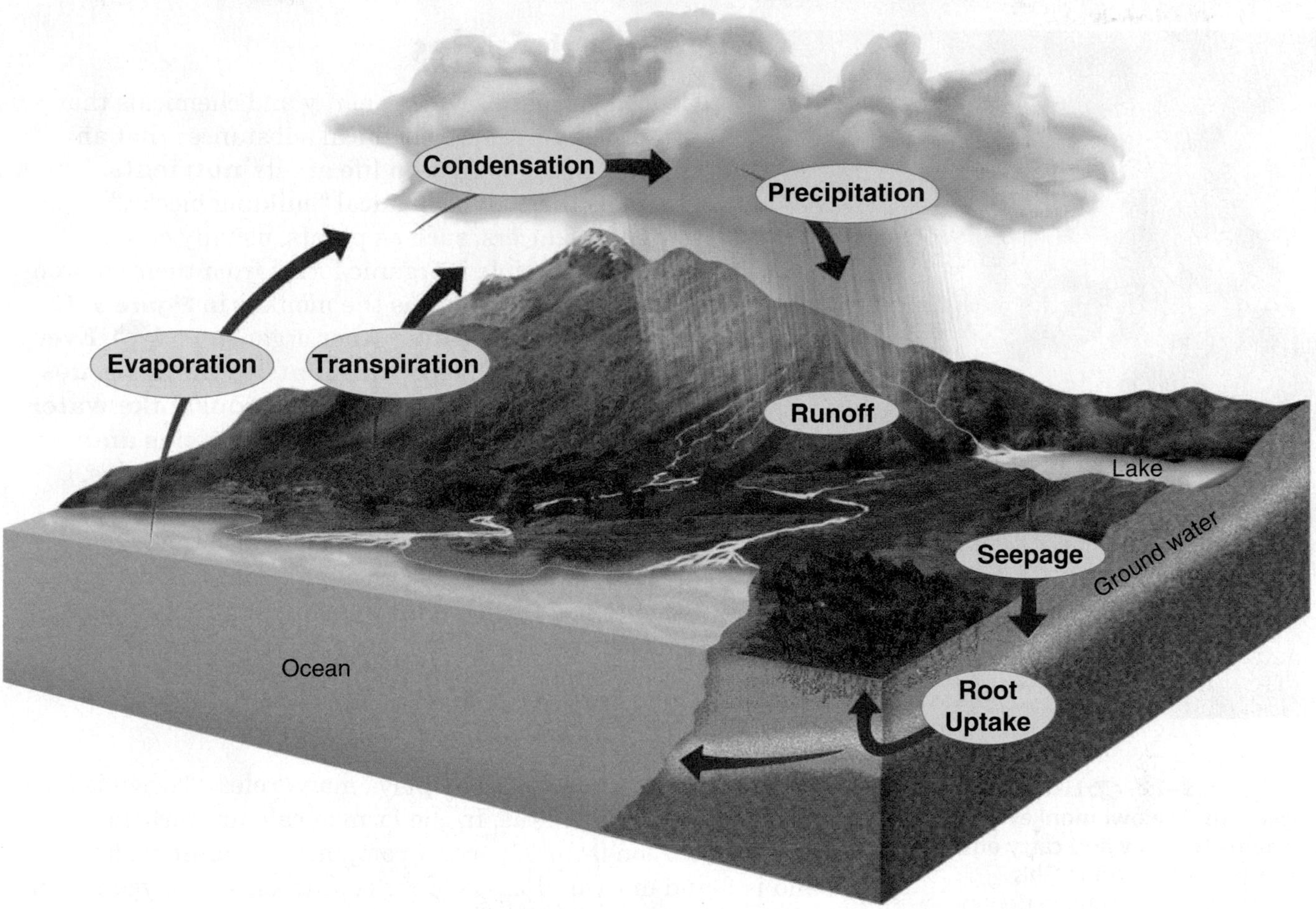

▲ **Figure 3–11** This diagram shows the main processes involved in the water cycle. Scientists estimate that it can take a single water molecule as long as 4000 years to complete one cycle. **Interpreting Graphics** *What happens to the water that evaporates from oceans and lakes?*

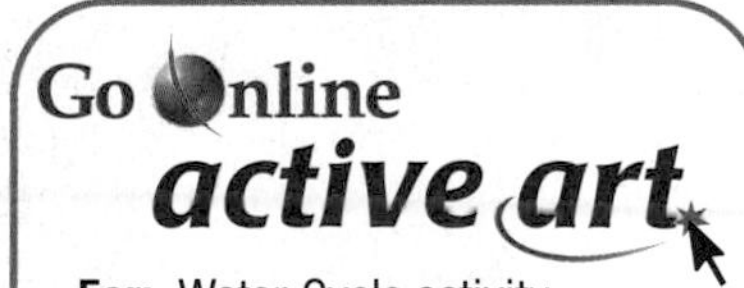

The Water Cycle

All living things require water to survive. Where does all this water come from? It moves between the ocean, atmosphere, and land. As **Figure 3–11** shows, water molecules enter the atmosphere as water vapor, a gas, when they evaporate from the ocean or other bodies of water. The process by which water changes from liquid form to an atmospheric gas is called **evaporation** (ee-vap-uh-RAY-shun). Water can also enter the atmosphere by evaporating from the leaves of plants in the process of **transpiration** (tran-spuh-RAY-shun).

During the day, the sun heats the atmosphere. As the warm, moist air rises, it cools. Eventually, the water vapor condenses into tiny droplets that form clouds. When the droplets become large enough, the water returns to Earth's surface in the form of precipitation—rain, snow, sleet, or hail.

On land, much of the precipitation runs along the surface of the ground until it enters a river or stream that carries the runoff back to an ocean or lake. Rain also seeps into the soil, some of it deeply enough to become ground water. Water in the soil enters plants through the roots, and the water cycle begins anew.

CHECKPOINT *How are evaporation and transpiration related?*

Go Online
active art
For: Water Cycle activity
Visit: PHSchool.com
Web Code: cbp-2033

▲ **Figure 3–12** **Like all living organisms, the owl monkey needs nutrients to grow and carry out essential life functions.** This monkey, which is found in Central and South America, obtains most of its nutrients by eating plants.

Nutrient Cycles

The food you eat provides energy and chemicals that keep you alive. All the chemical substances that an organism needs to sustain life are its **nutrients.** Think of them as the body's chemical "building blocks." Primary producers, such as plants, usually obtain nutrients in simple inorganic forms from their environment. Consumers, such as the monkey in **Figure 3–12,** obtain nutrients by eating other organisms. **Every living organism needs nutrients to build tissues and carry out essential life functions. Like water, nutrients are passed between organisms and the environment through biogeochemical cycles.**

The carbon cycle, nitrogen cycle, and phosphorus cycle are especially important. Note also that oxygen participates in all these cycles by combining with these elements and cycling with them during various parts of their journey.

CHECKPOINT *What is a nutrient?*

The Carbon Cycle Carbon plays many roles. Carbon is a key ingredient of living tissue. In the form of calcium carbonate ($CaCO_3$), carbon is an important component of animal skeletons and is found in several kinds of rocks. Carbon and oxygen form carbon dioxide gas (CO_2), an important component of the atmosphere. Carbon dioxide is taken in by plants during photosynthesis and is given off by both plants and animals during respiration. Four main types of processes move carbon through its cycle:

- Biological processes, such as photosynthesis, respiration, and decomposition, take up and release carbon and oxygen.
- Geochemical processes, such as erosion and volcanic activity, release carbon dioxide to the atmosphere and oceans.
- Mixed biogeochemical processes, such as the burial and decomposition of dead organisms and their conversion under pressure into coal and petroleum (fossil fuels), store carbon underground.
- Human activities, such as mining, cutting and burning forests, and burning fossil fuels, release carbon dioxide into the atmosphere.

Scientists identified these processes decades ago, but they are still actively investigating them. For example, how much carbon moves through each part of the cycle? How do other parts of the carbon cycle respond to changes in atmospheric carbon dioxide? How much carbon dioxide can the ocean absorb? Later in this unit, you will learn why answers to these questions are so important.

For: Links on cycles of matter
Visit: www.SciLinks.org
Web Code: cbn-2033

Figure 3–13 shows how these processes move carbon through the biosphere. In the atmosphere, carbon is present as carbon dioxide gas. Carbon dioxide is released into the atmosphere by volcanic activity, by respiration, by human activities such as the burning of fossil fuels and vegetation, and by the decomposition of organic matter. Plants take in carbon dioxide and use the carbon to build carbohydrates during photosynthesis. The carbohydrates are passed along food webs to animals and other consumers. In the ocean, carbon is also found, along with calcium and oxygen, in calcium carbonate, which is formed by many marine organisms. Calcium carbonate can also be formed chemically in certain marine environments. This chalky, carbon-based compound accumulates in marine sediments and in the bones and shells of organisms. Eventually these compounds break down and the carbon returns to the atmosphere.

▼ **Figure 3–13** Carbon is found in several large reservoirs in the biosphere. In the atmosphere, it is found as carbon dioxide gas; in the oceans as dissolved carbon dioxide; on land in organisms, rocks, and soil; and underground as coal, petroleum, and calcium carbonate rock. **Interpreting Graphics** ***What are the main sources of carbon dioxide in the ocean?***

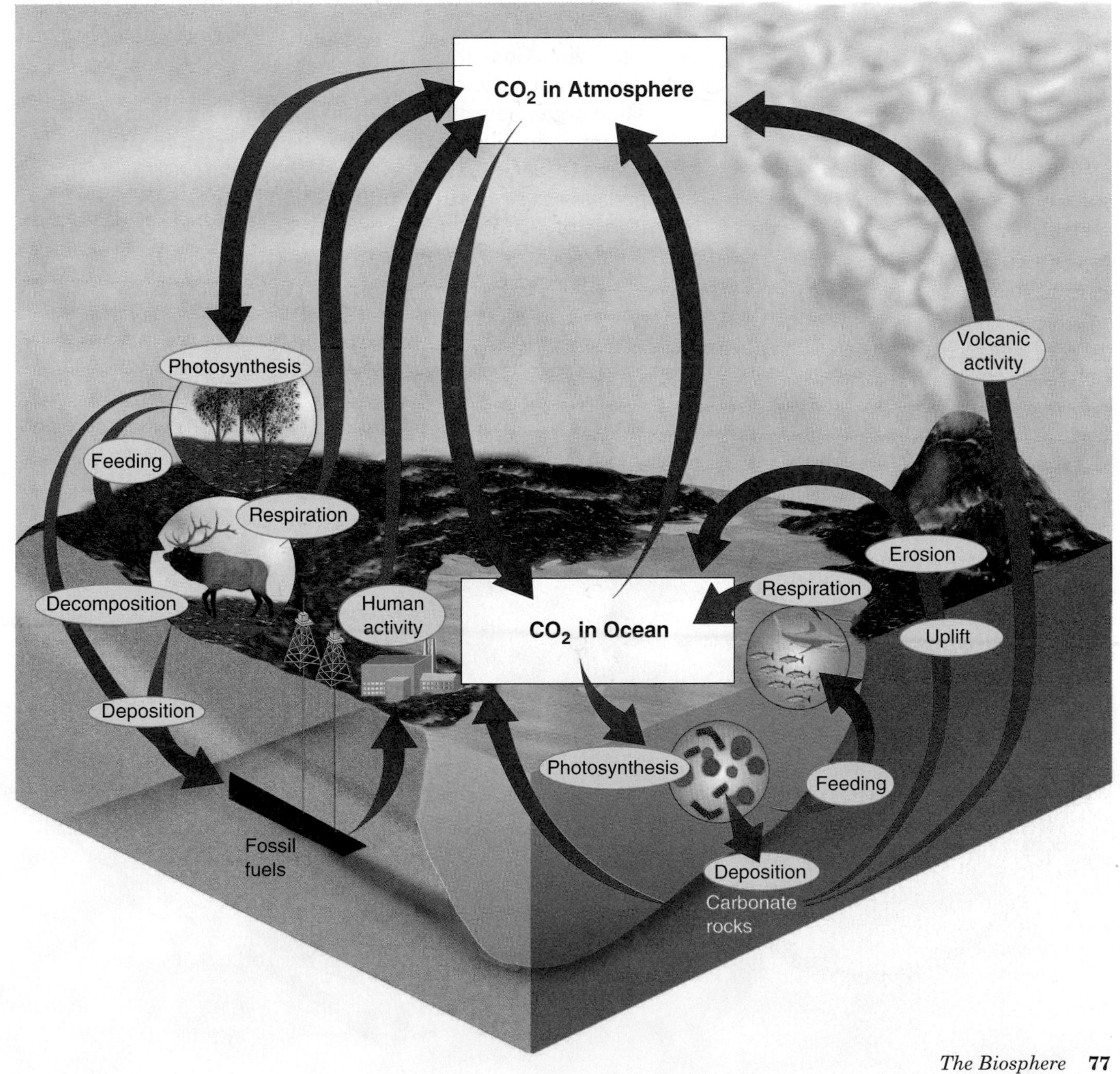

The Nitrogen Cycle All organisms require nitrogen to make amino acids, which in turn are used to build proteins. Many different forms of nitrogen occur naturally in the biosphere. Nitrogen gas (N_2) makes up 78 percent of Earth's atmosphere. Nitrogen-containing substances such as ammonia (NH_3), nitrate ions (NO_3^-), and nitrite ions (NO_2^-) are found in the wastes produced by many organisms and in dead and decaying organic matter. Nitrogen also exists in several forms in the ocean and other large water bodies. Human activity adds nitrogen to the biosphere in the form of nitrate—a major component of plant fertilizers.

Figure 3–14 shows how the different forms of nitrogen cycle through the biosphere. Although nitrogen gas is the most abundant form of nitrogen on Earth, only certain types of bacteria can use this form directly. Such bacteria, which live in the soil and on the roots of plants called legumes, convert nitrogen gas into ammonia in a process known as **nitrogen fixation.** Other bacteria in the soil convert ammonia into nitrates and nitrites. Once these products are available, producers can use them to make proteins. Consumers then eat the producers and reuse the nitrogen to make their own proteins.

When organisms die, decomposers return nitrogen to the soil as ammonia. The ammonia may be taken up again by producers. Other soil bacteria convert nitrates into nitrogen gas in a process called **denitrification.** This process releases nitrogen into the atmosphere once again.

▼ **Figure 3–14** The atmosphere is the main reservoir of nitrogen in the biosphere. Nitrogen also cycles through the soil and through the tissues of living organisms. **Interpreting Graphics** *What are the main nitrogen-containing nutrients in the biosphere?*

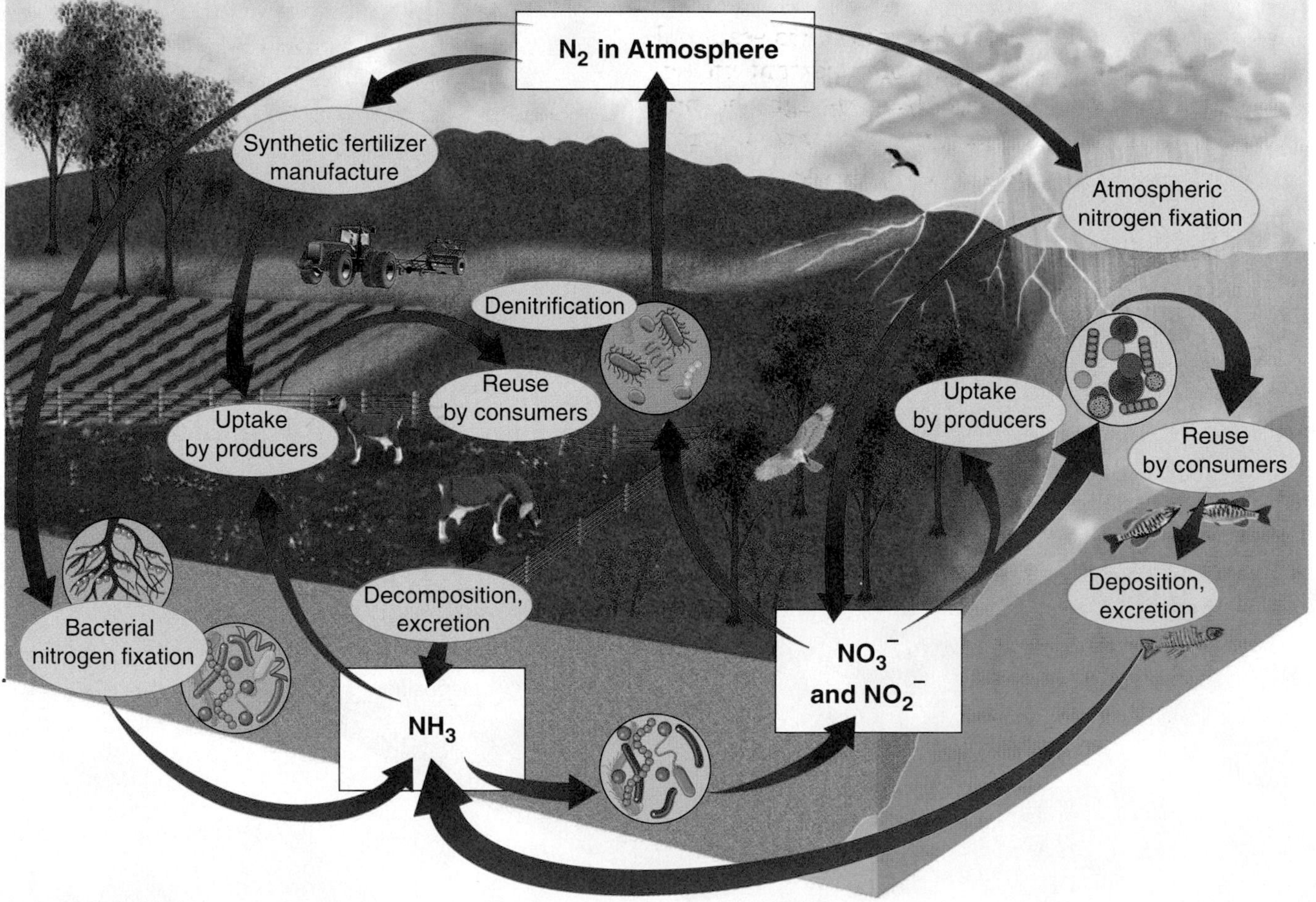

Analyzing Data

Farming in the Rye

Sometimes, farmers grow crops of rye and other grasses and then plow them under the soil to decay. This practice helps to increase crop yields of other plants. Farmers may also plow under legumes such as peas, vetch, and lentils. Legumes are plants that have colonies of nitrogen-fixing bacteria living in nodules on the plant roots.

In an effort to determine which practice produces the best crop yields, scientists performed an experiment in Georgia. They grew corn on land that had previously received one of five treatments. Three fields had previously been planted with three different legumes. A fourth field had been planted with rye. The fifth field was left bare before the corn was planted. None of the fields received fertilizer while the corn was growing. The table shows how much corn was produced per hectare of land (kg/ha) in each field. One hectare is equivalent to 10,000 square meters.

Corn Production

Previous Crop	Average Yield of Corn (kg/ha)
Monantha vetch	2876
Hairy vetch	2870
Austrian peas	3159
Rye	1922
None	1959

1. **Using Tables and Graphs** Use the data in the table to create a bar graph.
2. **Comparing and Contrasting** Compare the effect of growing legumes to that of growing grass on the yield of corn. How do the yields differ from the yield on the field that had received no prior treatment?
3. **Using Tables and Graphs** Which treatment produced the best yield of corn? The worst yield?
4. **Applying Concepts** Based on your knowledge of the nitrogen cycle, how can you explain these results?

The Phosphorus Cycle Phosphorus is essential to living organisms because it forms part of important life-sustaining molecules such as DNA and RNA. Although phosphorus is of great biological importance, it is not very common in the biosphere. Unlike carbon, oxygen, and nitrogen, phosphorus does not enter the atmosphere. Instead, phosphorus remains mostly on land in rock and soil minerals, and in ocean sediments. There, phosphorus exists in the form of inorganic phosphate. As the rocks and sediments gradually wear down, phosphate is released. On land, some of the phosphate washes into rivers and streams, where it dissolves. The phosphate eventually makes its way to the oceans, where it is used by marine organisms.

As **Figure 3–15** shows, some phosphate stays on land and cycles between organisms and the soil. When plants absorb phosphate from the soil or from water, the plants bind the phosphate into organic compounds. Organic phosphate moves through the food web, from producers to consumers, and to the rest of the ecosystem.

CHECKPOINT *Where is most of the phosphorus stored in the biosphere?*

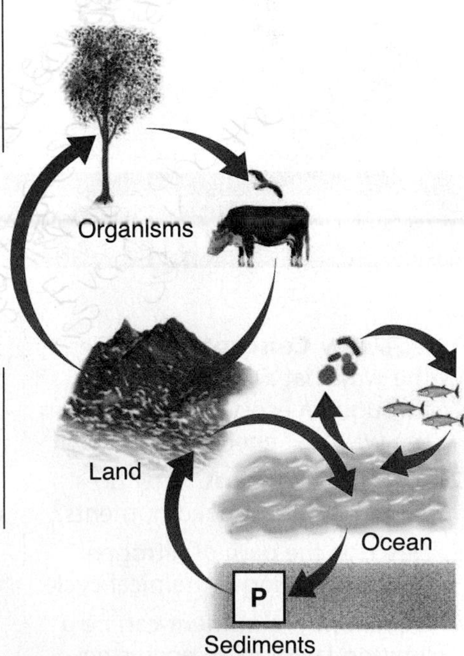

▶ **Figure 3–15** Phosphorus in the biosphere cycles among the land, ocean sediments, and living organisms. **Interpreting Graphics** *How is phosphorus important to living organisms?*

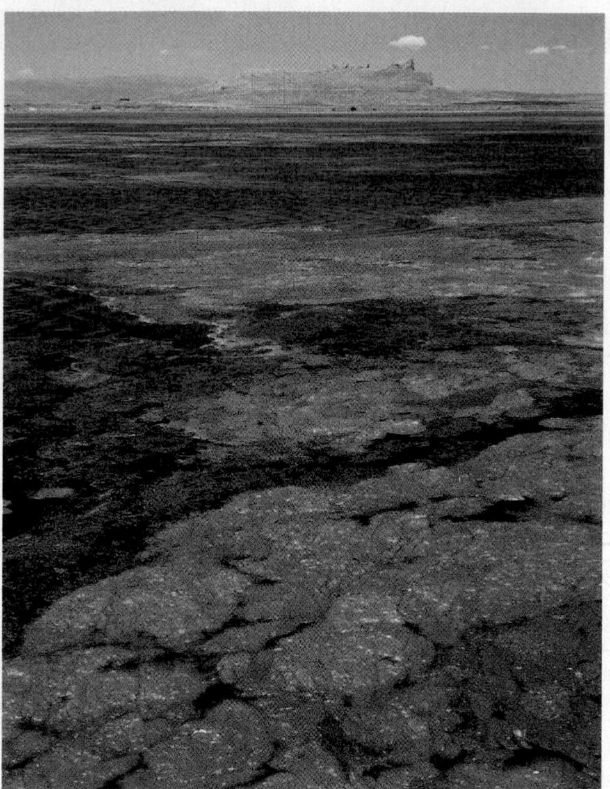

▲ **Figure 3–16** When an aquatic ecosystem receives a large input of a limiting nutrient, the result is often an increase in the number of producers. Here, an extensive algal bloom covers the shoreline of Tule Lake in California. **Using Analogies** *How is this situation similar to the one that occurs in a fish tank in which the fish have been overfed?*

Nutrient Limitation

Ecologists are often interested in the **primary productivity** of an ecosystem, which is the rate at which organic matter is created by producers. One factor that controls the primary productivity of an ecosystem is the amount of available nutrients. If a nutrient is in short supply, it will limit an organism's growth. When an ecosystem is limited by a single nutrient that is scarce or cycles very slowly, this substance is called a **limiting nutrient.**

Because they are well aware of this phenomenon, farmers apply fertilizers to their crops to boost their productivity. Fertilizers usually contain three important nutrients—nitrogen, phosphorus, and potassium. These nutrients help plants grow larger and more quickly than they would in unfertilized soil.

The open oceans of the world can be considered nutrient-poor environments compared to the land. Sea water contains at most only 0.00005 percent nitrogen, or 1/10,000 of the amount typically found in soil. In the ocean and other saltwater environments, nitrogen is often the limiting nutrient. In some areas of the ocean, however, silica or even iron can be the limiting nutrient. In streams, lakes, and freshwater environments, phosphorus is typically the limiting nutrient.

When an aquatic ecosystem receives a large input of a limiting nutrient—for example, runoff from heavily fertilized fields—the result is often an immediate increase in the amount of algae and other producers. This result is called an **algal bloom.** Why do algal blooms occur? There are more nutrients available, so the producers can grow and reproduce more quickly. If there are not enough consumers to eat the excess algae, conditions can become so favorable for growth that algae cover the surface of the water. Algal blooms, like the one shown in **Figure 3–16,** can sometimes disrupt the equilibrium of an ecosystem.

3–3 Section Assessment

1. **Key Concept** How does the way that matter flows through an ecosystem differ from the way that energy flows?
2. **Key Concept** Why do living organisms need nutrients?
3. Describe the path of nitrogen through its biogeochemical cycle.
4. Explain how a nutrient can be a limiting factor in an ecosystem.
5. **Critical Thinking Predicting** Based on your knowledge of the carbon cycle, what do you think might happen if vast areas of forests are cleared?
6. **Critical Thinking Applying Concepts** Summarize the role of algal blooms in disrupting the equilibrium in an aquatic ecosystem.

Thinking Visually

Making a Flowchart
Use a flowchart to trace the flow of energy in the carbon cycle. *Hint*: You may wish to refer to **Figure 3–13,** especially to the labels Photosynthesis, Feeding, Respiration, and Decomposition. Also, you may want to refer to **Figure 3–7** in Section 3–2 for a description of energy flow in an ecosystem.

Identifying a Limiting Nutrient

Limiting nutrients control the growth of organisms in many ecosystems. Excess nutrients can promote the growth of weeds, disease-causing bacteria, and other undesirable organisms. In this investigation, you will determine whether phosphate is a limiting nutrient for the growth of algae.

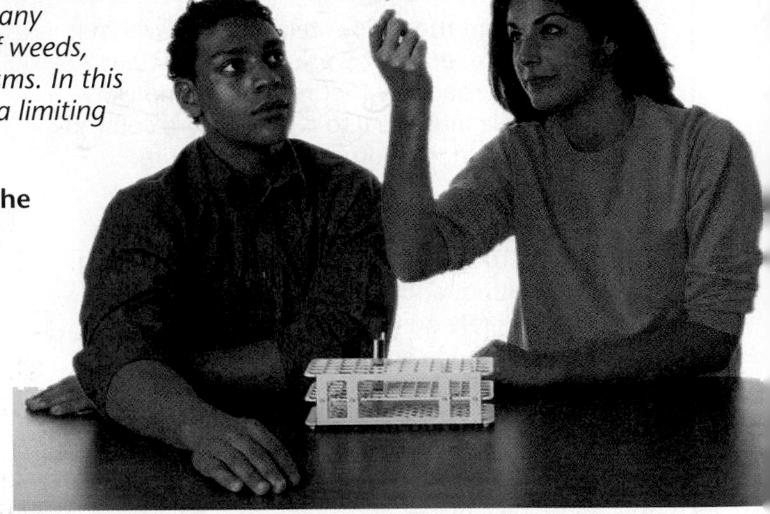

Problem

Does the supply of phosphate limit the growth of algae?

Materials

- dropper pipette
- algae culture
- 2 test tubes with stoppers
- test-tube rack
- 50-mL graduated cylinder
- pond water
- glass-marking pencil
- 10% trisodium phosphate solution

Skills

Formulating Hypotheses, Predicting

Procedure

1. Put on your safety goggles, apron, and plastic gloves. Use a dropper pipette to place 20 drops of algae culture in each of two test tubes.
2. Use a 50-mL graduated cylinder to add 19 mL of pond water to each test tube.
3. Use the glass-marking pencil to label one test tube "control" and the other test tube "phosphate." Use a dropper pipette to add 2 drops of trisodium phosphate to the "phosphate" test tube. **CAUTION:** *Trisodium phosphate can injure your skin. Do not get it on your skin or touch your face after handling it.*
4. Stopper both test tubes and place them in a sunny place. Wash your hands.
5. **Formulating Hypotheses** Record your hypothesis of how phosphate will affect the growth of the algae if it is a limiting nutrient. Also, record your prediction of how the two test tubes will appear after 7 days.
6. Observe the two test tubes each day for the next week. Record your observations each day, including a labeled sketch of each test tube.

Analyze and Conclude

1. **Observing** How did the added phosphate affect the growth of the algae?
2. **Drawing Conclusions** Do your results indicate that phosphate is a limiting nutrient for algae?
3. **Evaluating and Revising** Do your results support your hypothesis? If not, how would you revise your hypothesis?
4. **Predicting** Some detergents are labeled as environmentally safe because they contain little or no phosphate. What differences might you expect to find between a lake that contains high levels of phosphate detergents and one that contains low levels of phosphate detergents?

Go Further

Designing Experiments Select another nutrient and design an experiment to determine whether it is a limiting nutrient for the growth of algae. With your teacher's permission, conduct the experiment and share your findings with the class.

To find out more about how scientists investigate algal blooms, view the segment "*Pfiesteria:* A Killer in the Water," on Videotape One.

Chapter 3 Study Guide

3–1 What Is Ecology?

Key Concepts

- To understand the various relationships within the biosphere, ecologists ask questions about events and organisms that range in complexity from a single individual to a population, community, ecosystem, or biome, or to the entire biosphere.
- Scientists conduct modern ecological research according to three basic approaches: observing, experimenting, and modeling. All of these approaches rely on the application of scientific methods to guide ecological inquiry.

Vocabulary

ecology, p. 63
biosphere, p. 63
species, p. 64
population, p. 64
community, p. 64
ecosystem, p. 64
biome, p. 64

3–2 Energy Flow

Key Concepts

- Sunlight is the main energy source for life on Earth. In a few ecosystems, some organisms rely on the energy stored in inorganic chemical compounds.
- Energy flows through an ecosystem in one direction, from the sun or inorganic compounds to autotrophs (producers) and then to various heterotrophs (consumers).
- Only about 10 percent of the energy available within one trophic level is transferred to organisms at the next trophic level.

Vocabulary

autotroph, p. 67
producer, p. 67
photosynthesis, p. 68
chemosynthesis, p. 68
heterotroph, p. 68
consumer, p. 68
herbivore, p. 69
carnivore, p. 69
omnivore, p. 69
detritivore, p. 69
decomposer, p. 69
food chain, p. 69
food web, p. 70
trophic level, p. 70
ecological pyramid, p. 72
biomass, p. 72

3–3 Cycles of Matter

Key Concepts

- Unlike the one-way flow of energy, matter is recycled within and between ecosystems.
- Every living organism needs nutrients to grow and carry out essential life functions. Like water, nutrients are passed between organisms and the environment through biogeochemical cycles.

Vocabulary

biogeochemical cycle, p. 74
evaporation, p. 75
transpiration, p. 75
nutrient, p. 76
nitrogen fixation, p. 78
denitrification, p. 78
primary productivity, p. 80
limiting nutrient, p. 80
algal bloom, p. 80

Thinking Visually

Using information from this chapter, complete the following flowchart:

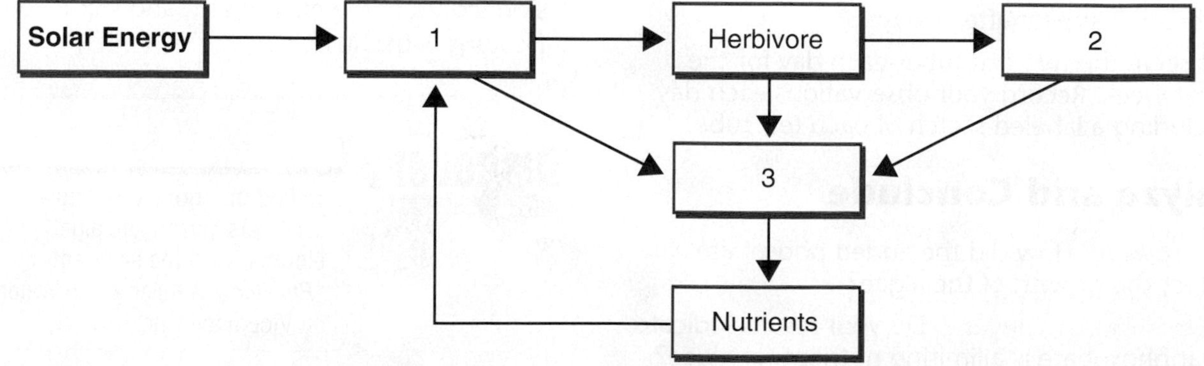

Preparing for the Living Environment Exam

Blue questions emphasize Regents Exam content

Chapter 3

Part A

Multiple Choice

For each statement or question, select the number of the word or expression that, of those given, best completes the statement or answers the question.

1 All of life on Earth interacts with the nonliving environment and exists in a region known as
(1) an ecosystem (3) the biosphere
(2) a niche (4) a food web

2 The linked and changing interactions of populations and the physical environment in a region compose a(an)
(1) food chain (3) ecosystem
(2) biosphere (4) food web

3 Autotrophs are organisms that
(1) rely on other organisms for their energy and food supply
(2) consume plant and animal remains and other dead matter
(3) use energy they take in from the environment to convert inorganic molecules into complex organic molecules
(4) obtain energy by eating plants

4 The series of steps in which a large fish eats a small fish that has eaten algae is a(an)
(1) food web (3) cyclic change
(2) food chain (4) energy pyramid

5 Which organism is a decomposer?

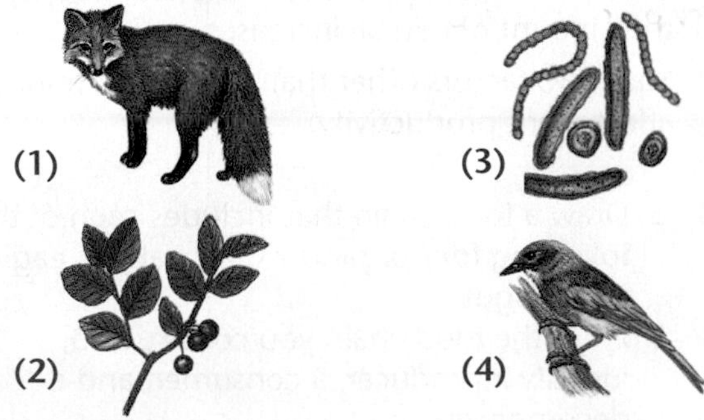

6 An ecosystem is *not* considered to be self-sustaining if
(1) there is interaction between biotic and abiotic factors
(2) some of its living organisms incorporate energy into organic compounds
(3) cycling of materials occurs between organisms and their environment
(4) it lacks a constant supply of energy

7 Which foods are derived from organisms that occupy the level that contains the greatest amount of energy in an energy pyramid?
(1) bread and corn (3) fish and rice
(2) hamburger and fries (4) chicken and shrimp

8 Which is *not* true about matter in the biosphere?
(1) Matter is recycled in the biosphere.
(2) Nutrient cycles transform and reuse molecules.
(3) The total amount of matter decreases over time.
(4) The lack of a specific nutrient can reduce productivity in an ecosystem.

9 Native Americans taught European settlers to bury pieces of fish with the seeds of corn they planted. Why might this practice ensure a good harvest?
(1) Corn grows best by the ocean where fish are plentiful.
(2) The nutrients from decomposing fish can be used by corn plants.
(3) Fish bones should be recycled.
(4) Fish provide water that is essential for plants to grow.

10 Two ways in which water enters the atmosphere in the water cycle are
(1) evaporation and transpiration
(2) respiration and runoff
(3) precipitation and condensation
(4) osmosis and diffusion

11 Which group of organisms is most likely found at the base of a food chain or food web?
(1) viruses (3) insects
(2) plants (4) fungi

Test-Taking Tip As you briefly scan the questions, identify those that may require pure guesswork on your part and save them for last. (Do not write in this book.) Then, use your time on those questions to reason through them and eliminate incorrect choices.

Preparing for the Living Environment Exam

Part B

Multiple Choice and Extended Response
For those questions that ask you to select a response, choose the one that best completes the statement or answers the question. For all others follow the directions given.

12 Phosphorus is an element essential to living things. Based on the diagram below, living things obtain the phosphorus they need from
(1) the atmosphere
(2) sunlight
(3) the food chain
(4) ATP

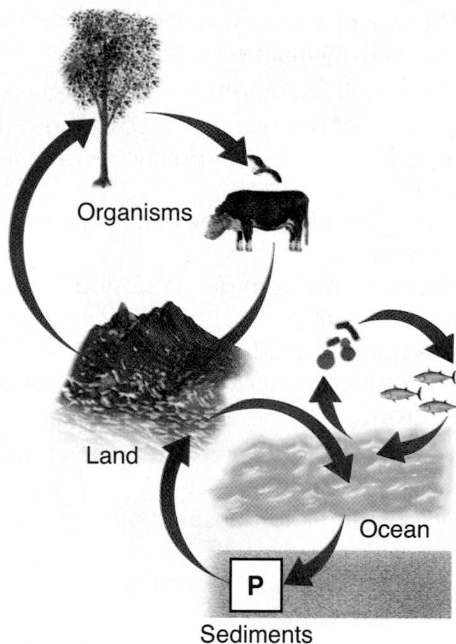

13 One hypothesis attributes the extinction of the dinosaurs to the collision of Earth with a large asteroid. The collision created a large dust cloud that circled Earth blocking the sun's rays. State one reason why this would cause the dinosaurs and many other organisms to die.

14 In a particular environment, the growth and survival of organisms depends on physical conditions (abiotic factors). State *two* abiotic factors important to land-dwelling organisms.

15 State what would happen to the plant population in an area if the number of decomposers decreased. Explain why this would happen.

Base your answers to questions 16 through 17 on the graph below and on your knowledge of biology. The graph shows the effect of rainfall on the rate of plant productivity (growth) in an ecosystem.

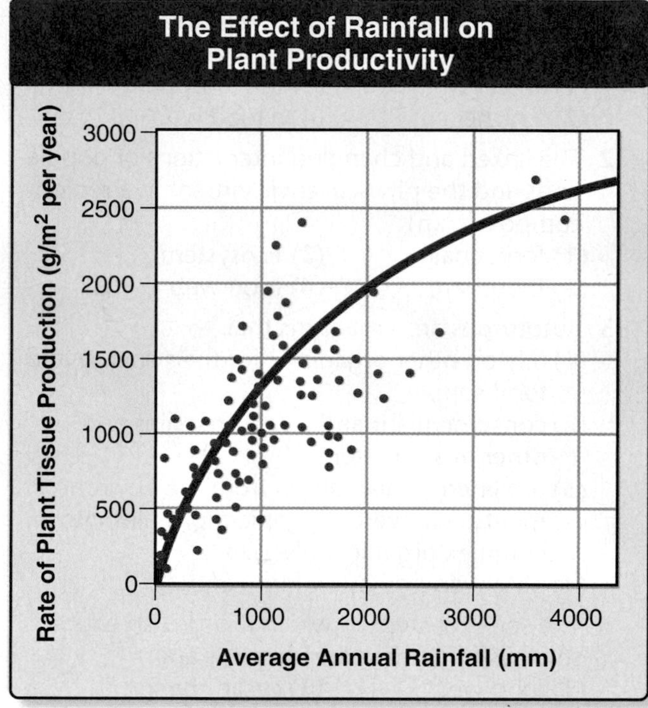

16 Describe what happens to plant productivity as the amount of rainfall increases.

17 State *two* factors other than water that might affect plant productivity.

18 *a* Draw a food chain that includes each of the following four organisms: fish, algae, eagle, and fungus.
b From the food chain you constructed, identify a producer, a consumer, and a decomposer.

Base your answers to questions 19 through 21 on the diagram of a food web below and on your knowledge of biology.

19 Make a diagram to show one food chain shown in this food web.

20 State what would happen to the rabbit population if a disease were to destroy all of the mice. Support your answer.

21 Identify which group of organisms is missing from the food web diagram and describe the function of this group of organisms in the flow of materials.

Part C

Extended Response
Answer the questions or follow the directions given.

22 Photosynthesis, respiration, and decomposition are all involved in the cycling of carbon through the ecosystem. Explain how these processes help in the cycling of carbon. In your answer, be sure to:
- identify which of these processes releases carbon dioxide into the atmosphere
- identify which of these processes removes carbon dioxide from the atmosphere
- describe how all three processes are important in maintaining a balanced ecosystem

23 Food chains and food webs both show how energy flows through ecosystems. Compare a food chain with a food web. In your answer be sure to:
- identify which (a food chain or a food web) is the most accurate representation of energy and material flow
- explain why it is more accurate

24 Some people claim that certain carnivores such as wolves and coyotes should be destroyed because they kill beneficial animals. Explain why these carnivores should be protected. In your answer be sure to:
- discuss prey population growth
- describe the role of carnivores in the ecosystem
- explain how the removal of these predators could lead to the extinction of the predators and other species.

Go Online
PHSchool.com

For: An interactive self-test
Visit: PHSchool.com
Web Code: cba-2030

CHAPTER 4

Ecosystems and Communities

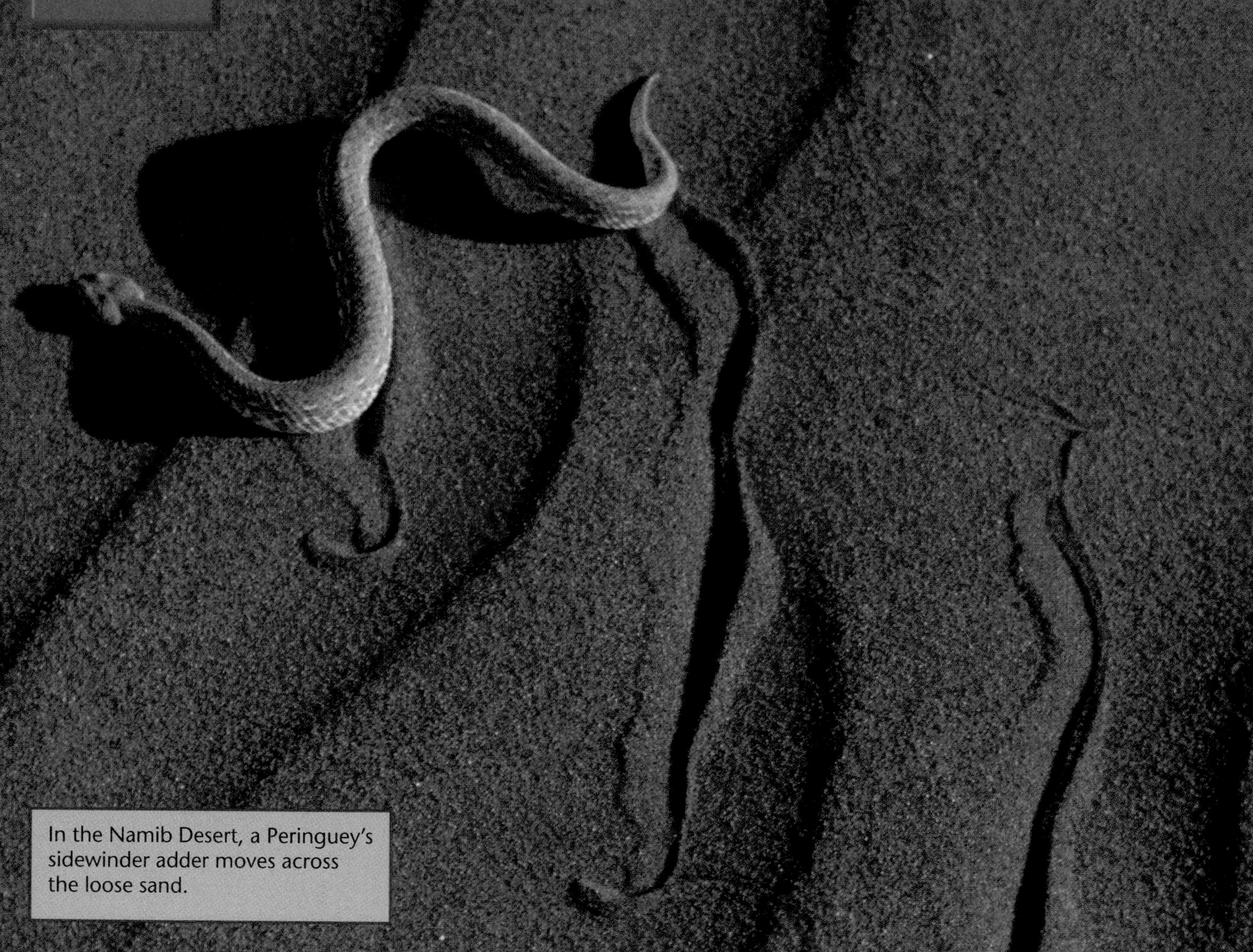

In the Namib Desert, a Peringuey's sidewinder adder moves across the loose sand.

Inquiry Activity

What relationships exist in an ecosystem?

Procedure

1. Observe a terrarium, aquarium, or other small ecosystem that your teacher provides.
2. Use your observations to construct a diagram (similar to a concept map) showing all the relationships that exist among the parts of the ecosystem.
3. Indicate on your diagram which relationships involve nonliving parts of the ecosystem.

Think About It

1. **Classifying** What types of relationships did you find among the organisms? What types of relationships did you find between the organisms and the nonliving parts of their environment?
2. **Predicting** How might your diagram change if the ecosystem were in the dark for a week?

4–1 The Role of Climate

4-1.1 Ecosystems are shaped by physical conditions
4-6.1 Organism survival
LS- Make observations

If you live in Michigan, you know you cannot grow banana trees in your backyard. Bananas are tropical plants that need plenty of water and heat. They won't survive in freezing temperatures. It may not be as obvious that cranberries won't grow in the Rio Grande Valley of Texas. Cranberries need plenty of water and a cold rest period. They cannot tolerate the months of very hot weather that often occur in the Rio Grande Valley.

Bananas and cranberries, like other plants and animals, vary in their adaptations to temperature, rainfall, and other environmental conditions. Species also vary in their tolerances for conditions outside their normal ranges. That's why climate is important in shaping ecosystems—and why understanding climate is important in ecology.

Guide for Reading

Key Concepts
- How does the greenhouse effect maintain the biosphere's temperature range?
- What are Earth's three main climate zones?

Vocabulary
weather • climate
greenhouse effect • polar zone
temperate zone • tropical zone

Reading Strategy: Outlining Before you read, use the headings in this section to make an outline about climate. As you read, fill in the subtopics and smaller topics. Then, add phrases or a sentence after each subtopic to provide key information.

What Is Climate?

In the atmosphere, temperature, precipitation, and other environmental factors combine to produce weather and climate. **Weather** is the day-to-day condition of Earth's atmosphere at a particular time and place. The weather where you live may be clear and sunny one day but cloudy and cold the next. **Climate,** on the other hand, refers to the average, year-after-year conditions of temperature and precipitation in a particular region.

Climate is caused by the interplay of many factors, including the trapping of heat by the atmosphere, the latitude, the transport of heat by winds and ocean currents, and the amount of precipitation that results. The shape and elevation of landmasses also contribute to global climate patterns.

The energy of incoming sunlight drives Earth's weather and helps determine climate. As you might expect, solar energy has an important effect on the temperature of the atmosphere. At the same time, the presence of certain gases in the atmosphere also has an effect on its temperature.

The Greenhouse Effect

Temperatures on Earth remain within a range suitable for life because the biosphere has a natural insulating blanket—the atmosphere. **Carbon dioxide, methane, water vapor, and a few other atmospheric gases trap heat energy and maintain Earth's temperature range.** These gases function like the glass windows of a greenhouse. Just as the glass keeps the greenhouse plants warm, these gases trap the heat energy of sunlight inside Earth's atmosphere. The natural situation in which heat is retained by this layer of greenhouse gases is called the **greenhouse effect,** shown in **Figure 4–1.**

▼ **Figure 4–1** **Carbon dioxide, water vapor, and several other gases in the atmosphere allow solar radiation to enter the biosphere but slow down the loss of heat to space.** These greenhouse gases cause the greenhouse effect, which helps maintain Earth's temperature range.

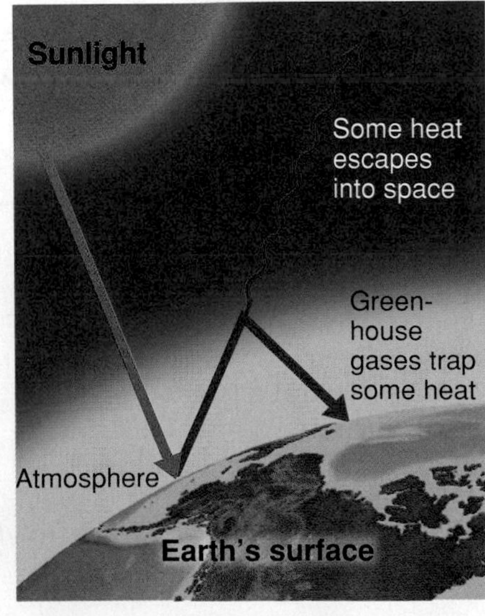

Greenhouse gases allow solar energy to penetrate the atmosphere in the form of sunlight. Much of the sunlight that hits the surface of our planet is converted into heat energy and then radiated back into the atmosphere. However, those same gases do not allow heat energy to pass out of the atmosphere as readily as light energy enters it. Instead, the gases trap heat inside Earth's atmosphere. If these gases were not present in the atmosphere, Earth would be 30 degrees Celsius cooler than it is today.

The Effect of Latitude on Climate

Because Earth is a sphere that is tilted on its axis, solar radiation strikes different parts of Earth's surface at an angle that varies throughout the year. At the equator, the sun is almost directly overhead at noon all year. At the North and South poles, however, the sun is much lower in the sky for months at a time. Look at **Figure 4–2,** and you will see that differences in the angle of sunlight directed at different latitudes result in the delivery of more heat to the equator than to the poles. The difference in heat distribution with latitude has important effects on Earth's climate zones.

As a result of differences in latitude and thus the angle of heating, Earth has three main climate zones: polar, temperate, and tropical. The **polar zones** are cold areas where the sun's rays strike Earth at a very low angle. These zones are located in the areas around the North and South poles, between 66.5° and 90° North and South latitudes. The **temperate zones** sit between the polar zones and the tropics. Because temperate zones are more affected by the changing angle of the sun over the course of a year, the climate in these zones ranges from hot to cold, depending on the season. The **tropical zone,** or tropics, is near the equator, between 23.5° North and 23.5° South latitudes. The tropics thus receive direct or nearly direct sunlight year-round, making the climate almost always warm. **Figure 4–2** shows Earth's main climate zones.

CHECKPOINT *What effect does latitude have on climate?*

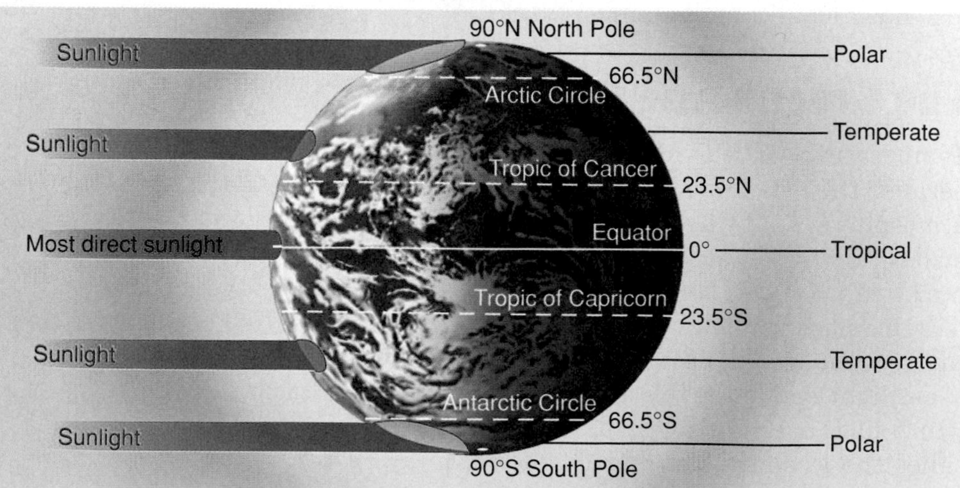

▶ **Figure 4–2** **Earth has three main climate zones.** These climate zones are caused by the unequal heating of Earth's surface. Near the equator, energy from the sun strikes Earth almost directly. Near the poles, the sun's rays strike Earth's surface at a lower angle. The same amount of solar energy is spread out over a larger area, heating the surface less than at the equator.

Heat Transport in the Biosphere

The unequal heating of Earth's surface drives winds and ocean currents, which transport heat throughout the biosphere. Winds form because warm air tends to rise and cool air tends to sink. Consequently, air that is heated near the equator rises. At the same time, cooler air over the poles sinks toward the ground. The upward movement of warm air and the downward movement of cool air create air currents, or winds, that move heat throughout the atmosphere, from regions of sinking air to regions of rising air. The prevailing winds, shown in **Figure 4–3,** bring warm or cold air to a region, affecting its climate.

Similar patterns of heating and cooling occur in Earth's oceans. Cold water near the poles sinks and then flows parallel to the ocean bottom, eventually rising again in warmer regions through a process called upwelling. Meanwhile, surface water is moved by winds. In both cases, the water flow creates ocean currents. Like air currents, ocean currents transport heat energy within the biosphere. Surface ocean currents warm or cool the air above them, thus affecting the weather and climate of nearby landmasses.

Continents and other landmasses can also affect winds and ocean currents. Landmasses can interfere with the movement of air masses. For example, a mountain range causes a moist air mass to rise. As this happens, the air mass cools and moisture condenses, forming clouds that bring precipitation to the mountains. Once the air mass reaches the far side of the mountains, it has lost much of its moisture. The result is a rain shadow—an area with a dry climate—on the far side of the mountains.

WINDS

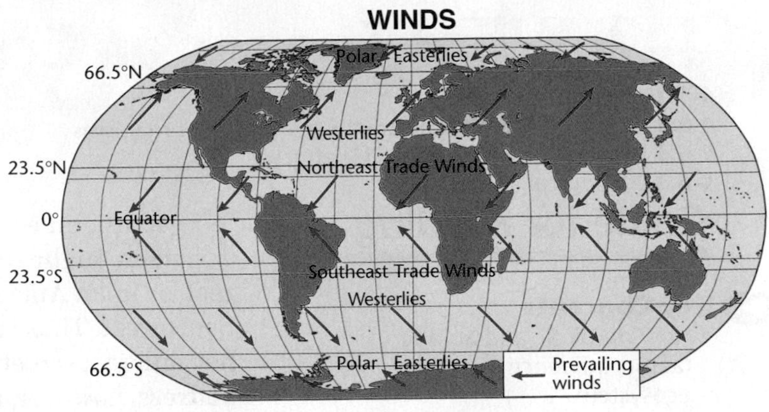

OCEAN CURRENTS

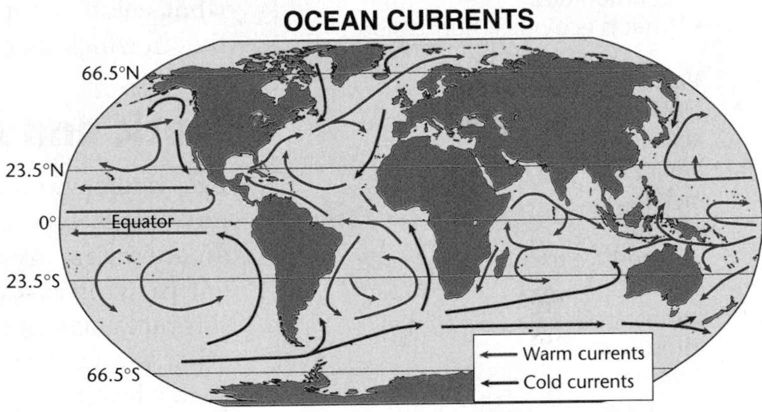

▲ **Figure 4–3** Earth's winds (top) and ocean currents (bottom) interact to help produce Earth's climates. The curved paths of some currents and winds are the result of Earth's rotation. **Interpreting Graphics** ***In what direction do cold currents in Earth's oceans generally move?***

4–1 Section Assessment

1. **Key Concept** What is the greenhouse effect?
2. **Key Concept** Describe Earth's three main climate zones.
3. What are the main factors that determine Earth's climate?
4. Describe two ways in which heat is transported in the biosphere.
5. **Critical Thinking Applying Concepts** A biologist recorded the bird species in her region. Then, she spotted a bird that was not supposed to live in the region. How might variations relate to this occurrence?

Sharpen Your Skills

Modeling

Earth rotates daily on its axis and is tilted at an angle of 23.5° in relation to the sun. Using a flashlight to represent the sun and a globe to represent Earth, demonstrate different levels of light in Earth's three climate zones.

4–2 What Shapes an Ecosystem?

4-1.1 Ecosystems
4-6.1 Relationships and interactions between organisms
4-6.3 A stable ecosystem can be altered
4-6.3 Ecological succession

Guide for Reading

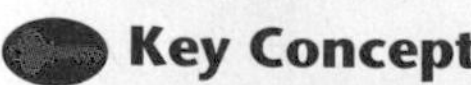

Key Concepts
- How do biotic and abiotic factors influence an ecosystem?
- What interactions occur within communities?
- What is ecological succession?

Vocabulary
biotic factor
abiotic factor
habitat
niche
resource
competitive exclusion principle
predation
symbiosis
mutualism
commensalism
parasitism
ecological succession
primary succession
pioneer species
secondary succession

Reading Strategy: Building Vocabulary Before you read, preview new vocabulary terms by skimming the section and making a list of the highlighted, boldface terms. Leave space to make notes as you read.

If you ask an ecologist where a particular organism lives, that person might say the organism lives on a Caribbean coral reef, or in an Amazon rain forest, or in a desert in the American Southwest. Those answers provide a kind of ecological address not unlike a street address in a city or town. An ecological address, however, tells you more than where an organism lives. It tells you about the climate the organism experiences and what neighbors it is likely to have. But what shapes the ecosystem in which an organism lives?

Biotic and Abiotic Factors

Ecosystems are influenced by a combination of biological and physical factors. The biological influences on organisms within an ecosystem are called **biotic factors.** These include the entire living cast of characters with which an organism might interact, including birds, trees, mushrooms, and bacteria—in other words, the ecological community. Biotic factors that influence a bullfrog, for example, might include the tiny plants and algae it eats as a tadpole, the herons that eat the adult frog, and other species that compete with the bullfrog for food or space.

Physical, or nonliving, factors that shape ecosystems are called **abiotic** (ay-by-AHT-ik) **factors.** For example, the climate of an area includes abiotic factors such as temperature, precipitation, and humidity. Other abiotic factors are wind, nutrient availability, soil type, and sunlight. For example, the bullfrog in **Figure 4–4** is affected by abiotic factors such as the availability of water and the temperature of the air. **Together, biotic and abiotic factors determine the survival and growth of an organism and the productivity of the ecosystem in which the organism lives.** The area where an organism lives is called its **habitat.** A habitat includes both biotic and abiotic factors.

Give an example of an abiotic factor.

◀ **Figure 4–4** **Like all ecosystems, this pond is shaped by a combination of biotic and abiotic factors.** The bullfrog, plants, and other organisms in the pond are biotic factors. The water, the air, and the rock on which the bullfrog sits are abiotic factors.

Quick Lab

How do abiotic factors affect different plant species?

Materials presoaked rye and rice seeds, sand, potting soil, 4 paper cups

Procedure   

1. Use a pencil to punch three holes in the bottom of each cup. Fill 2 cups with equal amounts of sand and 2 cups with the same amount of potting soil.
2. Plant 5 rice seeds in one sand-filled cup and 5 rice seeds in one soil-filled cup. Plant 5 rye seeds in each of the other 2 cups. Label each cup with the type of seeds and soil it contains.
3. Place all the cups in a warm, sunny location. Each day for 2 weeks, water the cups equally and record your observations of any plant growth. **CAUTION:** *Wash your hands well with soap and warm water after handling plants or soil.*

Analyze and Conclude

1. **Analyzing Data** In which medium did the rice grow best—sand or soil? Which was the better medium for the growth of rye?
2. **Inferring** Soil retains more water than sand, providing a moister environment. What can you infer from your observations about the kind of environment that favors the growth of rice? The growth of rye?
3. **Drawing Conclusions** Which would compete more successfully in a dry environment—rye or rice? In a moist environment?

The Niche

If an organism's habitat is its address, its niche is its occupation. A **niche** (NITCH) is the full range of physical and biological conditions in which an organism lives and the way in which the organism uses those conditions. For instance, part of the description of an organism's niche includes its place in the food web. Another part of the description might include the range of temperatures that the organism needs to survive. The combination of biotic and abiotic factors in an ecosystem often determines the number of different niches in that ecosystem.

A niche includes the type of food the organism eats, how it obtains this food, and which other species use the organism as food. For example, a mature bullfrog catches insects, worms, spiders, small fish, or even mice. Predators such as herons, raccoons, and snakes prey on bullfrogs.

The physical conditions that the bullfrog requires to survive are part of its niche. Bullfrogs spend their lives in or near the water of ponds, lakes, and slow-moving streams. A bullfrog's body temperature varies with that of the surrounding water and air. As winter approaches, bullfrogs burrow into the mud of pond or stream bottoms to hibernate.

The bullfrog's niche also includes when and how it reproduces. Female bullfrogs lay their eggs in water during the warmer months of the year. The young frogs, called tadpoles, live in the water until their legs and lungs develop.

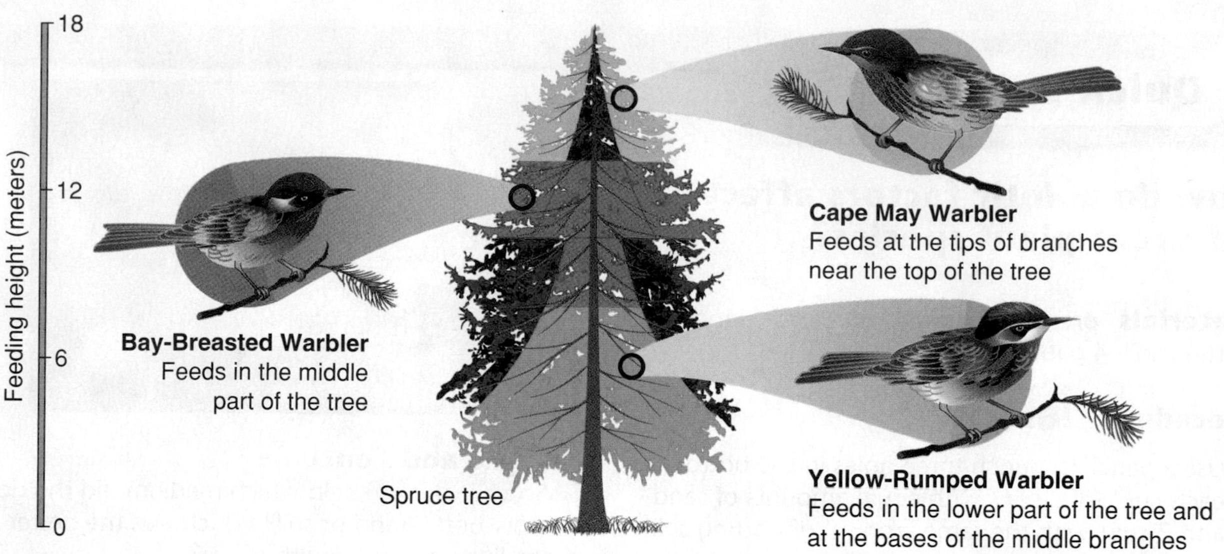

▲ **Figure 4–5** Each of these warbler species has a different niche in its spruce tree habitat. By feeding in different areas of the tree, the birds avoid competing with one another for food. **Inferring** ***What would happen if two of the warbler species attempted to occupy the same niche?***

As you will see, no two species can share the same niche in the same habitat. However, different species can occupy niches that are very similar. For instance, the three species of North American warblers shown in **Figure 4–5** live in the same spruce trees but feed at different elevations and in different parts of those trees. The species are similar, yet each warbler has a different niche within the forest.

What is a niche?

Community Interactions

When organisms live together in ecological communities, they interact constantly. These interactions help shape the ecosystem in which they live. **Community interactions, such as competition, predation, and various forms of symbiosis, can powerfully affect an ecosystem.**

Competition Competition occurs when organisms of the same or different species attempt to use an ecological resource in the same place at the same time. The term **resource** refers to any necessity of life, such as water, nutrients, light, food, or space. In a forest, for example, broad-leaved trees such as oak or hickory may compete for sunlight by growing tall, spreading out their leaves, and blocking the sunlight from shorter trees. Similarly, two species of lizards in a desert might compete by attempting to eat the same type of insect.

Direct competition in nature often results in a winner and a loser—with the losing organism failing to survive. A fundamental rule in ecology, the **competitive exclusion principle,** states that no two species can occupy the same niche in the same habitat at the same time. Look again at the distribution of the warblers in **Figure 4–5.** Can you see how this distribution avoids direct competition among the different warbler species?

Predation An interaction in which one organism captures and feeds on another organism is called **predation** (pree-DAY-shun). The organism that does the killing and eating is called the predator (PRED-uh-tur), and the food organism is the prey. Cheetahs are active predators with claws and sharp teeth. Their powerful legs enable them to run after prey. Other predators, such as anglerfishes, are more passive. An anglerfish has a fleshy appendage that resembles a fishing lure, which it uses to draw unsuspecting prey close to its mouth.

Symbiosis Any relationship in which two species live closely together is called **symbiosis** (sim-by-OH-sis), which means "living together." Biologists recognize three main classes of symbiotic relationships in nature: mutualism, commensalism, and parasitism. Examples of these three symbiotic relationships are shown in **Figure 4–6.**

Mutualism In **mutualism** (MYOO-choo-ul-iz-um), both species benefit from the relationship. Many flowers, for example, depend on certain species of insects to pollinate them. The flowers provide the insects with food in the form of nectar, pollen, or other substances, and the insects help the flowers reproduce.

Commensalism In **commensalism** (kuh-MEN-sul-iz-um), one member of the association benefits and the other is neither helped nor harmed. Small marine animals called barnacles, for example, often attach themselves to a whale's skin. The barnacles perform no known service to the whale, nor do they harm it. Yet, the barnacles benefit from the constant movement of water past the swimming whale, because the water carries food particles to them.

Parasitism In **parasitism** (PAR-uh-sit-iz-um), one organism lives on or inside another organism and harms it. The parasite obtains all or part of its nutritional needs from the other organism, called the host. Generally, parasites weaken but do not kill their host, which is usually larger than the parasite. Tapeworms, for example, are parasites that live in the intestines of mammals. Fleas, ticks, and lice live on the bodies of mammals, feeding on the blood and skin of the host.

Mutualism The ant cares for the aphids and protects them from predators. The aphids produce a sweet liquid that the ant drinks.

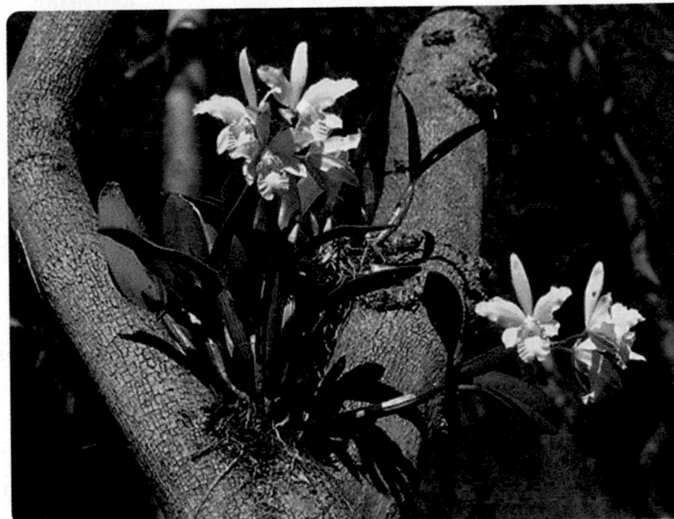

Commensalism The orchid benefits from its perch in the tree as it absorbs water and minerals from rainwater and runoff, but the tree is not affected.

Parasitism A tick feeds on the blood of its host and may also carry disease-causing microorganisms.

Figure 4–6 Three examples of symbiosis are shown: mutualism, commensalism, and parasitism. **Predicting** *What would happen to the aphids if the ant died?*

Ecological Succession

On the time scale of a human life, some ecosystems may seem stable. The appearance of stability is often misleading, because ecosystems and communities are always changing. Sometimes, an ecosystem changes in response to an abrupt disturbance, such as a severe storm. At other times, change occurs as a more gradual response to natural fluctuations in the environment. **Ecosystems are constantly changing in response to natural and human disturbances. As an ecosystem changes, older inhabitants gradually die out and new organisms move in, causing further changes in the community.** This series of predictable changes that occurs in a community over time is called **ecological succession.** Sometimes succession results from slow changes in the physical environment. A sudden natural disturbance from human activities, such as clearing a forest, may also be a cause of succession.

Primary Succession On land, succession that occurs on surfaces where no soil exists is called **primary succession.** For example, primary succession occurs on the surfaces formed as volcanic eruptions build new islands or cover the land with lava rock or volcanic ash. Primary succession also occurs on bare rock exposed when glaciers melt.

In **Figure 4–7,** you can follow the stages of primary succession after a volcanic eruption. When primary succession begins, there is no soil, just ash and rock. The first species to populate the area are called **pioneer species.** The pioneer species on volcanic rocks are often lichens (LY-kunz). A lichen is made up of a fungus and an alga and can grow on bare rock. As lichens grow, they help break up the rocks. When they die, the lichens add organic material to help form soil in which plants can grow.

What are pioneer species?

▼ **Figure 4–7** Primary succession occurs on newly exposed surfaces, such as this newly deposited volcanic rock and ash. (1) A volcanic eruption destroys the previous ecosystem. (2) The first organisms to appear are lichens. (3) Mosses soon appear, and grasses take root in the thin layer of soil. (4) Eventually, tree seedlings and shrubs sprout among the plant community. **Predicting** ***What types of animals would you expect to appear at each stage, and why?***

Secondary Succession Components of an ecosystem can be changed by natural events, such as fires, or by human activities, such as farming. These changes may affect the ecosystem in predictable or unpredictable ways. When the disturbance is over, community interactions tend to restore the ecosystem to its original condition through **secondary succession.** For example, secondary succession occurs after wildfires burn woodlands and when land cleared for farming is abandoned. **Figure 4–8** shows trees regrowing after a wildfire. In fact, fires set by lightning occur in many ecosystems, and some plants are so adapted to periodic fires that their seeds won't sprout unless exposed to fire!

Ecologists used to think that succession in a given area always proceeded through predictable stages to produce the same stable "climax community." Old-growth forests in the Pacific Northwest, for example, were considered climax communities. But natural disasters, climate change, and human activity such as introduction of nonnative species profoundly affect these communities today. Healthy ecosystems usually recover from natural disturbances because of the way components of the system interact. Ecosystems may or may not recover from long-term, human-caused disturbances.

▲ **Figure 4–8** Ten years after wildfires burned regions of Yellowstone National Park, small evergreen trees have begun to regenerate the forest. **Predicting** ***How do you think this region will look 20 years after the fires?***

Careers in Biology

Forestry Technician

Job Description: work outdoors to help maintain, protect, and develop forests (by planting trees, fighting insects and diseases that attack trees, and controlling soil erosion)

Education: two- or four-year college degree in forestry, wildlife, or conservation; summer work in parks, state and national forests; and private industry provides on-the-job training

Skills: knowledge of the outdoors and basic safety precautions; communication skills for working with the public; keen observational skills; physical fitness for jobs that require walking long distances through forests

Highlights: help to manage and conserve forest biomes by analyzing data, planting trees, and managing fires when necessary; contribute to people's enjoyment of outdoor recreation

For: Career links
Visit: PHSchool.com
Web Code: cbb-2042

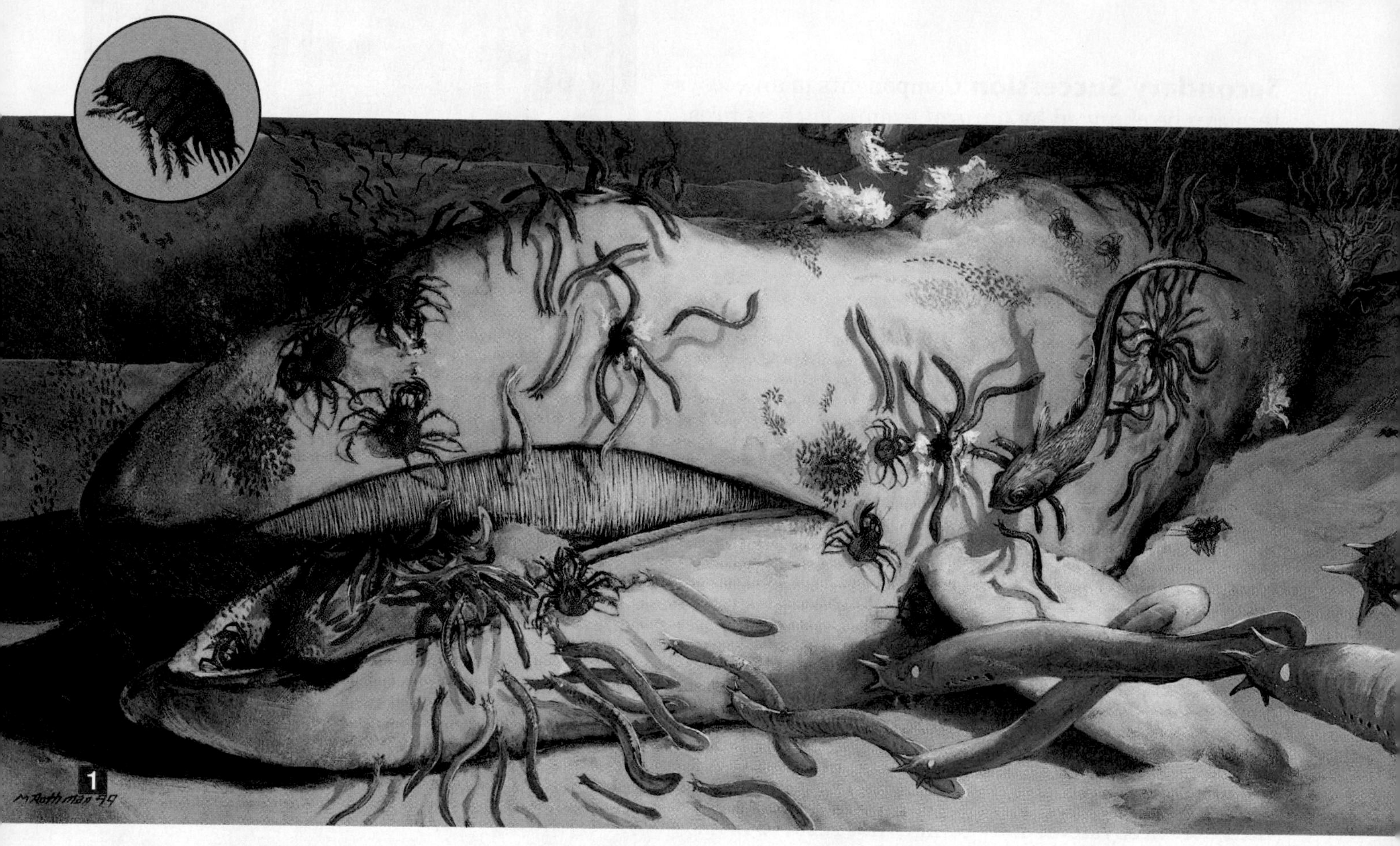

Figure 4–9 **Ecosystems are constantly changing in response to disturbances.** In natural environments, succession occurs in stages. A dead whale that falls to the ocean floor is soon covered with scavengers. After a time, only bare bones are left. The bones contain oil that supports several types of deep-sea bacteria. In the next stage of succession, the bacteria provide energy and nutrients for a different community of organisms that live on the bones and in the surrounding sediments.

Succession in a Marine Ecosystem Succession can occur in any ecosystem—even in the permanently dark, deep ocean. In 1987, scientists found an unusual community of organisms living on the remains of a dead whale in the deep waters off the coast of southern California. At first, ecologists did not know what to make of this extraordinary community. After several experiments and hours of observation, the ecologists found that the community represented a stage in succession amid an otherwise stable and well-documented deep-sea ecosystem. Since that discovery, several more whale carcasses have been found in other ocean basins with similar organisms surrounding them. **Figure 4–9** illustrates three stages in the succession of a whale-fall community.

1 The disturbance that causes this kind of succession begins when a large whale, such as a blue or fin whale, dies and sinks to the normally barren ocean floor. The whale carcass attracts a host of scavengers and decomposers, including amphipods (inset), hagfishes, and sharks, that feast on the decaying meat.

2 Within a year, most of the whale's tissues have been eaten. The carcass then supports only a much smaller number of fishes, crabs, marine snails (inset), and other marine animals. The decomposition of the whale's body, however, enriches the surrounding sediments with nutrients, forming an oasis of sediment dwellers, including many different species of marine worms.

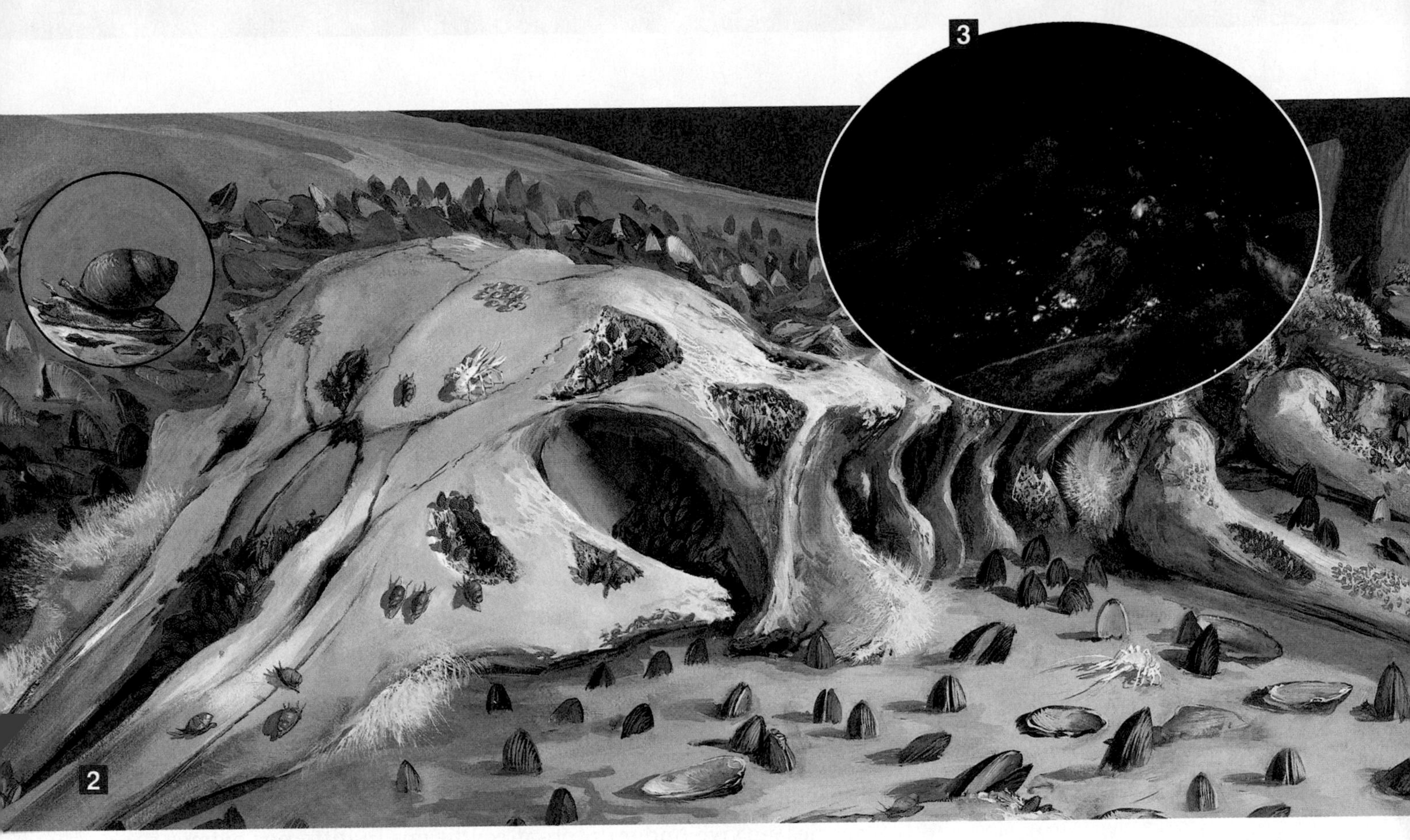

3 When only the whale's skeleton remains, a third community moves in. Heterotrophic bacteria begin to decompose oils inside the whale bones. In doing so, they release chemical compounds that serve as energy sources for other bacteria that are chemosynthetic autotrophs. The chemosynthetic bacteria, in turn, support a diverse community of mussels, limpets, snails, worms, crabs, clams, and other organisms that live on the bones and within the nearby sediments.

4–2 Section Assessment

1. **Key Concept** What is the difference between a biotic factor and an abiotic factor?
2. **Key Concept** Name three types of community interactions that can affect an ecosystem.
3. **Key Concept** What is the difference between primary succession and secondary succession?
4. How is an organism's niche determined?
5. **Critical Thinking Comparing and Contrasting** How are the three types of symbiotic relationships different? Similar?
6. **Critical Thinking Applying Concepts** Summarize the role of organisms, including microorganisms, in maintaining the equilibrium of a marine ecosystem while a dead whale decays on the ocean floor.

Writing in Science

Creative Writing
Use the information from this section to write a short story about an ecosystem that is disturbed and undergoes succession. *Hint*: Include a flowchart with your story to show the main stages of change.

4–3 Biomes

4-1.1 Ecosystems are shaped by physical conditions
4-1.1 Ecosystems include populations
4-6.1 Organism survival depends on physical environment
4-6.3 Development of stable ecosystems

Guide for Reading

Key Concept
- What are the unique characteristics of the world's major biomes?

Vocabulary
biome • tolerance
microclimate • canopy
understory • deciduous
coniferous • humus
taiga • permafrost

Reading Strategy: Using Visuals Before you read, preview **Figure 4–11.** Write down the names of the different biomes. As you read, examine the photographs and list the main characteristics of each biome.

Ecologists group Earth's diverse environments into biomes. A **biome** is a complex of terrestrial communities that covers a large area and is characterized by certain soil and climate conditions and particular assemblages of plants and animals.

Can all kinds of organisms live in every biome? No. Species vary in their adaptations to different conditions. An adaptation is an inherited characteristic that increases an organism's ability to survive and reproduce.

The leaves of the saguaro cactus, for example, are reduced to spines to minimize water loss, and its stems store water during dry spells. Its shallow, wide-spreading roots absorb water rapidly. Desert rodents, such as kangaroo rats, have adaptations in their kidneys that help conserve water, and they extract water from food. Many rain forest plants, such as certain anthuriums, have long, thin leaves whose pointed tips help shed excess water. Some rain forest animals, such as certain tree frogs, spend their life in trees—their tadpoles grow in water pockets in leaf bases of plants such as bromeliads.

These sorts of variations in plants and animals help different species survive under different conditions in different biomes. Plants and animals also exhibit variations in **tolerance,** or ability to survive and reproduce under conditions that differ from their optimal conditions. Plants and animals of the Arizona desert, for example, can tolerate temperatures that range from blisteringly hot to below freezing. Some rain forest plants and animals, by comparison, die quickly if the temperature drops below freezing or rises above 34°C for long. Either too much or too little of any environmental factor can make it difficult for an organism to survive. A saguaro would rot and die in a rain forest as surely as an anthurium or rain forest tree frog would shrivel and die in the desert!

▼ **Figure 4–10** Climate diagrams show the average temperature and precipitation at a given location during each month of the year. In this graph, and the others to follow, temperature is plotted as a red line. Precipitation is shown as vertical purple bars. **Interpreting Graphics** *What is the approximate average temperature and precipitation in New Orleans during the month of July?*

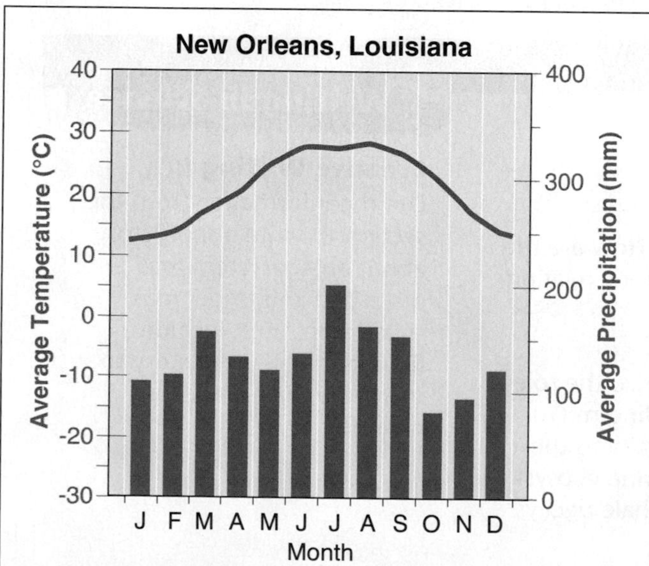

Biomes and Climate

Because each species is adapted to certain conditions, the climate of a region is an important factor in determining which organisms can survive there. Even within a biome, precise conditions of temperature and precipitation can vary over small distances. The climate in a small area that differs from the climate around it is called a **microclimate.** For example, certain streets in San Francisco are often blanketed in fog while the sun shines brightly just a few blocks away. Two main components of climate—temperature and precipitation—can be summarized in a graph called a climate diagram, as shown in **Figure 4–10.**

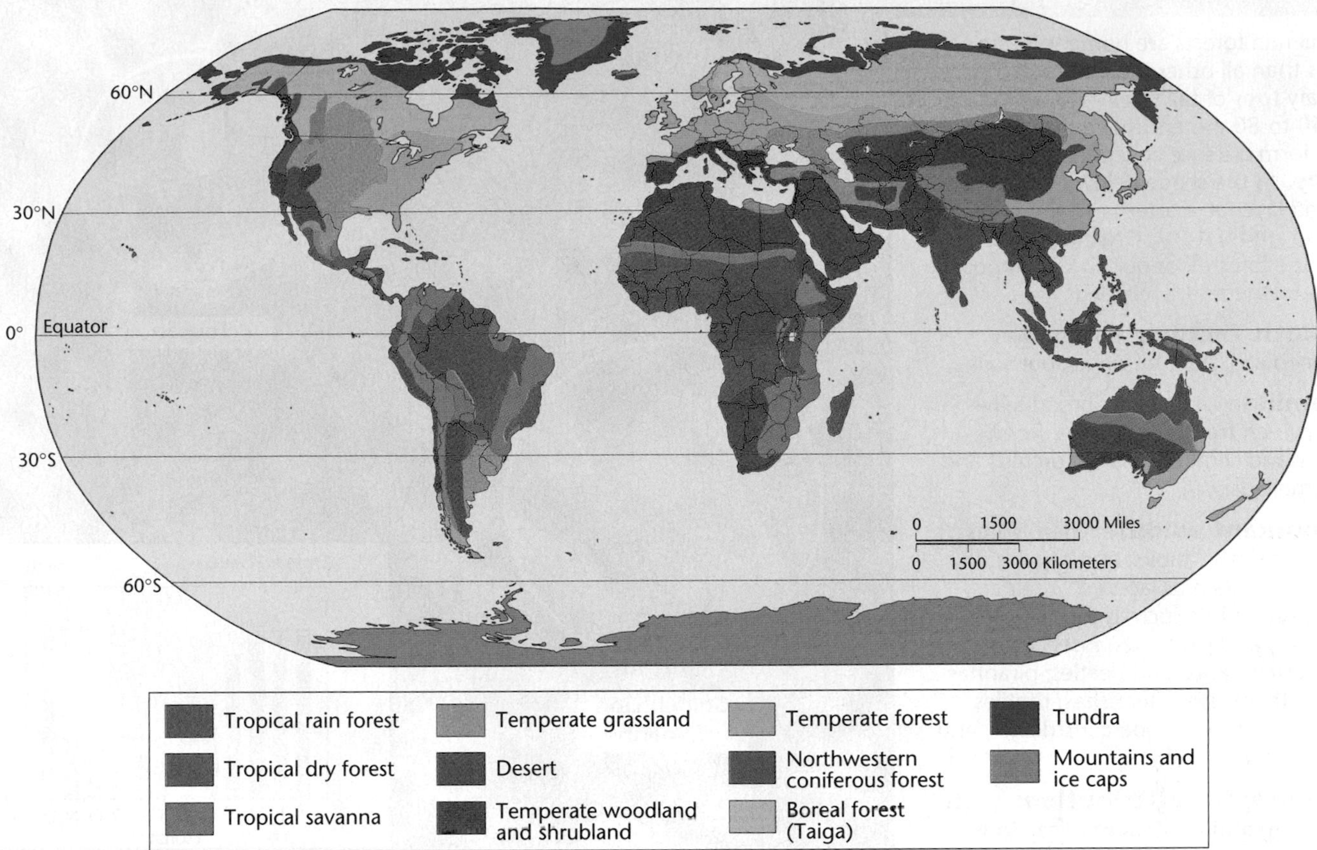

▲ **Figure 4–11** This map shows the locations of the world's major biomes. Other parts of Earth's surface are classified as mountains or ice caps. **Each biome has a characteristic climate and community of organisms.** These characteristics are shown on the pages that follow.

The Major Biomes

Ecologists recognize at least ten different biomes. **The world's major biomes include tropical rain forest, tropical dry forest, tropical savanna, desert, temperate grassland, temperate woodland and shrubland, temperate forest, northwestern coniferous forest, boreal forest, and tundra. Each of these biomes is defined by a unique set of abiotic factors—particularly climate—and a characteristic assemblage of plants and animals.** The distribution of major biomes is shown in **Figure 4–11**, and some of their most important characteristics are summarized over the next five pages.

There is often ecological variation within a biome. Sometimes, this variation is due to changes in microclimate caused by differences in exposure or elevation above sea level. Other times, variation may be related to local soil conditions or the presence of rock outcroppings. Note also that although boundaries between biomes on this map appear to be sharp, there are often transitional areas in which one biome's plants and animals become less common, whereas organisms of the adjacent biome become more common. These variations in distribution often can be related to the ranges of tolerances of plants and animals for different environmental factors. As you look at **Figure 4–11** and the following pages, see if you can relate the characteristics and locations of biomes to the patterns of global winds and ocean currents in **Figure 4–3.**

Tropical Rain Forest

Tropical rain forests are home to more species than all other biomes combined. The leafy tops of tall trees—extending from 50 to 80 meters above the forest floor—form a dense covering called a **canopy.** In the shade below the canopy, a second layer of shorter trees and vines forms an **understory.** Organic matter that falls to the forest floor quickly decomposes, and the nutrients are recycled.

- **Abiotic factors:** hot and wet year-round; thin, nutrient-poor soils
- **Dominant plants:** broad-leaved evergreen trees; ferns; large woody vines and climbing plants; orchids and bromeliads
- **Dominant wildlife:** herbivores such as sloths, tapirs, and capybaras; predators such as jaguars; anteaters; monkeys; birds such as toucans, parrots, and parakeets; insects such as butterflies, ants, and beetles; piranhas and other freshwater fishes; reptiles such as caymans, boa constrictors, and anacondas
- **Geographic distribution:** parts of South and Central America, Southeast Asia, parts of Africa, southern India, and northeastern Australia

Tropical Dry Forest

Tropical dry forests grow in places where rainfall is highly seasonal rather than year-round. During the dry season, nearly all the trees drop their leaves to conserve water. A tree that sheds its leaves during a particular season each year is called **deciduous.**

- **Abiotic factors:** generally warm year-round; alternating wet and dry seasons; rich soils subject to erosion
- **Dominant plants:** tall, deciduous trees that form a dense canopy during the wet season; drought-tolerant orchids and bromeliads; aloes and other succulents
- **Dominant wildlife:** tigers; monkeys; herbivores such as elephants, Indian rhinoceroses, hog deer; birds such as great pied hornbills, pied harriers, and spot-billed pelicans; insects such as termites; reptiles such as snakes and monitor lizards
- **Geographic distribution:** parts of Africa, South and Central America, Mexico, India, Australia, and tropical islands

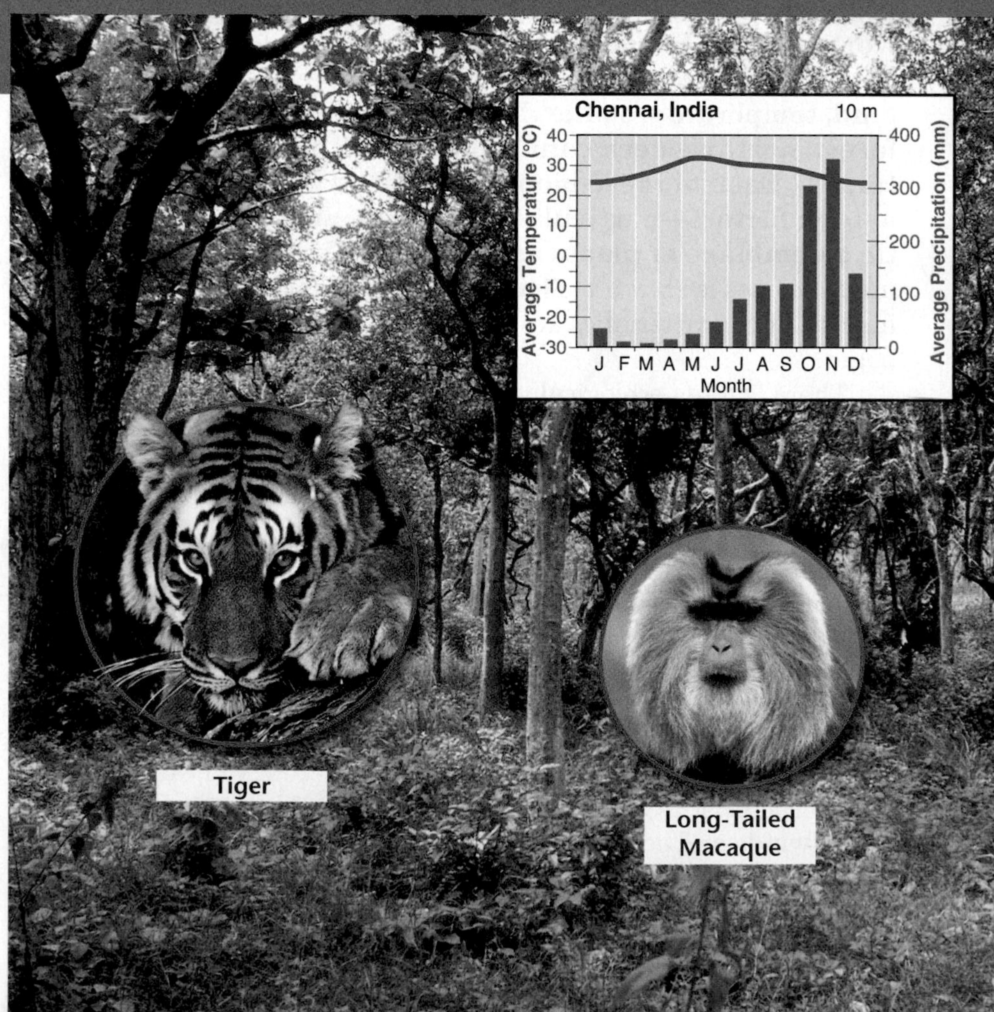

Nubian Vulture

White Rhinoceros

Tropical Savanna

Receiving more seasonal rainfall than deserts but less than tropical dry forests, tropical savannas, or grasslands, are characterized by a cover of grasses. Savannas are spotted with isolated trees and small groves of trees and shrubs. Compact soils, fairly frequent fires, and the action of large animals such as rhinoceroses prevent some savanna areas from turning into dry forest.

- **Abiotic factors:** warm temperatures; seasonal rainfall; compact soil; frequent fires set by lightning
- **Dominant plants:** tall, perennial grasses; sometimes drought-tolerant and fire-resistant trees or shrubs
- **Dominant wildlife:** predators such as lions, leopards, cheetahs, hyenas, and jackals; aardvarks; herbivores such as elephants, giraffes, antelopes, and zebras; baboons; birds such as eagles, ostriches, weaver birds, and storks; insects such as termites
- **Geographic distribution:** large parts of eastern Africa, southern Brazil, and northern Australia

Golden Eagle

Desert Hairy Scorpion

Desert

All deserts are dry—in fact, a desert biome is defined as having annual precipitation of less than 25 centimeters. Beyond that, deserts vary greatly, depending on elevation and latitude. Many undergo extreme temperature changes during the course of a day, alternating between hot and cold. The organisms in this biome can tolerate the extreme conditions.

- **Abiotic factors:** low precipitation; variable temperatures; soils rich in minerals but poor in organic material
- **Dominant plants:** cacti and other succulents; creosote bush and other plants with short growth cycles
- **Dominant wildlife:** predators such as mountain lions, gray foxes, and bobcats; herbivores such as mule deer, pronghorn antelopes, desert bighorn sheep, and kangaroo rats; bats; birds such as owls, hawks, and roadrunners; insects such as ants, beetles, butterflies, flies, and wasps; reptiles such as tortoises, rattlesnakes, and lizards
- **Geographic distribution:** Africa, Asia, the Middle East, United States, Mexico, South America, and Australia

Temperate Grassland

Characterized by a rich mix of grasses and underlaid by some of the world's most fertile soils, temperate grasslands—such as plains and prairies—once covered vast areas of the midwestern and central United States. Since the development of the steel plow, however, most have been converted to agricultural fields. Periodic fires and heavy grazing by large herbivores maintain the characteristic plant community.

- **Abiotic factors:** warm to hot summers; cold winters; moderate, seasonal precipitation; fertile soils; occasional fires
- **Dominant plants:** lush, perennial grasses and herbs; most are resistant to drought, fire, and cold
- **Dominant wildlife:** predators such as coyotes and badgers—historically included wolves and grizzly bears; herbivores such as mule deer, pronghorn antelopes, rabbits, prairie dogs, and introduced cattle—historically included bison; birds such as hawks, owls, bobwhites, prairie chickens, mountain plovers; reptiles such as snakes; insects such as ants and grasshoppers
- **Geographic distribution:** central Asia, North America, Australia, central Europe, and upland plateaus of South America

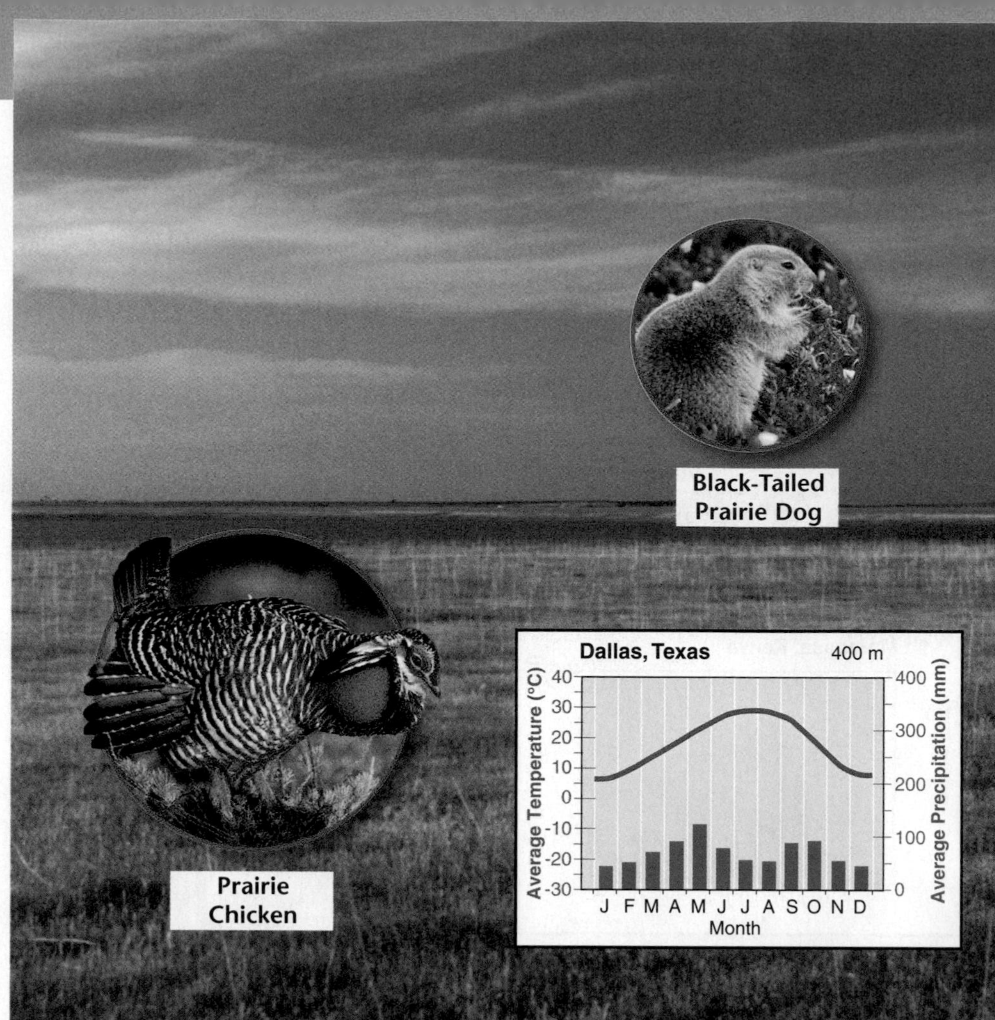

Temperate Woodland and Shrubland

This biome is characterized by a semiarid climate and a mix of shrub communities and open woodlands. In the open woodlands, large areas of grasses and wildflowers such as poppies are interspersed with oak trees. Communities that are dominated by shrubs are also known as chaparral. The growth of dense, low plants that contain flammable oils makes fires a constant threat.

- **Abiotic factors:** hot, dry summers; cool, moist winters; thin, nutrient-poor soils; periodic fires
- **Dominant plants:** woody evergreen shrubs with small, leathery leaves; fragrant, oily herbs that grow during winter and die in summer
- **Dominant wildlife:** predators such as coyotes, foxes, bobcats, and mountain lions; herbivores such as blacktailed deer, rabbits, and squirrels; birds such as hawks, California quails, warblers and other songbirds; reptiles such as lizards and snakes; butterflies
- **Geographic distribution:** western coasts of North and South America, areas around the Mediterranean Sea, South Africa, and Australia

Tiger Beetle

Philadelphia, Pennsylvania 4 m

Whitetail Deer

Temperate Forest

Temperate forests contain a mixture of deciduous and coniferous (koh-NIF-ur-us) trees. **Coniferous** trees, or conifers, produce seed-bearing cones and most have leaves shaped like needles. These forests have cold winters that halt plant growth for several months. In autumn, the deciduous trees shed their leaves. In the spring, small plants burst out of the ground and flower. Soils of temperate forests are often rich in **humus** (HYOO-mus), a material formed from decaying leaves and other organic matter that makes soil fertile.

- **Abiotic factors:** cold to moderate winters; warm summers; year-round precipitation; fertile soils
- **Dominant plants:** broadleaf deciduous trees; some conifers; flowering shrubs; herbs; a ground layer of mosses and ferns
- **Dominant wildlife:** Deer; black bears; bobcats; nut and acorn feeders such as squirrels; omnivores such as raccoons and skunks; numerous songbirds; turkeys
- **Geographic distribution:** eastern United States; southeastern Canada; most of Europe; and parts of Japan, China, and Australia

Seattle, Washington 150 m

Black Bear

Flying Squirrel

Northwestern Coniferous Forest

Mild, moist air from the Pacific Ocean provides abundant rainfall to this biome. The forest is made up of a variety of conifers, ranging from giant redwoods along the coast of northern California to spruce, fir, and hemlock farther north. Moss often covers tree trunks and the forest floor. Flowering trees and shrubs such as dogwood and rhododendron are also abundant. Because of its lush vegetation, the northwestern coniferous forest is sometimes called a "temperate rain forest."

- **Abiotic factors:** mild temperatures; abundant precipitation during fall, winter, and spring; relatively cool, dry summer; rocky, acidic soils
- **Dominant plants:** Douglas fir, Sitka spruce, western hemlock, redwood
- **Dominant wildlife:** bears; large herbivores such as elk and deer; beavers; predators such as owls, bobcats, and members of the weasel family
- **Geographic distribution:** Pacific coast of northwestern United States and Canada, from northern California to Alaska

Boreal Forest

Along the northern edge of the temperate zone are dense evergreen forests of coniferous trees. These biomes are called boreal forests, or **taiga** (TY-guh). Winters are bitterly cold, but summers are mild and long enough to allow the ground to thaw. The word *boreal* comes from the Greek word for "north," reflecting the fact that boreal forests occur mostly in the Northern Hemisphere.

- **Abiotic factors:** long, cold winters; short, mild summers; moderate precipitation; high humidity; acidic, nutrient-poor soils
- **Dominant plants:** needleleaf coniferous trees such as spruce and fir; some broadleaf deciduous trees; small, berry-bearing shrubs
- **Dominant wildlife:** predators such as lynxes and timber wolves and members of the weasel family; small herbivorous mammals; moose and other large herbivores; beavers; songbirds and migratory birds
- **Geographic distribution:** North America, Asia, and northern Europe

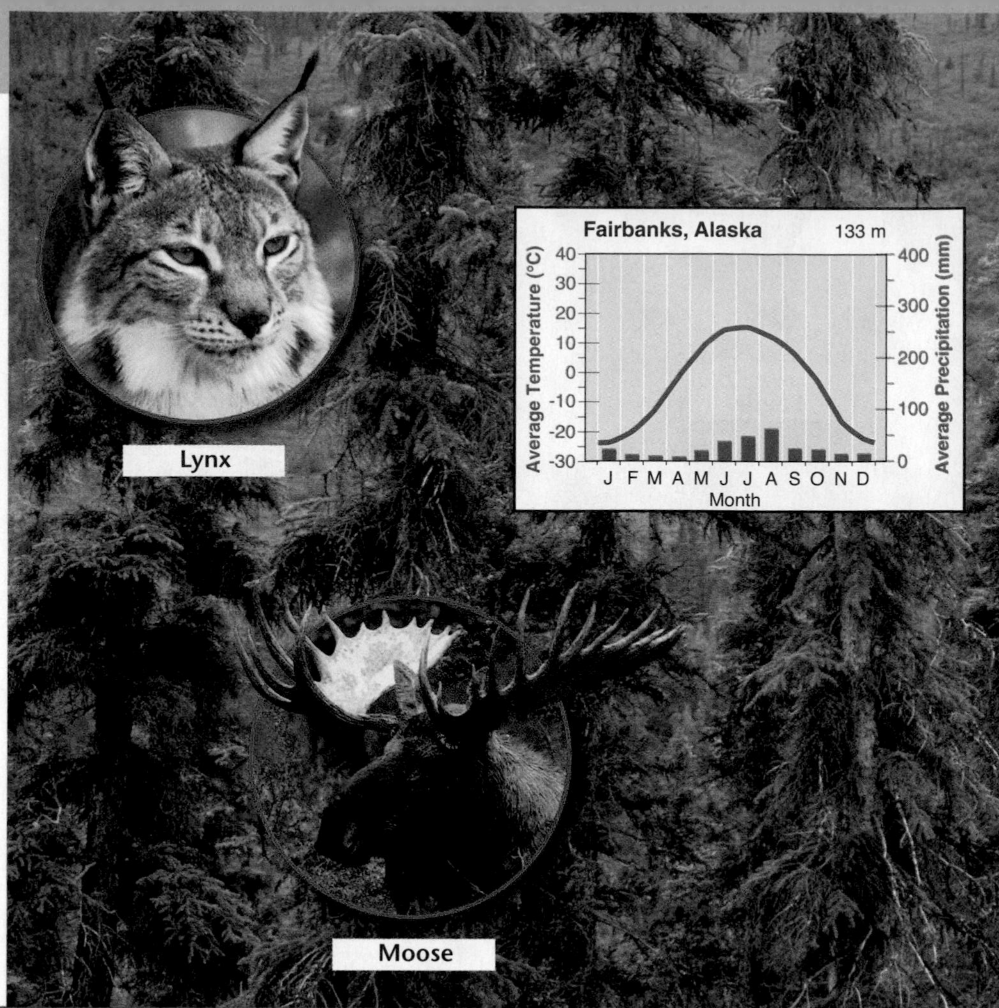

Tundra

The tundra is characterized by **permafrost,** a layer of permanently frozen subsoil. During the short, cool summer, the ground thaws to a depth of a few centimeters and becomes soggy and wet. In winter, the topsoil freezes again. This cycle of thawing and freezing, which rips and crushes plant roots, is one reason that tundra plants are small and stunted. Cold temperatures, high winds, the short growing season, and humus-poor soils also limit plant height.

- **Abiotic factors:** strong winds; low precipitation; short and soggy summers; long, cold, and dark winters; poorly developed soils; permafrost
- **Dominant plants:** ground-hugging plants such as mosses, lichens, sedges, and short grasses
- **Dominant wildlife:** a few resident birds and mammals that can withstand the harsh conditions; migratory waterfowl, shore birds, musk ox, Arctic foxes, and caribou; lemmings and other small rodents
- **Geographic distribution:** northern North America, Asia, and Europe

Snowy Owl

Caribou

Barrow, Alaska 8 m

Other Land Areas

Some areas of land on Earth do not fall neatly into the major biome categories described on the previous pages. These areas include mountain ranges and polar ice caps.

Mountain Ranges Mountain ranges can be found on all continents. On mountains like the one in **Figure 4–12,** the abiotic and biotic conditions vary with elevation. As you move up from base to summit, temperatures become colder and precipitation increases. Therefore, the types of plants and animals also change. If you were to climb the Rocky Mountains in Colorado, for example, you would begin in a grassland. Then, you would pass through an open woodland of pines. Next, you would hike through a forest of spruce and other conifers. Near the summit, you would reach open areas of wildflowers and stunted vegetation resembling tundra. In the Canadian Rockies, ice fields occur at the peaks of some ranges.

Polar Ice Caps The icy polar regions that border the tundra are cold year-round. Outside of the ice and snow, plants and algae are few but do include mosses and lichens. In the north polar region, the Arctic Ocean is covered with sea ice, and a thick ice cap covers most of Greenland. Polar bears, seals, insects, and mites are the dominant animals. In the south polar region, the continent of Antarctica is covered by a layer of ice that is nearly 5 kilometers thick in some places. There, the dominant wildlife includes penguins and marine mammals.

▲ **Figure 4–12** Washington's Mount Rainier towers above the tree line. **Applying Concepts** *Based on what you have seen in the previous pages, which biome lies at the base of this mountain?*

For: Links on biomes
Visit: www.SciLinks.org
Web Code: cbn-2043

4–3 Section Assessment

1. **Key Concept** List the major biomes, and give one characteristic feature of each.
2. How are biomes classified?
3. What are the two types of tropical forest? How do they differ?
4. How might a mountain range affect the types of plants and animals found in an area?
5. **Critical Thinking Inferring** What characteristics would you expect tundra animals to have?
6. **Critical Thinking Comparing and Contrasting** Choose two very different biomes. From each biome, select a plant and an animal that are dominant. Compare how these plants' adaptations are suited to their biomes. Compare how these animals' adaptations are suited to their biomes.

Thinking Visually

Creating Artwork

Choose one of the biomes discussed in this section. Then, depict the biome in a piece of artwork. Include the biome's characteristic plant and animal life in your art. Add labels to identify the organisms, and write a caption describing the content of the artwork.

4–4 Aquatic Ecosystems

1-S1.2 Judging the reliability of information
1-S3.1 Interpreting data may lead to new hypotheses
4-1.1 Ecosystems are shaped by physical conditions
4-1.1 Ecosystems include populations that interact
LS- Analyze, formulate, and organize data in tables/graphs

Guide for Reading

Key Concepts
- What are the main factors that govern aquatic ecosystems?
- What are the two types of freshwater ecosystems?
- What are the characteristics of the different marine zones?

Vocabulary
plankton • phytoplankton
zooplankton • wetland
estuary • detritus • salt marsh
mangrove swamp
photic zone • aphotic zone
zonation • coastal ocean
kelp forest • coral reef
benthos

Reading Strategy: Making Comparisons As you read, write down statements about similarities and differences among the different types of aquatic ecosystems.

Nearly three fourths of Earth's surface is covered with water, so it is not surprising that many organisms make their homes in aquatic habitats. Oceans, streams, lakes, and marshes—indeed, nearly any body of water—contain a wide variety of communities. These aquatic communities are governed by biotic and abiotic factors, including light, nutrient availability, and oxygen.

Aquatic ecosystems are determined primarily by the depth, flow, temperature, and chemistry of the overlying water. In contrast to land biomes, which are grouped geographically, aquatic ecosystems are often grouped according to the abiotic factors that affect them. One such factor is the depth of water, or distance from shore. The depth of water, in turn, determines the amount of light that organisms receive. Water chemistry refers primarily to the amount of dissolved chemicals—especially salts, nutrients, and oxygen—on which life depends. For example, communities of organisms found in shallow water close to shore can be very different from the communities that occur away from shore in deep water. One abiotic factor that is important both to biomes and aquatic ecosystems is latitude. Aquatic ecosystems in polar, temperate, and tropical oceans all have distinctive characteristics.

Freshwater Ecosystems

It may surprise you to know that only 3 percent of the surface water on Earth is fresh water. **Freshwater ecosystems can be divided into two main types: flowing-water ecosystems and standing-water ecosystems.**

Flowing-Water Ecosystems Rivers, streams, creeks, and brooks are all freshwater ecosystems that flow over the land. Organisms that live there are well adapted to the rate of flow. Some insect larvae have hooks that allow them to take hold of aquatic plants. Certain catfish have suckers that anchor them to rocks. Trout and many other fishes have streamlined bodies that help them move with or against the current.

Flowing-water ecosystems like the river in **Figure 4–13** originate in mountains or hills, often springing from an underground water source. Near the source, the turbulent water has plenty of dissolved oxygen but little plant life. As the water flows downhill, sediments build up and enable plants to establish themselves. Farther downstream, the water may meander more slowly through flat areas, where turtles, beavers, or river otters make their homes.

▼ **Figure 4–13** The Menominee River in Michigan is a flowing-water ecosystem. **Like all aquatic ecosystems, this river's communities are determined by the depth, flow, and chemistry of the water.**

Standing-Water Ecosystems Lakes and ponds are the most common standing-water ecosystems. In addition to the net flow of water in and out of these systems, there is usually water circulating within them. This circulation helps to distribute heat, oxygen, and nutrients throughout the ecosystem.

The relatively still waters of lakes and ponds provide habitats for many organisms, such as plankton, that would be quickly washed away in flowing water. **Plankton** is a general term for the tiny, free-floating organisms that live in both freshwater and saltwater environments. See **Figure 4–14** for examples. Unicellular algae, or **phytoplankton** (fyt-oh-PLANK-tun), are supported by nutrients in the water and form the base of many aquatic food webs. Planktonic animals, or **zooplankton** (zoh-oh-PLANK-tun), feed on the phytoplankton.

CHECKPOINT *What are phytoplankton?*

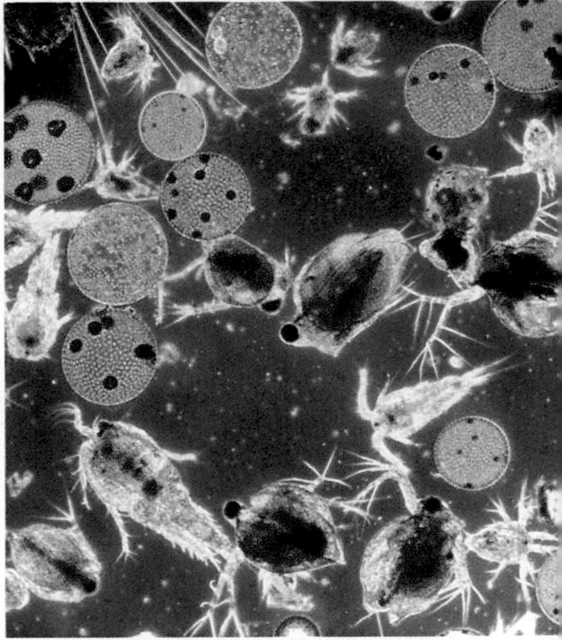

▲ **Figure 4–14** Both freshwater and saltwater ecosystems often include plankton. This photograph shows phytoplankton, zooplankton, and larger animals called water fleas. **Predicting** *What might happen to an aquatic food web if phytoplankton were removed from the ecosystem?*

Freshwater Wetlands A **wetland** is an ecosystem in which water either covers the soil or is present at or near the surface of the soil for at least part of the year. The water in wetlands may be flowing or standing and fresh, salty, or brackish, which is a mixture of fresh and salt water. Many wetlands are very productive ecosystems that serve as breeding grounds for insects, fishes and other aquatic animals, amphibians, and migratory birds.

The three main types of freshwater wetlands are bogs, marshes, and swamps. Bogs, which are wetlands that are often dominated by sphagnum moss, typically form in depressions where water collects. The water in sphagnum bogs is often very acidic. Marshes are shallow wetlands along rivers. They may be underwater for all or part of the year. Marshes often contain cattails, rushes, and other tall, grasslike plants. Water flows slowly through swamps, which often look like flooded forests. The presence of trees and shrubs is what distinguishes a swamp from a marsh.

Some wetlands, such as the swamp shown in **Figure 4–15**, are wet year-round. Other kinds of wetlands, however, may not always be covered in standing water. Such areas may be classified as wetlands because they have certain kinds of soils and are wet enough to support a specific community of water-loving plants and animals.

▼ **Figure 4–15** **Freshwater ecosystems can be divided into two main types: flowing-water ecosystems and standing-water ecosystems.** Although this swamp along the Loxahatchee River in Florida appears stagnant, water actually flows through it slowly. The swamp is home to turtles, otters, alligators, and herons that live among the baldcypress trees.

Word Origins

Detritus is a Latin word meaning "worn away." In ecology, detritus refers to particles that have worn away from decaying organic material. **If the Latin word *vorare* means "to devour," what is a *detritivore*?**

Estuaries

Estuaries (ES-tyoo-ehr-eez) are wetlands formed where rivers meet the sea. Estuaries thus contain a mixture of fresh water and salt water, and are affected by the rise and fall of ocean tides. Many are shallow, so sufficient sunlight reaches the bottom to power photosynthesis. Primary producers include plants, algae, and both photosynthetic and chemosynthetic bacteria. Estuary food webs differ from those of more familiar ecosystems because most primary production is not consumed by herbivores. Instead, much of that organic material enters the food web as detritus. **Detritus** is made up of tiny pieces of organic material that provide food for organisms at the base of the estuary's food web. Organisms that feed on detritus include clams, worms, and sponges.

Estuaries support an astonishing amount of biomass, although they usually contain fewer species than freshwater or marine ecosystems. Estuaries serve as spawning and nursery grounds for commercially important fishes and for shellfish such as shrimps and crabs. Many young animals feed and grow in estuaries, then head out to sea to mature, and return to reproduce. Many waterfowl use estuaries for nesting, feeding, and resting during migrations.

Salt marshes are temperate-zone estuaries dominated by salt-tolerant grasses above the low-tide line, and by seagrasses under water. Salt marshes like the one shown in **Figure 4–16** (left) are (or were once) found along great stretches of eastern North America from southern Maine to Georgia. One of the largest systems of connected salt marshes in America surrounds the Chesapeake Bay estuary in Maryland.

Mangrove swamps, shown in **Figure 4–16** (right), are coastal wetlands that are widespread across tropical regions, including southern Florida and Hawaii. Here, the dominant plants are several species of salt-tolerant trees, collectively called mangroves. Seagrasses are also common below the low-tide line. Like salt marshes, mangrove swamps are valuable nurseries for fish and shellfish. The largest mangrove area in the continental United States is within Florida's Everglades National Park.

Figure 4–16 Salt marshes occur in estuaries along seacoasts in the temperate zone. Salt-tolerant grasses are the dominant plants in this salt marsh (left) along the coast of Mount Desert Island in Maine. Mangrove swamps (right) occur in bays and estuaries along tropical coasts. The stiltlike roots of mangrove trees trap sediment that accumulates as mud behind the trees. This allows other plants to take root and helps to build the mangrove forest out from the shoreline. **Predicting** ***Would you expect to find mangrove swamps or salt marshes on a coast exposed to large ocean waves? Explain.***

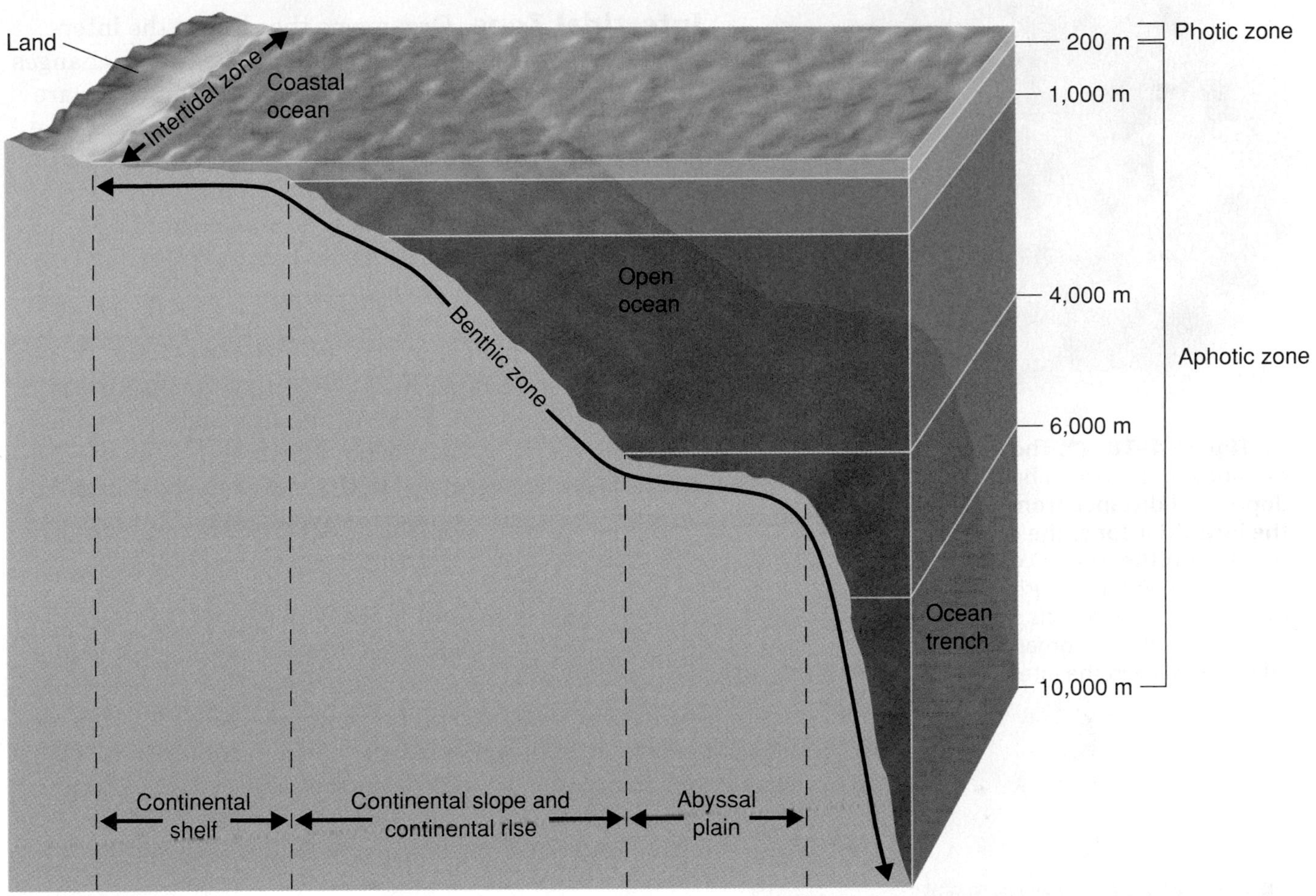

▲ **Figure 4–17** **The ocean can be divided into zones based on light penetration and into zones based on depth and the distance from shore.** Each zone contains a characteristic assemblage of organisms.

Marine Ecosystems

Unless you are an avid diver or snorkeler, it takes some imagination to picture what life is like in the vast, three-dimensional ocean. Sunlight penetrates only a relatively short distance through the surface of the water. Photosynthesis is limited to this well-lit upper layer known as the **photic** (FOH-tik) **zone.** Only in this relatively thin surface layer—typically down to a depth of about 200 meters—can algae and other producers grow. Below the photic zone is the **aphotic** (ay-FOH-tik) **zone,** which is permanently dark. Chemosynthetic autotrophs are the only producers that can survive in the aphotic zone.

There are several different classification systems that scientists use to describe marine ecosystems. **In addition to the division between the photic and aphotic zones, marine biologists divide the ocean into zones based on the depth and distance from shore: the intertidal zone, the coastal ocean, and the open ocean.** Each of these zones supports distinct ecological communities. The benthic zone covers the ocean floor and is, therefore, not exclusive to any of the other marine zones. **Figure 4–17** shows a generalized diagram of the marine zones.

CHECKPOINT *What factor is absent in the aphotic zone?*

Go Online
NSTA SCiLINKS
For: Links on aquatic ecosystems
Visit: www.SciLinks.org
Web Code: cbn-2044

▲ **Figure 4–18 The main divisions in the ocean based on depth and distance from shore are the intertidal zone, the coastal ocean, and the open ocean.** Along the coast of Vancouver Island in Canada, low tide reveals sea stars, seaweed, and other organisms adapted to life in the intertidal zone.

Intertidal Zone Organisms that live in the intertidal zone are exposed to regular and extreme changes in their surroundings. Once or twice a day, they are submerged in sea water. The remainder of the time, they are exposed to air, sunlight, and temperature changes. Often, organisms in this zone are battered by waves and sometimes by strong currents.

There are many different types of intertidal communities. One of the most interesting is the rocky intertidal, shown in **Figure 4–18,** which exists in temperate regions where exposed rocks line the shore. There, barnacles and seaweed permanently attach themselves to the rocks. Other organisms, such as snails, sea urchins, and sea stars, cling to the rocks by their feet or suckers.

Competition among organisms in the rocky intertidal zone often leads to zonation (zoh-NAY-shun). **Zonation** is the prominent horizontal banding of organisms that live in a particular habitat. In the rocky intertidal zone, each band can be distinguished by differences in color or shape of the major organisms. For example, a band of black algae might grow at the highest high-tide line, followed by encrusting barnacles. Lower down, clusters of blue mussels might stick out amid clumps of green algae. This zonation is similar to the pattern that you might observe as you climb up a mountain. In the intertidal zone, however, zonation exists on a smaller vertical scale—just a few meters compared to the kilometers you would ascend on a mountain.

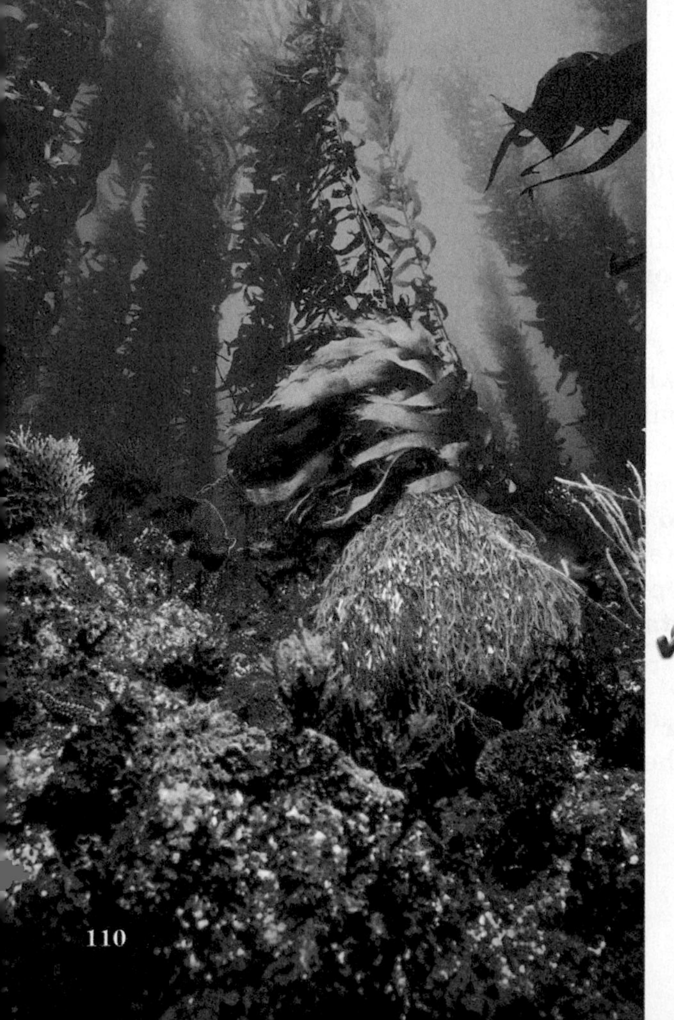

Coastal Ocean The **coastal ocean** extends from the low-tide mark to the outer edge of the continental shelf, the relatively shallow border that surrounds the continents. The continental shelf is often shallow enough to fall mostly or entirely within the photic zone, so photosynthesis can usually occur throughout its depth. As a result, the coastal ocean is often rich in plankton and many other organisms.

One of the most productive coastal ocean communities is the kelp forest. **Kelp forests** are named for their dominant organism: a giant brown alga that can grow at extraordinary rates—as much as 50 centimeters a day. Huge forests of this seaweed are found in cold-temperate seas around the world, including those along the coasts of California and the Pacific Northwest. Kelp forests, like the one shown in **Figure 4–19,** support a complex food web that includes snails, sea urchins, sea otters, a variety of fishes, seals, and whales.

What is the coastal ocean?

◀ **Figure 4–19** Kelp forests are ecosystems that occur in coastal oceans. The long strands of kelp create a habitat that shelters a variety of organisms. This kelp forest off the coast of California is part of a larger zone of kelp forests found along the western coast of North America from Alaska to Mexico. **Comparing and Contrasting** *How is a kelp forest like a forest on land?*

Coral Reefs In the warm, shallow water of tropical coastal oceans are coral reefs, among the most diverse and productive environments on Earth. **Coral reefs** are named for the coral animals whose hard, calcium carbonate skeletons make up their primary structure. As you can see in **Figure 4–20,** an extraordinary diversity of organisms flourishes in these spectacular habitats.

Coral animals are tiny relatives of jellyfish that live together in vast numbers. Most coral animals are the size of your fingernail, or even smaller. Each one looks like a small sack with a mouth surrounded by tentacles. These animals use their tentacles to capture and eat microscopic creatures that float by. Coral animals cannot grow in cold water or water that is low in salt.

The types of corals that build reefs grow with the help of algae that live symbiotically within their tissues. These algae carry out photosynthesis using the coral animals' wastes as nutrients. In turn, the algae provide their coral hosts with certain essential carbon compounds. Because their algae require strong sunlight, most reef-building corals thrive only in brightly lit areas within 40 meters of the surface.

▶ **Figure 4–20** This coral reef off the island of New Britain in the Pacific Ocean supports a dazzling variety of corals and fishes. Reefs are most abundant around islands and along the eastern coasts of continents. In the United States, only the coasts of southern Florida and Hawaii have coral reefs. **Applying Concepts** ***In what types of community interactions are coral animals involved?***

Analyzing Data

Ecosystem Productivity

The data table on the right compares the primary productivity of some of the world's ecosystems. Use the data table to answer the following questions:

1. **Using Tables and Graphs** Construct a bar graph to display the data. Use different colors to distinguish aquatic and land ecosystems.
2. **Using Tables and Graphs** According to your graph, which ecosystem is most productive? Use what you know to explain that fact.
3. **Inferring** Although the open ocean is among the least productive ecosystems, it contributes greatly to the overall productivity of the biosphere. How can this situation be explained?
4. **Applying Concepts** What are two abiotic factors that might account for the differences in productivity among the land ecosystems in the table? (*Hint:* Review the relevant biomes on pages 100–104.)

Productivity of Aquatic and Land Ecosystems

Ecosystem	Average Primary Productivity (grams of organic matter produced per square meter per year)
Aquatic Ecosystems:	
Coral reef	2500
Estuary	1800
Lake	500
Open ocean	125
Land Ecosystems:	
Tropical rain forest	2200
Temperate forest	1250
Tropical savanna	900
Tundra	90

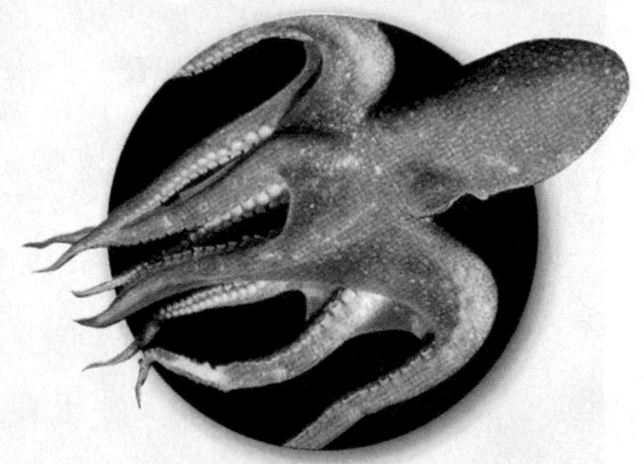

▲ **Figure 4–21** In the open ocean, the swordfish (top) can sometimes be seen swimming near the surface, yet these fish can also dive to more than 600 meters to prey on fishes of the deep ocean. Some types of octopus (bottom) live in the depths of the open ocean, although other types live in shallow coastal waters.

Open Ocean The open ocean, often referred to as the oceanic zone, begins at the edge of the continental shelf and extends outward. It is the largest marine zone, covering more than 90 percent of the surface area of the world's oceans. The open ocean ranges from about 500 meters deep along continental slopes to more than 11,000 meters at the deepest ocean trench. Organisms in the deep ocean are exposed to high pressure, frigid temperatures, and total darkness.

Typically, the open ocean has very low levels of nutrients and supports only the smallest producers. Productivity is generally low. Still, because of the enormous area, most of the photosynthetic activity on Earth occurs in the part of the open ocean within the photic zone. Fishes of all shapes and sizes dominate the open ocean. The swordfish and the octopus in **Figure 4–21** are just two examples of the organisms found in this zone. Marine mammals such as dolphins and whales also live there but must stay close to the surface to breathe.

Benthic Zone The ocean floor contains organisms that live attached to or near the bottom, such as sea stars, anemones, and marine worms. Scientists refer to these organisms as the **benthos.** That is why the ocean floor is called the benthic zone. This zone extends horizontally along the ocean floor from the coastal ocean through the open ocean.

Benthic ecosystems often depend on food from organisms that grow in the photic zone, particularly the producers. Animals that are attached to the bottom or do not move around much, such as clams and sea cucumbers, feed on pieces of dead organic material, or detritus, that drift down from the surface waters. Near deep-sea vents, where superheated water boils out of cracks on the ocean floor, dwell chemosynthetic primary producers that support life without light and photosynthesis.

4–4 Section Assessment

1. **Key Concept** List three characteristics that determine the structure of aquatic ecosystems.
2. **Key Concept** Compare standing-water ecosystems to flowing-water ecosystems. How are they alike? How are they different?
3. **Key Concept** List six distinct ecological zones that can be found in the ocean. Give two abiotic factors for each zone.
4. Define the terms *wetland* and *estuary*. Give at least one example of a freshwater wetland and of an estuary.
5. **Critical Thinking Predicting** How might the damming of a river affect an estuary at the river's mouth?

Writing in Science

Comparing and Contrasting

Choose three different aquatic ecosystems. From each of these ecosystems, select a plant and an animal and describe how the organisms are adapted to their environments. Show comparisons. *Hint*: Create a table to organize your ideas.

Exploration

Observing Succession

The most obvious examples of succession involve large organisms, such as plants and animals. In this investigation, you will determine whether succession also occurs in a community of microorganisms.

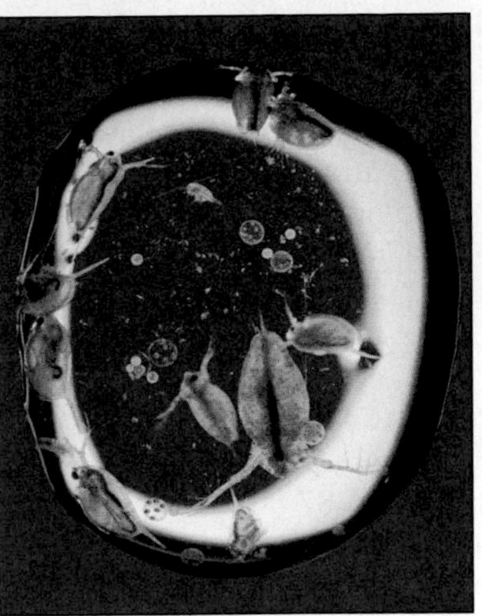

Problem **What changes occur in a microscopic community over time?**

Materials

- 1000-mL beaker or large jar
- soil
- grass clippings
- dried leaves
- 600 mL aged water
- 4 coverslips
- 4 glass slides
- 4 dropper pipettes
- microscope
- reference book or chart for identifying common microorganisms

Skills Using Tables and Graphs, Analyzing Data

Procedure   

1. Place enough soil in the 1000-mL beaker to cover the bottom. Fill the beaker with a loosely packed mixture of grass clippings and dried leaves, and add the aged water.
2. Set the beaker aside in a cool place where it can remain undisturbed for 24 hours.
3. After 24 hours, check the water for signs of life. A strong odor or cloudy water is evidence of bacterial growth; fuzzy growths or threads indicate the presence of mold; and a green tint is due to algae. Record your observations.
4. Use a dropper pipette to transfer a drop of water from the beaker to a microscope slide. Add a coverslip.
5. Examine the slide under the low-power objective of the microscope to locate any microorganisms. Then, switch to high power. Use a reference book or chart to identify the organisms. Record the date and your observations, including labeled drawings, the number of each type of organism in your field of view, and the magnification.
6. Repeat steps 4 and 5 with water samples from several different areas of the beaker.
7. Repeat steps 3 through 6 every day for 2 weeks. Note any changes in the number or types of organisms in the beaker.
8. Wash your hands thoroughly with soap and warm water before leaving the lab.

Analyze and Conclude

1. **Using Tables and Graphs** Make a graph of the population of each type of organism. Plot time on the *x*-axis and number of organisms per field of view on the *y*-axis. With your teacher's guidance, select the equipment and technology to use—either graph paper or a graphing calculator.
2. **Observing** How did the number and variety of organisms in the beaker change over the 2-week period?
3. **Analyzing Data** What kinds of organisms appeared first in the microscopic water community? Which appeared last? How can you explain these changes?
4. **Drawing Conclusions** Do your observations support the idea that succession occurs in communities of microorganisms? Explain your answer.

Go Further

Analyzing Data With your teacher's approval, set up a simple community of only a few known species of microorganisms. Observe the community for two weeks, and try to explain any evidence of succession that you observe.

Chapter 4 Study Guide

4–1 The Role of Climate

Key Concepts

- Carbon dioxide, methane, water vapor, and a few other atmospheric gases trap heat energy and maintain Earth's temperature range.
- As a result of differences in latitude and thus the angle of heating, Earth has three main climate zones: polar, temperate, and tropical.

Vocabulary

weather, p. 87
climate, p. 87
greenhouse effect, p. 87
polar zone, p. 88
temperate zone, p. 88
tropical zone, p. 88

4–2 What Shapes an Ecosystem?

Key Concepts

- Together, biotic and abiotic factors determine the survival and growth of an organism and the productivity of the ecosystem in which the organism lives.
- Community interactions, such as competition, predation, and various forms of symbiosis, can powerfully affect an ecosystem.
- Ecosystems are constantly changing in response to natural and human disturbances. As an ecosystem changes, older inhabitants gradually die out and new organisms move in, causing further changes in the community.

Vocabulary

biotic factor, p. 90
abiotic factor, p. 90
habitat, p. 90
niche, p. 91
resource, p. 92
competitive exclusion principle, p. 92
predation, p. 93
symbiosis, p. 93
mutualism, p. 93
commensalism, p. 93
parasitism, p. 93
ecological succession, p. 94
primary succession, p. 94
pioneer species, p. 94
secondary succession, p. 95

4–3 Biomes

Key Concept

- The world's major biomes include tropical rain forest, tropical dry forest, tropical savanna, temperate grassland, desert, temperate woodland and shrubland, temperate forest, northwestern coniferous forest, boreal forest, and tundra. Each of these biomes is defined by a unique set of abiotic factors—particularly climate—and has a characteristic ecological community.

Vocabulary

biome, p. 98 • tolerance, p. 98
microclimate, p. 98 • canopy, p. 100
understory, p. 100 • deciduous, p. 100
coniferous, p. 103 • humus, p. 103
taiga, p. 104 • permafrost, p. 104

4–4 Aquatic Ecosystems

Key Concepts

- Aquatic ecosystems are determined primarily by the depth, flow, temperature, and chemistry of the overlying water.
- Freshwater ecosystems can be divided into two main types: flowing-water ecosystems and standing-water ecosystems.
- In addition to the division between the photic and aphotic zones, marine biologists also divide the ocean into zones based on the depth and distance from shore: the intertidal zone, the coastal ocean, and the open ocean.

Vocabulary

plankton, p. 107 • phytoplankton, p. 107
zooplankton, p. 107 • wetland, p. 107
estuary, p. 108 • detritus, p. 108
salt marsh, p. 108 • mangrove swamp, p. 108
photic zone, p. 109 • aphotic zone, p. 109
zonation, p. 110 • coastal ocean, p. 110
kelp forest, p. 110 • coral reef, p. 111
benthos, p. 112

Thinking Visually

Using information from this chapter, create a concept map that includes the following terms: *abiotic factors, biotic factors, community interactions, predation, competition, symbiosis, nutrients, ecosystems, light, oxygen.*

Preparing for the Living Environment Exam

NEW YORK LIVING ENVIRONMENT

Blue questions emphasize Regents Exam content

Chapter 4

Part A

Multiple Choice

For each statement or question, select the number of the word or expression that, of those given, best completes the statement or answers the question.

1 The average, year-after-year conditions of temperature and precipitation in a particular region are its
(1) weather (3) biotic factors
(2) climate (4) biome

2 Generally, which has the greatest effect on determining the climate of a region?
(1) longitude
(2) dominant plant species
(3) distance from the equator
(4) month of the year

3 The burning of fossil fuels causes an increase in the air of
(1) oxygen (3) carbon dioxide
(2) water (4) nitrogen

4 All of the biotic and abiotic factors in a pond form a(an)
(1) biosphere (3) population
(2) ecosystem (4) niche

5 Tapeworms can live inside a dog's intestines and prevent the dog from getting all the nutrients it needs. In this relationship, the tapeworms are
(1) producers (3) scavengers
(2) parasites (4) decomposers

6 Which biome would you expect to find in a region with an average monthly temperature of 25°C and high year-round rainfall?
(1) tropical rain forest
(2) tropical dry forest
(3) desert
(4) tundra

7 Which biome is correctly paired with a factor or organism that is found there?
(1) boreal forest—moss
(2) tundra—permafrost
(3) temperate forest—prairie dog
(4) grassland—bear

8 The photic zone in marine ecosystems is important because
(1) it provides a habitat for chemosynthetic organisms
(2) it is the layer where photosynthesis takes place
(3) it is an area free from predator-prey relationships
(4) all organisms in this layer are consumers

9 The water in an estuary is
(1) salt water, only
(2) poor in nutrients
(3) fresh water, only
(4) a mixture of fresh water and salt water

10 In a stable, long-existing community, the establishment of a single species per niche is most directly the result of
(1) parasitism (3) competition
(2) interbreeding (4) overproduction

11 Following a major forest fire, an area that was once wooded is converted to barren soil. Which of the following schemes describes the most likely sequence of changes in vegetation following the fire?
(1) shrubs → maples → pines → grasses
(2) maples → pines → grasses → shrubs
(3) pines → shrubs → maples → grasses
(4) grasses → shrubs → pines → maples

12 Different species of animals in an ecosystem would most likely be similar in
(1) physical structure
(2) food requirements
(3) abiotic requirements
(4) number of offspring produced

13 A student measured some abiotic factors present in a stream during a biology class field trip. Which data did the student most likely record?
(1) the size and number of each species of fish
(2) the number of each type of green plant and each type of snail
(3) the number of species and total mass of decomposers
(4) the temperature and oxygen content of the water

Test-Taking Tip When you are asked to analyze a graph showing experimental data, first look at the shape of the curve. Identify the variables and try to determine how they are related. Then, read and answer the questions about the graph.

Preparing for the Living Environment Exam

Part B

Multiple Choice and Extended Response

For those questions that ask you to select a response, choose the one that best completes the statement or answers the question. For all others follow the directions given.

14 In a tropical rain forest, the leafy tops of tall trees get more sunlight than the shorter trees and vines that form the understory. Explain how all of the plants in this ecosystem can survive when they receive different amounts of sunlight.

15 List the major abiotic factors that help to shape ecosystems.

Base your answers to questions 16 and 17 on the information below and on your knowledge of biology.

A windstorm blows down the large trees in one part of a forest. Soon, sun-loving plants sprout in the new clearing.

16 Identify the type of ecological succession taking place.

17 Describe how this area will change over the next 50 years if no more storms or other interruptions occur.

---

18 List *two* ways the photic zone differs from the aphotic zone.

19 On a separate sheet of paper, draw the chart below. Then, fill in the chart with the following organisms in their correct marine zone(s): sea star, phytoplankton, dolphin, sea otter, clam, kelp, coral. (Do not write in this book.)

Zone	Organism(s)
Intertidal	
Costal ocean	
Open ocean	
Benthic	

Base your answers to questions 20 and 21 on the information below and on your knowledge of biology.

As cattle graze in the grasslands of East Africa, they stir up insects living in the grass. This is why birds known as cattle egrets can capture more insects when they hunt near cattle than when they hunt on their own. Some scientists want to design an experiment to determine if the relationship between the cattle and egrets is one of mutualism, parasitism, or commensalism. In a mutualistic relationship, both species benefit. In the case of parasitism, one species benefits while the other is harmed. In commensalism, one species benefits and the other species is unaffected.

20 The egrets benefit from their relationship with the cattle. The scientists hypothesize that the behavior of the cattle remains the same whether egrets are present or not present, indicating commensalism. Describe a controlled experiment the scientists could conduct to test their hypothesis.

21 The scientists observed two herds of cattle repeatedly. Then, they averaged their data and displayed it in the table below.

Relationship Between Cattle and Egrets

Behavior	Herd 1		Herd 2	
	Birds	No birds	Birds	No birds
Grazing (hours/day)	4.5	4.25	5.25	5
Visits to pond	4	4	3	3
No. in shade (measured at noon each day)	5	4	8	8
Resting (hours/day)	2.5	2.5	4	4.25

Based on the data, the scientists concluded that the relationship between the cattle and egrets could be classified as commensalism. Explain why the scientists were able to come to this conclusion. Use specific data from the table to support your answer.

---

22 State the competitive exclusion principle and provide one example.

23 State *two* abiotic factors that cause deciduous trees to shed their leaves.

24 Although the amount of precipitation is low, most parts of the tundra biome are very wet during the summer. Explain this apparent contradiction.

25 The cowbird lays its eggs in other birds' nests. When the cowbird egg hatches, the "parents" feed the cowbird along with their own young, which the young cowbird then pushes out of the nest. Is this an example of mutualism, parasitism, or commensalism? Support your answer with an explanation.

For each description in questions 26 through 28, select the interaction, chosen from the list below that is most closely associated with that description. Then record the number of the question and description on your paper.

Interactions		
(1) Organism A	+++++++>	Organism B
Organism B	+++++++>	Organism A
(2) Organism A	------------>	Organism B
Organism B	+++++++>	Organism A
(3) Organism A	ooooooo>	Organism B
Organism B	------------>	Organism A
(4) Organism A	------------>	Organism B
Organism B	------------>	Organism A
Key	+++++++>	Positive Effect
	ooooooo>	No Effect
	------------>	Negative Effect

26 The rhinoceros bird (Organism A) feeds on parasites that live on the body of the rhinoceros (Organism B). The rhinoceros allows the birds to feed on the parasites.

27 Ants (Organism A) defend acacia trees (Organism B) from attacks by insects that are herbivores. The ants live in the hollow thorns of the trees.

28 Wasp larvae (Organism A) obtain nutrition from tomato hornworms (Organism B). The tomato hornworms do not survive.

Part C

Extended Response

Answer the questions or follow the directions given.

29 A developer has proposed filling in a salt marsh to create a coastal resort. You have been asked by the local residents to prepare a report that will help them decide whether or not the proposal should be supported. Your report should include the following:

- definitions of wetlands and salt marshes
- examples of organisms found in salt marshes
- description of the role of salt marshes in the lives of insects, fishes, birds, and other organisms
- description of the role of salt marshes in the water cycle
- state one reason to support why the resort should be built and one reason why it should not be built

30 Habitat destruction is an environmental problem that affects our own generation and will affect future generations if it is not solved. Describe how the destruction of this habitat relates to humans and the overall ecosystem. In your answer, be sure to:

- identify the habitat you are describing
- describe *two* human activities that contribute to the destruction of this habitat
- describe *three* ways the destruction of this habitat has affected plants, humans, and other animals
- list *two* ways to limit further destruction of this habitat

For: An interactive self-test
Visit: PHSchool.com
Web Code: cba-2040

CHAPTER 5

Populations

This trio of sea otters is part of the population that lives near Monterey, California. Sea otters often rest by wrapping themselves in kelp to keep from drifting away.

Inquiry Activity

How do populations grow?

Procedure

1. Assume that a pair of rabbits produces 6 offspring, and that half the offspring are male and half are female. Assume that no offspring die. If each pair of rabbits breeds only once, how many offspring would be produced each year for 5 years?
2. Construct a graph of your data. Plot time on the *x*-axis and population on the *y*-axis.

Think About It

1. **Using Tables and Graphs** Describe the shape of your graph.
2. **Using Tables and Graphs** Use your graph to predict the population of rabbits in 10 years and in 20 years.
3. **Formulating Hypotheses** How can you explain the fact that Earth is not covered by rabbits?

5–1 How Populations Grow

4-1.1 Ecosystems
4-6.1 The carrying capacity of an environment
4-6.1 Environments and resources are finite
LS- Analyze, formulate, and organize data in tables/graphs

Sea otters are important members of the kelp forest community of America's Pacific Northwest coast. This "forest" is made up of algae called giant kelp, with stalks up to 30 meters long, and smaller types of kelp. The kelp forest provides a habitat for a variety of animals. Sea otters need a lot of energy to stay warm in cold water, so they eat large quantities of their favorite food: sea urchins. Sea urchins, in turn, feed on kelp.

The relationships along this food chain set the stage for a classic tale of population growth and decline. A century ago, otters were nearly eliminated by hunting. Sea urchin populations increased greatly, and kelp forests nearly disappeared. Why? Because the kelp was eaten down to the bare rock by hordes of sea urchins! The future of the kelp forests looked grim. Then, sea otters were declared an endangered species and were protected from hunting. With hunters out of the picture, otter populations recovered. Sea urchin numbers dropped dramatically. Kelp grew back. But now, some otter populations are shrinking again because otters are being eaten by killer whales. To better understand why populations such as these change as they do, we turn to the study of population biology.

Guide for Reading

Key Concepts
- What characteristics are used to describe a population?
- What factors affect population size?
- What are exponential growth and logistic growth?

Vocabulary
population density
immigration
emigration
exponential growth
logistic growth
carrying capacity

Reading Strategy: Asking Questions Before you read, rewrite the headings in the section as *how, why,* or *what* questions about populations. As you read, write down the answers to your questions.

Characteristics of Populations

Several terms can be used to describe a population in nature. **Three important characteristics of a population are its geographic distribution, density, and growth rate.** A fourth characteristic, the population's age structure, will be discussed later in this chapter. Geographic distribution, or range, is a term that describes the area inhabited by a population. The range can vary in size from a few cubic centimeters occupied by bacteria in a rotting apple to the millions of square kilometers occupied by migrating whales in the Pacific Ocean.

Population density is the number of individuals per unit area. This number can vary tremendously depending on the species and its ecosystem. The population of saguaro cactus in the desert plant community shown in **Figure 5–1**, for example, has a low density, whereas other plants in that community have a relatively high density.

▶ **Figure 5–1** The tall saguaro cactuses in this Arizona desert have a low population density compared to the smaller desert plants. **Density is one of the main characteristics that describe a natural population. Other characteristics of populations are their geographic distribution and growth rate.**

Word Origins

Immigration is formed from the Latin prefix *in-*, meaning "in," and *migrare,* meaning "to move from one place to another." **If the Latin prefix *e-* means "out," then what does *emigration* mean?**

Population Growth

Natural populations may stay the same size from year to year. But a population can grow rapidly, as sea otter populations did when they were first protected from hunting. Populations can also decrease in size, as otter populations are doing now because of predation by killer whales. But just how do interacting factors such as these influence population growth?

Three factors can affect population size: the number of births, the number of deaths, and the number of individuals that enter or leave the population. Simply put, a population will increase or decrease in size depending on how many individuals are added to it or removed from it.

Generally, populations grow if more individuals are born than die in any period of time. For some organisms, such as the penguins in **Figure 5–2,** being born may actually mean hatching. Plants can add new individuals as seeds sprout and begin to grow.

A population can grow when its birthrate is greater than its death rate. If the birthrate equals the death rate, the population stays more or less the same size. If the death rate is greater than the birthrate, the population shrinks. Sea otter populations grew when hunting stopped, because their death rate dropped. Those same otter populations are shrinking now because killer whales have raised the death rate of otters again.

Immigration (im-uh-GRAY-shun), the movement of individuals into an area, is another factor that can cause a population to grow. **Emigration** (em-uh-GRAY-shun), the movement of individuals out of an area, can cause a population to decrease in size. Wildlife biologists studying changes in populations of animals such as grizzly bears and wolves must consider immigration and emigration. For example, emigration can occur when young animals approaching maturity leave the area where they were born, find mates, and establish new territories. A shortage of food in one area may also lead to emigration. On the other hand, populations can increase by immigration as animals in search of mates or food arrive from outside.

▼ **Figure 5–2** This king penguin population has grown in size due to the recent births of chicks, recognizable by their downy brown feathers. **Population size is affected by the number of births, the number of deaths, and the number of individuals that enter or leave the population.**

Exponential Growth

If a population has abundant space and food, and is protected from predators and disease, then organisms in that population will multiply and the population size will increase. Let's conduct an imaginary investigation to understand how growth under ideal conditions might occur. Suppose you put a single bacterium in a petri dish. Supply it with enough nutrients and incubate the culture with the right amount of heat, moisture, and light. How will the population change over time?

Bacteria reproduce by splitting in half. If the bacteria have a doubling time of 20 minutes, then within 20 minutes the first bacterium will divide to produce 2 bacteria. Twenty minutes later, the 2 bacteria will divide to produce 4. After another 20 minutes, there will be 8 bacteria. In another hour, there will be 64 bacteria; and in just one more hour, there will be 512. And in just one day, this colony of bacteria will grow to an astounding size of 4,720,000,000,000,000,000,000. What would happen if this growth pattern continued for several days without slowing down? Bacteria would cover the planet!

Figure 5–3 shows a graph with the size of the bacterial population plotted against time. As you can see, the pattern of growth is a J-shaped curve. The J-shaped curve indicates that the population is undergoing exponential (eks-poh-NEN-shul) growth. **Exponential growth** occurs when the individuals in a population reproduce at a constant rate. At first, the number of individuals in an exponentially growing population increases slowly. Over time, however, the population becomes larger and larger until it approaches an infinitely large size. **Under ideal conditions with unlimited resources, a population will grow exponentially.**

With a doubling time of 20 minutes, some bacteria have the fastest rates of reproduction among living things. Populations of other species grow more slowly. For example, a female elephant can produce an infant only every 2 to 4 years, and then the offspring take about 10 years to mature. But as you can see in **Figure 5–3,** in the unlikely event that all the offspring of a single pair of elephants survived and reproduced for 750 years, there would be nearly 20 million elephants!

What is exponential growth?

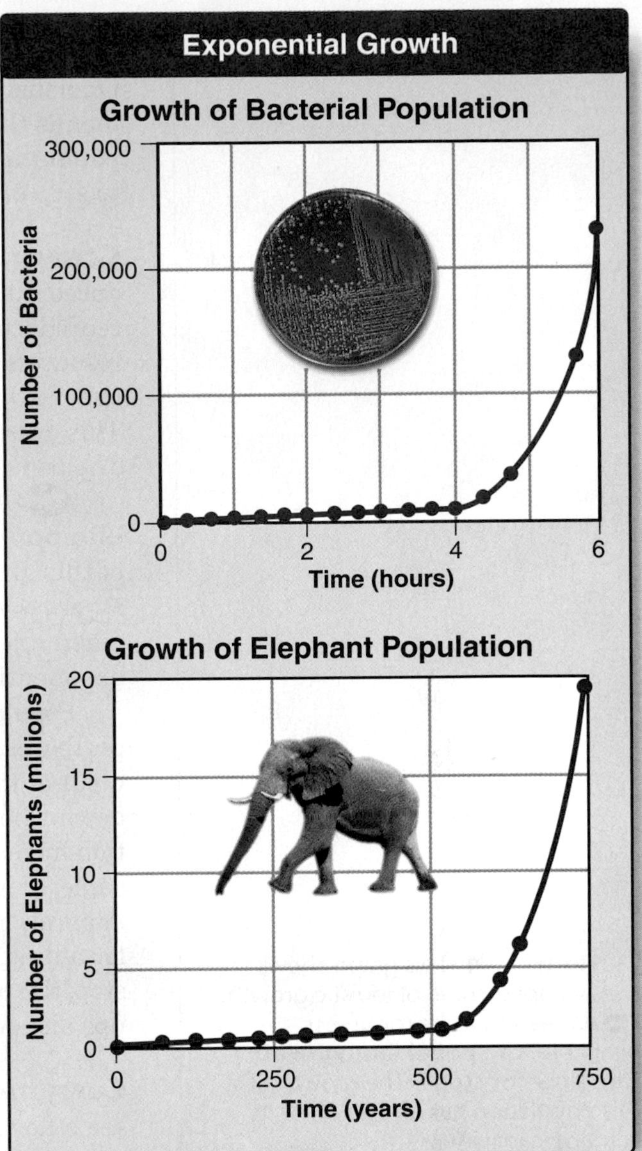

▲ **Figure 5–3 In the presence of unlimited resources and in the absence of predation and disease, a population will grow exponentially.** Both of these hypothetical graphs show the characteristic J-shape of exponential population growth.

Logistic Growth

Obviously, neither bacteria nor elephants cover the planet. This means that exponential growth does not continue in natural populations for very long. What might cause population growth to stop or to slow down?

Growth Slows Down Suppose that a few animals are introduced into a new environment. At first, as the animals begin to reproduce, the population increases slowly. Then, because resources are unlimited, the population grows exponentially. In time, however, the rate of population growth begins to slow down. This does not mean that the size of the population has dropped. The population is still growing, but at a much slower rate.

As resources become less available, the growth of a population slows or stops. The general, S-shaped curve of this growth pattern, called logistic growth, is shown in **Figure 5–4** in a yeast population. **Logistic growth** occurs when a population's growth slows or stops following a period of exponential growth. How might this happen?

Population growth may slow down when the birthrate decreases, when the death rate increases, or when both events occur at the same rate. Similarly, population growth may slow down when the rate of immigration decreases, the rate of emigration increases, or both. When the birthrate and death rate are the same, or when the rate of immigration is equal to the rate of emigration, then population growth will slow down or even stop for a time. Note that even when the population growth is said to stop, the population is still rising and falling somewhat, but the ups and downs average out around a certain population size.

▼ **Figure 5–4** This graph shows the S-shaped curve of logistic growth. **As resources become less available, the population growth rate slows or stops.** The growth of this population has leveled off at its carrying capacity.

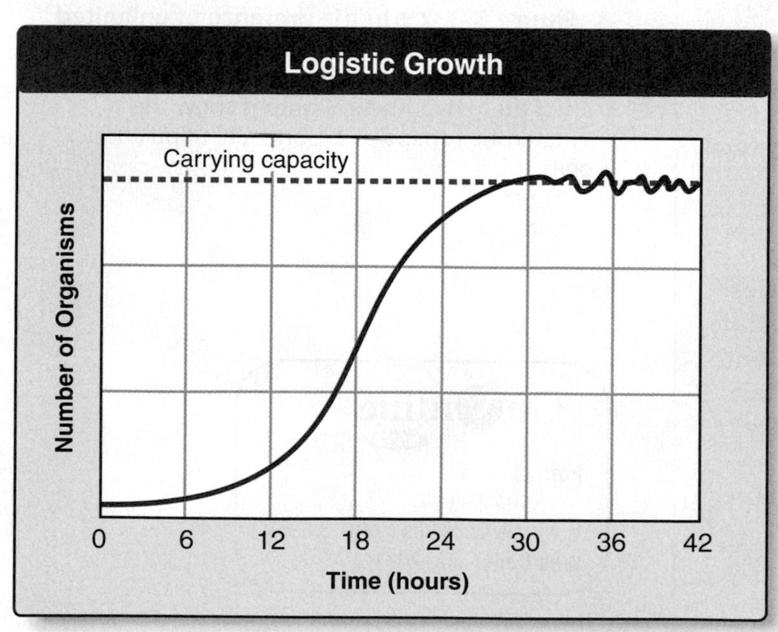

Carrying Capacity If you look again at **Figure 5–4**, you will see a horizontal line through the region of the graph where the growth of the yeast population has leveled off. The point at which that line intersects the y-axis tells you the size of the population when the average growth rate reaches zero. That number, in turn, represents the largest number of individuals—in this case, yeast cells—that a given environment can support. Ecologists call this number the **carrying capacity** of the environment for a particular species.

If you examine natural populations of familiar plant and animal species, you will find that many of them follow a logistic growth curve. In the natural world there are many factors that can slow the growth of a population. The factors that limit population growth are discussed in the next section.

Analyzing Data

Population Trends

Do fruit flies and rabbits show similar trends in population growth?

1. **Using Tables and Graphs** Make a graph using the data in each data table. One graph will show the growth rate of a fruit fly population. The other graph will show the growth rate of a population of rabbits.
2. **Using Tables and Graphs** What type of growth pattern is exhibited by the fruit fly population? Is it the same type of growth as in the rabbit population? Explain.
3. **Drawing Conclusions** Does either graph indicate that there is a carrying capacity for the population? If so, when does the population reach its carrying capacity? What is the maximum number of individuals that can be supported at that time?
4. **Predicting** Animals such as foxes and cats often prey on rabbits. Based on the growth curve of the rabbit population, what might happen if a group of predators move into the rabbits' habitat during the tenth generation and begin eating the rabbits?

Fruit Fly Population Growth

Days	Number of Fruit Flies
5	10
10	50
15	100
20	200
25	300
30	310
35	320
40	320

Rabbit Population Growth

Generations	Number of Rabbits
1	100
2	105
25	1000
37	1600
55	2400
72	3350
86	8000
100	13,150

5–1 Section Assessment

1. **Key Concept** List three characteristics that are used to describe a population.
2. **Key Concept** What factors can change a population's size?
3. **Key Concept** What is the difference between exponential growth and logistic growth?
4. What is meant by population density?
5. Define carrying capacity.
6. **Critical Thinking Inferring** What factors might cause the carrying capacity of a population to change?

Thinking Visually

Using Graphic Organizers
Draw a concept map that shows how populations grow. Include the following terms: *exponential growth, logistic growth, birthrate, death rate, immigration, emigration.* Add any other terms that you think are useful to complete the map.

5–2 Limits to Growth

4-1.1 Ecosystems
4-6.1 The carrying capacity of an environment
4-6.1 Environments and resources are finite
4-6.3 A stable ecosystem can be altered

Guide for Reading

Key Concept
- What factors limit population growth?

Vocabulary
limiting factor
density-dependent limiting factor
predator-prey relationship
density-independent limiting factor

Reading Strategy: Predicting Before you read, preview the diagram below. Predict how each factor might limit the growth of a population. As you read, note whether your predictions were correct.

Now that you know a few things about population growth, think again about the sea otter example in the beginning of the previous section. When a sea otter population declines, something has changed the relationship between the birthrate and the death rate, or between the rates of immigration and emigration. For instance, in part of the sea otter's range, the death rate of sea otters is increasing because killer whales are eating the otters. Predation by killer whales creates a situation that reduces the growth of the sea otter population.

Limiting Factors

Recall from Chapter 3 that the primary productivity of an ecosystem can be reduced when there is an insufficient supply of a particular nutrient. Ecologists call such substances limiting nutrients. A limiting nutrient is an example of a more general ecological concept: a limiting factor. In the context of populations, a **limiting factor** is a factor that causes population growth to decrease. Some of the limiting factors that can affect a population are shown in **Figure 5–5.**

▼ **Figure 5–5** Many different factors can limit population growth. Some of these factors are shown below. **Inferring** *How might each of these factors increase the death rate in a population?*

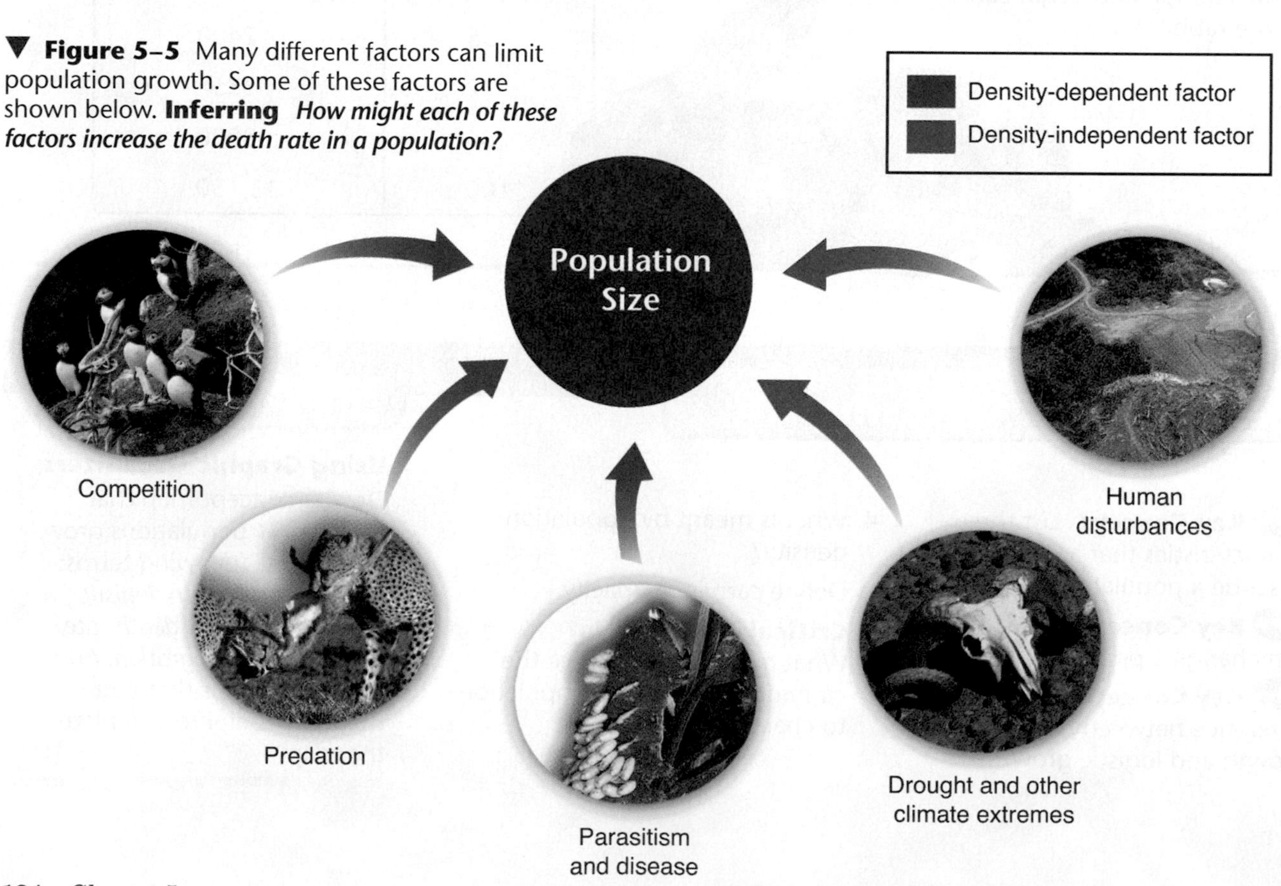

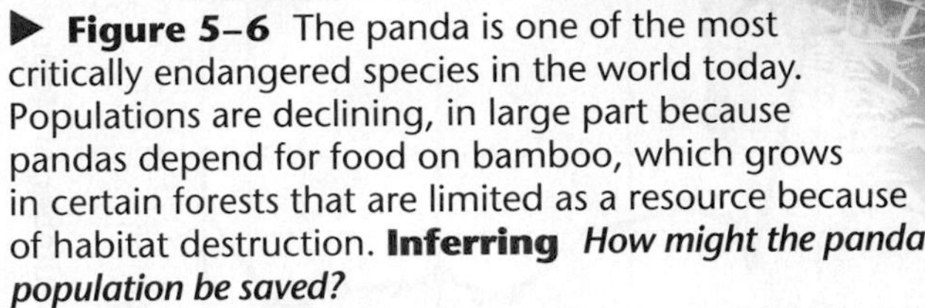

▶ **Figure 5–6** The panda is one of the most critically endangered species in the world today. Populations are declining, in large part because pandas depend for food on bamboo, which grows in certain forests that are limited as a resource because of habitat destruction. **Inferring** *How might the panda population be saved?*

A resource base that is limited can also affect the long-term survival of a species. As shown in **Figure 5–6,** pandas depend for food on bamboo that grows in certain kinds of temperate forests in China. Since the time that these forests have been cleared for timber and farmland, panda populations have fallen dramatically and have become isolated in small pockets of remaining forest.

Density-Dependent Factors

A limiting factor that depends on population size is called a **density-dependent limiting factor.** Density-dependent factors become limiting only when the population density—the number of organisms per unit area—reaches a certain level. These factors operate most strongly when a population is large and dense. They do not affect small, scattered populations as greatly. **Density-dependent limiting factors include competition, predation, parasitism, and disease.**

Competition When populations become crowded, organisms compete with one another for food, water, space, sunlight, and other essentials. For example, puffins must compete for limited nesting sites. Competition among members of the same species is a density-dependent limiting factor. The more individuals living in an area, the sooner they use up the available resources. Likewise, the fewer the number of individuals, the more resources are available to them and the less they must compete with one another.

Competition can also occur between members of different species. This type of competition is a major force behind evolutionary change. When two species compete for the same resources, both species are under pressure to change in ways that decrease their competition. Over time, the species may evolve to occupy separate niches. That is because, as you may recall, no two species can occupy the same niche in the same place at the same time.

CHECKPOINT *What is a density-dependent limiting factor?*

Quick Lab

How does competition affect growth?

Materials bean seeds, 2 paper cups, potting soil

Procedure 

1. Label two paper cups 3 and 15. Use a pencil to make several holes in the bottom of each paper cup. Fill each paper cup two-thirds full with potting soil. Plant 3 bean seeds in cup 3, and plant 15 bean seeds in cup 15.
2. Water both cups so that the soil is moist but not wet. Put them in a location that receives bright indirect light. Water the cups equally as needed.
3. Count the seedlings every other day for 2 weeks. **CAUTION:** *Wash your hands with soap and warm water before leaving the lab.*

Analyze and Conclude

Observing What differences did you observe between the two cups?

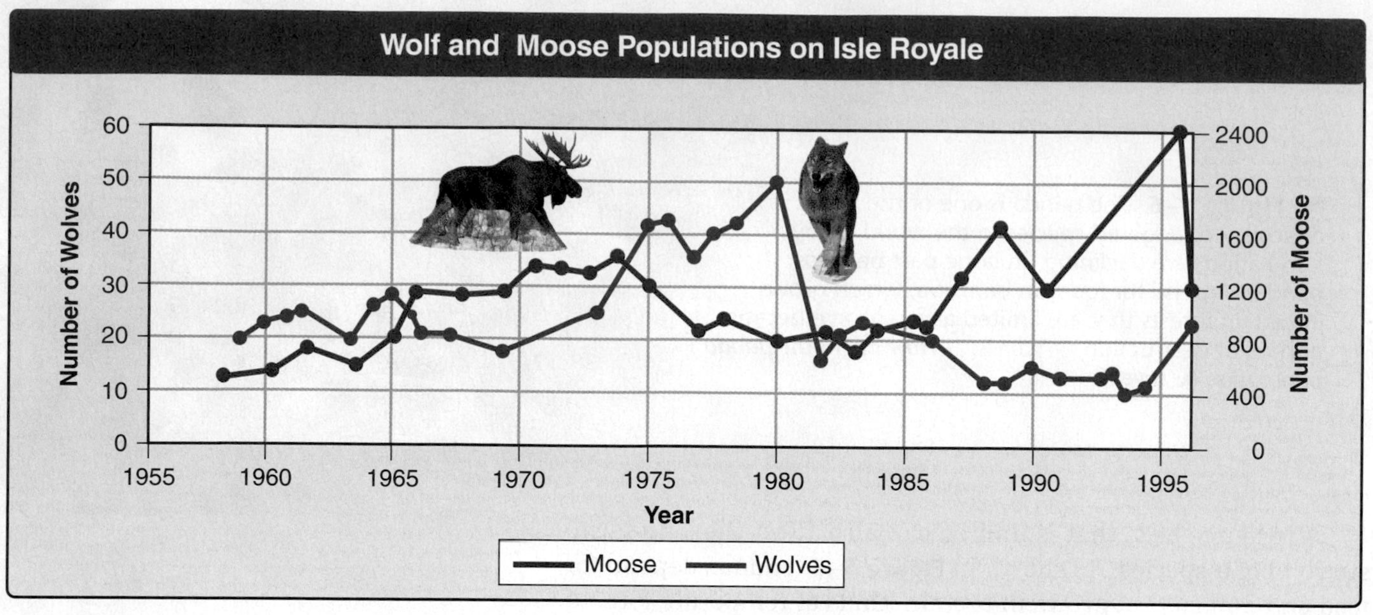

▲ **Figure 5–7** The relationship between moose and wolves on Isle Royale illustrates how predation can affect population growth. In this example, the moose population was also affected by changes in food supply, and the wolf population was also affected by disease. **Interpreting Graphics** *How are the increases and decreases in the moose population related to the changes in the wolf population?*

Predation Populations in nature are often controlled by predation. The regulation of a population by predation takes place within a **predator-prey relationship,** one of the best-known mechanisms of population control. The relationships between sea otters and sea urchins and between sea otters and killer whales are examples of predator-prey interactions that affect population growth.

A well-documented example of a predator-prey relationship is the interaction between wolves and moose on Isle Royale, an island in Lake Superior. The graph in **Figure 5–7** shows how periodic increases in the moose population—the prey—on Isle Royale are quickly followed by increases in the wolf population—the predators. As the wolves prey on the moose, the moose population falls. The decline in the moose population is followed, sooner or later, by a decline in the wolf population because there is less for the wolves to feed upon. A decline in the wolf population means that the moose have fewer enemies, so the moose population rises again. This cycle of predator and prey populations can be repeated indefinitely.

Parasitism and Disease Parasites can also limit the growth of a population. Parasitic organisms range in size from microscopic, disease-causing bacteria to tapeworms 30 centimeters or more in length. These organisms are similar to predators in many ways. Like predators, parasites take nourishment at the expense of their hosts, often weakening them and causing disease or death. The wasp cocoons in **Figure 5–8**, for example, can weaken or kill many caterpillars.

◀ **Figure 5–8** This larval sphinx moth has been attacked by a parasitic wasp. The wasp inserted its eggs beneath the moth's skin. After hatching, the wasp larvae fed on their host internally until they appeared as white cocoons on its back. **Predicting** *How might the wasp larvae affect the sphinx moth population?*

Density-Independent Factors

Density-independent limiting factors affect all populations in similar ways, regardless of the population size. **Unusual weather, natural disasters, seasonal cycles, and certain human activities—such as damming rivers and clear-cutting forests—are all examples of density-independent limiting factors.** In response to such factors, many species show a characteristic crash in population size. After the crash, the population may soon build up again, or it may stay low for some time.

For some species, storms or hurricanes can nearly extinguish a population. For example, thrips, aphids, and other insects that feed on plant buds and leaves might be washed out by a heavy rainstorm. Extremes of cold or hot weather also can take their toll on a population, regardless of the population's density. A severe winter frost, for example, can kill giant saguaro cactuses in the Arizona desert. In some areas, periodic droughts can affect entire populations of vegetation, as shown in **Figure 5–9.** Such events can, in turn, affect the populations of consumers within the food web.

Environments are always changing, and most populations can adapt to a certain amount of change. Populations often grow and shrink in response to such changes. Major upsets in an ecosystem, however, can lead to long-term declines in certain populations. Human activities have caused some of these major upsets, as you will soon read.

▶ **Figure 5–9** A drought can result in the abrupt decrease of a population, regardless of its size. **Droughts and other natural disasters are density-independent limiting factors.**

5–2 Section Assessment

1. **Key Concept** List three density-dependent factors and three density-independent factors that can limit the growth of a population.
2. What is the relationship between competition and population size?
3. If an entire lynx population disappears, what is likely to happen to the hare population on which it preys?
4. Identify how a limited resource can affect the size of a population. Give an example that illustrates this situation.
5. **Critical Thinking Applying Concepts** Give an example of a density-independent limiting factor that has affected a human population. Describe how this factor changed the human population.

Connecting Concepts

Biotic and Abiotic Factors
Study the factors that limit population growth as shown in **Figure 5–5.** Classify each factor as either biotic or abiotic. Refer to the information on biotic and abiotic factors in Section 4–2.

Does the Gray Wolf Population Need Protection?

Wolves were once widely distributed around the world, occupying almost every habitat except tropical jungles. Today, however, wolves occupy only a fraction of their former range. In 1973, the Endangered Species Act was passed by the U.S. Congress to protect declining populations of gray wolves from becoming extinct. At the time, there were only about 400 wolves in the lower 48 states. By 2002, the population had swelled to an estimated 4000 individuals scattered mostly throughout the Rocky Mountains and Great Lakes areas.

Classifying the status of animals is a judgment call. In some cases, the judgment is easy. For instance, the California condor population now includes only a few remaining members and is clearly in great danger. With other species, such as the gray wolf, the situation is much more complex. How should the gray wolf be classified—and therefore managed—in the United States?

The Viewpoints

Keep the Endangered Classification

People who want to keep the gray wolf's status as an endangered species say that most of its former habitat in the 48 contiguous states is unsuitable because of human encroachment. Proponents of this view cite the fact that only after gray wolves were given protection under the Endangered Species Act did the wolf population in the United States begin to increase. There is concern that persecution by people and loss of habitat will confine gray wolves to more remote areas, or reduce their habitat even further, unless federal protection continues.

Reclassify the Wolf and Remove Federal Protection

Opponents of the endangered species classification counter that in states like Minnesota, the gray wolf population is growing at a rate of 4 to 5 percent each year. These people are confident that, because the populations are increasing at a healthy rate, the wolves no longer need federal protection. Ranchers are concerned that, at the current growth rate, wolves will encroach on their livestock. Many feel strongly that landowners should have the right to protect themselves from potential losses. The protection of wolves currently costs the U.S. government over $200,000 per year. If the wolves could be legally hunted and trapped, the money that would be saved could be used to help protect other, more endangered species.

Research and Decide

1. **Analyzing the Viewpoints** To make an informed decision, learn more about this issue by consulting library or Internet resources. List the pros and cons of each option as they relate to both humans and wolves. Consider the different perspectives of landowners, conservationists, and other interested groups.
2. **Forming Your Opinion** Decide whether the federal government should change the status of the gray wolf. Write a persuasive statement to support your decision.

For: Links from the authors
Visit: PHSchool.com
Web Code: cbe-2052

5–3 Human Population Growth

1-S1.1 Values are essential in applying scientific knowledge
4-1.1 Ecosystems include populations that interact
4-6.1 The carrying capacity of an environment is limited
4-6.1 Environments and resources are finite

Guide for Reading

Key Concepts
- How has the size of the human population changed over time?
- Why do population growth rates differ in countries throughout the world?

Vocabulary
demography
demographic transition
age-structure diagram

Reading Strategy: Asking Questions Before you read, preview the graphs in **Figures 5–10**, **5–12**, and **5–13.** Make a list of questions about the graphs. As you read, write down the answers to your questions.

How quickly is the world's human population growing? In the United States and other developed countries, the current growth rate is very low. In some developing countries, the human population is growing at a rate of nearly 3 people per second. Because of this bustling growth rate, the human population is well on its way to reaching 9 billion within your lifetime.

Historical Overview

Like the populations of many other living organisms, the size of the human population tends to increase with time. For most of human existence, the population grew slowly. Life was harsh, and limiting factors kept population sizes low. Food was scarce. Incurable diseases were rampant. Until fairly recently, only half the children in the world survived to adulthood. Because death rates were so high, families had many children, just to make sure that some would survive.

About 500 years ago, the human population began growing more rapidly. Agriculture and industry made life easier and safer. The world's food supply became more reliable, and essential goods could be shipped around the globe. Improved sanitation, medicine, and health care dramatically reduced the death rate and increased longevity. At the same time, birthrates in most places remained high. With these advances, the human population experienced exponential growth, as shown in **Figure 5–10.**

▼ **Figure 5–10** **The size of the human population has increased over time.** After a long, slow start, the worldwide population grew exponentially following improvements in medicine, sanitation, agriculture, energy use, and technology.

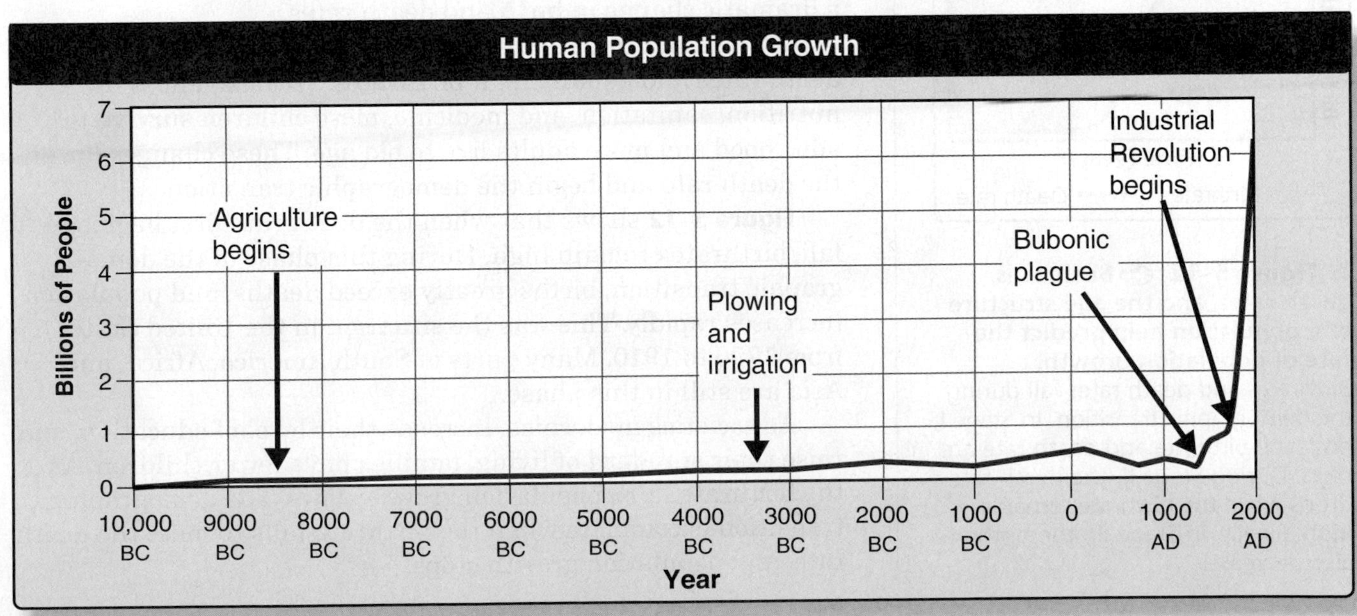

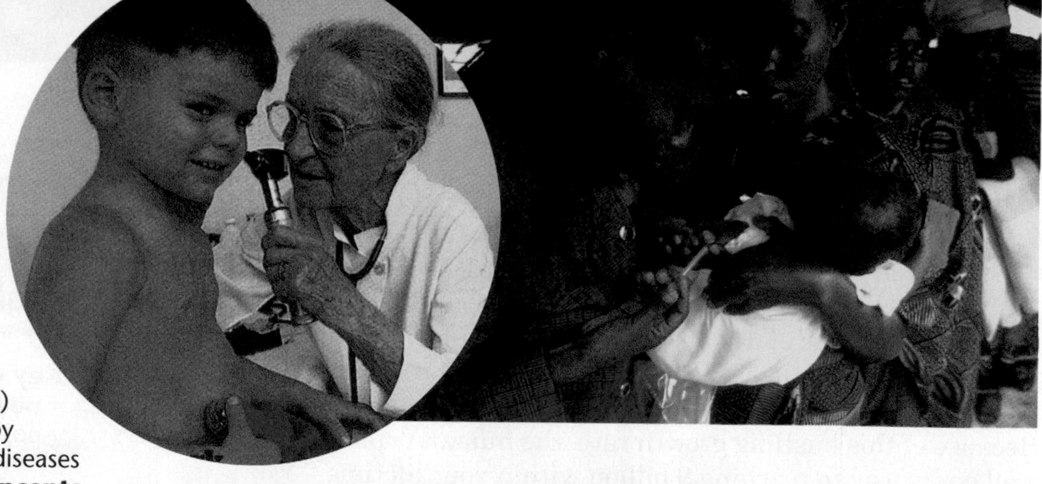

Figure 5–11 Medical advances can lead to a dramatic drop in a population's death rate. Dr. Leila Denmark (near right), who practiced medicine for 73 years, helped to invent the whooping cough vaccine in 1936. A healthcare worker in Rwanda (far right) vaccinates an infant, thereby helping to prevent certain diseases in that child. **Applying Concepts** *Which other advances can reduce a population's death rate?*

Patterns of Population Growth

The human population cannot keep growing exponentially forever, because Earth and its resources are limited. The question is, when and how will our population growth slow? Two centuries ago, English economist Thomas Malthus observed that human populations were growing rapidly. Malthus predicted that such growth would not continue indefinitely. Instead, according to Malthus, war, famine, and disease would limit human population growth.

Today, scientists have identified a variety of other social and economic factors that can affect human populations. The scientific study of human populations is called **demography** (duh-MAH-gruh-fee). Demography examines the characteristics of human populations and attempts to explain how those populations will change over time. **Birthrates, death rates, and the age structure of a population help predict why some countries have high growth rates while other countries grow more slowly.**

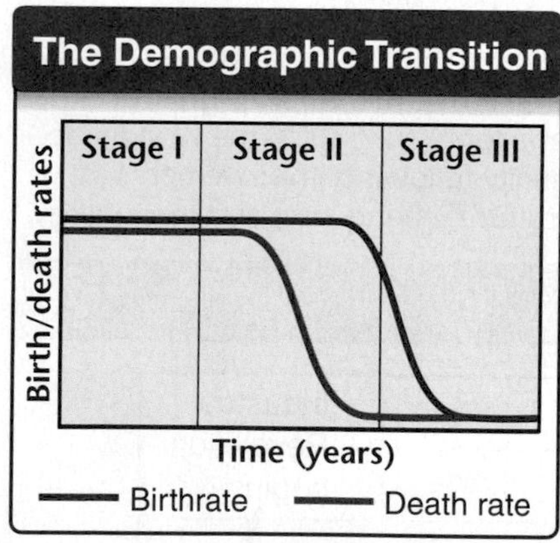

▲ **Figure 5–12** **Birthrates, death rates, and the age structure of a population help predict the rate of population growth.** Birthrates and death rates fall during the demographic transition. In Stage I, both the birthrate and death rate are high. During Stage II, the death rate drops while the birthrate remains high. Finally, in Stage III, the birthrate also decreases.

The Demographic Transition Over the past century, population growth in the United States, Japan, and much of Europe has slowed dramatically. Demographers have developed a hypothesis to explain this shift. According to this hypothesis, these countries have completed the **demographic transition,** a dramatic change in birth and death rates.

Throughout most of history, human societies have had high death rates and equally high birthrates. With advances in nutrition, sanitation, and medicine, more children survive to adulthood and more adults live to old age. These changes lower the death rate and begin the demographic transition.

Figure 5–12 shows that when the death rate first begins to fall, birthrates remain high. During this phase of the demographic transition, births greatly exceed deaths, and population increases rapidly. This was the situation in the United States from 1790 to 1910. Many parts of South America, Africa, and Asia are still in this phase.

As societies modernize, increase their level of education, and raise their standard of living, families have fewer children. As the birthrate falls, population growth slows. The demographic transition is complete when the birthrate falls to meet the death rate, and population growth stops.

So far, the demographic transition has been completed in only a few countries. Despite the trend in the United States, Europe, and Japan, the worldwide human population is still growing exponentially. Most people live in countries that have not yet completed the demographic transition. Much of the population growth today is contributed by only 10 countries, with India and China in the lead, where birthrates remain high.

Age Structure Population growth depends, in part, on how many people of different ages make up a given population. Demographers can predict future growth using models called **age-structure diagrams,** or population profiles. Age-structure diagrams show the population of a country broken down by gender and age group. Each bar in the age-structure diagram represents individuals within a 5-year group. Percentages of males are to the left of the center line and females to the right in each group.

Consider **Figure 5–13,** which compares the age structure of the U.S. population with that of Rwanda, a country in east-central Africa. In the United States, there are nearly equal numbers of people in each age group. This age structure predicts a slow but steady growth rate for the near future. In Rwanda, on the other hand, there are many more young children than teenagers, and many more teenagers than adults. This age structure predicts a population that will double in about 30 years.

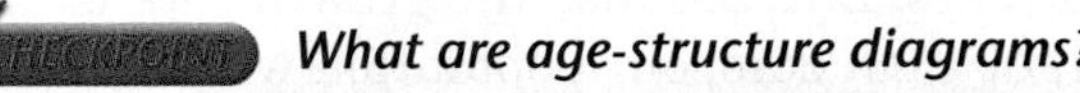
What are age-structure diagrams?

Go Online NSTA SCiLINKS
For: Links on population growth
Visit: www.SciLinks.org
Web Code: cbn-2053

▼ **Figure 5–13** These graphs show the age structure of the U.S. population and the Rwandan population. **Analyzing Data** *How do the United States and Rwanda differ in the percentages of 10- to 14-year-olds in the population?*

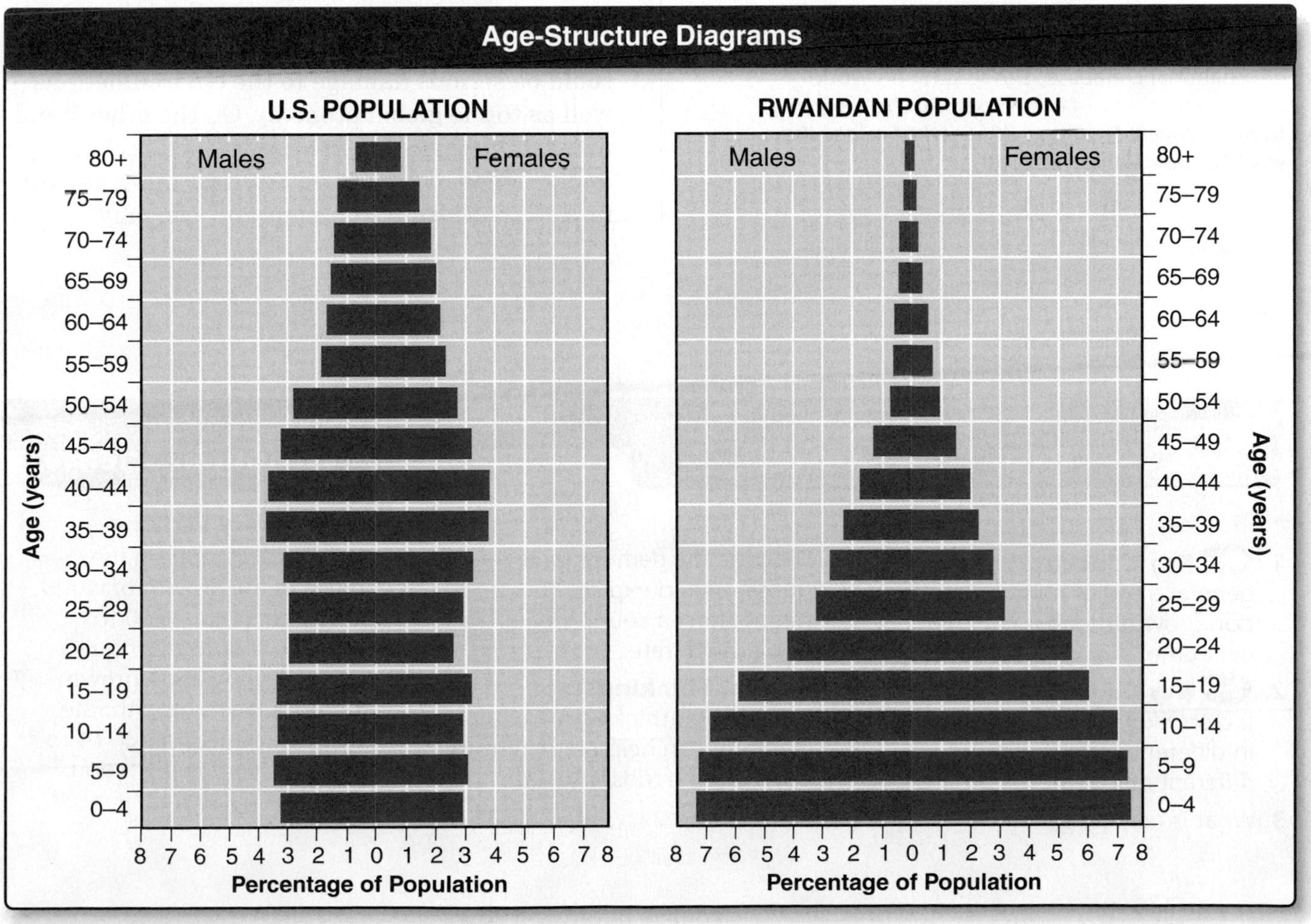

Age-Structure Diagrams

U.S. POPULATION

Males Females

80+ 75–79 70–74 65–69 60–64 55–59 50–54 45–49 40–44 35–39 30–34 25–29 20–24 15–19 10–14 5–9 0–4

Age (years)

8 7 6 5 4 3 2 1 0 1 2 3 4 5 6 7 8

Percentage of Population

RWANDAN POPULATION

Males Females

80+ 75–79 70–74 65–69 60–64 55–59 50–54 45–49 40–44 35–39 30–34 25–29 20–24 15–19 10–14 5–9 0–4

Age (years)

8 7 6 5 4 3 2 1 0 1 2 3 4 5 6 7 8

Percentage of Population

World Population: 1950–2050		
Year	Average Annual Growth Rate (%)	Population
1950	1.47	2,555,360,972
1960	1.33	3,039,669,330
1962*	2.19	3,136,556,092
1963*	2.19	3,206,072,286
1970	2.07	3,708,067,105
1980	1.69	4,454,607,332
1990	1.58	5,275,407,789
2000	1.23	6,078,684,329
2010	1.06	6,812,009,338
2020	0.87	7,515,218,898
2030	0.68	8,127,277,506
2040	0.54	8,646,671,023
2050	0.43	9,078,850,714

*Highest growth rate during 100-year period

▲ **Figure 5–14** This table, based on actual and projected data from the U.S. Census Bureau, International Database, shows data on world population. **Predicting** ***Based on the projected trend between 2040 and 2050, what might the world population be in 2060?***

Future Population Growth

To predict how the world's human population will grow, demographers must consider many factors, including the age structure of each country and the prevalence of life-threatening diseases, such as AIDS, malaria, and cholera. The table in **Figure 5–14** shows statistics for world population growth from 1950 to 2000 with projected figures through the year 2050. Current projections suggest that by 2050, the world population may reach more than 9 billion people.

Will the human population grow at its current rate, or will it level out to a logistic growth curve and become stable? By 2050 the growth rate may level off or even decrease. This may happen if countries that are currently growing rapidly move toward the demographic transition. The figures in the table show that the growth rate in 2050 is projected to be 0.43 percent. This rate is a decrease from the peak growth rate of 2.19 percent, reached in the early 1960s.

A lower growth rate means that the human population will be growing more slowly over the next 50 years. But, because the growth rate is still larger than zero, our population will continue to grow. Most ecologists suggest that if this growth does not slow down even more, there could be serious damage to the environment as well as to the global economy. On the other hand, many economists assert that science, technology, and changes in society will control those negative impacts on the environment and economy.

5–3 Section Assessment

1. **Key Concept** Describe the general trend of human population growth that has occurred over time.
2. **Key Concept** What factors explain why populations in different countries grow at different rates?
3. What is demography?
4. Describe the demographic transition and explain how it might affect a country's population growth rate.
5. **Critical Thinking Evaluating** Why do you think age-structure diagrams can help predict future population trends?

Writing in Science

Explanatory Writing

Write a paragraph on the trends in the growth of world population from 1950 to 2050. Be sure to distinguish between population growth and population growth rate. *Hint:* Refer to **Figure 5–14** to help with your explanation.

Exploration

Investigating the Growth of a Population of Bacteria

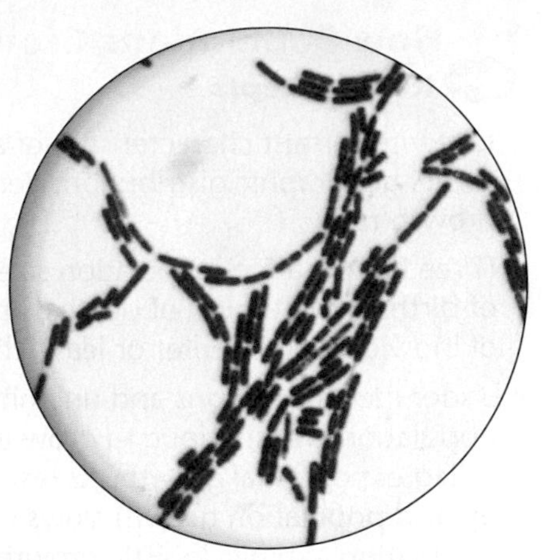

Bacteria are convenient for laboratory studies of populations because large numbers of bacteria live in a very small space and bacteria reproduce rapidly. In this investigation, you will examine the growth of a bacterial culture.

Problem

What happens to a population that depends on limited resources?

Materials

- 2 lima beans
- 2 dropper pipettes
- 100-mL beaker
- coverslips
- microscope slides
- 10-mL graduated cylinder
- 100-mL graduated cylinder
- methylene blue stain
- microscope
- test-tube rack
- 4 test tubes
- aluminum foil

Skills

Calculating, Using Tables and Graphs

Procedure

1. Before you begin, review the rules for sterile procedure with your teacher.
2. Wash your hands. Put on your plastic gloves. Then, to start a bacterial culture, put 2 lima beans into a 100-mL beaker. Add 50 mL of water. Allow this mixture to sit for 48 hours.
3. Construct a data table with four columns and five blank rows. At the top of the table, label the columns "Day," "Bacteria Observed," "Dilution Factor," and "Bacteria Present."
4. After 48 hours, use a dropper pipette to place a drop of the culture on a microscope slide. Add a coverslip. Place a drop of methylene blue stain on the slide next to the coverslip. Lightly touch a paper towel on the opposite side of the coverslip to draw the stain under the coverslip.
5. Use the high-power objective of a microscope to locate some bacteria. If you can count the bacteria in your field of view, go to step 7. If there are too many bacteria to count, go to step 6.
6. Use a dropper pipette to put 1 mL of the culture into a 10-mL graduated cylinder. Add 9 mL of water to the graduated cylinder. Empty the graduated cylinder into a test tube. This procedure dilutes the culture by a factor of 10. Examine the diluted sample under the microscope as in step 5. If there are still too many bacteria to count, dilute the sample again in the same way. Stop diluting when you can count the bacteria. Each time you dilute, multiply the dilution by 10.
7. Record the number of bacteria and the dilution factor in your data table. If you did not dilute, the dilution factor is 1. To determine the number of bacteria present, multiply the number of bacteria you observed by the dilution factor.
8. Cover the beaker with aluminum foil and set it aside overnight. Wash your hands thoroughly with soap and warm water when you are finished.
9. **Predicting** Record a prediction of how the population of bacteria will change.
10. Repeat steps 5 through 8 every day for 5 days.

Analyze and Conclude

1. **Using Tables and Graphs** Make a graph of the data from your data table. When did the population grow most quickly? Most slowly?
2. **Drawing Conclusions** How can you explain the changes in population growth?
3. **Inferring** What caused the changes in the population growth rate?

Go Further

Designing Experiments Design an experiment to investigate how a change in the food supply affects the growth of a bacterial population. With your teacher's approval, carry out your experiment.

Chapter 5 Study Guide

5–1 How Populations Grow

Key Concepts

- Three important characteristics of a population are its geographic distribution, density, and growth rate.
- Three factors affect population size: the number of births, the number of deaths, and the number of individuals that enter or leave the population.
- Under ideal conditions and unlimited resources, a population will continue to grow in a pattern called exponential growth. As resources are used up and population growth slows or stops, the population exhibits logistic growth.

Vocabulary

population density, p. 119
immigration, p. 120
emigration, p. 120
exponential growth, p. 121
logistic growth, p. 122
carrying capacity, p. 122

5–2 Limits to Growth

Key Concepts

- Density-dependent limiting factors include competition, predation, parasitism, and disease.
- Unusual weather, natural disasters, seasonal cycles, and certain human activities—such as damming rivers and clear-cutting forests—are all examples of density-independent limiting factors.

Vocabulary

limiting factor, p. 124
density-dependent limiting factor, p. 125
predator-prey relationship, p. 126
density-independent limiting factor, p. 127

5–3 Human Population Growth

Key Concepts

- Like the populations of many other living organisms, the size of the human population tends to increase with time.
- The characteristics of populations, and the social and economic factors that affect them, explain why some countries have high population growth rates while populations of other countries grow slowly or not at all.

Vocabulary

demography, p. 130
demographic transition, p. 130
age-structure diagram, p. 131

Thinking Visually

Using information from this chapter, complete the following concept map:

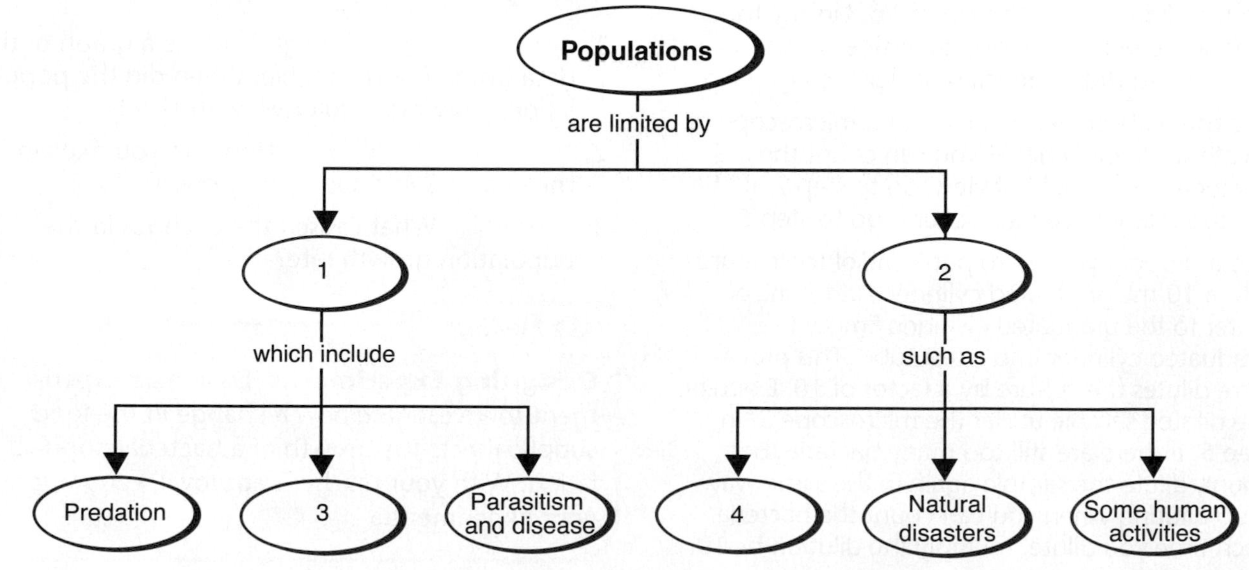

Preparing for the Living Environment Exam

Blue questions emphasize Regents Exam content

Chapter 5

Part A

Multiple Choice

For each statement or question, select the number of the word or expression that, of those given, best completes the statement or answers the question.

1 The movement of individuals into an area occupied by an existing population is called
(1) demography (3) carrying capacity
(2) immigration (4) emigration

2 The area occupied by a population is its
(1) growth rate
(2) geographic distribution
(3) age structure
(4) population density

3 What portion of the graph below is most similar to a graph representing human population growth during this century?
(1) A (3) C
(2) B (4) E

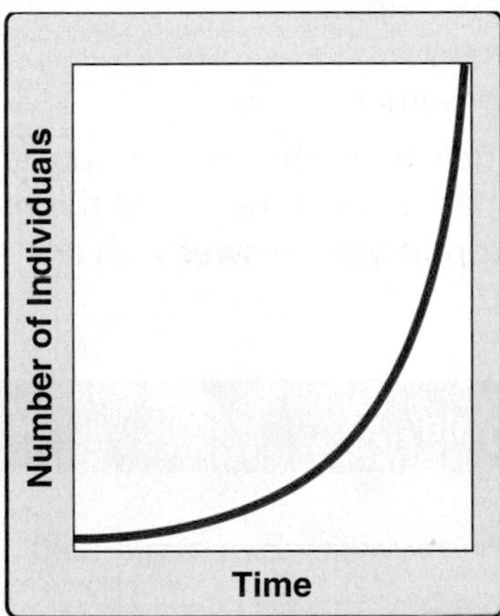

4 The maximum number of organisms of a particular species that can be supported by an environment is called
(1) growth rate
(2) carrying capacity
(3) food chain
(4) ecological succession

5 If a population grows larger than the carrying capacity of its environment, the
(1) death rate may rise
(2) birthrate may rise
(3) death rate may fall
(4) immigration rate may increase

6 A limiting factor that depends on abiotic components of the ecosystem is
(1) predation (3) hurricanes
(2) competition (4) parasitism

7 The limiting factor that depends most on population size is
(1) amount of competition
(2) soil and rock type
(3) amount of precipitation
(4) air temperature

8 The scientific study of human populations is called
(1) immigration
(2) emigration
(3) geography
(4) demography

9 The demographic transition is complete when
(1) population growth stops
(2) the birthrate is greater than the death rate
(3) the death rate begins to fall
(4) the death rate is greater than the birthrate

10 The number of individuals of a single species per unit area is known as
(1) carrying capacity
(2) logistic growth
(3) population density
(4) population growth rate

11 Density-independent limiting factors include
(1) predation
(2) drought
(3) competition
(4) parasitism

12 What is the major environmental factor limiting the number of autotrophs at great depths in the ocean?
(1) type of seafloor
(2) amount of light
(3) availibility of minerals
(4) absence of biotic factors

Test-Taking Tip To answer questions that have different combinations of Roman numerals as answer choices, you must evaluate each Roman numeral separately in relation to the question. Then, look to see which answer choice corresponds to the numerals you have selected.

Preparing for the Living Environment Exam

Part B

Multiple Choice and Extended Response
For those questions that ask you to select a response, choose the one that best completes the statement or answers the question. For all others follow the directions given.

13 State the difference between immigration and emigration.

14 On your own paper, draw the *x*- and *y*-axes for a line graph. Label the axes appropriately, and then draw a line on the graph to indicate how the human population has grown over the last 2,000 years.

15 Many species of organisms, including grasshoppers and foxes, live in an abandoned field. Is the carrying capacity of the field the same for both grasshoppers and foxes? Support your answer with an explanation.

16 State how a predator-prey relationship can be a mechanism of population control. Support your answer with an explanation.

17 State how parasites serve as a limiting factor.

18 Explain how factors such as atmospheric changes and soil erosion act as limiting factors on the growth of populations.

19 What will happen to a population of predators if there is a sudden increase in food for the prey? Support your answer with an explanation.

Base your answers to questions 20 and 21 on the information below and on your knowledge of biology.

A farm field is used year after year to grow the same crop. Slowly, the amount of potassium in the soil decreases. All the other nutrients the crop requires are present in adequate levels.

20 State what effect the decrease in potassium would eventually have on the ability of the crop to grow.

21 Explain how potassium in this field is an example of a limiting factor.

---

22 What questions would a demographer need to answer in order to determine whether a country is approaching the demographic transition?

Base your answers to questions 23 and 24 on the graph below and on your knowledge of biology.

23 The relationship between wolf and moose populations can best be described as
(1) parasite-host
(2) scavenger-decomposer
(3) predator-prey
(4) producer-consumer

24 State how an increase in the rabbit population on Isle Royale might affect the size of the moose population. Support your answer with an explanation.

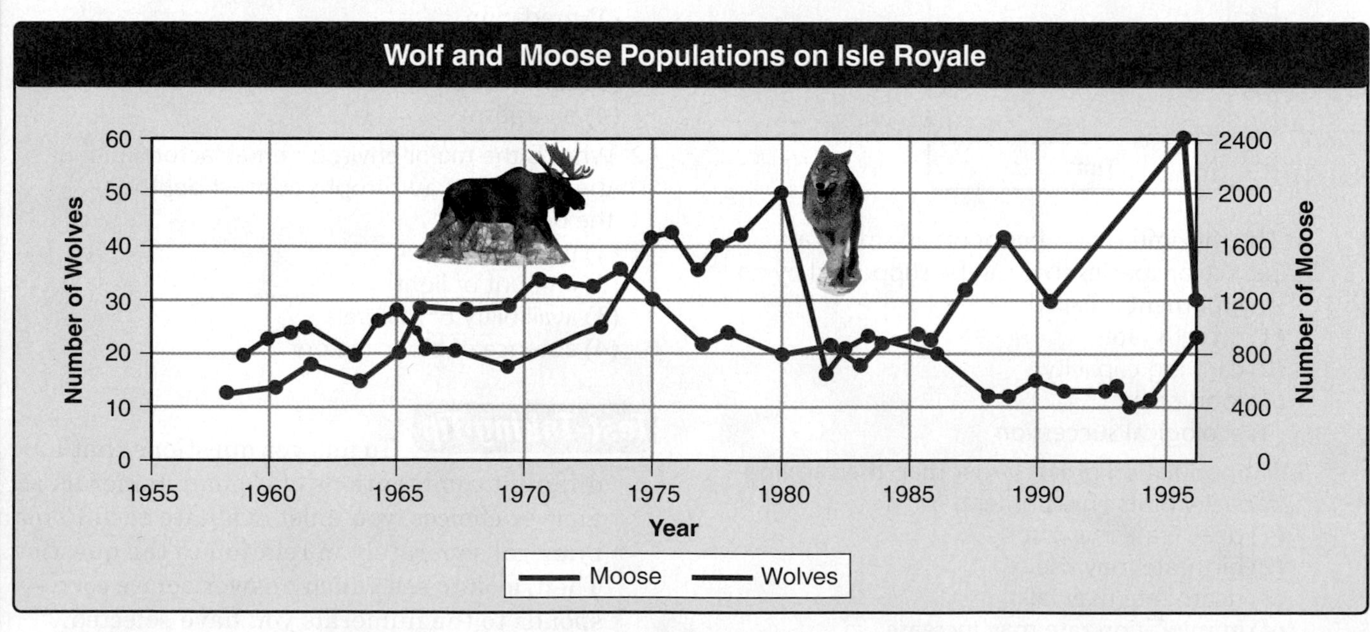

25 Explain how the introduction of a limiting nutrient such as phosphorus into a pond ecosystem would affect the carrying capacity of the pond.

Part C

Extended Response

Answer the questions or follow the directions given.

Base your answer to question 26 on the information below and on your knowledge of biology.

A student designed an experiment to determine if the type of food present in a yeast culture influenced the growth rate of the population. He set up one culture with table sugar and the other with an equal mass of molasses. The student examined the cultures through a microscope each day for four days. The illustrations below show the number of yeast cells observed each day.

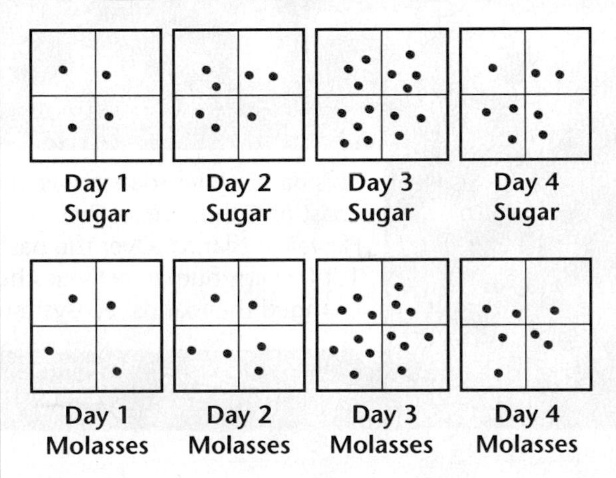

26 Interpret and explain the results of this experiment. In your answer, be sure to:
- describe the growth trend illustrated by both cultures
- state *two* factors that could cause the change observed in the molasses culture between Day 3 and Day 4
- describe how each population will be expected to change between Day 4 and Day 5
- based on the data above, state whether the type of food used influenced the population growth of the yeast

Base your answers to questions 27 through 29 on the information below and on your knowledge of biology.

Mountain lions, and their prey big horn sheep, are part of the natural food web in the Sierra Nevada Mountains. The Fish and Wildlife Service recently declared the sheep an endangered species. This action could lead to the shooting of mountain lions.

27 State one reason placing these sheep on the endangered species list could lead to the shooting of mountain lions where the sheep live.

28 State *two* reasons people would oppose the shooting of mountain lions.

29 Sheep and mountain lions were able to coexist for thousands of years. Explain what has caused the population of big horn sheep to decline to dangerously low numbers within just the last few decades.

30 Nitrogen is a limiting factor in aquatic ecosystems. Runoff from a field or lawn may wash nitrogen-rich fertilizer into a pond. Explain how the fertilizer will affect the carrying capacity of the pond for algae. In your answer, be sure to include:
- a definition of carrying capacity
- an explanation of how nitrogen serves as a limiting factor for the algae population
- a description of what will happen to the algae population as the level of nitrogen in the pond increases

For: An interactive self-test
Visit: PHSchool.com
Web Code: cba-2050

CHAPTER 6

Humans in the Biosphere

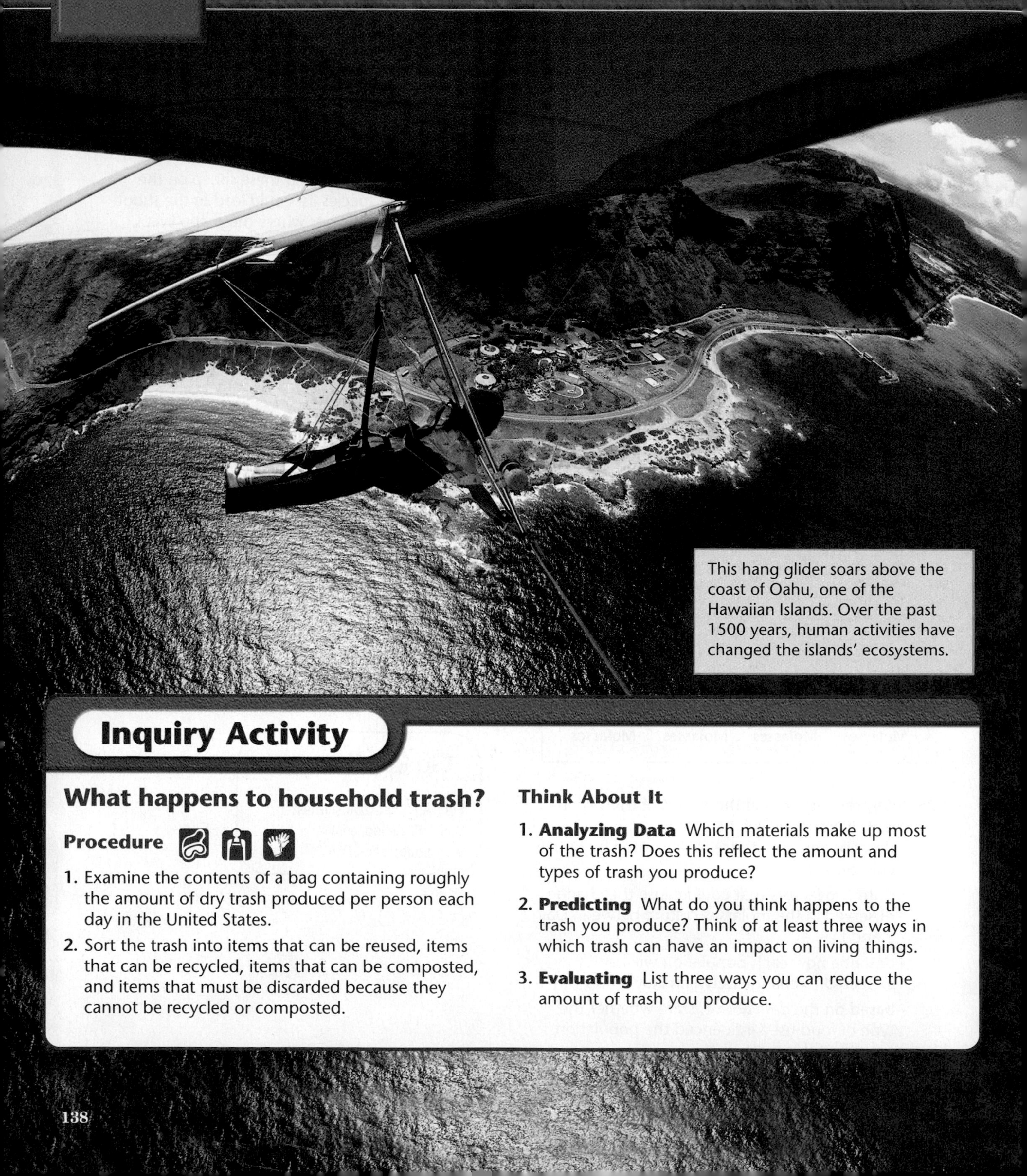

This hang glider soars above the coast of Oahu, one of the Hawaiian Islands. Over the past 1500 years, human activities have changed the islands' ecosystems.

Inquiry Activity

What happens to household trash?

Procedure   

1. Examine the contents of a bag containing roughly the amount of dry trash produced per person each day in the United States.
2. Sort the trash into items that can be reused, items that can be recycled, items that can be composted, and items that must be discarded because they cannot be recycled or composted.

Think About It

1. **Analyzing Data** Which materials make up most of the trash? Does this reflect the amount and types of trash you produce?
2. **Predicting** What do you think happens to the trash you produce? Think of at least three ways in which trash can have an impact on living things.
3. **Evaluating** List three ways you can reduce the amount of trash you produce.

6–1 A Changing Landscape

1-S1.1 Values are essential in applying scientific knowledge
4-6.3, 7.1 Stable ecosystems can be altered
4-7.2 Humans altering ecosystems
4-7.2 Industrialization increases demand for resources

About 1600 years ago, people from Polynesia began settling in the islands of Hawaii. These island people were accustomed to limited living space, so they farmed and fished with limited resources in mind. To cut down a coconut palm, a person had to plant two palm trees in its place. Fishing for certain species was prohibited during the season in which the fishes reproduce. The first Hawaiians maintained the ecosystem in such a way that it continued to provide fresh water, fertile soil, and the other resources they needed to survive. Their society was self-sufficient.

Even though they respected the land, these early settlers changed Hawaii's ecology. They cleared forests for farmland and introduced nonnative crop plants, along with animals such as pigs and rats. Eventually, as a result of the Polynesian settlers' activities, many native plants and animals became extinct.

Beginning in the late 1700s, new settlers began to arrive in Hawaii. These new settlers, who eventually included Americans, Europeans, and Asians, continued the process of change begun by the Polynesians. For example, farmers cleared vast areas to grow sugar cane, pineapples, and other crops, and they used large amounts of water for agriculture.

Hawaii today is very different from the islands the Polynesians settled. Many native species, such as the bird in **Figure 6–1,** are becoming scarce. Although the islands boast some of the wettest spots on Earth, agricultural practices have seriously depleted drinking water in places. Because of overfishing, some fish species that were once common are now rare. And Hawaiians today, unlike their Polynesian predecessors, must import some necessities, including part of their food, that were once provided by local ecosystems.

Guide for Reading

Key Concept
- What types of human activities can affect the biosphere?

Vocabulary
agriculture
monoculture
green revolution

Reading Strategy: Finding Main Ideas
As you read, make a list of facts that support the statement "The spreading influence of humans can and does affect the biosphere."

Earth as an Island

The history of humans in Hawaii offers an important lesson for the twenty-first century. In a sense, Earth, too, is an island. All of the organisms—including humans—that live on Earth share a limited resource base and depend on it for their long-term survival. We all rely on the natural ecological processes that sustain these resources.

To protect these resources, we need to understand how humans interact with the biosphere. You have learned about energy flow, chemical cycling, climate, and population-limiting factors. You must also understand how scientific models can be used to make predictions about complex systems. Studies of islands like Hawaii are important to people who don't live on an island—or don't think they do.

▼ **Figure 6–1** The iiwi, or Hawaiian honeycreeper, is one of the most beautiful birds in Hawaii. Like many native species in Hawaii, the iiwi is becoming scarce. Disease, habitat loss, and predation by introduced animals have taken their toll on the species. **Inferring** ***Based on the photograph, what can you infer about the iiwi's niche?***

▲ **Figure 6–2** People of the Paleolithic, or Stone Age, relied on hunting and gathering for their existence. This cave painting from Northern Spain shows ancient hunters slaying a herd of deer with bows and arrows. **Hunting and gathering are among the many human activities that have changed the biosphere.**

▼ **Figure 6–3** Like his Stone Age predecessors, this modern subsistence hunter from the Asmat tribe in New Guinea uses bows and spears. Other subsistence hunters may use modern tools like guns or motorized vehicles. **Predicting** ***What effects might subsistence hunters have on the environment in which they live?***

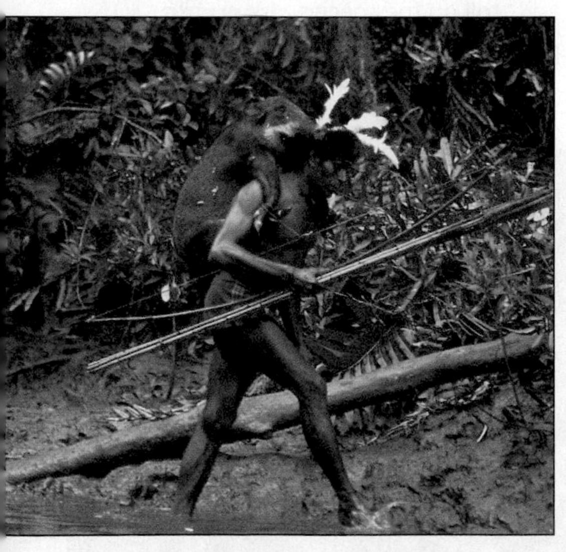

Human Activities

Like all organisms, we humans participate in food webs and chemical cycles. We depend on these ecological life-support systems to provide breathable air, drinkable water, and fertile soil that supports farming. In addition, ecosystem processes provide us with "services" such as storage and recycling of nutrients. Ecologists refer to these necessities as "ecosystem goods and services" because they have real value to us as individuals and societies. If we do not get these goods and services from the environment, we will need to spend money to produce them.

Since we depend on ecosystem goods and services, we must be aware that human activities can change local and global environments. According to a recent study, global human activities use as much energy, and transport almost as much material, as all Earth's other multicellular species combined. We have become the most important source of environmental change on the planet. **Among human activities that affect the biosphere are hunting and gathering, agriculture, industry, and urban development.** We do not yet fully understand how human activities affect ecosystems. Happily, ecological research can help us understand and manage our impact on the environment.

Hunting and Gathering

For most of human history, our ancestors obtained food by hunting and gathering. They hunted birds and mammals, as shown in **Figure 6–2**, and fished in rivers and oceans. They gathered wild seeds, fruits, and nuts. Even these prehistoric hunters and gatherers changed their environments. For example, some scientists hypothesize that the first humans to arrive in North America about 12,000 years ago caused a major mass extinction of animals. Woolly mammoths, giant ground sloths, and saber-toothed cats all became extinct. In addition, species that once lived in North America—cheetahs, zebras, and yaks, for example—disappeared from the continent.

Today groups of people in scattered parts of the world, from the Arctic to Central Africa, still follow the hunter-gatherer way of life to some degree. These people, such as the hunter shown in **Figure 6–3**, make relatively few demands on the environment. However, most of them use some form of technology, such as guns, snowmobiles, or manufactured tools.

What are ecosystem goods and services?

Agriculture

During thousands of years of searching for food, early hunter-gatherers learned how plants grew and ripened. They also discovered which ones were useful for food and medicines. By the end of the last ice age—about 11,000 years ago—humans began the practice of farming, or **agriculture.** Soon, people in different regions of the world were growing wheat, rice, and potatoes. The development of agriculture also included raising animals, such as sheep, goats, cows, pigs, and horses.

The spread of agriculture was among the most important developments in human history. Why? Because agriculture provides human societies with a fundamental need: a dependable supply of food that can be produced in large quantity and stored for later use. With a stable and predictable food supply, humans began to gather in larger settlements rather than travel in search of food. Stable communities, including towns and cities, enabled the development of the elements of civilization, such as government, laws, and writing.

From Traditional to Modern Agriculture Farming continued to develop for thousands of years. Farmers gradually acquired machinery, such as plows and the seed drill shown in **Figure 6–4,** to help with cultivation. World exploration led to an exchange of crops around the globe. For example, Europeans began to grow crops native to North and South America, such as potatoes and squash. Americans and Europeans cultivated rice, which is native to Asia.

In the 1800s and 1900s, advances in science and technology set the stage for a remarkable change in agriculture. Large-scale irrigation in dry areas such as the western United States allowed deserts to become breadbaskets. Machinery for plowing, planting, and harvesting helped farmers increase their yields tremendously. Agricultural scientists developed new varieties of crops that produce higher yields. These new crops were often grown using a practice called **monoculture,** in which large fields are planted with a single variety year after year. Chemical fertilizers boosted plant growth and pesticides controlled crop-damaging insects.

Word Origins

Agriculture is a combination of the Latin words *ager,* meaning "a field," and *cultura,* meaning "care." *Agriculture* is the science and art of farming, which includes the cultivation of field soils, production of crops, and the raising of livestock. **If the prefix *agro-* has the same meaning as *agri-,* what do you think the definition of the noun *agrochemical* is?**

▼ **Figure 6–4** By the 1700s, most Europeans relied on simple tools and animal-drawn plows and vehicles to work the land. This illustration shows a farmer guiding a four-wheeled seed drill as his horse pulls it across a field. The seed drill was invented to help farmers plant seeds in straight lines. **Inferring** ***Why is planting seeds in straight lines an advantage?***

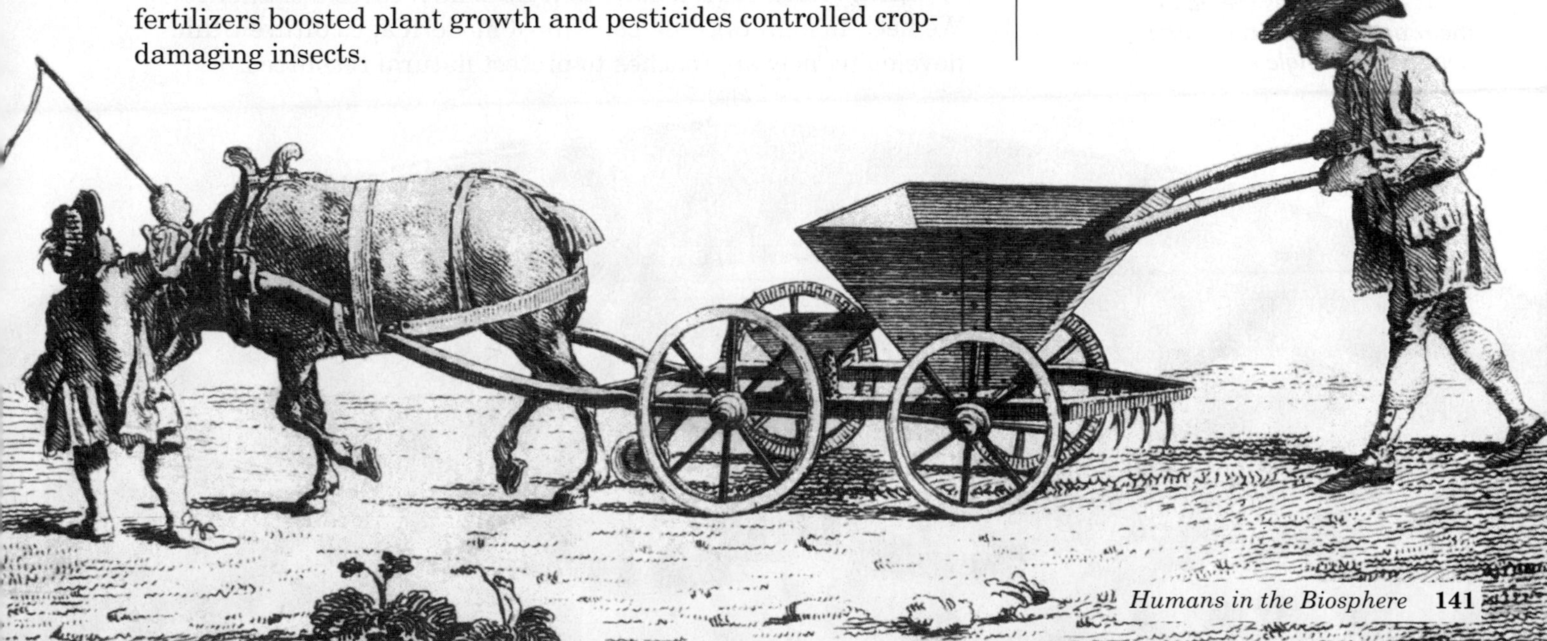

The Green Revolution By the middle of the twentieth century, despite agricultural advances, there were food shortages in many parts of the world. Governments and scientists began a major effort to increase food production in those countries. Plant breeders developed highly productive "miracle strains" of wheat and rice. Modern agricultural techniques were introduced, such as monoculture and the use of chemical fertilizers. This effort came to be called the **green revolution,** because it greatly increased the world's food supply.

The benefits of the green revolution have been enormous. In 20 years, Mexican farmers increased their wheat production ten times. India and China, countries with the world's largest populations, produced enough food to feed their own people for the first time in years. Over the last 50 years, the green revolution has helped world food production double. Even though hunger is still a major problem in parts of the world, the green revolution has provided many people with better nutrition.

Challenges for the Future While increasing world food supplies, modern agriculture has created ecological challenges. For example, large-scale monoculture can lead to problems with insect pests and diseases. To a corn-eating insect, enormous fields of corn look like huge dinner tables, filled with tasty treats! When an insect population is surrounded by food, the population can grow rapidly. When populations of insect pests increase, farmers may increase their use of pesticides. Unfortunately, chemical pesticides can damage beneficial insects, contaminate water supplies, and accumulate in the environment.

A second challenge is finding enough water for irrigation. Less than a quarter of American farmland relies heavily on irrigation, but that land produces a major portion of our harvest. Several states in the West and Midwest, for example, depend heavily on an underground water deposit called the Ogallala aquifer for their water needs. However, evidence indicates that the Ogallala may run dry within 20 to 40 years.

Most ecologists conclude that humanity faces a challenge. We need to maintain the benefits of modern agriculture while developing new approaches to protect natural resources.

▼ **Figure 6–5** This farmer is using a tractor to cultivate a field of soybeans. Modern agricultural machinery such as this has helped increase crop yields. **Applying Concepts** *What is the name for the practice of planting large fields with a single crop?*

Industrial Growth and Urban Development

Human society and its impact on the biosphere were transformed by the Industrial Revolution, which added machines and factories to civilization during the 1800s. That revolution led to the combination of industrial productivity and scientific know-how that provides us with most of the conveniences of modern life, from the homes we live in and the clothes we wear to the electronic devices we use in work and play. Mass-produced farm machinery makes efficient, large-scale agriculture possible. Automobiles give us mobility. Of course, to produce and power these machines, we need energy. We obtain most of this energy from fossil fuels—coal, oil, and natural gas.

For many years, cities and industries discarded wastes from manufacturing, energy production, and other sources into the air, water, and soil. Meanwhile, as urban centers became crowded, many people moved from the cities to the suburbs. The result of this movement was the growth of suburbs and the spread of suburban communities across the American landscape, as shown in **Figure 6–6.** Industrial development and the growth of cities and suburbs are closely tied to the high standard of living that so many people enjoy.

Many ecologists, however, are concerned about the effects of human activity on both local and global environments. Certain kinds of industrial processes pollute air, water, and soil. Dense human communities produce wastes that must be disposed of. Suburban growth consumes farmland and natural habitats, and can place additional stress on plant and animal populations and on the biosphere's life-support systems. Can we learn to control these harmful effects of human activity while preserving—or even improving—our standard of living? This is the enormous challenge that you and your children will face.

Figure 6–6 In the United States today, most people live and work either in cities or in the suburbs that surround them. **Problem Solving** *List some ways that problems associated with the growth of cities and suburbs can be prevented.*

6–1 Section Assessment

1. **Key Concept** List three types of human activities that can affect the biosphere. For each activity, give one environmental cost and one benefit.
2. Identify three of Earth's resources on which humans and other organisms depend for the long-term survival of their species.
3. What did agriculture provide that changed the course of human history?
4. Identify two ways in which the Industrial Revolution has affected living things.
5. **Critical Thinking Predicting** How might improved agricultural practices in a developing nation affect that nation's human population?

You & Your Community

Mapping Community Growth

Are there signs of growth in your community, or in some other community you know? Map out some of the residential areas, shopping malls, and industrial parks in the community. Then, write a brief paragraph telling how this growth might impact local ecosystems.

6–2 Renewable and Nonrenewable Resources

1-S1.1 Values are essential in applying scientific knowledge
4-6.3, 7.1 Stable ecosystems can be altered
4-7.2 Humans altering ecosystems
4-7.2 Industrialization increases demand for resources

Guide for Reading

Key Concepts

- How are environmental resources classified?
- What effects do human activities have on natural resources?

Vocabulary
renewable resource
nonrenewable resource
sustainable development
soil erosion • desertification
deforestation • aquaculture
smog • pollutant • acid rain

Reading Strategy: Building Vocabulary
As you read, make notes about the meaning of each new term in the list above. Then, draw a concept map to show the relationships among the terms in this section.

A few hundred years ago, inhabitants of English villages could graze their cattle on shared pasture land called commons. Since grazing was free of charge, villagers often put as many cattle as possible on those commons. Occasionally there were more cattle on the commons than the land could support. Even as the land became overused, people kept putting more animals on it. After all, those who didn't use that free land would sacrifice their own profit while others would continue to benefit. Overgrazing on village commons sometimes caused the pastures to deteriorate so badly that they could no longer support cattle.

Today, environmentalists often talk about the *tragedy of the commons.* This phrase expresses the idea that any resource, such as water in the ground or fish in the sea, that is free and accessible to everyone, may eventually be destroyed. Why? Because if no one is responsible for protecting a resource, and if no one benefits from preserving it, people will use it up. If humans do not preserve the goods and services of an ecosystem, these resources may suffer the same fate as the common grazing lands in English villages.

Classifying Resources

Environmental goods and services may be classified as either renewable or nonrenewable. A tree is an example of a renewable resource, because a new tree can grow in place of an old tree that dies or is cut down. **Renewable resources** can regenerate if they are alive or can be replenished by biochemical cycles if they are nonliving. However, a renewable resource is not necessarily unlimited. Fresh water, for example, is a renewable resource that can easily become limited by drought or overuse.

▼ **Figure 6–7 Natural resources can be classified as renewable or nonrenewable.** The grass growing in these pastures is a renewable resource—as long as the number of sheep grazing there is limited.

A **nonrenewable resource** is one that cannot be replenished by natural processes. The fossil fuels coal, oil, and natural gas are nonrenewable resources. Fossil fuels formed over hundreds of millions of years from deeply buried organic materials. When these fuels are depleted, they are gone forever.

The classification of a resource as renewable or nonrenewable depends on its context. Although a single tree is renewable, a population of trees in a forest ecosystem—on which a community of organisms depends—may not be renewable, because that ecosystem may change forever once those trees are gone.

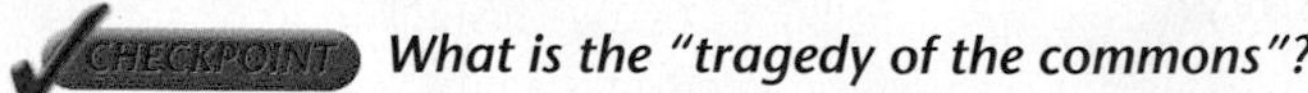
CHECKPOINT *What is the "tragedy of the commons"?*

Sustainable Development

How can we provide for our needs while maintaining ecosystem goods and services that are renewable? The concept of sustainable development is one answer to this major question. **Sustainable development** is a way of using natural resources without depleting them and of providing for human needs without causing long-term environmental harm.

Human activities can affect the quality and supply of renewable resources such as land, forests, fisheries, air, and fresh water. Ecological research can help us understand how human activities affect the functioning of ecosystems. To work well, sustainable development must take into account both the functioning of ecosystems and the ways that human economic systems operate. Sustainable strategies must enable people to live comfortably and improve their situation. The use of insects to control insect pests, as shown in **Figure 6–8,** is one such strategy. In finding sustainable-development strategies, ecological research can have a practical, positive impact on the environment we create for ourselves and future generations.

▲ **Figure 6–8** This ladybug is eating an insect pest—a black aphid. New strategies for pest control that employ beneficial insects may help farmers reduce the use of pesticides. **Inferring** *How does biological pest control contribute to sustainable development?*

Land Resources

Land is a resource that provides space for human communities and raw materials for industry. Land also includes the soils in which crops are grown. If managed properly, soil is a renewable resource. Soil, however, can be permanently damaged if it is mismanaged.

Food crops grow best in fertile soil, which is a mixture of sand, clay, rock particles, and humus (material from decayed organisms). Most of the humus that makes soil fertile is in the uppermost layer of the soil, called topsoil. Good topsoil absorbs and retains moisture yet allows excess water to drain. It is rich in nutrients but low in salts. Such soil is produced by long-term interactions between the soil and plants growing in it. Much agricultural land in the American Midwest, for example, was once covered by prairie ecosystems that produced and maintained a meter or more of very fertile topsoil. Deep roots of long-lived grasses held soil in place against rain and wind.

Plowing the land removes the roots that hold the soil in place. This increases the rate of **soil erosion**—the wearing away of surface soil by water and wind. A typical field on the High Plains of the Midwest loses roughly 47 metric tons of topsoil per hectare every year! In certain parts of the world with dry climates, a combination of farming, overgrazing, and drought has turned once productive areas into deserts, as shown in **Figure 6–9.** This process is called **desertification.** There are, however, a variety of sustainable-development practices that can guard against these problems. One practice is contour plowing, in which fields are plowed across the slope of the land to reduce erosion. Other strategies include leaving the stems and roots of the previous year's crop in place to help hold the soil and planting a field with rye rather than leaving it unprotected from erosion.

▼ **Figure 6–9** **Human activities affect the supply and the quality of renewable resources.** In dry regions, human activities, such as farming practices that fail to protect the soil, can contribute to desertification.

Forest Resources

Earth's forests are an important resource for the products they provide and for the ecological functions they perform. People use the wood from forests to make products ranging from homes to paper. In many parts of the world, wood is still burned as fuel for cooking and heating. But living forests also provide a number of important ecological services. Forests have been called "lungs of the Earth" because they remove carbon dioxide and produce oxygen. Forests also store nutrients, provide habitats and food for organisms, moderate climate, limit soil erosion, and protect freshwater supplies.

Whether a forest can be considered a renewable resource depends partly on the type of forest. For example, the temperate forests of the northeastern United States can be considered renewable. Most of these forests have been logged at least once in the past and have grown back naturally. However, today's forests differ somewhat in species composition from the forests they replaced.

Other forests, such as those in Alaska and the Pacific Northwest, are called old-growth forests because they have never before been cut. Worldwide, about half of the area originally covered by forests and woodlands has been cleared. Because it takes many centuries to produce old-growth forests, they are in effect nonrenewable resources. Old-growth forests often contain a rich variety of species. When logging occurs in these forests, the species they contain may be lost.

▼ **Figure 6–10** Planting new trees is one way to counteract the effects of deforestation. **Applying Concepts** *What are two ways in which reforestation might affect the biosphere?*

Deforestation Loss of forests, or **deforestation,** has several effects. Deforestation can lead to severe erosion as soil is exposed to heavy rains. Erosion can wash away nutrients in the topsoil. Grazing or plowing after deforestation can cause permanent changes to local soils and microclimates that in turn prevent the regrowth of trees.

Forest Management There are a variety of sustainable-development strategies for forest management. In some forests, mature trees can be harvested selectively to promote the growth of younger trees and preserve the forest ecosystem. In areas where forests have already been cut, foresters today often plant, manage, harvest, and replant tree farms, as shown in **Figure 6–10.** Tree farms can now be planted and harvested efficiently, making them fully renewable resources. Tree geneticists are also breeding new, faster-growing tree varieties that produce high-quality wood.

What is deforestation?

Fishery Resources

Fishes and other animals that live in water are a valuable source of food for humanity. For example, consider the food provided by the Chesapeake Bay and its watershed, which includes the saltwater bay itself and the freshwater rivers and streams that flow into it. This complex ecosystem supplies people with fishes such as striped bass and American shad, and shellfishes such as crabs and oysters. The recent history of fisheries, or fishing grounds, is an example of the tragedy of the commons. Fortunately, it also shows how ecological research can help people begin to correct an environmental problem.

Overfishing Overfishing, or harvesting fish faster than they can be replaced by reproduction, greatly reduced the amount of fish in parts of the world's oceans. Between 1950 and 1990, the world fish catch grew from 19 million tons to more than 90 million tons. The fish that were caught helped feed the world's people. But as the catch increased, the populations of some fish species began to shrink. By the early 1990s, populations of cod and haddock had dropped so low that researchers feared these fishes might disappear from the sea.

The declining fish populations are an example of the tragedy of the commons. People from several countries were taking advantage of a resource—fisheries—but no one took responsibility for maintaining that resource. Until fairly recently, fisheries seemed to be a renewable resource, one that could be harvested indefinitely. But overfishing threatened to destroy what was once a renewable resource.

Sustainable Development Is there a way to manage fisheries sustainably? That's where ecological research has entered the picture. Fishery ecologists gathered data on the size of fish populations and their growth rate. The U.S. National Marine Fisheries Service used these data to create guidelines for United States commercial fishing. The guidelines specified how many fish, and of what size, could be caught in various parts of the oceans. The regulations are helping fish populations recover, as shown in **Figure 6–11.** The regulations caused loss of jobs in the short term, but are designed to protect the fishing industry for the future.

Aquaculture The raising of aquatic animals for human consumption, which is called **aquaculture,** is also helping to sustain fish resources. If not properly managed, aquaculture can pollute water and damage aquatic ecosystems. However, environment-friendly aquaculture techniques are being developed.

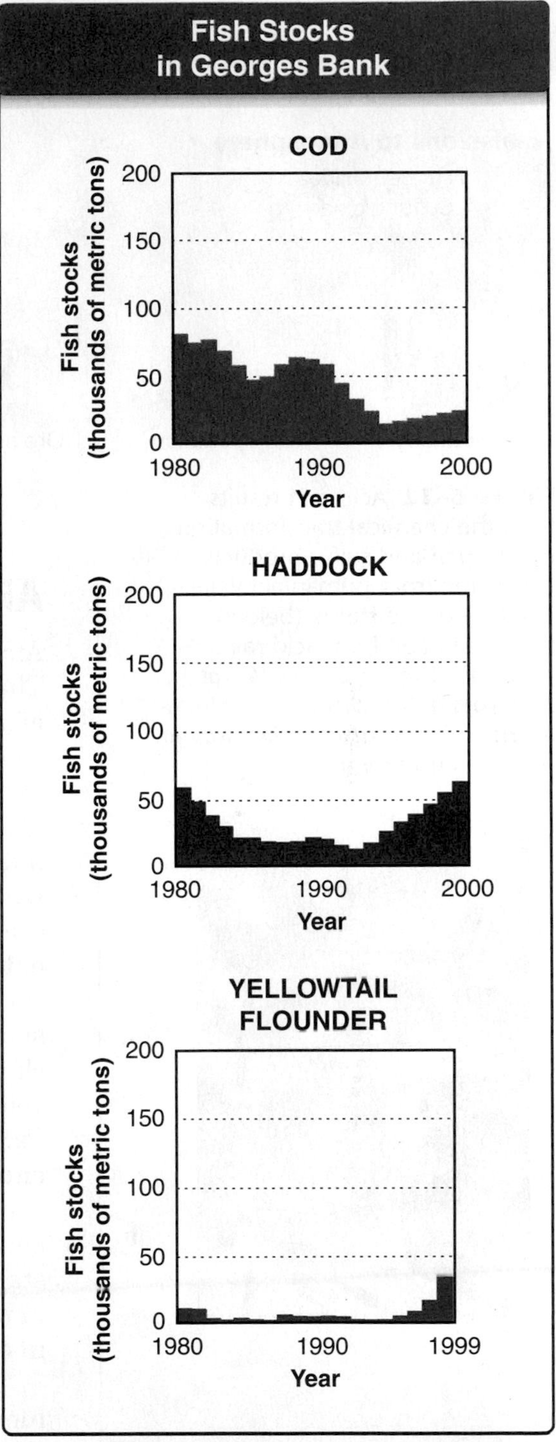

▲ **Figure 6–11** The graphs show how three fish populations—cod, haddock, and yellowtail flounder—have changed in Georges Bank, a fishery off the New England coast. The fish populations began to rise after regulations restricted commercial fishing. **Interpreting Graphics** *Describe the history of the cod population in Georges Bank between 1980 and 2000.*

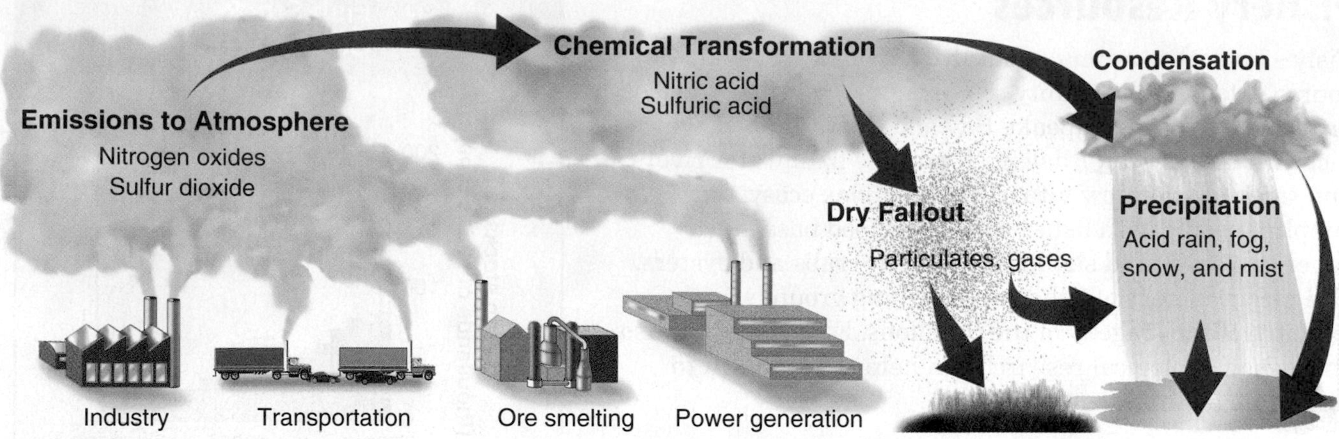

Figure 6–12 Acid rain results from the chemical transformation of nitrogen and sulfur products that come from human activities. The face of the statue (below) shows damage from acid rain. **Interpreting Graphics** *What pathways do the chemicals in atmospheric emissions take on their way to becoming acid rain?*

Air Resources

Air is a common resource that we use every time we breathe. The condition of the air affects people's health. The preservation of air quality remains a challenge for modern society.

If you live in a large city, you have probably seen **smog,** a mixture of chemicals that occurs as a gray-brown haze in the atmosphere. Smog is primarily due to automobile exhausts and industrial emissions. Because it threatens the health of people with asthma and other respiratory conditions, smog is considered a pollutant. A **pollutant** is a harmful material that can enter the biosphere through the land, air, or water.

The burning of fossil fuels can release pollutants that cause smog and other problems in the atmosphere. Potentially toxic chemicals, like nitrates, sulfates, and particulates (pahr-TIK-yoo-lits), are especially troublesome in large concentrations. Particulates are microscopic particles of ash and dust that can enter the nose, mouth, and lungs, causing health problems over the long term. Today, most industries use technology to control emissions from factory smokestacks. Strict automobile emission standards and clean-air regulations have improved air quality in many American cities, but air pollution is an ongoing problem in other parts of the world.

Many combustion processes, such as the burning of fossil fuels, release nitrogen and sulfur compounds into the atmosphere. When these compounds combine with water vapor in the air, they form drops of nitric and sulfuric acids. These strong acids can drift for many kilometers before they fall as **acid rain.** Acid rain can kill plants by damaging their leaves and changing the chemistry of soils and standing-water ecosystems. Acid rain may also dissolve and release toxic elements, such as mercury, from the soil, freeing those elements to enter other portions of the biosphere. **Figure 6–12** shows the processes that lead to the formation of acid rain.

What is a pollutant?

For: Articles on natural resources and pollution
Visit: PHSchool.com
Web Code: cbe-2062

Freshwater Resources

Americans use billions of liters of fresh water daily for everything from drinking and washing to watering crops and making steel. Although water is a renewable resource, the total supply of fresh water is limited. For this reason, protecting water supplies from pollution and managing society's ever-growing demand for water are major priorities.

Pollution threatens water supplies in several ways. Improperly discarded chemicals can enter streams and rivers. Wastes discarded on land can seep through soil and enter underground water supplies that we tap with wells. Domestic sewage, which is the wastewater from sinks and toilets, contains nitrogen and phosphorous compounds that can encourage the growth of algae and bacteria in aquatic habitats. Sewage can also contain microorganisms that can spread disease among humans and animals. In this country, most cities and towns now treat their sewage in order to make it safer.

One way of ensuring the sustainable use of water resources is to protect the natural systems involved in the water cycle. For example, wetlands such as the one shown in **Figure 6–13** can help to purify the water passing through them. As water flows slowly through a swamp, densely growing plants filter certain pollutants out of the water. Similarly, forests and other vegetation help to purify the water that seeps into the ground or runs off into rivers and lakes.

As demand for water grows rapidly in many parts of the United States, water conservation is becoming an increasingly important aspect of sustainable development. There are many strategies for conserving water—in homes, industry, and agriculture. More than three quarters of all water consumed in this country is used in agriculture, so conservation in this area can save large amounts of water. For example, drip irrigation delivers water directly to plant roots. This reduces the amount of water lost through evaporation.

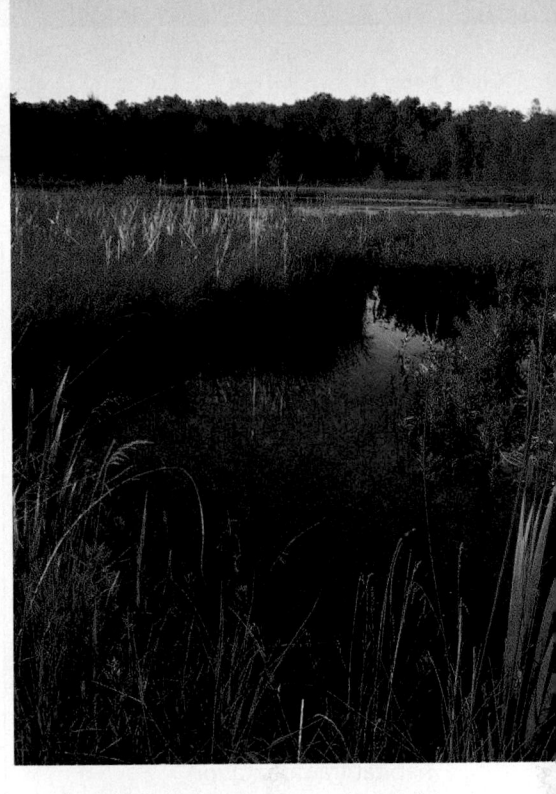

▲ **Figure 6–13** Wetlands provide a valuable ecosystem service by filtering certain pollutants from the water. **Applying Concepts** *How does this filtering process happen?*

6–2 Section Assessment

1. **Key Concept** What is the difference between a renewable and a nonrenewable resource?
2. **Key Concept** List two human activities that affect land resources, and explain the changes that can result. Do the same for air and water resources.
3. How does the decline in world fisheries represent a "tragedy of the commons"?
4. Identify two ways in which environmental resources are important to human health.
5. **Critical Thinking Applying Concepts** Describe sustainable development strategies to manage forests as a renewable resource.

Writing in Science

Cause-Effect Paragraph
Write a paragraph explaining the effect of fishing restrictions on fish populations. Your paragraph should explain why the regulations were needed as well as the effect of the regulations. *Hint*: For specific details to include, look at **Figure 6–11.**

6–3 Biodiversity

1-S1.1 Values are essential in applying scientific knowledge
4-6.2 Biodiversity and the stability of an ecosystem
4-7.2 Humans altering ecosystems
4-7.2 Industrialization increases demand for resources
4-7 Assessing risks, costs, and benefits of actions

Guide for Reading

Key Concepts
- What is the value of biodiversity?
- What are the current threats to biodiversity?
- What is the goal of conservation biology?

Vocabulary
biodiversity
ecosystem diversity
species diversity
genetic diversity
extinction
endangered species
habitat fragmentation
biological magnification
invasive species
conservation

Reading Strategy: Asking Questions Before you read, rewrite the headings in the section as *how, why,* or *what* questions about biodiversity. As you read, write brief answers to your questions.

Those of us who love nature find much to admire in the many forms of life that surround us. We marvel at the soaring flight of an eagle, the majestic movements of a whale, and the colors of spring wildflowers. "Variety," the saying goes, "is the spice of life." But variety in the biosphere gives us more than just interesting things to look at. Human society takes part in local and global food webs and energy cycles, and depends on both the physical and biological life-support systems of our planet. For that reason, our well-being is closely tied to the well-being of a great variety of other organisms—including many that are neither majestic nor beautiful to our eyes.

The Value of Biodiversity

Another word for variety is diversity. Therefore, biological diversity, or **biodiversity,** is the sum total of the genetically based variety of all organisms in the biosphere. **Ecosystem diversity** includes the variety of habitats, communities, and ecological processes in the living world. **Species diversity** refers to the number of different species in the biosphere. So far, biologists have identified and named about 1.5 million species and estimate that millions more may be discovered in the future. **Genetic diversity** refers to the sum total of all the different forms of genetic information carried by all organisms living on Earth today. Within each species, genetic diversity refers to the total of all different forms of genes present in that species. You will read about genetic information later in the book.

Biodiversity is one of Earth's greatest natural resources. Species of many kinds have provided us with foods, industrial products, and medicines—including painkillers, antibiotics, heart drugs, antidepressants, and anticancer drugs. For example, the rosy periwinkle plant in **Figure 6–14** is the source of substances used to treat certain cancers. The biodiversity represented by wild plants and animals is a kind of "library" of genetic information upon which humans can draw for future use. For example, most crop plants have wild relatives with useful traits such as resistance to disease or pests. When biodiversity is lost, potential sources of material with significant value to the biosphere and to humankind may be lost with it.

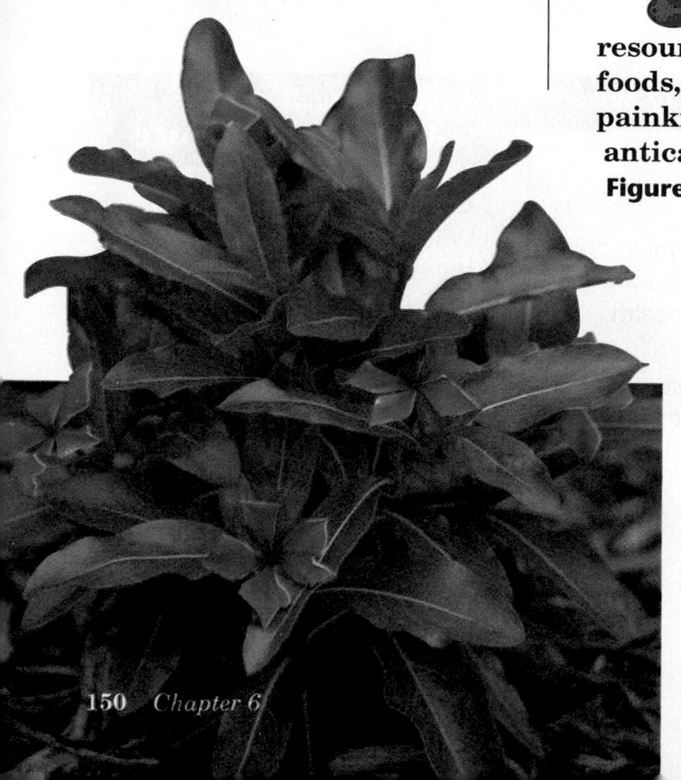

◀ **Figure 6–14** **Biodiversity is one of Earth's greatest natural resources. Species of many kinds have provided us with foods, industrial products, and medicines.** The rosy periwinkle is a pink-petaled flowering plant native only to Madagascar. Drugs derived from this plant, such as vincristine, are used to treat certain cancers, including leukemia.

Threats to Biodiversity

Human activity can reduce biodiversity by altering habitats, hunting species to extinction, introducing toxic compounds into food webs, and introducing foreign species to new environments. As human activities alter ecosystems, this may lead to the extinction of species. **Extinction** occurs when a species disappears from all or part of its range. A species whose population size is declining in a way that places it in danger of extinction is called an **endangered species.** As the population of an endangered species declines, the species loses genetic diversity—an effect that can make it even more vulnerable to extinction.

▲ **Figure 6–15** **Human activity can reduce biodiversity by altering habitats, hunting species to extinction, introducing toxic compounds into food webs, and introducing foreign species to new environments.** The Carolina parakeet was once common in the southeastern United States. This colorful bird was hunted to extinction by the early twentieth century because its feathers were in demand to decorate hats.

Habitat Alteration

When land is developed, natural habitats may be destroyed. Habitats supply organisms' needs, and they are a limited resource. Species' long-term survival depends on the preservation of this limited resource.

As habitats disappear, the species that live in those habitats vanish. In addition, development often splits ecosystems into pieces, a process called **habitat fragmentation.** As a result, remaining pieces of habitat become biological "islands." We usually think of islands as bits of land surrounded by water. But a biological island can be any patch of habitat surrounded by a different habitat. New York's Central Park is an island of trees and grass in a sea of concrete. In suburbs, patches of forest can be surrounded by farms, houses, and shopping malls. Habitat islands are very different from large, continuous ecosystems. The smaller the "island," the fewer species can live there, the smaller their populations can be, and the more vulnerable they are to further disturbance or climate change.

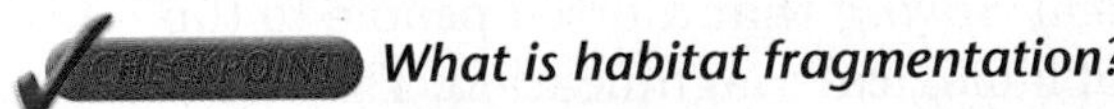
What is habitat fragmentation?

Demand for Wildlife Products

Throughout history, humans have pushed some animal species to extinction by hunting them for food or other products. In the 1800s, hunting caused the extinction of species such as the Carolina parakeet, in **Figure 6–15,** and the passenger pigeon.

Today, in the United States, endangered species are protected from hunting. Hunting, however, still threatens rare animals in parts of Africa, South America, and Southeast Asia. Some species are hunted for meat, fur, or hides. Others are hunted because people think that their body parts such as horns have medicinal properties. The Convention on International Trade in Endangered Species, CITES, bans international trade in products derived from a list of endangered species. Unfortunately, it is difficult to enforce laws in remote wilderness areas.

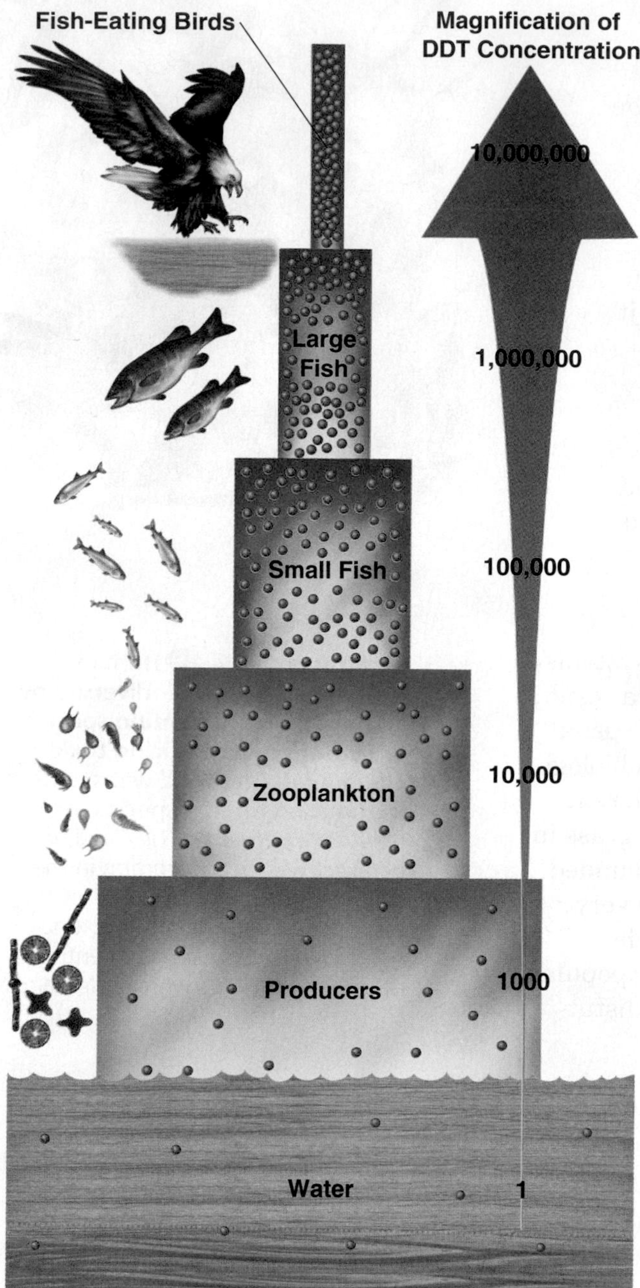

▲ **Figure 6–16** In the process of biological magnification, the concentration of a pollutant such as DDT—represented here by orange dots—is multiplied as it passes up the food chain from producers to consumers. By the time it reaches the top-level consumers, shown here as fish-eating birds, the amount of DDT in biological tissues can be magnified nearly 10 million times. **Calculating** *By what number is the concentration of DDT multiplied at each successive trophic level?*

Pollution

Many forms of pollution can threaten biodiversity, but one of the most serious problems occurs when toxic compounds accumulate in the tissues of organisms. The history of DDT, one of the first widely used pesticides, explains the situation well. At first, DDT seemed to be a perfect pesticide. It is cheap, remains active for a long time, kills many different insects, and can control agricultural pests and disease-carrying mosquitoes.

When DDT was sprayed, it drained into rivers and streams at low concentrations that seemed harmless. But DDT has two properties that make it hazardous. First, DDT is nonbiodegradable, which means that it is not broken down by metabolic processes in bacteria, plants, or animals. Second, when DDT is picked up by organisms, they do not eliminate it from their bodies. When aquatic plants pick up DDT from water, the pesticide is stored in their tissues. When herbivores eat those plants, they too store DDT. Because an herbivore eats many plants during its life, the DDT can become concentrated to levels ten times higher than levels found in the plants! When carnivores eat herbivores, the toxic substance is concentrated further, as shown in **Figure 6–16.** In this process, called **biological magnification,** concentrations of a harmful substance increase in organisms at higher trophic levels in a food chain or food web. Biological magnification affects the entire food web, although top-level carnivores are at highest risk.

In 1962, biologist Rachel Carson wrote a book called *Silent Spring* that alerted people to the dangers of biological magnification. The widespread spraying of DDT over many years had threatened populations of many animals—especially fish-eating birds like the osprey, brown pelican, and bald eagle—with extinction. One effect of DDT was to make eggs of these birds so fragile that the eggs could not survive intact. By the early 1970s, DDT was banned in the United States and in most other industrialized countries. In the years since, scientists have noted a marked recovery in the populations of birds that had been affected. Bald eagles, for example, can once again be seen around rivers, lakes, and estuaries in the lower 48 states.

CHECKPOINT *What is biological magnification?*

Quick Lab

How does biological magnification occur?

Materials paper cups (3 small, 1 medium, and 1 large); 1-L beaker; sand; 12 beads; masking tape

Procedure  

1. Use a pencil to punch five holes in the bottom of each paper cup. Place tape over the outsides of the holes. The small cups represent grasshoppers, the medium-sized cup represents an insect-eating lizard, and the large cup represents a hawk.
2. Half-fill each small cup with sand and 4 beads. The sand represents food. The beads represent a chlorinated pesticide.
3. Hold each small cup over a beaker to catch the sand and remove the tape. The sand that flows out of the cup represents digested food. Record the number of beads in each cup.
4. To model the effects of biological magnification on the lizard, empty the contents of the three small cups into the medium-sized cup. Repeat step 3 with the medium-sized cup.
5. Empty your medium-sized cup and those of two classmates into a large cup to model a hawk eating the lizard. Repeat step 3 with the large cup.

Analyze and Conclude

1. **Inferring** Which animals accumulated the most pesticide?
2. **Predicting** Which level of the food chain is most affected by biological magnification?

Introduced Species

One of the most important threats to biodiversity today comes from an unexpected source: apparently harmless plants and animals that humans transport around the world either accidentally or intentionally. Introduced into new habitats, these organisms often become **invasive species** that reproduce rapidly. Invasive species increase their populations because their new habitat lacks the parasites and predators that control their population "back home."

Hundreds of invasive species, including the one in **Figure 6–17**, are already causing ecological problems in the United States. Zebra mussels, an aquatic pest, came on ships from Europe during the 1980s. They spread through the Great Lakes and several major rivers. These mussels reproduce and grow so quickly that they cause major ecological changes and are driving several native species close to extinction. There are also many examples on land. One European weed, the leafy spurge, now infests millions of hectares of grasslands across the Northern Great Plains, where it displaces native plants.

▶ **Figure 6–17** **Human activity can reduce biodiversity by introducing foreign species to new environments.** Native to South America, nutrias have become pests in coastal areas of the southeastern United States. These furry rodents eat water plants that protect fragile shorelines from erosion. This destroys the habitats of species native to those ecosystems.

Conserving Biodiversity

Most people would like to preserve Earth's biodiversity for future generations. In ecology, the term **conservation** is used to describe the wise management of natural resources, including the preservation of habitats and wildlife. The modern science of conservation biology seeks to protect biodiversity. To do so requires detailed information about ecological relationships—such as the way natural populations use their habitats—and integrates information from other scientific disciplines, such as genetics, geography, and natural resource management.

Strategies for Conservation Many conservation efforts are aimed at managing individual species to keep them from becoming extinct. Some zoos, for example, have established captive breeding programs, in which young animals are raised in protected surroundings until the population is stable, then are later returned to the wild. This strategy has succeeded with a few species, including the black-footed ferret. **Today, conservation efforts focus on protecting entire ecosystems as well as single species. Protecting an ecosystem will ensure that the natural habitats and the interactions of many different species are preserved at the same time.** This effort is a much bigger challenge. Governments and conservation groups worldwide are working to set aside land, or expand existing areas, as parks and reserves.

Biology and History

Success in Conservation

Human activity can have a dramatic impact on the biosphere, to the point where other forms of life are threatened. Many efforts have been made to protect and preserve Earth's natural environments.

1854
Henry David Thoreau
Thoreau recommends the preservation of wildlife. In his book *Walden,* he cautions against seeking to dominate nature and suggests living in harmony with it.

1872
Yellowstone becomes the world's first national park.

1896
Harriet Hemenway
Hemenway and her cousin, Minna Hall, petition in Boston for legislation to prevent the extinction of birds due to unregulated hunting. By refusing to buy or wear plumed hats, the two cousins are among the first founders of the conservation movement.

1900
Lacey Act
Enacted by the U.S. Congress, the Lacey Act is the first major national conservation law. Transporting illegally killed animals across state borders becomes a federal crime.

1900

The United States has an extensive system of national parks, forests, and other protected areas. Marine sanctuaries are being designated to protect resources such as coral reefs and marine mammals. However, these areas may not be large enough, or contain the right resources, to protect biodiversity.

Protecting species and ecosystem diversity in many places around the world is an enormous challenge. As part of the effort to locate problem areas and set up a list of priorities, conservation biologists often identify biodiversity "hot spots," including those shown in **Figure 6–18** on the following page. Each hot spot is a place where significant numbers of habitats and species are in immediate danger of extinction as a result of human activity. The hot-spot strategy may help scientists and governments to focus their efforts where they are most needed.

Conservation Challenges Protecting resources for the future can require people to change the way they earn their living today. Regulations that restrict fishing, for example, can impose severe financial hardships on fishers for several years. That's why conservation regulations must be informed by solid research, and must try to maximize benefits while minimizing economic costs. But an ecological perspective tells us that if we do not take some difficult steps today, some resources may disappear. If that happens, many jobs that depend on ecosystem goods and services, such as fishing, will be lost permanently.

Why is it important to preserve entire ecosystems?

Writing in Science

Choose and research a specific endangered species and its habitat. Then, write a proposal that explains the problem and offers one or more possible conservation efforts for that species.

1933
Civilian Conservation Corps
President Roosevelt establishes the CCC, providing work in reforestation, prevention of soil erosion, and park and flood control projects.

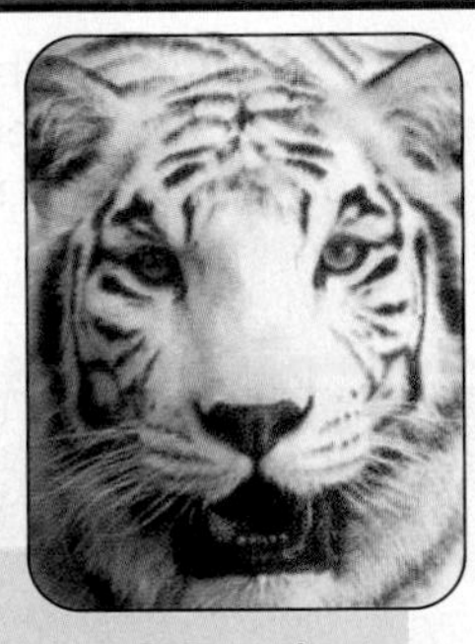

1966
Endangered Species Preservation Act
This act allows for the identification of and research on endangered species.

1970
Earth Day
The first celebration takes place in New York to rally against pollution and population overgrowth.

1992
Earth Summit
A United Nations conference in Brazil seeks international solutions for environmental issues, including the worldwide loss of species.

1950 2000

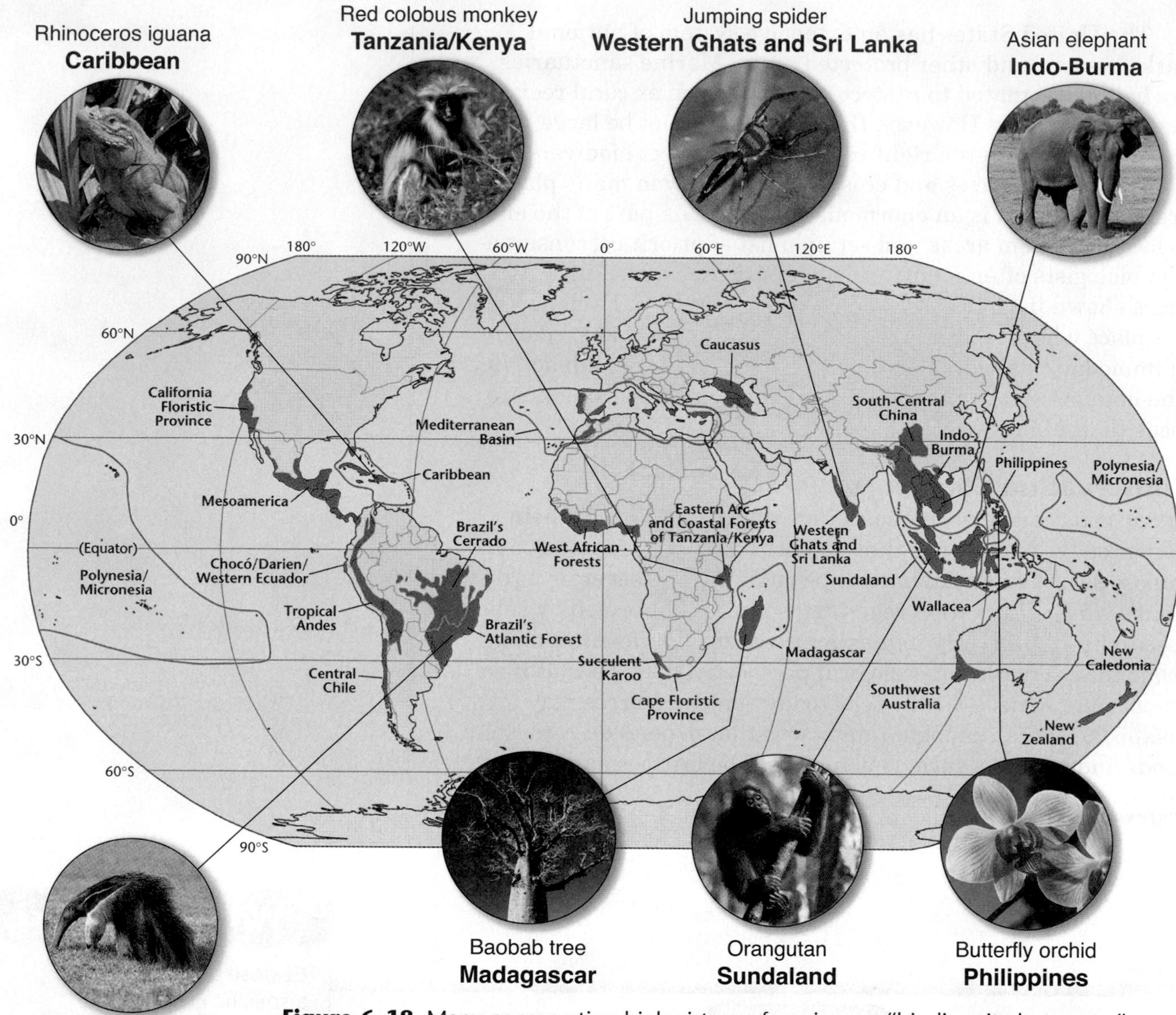

Figure 6–18 Many conservation biologists are focusing on "biodiversity hot spots," where the biodiversity of these unique ecosystems is threatened. The hot spots are shown in orange on the map. **By focusing on protecting specific ecosystems, biologists hope to preserve global biodiversity.**

6–3 Section Assessment

1. **Key Concept** Why is biodiversity worth preserving?
2. **Key Concept** List four activities that can threaten biodiversity.
3. **Key Concept** What is the current focus of conservation biologists worldwide?
4. Explain the relationship between habitat size and species diversity.
5. Why are habitats limited resources? How might their destruction affect the long-term survival of species?
6. **Critical Thinking Predicting** What problems could result if an endangered species were introduced into a nonnative habitat?

Connecting Concepts

Exploring Biomes
Review biomes in Chapter 4. Then, choose one of the hot spots shown above. Find out about the biome in which these unique ecosystems and endangered species occur. Report on your findings and suggest specific actions that can be taken to preserve the biome's biodiversity.

6–4 Charting a Course for the Future

1-S1.1 Values are essential in applying scientific knowledge
4-6.3 Ecosystems can be altered by climatic changes
4-7.1 Consumption of finite resources causes stress
4-7.1 Humans are changing many natural processes
4-7.2 Industrialization increases demand for energy

For most of human history, environmental change was a local affair. For example, many animals in the Hawaiian islands became extinct after humans arrived there. The effect of these extinctions on the biosphere at large was negligible. Since your parents and grandparents were born, however, global human population has grown from around 2.5 billion to more than 6.1 billion! Today, much of Earth's land surface has been altered by human activity.

In order to plan a sound environmental strategy for the twenty-first century, we need data provided by research. This research requires information from geology, chemistry, physics, and meteorology, as well as ecology.  **Researchers are gathering data to monitor and evaluate the effects of human activities on important systems in the biosphere. Two of these systems are the ozone layer high in the atmosphere and the global climate system.** Scientists' investigations of these two systems—and the actions taken as a result—show how research can have a positive impact on the global environment.

Guide for Reading

Key Concept
- What are two types of global change of concern to biologists?

Vocabulary
ozone layer
global warming

Reading Strategy: Summarizing As you read, find the key concept in the section. Write down a few words or phrases from the key concept, then use them in a summary of Section 6–4.

Ozone Depletion

Between 20 and 50 kilometers above Earth's surface, the atmosphere contains a relatively high concentration of ozone gas called the **ozone layer.** Molecules of ozone consist of three oxygen atoms. Although ozone at ground level is a pollutant, the naturally occurring ozone layer serves an important function. It absorbs a good deal of harmful ultraviolet, or UV, radiation from sunlight before it reaches Earth's surface. You may know that overexposure to UV radiation is the principal cause of sunburn. You may not know that exposure to UV can also cause cancer, damage eyes, and decrease organisms' resistance to disease. Intense UV radiation can also damage tissue in plant leaves and even phytoplankton in the oceans. Thus, by shielding the biosphere from UV light, the ozone layer serves as a global sunscreen.

Early Evidence Beginning in the 1970s, scientists found evidence from satellite data that the ozone layer was in trouble. The first problem sign was a gap, or "hole," in the ozone layer over Antarctica during winter. Since it was first discovered, the ozone hole has grown larger and lasted longer. A similar ozone hole also appeared over the Arctic. In 1974, a research team including Mario Molina of the Massachusetts Institute of Technology and F. Sherwood Rowland of the University of California at Irvine published data showing that gases called chlorofluorocarbons, or CFCs, could damage the ozone layer.

▼ **Figure 6–19** **Many biologists are concerned about the thinning of the ozone layer.** This image, taken by satellite in 2001, shows the thinning of the ozone layer in the Southern Hemisphere. The image is color-coded, with yellow being the area with the highest concentration of ozone and blue the lowest. The ozone hole is the bright blue area surrounding Antarctica.

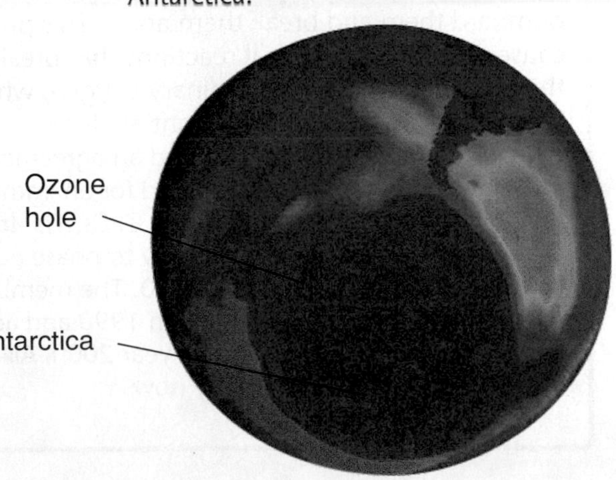

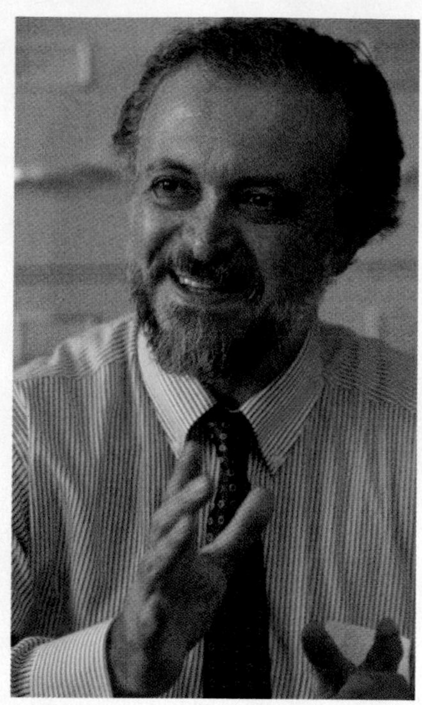

◀ **Figure 6–20** Mario Molina (left), F. Sherwood Rowland, and Paul Crutzen shared the Nobel Prize in 1995 for their research on factors that can destroy ozone. **Applying Concepts** *What action did nations take to deal with the ozone hole?*

One Solution CFCs were once widely used as propellants in aerosol cans; as coolant in refrigerators, freezers, and air conditioners; and in the production of plastic foams. Because of the research of Molina, Rowland, and other scientists, the United States and many other nations began reducing the use of CFCs in 1987. Today, most uses of CFCs are banned.

Because CFC molecules can linger for as long as a century, their effects are not yet over. But the level of chlorine from CFCs in the atmosphere has already begun to fall, indicating that the CFC ban will have positive, long-term effects on the global environment. Current data predict that the ozone holes should shrink and disappear within 50 years.

What is ozone depletion?

Analyzing Data

Banning CFCs

A layer of ozone is normally present in Earth's upper atmosphere, or stratosphere. The ozone layer prevents much of the ultraviolet light emitted by the sun from reaching Earth's surface. In the 1970s, scientists noticed that ozone levels in the stratosphere were dropping. Evidence indicated that this was caused by the introduction of chlorofluorocarbons into the atmosphere.

In the lower atmosphere, CFCs are stable. However, when CFCs are carried into the stratosphere, UV rays bombard them and break them apart. This process causes a series of chemical reactions that break down the ozone molecules into ordinary oxygen, which offers no protection from UV light at all.

In 1987, forty-six nations signed an agreement called the Montreal Protocol, which called for an immediate reduction in production and use of CFCs. The following year, the United States passed a law to phase out the use of CFCs in aerosol cans by 2000. The members of the Montreal Protocol met again in 1990 and agreed to end the use of most CFCs by the year 2000. All of these resolutions have taken effect by now.

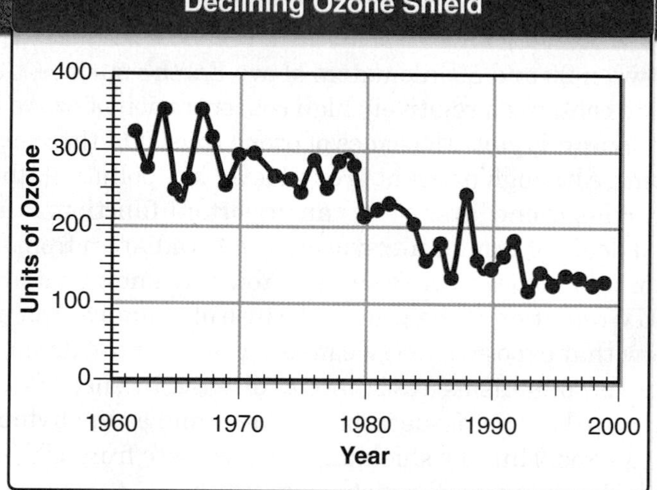

The graph shows ozone levels in the stratosphere from the 1960s to the late 1990s. Use the graph to answer the following questions.

1. **Using Tables and Graphs** Describe the general trend shown by the graph.
2. **Using Tables and Graphs** In what year did ozone drop to its lowest level?
3. **Applying Concepts** What happened between 1995 and 1999? Relate this to international actions regarding CFCs.

Global Climate Change

All life on Earth depends on climate conditions such as temperature and rainfall. That's why many ecologists are concerned about strong evidence that climate is changing. Since the late nineteenth century, average atmospheric temperatures on Earth's surface have risen about 0.6 Celsius degrees. Data from sources such as the National Oceanic and Atmospheric Administration indicate that since about 1980, average temperatures have risen between 0.2 and 0.3 Celsius degrees. The 1990s were the warmest decade ever recorded, and 1998 was the warmest year since record-keeping began. The term used to describe this increase in the average temperature of the biosphere is **global warming.** One sign of global warming is melting polar ice, as shown in **Figure 6–21.**

For: Links on global warming
Visit: www.SciLinks.org
Web Code: cbn-2064

Evidence of Global Warming The geological record shows that Earth's climate has changed repeatedly during its history. Therefore, researchers must determine whether the current warming trend is part of a larger, natural cycle of climate change, or whether it is caused by human activity. Research focuses on describing the warming trend, determining its cause, and predicting its effects on the biosphere.

The most widely accepted hypothesis is that current warming is related, at least in part, to human activities that are adding carbon dioxide and other greenhouse gases to the atmosphere. According to this hypothesis, the burning of fossil fuels, combined with the cutting and burning of forests worldwide, is adding carbon dioxide to the atmosphere faster than the carbon cycle removes it. Data show that concentrations of carbon dioxide in the atmosphere have been rising for 200 years. As a result, the atmosphere's natural greenhouse effect is intensified, causing the atmosphere to retain more heat.

Possible Effects of Global Warming How far might this warming go and what might its effects be? Researchers attempt to answer these questions with computer models based on data. Because these models are complex and involve assumptions, their predictions are open to debate. Nevertheless, most recent models suggest that average global surface temperatures will increase by 1 to 2 Celsius degrees by the year 2050.

What might this change mean? Sea levels may rise enough to flood some coastal areas. Flooding would affect coastal ecosystems as well as human communities. Some models suggest that parts of North America may experience more droughts during the summer growing season. Any long-term change in climate will affect ecosystems. New organisms may be able to live in places where they once could not. Other organisms may become threatened or extinct in areas where they once thrived.

Researchers are continuing to gather data and will use the data to refine current models. The new information should help provide society with ways of dealing with climate change.

▼ **Figure 6–21** **Biologists are concerned about global warming.** This map of the Arctic is based on images taken by satellites in 1979 and 1999. Sea ice in the Arctic Ocean has receded so quickly that some scientists suggest that, within the next 50 years, the ice could disappear completely.

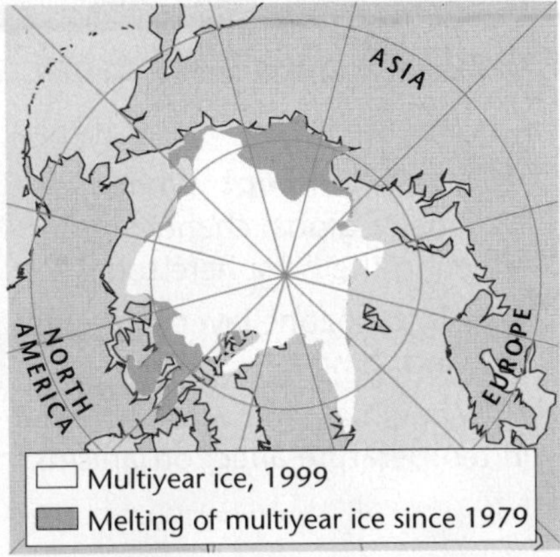

Ecosystem Services
Solar Energy
Production of oxygen
Storage and recycling of nutrients
Regulation of climate
Purification of water and air
Storage and distribution of fresh water
Food production
Nursery habitats for wildlife
Detoxification of human and industrial waste
Natural pest and disease control
Management of soil erosion and runoff

▲ **Figure 6–22** Human society depends on healthy, diverse, and productive ecosystems because of the environmental and economic benefits they provide. **Classifying** ***Should the ecosystem services in the chart be considered renewable or nonrenewable resources? Explain.***

The Value of a Healthy Biosphere

You might wonder why ecologists work so hard to study what seem to be small environmental changes. To understand, remember the concept of ecosystem goods and services. As shown in **Figure 6–22,** these range from water purification to waste recycling. Ecosystems provide many services besides these, however, such as the pollination of many crop plants by insects. Ecosystems are also a reservoir of organisms that might one day provide humans with new medicines and new varieties of crops. There is much that we don't understand about the systems that provide these services. Biologists are therefore concerned that human activities might affect them in unexpected ways.

Is there any way that people can help maintain the health of the biosphere without drastically changing their lifestyles? The answer is yes. People can make wise choices in the use and conservation of resources. For example, when people water gardens or take showers, they can avoid using more water than necessary. Like the Polynesians who settled Hawaii, people can plant trees to replace the ones they have cut down. Trash and other wastes can often be reused or recycled, and dangerous chemical wastes can be disposed in a way that does not harm ecosystems. Many communities now have facilities for recycling trash and methods of safely removing hazardous materials.

Studies of human impact on the environment are not about predicting disaster. You have seen how research led to actions that are replenishing fisheries in the North Atlantic and preserving the ozone layer. The biosphere is strong. Humans are very clever. Both humans and natural ecosystems can adapt to change of different kinds.

6–4 Section Assessment

1. **Key Concept** What are two major global changes affecting the biosphere today?
2. Why is the ozone layer important to living things?
3. How could a worldwide increase in temperature affect organisms?
4. What actions can people take in their daily lives to make wise choices in the use and conservation of resources?
5. **Thinking Critically Evaluating** Evaluate the impact of environmental research on the problem of ozone depletion. How did research identify the cause of the problem? To what action did this research lead?

You & Your Community

Comparing Media
Locate five print, radio, television, or Internet sources about global warming or the ozone hole. What attitudes and opinions are expressed in these sources? Compare them with the information in this section.

Observing the Effects of Acid Rain

Acid rain is formed when the combustion of fossil fuels releases gases containing nitrogen and sulfur compounds into the atmosphere. It can damage crops, forests, soil, and buildings. In this investigation, you will design and perform an experiment to simulate and test the effect of acid rain on the germination of seeds.

Problem

How does acid rain affect the germination of seeds?

Materials

- diluted sulfuric acid
- filter paper
- glass-marking pencil
- 2 petri dishes
- 100-mL graduated cylinder
- 100 seeds (mustard or radish)
- pH paper
- 2 100-mL beakers
- hand lens

Skills

Designing Experiments, Controlling Variables

Design Your Experiment

1. **Formulating Hypotheses** Use your knowledge of acid rain to develop a hypothesis about its effect on plant growth and development. Record your hypothesis.
2. **Predicting** Record a prediction about how acid rain will affect seed germination.
3. Design an experiment to test your prediction. It is not practical in the classroom to expose some plants to acid rain and others to rain without acid. You will need to choose a way to simulate acid rain.
4. As you plan your investigative procedures, refer to the Lab Tips box on page 55 for information on demonstrating safe practices, making wise choices in the use of materials, and selecting equipment and technology. With your teacher's guidance, select the equipment and technology to use to measure pH: either pH paper or a pH probe. If using a pH probe, see your teacher for instructions.
5. Check your experimental design to make sure you are testing only one variable and have included any necessary controls. Construct any data tables you will need to use for recording the results of your experiment. With your teacher's approval, carry out your experiment. **CAUTION:** *Wear goggles, an apron, and plastic gloves when handling diluted sulfuric acid.* Wash your hands thoroughly with soap and warm water before leaving the lab.

Analyze and Conclude

1. **Analyzing Data** What percentage of your control seeds germinated? What percentage of your acid-treated seeds germinated?
2. **Drawing Conclusions** What do your results imply about the short-term effects of acid rain?
3. **Predicting** Would you expect acid rain to injure plants after they have completed germination? Explain your answer.
4. **SAFETY** Explain how you demonstrated safe practices as you carried out this investigation.
5. **Asking Questions** What additional questions might you ask about the effects of acid rain on plants? (*Hint:* Think about seedlings that have already germinated.) Describe an experiment that might provide the answer.

Go Further

Problem Solving Conduct research and report to the class on the various methods used in industry to reduce the amounts of sulfur dioxide and nitrogen oxides being emitted into the atmosphere.

Chapter 6 Study Guide

6–1 A Changing Landscape

Key Concept

- Among human activities that affect the biosphere are hunting and gathering, agriculture, industry, and urban development.

Vocabulary

agriculture, p. 141 • monoculture, p. 141
green revolution, p. 142

6–2 Renewable and Nonrenewable Resources

Key Concepts

- Environmental goods and services may be classified as either renewable or nonrenewable.
- Human activities can affect the quality and supply of renewable resources such as land, forests, fisheries, air, and fresh water.

Vocabulary

renewable resource, p. 144
nonrenewable resource, p. 144
sustainable development, p. 145
soil erosion, p. 145 • desertification, p. 145
deforestation, p. 146 • aquaculture, p. 147
smog, p. 148 • pollutant, p. 148
acid rain, p. 148

6–3 Biodiversity

Key Concepts

- Biodiversity is one of Earth's greatest natural resources. Many species have provided us with foods, industrial products, and medicines—including painkillers, antibiotics, heart drugs, antidepressants, and anticancer drugs.
- Human activity can reduce biodiversity by altering habitats, hunting species to extinction, introducing toxic compounds into food webs, and introducing foreign species to new environments.
- Today, conservation efforts focus on protecting entire ecosystems as well as single species. Protecting an ecosystem will ensure that the natural habitats and interactions of many different species are preserved at the same time.

Vocabulary

biodiversity, p. 150 • ecosystem diversity, p. 150
species diversity, p. 150 • genetic diversity, p. 150
extinction, p. 151 • endangered species, p. 151
habitat fragmentation, p. 151
biological magnification, p. 152
invasive species, p. 153 • conservation, p. 154

6–4 Charting a Course for the Future

Key Concept

- Researchers are gathering data to monitor and evaluate the effects of human activities on important systems in the biosphere. Two of these systems are the ozone layer high in the atmosphere and the global climate system.

Vocabulary

ozone layer, p. 157
global warming, p. 159

Thinking Visually

Using information from this chapter, complete the following concept map:

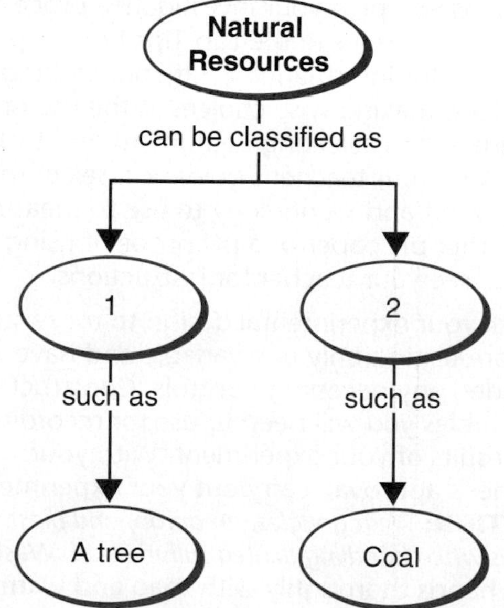

Preparing for the Living Environment Exam

NEW YORK LIVING ENVIRONMENT

Blue questions emphasize Regents Exam content

Chapter 6

Part A

Multiple Choice

For each statement or question, select the number of the word or expression that, of those given, best completes the statement or answers the question.

1 Which human activity is most responsible for the other three human activities?
(1) increasing demand for food
(2) increasing human population
(3) increasing loss of farmland
(4) increasing air pollution

2 When humans use more ground water for industry than is being replaced, the soil above the ground water may collapse and disrupt natural habitats. This human activity is an example of
(1) species exploitation
(2) renewal of natural resources
(3) a disposal problem
(4) poor use of finite resources

3 Which human activity has probably contributed most to the acidification of lakes in the Adirondack region?
(1) passing environmental protection laws
(2) establishing reforestation projects in lumbered areas
(3) burning fossil fuels that produce air pollutants containing sulfur and nitrogen
(4) using pesticides for the control of insects that feed on trees

4 Compared to a natural forest, the wheat field of a farmer *lacks*
(1) heterotrophs (3) autotrophs
(2) significant biodiversity (4) stored energy

5 Chittenango Falls State Park in central New York State is the only known habitat for an endangered species of aquatic snail. Contamination of its water supply and reduction of its habitat into isolated "islands" have threatened the future of this snail. Which step could be taken to protect this species of snail?
(1) banning human activities that damage the snail's habitat
(2) introducing a new snail predator into the habitat
(3) transferring the snail to a terrestrial environment
(4) crossbreeding the snail with another species

6 A species that enters an environment where it has not lived before
(1) always goes extinct
(2) mates with other species living there
(3) may not have natural enemies there
(4) will have no effect on the new environment

7 A species whose population size is declining and may become extinct is referred to as
(1) fragmented (3) biodiverse
(2) endangered (4) invasive

8 Ozone depletion is to CFCs as deforestation is to
(1) ozone (3) suburban sprawl
(2) soil erosion (4) pollution

9 Deforestation would most immediately result in
(1) the disappearance of native species
(2) industrialization of an area
(3) the depletion of the ozone shield
(4) global warming

10 In some areas, foresters plant one tree for every tree they cut. This activity is an example of
(1) lack of management of nonrenewable natural resources
(2) a good conservation practice for renewable natural resources
(3) a good conservation practice for nonrenewable natural resources
(4) lack of concern for renewable natural resources

11 Which energy sources are considered nonrenewable?
(1) wood
(2) paper
(3) solar and wind
(4) coal and oil

Test-Taking Tip When evaluating multiple choice answers, be sure to read all of the answer choices, even if the first choice seems to be the correct one. By doing so, you can make sure that the answer you chose is the best one.

Preparing for the Living Environment Exam

Part B

Multiple Choice and Extended Response

For those questions that ask you to select a response, choose the one that best completes the statement or answers the question. For all others follow the directions given.

12 Based on the map below, which statement is correct?

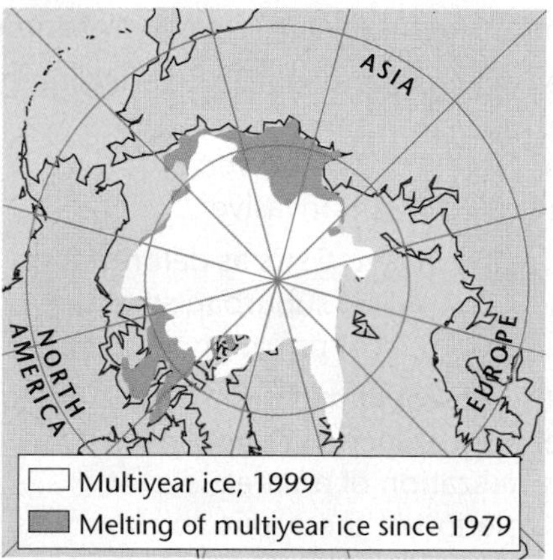

(1) Earth's ice caps are increasing in size.
(2) Earth's ice caps are decreasing in size.
(3) Global warming has not affected Earth's ice caps.
(4) The changes shown are due to acid rain.

Base your answers to questions 13 through 15 on the graph below and on your knowledge of biology.

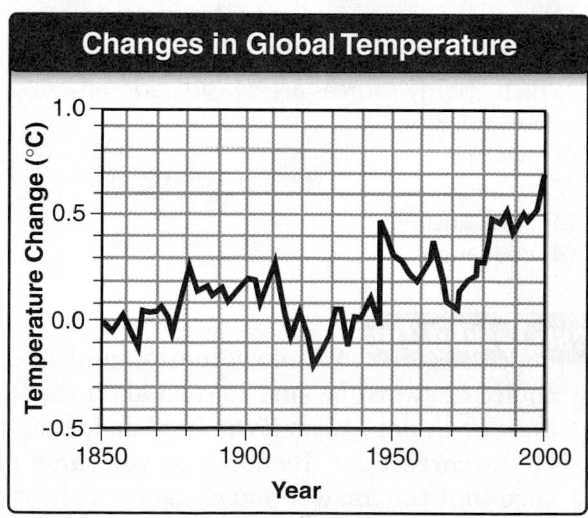

13 What is the change in temperature between the years 1850 and 2000?

14 Describe the trend in global temperature between the years 1970 and 2000.

15 Does the graph predict the pattern of global temperature change in the future? Support your answers with an explanation.

16 Specific human activities that have modified the composition of Earth's atmosphere are being blamed for the change in global temperature.

a State one change in the atmosphere's composition that could be responsible for the observed trend in temperature change.

b List the human activity that led to the atmospheric change.

17 State one environmental impact of reduced funding for public transportation (trains, city buses, school buses, etc.) on future generations. Support your answer with an explanation.

18 In the early 1980s, scientists discovered holes in the ozone shield surrounding Earth. State one negative effect this environmental change could have on humans.

Part C

Extended Response

Answer the questions or follow the directions given.

Base your answer to question 19 on the food web diagram below and on your knowledge of biology.

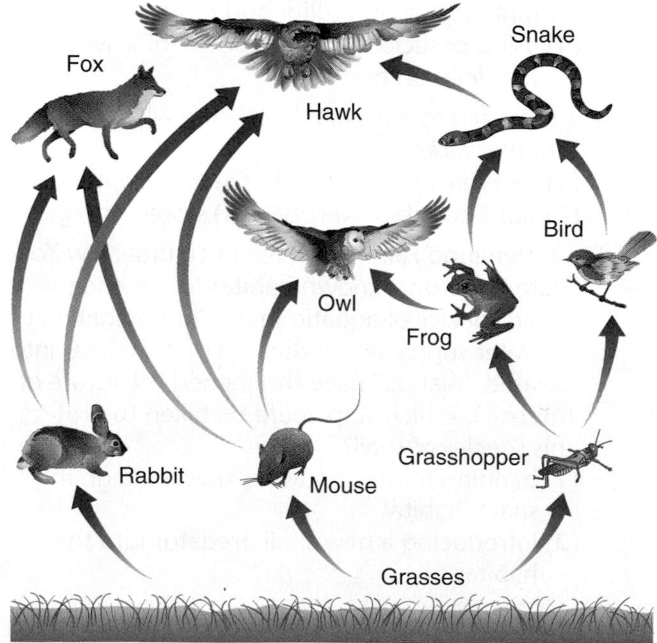

NEW YORK LIVING ENVIRONMENT

19 Some of the animals in the food web shown could accumulate high levels of a chlorinated pesticide, such as DDT, creating a significant environmental problem. Explain how pesticides move through an ecosystem and sometimes become present in high levels in certain organisms in that ecosystem. In your answer, be sure to include:

- an explanation of bioaccumulation as it applies to this food web
- a description of *two* ways a pesticide used to control a pest in the food chain pictured could enter the human food chain through fish caught in a nearby pond
- one explanation of how a pesticide applied to a field two years ago might still be present in that ecosystem

20 All living organisms are dependent on a stable environment.

a Describe how humans have made the environment less stable by:

- changing the chemical composition of air, soil, and water
- reducing the biodiversity of an area
- introducing technologies

b Describe *two* specific ways recently used by humans to reduce the amount of chemicals being added to the environment.

21 Choose one ecological problem from the list below.

Global warming
Destruction of the ozone shield
Loss of biodiversity

Discuss the ecological problem you chose. In your answer, be sure to state:

- the problem you selected and one human action that may have caused the problem
- one way in which the problem may negatively affect humans
- one positive action that could be taken to reduce the problem

Base your answers to questions 22 through 23 on the following reading passage and on your knowledge of biology.

Deforestation: New Term, Old Technique

The clearing of tropical rain forests has been going on for centuries. The clearing is done in order to create areas for grazing cattle or planting crops, to harvest trees for lumber or papermaking, or to build dams or towns. When the trees are cut and burned, the carbon stored in them is released into the atmosphere, increasing levels of carbon dioxide and adding to the greenhouse effect and global warming. With fewer trees, there is also a lower rate of evaporation of moisture from the tree canopy. This leads to less cloud cover and higher temperatures. In addition, more than half of all the species alive today live in tropical rain forests. When the trees are cleared, habitats are destroyed and species risk extinction. Finally, soils of tropical rain forests are low in nutrients, which are quickly depleted when the forests are cleared and the land is used to grow crops. As a result, farmers soon move on to clear and farm other parts of the forest.

22 State *two* consequences of clearing tropical rain forests.

23 Explain how deforestation affects the cycling of carbon through the ecosystem. In your explanation, be sure to:

- list *two* processes the put carbon into the atmosphere
- list one process that removes carbon from the atmosphere
- describe how deforestation disrupts the balance of carbon entering and being removed from the atmosphere

For: An interactive self-test
Visit: PHSchool.com
Web Code: cba-2060

UNIT 3

Cells

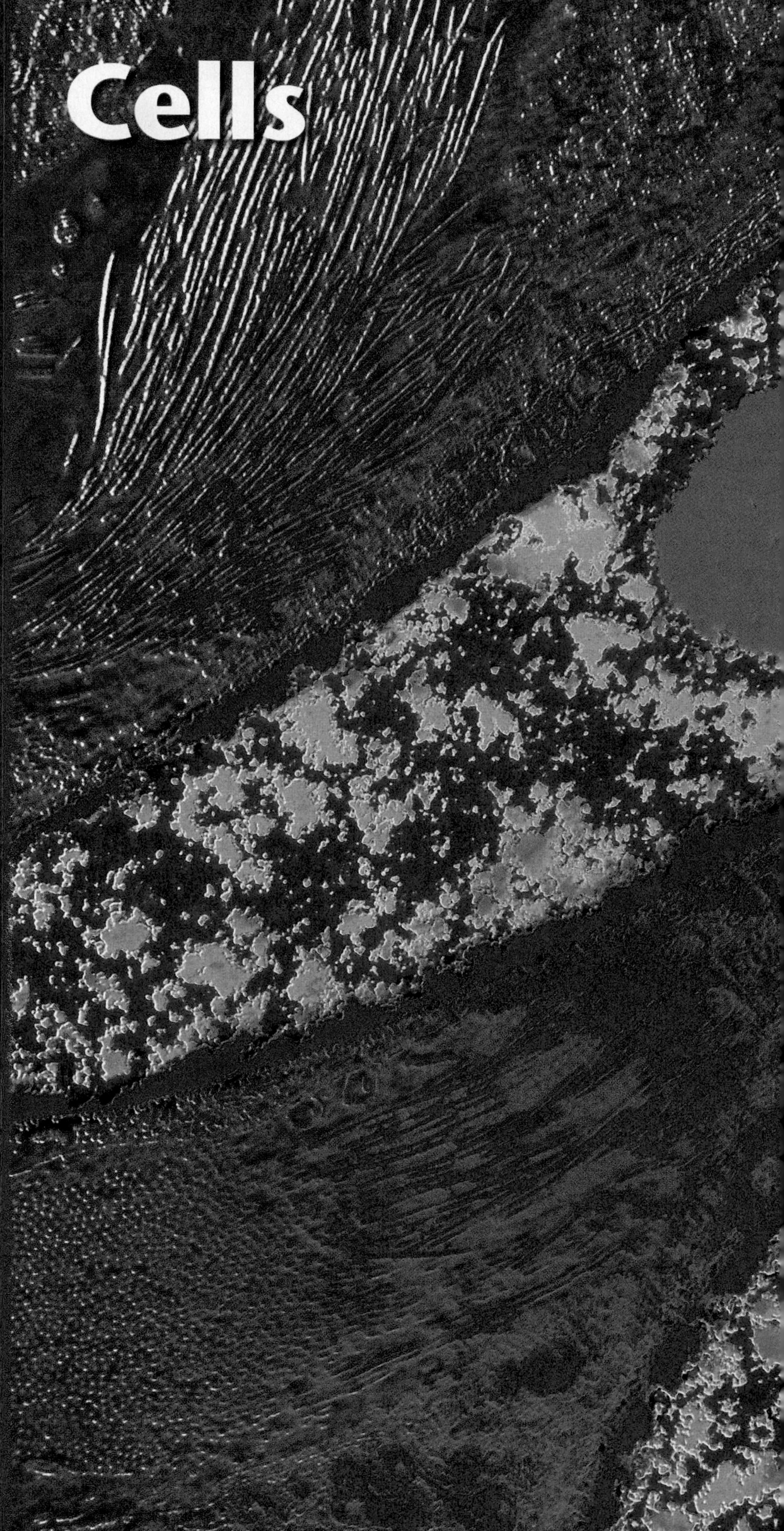

Chapters

This color-enhanced transmission electron micrograph shows two long cell nuclei (colored blue and yellow) from a human sarcoma, or cancer of the connective tissue. The round, orange structure near the middle of each nucleus is the nucleolus.

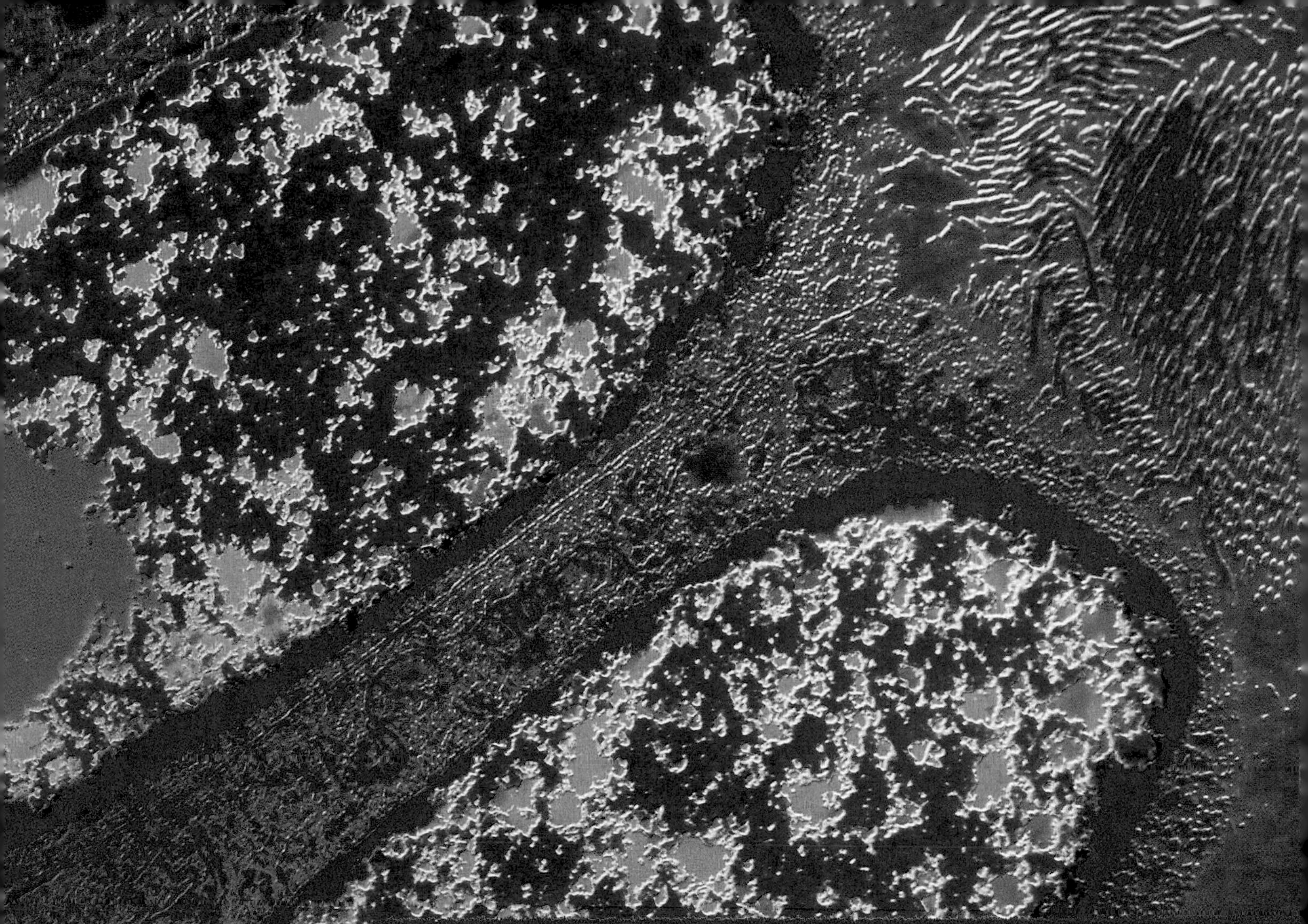

From the Author

"Life—it's all about the cell." I once saw that slogan on a T-shirt. Right away, I knew the point that the person was making. Everything in biology, even population growth and ecosystem organization, depends upon events in the cell. Understanding the cell—how it grows, reproduces, changes, and reacts to the world around it—is the key to all of life.

What discoveries lie ahead?

- What are the signals that determine whether cells will develop into bones, muscles, nerves, or other tissues in the body?
- Can we use our understanding of photosynthesis to improve crop yields and help feed the world's hungry?
- Will we learn enough about the control of cell division to find ways to stop the uncontrolled growth of cells known as cancer?

For: Latest discoveries
Visit: PHSchool.com
Web Code: cbe-3000

CHAPTER 7

Cell Structure and Function

This is a transmission electron micrograph of a neutrophil, a cell found in bone marrow. Color has been added to highlight the various organelles (magnification: 27,500×).

Inquiry Activity

What is a cell?

Procedure

1. Look through a microscope at a slide of a plant leaf or stem cross section. **CAUTION:** *Handle the microscope and slide carefully to avoid breaking them.* Sketch one or more cells. Record a description of their features, such as shape and internal parts.
2. Repeat step 1 with slides of nerve cells, bacteria, and paramecia.
3. Compare the cells by listing the characteristics they have in common and some of the differences among them.

Think About It

1. **Forming Operational Definitions** Use your observations to write a definition of "cell."
2. **Classifying** Classify the cells you observed into two or more groups. Explain what characteristics you used to put each cell in a particular group.

7–1 Life Is Cellular

1-S1.1 Historical development of ideas in science
1-S1.4 Theories supported by many individuals
4-1.2 Cell organelles have specialized parts and functions
LS- Observation, compare cells, use microscope

Guide for Reading

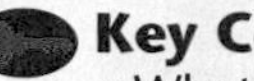

Key Concepts
- What is the cell theory?
- What are the characteristics of prokaryotes and eukaryotes?

Vocabulary
cell
cell theory
nucleus
eukaryote
prokaryote

Reading Strategy: Finding Main Ideas
As you read, look for evidence to support the statement "The cell theory revolutionized how biologlsts thought about living things."

Look closely at a part of a living thing, and what do you see? Hold a blade of grass up against the light, and you see tiny lines running the length of the blade. Examine the tip of your finger, and you see the ridges and valleys that make up fingerprints. Place an insect under a microscope, and you see the intricate structures of its wings and the spikes and bristles that protect its body. As interesting as these close-up views may be, however, they're only the beginning of the story. Look closer and deeper with a more powerful microscope, and you'll see that there is a common structure that makes up every living thing—the cell.

The Discovery of the Cell

"Seeing is believing," an old saying goes. It would be hard to find a better example of this than the discovery of the cell. Without the instruments to make them visible, cells remained out of sight and, therefore, out of mind for most of human history. All of this changed with a dramatic advance in technology—the invention of the microscope.

Early Microscopes It was not until the mid-1600s that scientists began to use microscopes to observe living things. In 1665, Englishman Robert Hooke used an early compound microscope to look at a thin slice of cork, a plant material. Under the microscope, cork seemed to be made of thousands of tiny, empty chambers. Hooke called these chambers "cells" because they reminded him of a monastery's tiny rooms, which were called cells. One of Hooke's illustrations of cells is shown in **Figure 7–1.** The term *cell* is used in biology to this day. We now know, however, that cells are not empty but contain living matter.

In Holland around the same time, Anton van Leeuwenhoek used a single-lens microscope to observe pond water and other things. To his amazement, the microscope revealed a fantastic world of tiny living organisms that seemed to be everywhere, even in the very water he and his neighbors drank.

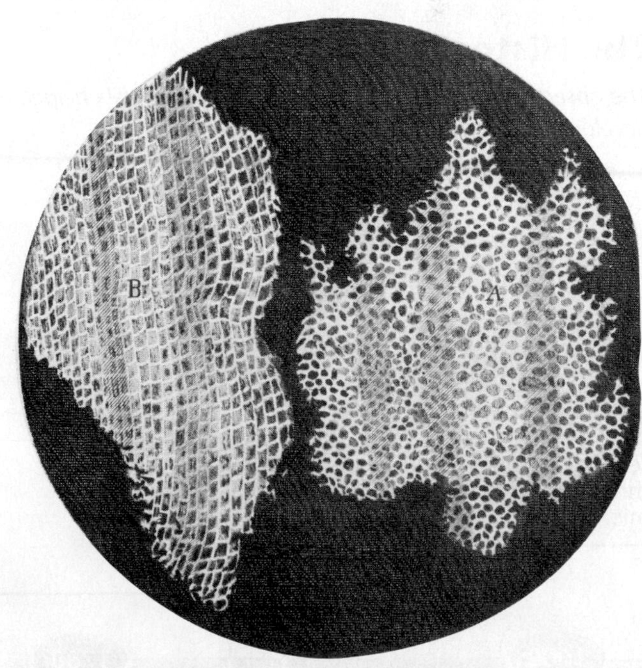

▶ **Figure 7–1** Using an early microscope, Hooke made this drawing of cork cells. In Hooke's drawings, the cells look like empty chambers because he was looking at dead plant matter. Today, we know that living cells are made up of many structures.

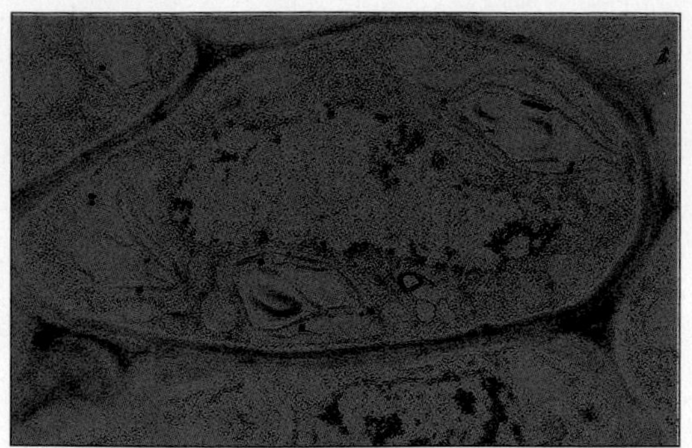

(magnification: 12,000×)

▲ **Figure 7–2** **The cell theory states that cells are the basic units of all living things.** This cell is from a plant leaf. Compare this micrograph with Hooke's drawing in **Figure 7–1.**

The Cell Theory Soon, numerous observations made it clear that **cells** were the basic units of life. In 1838, German botanist Matthias Schleiden concluded that all plants were made of cells like the one in **Figure 7–2.** The next year, German biologist Theodor Schwann stated that all animals were made of cells. In 1855, the German physician Rudolf Virchow concluded that new cells could be produced only from the division of existing cells. These discoveries, confirmed by other biologists, are summarized in the **cell theory,** a fundamental concept of biology. **The cell theory states:**

- **All living things are composed of cells.**
- **Cells are the basic units of structure and function in living things.**
- **New cells are produced from existing cells.**

Exploring the Cell

Following in the footsteps of Hooke, Virchow, and others, modern biologists still use microscopes to explore the cell. However, today's researchers use microscopes and techniques more powerful than the pioneers of biology could have imagined. Researchers can use fluorescent labels and light microscopy to follow molecules moving through the cell. Confocal light microscopy, which scans cells with a laser beam, makes it possible to build three-dimensional images of cells and their parts. High-resolution video technology makes it easy to produce movies of cells as they grow, divide, and develop.

Biology and History

The History of the Cell

The observations and conclusions of many scientists helped to develop the current understanding of the cell.

1665
Robert Hooke
Hooke publishes his book *Micrographia,* which contains his drawings of sections of cork as seen through one of the first microscopes.

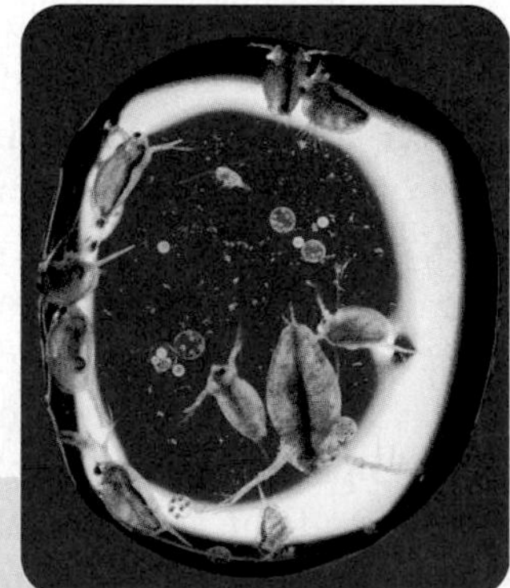

1674
Anton van Leeuwenhoek
Leeuwenhoek observes tiny living organisms in drops of pond water through his simple microscope.

1600 1700 1800

These new technologies make it possible for researchers to study the structure and movement of living cells in great detail. Unfortunately, light itself limits the detail, or resolution, of images that can be made with the light microscope. Like all forms of radiation, light waves are diffracted, or scattered, as they pass through matter, making it impossible to visualize tiny structures such as proteins and viruses with light microscopy.

By contrast, electron microscopes are capable of revealing details as much as 1000 times smaller than those visible in light microscopes because the wavelengths of electrons are much shorter than those of light. Transmission electron microscopes (TEMs) make it possible to explore cell structures and large protein molecules. Because beams of electrons can only pass through thin samples, cells and tissues must be cut first into ultrathin slices before they can be examined under a microscope.

With scanning electron microscopes (SEMs), a pencillike beam of electrons is scanned over the surface of a specimen. For SEM images, specimens do not have to be cut into thin slices to be visualized. The scanning electron microscope produces stunning three-dimensional images of cells. Because electrons are easily scattered by molecules in the air, samples examined in both types of electron microscopes must be placed in a vacuum in order to be studied. As a result, researchers chemically preserve their samples first and then carefully remove all of the water before placing them in the microscope. This means that electron microscopy can be used to visualize only nonliving, preserved cells and tissues.

For: Links on cell theory
Visit: www.SciLinks.org
Web Code: cbn-3071

Writing in Science

Use the library or the Internet to research a new discovery relating to the cell or its structures. Be sure to include the scientist(s) responsible for the discovery. Then, present your findings in the form of an oral report.

1838
Matthias Schleiden
Schleiden concludes that all plants are made up of cells.

1839
Theodor Schwann
Schwann concludes that all animals are made up of cells.

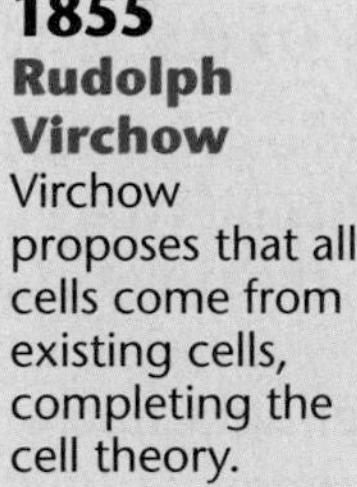

1855
Rudolph Virchow
Virchow proposes that all cells come from existing cells, completing the cell theory.

1970
Lynn Margulis
Margulis proposes the idea that certain organelles, tiny structures within some cells, were once free-living cells themselves.

1800 1900 2000

FIGURE 7–3 VARIETY OF MICROGRAPHS

Different types of microscopes produce a variety of images of cells and cell parts.

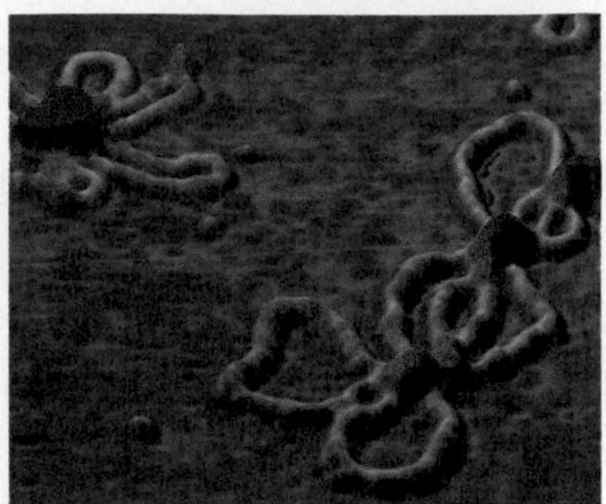

Scanning Probe Micrograph
A scanning probe microscope scans a tiny probe just above the surface of a sample and produces an image by recording the position of the probe. These powerful instruments can even visualize single molecules, such as DNA, on carefully prepared surfaces. (magnification: 320,000X)

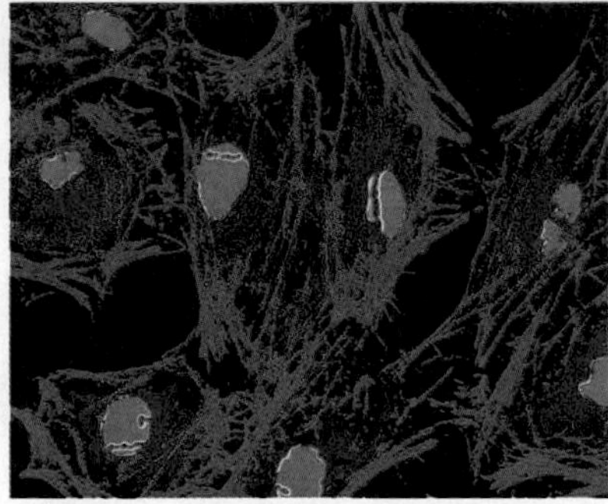

Confocal Light Micrograph
Confocal light microscopes construct images by scanning cells with a computer-controlled laser beam. In this fluorescent confocal light micrograph of HeLa cells, researchers attached fluorescent labels to the different molecules. By doing this, researchers can follow molecules as they move through a living cell. (magnification: 500X)

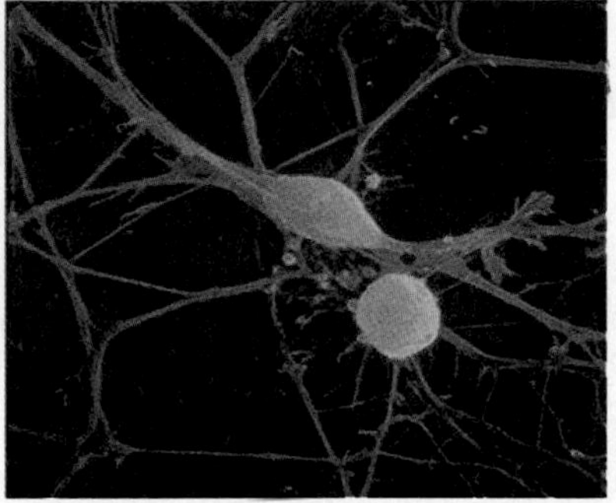

Scanning Electron Micrograph
Scanning electron microscopes produce three-dimensional images of the surfaces of cells, such as these neurons, and tissues. (magnification: 8900X)

In the 1990s, researchers perfected a new class of microscopes that produce images by tracing the surfaces of samples with a fine probe. These scanning probe microscopes have revolutionized the study of surfaces and made it possible to observe single atoms. Unlike electron microscopes, scanning probe microscopes can operate in ordinary air and can even show samples in solution. Researchers have already used scanning probe microscopes to image DNA and protein molecules as well as a number of important biological structures.

Prokaryotes and Eukaryotes

Cells come in a great variety of shapes and an amazing range of sizes. Although typical cells range from 5 to 50 micrometers in diameter, the tiniest mycoplasma bacteria are only 0.2 micrometers across, so small that they are difficult to see under even the best light microscopes. In contrast, the giant amoeba *Chaos chaos* may be 1000 micrometers in diameter, large enough to be seen with the unaided eye as a tiny speck in pond water. Despite their differences, all cells have two characteristics in common. They are surrounded by a barrier called a cell membrane; and, at some point in their lives, they contain the molecule that carries biological information—DNA.

For: Articles on cells
Visit: PHSchool.com
Web Code: cbe-3071

Cells fall into two broad categories, depending on whether they contain a nucleus. The **nucleus** (plural: nuclei) is a large membrane-enclosed structure that contains the cell's genetic material in the form of DNA. (A membrane is a thin layer of material that serves as a covering or lining.) The nucleus controls many of the cell's activities. **Eukaryotes** (yoo-KAR-ee-ohts) are cells that contain nuclei. **Prokaryotes** (pro-KAR-ee-ohts) are cells that do not contain nuclei. Both words derive from the Greek words *karyon,* meaning "kernel," or nucleus, and *eu,* meaning "true," or *pro,* meaning "before." These words reflect the idea that prokaryotic cells evolved before nuclei developed.

Prokaryotes Prokaryotic cells are generally smaller and simpler than eukaryotic cells, although there are many exceptions to this rule. **Prokaryotic cells have genetic material that is not contained in a nucleus.** Some prokaryotes contain internal membranes, but prokaryotes are generally less complicated than eukaryotes. Despite their simplicity, prokaryotes carry out every activity associated with living things. They grow, reproduce, respond to the environment, and some can even move by gliding along surfaces or swimming through liquids. The organisms we call bacteria are prokaryotes.

Eukaryotes Eukaryotic cells are generally larger and more complex than prokaryotic cells. As you can see in **Figure 7–4,** eukaryotic cells generally contain dozens of structures and internal membranes, and many are highly specialized. **Eukaryotic cells contain a nucleus in which their genetic material is separated from the rest of the cell.** Eukaryotes display great variety. Some eukaryotes live solitary lives as single-celled organisms. Others form large, multicellular organisms. Plants, animals, fungi, and protists are eukaryotes.

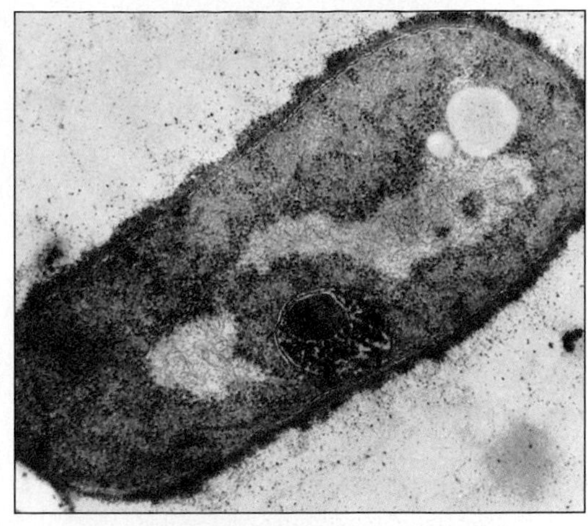

(magnification: 18,300×)

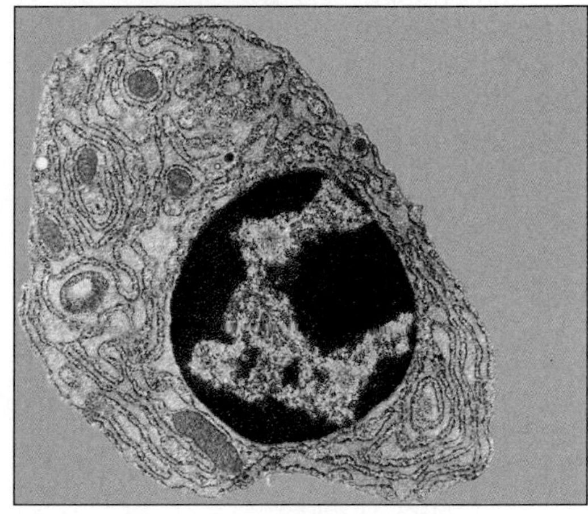

(magnification: 350×)

Figure 7–4 **The cells of eukaryotes have a nucleus, but the cells of prokaryotes do not.** Notice how many more structures are located in the eukaryotic cell (bottom) as compared with the prokaryotic cell (top).

7–1 Section Assessment

1. **Key Concept** What three statements describe the cell theory?
2. **Key Concept** What are the differences between prokaryotic cells and eukaryotic cells?
3. Compare the processes used to produce a TEM and an SEM.
4. What structures do all cells have?
5. **Critical Thinking Inferring** How did the invention of the microscope help the development of the cell theory?

Thinking Visually

Constructing a Chart
Make a three-column chart comparing prokaryotes with eukaryotes. In the first column, list the traits found in all cells. In the second column, list the features of prokaryotes. In the third column, list the features of eukaryotes.

7–2 Eukaryotic Cell Structure

4-1 Levels of organization: organelles to organisms **LS-** Make observations
4-1 Organelles
4-2 Nucleus
4-5 Chloroplasts

Guide for Reading

Key Concept
- What are the functions of the major cell structures?

Vocabulary
organelle
cytoplasm
nuclear envelope
chromatin
chromosome
nucleolus
ribosome
endoplasmic reticulum
Golgi apparatus
lysosome
vacuole
mitochondrion
chloroplast
cytoskeleton
centriole

Reading Strategy: Building Vocabulary
Before you read, preview the vocabulary by skimming the section and making a list of the highlighted boldface terms. Leave space to make notes as you read.

At first glance, a factory is a puzzling place. A bewildering variety of machines buzz and clatter, people move quickly in different directions, and the sheer diversity of so much activity can be confusing. However, if you take your time and watch carefully, before long you will begin to identify patterns. What might at first have seemed like chaos begins to make sense.

Comparing the Cell to a Factory

In some respects, the eukaryotic cell is like a factory. The first time you look at a microscope image of a cell, such as the one in **Figure 7–5,** the cell seems impossibly complex. Look closely at a eukaryotic cell, however, and patterns begin to emerge. To see those patterns more clearly, we'll look at some structures that are common to eukaryotic cells, shown in **Figure 7–6.** Because many of these structures act as if they are specialized organs, these structures are known as **organelles,** literally "little organs."

Cell biologists divide the eukaryotic cell into two major parts: the nucleus and the cytoplasm. The **cytoplasm** is the portion of the cell outside the nucleus. As you will see, the nucleus and cytoplasm work together in the business of life.

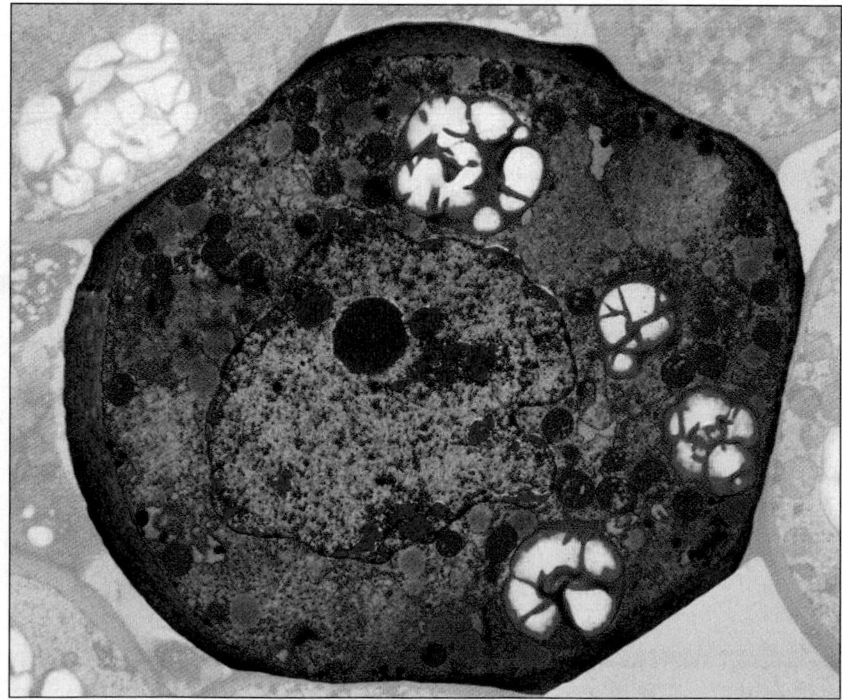

(magnification: 1500×)

▶ **Figure 7–5** This electron micrograph of a plant cell shows many of the different types of structures that are found in eukaryotic cells. The cell has been artificially colored so that you can distinguish one structure from another.

PLANT AND ANIMAL CELLS

Figure 7–6 Both plant and animal cells contain a variety of organelles. Some structures are specific to either plant cells or animal cells only. **Interpreting Graphics** *What structures do plant cells have that animal cells do not?*

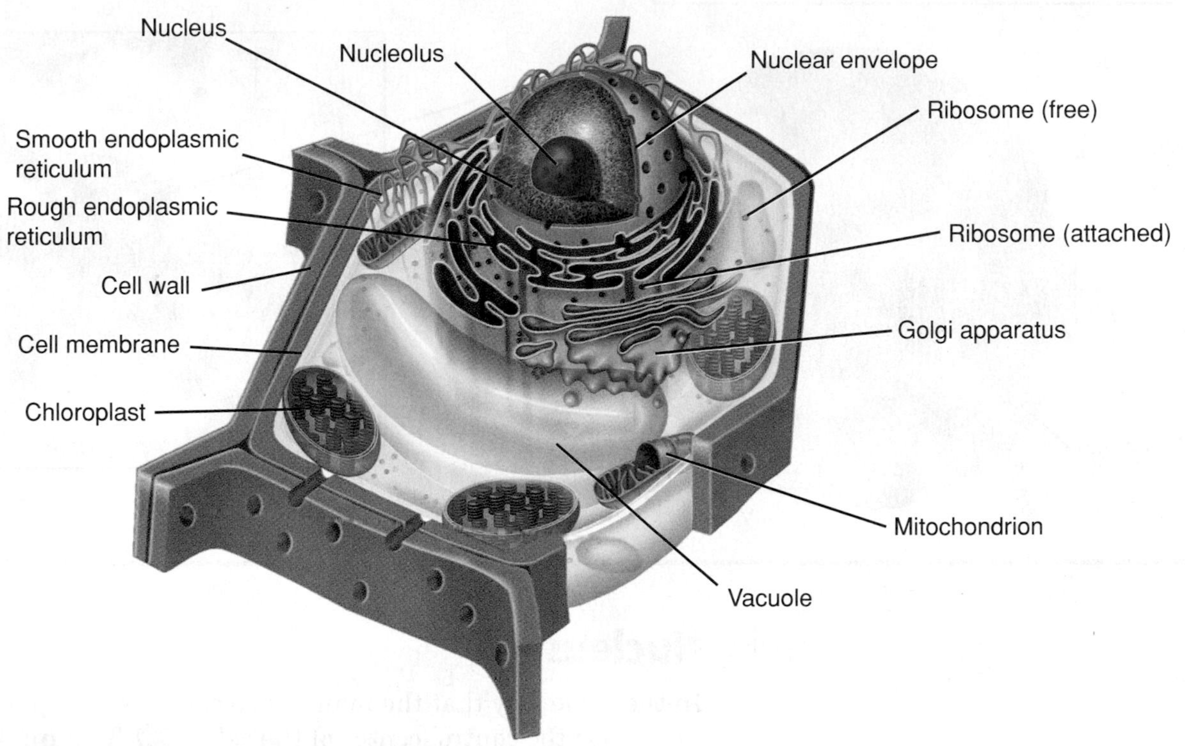

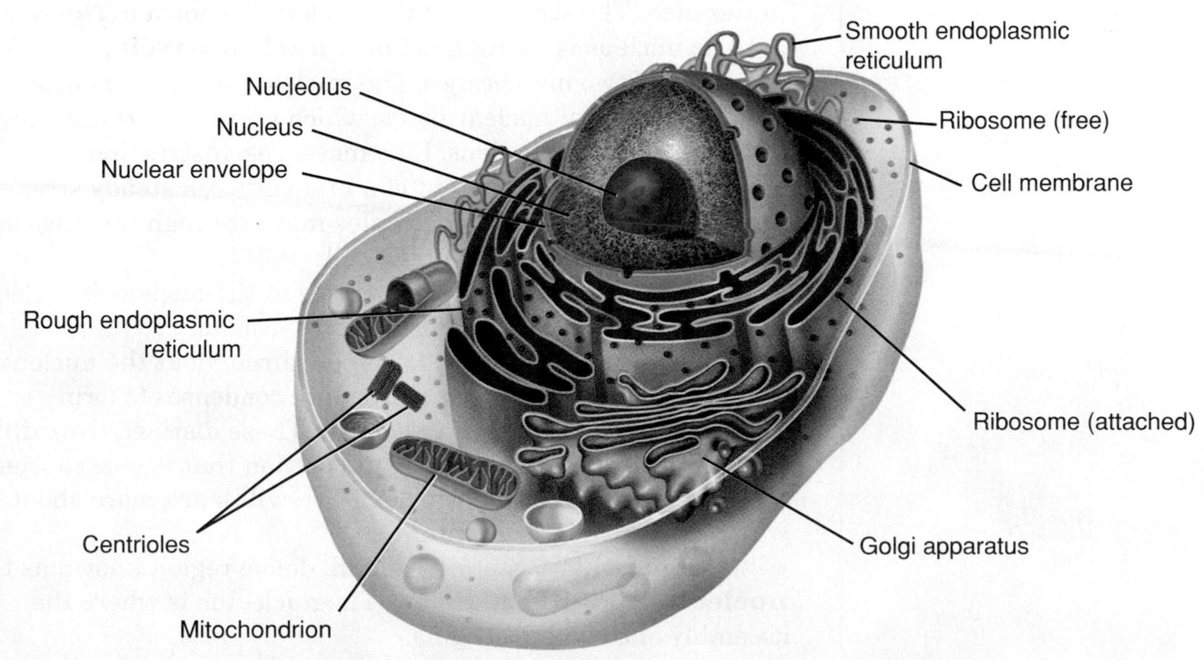

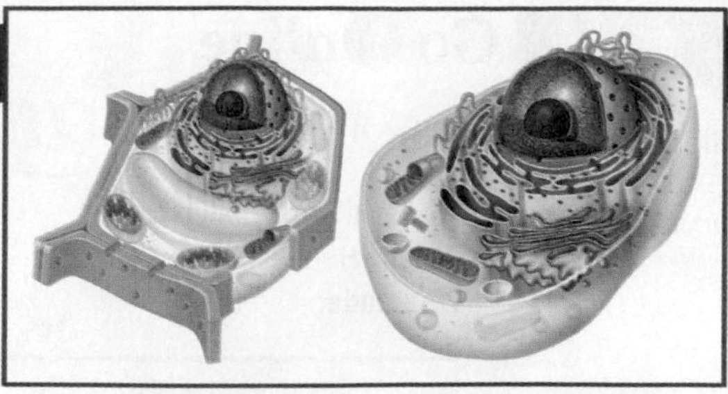

Figure 7–7 The Nucleus

The nucleus controls most cell processes and contains the hereditary information of DNA. The DNA combines with protein to form chromatin, which is found throughout the nucleus. The small, dense region in the nucleus is the nucleolus.

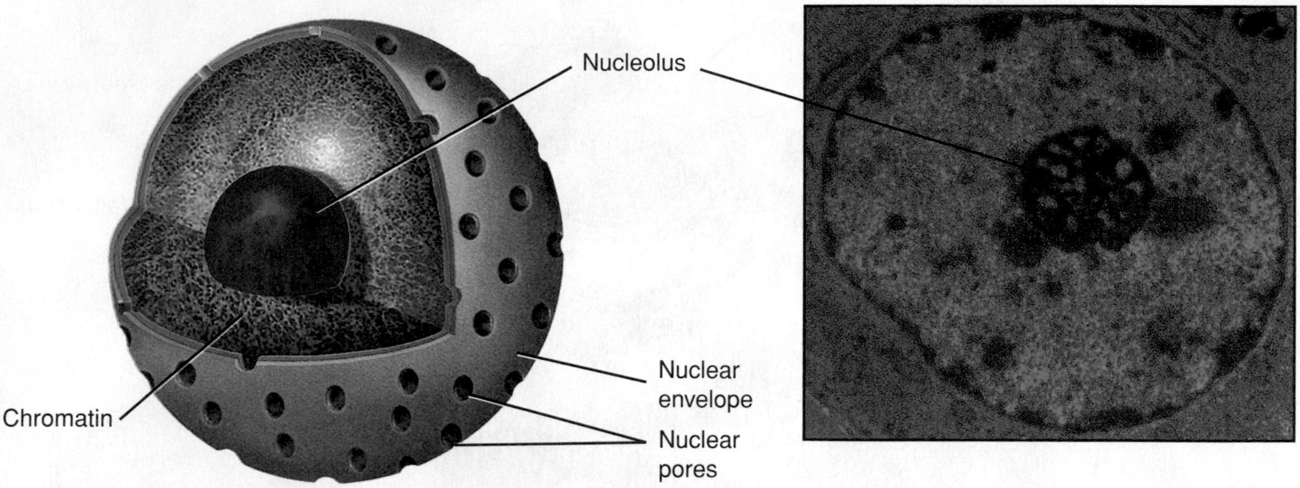

Nucleolus

Nuclear envelope

Nuclear pores

Chromatin

Nucleus

In the same way that the main office controls a large factory, the nucleus is the control center of the cell. **The nucleus contains nearly all the cell's DNA and with it the coded instructions for making proteins and other important molecules.** The structure of the nucleus is shown in **Figure 7–7.**

The nucleus is surrounded by a **nuclear envelope** composed of two membranes. The nuclear envelope is dotted with thousands of nuclear pores, which allow material to move into and out of the nucleus. Like messages, instructions, and blueprints moving in and out of a main office, a steady stream of proteins, RNA, and other molecules move through the nuclear pores to and from the rest of the cell.

The granular material you can see in the nucleus is called **chromatin.** Chromatin consists of DNA bound to protein. Most of the time, chromatin is spread throughout the nucleus. When a cell divides, however, chromatin condenses to form **chromosomes** (KROH-muh-sohms). These distinct, threadlike structures contain the genetic information that is passed from one generation of cells to the next. You will learn more about chromosomes in later chapters.

Most nuclei also contain a small, dense region known as the **nucleolus** (noo-KLEE-uh-lus). The nucleolus is where the assembly of ribosomes begins.

What kind of information is contained in chromosomes?

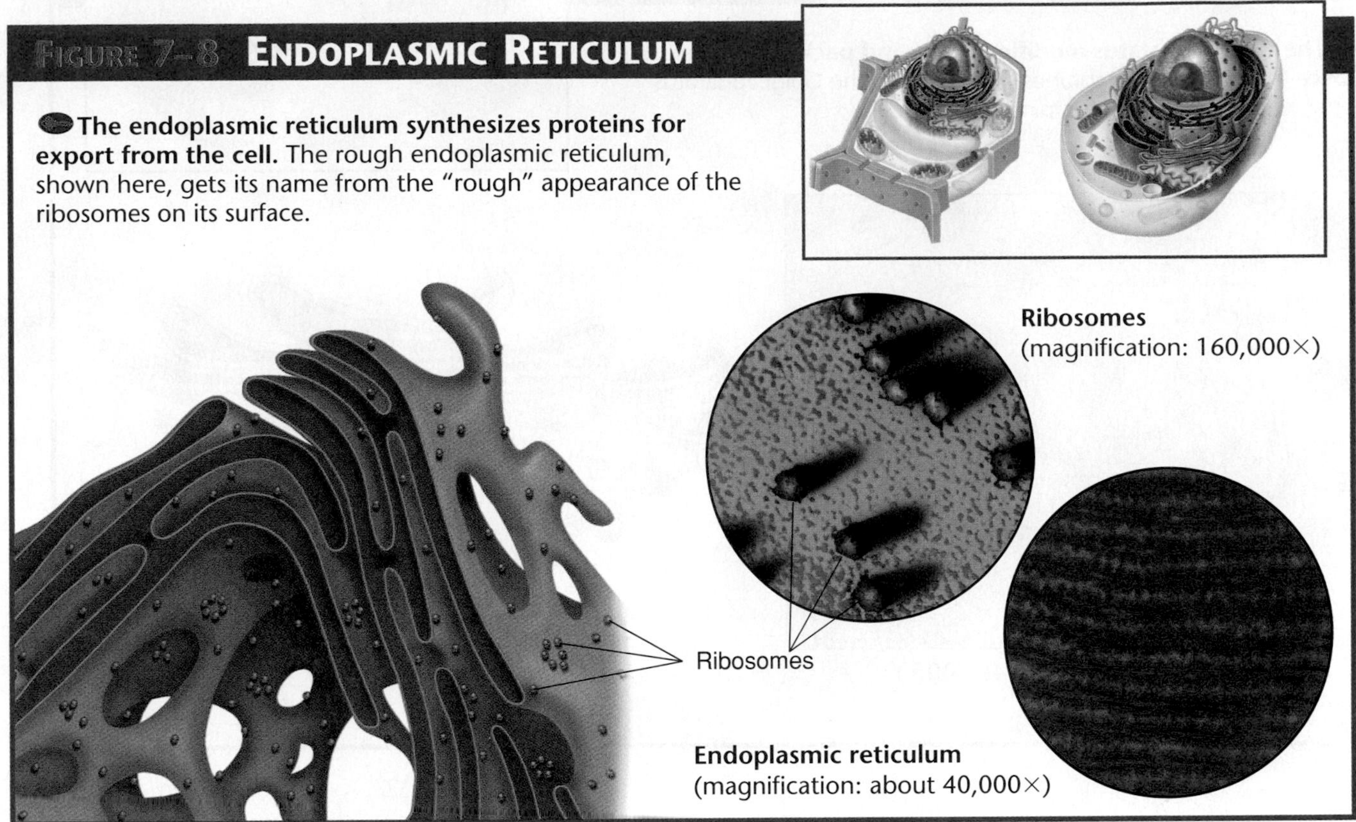

FIGURE 7–8 ENDOPLASMIC RETICULUM
The endoplasmic reticulum synthesizes proteins for export from the cell. The rough endoplasmic reticulum, shown here, gets its name from the "rough" appearance of the ribosomes on its surface.
Ribosomes
(magnification: 160,000×)
Ribosomes
Endoplasmic reticulum
(magnification: about 40,000×)

Ribosomes

One of the most important jobs carried out in the cellular "factory" is making proteins. **Proteins are assembled on ribosomes. Ribosomes** are small particles of RNA and protein found throughout the cytoplasm. They produce proteins by following coded instructions that come from the nucleus. Each ribosome, in its own way, is like a small machine in a factory, turning out proteins on orders that come from its "boss"—the cell nucleus. Cells that are active in protein synthesis are often packed with ribosomes.

Endoplasmic Reticulum

Eukaryotic cells also contain an internal membrane system known as the **endoplasmic reticulum** (en-doh-PLAZ-mik rih-TIK-yuh-lum), or ER. **The endoplasmic reticulum is the site where lipid components of the cell membrane are assembled, along with proteins and other materials that are exported from the cell.**

The portion of the ER involved in the synthesis of proteins is called rough endoplasmic reticulum, or rough ER. It is given this name because of the ribosomes found on its surface. Newly made proteins leave these ribosomes and are inserted into the rough ER, where they may be chemically modified.

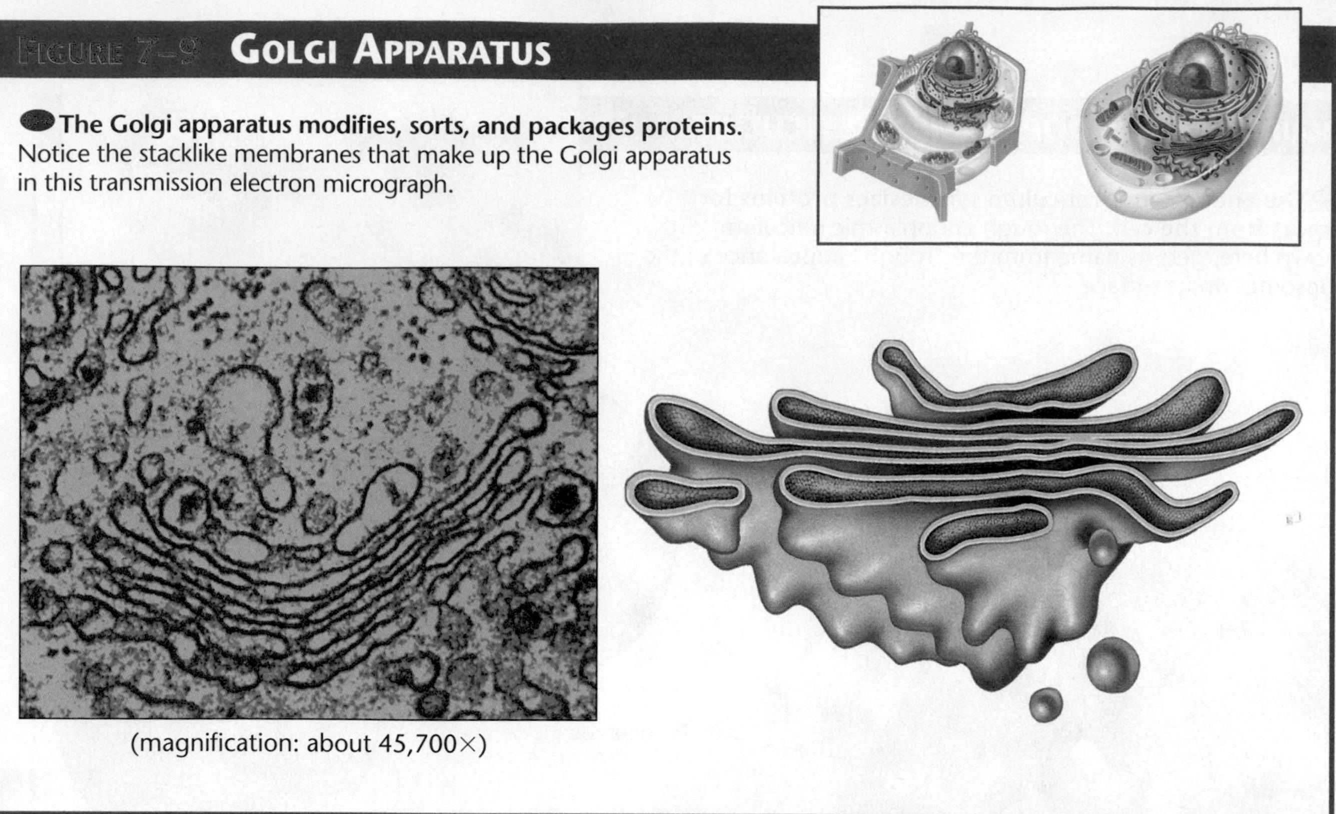

FIGURE 7–9 Golgi Apparatus

The Golgi apparatus modifies, sorts, and packages proteins. Notice the stacklike membranes that make up the Golgi apparatus in this transmission electron micrograph.

(magnification: about 45,700×)

Proteins that are released, or exported, from the cell are synthesized on the rough ER, as are many membrane proteins. Rough ER is abundant in cells that produce large amounts of protein for export. Other cellular proteins are made on "free" ribosomes, which are not attached to membranes.

The other portion of the ER is known as smooth endoplasmic reticulum (smooth ER) because ribosomes are not found on its surface. In many cells, the smooth ER contains collections of enzymes that perform specialized tasks, including the synthesis of membrane lipids and the detoxification of drugs. Liver cells, which play a key role in detoxifying drugs, often contain large amounts of smooth ER.

Golgi Apparatus

Proteins produced in the rough ER move next into an organelle called the **Golgi apparatus,** discovered by the Italian scientist Camillo Golgi. As you can see in **Figure 7–9,** Golgi appears as a stack of closely apposed membranes. **The function of the Golgi apparatus is to modify, sort, and package proteins and other materials from the endoplasmic reticulum for storage in the cell or secretion outside the cell.** The Golgi apparatus is somewhat like a customization shop, where the finishing touches are put on proteins before they are ready to leave the "factory." From the Golgi apparatus, proteins are then "shipped" to their final destinations throughout the cell or outside of the cell.

Lysosomes

Even the neatest, cleanest factory needs a cleanup crew, and that's what lysosomes (LY-suh-sohmz) are. **Lysosomes** are small organelles filled with enzymes. One function of lysosomes is the digestion, or breakdown, of lipids, carbohydrates, and proteins into small molecules that can be used by the rest of the cell.

Lysosomes are also involved in breaking down organelles that have outlived their usefulness. Lysosomes perform the vital function of removing "junk" that might otherwise accumulate and clutter up the cell. A number of serious human diseases, including Tay-Sachs disease, can be traced to lysosomes that fail to function properly.

What is the role of lysosomes?

Vacuoles

Every factory needs a place to store things, and cells contain places for storage as well. Some kinds of cells contain saclike structures called **vacuoles** (VAK-yoo-ohlz) that store materials such as water, salts, proteins, and carbohydrates. In many plant cells there is a single, large central vacuole filled with liquid. The pressure of the central vacuole in these cells makes it possible for plants to support heavy structures such as leaves and flowers.

Vacuoles are also found in some single-celled organisms and in some animals. The paramecium in **Figure 7–10** contains a vacuole called a contractile vacuole. By contracting rhythmically, this specialized vacuole pumps excess water out of the cell. The control of water content within the cell is just one example of an important process known as homeostasis. Homeostasis is the maintenance of a controlled internal environment.

Mitochondria and Chloroplasts

All living things require a source of energy. Factories are hooked up to the local power company, but what about cells? Most cells get energy in one of two ways—from food molecules or from the sun.

Mitochondria Nearly all eukaryotic cells, including plants, contain **mitochondria** (myt-oh-KAHN-dree-uh; singular: mitochondrion). **Mitochondria are organelles that convert the chemical energy stored in food into compounds that are more convenient for the cell to use.** Mitochondria are enclosed by two membranes—an outer membrane and an inner membrane. The inner membrane is folded up inside the organelle.

One of the most interesting aspects of mitochondria is the way in which they are inherited. In humans, all or nearly all of our mitochondria come from the cytoplasm of the ovum, or egg cell. This means that when your relatives are discussing which side of the family should take credit for your best characteristics, you can tell them that you got your mitchondria from Mom!

Figure 7–10 Vacuoles have a variety of functions. In the *Coleus* plant cell (top), the large blue structure is the central vacuole that stores salts, proteins, and carbohydrates. The paramecium (bottom) contains contractile vacuoles that fill with water and then pump the water out of the cell. **Applying Concepts** ***How do vacuoles help support plant structures?***

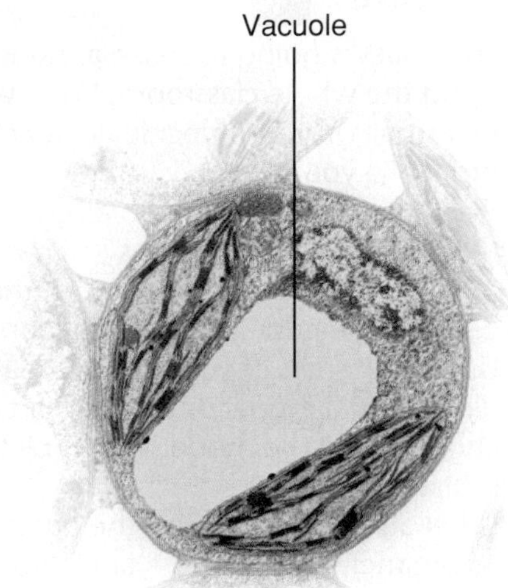

(magnification: about 3000×)

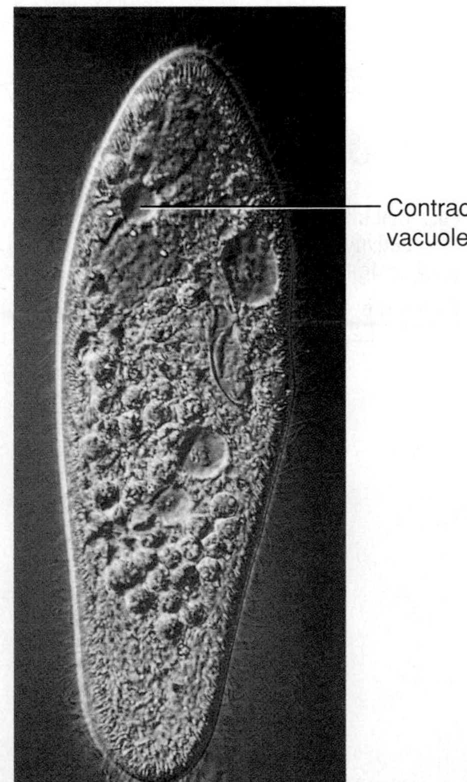

Quick Lab

How can you make a model of a cell?

Materials variety of craft supplies, index cards

Procedure 

1. Your class is going to make a model of a plant cell using the whole classroom. Work with a partner or in a small group to decide what cell part or organelle you would like to model. (Use **Figure 7–6** as a starting point. It will give you an idea of the relative sizes of various cell parts and their possible positions. **Figures 7–7** through **7–10** can provide additional information.)
2. Using materials of your choice, make a three-dimensional model of the cell part or organelle you chose. Make the model as complete and as accurate as you can.
3. Label an index card with the name of your cell part or organelle and list its main features and functions. Attach the card to your model.
4. Attach your model to an appropriate place in the room. If possible, attach your model to another related cell part or organelle.

Analyze and Conclude

1. **Inferring** What are the functions of the different organelles in plant cells?
2. **Calculating** Assume that a typical plant cell is 50 micrometers wide. Calculate the scale of your classroom cell model. (*Hint:* Divide the width of the classroom by the width of a cell, making sure to use the same units.)
3. **Comparing and Contrasting** How is your model cell part or organelle similar to the real cell part or organelle? How is it different?
4. **Evaluating** Based on your work with this model, describe how you could make a better model. Specify what new information the improved model would demonstrate.

For: Cell structure activity
Visit: PHSchool.com
Web Code: cbd-3072

Chloroplasts Plants and some other organisms contain **chloroplasts.** **Chloroplasts are organelles that capture the energy from sunlight and convert it into chemical energy in a process called photosynthesis.** Chloroplasts are the biological equivalents of solar power plants. Like mitochondria, chloroplasts are surrounded by two membranes. Inside the organelle are large stacks of other membranes, which contain the green pigment chlorophyll.

Organelle DNA Unlike other organelles that contain no DNA, chloroplasts and mitochondria contain their own genetic information in the form of small DNA molecules. Lynn Margulis, an American biologist, has suggested that mitochondria and chloroplasts are actually the descendants of ancient prokaryotes. Margulis suggests that the prokaryotic ancestors of these organelles evolved a symbiotic relationship with early eukaryotes, taking up residence within the eukaryotic cell. One group of prokaryotes had the ability to use oxygen to generate ATP. These prokaryotes evolved into mitochondria. Other prokaryotes that carried out photosynthesis evolved into chloroplasts. This idea is called the endosymbiotic theory.

Cytoskeleton

A supporting structure and a transportation system complete our picture of the cell as a factory. As you know, a factory building is supported by steel or cement beams and by columns that support its walls and roof. Eukaryotic cells have a structure—the **cytoskeleton**—that helps support the cell. **The cytoskeleton is a network of protein filaments that helps the cell to maintain its shape. The cytoskeleton is also involved in movement.** Microfilaments and microtubules are two of the principal protein filaments that make up the cytoskeleton.

Microfilaments are threadlike structures made of a protein called actin. They form extensive networks in some cells and produce a tough, flexible framework that supports the cell. Microfilaments also help cells move. Microfilament assembly and disassembly is responsible for the cytoplasmic movements that allow cells, such as amoebas, to crawl along surfaces.

Microtubules, as shown in **Figure 7–11**, are hollow structures made up of proteins known as tubulins. In many cells, they play critical roles in maintaining cell shape. Microtubules are also important in cell division, where they form a structure known as the mitotic spindle, which helps to separate chromosomes. In animal cells, tubulin is also used to form a pair of structures known as centrioles. **Centrioles** are located near the nucleus and help to organize cell division. Centrioles are not found in plant cells.

Microtubules also help to build projections from the cell surface, which are known as cilia (singular: cilium) and flagella (singular: flagellum), that enable cells to swim rapidly through liquids. Cilia and flagella can produce considerable force; and in some cells they move almost like the oars of a boat, pulling or pushing cells through the water. You will learn more about cilia and flagella in later chapters.

(magnification: 1000×)

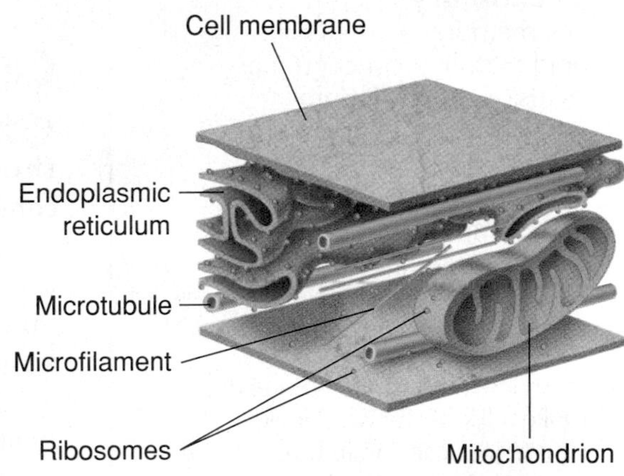

▲ **Figure 7–11 The cytoskeleton is a network of protein filaments that helps the cell to maintain its shape and is involved in many forms of cell movement.** The micrograph shows the microtubules of kidney cells. Microtubules are part of the cytoskeleton that help maintain cell shape.

7–2 Section Assessment

1. **Key Concept** Describe the functions of the endoplasmic reticulum, Golgi apparatus, chloroplast, and mitochondrion.
2. Describe the role of the nucleus in the cell.
3. What are two functions of the cytoskeleton?
4. How is a cell like a factory?
5. **Critical Thinking Inferring** You examine an unknown cell under the microscope and discover that the cell contains chloroplasts. What type of organism could you infer that the cell came from?

Writing in Science

Persuasive Writing

Image that you are Lynn Margulis. Write a persuasive letter to the editor of a magazine, explaining your idea. Your explanation should be clear to people who do not have a biology background. *Hint*: Review the concept of symbiosis in Section 4–2.

7–3 Cell Boundaries

4-1 Cell parts have specialized functions
4-1 Cell membranes
4-1 Organic and inorganic molecules react
1-S3, LS- State a hypothesis and interpret experimental data

Guide for Reading

Key Concepts
- What are the main functions of the cell membrane and the cell wall?
- What happens during diffusion?
- What is osmosis?

Vocabulary
cell membrane • cell wall
lipid bilayer • concentration
diffusion • equilibrium
osmosis • isotonic
hypertonic • hypotonic
facilitated diffusion
active transport • endocytosis
phagocytosis • pinocytosis
exocytosis

Reading Strategy: Summarizing As you read, make a list of the ways in which substances can move through the cell membrane. Write one sentence describing each process.

When you first study a country, you may begin by examining a map of the country's borders. Before you can learn anything about a nation, it's important to understand where it begins and where it ends. The same principle applies to cells. Among the most important parts of a cell are its borders, which separate the cell from its surroundings. All cells are surrounded by a thin, flexible barrier known as the **cell membrane.** Many cells also produce a strong supporting layer around the membrane known as a **cell wall.**

Cell Membrane

The cell membrane regulates what enters and leaves the cell and also provides protection and support. The composition of nearly all cell membranes is a double-layered sheet called a **lipid bilayer.** As you can see in **Figure 7–12**, there are two layers of lipids, hence the name bilayer. The lipid bilayer gives cell membranes a flexible structure that forms a strong barrier between the cell and its surroundings.

In addition to lipids, most cell membranes contain protein molecules that are embedded in the lipid bilayer. Carbohydrate molecules are attached to many of these proteins. In fact, there are so many kinds of molecules in cell membranes that scientists describe the membrane as a "mosaic" of different molecules. A mosaic is a work of art made of individual tiles or other pieces assembled to form a picture or design. As you will see, some of the proteins form channels and pumps that help to move material across the cell membrane. Many of the carbohydrates act like chemical identification cards, allowing individual cells to identify one another.

▼ **Figure 7–12** **The cell membrane regulates what enters and leaves the cell.** This illustration of the cell membrane shows that it is made up of a lipid bilayer in which proteins are embedded.

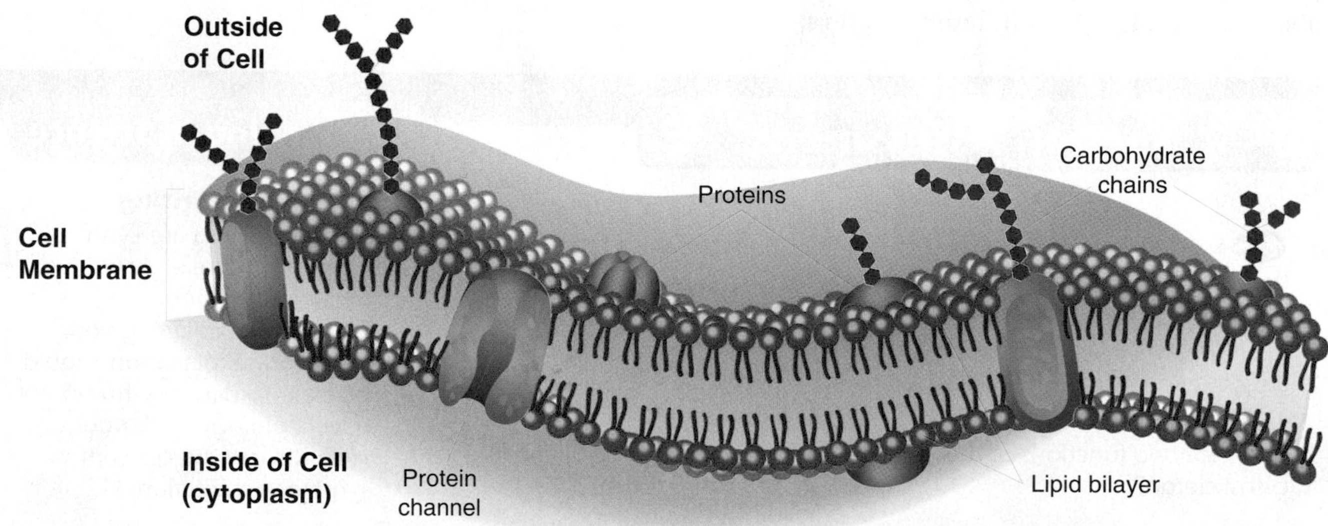

Cell Walls

Cell walls are present in many organisms, including plants, algae, fungi, and many prokaryotes. Cell walls lie outside the cell membrane. Most cell walls are porous enough to allow water, oxygen, carbon dioxide, and certain other substances to pass through easily. **The main function of the cell wall is to provide support and protection for the cell.**

Most cell walls are made from fibers of carbohydrate and protein. These substances are produced within the cell and then released at the surface of the cell membrane where they are assembled to form the wall. Plant cell walls are composed mostly of cellulose, a tough carbohydrate fiber. Cellulose is the principal component of both wood and paper, so every time you pick up a sheet of paper, you are holding the stuff of cell walls in your hand.

For: Links on cell membranes
Visit: www.SciLinks.org
Web Code: cbn-3073

Diffusion Through Cell Boundaries

Every living cell exists in a liquid environment that it needs to survive. It may not always seem that way; yet even in the dust and heat of a desert like the one in **Figure 7–13,** the cells of cactus plants, scorpions, and vultures are bathed in liquid. One of the most important functions of the cell membrane is to regulate the movement of dissolved molecules from the liquid on one side of the membrane to the liquid on the other side.

Measuring Concentration The cytoplasm of a cell contains a solution of many different substances in water. Recall that a solution is a mixture of two or more substances. The substances dissolved in the solution are called solutes. The **concentration** of a solution is the mass of solute in a given volume of solution, or mass/volume. For example, if you dissolved 12 grams of salt in 3 liters of water, the concentration of the solution would be 12 g/3 L, or 4 g/L (grams per liter). If you had 12 grams of salt in 6 liters of water, the concentration would be 12 g/6 L, or 2 g/L. The first solution is twice as concentrated as the second solution.

▼ **Figure 7–13** The cells of living things are bathed in liquid even in dry environments. When it rains, these cactus plants store the water in their stems. **Applying Concepts** *Which cell structure could serve as a storage location for water?*

DIFFUSION

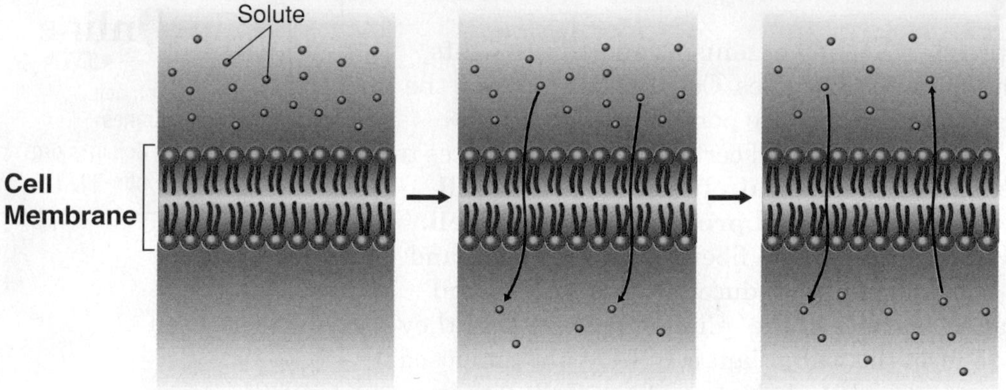

Solute

Cell Membrane

A There is a higher concentration of solute on one side of the membrane as compared to the other side of the membrane.

B Solute particles move from the side of the membrane with a higher concentration of solute to the side of the membrane with a lower concentration of solute. The solute particles will continue to diffuse across the membrane until equilibrium is reached.

C When equilibrium is reached, solute particles continue to diffuse across the membrane in both directions.

▲ **Figure 7–14** Diffusion is the process by which molecules of a substance move from areas of higher concentration to areas of lower concentration. **Diffusion does not require the cell to use energy.**

Diffusion In a solution, particles move constantly. They collide with one another and tend to spread out randomly. As a result, the particles tend to move from an area where they are more concentrated to an area where they are less concentrated, a process known as **diffusion** (dih-FYOO-zhun). When the concentration of the solute is the same throughout a system, the system has reached **equilibrium.**

What do diffusion and equilibrium have to do with cell membranes? Suppose a substance is present in unequal concentrations on either side of a cell membrane, as shown in **Figure 7–14.** If the substance can cross the cell membrane, its particles will tend to move toward the area where it is less concentrated until equilibrium is reached. At that point, the concentration of the substance on both sides of the cell membrane will be the same.

Because diffusion depends upon random particle movements, substances diffuse across membranes without requiring the cell to use energy. Even when equilibrium is reached, particles of a solution will continue to move across the membrane in both directions. However, because almost equal numbers of particles move in each direction, there is no further change in concentration.

CHECKPOINT ***What conditions are present when equilibrium is reached in a solution?***

Osmosis

Although many substances can diffuse across biological membranes, some are too large or too strongly charged to cross the lipid bilayer. If a substance is able to diffuse across a membrane, the membrane is said to be permeable to it. A membrane is impermeable to substances that cannot pass across it. Most biological membranes are selectively permeable, meaning that some substances can pass across them and others cannot.

Water passes quite easily across most membranes, even though many solute molecules cannot. An important process known as **osmosis** is the result. **Osmosis is the diffusion of water through a selectively permeable membrane.**

How Osmosis Works Look at the beaker on the left in **Figure 7–15.** There are more sugar molecules on the left side of the selectively permeable membrane than on the right side. That means that the concentration of water is lower on the left than it is on the right. The membrane is permeable to water but not to sugar. This means that water can cross the membrane in both directions, but sugar cannot. As a result, there is a net movement of water from the area of high concentration to the area of low concentration.

Water will tend to move across the membrane until equilibrium is reached. At that point, the concentrations of water and sugar will be the same on both sides of the membrane. When this happens, the two solutions will be **isotonic,** which means "same strength." When the experiment began, the more concentrated sugar solution was **hypertonic,** which means "above strength," as compared to the dilute sugar solution. The dilute sugar solution was **hypotonic,** or "below strength."

Word Origins

Hypotonic comes from the Greek word *hupo,* meaning "under," and the New Latin word *tonicus,* meaning "tension" or "strength." So a hypotonic solution is less strong, or less concentrated, than another solution of the same type. **If *derma* means "skin," how would you describe a hypodermic injection?**

For: Osmosis activity
Visit: PHSchool.com
Web Code: cbp-3075

▼ **Figure 7–15 Osmosis is the diffusion of water through a selectively permeable membrane.** In the first beaker, water is more concentrated on the right side of the membrane. As a result, the water diffuses (as shown in the second beaker) to the area of lower concentration.

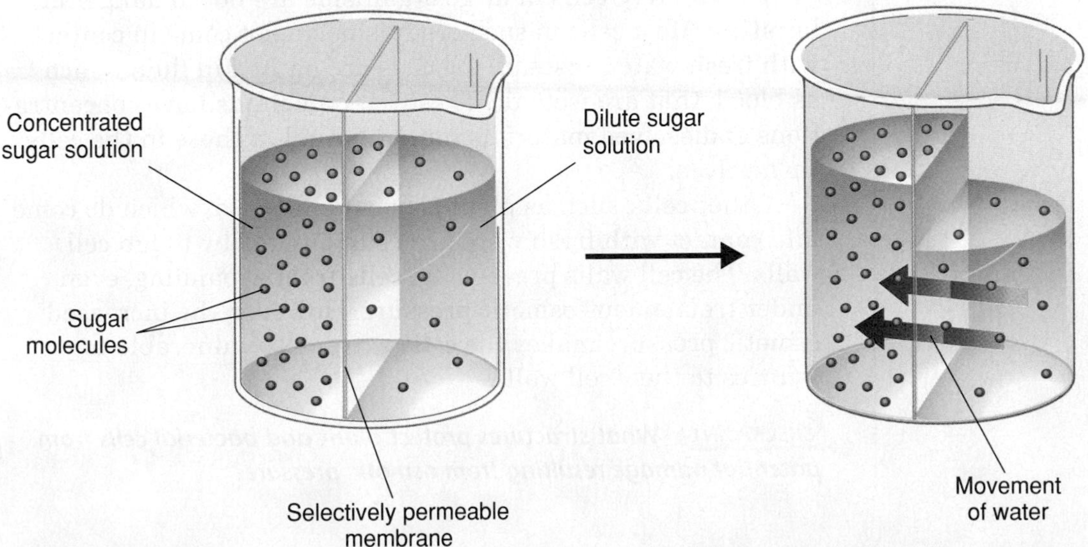

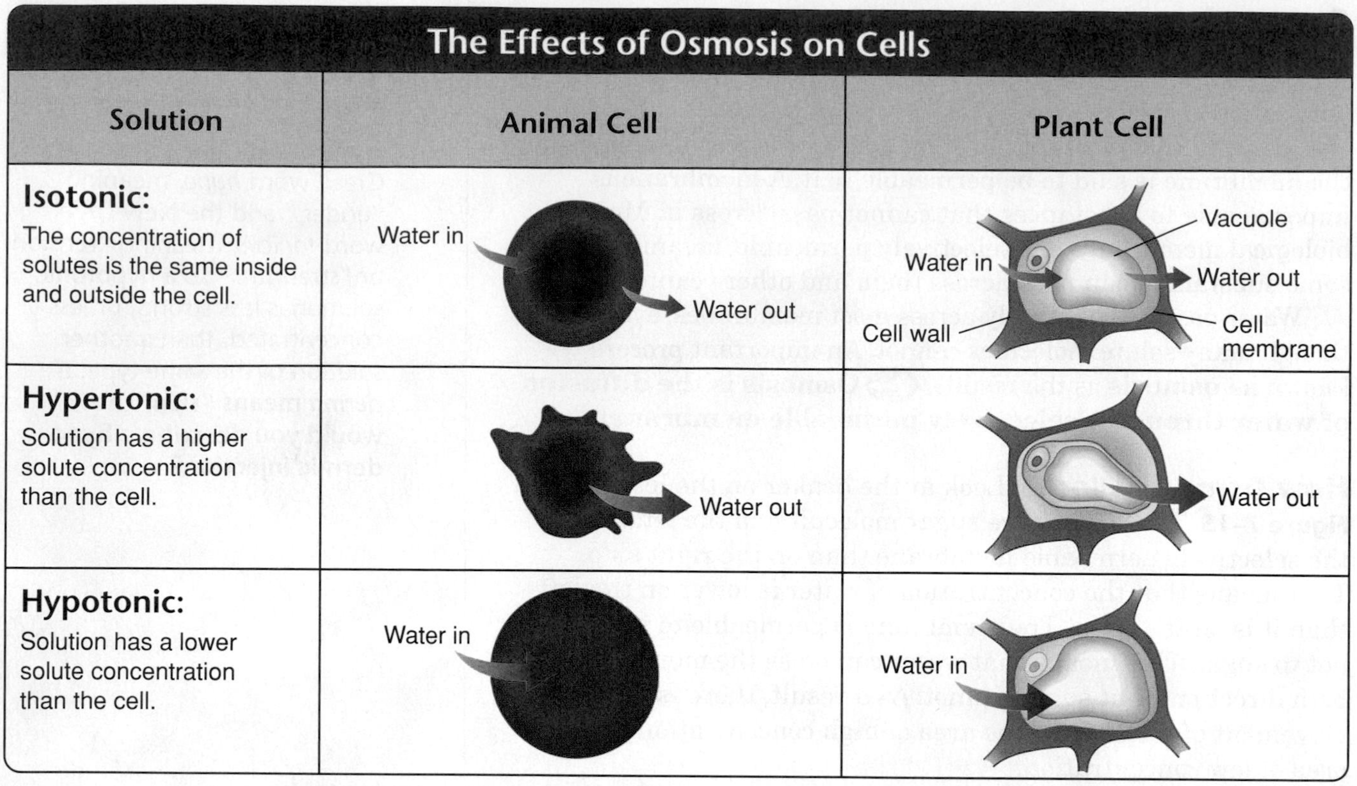

The Effects of Osmosis on Cells

Solution	Animal Cell	Plant Cell
Isotonic: The concentration of solutes is the same inside and outside the cell.	Water in; Water out	Vacuole; Water in; Water out; Cell wall; Cell membrane
Hypertonic: Solution has a higher solute concentration than the cell.	Water out	Water out
Hypotonic: Solution has a lower solute concentration than the cell.	Water in	Water in

▲ **Figure 7–16** Cells placed in an isotonic solution neither gain nor lose water. In a hypertonic solution, animal cells shrink, and plant cell vacuoles collapse. In a hypotonic solution, animal cells swell and burst. The vacuoles of plant cells swell, pushing the cell contents out against the cell wall. **Predicting** ***What would happen to the animal cell in the isotonic solution if it were placed in pure water?***

Osmotic Pressure For organisms to survive, they must have a way to balance the intake and loss of water. Osmosis exerts a pressure known as osmotic pressure on the hypertonic side of a selectively permeable membrane. Osmotic pressure can cause serious problems for a cell. Because the cell is filled with salts, sugars, proteins, and other molecules, it will almost always be hypertonic to fresh water. This means that osmotic pressure should produce a net movement of water into a typical cell that is surrounded by fresh water. If that happens, the volume of a cell will increase until the cell becomes swollen. Eventually, the cell may burst like an overinflated balloon.

Fortunately, cells in large organisms are not in danger of bursting. Most cells in such organisms do not come in contact with fresh water. Instead, the cells are bathed in fluids, such as blood, that are isotonic. These isotonic fluids have concentrations of dissolved materials roughly equal to those in the cells themselves.

Other cells, such as plant cells and bacteria, which do come into contact with fresh water, are surrounded by tough cell walls. The cell walls prevent the cells from expanding, even under tremendous osmotic pressure. However, the increased osmotic pressure makes the cells extremely vulnerable to injuries to their cell walls.

CHECKPOINT ***What structures protect plant and bacterial cells from potential damage resulting from osmotic pressure?***

Facilitated Diffusion

A few molecules, such as the sugar glucose, seem to pass through the cell membrane much more quickly than they should. One might think that these molecules are too large or too strongly charged to cross the membrane, and yet they diffuse across quite easily.

How does this happen? The answer is that cell membranes have protein channels that make it easy for certain molecules to cross the membrane. Red blood cells, for example, have a cell membrane protein with an internal channel that allows glucose to pass through it. Only glucose can pass through this channel, and it can move through in either direction. This cell membrane protein is said to facilitate, or help, the diffusion of glucose across the membrane. The process, shown in **Figure 7–17**, is known as **facilitated** (fuh-SIL-uh-tayt-ud) **diffusion.** Hundreds of different protein channels have been found that allow particular substances to cross different membranes.

Although facilitated diffusion is fast and specific, it is still diffusion. Therefore, a net movement of molecules across a cell membrane will occur only if there is a higher concentration of the particular molecules on one side than on the other side. This movement does not require the use of the cell's energy.

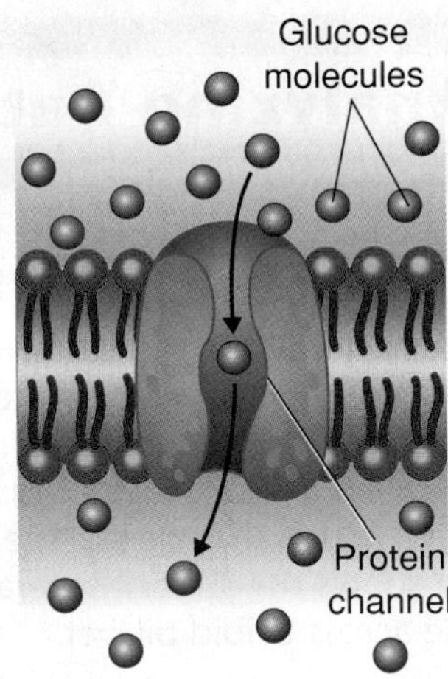

▲ **Figure 7–17** During facilitated diffusion, molecules, such as glucose, that cannot diffuse across the cell membrane's lipid bilayer on their own move through protein channels instead. **Applying Concepts** ***Does facilitated diffusion require the cell to use energy?***

Quick Lab

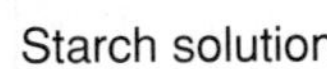
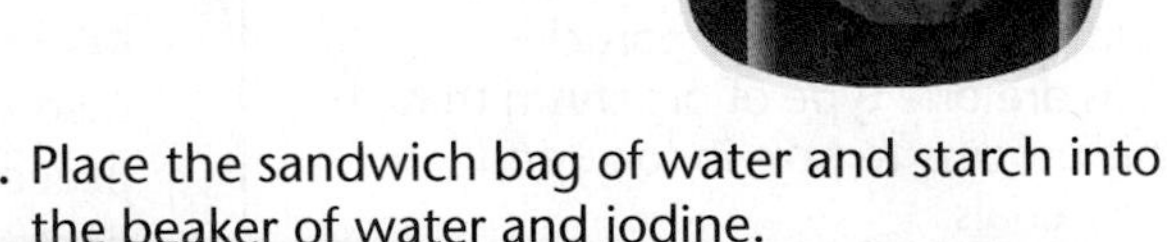

How can you model permeability in cells?

Materials graduated cylinder, plastic sandwich bag, starch, twist tie, 500-mL beaker, iodine solution

Procedure    

1. Pour about 50 mL of water into a plastic sandwich bag. Add 10 mL of starch. Secure the bag with a twist tie, and shake it gently to mix in the starch.
2. Put on your goggles, plastic gloves, and apron.
3. Pour 250 mL of water into a 500-mL beaker. **CAUTION:** *Handle the beaker carefully*. Add 15 drops of iodine. **CAUTION:** *Iodine is corrosive and irritating to the skin and can stain skin and clothing. Be careful not to spill it on yourself.*
4. Place the sandwich bag of water and starch into the beaker of water and iodine.
5. After 20 minutes, look at the sandwich bag in the beaker. Observe and record any changes that occurred.

Analyze and Conclude

1. **Using Models** What cell structure does the sandwich bag represent?
2. **Observing** What did you see inside the sandwich bag? Outside the sandwich bag?
3. **Inferring** Iodine turns blue-black in the presence of starch. What process do you think occurred that caused the results you observed? Explain.

Analyzing Data

Crossing the Cell Membrane

The cell membrane regulates what enters and leaves the cell and also provides protection and support. The core of nearly all cell membranes is a double-layered sheet called a lipid bilayer. Most materials entering the cell pass across this membrane by diffusion. The graph shows the sizes of several molecules that can diffuse across a lipid bilayer.

1. **Predicting** Which substances do you think will diffuse across the lipid bilayer most quickly? Most slowly? Explain your answers.
2. **Formulating Hypotheses** Formulate a hypothesis about the relationship between molecule size and rate of diffusion.
3. **Designing Experiments** Design an experiment to test your hypothesis.

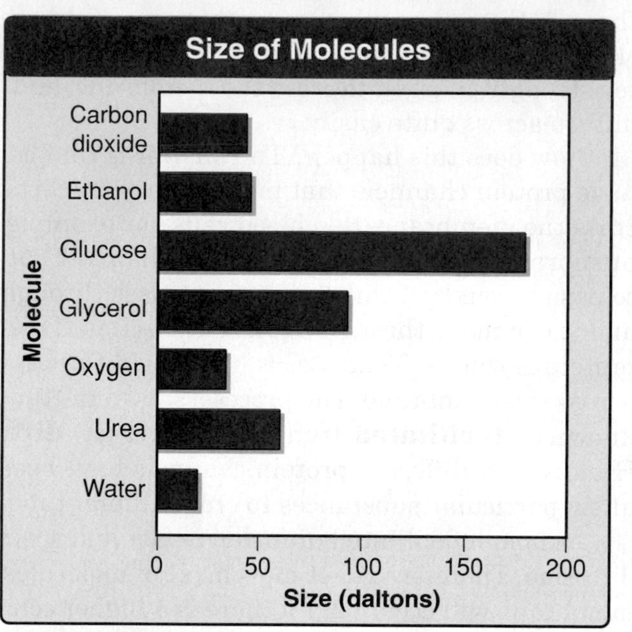

Active Transport

As powerful as diffusion is, cells sometimes must move materials in the opposite direction—against a concentration difference. This is accomplished by a process known as **active transport.** As its name implies, active transport requires energy. The active transport of small molecules or ions across a cell membrane is generally carried out by transport proteins or "pumps" that are found in the membrane itself. Larger molecules and clumps of material can also be actively transported across the cell membrane by processes known as endocytosis and exocytosis. The transport of these larger materials sometimes involves changes in the shape of the cell membrane.

Molecular Transport Small molecules and ions are carried across membranes by proteins in the membrane that act like energy-requiring pumps. Many cells use such proteins to move calcium, potassium, and sodium ions across cell membranes. Changes in protein shape, as shown in **Figure 7–19,** seem to play an important role in the pumping process. A considerable portion of the energy used by cells in their daily activities is devoted to providing the energy to keep this form of active transport working. The use of energy in these systems enables cells to concentrate substances in a particular location, even when the forces of diffusion might tend to move these substances in the opposite direction.

▼ **Figure 7–18** Phagocytosis is one form of active transport. During phagocytosis, extensions of cytoplasm surround and engulf large particles. Amoebas are one type of organism that uses this process to take in food and other materials.

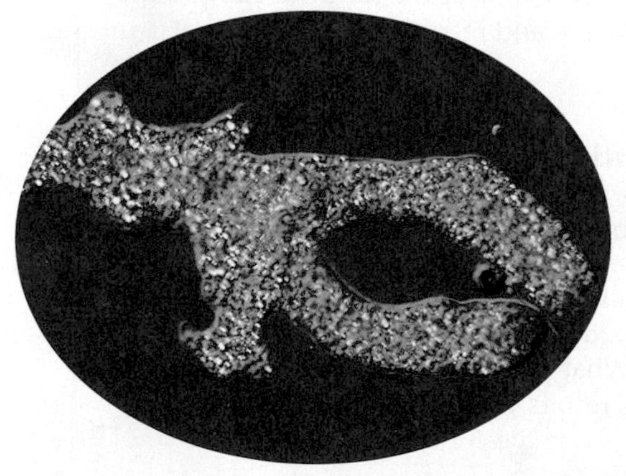

Endocytosis and Exocytosis Larger molecules and even solid clumps of material may be transported by movements of the cell membrane. One of these movements is called endocytosis (en-doh-sy-TOH-sis). **Endocytosis** is the process of taking material into the cell by means of infoldings, or pockets, of the cell membrane. The pocket that results breaks loose from the outer portion of the cell membrane and forms a vacuole within the cytoplasm. Large molecules, clumps of food, and even whole cells can be taken up in this way. Two examples of endocytosis are phagocytosis (fag-oh-sy-TOH-sis) and pinocytosis (py-nuh-sy-TOH-sis).

Phagocytosis means "cell eating." In **phagocytosis,** extensions of cytoplasm surround a particle and package it within a food vacuole. The cell then engulfs it. Amoebas use this method of taking in food. Engulfing material in this way requires a considerable amount of energy and, therefore, is correctly considered a form of active transport.

In a process similar to endocytosis, many cells take up liquid from the surrounding environment. Tiny pockets form along the cell membrane, fill with liquid, and pinch off to form vacuoles within the cell. This process is known as **pinocytosis.**

Many cells also release large amounts of material from the cell, a process known as exocytosis (ek-soh-sy-TOH-sis). During **exocytosis,** the membrane of the vacuole surrounding the material fuses with the cell membrane, forcing the contents out of the cell. The removal of water by means of a contractile vacuole is one example of this kind of active transport.

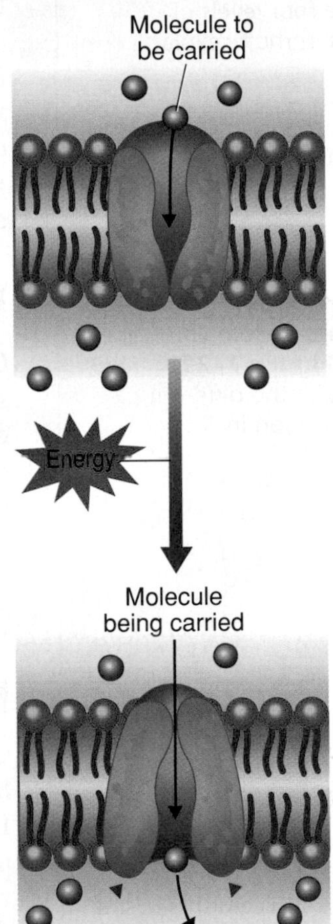

▶ **Figure 7–19** Active transport of particles against a concentration difference requires transport proteins and energy. **Interpreting Graphics** *What is happening in the illustration?*

7–3 Section Assessment

1. **Key Concept** Describe the functions of the cell membrane and cell wall.
2. **Key Concept** What happens during diffusion?
3. **Key Concept** Describe how water moves during osmosis.
4. What is the basic structure of a cell membrane?
5. What is the difference between phagocytosis and pinocytosis?
6. **Critical Thinking Comparing and Contrasting** What is the main way that active transport differs from diffusion?

Connecting Concepts

Homeostasis
What is the relationship between active transport and homeostasis? Give one example of active transport in an organism, and explain how the organism uses energy to maintain homeostasis. You may want to refer to Section 1–3.

7–4 The Diversity of Cellular Life

4-1 Levels of organization: from organelles to organisms **4-1** Cell parts are coordinated and work together
4-1 Functioning of organelles in single-celled organisms
4-1 Human homeostasis
4-1 Cell groupings

Guide for Reading

Key Concepts
- What is cell specialization?
- What are the four levels of organization in multicellular organisms?

Vocabulary
cell specialization
tissue
organ
organ system

Reading Strategy: Using Visuals Before you read, preview **Figure 7–22.** As you read, note the different levels of organization in the body.

Earth is sometimes called a living planet, and for good reason. From its simple beginnings, life has spread to every corner of the globe, penetrating deep into the earth and far beneath the surface of the seas. The diversity of life is so great that you might have to remind yourself that all living things are composed of cells, use the same basic chemistry, follow the same genetic code, and even contain the same kinds of organelles. This does not mean that all living things are the same. It does mean that their differences arise from the ways in which cells are specialized to perform certain tasks and the ways in which cells associate with each other to form multicellular organisms.

Unicellular Organisms

Cells are the basic living units of all organisms, but sometimes a single cell is a little more than that. Sometimes, a cell *is* the organism. A single-celled organism is also called a unicellular organism. Unicellular organisms do everything that you would expect a living thing to do. They grow, respond to the environment, transform energy, and reproduce. In terms of their numbers, unicellular organisms dominate life on Earth. Some examples of unicellular organisms are shown in **Figure 7–20.**

Multicellular Organisms

Organisms that are made up of many cells are called multicellular. There is a great variety among multicellular organisms. However, all multicellular organisms depend on communication and cooperation among specialized cells. **Cells throughout an organism can develop in different ways to perform different tasks.** This process is called **cell specialization.** Some examples of specialized cells are shown in **Figure 7–21.**

Figure 7–20 Yeasts, which are often used in bread making, are unicellular fungi. The *Volvox aureus* cells shown are actually individual alga cells that live together in a colony. The unicellular spiral-shaped bacterium *Leptospira interrogans* causes a serious disease in humans.

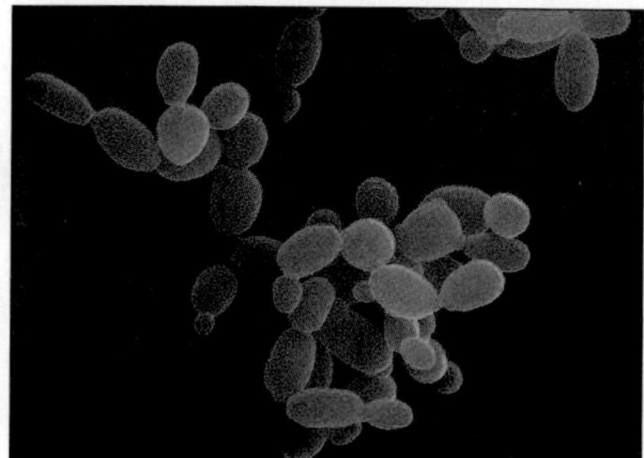

Yeast (magnification: 3400×)

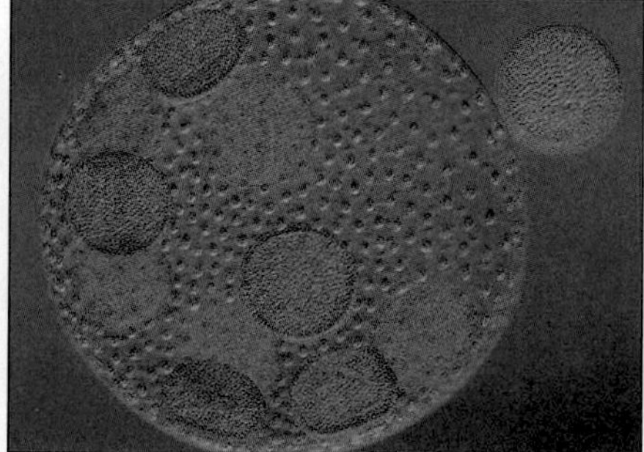

Volvox aureus (magnification: 250×)

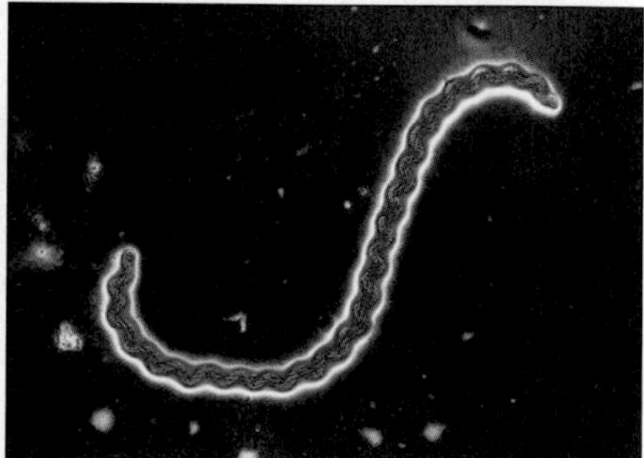

Leptospira interrogans (magnification: 27,000×)

FIGURE 7-21 CELL SPECIALIZATION

Cells in multicellular organisms are specialized to perform particular functions within the organism. Red blood cells transport oxygen throughout the body. Pancreatic cells produce compounds such as insulin that the body needs. Muscle cells contract and relax to move parts of the body. Guard cells control the opening and closing of stomata on the undersides of leaves.

Red Blood Cells (magnification: 13,000×)

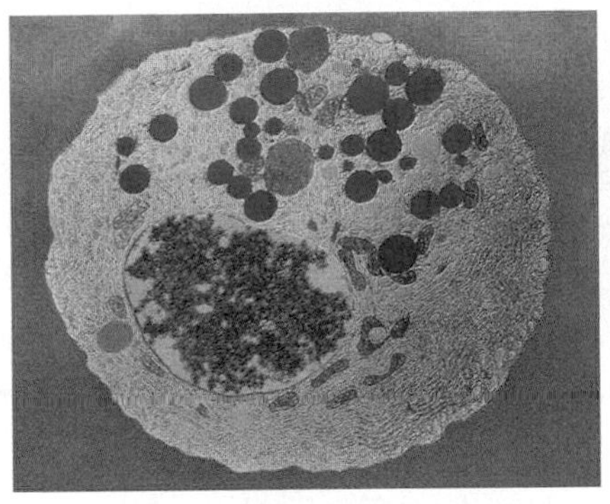

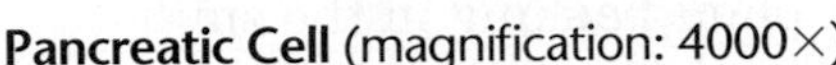

Pancreatic Cell (magnification: 4000×)

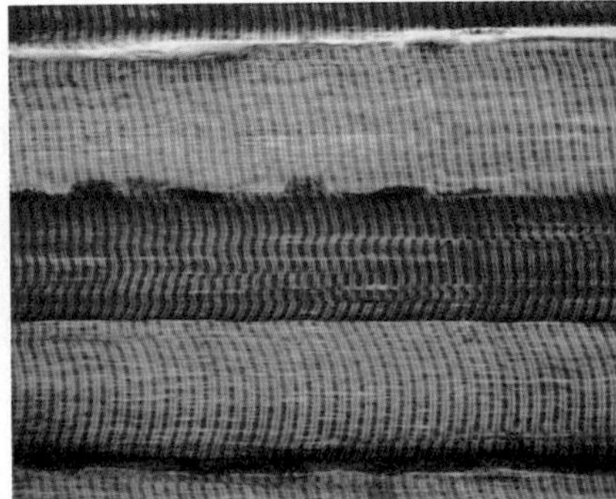

Muscle Cell (magnification: 350×)

Stomata (magnification: 510×)

Specialized Animal Cells Animal cells are specialized in many ways. Red blood cells are specialized to transport oxygen. Red blood cells contain a protein that binds to oxygen in the lungs and transports the oxygen throughout the body where it is released. Cells specialized to produce proteins, for example, are found in the pancreas. The pancreas is a gland that produces enzymes that make it possible to digest food. As you might expect, pancreatic cells are packed with ribosomes and rough ER, which are where proteins are produced. Pancreatic cells also possess large amounts of other organelles needed for protein export, including a well-developed Golgi apparatus and clusters of storage vacuoles loaded with enzymes.

The human ability to move is result of the specialized structures of muscle cells. These cells generate force by using a dramatically overdeveloped cytoskeleton. Skeletal muscle cells are packed with fibers arranged in a tight, regular pattern. Those fibers are actin microfilaments and a cytoskeletal protein called myosin. When they contract, muscle cells use chemical energy to pull these fibers past each other, generating force. Whether your muscles are large or small, your muscle cells themselves are "bulked up" with these specialized cytoskeletal proteins to a degree that makes them the body's undisputed heavy-lifting champions.

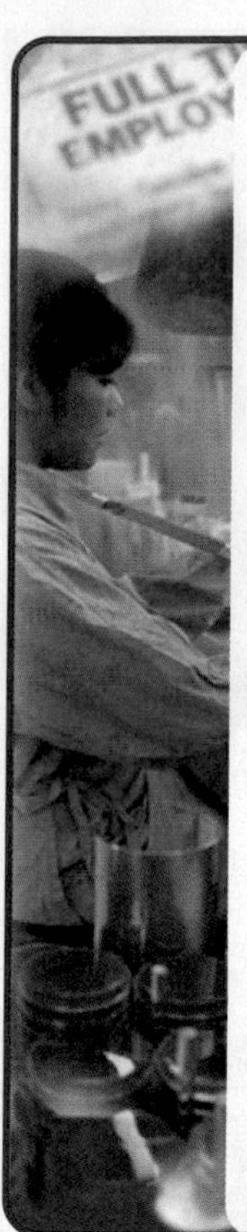

Careers in Biology

Histotechnologist

Job Description: work in a hospital laboratory, research institution, industrial laboratory, or government agency to prepare slides of body tissues for microscopic examination using special dyes and more advanced techniques, such as electron microscopy

Education: a bachelor's degree from a certified histotechnology program or a bachelor's degree with emphasis in biology and chemistry and one year's experience under a board-certified pathologist to become eligible for national certification exam, leading to a histotechnologist (HTL) certification

Skills: background in biology, anatomy, pathology, and/or chemistry; manual dexterity; attention to detail; good organizational skills; strong writing skills; computer literacy

Go Online
PHSchool.com
For: Career links
Visit: PHSchool.com
Web Code: cbb-3074

Specialized Plant Cells A plant basking in the sunlight may seem quiet and passive, but it is actually interacting with the environment at every moment. It rapidly exchanges carbon dioxide, oxygen, water vapor, and other gases through tiny openings called stomata on the undersides of leaves. Highly specialized cells, known as guard cells, regulate this exchange. Guard cells monitor the plant's internal conditions, changing their shape according to those conditions. For example, when the plant can benefit from gas exchange, the stomata open. The stomata close tightly when the plant's internal conditions change.

Levels of Organization

Biologists have identified levels of organization that make it easier to describe the cells within a multicellular organism. **The levels of organization in a multicellular organism are individual cells, tissues, organs, and organ systems.** These levels of organization are shown in **Figure 7–22.**

Tissues In multicellular organisms, cells are the first level of organization. Similar cells are grouped into units called tissues. A **tissue** is a group of similar cells that perform a particular function. The collection of cells that produce digestive enzymes in the pancreas makes up one kind of tissue. Most animals have four main types of tissue: muscle, epithelial, nervous, and connective tissue. You will read about these tissues in later chapters.

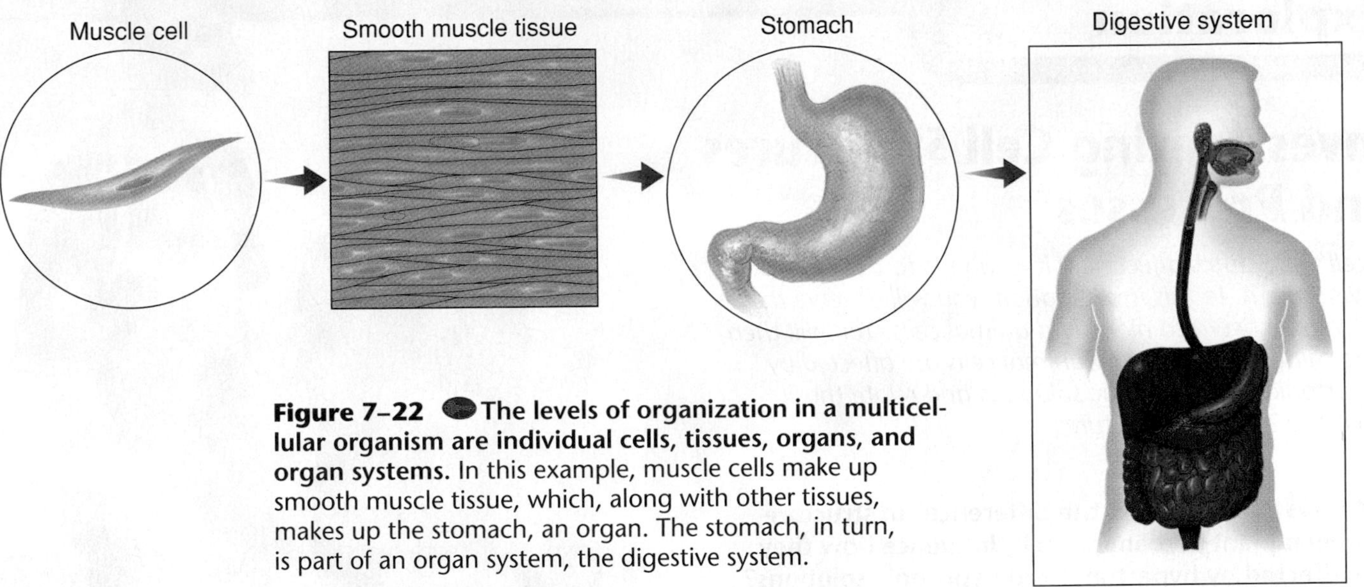

Figure 7–22 **The levels of organization in a multicellular organism are individual cells, tissues, organs, and organ systems.** In this example, muscle cells make up smooth muscle tissue, which, along with other tissues, makes up the stomach, an organ. The stomach, in turn, is part of an organ system, the digestive system.

Organs Many tasks within the body are too complicated to be carried out by just one type of tissue. In these cases, many groups of tissues work together as an **organ.** For example, each muscle in your body is an individual organ. Within a muscle, however, there is much more than muscle tissue. There are nerve tissues and connective tissues. Each type of tissue performs an essential task to help the organ function.

Organ Systems In most cases, an organ completes a series of specialized tasks. A group of organs that work together to perform a specific function is called an **organ system.**

The organization of the body's cells into tissues, organs, and organ systems creates a division of labor among those cells that makes multicellular life possible. Specialized cells such as nerve and muscle cells are able to function precisely because other cells are specialized to obtain the food and oxygen needed by those cells. This overall specialization and interdependence is one of the remarkable attributes of living things. Appreciating this characteristic is an important step in understanding the nature of living things.

7–4 Section Assessment

1. **Key Concept** In what kinds of organisms is cell specialization a characteristic?
2. **Key Concept** List the levels of biological organization in multicellular organisms from most simple to most complex.
3. How are unicellular organisms similar to multicellular organisms?
4. **Critical Thinking Predicting** Using what you know about the ways muscle moves, predict which organelles would be most common in muscle cells.

Writing in Science

Using Analogies

Use an organized area in your life—such as school, sports, or extracurricular activities—to construct an analogy to explain how the levels of organization in that chosen area can be compared with those of living organisms.

Investigating Cell Structures and Processes

A cell's structures affect how it responds to changes in its environment. In this investigation, you will observe the differences between plant and animal cells. You will then determine how plant and animal cells are affected by hypertonic and hypotonic solutions and relate those effects to the cells' structures.

Problem How do the differences in structure between plant and animal cells influence how they are affected by hypertonic and hypotonic solutions?

Materials

- forceps
- piece of red onion
- scalpel
- 4 glass slides
- dropper pipette
- 4 coverslips
- iodine solution
- paper towel
- microscope
- prepared slide of human cheek cells
- concentrated salt solution
- distilled water
- treated animal blood

Skills Observing, Comparing and Contrasting, Drawing Conclusions

Procedure

Part A: Plant and Animal Cell Structures

1. Put on safety goggles and a lab apron. Using forceps, peel a thin layer from the inner surface of a piece of a red onion, as shown in the photograph.
2. Use a scalpel to cut a small piece out of the layer you removed. **CAUTION:** *The scalpel is very sharp. Handle it carefully, and make sure to cut away from yourself.*
3. Place the piece of onion in the center of a glass slide. Add a drop of distilled water to the piece of onion, and cover it with a coverslip.
4. Put on your plastic gloves. Use a dropper pipette to place a drop of iodine solution at one end of the coverslip. **CAUTION:** *Iodine can stain skin and clothing. Be careful not to spill it on yourself.* Hold a piece of paper towel near the opposite edge of the coverslip, as shown in the diagram on page 195. This will draw the iodine under the coverslip, where it will stain the onion cells.
5. Examine your slide under the low-power objective of the microscope. **CAUTION:** *Microscopes and slides are fragile. Handle them carefully.* Sketch one cell, and label any structures you recognize.
6. Carefully switch to high power, and observe the cell again. Try to identify other cell structures, and add them to your sketch with appropriate labels.
7. Repeat steps 5 and 6 using a prepared slide of human cheek cells.

Part B: Effects of Hypertonic and Hypotonic Solutions

8. Repeat steps 1 to 3 to prepare another onion cell wet mount. Using the same method as in step 4, add a drop of concentrated salt solution to the slide, and use a paper towel to draw it under the coverslip.

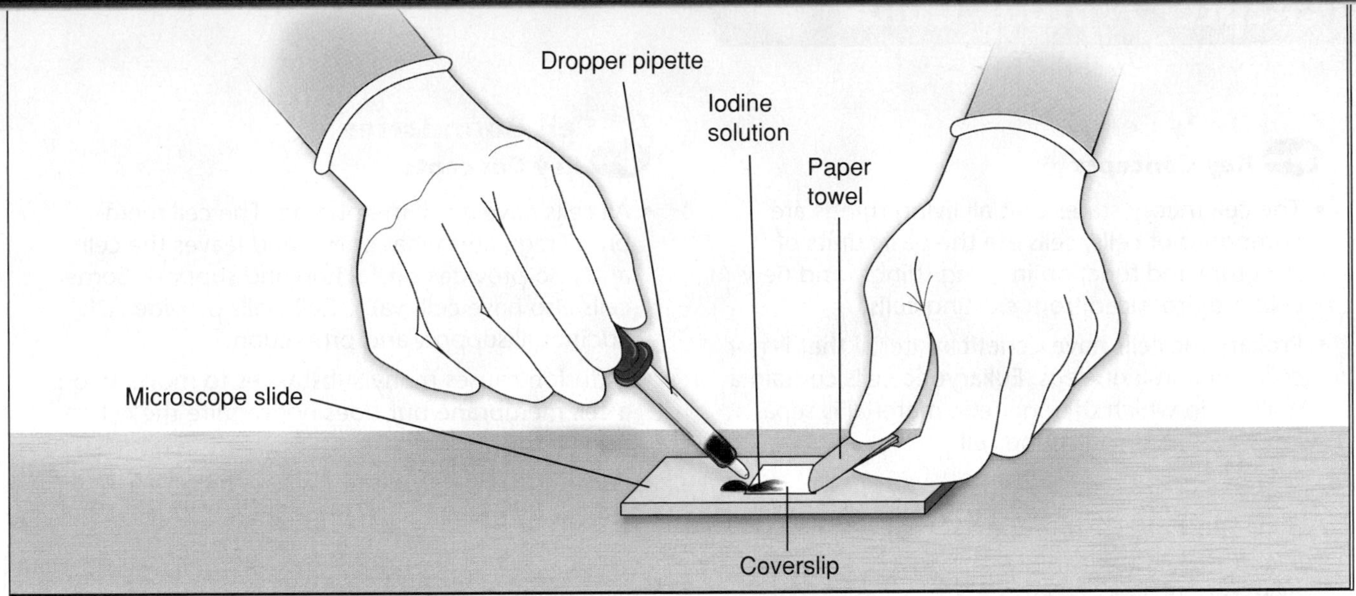

9. Observe the onion cells under the microscope under both low power and high power. Record your observations.
10. Prepare a wet-mount slide using treated animal blood. **CAUTION:** *Use only blood samples provided by your teacher.* Do not add water as you did with the onion cells.
11. Observe the blood cells under the microscope under both low power and high power. Sketch one cell, and label any structures you recognize.
12. Using the same method as in step 4, add a drop of concentrated salt solution to the slide, and use a paper towel to draw it under the coverslip.
13. Observe the blood cells under the microscope under both low power and high power. Record your observations. Rinse out the dropper pipette with distilled water.
14. Prepare another wet-mount slide of blood cells. This time, add a drop of distilled water to the slide and draw it under the coverslip.
15. Observe the blood cells under the microscope under both low power and high power. Record your observations.
16. Remove the plastic gloves and discard them according to your teacher's instructions. Wash your hands thoroughly with warm water and soap.

Analyze and Conclude

1. **Applying Concepts** Describe the shapes of the onion cells and the cheek cells you observed in Part A. What structures did you see in the onion cells? The cheek cells? Describe the functions of each of the structures you saw.
2. **Comparing and Contrasting** How are plant and animal cells similar in structure? How are they different?
3. **Drawing Conclusions** Explain your observations in step 9 of Part B in terms of osmosis and permeability.
4. **Drawing Conclusions** Explain your observations in steps 13 and 15 in terms of osmosis and permeability.
5. **Applying Concepts** What part of the cell is involved in the processes you observed in steps 9, 13, and 15? Explain your answer.
6. **Comparing and Contrasting** Why didn't the onion cells burst when they are in distilled water as in step 3? Relate your answer to the differences between plant and animal cells.

Go Further

Designing Experiments Design one or more experiments to test the effects of hypotonic and hypertonic solutions on other cells. Write a hypothesis for each experiment and control all variables. Get your teacher's permission before carrying out your experiments.

Chapter 7 Study Guide

7–1 Life Is Cellular

Key Concepts

- The cell theory states that all living things are composed of cells, cells are the basic units of structure and function in living things, and new cells are produced from existing cells.
- Prokaryotic cells have genetic material that is not contained in a nucleus. Eukaryotic cells contain a nucleus in which their genetic material is separated from the rest of the cell.

Vocabulary
cell, p. 170 • cell theory, p. 170
nucleus, p. 173 • eukaryote, p. 173
prokaryote, p. 173

7–2 Eukaryotic Cell Structure

Key Concepts

- The nucleus contains nearly all the cell's DNA and the coded instructions for making proteins and other important molecules.
- Proteins are assembled on ribosomes.
- One type of endoplasmic reticulum makes membranes and secretory proteins. The other type of ER makes lipids and helps to detoxify, or remove harmful substances.
- The Golgi apparatus modifies, sorts, and packages proteins and other materials from the endoplasmic reticulum for storage or secretion outside the cell.
- Mitochondria convert the chemical energy stored in food into compounds that are more convenient for the cell to use.
- Chloroplasts capture the energy from sunlight and convert it into chemical energy.
- The cytoskeleton is a network of protein filaments that helps the cell to maintain its shape. The cytoskeleton is also involved in movement of materials within and outside the cell.

Vocabulary
organelle, p. 174 • cytoplasm, p. 174
nuclear envelope, p. 176
chromatin, p. 176 • chromosome, p. 176
nucleolus, p. 176 • ribosome, p. 177
endoplasmic reticulum, p. 177
Golgi apparatus, p. 178
lysosome, p. 179 • vacuole, p. 179
mitochondrion, p. 179 • chloroplast, p. 180
cytoskeleton, p. 181 • centriole, p. 181

7–3 Cell Boundaries

Key Concepts

- All cells have a cell membrane. The cell membrane regulates what enters and leaves the cell and also provides protection and support. Some cells also have cell walls. Cell walls provide additional support and protection.
- Diffusion causes many substances to move across a cell membrane but does not require the cell to use energy.
- Osmosis is the diffusion of water through a selectively permeable membrane.

Vocabulary
cell membrane, p. 182 • cell wall, p. 182
lipid bilayer, p. 182 • concentration, p. 183
diffusion, p. 184 • equilibrium, p. 184
osmosis, p. 185 • isotonic, p. 185
hypertonic, p. 185 • hypotonic, p. 185
facilitated diffusion, p. 187
active transport, p. 188
endocytosis, p. 189 • phagocytosis, p. 189
pinocytosis, p. 189 • exocytosis, p. 189

7–4 The Diversity of Cellular Life

Key Concepts

- Cells in multicellular organisms develop in different ways to perform particular functions within the organism.
- The levels of organization in a multicellular organism are individual cells, tissues, organs, and organ systems.

Vocabulary
cell specialization, p. 190
tissue, p. 192
organ, p. 193
organ system, p. 193

Thinking Visually

Use the information in this chapter to create a concept map about the ways substances can move into and out of cells. Use the following terms in your concept map: *diffusion, osmosis, facilitated diffusion, active transport, phagocytosis, endocytosis, pinocytosis, exocytosis.*

Preparing for the Living Environment Exam

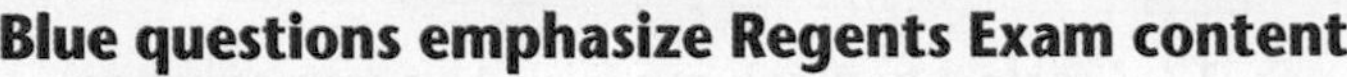

Blue questions emphasize Regents Exam content

Chapter 7

Part A

Multiple Choice

For each statement or question, select the number of the word or expression that, of those given, best completes the statement or answers the question.

1 Which structure in most cells controls the cell's activities?
(1) cell membrane (3) ribosome
(2) mitochondrion (4) nucleus

2 Despite differences in size and shape, all cells must have cytoplasm and a
(1) chloroplast (3) mitochondrion
(2) nucleus (4) cell membrane

3 Distinct threadlike structures containing genetic information are called
(1) ribosomes (3) nuclei
(2) chromosomes (4) mitochondria

4 Which organelle makes energy stored in high-energy compounds available for the cell?
(1) ribosome (3) mitochondrion
(2) chromosome (4) chloroplast

5 Cell membranes are constructed mainly of
(1) lipid bilayers (3) carbohydrate gates
(2) protein pumps (4) free-moving proteins

6 A substance that moves across a cell membrane without using the cell's energy tends to move
(1) away from the area of equilibrium
(2) away from the area where it is less concentrated
(3) away from the area where it is more concentrated
(4) toward the area where it is more concentrated

7 Which cell is best suited to transmit information through the human body?

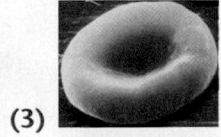

(1) 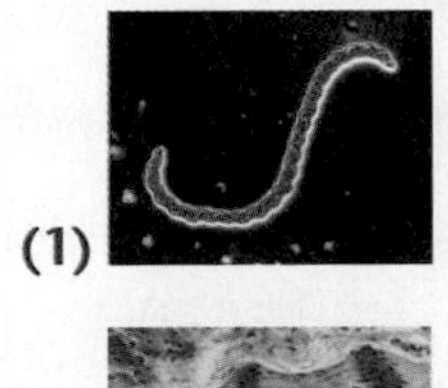
(3) 
(2) 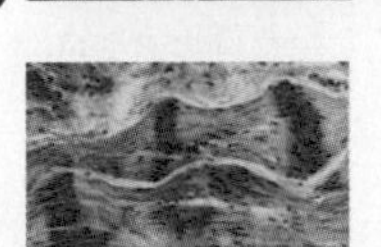
(4) 

8 A tissue is composed of a group of
(1) similar cells
(2) related organelles
(3) organ systems
(4) related organs

9 Which structure is *not* associated with animal cells?
(1) mitochondrion (3) nucleus
(2) chloroplast (4) cell membrane

10 The nucleus consists of all structures *except*
(1) cytoplasm
(2) chromatin
(3) genetic material
(4) a nuclear envelope

11 Which statement best describes the expected result when a typical cell is placed into fresh water?
(1) There would be a net movement of water out of the cell.
(2) There would be a net movement of water into the cell.
(3) Active transport of water into the cell would begin.
(4) No change in the cell's water content would occur.

12 Which cell structure is sometimes found attached to the endoplasmic reticulum?
(1) chloroplast (3) nucleus
(2) mitochondrion (4) ribosome

For questions 13 and 14, complete each analogy by selecting the correct number. In analogies, A : B :: C : means "A is to B as C is to ___?___."

13 Chloroplast : energy transfer :: nucleus :
(1) mitochondrion (3) protein manufacture
(2) DNA (4) information storage

14 Factory : assembly-line workers :: cell :
(1) vacuoles (3) ribosomes
(2) nuclei (4) mitochondria

Test-Taking Tip When you answer a question based on experimental data, read the description of the experiment carefully to determine the steps followed. Then, try to see if there are any trends in the data. For example, "if *x* increases, what happens to *y*"?

Preparing for the Living Environment Exam

Part B

Multiple Choice and Extended Response

For those questions that ask you to select a response, choose the one that best completes the statement or answers the question. For all others follow the directions given.

Base your answers to questions 15 and 16 on the information and graph below and on your knowledge of biology.

In an experiment, plant cells were placed in sucrose solutions of varying concentrations. The rate at which the plant cells absorbed sucrose from the solution was then measured for the different concentrations. The results are summarized in the graph.

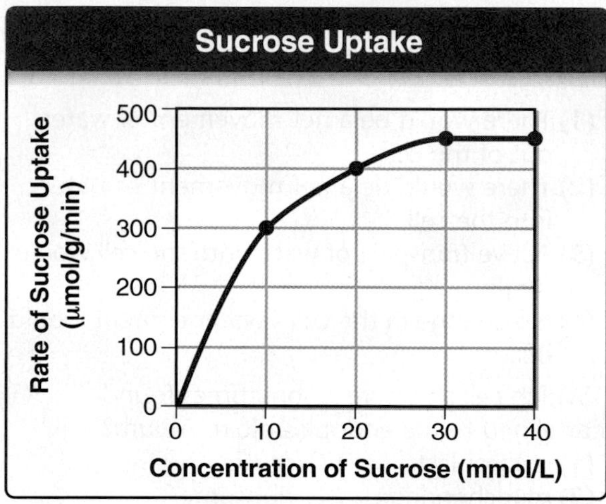

15 Which statement is best supported by information in the graph?
- **(1)** The rate of sucrose uptake increases at a constant rate from 0 to 30 mmol/L.
- **(2)** The rate of sucrose uptake decreases at a varying rate from 0 to 30 mmol/L.
- **(3)** The rate of sucrose uptake is less at 25 mmol/L than at 5 mmol/L.
- **(4)** The rate of sucrose uptake is constant between 30 and 40 mmol/L.

16 The graph shows that as the concentration of sucrose increases from 10 to 30 mmol/L, the plant cells
- **(1)** take in sucrose more slowly
- **(2)** take in sucrose more quickly
- **(3)** secrete sucrose more slowly
- **(4)** secrete sucrose more quickly

17 Create a two-column table to summarize the contributions made to the cell theory by Robert Hooke, Matthias Schleiden, Theodor Schwann, and Rudolf Virchow.

18 Many cells produce proteins that are secreted from the cell. Identify the two cell structures that cooperate to produce these specific proteins and describe the role of each in the process.

19 Chloroplasts and mitochondria are each involved in the transfer of energy. Explain how these two organelles work together in plant cells to take care of the plant's energy needs.

20 *a* Identify *two* cell structures, other than the nucleus, that contain their own DNA.

b Describe the hypothesis Lynn Margulis has proposed to account for the presence of DNA in these organelles.

21 State one function of the protein molecules that are located in cell membranes.

22 Which salt solution is more concentrated, Solution A, which contains 18 g of salt in 6 L of water, or Solution B, which contains 24 g of salt in 12 L of water? Support your answer with an explanation.

23 Identify the plant cell structure that helps prevent damage to cells when they are subjected to high osmotic pressure.

24 The beaker in the diagram has a selectively permeable membrane separating two solutions. Assume that the salt molecules can pass freely through the membrane. Will the water level on either side of the membrane be different when equilibrium is reached? Support your answer with an explanation.

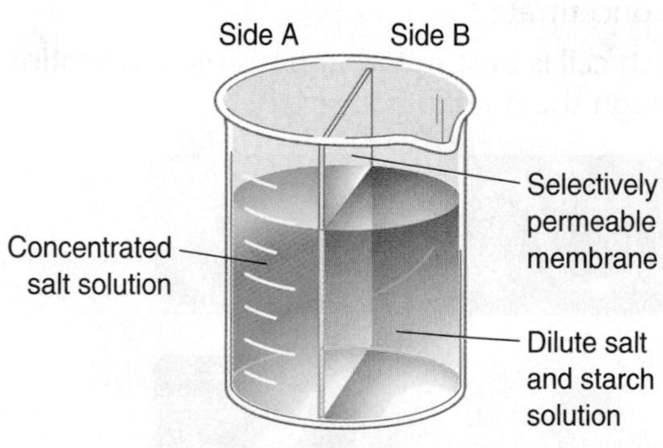

25 Single-celled organisms are able to function and maintain homeostasis, yet they do not have the tissues, organs, or organ systems that multicellular organisms use for this purpose. Identify the features that are found in most single-celled organisms that serve a similar purpose and enable them to function normally.

26 Many cells produce proteins that are secreted from the cell. Identify the *two* cell structures that cooperate to produce these specific proteins, and describe the role of each in the process.

Part C

Extended Response

Answer the questions or follow the directions given.

27 Describe the process of diffusion across a membrane. In your description, be sure to
- state how cellular energy is involved in this process
- state the direction substances move in relation to their concentrations

28 As waste chemicals build up in a cell, homeostasis is threatened. Explain how diffusion helps cells maintain low levels of waste chemicals.

29 Digestion of many food substances is necessary to make nutrients available to an organism's cells. To accomplish digestion, cells lining the digestive organs produce proteins called enzymes that are secreted by the cells into the digestive tract.
   a Explain why it is necessary for most food substances to be broken down into smaller molecules before they can be used within the body's cells.
   b Explain the role of the ribosomes and cell membrane in this process.

30 Diffusion and active transport are processes that are important to the maintenance of homeostasis in organisms. Compare the two processes, including examples that describe how they are important to living organisms. In your answer be sure to
- state *two* ways in which active transport differs from diffusion
- state one way the two processes are similar
- state an example of each process as used by a living organism

Base your answer to question 31 on the information below and on your knowledge of biology.

In an investigation to test the effects of varying salt concentrations on potato cells, a student placed a slice of raw potato into each of three beakers. Different solutions were added to the beakers, and the beakers were sealed. After 24 hours, the condition of each potato slice was observed. The results are summarized in the table below.

Experiment Results

Beaker	Contents of Beaker	Condition of Potato Slice After 24 Hours
A	Pure water	Very firm
B	2% salt solution	Near normal firmness
C	4% salt solution	Very flexible—not firm

31 Interpret and explain the results of this experiment. In your answer be sure to:
   a Predict the approximate concentration of water in the cytoplasm of normal potato cells. Support your prediction with an explanation.
   b Predict how the cells of the potato slice in Beaker A would differ in appearance from normal potato cells when viewed with a compound microscope. Support your prediction with an explanation.
   c Identify the process responsible for the changes in the potato cells

For: An interactive self-test
Visit: PHSchool.com
Web Code: cba-3070

CHAPTER 8

Photosynthesis

This leaf is carrying out photosynthesis, which converts light energy into chemical energy that the grasshoppers can use.

Inquiry Activity

How do organisms capture and use energy?

Procedure 

1. Obtain two test tubes wrapped in foil. Note the hole in the foil surrounding one test tube.
2. **Predicting** The test tubes contain *Euglena,* photosynthetic microorganisms that have chloroplasts and can move. Record your prediction of where in each test tube you will find *Euglena.*
3. Without shaking or disturbing the contents of the test tubes, carefully remove the foil. Record where *Euglena* are located in each test tube.

Think About It

1. **Observing** What pattern did you observe in the distribution of the *Euglena?* Why do you think they behave this way?
2. **Inferring** What is the source of energy that powers the *Euglena*'s swimming?

8–1 Energy and Life

4-5.1 Photosynthesis
4-5.1 Energy stored in chemical bonds
4-5.1 Energy from ATP
LS- Make observations

Energy is the ability to do work. Nearly every activity in modern society depends on one kind of energy or another. When a car runs out of fuel—more precisely, out of the chemical energy in gasoline—it comes to a sputtering halt. Without electrical energy, lights, appliances, and computers stop working.

Living things depend on energy, too. Sometimes, the need for energy is easy to see. It is obvious that energy is needed to play soccer or other sports. However, there are times when that need is less obvious. For example, when you are sleeping, your cells are busy using energy to build new proteins and amino acids. Clearly, without the ability to obtain and use energy, life would cease to exist.

Guide for Reading

Key Concepts
- Where do plants get the energy they need to produce food?
- What is the role of ATP in cellular activities?

Vocabulary
autotroph
heterotroph
adenosine triphosphate (ATP)

Reading Strategy: Asking Questions Before you read, study the diagram in **Figure 8–3.** Make a list of questions that you have about the diagram. As you read, write down the answers to your questions.

Autotrophs and Heterotrophs

Where does the energy that living things need come from? The simple answer is that it comes from food. Originally, though, the energy in most food comes from the sun. **Plants and some other types of organisms are able to use light energy from the sun to produce food.** Organisms such as plants, which make their own food, are called **autotrophs** (AW-toh-trohfs).

Other organisms, such as animals, cannot use the sun's energy directly. These organisms, known as **heterotrophs** (HET-uh-roh-trohfs), obtain energy from the foods they consume. Impalas, for example, eat grasses, which are autotrophs. Other heterotrophs, such as the leopard shown in **Figure 8–1,** obtain the energy stored in autotrophs indirectly by feeding on animals that eat autotrophs. Still other heterotrophs—mushrooms, for example—obtain food by decomposing other organisms. To live, all organisms, including plants, must release the energy in sugars and other compounds.

Figure 8–1 **Autotrophs use light energy from the sun to produce food.** These impalas get their energy by eating grass, while this leopard gets its energy by eating impalas and other animals. Impalas and leopards are both heterotrophs.

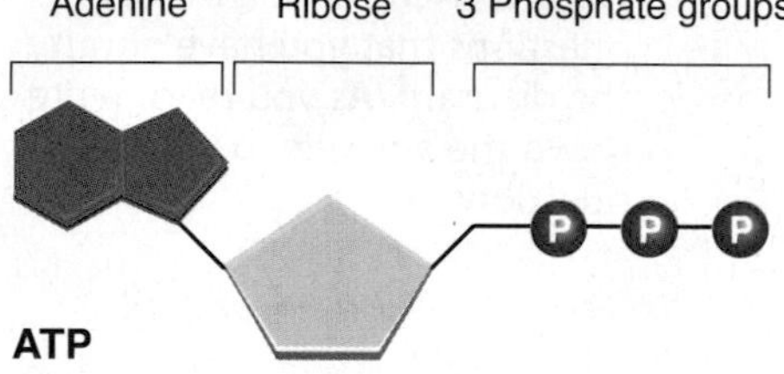

▲ **Figure 8–2** **ATP is used by all types of cells as their basic energy source.** The energy needed by the cells of this soccer player comes from ATP.

Chemical Energy and ATP

Energy comes in many forms, including light, heat, and electricity. Energy can be stored in chemical compounds, too. For example, when you light a candle, the wax melts, soaks into the wick, and is burned, releasing energy in the form of light and heat. As the candle burns, high-energy chemical bonds between carbon and hydrogen atoms in the wax are broken. The high-energy bonds are replaced by low-energy bonds between these atoms and oxygen. The energy of a candle flame is released from electrons. When the electrons in those bonds are shifted from higher energy levels to lower energy levels, the extra energy is released as heat and light.

Living things use chemical fuels as well. One of the principal chemical compounds that cells use to store and release energy is **adenosine triphosphate** (uh-DEN-uh-seen try-FAHS-fayt), abbreviated **ATP.** As **Figure 8–2** shows, ATP consists of adenine, a 5-carbon sugar called ribose, and three phosphate groups. Those three phosphate groups are the key to ATP's ability to store and release energy.

Storing Energy Adenosine diphosphate (ADP) is a compound that looks almost like ATP, except that it has two phosphate groups instead of three. This difference is the key to the way in which living things store energy. When a cell has energy available, it can store small amounts of it by adding a phosphate group to ADP molecules, producing ATP, as shown in **Figure 8–3.** In a way, ATP is like a fully charged battery, ready to power the machinery of the cell.

Releasing Energy How is the energy that is stored in ATP released? Simply by breaking the chemical bond between the second and third phosphates, energy is released. Because a cell can subtract that third phosphate group, it can release energy as needed. ATP has enough energy to power a variety of cellular activities, including active transport across cell membranes, protein synthesis, and muscle contraction. **The characteristics of ATP make it exceptionally useful as the basic energy source of all cells.**

What is the difference between ATP and ADP?

Using Biochemical Energy

One way cells use the energy provided by ATP is to carry out active transport. Many cell membranes contain a sodium-potassium pump, a membrane protein that pumps sodium ions (Na^+) out of the cell and potassium ions (K^+) into it. ATP provides the energy that keeps this pump working, maintaining a carefully regulated balance of ions on both sides of the cell membrane. ATP produces movement, too, providing the energy for motor proteins that move organelles throughout the cell.

For: ATP activity
Visit: PHSchool.com
Web Code: cbd-3081

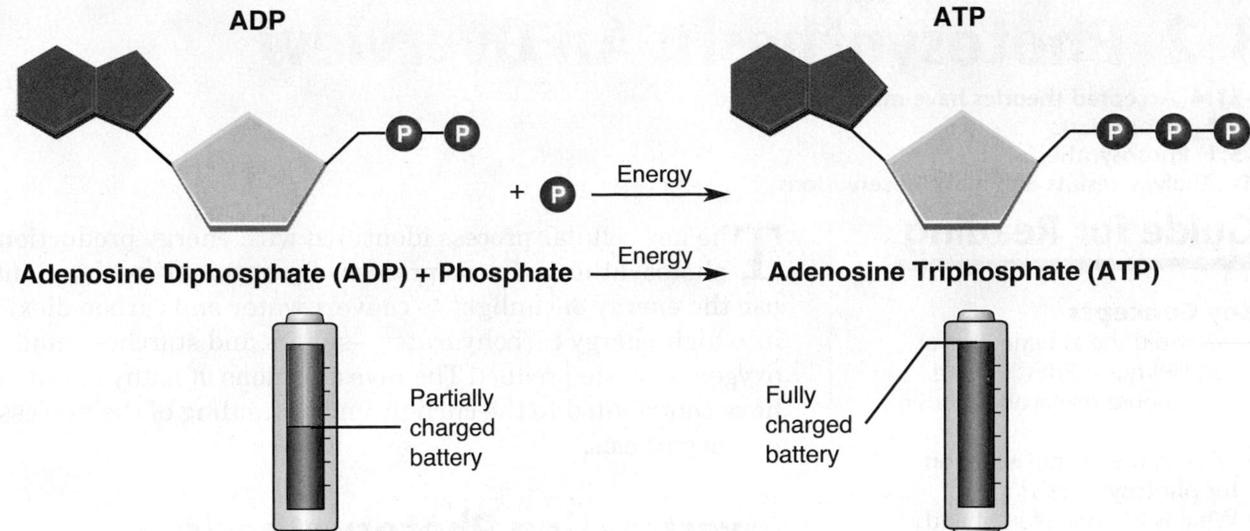

▲ **Figure 8–3** ATP can be compared to a fully charged battery because both contain stored energy, whereas ADP resembles a partially charged battery. **Predicting** ***What happens when a phosphate group is removed from ATP?***

Energy from ATP powers other important events in the cell, including the synthesis of proteins and nucleic acids and responses to chemical signals at the cell surface. The energy from ATP can even be used to produce light. In fact, the blink of a firefly on a summer night comes from an enzyme powered by ATP!

ATP is such a useful source of energy that you might think the cells would be packed with ATP to get them through the day, but this is not the case. In fact, most cells have only a small amount of ATP, enough to last them for a few seconds of activity. Why? Even though ATP is a great molecule for transferring energy, it is not a good one for storing large amounts of energy over the long term. A single molecule of the sugar glucose stores more than 90 times the chemical energy of a molecule of ATP. Therefore, it is more efficient for cells to keep only a small supply of ATP on hand. Cells can regenerate ATP from ADP as needed by using the energy in foods like glucose. As you will see, that's exactly what they do.

8–1 Section Assessment

1. **Key Concept** What is the ultimate source of energy for plants?
2. **Key Concept** What is ATP and what is its role in the cell?
3. Describe one cellular activity that uses the energy released by ATP.
4. How do autotrophs obtain energy? How do heterotrophs obtain energy?
5. **Critical Thinking Comparing and Contrasting** With respect to energy, how are ATP and glucose similar? How are they different?

Connecting Concepts

Ecology

Recall that energy flows and that nutrients cycle through the biosphere. How does the process of photosynthesis impact the flow of energy and the cycling of nutrients? You may wish to refer to Chapter 3 to help you answer this question.

8–2 Photosynthesis: An Overview

1-S1.4 Accepted theories have much support
4-5.1 Chloroplasts
4-5.1 Photosynthesis
LS- Analyze results and make observations

Guide for Reading

Key Concepts

- What did the experiments of van Helmont, Priestley, and Ingenhousz reveal about how plants grow?
- What is the overall equation for photosynthesis?
- What is the role of light and chlorophyll in photosynthesis?

Vocabulary
photosynthesis
pigment
chlorophyll

Reading Strategy: Summarizing As you read, find the key ideas under each blue head. Write down a few key words from each key idea. Then, use the key words in your summary.

The key cellular process identified with energy production is photosynthesis. In the process of **photosynthesis,** plants use the energy of sunlight to convert water and carbon dioxide into high-energy carbohydrates—sugars and starches—and oxygen, a waste product. The investigations of many scientists have contributed to the current understanding of the process of photosynthesis.

Investigating Photosynthesis

Research into photosynthesis began centuries ago with a simple question: When a tiny seedling grows into a tall tree with a mass of several tons, where does the tree's increase in mass come from? From the soil? From the water? From the air?

Van Helmont's Experiment In the 1600s, the Belgian physician Jan van Helmont devised an experiment to find out if plants grew by taking material out of the soil. Van Helmont determined the mass of a pot of dry soil and a small seedling. Then, he planted the seedling in the pot of soil. He watered it regularly. At the end of five years, the seedling, which by then had grown into a small tree, had gained about 75 kg.

Biology and History

Understanding Photosynthesis

Many scientists have contributed to understanding how plants carry out photosynthesis. Early research focused on the overall process. Later researchers investigated the detailed chemical pathways.

1643
Jan van Helmont
After careful measurements of a plant's water intake and mass increase, van Helmont concludes that trees gain most of their mass from water.

1771
Joseph Priestley
Using a bell jar, a candle, and a plant, Priestley finds that the plant releases oxygen.

1779
Jan Ingenhousz
Ingenhousz finds that aquatic plants produce oxygen bubbles in the light but not in the dark. He concludes that plants need sunlight to produce oxygen.

1600 1700 1800

The mass of the soil, however, was almost unchanged. He concluded that most of the gain in mass had come from water, because that was the only thing that he had added.

Van Helmont's experiment accounts for the "hydrate," or water, portion of the carbohydrate produced by photosynthesis. But where does the carbon of the "carbo-" portion come from? Although van Helmont did not realize it, carbon dioxide in the air made a major contribution to the mass of his tree. The carbon in carbon dioxide is used to make sugars and other carbohydrates in photosynthesis. Van Helmont had only part of the story, but he had made a major contribution to science.

Priestley's Experiment More than 100 years after van Helmont's experiment, the English minister Joseph Priestley performed an experiment that would give another insight into the process of photosynthesis. Priestley took a candle, placed a glass jar over it, and watched as the flame gradually died out. Something in the air, Priestley reasoned, was necessary to keep a candle flame burning. When that substance was used up, the candle went out. That substance was oxygen.

Priestley then found that if he placed a live sprig of mint under the jar and allowed a few days to pass, the candle could be relighted and would remain lighted for a while. The mint plant had produced the substance required for burning. In other words, it released oxygen.

CHECKPOINT *What did Priestley discover about photosynthesis?*

Word Origins

Photosynthesis comes from the Greek words *photo,* meaning "light," and *synthesis,* meaning "putting together." Therefore, *photosynthesis* means "using light to put something together," specifically, carbohydrates. *Chemo* means "having to do with chemicals or chemical reactions." **What do you think *chemosynthesis* means?**

Writing in Science

Use the Internet or library resources to research the experiments conducted by one of these scientists. Then, write a summary describing how the scientist contributed to the modern understanding of photosynthesis.

1845
Julius Robert Mayer
Mayer proposes that plants convert light energy into chemical energy.

1948
Melvin Calvin
Calvin traces the chemical path that carbon follows to form glucose. These reactions are also known as the Calvin cycle.

1992
Rudolph Marcus
Marcus wins the Nobel Prize in chemistry for describing the process by which electrons are transferred from one molecule to another in the electron transport chain.

1900

2000

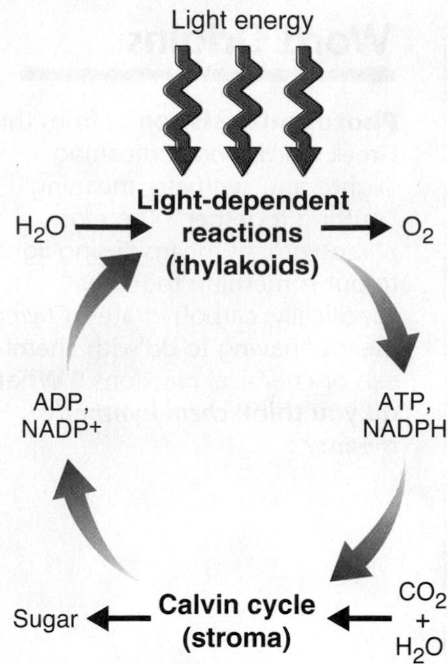

▲ **Figure 8–4**  **Photosynthesis is a series of reactions that uses light energy from the sun to convert water and carbon dioxide into sugars and oxygen.**

Jan Ingenhousz Later, the Dutch scientist Jan Ingenhousz showed that the effect observed by Priestley occurred only when the plant was exposed to light. The results of both Priestley's and Ingenhousz's experiments showed that light is necessary for plants to produce oxygen. **The experiments performed by van Helmont, Priestley, and Ingenhousz led to work by other scientists who finally discovered that in the presence of light, plants transform carbon dioxide and water into carbohydrates, and they also release oxygen.**

The Photosynthesis Equation

Because photosynthesis usually produces 6-carbon sugars ($C_6H_{12}O_6$) as the final product, the overall equation for photosynthesis can be shown as follows:

$$6CO_2 + 6H_2O \xrightarrow{\text{light}} C_6H_{12}O_6 + 6O_2$$

$$\text{carbon dioxide} + \text{water} \xrightarrow{\text{light}} \text{sugars} + \text{oxygen}$$

Photosynthesis uses the energy of sunlight to convert water and carbon dioxide into high-energy sugars and oxygen. Plants then use the sugars to produce complex carbohydrates such as starches. Plants obtain carbon dioxide from the air or water in which they grow. The process of photosynthesis is shown in **Figure 8–4.**

Quick Lab

What waste material is produced during photosynthesis?

Materials large clear plastic cup, sodium bicarbonate solution, elodea plant, large test tube

Procedure

1. Fill a large clear plastic cup about half full with sodium bicarbonate solution. The sodium bicarbonate solution is a source of carbon dioxide.
2. Place an elodea plant in a large test tube with the cut stem at the bottom. Fill the tube with sodium bicarbonate solution. **CAUTION:** *Handle the test tube carefully.*
3. Hold your thumb over the mouth of the tube. Turn the tube over, and lower it to the bottom of the cup. Make sure there is no air trapped in the tube.
4. Place the cup in bright light.
5. After at least 20 minutes, look closely at the elodea leaves. Record your observations.

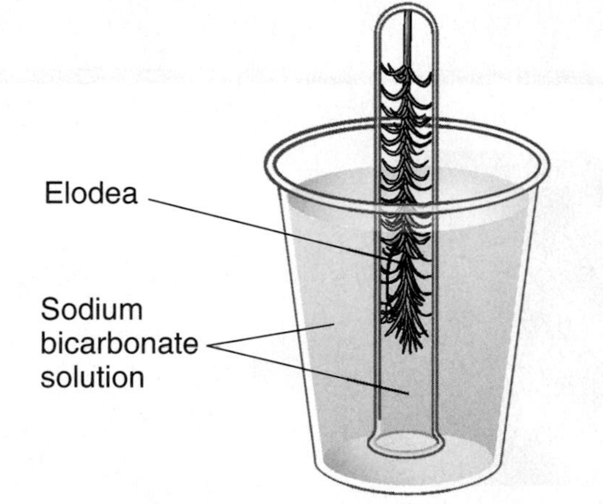

Analyze and Conclude

1. **Observing** What did you observe on the elodea leaves?
2. **Inferring** What substance accumulated in the leaves? Should that substance be considered a waste product? Explain.
3. **Applying Concepts** What plant organelle carries out photosynthesis and produces the gas?

Light and Pigments

Although the equation tells you that water and carbon dioxide are required for photosynthesis, it does not tell you how plants use these low-energy raw materials to produce high-energy sugars. To answer that question, you have to know how plants capture the energy of sunlight. **In addition to water and carbon dioxide, photosynthesis requires light and chlorophyll, a molecule in chloroplasts.**

Energy from the sun travels to Earth in the form of light. Sunlight, which your eyes perceive as "white" light, is actually a mixture of different wavelengths of light. Many of these wavelengths are visible to your eyes and make up what is known as the visible spectrum. Your eyes see the different wavelengths of the visible spectrum as different colors.

Plants gather the sun's energy with light-absorbing molecules called **pigments.** The plants' principal pigment is **chlorophyll** (KLAWR-uh-fil). There are two main types of chlorophyll: chlorophyll *a* and chlorophyll *b*.

As **Figure 8–5** shows, chlorophyll absorbs light very well in the blue-violet and red regions of the visible spectrum. However, chlorophyll does not absorb light well in the green region of the spectrum. Green light is reflected by leaves, which is why plants look green. Plants also contain red and orange pigments such as carotene that absorb light in other regions of the spectrum.

Because light is a form of energy, any compound that absorbs light also absorbs the energy from that light. When chlorophyll absorbs light, much of the energy is transferred directly to electrons in the chlorophyll molecule, raising the energy levels of these electrons. These high-energy electrons make photosynthesis work.

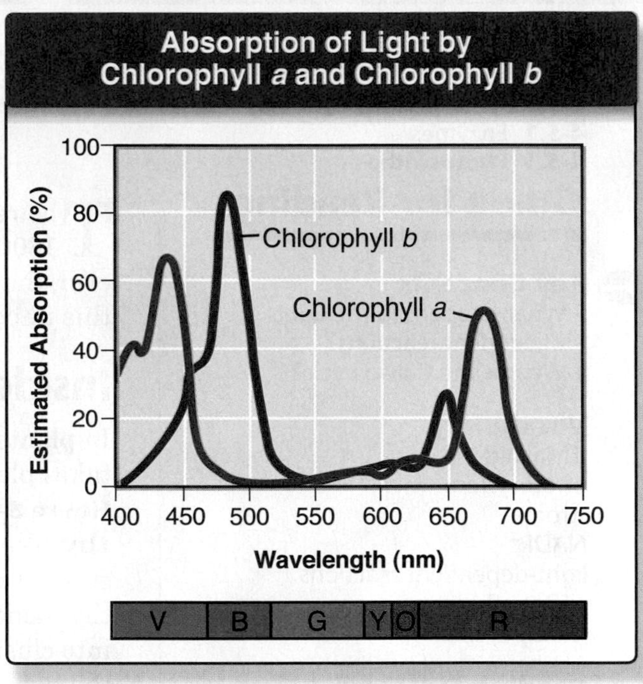

▲ **Figure 8–5** **Photosynthesis requires light and chlorophyll.** In the graph above, notice how chlorophyll *a* absorbs light mostly in the blue-violet and red regions of the visible spectrum, whereas chlorophyll *b* absorbs light in the blue and red regions of the visible spectrum.

8–2 Section Assessment

1. **Key Concept** What did van Helmont, Priestley, and Ingenhousz discover about plants?
2. **Key Concept** Describe the process of photosynthesis, including the reactants and products.
3. **Key Concept** Why are light and chlorophyll needed for photosynthesis?
4. Describe the relationship between chlorophyll and the color of plants.
5. **Critical Thinking Predicting** How well would a plant grow under pure yellow light? Explain your answer.

Writing in Science

Descriptive Writing

Write a summary paragraph describing either van Helmont's, Priestley's, or Ingenhousz's experiments with plants and light. *Hint:* Use the first boldface key sentence on page 206 to give you an idea for the topic sentence.

8–3 The Reactions of Photosynthesis

1-S3.1 Interpreting data may lead to new hypotheses
4-5.1 Enzymes
4-5.1 Photosynthesis
4-6.1 Organism survival depends on the physical conditions

Guide for Reading

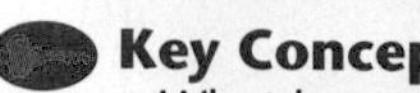

Key Concepts
- What happens in the light-dependent reactions?
- What is the Calvin cycle?

Vocabulary
thylakoid
photosystem
stroma
$NADP^+$
light-dependent reactions
ATP synthase
Calvin cycle

Reading Strategy: Using Visuals Before you read, preview **Figures 8–7, 8–10,** and **8–11.** As you read, notice where in the chloroplast each stage of photosynthesis takes place.

The requirements of photosynthesis were discovered in the 1800s. It was not until the second half of the 1900s, however, that biologists understood the complex reactions that make this important cellular process possible.

Inside a Chloroplast

In plants and other photosynthetic eukaryotes, photosynthesis takes place inside chloroplasts. The chloroplasts, shown in **Figure 8–6,** contain saclike photosynthetic membranes called **thylakoids** (THY-luh-koydz). Thylakoids are arranged in stacks known as grana (singular: granum). Proteins in the thylakoid membrane organize chlorophyll and other pigments into clusters known as **photosystems.** These photosystems are the light-collecting units of the chloroplast.

Scientists describe the reactions of photosystems in two parts: the light-dependent reactions and the light-independent reactions, or Calvin cycle. The relationship between these two sets of reactions is shown in **Figure 8–7.** The light-dependent reactions take place within the thylakoid membranes. The Calvin cycle takes place in the **stroma,** the region outside the thylakoid membranes.

Figure 8–6 In plants, photosynthesis takes place inside chloroplasts. **Observing** *What are thylakoids?*

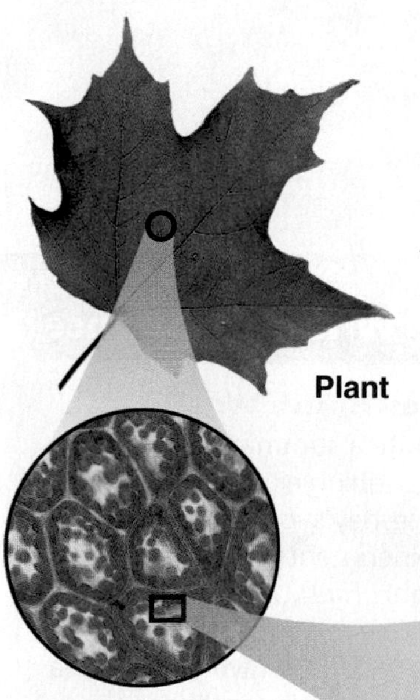
Plant
Plant Cells
(magnification: 500×)

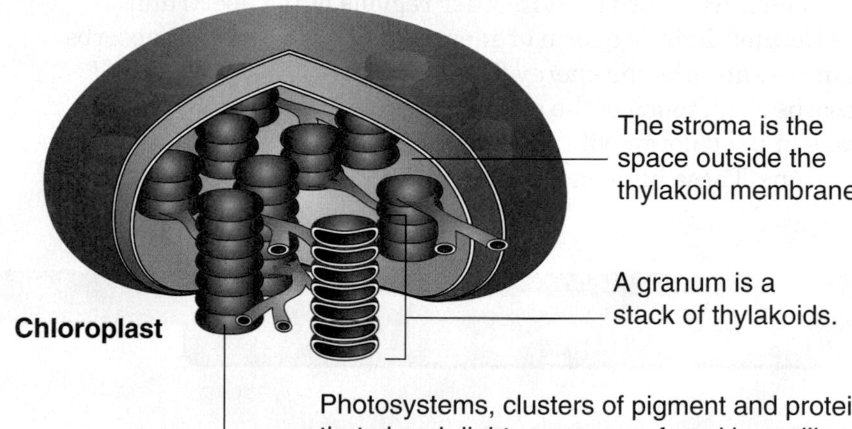
Chloroplast
The stroma is the space outside the thylakoid membranes.
A granum is a stack of thylakoids.
Photosystems, clusters of pigment and protein that absorb light energy, are found in saclike photosynthetic membranes called thylakoids.

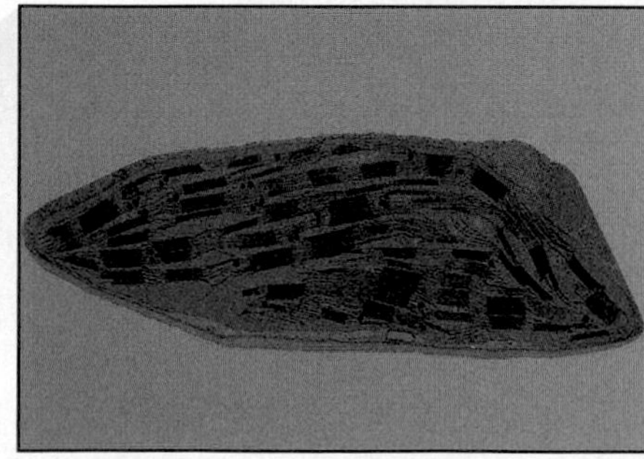
Chloroplast
(magnification: 10,000×)

FIGURE 8–7 PHOTOSYNTHESIS: AN OVERVIEW

The process of photosynthesis includes the light-dependent reactions as well as the Calvin cycle. **Interpreting Graphics** *What are the products of the light-dependent reactions?*

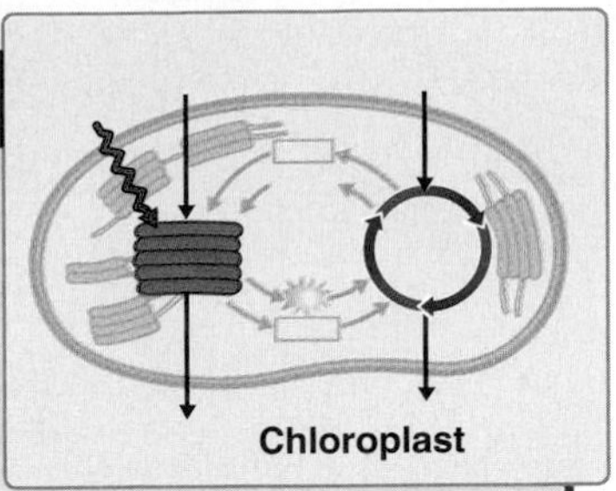

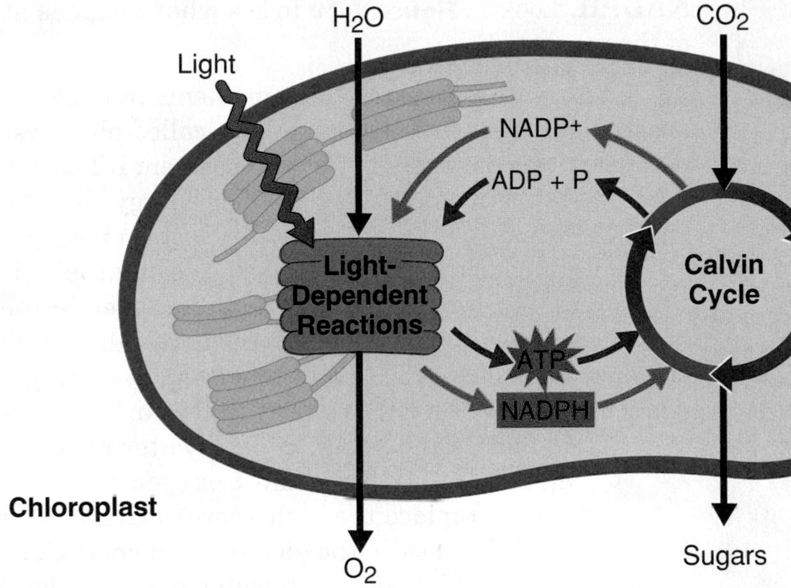

Electron Carriers

When sunlight excites electrons in chlorophyll, the electrons gain a great deal of energy. These high-energy electrons require a special carrier. Think of a high-energy electron as being similar to a red-hot coal from a fireplace or campfire. If you wanted to move the coal from one place to another, you wouldn't pick it up in your hands. You would use a pan or bucket—a carrier—to transport it. Cells treat high-energy electrons in the same way. Instead of a pan or bucket, they use electron carriers to transport high-energy electrons from chlorophyll to other molecules, as shown in **Figure 8–8.** A carrier molecule is a compound that can accept a pair of high-energy electrons and transfer them along with most of their energy to another molecule. This process is called electron transport, and the electron carriers themselves are known as the electron transport chain.

One of these carrier molecules is a compound known as **$NADP^+$** (nicotinamide adenine dinucleotide phosphate). The name is complicated, but the job that $NADP^+$ has is simple. $NADP^+$ accepts and holds 2 high-energy electrons along with a hydrogen ion (H^+). This converts the $NADP^+$ into NADPH. The conversion of $NADP^+$ into NADPH is one way in which some of the energy of sunlight can be trapped in chemical form.

The NADPH can then carry high-energy electrons produced by light absorption in chlorophyll to chemical reactions elsewhere in the cell. These high-energy electrons are used to help build a variety of molecules the cell needs, including carbohydrates like glucose.

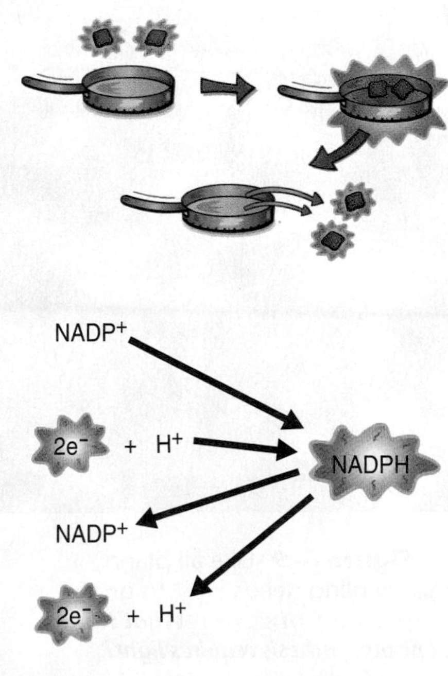

▲ **Figure 8–8** Like a pan being used to carry hot coals, electron carriers such as $NADP^+$ transport electrons. **Interpreting Graphics** *What eventually happens to those electrons?*

Light-Dependent Reactions

As you might expect from their name, the **light-dependent reactions** require light. That is why plants like the one in **Figure 8–9** need light to grow. The light-dependent reactions use energy from light to produce ATP and NADPH. **The light-dependent reactions produce oxygen gas and convert ADP and $NADP^+$ into the energy carriers ATP and NADPH.** Look at **Figure 8–10** to see what happens at each step of the process.

A Photosynthesis begins when pigments in photosystem II absorb light. That first photosystem is called photosystem II because it was discovered after photosystem I. The light energy is absorbed by electrons, increasing their energy level. These high-energy electrons are passed on to the electron transport chain.

As light continues to shine, does the chlorophyll run out of electrons? No, it does not. The thylakoid membrane contains a system that provides new electrons to chlorophyll to replace the ones it has lost. These new electrons come from water molecules (H_2O). Enzymes on the inner surface of the thylakoid membrane break up each water molecule into 2 electrons, 2 H^+ ions, and 1 oxygen atom. The 2 electrons replace the high-energy electrons that chlorophyll has lost to the electron transport chain. As plants remove electrons from water, oxygen is left behind and is released into the air. This reaction is the source of nearly all of the oxygen in Earth's atmosphere, and it is another way in which photosynthesis makes our lives possible. The hydrogen ions left behind when water is broken apart are released inside the thylakoid membrane.

B High-energy electrons move through the electron transport chain from photosystem II to photosystem I. Energy from the electrons is used by the molecules in the electron transport chain to transport H^+ ions from the stroma into the inner thylakoid space.

C Pigments in photosystem I use energy from light to reenergize the electrons. $NADP^+$ then picks up these high-energy electrons, along with H^+ ions, at the outer surface of the thylakoid membrane, plus an H^+ ion, and becomes NADPH.

D As electrons are passed from chlorophyll to $NADP^+$, more hydrogen ions are pumped across the membrane. After a while, the inside of the membrane fills up with positively charged hydrogen ions. This makes the outside of the thylakoid membrane negatively charged and the inside positively charged. The difference in charges across the membrane provides the energy to make ATP. This is why the H^+ ions are so important.

E H^+ ions cannot cross the membrane directly. However, the cell membrane contains a protein called **ATP synthase** (SIN-thays) that spans the membrane and allows H^+ ions to pass through it. As H^+ ions pass through ATP synthase, the protein rotates like a turbine being spun by water in a hydroelectric power plant.

▲ **Figure 8–9** Like all plants, this seedling needs light to grow. **Applying Concepts** *What stage of photosynthesis requires light?*

Light-Dependent Reactions

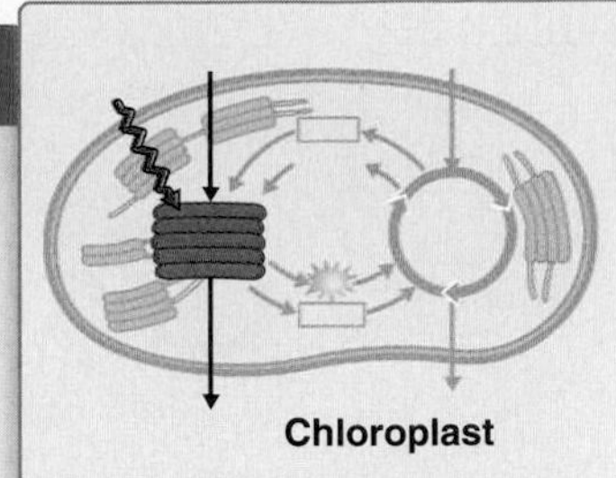

Figure 8–10 The light-dependent reactions use energy from sunlight to produce ATP, NADPH, and oxygen. The light-dependent reactions take place within the thylakoid membranes of chloroplasts.

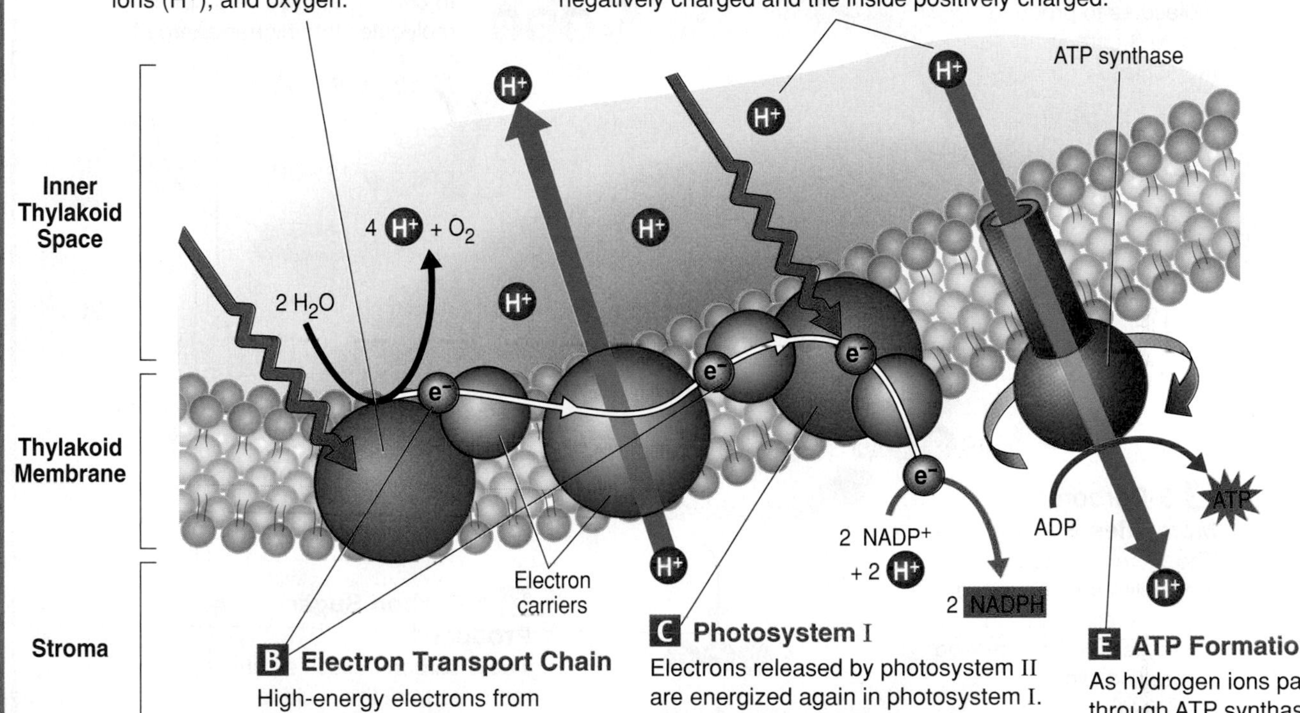

A Photosystem II
Light absorbed by photosystem II is used to break up water molecules into energized electrons, hydrogen ions (H^+), and oxygen.
D Hydrogen Ion Movement
The inside of the thylakoid membrane fills up with positively charged hydrogen ions. This action makes the outside of the thylakoid membrane negatively charged and the inside positively charged.
ATP synthase
Inner Thylakoid Space
Thylakoid Membrane
Stroma
$4\ H^+ + O_2$
$2\ H_2O$
H^+
e^-
Electron carriers
$2\ NADP^+$
$+ 2\ H^+$
2 NADPH
ADP
ATP
B Electron Transport Chain
High-energy electrons from photosystem II move through the electron transport chain to photosystem I.
C Photosystem I
Electrons released by photosystem II are energized again in photosystem I. Enzymes in the membrane use the electrons to form NADPH. NADPH is used to make sugar in the Calvin cycle.
E ATP Formation
As hydrogen ions pass through ATP synthase, their energy is used to convert ADP into ATP.

As it rotates, ATP synthase binds ADP and a phosphate group together to produce ATP. Because of this system, light-dependent electron transport produces not only high-energy electrons but ATP as well.

As we have seen, the light-dependent reactions use water, ADP, and $NADP^+$, and they produce oxygen and two high-energy compounds: ATP and NADPH. What good are these compounds? As we will see, they have an important role to play in the cell: They provide the energy to build energy-containing sugars from low-energy compounds.

CHECKPOINT *What is the role of photosystem II? How does that role compare with the role of photosystem I?*

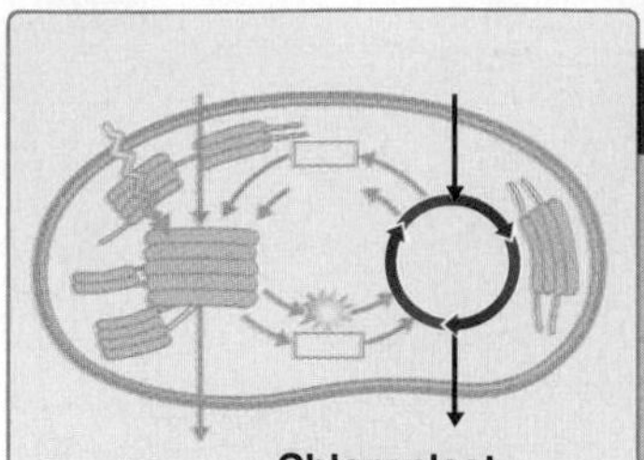

Figure 8–11 Calvin Cycle

The Calvin cycle uses ATP and NADPH to produce high-energy sugars. The Calvin cycle takes place in the stroma of chloroplasts and does not require light.

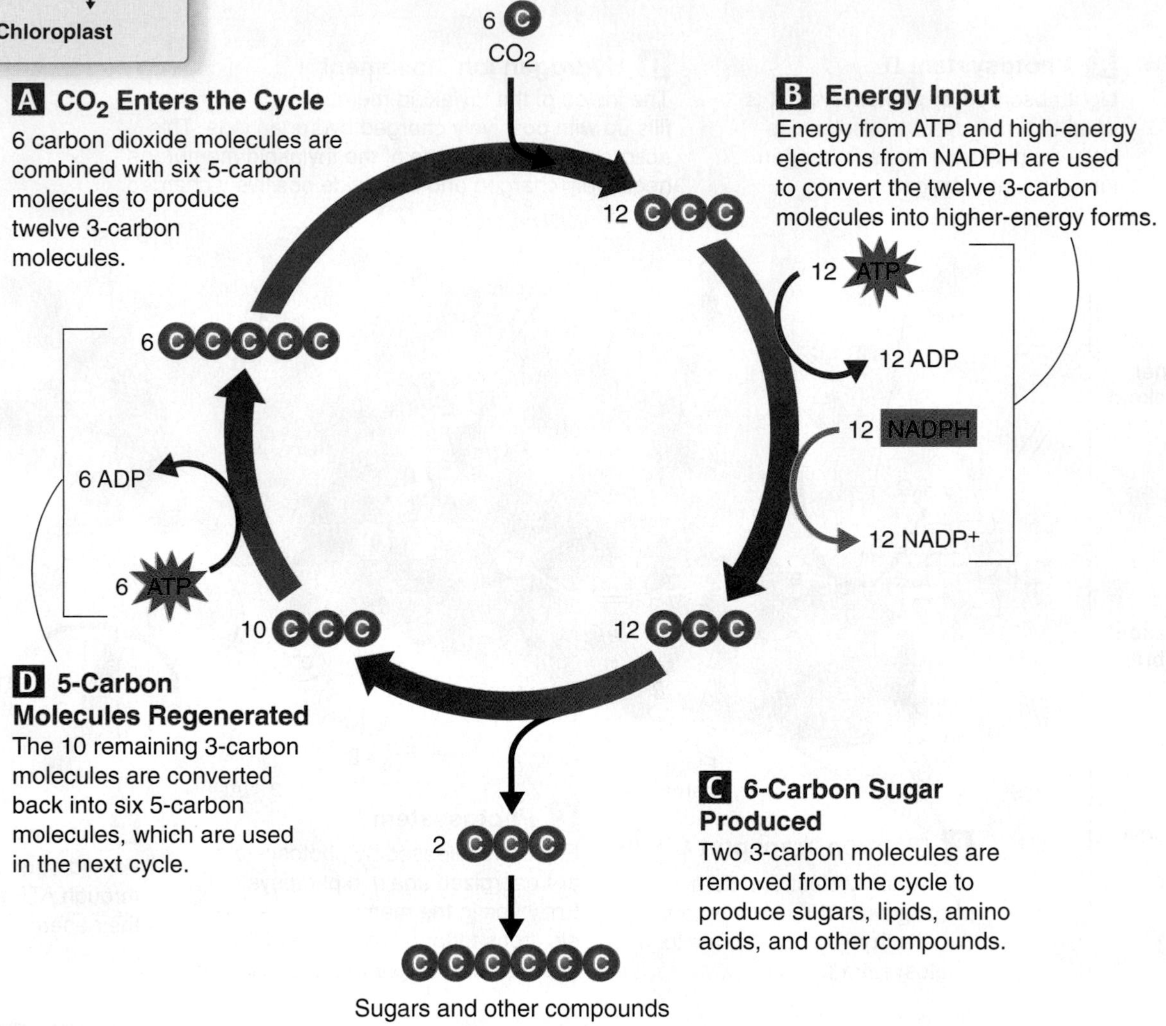

Chloroplast

6 C
CO_2

A CO_2 Enters the Cycle
6 carbon dioxide molecules are combined with six 5-carbon molecules to produce twelve 3-carbon molecules.

B Energy Input
Energy from ATP and high-energy electrons from NADPH are used to convert the twelve 3-carbon molecules into higher-energy forms.

12 CCC

12 ATP

12 ADP

12 NADPH

12 $NADP^+$

12 CCC

6 CCCCC

6 ADP

6 ATP

10 CCC

D 5-Carbon Molecules Regenerated
The 10 remaining 3-carbon molecules are converted back into six 5-carbon molecules, which are used in the next cycle.

2 CCC

CCCCCC
Sugars and other compounds

C 6-Carbon Sugar Produced
Two 3-carbon molecules are removed from the cycle to produce sugars, lipids, amino acids, and other compounds.

The Calvin Cycle

The ATP and NADPH formed by the light-dependent reactions contain an abundance of chemical energy, but they are not stable enough to store that energy for more than a few minutes. During the **Calvin cycle,** plants use the energy that ATP and NADPH contain to build high-energy compounds that can be stored for a long time. **The Calvin cycle uses ATP and NADPH from the light-dependent reactions to produce high-energy sugars.** The Calvin cycle is named after the American scientist Melvin Calvin, who worked out the details of this remarkable cycle. Because the Calvin cycle does not require light, these reactions are also called the light-independent reactions. Follow **Figure 8–11** to see how the Calvin cycle works.

A Six carbon dioxide molecules enter the cycle from the atmosphere. The carbon dioxide molecules combine with six 5-carbon molecules. The result is twelve 3-carbon molecules.

B The twelve 3-carbon molecules are then converted into higher-energy forms. The energy for this conversion comes from ATP and high-energy electrons from NADPH.

C Two of the twelve 3-carbon molecules are removed from the cycle. The plant cell uses these molecules to produce sugars, lipids, amino acids, and other compounds needed for plant metabolism and growth.

D The remaining ten 3-carbon molecules are converted back into six 5-carbon molecules. These molecules combine with six new carbon dioxide molecules to begin the next cycle.

The Calvin cycle uses six molecules of carbon dioxide to produce a single 6-carbon sugar molecule. As photosynthesis proceeds, the Calvin cycle works steadily removing carbon dioxide from the atmosphere and turning out energy-rich sugars. The plant uses the sugars to meet its energy needs and to build more complex macromolecules such as cellulose that it needs for growth and development. When other organisms eat plants, they can also use the energy stored in carbohydrates.

CHECKPOINT *What are the main products of the Calvin cycle?*

For: Links on photosynthesis
Visit: www.SciLinks.org
Web Code: cbn-3083

Analyzing Data

Rates of Photosynthesis

The rate at which a plant carries out photosynthesis depends in part on its environment. Plants that grow in the shade, for example, carry out photosynthesis at low levels of light. Plants that grow in the sun, such as desert plants, typically carry out photosynthesis at much higher levels of light.

The graph compares the rates of photosynthesis between plants that grow in the shade and plants that grow in the sun. It shows how the rate of photosynthesis changes with the number of micromoles of photons per square meter per second (μmol photons/m²/s), a standard unit of light intensity.

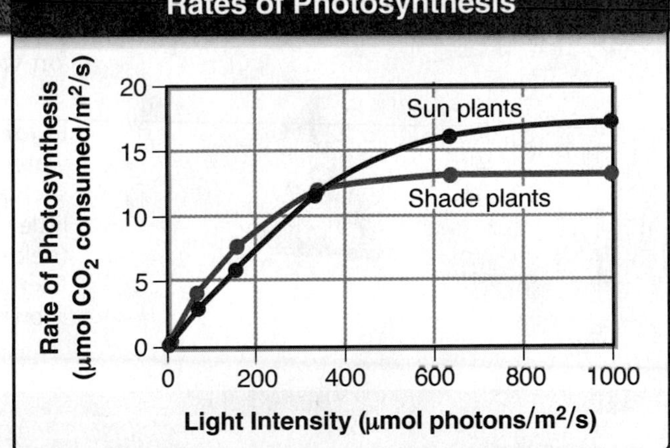

1. **Using Tables and Graphs** When light intensity is below 200 μmol photons/m²/s, do sun plants or shade plants have a higher rate of photosynthesis?
2. **Drawing Conclusions** Does the relationship in question 1 change when light intensity increases above 400 μmol photons/m²/s? Explain your answer.
3. **Inferring** The average light intensity in the Sonoran Desert is about 400 μmol photons/m²/s. According to the graph, what would be the approximate rate of photosynthesis for sun plants that grow in this environment?
4. **Going Further** Suppose you transplant a sun plant to a shaded forest floor that receives about 100 μmol photons/m²/s. Do you think this plant will grow and thrive? Why or why not? How does the graph help you answer this question?

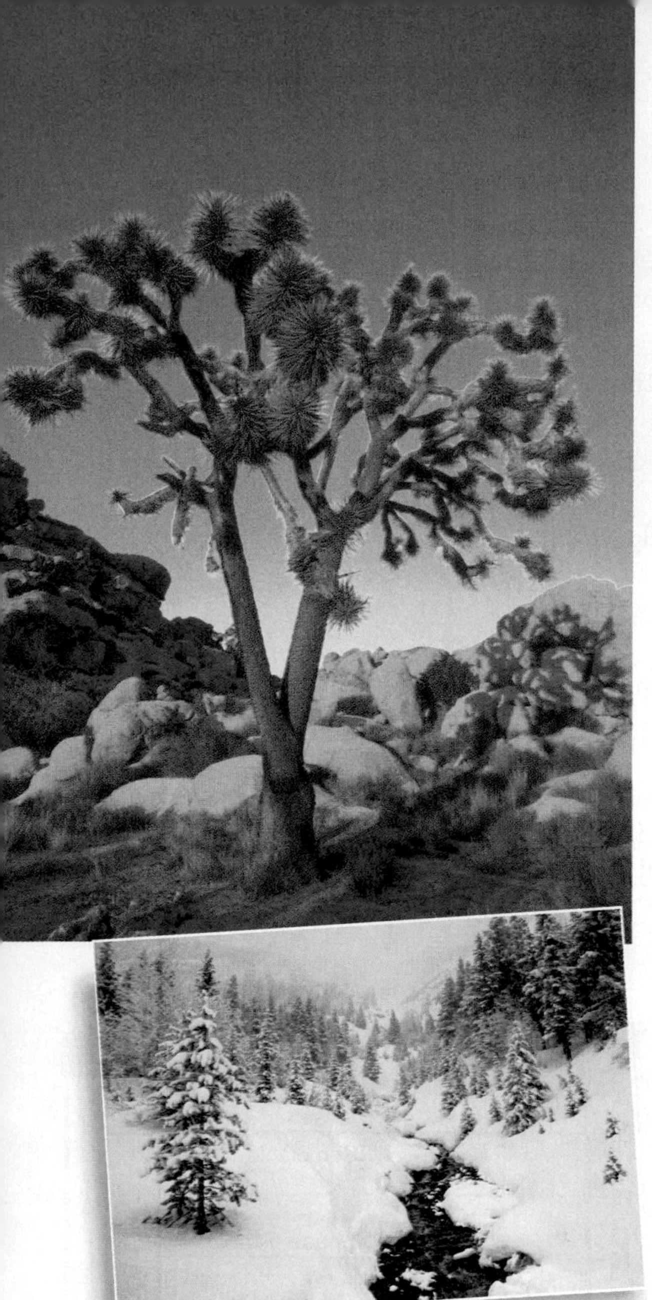

The two sets of photosynthetic reactions work together—the light-dependent reactions trap the energy of sunlight in chemical form, and the light-independent reactions use that chemical energy to produce stable, high-energy sugars from carbon dioxide and water. And, in the process, we animals get an atmosphere filled with oxygen. Not a bad deal at all.

Factors Affecting Photosynthesis

Many factors affect the rate at which photosynthesis occurs. Because water is one of the raw materials of photosynthesis, a shortage of water can slow or even stop photosynthesis. Plants that live in dry conditions, such as desert plants and conifers, have a waxy coating on their leaves that reduces water loss.

Temperature is also a factor. Photosynthesis depends on enzymes that function best between 0°C and 35°C. Temperatures above or below this range may damage the enzymes, slowing down the rate of photosynthesis. At very low temperatures, photosynthesis may stop entirely.

The intensity of light also affects the rate at which photosynthesis occurs. As you might expect, increasing light intensity increases the rate of photosynthesis. After the light intensity reaches a certain level, however, the plant reaches its maximum rate of photosynthesis. The level at which light intensity no longer affects photosynthesis varies from plant type to plant type. The conifers shown in **Figure 8–12** can carry out photosynthesis only on warm, sunny days.

Figure 8–12 Both temperature and the availability of water can affect rates of photosynthesis. Desert plants such as this Joshua tree (above) are adapted to survive with little water. During the cold winter months these conifers (below) may only occasionally carry out photosynthesis. **Comparing and Contrasting** ***What do both plants shown have that helps them conserve water?***

8–3 Section Assessment

1. **Key Concept** Summarize the light-dependent reactions.
2. **Key Concept** What reactions make up the Calvin cycle?
3. How is light energy converted into chemical energy during photosynthesis?
4. What is the function of NADPH?
5. **Critical Thinking Applying Concepts** Why are the light-dependent reactions important to the Calvin cycle?

Thinking Visually

Making a Flowchart
Construct a flowchart that illustrates the steps of photosynthesis. Begin with the energy of sunlight and end with the production of sugars. Include as much detail as possible in the numerous steps.

Design an Experiment

Investigating Photosynthesis

If only part of a leaf receives light, does the whole leaf perform photosynthesis? What if a leaf receives only light of one color? You are going to design an experiment to test the effects of colored light on photosynthesis.

Problem How do different colors of light affect starch synthesis during photosynthesis?

Materials

- scissors
- black construction paper
- potted plant
- tape
- blue, red, and green cellophane
- 5 large test tubes
- glass-marking pencil
- forceps
- 400-mL beaker
- 5 petri dishes
- iodine solution
- paper towels

Skills Predicting, Formulating Hypotheses

Design Your Experiment

1. **Predicting** As a result of photosynthesis, new starch molecules are synthesized and accumulate in leaves. Record your prediction of how keeping part of a leaf in darkness will affect starch synthesis.
2. Cut two pieces of black construction paper large enough to cover half of one leaf of the plant.
3. Sandwich half of the leaf between the pieces of black paper and tape the paper in place.
4. **Formulating Hypotheses** Develop a hypothesis that predicts how the color of light will affect photosynthesis. Record your hypothesis.
5. Design an experiment to test your hypothesis. Refer to the Lab Tips box on page 55. Have your teacher check your plan. Set up your experiment using whole leaves from the same plant as in step 3.
6. Leave your plant in a sunlit area for 2 days.
7. Cut off one leaf that was not treated as well as each of the experimental leaves, including the half-covered leaf. Roll up each leaf and put it in a large test tube. Label each tube and petri dish with the treatment the leaf received.
8. Put on your goggles and lab apron. Before you test the leaves for starch, the chlorophyll must be removed from the leaves. Your teacher will add alcohol to your test tubes and heat them in hot water. **CAUTION:** *Alcohol is toxic and flammable, and its fumes are irritating.* When the color has disappeared from each leaf, use forceps to swirl each leaf in a beaker of water. Place it in a labeled petri dish.
9. Put on your plastic gloves. Cover each leaf with iodine solution. Iodine solution stains starch blue or black. **CAUTION:** *Iodine is corrosive and irritating to the skin and can stain clothes and skin. Be careful not to spill it.*
10. After 1 minute, use forceps to gently swirl each leaf in the beaker of water and lay the leaf flat on a paper towel.
11. Observe each leaf and record your observations. Wash your hands before leaving the lab.

Analyze and Conclude

1. **Observing** Was your prediction about starch synthesis in the part of the first leaf covered in black paper correct? Explain your answer.
2. **Observing** What effect did each color of light have on starch synthesis in the leaves? Was your hypothesis correct?
3. **Communicating Results** Use your knowledge of chlorophyll to explain your results.

Go Further

Designing Experiments Where is starch found in the multicolored leaves of a coleus plant? Use your observations to propose a hypothesis. With your teacher's approval, perform an experiment to test your hypothesis. Explain your results.

Chapter 8 Study Guide

8–1 Energy and Life

Key Concepts

- Plants and some other types of organisms are able to use light energy from the sun to produce food.
- The characteristics of ATP make it exceptionally useful as the basic energy source of all cells.

Vocabulary
autotroph, p. 201
heterotroph, p. 201
adenosine triphosphate (ATP), p. 202

8–2 Photosynthesis: An Overview

Key Concepts

- The experiments performed by van Helmont, Priestley, and Ingenhousz led to work by other scientists who finally discovered that in the presence of light, plants transform carbon dioxide and water into carbohydrates, and they also release oxygen.
- Photosynthesis uses the energy of sunlight to convert water and carbon dioxide into high-energy sugars and oxygen.
- In addition to water and carbon dioxide, photosynthesis requires light and chlorophyll, a molecule found in chloroplasts.

Vocabulary
photosynthesis, p. 204
pigment, p. 207
chlorophyll, p. 207

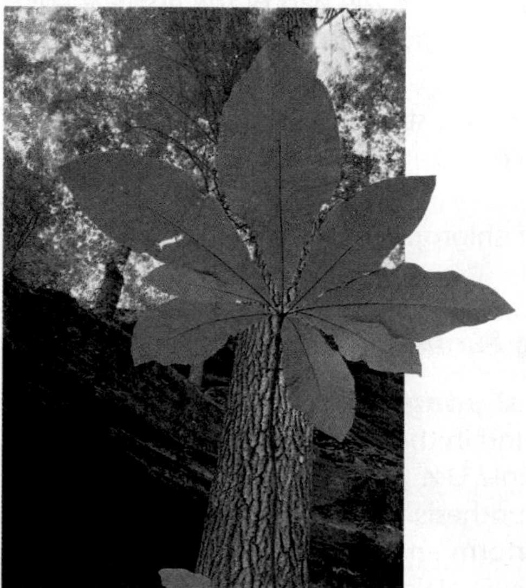

8–3 The Reactions of Photosynthesis

Key Concepts

- The process of photosynthesis includes the light-dependent reactions as well as the Calvin cycle.
- The light-dependent reactions produce oxygen gas and convert ADP and NADP+ into ATP and NADPH. The light-dependent reactions occur in the thylakoid.
- The Calvin cycle uses ATP and NADPH from the light-dependent reactions to produce high-energy sugars. The Calvin cycle is also known as the light-independent reactions.

Vocabulary
thylakoid, p. 208
photosystem, p. 208
stroma, p. 208
NADP+, p. 209
light-dependent reactions, p. 210
ATP synthase, p. 210
Calvin cycle, p. 212

Thinking Visually

Using the information in this chapter, complete the following flowchart about photosynthesis:

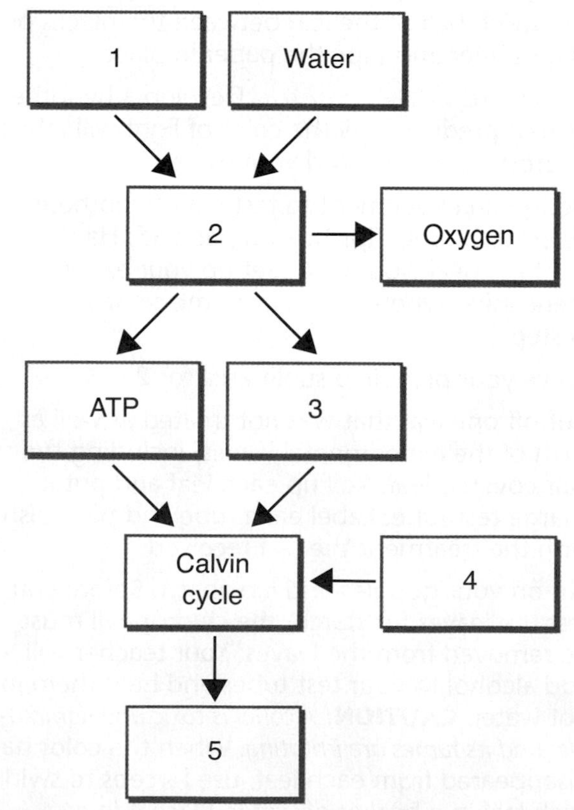

Preparing for the Living Environment Exam

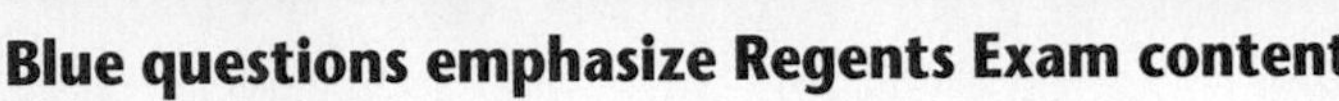

Blue questions emphasize Regents Exam content

Chapter 8

Part A

Multiple Choice

For each statement or question, select the number of the word or expression that, of those given, best completes the statement or answers the question.

1 Maple trees, algae, and wheat are all
(1) autotrophs (3) heterotrophs
(2) decomposers (4) scavengers

2 One of the principal chemical compounds that living things use to store energy is
(1) DNA (3) ATP
(2) H_2O (4) CO_2

3 Van Helmont placed a known mass of soil in a large container. He then planted a small tree with a known mass in the container of soil. For five years, he watered and observed the tree. At the conclusion of his experiment, he discovered that the tree had gained 75 kilograms, while the mass of the soil was almost unchanged. A reasonable conclusion van Helmont could make based on his data is that
(1) plants obtain food from the soil
(2) plants convert soil compounds into new plant cells
(3) plants obtain their food from a source other than water
(4) plants may use water as a source of building materials

4 In addition to light and chlorophyll, photosynthesis requires
(1) water and oxygen
(2) water and sugars
(3) oxygen and carbon dioxide
(4) water and carbon dioxide

5 The leaves of a plant appear green because chlorophyll
(1) reflects blue and orange light
(2) absorbs blue and orange light
(3) reflects green light
(4) absorbs green light

6 The products of photosynthesis are
(1) sugars and oxygen
(2) sugars and carbon dioxide
(3) water and carbon dioxide
(4) hydrogen and oxygen

7 Which organelle contains chlorophyll?

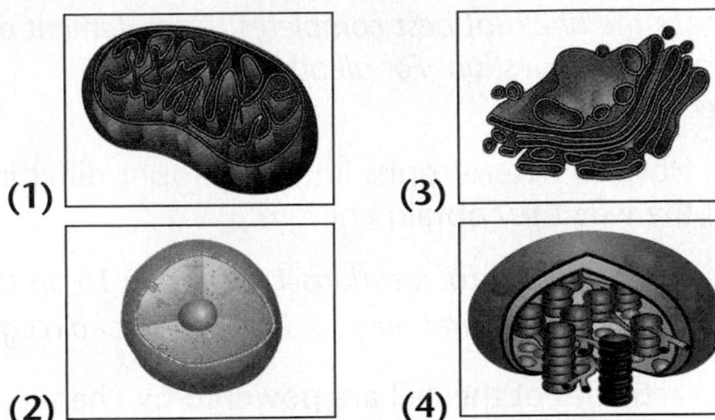

8 The first process in the light-dependent reactions of photosynthesis is
(1) light absorption
(2) electron transport
(3) oxygen production
(4) ATP formation

9 The light-independent reactions of photosynthesis are also known as the
(1) Calvin cycle (3) Ingenhousz cycle
(2) Priestley cycle (4) van Helmont cycle

10 Energy for use in cells is stored in the form of
(1) chemical-bond energy
(2) solar energy
(3) heat energy
(4) mechanical energy

For questions 11 and 12, complete each analogy by selecting the correct number. In analogies, A : B :: C : means "A is to B as C is to ___?___."

11 Oak tree : autotroph :: human :
(1) parasite (3) autotroph
(2) producer (4) heterotroph

12 Light-dependent reactions : oxygen :: Calvin cycle :
(1) sugar (3) carbon dioxide
(2) NADPH (4) ADP

Test-Taking Tip In tests, analogies compare pairs of items, such as *kitten* : *cat* :: *puppy* ___?___. Before looking at the possible answers, identify how the first pair is related. For example, since a kitten is a young cat, the relationship is *baby* : *adult*, so the correct answer is *puppy* : *dog*.

Preparing for the Living Environment Exam

Part B

Multiple Choice and Extended Response

For those questions that ask you to select a response, choose the one that best completes the statement or answers the question. For all others follow the directions given.

13 How do heterotrophs and autotrophs differ in the way they obtain energy?

Base your answers to questions 14 through 19 on the information below and on your knowledge of biology.

The activities of the cell are powered by chemical fuels. One of the principal chemical compounds that living organisms use to store energy is ATP.

14 Make a copy of the chart below on your answer paper. Complete the comparison of ATP and ADP by filling in the missing information. (Do not write in this book.)

Comparison of ATP and ADP

Name of Part	Number in ATP	Number in ADP
Adenine		
Ribose		
Phosphate groups		

15 Using the completed chart as a reference, state the primary difference between ATP and ADP.

16 Explain how the difference between ATP and ADP is important in the way a cell stores energy.

17 Compare the amounts of energy stored by ATP and glucose.

18 Which compound is used by the cell as an immediate source of energy?

19 Without light and chlorophyll, photosynthesis in green plants could not occur. Explain why each of these is important in the process of photosynthesis.

Base your answers to questions 20 and 21 on the information below and on your knowledge of biology.

Several drops of concentrated pigment were extracted from spinach leaves. These drops were placed at the bottom of a strip of highly absorbent paper. After the extract dried, the paper was suspended in a test tube containing alcohol so that only the tip of the paper was in the alcohol. As the alcohol was absorbed and moved up the paper, the various pigments contained in the extract separated, leaving different colored areas on the paper.

20 The process used to separate pigments in the above investigation is
(1) electrophoresis
(2) homeostatic identification
(3) chromatography
(4) enzymatic isolation

21 A valid conclusion that can be drawn from this information is that spinach leaves
(1) use only chlorophyll during photosynthesis
(2) contain several pigments
(3) contain more orange pigment than yellow pigment
(4) have only one color of pigment

22 Explain how the events in the Calvin cycle depend on the light-dependent reactions.

Base your answers to questions 23 through 27 on the information below and on your knowledge of biology.

A water plant placed in a bright light gives off bubbles of oxygen. In the laboratory, you notice that if the light is placed at different distances from the plant, the rate at which the plant produces bubbles changes. Your data are shown in the following table.

Oxygen Production

Distance From Light (cm)	Bubbles Produced per Minute
10	39
20	22
30	8
40	5

23 Using the information in the data table, make a line graph on a piece of graph paper. As you make your graph, be sure you
- mark an appropriate scale on each axis
- label each axis

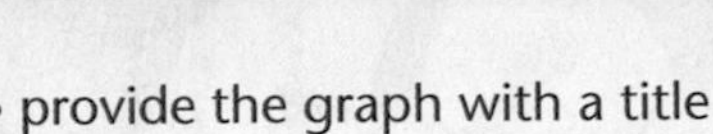

- provide the graph with a title
- plot the data for "Bubbles Produced per Minute" on the grid. Surround each point with a small circle, and connect the points

24 Describe the trend you observe on the graph.

25 When the light was farther from the plant, did the number of bubbles produced increase or decrease? Support your answer with an explanation.

26 At what distance is gas production at its highest?

(1) 10 cm (3) 30 cm
(2) 20 cm (4) 40 cm

27 State the relationship that exists between the distance from the plant to the light and the number of bubbles produced. Support your answer with an explanation.

---

28 Many of the sun's rays may be blocked by dust or clouds formed by volcanic eruptions or pollution. State one possible short-term effect and one possible long-term effect of this on photosynthesis.

29 Write a word equation that summarizes the process of photosynthesis. Use the following terms in your equation: light, sugars, oxygen, water, carbon dioxide.

Part C

Extended Response

Answer the questions or follow the directions given.

30 Some plant leaves contain yellow and red pigments as well as chlorophyll. In the fall, those leaves may become red or yellow. Explain the basis for these color changes. In your answer be sure to:

- state what process requires the presence of chlorophyll and the other pigments
- identify *two* external stimuli that can cause plants to change color

31 Design an experiment that uses pond water and algae to demonstrate the importance of light energy to pond life. In your answer be sure to

- identify the variables you will control
- identify the manipulated (independent) variable
- identify the responding (dependent) variable
- list the materials you will use
- outline the procedure you will follow

32 The greenhouse effect leads to global warming as Earth's atmosphere traps heat. Carbon dioxide is one of the main atmospheric gases contributing to this problem. This gas is produced through the burning of coal and oil for industry, power generation, and transportation. Some people have suggested that planting many long-lived trees along the interstate highways in New York and other states could help alleviate the greenhouse effect. Explain how the planting of trees along highways might help. In your explanation, be sure to

- identify the process in plants that relates most directly to their being helpful in alleviating the greenhouse effect
- explain what happens to much of the CO_2 used by plants in this process
- explain specifically why these trees, rather than short-lived plants such as grasses, would be more effective in combating the greenhouse effect

For: An interactive self-test
Visit: PHSchool.com
Web Code: cba-3080

CHAPTER 9

Cellular Respiration

Athletes get the energy they need from the breakdown of glucose during cellular respiration.

Inquiry Activity

How do living things release energy?

Procedure

1. Draw a table with 5 rows and 4 columns. Label the columns from left to right: Item, Activities, Energy Source, and How Energy Is Released.
2. Fill in each row of your table for every item your teacher provides. List yourself as the last item and complete that row.

Think About It

1. **Using Tables and Graphs** Was it easier to describe how living things use energy or how nonliving things use energy?
2. **Using Tables and Graphs** What is the most common energy source for living things?
3. **Formulating Hypotheses** How do you think living things release the energy they need?

9–1 Chemical Pathways

1-S2.2, S2.3 Development of a research plan
4-5.1 Energy stored in chemical bonds
4-5.1 Energy stored in organic molecules
LS- State appropriate hypotheses and organize data in tables

When you are hungry, how do you feel? If you are like most people, your stomach may seem empty, you might feel a little dizzy, and above all, you feel weak. The sensations produced by hunger vary from one person to the next, but the bottom line is always the same. Our bodies have a need for food, and they have their own ways of telling us when we need it.

Food provides living things with the chemical building blocks they need to grow and reproduce. Food serves as a source of raw materials from which the cells of the body can synthesize new molecules. Most of all, food serves as a source of energy.

Guide for Reading

Key Concepts

- What is cellular respiration?
- What happens during the process of glycolysis?
- What are the two main types of fermentation?

Vocabulary

calorie
glycolysis
cellular respiration
NAD^+
fermentation
anaerobic

Reading Strategy: Asking Questions Before you read this section, rewrite the headings as *how, why,* or *what* questions about releasing energy. Then, as you read, write brief answers to your questions.

Chemical Energy and Food

How much energy is actually present in food? Quite a lot. One gram of the sugar glucose ($C_6H_{12}O_6$), when burned in the presence of oxygen, releases 3811 calories of heat energy. A **calorie** is the amount of energy needed to raise the temperature of 1 gram of water 1 degree Celsius. The Calorie (capital "C") that is used on food labels is a kilocalorie, or 1000 calories. Cells, of course, don't "burn" glucose. Instead, they gradually release the energy from glucose and other food compounds.

This process begins with a pathway called **glycolysis** (gly-KAHL-ih-sis). Glycolysis releases only a small amount of energy. If oxygen is present, glycolysis leads to two other pathways that release a great deal of energy. If oxygen is not present, however, glycolysis is followed by a different pathway.

Figure 9–1 Living things get the energy they need from food. Both plant and animal cells carry out the final stages of cellular respiration in the mitochondria.

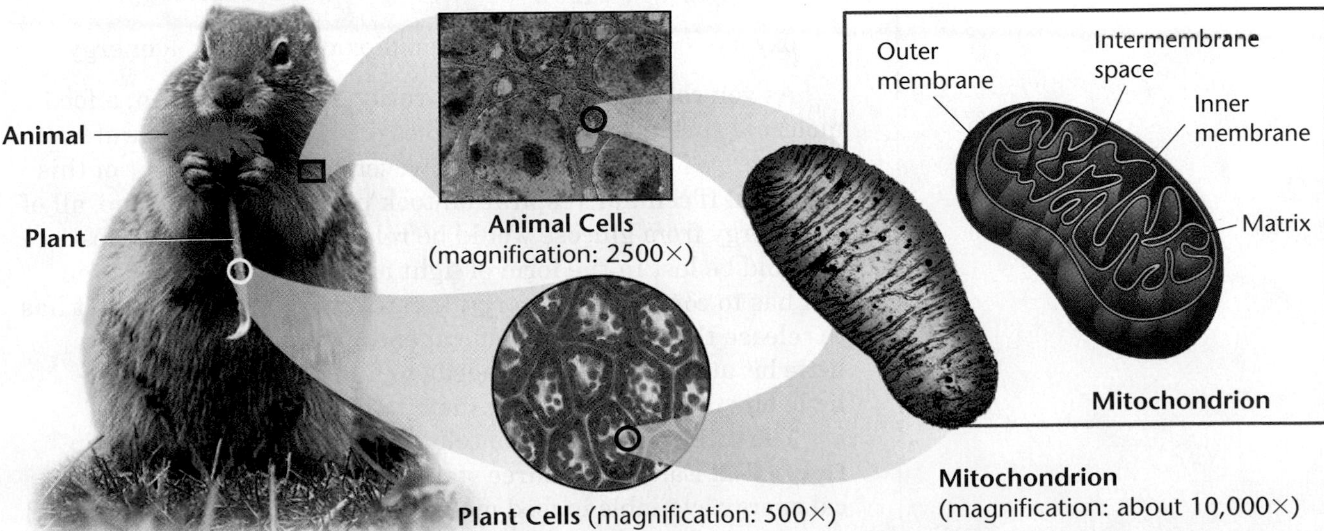

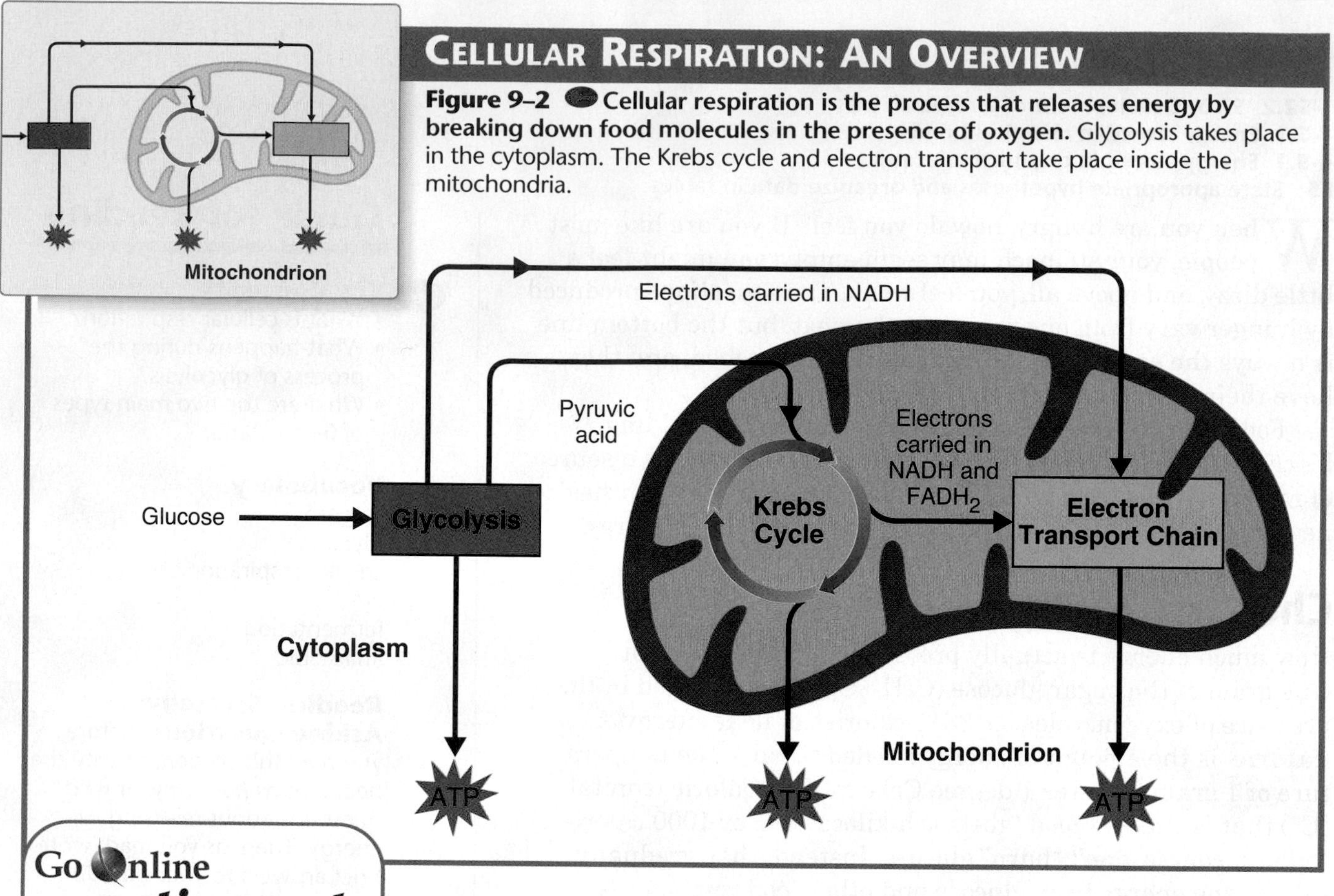

CELLULAR RESPIRATION: AN OVERVIEW

Figure 9–2 **Cellular respiration is the process that releases energy by breaking down food molecules in the presence of oxygen.** Glycolysis takes place in the cytoplasm. The Krebs cycle and electron transport take place inside the mitochondria.

Go Online
active art
For: Cellular Respiration activity
Visit: PHSchool.com
Web Code: cbp-3091

Overview of Cellular Respiration

In the presence of oxygen, glycolysis is followed by the Krebs cycle and the electron transport chain. Glycolysis, the Krebs cycle, and the electron transport chain make up a process called **cellular respiration.** **Cellular respiration is the process that releases energy by breaking down glucose and other food molecules in the presence of oxygen.** The equation for cellular respiration is:

$$6O_2 + C_6H_{12}O_6 \longrightarrow 6CO_2 + 6H_2O + \text{Energy}$$

oxygen + glucose ⟶ carbon dioxide + water + energy

As you can see, cellular respiration requires oxygen, a food molecule such as glucose, and gives off carbon dioxide, water, and energy. Do not be misled, however, by the simplicity of this equation. If cellular respiration took place in just one step, all of the energy from glucose would be released at once, and most of it would be lost in the form of light and heat. Clearly, a living cell has to control that energy. It can't simply start a fire—it has to release the explosive chemical energy in food molecules a little bit at a time. The cell needs to find a way to trap those little bits of energy by using them to make ATP.

The three main stages of cellular respiration are shown in **Figure 9–2.** Each of the three stages captures some of the chemical energy available in food molecules and uses it to produce ATP.

Glycolysis

The first set of reactions in cellular respiration is glycolysis. **Glycolysis is the process in which one molecule of glucose is broken in half, producing two molecules of pyruvic acid, a 3-carbon compound.** The process of glycolysis is shown in **Figure 9–3.**

ATP Production Even though glycolysis is an energy-releasing process, the cell needs to put in a little energy to get things going. At the pathway's beginning, 2 molecules of ATP are used up. In a way, those 2 ATP molecules are like an investment that pays back interest. In order to earn interest from a bank, first you have to put money into an account. Although the cell puts 2 ATP molecules into its "account" to get glycolysis going, when glycolysis is complete, 4 ATP molecules have been produced. This gives the cell a net gain of 2 ATP molecules.

NADH Production One of the reactions of glycolysis removes 4 high-energy electrons and passes them to an electron carrier called **NAD^+,** or nicotinamide adenine dinucleotide. Like $NADP^+$ in photosynthesis, each NAD^+ accepts a pair of high-energy electrons. This molecule, known as NADH, holds the electrons until they can be transferred to other molecules. By doing this, NAD^+ helps to pass energy from glucose to other pathways in the cell.

Although the energy yield from glycolysis is small, the process is so fast that cells can produce thousands of ATP molecules in just a few milliseconds. Besides speed, another advantage is that glycolysis itself does not require oxygen. This means that glycolysis can supply chemical energy to cells when oxygen is not available.

However, when a cell generates large amounts of ATP from glycolysis, it runs into a problem. In just a few seconds, all of the cell's available NAD^+ molecules are filled up with electrons. Without NAD^+, the cell cannot keep glycolysis going, and ATP production stops.

What does glycolysis break down?

Word Origins

Glycolysis comes from the Greek word *glukus,* meaning "sweet," and the Latin word *lysis,* which indicates a process of loosening or decomposing. Thus, *glycolysis* means "breaking glucose." **If *hydro* means "water," what do you think the term *hydrolysis* means?**

▼ **Figure 9–3** Glycolysis is the first stage in cellular respiration. **During glycolysis, glucose is broken down into 2 molecules of pyruvic acid.**

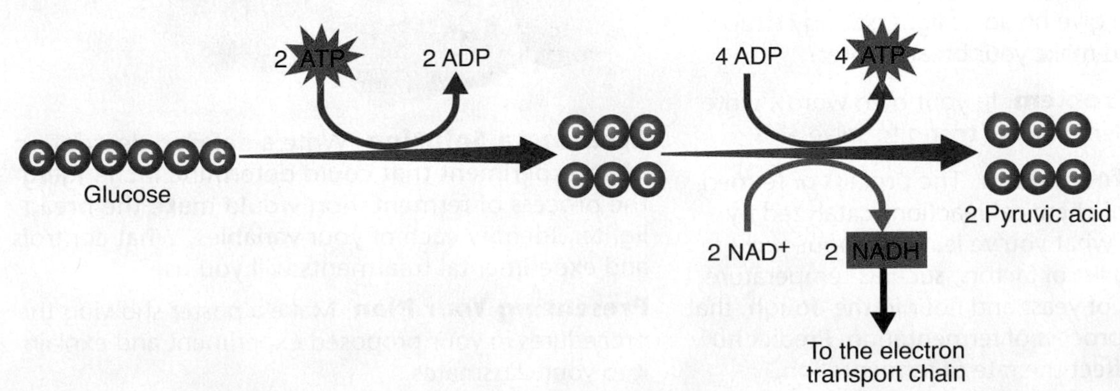

Fermentation

When oxygen is not present, glycolysis is followed by a different pathway. The combined process of this pathway and glycolysis is called fermentation. **Fermentation** releases energy from food molecules by producing ATP in the absence of oxygen.

During fermentation, cells convert NADH to NAD^+ by passing high-energy electrons back to pyruvic acid. This action converts NADH back into the electron carrier NAD^+, allowing glycolysis to continue producing a steady supply of ATP. Because fermentation does not require oxygen, it is said to be **anaerobic.** The term *anaerobic* means "not in air." **The two main types of fermentation are alcoholic fermentation and lactic acid fermentation.**

Alcoholic Fermentation Yeasts and a few other microorganisms use alcoholic fermentation, forming ethyl alcohol and carbon dioxide as wastes. The equation for alcoholic fermentation after glycolysis is:

$$\text{pyruvic acid} + \text{NADH} \longrightarrow \text{alcohol} + CO_2 + NAD^+$$

Alcoholic fermentation produces carbon dioxide as well as alcohol. Alcoholic fermentation causes bread dough to rise. When yeast in the dough runs out of oxygen, it begins to ferment, giving off bubbles of carbon dioxide that form the air spaces you see in a slice of bread. The small amount of alcohol produced in the dough evaporates when the bread is baked.

Problem Solving

A Family Recipe

You have opened a bakery, selling bread made according to your family's favorite recipe. Unfortunately, most of your customers find your bread too heavy. You need to make your bread more appealing to your customers. Before bread is baked, yeast cells in the dough ferment some of the carbohydrate in the flour, producing bubbles of carbon dioxide. These bubbles cause the dough to rise and give bread its light, spongy structure. How can you make your bread lighter?

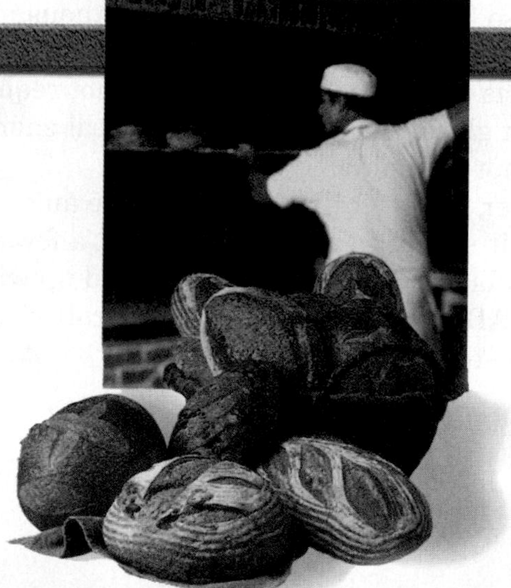

Defining the Problem In your own words, write down what problem you are trying to solve.

Organizing Information The process of fermentation is a series of chemical reactions catalyzed by enzymes. Review what you've learned about such reactions. Make a list of factors, such as temperature and the amounts of yeast and flour in the dough, that might affect the process of fermentation. Predict how each factor will affect the rate of fermentation.

Creating a Solution Write a detailed description of an experiment that could determine if changing the process of fermentation would make the bread lighter. Identify each of your variables. What controls and experimental treatments will you use?

Presenting Your Plan Make a poster showing the procedures in your proposed experiment and explain it to your classmates.

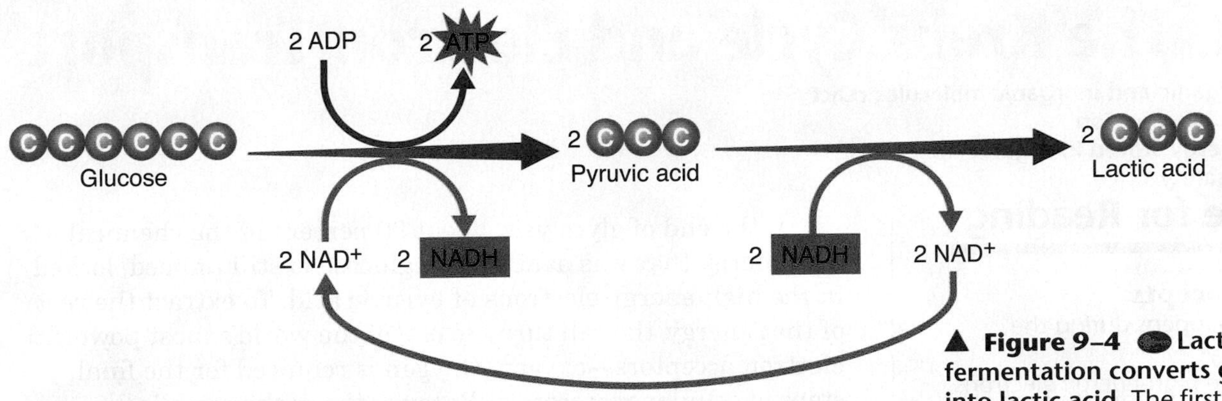

▲ **Figure 9–4** **Lactic acid fermentation converts glucose into lactic acid.** The first part of the equation is glycolysis. The second part shows the conversion of pyruvic acid to lactic acid.

Lactic Acid Fermentation In many cells, the pyruvic acid that accumulates as a result of glycolysis can be converted to lactic acid. Because this type of fermentation produces lactic acid, it is called lactic acid fermentation. This process regenerates NAD^+ so that glycolysis can continue, as shown in **Figure 9–4.** The equation for lactic acid fermentation after glycolysis is:

pyruvic acid + NADH ⟶ lactic acid + NAD^+

Lactic acid is produced in your muscles during rapid exercise when the body cannot supply enough oxygen to the tissues. Without enough oxygen, the body is not able to produce all of the ATP that is required. When you exercise vigorously by running, swimming, or riding a bicycle as fast as you can, the large muscles of your arms and legs quickly run out of oxygen. Your muscle cells rapidly begin to produce ATP by lactic acid fermentation. The buildup of lactic acid causes a painful, burning sensation. This is why muscles may feel sore after only a few seconds of intense activity.

Unicellular organisms also produce lactic acid as a waste product during fermentation. For example, prokaryotes are used in the production of a wide variety of foods and beverages, such as cheese, yogurt, buttermilk, and sour cream. Pickles, sauerkraut, and kimchi are also produced using lactic acid fermentation.

9–1 Section Assessment

1. **Key Concept** Describe the process of cellular respiration.
2. **Key Concept** What are the products of glycolysis?
3. **Key Concept** Name the two main types of fermentation.
4. What is a calorie? A Calorie?
5. How is the function of NAD^+ similar to that of $NADP^+$?
6. **Critical Thinking Comparing and Contrasting** How are lactic acid fermentation and alcoholic fermentation similar? How are they different?

Connecting Concepts

Chemical Equations
Write the conversion of ADP to ATP as a chemical equation. What are the reactants and the product? You may wish to refer back to Chapter 2 to review chemical equations.

9–2 The Krebs Cycle and Electron Transport

4-1.2 Organic and inorganic molecules react
4-5.1 Cell respiration
4-5.1 Energy stored in organic molecules
LS- Lab safety

Guide for Reading

Key Concepts

- What happens during the Krebs cycle?
- How are high-energy electrons used by the electron transport chain?

Vocabulary
aerobic
Krebs cycle
electron transport chain

Reading Strategy: Using Visuals Before you read, review **Figure 9–2** on page 222. Then, preview **Figures 9–6** and **9–7.** As you read, notice where the Krebs cycle and electron transport take place.

▲ **Figure 9–5** Hans Krebs won the Nobel Prize in 1953 for his discovery of the citric acid cycle, or Krebs cycle.

At the end of glycolysis, about 90 percent of the chemical energy that was available in glucose is still unused, locked in the high-energy electrons of pyruvic acid. To extract the rest of that energy, the cell turns to one of the world's most powerful electron acceptors—oxygen. Oxygen is required for the final steps of cellular respiration. Because the pathways of cellular respiration require oxygen, they are said to be **aerobic.**

As you know, the word *respiration* is often used as a synonym for breathing. This is why we have used the term *cellular respiration* to refer to energy-releasing pathways within the cell. The double meaning of respiration points out a crucial connection between cells and organisms: The energy-releasing pathways within cells require oxygen, and that is the reason we need to breathe, to respire.

The Krebs Cycle

In the presence of oxygen, pyruvic acid produced in glycolysis passes to the second stage of cellular respiration, the **Krebs cycle.** The Krebs cycle is named after Hans Krebs, the British biochemist who demonstrated its existence in 1937. **During the Krebs cycle, pyruvic acid is broken down into carbon dioxide in a series of energy-extracting reactions.** Because citric acid is the first compound formed in this series of reactions, the Krebs cycle is also known as the citric acid cycle.

A The Krebs cycle begins when pyruvic acid produced by glycolysis enters the mitochondrion. One carbon atom from pyruvic acid becomes part of a molecule of carbon dioxide, which is eventually released into the air. The other two carbon atoms from pyruvic acid are joined to a compound called coenzyme A to form acetyl-CoA. (The acetyl part of acetyl-CoA is made up of 2 carbon atoms, 1 oxygen atom, and 3 hydrogen atoms.) Acetyl-CoA then adds the 2-carbon acetyl group to a 4-carbon molecule, producing a 6-carbon molecule called citric acid.

B As the cycle continues, citric acid is broken down into a 4-carbon molecule, more carbon dioxide is released, and electrons are transferred to energy carriers. Follow the reactions in **Figure 9–6,** and you will see how this happens. First, look at the 6 carbon atoms in citric acid. One is removed, and then another, releasing 2 molecules of carbon dioxide and leaving a 4-carbon molecule. This 4-carbon molecule is then ready to accept another 2-carbon acetyl group, which starts the cycle all over again.

Next, look for ATP. For each turn of the cycle, a molecule similar to ADP is converted to a molecule that is similar to ATP. Finally, look at the electron carriers, NAD^+ and FAD.

Figure 9–6 The Krebs Cycle

During the Krebs cycle, pyruvic acid from glycolysis is used to make carbon dioxide, NADH, ATP, and $FADH_2$.

A Citric Acid Production
As pyruvic acid enters the mitochondrion, a carbon is removed, forming CO_2, and electrons are removed, changing NAD^+ to NADH. Coenzyme A joins the 2-carbon molecule, forming acetyl-CoA. Acetyl-CoA then adds the 2-carbon acetyl group to a 4-carbon compound, forming citric acid.

B Energy Extraction
Citric acid is broken down into a 5-carbon compound, then into a 4-carbon compound. Along the way, two more molecules of CO_2 are released, and electrons join NAD^+ and FAD, forming NADH and $FADH_2$. In addition, one molecule of ATP is generated. The energy tally from one molecule of pyruvic acid is 4 NADH, 1 $FADH_2$, and 1 molecule of ATP.

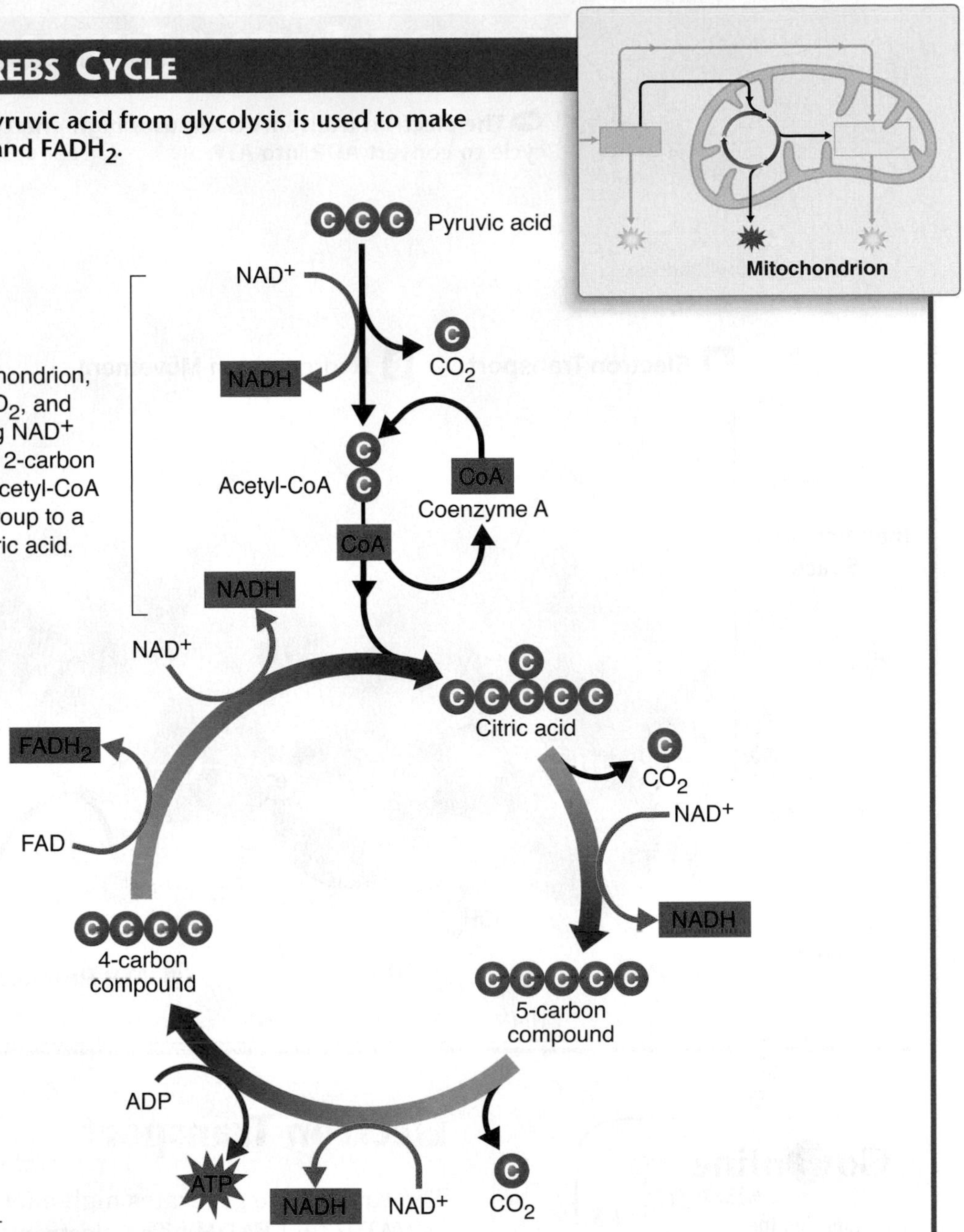

At five places in the cycle, a pair of high-energy electrons is accepted by electron carriers, changing NAD^+ to NADH and FAD to $FADH_2$. FAD (flavine adenine dinucleotide) and $FADH_2$ are molecules similar to NAD^+ and NADH, respectively.

What happens to each of these Krebs cycle products? First, the carbon dioxide released is the source of all the carbon dioxide in your breath. Every time you exhale, you expel the carbon dioxide produced by the Krebs cycle. Next, the ATP produced directly in the Krebs cycle can be used for cellular activities. However, what does the cell do with all those high-energy electrons in carriers like NADH? In the presence of oxygen, those high-energy electrons can be used to generate huge amounts of ATP.

CHECKPOINT *Why is the Krebs cycle also known as the citric acid cycle?*

FIGURE 9–7 ELECTRON TRANSPORT CHAIN

The electron transport chain uses high-energy electrons from the Krebs cycle to convert ADP into ATP.

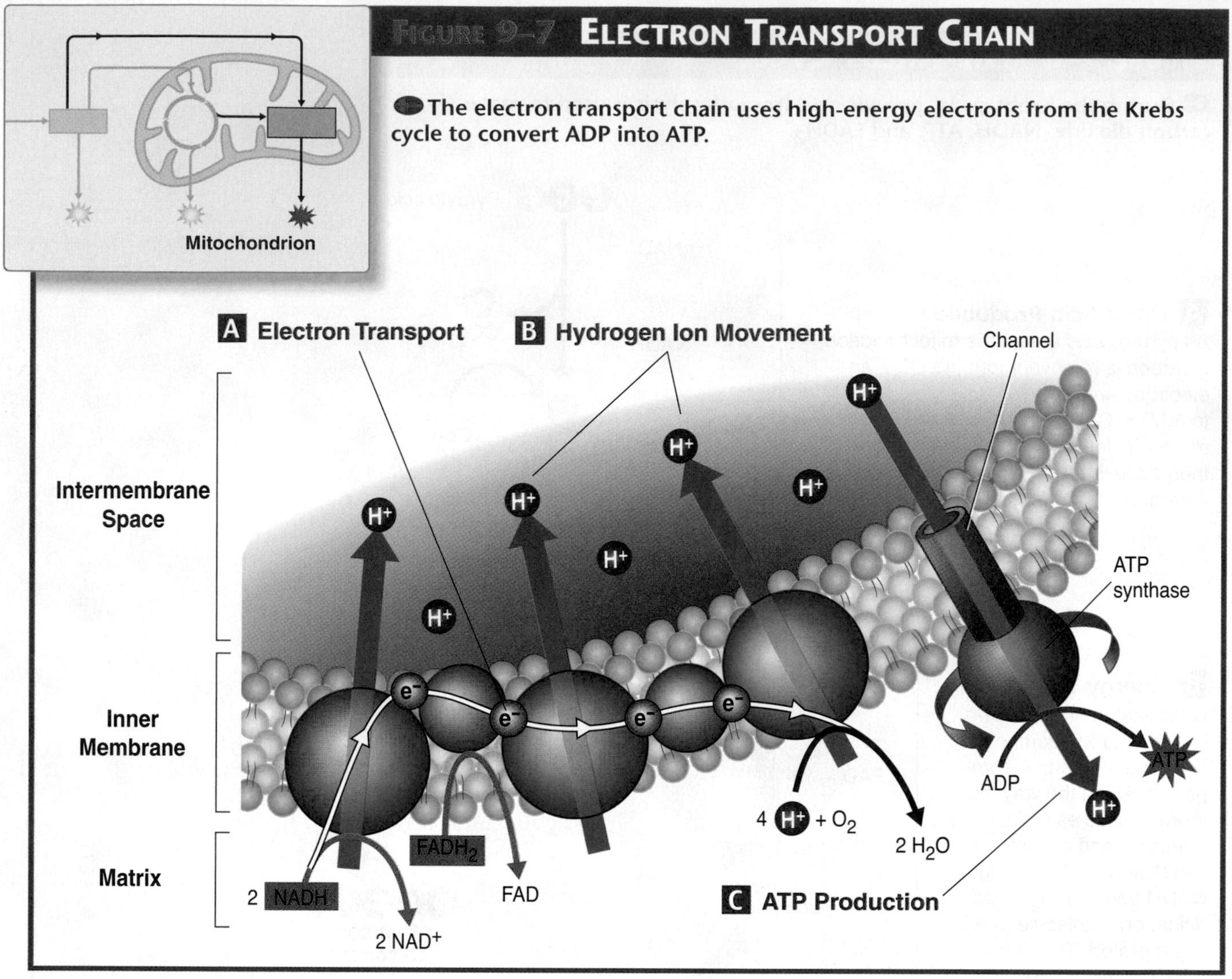

Mitochondrion
A Electron Transport
B Hydrogen Ion Movement
Channel
Intermembrane Space
Inner Membrane
Matrix
H+
e−
ATP synthase
ADP
ATP
2 NADH
2 NAD+
FADH2
FAD
4 H+ + O2
2 H2O
C ATP Production

Go Online NSTA SCiLINKS
For: Links on the Krebs cycle
Visit: www.SciLinks.org
Web Code: cbn-3092

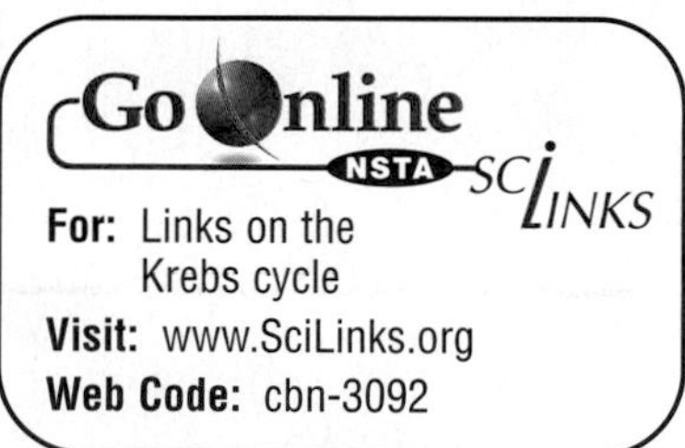

Electron Transport

The Krebs cycle generates high-energy electrons that are passed to NADH and $FADH_2$. The electrons are then passed from those carriers to the **electron transport chain.** **The electron transport chain uses the high-energy electrons from the Krebs cycle to convert ADP into ATP.** Look at **Figure 9–7** to see how this happens.

A High-energy electrons from NADH and $FADH_2$ are passed along the electron transport chain. In eukaryotes, the electron transport chain is composed of a series of carrier proteins located in the inner membrane of the mitochondrion. In prokaryotes, the same chain is in the cell membrane. High-energy electrons are passed from one carrier protein to the next. At the end of the electron transport chain is an enzyme that combines these electrons with hydrogen ions and oxygen to form water. Oxygen serves as the final electron acceptor of the electron transport chain. Thus, oxygen is essential for getting rid of low-energy electrons and hydrogen ions, the wastes of cellular respiration.

B Every time 2 high-energy electrons transport down the electron transport chain, their energy is used to transport hydrogen ions (H^+) across the membrane. During electron transport, H^+ ions build up in the intermembrane space, making it positively charged. The other side of the membrane, from which those H^+ ions have been taken, is now negatively charged.

C How does the cell use the charge differences that build up as a result of electron transport? The inner membranes of the mitochondria contain protein spheres called ATP synthases. As H^+ ions escape through channels into these proteins, the ATP synthases spin. Each time it rotates, the enzyme grabs a low-energy ADP and attaches a phosphate, forming high-energy ATP.

The beauty of this system is the way in which it couples the movement of high-energy electrons with the production of ATP. Every time a pair of high-energy electrons moves down the electron transport chain, the energy is used to move H^+ ions across the membrane. These ions then rush back across the membrane, producing enough force to spin the ATP synthase and generate enormous amounts of ATP. On average, each pair of high-energy electrons that moves down the electron transport chain provides enough energy to produce three molecules of ATP from ADP.

What is the role of ATP synthase in cellular respiration?

The Totals

How much chemical energy does cellular respiration yield from a single molecule of glucose? Recall that glycolysis produces just 2 ATP molecules per glucose. In the absence of oxygen, that is all the energy that a cell can extract from each molecule of glucose.

In the presence of oxygen, everything changes. As **Figure 9–8** shows, the Krebs cycle and electron transport enable the cell to produce 34 more ATP molecules per glucose molecule, in addition to the 2 ATP molecules obtained from glycolysis. This means that 18 times as much ATP can be generated from glucose in the presence of oxygen. The final wastes of cellular respiration are water and carbon dioxide.

How efficient is the process of cellular respiration? The 36 ATP molecules the cell makes per glucose represent about 38 percent of the total energy of glucose. That might not seem like much, but it means that the cell is actually more efficient at using food than the engine of a typical automobile is at burning gasoline. What happens to the remaining 62 percent? It is released as heat, which is one of the reasons your body feels warmer after vigorous exercise.

▼ **Figure 9–8** The complete breakdown of glucose through cellular respiration, including glycolysis, results in the production of 36 molecules of ATP. **Interpreting Graphics** *How many molecules of ATP are produced during glycolysis?*

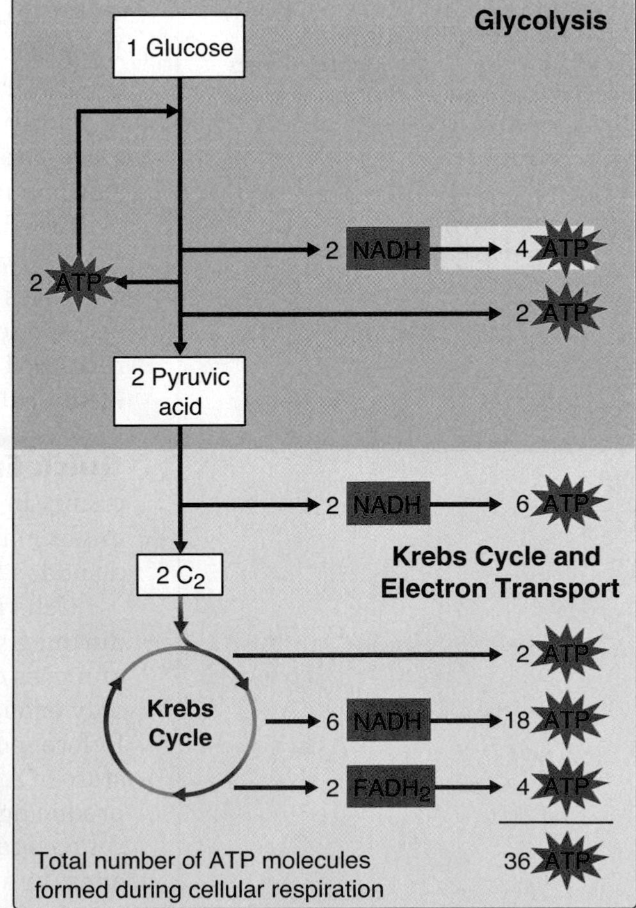

▲ **Figure 9–9** During a race, runners rely on the energy supplied by ATP to make it to the finish line. **Applying Concepts** *When runners begin a race, how do their bodies obtain energy?*

Energy and Exercise

Bang! The starter's pistol goes off, and the runners push off their starting blocks and sprint down the track. The initial burst of energy soon fades, and the runners settle down to a steady pace. After the runners hit the finish line, they walk around slowly and breathe deeply to catch their breath.

Let's look at what happens at each stage of the race in terms of the pathways the body uses to release energy. To obtain energy, the body uses ATP already in muscles and new ATP made by lactic acid fermentation and cellular respiration. At the beginning of a race, the body uses all three ATP sources, but stored ATP and lactic acid fermentation can only supply energy for a limited time.

Quick Energy What happens when your body needs lots of energy in a hurry? In response to sudden danger, quick actions might make the difference between life and death. To an athlete, a sudden burst of speed might win a race.

Cells normally contain small amounts of ATP produced during glycolysis and cellular respiration. When the starting gun goes off in a footrace, the muscles of the runners contain only enough of this ATP for a few seconds of intense activity. Before most of the runners have passed the 50-meter mark, that store of ATP is nearly gone. At this point, their muscle cells are producing most of their ATP by lactic acid fermentation. These sources can usually supply enough ATP to last about 90 seconds. In a 200- or 300-meter sprint, such as in **Figure 9–9,** this may be just enough to reach the finish line.

Fermentation produces lactic acid as a byproduct. When the race is over, the only way to get rid of lactic acid is in a chemical pathway that requires extra oxygen. For that reason, you can think of a quick sprint building up an oxygen debt that a runner has to repay after the race with plenty of heavy breathing.

Long-Term Energy What happens if a race is longer? How does your body generate the ATP it needs to run 2 kilometers or more, or to play in a soccer game that lasts more than an hour? For exercise longer than about 90 seconds, cellular respiration is the only way to generate a continuing supply of ATP. Cellular respiration releases energy more slowly than fermentation, which is why even well-conditioned athletes have to pace themselves during a long race or over the course of a game. Your body stores energy in muscle and other tissues in the form of the carbohydrate glycogen. These stores of glycogen are usually enough to last for 15 or 20 minutes of activity. After that, your body begins to break down other stored molecules, including fats, for energy. This is one reason why aerobic forms of exercise such as running, dancing, and swimming are so beneficial for weight control.

Why do runners breathe heavily after a race?

Quick Lab

How does exercise affect disposal of wastes from cellular respiration?

Materials 2 small test tubes, glass-marking pencil, 10-mL graduated cylinder, bromthymol blue solution, 2 straws, clock or watch with second hand

Procedure   

1. **Predicting** Record your prediction of how exercise will affect your body's production of carbon dioxide.
2. If you are using a carbon dioxide probe, see your teacher for instructions.
3. Label two test tubes A and B. Put 10 mL of water and a few drops of bromthymol blue solution in each test tube. Carbon dioxide causes bromthymol blue to turn yellow or green.
4. Your partner will time you during this step. When your partner says "go," slowly blow air through a straw into the bottom of test tube A. **CAUTION:** *Do not inhale through the straw.*
5. When the solution changes color, your partner should say "stop," and then record how long the color change took.
6. Jog in place for 1 minute. **CAUTION:** *Do not do this if you have a medical condition that interferes with exercise. If you feel faint or dizzy, stop immediately and sit down.*
7. Repeat steps 4 and 5 using test tube B.
8. Trade roles with your partner. Repeat steps 3 through 7.

Analyze and Conclude

1. **Analyzing Data** How did exercise affect the time for the solution to change color? Did these results support your prediction?
2. **Inferring** What process in your body produces carbon dioxide? How does exercise affect this process?
3. **SAFETY** What safety procedures did you follow? Why were these procedures important?

Figure 9–10 Photosynthesis and cellular respiration can be thought of as opposite processes. **Comparing and Contrasting** *Exactly how is the equation for photosynthesis different from the equation for cellular respiration?*

Comparing Photosynthesis and Cellular Respiration

	Photosynthesis	Cellular Respiration
Function	Energy capture	Energy release
Location	Chloroplasts	Mitochondria
Reactants	CO_2 and H_2O	$C_6H_{12}O_6$ and O_2
Products	$C_6H_{12}O_6$ and O_2	CO_2 and H_2O
Equation	$6CO_2 + 6H_2O \rightarrow C_6H_{12}O_6 + 6O_2$ (Energy)	$6O_2 + C_6H_{12}O_6 \rightarrow 6CO_2 + 6H_2O$ (Energy)

Comparing Photosynthesis and Cellular Respiration

The energy flows in photosynthesis and cellular respiration take place in opposite directions. Earlier in this chapter, the chemical energy in carbohydrates was compared to money in a savings account. Photosynthesis is the process that "deposits" energy. Cellular respiration is the process that "withdraws" energy. As you might expect, the equations for photosynthesis and cellular respiration, shown in **Figure 9–10,** are the reverse of each other.

On a global level, photosynthesis and cellular respiration are also opposites. Photosynthesis removes carbon dioxide from the atmosphere, and cellular respiration puts it back. Photosynthesis releases oxygen into the atmosphere, and cellular respiration uses that oxygen to release energy from food. The release of energy by cellular respiration takes place in all eukaryotes and some prokaryotes. Energy capture by photosynthesis, however, occurs only in plants, algae, and some bacteria.

9–2 Section Assessment

1. **Key Concept** What happens to pyruvic acid during the Krebs cycle?
2. **Key Concept** How does the electron transport chain use the high-energy electrons from the Krebs cycle?
3. Why is cellular respiration considered to be much more efficient than glycolysis alone?
4. How many molecules of ATP are produced in the entire breakdown of glucose?
5. **Critical Thinking Comparing and Contrasting** Compare the energy flow in photosynthesis to the energy flow in cellular respiration.
6. **Critical Thinking Using Analogies** How is the chemical energy in glucose similar to money in a savings account?

Thinking Visually

Organizing Information
Using **Figure 9–6** and **Figure 9–7** as guides, prepare a poster showing the main events of the process of cellular respiration. For each event, show the reactant and products and where in the mitochondrion the event occurs. Use your poster to explain cellular respiration to a classmate.

Should Creatine Supplements Be Banned?

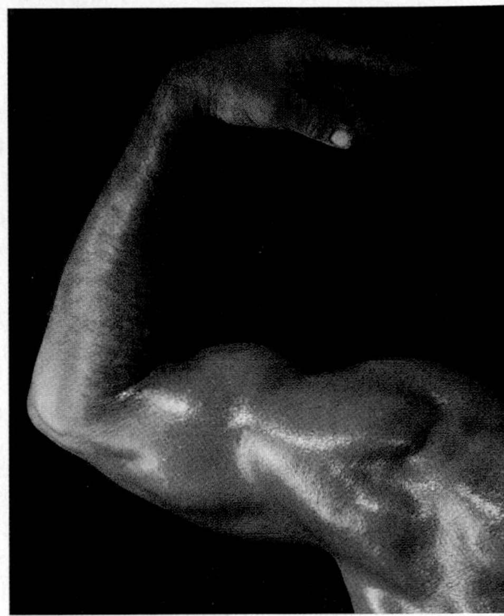

Many athletes now use a dietary supplement called creatine to enhance their performance. Creatine may improve athletic performance, but critics point to potentially serious side effects as a reason to control its use.

Although muscle cells contain only enough ATP for a few seconds of intense activity, most have a reserve nearly twice as large in the form of a molecule called creatine phosphate. When the muscle goes to work and starts to use up its available ATP, phosphates are transferred from creatine phosphate directly to ADP, regenerating ATP in a matter of milliseconds. The more creatine phosphate a muscle contains, the longer it can sustain intense activity. Hoping to increase their capacity for strong, short-term muscle contractions, many athletes have added creatine to their diets. Should athletes be allowed to use creatine supplements?

The Viewpoints

Creatine Supplements Should Be Allowed

Creatine is a natural substance found in human cells and in foods such as meat. Taken in recommended doses, creatine helps build muscle strength and performance, which can mean the difference between winning and losing. When athletes have followed instructions on container labels, no serious side effects have been reported. The risks are small and the rewards of winning are large enough to justify its use.

Creatine Supplements Should Be Banned

Like any natural substance, creatine can be abused. Creatine is known to cause water loss, putting the athletes who use it at risk for dehydration, muscle injury, diarrhea, kidney failure, and perhaps even death. Because creatine is considered a dietary supplement and not a drug, the Food and Drug Administration (FDA) has never determined its safety. Until a truly safe dose has been determined by careful scientific studies, athletes should not be allowed to use creatine.

Research and Decide

1. **Analyzing the Viewpoints** To make an informed decision, learn more about this issue by consulting library or Internet resources. Then, list the key arguments expressed by the proponents and critics of using creatine as a dietary supplement. What is known? What is not known? What are the benefits? What are the risks?
2. **Forming Your Opinion** Should athletes be allowed to take creatine to enhance performance? Weigh the pro and con arguments. Research to find out if some professional sports have banned the use of creatine by athletes. What were the reasons for this decision? Do some arguments outweigh others? Which arguments? Explain your answer.
3. **Writing an Editorial** Write an editorial for a sports magazine that takes a stand on creatine. Your editorial should persuade your readers that your opinion is justified.

For: Links from the authors
Visit: PHSchool.com
Web Code: cbe-3093

Investigating Fermentation by Making Kimchi

In this investigation, you will make a popular Korean side dish known as kimchi. Kimchi is made by allowing microorganisms to ferment Chinese cabbage. The main microorganism involved is a bacterium called Lactobacillus. *This bacterium mainly carries out lactic acid fermentation. Some species of* Lactobacillus *and other microorganisms on the cabbage carry out alcoholic fermentation. All of these microorganisms occur naturally on the surface of the Chinese cabbage. As these microorganisms ferment the Chinese cabbage, you will measure the chemical changes that occur during this process. You will use your knowledge of fermentation to explain the observations that you make.*

Problem
How does fermentation affect pH?

Materials

- 2 resealable plastic sandwich bags
- chopped Chinese cabbage
- noniodized salt
- 2.5-mL (1/2 teaspoon) measuring spoon
- pH-indicator paper
- thermometer

Skills
Predicting, Measuring, Drawing Conclusions

Procedure

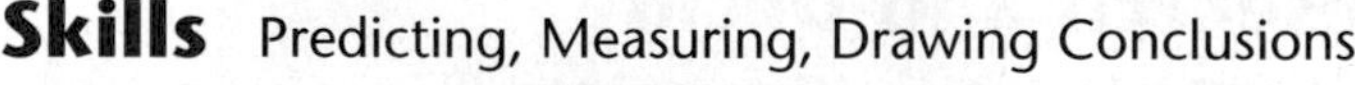

1. **Formulating Hypotheses** Recall that pH is a measure of how acidic or basic a solution is. Bases have pH levels between 7 and 14, and acids have pH levels between 0 and 7. Formulate a hypothesis that explains how fermentation leads to changes in pH. Record your hypothesis and your prediction of how the pH of the kimchi will change over time as it ferments.
2. Put one resealable plastic bag inside the other. Half-fill the inner bag with chopped cabbage. Add 2.5 mL of salt. Seal both bags and turn them upside down several times to mix the ingredients.
3. Unseal the bags and press down on them to expel any air. Then, reseal the bags. Label the plastic bags containing the kimchi with your name and place them in a cool area where they will remain undisturbed. Copy the data table shown. Measure and record the air temperature in your copy of the data table. Wash your hands at the end of each lab period.
4. Each day, observe the kimchi in the bags. Record your observations of any changes in the appearance of the kimchi or the bags in your data table. When a small amount of liquid appears in the bottom of the inner bag, open the bags. **CAUTION:** *Do not eat the kimchi.*

Data Table

Day	pH	Temperature	Observations
1			
8			
15			
22			
29			

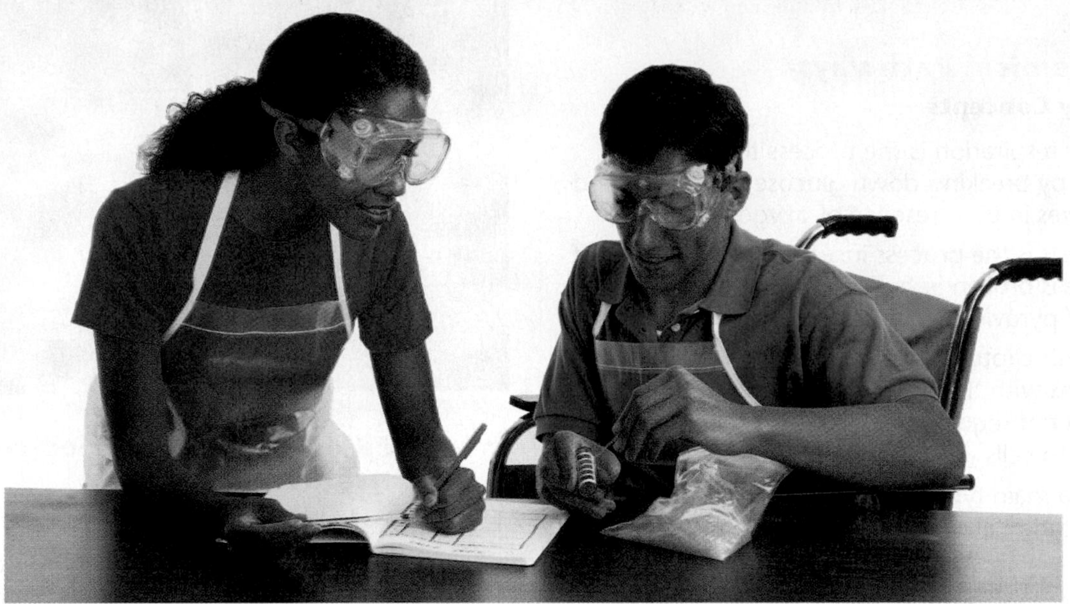

5 With your teacher's guidance, select the equipment and technology needed to measure pH—either pH-indicator paper or a pH probe. If you are using a pH probe, see your teacher for instructions.

6 Use pH-indicator paper to measure the pH of the liquid. Record the pH in your data table.

7 Press out any gas in the bags and reseal them. Return the bags to the cool area and leave them undisturbed for a week.

8 One week after you first measured the pH, repeat steps 6 and 7. Then, move the bags containing the kimchi to a refrigerator. Record the temperature of the refrigerator in your data table. Continue to observe the kimchi and record its pH every week for 4 weeks.

Analyze and Conclude

1. **Using Tables and Graphs** Use your data table to construct a graph showing the relationship between pH and time. With your teacher's guidance, select the appropriate equipment and technology—either graph paper or a graphing calculator. Describe how the pH of the kimchi changed over time.
2. **Inferring** What substance do you think was responsible for the change in pH? What process could have produced this substance?
3. **Evaluating and Revising** Was your prediction correct? What changes would you make in your hypothesis as a result of your observations?
4. **Inferring** Did you see any evidence that a gas was produced or consumed in the bags? If so, what was this gas? What process was responsible for this change? Explain the reasons for your answers.

Go Further

Designing Experiments Yogurt is made from milk using microorganisms that carry out lactic acid fermentation. Do research using scientific literature to form a hypothesis to determine how a factor, such as temperature or sugar concentration, affects the fermentation of yogurt. Your description should state your hypothesis, identify all variables, and explain how the outcome of the experiment could support or contradict your hypothesis.

For: Data Sharing
Visit: PHSchool.com
Web Code: cbd-3094

Share Your Data Online Enter your pH values in the data-sharing table online. Then, look at the data entered by other students. Based on the available data, how do you think a change in pH over time is related to fermentation? Why might your results differ from those of other students?

Chapter 9 Study Guide

9–1 Chemical Pathways

Key Concepts

- Cellular respiration is the process that releases energy by breaking down glucose and other food molecules in the presence of oxygen.
- Glycolysis is the process in which one molecule of glucose is broken in half, producing two molecules of pyruvic acid, a 3-carbon compound.
- Glycolysis captures two pairs of high-energy electrons with the carrier NAD^+. Because glycolysis does not require oxygen, it supplies chemical energy to cells when oxygen is not available.
- The two main types of fermentation are alcoholic fermentation and lactic acid fermentation.
- In the absence of oxygen, yeast and a few other microorganisms use alcoholic fermentation, forming ethyl alcohol and carbon dioxide as wastes.
- Animals cannot perform alcoholic fermentation, but some cells, such as human muscle cells, can convert glucose into lactic acid. This is called lactic acid fermentation.

Vocabulary
calorie, p. 221
glycolysis, p. 221
cellular respiration, p. 222
NAD^+, p. 223
fermentation, p. 224
anaerobic, p. 224

9–2 The Krebs Cycle and Electron Transport

Key Concepts

- During the Krebs cycle, pyruvic acid is broken down into carbon dioxide in a series of energy-extracting reactions.
- The electron transport chain uses the high-energy electrons from the Krebs cycle to convert ADP into ATP.
- The products of photosynthesis are similar to the reactants of cellular respiration. The products of cellular respiration are the reactants of photosynthesis.

Vocabulary
aerobic, p. 226
Krebs cycle, p. 226
electron transport chain, p. 228

Thinking Visually

Using the information in this chapter, complete the following compare-and-contrast table about fermentation and cellular respiration:

Comparing Fermentation and Cellular Respiration

Characteristic	Fermentation	Cellular Respiration
Starting reactants	1	2
Pathways involved	3	4
End products	5	6
Number of ATP molecules produced	7	8

Preparing for the Living Environment Exam

Blue questions emphasize Regents Exam content

Chapter 9

Part A

Multiple Choice

For each statement or question, select the number of the word or expression that, of those given, best completes the statement or answers the question.

1 In cells, the energy available in food is used to make an energy-rich compound called
(1) water (3) glucose
(2) ATP (4) ADP

2 The process most directly associated with the release of energy from molecules in the presence of oxygen is
(1) cellular respiration (3) photosynthesis
(2) DNA replication (4) regulation

3 Which of the organisms illustrated below perform cellular respiration?

A  B  C  D 

(1) A and B, only (3) B, C, and D, only
(2) B and D, only (4) A, B, C, and D

4 ATP is a compound that is synthesized when
(1) chemical bonds between carbon atoms are formed during photosynthesis
(2) energy stored in chemical bonds is released during cellular respiration
(3) energy stored in nitrogen is released, forming amino acids
(4) digestive enzymes break amino acids into smaller parts

5 Which phrase best describes cellular respiration, a process that occurs continuously in the cells of organisms?
(1) removal of oxygen from the cells of an organism
(2) conversion of light energy into the chemical bond energy of organic molecules
(3) transport of materials within cells and throughout the bodies of multicellular organisms
(4) changing of stored chemical energy in food molecules to a form usable by organisms

6 The flow of energy through an ecosystem involves many energy transfers. The diagram below summarizes the transfer of energy that eventually powers muscle activity.

Sun $\rightarrow$ *Food* $\rightarrow$ *ATP* $\rightarrow$ *Muscle Activity*
A B C

The process of cellular respiration is represented by
(1) arrow A, only
(2) arrow B, only
(3) arrow C, only
(4) arrows A, B, and C

7 During heavy exercise, the buildup of lactic acid in muscle cells results in
(1) alcoholic fermentation
(2) the Calvin cycle
(3) oxygen debt
(4) the Krebs cycle

8 The raw materials needed for cellular respiration include
(1) glucose and carbon dioxide
(2) glucose and oxygen
(3) carbon dioxide and oxygen
(4) oxygen and lactic acid

9 Chemical reactions that yield the greatest amount of ATP occur during the conversion of pyruvic acid to
(1) ethyl alcohol
(2) carbon dioxide and water
(3) glucose and oxygen
(4) lactic acid

10 Which best represents the waste products of cellular respiration?
(1) O_2 (3) H_2O and O_2
(2) CO_2 and H_2O (4) CO_2 and O_2

Test-Taking Tip When you are asked to analyze a graph showing experimental data, first look at the shape of the curve. Identify the variables and try to determine how they are related. Then, read and answer the questions about the graph.

Preparing for the Living Environment Exam

Part B

Multiple Choice and Extended Response

For those questions that ask you to select a response, choose the one that best completes the statement or answers the question. For all others follow the directions given.

Base your answers to questions 11 and 12 on the information and data table below and on your knowledge of biology.

The rate of respiration of a freshwater sunfish was determined at different temperatures. The rate of respiration was determined by counting the number of times the gill covers of the fish opened and closed during 1-minute intervals at the various temperatures. The following data were collected.

Data Table

Temperature (°C)	Gill Cover Opening and Closing Per Minute
10	15
15	25
18	30
20	38
23	60
25	57
27	25

11 According to the data, as the temperature increases, the rate of respiration of the sunfish
- **(1)** increases steadily
- **(2)** decreases steadily
- **(3)** increases, then decreases
- **(4)** decreases, then increases

12 Which title is appropriate for this data table?
- **(1)** The Effect of Temperature on Rate of Respiration in Sunfish
- **(2)** The Effect of Gill Movement on Rate of Respiration in Sunfish
- **(3)** The Relationship Between Temperature and Dissolved Oxygen
- **(4)** The Relationship Between Sunfish Population and Temperature Change in Freshwater Habitats

13 List the *three* products that are produced as a result of glycolysis.

Base your answers to questions 14 through 16 on the graph below and on your knowledge of biology.

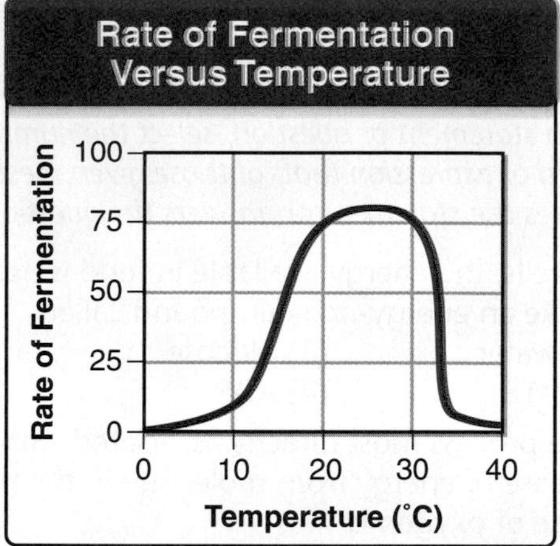

14 Which statement best describes the relationship between the rate of fermentation and temperature?
- **(1)** The rate of fermentation continually increases as temperature increases.
- **(2)** The rate of fermentation continually decreases as temperature increases.
- **(3)** The rate of fermentation increases with temperature, then it rapidly decreases.
- **(4)** The rate of fermentation decreases with temperature, then it increases.

15 Which statement best explains the data shown in the graph?
- **(1)** The molecules that regulate fermentation perform optimally at temperatures above 30°C.
- **(2)** The yeast begins releasing carbon dioxide at 30°C.
- **(3)** The yeast cannot survive at temperatures above 30°C.
- **(4)** The molecules that regulate fermentation perform optimally at temperatures below 10°C.

16 State the hypothesis that was most likely being investigated in the experiment that produced the data in the graph.

17 Yeast cells can carry out both fermentation and cellular respiration, depending on whether oxygen is present. In which case would you expect yeast cells to grow more rapidly? Support your answer with an explanation.

NEW YORK LIVING ENVIRONMENT

Part C

Extended Response

Answer the questions or follow the directions given.

Base your answer to question 18 on the information below and your knowledge of biology.

18 The flowchart below represents the flow of materials and energy typical of many ecosystems. Trace the flow of energy, using the flowchart as a reference. In your answer be sure to:
- identify the words that should be written in the ovals numbered *1* and *2*
- identify the *two* materials in the flowchart that contain stored energy and are part of the energy flow
- explain what happens to the ATP shown in the flowchart

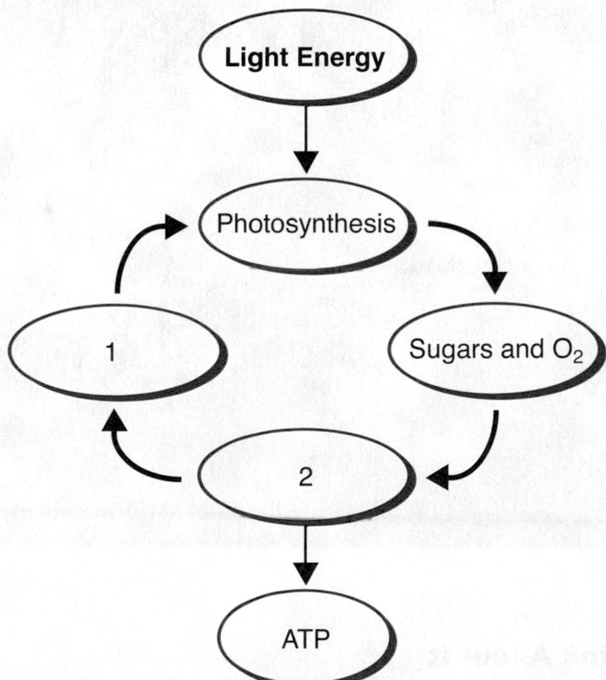

19 In all organisms, ATP and ADP are important molecules. Explain how ATP and ADP are important in sustaining life. In your explanation be sure to:
- state the primary function of ATP and ADP
- compare ATP to ADP
- describe what is involved in converting one to the other

Base your answers to questions 20 through 22 on the reading passage below and on your knowledge of biology.

The Carbon Cycle

Atoms and molecules on Earth are cycled and recycled through living and nonliving parts of the environment. In this way, carbon, hydrogen, nitrogen, and oxygen are used and reused. Energy from the sun keeps this process going in biogeochemical cycles.

Carbon cycles through the environment during biological processes like photosynthesis, respiration, and decomposition of plants and animals.

20 Explain why atoms and molecules can be cycled through an ecosystem but energy cannot.

21 It is sometimes said that, "photosynthesis and respiration are reverse processes." Support this statement by explaining how each of the following is involved in both photosynthesis and respiration:
- oxygen and carbon dioxide
- energy
- enzymes
- glucose

22 How are the sites of photosynthesis and respiration in the cell different?

For: An interactive self-test
Visit: PHSchool.com
Web Code: cba-3090

CHAPTER 10

Cell Growth and Division

This liver cell has almost completed the process of cell division. During cell division, a cell splits into two daughter cells (magnification: 11,500×).

Inquiry Activity

How do organisms grow?

Procedure

1. Use a microscope to compare the sizes of similar cells in large and small plants. For example, you might compare the leaf cells of grass to the leaf cells of a tree. Be sure to use the same magnification when comparing the sizes of the cells.
2. Use a microscope to compare the sizes of cells in similar tissues from small and large animals, such as muscle tissue from a frog and from a human.

Think About It

1. **Observing** Are the cells of the small plant larger or smaller than those of the large plant? Are the cells of the small animal larger or smaller than those of the large animal?
2. **Comparing and Contrasting** Make a general statement that compares the number and size of cells in small organisms to those in larger organisms.

10–1 Cell Growth

4-1.2 Cell membranes
LS- Observe, measure length, volume of liquids
LS- Use of compound microscope

Guide for Reading

 **Key Concept**

- What problems does growth cause for cells?

Vocabulary
cell division

Reading Strategy: Asking Questions Before reading this section, rewrite each blue heading as a *what, where,* or *how* question. Then, as you read, fill in the answer to each question.

When a living thing grows, what happens to its cells? Does an animal get larger because each cell increases in size or because it produces more of them? In most cases, living things grow by producing more cells. On average, the cells of an adult animal are no larger than those of a young animal—there are just more of them.

Limits to Cell Growth

There are two main reasons why cells divide rather than continuing to grow indefinitely. **The larger a cell becomes, the more demands the cell places on its DNA. In addition, the cell has more trouble moving enough nutrients and wastes across the cell membrane.**

DNA "Overload" As you may recall, the information that controls a cell's function is stored in a molecule known as DNA. In eukaryotic cells, DNA is found in the nucleus of the cell. When a cell is small, the information stored in that DNA is able to meet all of the cell's needs. But as a cell increases in size, it usually does not make extra copies of DNA. If a cell were to grow without limit, an "information crisis" would occur.

To help understand why a larger cell has a more difficult time functioning efficiently than a smaller cell, compare the cell to a growing town. Suppose a small town has a library with a few thousand books. If more people move into the town, the town will get larger. There will be more people borrowing books, and sometimes people may have to wait to borrow popular titles. Similarly, a larger cell would have to make greater demands on its available genetic "library." In time, the cell's DNA would no longer be able to serve the increasing needs of the growing cell.

Exchanging Materials There is another reason why the size of cells is limited. You may recall that food, oxygen, and water enter a cell through its cell membrane. Waste products leave in the same way. The rate at which this exchange takes place depends on the surface area of the cell, which is the total area of its cell membrane. However, the rate at which food and oxygen are used up and waste products are produced depends on the cell's volume. Understanding the relationship between a cell's volume and its surface area is the key to understanding why cells must divide as they grow.

▼ **Figure 10–1** Living things grow by producing more cells. Although the adult snail is larger than the young snail, the cells of both are the same size.

For: Links on cell growth
Visit: PHSchool.com
Web Code: cbd-3101

Ratio of Surface Area to Volume Imagine a cell that is shaped like a cube, like those in **Figure 10–2.** If this cell has a length of 1 cm, its surface area would be equal to length × width × number of sides, or 1 cm × 1 cm × 6 = 6 cm^2. The volume of the cell would be equal to length × width × height, or 1 cm × 1 cm × 1 cm = 1 cm^3. To obtain the ratio of surface area to volume, divide the surface area by the volume. In this case, the ratio of surface area to volume would be 6 / 1, or 6 : 1.

If the length of the cell doubled, what would happen to the cell's surface area compared to its volume? The cell's surface area would be equal to 2 cm × 2 cm × 6 = 24 cm^2. The volume would be equal to 2 cm × 2 cm × 2 cm = 8 cm^3. The cell's ratio of surface area to volume would be 24 / 8, or 3 : 1.

What if the length of the cell triples? The cell's surface area now would be 3 cm × 3 cm × 6 = 54 cm^2. The volume would be 3 cm × 3 cm × 3 cm = 27 cm^3. The ratio of surface area to volume would be 54 / 27, or 2 : 1.

Note that the volume increases much more rapidly than the surface area, causing the ratio of surface area to volume to decrease. This decrease creates serious problems for the cell.

To use the town analogy again, suppose that the small town has a two-lane main street. As the town grows, more people will begin to use this street. The main street leading through town, however, has not increased in size. As a result, people will encounter more traffic as they enter and leave the town. A cell that continues to grow larger would experience similar problems.

Quick Lab

What limits the sizes of cells?

Materials 2 peeled hard-boiled eggs, blue food coloring, 150-mL beaker, scalpel, spoon, paper towels, metric ruler

Procedure    

1. Put on your plastic gloves and apron. Place 100 mL of water in a beaker. Add 10 drops of blue food coloring, and stir with a spoon. **CAUTION:** *Food coloring may stain hands and clothing.*
2. Use the scalpel to cut through the middle of 1 hard-boiled egg. **CAUTION:** *Be careful with the scalpel.* Remove the yolk. Cut an 8-mm cube from the thickest part of the egg white.
3. Place the egg cube and a peeled hard-boiled egg gently into the beaker of food coloring and water. Allow the eggs to sit in the beaker for 10 minutes.

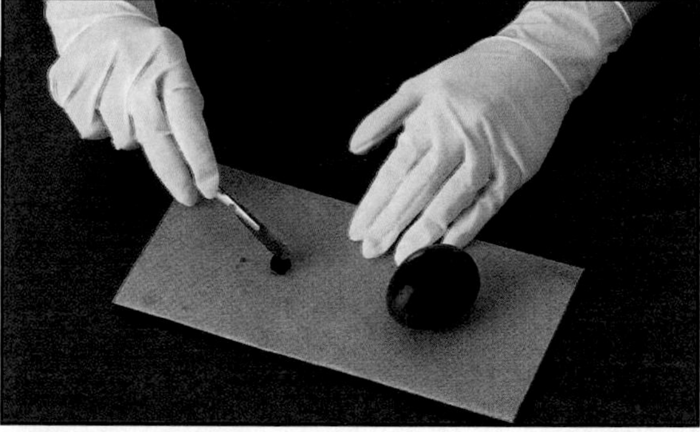

4. After 10 minutes, use a spoon to carefully remove the egg cube and the whole egg from the beaker, and place them on a paper towel. Cut the egg cube in half. Clean the scalpel blade and cut the whole egg in half. Measure how far the blue color penetrated the egg cube and the whole egg.

Analyze and Conclude

1. **Observing** How close to the centers of the egg cube and the whole egg did the color reach?
2. **Using Models** Compare the whole egg and the egg cube to cells to explain why a cell cannot continue to grow indefinitely.

Ratio of Surface Area to Volume in Cells			
Cell Size	 1 cm, 1 cm, 1 cm	 2 cm, 2 cm, 2 cm	 3 cm, 3 cm, 3 cm
Surface Area (length x width x 6)	1 cm x 1 cm x 6 = 6 cm^2	2 cm x 2 cm x 6 = 24 cm^2	3 cm x 3 cm x 6 = 54 cm^2
Volume (length x width x height)	1 cm x 1 cm x 1 cm = 1 cm^3	2 cm x 2 cm x 2 cm = 8 cm^3	3 cm x 3 cm x 3 cm = 27 cm^3
Ratio of Surface Area to Volume	6 / 1 = 6 : 1	24 / 8 = 3 : 1	54 / 27 = 2 : 1

▲ **Figure 10–2** As the length of a cell increases, its volume increases faster than its surface area. **The resulting decrease in the cell's ratio of surface area to volume makes it more difficult for the cell to move needed materials in and waste products out.**

If a cell got too large, it would be more difficult to get sufficient amounts of oxygen and nutrients in and waste products out. This is one reason why cells do not grow much larger even if the organism of which they are a part does.

Division of the Cell

Before it becomes too large, a growing cell divides forming two "daughter" cells. The process by which a cell divides into two new daughter cells is called **cell division.**

Before cell division occurs, the cell replicates, or copies, all of its DNA. This replication of DNA solves the problem of information storage because each daughter cell gets one complete set of genetic information. Thus, each daughter cell receives its own genetic "library." Cell division also solves the problem of increasing size by reducing cell volume. Each daughter cell has an increased ratio of surface area to volume. This allows efficient exchange of materials with the environment.

10–1 Section Assessment

1. **Key Concept** Give two reasons why cells divide.
2. How is a cell's DNA like the books in a library?
3. As a cell increases in size, which increases more rapidly, its surface area or its volume?
4. **Critical Thinking Calculating** Calculate the surface area, volume, and ratio of surface area to volume of an imaginary cubic cell measuring 4 cm on each side.

Connecting Concepts

Stability and Equilibrium
Select two cell organelles and describe how their functions might be impaired if the cell were to become too large. A review of Chapter 7 may help you with this task.

10–2 Cell Division

1-S2.3, 3.1 Hypotheses lead to predictions
4-2.1 Heredity specifies traits
4-2.1 Genes, chromosomes in the nucleus
4-4.1 The importance and events of mitotic cell division
LS- State an appropriate hypothesis and analyze results

Guide for Reading

Key Concepts
- What are the main events of the cell cycle?
- What are the four phases of mitosis?

Vocabulary
mitosis
cytokinesis
chromatid
centromere
interphase
cell cycle
prophase
centriole
spindle
metaphase
anaphase
telophase

Reading Strategy: Outlining As you read this section, outline the major events of the cell cycle. Write a few sentences to describe the activity of chromosomes as they progress through each part of the cell cycle.

What do you think would happen if a cell were simply to split into two, without any advance preparation? Would each daughter cell have everything it needed to survive? Because each cell has only one set of genetic information, the answer is no. Every cell must first copy its genetic information before cell division begins. Each daughter cell then gets a complete copy of that information.

In most prokaryotes, the rest of the process of cell division is a simple matter of separating the contents of the cell into two parts. In eukaryotes, cell division is more complex and occurs in two main stages. The first stage, division of the cell nucleus, is called **mitosis** (my-TOH-sis). The second stage, division of the cytoplasm, is called **cytokinesis** (sy-toh-kih-NEE-sis).

Many organisms, especially unicellular ones, reproduce by means of mitosis and cytokinesis. Reproduction by mitosis is classified as asexual, since the cells produced by mitosis are genetically identical to the parent cell. Mitosis is also the source of new cells when a multicellular organism grows and develops. In humans, for example, mitosis begins shortly after the egg is fertilized, producing the vast numbers of cells needed for the embryo to take form.

Chromosomes

In eukaryotic cells, the genetic information that is passed on from one generation of cells to the next is carried by chromosomes. Chromosomes are made up of DNA—which carries the cell's coded genetic information—and proteins. The cells of every organism have a specific number of chromosomes. The cells of fruit flies, for example, have 8 chromosomes; human cells have 46 chromosomes; and carrot cells have 18 chromosomes.

Chromosomes are not visible in most cells except during cell division. This is because the DNA and protein molecules that make up the chromosomes are spread throughout the nucleus. At the beginning of cell division, however, the chromosomes condense into compact, visible structures that can be seen through a light microscope.

Well before cell division, each chromosome is replicated, or copied. Because of this, each chromosome consists of two identical "sister" **chromatids** (KROH-muh-tidz), as shown in **Figure 10–3.** When the cell divides, the "sister" chromatids separate from each other. One chromatid goes to each of the two new cells.

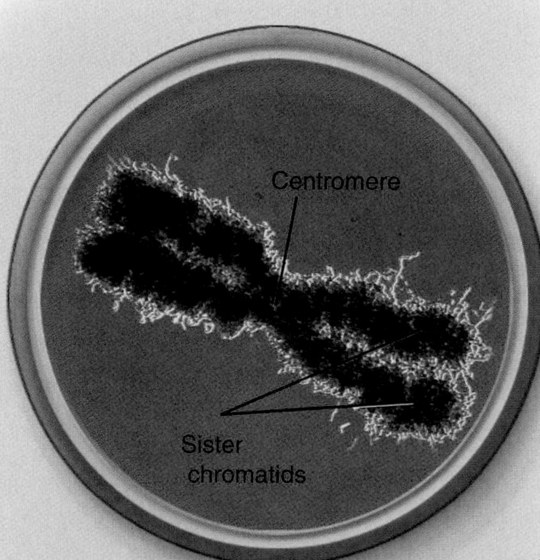

(magnification: 20,000×)

◀ **Figure 10–3** This is a human chromosome shown as it appears through an electron microscope. Each chromosome has two sister chromatids attached at the centromere. **Inferring** *Why is it important that the sister chromatids are identical?*

Each pair of chromatids is attached at an area called the centromere (SEN-troh-meer). **Centromeres** are usually located near the middle of the chromatids, although some lie near the ends. A human body cell entering cell division contains 46 chromosomes, each of which consists of two chromatids.

The Cell Cycle

At one time, biologists described the life of a cell as one cell division after another separated by an "in-between" period of growth called **interphase.** We now appreciate that a great deal happens in the time between cell divisions, and use a concept known as the cell cycle to represent recurring events in the life of the cell. The **cell cycle** is the series of events that cells go through as they grow and divide. **During the cell cycle, a cell grows, prepares for division, and divides to form two daughter cells, each of which then begins the cycle again.** The cell cycle is shown in **Figure 10–4.**

The cell cycle consists of four phases. Mitosis and cytokinesis take place during the M phase. Chromosome replication, or synthesis, takes place during the S phase. When the cell copies the chromosomes, it makes a duplicate set of DNA. Between the M and S phases are G_1 and G_2. The *G* in the names of these phases stands for "gap," but the G_1 and G_2 are definitely not periods when nothing takes place. They are actually periods of intense growth and activity.

Go Online NSTA SCILINKS
For: Links on the cell cycle
Visit: www.SciLinks.org
Web Code: cbn-3103

Events of the Cell Cycle

During the normal cell cycle, interphase can be quite long, whereas the process of cell division takes place quickly. Interphase is divided into three phases: G_1, S, and G_2.

The G_1 phase is a period of activity in which cells do most of their growing. During this phase, cells increase in size and synthesize new proteins and organelles.

G_1 is followed by the S phase, in which chromosomes are replicated and the synthesis of DNA molecules takes place. Key proteins associated with the chromosomes are also synthesized during the S phase. Usually, once a cell enters the S phase and begins the replication of its chromosomes, it completes the rest of the cell cycle.

When the DNA replication is completed, the cell enters the G_2 phase. G_2 is usually the shortest of the three phases of interphase. During the G_2 phase, many of the organelles and molecules required for cell division are produced. When the events of the G_2 phase are completed, the cell is ready to enter the M phase and begin the process of cell division.

CHECKPOINT *What happens during the G_1 phase?*

▼ **Figure 10–4** **During the cell cycle, the cell grows, replicates its DNA, and divides into two daughter cells.** DNA synthesis takes place during the S phase. Cell division takes place during the M phase. G_1 and G_2 are gap phases.

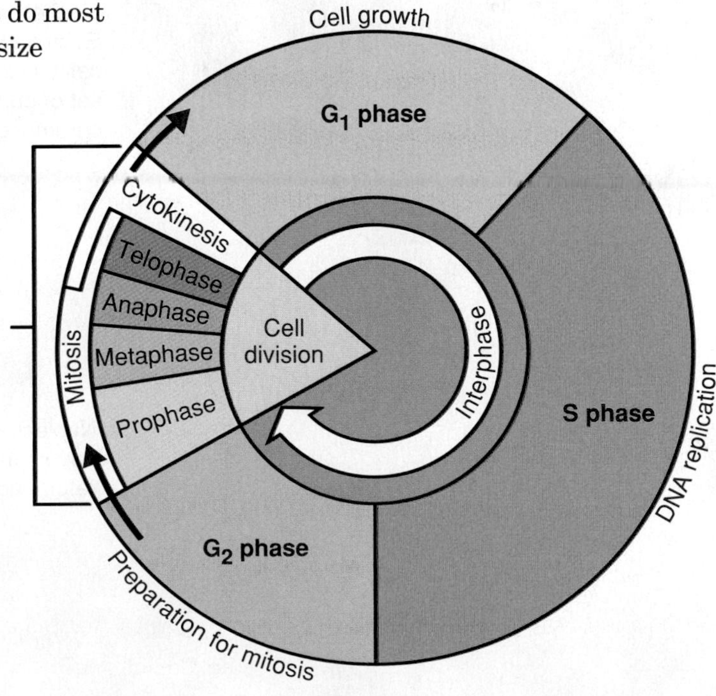

Mitosis

Biologists divide the events of mitosis into four phases: prophase, metaphase, anaphase, and telophase. Depending on the type of cell, the four phases of mitosis may last anywhere from a few minutes to several days. As you read about each phase of mitosis, look at **Figure 10–5.**

Prophase The first and longest phase of mitosis, **prophase,** can take as much as 50 to 60 percent of the total time required to complete mitosis. During prophase, the chromosomes become visible. The **centrioles** (SEN-tree-ohlz), two tiny structures located in the cytoplasm near the nuclear envelope, separate and take up positions on opposite sides of the nucleus.

▼ **Figure 10–5** Most eukaryotic cells go through a regular cycle of interphase, mitosis, and cytokinesis. **Mitosis has four phases: prophase, metaphase, anaphase, and telophase.** The events shown here are typical of animal cells. The photographs shown are from a developing whitefish embryo (magnification: 625×).

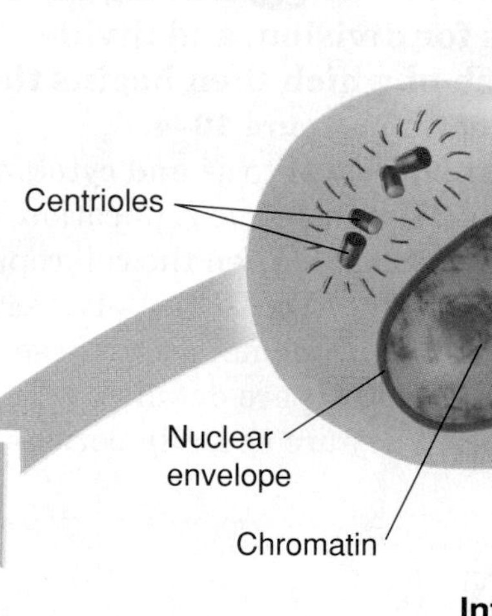

Interphase
The cell grows and replicates its DNA and centrioles.

Cytokinesis
The cytoplasm pinches in half. Each daughter cell has an identical set of duplicate chromosomes.

Telophase
The chromosomes gather at opposite ends of the cell and lose their distinct shapes. Two new nuclear envelopes will form.

Nuclear envelope reforming

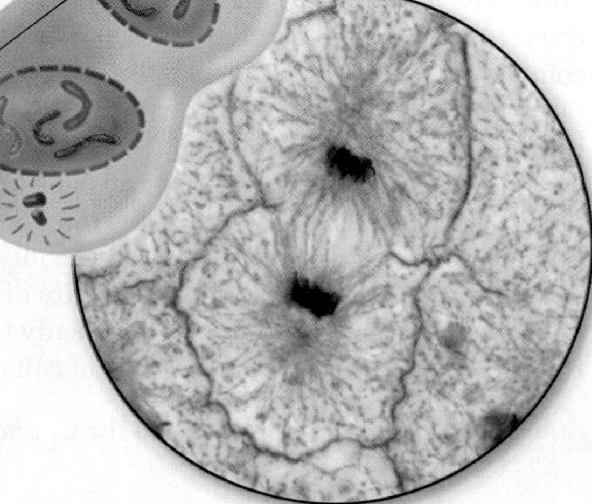

The centrioles lie in a region called the centrosome that helps to organize the **spindle,** a fanlike microtubule structure that helps separate the chromosomes. During prophase, the condensed chromosomes become attached to fibers in the spindle at a point near the centromere of each chromatid. Interestingly, plant cells do not have centrioles, but still organize their mitotic spindles from similar regions.

Near the end of prophase, the chromosomes coil more tightly. In addition, the nucleolus disappears, and the nuclear envelope breaks down.

What is the function of the spindle?

Spindle forming

Prophase
The chromatin condenses into chromosomes. The centrioles separate, and a spindle begins to form. The nuclear envelope breaks down.

Centromere

Chromosomes (paired chromatids)

Centriole

Metaphase
The chromosomes line up across the center of the cell. Each chromosome is connected to a spindle fiber at its centromere.

Spindle

Centriole

Anaphase
The sister chromatids separate into individual chromosomes and are moved apart.

Individual chromosomes

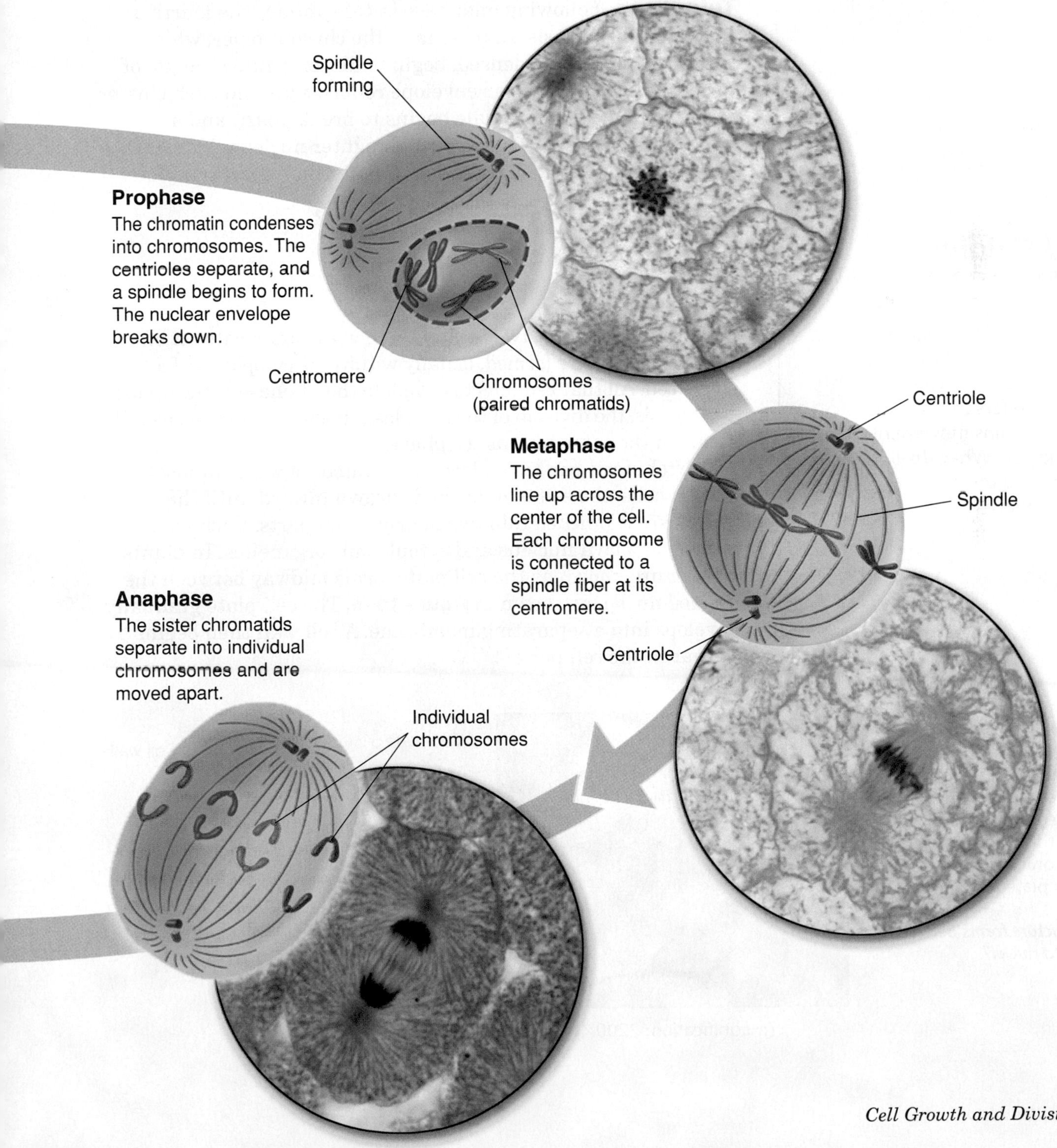

Metaphase The second phase of mitosis, **metaphase,** often lasts only a few minutes. During metaphase, the chromosomes line up across the center of the cell. Microtubules connect the centromere of each chromosome to the two poles of the spindle.

Anaphase **Anaphase** is the third phase of mitosis. During anaphase, the centromeres that join the sister chromatids split, allowing the sister chromatids to separate and become individual chromosomes. The chromosomes continue to move until they have separated into two groups near the poles of the spindle. Anaphase ends when the chromosomes stop moving.

Telophase Following anaphase is **telophase,** the fourth and final phase of mitosis. In telophase, the chromosomes, which were distinct and condensed, begin to disperse into a tangle of dense material. A nuclear envelope re-forms around each cluster of chromosomes. The spindle begins to break apart, and a nucleolus becomes visible in each daughter nucleus. Mitosis is complete. However, the process of cell division is not complete.

CHECKPOINT ***What happens during anaphase?***

Cytokinesis

As a result of mitosis, two nuclei—each with a duplicate set of chromosomes—are formed, usually within the cytoplasm of a single cell. All that remains to complete the M phase of the cycle is cytokinesis, the division of the cytoplasm itself. Cytokinesis usually occurs at the same time as telophase.

Cytokinesis can take place in a number of ways. In most animal cells, the cell membrane is drawn inward until the cytoplasm is pinched into two nearly equal parts. Each part contains its own nucleus and cytoplasmic organelles. In plants, a structure known as the cell plate forms midway between the divided nuclei, as shown in **Figure 10–6.** The cell plate gradually develops into a separating membrane. A cell wall then begins to appear in the cell plate.

Word Origins

Cytokinesis comes from the Greek words *kytos,* meaning "hollow vessel," and *kinesis,* meaning "motion." The prefix *cyto-* refers to cells, so *cytokinesis* means movement within the cell. **What do you think the term *cytotoxic* means?**

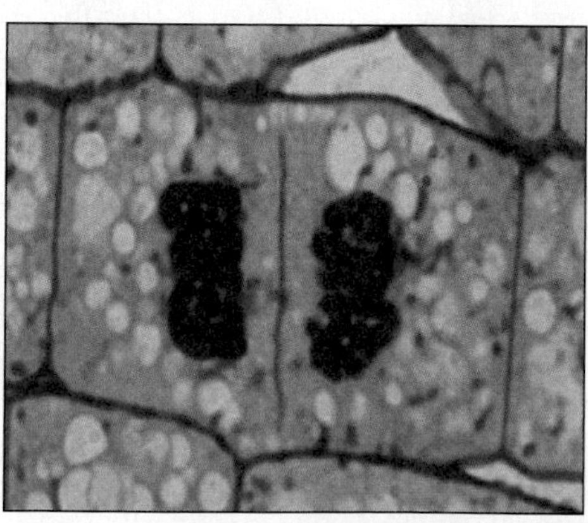

(magnification: 2200×)

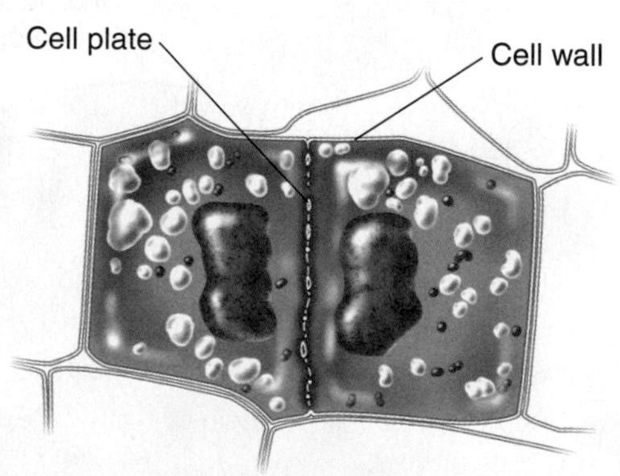

▶ **Figure 10–6** During cytokinesis in plant cells, the cytoplasm is divided by a cell plate. The thin line you can see between the two dark nuclei in this electron micrograph of onion cells dividing is the cell plate forming. **Interpreting Graphics** ***What structure forms between the divided nuclei?***

Analyzing Data

Life Spans of Human Cells

Like all organisms, cells have a given life span from birth to death. In multicellular organisms, such as humans, the health of the organism depends on cells not exceeding their life span. This is especially true of cells that tend to divide rapidly. If these cells did not die on schedule, overcrowding of cells would occur, causing uncontrolled growth that would be life-threatening.

The data table shows the life spans of various human cells. It also contains information about the ability of the cells to multiply through cell division.

1. **Inferring** White blood cells help protect the body from infection and disease-producing organisms. How might their function relate to their life span?
2. **Comparing and Contrasting** Based on the data, how are the consequences of injuries to the heart and spinal cord similar to each other? How are they different from the consequences of injuries to smooth muscle?
3. **Formulating Hypotheses** Propose a hypothesis to account for the data related to the cell life spans of the lining of the esophagus, small intestine, and large intestine.

Life Spans of Various Human Cells

Cell Type	Life Span	Cell Division
Lining of esophagus	2–3 days	Can divide
Lining of small intestine	1–2 days	Can divide
Lining of large intestine	6 days	Can divide
Red blood cells	Less than 120 days	Cannot divide
White blood cells	10 hours to decades	Many do not divide
Smooth muscle	Long-lived	Can divide
Cardiac (heart) muscle	Long-lived	Cannot divide
Skeletal muscle	Long-lived	Cannot divide
Neuron (nerve cell)	Long-lived	Most do not divide

4. **Going Further** Cancer is a disease related to cell life span and cell division. If cancer cells were added to the data table, predict what would be written under the columns headed "Life Span" and "Cell Division." Explain the reasoning underlying your predictions.

10–2 Section Assessment

1. **Key Concept** Name the main events of the cell cycle.
2. **Key Concept** Describe what happens during each of the four phases of mitosis.
3. Describe what happens during interphase.
4. What are chromosomes made of?
5. How do prokaryotic cells divide?
6. **Critical Thinking Comparing and Contrasting** How is cytokinesis in plant cells similar to cytokinesis in animal cells? How is it different?

Writing in Science

Creative Writing

Suppose you were small enough to hitch a ride on a chromosome located in a plant cell that goes through mitosis and cytokinesis. Describe what you would see happening during each phase of the process.

10–3 Regulating the Cell Cycle

4-2.1 The environment can influence gene expression
4-5.3 Feedback mechanisms help maintain homeostasis
4-5.2 Exposure of cells
4-5.2 Gene mutations
4-5.2 Biological research

Guide for Reading

Key Concepts
- How is the cell cycle regulated?
- How are cancer cells different from other cells?

Vocabulary
cyclin
cancer

Reading Strategy: Summarizing Summarizing helps you understand and remember what you read. Write a main-idea statement for each blue head. When you have finished the section, compare your statements with those in the study guide.

One of the most striking aspects of cell behavior in a multicellular organism is how carefully cell growth and cell division are controlled. Not all cells move through the cell cycle at the same rate. In the human body, most muscle cells and nerve cells do not divide at all once they have developed. In contrast, the cells of the skin and digestive tract, and cells in the bone marrow that make blood cells, grow and divide rapidly throughout life. Such cells may pass through a complete cycle every few hours. This process provides new cells to replace those that wear out or break down.

Controls on Cell Division

Scientists can observe the effects of controlled cell growth in the laboratory by placing some cells in a petri dish containing nutrient broth. The nutrient broth provides food for the cells. Most cells will grow until they form a thin layer covering the bottom of the dish, as shown in **Figure 10–7.** Then, the cells stop growing. When cells come into contact with other cells, they respond by not growing.

If cells are removed from the center of the dish, however, the cells bordering the open space will begin dividing until they have filled the empty space. These experiments show that the controls on cell growth and cell division can be turned on and off.

Something similar happens within the body. When an injury such as a cut in the skin or a break in a bone occurs, cells at the edges of the injury are stimulated to divide rapidly. This action produces new cells, starting the process of healing. When the healing process nears completion, the rate of cell division slows down, controls on growth are restored, and everything returns to normal.

▼ **Figure 10–7** Cells in a petri dish will continue to grow until they come into contact with other cells. **Applying Concepts** *What would happen if the cells continued to divide?*

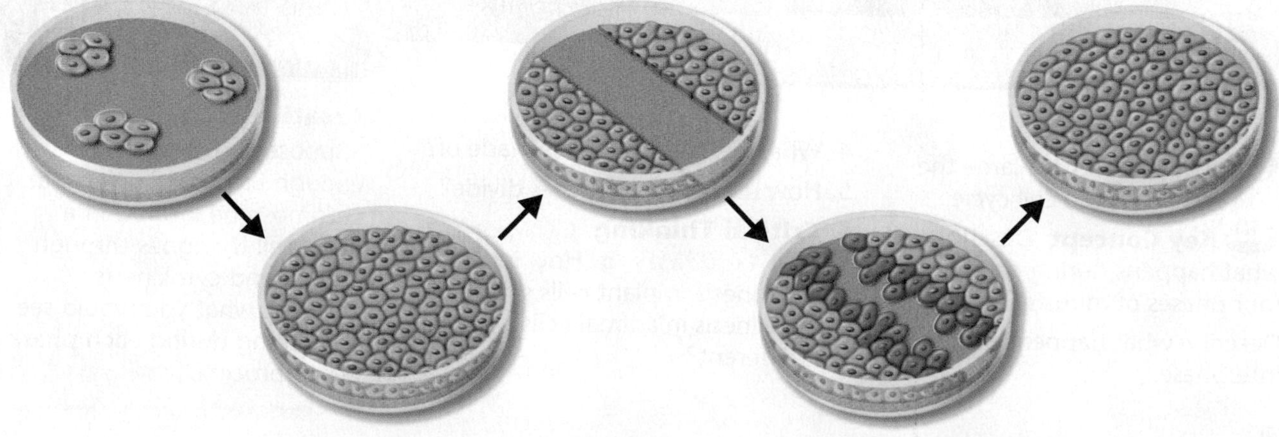

Cell Cycle Regulators

For many years, biologists searched for a substance that might regulate the cell cycle—something that would "tell" cells when it was time to divide, duplicate their chromosomes, or enter another phase of the cycle. In the early 1980s, biologists found the substance.

Several scientists, including Tim Hunt of Great Britain and Mark Kirschner of the United States, discovered that cells in mitosis contained a protein that when injected into a nondividing cell, would cause a mitotic spindle to form. Such an experiment is shown in **Figure 10–8.** To their surprise, they discovered that the amount of this protein in the cell rose and fell in time with the cell cycle. They decided to call this protein **cyclin** because it seemed to regulate the cell cycle. Investigators have since discovered a family of closely related proteins, known as cyclins, that are involved in cell cycle regulation. **Cyclins regulate the timing of the cell cycle in eukaryotic cells.**

The discovery of cyclins was just the beginning. More recently, dozens of other proteins have been discovered that also help to regulate the cell cycle. There are two types of regulatory proteins: those that occur inside the cell and those that occur outside the cell.

Internal Regulators Proteins that respond to events inside the cell are called internal regulators. Internal regulators allow the cell cycle to proceed only when certain processes have happened inside the cell. For example, several regulatory proteins make sure that a cell does not enter mitosis until all its chromosomes have been replicated. Another regulatory protein prevents a cell from entering anaphase until all its chromosomes are attached to the mitotic spindle.

External Regulators Proteins that respond to events outside the cell are called external regulators. External regulators direct cells to speed up or slow down the cell cycle. Growth factors are among the most important external regulators. They stimulate the growth and division of cells. Growth regulators are especially important during embryonic development and wound healing. Molecules found on the surfaces of neighboring cells often have an opposite effect, causing cells to slow down or stop their cell cycles. These signals prevent excessive cell growth and keep the tissues of the body from disrupting each other.

CHECKPOINT *What are cyclins?*

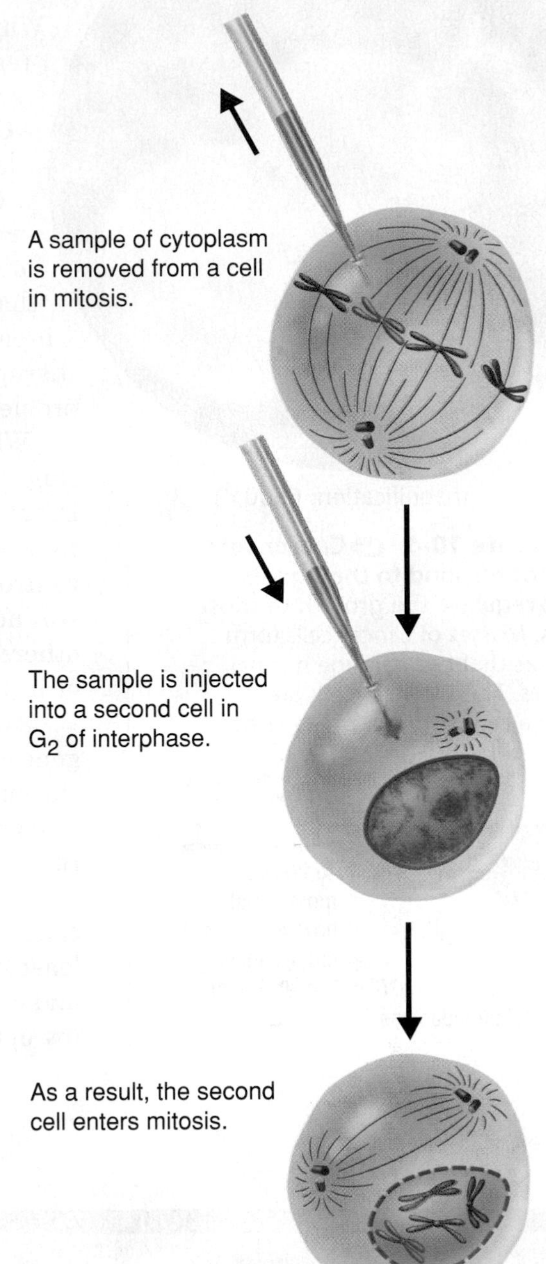

A sample of cytoplasm is removed from a cell in mitosis.
The sample is injected into a second cell in G_2 of interphase.
As a result, the second cell enters mitosis.

▲ **Figure 10–8** **The timing of the cell cycle is regulated by cyclins.** When cytoplasm from a cell in mitosis is injected into another cell, the second cell enters mitosis. The reason for this effect is a protein called cyclin, which triggers cell division.

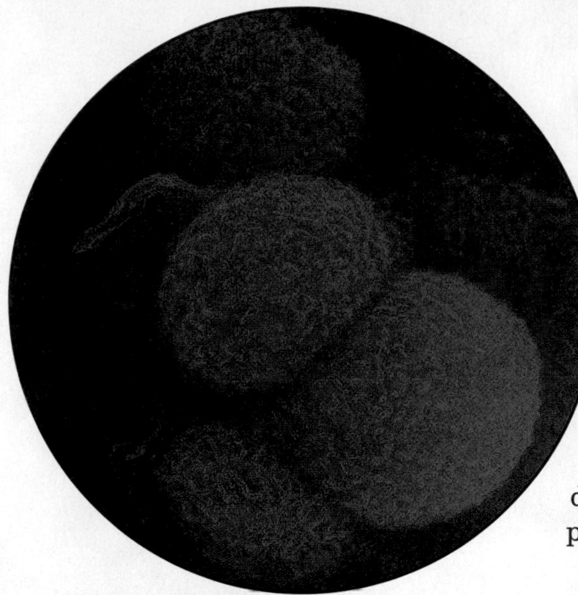

(magnification: 6900×)

▲ **Figure 10–9** **Cancer cells do not respond to the signals that regulate the growth of most cells.** Masses of cancer cells form tumors that can damage normal tissues. These cancer cells are from a cancer tumor in the large intestine.

To find out more about how scientists study cancer, view the segment "Skin Cancer: Deadly Cells," on Videotape Two.

Uncontrolled Cell Growth

Why is cell growth regulated so carefully? The principal reason may be that the consequences of uncontrolled cell growth in a multicellular organism are very severe. **Cancer,** a disorder in which some of the body's own cells lose the ability to control growth, is one such example. **Cancer cells do not respond to the signals that regulate the growth of most cells.** As a result, they divide uncontrollably and form masses of cells called tumors that can damage the surrounding tissues. Cancer cells may break loose from tumors and spread throughout the body, disrupting normal activities and causing serious medical problems or even death. **Figure 10–9** shows typical cancer cells.

What causes the loss of growth control that characterizes cancer? The various forms of cancer have many causes, including smoking tobacco, radiation exposure, and even viral infection. All cancers, however, have one thing in common: The control over the cell cycle has broken down. Some cancer cells will no longer respond to external growth regulators, while others fail to produce the internal regulators that ensure orderly growth.

An astonishing number of cancer cells have a defect in a gene called p53, which normally halts the cell cycle until all chromosomes have been properly replicated. Damaged or defective p53 genes cause the cells to lose the information needed to respond to signals that would normally control their growth.

Cancer is a serious disease. Understanding and combating cancer remains a major scientific challenge, but scientists at least know where to start. Cancer is a disease of the cell cycle, and conquering cancer will require a much deeper understanding of the processes that control cell division.

10–3 Section Assessment

1. **Key Concept** What chemicals regulate the cell cycle? How do they work?
2. **Key Concept** What happens when cells do not respond to the signals that normally regulate their growth?
3. How do cells respond to contact with other cells?
4. Why can cancer be considered a disease of the cell cycle?
5. **Critical Thinking Formulating Hypotheses** Write a hypothesis about what you think would happen if cyclin were injected into a cell that was in mitosis.

Sharpen Your Skills

Problem Solving
Imagine that you are developing a drug that will inhibit the growth of cancer cells. Use your knowledge of the cell cycle to describe how the drug would target and prevent the multiplication of cancer cells. Use the Internet to compare your anticancer drug with those currently in use.

Stem Cells: Promises and Problems

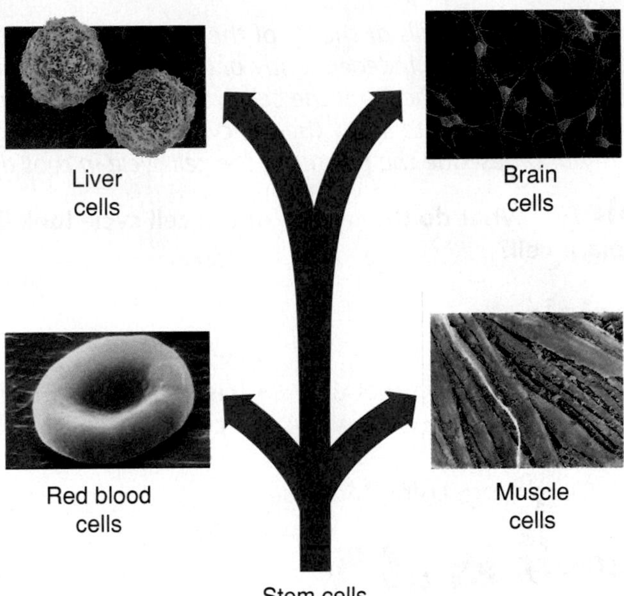

Where do the different cells and tissues in your body come from? Incredible as it seems, every cell was produced by mitosis from a small number of cells called stem cells. Stem cells are unspecialized cells that have the potential to differentiate—to become specialized in structure and function—into a wide variety of cell types. In early embryonic development, stem cells produce every tissue in the body. Evidence indicates that stem cells also are found in adults. Stem cells in the bone marrow, for example, produce more than a dozen types of blood cells, replacing those lost due to normal wear and tear.

Stem Cells in Medicine

Although your body produces billions of new cells every day, it is not always able to produce the right kind of cell to replace those damaged by injury or disease. For example, the body is not able to produce new neurons to repair serious spinal cord injuries, such as those that cause paralysis. Because of this, at present, there is no way for doctors to restore movement and feeling to people who are paralyzed.

Stem cells may be the perfect solution to this problem. Recently, researchers have found that implants of stem cells can reverse the effects of brain injuries in mice. There is hope that the same will hold true for humans and that stem cells might be used to reverse brain and spinal cord injuries. It also may be possible to use stem cells to grow new liver tissue, to replace heart valves, and to reverse the effects of diabetes.

Sources of Stem Cells

Human embryonic stem cells were first isolated in 1998 by scientists in Wisconsin. In 2004, Korean scientists produced such cells by transferring adult cell nuclei into the cytoplasms of egg cells. However, since such cells are taken from human embryos, these techniques raise serious moral and ethical questions. Because of such issues, embryonic stem cell research is highly controversial.

Researchers have also found that nerve, muscle, and liver cells sometimes can be grown from adult stem cells isolated from the bone marrow and other tissues in the body. Experiments such as these, although still in the early stages of development, may usher in a new era of therapy in which replacement tissue is grown from a person's own stem cells.

Research and Decide

Use library or Internet resources to learn more about stem-cell research. Then, write a brief report on how this technology will impact the future of medicine.

For: Links from the authors
Visit: PHSchool.com
Web Code: cbe-3104

Exploration

Modeling the Phases of the Cell Cycle

In a growing root, the cells at the tip of the root are constantly dividing. Because each cell divides independently of the others, a root tip contains many cells at different phases of the cell cycle. This makes a root tip an excellent tissue in which to study the cell cycle. In this investigation, you will identify and describe the phases of the cell cycle in root tip cells.

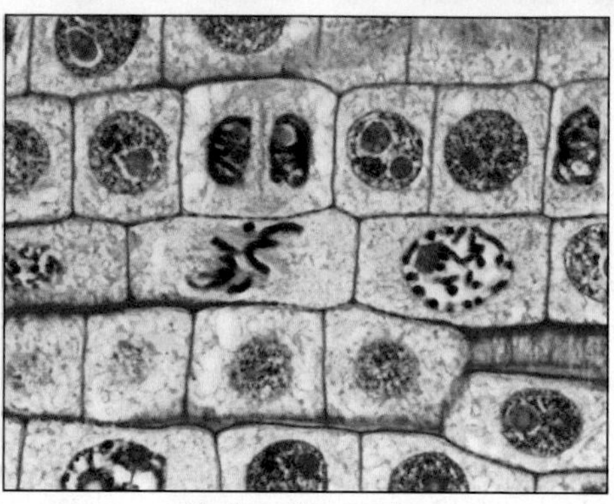

Onion Root Tip
(magnification: 700×)

Problem **What do the phases of the cell cycle look like in a typical plant cell?**

Materials

- microscope
- prepared slides of onion root tips
- craft materials such as beads, yarn, and pipe cleaners
- tape or glue
- scissors

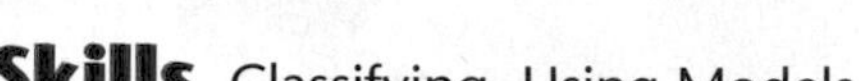

Skills Classifying, Using Models

Procedure   

1. Obtain a prepared slide of an onion root tip. Hold the slide up to the light and find the pointed end of the root section. This is the root tip where cells were actively dividing.
2. Place the slide on the microscope stage with the root tip pointing away from you. Using the low-power objective, adjust the focus of the microscope until the root tip is clearly visible. Just above the root tip is a region that contains many new small cells. The larger cells of this region were in the process of dividing when the slide was made. These are the cells you will be observing.
3. Observe the boxlike cells that are arranged in rows. Scan across one row and down to the next row to compare the cells. The chromosomes of the cells have been stained to make them easily visible. Select one cell whose chromosomes are clearly visible. Switch to high power and sketch this cell.
4. Use the craft materials to make a model of the cell that you sketched, showing how its chromosomes are arranged.
5. Select at least four more cells whose internal appearances are different from the first cell you sketched. Switch to high power and sketch each of these cells. Repeat step 4 for each cell you sketch.
6. On a separate sheet of paper, make a copy of the data table shown. Choose 25 root tip cells at random and decide which phase of the cell cycle each is in. Record the number of cells in each phase in your copy of the data table. If you find that some cells appear to be between two phases, record those observations as well.
7. Look closely at your sketches and models. Arrange the models in order to represent the process of cell division.
8. Refer to **Figure 10–5** on pages 246 and 247 to determine whether you have ordered the phases of the cell cycle accurately. Correct the order of your models, if necessary. Label each of the models and sketches with the name of the phase it represents. Use the models to explain the process of cell division to another student.
9. Wash your hands with soap and warm water before you leave the lab.

Data Table

Phase	Number of Cells
Interphase	
Prophase	
Metaphase	
Anaphase	
Telophase	

Analyze and Conclude

1. **Analyzing Data** Do your results indicate that there were more cells in some phases than in others? Identify the most common phase(s) and explain what these differences in numbers of cells might mean.
2. **Drawing Conclusions** What evidence did you observe that shows mitosis is a continuous process, not a series of separate events?
3. **Using Models** Describe what is happening in each phase of your cell models.
4. **Using Models** Propose an alternative model to illustrate the same concept.
5. **Applying Concepts** Cells in the root divide many times as the root grows longer and thicker. With each cell division, the chromosomes are divided between two daughter cells, yet the number of chromosomes in each cell does not change. What process ensures that the normal number of chromosomes is restored after each cell division? During which part of the cell cycle does this process occur?

Go Further

Making Models In muscle cells, mitosis is not always followed by cell division. Instead, repeated cycles of mitosis result in long, tubular cells with many nuclei. Make a model that shows mitosis in a muscle cell.

For: Data sharing
Visit: PHSchool.com
Web Code: cbd-3104

Share Your Data Online Enter your data on the number of cells in the phases of the cell cycle. Then, look at the data entered by other students. Based on the available data, were there more cells in some phases than in others? Why might your results differ from those of other students?

Chapter 10 Study Guide

10–1 Cell Growth

Key Concept

- The larger a cell becomes, the more demands the cell places on its DNA. In addition, the cell has more trouble moving enough nutrients and wastes across the cell membrane.

Vocabulary
cell division, p. 243

10–2 Cell Division

Key Concepts

- During the cell cycle, a cell grows, prepares for division, and divides to form two daughter cells, each of which then begins the cycle again.
- Biologists divide the events of mitosis into four phases: prophase, metaphase, anaphase, and telophase. Mitosis insures that each daughter cell has the same genetic information as the parent cell.
- During prophase in animal cells, the centrioles separate and take up positions on opposite sides of the nucleus. In addition, chromosomes condense and the spindle appears.
- During metaphase, the chromosomes line up across the center of the cell. Microtubules connect the chromosome to each pole of the spindle.
- During anaphase, the centromeres that join the sister chromatids split, and the sister chromatids separate and become individual chromosomes.
- In telophase, the chromosomes, which were distinct and condensed, uncoil and disperse as the nuclear envelope re-forms.
- Cytokinesis is the division of the cytoplasm.

Vocabulary
mitosis, p. 244
cytokinesis, p. 244
chromatid, p. 244
centromere, p. 245
interphase, p. 245
cell cycle, p. 245
prophase, p. 246
centriole, p. 246
spindle, p. 247
metaphase, p. 248
anaphase, p. 248
telophase, p. 248

10–3 Regulating the Cell Cycle

Key Concepts

- Cyclins regulate the timing of the cell cycle in eukaryotic cells.
- Cancer cells do not respond to the signals that regulate the growth of most cells.

Vocabulary
cyclin, p. 251
cancer, p. 252

Thinking Visually

Using the information in this chapter, complete the following cycle diagram of the cell cycle.

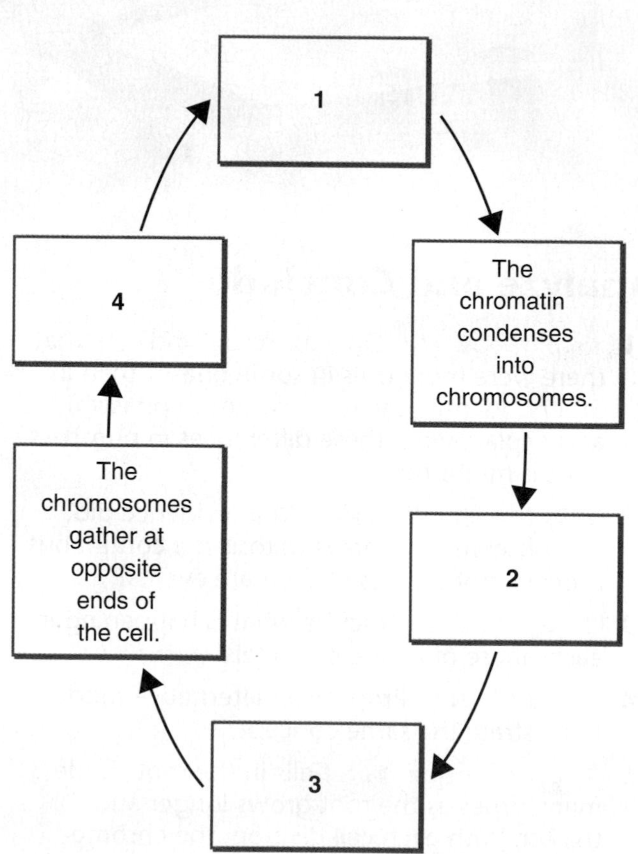
1
The chromatin condenses into chromosomes.
2
3
The chromosomes gather at opposite ends of the cell.
4

Preparing for the Living Environment Exam

NEW YORK LIVING ENVIRONMENT

Blue questions emphasize Regents Exam content

Chapter 10

Part A

Multiple Choice

For each statement or question, select the number of the word or expression that, of those given, best completes the statement or answers the question.

1 Normal mitotic cell division results in the production of
(1) two daughter cells
(2) double the number of chromosomes
(3) two sex cells
(4) half the number of chromosomes

2 Each pair of chromatids is attached at an area called the
(1) centriole (3) spindle
(2) centromere (4) chromosome

3 If a cell has 12 chromosomes, how many chromosomes will each of its daughter cells have after mitosis?
(1) 4 (3) 12
(2) 6 (4) 24

4 For a cell to divide successfully, it must first
(1) duplicate its genetic information
(2) increase its ratio of surface area to volume
(3) increase its number of chromosomes
(4) decrease its number of organelles

5 Which statement best describes the genetic information associated with the two chromatids of a chromosome?
(1) Each of the two chromatids normally contains the same genetic information.
(2) Each of the two chromatids normally contains different genetic information.
(3) Each chromatid normally contains one-half of the chromosome's genetic information.
(4) Only one chromatid normally carries the chromosome's genetic information.

6 In plant cells, what forms midway between the divided nuclei during cytokinesis?
(1) nuclear membrane
(2) centromere
(3) cell membrane
(4) cell plate

7 The process of mitosis insures equal distribution to the new cells of the
(1) mitochondria (3) cytoplasm
(2) chloroplasts (4) chromosomes

8 Which of the illustrations below best represents metaphase of mitosis?

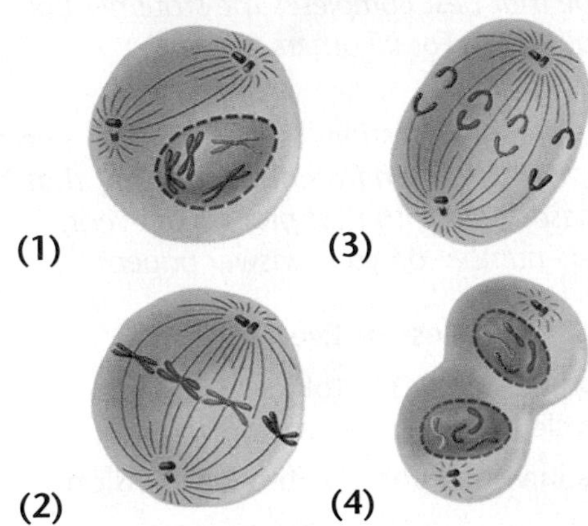

9 The timing of the cell cycle in eukaryotic cells is controlled by a group of closely related proteins known as
(1) chromatids (3) centromeres
(2) cyclins (4) centrioles

10 Which does *not* occur during mitosis?
(1) duplication of cell DNA
(2) formation of a new nuclear membrane
(3) separation of "sister" chromatids
(4) breakdown of the nuclear membrane

11 Each of the two daughter cells that results from the normal mitotic division of the original parent cell contains
(1) the same number of chromosomes, but has genes different from the parent cell
(2) the same number of chromosomes and has genes identical to those of the parent cell
(3) one-half of the number of chromosomes, but has genes different from those of the parent cell
(4) one-half of the number of chromosomes and has genes identical to those of the parent cell

Test-Taking Tip If after reading all of the answer choices you are not sure which one is correct, eliminate the choices that you know are wrong. Then, select your answer from the remaining choices.

Preparing for the Living Environment Exam

Part B

Multiple Choice and Extended Response

For those questions that ask you to select a response, choose the one that best completes the statement or answers the question. For all others follow the directions given.

For each description in questions 12 through 14, select the process or event, chosen from the list below, that is most closely associated with that process or event. Then, record its number on your answer paper.

Process or Event

(1) Interphase (3) Cytokinesis
(2) Cell cycle (4) Cancer

12 A process in which unregulated cell division occurs

13 A process by which the cytoplasm divides

14 A series of events that cells go through as they divide and grow

Base your answers to questions 15 through 16 on the information and illustration below and on your knowledge of biology.

The spindle fibers of a dividing cell were labeled with a fluorescent dye. At the beginning of anaphase, a laser beam was used to stop the dye from glowing on one side of the cell, thereby marking the fibers, as shown in the second diagram. The laser did not inhibit the normal function of the fibers.

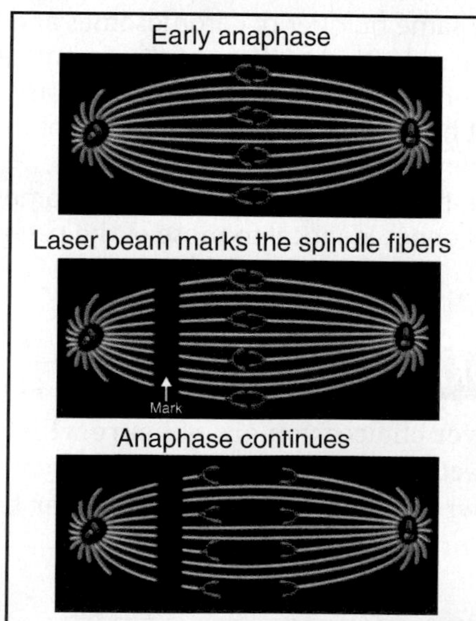

15 This experiment tests a hypothesis about
(1) how chromosomes migrate during cell division
(2) how fluorescent dyes work in the cell
(3) the effect of lasers on cells
(4) why cells divide

16 Would this experiment have provided the same information if the laser beam were focused on the fibers at the point where they contact the chromatids? Support your answer with an explanation.

17 State how a cell's chromosomes change as the cell prepares to divide.

18 Compare the quantity of DNA in a cell at the beginning of mitosis with the quantity of DNA in each of the two newly produced daughter cells.

19 Molecules found on the surfaces of cells might play a role in the process by which cells divide until they contact other cells. Explain how an alteration of a cell's DNA could produce cells that would continue to grow and divide even after coming into contact with other cells.

20 A classmate suggests that temperature might affect the rate of mitosis in plant cells. Describe an experiment that could be done to test this hypothesis.

21 Each type of eukaryotic organism has a characteristic number of chromosomes. All human cells, for example, have 46 chromosomes in their nuclei; fruit fly cells have 8 chromosomes. Describe how an organism such as a fruit fly would be affected if one of its body cells lost a chromosome during cell division in its very early development.

22 The nerve cells in the human nervous system seldom undergo mitosis. Based on this information, explain why complete recovery from injuries to the nervous system may not occur.

Base your answers to questions 23 and 24 on the information provided in the reading passage and on your knowledge of biology.

Stem Cells

Almost all human tissue can repair itself due to stem cells. These cells reproduce repeatedly, forming exact copies of themselves. They also form other kinds of cells. For example, stem cells in bone marrow can give rise to all of the structures in the blood.

For many years, biologists believed that the brain could not repair itself because it lacked stem cells. A recent discovery, however, indicates that a mature human brain produces neurons routinely at one site. This raises the prospect that stem cells might be found in other areas. If investigators learn how to cause existing stem cells to produce nerve cells, it might be possible to correct disorders such as Alzheimer's disease, Parkinson's disease, and brain injuries.

23 Until recently, many biologists thought that the brain could not repair itself because they thought it
- **(1)** could not make new connections between neurons
- **(2)** had DNA different from DNA in reproductive cells
- **(3)** could form new cells only in certain areas of the brain
- **(4)** lacked stem cells needed to produce new neurons

24 Describe how this new discovery concerning stem cells might help to treat diseases such as Alzheimer's disease or Parkinson's disease.

Part C

Extended Response

Answer the questions or follow the directions given.

25 Summarize what happens to a cell's genetic material both before and during the process of cell division. In your answer, be sure to
- explain the changes in chromosomes that occur before cell division and the process that brings about the change
- describe how chromosomes are arranged at the beginning of cell division
- describe specifically how the chromosomes change during cell division
- describe what happens to chromosomes at the end of cell division
- compare the amount of genetic material present in the cell with the amount present in the daughter (offspring) cells

26 The following diagram shows a phase of mitosis. The four chromosomes shown in the center of the cell each consist of two connected strands.

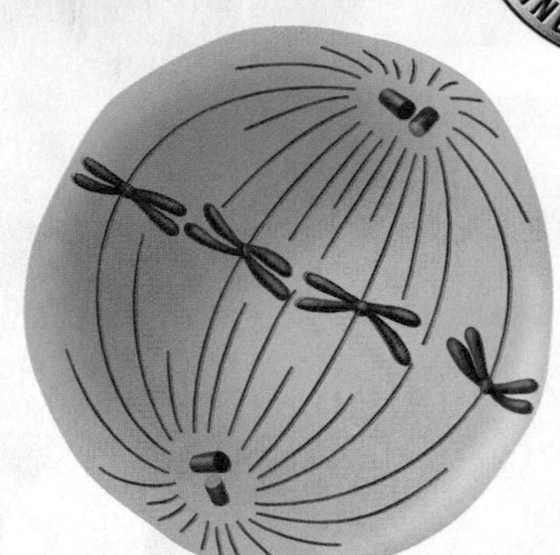

Explain how the two strands of the same chromosome compare with regard to the genetic information they carry. In your explanation be sure to:
- state the name of the process responsible for converting a single-stranded chromosome into a double-stranded chromosome
- compare the number and type of genes on one strand of a doubled chromosome to the number and type of genes located on the attached strand
- state why it is important that the number and type of genes present on each strand of a double chromosome compare in the way you described
- describe what the end result of the process illustrated will be

For: An interactive self-test
Visit: PHSchool.com
Web Code: cba-3100

UNIT 4

Genetics

Chapters

▶ Genetics is the study of heredity, or the transmission of characteristics from parent to offspring. Why didn't this normal-colored, white-tail fawn inherit the white fur from its albino mother? Read on to find out.

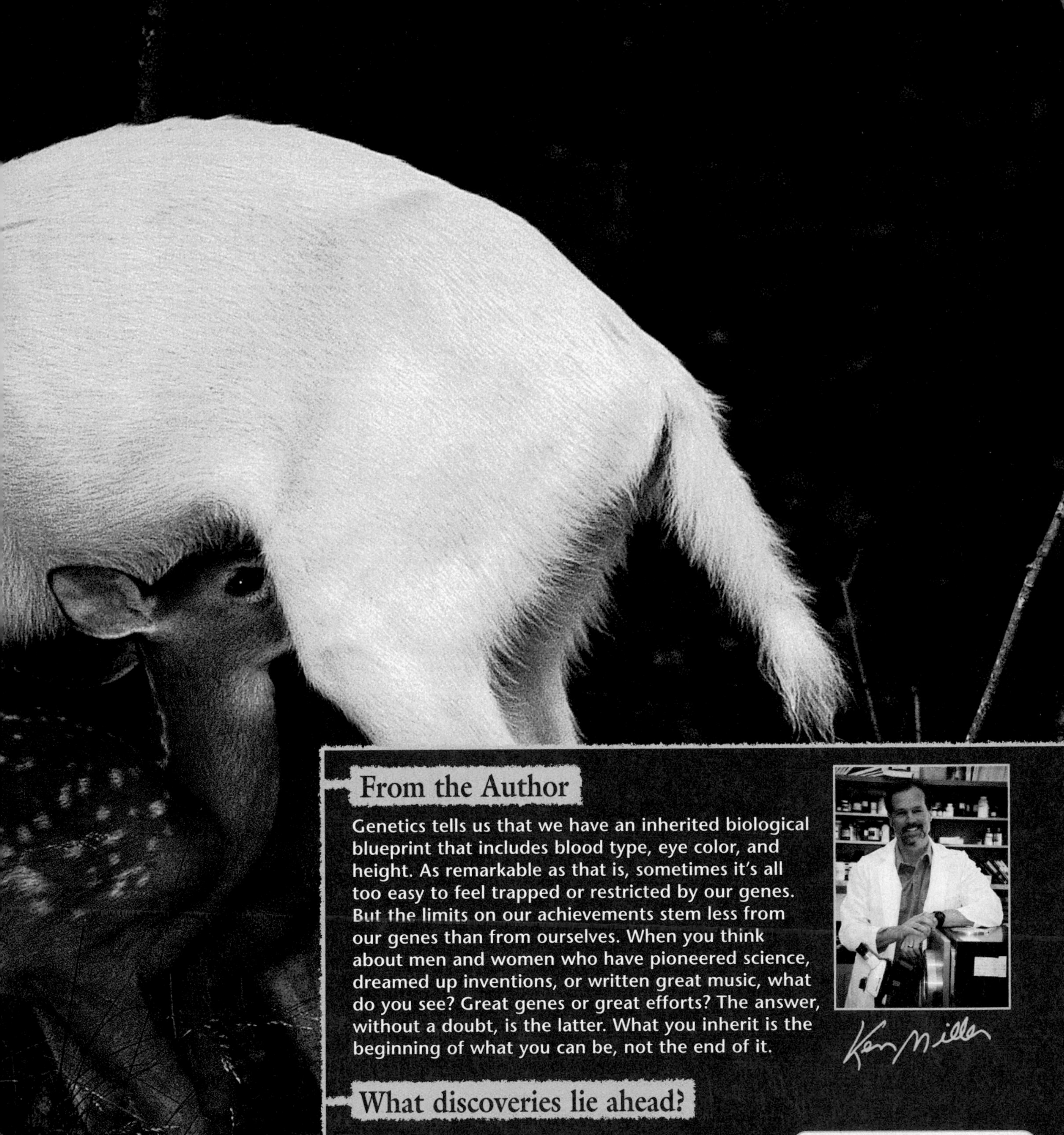

From the Author

Genetics tells us that we have an inherited biological blueprint that includes blood type, eye color, and height. As remarkable as that is, sometimes it's all too easy to feel trapped or restricted by our genes. But the limits on our achievements stem less from our genes than from ourselves. When you think about men and women who have pioneered science, dreamed up inventions, or written great music, what do you see? Great genes or great efforts? The answer, without a doubt, is the latter. What you inherit is the beginning of what you can be, not the end of it.

What discoveries lie ahead?

- Can we use the information from the Human Genome Project effectively to cure disease and alleviate suffering?
- Will we develop ways to use genetic engineering wisely and respect the natural environment of the world in which we live?

Go Online PHSchool.com

For: Latest discoveries
Visit: PHSchool.com
Web Code: cbe-4000

CHAPTER 11

Introduction to Genetics

The varied patterns of stripes on zebras are due to differences in genetic makeup. No two zebras have identical stripe patterns.

Inquiry Activity

Are traits inherited?

Procedure

1. Look at your classmates. Note how they vary in the shape of the front hairline, the space between the two upper front teeth, and the way in which the earlobes are attached.
2. Make a list of the different forms of these traits that you have observed in the class or among other people you know.

Think About It

1. **Inferring** Could these traits be inherited? From whom could they be inherited?
2. **Inferring** How is it possible that these traits could be found in a person and his or her biological grandparents but not in the biological parents?

11–1 The Work of Gregor Mendel

1-S1. Historical development of ideas in science
4-2.1 Heredity specifies traits
4-2.1 Sexual reproduction
4-3.1 New inheritable characteristics

What is an inheritance? To most people, it is money or property left to them by a relative who has passed away. That kind of inheritance is important, of course. There is another form of inheritance, however, that matters even more. This inheritance has been with you from the very first day you were alive—your genes.

Every living thing—plant or animal, microbe or human being—has a set of characteristics inherited from its parent or parents. Since the beginning of recorded history, people have wanted to understand how that inheritance is passed from generation to generation. More recently, however, scientists have begun to appreciate that heredity holds the key to understanding what makes each species unique. As a result, **genetics,** the scientific study of heredity, is now at the core of a revolution in understanding biology.

Guide for Reading

Key Concepts
- What is the principle of dominance?
- What happens during segregation?

Vocabulary
genetics • fertilization
true-breeding • trait • hybrid
gene • allele • segregation
gamete

Reading Strategy: Finding Main Ideas As you read, find evidence to support the following statement: Mendel's ideas about genetics were the beginning of a new area of biology.

Gregor Mendel's Peas

The work of an Austrian monk named Gregor Mendel, shown in **Figure 11–1,** was particularly important to understanding biological inheritance. Gregor Mendel was born in 1822 in what is now the Czech Republic. After becoming a priest, Mendel spent several years studying science and mathematics at the University of Vienna. He spent the next 14 years working in the monastery and teaching at the high school. In addition to his teaching duties, Mendel was in charge of the monastery garden. In this ordinary garden, he was to do the work that changed biology forever.

Mendel carried out his work with ordinary garden peas. He knew that part of each flower produces pollen, which contains the plant's male reproductive cells, or sperm. Similarly, the female portion of the flower produces egg cells. During sexual reproduction, male and female reproductive cells join, a process known as **fertilization.** Fertilization produces a new cell, which develops into a tiny embryo encased within a seed. Pea flowers are normally self-pollinating, which means that sperm cells in pollen fertilize the egg cells in the same flower. The seeds that are produced by self-pollination inherit all of their characteristics from the single plant that bore them. In effect, they have a single parent.

When Mendel took charge of the monastery garden, he had several stocks of pea plants. These peas were **true-breeding,** meaning that if they were allowed to self-pollinate, they would produce offspring identical to themselves. One stock of seeds would produce only tall plants, another only short ones. One line produced only green seeds, another only yellow seeds. These true-breeding plants were the basis of Mendel's experiments.

▲ **Figure 11–1** Gregor Mendel's experiments with pea plants laid the foundations of the science of genetics.

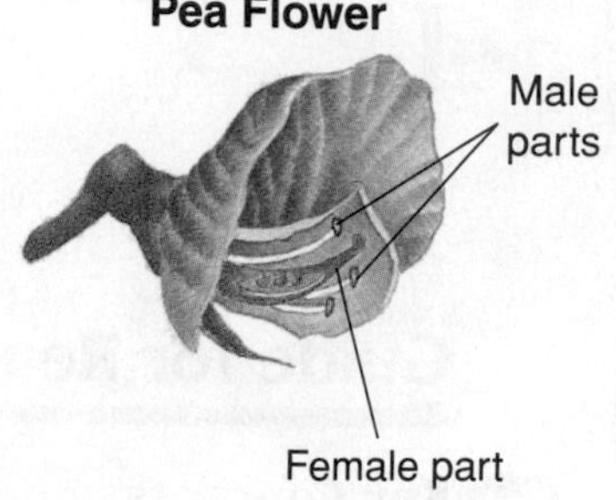

◀ **Figure 11–2** To cross-pollinate pea plants, Mendel cut off the male parts of one flower and then dusted it with pollen from another flower. **Applying Concepts** ***How did this procedure prevent self-pollination?***

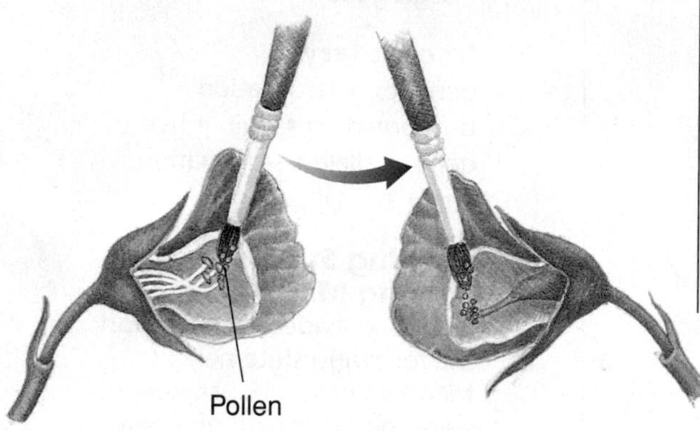

Mendel wanted to produce seeds by joining male and female reproductive cells from two different plants. To do this, he had to prevent self-pollination. He accomplished this by cutting away the pollen-bearing male parts as shown in **Figure 11–2** and then dusting pollen from another plant onto the flower. This process, which is known as cross-pollination, produced seeds that had two different plants as parents. This made it possible for Mendel to cross-breed plants with different characteristics, and then to study the results.

CHECKPOINT ***What is fertilization?***

Genes and Dominance

Mendel studied seven different pea plant traits. A **trait** is a specific characteristic, such as seed color or plant height, that varies from one individual to another. Each of the seven traits Mendel studied had two contrasting characters, for example, green seed color and yellow seed color. Mendel crossed plants with each of the seven contrasting characters and studied their offspring. We call each original pair of plants the P (parental) generation. The offspring are called the F_1, or "first filial," generation. *Filius* and *filia* are the Latin words for "son" and "daughter." The offspring of crosses between parents with different traits are called **hybrids.**

▼ **Figure 11–3** When Mendel crossed plants with contrasting characters for the same trait, the resulting offspring had only one of the characters. **From these experiments, Mendel concluded that some alleles are dominant and others are recessive.**

Mendel's Seven F_1 Crosses on Pea Plants

	Seed Shape	Seed Color	Seed Coat Color	Pod Shape	Pod Color	Flower Position	Plant Height
P	Round X Wrinkled	Yellow X Green	Gray X White	Smooth X Constricted	Green X Yellow	Axial X Terminal	Tall X Short
F_1	Round	Yellow	Gray	Smooth	Green	Axial	Tall

What were those F_1 hybrid plants like? Did the characters of the parent plants blend in the offspring? Not at all. To Mendel's surprise, all of the offspring had the character of only one of the parents, as shown in **Figure 11–3.** In each cross, the character of the other parent seemed to have disappeared.

From this set of experiments, Mendel drew two conclusions. Mendel's first conclusion was that biological inheritance is determined by factors that are passed from one generation to the next. Today, scientists call the chemical factors that determine traits **genes.** Each of the traits Mendel studied was controlled by one gene that occurred in two contrasting forms. These contrasting forms produced the different characters of each trait. For example, the gene for plant height occurs in one form that produces tall plants and in another form that produces short plants. The different forms of a gene are called **alleles** (uh-LEELZ).

Mendel's second conclusion is called the principle of dominance. **The principle of dominance states that some alleles are dominant and others are recessive.** An organism with a dominant allele for a particular form of a trait will always exhibit that form of the trait. An organism with a recessive allele for a particular form of a trait will exhibit that form only when the dominant allele for the trait is not present. In Mendel's experiments, the allele for tall plants was dominant and the allele for short plants was recessive. The allele for yellow seeds was dominant, while the allele for green seeds was recessive.

For: Articles on genetics
Visit: PHSchool.com
Web Code: cbe-4111

Segregation

Mendel wanted the answer to another question: Had the recessive alleles disappeared, or were they still present in the F_1 plants? To answer this question, he allowed all seven kinds of F_1 hybrid plants to produce an F_2 (second filial) generation by self-pollination. In effect, he crossed the F_1 generation with itself to produce the F_2 offspring, as shown in **Figure 11–4.**

▼ **Figure 11–4** When Mendel allowed the F_1 plants to reproduce by self-pollination, the traits controlled by recessive alleles reappeared in about one fourth of the F_2 plants in each cross. **Calculating** *What proportion of the F_2 plants had a trait controlled by a dominant allele?*

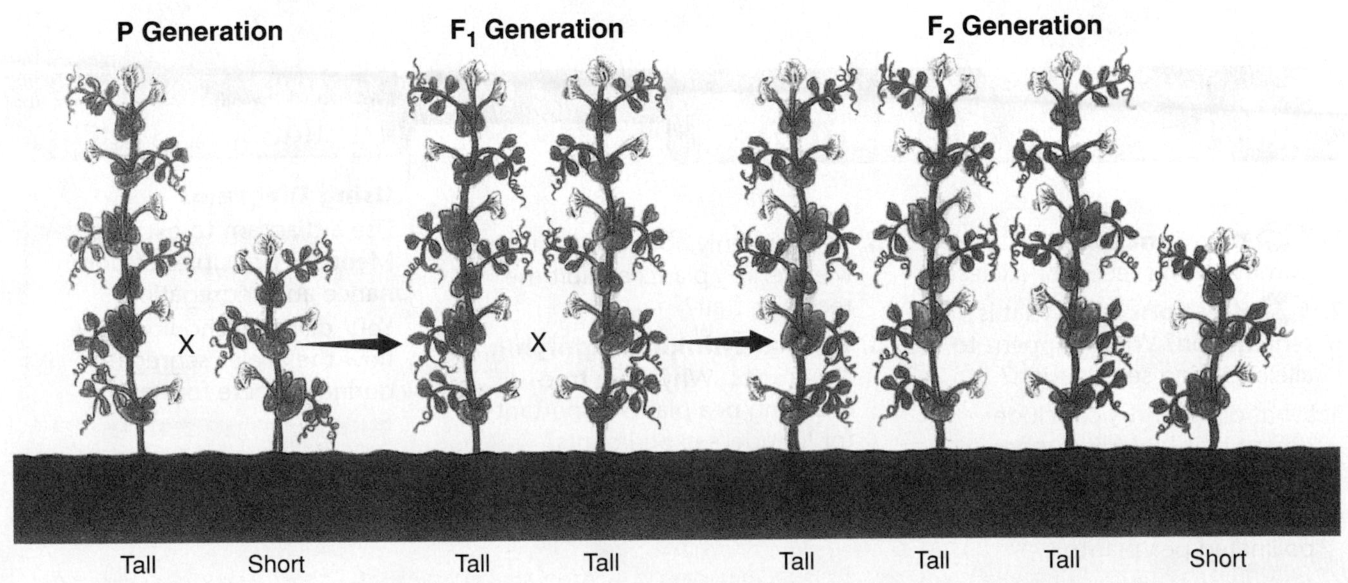

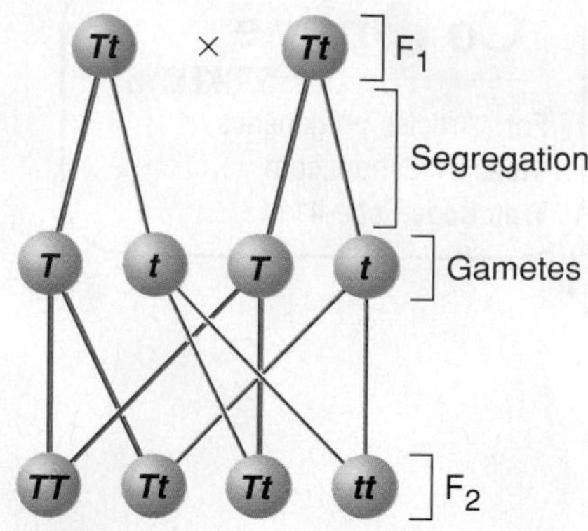

▲ **Figure 11–5** **During gamete formation, alleles segregate from each other so that each gamete carries only a single copy of each gene. Each F_1 plant produces two types of gametes—those with the allele for tallness and those with the allele for shortness.** The alleles are paired up again when gametes fuse during fertilization. The *TT* and *Tt* allele combinations produce tall pea plants; *tt* is the only allele combination that produces a short pea plant.

The F_1 Cross The results of the F_1 cross were remarkable. When Mendel compared the F_2 plants, he discovered that the traits controlled by the recessive alleles had reappeared! Roughly one fourth of the F_2 plants showed the trait controlled by the recessive allele. Why did the recessive alleles seem to disappear in the F_1 generation and then reappear in the F_2 generation? To answer this question, let's take a closer look at one of Mendel's crosses.

Explaining the F_1 Cross To begin with, Mendel assumed that a dominant allele had masked the corresponding recessive allele in the F_1 generation. However, the trait controlled by the recessive allele showed up in some of the F_2 plants. This reappearance indicated that at some point the allele for shortness had been separated from the allele for tallness. How did this separation, or **segregation,** of alleles occur? Mendel suggested that the alleles for tallness and shortness in the F_1 plants segregated from each other during the formation of the sex cells, or **gametes** (GAM-eetz). Did that suggestion make sense?

Let's assume, as perhaps Mendel did, that the F_1 plants inherited an allele for tallness from the tall parent and an allele for shortness from the short parent. Because the allele for tallness is dominant, all the F_1 plants are tall. **When each F_1 plant flowers and produces gametes, the two alleles segregate from each other so that each gamete carries only a single copy of each gene. Therefore, each F_1 plant produces two types of gametes—those with the allele for tallness and those with the allele for shortness.**

Look at **Figure 11–5** to see how alleles separated during gamete formation and then paired up again in the F_2 generation. A capital letter *T* represents a dominant allele. A lowercase letter *t* represents a recessive allele. The result of this process is an F_2 generation with new combinations of alleles.

11–1 Section Assessment

1. **Key Concept** What are dominant and recessive alleles?
2. **Key Concept** What is segregation? What happens to alleles during segregation?
3. What did Mendel conclude determines biological inheritance?
4. Describe how Mendel cross-pollinated pea plants.
5. Why did only about one fourth of Mendel's F_2 plants exhibit the recessive trait?
6. **Critical Thinking Applying Concepts** Why were true-breeding pea plants important for Mendel's experiments?

Thinking Visually

Using Diagrams
Use a diagram to explain Mendel's principles of dominance and segregation. Your diagram should show how the alleles segregate during gamete formation.

11–2 Probability and Punnett Squares

4-2.1 Heredity specifies traits
4-3.1 New inheritable characteristics
4-3.1 Genetic recombination
1-S3.2 Test experimental data using statistical analysis
LS- Formulate a conclusion

Guide for Reading

 **Key Concepts**

- How do geneticists use the principles of probability?
- How do geneticists use Punnett squares?

Vocabulary
probability
Punnett square
homozygous
heterozygous
phenotype
genotype

Reading Strategy: Building Vocabulary Before you read, preview the list of new vocabulary words. Predict the relationship between phenotype and genotype. As you read, check to see if your predictions were correct.

Whenever Mendel performed a cross with pea plants, he carefully categorized and counted the many offspring. Every time Mendel repeated a particular cross, he obtained similar results. For example, whenever Mendel crossed two plants that were hybrid for stem height (*Tt*), about three fourths of the resulting plants were tall and about one fourth were short. Mendel realized that the principles of probability could be used to explain the results of genetic crosses.

Genetics and Probability

The likelihood that a particular event will occur is called **probability.** As an example of probability, consider an ordinary event like the coin flip shown in **Figure 11–6.** There are two possible outcomes: The coin may land heads up or tails up. The chances, or probabilities, of either outcome are equal. Therefore, the probability that a single coin flip will come up heads is 1 chance in 2. This is 1/2, or 50 percent.

If you flip a coin three times in a row, what is the probability that it will land heads up every time? Because each coin flip is an independent event, the probability of each coin's landing heads up is 1/2. Therefore, the probability of flipping three heads in a row is:

$$\frac{1}{2} \times \frac{1}{2} \times \frac{1}{2} = \frac{1}{8}.$$

As you can see, you have 1 chance in 8 of flipping heads three times in a row. That the individual probabilities are multiplied together illustrates an important point—past outcomes do not affect future ones.

How is coin flipping relevant to genetics? The way in which alleles segregate is completely random, like a coin flip. **The principles of probability can be used to predict the outcomes of genetic crosses.**

CHECKPOINT *What is the probability that a tossed coin will come up tails twice in a row?*

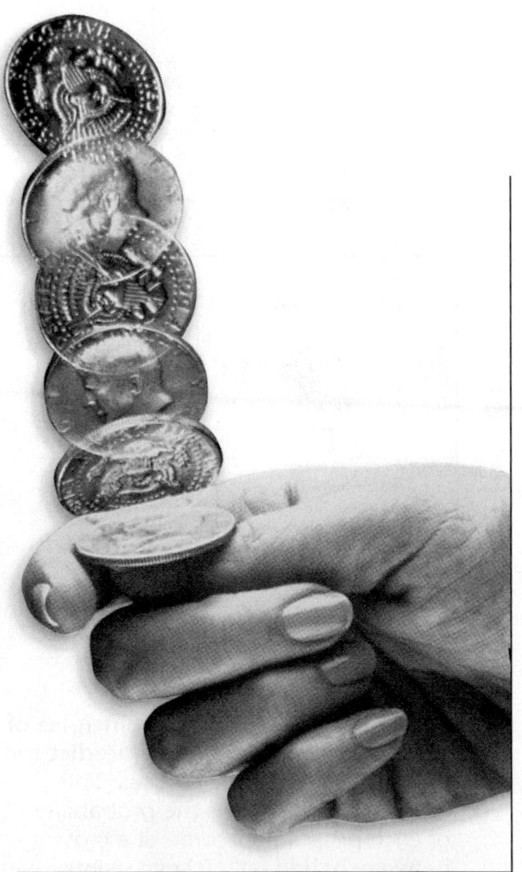

▶ **Figure 11–6** The mathematical concept of probability allows you to calculate the likelihood that a particular event will occur. **Predicting** *What is the probability that the coin will land heads up?*

Quick Lab

How are dimples inherited?

Materials copy of page from telephone book, calculator

Procedure

1. Write the last 4 digits of any telephone number. These 4 random digits represent the alleles of a gene that determines whether a person will have dimples. Odd digits represent the allele for the dominant trait of dimples. Even digits stand for the allele for the recessive trait of no dimples.
2. Use the first 2 digits to represent a certain father's genotype. Use the symbols *D* and *d* to write his genotype, as shown in the example.
3. Use the last 2 digits the same way to find the mother's genotype. Write her genotype.

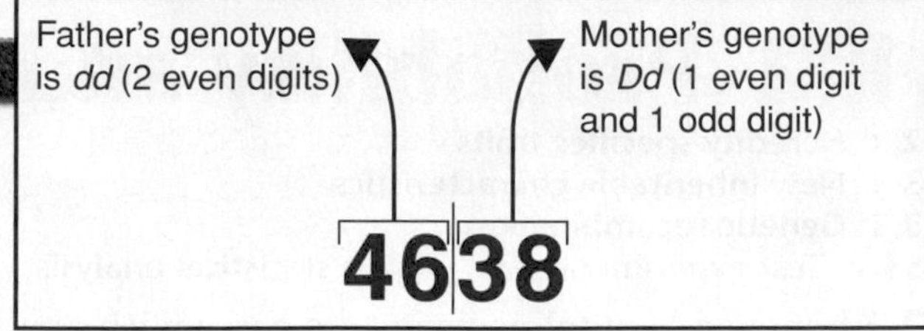

4. Use **Figure 11–7** as an example to construct a Punnett square for the cross of these parents. Then, using the Punnett square, determine the probability that their child will have dimples.
5. Determine the class average of the percent of children with dimples.

Analyze and Conclude

1. **Applying Concepts** How does the class average compare with the result of a cross of two heterozygous parents?
2. **Drawing Conclusions** What percentage of the children will be expected to have dimples if one parent is homozygous for dimples *(DD)* and the other is heterozygous *(Dd)*?

Punnett Squares

The gene combinations that might result from a genetic cross can be determined by drawing a diagram known as a **Punnett square.** The Punnett square in **Figure 11–7** shows one of Mendel's segregation experiments. The types of gametes produced by each F_1 parent are shown along the top and left sides of the square. The possible gene combinations for the F_2 offspring appear in the four boxes that make up the square. The letters in the Punnett square represent alleles. In this example, *T* represents the dominant allele for tallness and *t* represents the recessive allele for shortness. **Punnett squares can be used to predict and compare the genetic variations that will result from a cross.**

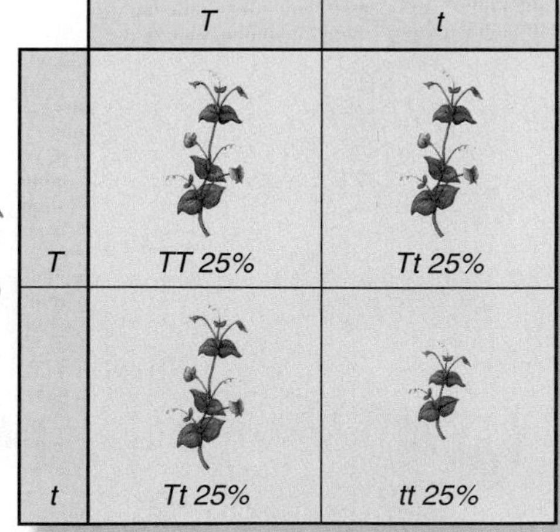

▲ **Figure 11–7 The principles of probability can be used to predict the outcomes of genetic crosses.** This Punnett square shows the probability of each possible outcome of a cross between hybrid tall *(Tt)* pea plants.

Organisms that have two identical alleles for a particular trait—*TT* or *tt* in this example—are said to be **homozygous** (hoh-moh-ZY-gus). Organisms that have two different alleles for the same trait are **heterozygous** (het-ur-oh-ZY-gus). Homozygous organisms are true-breeding for a particular trait. Heterozygous organisms are hybrid for a particular trait.

All of the tall plants have the same **phenotype,** or physical characteristics. They do not, however, have the same **genotype,** or genetic makeup. The genotype of one third of the tall plants is *TT,* while the genotype of two thirds of the tall plants is *Tt.* The plants in **Figure 11–8** have the same phenotype but different genotypes.

Probability and Segregation

Look again at **Figure 11–7.** One fourth (1/4) of the F_2 plants have two alleles for tallness *(TT)*; 2/4, or 1/2, of the F_2 plants have one allele for tallness and one allele for shortness *(Tt)*. Because the allele for tallness is dominant over the allele for shortness, 3/4 of the F_2 plants should be tall. Overall, there are 3 tall plants for every 1 short plant in the F_2 generation. Thus, the ratio of tall plants to short plants is 3 : 1. This assumes, of course, that Mendel's model of segregation is correct.

Did the data from Mendel's experiments fit his model? Yes. The predicted ratio—3 dominant to 1 recessive—showed up consistently, indicating that Mendel's assumptions about segregation had been correct. For each of his seven crosses, about 3/4 of the plants showed the trait controlled by the dominant allele. About 1/4 showed the trait controlled by the recessive allele. Segregation did indeed occur according to Mendel's model.

▲ **Figure 11–8** Although these plants have different genotypes (*TT* and *Tt*), they have the same phenotype (tall). **Predicting** *If you crossed these two plants, would their offspring be tall or short?*

Probabilities Predict Averages

Probabilities predict the average outcome of a large number of events. However, probability cannot predict the precise outcome of an individual event. If you flip a coin twice, you are likely to get one head and one tail. However, you might also get two heads or two tails. To be more likely to get the expected 50 : 50 ratio, you would have to flip the coin many times.

The same is true of genetics. The larger the number of offspring, the closer the resulting numbers will get to expected values. If an F_1 generation contains just three or four offspring, it may not match Mendelian predicted ratios. When an F_1 generation contains hundreds or thousands of individuals, however, the ratios usually come very close to matching expectations.

11–2 Section Assessment

1. **Key Concept** How are the principles of probability used to predict the outcomes of genetic crosses?
2. **Key Concept** How are Punnett squares used?
3. What is probability?
4. Define the terms *genotype* and *phenotype.*
5. **Critical Thinking Problem Solving** An F_1 plant that is homozygous for shortness is crossed with a heterozygous F_1 plant. What is the probability that a seed from the cross will produce a tall plant? Use a Punnett square to explain your answer and to compare the probable genetic variations in the F_2 plants.

Thinking Visually

Drawing Punnett Squares
Imagine that you came upon a tall pea plant similar to those Mendel used in his experiments. How could you determine the plant's genotype with respect to height? Draw two Punnett squares to show your answer.

11–3 Exploring Mendelian Genetics

1-S1.1 Science combines what is known with new evidence
1-S1.2 Inquiry—processing/interpreting information
4-2.1 Heredity involves passing coded instructions
4-3.1 New inheritable characteristics

Guide for Reading

Key Concepts

- What is the principle of independent assortment?
- What inheritance patterns exist aside from simple dominance?

Vocabulary
independent assortment
incomplete dominance
codominance
multiple alleles
polygenic traits

Reading Strategy: Finding Main Ideas Before you read, draw a line down the center of a sheet of paper. On the left side, write down the main topics of the section. On the right side, note supporting details and examples.

After showing that alleles segregate during the formation of gametes, Mendel wondered if they did so independently. In other words, does the segregation of one pair of alleles affect the segregation of another pair of alleles? For example, does the gene that determines whether a seed is round or wrinkled in shape have anything to do with the gene for seed color? Must a round seed also be yellow?

Independent Assortment

To answer these questions, Mendel performed an experiment to follow two different genes as they passed from one generation to the next. Mendel's experiment is known as a two-factor cross.

The Two-Factor Cross: F_1 First, Mendel crossed true-breeding plants that produced only round yellow peas (genotype *RRYY*) with plants that produced wrinkled green peas (genotype *rryy*). All of the F_1 offspring produced round yellow peas. This shows that the alleles for yellow and round peas are dominant over the alleles for green and wrinkled peas. A Punnett square for this cross, shown in **Figure 11–9,** shows that the genotype of each of these F_1 plants is *RrYy*.

This cross does not indicate whether genes assort, or segregate, independently. However, it provides the hybrid plants needed for the next cross—the cross of F_1 plants to produce the F_2 generation.

Figure 11–9 Mendel crossed plants that were homozygous dominant for round yellow peas with plants that were homozygous recessive for wrinkled green peas. All of the F_1 offspring were heterozygous dominant for round yellow peas. **Interpreting Graphics** *How is the genotype of the offspring different from that of the homozygous dominant parent?*

rryy (columns) × *RRYY* (rows)

	ry	*ry*	*ry*	*ry*
RY	*RrYy*	*RrYy*	*RrYy*	*RrYy*
RY	*RrYy*	*RrYy*	*RrYy*	*RrYy*
RY	*RrYy*	*RrYy*	*RrYy*	*RrYy*
RY	*RrYy*	*RrYy*	*RrYy*	*RrYy*

The Two-Factor Cross: F_2 Mendel knew that the F_1 plants had genotypes of *RrYy*. In other words, the F_1 plants were all heterozygous for both the seed shape and seed color genes. How would the alleles segregate when the F_1 plants were crossed to each other to produce an F_2 generation? Remember that each plant in the F_1 generation was formed by the fusion of a gamete carrying the dominant *RY* alleles with another gamete carrying the recessive ry alleles. Did this mean that the two dominant alleles would always stay together? Or would they "segregate independently," so that any combination of alleles was possible?

In Mendel's experiment, the F_2 plants produced 556 seeds. Mendel compared the variation in the seeds. He observed that 315 seeds were round and yellow and another 32 were wrinkled and green, the two parental phenotypes. However, 209 of the seeds had combinations of phenotypes—and therefore combinations of alleles—not found in either parent. This clearly meant that the alleles for seed shape segregated independently of those for seed color—a principle known as **independent assortment.** Put another way, genes that segregate independently—such as the genes for seed shape and seed color in pea plants—do not influence each other's inheritance. Mendel's experimental results were very close to the 9 : 3 : 3 : 1 ratio that the Punnett square shown in **Figure 11–10** predicts. Mendel had discovered the principle of independent assortment. **The principle of independent assortment states that genes for different traits can segregate independently during the formation of gametes. Independent assortment helps account for the many genetic variations observed in plants, animals, and other organisms.**

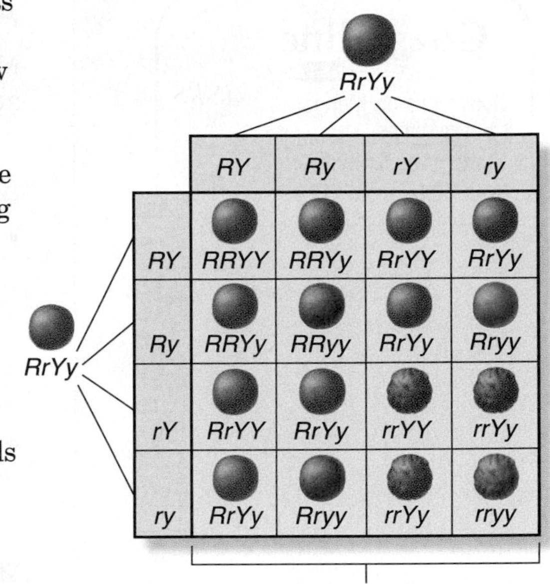

▲ **Figure 11–10** **When Mendel crossed plants that were heterozygous dominant for round yellow peas, he found that the alleles segregated independently to produce the F_2 generation.**

Problem Solving

Producing True-Breeding Seeds

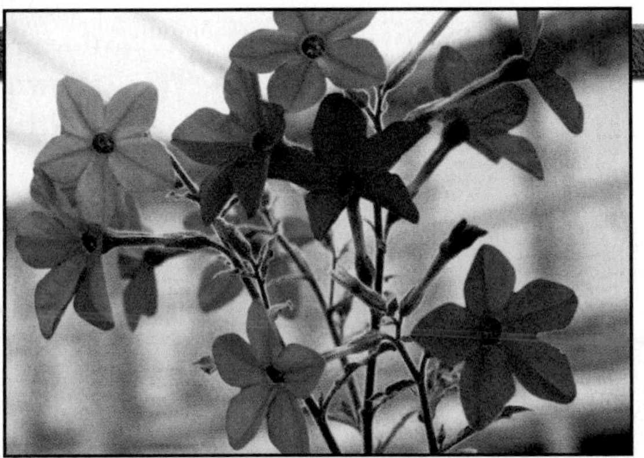

Suppose you work for a company that specializes in ornamental flowers. One spring, you find an ornamental plant with beautiful lavender flowers. Knowing that these plants are self-pollinating, you harvest seeds from it. You plant the seeds the following season. Of the 106 test plants, 31 have white flowers. Is there a way to develop seeds that produce only lavender flowers?

Defining the Problem Describe the problem that must be solved to make the lavender-flowered plants a commercial success.

Organizing Information The first lavender flower produced offspring with both lavender and white flowers when allowed to self-pollinate. Use your knowledge of Mendelian genetics, including Punnett squares, to draw conclusions about the nature of the allele for these lavender flowers.

Creating a Solution Write a description of how you would produce seeds guaranteed to produce 100 percent lavender plants. A single plant can produce as many as 1000 seeds.

Presenting Your Plan Prepare a step-by-step outline of your plan, including Punnett squares when appropriate. Present the procedure to your class.

For: Links on Mendelian genetics
Visit: www.SciLinks.org
Web Code: cbn-4113

A Summary of Mendel's Principles

Mendel's principles form the basis of the modern science of genetics. These principles can be summarized as follows:

- The inheritance of biological characteristics is determined by individual units known as genes. Genes are passed from parents to their offspring.
- In cases in which two or more forms (alleles) of the gene for a single trait exist, some forms of the gene may be dominant and others may be recessive.
- In most sexually reproducing organisms, each adult has two copies of each gene—one from each parent. These genes are segregated from each other when gametes are formed.
- The alleles for different genes usually segregate independently of one another.

Beyond Dominant and Recessive Alleles

Despite the importance of Mendel's work, there are important exceptions to most of his principles. For example, not all genes show simple patterns of dominant and recessive alleles. In most organisms, genetics is more complicated, because the majority of genes have more than two alleles. In addition, many important traits are controlled by more than one gene. **Some alleles are neither dominant nor recessive, and many traits are controlled by multiple alleles or multiple genes.**

Incomplete Dominance A cross between two four o'clock (Mirabilis) plants shows one of these complications. The F_1 generation produced by a cross between red-flowered *(RR)* and white-flowered *(WW)* plants consists of pink-colored flowers *(RW),* as shown in **Figure 11–11.** Which allele is dominant in this case? Neither one. Cases in which one allele is not completely dominant over another are called **incomplete dominance.** In incomplete dominance, the heterozygous phenotype is somewhere in between the two homozygous phenotypes.

▼ **Figure 11–11** **Some alleles are neither dominant nor recessive.** In four o'clock plants, for example, the alleles for red and white flowers show incomplete dominance. Heterozygous *(RW)* plants have pink flowers—a mix of red and white coloring.

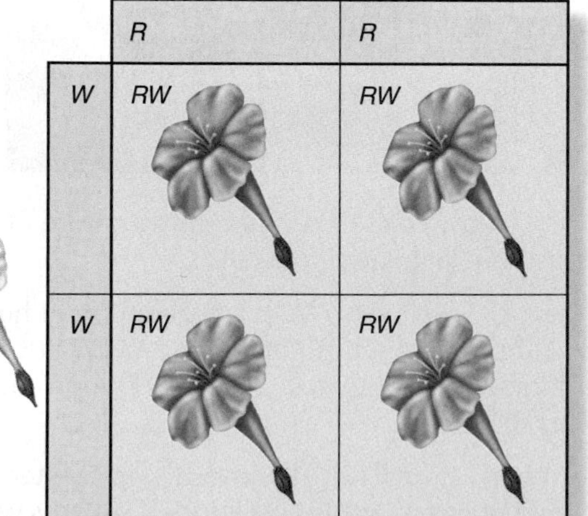

Codominance A similar situation is **codominance,** in which both alleles contribute to the phenotype. For example, in certain varieties of chicken, the allele for black feathers is codominant with the allele for white feathers. Heterozygous chickens have a color described as "erminette," speckled with black and white feathers. Unlike the blending of red and white colors in heterozygous four o'clocks, black and white colors appear separately. Many human genes show codominance, too, including one for a protein that controls cholesterol levels in the blood. People with the heterozygous form of the gene produce two different forms of the protein, each with a different effect on cholesterol levels.

Figure 11–12 Multiple Alleles

Coat color in rabbits is determined by a single gene that has at least four different alleles. Different combinations of alleles result in the four colors you see here. **Interpreting Graphics** *What allele combinations can a chinchilla rabbit have?*

Full color: CC, Cc^{ch}, Cc^{h}, or Cc

Chinchilla: $c^{ch}c^{h}$, $c^{ch}c^{ch}$, or $c^{ch}c$

Himalayan: $c^{h}c$ or $c^{h}c^{h}$

Albino: cc

Key

C = full color; dominant to all other alleles

c^{ch} = chinchilla; partial defect in pigmentation; dominant to c^{h} and c alleles

c^{h} = Himalayan; color in certain parts of body; dominant to c allele

c = albino; no color; recessive to all other alleles

Multiple Alleles Many genes have more than two alleles and are therefore said to have **multiple alleles.** This does not mean that an individual can have more than two alleles. It only means that more than two possible alleles exist in a population. One of the best-known examples is coat color in rabbits. A rabbit's coat color is determined by a single gene that has at least four different alleles. The four known alleles display a pattern of simple dominance that can produce four possible coat colors, as shown in **Figure 11–12.** Many other genes have multiple alleles, including the human genes for blood type.

Polygenic Traits Many traits are produced by the interaction of several genes. Traits controlled by two or more genes are said to be **polygenic traits,** which means "having many genes." For example, at least three genes are involved in making the reddish-brown pigment in the eyes of fruit flies. Different combinations of alleles for these genes produce very different eye colors. Polygenic traits often show a wide range of phenotypes. For example, the wide range of skin color in humans comes about partly because more than four different genes probably control this trait.

What are multiple alleles?

For: Links on Punnett squares
Visit: www.SciLinks.org
Web Code: cbn-4112

▲ **Figure 11–13** The common fruit fly is a popular organism for genetic research. **Inferring** *Why are fruit flies easier to use for genetic research than large animals, such as dogs?*

Applying Mendel's Principles

Mendel's principles don't apply only to plants. At the beginning of the 1900s, the American geneticist Thomas Hunt Morgan decided to look for a model organism to advance the study of genetics. He wanted an animal that was small, easy to keep in the laboratory, and able to produce large numbers of offspring in a short period of time. He decided to work on a tiny insect that kept showing up, uninvited, in his laboratory. The insect was the common fruit fly, *Drosophila melanogaster,* shown in **Figure 11–13.**

Morgan grew the flies in small milk bottles stoppered with cotton gauze. *Drosophila* was an ideal organism for genetics because it could produce plenty of offspring, and it did so quickly. A single pair of flies could produce as many as 100 offspring. Before long, Morgan and other biologists had tested every one of Mendel's principles and learned that they applied not just to pea plants but to other organisms as well.

Mendel's principles also apply to humans. The basic principles of Mendelian genetics can be used to study the inheritance of human traits and to calculate the probability of certain traits appearing in the next generation. You will learn more about human genetics in Chapter 14.

Genetics and the Environment

The characteristics of any organism, whether bacterium, fruit fly, or human being, are not determined solely by the genes it inherits. Rather, characteristics are determined by interaction between genes and the environment. For example, genes may affect a sunflower plant's height and the color of its flowers. However, these same characteristics are also influenced by climate, soil conditions, and the availability of water. Genes provide a plan for development, but how that plan unfolds also depends on the environment.

11–3 Section Assessment

1. **Key Concept** Explain what *independent assortment* means.
2. **Key Concept** Describe two inheritance patterns besides simple dominance.
3. What is the difference between incomplete dominance and codominance?
4. Why are fruit flies an ideal organism for genetic research?
5. **Critical Thinking Comparing and Contrasting** A geneticist studying coat color in animals crosses a male rabbit having the genotype CC with a female having genotype Cc^{ch}. The geneticist then crosses a cc^{ch} male with a Cc^{c} female. In which of the two crosses are the offspring more likely to show greater genetic variation? Use Punnett squares to explain your answer.

Sharpen Your Skills

Problem Solving

Construct a genetics problem to be given as an assignment to a classmate. The problem must test incomplete dominance, codominance, multiple alleles, or polygenic traits. Your problem must have an answer key that includes all of your work.

11–4 Meiosis

4-2.1 Sexual reproduction involves two parents
4-2.1 Heredity involves passing coded instructions
4-3.1 New inheritable characteristics
4-4.1 Meiosis

Gregor Mendel did not know where the genes he had discovered were located in the cell. Fortunately, his predictions of how genes should behave were so specific that it was not long before biologists were certain they had found them. Genes are located on chromosomes in the cell nucleus.

Mendel's principles of genetics require at least two things. First, each organism must inherit a single copy of every gene from each of its "parents." Second, when an organism produces its own gametes, those two sets of genes must be separated from each other so that each gamete contains just one set of genes. This means that when gametes are formed, there must be a process that separates the two sets of genes so that each gamete ends up with just one set. Although Mendel didn't know it, gametes are formed through exactly such a process.

Guide for Reading

 **Key Concepts**

- What happens during the process of meiosis?
- How is meiosis different from mitosis?

Vocabulary
homologous
diploid
haploid
meiosis
tetrad
crossing-over

Reading Strategy: Using Visuals Before you read, preview **Figure 11–15.** As you read, note what happens at each stage of meiosis.

Chromosome Number

As an example of how this process works, let's consider the fruit fly, *Drosophila.* A body cell in an adult fruit fly has 8 chromosomes, as shown in **Figure 11–14.** Four of the chromosomes came from the fruit fly's male parent, and 4 came from its female parent. These two sets of chromosomes are **homologous** (hoh-MAHL-uh-guhs), meaning that each of the 4 chromosomes that came from the male parent has a corresponding chromosome from the female parent.

A cell that contains both sets of homologous chromosomes is said to be **diploid,** which means "two sets." The number of chromosomes in a diploid cell is sometimes represented by the symbol 2N. Thus for *Drosophila,* the diploid number is 8, which can be written 2N = 8. Diploid cells contain two complete sets of chromosomes and two complete sets of genes. This agrees with Mendel's idea that the cells of an adult organism contain two copies of each gene.

By contrast, the gametes of sexually reproducing organisms, including fruit flies and peas, contain only a single set of chromosomes, and therefore only a single set of genes. Such cells are said to be **haploid,** which means "one set." For *Drosophila,* this can be written as N = 4, meaning that the haploid number is 4.

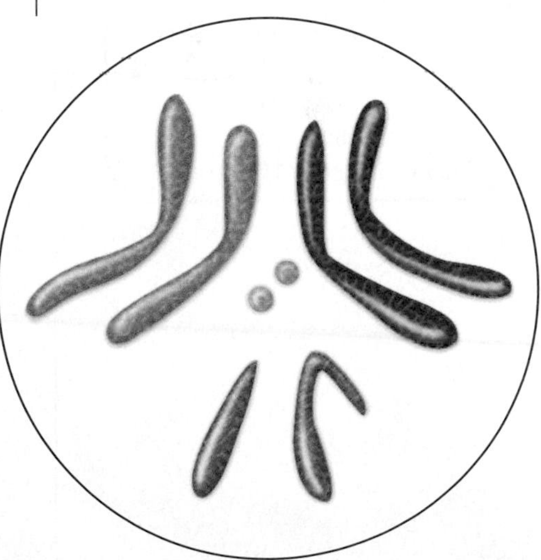

▶ **Figure 11–14** These chromosomes are from a fruit fly. Each of the fruit fly's body cells has 8 chromosomes.

Phases of Meiosis

How are haploid (N) gamete cells produced from diploid (2N) cells? That's where **meiosis** (my-OH-sis) comes in. **Meiosis is a process of reduction division in which the number of chromosomes per cell is cut in half through the separation of homologous chromosomes in a diploid cell.**

Meiosis

Figure 11–15 **During meiosis, the number of chromosomes per cell is cut in half through the separation of the homologous chromosomes.** The result of meiosis is 4 haploid cells that are genetically different from one another and from the original cell.

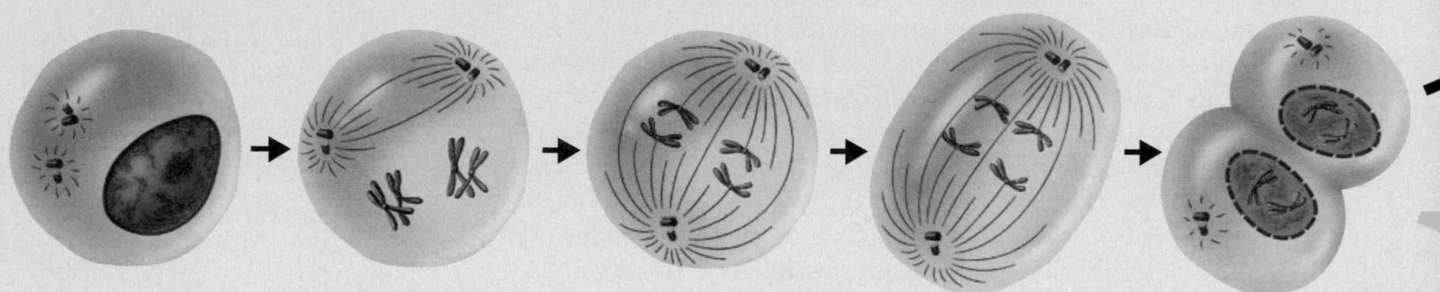

MEIOSIS I

Interphase I
Cells undergo a round of DNA replication, forming duplicate chromosomes.

Prophase I
Each chromosome pairs with its corresponding homologous chromosome to form a tetrad.

Metaphase I
Spindle fibers attach to the chromosomes.

Anaphase I
The fibers pull the homologous chromosomes toward opposite ends of the cell.

Telophase I and Cytokinesis
Nuclear membranes form. The cell separates into two cells.

For: Meiosis activity
Visit: PHSchool.com
Web Code: cbp-4114

Meiosis usually involves two distinct divisions, called meiosis I and meiosis II. By the end of meiosis II, the diploid cell that entered meiosis has become 4 haploid cells. **Figure 11–15** shows meiosis in an organism that has a diploid number of 4 (2N = 4).

Meiosis I Prior to meiosis I, each chromosome is replicated. The cells then begin to divide in a way that looks similar to mitosis. In mitosis, the 4 chromosomes line up individually in the center of the cell. The 2 chromatids that make up each chromosome then separate from each other.

In prophase of meiosis I, however, each chromosome pairs with its corresponding homologous chromosome to form a structure called a **tetrad.** There are 4 chromatids in a tetrad. This pairing of homologous chromosomes is the key to understanding meiosis.

As homologous chromosomes pair up and form tetrads in meiosis I, they exchange portions of their chromatids in a process called **crossing-over.** Crossing-over, shown in **Figure 11–16,** results in the exchange of alleles between homologous chromosomes and produces new combinations of alleles.

What happens next? The homologous chromosomes separate, and two new cells are formed. Although each cell now has 4 chromatids (as it would after mitosis), something is different.

For: Links on meiosis
Visit: www.SciLinks.org
Web Code: cbn-4114

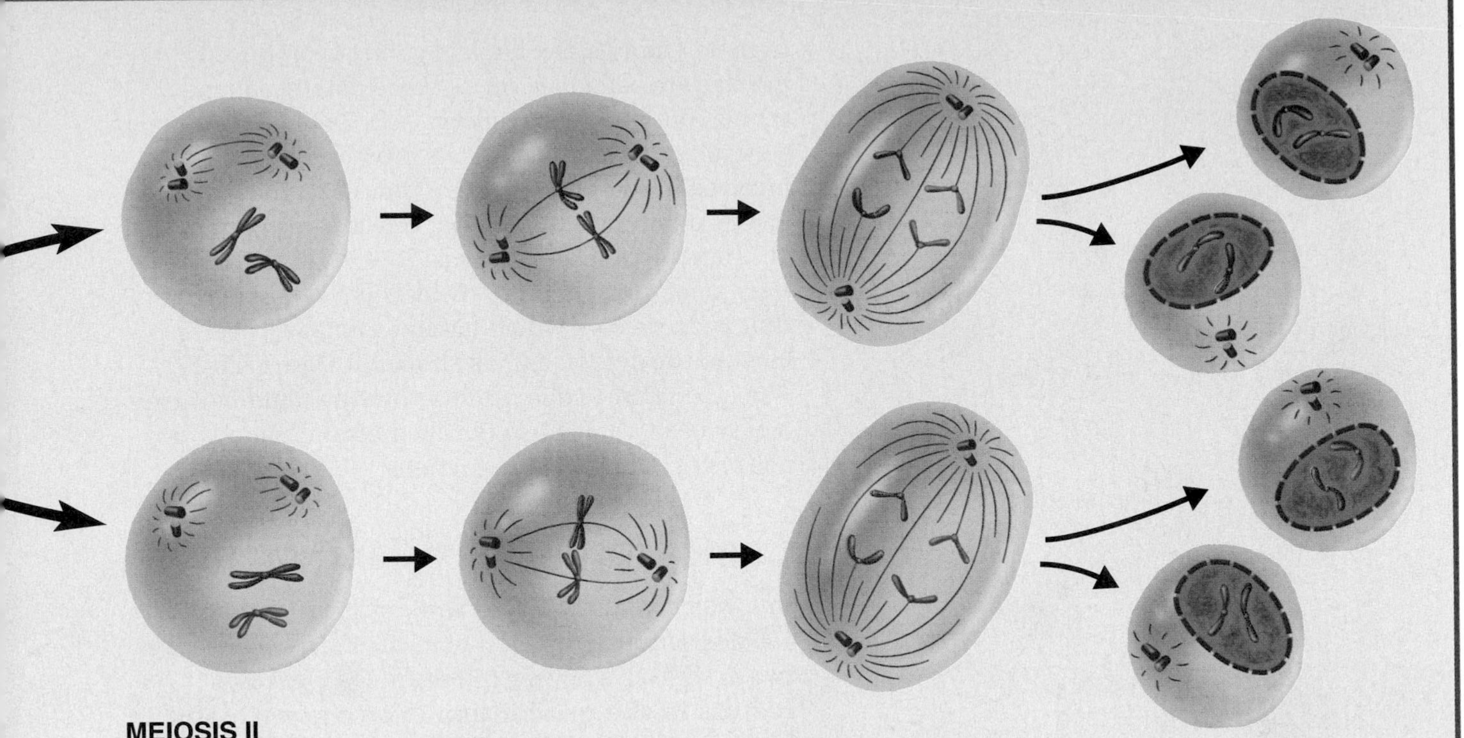

MEIOSIS II

Prophase II
Meiosis I results in two haploid (N) daughter cells, each with half the number of chromosomes as the original cell.

Metaphase II
The chromosomes line up in a similar way to the metaphase stage of mitosis.

Anaphase II
The sister chromatids separate and move toward opposite ends of the cell.

Telophase II and Cytokinesis
Meiosis II results in four haploid (N) daughter cells.

Because each pair of homologous chromosomes was separated, neither of the daughter cells has the two complete sets of chromosomes that it would have in a diploid cell. Those two sets have been shuffled and sorted almost like a deck of cards. The two cells produced by meiosis I have sets of chromosomes and alleles that are different from each other and from the diploid cell that entered meiosis I.

Meiosis II The two cells produced by meiosis I now enter a second meiotic division. Unlike the first division, neither cell goes through a round of chromosome replication before entering meiosis II. Each of the cell's chromosomes has 2 chromatids. During metaphase II of meiosis, chromosomes line up in the center of each cell. In anaphase II, the paired chromatids separate. In this example, each of the four daughter cells produced in meiosis II receives 2 chromatids. Those four daughter cells now contain the haploid number (N)—just 2 chromosomes each.

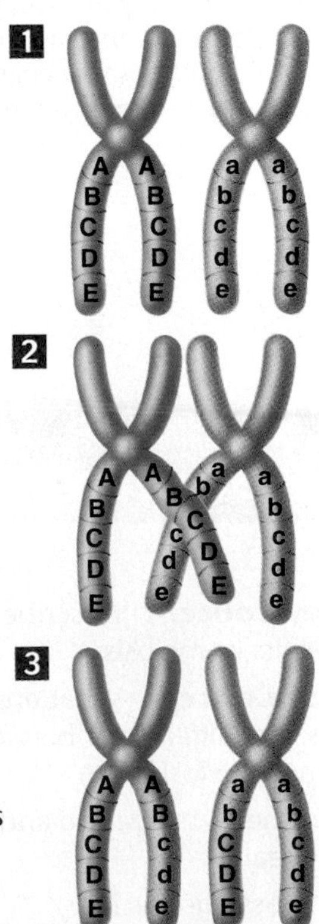

▶ **Figure 11–16** Crossing-over occurs during meiosis. (1) Homologous chromosomes form a tetrad. (2) Chromatids cross over one another. (3) The crossed sections of the chromatids are exchanged. **Interpreting Graphics** *How does crossing-over affect the alleles on a chromatid?*

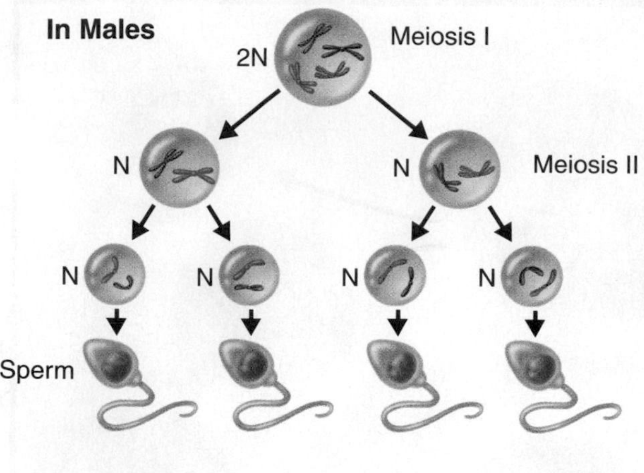

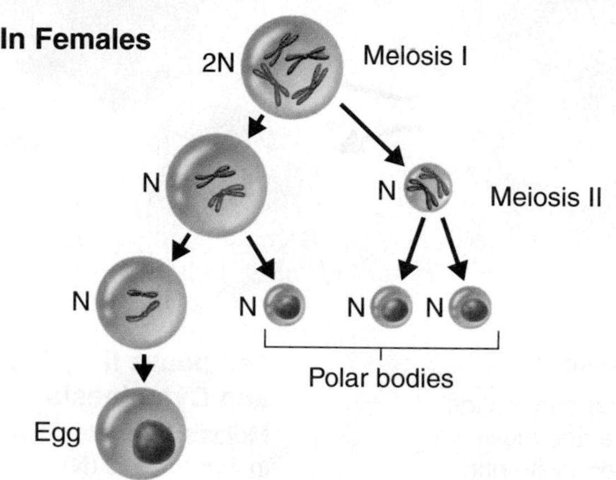

▲ **Figure 11–17** **Meiosis produces four genetically different haploid cells.** In males, meiosis results in four equal-sized gametes called sperm. In females, only one large egg cell results from meiosis. The other three cells, called polar bodies, usually are not involved in reproduction.

Gamete Formation

In male animals, the haploid gametes produced by meiosis are called sperm. In some plants, pollen grains contain haploid sperm cells. In female animals, generally only one of the cells produced by meiosis is involved in reproduction. This female gamete is called an egg in animals and an egg cell in some plants.

In many female animals, the cell divisions at the end of meiosis I and meiosis II are uneven, so that a single cell, which becomes an egg, receives most of the cytoplasm, as shown in **Figure 11–17.** The other three cells produced in the female during meiosis are known as polar bodies and usually do not participate in reproduction.

Comparing Mitosis and Meiosis

In a way, it's too bad that the words *mitosis* and *meiosis* sound so much like each other, because the two processes are very different. **Mitosis results in the production of two genetically identical diploid cells, whereas meiosis produces four genetically different haploid cells.**

A diploid cell that divides by mitosis gives rise to two diploid (2N) daughter cells. The daughter cells have sets of chromosomes and alleles that are identical to each other and to the original parent cell. Mitosis allows an organism's body to grow and replace cells. In asexual reproduction, a new organism is produced by mitosis of the cell or cells of the parent organism.

Meiosis, on the other hand, begins with a diploid cell but produces four haploid (N) cells. These cells are genetically different from the diploid cell and from one another. Meiosis is how sexually reproducing organisms produce gametes. In contrast, asexual reproduction involves only mitosis.

11–4 Section Assessment

1. **Key Concept** Describe the main results of meiosis.
2. **Key Concept** What are the principal differences between mitosis and meiosis?
3. What do the terms *diploid* and *haploid* mean?
4. What is crossing-over?
5. **Critical Thinking Applying Concepts** In human cells, 2N = 46. How many chromosomes would you expect to find in a sperm cell? In an egg cell? In a white blood cell? Explain.

Connecting Concepts

Sexual and Asexual Reproduction
In asexual reproduction, mitosis occurs, but not meiosis. Which type of reproduction—sexual or asexual—results in offspring with greater genetic variation? Explain your answer.

11–5 Linkage and Gene Maps

4-2.1 Heredity specifies traits
4-2.1 Genes and chromosomes in the nucleus
4-3.1 New inheritable characteristics
4-3.1 Genetic recombination

If you thought carefully about Mendel's principle of independent assortment as you analyzed meiosis, one question might have been bothering you. It's easy to see how genes located on different chromosomes assort independently, but what about genes located on the same chromosome? Wouldn't they generally be inherited together?

Guide for Reading

Key Concept
- What structures actually assort independently?

Vocabulary
gene map

Reading Strategy: Predicting Before you read, preview **Figure 11–19.** Predict how a diagram like this one can be used to determine how likely genes are to assort independently. As you read, note whether or not your prediction was correct.

Gene Linkage

The answer to these questions, as Thomas Hunt Morgan first realized in 1910, is yes. Morgan's research on fruit flies led him to the principle of linkage. After identifying more than 50 *Drosophila* genes, Morgan discovered that many of them appeared to be "linked" together in ways that, at first glance, seemed to violate the principle of independent assortment. For example, a fly with reddish-orange eyes and miniature wings, like the one shown in **Figure 11–18,** was used in a series of crosses. The results showed that the genes for those traits were almost always inherited together and only rarely became separated from each other.

Morgan and his associates observed so many genes that were inherited together that before long they could group all of the fly's genes into four linkage groups. The linkage groups assorted independently, but all of the genes in one group were inherited together. *Drosophila* has four linkage groups. It also has four pairs of chromosomes, which led to two remarkable conclusions. First, each chromosome is actually a group of linked genes. Second, Mendel's principle of independent assortment still holds true. **It is the chromosomes, however, that assort independently, not individual genes.**

How did Mendel manage to miss gene linkage? By luck, or by design, six of the seven genes he studied are on different chromosomes. The two genes that are found on the same chromosome are so far apart that they also assort independently.

▼ **Figure 11–18** The genes for this fruit fly's reddish-orange eyes and miniature wings are almost always inherited together. The reason for this is that the genes are close together on a single chromosome. **It is the chromosomes that assort independently, not individual genes.**

Gene Maps

If two genes are found on the same chromosome, does this mean that they are linked forever? Not at all. Crossing-over during meiosis sometimes separates genes that had been on the same chromosome onto homologous chromosomes. Crossover events occasionally separate and exchange linked genes and produce new combinations of alleles. This is important because it helps to generate genetic diversity.

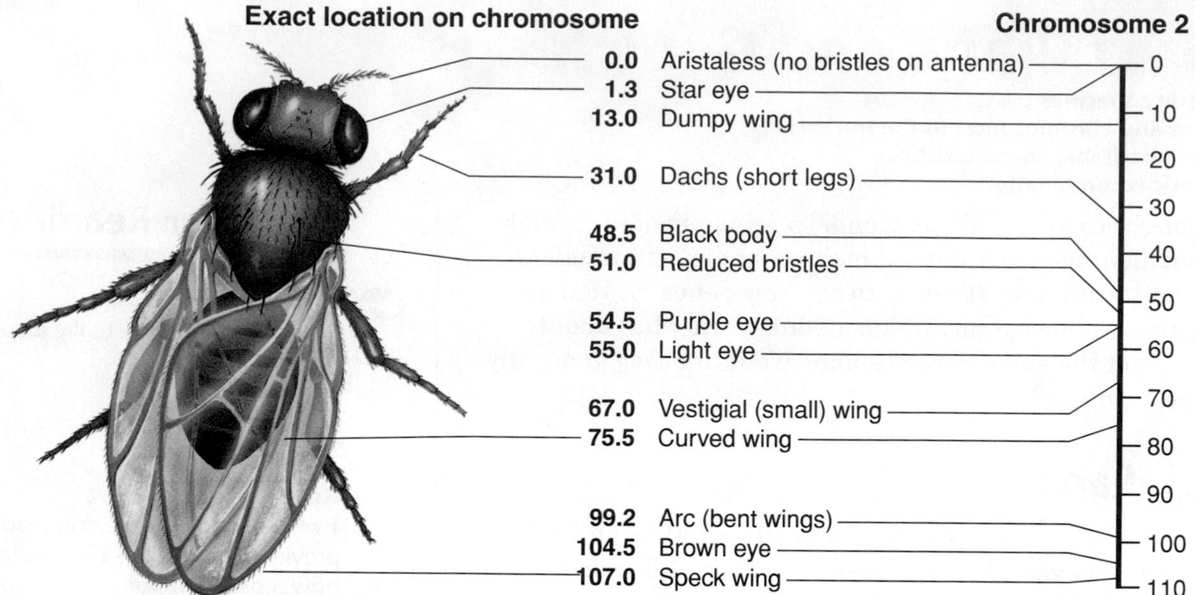

▲ **Figure 11–19** This gene map shows the location of a variety of genes on chromosome 2 of the fruit fly. The genes are named after the problems abnormal alleles cause, not the normal structure. **Interpreting Graphics** *Where on the chromosome is the "purple eye" gene located?*

In 1911, a Columbia University student was working part time in Morgan's lab. This student, Alfred Sturtevant, hypothesized that the rate at which crossing-over separated linked genes could be the key to an important discovery. Sturtevant reasoned that the farther apart two genes were, the more likely they were to be separated by a crossover in meiosis. The rate at which linked genes were separated and recombined could then be used to produce a "map" of distances between genes. Sturtevant gathered up several notebooks of lab data and took them back to his room. The next morning, he presented Morgan with a **gene map** showing the relative locations of each known gene on one of the *Drosophila* chromosomes, as shown in **Figure 11–19.** Sturtevant's method of using recombination rates, which measure the frequencies of crossing-over between genes, has been used to construct genetic maps, including maps of the human genome, ever since.

11–5 Section Assessment

1. **Key Concept** How does the principle of independent assortment apply to chromosomes?
2. What are gene maps, and how are they produced?
3. How does crossing-over make gene mapping possible?
4. **Critical Thinking Inferring** If two genes are on the same chromosome but usually assort independently, what does that tell you about how close together they are?

Writing in Science

Cause-Effect Paragraph
In your own words, explain why the alleles for reddish-orange eyes and miniature wings in *Drosophila* are usually inherited together. Include the idea of gene linkage. *Hint:* To organize your ideas, draw a cause-effect diagram that shows what happens to the two alleles during meiosis.

Exploration

Modeling Meiosis

Meiosis results in 4 new cells, each containing half the number of chromosomes in the original cells. Using the procedures below, you will build a model to demonstrate the process of meiosis and explore how it can lead to genetic changes.

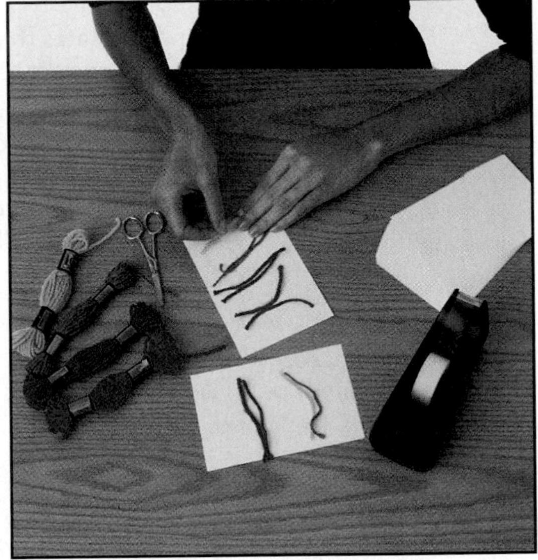

Problem **What happens to the chromosomes in cells during meiosis?**

Materials

- 4 colors of yarn (2 shades of red and 2 shades of green)
- scissors
- transparent tape
- index cards
- felt-tip marker

Skills Using Models, Communicating Results

Procedure 

1. You will use yarn and index cards to model each stage of meiosis. Use two shades of red yarn to represent one homologous pair of chromosomes and two shades of green yarn to represent another pair. Use an index card to represent a cell.
2. Cut two pieces of yarn about 5 cm long from each color of yarn. Each piece of yarn will represent a chromatid.
3. Tape pieces of red and green yarn to an index card to show the appearance of two tetrads in a cell at the beginning of meiosis.
4. Tape pieces of yarn to additional index cards to model the numbers and positions of the chromosomes and cells at each stage of meiosis. Be sure to include an example of crossing-over at the correct stage. Use a felt-tip marker to label each card with the name of the stage it represents.
5. Arrange the finished cards to show the complete process of meiosis. Label the stages at which genetic segregation and crossing-over occur and chromosome number changes.
6. Use your cards to explain the process of meiosis to a classmate. Then, trade roles and have your classmate use his or her models to explain the process of meiosis to you.

Analyze and Conclude

1. **Using Models** What is the result of the first meiotic division (meiosis I)?
2. **Using Models** What is the result of the second meiotic division (meiosis II)?
3. **Drawing Conclusions** How does meiosis lead to increased genetic variation?
4. **Predicting** How would the gametes be affected if a pair of chromatids failed to separate in the second meiotic division?
5. **Using Models** What parts of the cell did the yarn represent?
6. **Evaluating** How well do you think this investigation modeled the process of meiosis? Explain your answer.

Go Further

Using Models Make a second set of models that shows the differences between the formation of sperm and the formation of eggs.

Chapter 11 Study Guide

11–1 The Work of Gregor Mendel

Key Concepts

- The principle of dominance states that some alleles are dominant and others are recessive.
- When each F_1 plant flowers, the two alleles segregate from each other so that each gamete carries only a single copy of each gene. Therefore, each F_1 plant produces two types of gametes—those with the allele for tallness and those with the allele for shortness.

Vocabulary

genetics, p. 263 • fertilization, p. 263
true-breeding, p. 263
trait, p. 264 • hybrid, p. 264
gene, p. 265 • allele, p. 265
segregation, p. 266 • gamete, p. 266

11–2 Probability and Punnett Squares

Key Concepts

- The principles of probability can be used to predict the outcomes of genetic crosses.
- Punnett squares can be used to predict and compare the genetic variations that will result from a cross.

Vocabulary

probability, p. 267 • Punnett square, p. 268
homozygous, p. 268 • heterozygous, p. 268
phenotype, p. 268 • genotype, p. 268

11–3 Exploring Mendelian Genetics

Key Concepts

- The principle of independent assortment states that genes for different traits can segregate independently during the formation of gametes. Independent assortment helps account for the many genetic variations observed in plants, animals, and other organisms.
- Some alleles are neither dominant nor recessive, and many traits are controlled by multiple alleles or multiple genes.

Vocabulary

independent assortment, p. 271
incomplete dominance, p. 272
codominance, p. 272
multiple alleles, p. 273
polygenic traits, p. 273

11–4 Meiosis

Key Concepts

- Meiosis is a process of reduction division in which the number of chromosomes per cell is cut in half through the separation of homologous chromosomes in a diploid cell.
- Mitosis results in the production of two genetically identical diploid cells, whereas meiosis produces four genetically different haploid cells.

Vocabulary

homologous, p. 275 • diploid, p. 275
haploid, p. 275 • meiosis, p. 276
tetrad, p. 276 • crossing-over, p. 277

11–5 Linkage and Gene Maps

Key Concept

- Chromosomes assort independently; individual genes do not.

Vocabulary

gene map, p. 280

Thinking Visually

Using the information in this chapter, complete the following flowchart about meiosis.

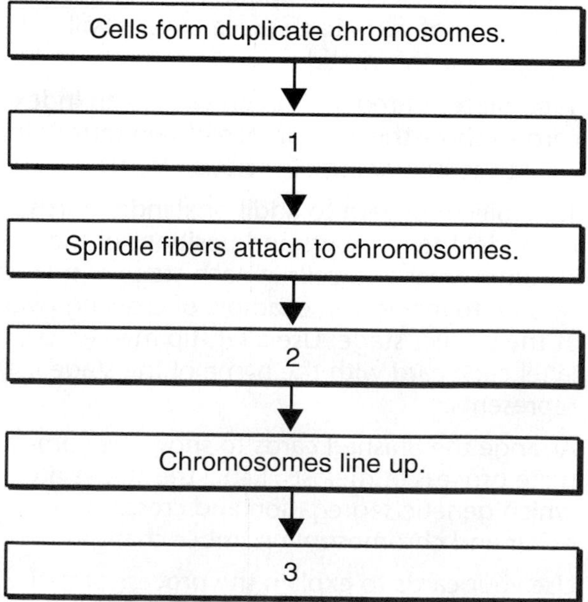

Cells form duplicate chromosomes.
1
Spindle fibers attach to chromosomes.
2
Chromosomes line up.
3

Preparing for the Living Environment Exam

Blue questions emphasize Regents Exam content

Chapter 11

Part A

Multiple Choice

For each statement or question, select the number of the word or expression that, of those given, best completes the statement or answers the question.

1 What happens to the chromosome number of a cell during meiosis?
(1) It doubles. (3) It stays the same.
(2) It quadruples. (4) It halves.

2 Which arrangement of cell-related terms correctly represents the relationships involved?
(1) A nucleus includes chromosomes that contain several genes.
(2) Several nuclei make up genes that are located on chromosomes.
(3) A gene is made up of chromosomes that are located in the cytoplasm.
(4) Chromosomes are composed of nuclei that include several genes.

3 To maintain the chromosome number of an organism, the gametes must
(1) come with a complete set of genetic instructions
(2) result in genetically identical cells
(3) be produced by mitosis
(4) be produced by meiosis

4 What stage of meiosis is represented in the cell illustrated below?
(1) prophase I (3) anaphase II
(2) telophase I (4) metaphase I

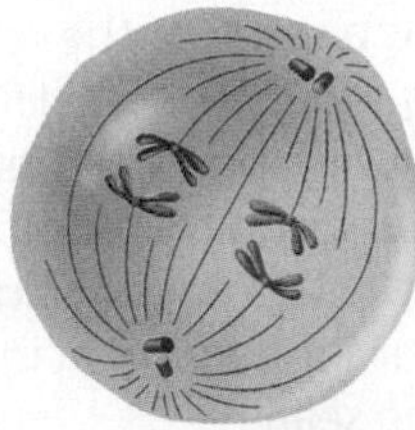

5 Unlike mitosis, meiosis results in the formation of
(1) two cells, each containing half the genetic information of the parent cell
(2) two cells, each containing a complete set of chromosomes
(3) four cells, each containing a complete set of chromosomes
(4) four cells, each containing half the genetic information of the parent cell

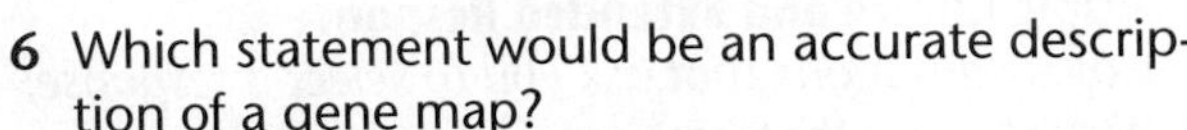

6 Which statement would be an accurate description of a gene map?
(1) A gene map shows the number of possible forms of a gene.
(2) A gene map shows the relative locations of genes on a chromosome.
(3) A gene map shows where chromosomes are located in a cell.
(4) A gene map shows how crossing-over occurs.

7 Two pink-flowering plants are crossed. The offspring flower as follows: 25% red, 25% white, 50% pink. What pattern of inheritance does flower color in these flowers follow?
(1) dominance
(2) multiple alleles
(3) incomplete dominance
(4) recessiveness

8 A genetic disease is one that can be inherited from one or both of an individual's parents. Examine the description of disease inheritance in a particular family.

Child:	has disease; possesses two abnormal forms of the gene for the trait
Father:	does not have the disease; possesses one abnormal form of the gene for the trait
Mother:	does not have the disease

What is *most likely* the genetic makeup of the mother for this genetic disease?
(1) possesses two normal forms of the gene for the trait
(2) possesses two abnormal forms of the gene for the trait
(3) possesses one normal and one abnormal form of the gene for the trait
(4) possesses an abnormal number of genes for the trait

Test-Taking Tip

To complete an analogy, write a sentence that uses the two given words of the first pair. Then, rewrite the sentence with the third given word and a blank. Try each of the answer choices in the blank to see which one works best. If more than one answer choice seems to fit, refine the original sentence and repeat the process.

Preparing for the Living Environment Exam

Part B

Multiple Choice and Extended Response

For those questions that ask you to select a response, choose the one that best completes the statement or answers the question. For all others follow the directions given.

9 Meiosis occurs in the development of sex cells. Mitosis occurs in most other cells. State *two* additional differences between these processes.

10 State why horse breeders will pay a lot of money to breed one of their horses with a horse that has won the Kentucky Derby.

11 State *two* ways that multiple alleles and polygenic traits differ.

Base your answers to questions 12 and 13 on the information below and on your knowledge of biology.

A student calculates the recombination frequency of genes A, B, C, and D on one chromosome. The recombination frequencies are as follows: C-D: 25 map units; A-B: 12 map units; B-D: 20 map units; and A-C: 17 map units.

12 Assuming the student's calculations are correct, how many map units apart are genes A and D?

(1) 5 (3) 10
(2) 8 (4) 12.5

13 Which gene map below best reflects the student's data?

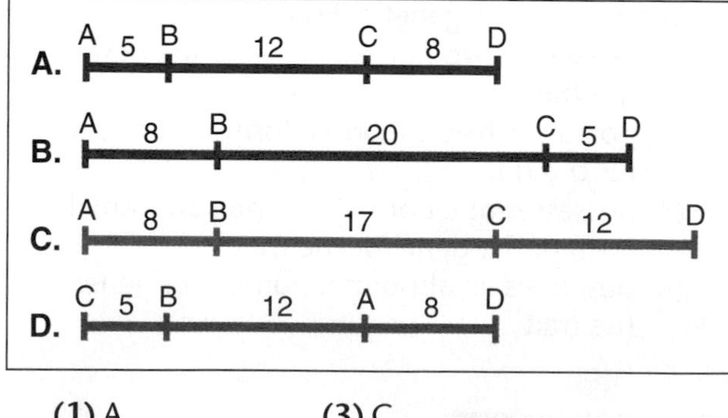

(1) A (3) C
(2) B (4) D

14 In sheep, the allele for white wool (*A*) is dominant over the allele for black wool (*a*). State how you would determine the genotype of a white ram (male sheep).

15 In rabbits, *B* is an allele for black coat and *b* is an allele for brown coat.

- Write the genotype for a rabbit that is homozygous for black coat.
- Write the genotype for a rabbit that is heterozygous for black coat.

Base your answers to questions 16 through 18 on the passage below and on your knowledge of biology.

DNA is a long, threadlike molecule. Basically it contains the instructions for everything our cells do from the moment of conception until death. Most human cells contain 46 chromosomes (23 pairs). Each chromosome contains a DNA molecule with hundreds or thousands of genes along it. Genes typically code for the production of specific proteins. The instructions for making proteins are in the form of a four-letter code. A single misspelling in the DNA sequence can result in an incorrect protein or no protein being made, which, in turn, may result in an upset in homeostasis—in this case a genetic disease.

Connecting a particular defective gene with a disease has been a very slow process. In 1989, geneticists had identified four genes associated with such diseases. They did this by sorting through the hereditary history of families and examining the genetic makeup of individuals with the disease and those not having the disease. As a result of the Human Genome Project (HGP), a huge study to find out more about all of the DNA in human cells and the cells of other organisms, the list of diseases known to be linked to specific genes was up to 100 by 1998.

One of the first diseases linked to a gene was cystic fibrosis. It took teams of scientists nine years to identify the gene. As a result of the technology and information sharing associated the HGP, the gene for Parkinson disease was mapped in nine days and precisely described in just nine months. This means that scientists knew the letter code and the location on a chromosome of the Parkinson in less than a year after they started the search!

As the understanding of diseases at the DNA level becomes clearer, scientists might be able to prevent such diseases, design individualized treatments for them, and in some cases, actually cure the diseases.

(Adapted from: "Genetics: The Future of Medicine" NIH Publication No. 00-4873)

16 According to the reading passage, two diseases linked to genes are
(1) the common cold and cystic fibrosis
(2) HGP and Parkinson disease
(3) Parkinson disease and cystic fibrosis
(4) the common cold and HGP

17 Which of the following would be the best title for this reading?
(1) Predicting the Inheritance of Human Genetic Diseases
(2) The Human Genome Project
(3) The Gene for Cystic Fibrosis
(4) Mapping Human Genetic Diseases

18 State one reason it is important to study the inheritance of human genetic diseases.

19 Explain why it is chromosomes, not individual genes, that assort independently.

20 In pea plants, the allele for yellow seeds is dominant to the allele for green seeds.
a Predict the genotypic ratio of offspring produced by crossing two parents heterozygous for this trait.
b Draw a Punnett square to illustrate your prediction.

Part C

Extended Response
Answer the questions or follow the directions given.

21 Gregor Mendel is called the Father of Genetics. His work led to the discovery of several basic principles that help to explain how traits are inherited.

Mendel's contributions to our understanding of heredity were made with no knowledge of chromosomes, genes, or the process of meiosis. One observation he made was that in most sexually reproducing organisms, each offspring inherits one allele (form of a gene) from each parent.

Explain the role of genes, chromosomes, and meiosis in the inheritance of traits. In your explanation be sure to include information concerning:
- the relationship between genes and chromosomes
- the distribution of chromosomes during meiosis
- how meiosis leads to the sorting and recombining of traits

22 Gregor Mendel realized that the principles of probability were important to an understanding of genetics.
a Explain what is meant by the term *probability*.
b State how probability is used in genetics.

23 Describe the process of meiosis. In your description, be sure to include
- the number of cells produced
- the number of chromosomes present in each cell at the start and at the conclusion of the process
- the number of cytoplasmic divisions that occur

24 Genes that control hair or feather color in some animals are expressed differently in the winter than in the summer. For example, snowshoe hares are white in winter and brown in summer.
a Explain how such a difference in the expression of the gene for fur color might be beneficial to the snowshoe hare.
b Describe how the snowshoe hare's fur color can change but the genes the animal inherited from its parents do not change.

For: An interactive self-test
Visit: PHSchool.com
Web Code: cba-4110

CHAPTER 12

DNA and RNA

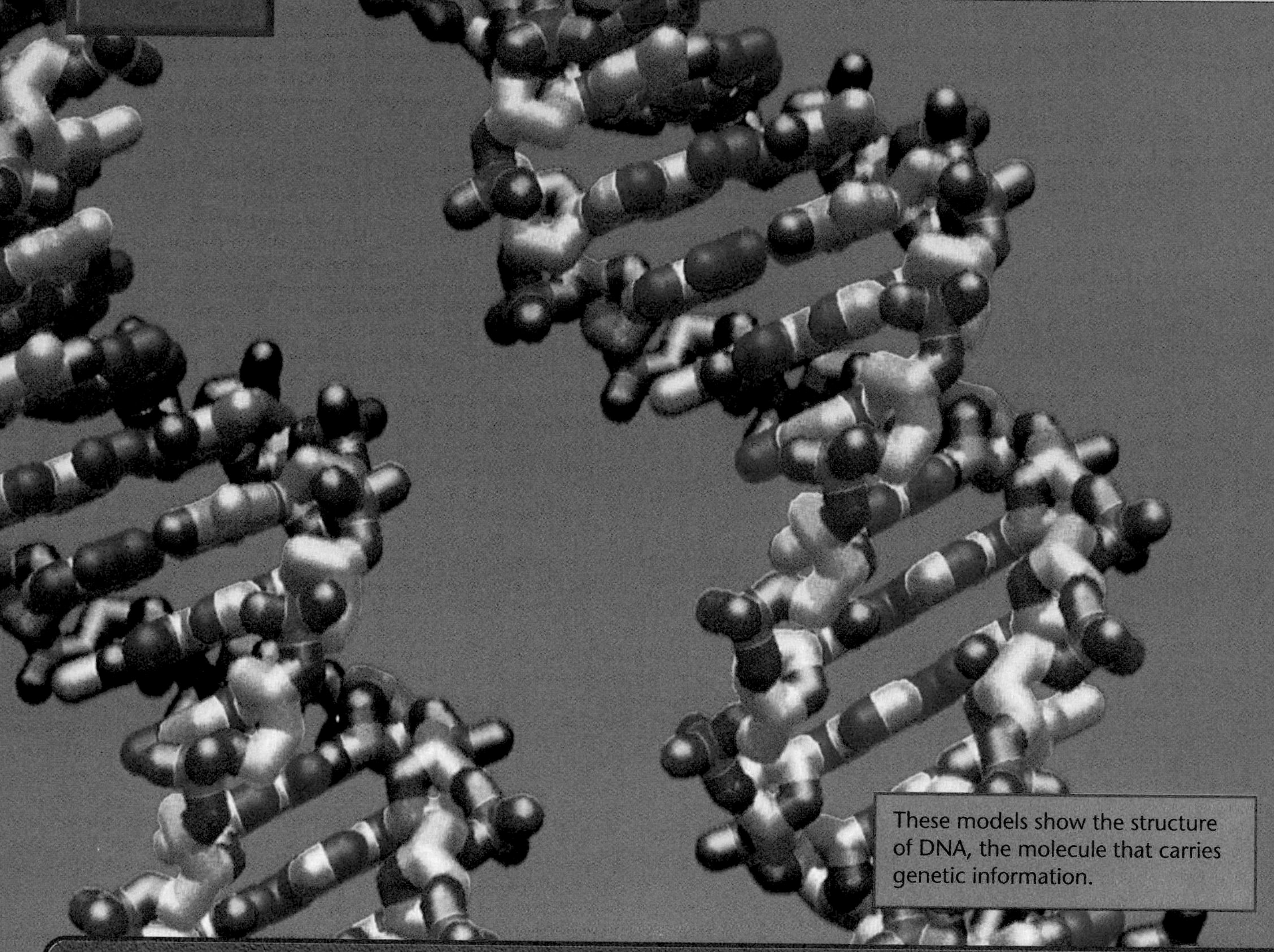

These models show the structure of DNA, the molecule that carries genetic information.

Inquiry Activity

How do codes work?

Procedure

1. Obtain 12 pop beads of four different colors.
2. Select a word that contains at least five different letters from the text on the next page. Use your beads to develop a code for your word.
3. Exchange your code and your coded bead chain with a classmate. Use the classmate's code to decipher his or her word.

Think About It

1. **Using Models** How were you able to encode five different letters using only four colors?
2. **Calculating** How many different letters could you encode by using two beads to stand for each letter used in your message?
3. **Analyzing Data** Could you encode the whole alphabet by using three beads for each letter?

12–1 DNA

1-S1. Historical development of ideas in science
1-S1.3, S1.4 Scientific explanations
4-2.1 DNA carries the genetic code and can replicate
4-5.1 Organic compounds
LS- Make observations and analyze results

How do genes work? What are they made of, and how do they determine the characteristics of organisms? Are genes single molecules, or are they longer structures made up of many molecules? In the middle of the 1900s, questions like these were on the minds of biologists everywhere.

To truly understand genetics, biologists first had to discover the chemical nature of the gene. If the structures that carry genetic information could be identified, it might be possible to understand how genes control the inherited characteristics of living things.

Guide for Reading

Key Concepts

- What did scientists discover about the relationship between genes and DNA?
- What is the overall structure of the DNA molecule?

Vocabulary

transformation
bacteriophage
nucleotide
base pairing

Reading Strategy: Summarizing As you read, find the key ideas for the text under each blue heading. Write down a few key words from each main idea. Then, use the key words in your summary. Revise your summary, keeping only the most important ideas.

Griffith and Transformation

Like many stories in science, the discovery of the molecular nature of the gene began with an investigator who was actually looking for something else. In 1928, British scientist Frederick Griffith was trying to figure out how bacteria make people sick. More specifically, Griffith wanted to learn how certain types of bacteria produce a serious lung disease known as pneumonia.

Griffith had isolated two slightly different strains, or types, of pneumonia bacteria from mice. Both strains grew very well in culture plates in his lab, but only one of the strains caused pneumonia. The disease-causing strain of bacteria grew into smooth colonies on culture plates, whereas the harmless strain produced colonies with rough edges. The differences in appearance made the two strains easy to distinguish.

◀ **Figure 12–1** White mice like these are commonly used in scientific experiments.

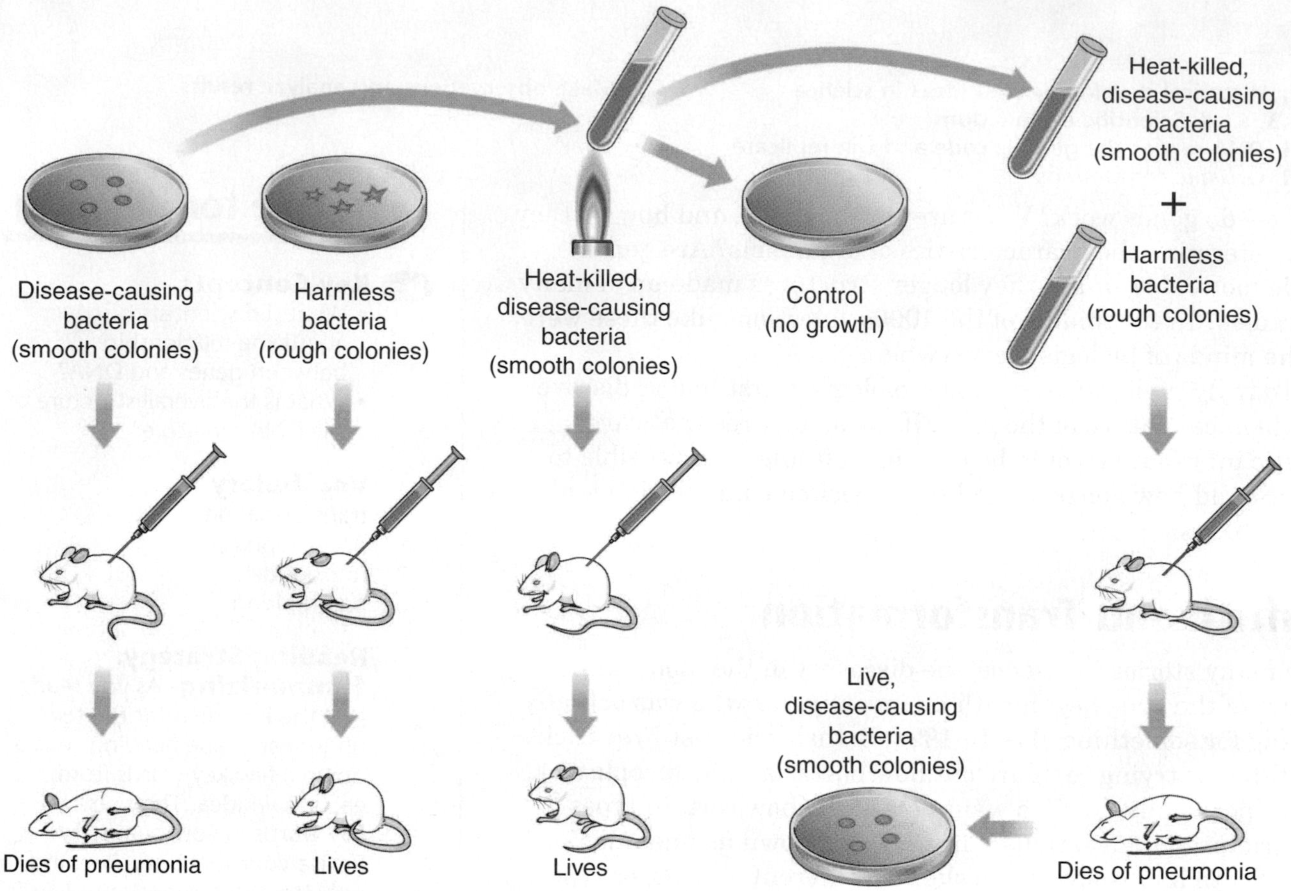

▲ **Figure 12–2** Griffith injected mice with four different samples of bacteria. When injected separately, neither heat-killed, disease-causing bacteria nor live, harmless bacteria killed the mice. The two types injected together, however, caused fatal pneumonia. From this experiment, biologists inferred that genetic information could be transferred from one bacterium to another. **Inferring** ***After heating the disease-causing bacteria, why did Griffith test whether material from the bacterial culture would produce new colonies in a petri dish?***

Griffith's Experiments When Griffith injected mice with the disease-causing strain of bacteria, the mice developed pneumonia and died. When mice were injected with the harmless strain, they didn't get sick at all. Griffith wondered if the disease-causing bacteria might produce a poison.

To find out, he took a culture of these cells, heated the bacteria to kill them, and injected the heat-killed bacteria into mice. The mice survived, suggesting that the cause of pneumonia was not a chemical poison released by the disease-causing bacteria. Griffith's experiments are shown in **Figure 12–2.**

Transformation Griffith's next experiment produced an amazing result. He mixed his heat-killed, disease-causing bacteria with live, harmless ones and injected the mixture into mice. By themselves, neither should have made the mice sick. But to Griffith's amazement, the mice developed pneumonia and many died. When he examined the lungs of the mice, he found them filled not with the harmless bacteria, but with the disease-causing bacteria. Somehow the heat-killed bacteria had passed their disease-causing ability to the harmless strain. Griffith called this process **transformation** because one strain of bacteria (the harmless strain) had apparently been changed permanently into another (the disease-causing strain).

Griffith hypothesized that when the live, harmless bacteria and the heat-killed bacteria were mixed, some factor was transferred from the heat-killed cells into the live cells. That factor, he hypothesized, must contain information that could change harmless bacteria into disease-causing ones. Furthermore, since the ability to cause disease was inherited by the transformed bacteria's offspring, the transforming factor might be a gene.

Avery and DNA

In 1944, a group of scientists led by Canadian biologist Oswald Avery at the Rockefeller Institute in New York decided to repeat Griffith's work. They did so to determine which molecule in the heat-killed bacteria was most important for transformation. If transformation required just one particular molecule, that might well be the molecule of the gene.

Avery and his colleagues made an extract, or juice, from the heat-killed bacteria. They then carefully treated the extract with enzymes that destroyed proteins, lipids, carbohydrates, and other molecules, including the nucleic acid RNA. Transformation still occurred. Obviously, since these molecules had been destroyed, they were not responsible for the transformation.

Avery and the other scientists repeated the experiment, this time using enzymes that would break down DNA. When they destroyed the nucleic acid DNA in the extract, transformation did not occur. There was just one possible conclusion. DNA was the transforming factor. **Avery and other scientists discovered that the nucleic acid DNA stores and transmits the genetic information from one generation of an organism to the next.**

The Hershey-Chase Experiment

Scientists are a skeptical group. It usually takes several experiments to convince them of something as important as the chemical nature of the gene. The most important of these experiments was performed in 1952 by two American scientists, Alfred Hershey and Martha Chase. They collaborated in studying viruses, nonliving particles smaller than a cell that can infect living organisms.

Bacteriophages One kind of virus that infects bacteria is known as a **bacteriophage** (bak-TEER-ee-uh-fayj), which means "bacteria eater." **Figure 12–3** shows typical bacteriophages. Bacteriophages are composed of a DNA or RNA core and a protein coat. When a bacteriophage enters a bacterium, the virus attaches to the surface of the cell and injects its genetic information into it. The viral genes act to produce many new bacteriophages, and they gradually destroy the bacterium. When the cell splits open, hundreds of new viruses burst out.

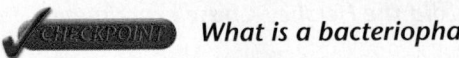

What is a bacteriophage?

▼ **Figure 12–3** A bacteriophage is a type of virus that infects and kills bacteria. This image shows two T2 bacteriophages (purple) invading an *E. coli* cell (green). **Comparing and Contrasting** *How large are viruses compared with bacteria?*

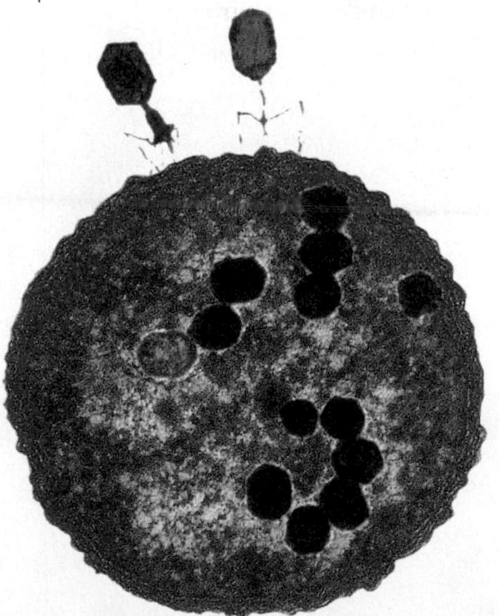

(magnification: 25,000×)

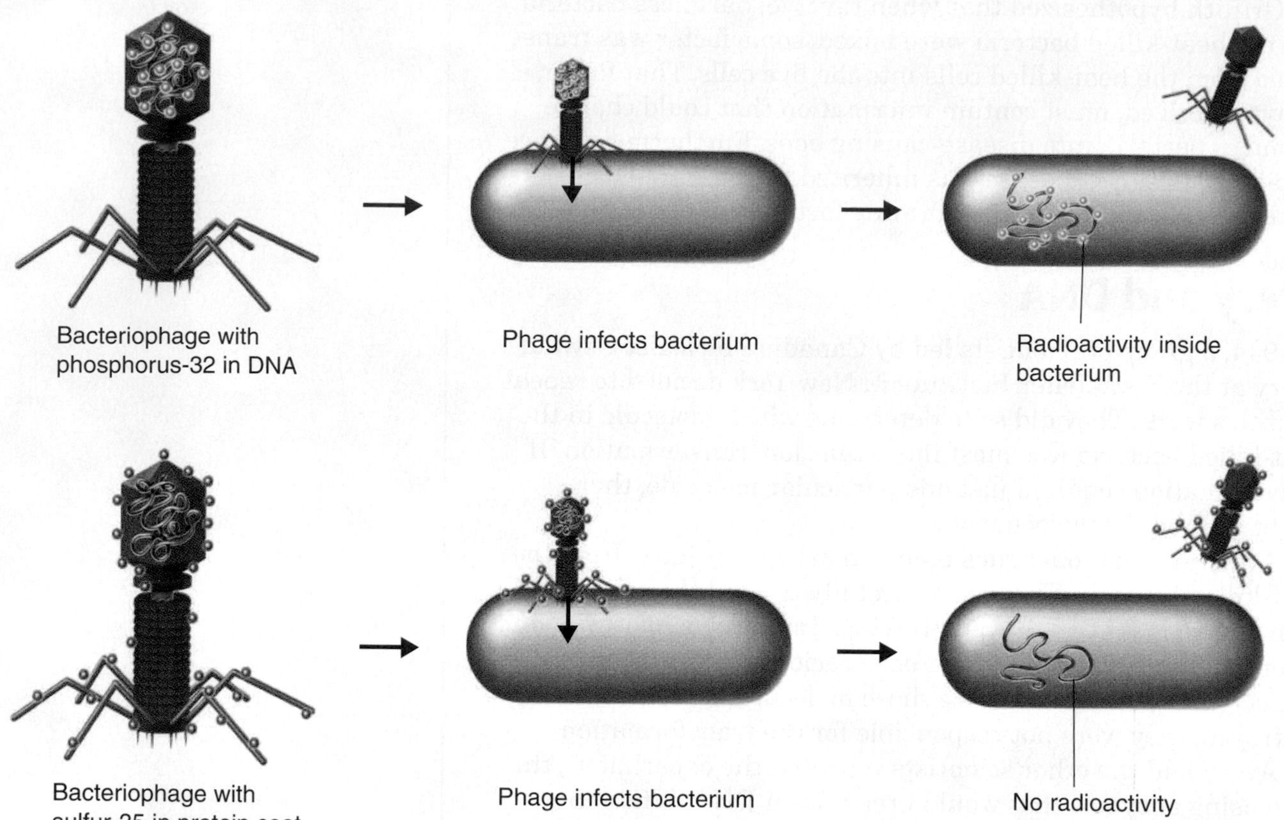

▲ **Figure 12–4** Alfred Hershey and Martha Chase used different radioactive markers to label the DNA and proteins of bacteriophages. The bacteriophages injected only DNA into the bacteria, not proteins. **From these results, Hershey and Chase concluded that the genetic material of the bacteriophage was DNA.**

Radioactive Markers Hershey and Chase reasoned that if they could determine which part of the virus—the protein coat or the DNA core—entered the infected cell, they would learn whether genes were made of protein or DNA. To do this, they grew viruses in cultures containing radioactive isotopes of phosphorus-32 (^{32}P) and sulfur-35 (^{35}S). This was a clever strategy because proteins contain almost no phosphorus and DNA contains no sulfur. The radioactive substances could be used as markers. If ^{35}S was found in the bacteria, it would mean that the viruses' protein had been injected into the bacteria. If ^{32}P was found in the bacteria, then it was the DNA that had been injected.

The Hershey-Chase experiment is shown in **Figure 12–4.** The two scientists mixed the marked viruses with bacteria. Then, they waited a few minutes for the viruses to inject their genetic material. Next, they separated the viruses from the bacteria and tested the bacteria for radioactivity. Nearly all the radioactivity in the bacteria was from phosphorus (^{32}P), the marker found in DNA. **Hershey and Chase concluded that the genetic material of the bacteriophage was DNA, not protein.**

CHECKPOINT *What part of the virus did the Hershey-Chase experiment show had entered the bacteria?*

The Components and Structure of DNA

For: Links on DNA
Visit: www.SciLinks.org
Web Code: cbn-4121

You might think that knowing genes were made of DNA would have satisfied scientists, but that was not the case at all. Instead, they wondered how DNA, or any molecule for that matter, could do the three critical things that genes were known to do: First, genes had to carry information from one generation to the next; second, they had to put that information to work by determining the heritable characteristics of organisms; and third, genes had to be easily copied, because all of a cell's genetic information is replicated every time a cell divides. For DNA to do all of that, it would have to be a very special molecule indeed.

DNA is a long molecule made up of units called **nucleotides.** As **Figure 12–5** shows, each nucleotide is made up of three basic components: a 5-carbon sugar called deoxyribose, a phosphate group, and a nitrogenous (nitrogen-containing) base. There are four kinds of nitrogenous bases in DNA. Two of the nitrogenous bases, adenine (AD-uh-neen) and guanine (GWAH-neen), belong to a group of compounds known as purines. The remaining two bases, cytosine (SY-tuh-zeen) and thymine (THY-meen), are known as pyrimidines. Purines have two rings in their structures, whereas pyrimidines have one ring.

The backbone of a DNA chain is formed by sugar and phosphate groups of each nucleotide. The nitrogenous bases stick out sideways from the chain. The nucleotides can be joined together in any order, meaning that any sequence of bases is possible.

If you don't see much in **Figure 12–5** that could explain the remarkable properties of the gene, don't be surprised. In the 1940s and early 1950s, the leading biologists in the world thought of DNA as little more than a string of nucleotides. They were baffled, too. The four different nucleotides, like the 26 letters of the alphabet, could be strung together in many different ways, so it was possible they could carry coded genetic information. However, so could many other molecules, at least in principle. Was there something more to the structure of DNA?

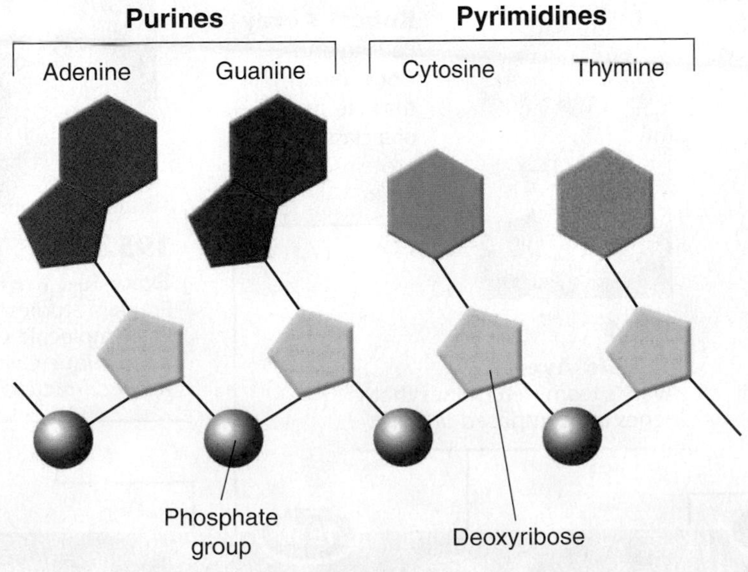

◀ **Figure 12–5** DNA is made up of nucleotides. Each nucleotide has three parts: a deoxyribose molecule, a phosphate group, and a nitrogenous base. There are four different bases in DNA: adenine, guanine, cytosine, and thymine. **Interpreting Graphics** *How are the nucleotides joined together to form the DNA chain?*

Source of DNA	A	T	G	C
Streptococcus	29.8	31.6	20.5	18.0
Yeast	31.3	32.9	18.7	17.1
Herring	27.8	27.5	22.2	22.6
Human	30.9	29.4	19.9	19.8

Percentages of Bases in Four Organisms

▲ **Figure 12–6** Erwin Chargaff showed that the percentages of guanine and cytosine in DNA are almost equal. The same is true for adenine and thymine. **Interpreting Graphics** *Which organism has the highest percentage of adenine?*

Chargaff's Rules One of the puzzling facts about DNA was a curious relationship between its nucleotides. Years earlier, Erwin Chargaff, an American biochemist, had discovered that the percentages of guanine [G] and cytosine [C] bases are almost equal in any sample of DNA. The same thing is true for the other two nucleotides, adenine [A] and thymine [T], as shown in **Figure 12–6.** The observation that [A] = [T] and [G] = [C] became known as Chargaff's rules. Despite the fact that DNA samples from organisms as different as bacteria and humans obeyed this rule, neither Chargaff nor anyone else had the faintest idea why.

X-Ray Evidence In the early 1950s, a British scientist named Rosalind Franklin began to study DNA. She used a technique called X-ray diffraction to get information about the structure of the DNA molecule. Aiming a powerful X-ray beam at concentrated DNA samples, she recorded the scattering pattern of the X-rays on film. Franklin worked hard to make better and better patterns from DNA until the patterns became clear.

Biology and History

Discovering the Role of DNA

Genes and the laws of heredity were discovered before scientists identified the molecules that genes are made of. With the discovery of DNA, scientists have been able to explain how genes are replicated and how they function.

1928
Frederick Griffith
Griffith discovers that a factor in heat-killed, disease-causing bacteria can "transform" harmless bacteria into ones that can cause disease.

1944
Oswald Avery
Avery's team determines that genes are composed of DNA.

1951
Linus Pauling
Robert Corey
Pauling and Corey determine that the structure of a class of proteins is a helix.

1952
Rosalind Franklin
Franklin studies the DNA molecule using a technique called X-ray diffraction.

1900 1925 1950

By itself, Franklin's X-ray pattern does not reveal the structure of DNA, but it does carry some very important clues. The X-shaped pattern in the photograph in the time line shows that the strands in DNA are twisted around each other like the coils of a spring, a shape known as a helix. The angle of the *X* suggests that there are two strands in the structure. Other clues suggest that the nitrogenous bases are near the center of the molecule.

What technique did Franklin use to study DNA?

The Double Helix At the same time that Franklin was continuing her research, Francis Crick, a British physicist, and James Watson, an American biologist, were trying to understand the structure of DNA by building three-dimensional models of the molecule. Their models were made of cardboard and wire. They twisted and stretched the models in various ways, but their best efforts did nothing to explain DNA's properties.

Then, early in 1953, Watson was shown a copy of Franklin's remarkable X-ray pattern. The effect was immediate. In his book *The Double Helix,* Watson wrote: "The instant I saw the picture my mouth fell open and my pulse began to race." Using clues from Franklin's pattern, within weeks Watson and Crick had built a structural model that explained the puzzle of how DNA could carry information, and how it could be copied. They published their results in a historic one-page paper in April of 1953. **Watson and Crick's model of DNA was a double helix, in which two strands were wound around each other.**

Writing in Science

Do research in the library or on the Internet to find out what James Watson or Francis Crick has worked on since discovering the structure of DNA. Organize your findings about the scientist's work and write a short essay describing it.

1953
James Watson
Francis Crick
Watson and Crick develop the double-helix model of the structure of DNA.

1960
Sydney Brenner
Brenner and other scientists show the existence of messenger RNA.

1977
Walter Gilbert
Gilbert, Allan Maxam, and Frederick Sanger develop methods to read the DNA sequence.

2000
Human Genome Project
The Human Genome Project—an attempt to sequence all human DNA—is essentially complete.

1950 1975 2000

Figure 12–7 **DNA is a double helix in which two strands are wound around each other.** Each strand is made up of a chain of nucleotides. The two strands are held together by hydrogen bonds between adenine and thymine and between guanine and cytosine.

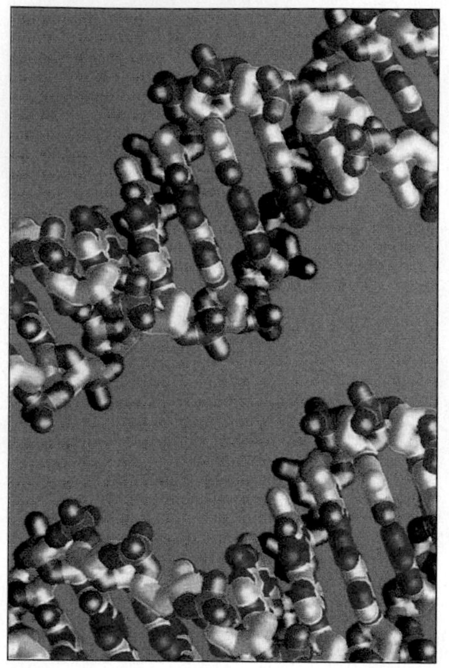

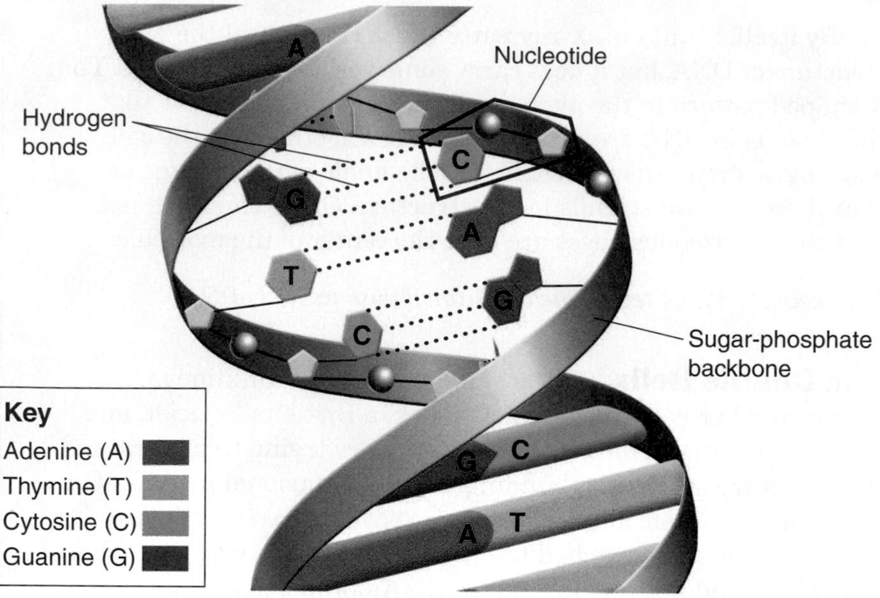

A double helix looks like a twisted ladder or a spiral staircase. When Watson and Crick evaluated their DNA model, they realized that the double helix accounted for many of the features in Franklin's X-ray pattern but did not explain what forces held the two strands together. They then discovered that hydrogen bonds could form between certain nitrogenous bases and provide just enough force to hold the two strands together. As **Figure 12–7** shows, hydrogen bonds can form only between certain base pairs—adenine and thymine, and guanine and cytosine. Once they saw this, they realized that this principle, called **base pairing,** explained Chargaff's rules. Now there was a reason that [A] = [T] and [G] = [C]. For every adenine in a double-stranded DNA molecule, there had to be exactly one thymine molecule; for each cytosine molecule, there was one guanine molecule.

12–1 Section Assessment

1. **Key Concept** List the conclusions Griffith, Avery, Hershey, and Chase drew from their experiments.
2. **Key Concept** Describe Watson and Crick's model of the DNA molecule.
3. What are the four kinds of bases found in DNA?
4. Did Watson and Crick's model account for the equal amounts of thymine and adenine in DNA? Explain.
5. **Critical Thinking Inferring** Why did Hershey and Chase grow viruses in cultures that contained both radioactive phosphorus and radioactive sulfur? What might have happened if they had used only one radioactive substance?

Connecting Concepts

Scientific Methods
Using the experiments of Griffith, Avery, or Hershey and Chase as an example, develop a flowchart that shows how the scientist or scientists used scientific processes. Be sure to identify each process. *Hint:* You may wish to review Chapter 1, which describes scientific methods.

12–2 Chromosomes and DNA Replication

4-2.1 Heredity
4-2.1 Genes and chromosomes in the nucleus
4-2.1 DNA carries the genetic code and can replicate
LS- Analyze results

DNA is present in such large amounts in many tissues that it's easy to extract and analyze. But where is DNA found in the cell? How is it organized? Where are the genes that Mendel first described a century and a half ago?

Guide for Reading

Key Concept
- What happens during DNA replication?

Vocabulary
chromatin
histone
replication
DNA polymerase

Reading Strategy: Asking Questions Before you read, study the diagram in **Figure 12–11.** Make a list of questions about the diagram. As you read, write down the answers to your questions.

DNA and Chromosomes

Prokaryotic cells lack nuclei and many of the organelles found in eukaryotes. Their DNA molecules are located in the cytoplasm. Most prokaryotes have a single circular DNA molecule that contains nearly all of the cell's genetic information. This large DNA molecule is usually referred to as the cell's chromosome, as shown in **Figure 12–8.**

Eukaryotic DNA is a bit more complicated. Many eukaryotes have as much as 1000 times the amount of DNA as prokaryotes. This DNA is not found free in the cytoplasm. Eukaryotic DNA is generally located in the cell nucleus in the form of a number of chromosomes. The number of chromosomes varies widely from one species to the next. For example, diploid human cells have 46 chromosomes, *Drosophila* cells have 8, and giant sequoia tree cells have 22.

DNA Length DNA molecules are surprisingly long. The chromosome of the prokaryote *E. coli,* which can live in the human colon (large intestine), contains 4,639,221 base pairs. The length of such a DNA molecule is roughly 1.6 mm, which doesn't sound like much until you think about the small size of a bacterium. To fit inside a typical bacterium, the DNA molecule must be folded into a space only one one-thousandth of its length.

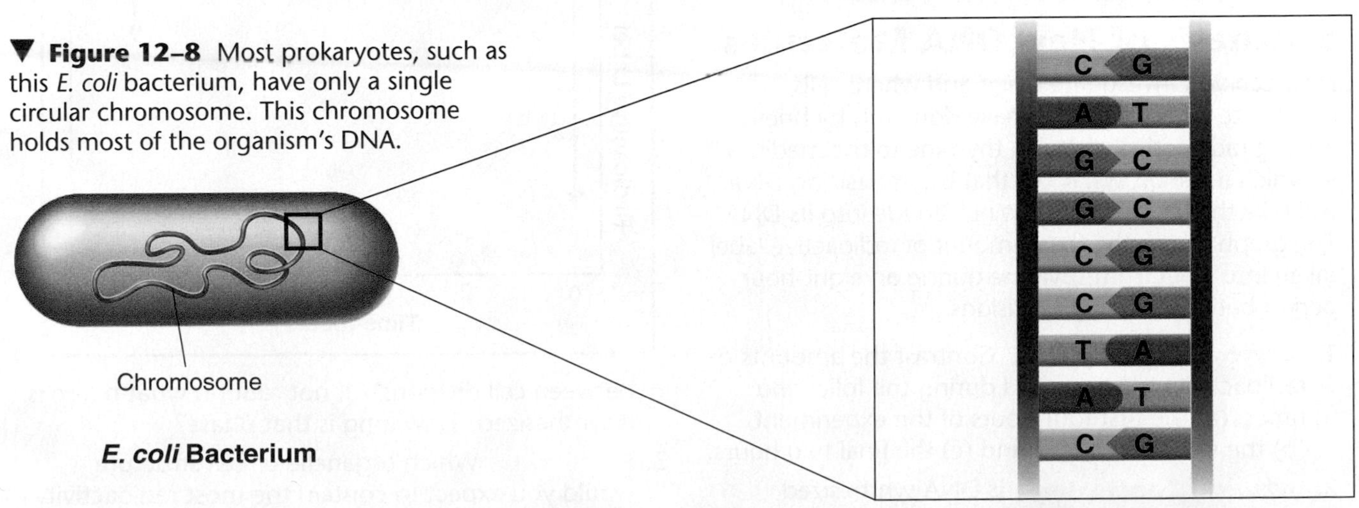

▼ **Figure 12–8** Most prokaryotes, such as this *E. coli* bacterium, have only a single circular chromosome. This chromosome holds most of the organism's DNA.

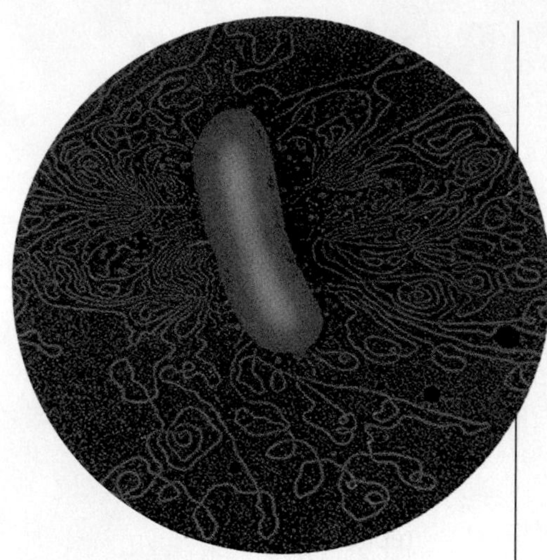

▲ **Figure 12–9** The DNA in a bacterium is about 1000 times as long as the bacterium itself. It must therefore be very tightly folded. **Using Analogies** *Compare DNA in a bacterium to a rope jammed into a backpack.*

To get a rough idea of what this means, think of a large school backpack. Then, imagine trying to pack a 300-meter length of rope into the backpack! **Figure 12–9,** which shows DNA spilling out from a ruptured bacterium, indicates how dramatically the DNA must be folded to fit within the cell.

Chromosome Structure The DNA in eukaryotic cells is packed even more tightly. A human cell contains almost 1000 times as many base pairs of DNA as a bacterium. The nucleus of a human cell contains more than 1 meter of DNA. How is so much DNA folded into tiny chromosomes? The answer can be found in the composition of eukaryotic chromosomes.

Eukaryotic chromosomes contain both DNA and protein, tightly packed together to form a substance called **chromatin.** Chromatin consists of DNA that is tightly coiled around proteins called **histones,** as shown in **Figure 12–10.** Together, the DNA and histone molecules form a beadlike structure called a nucleosome. Nucleosomes pack with one another to form a thick fiber, which is shortened by a system of loops and coils.

During most of the cell cycle, these fibers are dispersed in the nucleus so that individual chromosomes are not visible. During mitosis, however, the fibers of each individual chromosome are drawn together, forming the tightly packed chromosomes you can see through a light microscope in dividing cells. The tight packing of nucleosomes may help separate chromosomes during mitosis. There is also some evidence that changes in chromatin structure and histone-DNA binding are associated with changes in gene activity and expression.

Analyzing Data

Synthesis of New DNA Molecules

How can you investigate when and where cells synthesize DNA? Scientists have done this by briefly adding radioactively labeled thymine to the medium in which a cell grows. A cell that is synthesizing DNA will take the labeled thymine nucleotide into its DNA. The graph shows the total amount of radioactive label taken into DNA from thymine during an eight-hour period between two cell divisions.

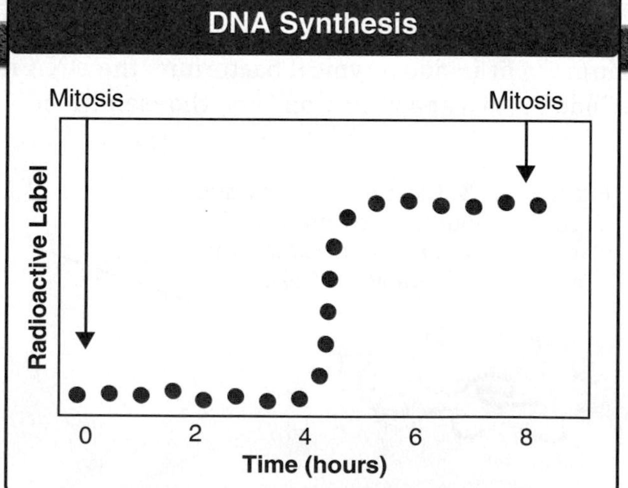

1. **Interpreting Graphics** Contrast the amounts of radioactivity incorporated during the following times: (a) the first four hours of the experiment, (b) the next two hours, and (c) the final two hours.
2. **Drawing Conclusions** Is DNA synthesized continually during the cell cycle (the period between cell divisions)? If not, during what phase is it synthesized? How long is that phase?
3. **Predicting** Which organelle or cell structure would you expect to contain the most radioactivity after this experiment? Explain.

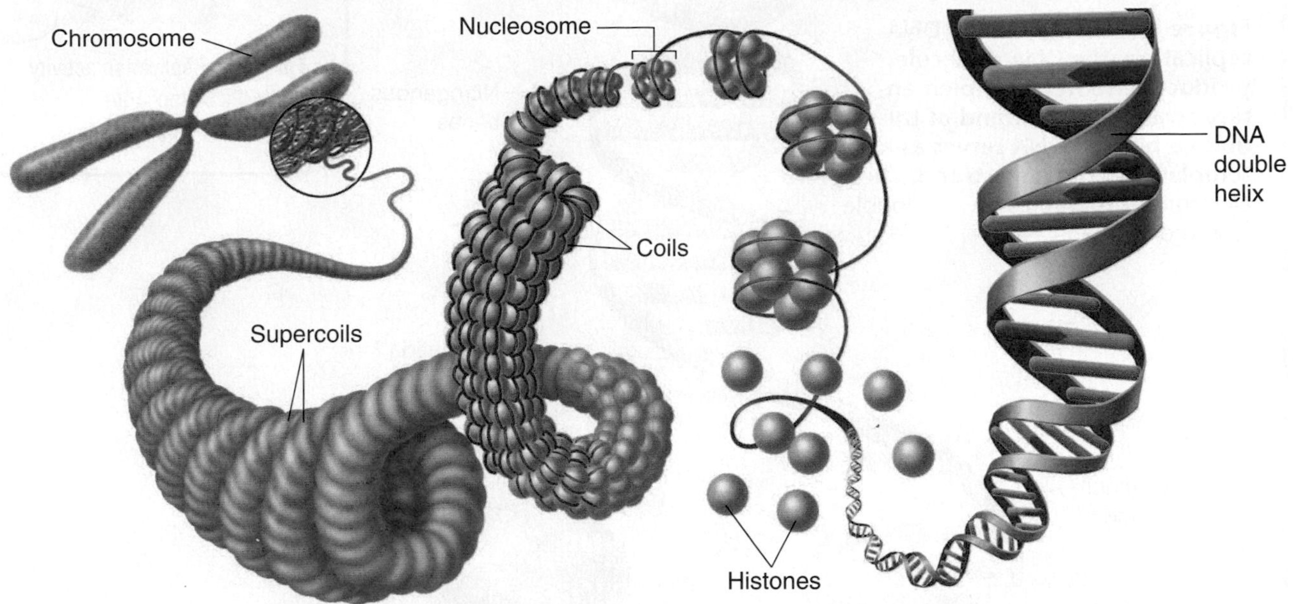

▲ **Figure 12–10** Eukaryotic chromosomes contain DNA wrapped around proteins called histones. The strands of nucleosomes are tightly coiled and supercoiled to form chromosomes. **Interpreting Graphics** ***What is each DNA-histone complex called?***

What do nucleosomes do? Nucleosomes seem to be able to fold enormous lengths of DNA into the tiny space available in the cell nucleus. This is such an important function that the histone proteins themselves have changed very little during evolution—probably because mistakes in DNA folding could harm a cell's ability to reproduce.

What is chromatin?

DNA Replication

When Watson and Crick discovered the double helix structure of DNA, there was one more remarkable aspect that they recognized immediately. The structure explained how DNA could be copied, or replicated. Each strand of the DNA double helix has all the information needed to reconstruct the other half by the mechanism of base pairing. Because each strand can be used to make the other strand, the strands are said to be complementary. If you could separate the two strands, the rules of base pairing would allow you to reconstruct the base sequence of the other strand.

In most prokaryotes, DNA replication begins at a single point in the chromosome and proceeds, often in two directions, until the entire chromosome is replicated. In the larger eukaryotic chromosomes, DNA replication occurs at hundreds of places. Replication proceeds in both directions until each chromosome is completely copied. The sites where separation and replication occur are called replication forks.

DNA Replication

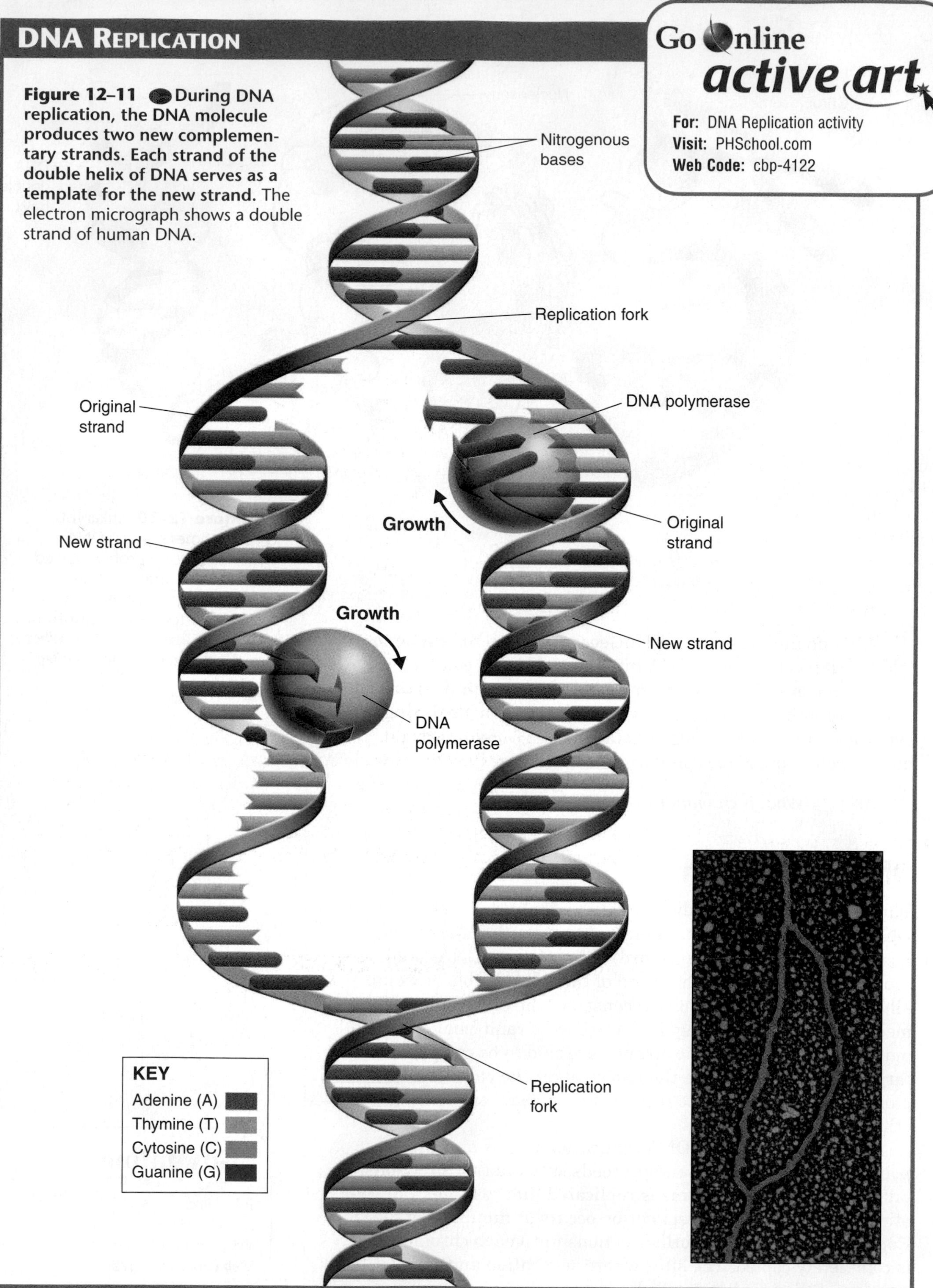

Figure 12–11 During DNA replication, the DNA molecule produces two new complementary strands. Each strand of the double helix of DNA serves as a template for the new strand. The electron micrograph shows a double strand of human DNA.

Duplicating DNA Before a cell divides, it duplicates its DNA in a copying process called **replication.** This process ensures that each resulting cell will have a complete set of DNA molecules. **During DNA replication, the DNA molecule separates into two strands, then produces two new complementary strands following the rules of base pairing. Each strand of the double helix of DNA serves as a template, or model, for the new strand.**

Figure 12–11 shows the process of DNA replication. The two strands of the double helix have separated, allowing two replication forks to form. As each new strand forms, new bases are added following the rules of base pairing. In other words, if the base on the old strand is adenine, thymine is added to the newly forming strand. Likewise, guanine is always paired to cytosine.

For example, a strand that has the bases TACGTT produces a strand with the complementary bases ATGCAA. The result is two DNA molecules identical to each other and to the original molecule. Note that each DNA molecule resulting from replication has one original strand and one new strand.

How Replication Occurs DNA replication is carried out by a series of enzymes. These enzymes "unzip" a molecule of DNA. The unzipping occurs when the hydrogen bonds between the base pairs are broken and the two strands of the molecule unwind. Each strand serves as a template for the attachment of complementary bases.

DNA replication involves a host of enzymes and regulatory molecules. You may recall that enzymes are highly specific. For this reason, they are often named for the reactions they catalyze. The principal enzyme involved in DNA replication is called **DNA polymerase** (PAHL-ih-mur-ayz) because it joins individual nucleotides to produce a DNA molecule, which is, of course, a polymer. DNA polymerase also "proofreads" each new DNA strand, helping to maximize the odds that each molecule is a perfect copy of the original DNA.

12–2 Section Assessment

1. **Key Concept** Explain how DNA is replicated.
2. Where and in what form is eukaryotic DNA found?
3. How are the long DNA molecules found in eukaryotes packed into short chromosomes?
4. How are histones related to nucleosomes?
5. What is the role of DNA polymerase in DNA replication?
6. **Critical Thinking Comparing and Contrasting** How is the structure of chromosomes in eukaryotes different from the structure of chromosomes in prokaryotes?

Thinking Visually

Creating a Venn Diagram
Make a Venn diagram that compares the process of DNA replication in prokaryotes and eukaryotes. Compare the location, steps, and end products of the process in each kind of cell. (For more on Venn diagrams, see Appendix A.)

12–3 RNA and Protein Synthesis

4-2.1 DNA
4-5.1 Organic compounds are used to assemble molecules
LS- Make observations

Guide for Reading

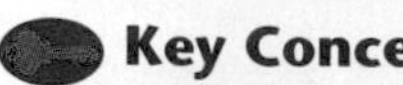

Key Concepts

- What are the three main types of RNA?
- What is transcription?
- What is translation?

Vocabulary

gene
messenger RNA
ribosomal RNA
transfer RNA
transcription
RNA polymerase
promoter
intron
exon
codon
translation
anticodon

Reading Strategy: Using Visuals Before you read, preview **Figure 12–18.** As you read, notice what happens in each step of translation, or protein synthesis.

The double helix structure explains how DNA can be copied, but it does not explain how a gene works. In molecular terms, **genes** are coded DNA instructions that control the production of proteins within the cell. The first step in decoding these genetic messages is to copy part of the nucleotide sequence from DNA into RNA, or ribonucleic acid. These RNA molecules contain coded information for making proteins.

The Structure of RNA

RNA, like DNA, consists of a long chain of nucleotides. As you may recall, each nucleotide is made up of a 5-carbon sugar, a phosphate group, and a nitrogenous base. There are three main differences between RNA and DNA: The sugar in RNA is ribose instead of deoxyribose, RNA is generally single-stranded, and RNA contains uracil in place of thymine.

You can think of an RNA molecule as a disposable copy of a segment of DNA. In many cases, an RNA molecule is a working copy of a single gene. The ability to copy a single DNA sequence into RNA makes it possible for a single gene to produce hundreds or even thousands of RNA molecules.

Types of RNA

RNA molecules have many functions, but in the majority of cells most RNA molecules are involved in just one job—protein synthesis. The assembly of amino acids into proteins is controlled by RNA. **There are three main types of RNA: messenger RNA, ribosomal RNA, and transfer RNA.** The structures of these molecules are shown in **Figure 12–12.**

▼ Figure 12–12 The three main types of RNA are messenger RNA, ribosomal RNA, and transfer RNA. Ribosomal RNA is combined with proteins to form ribosomes.

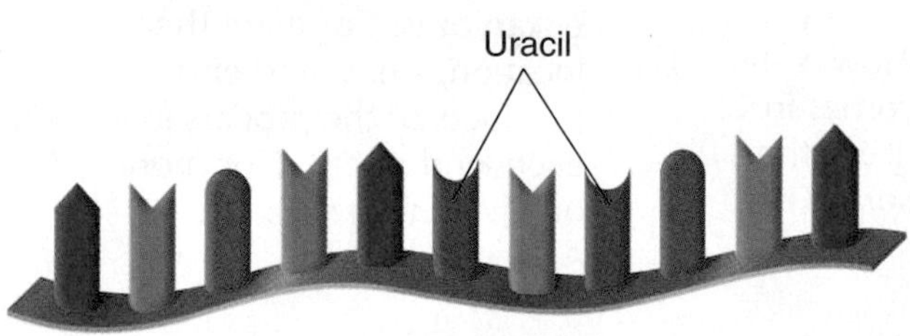

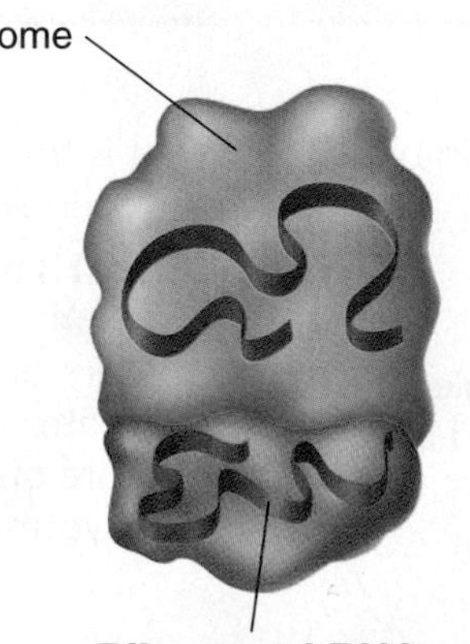

Most genes contain instructions for assembling amino acids into proteins. The RNA molecules that carry copies of these instructions are known as **messenger RNA** (mRNA) because they serve as "messengers" from DNA to the rest of the cell.

Proteins are assembled on ribosomes, shown in **Figure 12–13.** Ribosomes are made up of several dozen proteins, as well as a form of RNA known as **ribosomal RNA** (rRNA).

During the construction of a protein, a third type of RNA molecule transfers each amino acid to the ribosome as it is specified by coded messages in mRNA. These RNA molecules are known as **transfer RNA** (tRNA).

What are ribosomes made of?

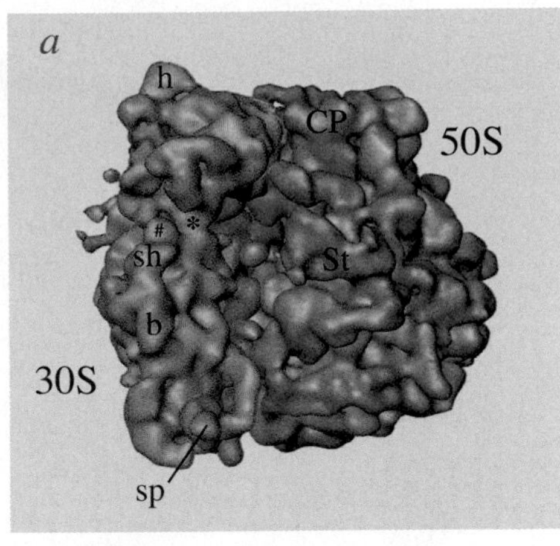

▲ **Figure 12–13** In this detailed model of a ribosome, the two subunits of the ribosome are shown in yellow and blue. The model was produced using cryo-electron microscopy. Data from more than 73,000 electron micrographs, taken at ultra-cold temperatures to preserve ribosome structure, were analyzed to produce the model.

Transcription

RNA molecules are produced by copying part of the nucleotide sequence of DNA into a complementary sequence in RNA, a process called **transcription.** Transcription requires an enzyme known as **RNA polymerase** that is similar to DNA polymerase. **During transcription, RNA polymerase binds to DNA and separates the DNA strands. RNA polymerase then uses one strand of DNA as a template from which nucleotides are assembled into a strand of RNA.** The process of transcription is shown in **Figure 12–14.**

How does RNA polymerase "know" where to start and stop making an RNA copy of DNA? The answer to this question begins with the observation that RNA polymerase doesn't bind to DNA just anywhere. The enzyme will bind only to regions of DNA known as **promoters,** which have specific base sequences. In effect, promoters are signals in DNA that indicate to the enzyme where to bind to make RNA. Similar signals in DNA cause transcription to stop when the new RNA molecule is completed.

▼ **Figure 12–14 During transcription, RNA polymerase uses one strand of DNA as a template to assemble nucleotides into a strand of RNA.**

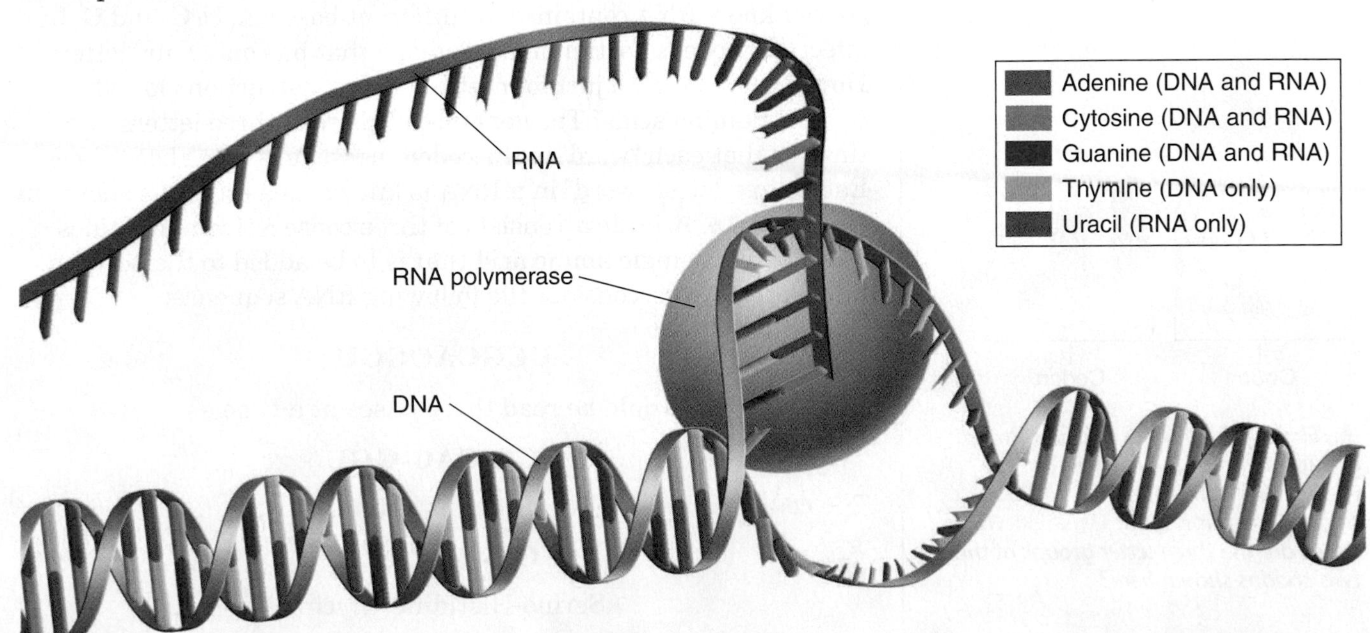

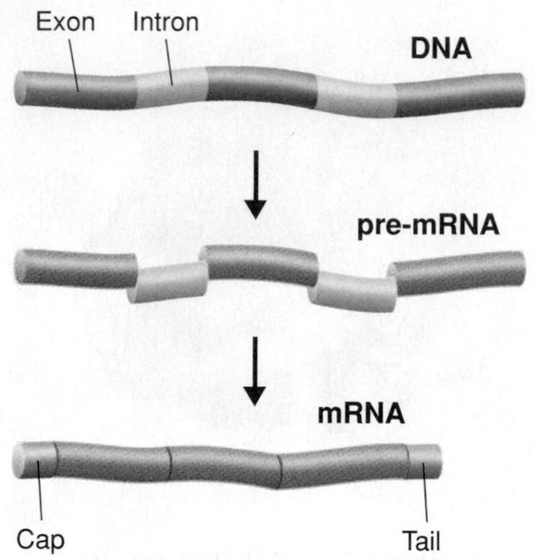

▲ **Figure 12–15** Many RNA molecules have sections, called introns, edited out of them before they become functional. The remaining pieces, called exons, are spliced together. Then, a cap and tail are added to form the final RNA molecule. **Predicting** *What do you think would happen if the introns were not removed from the pre-mRNA?*

RNA Editing

Like a writer's first draft, many RNA molecules require a bit of editing before they are ready to go into action. Remember that an RNA molecule is produced by copying DNA. Surprisingly, the DNA of eukaryotic genes contains sequences of nucleotides, called **introns,** that are not involved in coding for proteins. The DNA sequences that code for proteins are called **exons** because they are "expressed" in the synthesis of proteins. When RNA molecules are formed, both the introns and the exons are copied from the DNA. However, the introns are cut out of RNA molecules while they are still in the nucleus. The remaining exons are then spliced back together to form the final mRNA as shown in **Figure 12–15.**

Why do cells use energy to make a large RNA molecule and then throw parts of it away? That's a good question, and biologists still do not have a complete answer to it. Some RNA molecules may be cut and spliced in different ways in different tissues, making it possible for a single gene to produce several different forms of RNA. Introns and exons may also play a role in evolution. This would make it possible for very small changes in DNA sequences to have dramatic effects in gene expression.

What are introns and exons?

The Genetic Code

Proteins are made by joining amino acids into long chains called polypeptides. Each polypeptide contains a combination of any or all of the 20 different amino acids. The properties of proteins are determined by the order in which different amino acids are joined together to produce polypeptides. How, you might wonder, can a particular order of nitrogenous bases in DNA and RNA molecules be translated into a particular order of amino acids in a polypeptide?

The "language" of mRNA instructions is called the genetic code. As you know, RNA contains four different bases: A, U, C, and G. In effect, the code is written in a language that has only four "letters." How can a code with just four letters carry instructions for 20 different amino acids? The genetic code is read three letters at a time, so that each "word" of the coded message is three bases long. Each three-letter "word" in mRNA is known as a codon, as shown in **Figure 12–16.** A **codon** consists of three consecutive nucleotides that specify a single amino acid that is to be added to the polypeptide. For example, consider the following RNA sequence:

UCGCACGGU

This sequence would be read three bases at a time as:

UCG-CAC-GGU

The codons represent the different amino acids:

UCG-CAC-GGU

Serine-Histidine-Glycine

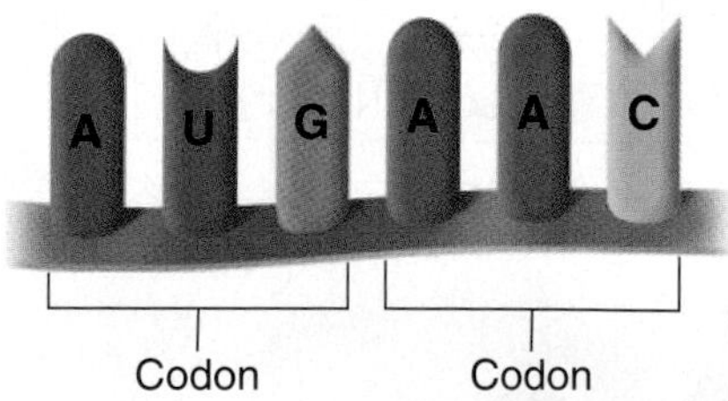

▲ **Figure 12–16** A codon is a group of three nucleotides on messenger RNA that specify a particular amino acid. **Observing** *What are the three-letter groups of the two codons shown here?*

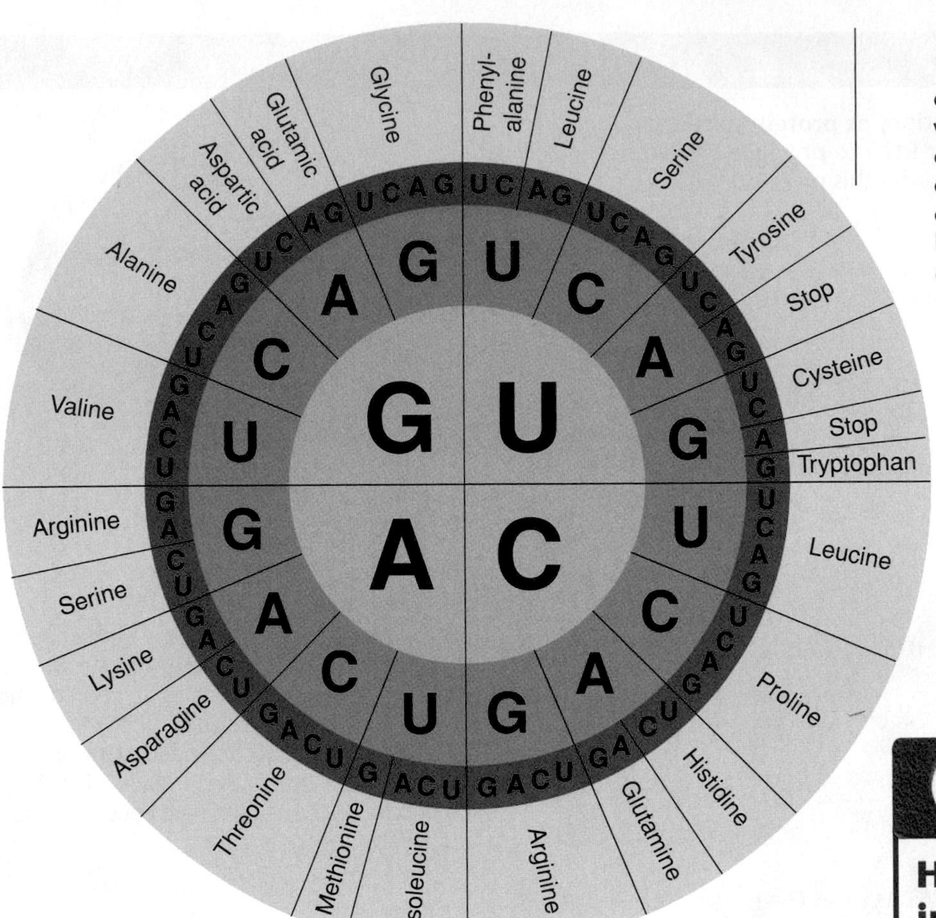

◀ **Figure 12–17** The genetic code shows the amino acid to which each of the 64 possible codons corresponds. To decode a codon, start at the middle of the circle and move outward. **Interpreting Graphics** *For what amino acid does the codon UGC code?*

Because there are four different bases, there are 64 possible three-base codons ($4 \times 4 \times 4 = 64$). **Figure 12–17** shows all 64 possible codons of the genetic code. As you can see, some amino acids can be specified by more than one codon. For example, six different codons specify the amino acid leucine, and six others specify arginine.

There is also one codon, AUG, that can either specify methionine or serve as the initiation, or "start," codon for protein synthesis. Notice also that there are three "stop" codons that do not code for any amino acid. Stop codons act like the period at the end of a sentence; they signify the end of a polypeptide, which consists of many amino acids.

Translation

The sequence of nucleotide bases in an mRNA molecule serves as instructions for the order in which amino acids should be joined together to produce a polypeptide. However, anyone who has tried to assemble a complex toy knows that instructions generally don't do the job themselves. They need something to read them and put them to use. In the cell, that "something" is a tiny factory called the ribosome.

Quick Lab

How does a cell interpret DNA?

Procedure

1. A certain gene has the following sequence of nucleotides:
   GACAAGTCCACAATC
   Write this sequence on a sheet of paper.
2. From left to right, write the sequence of the mRNA molecule transcribed from this gene.
3. Look at **Figure 12–17.** Reading the mRNA codons from left to right, write the amino acid sequence of the polypeptide translated from the mRNA.
4. Repeat step 3, reading the codons from right to left.

Analyze and Conclude

1. **Applying Concepts** Why did steps 3 and 4 produce different polypeptides?
2. **Inferring** Do cells usually decode nucleotides in one direction only or in either direction?

TRANSLATION

Figure 12–18 During translation, or protein synthesis, the cell uses information from messenger RNA to produce proteins. The cell uses all three main forms of RNA during this process.

A Messenger RNA
Messenger RNA is transcribed in the nucleus, then enters the cytoplasm and attaches to a ribosome.

Nucleus
A U G U U C A A A
mRNA
Lysine
Phenylalanine
tRNA
Methionine

B Transfer RNA
Translation begins at AUG, the start codon. Each transfer RNA has an anticodon whose bases are complementary to a codon on the mRNA strand. The ribosome positions the start codon to attract its anticodon, which is part of the tRNA that binds methionine. The ribosome also binds the next codon and its anticodon.

U U U
Ribosome
U A C A A G
A U G U U C A A A
mRNA
Start codon

The decoding of an mRNA message into a polypeptide chain (protein) is known as **translation.** Translation takes place on ribosomes. **During translation, the cell uses information from messenger RNA to produce proteins.** Refer to **Figure 12–18** as you read about translation.

A Before translation occurs, messenger RNA is transcribed from DNA in the nucleus and released into the cytoplasm.

B Translation begins when an mRNA molecule in the cytoplasm attaches to a ribosome. As each codon of the mRNA molecule moves through the ribosome, the proper amino acid is brought into the ribosome by tRNA. In the ribosome, the amino acid is transferred to the growing polypeptide chain.

Each tRNA molecule carries only one kind of amino acid. For example, some tRNA molecules carry methionine, others carry arginine, and still others carry serine. In addition to an amino acid, each tRNA molecule has three unpaired bases. These bases, called the **anticodon,** are complementary to one mRNA codon.

C The Polypeptide "Assembly Line"
The ribosome joins the two amino acids—methionine and phenylalanine—and breaks the bond between methionine and its tRNA. The tRNA floats away from the ribosome, allowing the ribosome to bind another tRNA. The ribosome moves along the mRNA, binding new tRNA molecules and amino acids.

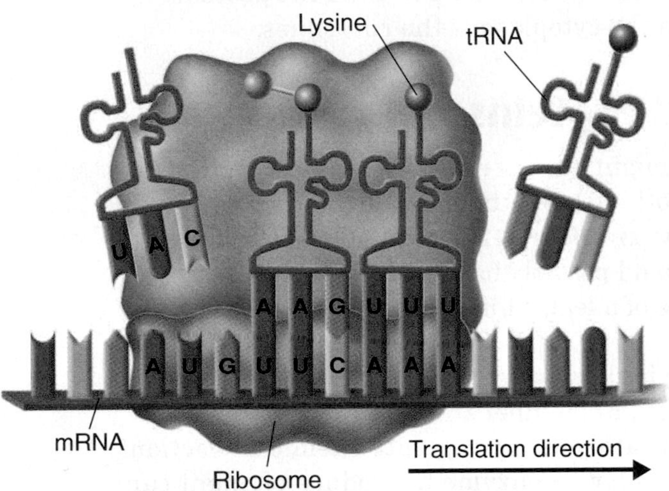

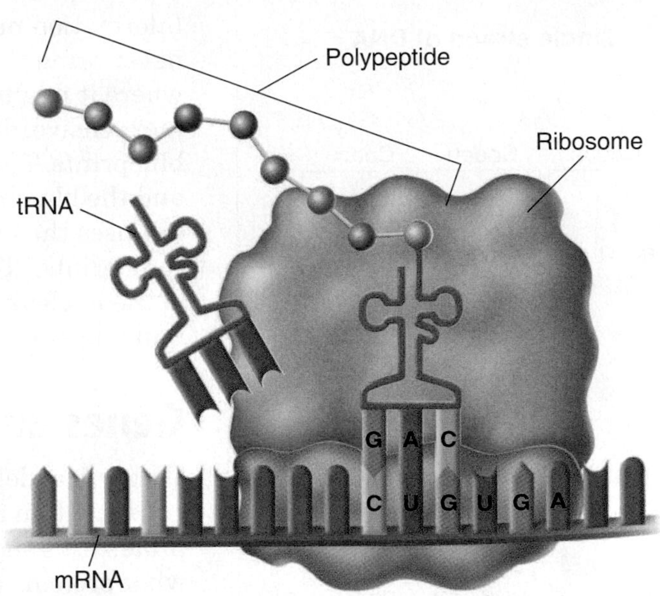

D Completing the Polypeptide
The process continues until the ribosome reaches one of the three stop codons. The result is a complete polypeptide.

Go Online
active art
For: Protein Synthesis activity
Visit: PHSchool.com
Web Code: cbp-4123

In the case of the tRNA molecule for methionine, the anticodon bases are UAC, which pair with the methionine codon, AUG. The ribosome has a second binding site for a tRNA molecule for the next codon. If that next codon is UUC, a tRNA molecule with an AAG anticodon would fit against the mRNA molecule held in the ribosome. That second tRNA molecule would bring the amino acid phenylalanine into the ribosome.

C Like an assembly line worker who attaches one part to another, the ribosome forms a peptide bond between the first and second amino acids, methionine and phenylalanine. At the same time, the ribosome breaks the bond that had held the first tRNA molecule to its amino acid and releases the tRNA molecule. The ribosome then moves to the third codon, where a tRNA molecule brings it the amino acid specified by the third codon.

D The polypeptide chain continues to grow until the ribosome reaches a stop codon on the mRNA molecule. When the ribosome reaches a stop codon, it releases the newly formed polypeptide and the mRNA molecule, completing the process of translation.

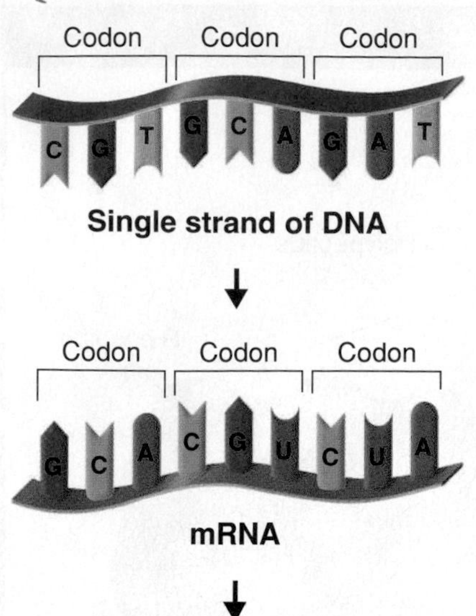

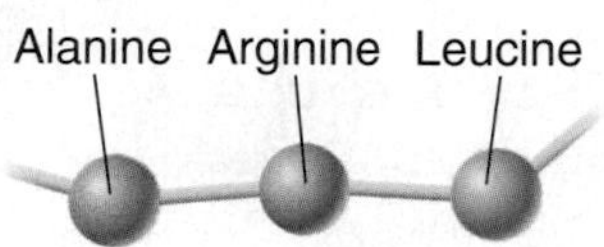

▲ **Figure 12–19** This diagram illustrates how information for specifying the traits of an organism is carried in DNA. The sequence of bases in DNA is used as a template for mRNA. The codons of mRNA specify the sequence of amino acids in a protein, and proteins play a key role in producing an organism's traits.

The Roles of RNA and DNA

You can compare the different roles played by DNA and RNA molecules in directing protein synthesis to the two types of plans used by builders. A master plan has all the information needed to construct a building. But builders never bring the valuable master plan to the building site, where it might be damaged or lost. Instead, they prepare inexpensive, disposable copies of the master plan called blueprints. The master plan is safely stored in an office, and the blueprints are taken to the job site. Similarly, the cell uses the vital DNA "master plan" to prepare RNA "blueprints." The DNA molecule remains within the safety of the nucleus, while RNA molecules go to the protein-building sites in the cytoplasm—the ribosomes.

Genes and Proteins

Gregor Mendel might have been surprised to learn that most genes contain nothing more than instructions for assembling proteins, as shown in **Figure 12–19.** He might have asked what proteins could possibly have to do with the color of a flower, the shape of a leaf, a human blood type, or the sex of a newborn baby.

The answer is that proteins have everything to do with these things. Remember that many proteins are enzymes, which catalyze and regulate chemical reactions. A gene that codes for an enzyme to produce pigment can control the color of a flower. Another gene produces an enzyme specialized for the production of red blood cell surface antigen. This molecule determines your blood type. Genes for certain proteins can regulate the rate and pattern of growth throughout an organism, controlling its size and shape. In short, proteins are microscopic tools, each specifically designed to build or operate a component of a living cell.

12–3 Section Assessment

1. **Key Concept** List the three main types of RNA.
2. **Key Concept** What happens during transcription?
3. **Key Concept** What happens during translation?
4. Describe the three main differences between RNA and DNA.
5. **Critical Thinking Applying Concepts** Using the genetic code, identify the amino acids that have the following messenger RNA strand codes: UGGCAGUGC.

Writing in Science

Creative Writing

An RNA molecule is looking for a job in a protein synthesis factory, and it asks you to write its résumé. This RNA molecule is not yet specialized and could, with some structural changes, function as either mRNA, tRNA, or rRNA. The résumé you create should reflect the qualifications needed for each type of RNA.

12–4 Mutations

4-2.1 Gene mutations are passed along when cells divide
4-2.1 Mutations involve changes in DNA segments (genes)
4-3.1 Mutations are random events
4-3.1 Inheritable characteristics can result from mutations

Now and then cells make mistakes in copying their own DNA, inserting an incorrect base or even skipping a base as the new strand is put together. These mistakes are called **mutations,** from a Latin word meaning "to change."  **Mutations are changes in the genetic material.**

Guide for Reading

Key Concept
- What are mutations?

Vocabulary
mutation
point mutation
frameshift mutation
polyploidy

Reading Strategy: Using Visuals Before you read, preview **Figure 12–20** and **Figure 12–21.** As you read, notice the changes that occur in gene and chromosomal mutations.

Kinds of Mutations

Like the mistakes that people make in their daily lives, mutations come in many shapes and sizes. Mutations that produce changes in a single gene are known as gene mutations. Those that produce changes in whole chromosomes are known as chromosomal mutations.

Gene Mutations Gene mutations involving changes in one or a few nucleotides are known as **point mutations,** because they occur at a single point in the DNA sequence. Point mutations include substitutions, in which one base is changed to another, as well as insertions and deletions, in which a base is inserted or removed from the DNA sequence.

Substitutions usually affect no more than a single amino acid. The effects of insertions or deletions can be much more dramatic. Remember that the genetic code is read in three-base codons. If a nucleotide is added or deleted, the bases are still read in groups of three, but now those groupings are shifted for every codon that follows, as shown in **Figure 12–20.** Changes like these are called **frameshift mutations** because they shift the "reading frame" of the genetic message. By shifting the reading frame, frameshift mutations may change every amino acid that follows the point of the mutation. Frameshift mutations can alter a protein so much that it is unable to perform its normal functions.

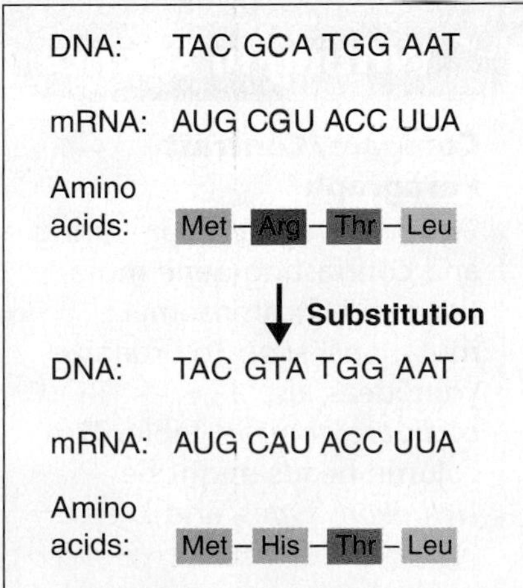

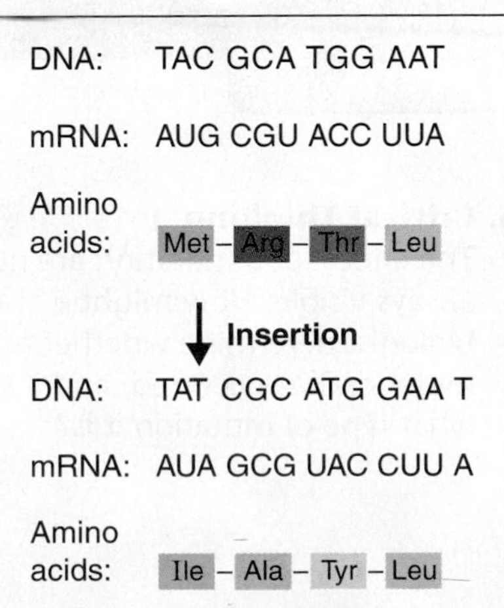

Figure 12–20 **Gene mutations result from changes in a single gene.** These diagrams illustrate the different types of mutations, or changes, in DNA. They also show how the mutations affect the amino acid sequences of the proteins for which they code. In a substitution (left), one base replaces another. In an insertion (center), an extra base is inserted into a base sequence. The loss of a single letter in a sentence (below) models the effects of the deletion of one base in a DNA sequence.

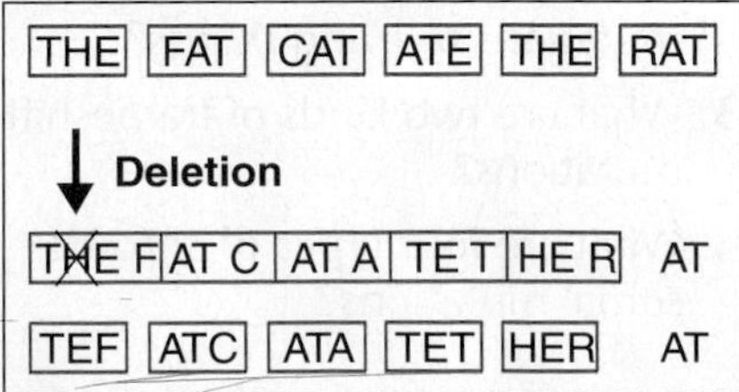

▼ **Figure 12–21** **Chromosomal mutations involve changes in whole chromosomes.** The illustration below shows four types of chromosomal mutations.

Original chromosome

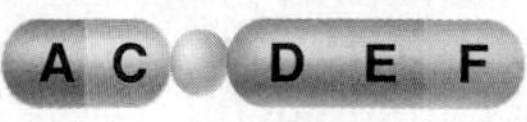

Deletion

Duplication

Inversion

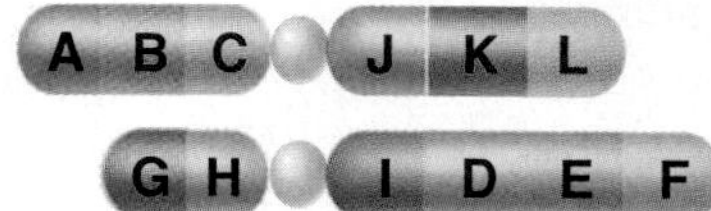

Translocation

Chromosomal Mutations Chromosomal mutations involve changes in the number or structure of chromosomes. Such mutations may change the locations of genes on chromosomes, and may even change the number of copies of some genes.

Figure 12–21 shows four types of chromosomal mutations: deletions, duplications, inversions, and translocations. Deletions involve the loss of all or part of a chromosome, while duplications produce extra copies of parts of a chromosome. Inversions reverse the direction of parts of chromosomes, and translocations occur when part of one chromosome breaks off and attaches to another.

Significance of Mutations

Many, if not most, mutations are neutral, meaning that they have little or no effect on the expression of genes or the function of the proteins for which they code. Mutations that cause dramatic changes in protein structure or gene activity are often harmful, producing defective proteins that disrupt normal biological activities. However, mutations are also the source of genetic variability in a species. Some of this variation may be highly beneficial.

Harmful mutations are the causes of many genetic disorders; you will learn about some human genetic disorders in Chapter 14. Harmful mutations are also associated with many types of cancer. In contrast, beneficial mutations may produce proteins with new or altered activities that can be useful to organisms in different or changing environments.

Plant and animal breeders often take advantage of such beneficial mutations. For example, when a complete set of chromosomes fails to separate during meiosis, the gametes that result may produce triploid (3N) or tetraploid (4N) organisms. The condition in which an organism has extra sets of chromosomes is called **polyploidy.** Polyploid plants are often larger and stronger than diploid plants. Important crop plants have been produced in this way, including bananas and many citrus fruits.

12–4 Section Assessment

1. **Key Concept** What is a mutation?
2. What is the significance of mutations to living things?
3. What are two kinds of frameshift mutations?
4. What are four types of chromosomal mutations?
5. **Critical Thinking Inferring** The effects of a mutation are not always visible. How might a biologist determine whether a mutation has occurred, and if so, what type of mutation it is?

Writing in Science

Compare/Contrast Paragraph

Write a paragraph comparing and contrasting gene mutations and chromosomal mutations. *Hint:* To organize your ideas, use a compare/contrast table. The column heads might be *Definition, Types,* and *Effects.*

12–5 Gene Regulation

4-2.1 Heredity specifies traits
4-2.1 Genes are segments of DNA molecules
4-2.1 Proteins are responsible for much of the work of cells
4-2.1 Differences between cells

Only a fraction of the genes in a cell are expressed at any given time. An expressed gene is a gene that is transcribed into RNA. How does the cell determine which genes will be expressed and which will remain "silent"? A close look at the structure of a gene provides some important clues.

At first glance, the DNA sequence of a gene is nothing more than a confusing jumble of the four letters that represent the bases in DNA. However, if we take the time to analyze those letters, patterns emerge. Molecular biologists have found that certain DNA sequences serve as promoters, binding sites for RNA polymerase. Others serve as start and stop signals for transcription. In fact, cells are filled with DNA-binding proteins that attach to specific DNA sequences and help to regulate gene expression. A typical gene might look something like **Figure 12–22.**

As we've seen, there is a promoter just to one side of the gene. But what are the "regulatory sites" next to the promoter? These are places where other proteins, binding directly to the DNA sequences at those sites, can regulate transcription. The actions of these proteins help to determine whether a gene is turned on or turned off.

Gene Regulation: An Example

How does an organism "know" whether to turn a gene on or off? The common bacterium *E. coli* provides us with a perfect example of how gene expression can be regulated. The 4288 protein-encoding genes in this bacterium include a cluster of three genes that are turned on or off together. A group of genes that operate together is known as an **operon.** Because these genes must be expressed in order for the bacterium to be able to use the sugar lactose as a food, they are called the *lac* operon.

Guide for Reading

Key Concepts
- How are *lac* genes turned off and on?
- How are most eukaryotic genes controlled?

Vocabulary
operon
operator
differentiation
hox gene

Reading Strategy: Outlining Before you read, use the headings of the section to make an outline about gene regulation. As you read, fill in subtopics and smaller topics. Then, add phrases or a sentence after each subtopic to provide key information.

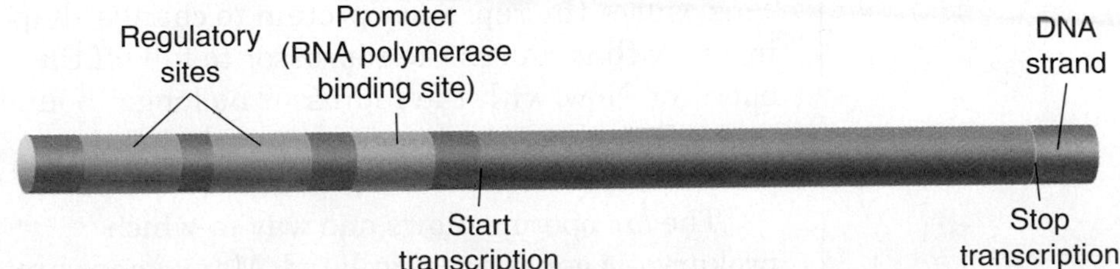

GAATTCTAATCTCCCTCTCAACCCTACAGTCACCCATTTGGTATATTAAAGATGTGTTG
TCTACTGTCTAGTATCCCTCAAGTAGTGTCAGGAATTAGTCATTTAAATAGTCTGCAAG
CCAGGAGTGGTGGCTCATGTCTGTAATTCCAGCACTGGAGAGGTAGAAGTGGGAG
GACTGCTTGAGCTCAAGAGTTTGATATTATCCTGGACAACATAGCAAGACCTCGTCT
CTACTTAAAAAAAAAAAAAATTAGCCAGGCATGTGATGTACACCTGTAGTCCCAGCTAC
TCAGGAGGCCGAAATGGGAGGATCCCTTGAGCTCAGGAGGTCAAGGCTGCAGTGA
GACATGATCTTGCCACTGCACTCCAGCCTGGACAGCAGAGTGAAACCTTGCCTCAC
GAAACAGAATACAAAAACAAACAAACAAAAAACTGCTCCGCAATGCGCTTCCTTGAT
GCTCTACCACATAGGTCTGGGTACTTT

◀ **Figure 12–22** A typical gene includes start and stop signals, with the nucleotides to be translated in between. The DNA sequence shown is only a very small part of an actual gene. **Interpreting Graphics** *What is the function of the promoter?*

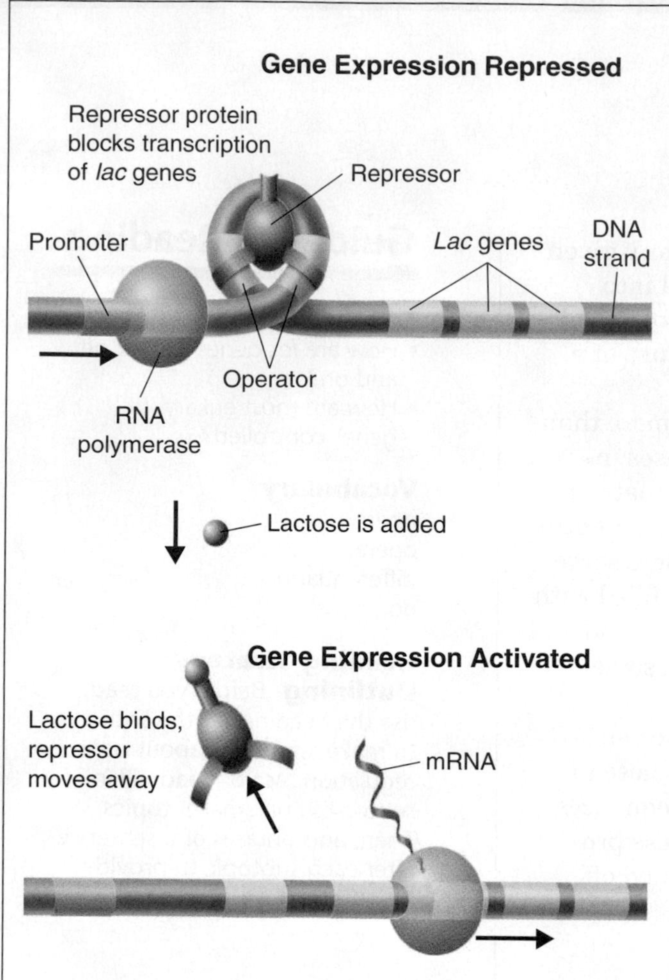

▲ **Figure 12–23** **The *lac* genes in *E. coli* are turned off by repressors and turned on by the presence of lactose.** When lactose is not present, the repressor binds to the operator region, preventing RNA polymerase from beginning transcription. Lactose causes the repressor to be released from the operator region.

Why must *E. coli* turn on the *lac* genes in order to use lactose for food? Lactose is a compound made up of two simple sugars, galactose and glucose. To use lactose for food, the bacterium must take lactose across its cell membrane and then break the bond between glucose and galactose. These tasks are performed by proteins coded for by the genes of the *lac* operon. This means, of course, that if the bacterium is grown in a medium where lactose is the only food source, it must transcribe the genes and produce these proteins. If grown on another food source, such as glucose, it would have no need for these proteins.

Remarkably, the bacterium almost seems to "know" when the products of these genes are needed. **The *lac* genes are turned off by repressors and turned on by the presence of lactose.** This process tells us a great deal about how genes are regulated.

On one side of the operon's three genes are two regulatory regions. In the promoter (P), RNA polymerase binds and then begins transcription. The other region is the **operator** (O). *E. coli* cells contain several copies of a DNA-binding protein known as the *lac* repressor, which can bind to the O region. As **Figure 12–23** shows, when the *lac* repressor binds to the O region, RNA polymerase is prevented from beginning the process of transcription. In effect, the binding of the repressor protein turns the operon "off" by preventing the transcription of its genes.

If the repressor protein is always present, how are the *lac* genes turned on in the presence of lactose? Besides its DNA binding site, the *lac* repressor protein has a binding site for lactose itself. When lactose is added to the medium in which *E. coli* is growing, sugar molecules diffuse into the cell and bind to the repressor proteins. This causes the repressor protein to change shape in a way that causes the repressor to fall off the operator. Now, with the repressor no longer bound to the O site, RNA polymerase can bind to the promoter and transcribe the genes of the operon.

The *lac* operon shows one way in which prokaryotic genes are regulated. Many genes are regulated by repressor proteins, while others use proteins that speed transcription. Sometimes regulation occurs at the level of protein synthesis. Regardless of the system, the result is the same: Cells turn their genes on and off as needed.

 ***What is the operator?***

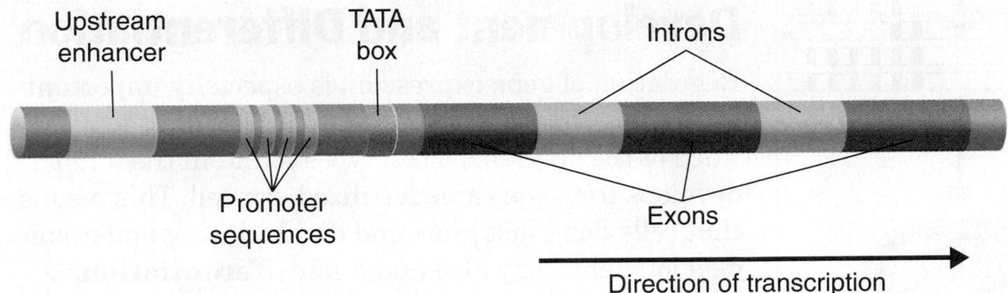

◀ **Figure 12–24** Many eukaryotic genes include a sequence called the TATA box that may help position RNA polymerase. **Eukaryotic genes have regulatory sequences that are more complex than prokaryotic genes.**

Eukaryotic Gene Regulation

The general principles of gene regulation in prokaryotes also apply to eukaryotic cells, although there are some important differences. Operons are generally not found in eukaryotes. **Most eukaryotic genes are controlled individually and have regulatory sequences that are much more complex than those of the *lac* operon.**

Figure 12–24 shows some of the features of a typical eukaryotic gene. One of the most interesting is a short region of DNA about 30 base pairs long, containing a sequence of TATATA or TATAAA, before the start of transcription. This region is found before so many eukaryotic genes that it even has a name: the "TATA box." The TATA box seems to help position RNA polymerase by marking a point just before the point at which transcription begins. Eukaryotic promoters are usually found just before the TATA box, and they consist of a series of short DNA sequences.

Genes are regulated in a variety of ways by enhancer sequences located before the point at which transcription begins. An enormous number of proteins can bind to different enhancer sequences, which is why eukaryotic gene regulation is so complex. Some of these DNA-binding proteins enhance transcription by opening up tightly packed chromatin. Others help to attract RNA polymerase. Still other proteins block access to genes, much like prokaryotic repressor proteins.

Why is gene regulation in eukaryotes more complex than in prokaryotes? Think for a moment about the way in which genes are expressed in a multicellular organism. The genes that code for liver enzymes, for example, are not expressed in nerve cells. Keratin, an important protein in skin cells, is not produced in blood cells. Cell specialization requires genetic specialization, but all of the cells in a multicellular organism carry the complete genetic code in their nucleus. Therefore, for proper overall function, only a tiny fraction of the available genes needs to be expressed in the appropriate cells of different tissues throughout the body. The complexity of gene regulation in eukaryotes makes this specificity possible.

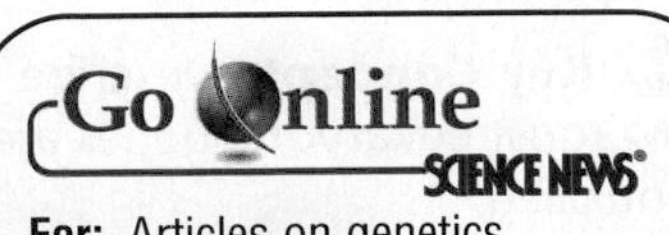

For: Articles on genetics
Visit: PHSchool.com
Web Code: cbe-4125

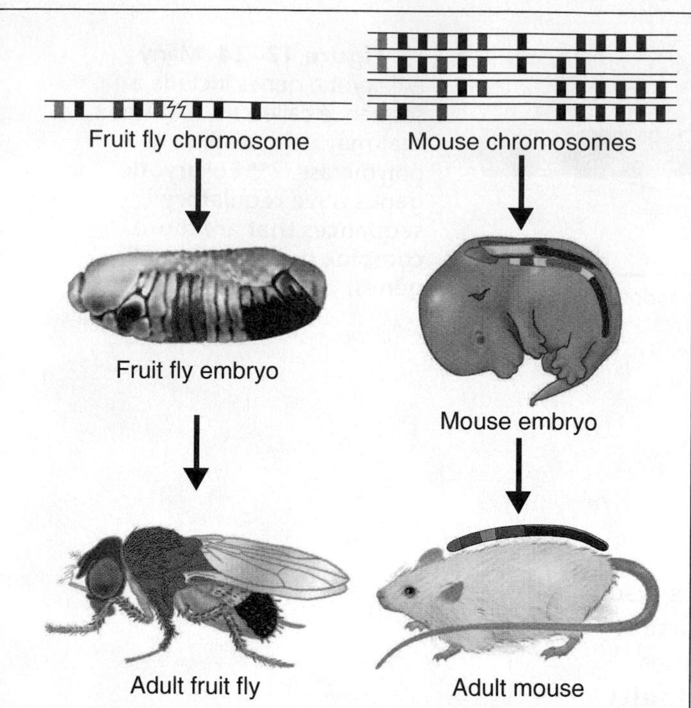

▲ **Figure 12–25** In fruit flies, a series of hox genes along a chromosome determines the basic structure of the fly's body. Mice have very similar genes on four different chromosomes. The color bars along the mouse's back show the approximate body area affected by genes of the corresponding colors. **Interpreting Graphics** *What section of the bodies of flies and mice is coded by the genes shown in blue?*

Development and Differentiation

Regulation of gene expression is especially important in shaping the way a complex organism develops. Each of the specialized cell types found in the adult develops from the same fertilized egg cell. This means that cells don't just grow and divide during embryonic development; they also undergo **differentiation,** meaning they become specialized in structure and function. The study of genes that control development and differentiation is one of the most exciting areas in biology today.

A series of genes, known as the **hox genes,** control the differentiation of cells and tissues in the embryo. A mutation in one of these "master control genes" can completely change the organs that develop in specific parts of the body. Mutations affecting the hox genes in the fruit fly, *Drosophila,* for example, can replace the fly's antennae with legs growing on its head!

In flies, the hox genes are located side-by-side in a single cluster, as shown in **Figure 12–25.** Remarkably, similar clusters exist in the DNA of other animals, including humans. The function of the hox genes in humans seems to be almost the same—to tell the cells of the body how they should differentiate as the body grows. Careful control of expression in these genes is essential for normal development.

The striking similarity of genes that control development has a simple scientific explanation: Common patterns of genetic control exist because all these genes have descended from the genes of common ancestors. One such gene, called Pax 6, controls eye growth in *Drosophila*. A similar gene was found to guide eye growth in mice and other mammals. When a copy of the mouse gene was inserted into the "knee" of a *Drosophila* embryo, the resulting fruit fly grew an eye on its leg! The fly gene and the mouse gene are similar enough to trade places and still function—even though they come from animals that have not shared a common ancestor in at least 600 million years.

12–5 Section Assessment

1. **Key Concept** How is the *lac* operon regulated?
2. **Key Concept** Describe how most eukaryotic genes are controlled.
3. What genes control cell differentiation during development?
4. What is a promoter?
5. **Critical Thinking Comparing and Contrasting** How is the way hox genes are expressed in mice similar to the way they are expressed in fruit flies? How is it different?

Writing in Science

Making an Analogy
Make an analogy to demonstrate the different components of the *lac* operon. Then, explain in a short paragraph—using your analogy—how the *lac* operon works.

Modeling DNA Replication

Living cells synthesize exact copies of DNA molecules that are passed on to each daughter cell during cell division. In this investigation, you will model DNA replication.

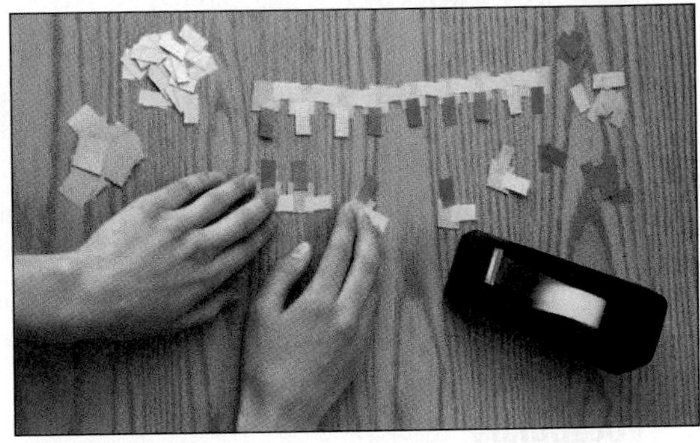

Problem How is DNA replicated?

Materials

- construction paper (tan, gray, green, yellow, red, and purple)
- metric ruler
- scissors
- transparent tape

Skills Using Models

Procedure

1. Cut out rectangles of construction paper in the sizes and colors indicated below:

   Sugars: 36 tan pieces, each 2 cm × 2 cm

   Phosphates: 36 gray pieces, each 1 cm × 2 cm

   Adenines (A): 12 green pieces, each 1 cm × 2 cm

   Thymines (T): 12 yellow pieces, each 1 cm × 2 cm

   Guanines (G): 6 red pieces, each 1 cm × 2 cm

   Cytosines (C): 6 purple pieces, each 1 cm × 2 cm

2. To model a nucleotide, tape together a phosphate group, a sugar, and a guanine molecule (G) (see **Figure 12–5**).
3. Assemble eight additional nucleotide models with the following nitrogenous bases: 3 thymines (T); 3 adenines (A); 2 cytosines (C).
4. To model a single strand of DNA, tape the sugar of each nucleotide to the phosphate group of the next nucleotide in the following order: G T T A C A A T C.
5. Construct a strand of DNA that is complementary to the first strand. Tape the nucleotides of the second strand together as you did in step 4. Record the positions of the bases in both strands of your model.
6. Place the two strands side by side so that their complementary nucleotides face each other. Do not tape the two strands together. Write "original" on each strand.
7. Separate the two strands. Simulate the action of DNA polymerase by constructing a new complementary strand for each original strand.
8. Tape the bases of each new strand to the complementary bases of its matching strand.

Analyze and Conclude

1. **Comparing and Contrasting** Compare the new double-stranded DNA models with your original DNA model. Are their nucleotide sequences identical?
2. **Using Models** After a cell's DNA is replicated, the cell may divide in two. Each new cell receives one copy of the original cell's DNA. According to your model, how are the new strands and the original strands divided between the two new cells?
3. **Drawing Conclusions** What problems would you expect to occur if DNA was not copied accurately as it is replicated?
4. **Evaluating** Do you consider this procedure an adequate model of DNA replication? Explain your answer.
5. Describe an alternative way of modeling DNA replication.

Go Further

Using Models Cells use the information in DNA to make proteins. First, part of the nucleotide sequence of DNA is copied into a complementary sequence of RNA in the process of transcription. Then, during translation, the cell uses information in the RNA to make proteins. Modify your model or make a new model to show how transcription and translation occur.

Chapter 12 Study Guide

12–1 DNA

Key Concepts

- Avery and other scientists discovered that DNA is the nucleic acid that stores and transmits the genetic information from one generation of an organism to the next.
- Hershey and Chase concluded that the genetic material of the bacteriophage was DNA.
- Watson and Crick's model of DNA was a double helix, in which two strands were wound around each other.

Vocabulary
transformation, p. 288 • bacteriophage, p. 289
nucleotide, p. 291 • base pairing, p. 294

12–2 Chromosomes and DNA Replication

Key Concept

- During DNA replication, the DNA molecule separates into two strands, then produces two new complementary strands following the rules of base pairing. Each strand of the double helix of DNA serves as a template, or model, for the new strand.

Vocabulary
chromatin, p. 296 • histone, p. 296
replication, p. 299 • DNA polymerase, p. 299

12–3 RNA and Protein Synthesis

Key Concepts

- There are three main types of RNA: messenger RNA, ribosomal RNA, and transfer RNA.
- During transcription, RNA polymerase binds to DNA and separates the DNA strands. RNA polymerase then uses one strand of DNA as a template from which nucleotides are assembled into a strand of RNA.
- During translation, the cell uses information from messenger RNA to produce proteins.

Vocabulary
gene, p. 300 • messenger RNA, p. 301
ribosomal RNA, p. 301
transfer RNA, p. 301 • transcription, p. 301
RNA polymerase, p. 301 • promoter, p. 301
intron, p. 302 • exon, p. 302 • codon, p. 302
translation, p. 304 • anticodon, p. 304

12–4 Mutations

Key Concept

- Mutations are changes in genetic material. Gene mutations result from changes in a single gene. Chromosomal mutations involve changes in whole chromosomes.

Vocabulary
mutation, p. 307 • point mutation, p. 307
frameshift mutation, p. 307 • polyploidy, p. 308

12–5 Gene Regulation

Key Concepts

- The *lac* genes are turned off by repressors and turned on by the presence of lactose.
- Most eukaryotic genes are controlled individually and have regulatory sequences that are much more complex than those of the *lac* operon.

Vocabulary
operon, p. 309 • operator, p. 310
differentiation, p. 312 • hox gene, p. 312

Thinking Visually

Using the information in this chapter, complete the following flowchart about protein synthesis:

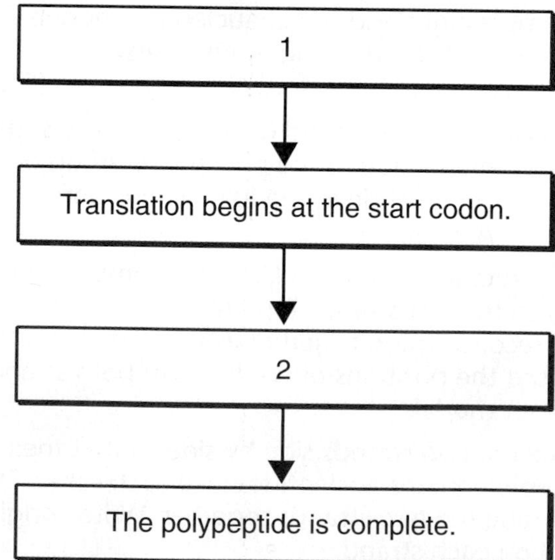

Preparing for the Living Environment Exam

NEW YORK LIVING ENVIRONMENT

Blue questions emphasize Regents Exam content

Chapter 12

Part A

Multiple Choice

For each statement or question, select the number of the word or expression that, of those given, best completes the statement or answers the question.

1 Bacteria in Culture A produce slime capsules around their cell walls. A biologist removed the DNA from some of the bacteria in Culture A and injected it into bacteria in Culture B, which normally do not produce slime capsules. After the injection, bacteria with slime capsules began to appear in Culture B. What conclusion can best be drawn from this investigation?
(1) The bacteria in Culture A are mutations.
(2) Bacteria reproduce faster when they have slime capsules.
(3) The slime capsules of bacteria in Culture B contain DNA.
(4) DNA is most likely involved in production of slime capsules.

2 Bacteriophages are composed of a DNA or RNA core and a protein coat. They are
(1) tiny bacteria
(2) ribosome complexes
(3) enzymes
(4) viruses

3 The kind of genes an organism possesses is dependent upon the
(1) type of proteins in the organism's nuclei
(2) sequence of bases in the organism's DNA
(3) number of ribosomes in the organism's cytoplasm
(4) size of mitochondria in the organism's cells

4 The diagram below shows the process of DNA
(1) replication (3) transcription
(2) translation (4) transformation

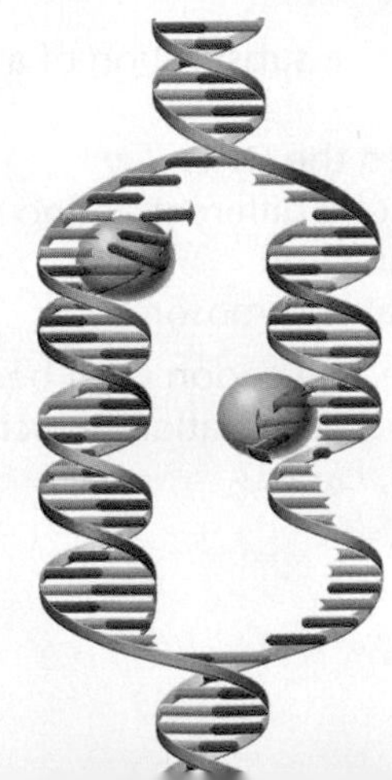

5 The main enzyme involved in DNA replication that joins individual nucleotides to produce DNA molecules is
(1) transfer RNA (3) ribose
(2) RNA polymerase (4) DNA polymerase

6 In which way does RNA differ from DNA?
(1) RNA contains uracil and deoxyribose.
(2) RNA contains ribose and thymine.
(3) RNA contains uracil and ribose.
(4) RNA contains adenine and ribose.

7 The process by which the genetic code of DNA is copied into a complementary sequence of RNA is called
(1) translation
(2) replication
(3) transcrlption
(4) transformation

8 A certain mutant bacterial cell cannot produce substance X. The mutation was most likely the result of a change in the
(1) structure of the cell membrane
(2) ability of the DNA to replicate
(3) amino acid sequence of DNA
(4) gene that codes for a specific protein

9 Changes in the DNA sequence that affect genetic information are known as
(1) replications
(2) transformations
(3) mutations
(4) translations

10 An expressed gene is one that
(1) functions as a promoter
(2) is transcribed into RNA
(3) codes for proteins
(4) contains an operon

11 In humans, DNA molecules are located in the
(1) nucleus (3) ribosome
(2) cytoplasm (4) histone

Test-Taking Tip When you answer a question based on experimental data, read the description of the experiment carefully to determine the steps followed. Then, try to see if there are any trends in the data. For example, "if x increases, what happens to y"?

Preparing for the Living Environment Exam

Part B

Multiple Choice and Extended Response
For those questions that ask you to select a response, choose the one that best completes the statement or answers the question. For all others follow the directions given.

12 Base pairing is an important part of the DNA replication process.

a State what is meant by the term *base pairing.*

b Explain how base pairing during DNA replication is important in maintaining the genetic code.

Base your answers to questions 13 and 14 on the data table below and on your knowledge of biology.

A scientist analyzed several DNA samples to determine the relative proportions of purine and pyrimidine bases. Her data are summarized in the table.

Percentages of Bases in Three Samples

Sample	G	C	A	T
A	35	35	15	15
B	40	10	40	10
C	25	25	25	25

13 Which sample(s) support(s) the base-pairing rules?
(1) Sample A, only **(3)** Samples A and B
(2) Sample B, only **(4)** Samples A and C

14 If the scientist had analyzed mRNA rather than DNA, what percentage of uracil would you expect to find in Sample A?
(1) 10 **(3)** 35
(2) 25 **(4)** 15

Base your answers to questions 15 and 16 on the illustration below and on your knowledge of biology.

Transcribed Strand of DNA

T A C C C G A A G T T C A T G

15 List the codons of the mRNA molecule that would be transcribed from this strand of DNA.

16 Using Figure 12–17 on page 303, list the sequence of amino acids that this mRNA molecule specifies.

Base your answers to questions 17 and 18 on the information below and on your knowledge of biology.

Hereditary information is stored in genes that are made of a *template* molecule. This template molecule can replicate, and it also controls the production of __A__.

17 A template molecule is referred to in the first sentence. Explain what *template* means.

18 Which molecules are represented by __A__?
(1) bases **(3)** amino acids
(2) proteins **(4)** simple sugars

Base your answers to questions 19 and 20 on the diagram below and on your knowledge of biology.

DNA: TAC GCA TGG AAT

mRNA: AUG CGU ACC UUA

Amino acids: Met–Arg–Thr–Leu

↓ **Substitution**

DNA: TAC GTA TGG AAT

mRNA: AUG CAU ACC UUA

Amino acids: Met–His–Thr–Leu

19 In this mutation, a substitution of a nucleotide results in
(1) no change to the DNA
(2) production of a different amino acid
(3) mRNA dysfunction
(4) an additional chromosome

20 In this example, the codon GCA becomes GTA. What is this kind of mutation, which affects only one nucleotide, called?

Part C

Extended Response

Answer the questions or follow the directions given.

Base your answers to questions 21 through 23 on the passage below and on your knowledge of biology.

Finding Griffith's "Factor"

In 1928, scientist Frederick Griffith tried to determine how certain strains of bacteria caused pneumonia. Figure 12-2 on page 288 shows the procedure that Griffith followed in his experiment. He was surprised to find that when heat-killed, disease-causing bacteria were combined with harmless bacteria and injected into healthy mice, the mice died.

From these results, Griffith hypothesized that some "factor" was transferred from the heat-killed cells to the live cells. Maybe that "factor" contained a gene.

Nearly 20 years later, Oswald Avery repeated Griffith's work. Avery and his colleagues wanted to know which part of the bacteria was most important for transformation. Using enzymes, the scientists destroyed the heat-killed bacteria's proteins, lipids, carbohydrates, and other molecules that might have been responsible for transforming the harmless bacteria. Finally, they identified the "factor" that Griffith had hypothesized about.

21 Griffith learned that some "factor" transformed harmless bacteria into disease-causing bacteria. State a hypothesis about this "factor" that Griffith might have formed.

22 State *two* kinds of information about Griffith's investigation that Avery and his colleagues needed in order to duplicate and expand on Griffith's experiments.

23 Enzymes were especially useful in carrying out Avery's experiment. Explain how the action of enzymes was necessary for Avery to conduct a controlled experiment. In your answer be sure to:
- state the importance of enzyme shape
- explain why separate trials were needed for different types of molecules (proteins, carbohydrates, and lipids)

Base your answers to questions 24 and 25 on the passage below and on your knowledge of biology.

A group of students used the following procedure to extract DNA from a sample of raw wheat germ. They made a solution of wheat germ and water by heating it and mixing until the wheat germ was dissolved. Once dissolved, the students added a small amount of detergent to the solution and stirred gently. After 5 minutes, they added meat tenderizer to the beaker. Then, they used a solution of baking soda to bring the pH of the mixture to about 8. The students poured 6 mL of the wheat germ mixture into a clean test tube, and then gently poured an equal amount of ethanol in a layer on top. After 5 minutes, DNA strands began to appear in the interface between the ethanol and the wheat germ mixture.

24 Detergent and certain enzymes in meat tenderizer work to break down cell parts. Identify *two* specific cell parts that must be destroyed in order to release DNA from wheat germ.

25 After removing the DNA strands from the mixture and allowing them to dry overnight, the students placed them in a test tube containing 3 mL of a 4% salt solution and added 3 mL of a diphenylamine solution. In a second test tube, they placed 3 mL "standard DNA solution" given to them by their teacher and 3 mL of the diphenylamine solution. Finally, in a third test tube, they placed 3 mL of the 4% salt solution and 3 mL of the diphenylamine solution.

Assuming that the students extracted their DNA successfully and knowing that diphenylamine is an indicator that turns blue in the presence of deoxyribose, which test tubes contain solutions that will turn blue? Support your answer with an explanation.

For: An interactive self-test
Visit: PHSchool.com
Web Code: cba-4120

CHAPTER 13

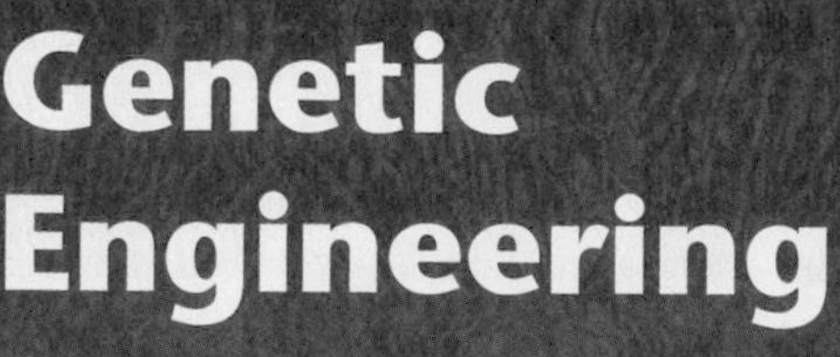

Genetic Engineering

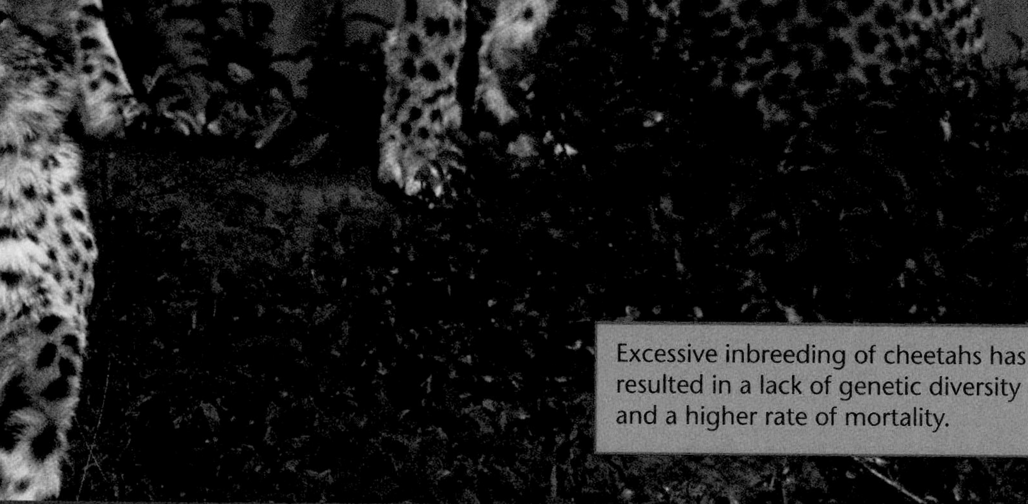

Excessive inbreeding of cheetahs has resulted in a lack of genetic diversity and a higher rate of mortality.

Inquiry Activity

Can you improve plant breeding?

Procedure 

1. Examine 5 apples of different varieties. Record the color, shape, and size of each apple.
2. Record your choices of the varieties that you consider best in color, shape, and size.

Think About It

1. **Formulating Hypotheses** How could you produce an apple that has the best traits of all 5 varieties?
2. **Formulating Hypotheses** Most apple trees do not produce fruit until they are about 15 years old. How could you use your knowledge of DNA to produce a new variety of apple more quickly?

13–1 Changing the Living World

4-2.1 The environment can influence gene expression
4-2.2 Selective breeding
4-3.1 New inheritable characteristics
4-3.1 Mutations are random events
LS- Make observations and state an appropriate hypothesis

Visit a dog show, and what do you see? You can compare dogs of every breed imaginable, distinguished from one another by an enormous range of characteristics that are the result of genetic variation. Striking contrasts are everywhere—the size of a tiny Chihuahua and that of a massive great Dane, the short coat of a Labrador retriever and the curly fur of a poodle, the long muzzle of the wolfhound and the pug nose of a bulldog. The differences among breeds of dogs are so great that someone who had never seen such animals before might think that many of these breeds are different species. They're not, of course, but where did such differences come from? What forces gave rise to the speed of a greyhound, the courage of a German shepherd, and the herding instincts of a border collie?

Guide for Reading

Key Concepts
- What is the purpose of selective breeding?
- Why might breeders try to induce mutations?

Vocabulary
selective breeding
hybridization
inbreeding

Reading Strategy: Outlining Before you read, write down the blue headings of the section. As you read, list the important information under each heading.

Selective Breeding

The answer, of course, is that *we* did it. Humans have kept and bred dogs for thousands of years, always looking to produce animals that might be better hunters, better retrievers, or better companions. By **selective breeding,** allowing only those animals with desired characteristics to produce the next generation, humans have produced many different breeds of dogs.

Humans use selective breeding, which takes advantage of naturally occurring genetic variation in plants, animals, and other organisms, to pass desired traits on to the next generation of organisms. Nearly all domestic animals—including horses, cats, and farm animals—and most crop plants have been produced by selective breeding. American botanist Luther Burbank (1849–1926) may have been the greatest selective plant breeder of all time. He developed the disease-resistant Burbank potato, which was later exported to Ireland to help fight potato blight and other diseases. During his lifetime, Burbank developed more than 800 varieties of plants.

Hybridization As one of his tools, Burbank used **hybridization,** crossing dissimilar individuals to bring together the best of both organisms. Hybrids, the individuals produced by such crosses, are often hardier than either of the parents. In many cases, Burbank's hybrid crosses combined the disease resistance of one plant with the food-producing capacity of another. The result was a new line of plants that had the characteristics farmers needed to increase food production. **Figure 13–1** shows hybrid daisies developed using Burbank's techniques.

▼ **Figure 13–1 Humans use selective breeding to pass desired traits on to the next generation of organisms.** Luther Burbank used selective breeding to develop these Shasta daisies, a popular variety.

▶ **Figure 13–2** Inbreeding is required to maintain the characteristics of pedigreed dogs, such as these golden retrievers. However, inbreeding has also increased the breed's susceptibility to diseases and deformities. **Applying Concepts** *What other animals are likely to be inbred?*

Inbreeding To maintain the desired characteristics of a line of organisms, breeders often use a technique known as inbreeding. **Inbreeding** is the continued breeding of individuals with similar characteristics. The many breeds of dogs—from beagles to poodles—are maintained by inbreeding. Inbreeding helps to ensure that the characteristics that make each breed unique will be preserved. The golden retrievers shown in **Figure 13–2** are an example of inbred animals.

Although inbreeding is useful in retaining a certain set of characteristics, it does have its risks. Most of the members of a breed are genetically similar. Because of this, there is always a chance that a cross between two individuals will bring together two recessive alleles for a genetic defect. Serious problems in many breeds of dogs, including blindness and joint deformities in German shepherds and golden retrievers, have resulted from excessive inbreeding.

CHECKPOINT *What is inbreeding?*

Increasing Variation

Selective breeding would be nearly impossible without the wide variation that is found in natural populations. This is one of the reasons biologists are interested in preserving the diversity of plants and animals in the wild. However, sometimes breeders want more variation than exists in nature. **Breeders can increase the genetic variation in a population by inducing mutations, which are the ultimate source of genetic variability.**

As you may recall, mutations are inheritable changes in DNA. Mutations occur spontaneously, but breeders can increase the mutation rate by using radiation and chemicals. Many mutations are harmful to the organism. With luck and perseverance, however, breeders can produce a few mutants—individuals with mutations—with desirable characteristics that are not found in the original population.

▼ **Figure 13–3** **Breeders can increase genetic variation by inducing mutations.** This process was used to produce the oil-eating bacteria shown here. This image was made using a scanning electron microscope and has been artificially colored.

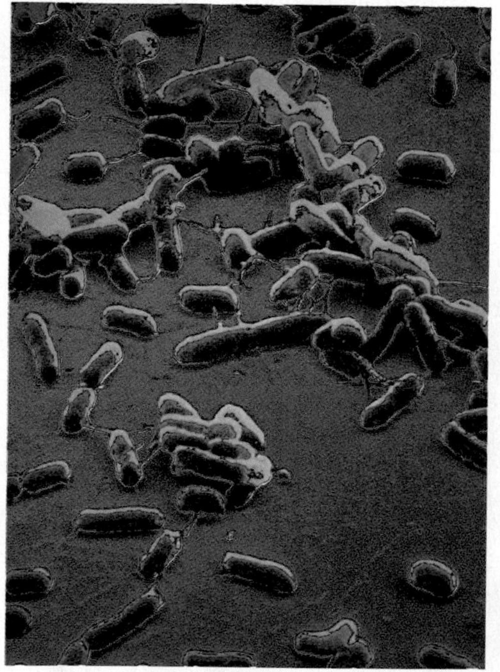

(magnification: 6200×)

Producing New Kinds of Bacteria This technique has been particularly useful with bacteria. Their small size enables millions of organisms to be treated with radiation or chemicals at the same time. This increases the chances of producing a useful mutant. Using this technique, scientists have been able to develop hundreds of useful bacterial strains. It has even been possible to produce bacteria that can digest oil, as shown in **Figure 13–3,** and that were once used to clean up oil spills. (Today, naturally occurring strains of oil-digesting bacteria are used to clean up oil spills.)

Producing New Kinds of Plants Drugs that prevent chromosomal separation during meiosis have been particularly useful in plant breeding. Sometimes these drugs produce cells that have double or triple the normal number of chromosomes. Plants grown from such cells are called polyploid because they have many sets of chromosomes. Polyploidy is usually fatal in animals. However, for reasons that are not clear, plants are much better at tolerating extra sets of chromosomes. Polyploidy may instantly produce new species of plants that are often larger and stronger than their diploid relatives. **Figure 13–4** shows some polyploid day lilies. Many important crop plants have been produced in this way, including bananas and many varieties of citrus fruits.

Word Origins

Polyploid comes from the Greek words *polus,* meaning "many," and *-ploos,* meaning "fold." So *polyploid* means "many-fold" or "many times." **How many sets of chromosomes do you think a triploid plant has?**

▶ **Figure 13–4** The day lilies at the right are examples of polyploid plants. New species of plants are produced when the chromosome number is doubled or tripled. **Applying Concepts** ***What are some other examples of polyploid plants?***

13–1 Section Assessment

1. **Key Concept** Give one example of selective breeding.
2. **Key Concept** Relate genetic variation and mutations to each other.
3. How might a breeder induce mutations?
4. What is polyploidy?
5. **Critical Thinking Comparing and Contrasting** You are a geneticist trying to develop a sunflower with red flowers and a short stem. As you compare the sunflowers you have, what genetic variations would you look for? What kinds of plants would you select for crossing?

Writing in Science

Solving a Problem
Write a paragraph in which you suggest ways that plants could be genetically altered to improve the world's food supply. *Hint:* The first sentence in your paragraph should express the paragraph's main idea.

13–2 Manipulating DNA

4-2.2 Genetic engineering
4-2.2 Special enzymes
4-2.2 Genes are altered when the DNA segments are altered
LS- Chromatography/electrophoresis
LS- Make observations

Guide for Reading

Key Concept
- How do scientists make changes to DNA?

Vocabulary
genetic engineering
restriction enzyme
gel electrophoresis
recombinant DNA
polymerase chain reaction (PCR)

Reading Strategy: Previewing Graphics Before you read this section, examine the figures. Read the captions, and identify questions about or predict relationships among the techniques illustrated.

Until very recently, animal and plant breeders could not modify the genetic code of living things. They were limited by the need to work with the variation that already exists in nature. Even when they tried to add to that variation by introducing mutations, the changes they produced in the DNA were random and unpredictable. Imagine, however, that one day biologists were able to go right to the genetic code and rewrite an organism's DNA. Imagine that biologists could transfer genes at will from one organism to another, designing new living things to meet specific needs. That day, as you may know from scientific stories in the news, is already here.

How are changes made to DNA? **Scientists use their knowledge of the structure of DNA and its chemical properties to study and change DNA molecules. Different techniques are used to extract DNA from cells, to cut DNA into smaller pieces, to identify the sequence of bases in a DNA molecule, and to make unlimited copies of DNA.** Understanding how these techniques work will help you develop an appreciation for what is involved in genetic engineering.

The Tools of Molecular Biology

Suppose you had a computer game you wanted to change. Knowing that the characteristics of that game are determined by a coded computer program, how would you set about rewriting parts of the program? To make such changes, a software engineer would need a way to get the program out of the computer, read it, make changes in it, and then put the modified code back into the game. **Genetic engineering,** making changes in the DNA code of a living organism, works almost the same way.

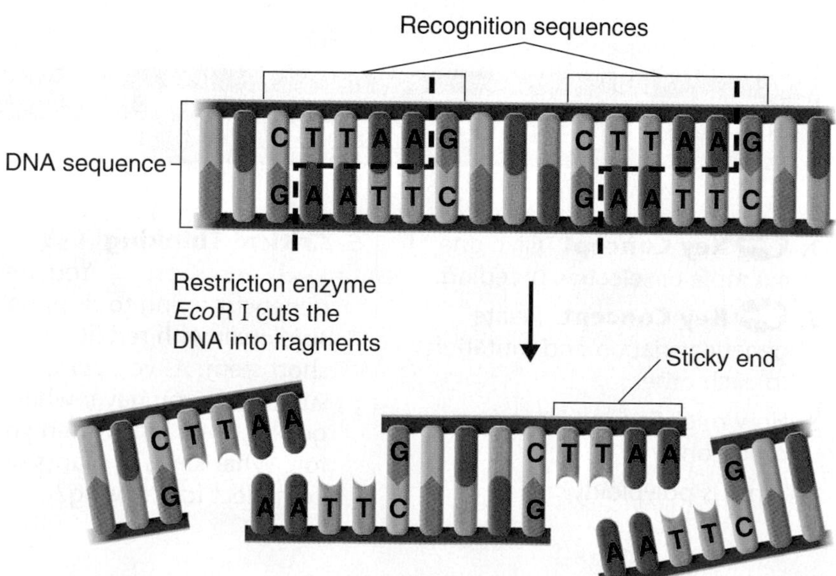

▶ **Figure 13–5 Molecular biologists have developed different techniques that allow them to study and change DNA molecules.** This drawing shows how restriction enzymes are used to edit DNA. The restriction enzyme *Eco*R I, for example, finds the sequence CTTAAG on DNA. Then, the enzyme cuts the molecule at each occurrence of CTTAAG. Different restriction enzymes recognize and cut different sequences of nucleotides on DNA molecules. The cut ends are called sticky ends because they may "stick" to complementary base sequences by means of hydrogen bonds.

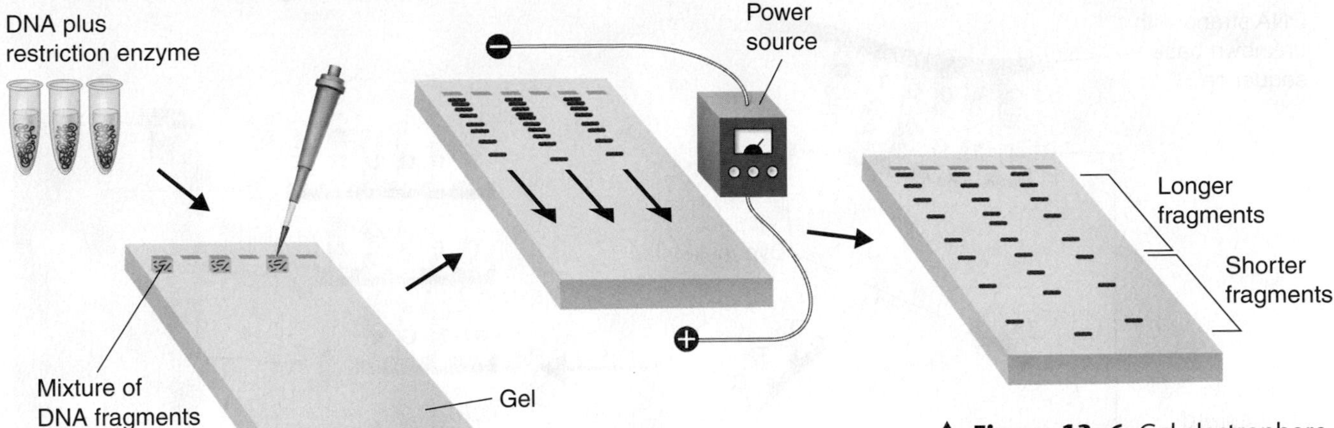

▲ **Figure 13–6** Gel electrophoresis is used to separate DNA fragments. First, restriction enzymes cut DNA into fragments. The DNA fragments are then poured into wells on a gel, which is similar to a thick piece of gelatin. An electric voltage moves the DNA fragments across the gel. Because longer fragments of DNA move through the gel more slowly, they do not migrate as far across the gel as shorter fragments of DNA. Based on size, the DNA fragments make a pattern of bands on the gel. These bands can then be compared with other samples of DNA. **Inferring** ***What kinds of information might the bands from two different DNA sources provide?***

DNA Extraction How do biologists get DNA out of a cell? DNA can be extracted from most cells by a simple chemical procedure: The cells are opened and the DNA is separated from the other cell parts.

Cutting DNA DNA molecules from most organisms are much too large to be analyzed, so biologists cut them precisely into smaller fragments using restriction enzymes. Hundreds of **restriction enzymes** are known, and each one cuts DNA at a specific sequence of nucleotides. As shown in **Figure 13–5,** restriction enzymes are amazingly precise. Like a key that fits only one lock, a restriction enzyme will cut a DNA sequence only if it matches the sequence precisely.

Separating DNA How can DNA fragments be separated and analyzed? One way, a procedure known as gel electrophoresis (ee-lek-troh-fuh-REE-sis), is shown in **Figure 13–6.** In **gel electrophoresis,** a mixture of DNA fragments is placed at one end of a porous gel, and an electric voltage is applied to the gel. When the power is turned on, DNA molecules, which are negatively charged, move toward the positive end of the gel. The smaller the DNA fragment, the faster and farther it moves. Gel electrophoresis can be used to compare the genomes, or gene composition, of different organisms or different individuals. It can also be used to locate and identify one particular gene out of the tens of thousands of genes in an individual's genome.

Using the DNA Sequence

Once DNA is in a manageable form, its sequence can be read, studied, and even changed. Knowing the sequence of an organism's DNA allows researchers to study specific genes, to compare them with the genes of other organisms, and to try to discover the functions of different genes and gene combinations. The following are some techniques scientists use to read and change the sequence of DNA molecules.

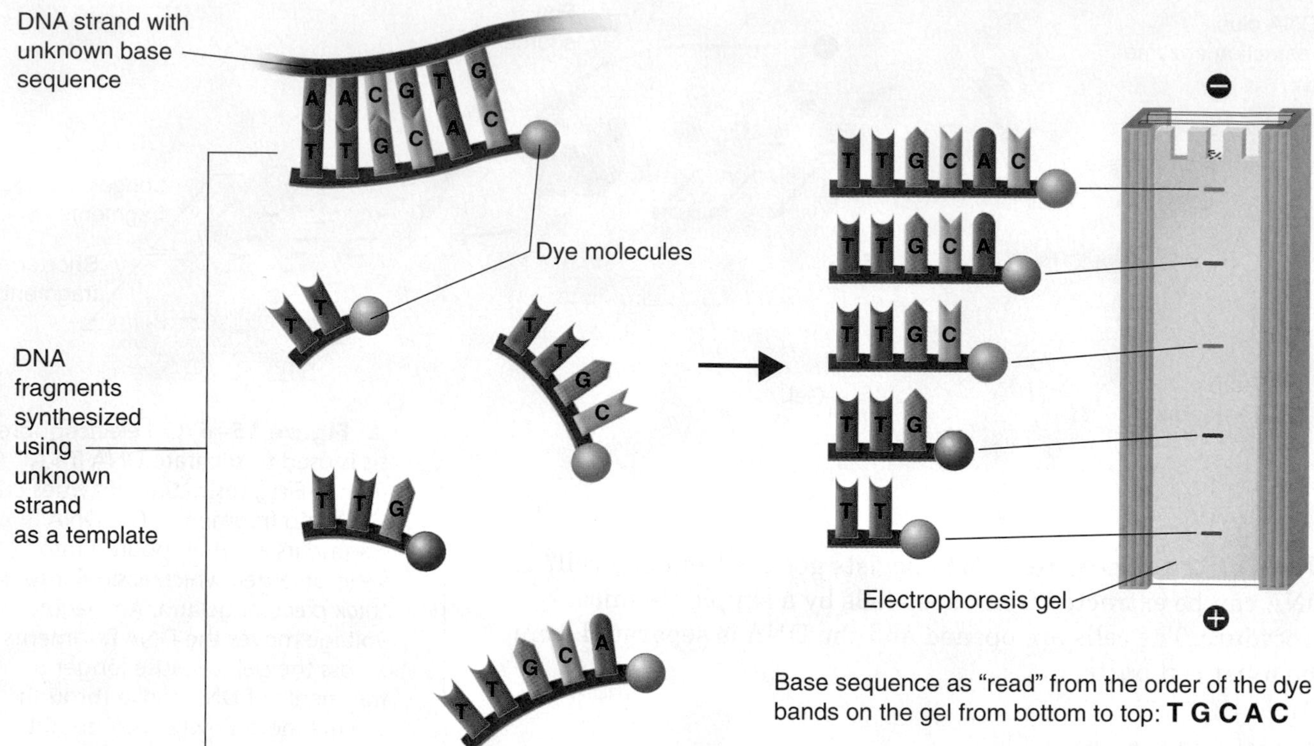

▲ **Figure 13–7 Knowing the sequence of an organism's DNA allows researchers to study specific genes.** In DNA sequencing, a complementary DNA strand is made using a small proportion of fluorescently labeled nucleotides. Each time a labeled nucleotide is added, it stops the process of replication, producing a short color-coded DNA fragment. When the mixture of fragments is separated on a gel, the DNA sequence can be read directly from the gel.

Reading the Sequence Researchers use a clever chemical trick to "read" DNA by determining the order of its bases. A single strand of DNA whose sequence of bases is not known is placed in a test tube. DNA polymerase, the enzyme that copies DNA, and the four nucleotide bases, A, T, G, and C, are added to the test tube. As the enzyme goes to work, it uses the unknown strand as a template to make one new DNA strand after another. The tricky part is that researchers also add a small number of bases that have a chemical dye attached.

Each time a dye-labeled base is added to a new DNA strand, the synthesis of that strand is terminated. When DNA synthesis is completed, the new DNA strands are different lengths, depending on how far synthesis had progressed when the dye-tagged base was added. Since each base is labeled with a different color, the result is a series of dye-tagged DNA fragments of different lengths. These fragments are then separated according to length, often by gel electrophoresis, as shown in **Figure 13–7.** The order of colored bands on the gel tells the exact sequence of bases in the DNA.

Cutting and Pasting DNA sequences can be changed in a number of ways. Short sequences can be assembled using laboratory machines known as DNA synthesizers. "Synthetic" sequences can then be joined to "natural" ones using enzymes that splice DNA together. The same enzymes make it possible to take a gene from one organism and attach it to the DNA of another organism. Such DNA molecules are sometimes called **recombinant DNA** because they are produced by combining DNA from different sources.

Making Copies In order to study genes, biologists often need to make many copies of a particular gene. Like a photocopy machine stuck on "print," a technique known as **polymerase chain reaction (PCR)** allows biologists to do exactly that. **Figure 13–8** shows how PCR works.

The idea behind PCR is surprisingly simple. At one end of a piece of DNA a biologist wants to copy, he or she adds a short piece of DNA that is complementary to a portion of the sequence. At the other end, the biologist adds another short piece of complementary DNA. These short pieces are known as "primers" because they provide a place for the DNA polymerase to start working.

The DNA is heated to separate its two strands, then cooled to allow the primers to bind to single-stranded DNA. DNA polymerase starts making copies of the region between the primers. Because the copies themselves can serve as templates to make still more copies, just a few dozen cycles of replication can produce millions of copies of the DNA between those primers.

Where did Kary Mullis, the American inventor of PCR, find a DNA polymerase enzyme that could stand repeated cycles of heating and cooling? Mullis found it in bacteria living in the hot springs of Yellowstone National Park—a perfect example of the importance of biodiversity to biotechnology.

What is a polymerase chain reaction?

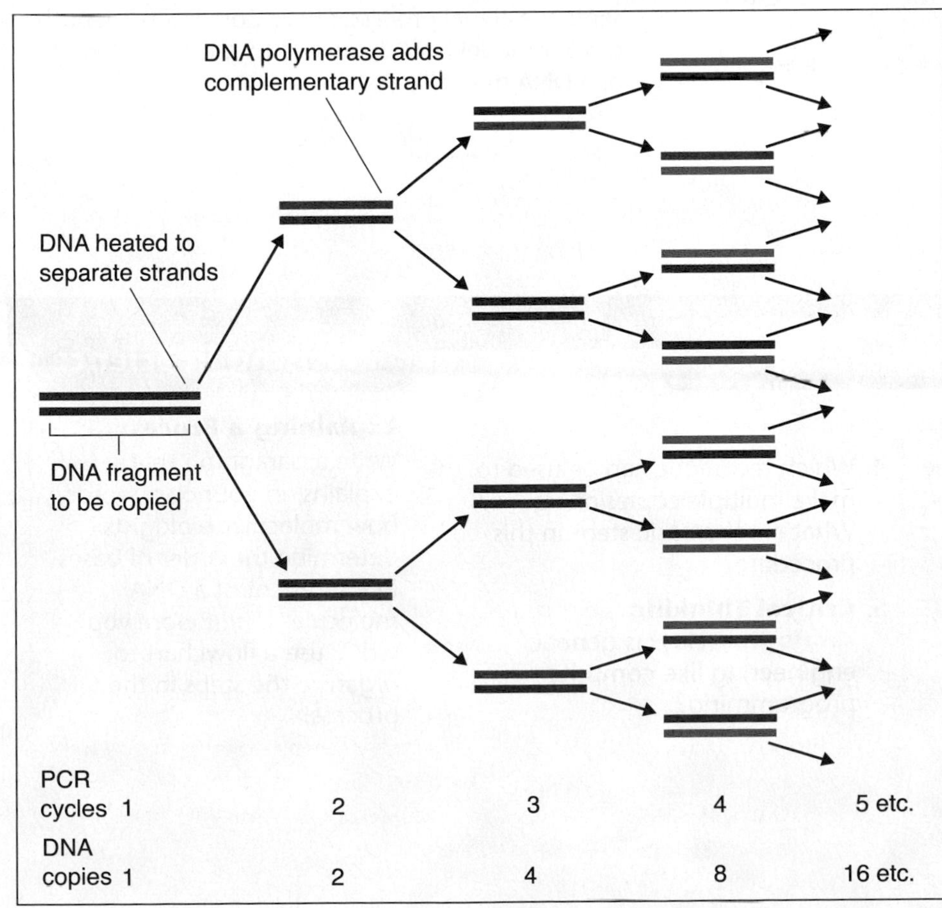

◀ **Figure 13–8** Polymerase chain reaction (PCR) is used to make multiple copies of genes. **Calculating** *How many copies of the DNA will there be after six cycles?*

Quick Lab

How can restriction enzymes be modeled?

Materials construction paper, scissors, transparent tape

Procedure 

1. Write a 50-base double-stranded DNA sequence using the letters A, C, G, and T in random order. Include each of the base sequences shown below at least once in your 50 base-pair sequences.
2. Make 3 copies of your double-stranded sequence on three different-colored strips of paper.
3. Use the drawings below to see how the restriction enzyme *Eco*R I would cut your double-stranded sequence. Use scissors to cut 1 copy of the sequence as *Eco*R I would.

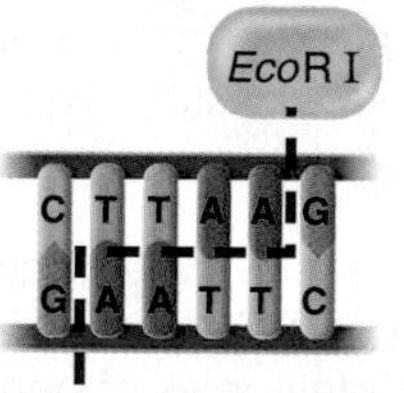

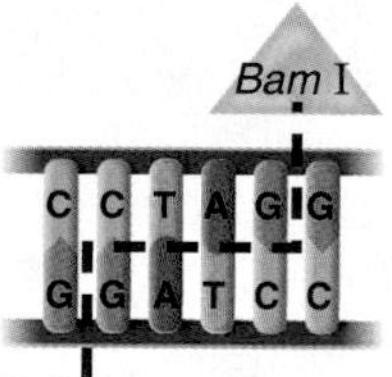

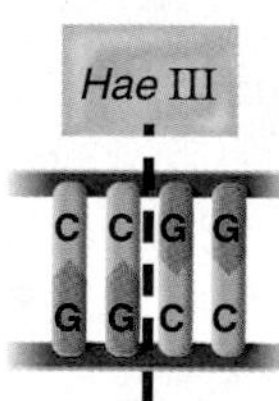

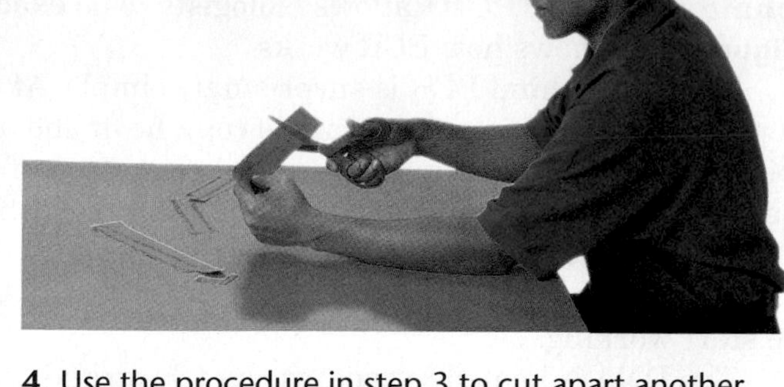

4. Use the procedure in step 3 to cut apart another copy of your sequence as the restriction enzyme *Bam* I would. Cut apart the third copy as the restriction enzyme *Hae* III would.
5. To model the building of recombinant DNA, tape the single-stranded end of one of your pieces of DNA sequences to a complementary, single-stranded end of one of a classmate's pieces. This will form a single, long DNA molecule.

Analyze and Conclude

1. **Observing** Which restriction enzyme produced the most pieces? The fewest pieces?
2. **Evaluating** Evaluate your model of restriction-enzyme function according to how well it represents the actual process. (*Hint:* Contrast the length of your model DNA sequence to the actual length of a DNA molecule.)

13–2 Section Assessment

1. **Key Concept** Describe the process scientists use to manipulate DNA.
2. Why might a scientist want to know the sequence of a DNA molecule?
3. How does gel electrophoresis work?
4. Which technique can be used to make multiple copies of a gene? What are the basic steps in this procedure?
5. **Critical Thinking Using Analogies** How is genetic engineering like computer programming?

Writing in Science

Explaining a Process

Write a paragraph that explains, in your own words, how molecular biologists determine the order of bases in a segment of a DNA molecule. *Hint:* Before you write, use a flowchart to organize the steps in the process.

13–3 Cell Transformation

4-2.2 Genetic engineering
4-2.2 Organisms may be modified

Guide for Reading

 **Key Concepts**
- What happens during cell transformation?
- How can you tell if a transformation experiment has been successful?

Vocabulary
plasmid
genetic marker

Reading Strategy: Summarizing As you read, take notes on how each kind of cell can be transformed. After you read, go back to your notes and compare the different techniques.

It would do little good to modify a DNA molecule in the test tube if it were not possible to put that DNA back into a living cell and make it work. This sounds tricky, and it is, but you have already seen an example of how this can be done. Remember Griffith's experiments on bacterial transformation? **During transformation, a cell takes in DNA from outside the cell. This external DNA becomes a component of the cell's DNA.**

Today, biologists understand that Griffith's extract of heat-killed bacteria must have contained DNA fragments. When he mixed those fragments with live bacteria, a few of them actually took up the DNA molecules. This suggests that bacteria can be transformed simply by placing them in a solution containing DNA molecules—and indeed they can.

Transforming Bacteria

Figure 13–9 shows how bacteria can be transformed using recombinant DNA. The foreign DNA is first joined to a small, circular DNA molecule known as a **plasmid.** Plasmids are found naturally in some bacteria and have been very useful for DNA transfer. Why? The plasmid DNA has two essential features. First, it has a DNA sequence that helps promote plasmid replication. If the plasmid containing the foreign DNA manages to get inside a bacterial cell, this sequence ensures that it will be replicated.

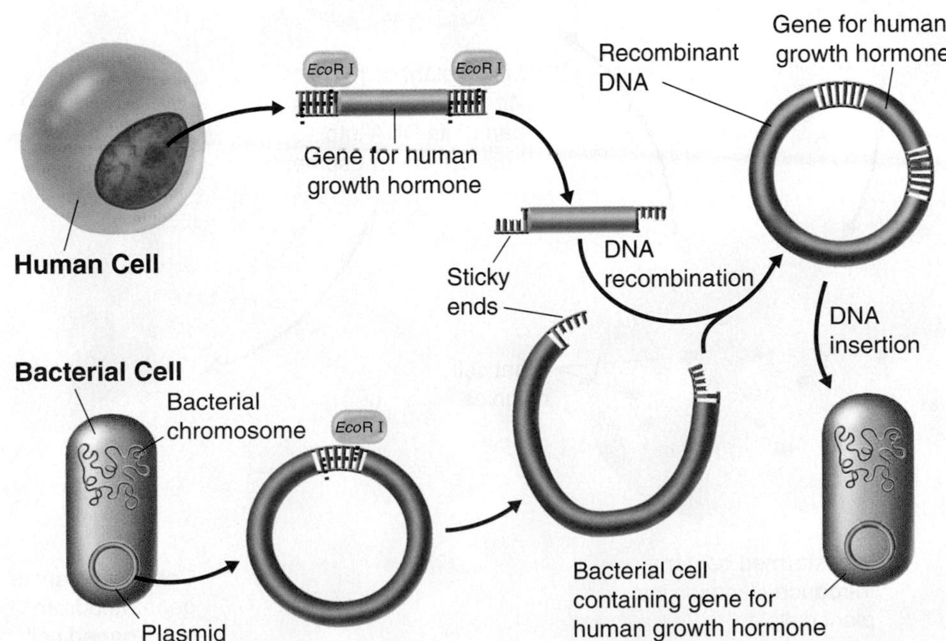

◀ **Figure 13–9** **During transformation, a cell incorporates DNA from outside the cell into its own DNA.** One way to use bacteria to produce human growth hormone is to insert a human gene into bacterial DNA. The new combination of genes is then returned to a bacterial cell. The bacterial cell containing the gene replicates over and over.

Second, the plasmid has a **genetic marker**—a gene that makes it possible to distinguish bacteria that carry the plasmid (and the foreign DNA) from those that don't. Genes for resistance to antibiotics, compounds that can kill bacteria, are commonly used as markers. A marker makes it possible for researchers to mix recombinant plasmids with a culture of bacteria, add enough DNA to transform one cell in a million, and still be able to "find" that cell. After transformation, the culture is treated with an antibiotic. Only those rare cells that have been transformed survive—because only they carry a resistance gene.

CHECKPOINT *What is a genetic marker?*

Transforming Plant Cells

Many plant cells can be transformed by using a process that takes advantage of a bacterium. In nature, this bacterium inserts a small DNA plasmid that produces tumors into a plant's cells. Researchers have discovered that they can inactivate the tumor-producing gene and insert a piece of foreign DNA into the plasmid. The recombinant plasmid can then be used to infect plant cells, as shown in **Figure 13–10.**

▼ **Figure 13–10** The bacterium *Agrobacterium tumefaciens* can be used to introduce foreign DNA into plant cells. **If the transformation is successful, the DNA will be integrated into one of the cell's chromosomes.**

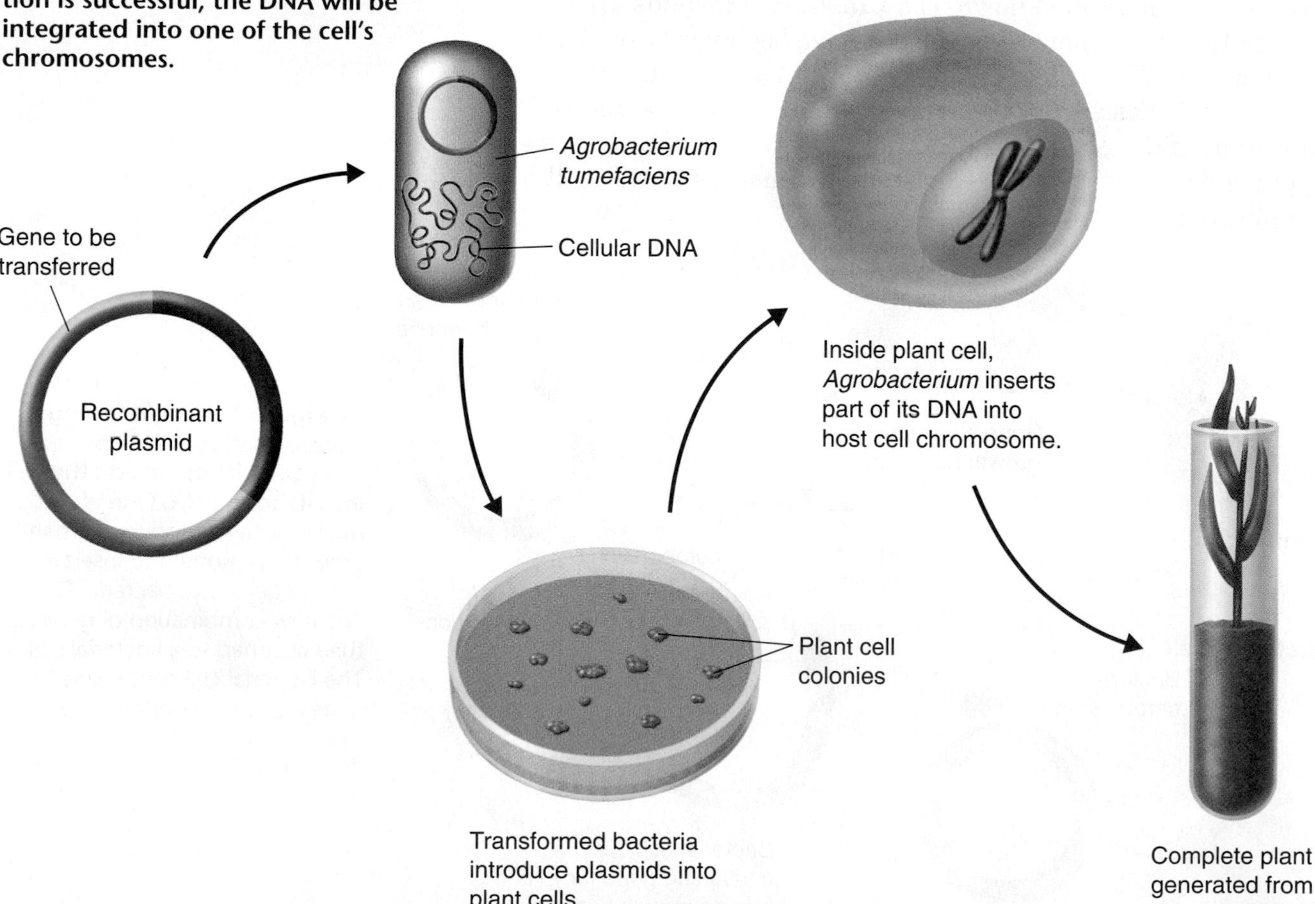
Gene to be transferred
Recombinant plasmid
Agrobacterium tumefaciens
Cellular DNA
Transformed bacteria introduce plasmids into plant cells.
Plant cell colonies
Inside plant cell, Agrobacterium inserts part of its DNA into host cell chromosome.
Complete plant is generated from transformed cell.

When their cell walls are removed, plant cells in culture will sometimes take up DNA on their own. DNA can also be injected directly into some cells. Cells transformed by either procedure can be cultured to produce adult plants. **If transformation is successful, the recombinant DNA is integrated into one of the chromosomes of the cell.**

Transforming Animal Cells

Animal cells can be transformed in some of the same ways as plant cells. Many egg cells are large enough that DNA can be directly injected into the nucleus. Once inside the nucleus, enzymes normally responsible for DNA repair and recombination may help to insert the foreign DNA into the chromosomes of the injected cell. Like bacterial plasmids, the DNA molecules used for transformation of animal and plant cells contain marker genes that enable biologists to identify which cells have been transformed.

Recently, it has become possible to eliminate particular genes by careful design of the DNA molecules that are used for transformation. As **Figure 13–11** shows, DNA molecules can be constructed with two ends that will sometimes recombine with specific sequences in the host chromosome. Once they do, the host gene normally found between those two sequences may be lost or specifically replaced with a new gene. This kind of gene replacement has made it possible to pinpoint the specific functions of genes in many organisms, including mice.

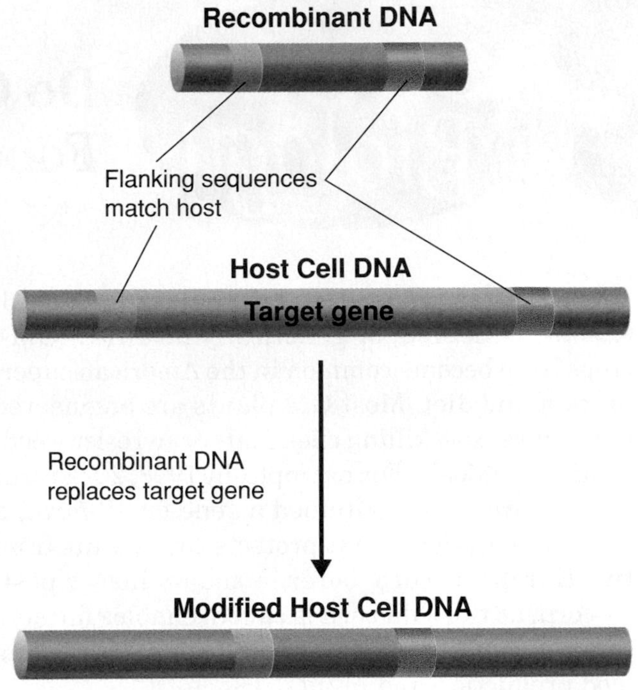

▲ **Figure 13–11** Recombinant DNA can replace a gene in an animal's genome. The ends of the recombinant DNA recombine with sequences in the host cell DNA. When the recombinant DNA is inserted into the target location, the host cell's original gene is lost or knocked out of its place. **Applying Concepts** ***How might this technique be used to treat disorders caused by a single gene? What might be some risks?***

13–3 Section Assessment

1. **Key Concept** What is transformation?
2. **Key Concept** How can you tell if a transformation experiment has been successful?
3. How are genetic markers related to transformation?
4. What are two features that make plasmids useful for transforming cells?
5. **Critical Thinking Comparing and Contrasting** Compare the transformation of a bacterium cell with the transformation of a plant cell.

Writing in Science

Writing a Plan for an Experiment

Imagine that you are a genetic engineer. Determine what your next experiment will be. Then, write up the steps you will follow and what your intended result will be.

Do Genetically Modified Foods Need Stricter Controls?

Since they were first introduced in 1994, bioengineered, or genetically modified (GM), crops have become common in the American supermarket and diet. Most GM plants are engineered to produce pest-killing chemicals or to resist weed-killing chemicals. For example, in 1998, 20 percent of U.S. corn crops contained a gene for *Bt-toxin,* a natural insecticide that protects corn plants from the European corn borer, a major insect pest. *Bt*-corn, as this GM corn is called, enables farmers to produce more food on fewer acres, increasing food production and profits.

Many consumers, however, are concerned about the long-term impact of these crops. The European Union, for example, has effectively stopped the import of many GM food crops and required that others be prominently labeled as genetically modified. Should GM foods be more tightly controlled?

The Viewpoints

GM Foods Need Tighter Controls

Some people are concerned that GM foods might have unexpected effects on people. For example, one type of GM corn approved only for animal feed has appeared accidentally in tortillas. The corn contains a protein that could cause allergic reactions in people. The contaminated tortillas show that GM crops can get mixed in with crops that have not been genetically modified.

Genetically modified crops also could pose a hazard to the environment. Antibiotic-resistant genes used as markers could spread into the environment, resulting in antibiotic-resistant bacteria. Pollen from GM plants might transfer genes to wild plants, resulting in "super weeds" that are impossible to control with weed killers. Plants engineered to produce insecticides can kill beneficial insects as well as pests. The spread of these pesticide genes from crop plants into wild plants might harm beneficial insects, such as bees and butterflies.

GM Foods Do Not Need Tighter Controls

Recently developed GM food crops contain essential vitamins that are lacking in the diets of many people. For example, golden rice contains genes that greatly increase its content of beta-carotene, which the body uses to make vitamin A. The high productivity and nutritional benefits of GM crops are especially important in developing countries, where their use may prevent famine and ease suffering.

Because they increase production and reduce the need for chemical pesticides, GM crops can be beneficial to the environment. Someday, GM plants could be sources of medicines, fuels, and plastics. If GM products are more strictly controlled, companies might not research new applications.

Research and Decide

1. **Analyzing the Viewpoints** To make an informed decision, learn more about this issue by consulting library or Internet resources. Then, list the risks and benefits of GM plants.
2. **Forming Your Opinion** Are stricter regulations needed? Give reasons for your opinion.

For: Links from the authors
Visit: PHSchool.com
Web Code: cbe-4133

13–4 Applications of Genetic Engineering

4-2.1 Asexually reproducing organisms and genes
4-2.2 Genetic manipulation
4-4.1 Cloning produces genetically alike individuals
4-7.3 Proposals that involve new technologies

Genetic engineering makes it possible to transfer DNA sequences, including whole genes, from one organism to another. Does this mean that genes from organisms as different as animals and plants can be made to work in each other? American researcher Steven Howell and his associates provided the answer in 1986. They isolated the gene for luciferase, an enzyme that allows fireflies to glow, and inserted it into tobacco cells. When whole plants were grown from the recombinant cells and the gene was activated, the plants glowed in the dark, as you can see in **Figure 13–12.** The gene for luciferase, which comes from an animal, can specify a trait in a plant. This shows that the basic mechanisms of gene expression are shared by plants and animals.

Guide for Reading

Key Concept
- How are transgenic organisms useful to human beings?

Vocabulary
transgenic
clone

Reading Strategy: Monitoring Your Understanding Make a table with three columns. Before you read, write what you already know about cloning in the first column. Under the next heading, write down what you want to learn about cloning. After you read, write down what you learned about cloning in the last column.

Transgenic Organisms

The universal nature of genetic mechanisms makes it possible to construct organisms that are **transgenic,** meaning that they contain genes from other species. Using the basic techniques of genetic engineering, a gene from one organism can be inserted into cells from another organism. These transformed cells can then be used to grow new organisms.  **Genetic engineering has spurred the growth of biotechnology, which is a new industry that is changing the way we interact with the living world.**

Transgenic Microorganisms Because they reproduce rapidly and are easy to grow, transgenic bacteria now produce a host of important substances useful for health and industry. The human forms of proteins such as insulin, growth hormone, and clotting factor, which are used to treat serious human diseases and conditions, were once rare and expensive. Bacteria transformed with the genes for human proteins now produce these important compounds cheaply and in great abundance. People with insulin-dependent diabetes are now treated with pure human insulin produced by human genes inserted into bacteria. In the future, transgenic microorganisms may produce substances designed to fight cancer, as well as the raw materials for plastics and synthetic fibers.

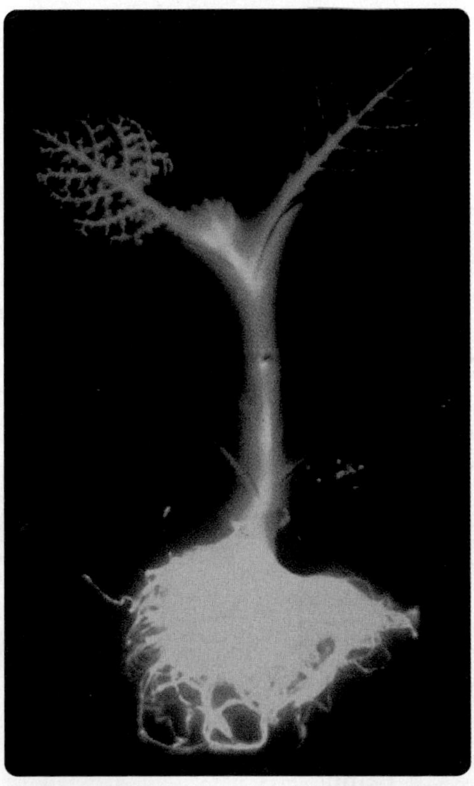

▶ **Figure 13–12 Genetic engineering has changed the way we interact with living things.** This transgenic tobacco plant, which glows in the dark, was grown from a tobacco cell transformed with the firefly luciferase gene. The plant illustrates how DNA from one organism contains information that can specify traits in another organism.

Go Online
NSTA SCiLINKS
For: Links on genetic engineering
Visit: www.SciLinks.org
Web Code: cbn-4134

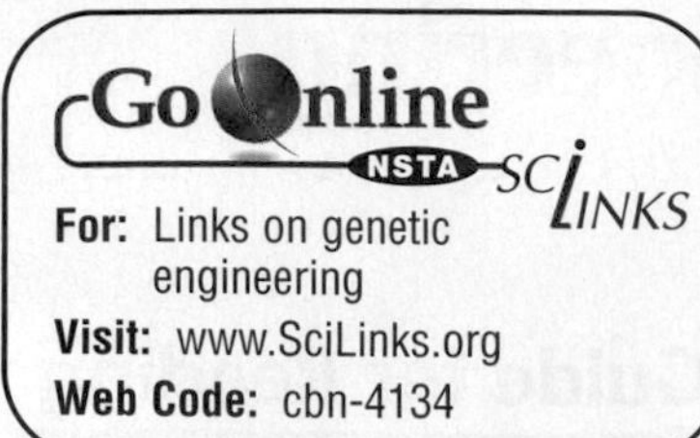

Transgenic Animals Transgenic animals have been used to study genes and to improve the food supply. Mice have been produced with human genes that make their immune systems act similarly to those of humans. This allows scientists to study the effects of diseases on the human immune system. Some transgenic livestock now have extra copies of growth hormone genes. Such animals grow faster and produce leaner meat than ordinary animals. Researchers are trying to produce transgenic chickens that will be resistant to the bacterial infections that can cause food poisoning.

In the future, transgenic animals might also provide us with an ample supply of our own proteins. Several labs have engineered transgenic sheep and pigs that produce human proteins in their milk, making it easy to collect and refine the proteins.

Transgenic Plants Transgenic plants are now an important part of our food supply. In the year 2000, 52 percent of the soybeans and 25 percent of the corn grown in the United States were transgenic, or genetically modified (GM). Many of these plants contain genes that produce a natural insecticide, so the crops do not have to be sprayed with synthetic pesticides. Other crop plants have genes that enable them to resist weed-killing chemicals. These genes allow crop plants to survive while weeds are still controlled.

▼ **Figure 13–13** In early 1997, Dolly made headlines as the first clone of an adult mammal. **Applying Concepts** *Why did Dolly not look like her foster mother?*

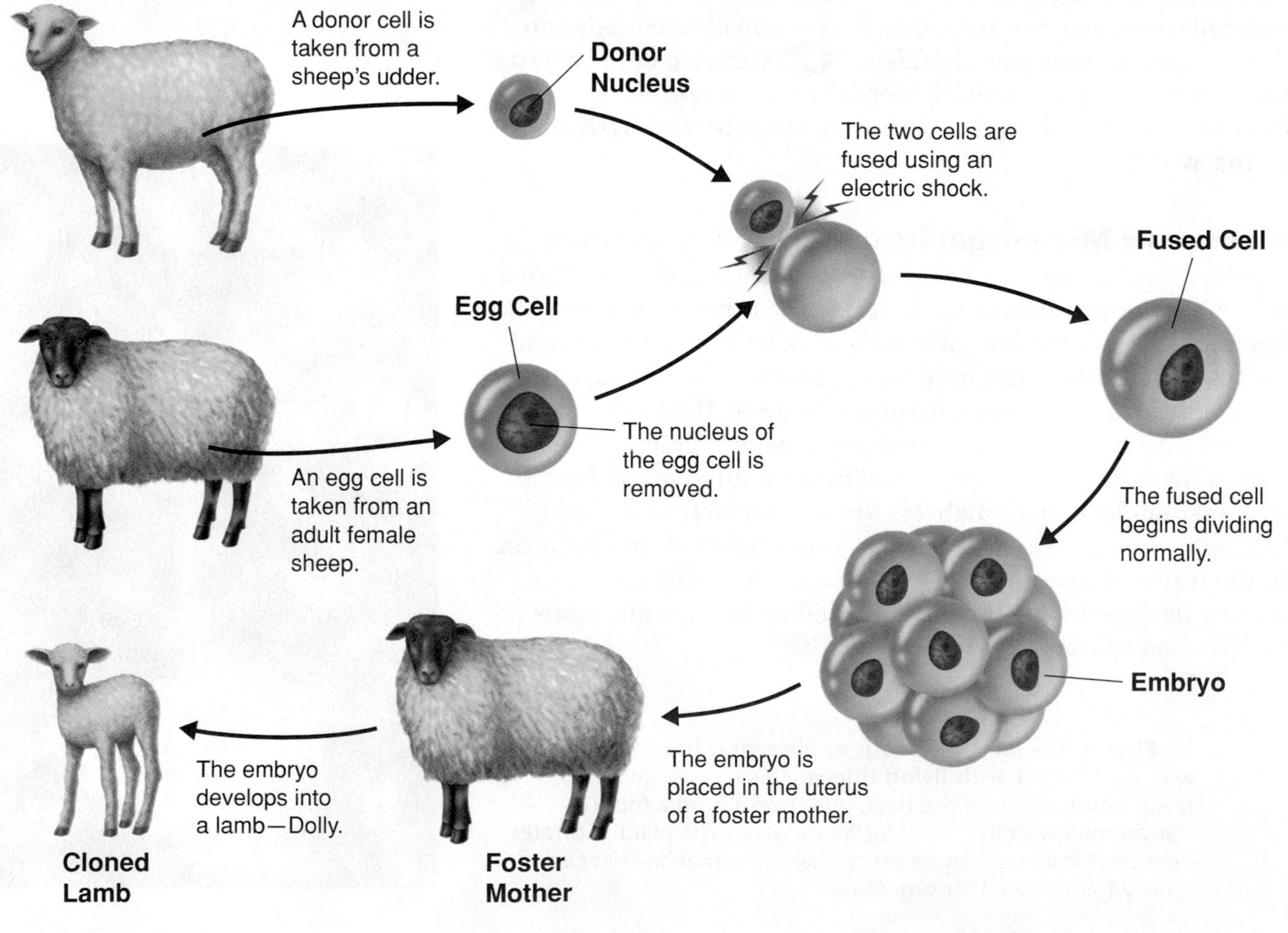

A donor cell is taken from a sheep's udder.
Donor Nucleus
The two cells are fused using an electric shock.
Fused Cell
Egg Cell
The nucleus of the egg cell is removed.
An egg cell is taken from an adult female sheep.
The fused cell begins dividing normally.
Embryo
The embryo is placed in the uterus of a foster mother.
The embryo develops into a lamb—Dolly.
Cloned Lamb
Foster Mother

Transgenic plants may soon produce human antibodies that can be used to fight disease, plastics that can now be produced only from petroleum, and foods that are resistant to rot and spoilage. One of the most important new developments in GM foods is a rice plant that contains vitamin A, a nutrient that is essential for human health. Since rice is the major food for billions of the world's people, this rice may improve the diets and health of many people by supplying an important nutrient.

▲ **Figure 13–14** The adult sheep is Dolly, the first mammal cloned from an adult cell. The lamb is Dolly's first offspring, called Bonnie. The fact that Dolly was cloned did not affect her ability to produce a live offspring. **Inferring** *Why might it be important for cloned animals to be able to reproduce?*

Cloning

A **clone** is a member of a population of genetically identical cells produced from a single cell. Cloned colonies of bacteria and other microorganisms are easy to grow, but this is not always true of multicellular organisms, especially animals. For many years, biologists wondered if it might be possible to clone a mammal—to use a single cell from an adult to grow an entirely new individual that is genetically identical to the organism from which the cell was taken. After years of research, many scientists had concluded that this was impossible.

In 1997, Scottish scientist Ian Wilmut stunned biologists by announcing that he had cloned a sheep. How did he do it? **Figure 13–13** shows the basic steps. In Wilmut's technique, the nucleus of an egg cell is removed. The cell is fused with a cell taken from another adult. The fused cell begins to divide and the embryo is then placed in the reproductive system of a foster mother, where it develops normally. The sheep, which Wilmut named Dolly, is shown in **Figure 13–14.** Cloned cows, pigs, mice, and other mammals have been produced by similar techniques. Researchers hope that cloning will enable them to make copies of transgenic animals and even help save endangered species. On the other hand, the technology is controversial for many reasons, including studies suggesting that cloned animals may suffer from a number of genetic defects and health problems.

The use of cloning technology on humans, while scientifically possible, raises serious ethical and moral issues that have caused many people to oppose such work. As techniques improve, these important issues will become even more pressing.

13–4 Section Assessment

1. **Key Concept** List one practical application for each of the following: transgenic bacteria, transgenic animals, transgenic plants.
2. **Key Concept** What is a transgenic organism?
3. What basic steps were followed to produce Dolly?
4. **Critical Thinking Making Judgments** List reasons you would or would not be concerned about eating genetically modified food.

You & Your Community

Conducting a Survey
Survey at least ten people about their viewpoints on cloning animals. To help the people you survey understand the topic, prepare an illustrated explanation of the process of cloning.

Design an Experiment

Investigating the Effects of Radiation on Seeds

Mutations occur naturally in all organisms. However, an organism's mutation rate increases when it is exposed to certain chemicals or types of radiation. In this investigation, you will design an experiment to test the effects of X-ray exposure on seeds.

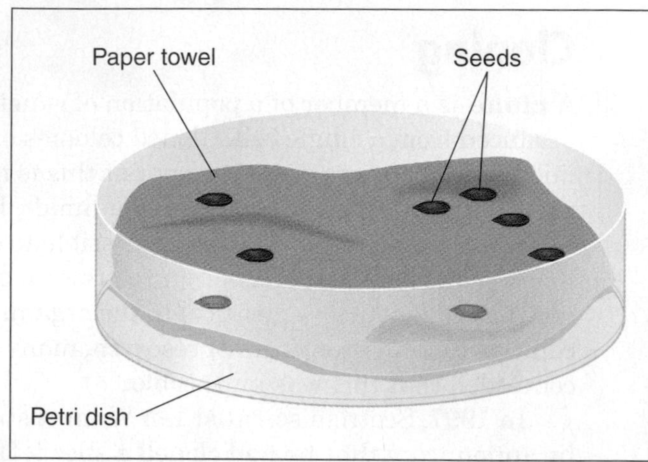

Problem

Do plants grown from irradiated seeds show evidence of increased mutation?

Materials

- irradiated seeds and nonirradiated seeds of the same species
- petri dishes
- paper towels
- plant pots with commercial potting soil
- glass-marking pencil

Skills

Forming Operational Definitions

Design Your Experiment

Part A: Plan the Experiment

1. **Designing Experiments** Working with two of your classmates, design an experiment to test the hypothesis that radiation increases the rate of mutation in seeds.
2. As you plan your investigative procedures, refer to the Lab Tips box on page 55 for information on demonstrating safe practices, making wise choices in the use of materials, and selecting equipment and technology.
3. Discuss your experimental plan with your group. Make certain that you have identified and controlled all important variables and included both irradiated and control seeds in your experimental plan.
4. You will not be able to observe mutations in DNA directly. What observations or measurements can you make that will provide evidence of the number of mutations that have occurred in a seed? With your group, plan what observations you will use to estimate the number of mutations that have occurred in a seed.
5. Design a data table in which to record your observations.
6. Show your experimental plan to your teacher. Once your teacher approves your plan, begin your experiment.

Part B: Carry Out Your Experiment

7. To grow the seeds, follow any instructions that are on the seed packages. If there are no instructions, line a petri dish with a paper towel for each experimental group of seeds. Place the seeds in the petri dishes, as shown in the diagram above. Cover the seeds with water. **CAUTION:** *Wash your hands well with warm water and plenty of soap after handling seeds, plants, or soil and before leaving the laboratory.*
8. Place the covers on the petri dishes to protect the seeds from mold and bacteria. Record everything you do to the seeds.
9. Use a glass-marking pencil to label each petri dish. Every petri dish that you use in this experiment should be identified by a different label that includes your name. Store the petri dishes in the location that your teacher designates.
10. Record your observations of each group of seeds every day for 2 weeks. Add water to the petri dishes as necessary to keep the seeds moist.
11. After 2 weeks, count the seeds that failed to germinate. Carefully transfer the young plants from the petri dishes to pots of soil. Water each plant. Label each pot with your name and the kind of plants it contains.

12. Place the potted plants in sunlight or under a fluorescent lamp as your teacher directs. Water the plants regularly. Continue to observe the plants daily, according to your experimental plans, for the next 2 weeks. Record your observations each day.

Analyze and Conclude

1. **Comparing and Contrasting** What differences did you observe between the irradiated seeds and the nonirradiated seeds?
2. **Designing Experiments** How could you best determine whether a seed contains mutant DNA?
3. **Forming Operational Definitions** What kinds of observations did you decide to use as evidence of mutations? Explain why you think that these observations are reliable evidence.
4. **Analyzing Data** Did the irradiated seeds show evidence of more mutations than the nonirradiated seeds?
5. **Formulating Hypotheses** Mutations sometimes cause part of an otherwise healthy-looking leaf or other plant part to appear abnormal. Did you see abnormal-looking areas on any plants? Would you expect this kind of abnormality to be inherited? Explain.
6. **Evaluating** What explanations, other than mutation, can you think of for the differences you observed between the irradiated seeds and the nonirradiated seeds?
7. **SAFETY:** Explain how you demonstrated safe practices during this investigation.

Go Further

Communicating Valid Conclusions
Compare your data to those of other students in your class. Work with the rest of the students in your class to reach a conclusion about the effect of radiation on seeds. Your conclusion should be based on class data. Then, write a short report about your experiment that would be suitable to submit to a scientific journal. Your report should communicate your conclusion and explain why it is valid.

Chapter 13 Study Guide

13–1 Changing the Living World

Key Concepts

- Humans use selective breeding, which takes advantage of naturally occurring genetic variation in plants, animals, and other organisms, to pass desired traits on to the next generation of organisms.
- Breeders can increase the genetic variation in a population by inducing mutations, which are the ultimate source of genetic variability.

Vocabulary
selective breeding, p. 319
hybridization, p. 319
inbreeding, p. 320

13–2 Manipulating DNA

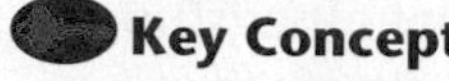
Key Concept

- Scientists use their knowledge of the structure of DNA and its chemical properties to study and change DNA molecules. Different techniques are used to extract DNA from cells, to cut DNA into smaller pieces, to identify the sequence of bases in a DNA molecule, and to make unlimited copies of DNA.

Vocabulary
genetic engineering, p. 322
restriction enzyme, p. 323
gel electrophoresis, p. 323
recombinant DNA, p. 324
polymerase chain reaction (PCR), p. 325

13–3 Cell Transformation

Key Concepts

- During transformation, a cell takes in DNA from outside the cell. This external DNA becomes a component of the cell's DNA.
- If transformation is successful, the recombinant DNA is integrated into one of the chromosomes of the cell.

Vocabulary
plasmid, p. 327
genetic marker, p. 328

13–4 Applications of Genetic Engineering

Key Concept

- Genetic engineering has spurred the growth of biotechnology, which is a new industry that is changing the way we interact with the living world.

Vocabulary
transgenic, p. 331
clone, p. 333

Thinking Visually

Using the information in this chapter, complete the following concept map.

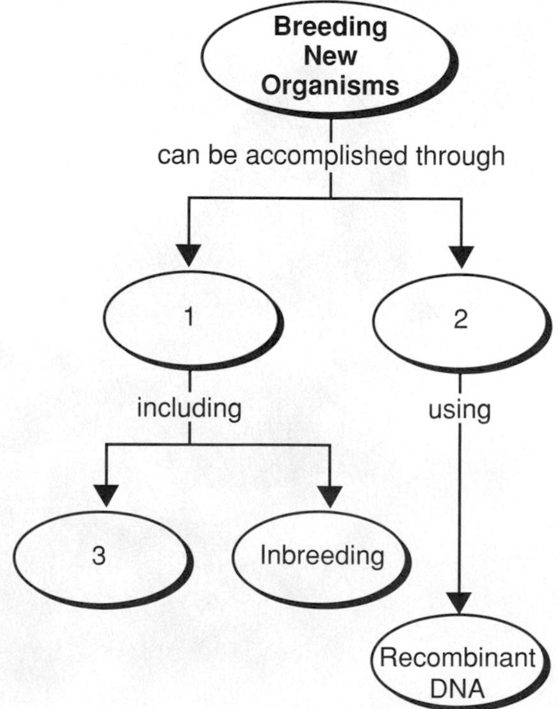

Preparing for the Living Environment Exam

NEW YORK
LIVING ENVIRONMENT

Blue questions emphasize Regents Exam content

Chapter 13

Part A

Multiple Choice

For each statement or question, select the number of the word or expression that, of those given, best completes the statement or answers the question.

1 When humans first domesticated dogs, there was relatively little diversity in the species. Today, there are many variations such as the German shepherd and the Dalmatian. This increase in diversity is most closely associated with
(1) cloning of selected body cells
(2) selective breeding
(3) mitotic cell division
(4) environmental influences on inherited traits

2 Many diabetics are now using insulin that was made by certain bacteria. The ability of these bacteria to produce insulin was most likely the result of
(1) deleting many DNA segments from bacterial DNA
(2) genetic mapping of bacterial DNA to activate the gene for insulin production
(3) inserting a portion of human DNA into the ring-shaped DNA of bacteria
(4) using radiation to trigger mutations

3 DNA molecules are cut into fragments having shorter sequences by using
(1) enzymes (3) electrophoresis
(2) chromatography (4) carbohydrates

4 A small amount of DNA was taken from a fossil of a mammoth found frozen in glacial ice. Genetic technology can be used to produce a large quantity of identical DNA from this mammoth's DNA. In this technology, the original DNA sample is used to
(1) stimulate differentiation in other mammoth cells
(2) provide fragments to replace certain human body chemicals
(3) act as a template for repeated replication
(4) trigger mitosis to obtain new base sequences

5 When cell transformation is successful, the recombinant DNA
(1) undergoes mutation
(2) is treated with antibiotics
(3) is integrated into a chromosome
(4) becomes a plasmid

6 What is the result of the process illustrated below?

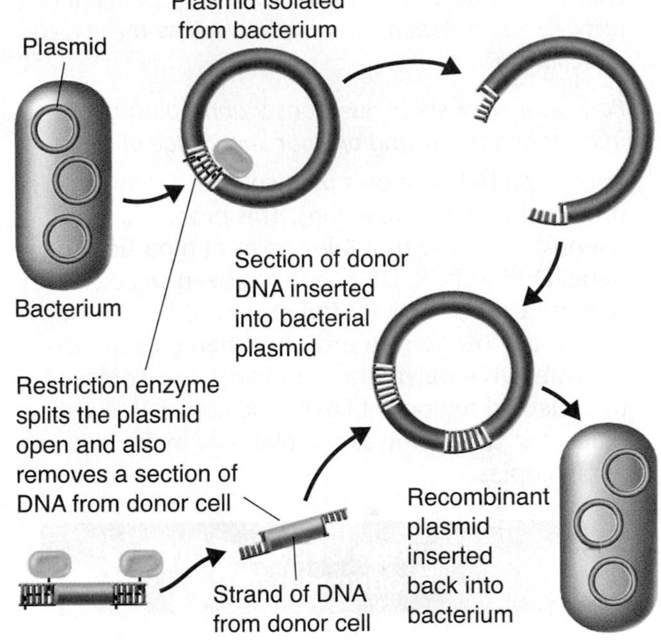
Plasmid
Plasmid isolated from bacterium
Bacterium
Section of donor DNA inserted into bacterial plasmid
Restriction enzyme splits the plasmid open and also removes a section of DNA from donor cell
Recombinant plasmid inserted back into bacterium
Strand of DNA from donor cell

(1) polymerase DNA (3) a new human gene
(2) recombinant DNA (4) a new human species

7 Bacteria often contain small circular molecules of DNA known as
(1) clones (3) plasmids
(2) restrictions (4) hybrids

8 Which statement concerning an organism produced by cloning is correct?
(1) The clone is genetically identical to the parent.
(2) The clone has the combined genes of both of its parents.
(3) The genetic makeup of the clone will be somewhat different than that of its parent.
(4) The appearance of the clone will be entirely different than that of its parents.

Test-Taking Tip For questions containing the words *not* or *except*, begin by eliminating each answer choice that does fit the characteristic in question. After eliminating all but one of the choices, check to see that your answer is correct by confirming that it does not fit the characteristic in question.

Preparing for the Living Environment Exam

Part B

Multiple Choice and Extended Response

For those questions that ask you to select a response, choose the one that best completes the statement or answers the question. For all others follow the directions given.

Base your answers to questions 9 and 10 on the information below and on your knowledge of biology.

The graph below shows data collected during PCR (polymerase chain reaction). This process allows scientists to make multiple copies of a particular gene. During PCR, DNA that has been selected and prepared specifically for the process is heated to separate it into two strands. It is then cooled. An enzyme, DNA polymerase starts making copies of the selected regions of DNA. The copies that are made can then serve as templates to make additional copies.

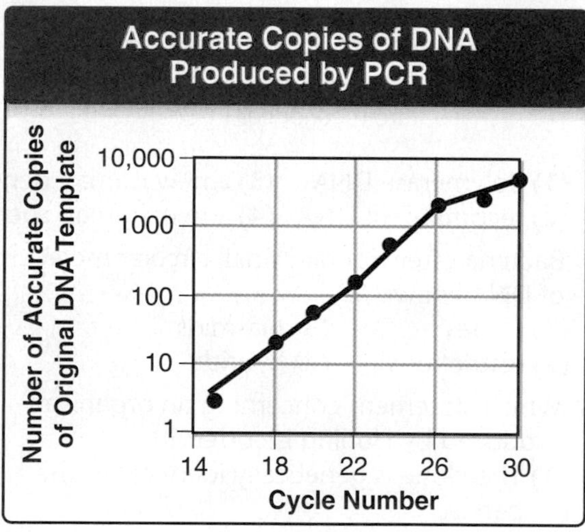

9 PCR is expected to double the amount of DNA with each cycle. State whether or not this is supported with information from the graph. Use specific data from the graph to explain the basis for your answer.

10 Explain why the amount of DNA produced with PCR is expected to double with each cycle.

11 The luciferase gene found in fireflies has been successfully transferred to several plant species. Under certain conditions, plants containing this gene will glow. State what this indicates about the functioning of genes in both plants and animals.

12 Describe what a transgenic organism is, and identify three examples of how transgenic bacteria have been used to benefit humans.

13 List *two* advantages of producing needed proteins such as insulin through genetic engineering.

14 A plant breeder has three rose bushes with the characteristics shown in the chart below.

Rosebush	Thorniness	Scent	Flower Color
A	thornless	scentless	pink
B	thorny	sweet smell	yellow
C	thorny	scentless	purple

Explain how a plant breeder could develop a purebred variety of thornless sweet-smelling purple roses.

Base your answers to questions 15 through 17 on the diagram below and on your knowledge of biology.

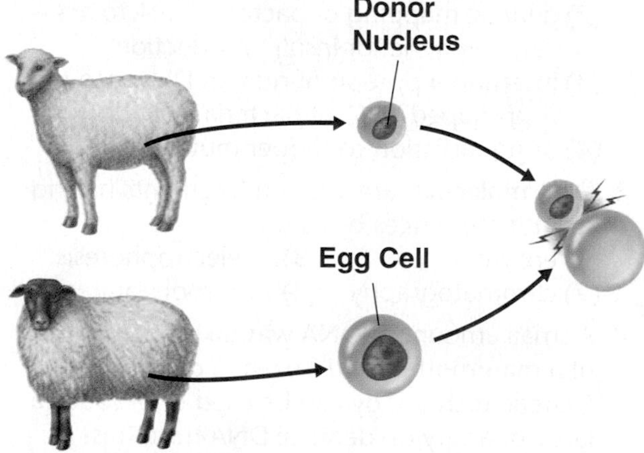

15 The events shown in the diagram represent part of the process of

(1) selective breeding (3) natural selection
(2) cloning (4) genetic modification

16 Compare the amount of genetic information in the nucleus of the donor cell with the amount of genetic information in an intact egg cell.

17 Explain why the nucleus of the egg must be removed before fusing the cells.

NEW YORK LIVING ENVIRONMENT

Base your answers to questions 18 through 19 on the passage below and on your knowledge of biology.

The DNA sequence for the Lyme disease pathogen *Borrelia burgdorferi,* comprising over 1.4 million base pairs, has been identified. This achievement, first featured in the scientific journal *Nature,* provides new information that will hopefully lead to better diagnostic tests, second-generation vaccines, discovery of the reasons behind individual susceptibility to chronic symptoms, and other discoveries in the ongoing quest to understand and prevent this multi-faceted disease.

18 Identify the technique used to separate a mixture of DNA fragments that vary in size.

19 State how knowledge of the DNA sequence of a disease-causing organism can be used by researchers to help fight the disease.

Part C

Extended Response

Answer the questions or follow the directions given.

20 Both genetic engineering and selective breeding have been used to make changes in the genetic information of certain organisms. Both processes rely on natural variations found in organisms, but use them differently. Compare the way these natural variations are used differently in the two processes. In your answer, be sure to

- explain how breeders use variations to produce offspring with combinations of traits that never existed in any one individual plant or animal before
- give an example of selective breeding that supports your explanation of how the process works
- explain how genetic engineers use variations to produce organisms with genetic traits that never existed in that species before
- give an example of genetic engineering that supports your explanation of how the process works

21 For many years, humans have used a variety of techniques that have influenced the genetic makeup of organisms. These techniques have led to the production of new varieties of organisms that possess characteristics that are useful to humans. Identify one technique presently being used to alter the genetic makeup of an organism, and explain how humans can benefit from this change. Your answer must include at least:

- the name of the technique used to alter the genetic makeup
- a brief description of what is involved in this technique
- one specific example of how this technique has been used
- a statement of how humans have benefited from the production of this new variety of organism

For: An interactive self-test
Visit: PHSchool.com
Web Code: cba-4130

CHAPTER 14

The Human Genome

The children in this family have some traits that are similar to their mother's and some that are similar to their father's.

Inquiry Activity

Can you predict chin shape?

Procedure

1. Two parents with cleft chins, both heterozygous for cleft chin *(Cc)*, have three children with cleft chins. The parents are sure that their fourth child will not have a cleft chin. Draw a Punnett square to see if this is possible.
2. Determine the probability that the fourth child will have a cleft chin.

Think About It

1. **Using Models** What information does a Punnett square give? Does the Punnett square support the parents' prediction? Explain your answer.
2. **Predicting** If these parents have a fifth child, what are the chances that the child will have a cleft chin? Explain your answer.

14–1 Human Heredity

4-2.1 Genes/chromosomes directly influence heredity
4-2.1 Mutations are changes in genes and can be inherited
4-2.2 Genetic research
4-5.2 Biological research

Of all the living things that inhabit this remarkable world, there is one in particular that has always drawn our interest, one that has always made us wonder, one that will always fire our imagination. That creature is, of course, ourselves, *Homo sapiens.*

Scientists once knew much less about humans than about other organisms. Until very recently, human genetics lagged far behind the genetics of "model" organisms such as fruit flies and mice. That, however, has changed. Scientists are now on the verge of understanding human genetics at least as well as they understand that of some other organisms. From that understanding will come a new responsibility to use that information wisely.

Guide for Reading

Key Concepts
- How is sex determined?
- How do small changes in DNA cause genetic disorders?

Vocabulary
karyotype
sex chromosome
autosome
pedigree

Reading Strategy: Using Prior Knowledge
Before you read, write down what you already know about the inheritance of traits. As you read, compare the information in the text to your notes.

Human Chromosomes

What makes us human? Biologists can begin to answer that question by taking a look under the microscope to see what is inside a human cell. To analyze chromosomes, cell biologists photograph cells in mitosis, when the chromosomes are fully condensed and easy to see. The biologists then cut out the chromosomes from the photographs and group them together in pairs. A picture of chromosomes arranged in this way is known as a **karyotype** (KAR-ee-uh-typ).

The chromosomes shown in **Figure 14–1** are from a typical human body cell. The number of chromosomes—46—helps identify this karyotype as human. This karyotype is the result of a haploid sperm, carrying just 23 chromosomes, fertilizing a haploid egg, also with 23 chromosomes. The diploid zygote, or fertilized egg, contained the full complement of 46 chromosomes.

Two of those 46 chromosomes are known as **sex chromosomes,** because they determine an individual's sex. Females have two copies of a large X chromosome. Males have one X and one small Y chromosome. To distinguish them from the sex chromosomes, the remaining 44 chromosomes are known as autosomal chromosomes, or **autosomes.** To quickly summarize the total number of chromosomes present in a human cell, both autosomes and sex chromosomes, biologists write 46,XX for females and 46,XY for males.

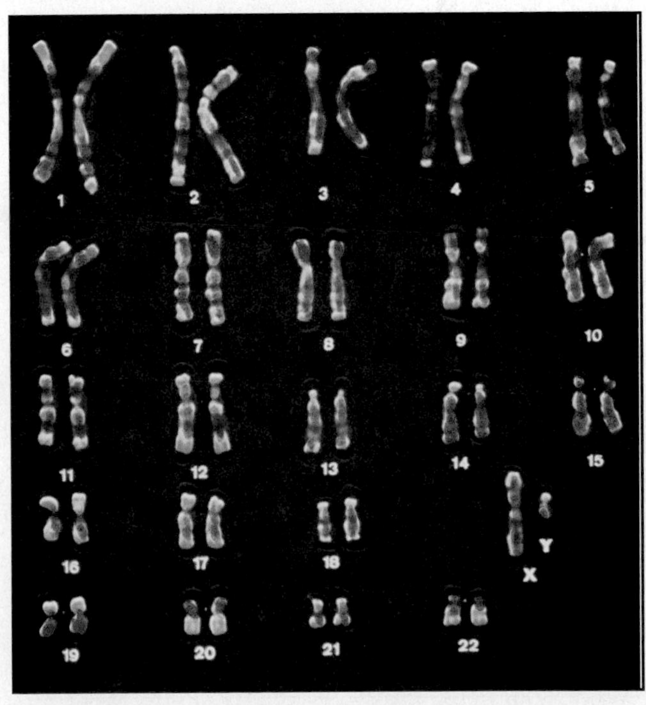

▶ **Figure 14–1** These human chromosomes have been cut out of a photograph and arranged to form a karyotype. **Interpreting Graphics** *Analyze this karyotype and identify the person's sex.*

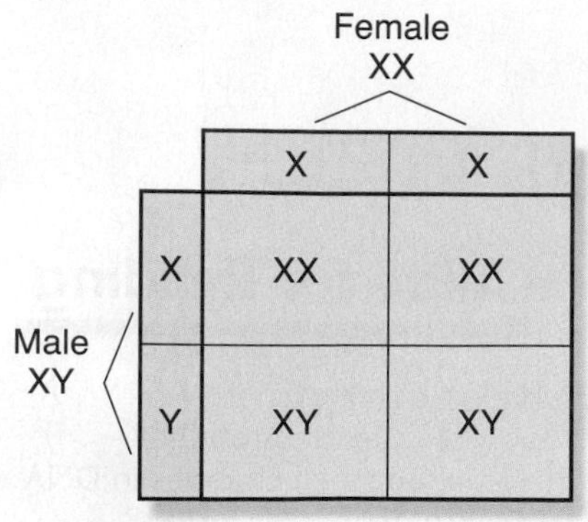
Female
XX
X
X
Male
XY
X
XX
XX
Y
XY
XY

▲ **Figure 14–2** **In humans, egg cells contain a single X chromosome. Sperm cells contain either one X chromosome or one Y chromosome.** In a population, approximately half of the zygotes are XX (female) and half are XY (male).

Go Online
active art
For: Pedigree activity
Visit: PHSchool.com
Web Code: cbp-4141

▼ **Figure 14–3** This drawing shows what the symbols in a pedigree represent. **Interpreting Graphics** *What are the genotypes of both parents on the left in the second row? How do you know?*

As you can see in **Figure 14–2**, males and females are born in a roughly 50 : 50 ratio because of the way in which sex chromosomes segregate during meiosis. **All human egg cells carry a single X chromosome (23,X). However, half of all sperm cells carry an X chromosome (23,X) and half carry a Y chromosome (23,Y). This ensures that just about half of the zygotes will be 46,XX and half will be 46,XY.**

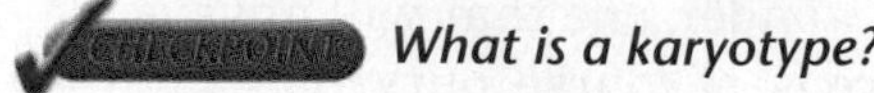
CHECKPOINT

What is a karyotype?

Human Traits

Human genes are inherited according to the same principles that Gregor Mendel discovered in his work with garden peas. However, in order to apply Mendelian genetics to humans, biologists must identify an inherited trait controlled by a single gene. First, they must establish that the trait is actually inherited and not the result of environmental influences. Then, they have to study how the trait is passed from one generation to the next.

Pedigree Charts A **pedigree** chart, which shows the relationships within a family, can be used to help with this task. The pedigree in **Figure 14–3** shows how an interesting human trait, a white lock of hair just above the forehead, is transmitted through three generations of a family. The allele for the white forelock trait is dominant. At the top of the chart is a grandfather who had the white forelock trait. Two of his three children inherited the trait, although one child did not. Three grandchildren have the trait, and two do not.

Genetic counselors analyze pedigree charts to infer the genotypes of family members. For example, since the white forelock trait is dominant, all the family members that lack the trait must have homozygous recessive alleles. Since one of the grandfather's children lacks the white forelock trait, the grandfather must be heterozygous for the trait.

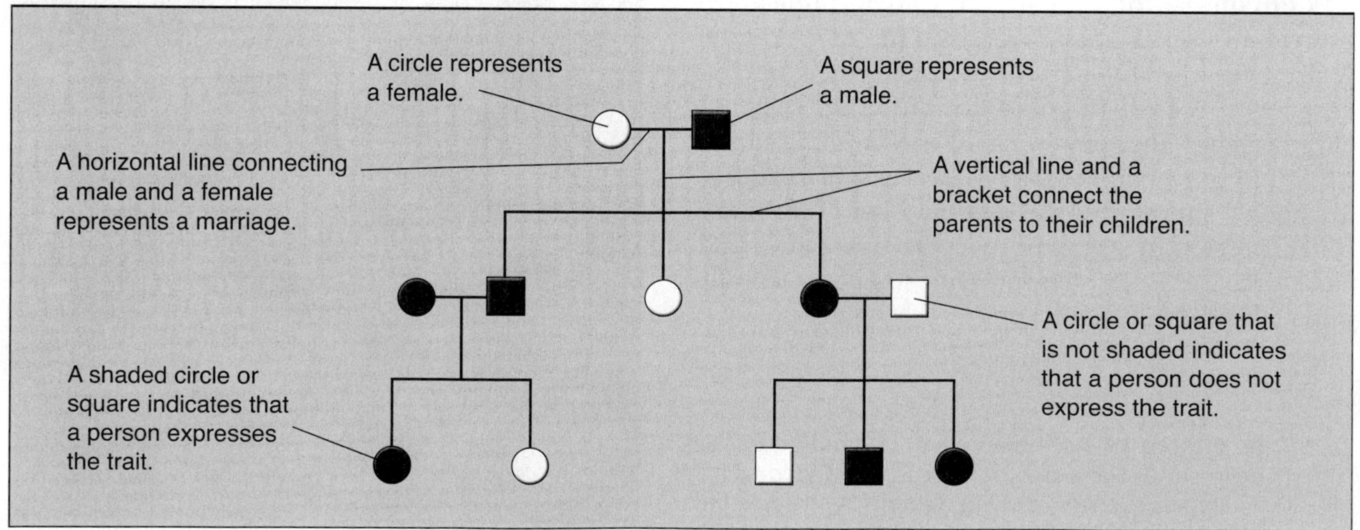
A circle represents a female.
A square represents a male.
A horizontal line connecting a male and a female represents a marriage.
A vertical line and a bracket connect the parents to their children.
A circle or square that is not shaded indicates that a person does not express the trait.
A shaded circle or square indicates that a person expresses the trait.

Genes and the Environment Unfortunately for folks who would like to settle burning issues, like which side of the family is responsible for your good looks, some of the most obvious human traits are almost impossible to associate with single genes. There are two reasons for this. First, things you might think of as single traits, such as the shape of your eyes or ears, are actually polygenic, meaning they are controlled by many genes. Second, many of your personal traits are only partly governed by genetics. Remember that the phenotype of an organism is only partly determined by its genotype. Many traits are strongly influenced by environmental, or nongenetic, factors, including nutrition and exercise. For example, even though a person's maximum possible height is largely determined by genetic factors, nutritional improvements in the United States and Europe have increased the average height of these populations about 10 centimeters over their average height in the 1800s.

Although it is important to consider the influence of the environment on the expression of some genes, it must be understood that environmental effects on gene expression are not inherited; genes are. Genes may be denied a proper environment in which to reach full expression in one generation. However, these same genes can, in a proper environment, achieve full potential in a later generation.

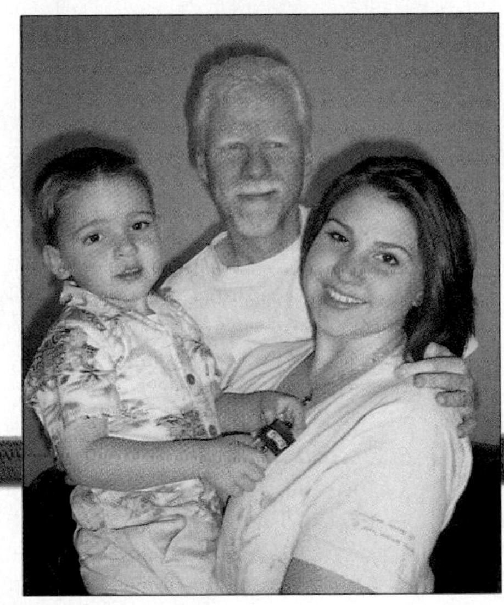

Problem Solving

Using a Pedigree

Imagine that you are a genetic counselor. The pedigree shown illustrates the inheritance of albinism, a condition in which a person's skin, hair, and eyes lack normal coloring, in three generations of a family. A couple from the family have come to you for advice about how the trait is inherited. Your task is to determine whether the allele for albinism is dominant or recessive.

Defining the Problem Define the problem that must be solved.

Organizing Information Copy the pedigree and the key onto a piece of paper. Label each person on the pedigree with his or her phenotype: normal-pigmented skin or albino.

Creating a Solution Write down how you would analyze the pattern in the inheritance of the albinism trait. Describe how you will use your analysis to infer the genotype of as many individuals as possible.

Presenting Your Plan Prepare a step-by-step outline of your plan. Present the plan to your class as if you were explaining the process to the couple involved.

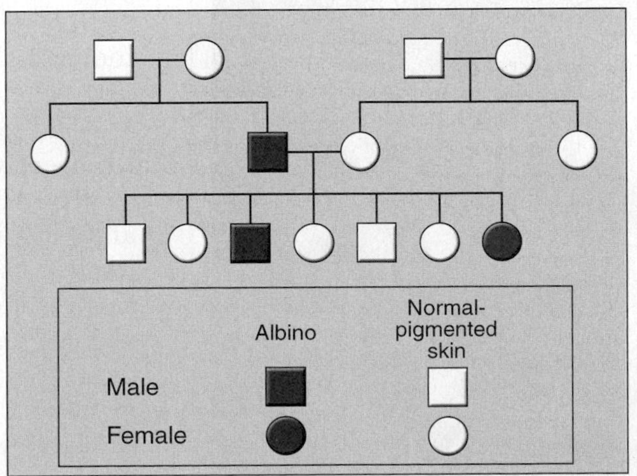

▶ **Figure 14–4** This table shows the relationship between genotype and phenotype for the ABO blood group. It also shows which blood types can safely be transfused into people with other blood types. **Applying Concepts** *How can there be four different phenotypes, even though there are six different genotypes?*

Blood Groups

Phenotype (Blood Type)	Genotype	Antigen on Red Blood Cell	Safe Transfusions	
			To	From
A	I^AI^A or I^Ai	A	A, AB	A, O
B	I^BI^B or I^Bi	B	B, AB	B, O
AB	I^AI^B	A and B	AB	A, B, AB, O
O	ii	none	A, B, AB, O	O

Human Genes

The human genome—our complete set of genetic information—includes tens of thousands of genes. The DNA sequences on these genes carry information for specifying many characteristics, from the color of your eyes to the detailed structures of proteins within your cells. The exploration of the human genome has been a major scientific undertaking. By 2000, the DNA sequence of the human genome was almost complete.

Studying the genetics of our species has not been easy. Until recently, the identification of a human gene took years of scientific work. Humans have long generation times and a complex life cycle, and they produce, at least compared with peas and fruit flies, very few offspring. Still, in a few cases, biologists were able to identify genes that directly control a single human trait. Some of the very first human genes to be identified were those that control blood type.

▼ **Figure 14–5** This medical worker is drawing blood from a patient. The blood will be tested to see what type of blood it is. **Applying Concepts** *Why is blood typing so important during a blood transfusion?*

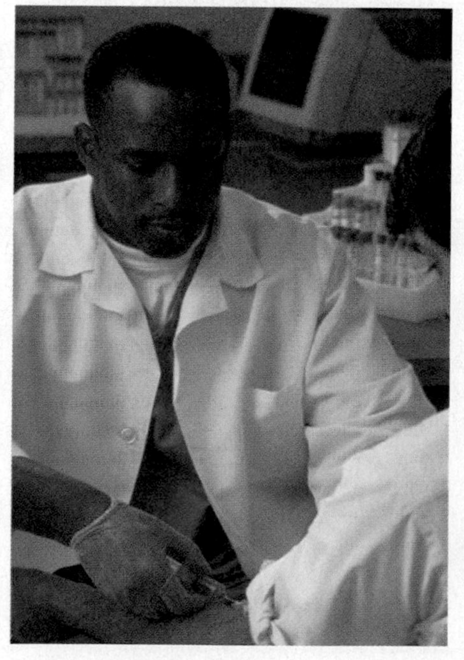

Blood Group Genes Human blood comes in a variety of genetically determined blood groups. Knowing a person's blood group is critical because using the wrong type of blood for a transfusion during a medical procedure can be fatal. A number of genes are responsible for human blood groups, but the best known are the ABO blood groups and the Rh blood groups.

The Rh blood group is determined by a single gene with two alleles—positive and negative. *Rh* stands for "rhesus monkey," the animal in which this factor was discovered. The positive (Rh^+) allele is dominant, so persons who are Rh^+/Rh^+ or Rh^+/Rh^- are said to be Rh-positive. Individuals with two Rh^- alleles are Rh-negative.

The ABO blood group is more complicated. There are three alleles for this gene, I^A, I^B, and i. Alleles I^A and I^B are codominant. These alleles produce molecules known as antigens on the surface of red blood cells. As **Figure 14–4** shows, individuals with alleles I^A and I^B produce both A and B antigens, making them blood type AB. The i allele is recessive. Individuals with alleles I^AI^A or I^Ai produce only the A antigen, making them blood type A. Those with I^BI^B or I^Bi alleles are type B. Those who are homozygous for the i allele (ii) produce no antigen and are said to have blood type O.

When a medical worker refers to blood groups, he or she usually mentions both groups at the same time. For example, if a patient has AB-negative blood, it means the individual has I^A and I^B alleles from the ABO gene and two Rh^- alleles from the Rh gene.

Recessive Alleles Many human genes have become known through the study of genetic disorders. **Figure 14–6** lists some common genetic disorders. In most cases, the presence of a normal, functioning gene is revealed only when an abnormal or nonfunctioning allele affects the phenotype.

One of the first genetic disorders to be understood this way was phenylketonuria (fen-ul-ket-oh-NOOR-ee-uh), or PKU. People with PKU lack the enzyme that is needed to break down phenylalanine. Phenylalanine is an amino acid found in milk and many other foods. If a newborn has PKU, phenylalanine may build up in the tissues during the child's first years of life and cause severe mental retardation. Fortunately, newborns can be tested for PKU and then placed on a low-phenylalanine diet that prevents most of the effects of PKU. PKU is caused by an autosomal recessive allele carried on chromosome 12.

Many other disorders are also caused by autosomal recessive alleles. One is Tay-Sachs disease, which is caused by an allele found mostly in Jewish families of central and eastern European ancestry. Tay-Sachs disease results in nervous system breakdown and death in the first few years of life. Although there is no treatment for Tay-Sachs disease, there is a test for the allele. By taking this test, prospective parents can learn whether they are at risk of having a child with the disorder.

▼ **Figure 14–6** This table shows the major symptoms of some well-known genetic disorders. **Interpreting Graphics** *Which disorder causes galactose to accumulate in the tissues?*

Some Autosomal Disorders in Humans

Type of Disorder	Disorder	Major Symptoms
Disorders caused by recessive alleles	Albinism	Lack of pigment in skin, hair, and eyes
	Cystic fibrosis	Excess mucus in lungs, digestive tract, liver; increased susceptibility to infections
	Galactosemia	Accumulation of galactose (a sugar) in tissues; mental retardation; eye and liver damage
	Phenylketonuria (PKU)	Accumulation of phenylalanine in tissues; lack of normal skin pigment; mental retardation
	Tay-Sachs disease	Lipid accumulation in brain cells; mental deficiency; blindness; death in early childhood
Disorders caused by dominant alleles	Achondroplasia	Dwarfism (one form)
	Huntington's disease	Mental deterioration and uncontrollable movements; symptoms usually appear in middle age
	Hypercholesterolemia	Excess cholesterol in blood; heart disease
Disorders caused by codominant alleles	Sickle cell disease	Misshapen, or sickled, red blood cells; damage to many tissues

Dominant Alleles Not all genetic disorders are caused by recessive alleles. You may recall that the effects of a dominant allele are expressed even when the recessive allele is present. Therefore, if you have a dominant allele for a genetic disorder, it will be expressed. Two examples of genetic disorders caused by autosomal dominant alleles are a form of dwarfism known as achondroplasia (ay-kahn-droh-PLAY-zhuh) and a nervous system disorder known as Huntington's disease. Huntington's disease causes a progressive loss of muscle control and mental function until death occurs. People who have this disease generally show no symptoms until they are in their thirties or older, when the gradual damage to the nervous system begins.

Codominant Alleles Sickle cell disease, a serious disorder found in about 1 out of 500 African Americans, is caused by a codominant allele. As you will read, the reason for the high incidence of sickle cell in the United States is a story that links genetics, human history, and molecular biology.

What type of allele causes Huntington's disease?

From Gene to Molecule

How do the actual DNA sequences in genes affect phenotype so profoundly? What is the link between the DNA bases in the allele for a genetic disorder and the disorder itself? For many genetic disorders, scientists are still working to find the answer. But for two disorders, the connection is understood very well indeed. **In both cystic fibrosis and sickle cell disease, a small change in the DNA of a single gene affects the structure of a protein, causing a serious genetic disorder.**

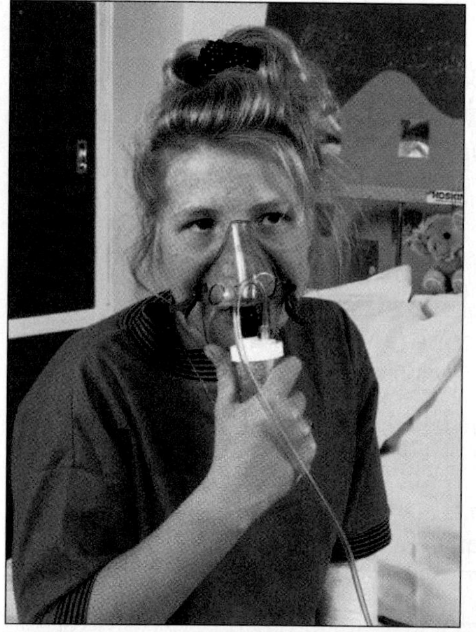

▲ **Figure 14–7** This girl is inhaling a fine mist through a nebulizer. The medication in the mist thins the mucus in the lungs, making breathing easier. **Inferring** *Why is it important for people with CF to thin the mucus in their lungs?*

Cystic Fibrosis Cystic fibrosis, or CF, is a common genetic disease. Cystic fibrosis is most common among people whose ancestors came from Northern Europe. The disease is caused by a recessive allele on chromosome 7. Children with cystic fibrosis have serious digestive problems. In addition, they produce a thick, heavy mucus that clogs their lungs and breathing passageways.

Cystic fibrosis involves a very small genetic change. **Figure 14–8** illustrates how information carried in a chromosome's DNA specifies the trait of cystic fibrosis. Most cases of cystic fibrosis are caused by the deletion of 3 bases in the middle of a sequence for a protein. This protein normally allows chloride ions (Cl^-) to pass across biological membranes. The deletion of these 3 bases removes just one amino acid from this large protein, causing it to fold improperly. Because of this, the cells do not transport the protein to the cell membrane, and the misfolded protein is destroyed. Unable to transport chloride ions, tissues throughout the body malfunction. People with one normal copy of the allele are unaffected, because they can produce enough of the chloride channel protein to allow their tissues to function properly.

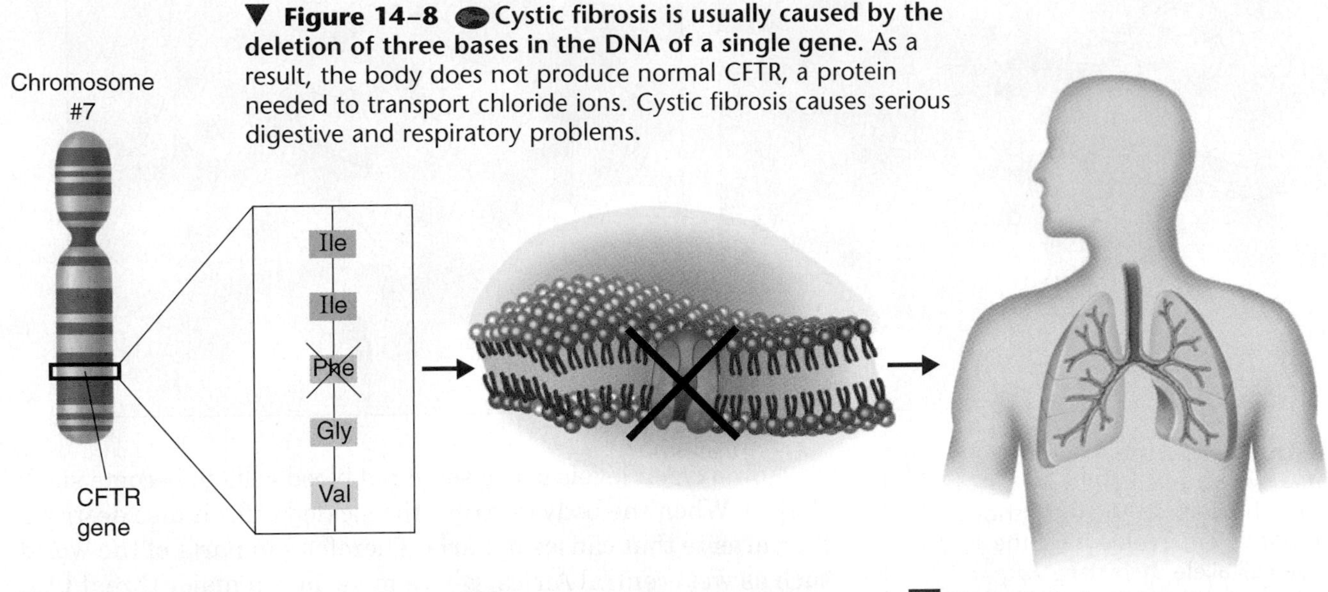

▼ **Figure 14–8** **Cystic fibrosis is usually caused by the deletion of three bases in the DNA of a single gene.** As a result, the body does not produce normal CFTR, a protein needed to transport chloride ions. Cystic fibrosis causes serious digestive and respiratory problems.

A The most common allele that causes cystic fibrosis is missing 3 DNA bases. As a result, the amino acid phenylalanine is missing from the CFTR protein.

B Normal CFTR is a chloride ion channel in cell membranes. Abnormal CFTR cannot be transported to the cell membrane.

C The cells in the person's airways are unable to transport chloride ions. As a result, the airways become clogged with a thick mucus.

Sickle Cell Disease Sickle cell disease is a common genetic disorder found in African Americans. Sickle cell disease is characterized by the bent and twisted shape of the red blood cells, like those shown in **Figure 14–9.** These sickle-shaped red blood cells are more rigid than normal cells and tend to get stuck in the capillaries, the narrowest blood vessels in the body. As a result, blood stops moving through these vessels, damaging cells, tissues, and organs. Sickle cell disease produces physical weakness and damage to the brain, heart, and spleen. In some cases, it may be fatal.

Hemoglobin is the protein in red blood cells that carries oxygen. The normal allele for the gene differs little from the sickle cell allele—just one DNA base is changed. This change substitutes the amino acid valine for glutamic acid. As a result, the abnormal hemoglobin is somewhat less soluble than normal hemoglobin. Any decrease in blood oxygen levels causes many of the hemoglobin molecules to come out of solution and stick together. The stuck-together molecules form long chains and fibers that produce the characteristic shape of sickled cells.

Why do so many African Americans carry the sickle cell allele? Most African Americans can trace their ancestry to west central Africa. Malaria, a serious parasitic disease that infects red blood cells, is common in this region of Africa. People who are heterozygous for the sickle cell allele are generally healthy. In addition, they have the benefit of being resistant to malaria. The relationship between the incidence of malaria and the presence of the sickle cell allele is shown in **Figure 14–10** on the next page.

▼ **Figure 14–9** These red blood cells contain the abnormal hemoglobin characteristic of sickle cell disease. **Observing** ***How is this cell different from a normal red blood cell?***

(magnification: 1800×)

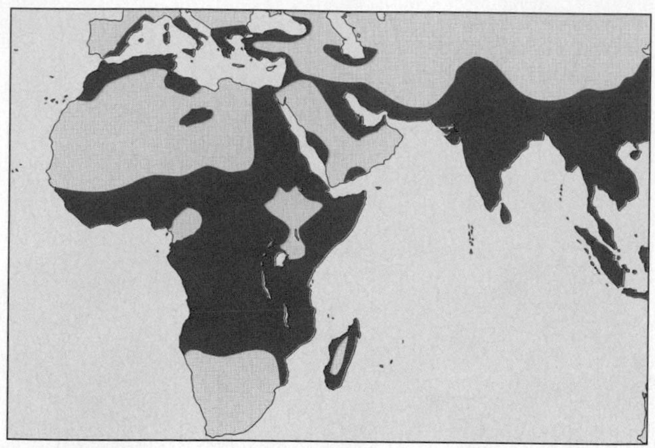

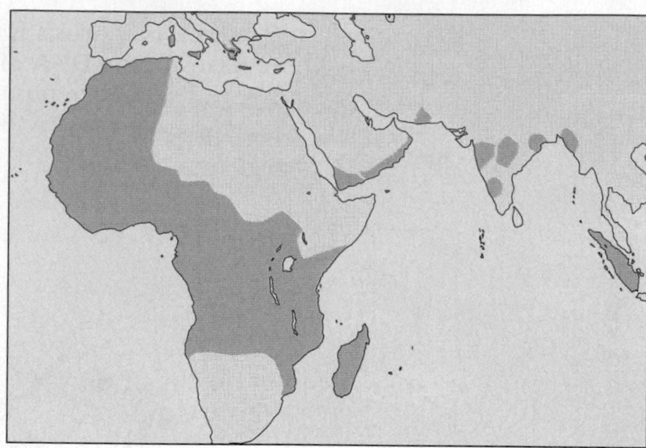

Figure 14–10 The map on the left shows where malaria is common. The map on the right shows regions where people have the sickle cell allele. **Interpreting Graphics** *What is the relationship between the places where malaria and the sickle cell allele are found?*

Low oxygen levels cause some red blood cells to become sickle shaped. When the body destroys the sickled cells, it also destroys the parasite that causes malaria. Therefore, in parts of the world such as west central Africa, where malaria is a major threat to health, the sickle cell allele is actually beneficial in heterozygous persons.

Dominant or Recessive? What makes an allele dominant, recessive, or codominant? CF and sickle cell disease show biologists that it all depends on the nature of a gene's protein product and its role in the cell. In the case of CF, just one copy of the normal allele can supply cells with enough chloride channel proteins to function. Therefore, the trait has only two phenotypes: the normal phenotype or the cystic fibrosis phenotype. Because of this, the normal allele is considered dominant over the recessive CF allele.

The allele for normal hemoglobin was once also considered dominant over the sickle cell allele, but biologists now know that this situation is more complex. In contrast to cystic fibrosis, there are three phenotypes associated with the sickle-cell gene. An individual with both normal and sickle cell alleles has a different phenotype—resistance to malaria—from someone with only normal alleles. Therefore, the sickle cell alleles are thought to be codominant because both alleles contribute to the phenotype.

14–1 Section Assessment

1. **Key Concept** What are sex chromosomes? What determines whether a person is male or female?
2. **Key Concept** Using an example, explain how a small change in a person's DNA can cause a genetic disorder.
3. How does studying genetic disorders such as PKU help biologists understand normal alleles?
4. **Critical Thinking Predicting** If a woman with type O blood and a man with type AB blood have children, what are the children's possible genotypes?

Thinking Visually

Drawing a Pedigree
Choose a family and a trait, such as facial dimples, that you can trace through three generations. Find out who in the family has had the trait and who has not. Then, draw a pedigree to represent the family history of the trait.

14–2 Human Chromosomes

4-2.1 Heredity
4-2.2 Genetic research
4-5.2 Biological research
LS- Make observations and organize data in tables/graphs

A human diploid cell contains more than 6 billion base pairs of DNA. All of this DNA is neatly packed into the 46 chromosomes present in every diploid human cell. In its own way, each of these chromosomes is like a library containing hundreds or even thousands of books. Although biologists are many decades away from mastering the contents of those books, biology is now in the early stages of learning just how many books there are and what they deal with.

You may be surprised to learn that genes make up only a small part of chromosomes. In fact, only about 2 percent of the DNA in your chromosomes functions as genes—that is, is transcribed into RNA. Genes are scattered among long segments of DNA that do not code for RNA. The average human gene consists of about 3000 base pairs, while the largest gene in the human genome has more than 2 million base pairs!

Guide for Reading

Key Concepts
- Why are sex-linked disorders more common in males than in females?
- What is nondisjunction, and what problems does it cause?

Vocabulary
sex-linked gene
nondisjunction

Reading Strategy: Outlining Before you read, use the headings of the section to make an outline about human chromosomes. As you read, write a sentence under each head to provide key information.

Human Genes and Chromosomes

Chromosomes 21 and 22 are the smallest human autosomes. Chromosome 22 contains approximately 43 million DNA base pairs. Chromosome 21 contains roughly 32 million base pairs. These chromosomes were the first two human chromosomes whose sequences were determined. Their structural features seem to be representative of other human chromosomes.

Chromosome 22 contains as many as 545 different genes, some of which are very important for health. Genetic disorders on chromosome 22 include an allele that causes a form of leukemia and another associated with neurofibromatosis, a tumor-causing disease of the nervous system. However, chromosome 22 also contains long stretches of repetitive DNA that do not code for proteins. These long stretches of repetitive DNA are unstable sites where rearrangements can occur.

The structure of chromosome 21 is similar. It contains about 225 genes, including one associated with amyotrophic lateral sclerosis (ALS), also known as Lou Gehrig's disease. Chromosome 21 also has many regions with no genes at all.

As exploration of the larger human chromosomes continues, molecular biologists may gradually learn more about how the arrangements of genes on chromosomes affect gene expression and development.

As you may recall, genes located close together on the same chromosome are linked, meaning that they tend to be inherited together. This is true for human genes. You also read earlier that linked genes may be separated by crossing-over during meiosis; this applies to human chromosomes as well.

▲ **Figure 14–11** Lou Gehrig died at age 37 of ALS. ALS causes a progressive loss of muscle control due to the destruction of nerves in the brain and spinal cord.

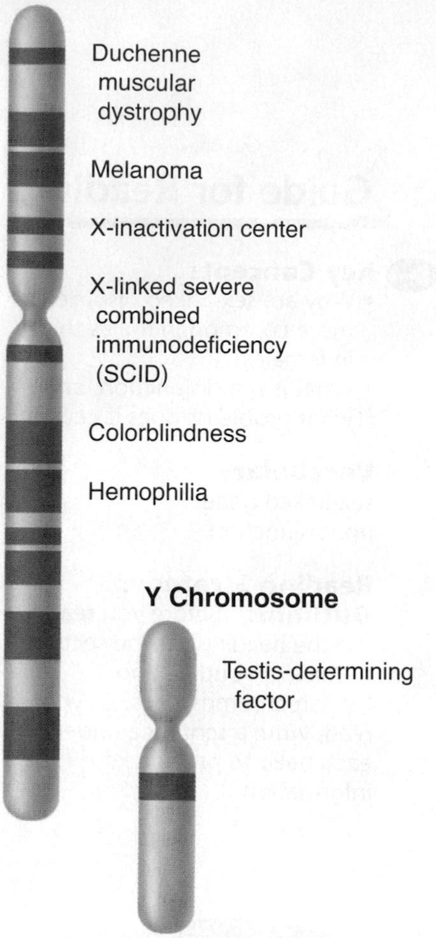

X Chromosome

Duchenne muscular dystrophy

Melanoma

X-inactivation center

X-linked severe combined immunodeficiency (SCID)

Colorblindness

Hemophilia

Y Chromosome

Testis-determining factor

▲ **Figure 14–12** Genes on X and Y chromosomes, such as those shown in the diagrams, are called sex-linked genes. **Interpreting Graphics** ***Which chromosome carries more genes?***

Sex-Linked Genes

Is there a special pattern of inheritance for genes located on the X chromosome or the Y chromosome? The answer is yes. Because these chromosomes determine sex, genes located on them are said to be **sex-linked genes.** Many sex-linked genes are found on the X chromosome, as shown in **Figure 14–12.** More than 100 sex-linked genetic disorders have now been mapped to the X chromosome. The human Y chromosome is much smaller than the X chromosome and appears to contain only a few genes.

Colorblindness Three human genes associated with color vision are located on the X chromosome. In males, a defective version of any one of these genes produces colorblindness, an inability to distinguish certain colors. The most common form of this disorder, red-green colorblindness, is found in about 1 in 10 males in the United States. Among females, however, colorblindness is rare—only about 1 female in 100 has colorblindness. Why the difference?

Males have just one X chromosome. Thus, all X-linked alleles are expressed in males, even if they are recessive. In order for a recessive allele, such as the one for colorblindness, to be expressed in females, there must be two copies of the allele, one on each of the two X chromosomes. This means that the recessive phenotype of a sex-linked genetic disorder tends to be much more common among males than among females. In addition, because men pass their X chromosomes along to their daughters, sex-linked genes move from fathers to their daughters and may then show up in the sons of those daughters, as shown in **Figure 14–13.**

Figure 14–13 **X-linked alleles are always expressed in males, because males have only one X chromosome.** Males who receive the recessive X^c allele all have colorblindness. Females, however, will have colorblindness only if they receive two X^c alleles.

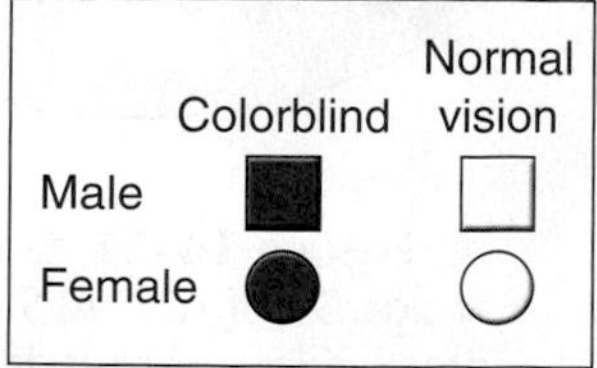

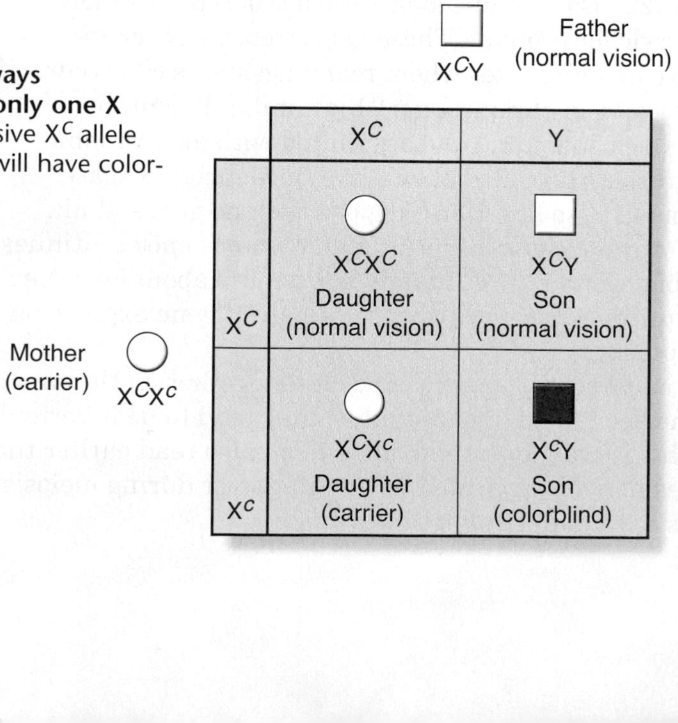

Father (normal vision) X^CY

Mother (carrier) X^CX^c

	X^C	Y
X^C	X^CX^C Daughter (normal vision)	X^CY Son (normal vision)
X^c	X^CX^c Daughter (carrier)	X^cY Son (colorblind)

Quick Lab

How is colorblindness transmitted?

Materials 2 plastic cups, 3 white beans, black marker, red bean

Procedure

1. On a sheet of paper, draw a data table with the column headings "Trial," "Colors," "Sex of Individual," and "Number of X-Linked Alleles." Draw 10 rows under the headings and fill in the numbers 1 through 10 under "Trial." Use the marker to label one cup "father" and the other "mother."
2. The white beans represent X chromosomes. Use the marker to mark a dot on 1 white bean to represent the X-linked allele for colorblindness. Place this bean, plus 1 unmarked white bean, into the cup labeled "mother."
3. Mark a black dot on 1 more white bean. Place this bean, plus 1 red bean, into the cup labeled "father." The red bean represents a Y chromosome.
4. Close your eyes and pick one bean from each cup to represent how each parent contributes a sex chromosome to a fertilized egg.
5. In your data table, record the color of each bean and the sex of an individual who would carry this pair of sex chromosomes. Also record how many X-linked alleles the individual has. Put the beans back in the cups they came from.
6. Determine whether the individual would have colorblindness.
7. Repeat steps 4 to 6 for a total of 10 pairs of beans.

Analyze and Conclude

1. **Drawing Conclusions** How do the sex chromosomes keep the numbers of males and females roughly equal?
2. **Calculating** Share your data with your classmates. Calculate the class totals for each table column. How many females were colorblind? How many males? How would you explain these results?
3. **Using Models** Evaluate the adequacy of your model. How accurately does it represent the transmission of colorblindness in a population?

Hemophilia Hemophilia is another example of a sex-linked disorder. Two important genes carried on the X chromosome help control blood clotting. A recessive allele in either of these two genes may produce a disorder called hemophilia (hee-moh-FIL-ee-uh). In hemophilia, a protein necessary for normal blood clotting is missing. About 1 in 10,000 males is born with a form of hemophilia. People with hemophilia can bleed to death from minor cuts and may suffer internal bleeding from bumps or bruises. Fortunately, hemophilia can be treated by injections of normal clotting proteins, which are now produced using recombinant DNA.

Duchenne Muscular Dystrophy Duchenne muscular dystrophy (DIS-truh-fee) is a sex-linked disorder that results in the progressive weakening and loss of skeletal muscle. In the United States, one out of every 3000 males is born with this condition. Duchenne muscular dystrophy is caused by a defective version of the gene that codes for a muscle protein. Researchers in many laboratories are trying to find a way to treat or cure this disorder, possibly by inserting a normal allele into the muscle cells of Duchenne muscular dystrophy patients.

What causes Duchenne muscular dystrophy?

▲ **Figure 14–14** This cat's fur color is controlled by a gene on the X chromosome. **Drawing Conclusions** *Is the cat shown a male or a female?*

▼ **Figure 14–15** **Nondisjunction causes gametes to have abnormal numbers of chromosomes.** The result of nondisjunction may be a chromosome disorder such as Down syndrome.

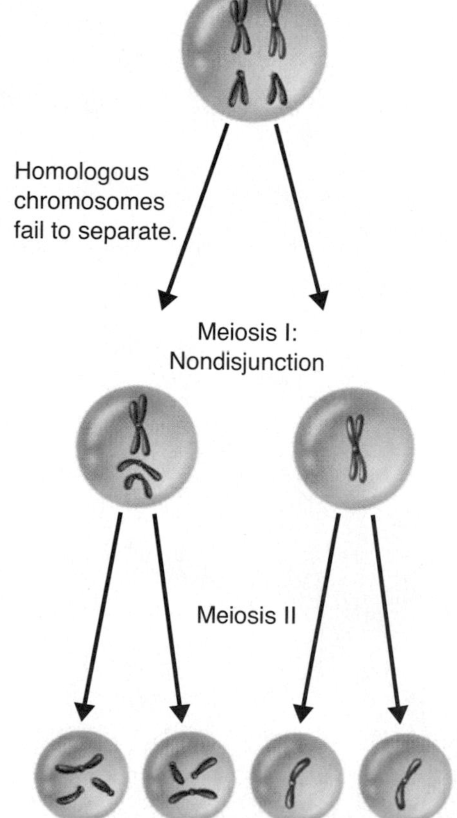

X-Chromosome Inactivation

Females have two X chromosomes, but males have only one. If just one X chromosome is enough for cells in males, how does the cell "adjust" to the extra X chromosome in female cells? The answer was discovered by the British geneticist Mary Lyon. In female cells, one X chromosome is randomly switched off. That turned-off chromosome forms a dense region in the nucleus known as a Barr body. Barr bodies are generally not found in males because their single X chromosome is still active.

The same process happens in other mammals. In cats, for example, a gene that controls the color of coat spots is located on the X chromosome. One X chromosome may have an allele for orange spots and the other may have an allele for black spots. In cells in some parts of the body, one X chromosome is switched off. In other parts of the body, the other X chromosome is switched off. As a result, the cat's fur will have a mixture of orange and black spots, as shown in **Figure 14–14.** Male cats, which have just one X chromosome, can have spots of only one color. By the way, this is one way to tell the sex of a cat. If the cat's fur has three colors—white with orange and black spots, for example—you can almost be certain that it is female.

Chromosomal Disorders

Most of the time, the mechanisms that separate human chromosomes in meiosis work very well, but every now and then something goes wrong. The most common error in meiosis occurs when homologous chromosomes fail to separate. This is known as **nondisjunction,** which means "not coming apart." Nondisjunction is illustrated in **Figure 14–15.** **If nondisjunction occurs, abnormal numbers of chromosomes may find their way into gametes, and a disorder of chromosome numbers may result.**

Down Syndrome If two copies of an autosomal chromosome fail to separate during meiosis, an individual may be born with three copies of a chromosome. This is known as a trisomy, meaning "three bodies." The most common form of trisomy involves three copies of chromosome 21 and is called Down syndrome. **Figure 14–16** shows a karyotype of a person with Down syndrome. In the United States, approximately 1 baby in 800 is born with Down syndrome. Down syndrome produces mild to severe mental retardation. It is also characterized by an increased susceptibility to many diseases and a higher frequency of some birth defects.

Why should an extra copy of one chromosome cause so much trouble? That is still not clear, and it is one of the reasons scientists have worked so hard to learn the DNA sequence for chromosome 21. Now that researchers know all of the genes on the chromosome, they can begin experiments to find the exact genes that cause problems when present in three copies.

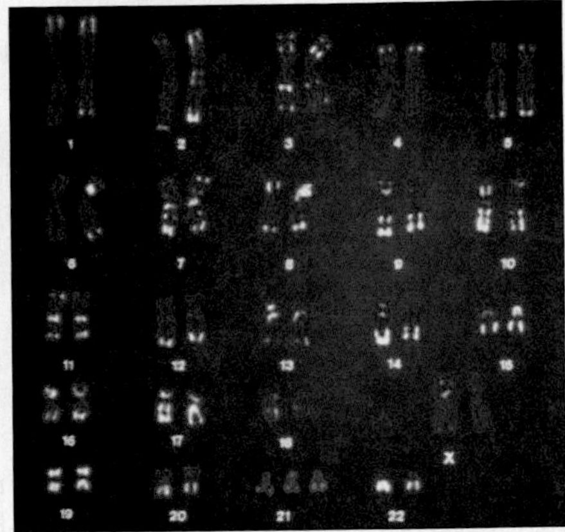

Figure 14–16 The karyotype on the right is from a person with Down syndrome. Down syndrome causes mental retardation and various physical problems. People with Down syndrome can, however, lead active, happy lives. **Observing** *Analyze this karyotype. What characteristic enables you to identify it as belonging to a person with Down syndrome? Is that person male or female?*

Sex Chromosome Disorders Disorders also occur among the sex chromosomes. Two of these abnormalities are Turner's syndrome and Klinefelter's syndrome.

In females, nondisjunction can lead to Turner's syndrome. A female with Turner's syndrome usually inherits only one X chromosome (karyotype 45,X). Women with Turner's syndrome are sterile, which means that they are unable to reproduce. Their sex organs do not develop at puberty.

In males, nondisjunction causes Klinefelter's syndrome (karyotype 47,XXY). The extra X chromosome interferes with meiosis and usually prevents these individuals from reproducing. Cases of Klinefelter's syndrome have been found in which individuals were XXXY or XXXXY. There have been no reported instances of babies being born without an X chromosome, indicating that the X chromosome contains genes that are vital for the survival and development of an embryo.

These sex chromosome abnormalities point out the essential role of the Y chromosome in male sex determination in humans. The human Y chromosome contains a sex-determining region that is necessary to produce male sexual development, and it can do this even if several X chromosomes are present. However, if this region of the Y chromosome is absent, the embryo develops as a female.

14–2 Section Assessment

1. **Key Concept** Why are sex-linked disorders more common in males than in females?
2. **Key Concept** How does nondisjunction cause chromosome number disorders?
3. List at least two examples of human sex-linked disorders.
4. Describe two sex chromosome disorders.
5. **Critical Thinking Comparing and Contrasting** Distinguish between sex-linked disorders and sex chromosome disorders.

Writing in Science

Explaining a Process
Write a paragraph explaining the process of nondisjunction. *Hint:* To organize your writing, refer to **Figure 14–15** and use this diagram to create a flowchart that shows the steps in the process.

Who Controls Your DNA?

The U.S. Department of Defense requires that soldiers submit DNA samples for a database that could be used to identify soldiers' remains. Two Marines, Corporal John C. Mayfield and Corporal Joseph Vlacovsky, refused. At their court martial, the two Marines argued that DNA samples could be examined for genes related to disease or even behavior and, therefore, the database was an invasion of privacy. As a result of the concerns raised by this case, the U.S. Department of Defense has changed its policies. It now destroys DNA samples upon request when an individual leaves military service. Do people have a right to control their own DNA samples?

The Viewpoints

DNA Information Is Not Private

As the court recognized, the U.S. Department of Defense had good reasons for requiring that DNA samples be taken and stored. Furthermore, DNA sequences are no more private and personal than fingerprints or photographs, which are taken by private and government agencies all the time. An employer has a right to take and keep such information. Individuals should have no reason to fear the abuse of such databases.

DNA Infomation Is Private and Personal

The use of DNA for personal identification by the military may be justified. An individual's genetic information, however, is a private matter. A recent study at Harvard and Stanford universities turned up more than 200 cases of discrimination because of genes individuals carried or were suspected of carrying. Employers with DNA information might use it to discriminate against workers who carry genes they suspect might cause medical or behavioral problems. Individuals must have the right to control their own DNA and to withhold samples from such databases.

Research and Decide

1. **Analyzing the Viewpoints** Learn more about this issue by consulting library or Internet resources. Then decide whether there are any circumstances in which an employer might be justified in demanding DNA samples from its employees. Why might an employee wish to withhold such samples?
2. **Forming Your Opinion** Should the control of DNA databases be a matter of law, or should it be a matter to be negotiated between people, their employers, and insurance companies?
3. **Persuasive Speaking** Suppose you were a doctor working as a consultant to a health insurance company. The insurance company is trying to decide whether to test adults for cystic fibrosis alleles before agreeing to insure their families. What advice would you give to the company about this?

For: Links from the authors
Visit: PHSchool.com
Web Code: cbe-4142

14–3 Human Molecular Genetics

4-2.2 Genetic research
4-5.2 Biological research
4-7.3 Proposals that involve new technologies
LS- Chromatography/electrophoresis

Guide for Reading

 **Key Concepts**

- What is the goal of the Human Genome Project?
- What is gene therapy?

Vocabulary
DNA fingerprinting

Reading Strategy: Finding Main Ideas As you read, find evidence to support the following statement: The influence of human molecular genetics on society is growing rapidly.

Watson and Crick took the first step in making genetics a molecular science when they discovered the double-helical structure of DNA in 1953. Today, the transformation they started is complete. The exploration of human genes is now a major scientific undertaking. Biologists can now read, analyze, and even change the molecular code of genes.

Human DNA Analysis

The roughly 6 billion base pairs you carry in your DNA are a bit like an encyclopedia with thousands of volumes. In principle, biologists would like to know everything the volumes contain, but as a practical matter there isn't enough time to read all of them. Nonetheless, if you've used an encyclopedia you've already learned one of the ways to handle huge amounts of information—you find a way to look up only what you need. In an encyclopedia, you can use an index or an alphabetical list of articles. As you might suspect, biologists search the volumes of the human genome using sequences of DNA bases.

Testing for Alleles If two prospective parents suspect they might be carrying recessive alleles for a genetic disorder such as cystic fibrosis (CF) or Tay-Sachs disease, how could they find out for sure? Because the Tay-Sachs and CF alleles have slightly different DNA sequences from their normal counterparts, a variety of genetic tests have been developed that can spot those differences. Sometimes these genetic tests use labeled DNA probes. These are specific DNA base sequences that detect the complementary base sequences found in disease-causing alleles. Other tests search for changes in restriction enzyme cutting sites. Tests also detect differences between the lengths of normal and abnormal alleles.

Genetic tests are now available for hundreds of disorders, making it possible to determine whether prospective parents risk passing such alleles to their children. In an increasing number of such cases, DNA testing can pinpoint the exact genetic basis of a disorder, making it possible to develop more effective treatment for individuals affected by genetic disease.

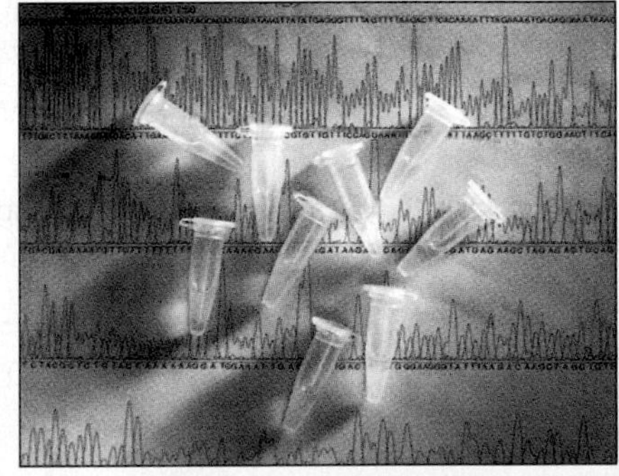

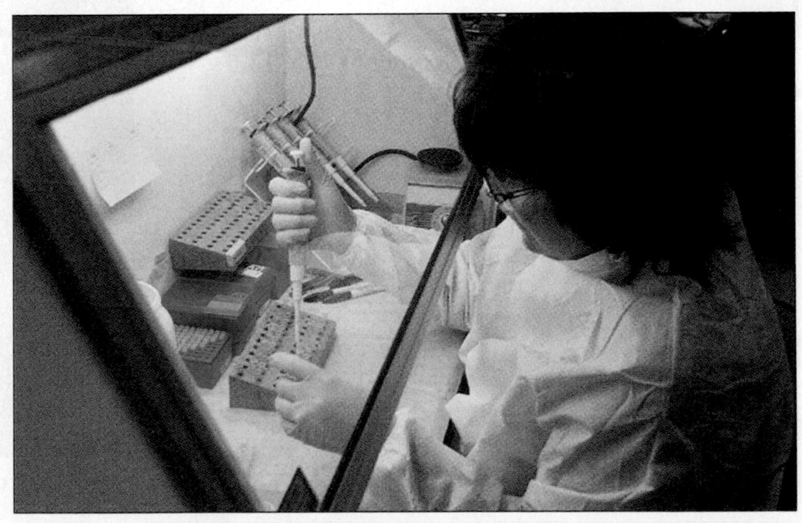

▶ **Figure 14–17** This laboratory worker is preparing a report on DNA evidence. The inset shows vials of DNA lying on a printout of a DNA analysis chart.

FIGURE 14–18 DNA FINGERPRINTING

DNA fingerprinting can be used to determine whether blood, sperm, or other material left at a crime scene matches DNA from a suspect. **Interpreting Graphics** *In the DNA fingerprint below, does the DNA fingerprint from the evidence (E) match suspect 1 (S1) or suspect 2 (S2)?*

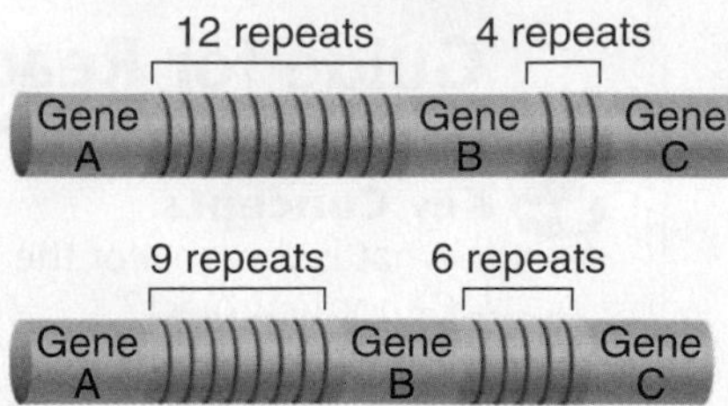

A Chromosomes contain large amounts of DNA called repeats that do not code for proteins. This DNA varies from person to person. Here, one sample has 12 repeats between genes A and B, while the second sample has 9 repeats.

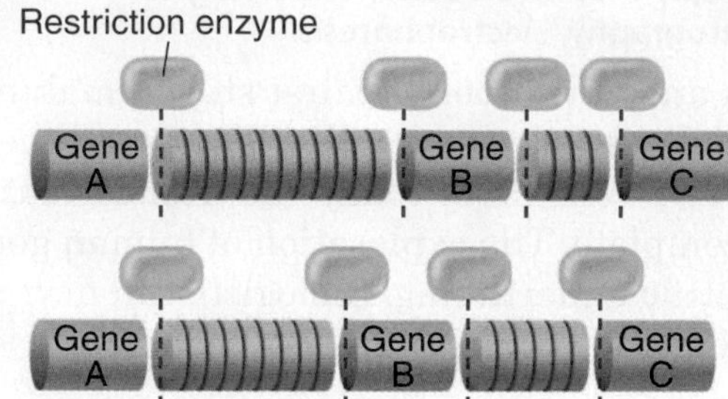

B Restriction enzymes are used to cut the DNA into fragments containing genes and repeats. Note that the repeat fragments from these two samples are of different lengths.

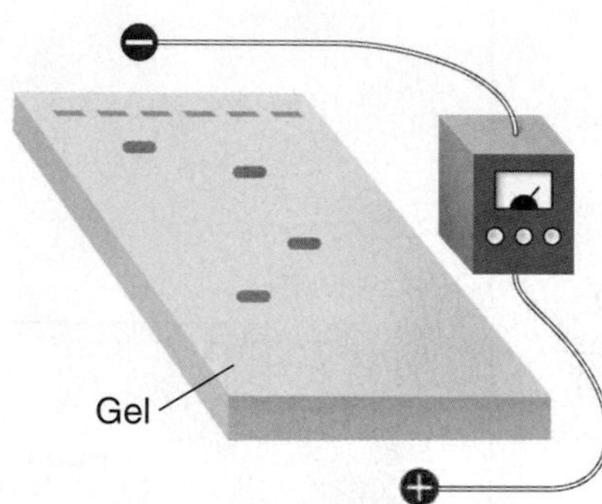

C The DNA fragments are separated according to size using gel electrophoresis. The fragments containing repeats are then labeled using radioactive probes. This produces a series of bands—the DNA fingerprint.

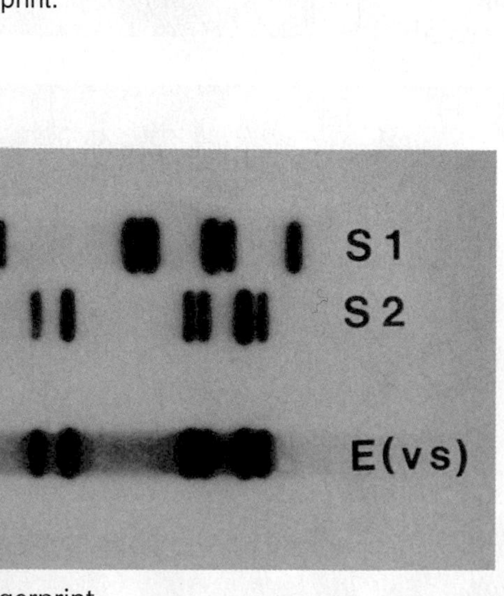

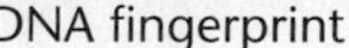

DNA fingerprint

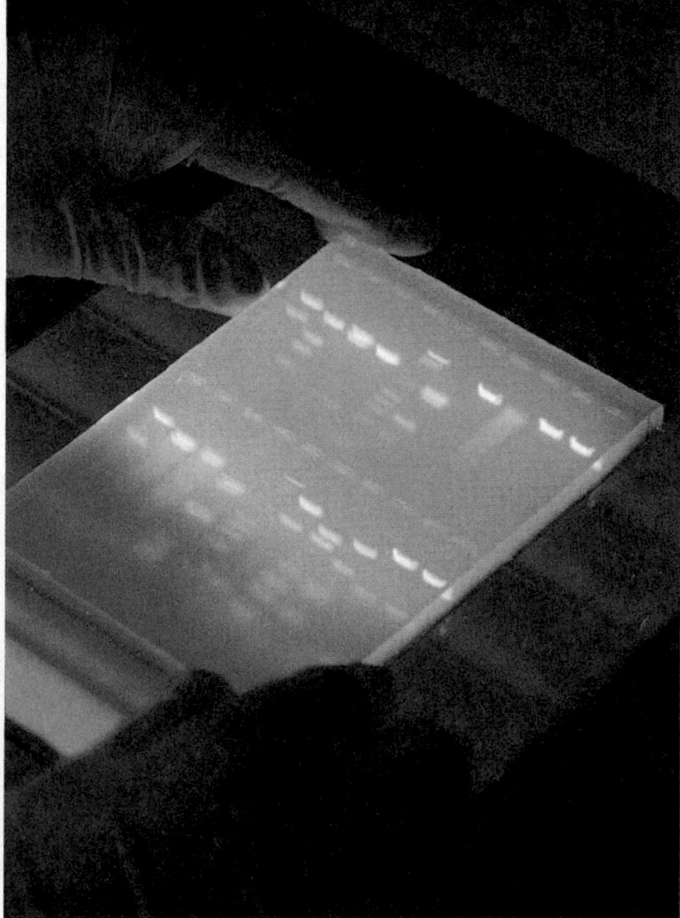

Gel electrophoresis

DNA Fingerprinting The great complexity of the human genome ensures that no individual is exactly like any other genetically—except, of course, for identical twins. Molecular biology has used this biological fact to add a powerful new tool called **DNA fingerprinting** to the identification of individuals. Unlike other forms of testing, DNA fingerprinting does not analyze the cell's most important genes, which are largely identical among most people. Rather, DNA fingerprinting analyzes sections of DNA that have little or no known function but vary widely from one individual to another.

Figure 14–18 shows how DNA fingerprinting works. A small sample of human DNA is cut with a restriction enzyme. The resulting fragments are separated by size using gel electrophoresis. Fragments containing these highly variable regions are then detected with a DNA probe, revealing a series of DNA bands of various sizes. If enough combinations of restriction enzymes and probes are used, a pattern of bands is produced that can be distinguished statistically from the pattern of any other individual in the world. DNA samples can be obtained from blood, sperm, and even hair strands with tissue at the base.

DNA fingerprinting has been used in the United States since the late 1980s. The reliability of DNA evidence has helped convict criminals as well as overturn many convictions. The precision that molecular biology brings to the justice system is good news not only for those who are victims of crime but also for those who have been wrongly convicted.

The Human Genome Project

Advances in DNA sequencing technologies at the close of the twentieth century made it possible, for the first time, to sequence entire genomes. At first, biologists worked on relatively small genomes, such as those of viruses and bacteria. The DNA sequence of the common bacterium *Escherichia coli,* which was determined in 1996, contains "only" 4,639,221 base pairs, making it just about as long as this textbook if it were printed on paper in a readable typeface. The genomes of even the simplest eukaryotic organisms are much larger, and the human genome, which contains over 6 billion base pairs, is nearly 1400 times as large.

Despite the problem of size, in 1990, scientists in the United States and other countries began the Human Genome Project. **The Human Genome Project is an ongoing effort to analyze the human DNA sequence.** Along the way, investigators completed the genomes of several other organisms, including yeast—a unicellular eukaryote—and *Drosophila melanogaster,* the fruit fly. In June 2000, scientists announced that a working copy of the human genome was essentially complete.

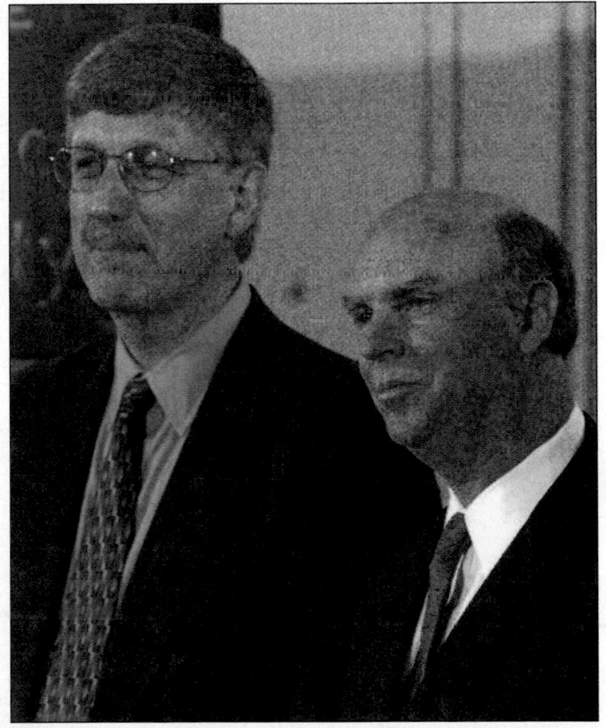

▲ **Figure 14–19** **The Human Genome Project is an ongoing effort to analyze the human DNA sequence.** Dr. Francis Collins and Dr. Craig Venter, who headed the public and private portions of the project, jointly announced the completion of a working draft of the human genome sequence.

Rapid Sequencing How did they do it? Scientists first determined the sequence of bases in widely separated regions of DNA. These regions were then used as markers, not unlike the mile markers along a road thousands of miles long. The markers made it possible to locate and return to specific locations in the genome.

Scientists then used a technique known as "shotgun sequencing." This method involved cutting DNA into random fragments and then determining the sequence of bases in each fragment. Computers found areas of overlap between the fragments and put the fragments together by linking the overlapping areas. The computers then aligned the fragments relative to the known markers on each chromosome. The entire process is something like putting a jigsaw puzzle together, but instead of matching shapes, the scientists match identical base sequences.

Searching for Genes Only a small part of a human DNA molecule is made up of genes. In fact, one of the genome's scientific surprises was how few genes it seems to contain—possibly as few as 25,000. Since the genome of the fruit fly *Drosophila* contains approximately 14,000 genes and that of a tiny worm roughly 20,000, many researchers had expected to find far more in our own DNA. The final number, however, is far from certain.

Molecular biologists continue to search for genes, which they can locate in several ways. In one method, they find genes by finding DNA sequences that are known to be promoters, which are binding sites for RNA polymerase. Promoters indicate the start of a gene. Shortly behind the promoter, there should be an open reading frame. An open reading frame is a sequence of DNA bases that will produce an mRNA sequence, which then specifies a series of amino acids. Recall that for most genes, the mRNA coding regions, or exons, are interrupted by introns, which are noncoding regions. Therefore, investigators have to find the introns as well as the exons in order to follow the gene through its complete length, as shown in **Figure 14–20.**

▼ **Figure 14–20** Researchers exploring the human genome can use DNA sequences to locate many genes. Promoters are sequences in which RNA polymerase can bind to DNA. A typical gene, such as the gene for insulin shown below, has other DNA sequences that may serve as signals for RNA polymerase to start and stop transcription. **Interpreting Graphics** ***In which direction would RNA polymerase move in transcribing the insulin gene?***

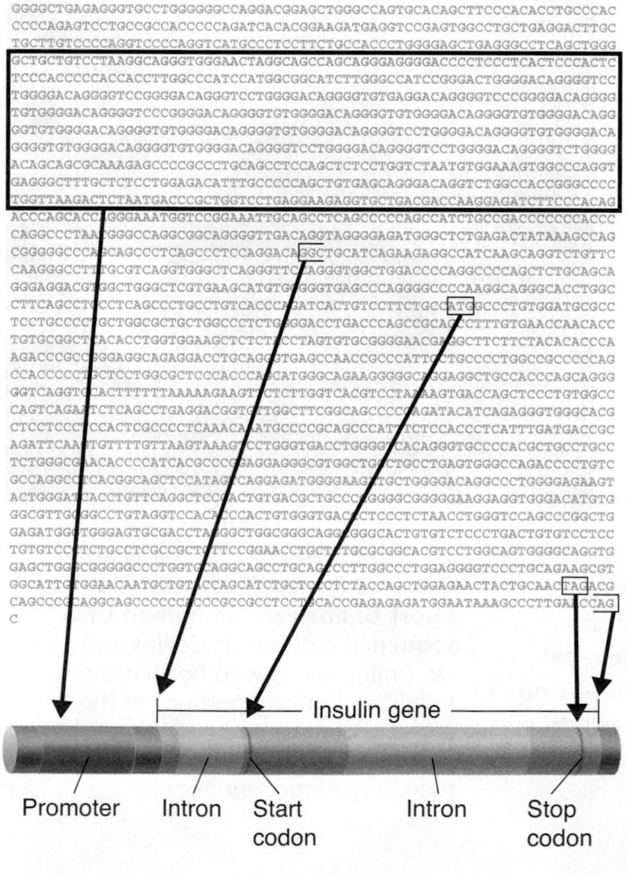

Research groups around the world are analyzing the huge amount of information in the DNA sequence, looking for genes that may provide useful clues to some of the basic properties of life. In addition to its scientific significance, understanding the structure and control of key genes may have commercial value. Biotechnology companies are rushing to find genetic information that may be useful in developing new drugs and treatments for diseases.

A Breakthrough for Everyone One of the remarkable things about genome research is the open availability of nearly all its data. From its very beginning, data from publicly supported research on the human genome have been posted on the Internet on a daily basis. You can read the latest genome data there and, if you wish, analyze it. The Web site for this textbook links to the Human Genome Project.

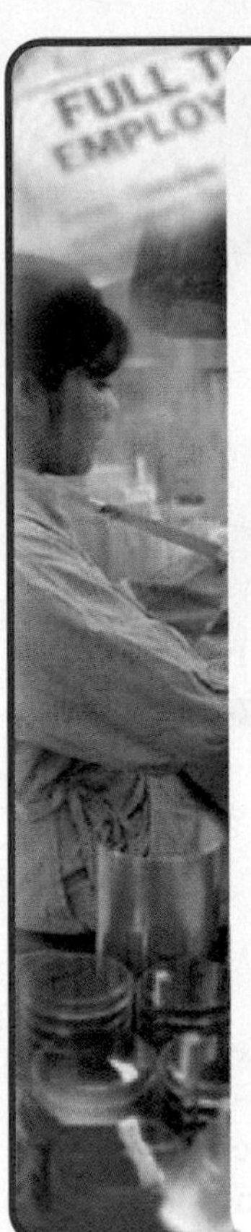

Careers in Biology

Geneticist

Job Description: work in the laboratories of universities or large companies doing molecular-level research, or work in a clinic collecting family histories and counseling people who have a genetic disorder or who may carry a genetic disorder

Education: a master's degree or doctorate in genetics or related field; some medical research positions require a medical degree, as well

Skills: good verbal and written communication skills, analytical, detail-oriented, caring, organized, curious, and able to meet deadlines

Highlights: You have the opportunity to discover new genes or patterns of heredity that can help treat or cure genetic disorders or to make sure that these types of discoveries are put into practice to improve public health.

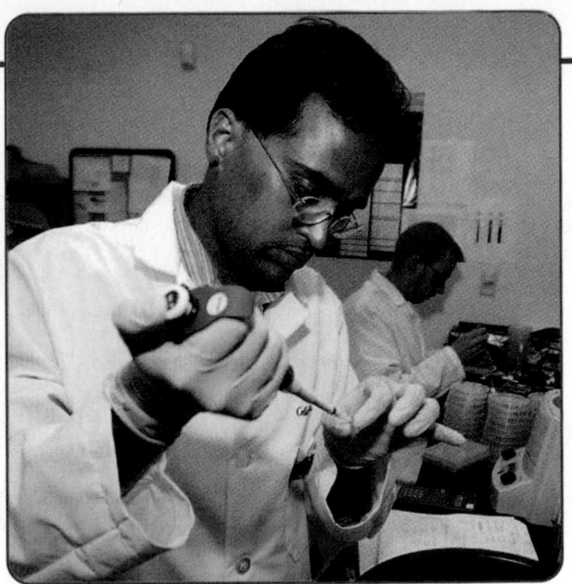

For: Career links
Visit: PHSchool.com
Web Code: cbb-4143

Gene Therapy

The Human Genome Project will have an impact on society as well as on scientific thought. For example, information about the human genome might be used to cure genetic disorders by gene therapy. Gene therapy is the process of changing the gene that causes a genetic disorder. **In gene therapy, an absent or faulty gene is replaced by a normal, working gene.** This way, the body can make the correct protein or enzyme it needs, which eliminates the cause of the disorder.

The first authorized attempt to cure a human genetic disorder by gene transfer occurred in 1990. Then, in 1999, a young French girl was apparently cured of an inherited immune disorder when cells from her bone marrow were removed, modified in the laboratory, and then placed back in her body. However, scientists do not yet know how long the beneficial effects of this treatment will last.

Figure 14–21 on the next page shows one of the ways in which researchers have attempted to practice gene therapy. Viruses are often used because of their ability to enter a cell's DNA. The virus particles are modified so that they cannot cause disease. Then, a DNA fragment containing a replacement gene is spliced to viral DNA. The patient is then infected with the modified virus particles, which should carry the gene into cells to correct genetic defects.

For: More information on the Human Genome Project
Visit: PHSchool.com
Web Code: cbe-4143

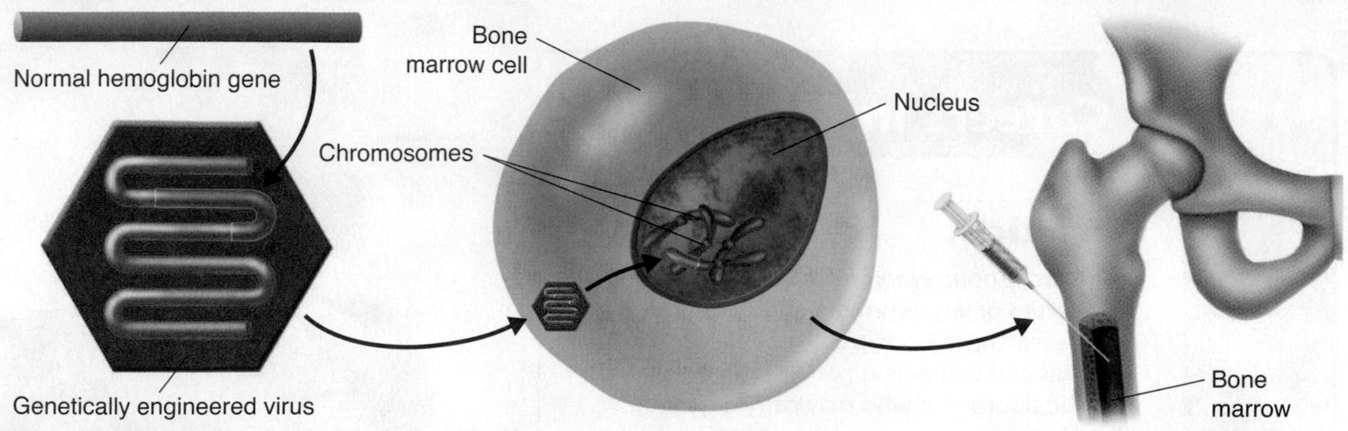

▲ **Figure 14–21** **Gene therapy is the process of changing the genes that cause a genetic disorder.** This drawing shows how a virus might be used to deliver the gene for normal hemoglobin into a person's bone marrow.

Unfortunately, gene therapy experiments have not always been successful. Attempts to treat cystic fibrosis by spraying genetically engineered viruses into the breathing passages have not produced a lasting cure. For all the promise it holds, in most cases gene therapy remains a high-risk, experimental procedure.

Ethical Issues in Human Genetics

It would be marvelous to be able to cure hemophilia or other genetic diseases. But if human cells can be manipulated to cure disease, should biologists try to engineer taller people or change their eye color, hair texture, sex, blood group, or appearance? What will happen to the human species if we gain the opportunity to design our bodies? What will be the consequences if biologists develop the ability to clone human beings by making identical copies of their cells? These are questions with which society must come to grips.

The goal of biology is to gain a better understanding of the nature of life. As our knowledge increases, however, so does our ability to manipulate the genetics of living things, including ourselves. In a democratic nation, all citizens—not just scientists—are responsible for ensuring that the tools science has given us are used wisely. This means that you should be prepared to help develop a thoughtful and ethical consensus of what should and should not be done with the human genome. To do anything less would be to lose control of two of our most precious gifts: our intellect and our humanity.

14–3 Section Assessment

1. **Key Concept** What is the Human Genome Project?
2. **Key Concept** Describe how gene therapy works.
3. Name two common uses for DNA testing.
4. Describe how molecular biologists identify genes in sequences of DNA.
5. **Critical Thinking Making Judgments** Evaluate the potential impact of the Human Genome Project on both scientific thought and society. How has it improved our understanding of human genetics? How might it be used to benefit humankind? What potential ethical problems might it create?

Writing in Science

Persuasive Paragraph

Biologists may one day be able to use genetic engineering to alter a child's inherited traits. Under what circumstances, if at all, should this ability be used? When should it not be used? Write a persuasive paragraph expressing your opinion. *Hint:* Use specific examples of traits to support your ideas.

Real-World Lab

Modeling DNA Probes

A DNA probe is a short, single-stranded DNA molecule bound to a detectable tag such as a fluorescent dye. Because the probe is single stranded, it can bind to other DNA that has a complementary sequence. To find a specific DNA sequence, scientists mix a probe with an unknown DNA sample. The probe will only bind to a DNA sample that has a complementary sequence, showing where the desired sequence is. In this lab, you will model how scientists use DNA probes.

Problem
How do DNA probes help to identify individuals?

Materials
- graph paper
- scissors
- colored pencil or marker

Skills
Using Models, Classifying

Procedure 

1. DNA sequences from five individuals are shown. Copy each individual's number and DNA sequence onto graph paper, putting one letter from the DNA sequence into each square. Skip five lines between each sequence and the next one.
2. Copy the following sequence for a six-base DNA probe onto graph paper, as you did the DNA sequences in step 1: T C C G A G
3. Fill in the square that follows the probe sequence with a colored pencil or marker to represent the fluorescent dye bound to the probe.
4. Cut out the strip of graph paper that represents the probe and its attached fluorescent dye.
5. Move the probe along each individual's DNA sequence. As you do so, look for parts of the DNA sequences that are complementary to the probe's sequence.
6. Circle the part of any individual's DNA sequence that is complementary to the sequence of the DNA probe.
7. Record the numbers of the individuals who were identified by the DNA probe.
8. Choose one of the five individuals, and construct a new DNA probe that will identify only that individual. Write out the DNA sequence of this new probe as you did in step 2. Your new probe does not have to be six bases long.
9. Cut out your new probe and exchange it for one written by a classmate.
10. Repeat steps 5 and 6 with the probe you received to identify the individual that your classmate selected.

Individual 1	ATCTCGAGACTGATAGGCTCTAAGCTCGAG
Individual 2	ATTGGCCACTCGAGACGTTGGCCAAGTCCG
Individual 3	ATGACCATGGCCAGGCTCGAGCTGATGACG
Individual 4	ATATGGCCATTGCTCGAGTGGCCAGATCCG
Individual 5	ACTCGAGGTCCCTCGAGTGTAGGCTCATCG

Analyze and Conclude

1. **Observing** What DNA sequence is complementary to the sequence of the probe shown in step 2?
2. **Classifying** Which individual(s) was (were) identified by the DNA probe given in step 2?
3. **Using Models** Is it possible for the same DNA probe to identify more than one individual? Explain your answer.
4. **Drawing Conclusions** Would DNA probes with longer or shorter sequences be more likely to identify only one individual? Explain your answer.

Go Further

Using Models Restriction enzymes cut DNA at specific base sequences. Make a model of a DNA probe and a restriction enzyme. Use your models to show how DNA probes and restriction enzymes could be used together to create DNA fingerprints for the five individuals shown.

Chapter 14 Study Guide

14–1 Human Heredity

Key Concepts

- All human egg cells carry a single X chromosome (23,X). However, half of all sperm cells carry an X chromosome (23,X) and half carry a Y chromosome (23,Y). This ensures that just about half of the zygotes will be 46,XX (female), and half will be 46,XY (male).
- In both cystic fibrosis and sickle cell disease, a small change in the DNA of a single gene affects the structure of a protein, causing a serious genetic disorder.

Vocabulary
karyotype, p. 341
sex chromosome, p. 341
autosome, p. 341
pedigree, p. 342

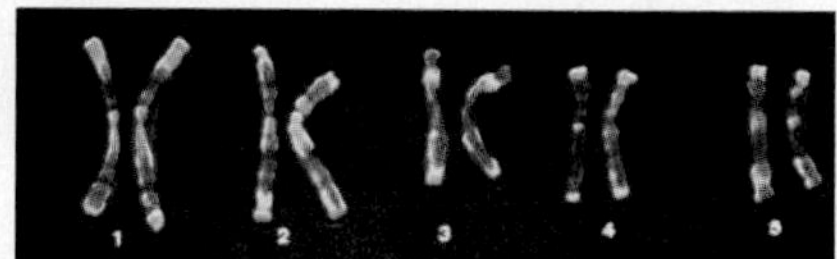

14–2 Human Chromosomes

Key Concepts

- Males have just one X chromosome. Thus, all X-linked alleles are expressed in males, even if they are recessive.
- If nondisjunction occurs, abnormal numbers of chromosomes may find their way into gametes, and a disorder of chromosome numbers may result.

Vocabulary
sex-linked gene, p. 350
nondisjunction, p. 352

14–3 Human Molecular Genetics

Key Concepts

- The Human Genome Project is an ongoing effort to analyze the human DNA sequence.
- In gene therapy, an absent or faulty gene is replaced by a normal, working gene.

Vocabulary
DNA fingerprinting, p. 357

Thinking Visually

Using the information in this chapter, complete the following concept map about chromosome disorders:

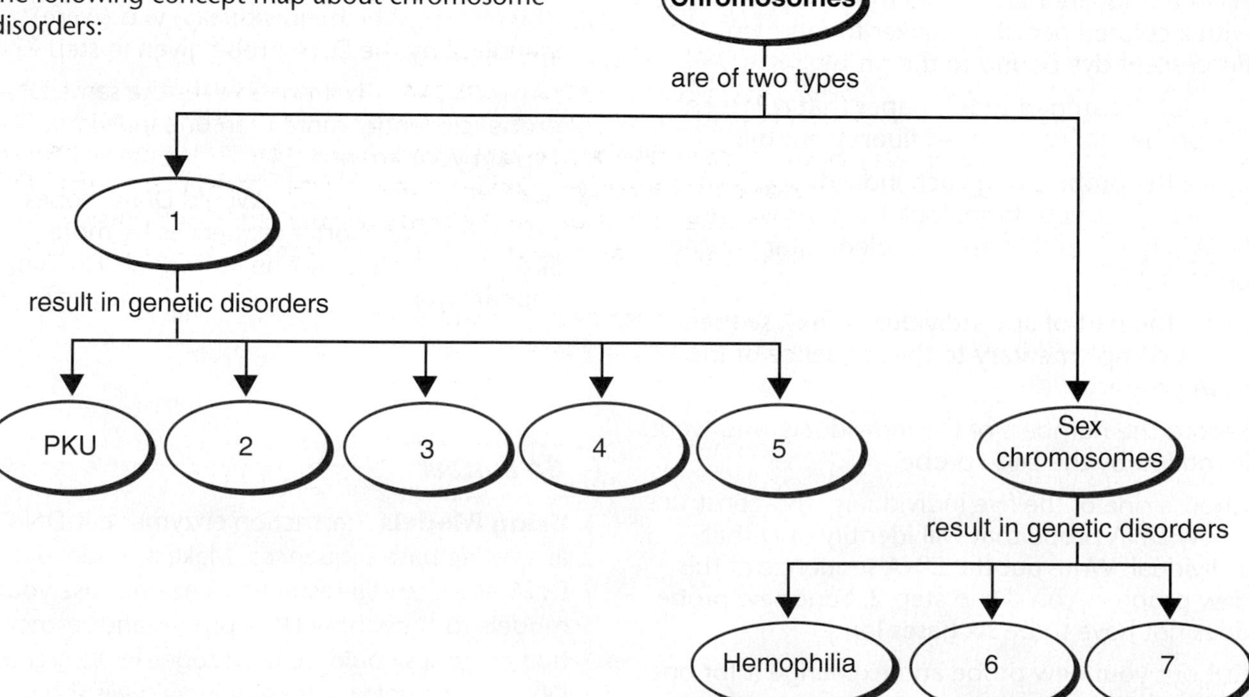

Preparing for the Living Environment Exam

NEW YORK LIVING ENVIRONMENT

Blue questions emphasize Regents Exam content

Chapter 14

Part A

Multiple Choice

For each statement or question, select the number of the word or expression that, of those given, best completes the statement or answers the question.

1 A normal human zygote contains a full set of
(1) 23 chromosomes, one half from each parent
(2) 46 chromosomes, one half from each parent
(3) chromosomes from the father, only
(4) chromosomes from the mother, only

2 Traits that are caused by the interaction of many genes are said to be
(1) polyploid (3) linked
(2) polygenic (4) autosomal

3 An example of a trait that is determined by multiple alleles is
(1) Huntington's disease
(2) Down syndrome
(3) ABO blood groups
(4) hemophilia

4 Hemophilia is a genetic disorder that is
(1) sex-linked
(2) sex-influenced
(3) fairly common
(4) more common in women than in men

5 To determine the identity of their biological parents, adopted children sometimes request DNA tests. These tests involve comparing DNA samples from the child to DNA samples taken from the likely parents. Possible relationships may be determined from these tests because the
(1) base sequence of the father determines the base sequence of the offspring
(2) DNA of parents and their offspring is more similar than the DNA of non-family members
(3) position of the genes on each chromosome is unique to each family
(4) mutation rate is the same in closely related individuals but varies in non-related individuals

6 The process of attempting to cure genetic disorders by placing copies of healthy genes into cells that lack them is known as
(1) gene therapy
(2) DNA fingerprinting
(3) rapid sequencing
(4) the Human Genome Project

7 Which can be observed in a person's karyotype?
(1) colorblindness and trisomy 21
(2) Turner's syndrome and cystic fibrosis
(3) colorblindness and cystic fibrosis
(4) Turner's syndrome and trisomy 21

8 A woman is heterozygous for type A blood. A man has AB blood. What is the probability that the couple's child will have type B blood?
(1) 0% (3) 50%
(2) 25% (4) 100%

9 According to the graph below, the frequency of Down syndrome
(1) increases with increase in maternal age
(2) is 15 times more in the 45+ age group than it is in the 30 to 34 age group
(3) is greater in the 25–29 age group than in the 40 to 44 age group
(4) levels off at 2 per 1000 live births in the 15 to 19 age group

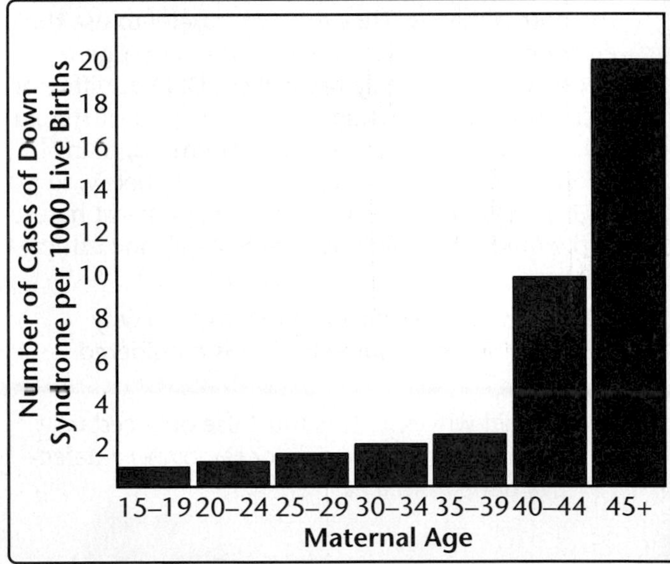

Test-Taking Tip When interpreting a pedigree, first read through all the generations given. Then, go back and assign (either mentally or on scratch paper) a possible genotype to each person represented in the pedigree. Use Punnett squares to test your assigned genotypes to ensure that they could produce each successive generation's phenotypes.

Preparing for the
Living Environment Exam

Part B

Multiple Choice and Extended Response

For those questions that ask you to select a response, choose the one that best completes the statement or answers the question. For all others follow the directions given.

Base your answers to questions 10 and 11 on the passage below and on your knowledge of biology.

The Human Genome Project

For a number of years, scientists at Cold Spring Harbor Laboratory have been attempting to map every known human gene. By mapping, scientists mean that they are trying to find out on which of the 46 chromosomes each gene is located and exactly where on the chromosome the gene is located. By locating the exact positions of defective genes, scientists hope to cure diseases by replacing defective genes with normal ones, a technique known as gene therapy. Scientists can use specific enzymes to cut out the defective genes and insert the normal genes. They must be careful to use the enzyme that will splice out only the target gene, because different enzymes will cut DNA at different locations. While the human genome project should eventually improve the health of humans, many people are skeptical and apprehensive, believing that gene therapy would be working against nature and would have religious, moral, legal, and ethical implications.

10 Using one specific example, explain why the Human Genome Project is considered important.

11 Explain why scientists must use only certain enzymes when inserting or removing a defective gene from a cell.

Base your answers to questions 12 and 13 on the passage below and on your knowledge of biology.

Knowing the DNA sequence of a gene provides researchers with information about the structure of the protein encoded by that gene. For example, when the cystic fibrosis (CF) gene was identified, the gene's DNA sequence suggested that the CF protein might be a channel protein embedded in the cell membrane. The gene's sequence also hinted to researchers that the protein might be specifically involved with the passage of salt through the cell membrane. This fit with what scientists already knew about cystic fibrosis. It made sense that mucus would accumulate in the lungs and digestive organs of individuals with CF as a result of problems with salt and water transport through a malformed channel protein.

12 Explain how knowing a gene's sequence allows researchers to determine the protein that might be the problem in a genetic disease such as CF.

13 Individuals with only one defective gene for CF do not have noticeable problems with the passage of salt across their cell membranes. Only individuals with two defective genes have CF. Explain how it is possible that a child who has a parent with CF would not necessarily inherit cystic fibrosis.

---

14 Explain why genetic disorders caused by dominant alleles are less common than genetic disorders caused by recessive alleles.

15 *Plasmodium falciparum,* a protist, causes a fatal form of malaria. Propose a hypothesis to explain why *P. falciparum* can live in red blood cells that contain normal hemoglobin but not in red blood cells that contain the sickle cell allele.

16 Explain how a family pedigree can be helpful in determining the probability of having a child with a genetic disorder.

17 State *two* examples of how an understanding of genetics is making new medical treatments or diagnoses possible.

18 Explain the relationship between meiosis and Down syndrome, Turner's syndrome, and Klinefelter's syndrome. (*Hint:* You might wish to refer to Chapter 11.)

19 Two prospective parents learn that they each carry one allele for Tay-Sachs disease.

- Explain why neither of them suffers from Tay-Sachs disease.
- If they have children, what are the chances they will have a baby with Tay-Sachs disease?
- What are the chances that one of their healthy children will carry the Tay-Sachs allele?

NEW YORK LIVING ENVIRONMENT

Part C

Extended Response

Answer the questions or follow the directions given.

20 Gel electrophoresis is a valuable new tool. When used as part of a procedure referred to as DNA fingerprinting, it can be helpful in identifying specific individuals. Describe the process of gel electrophoresis as it is involved in DNA fingerprinting. In your description be sure to include:

- the role of the enzymes used in the process
- why using several different enzymes is better than using only one
- how DNA is separated during the process

Base your answers to questions 21 through 24 on the reading passage below and on your knowledge of biology.

Gene Therapy Restores Vision in Dogs Which Have Rare Disease

Using gene therapy, scientists have restored vision in dogs with a version of a rare disease that blinds human infants. The dogs had a version of Leber congenital amaurosis, an untreatable condition that causes near-total blindness in infancy. About 10,000 Americans have it, and about 1000 of them have the particular genetic defect that was corrected in the dogs.

An associate professor of ophthalmology at the University of Pennsylvania reports their experiments on three dogs in the May 2001 issue of the journal *Nature Genetics.* The dogs were blind because they lacked a particular gene. Without it, their eyes could not make a pigment necessary to perceive light. Researchers used eye surgery to deliver a copy of the gene, which was carried by a virus that inserted the gene into the DNA of the eye cells. They treated one eye in each animal and used the other eye for comparison.

Four months after treatment, several tests showed that the animals had regained at least some sight in the treated eye. Putting the dogs in a room cluttered with furniture, the dogs were much better at avoiding objects on the same side of their body as the treated eye. The treatment's effects have lasted nine months so far, the researcher reported. If this same gene therapy technique works for human Leber patients, it might pave the way for treating a variety of hereditary vision diseases that strike the retina, known collectively as retinitis pigmentosa, which affects 100,000 to 200,000 Americans.

(Source: *Times Union*, Albany 4/28/01 AP Malcom Ritter)

21 State how scientists actually delivered the missing gene to the eye cells of dogs.

22 State how scientists demonstrated that gene therapy, and not some other factor, improved the dogs' ability to see.

23 List *three* things scientists should do before performing this procedure on people with retinitis pigmentosa to make sure there will be few problems and that the results will last. Support your answer with an explanation.

24 It is hoped that eventually people with retinitis pigmentosa will be able to undergo gene therapy similar to that done with dogs. If the gene is successfully inserted and their vision is corrected, will the new gene be passed along to the children of these individuals? Support your answer with an explanation.

For: An interactive self-test
Visit: PHSchool.com
Web Code: cba-4140

UNIT 5

Evolution

Chapters

▶ Named after the color of their feet, the blue-footed boobies belong to the most common of the three species of boobies found on the Galápagos Islands.

From the Author

This book contains information about animals, plants, ecology, genetics, geology, physiology, paleontology, medicine, and chemistry. Why is all that stuff in here? Because all parts of the living world—from the DNA in our cells to the air we breathe—are united by evolutionary theory into the story of life on Earth. That story, in addition to helping us understand our world, reminds us that all living things share a common past. To me, that unity of life is both fascinating and awesome. See if you agree!

Joe Levine

What discoveries lie ahead?

- Can evolutionary theory help predict which strains of flu, AIDS, and West Nile virus will be most deadly next year?
- What new forms of life will researchers discover?
- What will the study of fossils and genes reveal about the early evolution of plants and animals?

Go Online PHSchool.com

For: Latest discoveries
Visit: PHSchool.com
Web Code: cbe-5000

CHAPTER 15

Darwin's Theory of Evolution

If you look closely at the top of what appears to be a leaf in the center of this photograph, you can see a head. This walking-leaf insect is a superb example of camouflage.

Inquiry Activity

Do lima beans show variation?

Procedure 

1. Count out 10 lima beans and measure the length of each in millimeters. Record your results in a data table.
2. Combine your data with the data of two other classmates. Place all the data on one graph. Plot the length on the *x*-axis and the number of beans of each length on the *y*-axis.

Think About It

1. **Analyzing Data** Calculate the average length of the beans. Are most lima beans close to the average length?
2. **Predicting** How do you think a graph of data from the entire class would be different from your graph of data?

15–1 The Puzzle of Life's Diversity

1-S1.1 Historical development of ideas in science
1-S1.1 Scientific explanations
LS- Use laboratory instruments

Nature presents scientists with a puzzle. Humans share the Earth with millions of other kinds of organisms of every imaginable shape, size, and habitat. This variety of living things is called biological diversity. How did all these different organisms arise? How are they related? These questions make up the puzzle of life's diversity.

What scientific explanation can account for the diversity of life? The answer is a collection of scientific facts, observations, and hypotheses known as evolutionary theory. **Evolution,** or change over time, is the process by which modern organisms have descended from ancient organisms. A scientific **theory** is a well-supported testable explanation of phenomena that have occurred in the natural world.

Guide for Reading

Key Concepts

- What was Charles Darwin's contribution to science?
- What pattern did Darwin observe among organisms of the Galápagos Islands?

Vocabulary
evolution
theory
fossil

Reading Strategy: Using Visuals Before you read, examine **Figure 15–1.** Find the British Isles, where Darwin's journey began, then trace his route. Write a statement describing his travels.

Voyage of the *Beagle*

The individual who contributed more to our understanding of evolution than anyone was Charles Darwin. Darwin was born in England on February 12, 1809—the same day as Abraham Lincoln. Shortly after completing his college studies, Darwin joined the crew of the H.M.S. *Beagle*. In 1831, he set sail from England for a voyage around the world. His route is shown in **Figure 15–1.** Although no one knew it at the time, this was to be one of the most important voyages in the history of science. **During his travels, Darwin made numerous observations and collected evidence that led him to propose a revolutionary hypothesis about the way life changes over time.** That hypothesis, now supported by a huge body of evidence, has become the theory of evolution.

▼ **Figure 15–1** On a five-year voyage on the *Beagle,* Charles Darwin visited several continents and many remote islands. **Darwin's observations led to a revolutionary theory about the way life changes over time.**

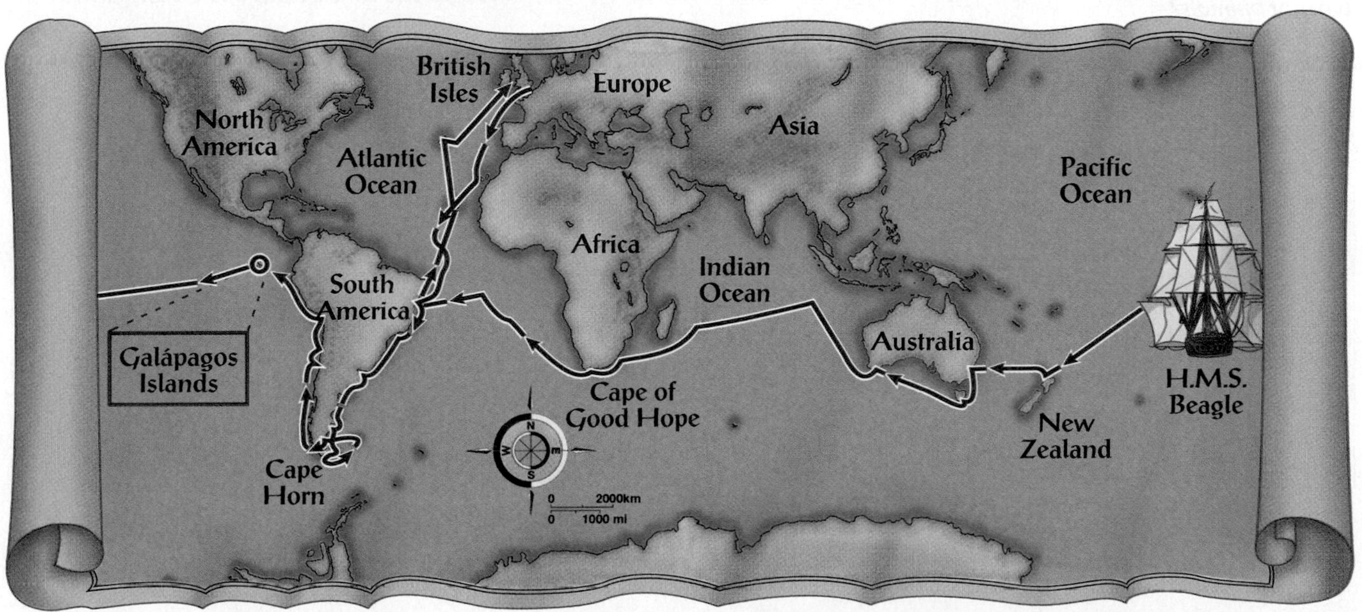

Wherever the ship anchored, Darwin went ashore to collect plant and animal specimens that he added to an ever-growing collection. At sea, he studied his specimens, read the latest scientific books, and filled many notebooks with his observations and thoughts. Darwin was well educated and had a strong interest in natural history. His curiosity and analytical nature were ultimately the keys to his success as a scientist. During his travels, Darwin came to view every new finding as a piece in an extraordinary puzzle: a scientific explanation for the diversity of life on this planet.

Darwin's Observations

Darwin knew a great deal about the plants and animals of his native country. But he saw far more diversity during his travels. For example, during a single day in a Brazilian forest, Darwin collected 68 different beetle species—despite the fact that he was not even searching for beetles! He began to realize that an enormous number of species inhabit the Earth.

Patterns of Diversity Darwin was intrigued by the fact that so many plants and animals seemed remarkably well suited to whatever environment they inhabited. He was impressed by the many ways in which organisms survived and produced offspring. He wondered if there was some process that led to such a variety of ways of reproducing.

Darwin was also puzzled by where different species lived—and did not live. He visited Argentina and Australia, for example, which had similar grassland ecosystems. Yet, those grasslands were inhabited by very different animals. Also, neither Argentina nor Australia was home to the sorts of animals that lived in European grasslands. For Darwin, these patterns posed challenging questions. Why were there no rabbits in Australia, despite the presence of habitats that seemed perfect for them? Similarly, why were there no kangaroos in England?

Figure 15–2 Many of the fossils that Darwin discovered resembled living organisms but were not identical to them. The glyptodon, an extinct animal known only from fossil remains, is an ancient relative of the armadillo of South America. **Comparing and Contrasting** *What are some similarities and differences between these two types of animals?*

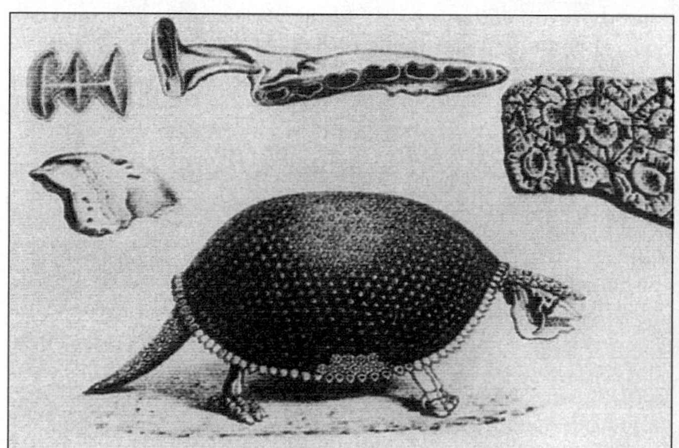

▲ **Figure 15–3 Darwin observed that the characteristics of many animals and plants varied noticeably among the different Galápagos Islands.** Among the tortoises, the shape of the shell corresponds to different habitats. The Hood Island tortoise (right) has a long neck and a shell that is curved and open around the neck and legs, allowing the tortoise to reach the sparse vegetation on Hood Island. The tortoise from Isabela Island (lower left) has a dome-shaped shell and a shorter neck. Vegetation on this island is more abundant and closer to the ground. The tortoise from Pinta Island has a shell that is intermediate between these two forms.

Living Organisms and Fossils Darwin soon realized that living animals represented just part of the puzzle posed by the natural world. In many places during his voyage, Darwin collected the preserved remains of ancient organisms, called **fossils.** Some of those fossils resembled organisms that were still alive, as shown in **Figure 15–2.** Others looked completely unlike any creature he had ever seen. As Darwin studied fossils, new questions arose. Why had so many of these species disappeared? How were they related to living species?

The Galápagos Islands Of all the *Beagle*'s ports of call, the one that influenced Darwin the most was a group of small islands located 1000 km west of South America. These are the Galápagos Islands. Darwin noted that although they were close together, the islands had very different climates. The smallest, lowest islands were hot, dry, and nearly barren. Hood Island, for example, had sparse vegetation. The higher islands had greater rainfall and a different assortment of plants and animals. Isabela Island had rich vegetation.

Darwin was fascinated in particular by the land tortoises and marine iguanas in the Galápagos. He learned that the giant tortoises varied in predictable ways from one island to another, as shown in **Figure 15–3.** The shape of a tortoise's shell could be used to identify which island a particular tortoise inhabited. Darwin later admitted in his notes that he "did not for some time pay sufficient attention to this statement."

✓ CHECKPOINT *How did the fossils Darwin observed compare with the living organisms he studied?*

For: Links on evolution
Visit: www.SciLinks.org
Web Code: cbn-5151

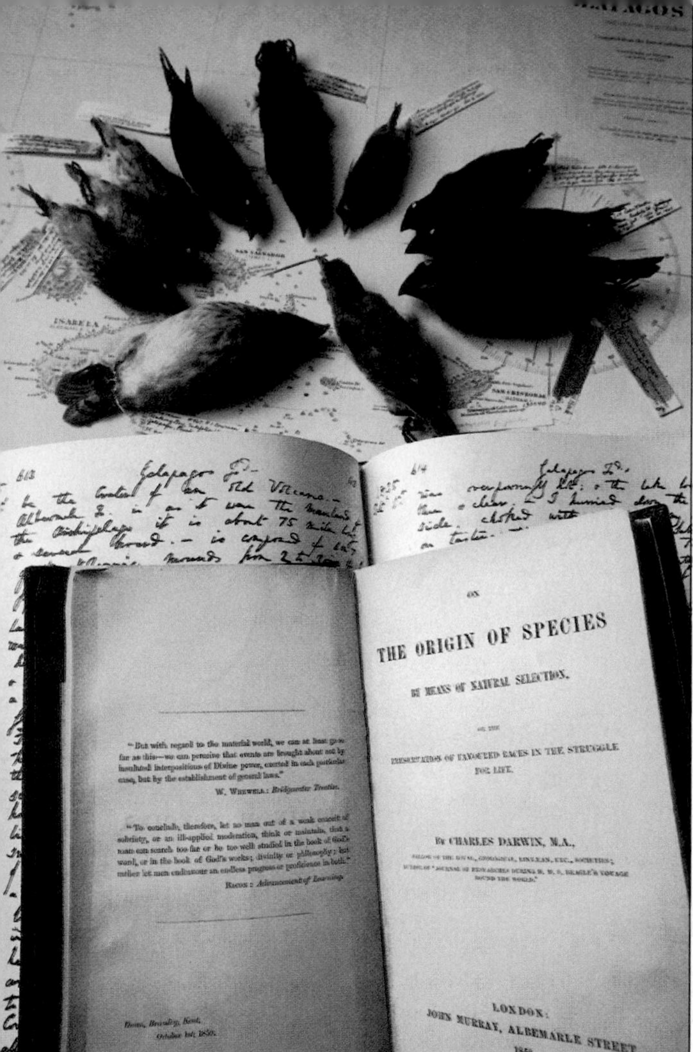

▲ **Figure 15–4** Darwin's notebooks and some of the finch specimens he collected have been preserved for today's scientists to study. **Inferring** *What might modern scientists learn from examining evidence collected by earlier investigators?*

Darwin also saw several types of small, ordinary-looking brown birds hopping around, looking for seeds. As an eager naturalist, he collected many specimens, several of which are shown in **Figure 15–4.** However, he did not find them particularly unusual or important. As Darwin examined the birds, he noted that they had differently shaped beaks. He thought that some of the birds were wrens, some were warblers, and some were blackbirds. But he came to no other conclusions—at first.

The Journey Home

While heading home, Darwin spent a great deal of time thinking about his findings. Examining different mockingbirds from the Galápagos, Darwin noticed that individual birds collected from the island of Floreana looked different from those collected on James Island. They also looked different from individuals collected on other islands. Darwin also remembered that the tortoises differed from island to island. Although Darwin did not immediately understand the reason for these patterns of diversity, he had stumbled across an important finding. **Darwin observed that the characteristics of many animals and plants varied noticeably among the different islands of the Galápagos.** After returning to England, Darwin began to wonder if animals living on different islands had once been members of the same species. According to this hypothesis, these separate species would have evolved from an original South American ancestor species after becoming isolated from one another. Was this possible? If so, it would turn people's view of the natural world upside down.

15–1 Section Assessment

1. **Key Concept** What did Darwin's travels reveal to him about the number and variety of living species?
2. **Key Concept** How did tortoises and birds differ among the islands of the Galápagos?
3. What is evolution? Why is evolution referred to as a theory?
4. What is a fossil?
5. **Critical Thinking Inferring** Darwin found fossils of many organisms that were different from any living species. How would this finding have affected his understanding of life's diversity?

Connecting Concepts

Biotic and Abiotic Factors
In Chapter 5, you learned that both biotic and abiotic factors affect ecosystems. Distinguish between these two factors, give some examples of each, and explain how they might have affected the tortoises that Darwin observed on the Galápagos Islands.

15–2 Ideas That Shaped Darwin's Thinking

1-S1.1 Historical development of ideas in science
1-S1.1 Combining existing knowledge with new evidence
1-S1.4 Accepted theories have support of many individuals
1-S3.5 Scientific findings evaluated

If Darwin had lived a century earlier, he might have done little more than think about the questions raised during his travels. But Darwin's voyage came during one of the most exciting periods in the history of Western science. Explorers were traversing the globe, and great thinkers were beginning to challenge established views about the natural world. Darwin was powerfully influenced by the work of these scientists, especially those who were studying the history of Earth. In turn, he himself greatly changed the thinking of many scientists and nonscientists. Some people, however, found Darwin's ideas too shocking to accept. To understand how radical Darwin's thoughts appeared, you must understand a few things about the world in which he lived.

Most Europeans in Darwin's day believed that the Earth and all its forms of life had been created only a few thousand years ago. Since that original creation, they concluded, neither the planet nor its living species had changed. A robin, for example, has always looked and behaved as robins had in the past. Rocks and major geological features were thought to have been produced suddenly by catastrophic events that humans rarely, if ever, witnessed.

By the time Darwin set sail, numerous discoveries had turned up important pieces of evidence. A rich fossil record, including the example in **Figure 15–5**, was challenging that traditional view of life. In light of such evidence, some scientists even adjusted their beliefs to include not one but several periods of creation. Each of these periods, they contended, was preceded by a catastrophic event that killed off many forms of life. At first, Darwin may have accepted these beliefs. But he began to realize that much of what he had observed did not fit neatly into this view of unchanging life. Slowly, after studying many scientific theories of his time, Darwin began to change his thinking dramatically.

Guide for Reading

Key Concepts
- How did Hutton and Lyell describe geological change?
- According to Lamarck, how did species evolve?
- What was Malthus's theory of population growth?

Reading Strategy: Finding Main Ideas
As you read about the individuals who influenced Darwin's thinking, write a sentence briefly describing what Darwin learned from each one.

▶ **Figure 15–5** This engraving, made around 1850, shows the fossil remains of a giant sloth from South America. During the 1800s, explorers were finding the remains of numerous animal types that had no living representatives. **Inferring** ***What did such fossil evidence indicate about life in the past?***

▲ **Figure 15–6** These huge rocks, which are composed of sandstone, show distinct layers that were laid down over millions of years. **Hutton and Lyell cited geological features such as these rocks as evidence that Earth is many millions of years old.**

An Ancient, Changing Earth

During the eighteenth and nineteenth centuries, scientists examined Earth in great detail. They gathered information suggesting that Earth was very old and had changed slowly over time. Two scientists who formed important theories based on this evidence were James Hutton and Charles Lyell. **Hutton and Lyell helped scientists recognize that Earth is many millions of years old, and the processes that changed Earth in the past are the same processes that operate in the present.**

Hutton and Geological Change In 1795, the geologist James Hutton published a detailed hypothesis about the geological forces that have shaped Earth. Hutton proposed that layers of rock, such as those shown in **Figure 15–6,** form very slowly. Also, some rocks are moved up by forces beneath Earth's surface. Others are buried, and still others are pushed up from the sea floor to form mountain ranges. The resulting rocks, mountains, and valleys are then shaped by a variety of natural forces—including rain, wind, heat, and cold temperatures. Most of these geological processes operate extremely slowly, often over millions of years. Hutton, therefore, proposed that Earth had to be much more than a few thousand years old.

Biology and History

Origins of Evolutionary Thought

The groundwork for the modern theory of evolution was laid during the 1700s and 1800s. Charles Darwin developed the central idea of evolution by natural selection, but others before and during his time also built essential parts of the theory.

1785
James Hutton
Hutton proposes that Earth is shaped by geological forces that took place over extremely long periods of time. He estimates Earth to be millions—not thousands—of years old.

1798
Thomas Malthus
In his *Essay on the Principle of Population,* Malthus predicts that the human population will grow faster than the space and food supplies needed to sustain it.

1809
Jean-Baptiste Lamarck
Lamarck publishes his hypotheses of the inheritance of acquired traits. The ideas are flawed, but he is one of the first to propose a mechanism explaining how organisms change over time.

1750

1800

Lyell's *Principles of Geology* Just before the *Beagle* set sail, Darwin had been given the first volume of geologist Charles Lyell's book *Principles of Geology*. Lyell stressed that scientists must explain past events in terms of processes that they can actually observe, since processes that shaped the Earth millions of years earlier continue in the present. Volcanoes release hot lava and gases now, just as they did on an ancient Earth. Erosion continues to carve out canyons, just as it did in the past.

Lyell's work explained how awesome geological features could be built up or torn down over long periods of time. Lyell helped Darwin appreciate the significance of geological phenomena that he had observed. Darwin had witnessed a spectacular volcanic eruption. Darwin wrote about an earthquake that had lifted a stretch of rocky shoreline—with mussels and other animals attached to it—more than 3 meters above its previous position. He noted that fossils of marine animals were displaced many feet above sea level. Darwin then understood how geological processes could have raised these rocks from the sea floor to a mountaintop.

This understanding of geology influenced Darwin in two ways. First, Darwin asked himself: If the Earth could change over time, might life change as well? Second, he realized that it would have taken many, many years for life to change in the way he suggested. This would have been possible only if the Earth were extremely old.

CHECKPOINT ***What are some ways the Earth has changed over time?***

For: Links on Darwin
Visit: www.SciLinks.org
Web Code: cbn-5152

Writing in Science

Use the library or the Internet to find out more about Darwin and Wallace. Write a dialogue between these two men, where the conversation shows the similarities in their careers and theories.

1831
Charles Darwin
Darwin sets sail on the H.M.S. *Beagle,* a voyage that will provide him with vast amounts of evidence leading to his theory of evolution.

1833
Charles Lyell
In the second and final volume of *Principles of Geology,* Lyell explains that processes occurring now have shaped Earth's geological features over long periods of time.

1858
Alfred Wallace
Wallace writes to Darwin, speculating on evolution by natural selection, based on his studies of the distribution of plants and animals.

1859
Darwin publishes *On the Origin of Species.*

1850

Lamarck's Evolution Hypotheses

The French naturalist Jean-Baptiste Lamarck was among the first scientists to recognize that living things have changed over time—and that all species were descended from other species. He also realized that organisms were somehow adapted to their environments. In 1809, the year that Darwin was born, Lamarck published his hypotheses.

Lamarck proposed that by selective use or disuse of organs, organisms acquired or lost certain traits during their lifetime. These traits could then be passed on to their offspring. Over time, this process led to change in a species.

Tendency Toward Perfection Lamarck proposed that all organisms have an innate tendency toward complexity and perfection. As a result, they are continually changing and acquiring features that help them live more successfully in their environments. In Lamarck's view, for instance, the ancestors of birds acquired an urge to fly. Over many generations, birds kept trying to fly, and their wings increased in size and became more suited to flying.

Use and Disuse Because of this tendency toward perfection, Lamarck proposed that organisms could alter the size or shape of particular organs by using their bodies in new ways. For example, by trying to use their front limbs for flying, birds could eventually transform those limbs into wings. Conversely, if a winged animal did not use its wings—an example of disuse—the wings would decrease in size over generations and finally disappear.

Inheritance of Acquired Traits Like many biologists of his time, Lamarck thought that acquired characteristics could be inherited. For example, if during its lifetime an animal somehow altered a body structure, leading to longer legs or fluffier feathers, it would pass that change on to its offspring. By this reasoning, if you spent much of your life lifting weights to build muscles, your children would inherit big muscles, too.

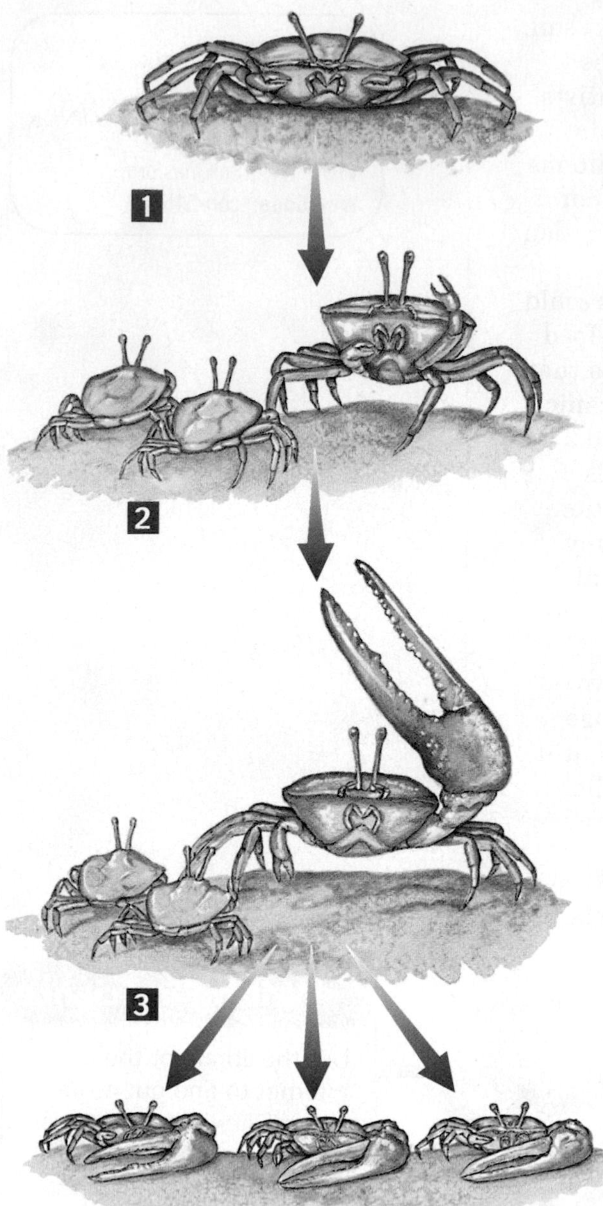

▲ **Figure 15–7** **Lamarck proposed that the selective use or disuse of an organ led to a change in that organ that was then passed on to offspring.** This proposed mechanism is shown here applied to fiddler crabs. (1) The male crab uses its small front claw to attract mates and ward off predators. (2) Because the front claw has been used repeatedly, it becomes larger. (3) The acquired characteristic, a larger claw, is then passed on to the crab's offspring. Lamarck's explanation, proposed in 1809, was found to be incorrect.

Evaluating Lamarck's Hypotheses

Lamarck's hypotheses of evolution, illustrated in **Figure 15–7**, are incorrect in several ways. Lamarck, like Darwin, did not know how traits are inherited. He did not know that an organism's behavior has no effect on its heritable characteristics. However, Lamarck was one of the first to develop a scientific hypothesis of evolution and to realize that organisms are adapted to their environments. He paved the way for the work of later biologists.

Population Growth

Another important influence on Darwin came from the English economist Thomas Malthus. In 1798, Malthus published a book in which he noted that babies were being born faster than people were dying. **Malthus reasoned that if the human population continued to grow unchecked, sooner or later there would be insufficient living space and food for everyone.** The only forces he observed that worked against this growth were war, famine, and disease. Conditions in certain parts of nineteenth-century England, illustrated in **Figure 15–8,** reinforced Malthus's somewhat pessimistic view of the human condition.

When Darwin read Malthus's work, he realized that this reasoning applied even more strongly to plants and animals than it did to humans. Why? Because humans produce far fewer offspring than most other species do. A mature maple tree can produce thousands of seeds in a single summer, and one oyster can produce millions of eggs each year. If all the offspring of almost any species survived for several generations, they would overrun the world.

Obviously, this has not happened, because continents are not covered with maple trees, and oceans are not filled with oysters. The overwhelming majority of a species' offspring die. Further, only a few of those offspring that survive succeed in reproducing. What causes the death of so many individuals? What factor or factors determine which ones survive and reproduce, and which do not? Answers to these questions became central to Darwin's explanation of evolutionary change.

▶ **Figure 15–8** **Malthus reasoned that if the human population continued to grow unchecked, sooner or later there would be insufficient food and living space for everyone.** He supported his theory with the evidence he observed in the streets of London.

15–2 Section Assessment

1. **Key Concept** What two ideas from geology were important to Darwin's thinking?
2. **Key Concept** According to Lamarck, how did organisms acquire traits?
3. **Key Concept** According to Malthus, what factors limited population growth?
4. How did Lyell's *Principles of Geology* influence Darwin?
5. **Critical Thinking Evaluating** Evaluate the strengths and weaknesses of Lamarck's hypotheses of evolution. How did they contribute to scientific thought? Why have they been rejected?

Writing in Science

Creative Writing
Imagine that you are Thomas Malthus. Write an article that would appear in a newspaper of the time that explains your ideas. Explain the impact of a growing population on society and the environment.

15–3 Darwin Presents His Case

4-3.1 Natural selection and evolution
4-2.2 Selective breeding
LS- Make observations and formulate a conclusion
LS- State an appropriate hypothesis

Guide for Reading

Key Concepts

- How is natural variation used in artificial selection?
- How is natural selection related to a species' fitness?
- What evidence of evolution did Darwin present?

Vocabulary

artificial selection
struggle for existence
fitness
adaptation
survival of the fittest
natural selection
descent with modification
common descent
homologous structure
vestigial organ

Reading Strategy: Building Vocabulary As you read, write a phrase or sentence in your own words to define each highlighted, boldface term.

When Darwin returned to England in 1836, he brought back specimens from around the world. Subsequent findings about these specimens soon had the scientific community abuzz. Darwin learned that his Galápagos mockingbirds actually belonged to three separate species found nowhere else in the world! Even more surprising, the brown birds that Darwin had thought to be wrens, warblers, and blackbirds were all finches. They, too, were found nowhere else. The same was true of the Galápagos tortoises, the marine iguanas, and many plants that Darwin had collected on the islands. Each island species looked a great deal like a similar species on the South American mainland. Yet, the island species were clearly different from the mainland species and from one another.

Publication of *On the Origin of Species*

Darwin began filling notebooks with his ideas about species diversity and the process that would later be called evolution. However, he did not rush out to publish his thoughts. Recall that Darwin's ideas challenged fundamental scientific beliefs of his day. Darwin was not only stunned by his discoveries, he was disturbed by them. Years later, he wrote, "It was evident that such facts as these . . . could be explained on the supposition that species gradually became modified, and the subject haunted me." Although he discussed his work with friends, he shelved his manuscript for years and told his wife to publish it in case he died.

In 1858, Darwin received a short essay from Alfred Russel Wallace, a fellow naturalist who had been doing field work in Malaysia. That essay summarized the thoughts on evolutionary change that Darwin had been mulling over for almost 25 years! Suddenly, Darwin had an incentive to publish his own work. At a scientific meeting later that year, Wallace's essay was presented together with some of Darwin's work.

◀ **Figure 15–9** Each zebra inherits genes that give it a distinctive pattern of stripes. Those visibly different patterns are an example of natural variation in a species. **Formulating Hypotheses** ***What might be some genetic variations that are not visible?***

Eighteen months later, in 1859, Darwin published the results of his work, *On the Origin of Species.* In his book, he proposed a mechanism for evolution that he called natural selection. He then presented evidence that evolution has been taking place for millions of years—and continues in all living things. Darwin's work caused a sensation. Many people considered his arguments to be brilliant, while others strongly opposed his message. But what did Darwin actually say?

What event motivated Darwin to publish his ideas?

Inherited Variation and Artificial Selection

One of Darwin's most important insights was that members of each species vary from one another in important ways. Observations during his travels and conversations with plant and animal breeders convinced him that variation existed both in nature and on farms. For example, some plants in a species bear larger fruit than others. Some cows give more milk than others. From breeders, Darwin learned that some of this was heritable variation—differences that are passed from parents to offspring. Darwin had no idea of how heredity worked. Today, we know that heritable variation in organisms is caused by variations in their genes. We also know that genetic variation is found in wild species as well as in domesticated plants and animals.

Darwin argued that this variation mattered. This was a revolutionary idea, because in Darwin's day, variations were thought to be unimportant, minor defects. But Darwin noted that plant and animal breeders used heritable variation—what we now call genetic variation—to improve crops and livestock. They would select for breeding only the largest hogs, the fastest horses, or the cows that produced the most milk. Darwin termed this process **artificial selection.** **In artificial selection, nature provided the variation, and humans selected those variations that they found useful.** Artificial selection has produced many diverse domestic animals and crop plants, including the plants shown in **Figure 15–10,** by selectively breeding for different traits.

Quick Lab

New vegetables from old?

Materials various *Brassica* (cabbage family) vegetables

Procedure 

Examine each of the vegetables and compare them. Determine which organ of the ancestral plant breeders may have chosen to produce each vegetable.

Analyze and Conclude

Formulating Hypotheses Choose one of the vegetables. Explain how breeders might have produced that variety from the ancestral plant, shown below.

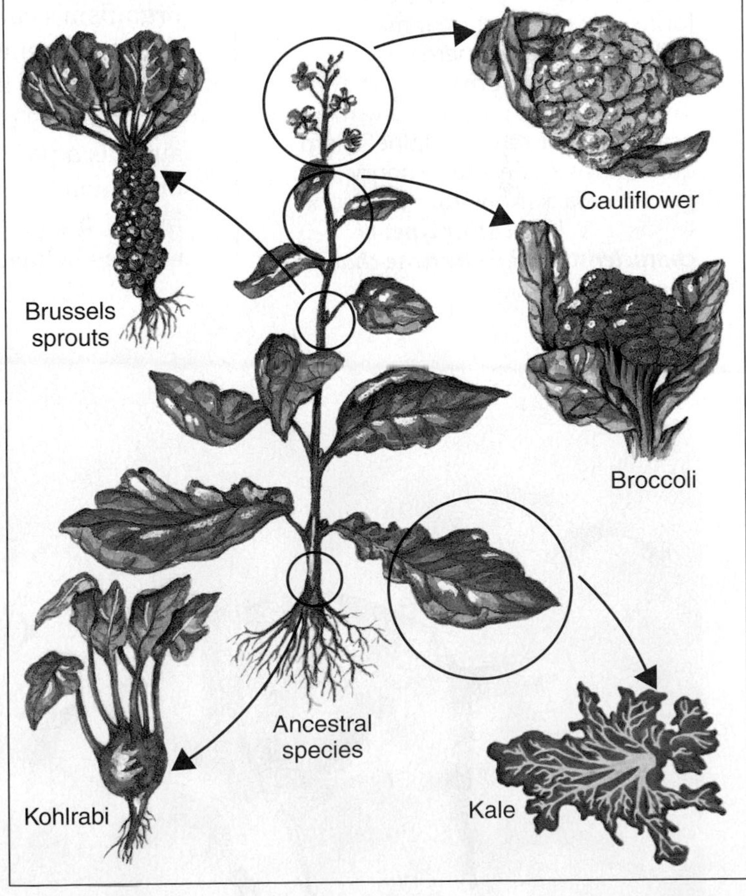

▶ **Figure 15–10 In artificial selection, humans select from among the naturally occurring genetic variations in a species.** From a single ancestral plant, breeders selecting for enlarged flower buds, leaf buds, leaves, or stems have produced all these plants.

For: Links on natural selection
Visit: www.SciLinks.org
Web Code: cbn-5153

Evolution by Natural Selection

Darwin's next insight was to compare processes in nature to artificial selection. By doing so, he developed a scientific hypothesis to explain how evolution occurs. This is where Darwin made his greatest contribution—and his strongest break with the past.

The Struggle for Existence Darwin was convinced that a process like artificial selection worked in nature. But how? He recalled Malthus's work on population growth. Darwin realized that high birth rates and a shortage of life's basic needs would eventually force organisms into a competition for resources. The **struggle for existence** means that members of each species compete regularly to obtain food, living space, and other necessities of life. In this struggle, the predators that are faster or have a particular way of ensnaring other organisms can catch more prey. Those prey that are faster, better camouflaged, or better protected, such as the porcupine shown in **Figure 15–11**, can avoid being caught. This struggle for existence was central to Darwin's theory of evolution.

Survival of the Fittest A key factor in the struggle for existence, Darwin observed, was how well suited an organism is to its environment. Darwin called the ability of an individual to survive and reproduce in its specific environment **fitness.** Darwin proposed that fitness is the result of adaptations. An **adaptation** is any inherited characteristic that increases an organism's chance of survival. Successful adaptations, Darwin concluded, enable organisms to become better suited to their environment and thus better able to survive and reproduce. Adaptations can be anatomical, or structural, characteristics, such as a porcupine's sharp quills. Adaptations also include an organism's physiological processes, or functions, such as the way in which a plant performs photosynthesis. More complex features, such as behavior in which some animals live and hunt in groups, can also be adaptations.

▼ **Figure 15–11** Survival of the fittest can take many different forms. For one species, it may be an ability to run fast, whereas for another species, it may be behavioral tactics that it uses to outsmart predators. For the porcupine, sharp quills make a powerful, hungry predator back away from an attack. **Inferring** *What other types of characteristics might increase chances of survival?*

◀ **Figure 15–12** Each of these baby tanagers has its own set of inherited traits that affect its survival. A stronger bird may take food from a weaker sibling. A faster bird may escape predators more easily. Only those birds that survive and reproduce have the chance to pass their traits to the next generation. **Over time, natural selection results in changes in the inherited characteristics of a population.**

The concept of fitness, Darwin argued, was central to the process of evolution by natural selection. Generation after generation, individuals compete to survive and produce offspring. The baby birds in **Figure 15–12,** for example, compete for food and space while in the nest. Because each individual differs from other members of its species, each has unique advantages and disadvantages. Individuals with characteristics that are not well suited to their environment—that is, with low levels of fitness—either die or leave few offspring. Individuals that are better suited to their environment—that is, with adaptations that enable fitness—survive and reproduce most successfully. Darwin called this process **survival of the fittest.**

Because of its similarities to artificial selection, Darwin referred to the survival of the fittest as **natural selection.** In both artificial selection and natural selection, only certain individuals of a population produce new individuals. However, in natural selection, the traits being selected—and therefore increasing over time—contribute to an organism's fitness in its environment. Natural selection also takes place without human control or direction. **Over time, natural selection results in changes in the inherited characteristics of a population. These changes increase a species' fitness in its environment.** Natural selection cannot be seen directly; it can only be observed as changes in a population over many successive generations.

CHECKPOINT *What did Darwin mean when he described certain organisms as "more fit" than others?*

Descent With Modification Darwin proposed that over long periods, natural selection produces organisms that have different structures, establish different niches, or occupy different habitats. As a result, species today look different from their ancestors. Each living species has descended, with changes, from other species over time. He referred to this principle as **descent with modification.**

For: Articles on evolution
Visit: PHSchool.com
Web Code: cbe-5154

Descent with modification also implies that all living organisms are related to one another. Look back in time, and you will find common ancestors shared by tigers, panthers, and cheetahs. Look farther back, and you will find ancestors that these felines share with horses, dogs, and bats. Farther back still are the common ancestors of mammals, birds, alligators, and fishes. If we look far enough back, the logic concludes, we could find the common ancestors of all living things. This is the principle known as **common descent.** According to this principle, all species—living and extinct—were derived from common ancestors. Therefore, a single "tree of life" links all living things.

Evidence of Evolution

With this unified, dynamic theory of life, Darwin could finally explain many of the observations he had made during his travels aboard the *Beagle.* **Darwin argued that living things have been evolving on Earth for millions of years. Evidence for this process could be found in the fossil record, the geographical distribution of living species, homologous structures of living organisms, and similarities in early development, or embryology.**

The Fossil Record By Darwin's time, scientists knew that fossils were the remains of ancient life, and that different layers of rock had been formed at different times during Earth's history. Darwin saw fossils as a record of the history of life on Earth. Darwin, like Lyell, proposed that Earth was many millions—rather than thousands—of years old. During this long time, Darwin proposed, countless species had come into being, lived for a time, and then vanished. By comparing fossils from older rock layers with fossils from younger layers, scientists could document the fact that life on Earth has changed over time as shown in **Figure 15–13.**

▼ **Figure 15–13 Darwin argued that the fossil record provided evidence that living things have been evolving for millions of years.** Often, the fossil record includes a variety of different extinct organisms that are related to one another and to living species. The four fossil organisms shown here are cephalopods, a group that includes squid, octopi, and the chambered nautilus. The fossil record contains more than 7500 species of cephalopods, which vary, as these fossils show, from species with short, straight shells, to species with longer, coiled shells. Darwin and his colleagues noticed that the sizes, shapes, and varieties of related organisms preserved in the fossil record changed over time.

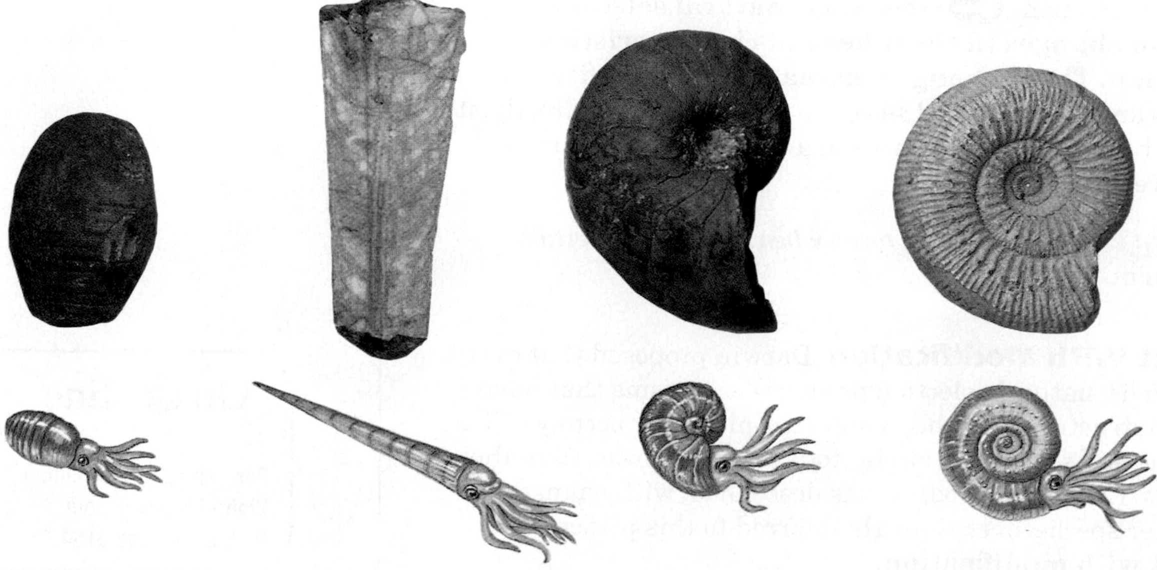

Since Darwin's time, the number of known fossil forms has grown enormously. Researchers have discovered many hundreds of transitional fossils that document various intermediate stages in the evolution of modern species from organisms that are now extinct. Gaps remain, of course, in the fossil records of many species, although a lot of them shrink each year as new fossils are discovered. These gaps do not indicate weakness in the theory of evolution itself. Rather, they point out uncertainties in our understanding of exactly how some species evolved.

Geographic Distribution of Living Species Remember that many parts of the biological puzzle that Darwin saw on his *Beagle* voyage involved living organisms. After Darwin discovered that those little brown birds he collected in the Galápagos were all finches, he began to wonder how they came to be similar, yet distinctly different from one another. Each species was slightly different from every other species. They were also slightly different from the most similar species on the mainland of South America. Could the island birds have changed over time, as populations in different places adapted to different local environments? Darwin struggled with this question for a long time. He finally decided that all these birds could have descended with modification from a common mainland ancestor.

There were other parts to the living puzzle as well. Recall that Darwin found entirely different species of animals on the continents of South America and Australia. Yet, when he looked at similar environments on those continents, he sometimes saw different animals that had similar anatomies and behaviors. Darwin's theory of descent with modification made scientific sense of this part of the puzzle as well. Species now living on different continents, as shown in **Figure 15–14,** had each descended from different ancestors. However, because some animals on each continent were living under similar ecological conditions, they were exposed to similar pressures of natural selection. Because of these similar selection pressures, different animals ended up evolving certain striking features in common.

CHECKPOINT *How can two species that look very different from each other be more closely related than two other species that look similar to each other?*

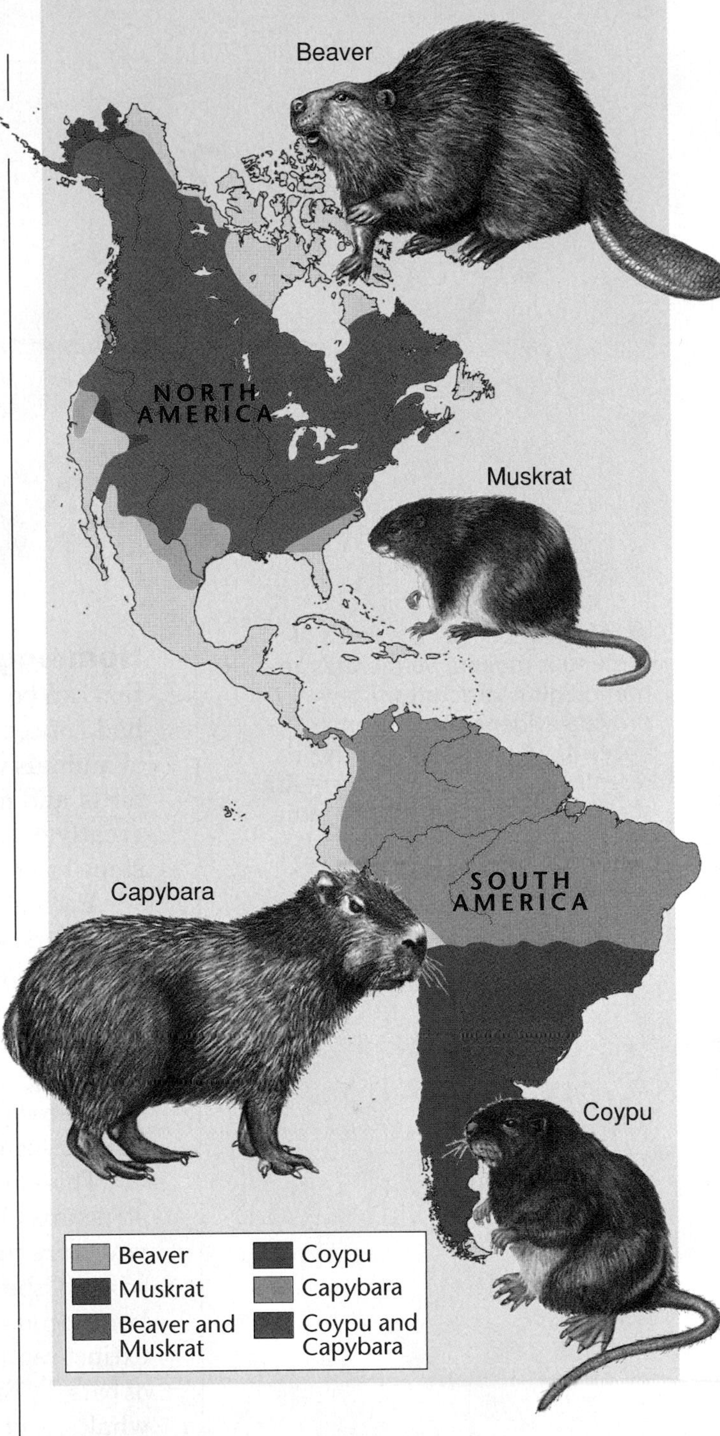

▲ **Figure 15–14** The existence of similar but unrelated species was a puzzle to Darwin. Later, he realized that similar animals in different locations were the product of different lines of evolutionary descent. Here, the beaver and the capybara are similar species that inhabit similar environments of North America and South America. The South American coypu also shares many characteristics with the North American muskrat. **Interpreting Graphics** *Which animal has a larger geographical range, the coypu or the muskrat?*

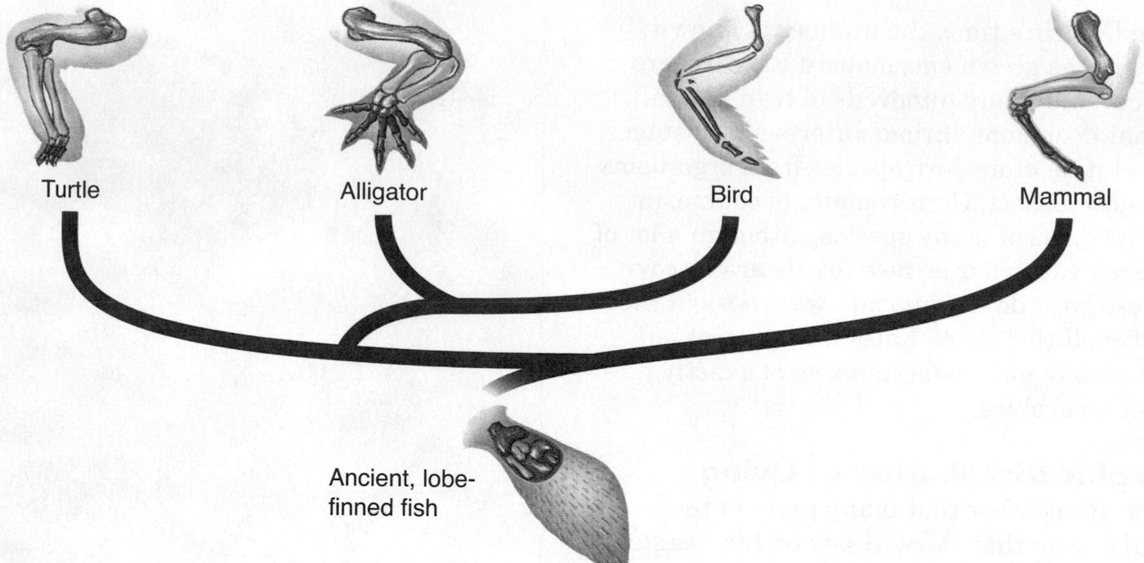

▲ **Figure 15–15** The limbs of these four modern vertebrates are homologous structures. They provide evidence of a common ancestor whose bones may have resembled those of the ancient fish shown here. Notice that the same colors are used to show related structures. **Homologous structures are one type of evidence for the evolution of living things.**

Homologous Body Structures Further evidence of evolution can be found in living animals. By Darwin's time, researchers had noticed striking anatomical similarities among the body parts of animals with backbones. For example, the limbs of reptiles, birds, and mammals—arms, wings, legs, and flippers—vary greatly in form and function. Yet, they are all constructed from the same basic bones, as shown in **Figure 15–15.**

Each of these limbs has adapted in ways that enable organisms to survive in different environments. Despite these different functions, however, these limb bones all develop from the same clumps of cells in embryos. Structures that have different mature forms but develop from the same embryonic tissues are called **homologous** (hoh-MAHL-uh-guhs) **structures.** Homologous structures provide strong evidence that all four-limbed vertebrates have descended, with modifications, from common ancestors.

There is still more information to be gathered from homologous structures. If we compare the front limbs, we can see that all bird wings are more similar to one another than any of them are to bat wings. Other bones in bird skeletons most closely resemble the homologous bones of certain reptiles—including crocodiles and extinct reptiles such as dinosaurs. The bones that support the wings of bats, by contrast, are more similar to the front limbs of humans, whales, and other mammals than they are to those of birds. These similarities and differences help biologists group animals according to how recently they last shared a common ancestor.

Not all homologous structures serve important functions. The organs of many animals are so reduced in size that they are just vestiges, or traces, of homologous organs in other species. These **vestigial organs** may resemble miniature legs, tails, or other structures. The legs of the skinks shown in **Figure 15–16** are an example of vestigial organs. Why would an organism possess organs with little or no function? One possibility is that the presence of a vestigial organ may not affect an organism's ability to survive and reproduce. In that case, natural selection would not cause the elimination of that organ.

Word Origins

Homologous, from the Greek words *homos,* meaning "same," and *legein,* meaning "say," describes similar body structures that come from a common ancestor. **If the word *morphe* means "shape," what are homomorphic structures?**

Figure 15–16 These three animals are skinks, a type of lizard. In some species of skinks, legs have become vestigial. They are so reduced that they no longer function in walking. In humans, the appendix is an example of a vestigial organ because it carries out no function in digestion. **Inferring** *How might vestigial organs provide clues to an animal's evolutionary history?*

Homologies also appear in other aspects of plant and animal anatomy and physiology. Certain groups of plants and algae, for example, share homologous variations in stem, leaf, root, and flower structures, and in the way they carry out photosynthesis. Mammals share many homologies that distinguish them from other vertebrates. Dolphins may look something like fishes, but homologies show that they are mammals. For example, like other mammals, they have lungs rather than gills and obtain oxygen from air rather than water.

Similarities in Embryology The early stages, or embryos, of many animals with backbones are very similar. This does not mean that a human embryo is ever identical to a fish or a bird embryo. However, as you can see in **Figure 15–17,** many embryos look especially similar during early stages of development. What do these similarities mean?

There have, in the past, been incorrect explanations for these similarities. Also, the biologist Ernst Haeckel fudged some of his drawings to make the earliest stages of some embryos seem more similar than they actually are! Errors aside, however, it is clear that the same groups of embryonic cells develop in the same order and in similar patterns to produce the tissues and organs of all vertebrates. These common cells and tissues, growing in similar ways, produce the homologous structures discussed earlier.

CHECKPOINT *What are homologous structures?*

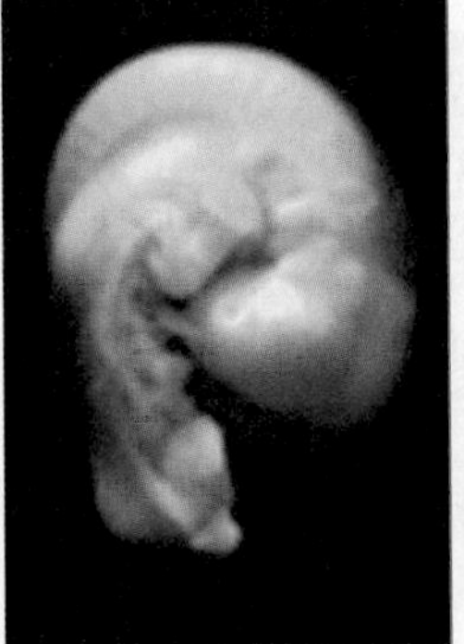

Chicken

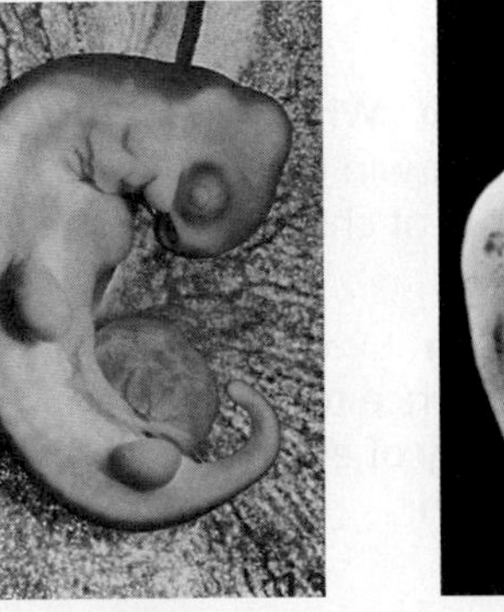

Turtle

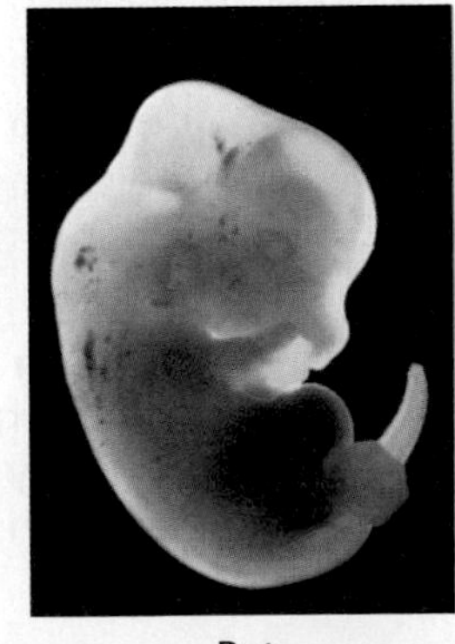

Rat

Figure 15–17 In their early stages of development, chickens, turtles, and rats look similar, providing evidence that they shared a common ancestry. **Inferring** *How could a study of these embryos help show the relationships among animals with backbones?*

▲ **Figure 15–18** Darwin's *On the Origin of Species* presented a revolutionary view of the living world. Many scientists agree with Darwin's statement that "There is a grandeur in this view of life, . . . that . . . from so simple a beginning, endless forms so beautiful and wonderful have been and are being evolved." **Applying Concepts** ***New species are continually being discovered. How could you use Darwin's theory to learn more about these new species?***

Summary of Darwin's Theory

Darwin's theory of evolution can be summarized as follows:

- Individual organisms differ, and some of this variation is heritable.
- Organisms produce more offspring than can survive, and many that do survive do not reproduce.
- Because more organisms are produced than can survive, they compete for limited resources.
- Each unique organism has different advantages and disadvantages in the struggle for existence. Individuals best suited to their environment survive and reproduce most successfully. These organisms pass their heritable traits to their offspring. Other individuals die or leave fewer offspring. This process of natural selection causes species to change over time.
- Species alive today are descended with modification from ancestral species that lived in the distant past. This process, by which diverse species evolved from common ancestors, unites all organisms on Earth into a single tree of life.

Strengths and Weaknesses of Evolutionary Theory

Scientific advances in many fields of biology, along with geology and physics, have confirmed and expanded most of Darwin's hypotheses. Today, evolutionary theory offers vital insights to all biological and biomedical sciences—from infectious-disease research to ecology. In fact, evolution is often called the "grand unifying theory of the life sciences."

Like any scientific theory, evolutionary theory continues to change as new data are gathered and new ways of thinking arise. As you will see shortly, researchers still debate such important questions as precisely how new species arise and why species become extinct. There is also uncertainty about how life began.

15–3 Section Assessment

1. **Key Concept** How is artificial selection dependent on variation in nature?
2. **Key Concept** The theory of evolution by natural selection explains, in scientific terms, how living things evolve over time. What is being selected in this process?
3. **Key Concept** What types of evidence did Darwin use to support his theory of change over time?
4. **Critical Thinking Evaluating** Use scientific evidence to evaluate Darwin's theory of evolution by natural selection.

Writing in Science

Newspaper Article
Write a newspaper article about the meeting in which Darwin's and Wallace's hypotheses of evolution were first presented. Explain the theory of evolution by natural selection for an audience who knows nothing about the subject.

Exploration

Modeling Adaptation

In this game, three families land on an alien planet. At home, the Hunter family survived by hunting in the cold north. The Seeder family farmed the temperate zone. The Fisher family lived on a tropical island. In this investigation, you will model how well each family survives in a new environment.

Problem How do organisms survive in new habitats?

Material

- coin

Skills Using Models, Using Tables and Graphs, Calculating

Procedure

1. Work in groups of three, with each member playing a Hunter, Seeder, or Fisher.
2. Flip a coin. Record the result as 1 for heads, 0 for tails. Toss the coin three more times to produce a series of four 1s and 0s. This 4-digit number is the code for your new habitat.
3. If the first digit in your code is 1, you live in a hot area. If it is 0, the climate is cold. If the second digit is 1, the climate is wet. If it is 0, it's dry. If the third digit is 1, you have a dry cave to live in. If it is 0, you sleep under the stars. If the last digit is 1, there is enough food. If it is 0, food is scarce. Record a description of your habitat.
4. Find your family in the table below. Then, record each number in your row that falls under a heading that describes your habitat (hot or cold and so forth). Record the total of these 4 numbers. This total represents the energy you have accumulated from your food.
5. Subtract 8 from your total to model the energy you must use to survive. If you don't have enough energy to do this, you're out of the game. The player with the most energy wins. Record the score and habitat of each family.
6. **Predicting** Record a prediction of what would happen if you reversed each player's habitat code by changing all the 1s to 0s and the 0s to 1s.
7. Reverse your habitat code as described in step 6. Play a second round with these conditions.

Analyze and Conclude

1. **Comparing and Contrasting** In which habitat were you most successful? Was it similar to your home environment?
2. **Using Models** The numbers in the table are different for each family. How did this fact help you model the survival of different organisms?
3. **Drawing Conclusions** Is one habitat best for all players? Explain in terms of adaptation.

Go Further

Applying Concepts Revise the game to reflect the different conditions of summer and winter. Then, demonstrate your game to the class.

Energy Points for Survival

	Temperature		Water		Shelter		Food	
	Cold	Hot	Dry	Wet	None	Cave	Scarce	Plenty
Hunter	8	-2	0	4	-6	7	-5	8
Seeder	0	3	2	2	-1	2	-2	6
Fisher	-5	8	-2	5	0	1	-1	4

Chapter 15 Study Guide

15–1 The Puzzle of Life's Diversity

Key Concepts

- During his travels, Charles Darwin made numerous observations and collected evidence that led him to propose a revolutionary hypothesis about the way life changes over time.
- Darwin observed that the characteristics of many animals and plants varied noticeably among the different islands of the Galápagos.

Vocabulary

evolution, p. 369
theory, p. 369
fossil, p. 371

15–2 Ideas That Shaped Darwin's Thinking

Key Concepts

- Hutton and Lyell helped scientists realize that Earth is many millions of years old, and the processes that changed Earth in the past are the same processes that operate in the present.
- Lamarck proposed that by selective use or disuse of organs, organisms acquired or lost certain traits during their lifetime. These traits could then be passed on to their offspring. Over time, this process led to change in a species.
- Malthus reasoned that if the human population continued to grow unchecked, sooner or later there would be insufficient living space and food for everyone.

15–3 Darwin Presents His Case

Key Concepts

- In artificial selection, nature provides the variation among different organisms, and humans select those variations that they find useful.
- Over time, natural selection results in changes in the inherited characteristics of a population. These changes increase a species' fitness in its environment.
- Darwin argued that living things have been evolving on Earth for millions of years. Evidence for this process could be found in the fossil record, the geographical distribution of living species, homologous structures of living organisms, and similarities in early development, or embryology.

Vocabulary

artificial selection, p. 379
struggle for existence, p. 380
fitness, p. 380
adaptation, p. 380
survival of the fittest, p. 381
natural selection, p. 381
descent with modification, p. 381
common descent, p. 382
homologous structure, p. 384
vestigial organ, p. 384

Thinking Visually

Use the information in this chapter to complete the table below.

Evidence of Evolution

Type of Evidence	Example	What Evidence Reveals
The fossil record	1	2
Geographic distribution of living species	3	4
Homologous body structures	5	6
Similarities in embryological development	7	8

Preparing for the Living Environment Exam

Blue questions emphasize Regents Exam content

Chapter 15

Part A

Multiple Choice

For each statement or question, select the number of the word or expression that, of those given, best completes the statement or answers the question.

1 Which concept is *not* a part of the theory of evolution?
(1) Present-day species developed from earlier species.
(2) Some species die out when environmental changes occur.
(3) Complex organisms develop from simple organisms over time.
(4) Change occurs according to the needs of an individual organism to survive.

2 Even though the environment changes, a population that occupies a given geographic area will *most likely* continue to be found in this area if the
(1) variations in the population decrease over time
(2) members of the population decrease in number
(3) members of the population exceed the carrying capacity
(4) population passes on those genes that result in favorable adaptations

3 Which statement does the fossil record *best* support?
(1) Many organisms that lived in the past are now extinct.
(2) Species occupying the same habitat have identical environmental needs.
(3) The struggle for existence between organisms results in changes in populations.
(4) Structures such as leg bones and wing bones can originate from the same type of tissue found in embryos.

4 One explanation for the variety of organisms present on Earth today is that over time
(1) new species have adapted to fill available niches in the environment
(2) evolution has caused the appearance of organisms that are similar to each other
(3) each niche has changed to support a certain variety of organism
(4) the environment has remained unchanged causing rapid evolution

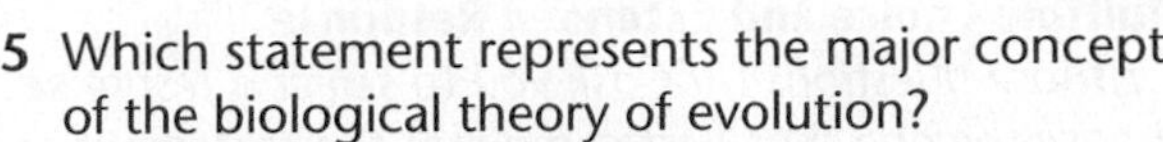

5 Which statement represents the major concept of the biological theory of evolution?
(1) A new species moves into a habitat when another species becomes extinct.
(2) Every period of time in Earth's history has its own group of organisms.
(3) Present-day organisms on Earth developed from earlier, distinctly different organisms.
(4) Every location on Earth's surface has its own unique group of organisms.

6 The diagram below best illustrates

(1) Lamarck's theory of evolution
(2) Darwin's theory of evolution
(3) Malthus's principles
(4) Lyell's theory about past changes

7 Which concepts are important in Darwin's theory of evolution by natural selection?
A Struggle for existence
B Survival of the fittest
C Descent with modification
(1) A and B, only
(2) A and C, only
(3) B and C, only
(4) A, B, and C

Test-Taking Tip If you have trouble answering a question, make a mark beside it and go on. (Do not write in this book.) You may find information in later questions that will allow you to eliminate some answer choices in your unanswered question.

Preparing for the Living Environment Exam

Part B

Multiple Choice and Extended Response

For those questions that ask you to select a response, choose the one that best completes the statement or answers the question. For all others follow the directions given.

Base your answers to questions 8 and 9 on the information and drawings below and on your knowledge of biology.

The birds pictured below are two of the 13 species of finches that Darwin found on the Galápagos Islands.

Woodpecker finch

Large ground finch

8 What process produced the two different types of beaks shown?
(1) selective breeding
(2) fossil variation
(3) natural selection
(4) inheritance of acquired traits

9 The large ground finch obtains food by cracking seeds. Its short, strong beak is an example of
(1) the struggle for survival
(2) overproduction of a species
(3) the cloning of desirable traits
(4) an adaptation

---

10 A protein similar to the mammalian hormone, prolactin (also a protein) is found in birds and amphibians. Prolactin stimulates the production of milk in mammals. In amphibians, the similar protein causes the animals to seek water when they lay their eggs. In birds, it causes the animals to regurgitate material from their crops (a part of the digestive system) to feed their young. State how similarities among these three chemicals can be explained. Support your answer with an explanation.

Base your answers to questions 11 through 13 on the information and chart below and on your knowledge of biology.

Plant scientists have produced a new variety of sunflower with seeds used for cooking oil and margarine. The scientists did tests to compare their new variety, C, with two existing varieties, A and B. Their data are shown in the chart.

Variety	Stem Strength (1–9 = weak-strong)	Oil Content per Seed (%)	Time for Seeds to Mature (1–9 = early-late)	Seed Yield (kg/acre)
A (old)	5	48	8	2050
B (old)	8	41	5	2200
C (new)	7	38	2	2600

11 To be productive economically, a variety of sunflower must have a strong stem, high yield of oil, and rapid rate of maturation. Should Variety C be planted instead of Varieties A and B? Support your answer with information from the chart.

12 State *two* things you would need to know about this investigation to determine the accuracy of the results presented in the chart.

13 If the scientists did not directly alter the sunflowers' genetic makeup, state how they could have developed Variety C.

Base your answers to questions 14 and 15 on the passage below and on your knowledge of biology.

Mule Deer

About 100 years ago, approximately 4000 mule deer roamed the Kaibab Plateau, which is located on the northern rim of the Grand Canyon in Arizona. Their natural enemies, which were wolves and pumas, kept the deer population in check. Then, early in the 1900s, the majority of wolves and pumas were killed by humans, because these predators were also killing cattle and sheep that grazed on the plateau. As a result, the deer population grew unchecked, rising to over 100,000 by the 1920s. The plateau was quickly overgrazed, and the deer population fell rapidly. Observers in the late 1920s discovered that some deer had begun to eat the leaves of trees instead of their usual diet of grasses and the leaves of low shrubs.

14 Compare the adaptations needed by the deer in the early 1900s with those needed in the 1920s.

15 Did the killing of wolves and pumas by humans interfere with the process of natural selection? Support your answer with an explanation.

Part C

Extended Response

Answer the questions or follow the directions given.

16 Using the modern theory of evolution as the basis, evaluate the accuracy of the following passage:

Modern giraffes evolved from a short-necked ancestor by stretching their necks to reach the leaves on high branches. Over time, adults with longer necks passed the trait on to their offspring. In your evaluation, be sure to:

- state whether or not the passage is accurate
- differentiate between a trait that can be passed from one generation to the next and one that cannot
- state why the number of giraffes with long necks will increase over time

17 In the past, a specific antibiotic was effective in killing a certain species of bacteria. Now, most members of this bacterial species are resistant to this antibiotic. Explain how this species of bacteria has become resistant. Your answer must include the concepts of:

- overproduction
- variation
- natural selection
- adaptation to the environment

Base your answers to questions 18 through 21 on the passage below and on your knowledge of biology.

Koalas

About 45 million years ago, Australia separated from Antarctica and gradually drifted northward. Fossil remains of koala-like animals in Australia date back to 25 million years ago. Around that time, the climate changed and Australia grew drier. Plants such as eucalyptus trees evolved, and koalas became dependent on them for food. When Europeans first arrived in Australia in 1788, they cleared forests for farmland, thus reducing the size of koala habitats and food sources. The Europeans also killed millions of koalas for their fur. Many additional koalas died from diseases, such as pneumonia and infections caused by the chlamydia bacteria, because koalas are particularly susceptible to disease when they are stressed by limited food. By 1924, koalas had disappeared from several areas of Australia.

18 State why fossils of koala-like animals have not been found in North America.

19 Cutting down trees for farmland resulted in smaller patches of forest for koalas. Additional trees died because of soil erosion and other related factors. Describe the effect of the loss of trees on the koala population. In your explanation, be sure to:

- state how the tree losses would increase the struggle for survival
- explain how the struggle for survival could lead to the formation of new species

20 Scientists think that chlamydia bacteria act as an agent of natural selection and keep the number of koala in the population under control. State why these bacteria may not continue to serve as selection agents in future generations of koala.

21 Since Europeans came to Australia, 80 percent of the eucalyptus trees have been cleared. Although there is government protection for koalas, there is no protection for eucalyptus trees. Assuming koalas do not adapt to the loss of habitat and food sources, describe their fate if the remaining eucalyptus trees are cleared.

For: An interactive self-test
Visit: PHSchool.com
Web Code: cba-5150

CHAPTER 16

Evolution of Populations

This group of ladybug beetles illustrates a population with a number of inherited traits. Darwin recognized such variation as the raw material for evolution.

Inquiry Activity

Does sexual reproduction change genotype ratios?

Procedure

1. Put 33 red and 67 black beads in a large paper cup to represent two alleles of a certain gene in a population.
2. To model the genotype of an offspring, remove two beads. Record the genotype. Return the beads.
3. Repeat step 2 for a total of 10 offspring. Add your data to the class total.

Think About It

1. **Calculating** What was the genotype ratio of the offspring?
2. **Comparing and Contrasting** Was the genotype ratio the same as the 1 : 2 : 1 genotype ratio for a cross between two heterozygotes ($Aa \times Aa$)? Explain.
3. **Predicting** If you repeated this activity over and over, would you expect the genotype ratios to change? Explain.

16–1 Genes and Variation

1-S1.3 Scientific explanations are subject to change **LS-** Organize data in tables/graphs
4-3.1 Inheritable characteristics
4-3.1 Natural selection and evolution
4-3.1 The variability of offspring due to mutation

As Darwin developed his theory of evolution, he worked under a serious handicap. He didn't know how heredity worked! Although Mendel's work on inheritance in peas was published during Darwin's lifetime, its importance wasn't recognized for decades. This lack of knowledge left two big gaps in Darwin's thinking. First, he had no idea how heritable traits, such as those shown in **Figure 16–1,** pass from one generation to the next. Second, although variation in heritable traits was central to Darwin's theory, he had no idea how that variation appeared.

Evolutionary biologists connected Mendel's work to Darwin's during the 1930s. By then, biologists understood that genes control heritable traits. They soon realized that changes in genes produce heritable variation on which natural selection can operate. Genes became the focus of new hypotheses and experiments aimed at understanding evolutionary change. Another revolution in evolutionary thought began with Watson and Crick's studies on DNA. Their model of the DNA molecule helped evolutionary biologists because it demonstrated the molecular nature of mutation and genetic variation.

Today, molecular techniques are used to test hypotheses about how heritable variation appears and how natural selection operates on that variation. As you will learn in this chapter, fitness, adaptation, species, and evolutionary change are now defined in genetic terms. We understand how evolution works better than Darwin ever could, beginning with heritable variation.

Guide for Reading

Key Concepts
- What are the main sources of heritable variation in a population?
- How is evolution defined in genetic terms?
- What determines the numbers of phenotypes for a given trait?

Vocabulary
gene pool
relative frequency
single-gene trait
polygenic trait

Reading Strategy: Building Vocabulary
Before you read, make a list of the vocabulary terms above. As you read, take notes about the meaning of each term.

How Common Is Genetic Variation?

We now know that many genes have at least two forms, or alleles. Animals such as horses, dogs, and mice often have several alleles for traits such as body size or coat color. Plants, such as peas, often have several alleles for flower color. All organisms have additional genetic variation that is "invisible" because it involves small differences in biochemical processes. In addition, an individual organism is heterozygous for many genes. An insect may be heterozygous for as many as 15 percent of its genes. Individual fishes, reptiles, and mammals are typically heterozygous for between 4 and 8 percent of their genes.

▼ **Figure 16–1** **There are two main sources of genetic variation: mutations and the gene shuffling that results from sexual reproduction.** Each of these babies has inherited a collection of traits. Some, such as hair color, are visible, while others, such as the ability to resist certain diseases, are not.

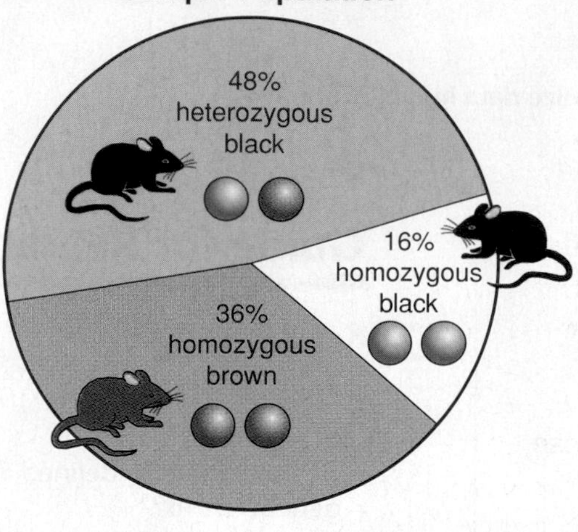

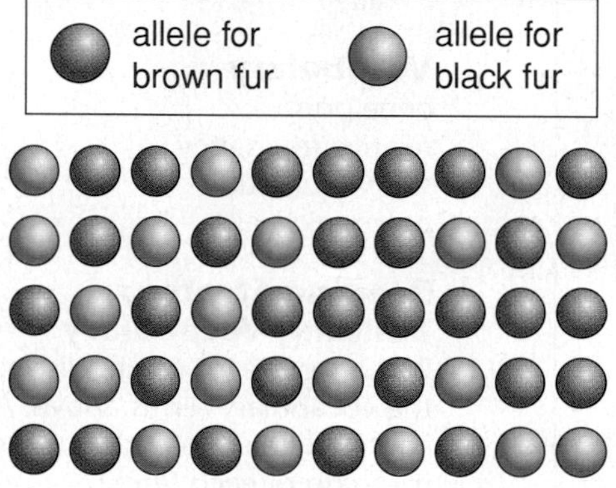

▲ **Figure 16–2** When scientists determine whether a population is evolving, they may look at the sum of the population's alleles, or its gene pool. This diagram shows the gene pool for fur color in a population of mice. **Calculating** *Here, in a total of 50 alleles, 20 alleles are B (black), and 30 are b (brown). How many of each allele would be present in a total of 100 alleles?*

Variation and Gene Pools

Genetic variation is studied in populations. A population is a group of individuals of the same species that interbreed. Because members of a population interbreed, they share a common group of genes called a gene pool. A **gene pool** consists of all genes, including all the different alleles, that are present in a population.

The **relative frequency** of an allele is the number of times that the allele occurs in a gene pool, compared with the number of times other alleles for the same gene occur. Relative frequency is often expressed as a percentage. For example, in the mouse population in **Figure 16–2,** the relative frequency of the dominant *B* allele (black fur) is 40 percent, and the relative frequency of the recessive *b* allele (brown fur) is 60 percent. The relative frequency of an allele has nothing to do with whether the allele is dominant or recessive. In this particular mouse population, the recessive allele occurs more frequently than the dominant allele.

Gene pools are important to evolutionary theory, because evolution involves changes in populations over time. **In genetic terms, evolution is any change in the relative frequency of alleles in a population.** For example, if the relative frequency of the *B* allele in the mouse population changed over time to 30 percent, the population is evolving.

 *What is a gene pool?*

Sources of Genetic Variation

Biologists can now explain how variation is produced. **The two main sources of genetic variation are mutations and the genetic shuffling that results from sexual reproduction.**

Mutations A mutation is any change in a sequence of DNA. Mutations can occur because of mistakes in the replication of DNA or as a result of radiation or chemicals in the environment. Mutations do not always affect an organism's phenotype. For example, a DNA codon altered from GGA to GGU will still code for the same amino acid, glycine. That mutation has no effect on phenotype. Many mutations do produce changes in phenotype, however. Some can affect an organism's fitness, or its ability to survive and reproduce in its environment. Other mutations may have no effect on fitness.

Gene Shuffling Mutations are not the only source of heritable variation. You do not look exactly like your biological parents, even though they provided you with all your genes. You probably look even less like any brothers or sisters you may have. Yet, no matter how you feel about your relatives, mutant genes are not primarily what makes them so different from you.

For: Links on population genetics
Visit: www.SciLinks.org
Web Code: cbn-5161

Most heritable differences are due to gene shuffling that occurs during the production of gametes. Recall that each chromosome of a homologous pair moves independently during meiosis. As a result, the 23 pairs of chromosomes found in humans can produce 8.4 million different combinations of genes!

Another process, crossing-over, also occurs during meiosis. Crossing-over further increases the number of different genotypes that can appear in offspring. Recall that a genotype is an organism's genetic makeup. When alleles are recombined during sexual reproduction, they can produce dramatically different phenotypes. Thus, sexual reproduction is a major source of variation within many populations.

Sexual reproduction can produce many different phenotypes, but it does not change the relative frequency of alleles in a population. To understand why, compare a population's gene pool to a deck of playing cards. Each card represents an allele found in the population. The exchange of genes during gene shuffling is similar to shuffling a deck of cards. Shuffling leads to different types of hands, but it can never change the relative numbers of aces, kings, or queens in the deck. The probability of drawing an ace off the top of the deck will always be 4 in 52, or one thirteenth (4/52 = 1/13). No matter how many times you shuffle the deck, this probability will remain the same. Similarly, sexual reproduction produces many different combinations of genes, but in itself it does not alter the relative frequencies of each type of allele in a population.

What are the sources of heritable variation?

Word Origins

Gene comes from the Greek word *gignesthai,* meaning "to be born," and refers to factors that produce an organism. The prefix *poly-* comes from the Greek word *polys,* meaning "many," so *polygenic* means "having many genes." The prefix *mono-* means "one." **What do you think the term *monogenic* means?**

Single-Gene and Polygenic Traits

Heritable variation can be expressed in a variety of ways. **The number of phenotypes produced for a given trait depends on how many genes control the trait.** Among humans, a widow's peak—a downward dip in the center of the hairline—is a **single-gene trait.** It is controlled by a single gene that has two alleles. The allele for a widow's peak is dominant over the allele for a hairline with no peak. As a result, variation in this gene leads to only two distinct phenotypes, as shown in **Figure 16–3.**

As you can see, the frequency of phenotypes caused by this single gene is represented on the bar graph. This graph shows that the presence of a widow's peak may be less common in a population than the absence of a widow's peak, even though the allele for a widow's peak is the dominant form. In real populations, phenotypic ratios are determined by the frequency of alleles in the population as well as by whether the alleles are in the dominant or recessive form. Allele frequencies may not match Mendelian ratios.

Figure 16–3 In humans, a single gene with two alleles controls whether a person has a widow's peak (left) or does not have a widow's peak (right). As a result, only two phenotypes are possible. **The number of phenotypes a given trait has is determined by how many genes control the trait.**

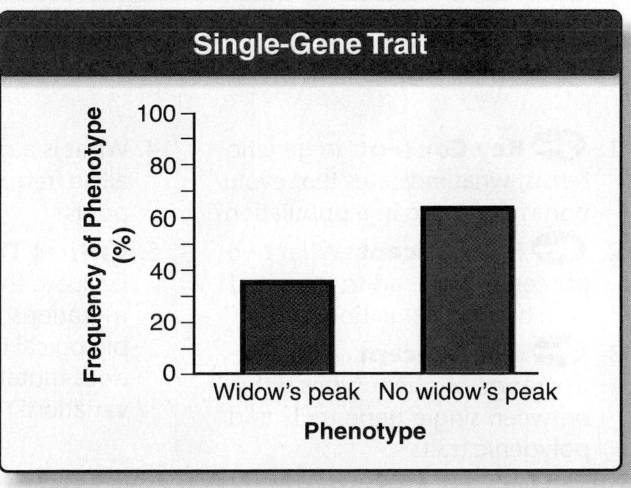

Figure 16–4 The graph below shows the distribution of phenotypes that would be expected for a trait if many genes contributed to the trait. The photograph shows the actual distribution of heights of a group of young men. **Using Tables and Graphs** ***What does the shape of the graph indicate about height in humans?***

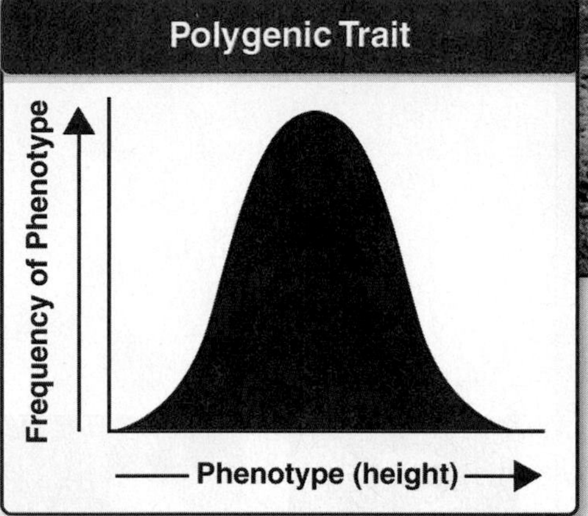

Many traits are controlled by two or more genes and are, therefore, called **polygenic traits.** Each gene of a polygenic trait often has two or more alleles. As a result, one polygenic trait can have many possible genotypes and phenotypes.

Height in humans is one example of a polygenic trait. You can sample phenotypic variation in this trait by measuring the height of all the students in your class. You can then calculate the average height of this group. Many students will be just a little taller or shorter than average. Some of your classmates, however, will be very tall or very short. If you graph the number of individuals of each height, you may get a graph similar to the one in **Figure 16–4.** The symmetrical bell-like shape of this curve is typical of polygenic traits. A bell-shaped curve is also called a normal distribution.

16–1 Section Assessment

1. **Key Concept** In genetic terms, what indicates that evolution is occurring in a population?
2. **Key Concept** What two processes can lead to inherited variation in populations?
3. **Key Concept** How does the range of phenotypes differ between single-gene traits and polygenic traits?
4. What is a gene pool? How are allele frequencies related to gene pools?
5. **Critical Thinking Evaluating** Evaluate the significance of mutations to the process of biological evolution. (*Hint*: How does mutation affect genetic variation?)

Connecting Concepts

Genetic Variation
How does the process known as independent assortment relate to the genetic variation that results from sexual reproduction? *Hint:* Refer to Chapter 11.

16–2 Evolution as Genetic Change

4-3.1 Inheritable characteristics
4-3.1 Natural selection and evolution
4-3.1 Variability of offspring
LS- Analyze results and make observations

Guide for Reading

 **Key Concepts**

- How does natural selection affect single-gene and polygenic traits?
- What is genetic drift?
- What five conditions are needed to maintain genetic equilibrium?

Vocabulary
directional selection
stabilizing selection
disruptive selection
genetic drift
founder effect
Hardy-Weinberg principle
genetic equilibrium

Reading Strategy: Outlining Before you read, use the headings to make an outline. As you read, add a sentence after each heading to provide key information.

A genetic view of evolution offers a new way to look at key evolutionary concepts. Each time an organism reproduces, it passes copies of its genes to its offspring. We can therefore view evolutionary fitness as an organism's success in passing genes to the next generation. In the same way, we can view an evolutionary adaptation as any genetically controlled physiological, anatomical, or behavioral trait that increases an individual's ability to pass along its genes.

Natural selection never acts directly on genes. Why? Because it is an entire organism—not a single gene—that either survives and reproduces or dies without reproducing. Natural selection, therefore, can only affect which individuals survive and reproduce and which do not. If an individual dies without reproducing, the individual does not contribute its alleles to the population's gene pool. If an individual produces many offspring, its alleles stay in the gene pool and may increase in frequency.

Now recall that evolution is any change over time in the relative frequencies of alleles in a population. This reminds us that it is populations, not individual organisms, that can evolve over time. Let us see how this can happen in different situations.

Natural Selection on Single-Gene Traits

Natural selection on single-gene traits can lead to changes in allele frequencies and thus to evolution. Imagine that a hypothetical population of lizards, shown in **Figure 16-5**, is normally brown, but experiences mutations that produce red and black forms. What happens to those new alleles? If red lizards are more visible to predators, they might be less likely to survive and reproduce, and the allele for red coloring might not become common.

▼ **Figure 16-5 Natural selection on single-gene traits can lead to changes in allele frequencies and thus to evolution.** Organisms of one color, for example, may produce fewer offspring than organisms of other colors.

Effect of Color Mutations on Lizard Survival

Initial Population	Generation 10	Generation 20	Generation 30
80%	80%	70%	40%
10%	0%	0%	0%
10%	20%	30%	60%

Black lizards, on the other hand, might absorb more sunlight and warm up faster on cold days. If high body temperature allows them to move faster to feed and to avoid predators, they might produce more offspring than brown forms. The allele for black color might then increase in relative frequency. If a color change has no effect on fitness, the allele that produces it would not be under pressure from natural selection.

Natural Selection on Polygenic Traits

When traits are controlled by more than one gene, the effects of natural selection are more complex. As you learned earlier, the action of multiple alleles on traits such as height produces a range of phenotypes that often fit a bell curve. The fitness of individuals close to one another on the curve will not be very different. But fitness can vary a great deal from one end of such a curve to the other. And where fitness varies, natural selection can act. **Natural selection can affect the distributions of phenotypes in any of three ways: directional selection, stabilizing selection, or disruptive selection.**

Directional Selection When individuals at one end of the curve have higher fitness than individuals in the middle or at the other end, **directional selection** takes place. The range of phenotypes shifts as some individuals fail to survive and reproduce while others succeed. To understand this, consider how limited resources, such as food, can affect the long-term survival of individuals and the evolution of populations.

Among seed-eating birds such as Darwin's finches, for example, birds with bigger, thicker beaks can feed more easily on larger, harder, thicker-shelled seeds. Suppose a food shortage causes the supply of small and medium-sized seeds to run low, leaving only larger seeds. Birds whose beaks enable them to open those larger seeds will have better access to food. Birds with the big-beak adaptation would therefore have higher fitness than small-beaked birds. The average beak size of the population would probably increase, as shown in **Figure 16–6.**

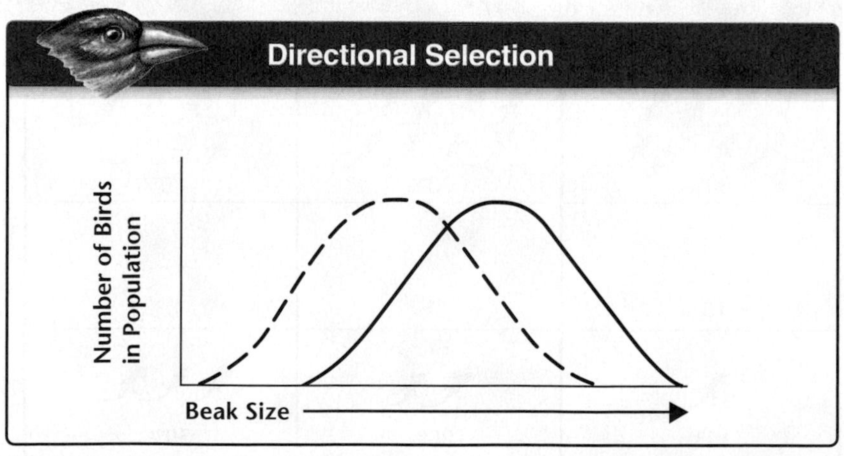

▶ **Figure 16–6** **Directional selection occurs when individuals at one end of the curve have higher fitness than individuals in the middle or at the other end.** In this example, a population of seed-eating birds experiences directional selection when a food shortage causes the supply of small seeds to run low. The dotted line shows the original distribution of beak sizes. The solid line shows how the distribution of beak sizes would change as a result of selection.

Stabilizing Selection When individuals near the center of the curve have higher fitness than individuals at either end of the curve, **stabilizing selection** takes place. This situation keeps the center of the curve at its current position, but it narrows the overall graph.

As shown in **Figure 16–7,** the mass of human infants at birth is under the influence of stabilizing selection. Human babies born much smaller than average are likely to be less healthy and thus less likely to survive. Babies that are much larger than average are likely to have difficulty being born. The fitness of these larger or smaller individuals is, therefore, lower than that of more average-sized individuals.

Disruptive Selection When individuals at the upper and lower ends of the curve have higher fitness than individuals near the middle, **disruptive selection** takes place. In such situations, selection acts most strongly against individuals of an intermediate type. If the pressure of natural selection is strong enough and lasts long enough, this situation can cause the single curve to split into two. In other words, selection creates two distinct phenotypes.

For example, suppose a population of birds lives in an area where medium-sized seeds become less common and large and small seeds become more common. Birds with unusually small or large beaks would have higher fitness. As shown in **Figure 16–8,** the population might split into two subgroups: one that eats small seeds and one that eats large seeds.

CHECKPOINT *How do stabilizing selection and disruptive selection differ?*

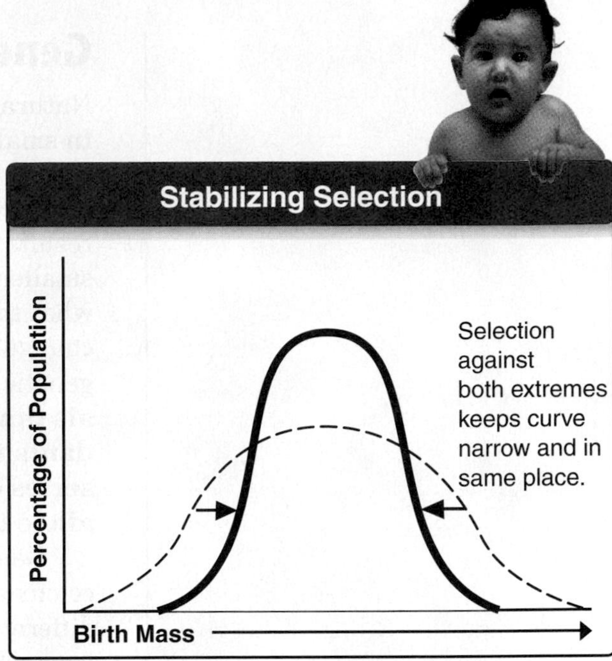

▲ **Figure 16–7** **Stabilizing selection takes place when individuals near the center of a curve have higher fitness than individuals at either end.** This example shows that human babies born at an average mass are more likely to survive than babies born either much smaller or much larger than average.

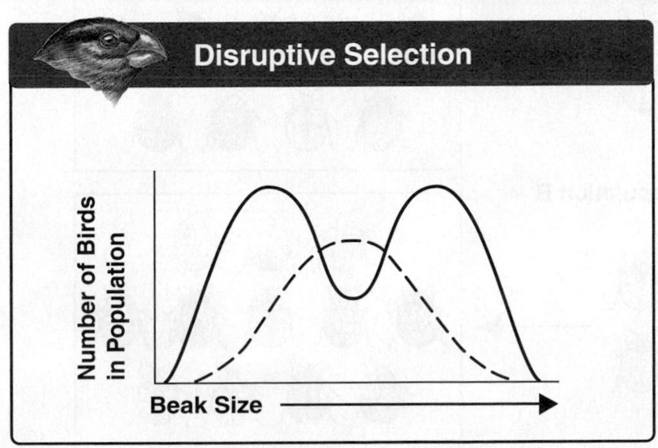

◀ **Figure 16–8** **When individuals at the upper and lower ends of the curve have higher fitness than individuals near the middle, disruptive selection takes place.** In this example, average-sized seeds become less common, and larger and smaller seeds become more common. As a result, the bird population splits into two subgroups specializing in eating different-sized seeds.

Genetic Drift

Natural selection is not the only source of evolutionary change. In small populations, an allele can become more or less common simply by chance. Recall that genetics is controlled by the laws of probability. These laws can be used to predict the overall results of genetic crosses in large populations. However, the smaller a population is, the farther the results may be from what the laws of probability predict. This kind of random change in allele frequency is called **genetic drift.** How does genetic drift take place? **In small populations, individuals that carry a particular allele may leave more descendants than other individuals, just by chance. Over time, a series of chance occurrences of this type can cause an allele to become common in a population.**

Genetic drift may occur when a small group of individuals colonizes a new habitat. These individuals may carry alleles in different relative frequencies than did the larger population from which they came. If so, the population that they found will be genetically different from the parent population. Here, however, the cause is not natural selection but simply chance—specifically, the chance that particular alleles were in one or more of the founding individuals, as shown in **Figure 16–9.** A situation in which allele frequencies change as a result of the migration of a small subgroup of a population is known as the **founder effect.** One example of the founder effect is the evolution of several hundred species of fruit flies found on different Hawaiian Islands. All of those species descended from the same original mainland population. Those species in different habitats on different islands now have allele frequencies that are different from those of the original species.

What is genetic drift?

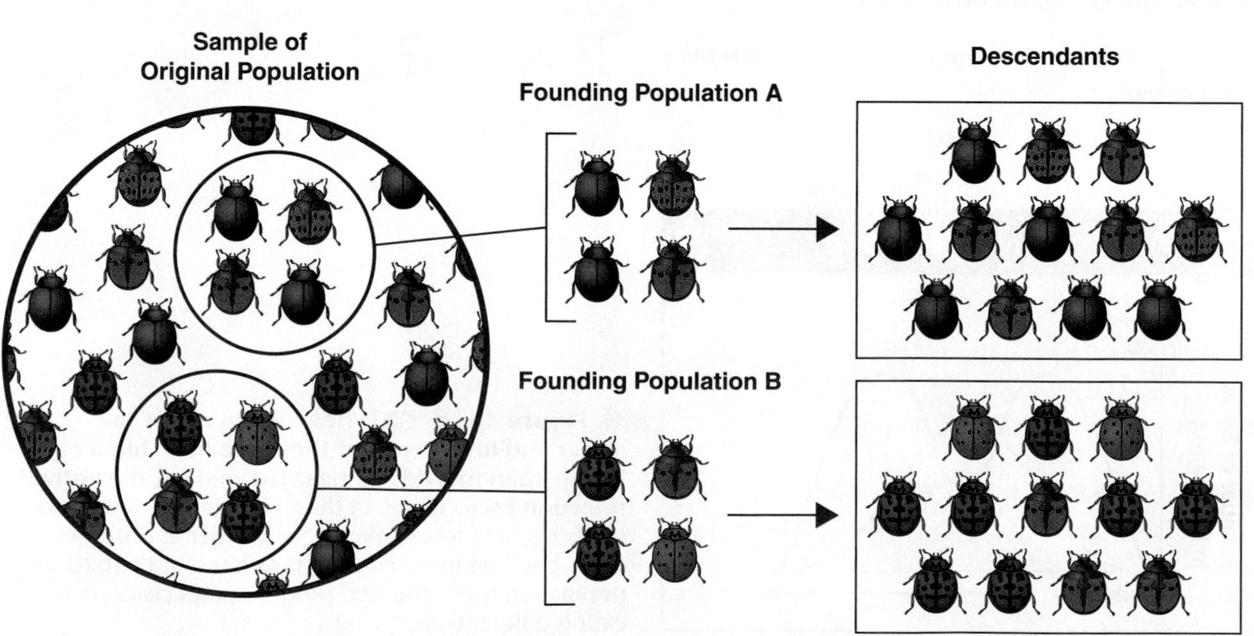

Figure 16–9 **In small populations, individuals that carry a particular allele may have more descendants than other individuals. Over time, a series of chance occurrences of this type can cause an allele to become more common in a population.** This model demonstrates how two small groups from a large, diverse population could produce new populations that differ from the original group.

Quick Lab

Can the environment affect survival?

Materials scissors, construction paper (several colors), transparent tape, 15-cm ruler, watch with a second hand

Procedure 

1. **Predicting** Predict what would happen to a population of butterflies that includes some individuals that are easy for predators to see and some that blend in with the environment.
2. Choose three different-colored sheets of construction paper. Cut out a butterfly shape from each sheet, 5 × 10 cm in size, as shown. **CAUTION:** *Be careful with scissors.*
3. Tape your butterflies to different-colored surfaces. Then, return to your seat.
4. Record how many shapes of each color you can count from your desk in 5 seconds.
5. Exchange your observations with your classmates to determine the class total for each color.

Analyze and Conclude

1. **Analyzing Data** According to your class data, which colors of butterfly are easiest to see? Which color of butterfly would be most easily caught by a predator?
2. **Inferring** What will happen to the butterfly population after many generations if predators consume most of the easy-to-see butterflies?

Evolution Versus Genetic Equilibrium

To clarify how evolutionary change operates, scientists often find it helpful to determine what happens when *no* change takes place. So biologists ask: Are there any conditions under which evolution will not occur? Is there any way to recognize when that is the case? The answers to those questions are provided by the Hardy-Weinberg principle, named after two researchers who independently proposed it in 1908.

The **Hardy-Weinberg principle** states that allele frequencies in a population will remain constant unless one or more factors cause those frequencies to change. The situation in which allele frequencies remain constant is called **genetic equilibrium.** If the allele frequencies do not change, the population will not evolve.

Under what conditions does the Hardy-Weinberg principle hold? **Five conditions are required to maintain genetic equilibrium from generation to generation: (1) There must be random mating; (2) the population must be very large; and (3) there can be no movement into or out of the population, (4) no mutations, and (5) no natural selection.**

In some populations, these conditions may be met or nearly met for long periods of time. If, however, the conditions are not met, the genetic equilibrium will be disrupted, and the population will evolve.

▲ **Figure 16–10 One of the five conditions that are needed to maintain genetic equilibrium from one generation to the next is large population size.** The allele frequencies of large populations, such as this group of birds, are less likely to be changed through the process of genetic drift.

Random Mating All members of the population must have an equal opportunity to produce offspring. Random mating ensures that each individual has an equal chance of passing on its alleles to offspring.

In natural populations, however, mating is rarely completely random. Many species, including lions and wolves, select mates based on particular heritable traits, such as size or strength. Such nonrandom mating means that the genes for those traits are *not* in equilibrium but are under strong selection pressure.

Large Population A large population size is also important in maintaining genetic equilibrium. That is because genetic drift has less effect on large populations, such as the population of birds shown in **Figure 16–10,** than on small ones.

No Movement Into or Out of the Population Because individuals may bring new alleles into a population, there must be no movement of individuals into or out of a population. In genetic terms, the population's gene pool must be kept together and kept separate from the gene pools of other populations.

No Mutations If genes mutate from one form into another, new alleles may be introduced into the population, and allele frequencies will change.

No Natural Selection All genotypes in the population must have equal probabilities of survival and reproduction. No phenotype can have a selective advantage over another. In other words, there can be no natural selection operating on the population.

16–2 Section Assessment

1. **Key Concept** Describe how natural selection can affect traits controlled by single genes.
2. **Key Concept** Describe three patterns of natural selection on polygenic traits. Which one leads to two distinct phenotypes?
3. **Key Concept** How does genetic drift lead to a change in a population's gene pool?
4. **Key Concept** What is the Hardy-Weinberg principle?
5. **Critical Thinking Comparing and Contrasting** How are directional selection and disruptive selection similar? How are they different?

Sharpen Your Skills

Using Models

Demonstrate natural selection on polygenic traits by cutting a sheet of paper into squares of five different sizes to represent sizes in a population. Use the squares to model directional, stabilizing, and disruptive selection. Then, think of an alternative way to model one type of selection. Decide which model works best, and give your reasons.

Should the Use of Antibiotics Be Restricted?

Natural selection is everywhere. One dramatic example of evolution in action poses a serious threat to public health. Many kinds of disease-causing bacteria are evolving resistance to antibiotics—drugs intended to kill them or interfere with their growth.

Antibiotics are one of medicine's greatest weapons against bacterial diseases. When antibiotics were discovered, they were called "magic bullets" and "wonder drugs" because they were so effective. They have made diseases like pneumonia much less of a threat than they were about sixty years ago. However, people may be overusing antibiotics. Doctors sometimes prescribe them for diseases for which they are not effective. Commercial feed for chickens and other farm animals is laced with antibiotics to prevent infection.

This wide use has caused many bacteria—including *Mycobacterium tuberculosis,* which causes tuberculosis—to evolve resistance to antibiotics. This resistance is a prime example of the evolution of a genetically controlled physiological trait. Resistance evolved because bacterial populations contained a few individuals with genes that enabled them to destroy, inactivate, or eliminate antibiotics. Descendants of those physiologically similar individuals survived and reproduced, and became today's resistant strains. Once-powerful antibiotics are now useless against resistant bacteria. Given this risk, should government agencies restrict the use of antibiotics?

The Viewpoints

Antibiotic Use Should Be Restricted

The danger of an incurable bacterial epidemic is so high that action must be taken on a national level as soon as possible. Doctors overuse antibiotics in humans because patients demand them. The livestock industry likes using antibiotics in animal feeds and will not change their practice unless forced to do so.

Antibiotic Use Should Not Be Restricted

Researchers are coming up with new drugs all the time. These drugs can be reserved for human use only. Doctors need to be able to prescribe antibiotics as they choose, and our food supply depends on the use of antibiotics in agriculture. The medical profession and the livestock industry need the freedom to find solutions that work best for them.

Research and Decide

1. **Analyzing the Viewpoints** To make an informed decision, learn more about this issue by consulting library and Internet resources. Then, list the advantages and disadvantages of restricting the use of antibiotics.
2. **Forming Your Opinion** Should antibiotics be restricted? Are there some situations in which such regulations would be more appropriate than others?

For: Links from the authors
Visit: PHSchool.com
Web Code: cbe-5162

16–3 The Process of Speciation

1-S1.1 Scientific explanations
4-3.1 Natural selection and evolution
4-3.1 Natural selection of behaviors
LS- Analyze results

Guide for Reading

Key Concepts
- What factors are involved in the formation of new species?
- Describe the process of speciation in the Galápagos finches.

Vocabulary
speciation
reproductive isolation
behavioral isolation
geographic isolation
temporal isolation

Reading Strategy: Using Visuals Before you read, preview **Figure 16–16.** As you read about speciation of Darwin's finches, notice what happens at each step in the diagram.

Factors such as natural selection and chance events can change the relative frequencies of alleles in a population. But how do these changes lead to the formation of new species, or **speciation**?

Recall that biologists define a species as a group of organisms that breed with one another and produce fertile offspring. This means that individuals in the same species share a common gene pool. Because a population of individuals has a shared gene pool, a genetic change that occurs in one individual can spread through the population as that individual and its offspring reproduce. If a genetic change increases fitness, that allele will eventually be found in many individuals of that population.

Isolating Mechanisms

Given this genetic definition of species, what must happen for a species to evolve into two new species? The gene pools of two populations must become separated for them to become new species. **As new species evolve, populations become reproductively isolated from each other.** When the members of two populations cannot interbreed and produce fertile offspring, **reproductive isolation** has occurred. At that point, the populations have separate gene pools. They respond to natural selection or genetic drift as separate units. Reproductive isolation can develop in a variety of ways, including behavioral isolation, geographic isolation, and temporal isolation.

Behavioral Isolation One type of isolating mechanism, **behavioral isolation,** occurs when two populations are capable of interbreeding but have differences in courtship rituals or other reproductive strategies that involve behavior. For example, the eastern and western meadowlarks shown in **Figure 16–11** are very similar birds whose habitats overlap in the center of the United States. Members of the two species will not mate with each other, however, partly because they use different songs to attract mates. Eastern meadowlarks will not respond to western meadowlark songs, and vice versa.

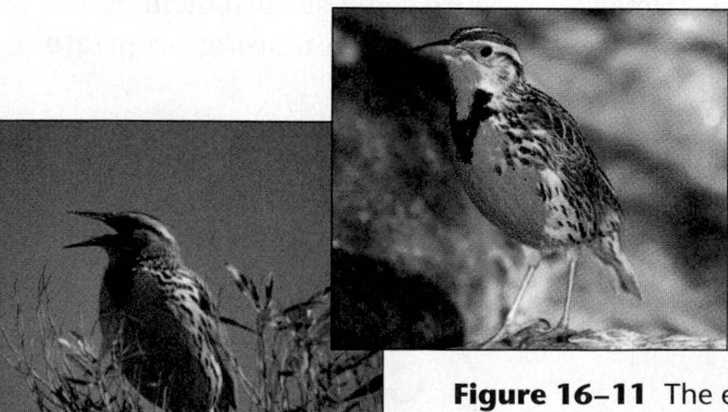

Figure 16–11 The eastern meadowlark (left) and western meadowlark (right) have overlapping ranges. They do not interbreed, however, because they have different mating songs. **Applying Concepts** *What type of reproductive isolation does this situation illustrate?*

Abert squirrel

Kaibab squirrel

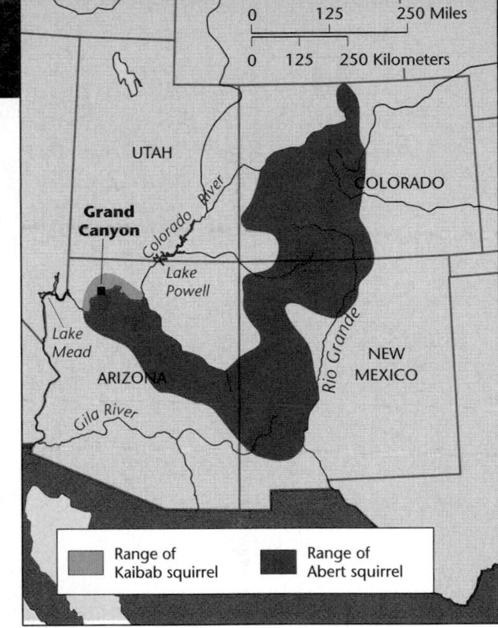

Figure 16–12 **When two populations of a species become reproductively isolated, new species can develop.** The Kaibab squirrel evolved from the Abert squirrel. The Kaibab squirrels were isolated from the main population by the Colorado River.

Geographic Isolation With **geographic isolation,** two populations are separated by geographic barriers such as rivers, mountains, or bodies of water. The Abert squirrel in **Figure 16–12,** for example, lives in the Southwest. About 10,000 years ago, the Colorado River split the species into two separate populations. Two separate gene pools formed. Genetic changes that appeared in one group were not passed to the other. Natural selection worked separately on each group and led to the formation of a distinct subspecies, the Kaibab squirrel. The Abert and Kaibab squirrels have very similar anatomical and physiological characteristics, indicating that they are closely related. However, the Kaibab squirrel differs from the Abert squirrel in significant ways, such as fur coloring.

Geographic barriers do not guarantee the formation of new species, however. Separate lakes may be linked for a time during a flood, or a land bridge may temporarily form between islands, enabling separated populations to mix. If two formerly separated populations can still interbreed, they remain a single species. Also, any potential geographic barrier may separate certain types of organisms but not others. A large river will keep squirrels and other small rodents apart, but it does not necessarily isolate bird populations.

Temporal Isolation A third isolating mechanism is **temporal isolation,** in which two or more species reproduce at different times. For example, three similar species of orchid all live in the same rain forest. Each species releases pollen only on a single day. Because the three species release pollen on different days, they cannot pollinate one another.

How can temporal isolation lead to speciation?

Galápagos Islands Finches						
Shape of Head and Beak						
Common Name of Finch Species	Vegetarian tree finch	Large insectivorous tree finch	Woodpecker finch	Cactus ground finch	Sharp-beaked ground finch	Large ground finch
Main Food	Fruits	Insects	Insects	Cacti	Seeds	Seeds
Feeding Adaptation	Parrotlike beak	Grasping beak	Uses cactus spines	Large crushing beak	Pointed crushing beak	Large crushing beak
Habitat	Trees	Trees	Trees	Ground	Ground	Ground

▲ **Figure 16–13** Detailed genetic studies have shown that these finches evolved from a species with a more-or-less general-purpose beak. **Formulating Hypotheses** *Suggest how one of these beaks could have resulted from natural selection.*

Go Online
NSTA SCILINKS
For: Links on speciation
Visit: www.SciLinks.org
Web Code: cbn-5163

Testing Natural Selection in Nature

Now that you know the basic mechanisms of evolutionary change, you might wonder if these processes can be observed in nature. The answer is yes. In fact, some of the most important studies showing natural selection in action involve descendants of the finches that Darwin observed in the Galápagos Islands.

Those finch species looked so different from one another that when Darwin first saw them, he did not realize they were all finches. He thought they were blackbirds, warblers, and other kinds of birds. The species he examined differed greatly in the sizes and shapes of their beaks and in their feeding habits, as shown in **Figure 16–13.** Some species fed on small seeds, while others ate large seeds with thick shells. One species used cactus spines to pry insects from dead wood. One species, not shown here, even pecked at the tails of large sea birds and drank their blood!

Once Darwin discovered that these birds were all finches, he hypothesized that they had descended from a common ancestor. Over time, he proposed, natural selection shaped the beaks of different bird populations as they adapted to eat different foods.

That was a reasonable hypothesis. But was there any way to test it? No one thought so, until the work of Peter and Rosemary Grant from Princeton University proved otherwise. For more than twenty years, the Grants, shown in **Figure 16–14,** have been collaborating to band and measure finches on the Galápagos Islands. They realized that Darwin's hypothesis relied on two testable assumptions. First, in order for beak size and shape to evolve, there must be enough heritable variation in those traits to provide raw material for natural selection. Second, differences in beak size and shape must produce differences in fitness that cause natural selection to occur.

The Grants tested these hypotheses on the medium ground finch on Daphne Major, one of the Galápagos islands. This island is large enough to support good-sized finch populations, yet small enough to enable the Grants to catch and identify nearly every bird belonging to the species under study.

Variation The Grants first identified and measured as many individual birds as possible on the island. They recorded which birds were still living and which had died, which had succeeded in breeding and which had not. For each individual, they also recorded anatomical characteristics such as wing length, leg length, beak length, beak depth, beak color, feather colors, and total mass. Many of these characteristics appeared in bell-shaped distributions typical of polygenic traits. These data indicate that there is great variation of heritable traits among the Galápagos finches.

Figure 16–14 Peter and Rosemary Grant have demonstrated that natural selection is still a force in the evolution of the Galápagos finches. **Applying Concepts** *How does their research demonstrate natural selection?*

Natural Selection Other researchers who had visited the Galápagos did not see the different finches competing or eating different foods. During the rainy season, when these researchers visited, there is plenty of food. Under these conditions, finches often eat the most available type of food. During dry-season drought, however, some foods become scarce, and others disappear altogether. At that time, differences in beak size can mean the difference between life and death. To survive, birds become feeding specialists. Each species selects the type of food its beak handles best. Birds with big, heavy beaks, for example, select big, thick seeds that no other species can crack open.

The Grants' most interesting discovery was that individual birds with different-sized beaks had different chances of survival during a drought. When food for the finches was scarce, individuals with the largest beaks were more likely to survive, as shown in **Figure 16–15.** Beak size also plays a role in mating behavior, because big-beaked birds tend to mate with other big-beaked birds. The Grants observed that average beak size in that finch population increased dramatically over time. This change in beak size is an example of directional selection operating on an anatomical trait.

By documenting natural selection in the wild, the Grants provided evidence of the process of evolution: The next generation of finches had larger beaks than did the generation before selection had occurred. An important result of this work was their finding that natural selection takes place frequently—and sometimes very rapidly. Changes in the food supply on the Galápagos caused measurable fluctuations in the finch populations over a period of only decades. This is markedly different from the slow, gradual evolution that Darwin envisioned.

CHECKPOINT *What type of natural selection did the Grants observe in the Galápagos?*

▼ **Figure 16–15** This graph shows the survival rate of one species of ground-feeding finches, the medium ground finch, *Geospiza fortis.* **Using Tables and Graphs** *What trend does this graph show?*

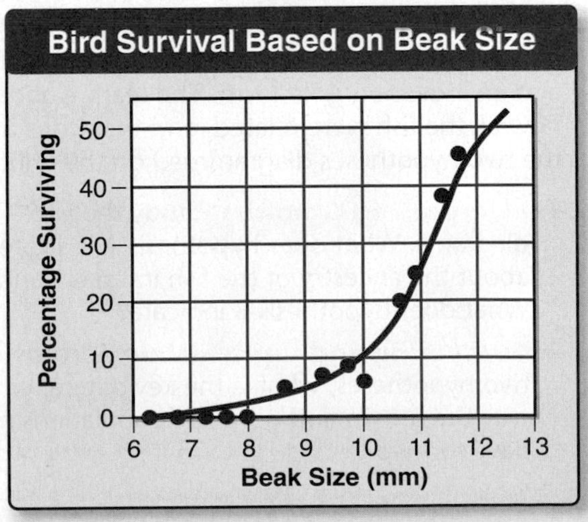

To find out more about ongoing research on the Galápagos, view the segment "The Galápagos Islands: A Glimpse Into the Past," on Videotape Two.

Speciation in Darwin's Finches

The Grants' work demonstrates that finch beak size can be changed by natural selection. If we combine this information with other evolutionary concepts you have learned in this chapter, we can show how natural selection can lead to speciation. We can devise a hypothetical scenario for the evolution of all Galápagos finches from a single group of founding birds. **Speciation in the Galápagos finches occurred by founding of a new population, geographic isolation, changes in the new population's gene pool, reproductive isolation, and ecological competition.**

Founders Arrive Many years ago, a few finches from the South American mainland—species A—flew or were blown to one of the Galápagos Islands, as shown in **Figure 16–16.** Finches are small birds that do not usually fly far over open water. These birds may have gotten lost, or they may have been blown off course by a storm. Once they arrived on one of the islands, they managed to survive and reproduce.

Geographic Isolation Later on, some birds from species A crossed to another island in the Galápagos group. Because these birds do not usually fly over open water, they rarely move from island to island. Thus, finch populations on the two islands were essentially isolated from each other and no longer shared a common gene pool.

How did finches arrive in the Galápagos Islands?

Analyzing Data

How Are These Fish Related?

A research team studied two lakes in an area that sometimes experiences flooding. Each lake contained two types of similar fish: a dull brown form and an iridescent gold form. The team wondered how all the fish were related, and they considered the two hypotheses diagrammed on the right.

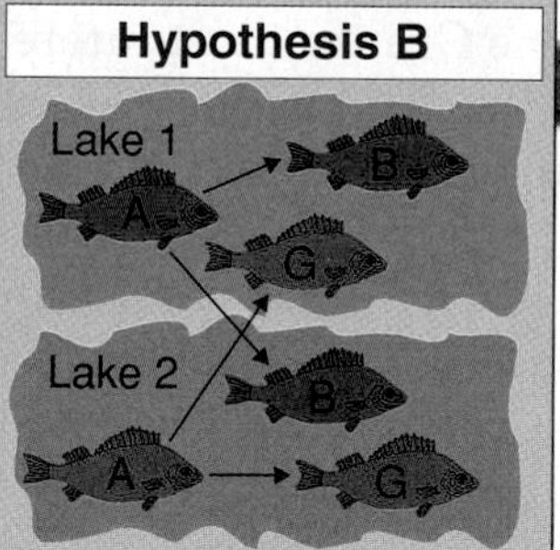

1. **Interpreting Graphics** Study the two diagrams. What does hypothesis A indicate about the ancestry of the fish in Lake 1 and Lake 2? What does hypothesis B indicate?
2. **Comparing and Contrasting** According to the two hypotheses, what is the key difference in the way the brown and gold fish populations might have formed?
3. **Drawing Conclusions** A DNA analysis showed that the brown and gold fish from Lake 1 are the most closely related. Which hypothesis does this evidence support?
4. **Asking Questions** To help determine whether the brown and gold fish are members of separate species, what question might scientists ask?

▶ **Figure 16–16 Speciation in the Galápagos finches occurred by founding of new populations, geographic isolation, gene pool changes, reproductive isolation, and ecological competition.** Small groups of finches moved from one island to another, became reproductively isolated, and evolved into new species.

Changes in the Gene Pool Over time, populations on each island became adapted to their local environments. The plants growing on the first island may have produced small thin-shelled seeds, whereas the plants on the second island may have produced larger thick-shelled seeds. On the second island, directional selection would favor individuals with larger, heavier beaks. These birds could crack open and eat the large seeds more easily. Thus, birds with large beaks would be better able to survive on the second island. Over time, natural selection would have caused that population to evolve larger beaks, forming a separate population, B.

Reproductive Isolation Now, imagine that a few birds from the second island cross back to the first island. Will the population-A birds breed with the population-B birds? Probably not. These finches choose their mates carefully. As part of their courtship behavior, they inspect a potential partner's beak very closely. Finches prefer to mate with birds that have the same-sized beak as they do. In other words, big-beaked birds prefer to mate with other big-beaked birds, and smaller-beaked birds prefer to mate with other smaller-beaked birds. Because the birds on the two islands have different-sized beaks, it is likely that they would not choose to mate with each other. Thus, differences in beak size, combined with mating behavior, could lead to reproductive isolation. The gene pools of the two bird populations remain isolated from each other—even when individuals live together in the same place. The two populations have now become separate species.

Ecological Competition As these two new species live together in the same environment (the first island), they compete with each other for available seeds. During the dry season, individuals that are most different from each other have the highest fitness. The more specialized birds have less competition for certain kinds of seeds and other foods, and the competition among individual finches is also reduced. Over time, species evolve in a way that increases the differences between them. The species-B birds on the first island may evolve into a new species, C.

Continued Evolution This process of isolation on different islands, genetic change, and reproductive isolation probably repeated itself time and time again across the entire Galápagos island chain. Over many generations, it produced the 13 different finch species found there today. Use the steps in this illustration to explain how other Darwin finches, such as the vegetarian tree finch that feeds on fruit, might have evolved.

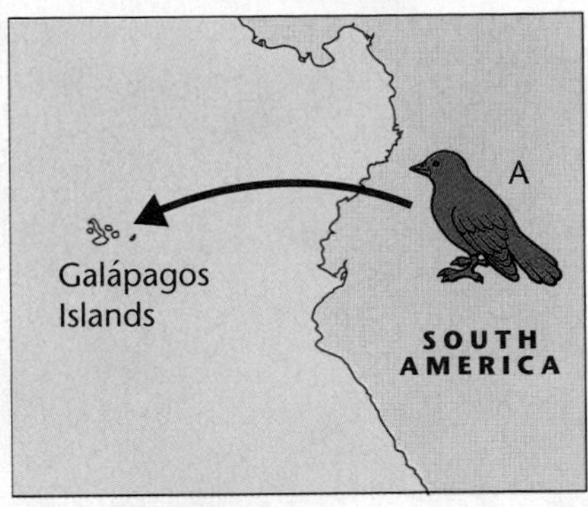

Founders Arrive
A few finches travel from South America to one of the islands. There, they survive and reproduce.

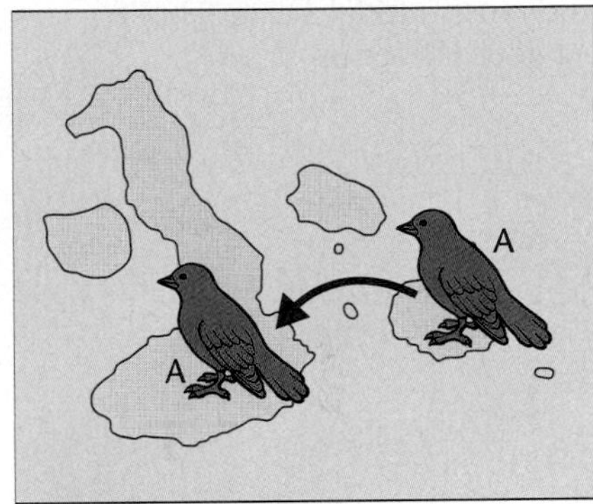

Geographic Isolation
Some birds from species A cross to a second island. The two populations no longer share a gene pool.

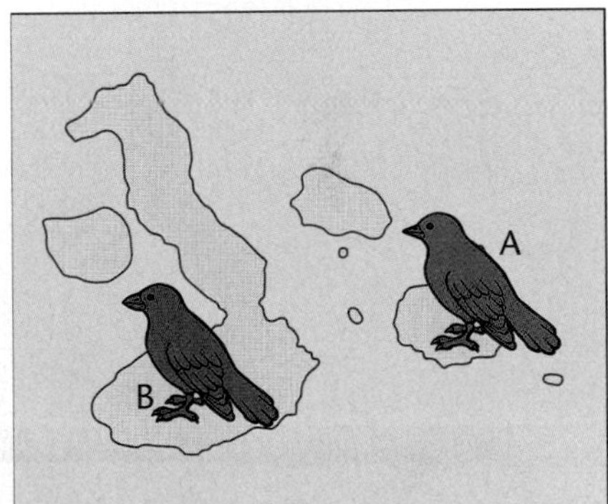

Changes in the Gene Pool
Seed sizes on the second island favor birds with larger beaks. The population on the second island evolves into a population, B, with larger beaks. Eventually, populations A and B evolve into separate species.

▲ **Figure 16–17** Paleontologists study fossils to find clues about previous life forms.

Studying Evolution Since Darwin

It is useful to review and critique the strengths and weaknesses of evolutionary theory. Darwin made bold assumptions about heritable variation, the age of Earth, and relationships among organisms. New data from genetics, physics, and biochemistry could have proved him wrong on many counts. They didn't. Scientific evidence supports the theory that living species descended with modification from common ancestors that lived in the ancient past.

Limitations of Research The Grants' research clearly shows the effects of directional selection in nature. The Grants' data also show how competition and climate change affect natural selection. The work does have limitations. For example, while the Grants observed changes in the size of the finches' beaks, they did not observe the formation of a new species. Scientists predict that as new fossils are found, they will continue to expand our understanding of how species evolved.

Unanswered Questions The studies of the Grants fit into an enormous body of scientific work supporting the theory of evolution. Millions of fossils show that life has existed on Earth for more than 3 billion years and that organisms have changed dramatically over this time. These fossils form just a part of the evidence supporting the conclusion that life has evolved. Remember that a scientific theory is defined as a well-tested explanation that accounts for a broad range of observations. Evolutionary theory fits this definition. To be sure, many new discoveries have led to new hypotheses that refine and expand Darwin's original ideas. No scientist suggests that all evolutionary processes are fully understood. Many unanswered questions remain.

Why is understanding evolution important? Because evolution continues today, driving changes in the living world such as drug resistance in bacteria and viruses, and pesticide resistance in insects. Evolutionary theory helps us understand and respond to these changes in ways that improve human life.

16–3 Section Assessment

1. **Key Concept** How is reproductive isolation related to the formation of new species?
2. **Key Concept** What type of isolating mechanism was important in the formation of Galápagos finch species?
3. Explain how behavior can play a role in the evolution of species.
4. What recent research findings support Darwin's theory of evolution?
5. **Critical Thinking Inferring** Suppose that a drought on an island eliminates all but plants that produce large, tough seeds. All the finches on the island have very small beaks. How might this environmental change impact the survival of this finch population?

Writing in Science

Summarizing
Write a paragraph that summarizes the Grants' research with Galápagos finches. Your summary should include the main points of the research. *Hint:* The first sentence in your summary might state the Grants' hypothesis.

Exploration

Investigating Genetic Diversity in Bacteria

Genetic diversity can make a population of organisms more adaptable. Some bacteria are able to survive in the presence of antibiotics that kill other bacteria. In this investigation, you will test a population of bacteria for the presence of antibiotic-resistant bacteria.

Problem
How common are antibiotic-resistant bacteria?

Materials

- liquid bacterial culture
- sterile swabs
- sterile agar plate
- glass-marking pencil
- antibiotic paper disks
- forceps
- transparent tape
- 70% alcohol
- metric ruler

Skills
Observing, Analyzing Data

Procedure

1. Wash your hands thoroughly with soap and warm water. Without opening the agar plate, use a glass-marking pencil to draw two lines at right angles on the bottom of the plate. This will divide the plate into four equal areas, or quadrants. Label the quadrants 1 to 4, as shown. Write your initials on the plate.
2. Wearing plastic gloves, dip a sterile swab in the bacterial culture. Remove the cover of the agar plate and rub the swab gently over the entire surface of the agar. Immediately replace the cover. Follow your teacher's directions for disposing of the swab.
3. Remove the cover of the agar plate again. Use clean forceps to place an antibiotic disk on the agar in the center of each quadrant. Replace the cover; then tape the plate closed.
4. Place the plate upside down in the area designated by your teacher.
5. Return the forceps to your teacher for disinfection. Wipe your work surface with 70% alcohol and a paper towel. Wash your hands well with soap and warm water before leaving the lab.
6. After 24 hours, observe the growth of bacteria around each antibiotic disk. Record your observations. **CAUTION:** *Do not open the plate.*
7. Use the metric ruler to measure the diameter of the zone of reduced bacterial growth, called the zone of inhibition, around each antibiotic disk. Record the diameter of each zone of inhibition.
8. Carefully observe the zones of inhibition. Do you see any evidence of bacterial growth there? Record your observations. Give the used plate to your teacher for safe disposal. Wipe your work surface with 70% alcohol and a paper towel. Wash your hands well with soap and warm water before leaving the lab.

Analyze and Conclude

1. **Observing** How did the antibiotic disks affect the growth of the bacteria?
2. **Classifying** What type of selection (directional, stabilizing, or disruptive) occurred in this experiment? Explain your answer.
3. **Drawing Conclusions** Did your data support the idea that antibiotic-resistant bacteria are common? Explain your answer.
4. **Evaluating** How do you know your data and conclusion are valid? (*Hint*: Compare your data and conclusion with those of other students.)

Go Further

Applying Concepts Investigate genetic diversity further by using your school library and the Internet to research the use of wild relatives of food crops to increase genetic variation in plants.

Chapter 16 Study Guide

16–1 Genes and Variation

Key Concepts

- In genetic terms, evolution is any change in the relative frequency of alleles in a population.
- Biologists have discovered that there are two main sources of genetic variation: mutations and the genetic shuffling that results from sexual reproduction.
- The number of phenotypes produced for a given trait depends on how many genes control the trait.

Vocabulary
gene pool, p. 394
relative frequency, p. 394
single-gene trait, p. 395
polygenic trait, p. 396

16–2 Evolution as Genetic Change

Key Concepts

- Natural selection on single-gene traits can lead to changes in allele frequencies and thus to evolution.
- Natural selection can affect the distributions of phenotypes in any of three ways: directional selection, stabilizing selection, or disruptive selection.
- In small populations, individuals that carry a particular allele may leave more descendants than other individuals, just by chance. Over time, a series of chance occurrences of this type can cause an allele to become common in a population.
- Five conditions are required to maintain genetic equilibrium from generation to generation: There must be random mating; the population must be very large; and there can be no movement into or out of the population, no mutations, and no natural selection.

Vocabulary
directional selection, p. 398
stabilizing selection, p. 399
disruptive selection, p. 399
genetic drift, p. 400
founder effect, p. 400
Hardy-Weinberg principle, p. 401
genetic equilibrium, p. 401

16–3 The Process of Speciation

Key Concepts

- As new species evolve, populations become reproductively isolated from each other.
- Speciation in the Galápagos finches occurred by founding of a new population, geographic isolation, changes in the new population's gene pool, reproductive isolation, and ecological competition.

Vocabulary
speciation, p. 404
reproductive isolation, p. 404
behavioral isolation, p. 404
geographic isolation, p. 405
temporal isolation, p. 405

Thinking Visually

Using the information in this chapter, complete the following concept map about evolution of populations:

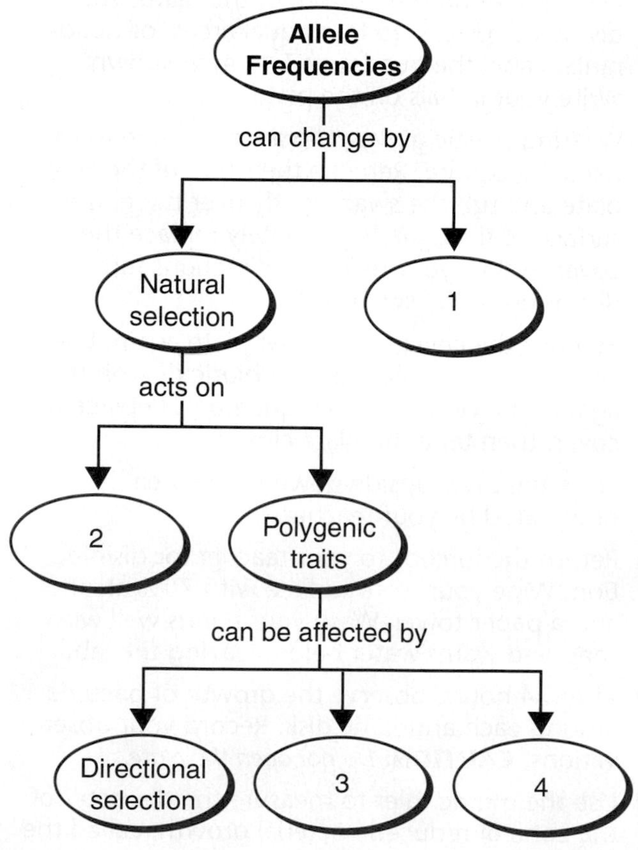

Preparing for the Living Environment Exam

NEW YORK LIVING ENVIRONMENT

Blue questions emphasize Regents Exam content

Chapter 16

Part A

Multiple Choice

For each statement or question, select the number of the word or expression that, of those given, best completes the statement or answers the question.

1 The combined genetic information of all the members of a particular population forms a
(1) gene pool (3) phenotype
(2) genotype (4) genetic drift

2 According to modern evolutionary theory, genes responsible for new traits that help a species survive in a particular environment will usually
(1) not change in frequency
(2) decrease gradually in frequency
(3) decrease rapidly in frequency
(4) increase in frequency

3 Traits, such as human height, that are controlled by more than one gene are known as
(1) single-gene traits
(2) polygenic traits
(3) recessive traits
(4) dominant traits

4 The type of selection in which individuals of average size have greater fitness than small or large individuals is called
(1) disruptive selection
(2) stabilizing selection
(3) directional selection
(4) artificial selection

5 Some behaviors such as mating and caring for young are genetically determined in certain species of birds. The presence of these behaviors is most likely due to the fact that
(1) birds do not have the ability to learn
(2) individual birds need to learn to survive and reproduce
(3) these behaviors helped birds to survive in the past
(4) within their lifetimes, birds developed these behaviors

6 Which term best describes a change in the frequency of an allele in a population that comes about by chance?
(1) a gene pool
(2) genetic drift
(3) genetic variation
(4) natural selection

7 A change in allele frequencies that results when a small subgroup of a population migrates to a new area is called
(1) natural selection
(2) the Hardy-Weinberg principle
(3) the founder effect
(4) genetic equilibrium

8 Similar organisms that can breed with each other and produce fertile offspring in the natural environment make up a
(1) species
(2) gene pool
(3) ecosystem
(4) temporal zone

9 The evolution of Darwin's finches is an example of
(1) genetic equilibrium
(2) speciation
(3) stabilizing selection
(4) artificial selection

10 Which situation would most likely result in the highest rate of natural selection?
(1) reproduction of organisms by an asexual method in an unchanging environment
(2) reproduction of a species having a very low mutation rate in a changing environment
(3) reproduction of organisms in an unchanging environment with little competition and few predators
(4) reproduction of organisms exhibiting genetic differences due to mutations and genetic recombinations in a changing environment

11 Change is to evolution as lack of change is to
(1) genetic equilibrium
(2) polygenic traits
(3) gene pool
(4) genetic variation

Test-Taking Tip If you have trouble answering a question, make a mark beside it and go on. (Do not write in this book.) You may find information in later questions that will allow you to eliminate some answer choices in your unanswered question.

Preparing for the Living Environment Exam

Part B

Multiple Choice and Extended Response

For those questions that ask you to select a response, choose the one that best completes the statement or answers the question. For all others follow the directions given.

12 If coat color in rabbits is a polygenic trait, which process might have produced the situation shown in the graph below?

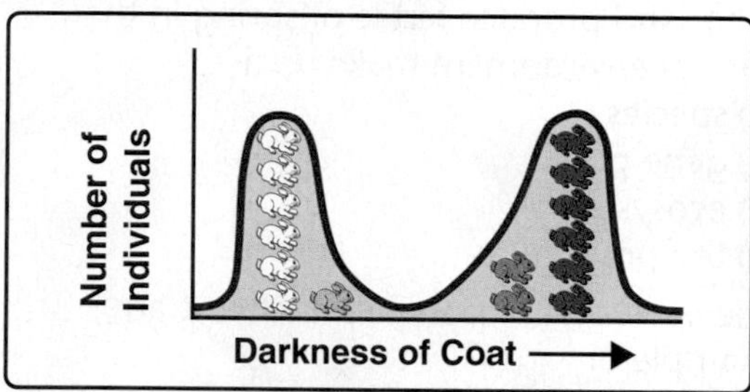

(1) stabilizing selection
(2) disruptive selection
(3) directional selection
(4) genetic equilibrium

Base your answers to questions 13 and 14 on the graphs below, which show the changes in a population of crabs living on a particular beach, and on your knowledge of biology.

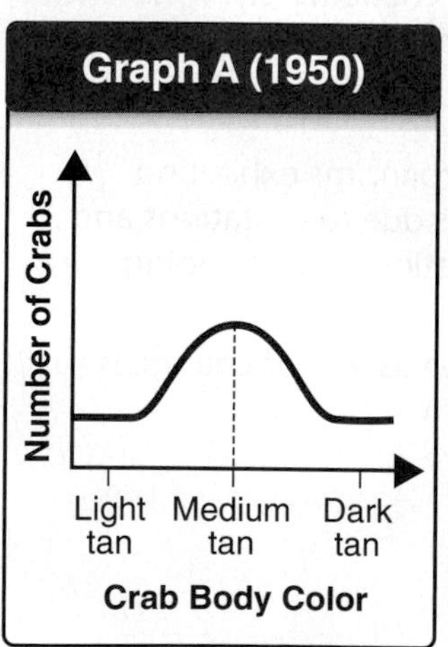

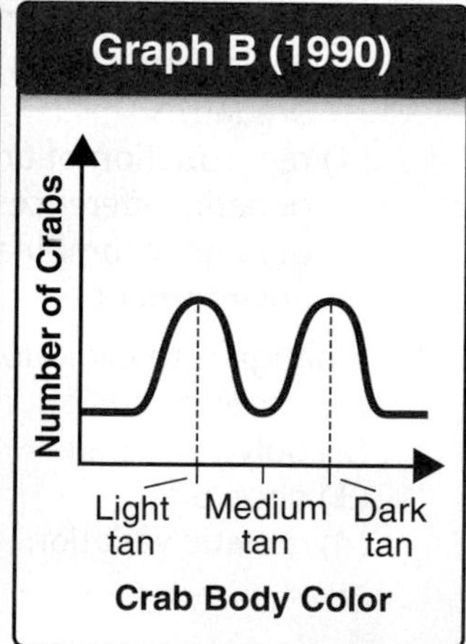

13 Describe how the coloration in the population of crabs changed between 1950 and 1990.

14 Between 1950 and 1990, the color of the sand got lighter. Also, large areas of the sandy beach eroded away, exposing areas of darker bedrock. Explain how these changes in the sand could account for the changes observed in the crab population. Use data from the graphs to support your answer.

15 Eastern and western meadowlarks do not interbreed because they have different mating songs. This situation is called
(1) geographic isolation
(2) behavioral isolation
(3) temporal isolation
(4) random mating

Base your answers to questions 16 through 18 on Figure 16–5 on page 397 and on your knowledge of biology.

16 State how the frequency of the brown allele changed over 30 generations.

17 Some scientists concluded that this lizard population is evolving. Explain how the data in the chart support this conclusion.

18 State the role that mutation played in the changes that occurred over 20 generations in this lizard population.

Base your answers to questions 19 through 21 on the graph below, which shows the data on the lengths of beaks of three finch species that live on the ground, and on your knowledge of biology.

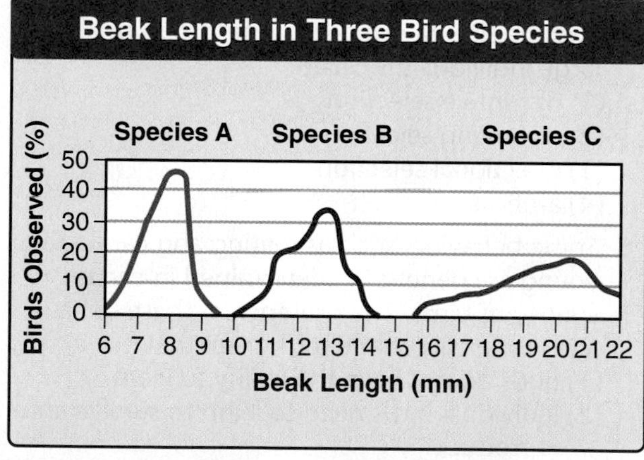

19 Which of the three species represented in the graph has the smallest range of beak sizes?

20 Identify the species that most likely eats the largest seeds. State the basis for your answer.

21 State how the graph for Species C would likely change if the seed characteristics changed to make it very difficult for birds with beaks 18 to 21 mm to use the seeds for food.

22 State how speciation and reproductive isolation are related.

23 State what could happen to a species in a changing environment if the members of that species do not express any genetic variations.

Base your answers to questions 24 and 25 on the chart below and on your knowledge of biology.

Frequency of Alleles

Year	Frequency of Allele B	Frequency of Allele b
1900	0.99	0.01
1910	0.81	0.19
1920	0.64	0.36
1930	0.49	0.51
1940	0.36	0.64
1950	0.25	0.75
1960	0.16	0.84
1970	0.10	0.90

24 Which statement about the frequencies of alleles between 1900 and 1970 is correct?
(1) Allele B increased in frequency as allele b decreased in frequency.
(2) Allele B decreased in frequency as allele b increased in frequency.
(3) Both alleles decreased in frequency.
(4) Both alleles increased in frequency.

25 The best explanation for the data is that
(1) allele b was needed by the species, and it therefore appeared
(2) organisms carrying allele b had a reduced rate of survival
(3) a change in the environment favored the trait controlled by allele B
(4) a change in the environment favored the trait controlled by allele b

26 Explain what the term *frequency* means as it applies to a trait such as fur color in a species of animal. Provide a specific example with your answer.

27 State what is meant by the term *single-gene trait.*

Part C

Extended Response
Answer the questions or follow the directions given.

28 Since antibiotics were discovered in the 1940s, they have become one of the most commonly prescribed types of drugs in the United States. More than 133 million prescriptions for antibiotics are written by doctors each year for nonhospitalized patients, and 190 million doses of antibiotics are administered in United States hospitals each day. However, antibiotics are becoming less effective, because the more they are used, the more resistant bacteria become to them. Explain how natural selection can result in an antibiotic becoming less effective against a particular species of bacteria. In your answer, be sure to explain how the
- bacteria originally became resistant to the antibiotic
- antibiotic acted as an "agent of natural selection"
- continued use of the antibiotic can lead to an almost totally resistant population of the bacteria.

29 When Charles Darwin was developing his theory of evolution, he considered variations in a population important. However, he could not explain how the variations occurred. Name *two* processes that can result in variation in a population. Explain how these processes actually cause variation.

For: An interactive self-test
Visit: PHSchool.com
Web Code: cba-5160

CHAPTER 17 The History of Life

About 25 million years ago, this scorpion was caught in sticky tree resin, which later hardened into amber. Fossils like this one provide evidence that enables scientists to build up a picture of Earth's history.

Inquiry Activity

How can you date a rock?

Procedure

1. Examine a piece of shale with a hand lens. This rock formed from the sediment deposited at the bottom of an ancient lake. As the shale formed, one dark layer and one light layer were deposited each year.
2. Place a transparent metric ruler next to the shale sample. Count and record the number of dark layers in a 5-mm section of the shale.
3. Divide your result in step 2 by 5 to determine the average number of layers per millimeter.

Think About It

1. **Inferring** How many years did it take for your specimen to form?
2. **Calculating** Suppose your specimen came from a deposit of shale that is 600 meters thick. How long did it take for the complete deposit to form?

17–1 The Fossil Record

4-3.1 Natural selection and the fossil record
4-3.1 Many organisms that lived long ago are extinct
LS- Analyze results and formulate a conclusion
LS- Make observations and use laboratory instruments
LS- Organize data in tables/graphs

Guide for Reading

Key Concepts
- What is the fossil record?
- What information do relative dating and radioactive dating provide about fossils?
- What are the main divisions of the geologic time scale?

Vocabulary
paleontologist • fossil record
extinct • relative dating
index fossil • half-life
radioactive dating
geologic time scale • era
period

Reading Strategy: Finding Main Ideas Before you read, write down this idea: Scientists use the fossil record to learn about the history of life on Earth. As you read, make a list of the kinds of evidence that support this main idea.

The history of life on Earth is filled with mystery, life-and-death struggles, and bizarre plants and animals as amazing as any mythological creatures. Studying life's history is one of the most fascinating and challenging parts of biology, and researchers go about it in several ways. One technique is to read the pieces of the story that are "written" in ancient rocks, in the petrified sap of ancient trees, in peat bogs and tar pits, and in polar glaciers. You may recall that these traces and preserved remains of ancient life are called fossils.

Fossils and Ancient Life

Paleontologists (pay-lee-un-TAHL-uh-jists) are scientists who study fossils. They collect fossils such as the one shown in **Figure 17–1.** From these fossils, they infer what past life forms were like—the structure of the organisms, what they ate, what ate them, and the environment in which they lived. Paleontologists also classify fossil organisms. They group similar organisms together and arrange them in the order in which they lived—from oldest to most recent. Together, all this information about past life is called the **fossil record.** **The fossil record provides evidence about the history of life on Earth. It also shows how different groups of organisms, including species, have changed over time.**

The fossil record reveals a remarkable fact: Fossils occur in a particular order. Certain fossils appear only in older rocks, and other fossils appear only in more recent rocks. In other words, the fossil record shows that life on Earth has changed over time. In fact, more than 99 percent of all species that have ever lived on Earth have become **extinct,** which means the species died out. Meanwhile, over billions of years, ancient unicellular organisms have given rise to the modern bacteria, protists, fungi, plants, and animals that you will study in later units.

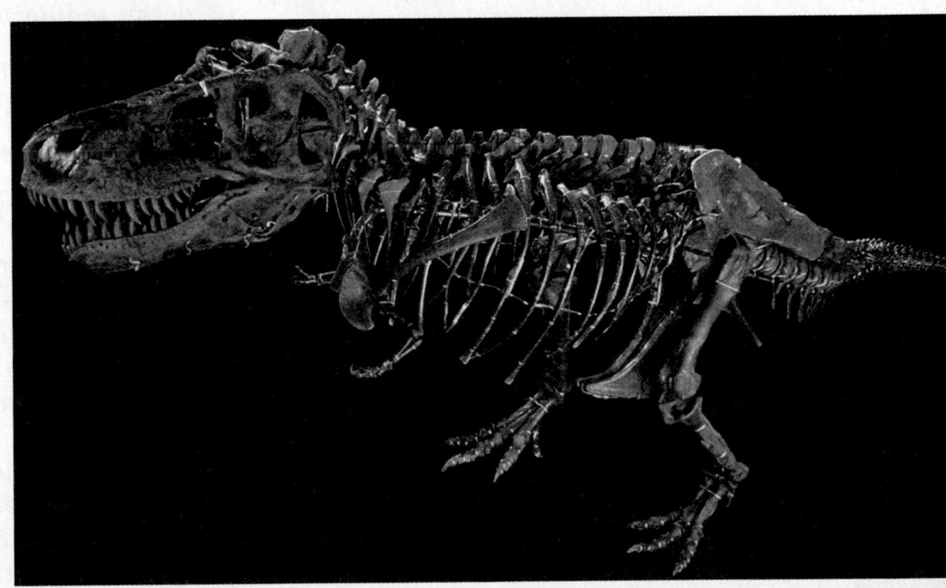

▶ **Figure 17–1** This remarkably complete dinosaur fossil reveals many characteristics of the original animal. **Observing** *What anatomical similarities can you observe between this fossil and any organism alive today?*

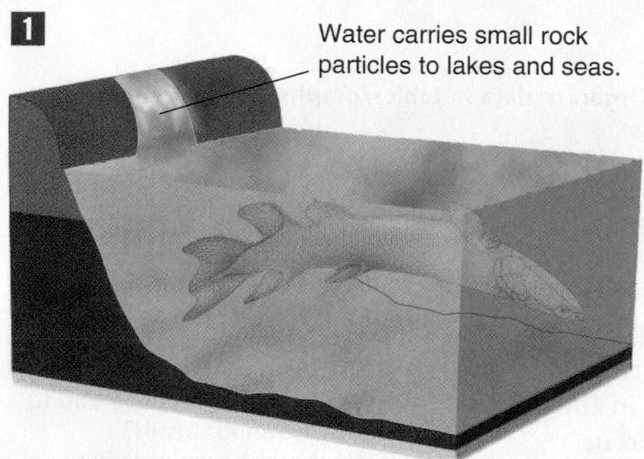

1
Water carries small rock particles to lakes and seas.

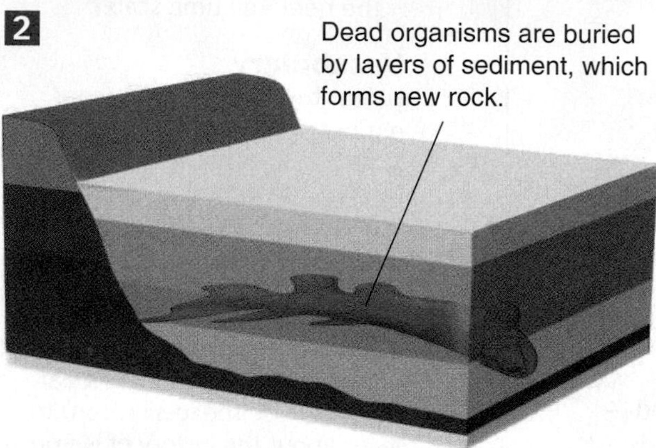

2
Dead organisms are buried by layers of sediment, which forms new rock.

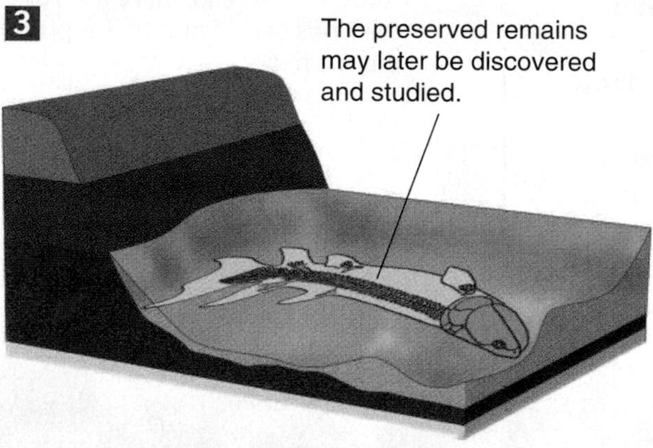

3
The preserved remains may later be discovered and studied.

▲ **Figure 17–2** **The fossil record provides evidence about the history of life on Earth.** Most fossils are formed in sedimentary rock.

How Fossils Form

A fossil can be as large and complete as an entire, perfectly preserved animal, or as small and incomplete as a tiny fragment of a jawbone or leaf. There are fossil eggs, fossil footprints, and even fossilized animal droppings. For a fossil to form, either the remains of the organism or some trace of its presence must be preserved. The formation of any fossil depends on a precise combination of conditions. Because of this, the fossil record provides incomplete information about the history of life. For every organism that leaves a fossil, many more die without leaving a trace.

Most fossils form in sedimentary rock, as shown in **Figure 17–2.** Sedimentary rock is formed when exposure to rain, heat, wind, and cold breaks down existing rock into small particles of sand, silt, and clay. These particles are carried by streams and rivers into lakes or seas, where they eventually settle to the bottom. As layers of sediment build up over time, dead organisms may also sink to the bottom and become buried. If conditions are right, the remains may be kept intact and free from decay. The weight of layers of sediment gradually compresses the lower layers and, along with chemical activity, turns them into rock.

The quality of fossil preservation varies. In some cases, the small particles of rock surrounding the remains of an organism preserve an imprint of its soft parts. In other cases, the hard parts are preserved when wood, shells, or bones are saturated or replaced with long-lasting mineral compounds. Occasionally, organisms are buried quickly in fine-grained clay or volcanic ash before they begin to decay, so they are perfectly preserved.

CHECKPOINT ***Why is the fossil record described as an incomplete record of life's history?***

Interpreting Fossil Evidence

The natural forces that form sedimentary rock can also reveal fossils that have been hidden in layers of rock for millions of years. Forces inside Earth lift rocks up into mountain ranges, where wind, rain, and running water erode the rock. Bit by bit, water and wind wear away the upper, younger layers, exposing the older fossil-bearing layers beneath.

When a fossil is exposed, a fortunate (and observant) paleontologist may happen along at just the right time and remove the fossil for study.

Paleontologists occasionally unearth the remains of an entire organism. More often, though, they must reconstruct an extinct species from a few fossil bits—remains of bone, a shell, leaves, or pollen. When paleontologists study a fossil, they look for anatomical similarities—and differences—between the fossil and living organisms. Also, a fossil's age is extremely important. Paleontologists determine the age of fossils using two techniques: relative dating and radioactive dating.

Relative Dating About two centuries ago, geologists noted that rock layers containing certain fossils consistently appeared in the same vertical order no matter where they were found. Also, a particular species of trilobite—a common fossil and an extinct relative of horseshoe crabs—might be found in one rock layer but be absent from layers above or below it. How might such a pattern be useful?

In **relative dating,** the age of a fossil is determined by comparing its placement with that of fossils in other layers of rock, as shown in **Figure 17–3.** Recall that sedimentary rock is formed from the gradual deposition of layers of sand, rock, and other types of sediment. The rock layers form in order by age—the oldest layers on the bottom, with more recent layers on top, closer to Earth's surface.

Scientists also use **index fossils** to compare the relative ages of fossils. To be used as an index fossil, a species must be easily recognized and must have existed for a short period but have had a wide geographic range. As a result, it will be found in only a few layers of rock, but these specific layers will be found in different geographic locations. **Relative dating allows paleontologists to estimate a fossil's age compared with that of other fossils.** However, it provides no information about its absolute age, or age in years.

Word Origins

The word part *paleo-* means "ancient" or "early," and *-zoic* means "life." The word part *meso-* means "middle." The word part *ceno-* means "recent." **Use this information to explain the meanings of *paleozoic, mesozoic,* and *cenozoic.***

▼ **Figure 17–3 In relative dating, a paleontologist estimates a fossil's age in comparison with that of other fossils.** Each of these fossils is an index fossil. It enables scientists to date the rock layer in which it is found. Scientists can also use index fossils to date rocks from different locations.

Quick Lab

What is a half-life?

Materials 100 1-cm squares of paper, plastic or paper cup

Procedure 

1. Construct a data table with 2 columns and 5 blank rows. Label the columns "Spill Number" and "Number of Squares Returned."
2. Place an *X* on each square of paper, and put all the squares in the cup.
3. Mix up the squares in the cup. Then, spill them out and separate all squares that overlap.
4. Remove the squares that have an *X* showing. Record the number of squares remaining and return them to the cup.
5. Repeat steps 3 and 4 until there are 5 or fewer squares remaining. Make a graph of your results with the number of spills on the *x*-axis and the number of squares remaining on the *y*-axis.

Analyze and Conclude

1. **Analyzing Data** How many spills were required to remove half of the squares? To remove three fourths?
2. **Calculating** If each spill represents one year, what is the half-life of the squares?

To find out about radioactive dating, view the segment "Mummies: Ties to the Past," on Videotape Two.

Radioactive Dating Scientists use radioactive decay to assign absolute ages to rocks. Some elements found in rocks are radioactive. Radioactive elements decay, or break down, into nonradioactive elements at a steady rate, which is measured in a unit called a half-life. A **half-life** is the length of time required for half of the radioactive atoms in a sample to decay. As shown in **Figure 17–4,** after one half-life, half of the original radioactive atoms in a sample have decayed. Of those remaining atoms, half again are decayed after another half-life.

Radioactive dating is the use of half-lives to determine the age of a sample. **In radioactive dating, scientists calculate the age of a sample based on the amount of remaining radioactive isotopes it contains.** Different radioactive elements have different half-lives and therefore provide natural clocks that "tick" at different rates. Carbon-14, for example, has a half-life of about 5730 years. Carbon-14 is taken up by living things while they are alive. After an organism dies, the carbon-14 in its body begins to decay to form nitrogen-14, which escapes into the air. Carbon-12, the most common isotope of carbon, is not radioactive and does not decay. By comparing the amounts of carbon-14 and carbon-12 in a fossil, researchers can determine when the organism lived. The more carbon-12 there is in a sample compared to carbon-14, the older the sample is.

Because carbon-14 has a relatively short half-life, it is useful only for dating fossils younger than about 60,000 years. To date older rocks, researchers use elements with longer half-lives. Potassium-40, for example, decays to the inert gas argon-40 and has a half-life of 1.26 billion years.

What is a half-life?

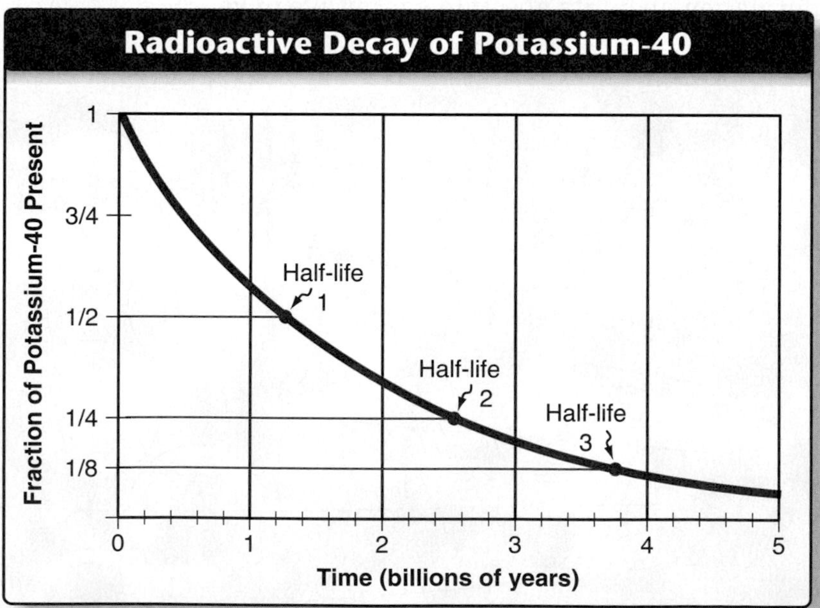

▲ **Figure 17–4** **Radioactive dating involves measuring the amounts of radioactive isotopes in a sample to determine its actual age.** Such measurements enable scientists to determine the absolute age of rocks and the fossils they contain.

Geologic Time Scale

Paleontologists use divisions of the **geologic time scale** to represent evolutionary time. **Figure 17–5** shows the most recent version of the geologic time scale. Scientists first developed the geologic time scale by studying rock layers and index fossils worldwide. With this information, they placed Earth's rocks in order according to relative age. As geologists studied the fossil record, they found major changes in the fossil animals and plants at specific layers in the rock. These times were used to mark where one segment of geologic time ends and the next begins—long before anyone knew how long these various segments actually were.

Years later, radioactive dating techniques were used to assign specific ages to the various rock layers. Not surprisingly, the divisions of the geologic time scale did not turn out to be of standard lengths, such as 100 million years. Instead, geologic divisions vary in duration by many millions of years. Scientists use several levels of divisions for the geologic time scale. Geologic time begins with Precambrian (pree-KAM-bree-un) Time. Although few multicellular fossils exist from this time, the Precambrian actually covers about 88 percent of Earth's history, as shown in **Figure 17–6** on the next page. **After Precambrian Time, the basic divisions of the geologic time scale are eras and periods.**

Eras Geologists divide the time between the Precambrian and the present into three **eras.** They are the Paleozoic Era, the Mesozoic Era, and the Cenozoic Era. The Paleozoic (pay-lee-oh-ZOH-ik) began about 544 million years ago and lasted for almost 300 million years. Many vertebrates and invertebrates—animals with and without backbones—lived during the Paleozoic.

The Mesozoic (mez-uh-ZOH-ik) began about 245 million years ago and lasted about 180 million years. Some people call the Mesozoic the Age of Dinosaurs, yet dinosaurs were only one of many kinds of organisms that lived during this era. Mammals began to evolve during the Mesozoic.

Earth's most recent era is the Cenozoic (sen-uh-ZOH-ik). It began about 65 million years ago and continues to the present. The Cenozoic is sometimes called the Age of Mammals because mammals became common during this time.

Geologic Time Scale

Era	Period	Time (millions of years ago)
Cenozoic	Quaternary	1.8 – present
	Tertiary	65 – 1.8
Mesozoic	Cretaceous	145 – 65
	Jurassic	208 – 145
	Triassic	245 – 208
Paleozoic	Permian	290 – 245
	Carboniferous	360 – 290
	Devonian	410 – 360
	Silurian	440 – 410
	Ordovician	505 – 440
	Cambrian	544 – 505
Precambrian Time	Vendian	650 – 544

▲ **Figure 17–5** **The basic units of the geologic time scale after Precambrian Time are eras and periods.** Each era is divided into periods.

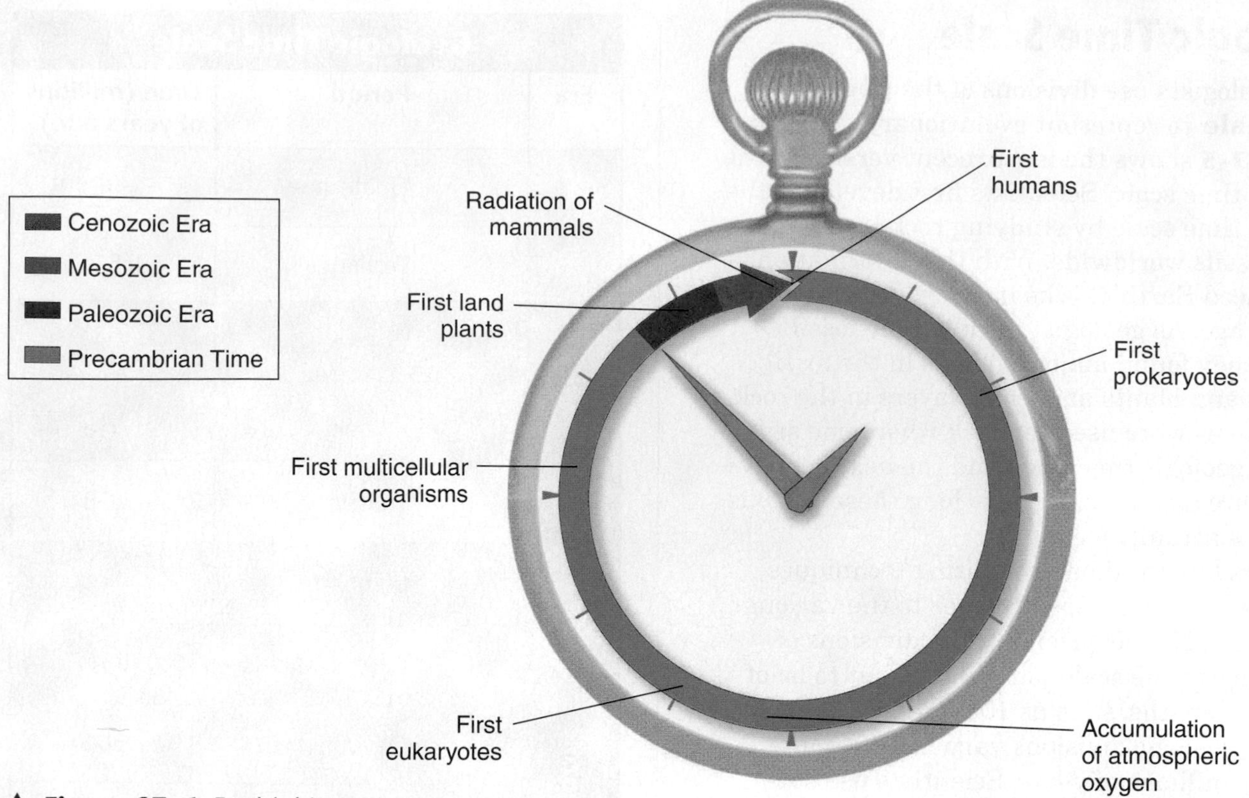

▲ **Figure 17–6** Earth's history is often compared to a familiar measurement, such as the twelve hours between noon and midnight. In such a comparison, notice that Precambrian Time lasts from noon until after 10:30 PM. **Interpreting Graphics** ***Using this model, about what time did life appear? The first plants? The first humans?***

Periods Eras are subdivided into **periods,** which range in length from tens of millions of years to less than two million years. The Mesozoic Era, for example, includes three periods: the Triassic Period, the Jurassic Period, and the Cretaceous Period. Many periods are named for places around the world where geologists first described the rocks and fossils of that period. The name Cambrian, for example, refers to Cambria, the old Roman name for Wales. Jurassic refers to the Jura Mountains in France. The Carboniferous ("carbon-bearing") Period, on the other hand, is named for the large coal deposits that formed during that period.

17–1 Section Assessment

1. **Key Concept** What can be learned from the fossil record?
2. **Key Concept** Which type of dating provides an absolute age for a given fossil? Describe how this is done.
3. **Key Concept** How are eras and periods related?
4. How do fossils form?
5. What geologic era is known as the Age of Mammals? When did this era begin?
6. **Critical Thinking Drawing Conclusions** Many more fossils have been found since Darwin's day, allowing several gaps in the fossil record to be filled. How might this information make relative dating more accurate?

Thinking Visually

Constructing a Time Line
Create a time line that shows the four main divisions in the geologic time scale and the key events that occurred during those divisions. Then, as you read Section 17–3, add more events to your time line.

17–2 Earth's Early History

1-S1.1 Historical development of ideas in science
1-S3.5 Experiments must be repeatable with the same results
1-S3.5 Scientific findings are evaluated through peer review
4-3.1 Evolutionary change
4-3.1 Evolution from simple to complex

If life comes only from life, then how did life on Earth first begin? This section presents the current scientific view of events on the early Earth. These hypotheses, however, are based on a relatively small amount of evidence. The gaps and uncertainties make it likely that scientific ideas about the origin of life will change.

Guide for Reading

Key Concepts
- What substances made up Earth's early atmosphere?
- What did Miller and Urey's experiments show?
- What occurred when oxygen was added to Earth's atmosphere?
- What hypothesis explains the origin of eukaryotic cells?

Vocabulary
proteinoid microsphere
microfossil
endosymbiotic theory

Reading Strategy: Making Comparisons
Before you read, write three sentences about Earth as it is today. As you read, write three sentences that describe how Earth was very different in the past.

Formation of Earth

Geologic evidence shows that Earth, which is about 4.6 billion years old, was not "born" in a single event. Instead, pieces of cosmic debris were probably attracted to one another over the course of about 100 million years. While the planet was young, it was struck by one or more objects, possibly as large as the planet Mars. This collision produced enough heat to melt the entire globe.

Once Earth melted, its elements rearranged themselves according to density. The most dense elements formed the planet's core. There, radioactive decay generated enough heat to convert Earth's interior into molten rock. Moderately dense elements floated to the surface, much as fat floats to the top of hot chicken soup. These elements ultimately cooled to form a solid crust. The least dense elements—including hydrogen and nitrogen—formed the first atmosphere.

This infant planet was very different from today's Earth. **Figure 17–7** shows how it might have looked. The sky was probably not blue but pinkish-orange. **Earth's early atmosphere probably contained hydrogen cyanide, carbon dioxide, carbon monoxide, nitrogen, hydrogen sulfide, and water.** Had you been there, a few deep breaths would have killed you!

▼ **Figure 17–7** The early Earth was much hotter than it is now, and there was little or no oxygen in the atmosphere. **Earth's early atmosphere was probably made up of hydrogen cyanide, carbon dioxide, carbon monoxide, nitrogen, hydrogen sulfide, and water.**

Geologists infer that about 4 billion years ago, Earth cooled enough to allow the first solid rocks to form on its surface. For millions of years afterward, violent volcanic activity shook Earth's crust. Comets and asteroids bombarded its surface. Oceans did not exist because the surface was extremely hot.

About 3.8 billion years ago, Earth's surface cooled enough for water to remain a liquid. Thunderstorms drenched the planet, and oceans covered much of the surface. Those primitive oceans were brown because they contained lots of dissolved iron. The earliest sedimentary rocks, which were deposited in water, have been dated to this period. This was the Earth on which life appeared.

 *Why did the early Earth not have oceans?*

The First Organic Molecules

For several reasons, atoms do not assemble themselves into complex organic molecules or living cells on Earth today. For one thing, the oxygen in the atmosphere is very reactive and would destroy many kinds of organic molecules not protected within cells. In addition, as soon as organic molecules appeared, something—bacteria or some other life form—would probably eat them! But the early Earth was a very different place. Could organic molecules have evolved under those conditions?

In the 1950s, American chemists Stanley Miller and Harold Urey tried to answer that question by simulating conditions on the early Earth in a laboratory setting. They filled a flask with hydrogen, methane, ammonia, and water to represent the atmosphere. They made certain that no microorganisms could contaminate the results. Then, as shown in **Figure 17–8,** they passed electric sparks through the mixture to simulate lightning.

The results were spectacular. Over a few days, several amino acids—the building blocks of proteins—began to accumulate. **Miller and Urey's experiments suggested how mixtures of the organic compounds necessary for life could have arisen from simpler compounds present on a primitive Earth.** Scientists now know that Miller and Urey's original simulations of Earth's early atmosphere were not accurate. However, similar experiments based on more current knowledge of Earth's early atmosphere have also produced organic compounds. In fact, one of Miller's experiments in 1995 produced cytosine and uracil, two of the bases found in RNA.

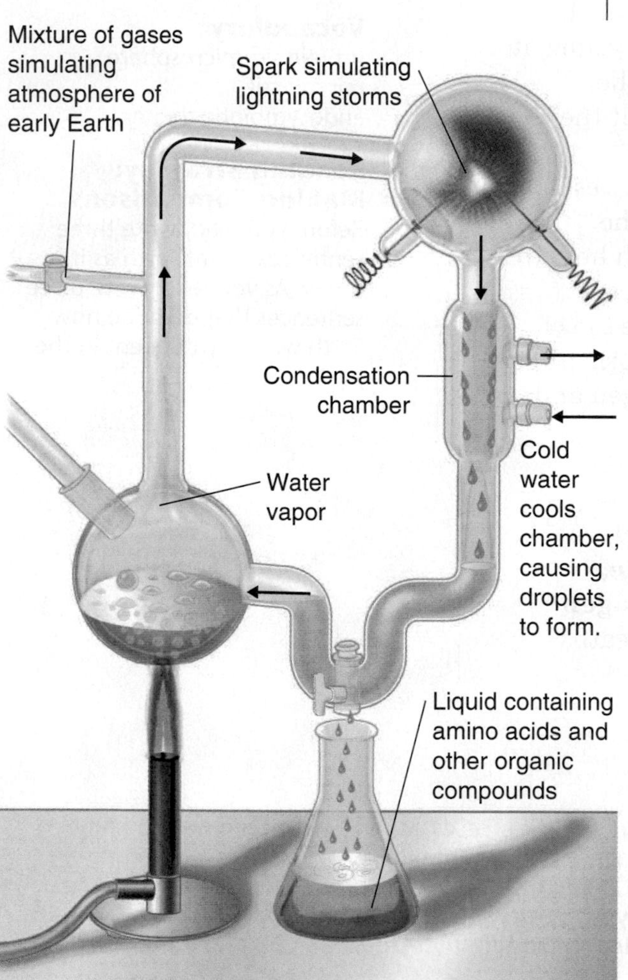

▲ **Figure 17–8** Miller and Urey produced amino acids, which are needed to make proteins, by passing sparks through a mixture of hydrogen, methane, ammonia, and water. **This and other experiments suggested how simple compounds found on the early Earth could have combined to form the organic compounds needed for life.**

The Puzzle of Life's Origins

A stew of organic molecules is a long way from a living cell, and the leap from nonlife to life is the greatest gap in scientific hypotheses of Earth's early history. Geological evidence suggests that about 200 to 300 million years after Earth cooled enough to carry liquid water, cells similar to modern bacteria were common. How might these cells have originated?

Formation of Microspheres Under certain conditions, large organic molecules can form tiny bubbles called **proteinoid microspheres,** as shown in **Figure 17–9.** Microspheres are not cells, but they have some characteristics of living systems. Like cells, they have selectively permeable membranes through which water molecules can pass. Microspheres also have a simple means of storing and releasing energy. Several hypotheses suggest that structures similar to proteinoid microspheres might have acquired more and more characteristics of living cells.

Evolution of RNA and DNA Another unanswered question in the evolution of cells is the origin of DNA and RNA. Remember that all cells are controlled by information stored in DNA, which is transcribed into RNA and then translated into proteins. How could this complex biochemical machinery have evolved?

Science cannot yet solve this puzzle, although molecular biologists have made surprising discoveries in this area. Under the right conditions, some RNA sequences can help DNA replicate. Other RNA sequences process messenger RNA after transcription. Still others catalyze chemical reactions. Some RNA molecules can even grow and duplicate themselves—suggesting that RNA might have existed before DNA. A series of experiments that simulated conditions of the early Earth have suggested that small sequences of RNA could have formed and replicated on their own. From this relatively simple RNA-based form of life, several steps could have led to the system of DNA-directed protein synthesis that exists now. This hypothesis is shown in **Figure 17–10.** Future experiments are aimed at refining and retesting this hypothesis.

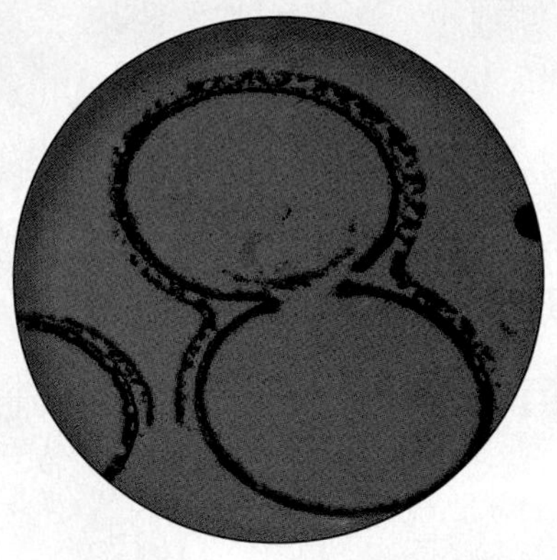

(magnification: about 10,000×)

▲ **Figure 17–9** Large organic molecules can sometimes form tiny proteinoid microspheres like the ones shown here. **Comparing and Contrasting** *How are proteinoid microspheres similar to cells? How are they different?*

▼ **Figure 17–10** One hypothesis about the origin of life, illustrated here, suggests that RNA could have evolved before DNA. Scientists have not yet demonstrated the later stages of this process in a laboratory setting. **Interpreting Graphics** *How might RNA have stored genetic information?*

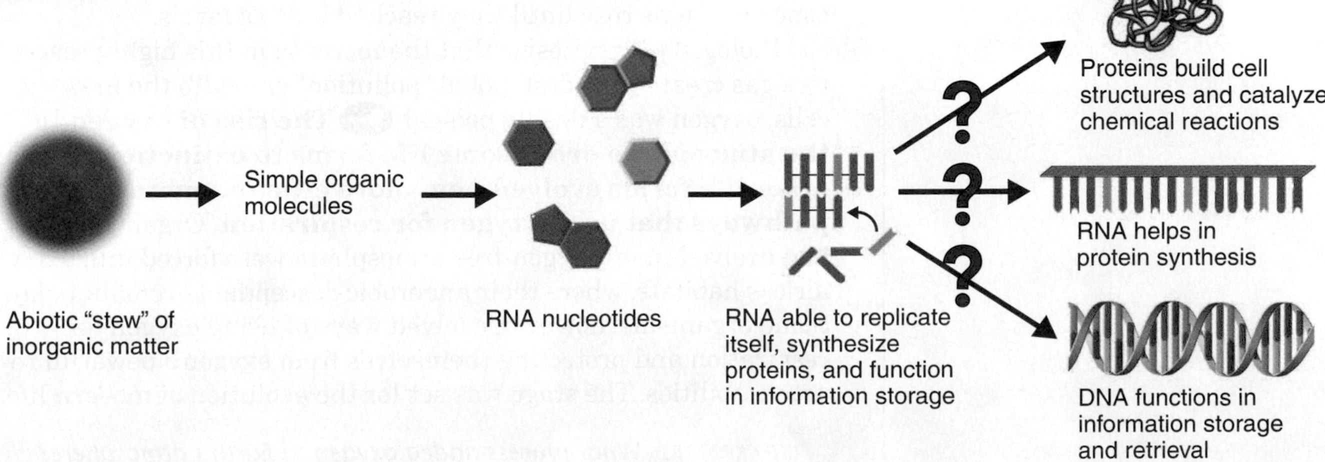
Abiotic "stew" of inorganic matter
Simple organic molecules
RNA nucleotides
RNA able to replicate itself, synthesize proteins, and function in information storage
?
?
?
Proteins build cell structures and catalyze chemical reactions
RNA helps in protein synthesis
DNA functions in information storage and retrieval

▲ **Figure 17–11** **Ancient photosynthetic organisms produced a rise in oxygen in Earth's atmosphere.** These rocklike formations, called stromatolites, were made by cyanobacteria, which were probably among the earliest organisms to evolve on Earth.

Free Oxygen

Microscopic fossils, or **microfossils,** of single-celled prokaryotic organisms that resemble modern bacteria have been found in rocks more than 3.5 billion years old, as shown in **Figure 17–11.** Those first life forms must have evolved in the absence of oxygen, because Earth's first atmosphere contained very little of that highly reactive gas.

Over time, as indicated by fossil evidence, photosynthetic bacteria became common in the shallow seas of the Precambrian. By 2.2 billion years ago at the latest, these organisms were steadily churning out oxygen, an end product of photosynthesis. One of the first things oxygen did was to combine with iron in the oceans. In other words, it caused the oceans to rust! When iron oxide was formed, it fell from the sea water to the ocean floor. There, it formed great bands of iron that are the source of most of the iron ore mined today. Without iron, the oceans changed color from brown to blue-green.

Next, oxygen gas started accumulating in the atmosphere. As atmospheric oxygen concentrations rose, concentrations of methane and hydrogen sulfide began to decrease, the ozone layer began to form, and the skies turned their present shade of blue. Over the course of several hundred million years, oxygen concentrations rose until they reached today's levels.

Biologists hypothesize that the increase in this highly reactive gas created the first global "pollution" crisis. To the first cells, oxygen was a deadly poison! **The rise of oxygen in the atmosphere drove some life forms to extinction, while other life forms evolved new, more efficient metabolic pathways that used oxygen for respiration.** Organisms that had evolved in an oxygen-free atmosphere were forced into a few airless habitats, where their anaerobic descendants remain today. Some organisms, however, evolved ways of using oxygen for respiration and protecting themselves from oxygen's powerful reactive abilities. The stage was set for the evolution of modern life.

What process added oxygen to Earth's atmosphere?

Origin of Eukaryotic Cells

Several important events in the history of life have been revealed through molecular studies of cells and their organelles. One of these events is the origin of eukaryotic cells, which are cells that have nuclei. About 2 billion years ago, prokaryotic cells—cells without nuclei—began evolving internal cell membranes. The result was the ancestor of all eukaryotic cells.

The Endosymbiotic Theory Then, something radical seems to have happened. Other prokaryotic organisms entered this ancestral eukaryote. These organisms did not infect their host, as parasites would have done, and the host did not digest them, as it would have digested prey. Instead, the smaller prokaryotes began living inside the larger cell, as shown in **Figure 17–12.** Over time, a symbiotic, or interdependent, relationship evolved. According to the **endosymbiotic theory,** eukaryotic cells formed from a symbiosis among several different prokaryotic organisms. One group of prokaryotes had the ability to use oxygen to generate energy-rich molecules of ATP. These evolved into the mitochondria that are now in the cells of all multicellular organisms. Other prokaryotes that carried out photosynthesis evolved into the chloroplasts of plants and algae. **The endosymbiotic theory proposes that eukaryotic cells arose from living communities formed by prokaryotic organisms.**

This hypothesis was proposed more than a century ago, when microscopists saw that the membranes of mitochondria and chloroplasts resembled the plasma membranes of free-living prokaryotes. Yet, the endosymbiotic theory did not receive much support until the 1960s, when it was championed by Lynn Margulis of Boston University.

Go Online NSTA SCILINKS
For: Links on eukaryotic cells
Visit: www.SciLinks.org
Web Code: cbn-5172

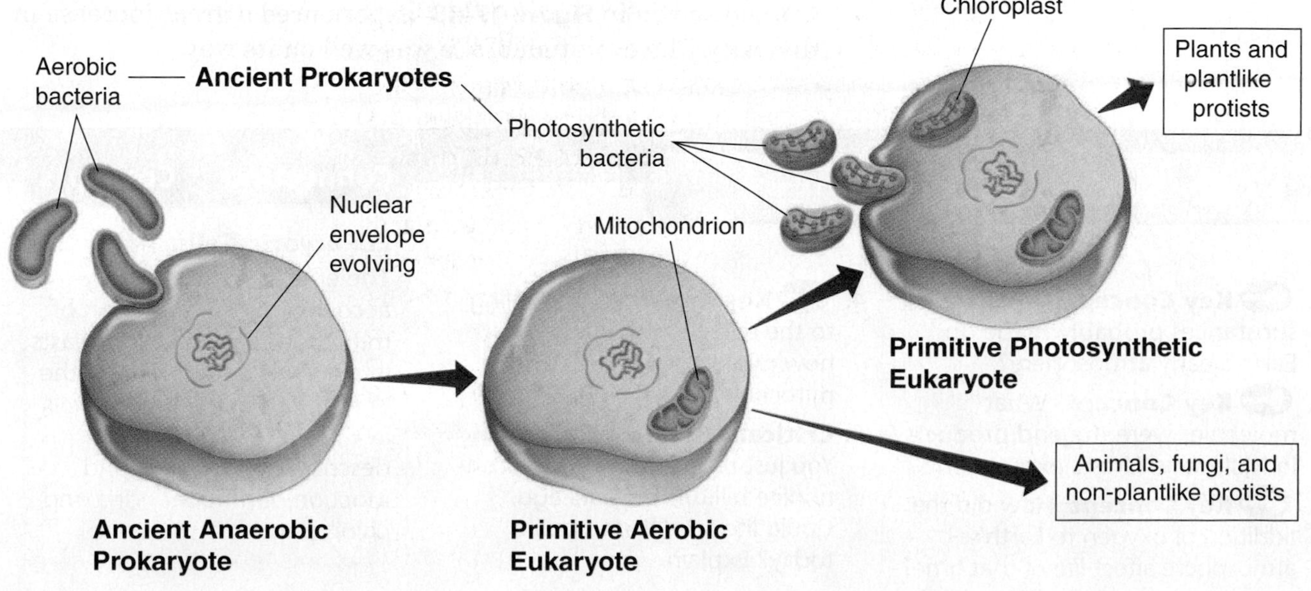

▼ **Figure 17–12** **The endosymbiotic theory proposes that eukaryotic cells arose from living communities formed by prokaryotic organisms.** Ancient prokaryotes may have entered primitive eukaryotic cells and remained there as organelles.

▲ **Figure 17–13** This ancient jellyfish, an early multicellular animal from Precambrian Time, did not have bones or other hard parts, but it left behind a fossil that allowed biologists to infer its overall shape. **Observing** *What evidence shows that this organism had body parts arranged around a central point?*

The Evidence Lynn Margulis and her supporters built their argument on several pieces of evidence: First, mitochondria and chloroplasts contain DNA similar to bacterial DNA. Second, mitochondria and chloroplasts have ribosomes whose size and structure closely resemble those of bacteria. Third, like bacteria, mitochondria and chloroplasts reproduce by binary fission when the cells containing them divide by mitosis. Thus, mitochondria and chloroplasts have many of the features of free-living bacteria. These similarities provide strong evidence of a common ancestry between free-living bacteria and the organelles of living eukaryotic cells.

Sexual Reproduction and Multicellularity

Some time after eukaryotic cells arose, those cells began to reproduce sexually. This development enabled evolution to take place at far greater speeds than ever before. How did sexual reproduction speed up the evolutionary process?

Most prokaryotes reproduce asexually. Often, they simply duplicate their genetic material and divide into two new cells. Although this process is efficient, it yields daughter cells that are exact duplicates of the parent cell. This type of reproduction restricts genetic variation to mutations in DNA. Sexual reproduction, on the other hand, shuffles and reshuffles genes in each generation, much like a person shuffling a deck of cards. The offspring of sexually reproducing organisms, therefore, never resemble their parents exactly. By increasing the number of gene combinations, sexual reproduction increases the probability that favorable combinations will be produced. Favorable gene combinations greatly increase the chances of evolutionary change in a species due to natural selection.

A few hundred million years after the evolution of sexual reproduction, evolving life forms crossed another great threshold: the development of multicellular organisms from single-celled organisms. These first multicellular organisms, such as the one shown in **Figure 17–13,** experienced a great increase in diversity. The evolution of life was well on its way.

17–2 Section Assessment

1. **Key Concept** What substances probably made up Earth's early atmosphere?
2. **Key Concept** What molecules were the end products in Miller and Urey's experiments?
3. **Key Concept** How did the addition of oxygen to Earth's atmosphere affect life of that time?
4. **Key Concept** According to the endosymbiotic theory, how might chloroplasts and mitochondria have originated?
5. **Critical Thinking Predicting** You just read that life arose from nonlife billions of years ago. Could life arise from nonlife today? Explain.

Connecting Concepts

Eukaryotic Cells
The endosymbiotic theory accounts for the evolution of mitochondria and chloroplasts in eukaryotic cells. Review the description of eukaryotic cells in Chapter 7, and then describe the structure and function of mitochondria and chloroplasts.

17–3 Evolution of Multicellular Life

4-3.1 Extinction of species
4-3.1 Fossil records of extinct species

Although the fossil record has missing pieces, paleontologists have assembled good evolutionary histories for many groups of organisms. Furthermore, the fossil record indicates that major changes occurred in Earth's climate, geography, and life forms. In this section, you will get an overview of how multicellular life evolved from its earliest forms to its present-day diversity.

Guide for Reading

 **Key Concept**

- What were the characteristic forms of life in the Paleozoic, Mesozoic, and Cenozoic eras?

Vocabulary
mass extinction

Reading Strategy: Using Graphic Organizers
As you read, make a table of the three geologic eras described in the section. Include information about the typical organisms and main evolutionary events of each era.

Precambrian Time

Recall that almost 90 percent of Earth's history occurred during the Precambrian. During this time, simple anaerobic forms of life appeared and were followed by photosynthetic forms, which added oxygen to the atmosphere. Aerobic forms of life evolved, and eukaryotes appeared. Some of those organisms gave rise to multicellular forms that continued to increase in complexity. Few fossils exist from this time because the animals were all soft-bodied. Life existed only in the sea.

Paleozoic Era

Rich fossil evidence shows that early in the Paleozoic Era, there was a diversity of marine life. Scientists once thought that those different forms of life evolved rapidly at the beginning of the Paleozoic, but increasing evidence from Precambrian fossils and DNA studies suggests that life began to diversify much earlier. Regardless of when these forms evolved, fossil evidence shows that life was highly diverse by the first part of the Paleozoic Era, the Cambrian Period. An artist's portrayal of Cambrian life, which included many kinds of invertebrate animals, is shown in **Figure 17–14.**

▼ **Figure 17–14** **The fossil record shows evidence of many types of marine life early in the Paleozoic Era.** These and other unfamiliar organisms dwelt in the sea during the Cambrian Period, a time when animals with hard parts evolved.

Cambrian Period Paleontologists call the diversification of life during the early Cambrian Period the "Cambrian Explosion." For the first time, many organisms had hard parts, including shells and outer skeletons. During the Cambrian Period, the first known representatives of most animal phyla evolved. Invertebrates—such as jellyfishes, worms, and sponges—drifted through the water, crawled along the sandy bottom, or attached themselves to the ocean floors. Brachiopods, which were small animals with two shells, were especially common. They resembled—but were unrelated to—modern clams. Trilobites were also common. Trilobites were arthropods, which are invertebrates with segmented bodies, jointed limbs, and an external skeleton.

CHECKPOINT *What is the "Cambrian Explosion"?*

▲ **Figure 17–15** During the Ordovician Period, aquatic arthropods like this eurypterid evolved. Eurypterids had segmented bodies and lived in water. Some of them grew to a length of almost 13 meters. Eurypterids are now extinct. **Comparing and Contrasting** *Which of today's animals do eurypterids resemble?*

Ordovician and Silurian Periods During the Ordovician (awr-duh-VISH-un) and Silurian (sih-LOOR-ee-un) periods, the ancestors of the modern octopi and squid appeared, as did aquatic arthropods like the one in **Figure 17–15.** Some arthropods became the first animals to live on land. Among the first vertebrates (animals with backbones) to appear were jawless fishes, which had suckerlike mouths. The first land plants evolved from aquatic ancestors. These simple plants grew low to the ground in damp areas.

Devonian Period By the Devonian (dih-VOH-nee-un) Period, some plants, such as ferns, had adapted to drier areas, allowing them to invade more habitats. Insects, which are arthropods, appeared on land. In the seas, both invertebrates and vertebrates thrived. Even though the invertebrates were far more numerous, the Devonian is often called the Age of Fishes because many groups of fishes were present in the oceans. Most fishes of this time had jaws, bony skeletons, and scales on their bodies. Sharks appeared in the late Devonian.

During the Devonian, vertebrates began to invade the land. The first fishes to develop the ability to crawl awkwardly on leglike fins were still fully aquatic animals. Some of these early four-legged vertebrates evolved into the first amphibians. An amphibian (am-FIB-ee-un) is an animal that lives part of its life on land and part of its life in water.

Carboniferous and Permian Periods Throughout the rest of the Paleozoic Era, life expanded over Earth's continents. Other groups of vertebrates, such as reptiles, evolved from certain amphibians. Reptiles are animals that have scaly skin and lay eggs with tough, leathery shells. Winged insects evolved into many forms, including huge dragonflies and cockroaches. Giant ferns and other plants formed vast swampy forests, shown in **Figure 17–16.** The remains of those ancient plants formed thick deposits of sediment that changed into coal over millions of years, giving the Carboniferous its name.

▲ **Figure 17–16** Ancient forests like this one from the Carboniferous Period were characterized by a huge variety of life forms. **At the end of the Paleozoic Era, many types of animals and plants became extinct.**

At the end of the Paleozoic, many organisms died out. This was a **mass extinction,** in which many types of living things became extinct at the same time. **The mass extinction at the end of the Paleozoic affected both plants and animals on land and in the seas. As much as 95 percent of the complex life in the oceans disappeared.** For example, trilobites, which had existed since early in the Paleozoic, suddenly became extinct. Many amphibians also became extinct. Not all organisms disappeared, however. The mass extinction did not affect many fishes. Numerous reptiles also survived.

Mesozoic Era

The Mesozoic Era lasted approximately 180 million years. **Events during the Mesozoic include the increasing dominance of dinosaurs. The Mesozoic is marked by the appearance of flowering plants.**

Triassic Period Those organisms that survived the Permian mass extinction became the main forms of life early in the Triassic (try-AS-ik) Period. Important organisms in this new ecosystem were fishes, insects, reptiles, and cone-bearing plants like the one in **Figure 17–17.** Reptiles were so successful during the Mesozoic Era that this time is often called the Age of Reptiles.

About 225 million years ago, the first dinosaurs appeared. One of the earliest dinosaurs, *Coelophysis,* was a meat-eater that had light, hollow bones and ran swiftly on its hind legs. Mammals also first appeared during the late Triassic Period, probably evolving from mammallike reptiles. Mammals of the Triassic were very small, about the size of a mouse or shrew.

▼ **Figure 17–17** Among the seed plants of the Triassic Period were cone-bearing plants called cycads, which left this modern descendant. **Applying Concepts** *What other organisms were important in the Triassic Period?*

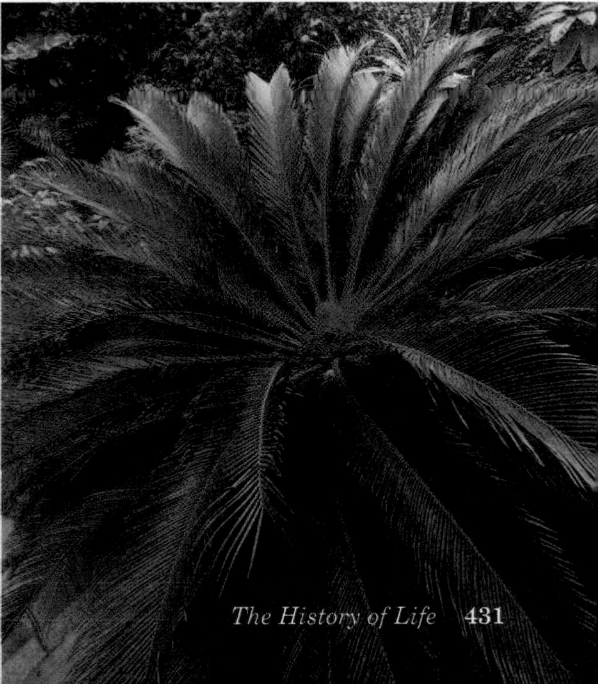

▲ **Figure 17–18** **During the Mesozoic Era, dinosaurs were dominant.** *Dicraeosaurus* (foreground) was a plant-eater that grew to about 20 meters in length.

Jurassic Period During the Jurassic (joo-RAS-ik) Period, dinosaurs became the dominant animals on land. Dinosaurs "ruled" Earth for about 150 million years, but different types lived at different times. At 20 meters long, *Dicraeosaurus*, shown in **Figure 17–18,** was one of the larger dinosaurs of the Jurassic Period.

One of the first birds, called *Archaeopteryx,* appeared during this time. Many paleontologists now think that birds are close relatives of dinosaurs. Since the 1990s, scientists working in China have found evidence for this hypothesis in other fossils that have the skulls and teeth of dinosaurs but the body structure and feathers of birds.

Cretaceous Period Reptiles were still the dominant vertebrates throughout the Cretaceous (krih-TAY-shus) Period. Dinosaurs such as the meat-eating *Tyrannosaurus rex* dominated land ecosystems, while flying reptiles and birds soared in the sky. Flying reptiles, however, became extinct during the Cretaceous. In the seas, turtles, crocodiles, and extinct reptiles such as plesiosaurs swam among fishes and marine invertebrates.

The Cretaceous also brought new forms of life, including leafy trees, shrubs, and small flowering plants like those you see today. Unlike the conifers, flowering plants produce seeds enclosed in a fruit, which protects the seed and aids in dispersing it to new locations.

At the close of the Cretaceous, another mass extinction occurred. More than half of all plant and animal groups were wiped out, including all of the dinosaurs.

When did flowering plants evolve?

▶ **Figure 17–19** **During the Cenozoic Era, mammals evolved adaptations that allowed them to live on land, in water, and even in the air.** Two of the traits that contributed to the success of mammals were a covering of hair that provided insulation against the cold and the protection of the young before and after birth.

Cenozoic Era

During the Mesozoic, early mammals competed with dinosaurs for food and places to live. The extinction of dinosaurs at the end of the Mesozoic, however, created a different world. **During the Cenozoic, mammals evolved adaptations that allowed them to live in various environments—on land, in water, and even in the air.** One land mammal from the early Cenozoic is shown in **Figure 17–19.** Paleontologists often call the Cenozoic the Age of Mammals.

Tertiary Period During the Tertiary Period, Earth's climates were generally warm and mild. In the oceans, marine mammals such as whales and dolphins evolved. On land, flowering plants and insects flourished. Grasses evolved, providing a food source that encouraged the evolution of grazing mammals, the ancestors of today's cattle, deer, sheep, and other grass-eating mammals. Some mammals became very large, as did some birds.

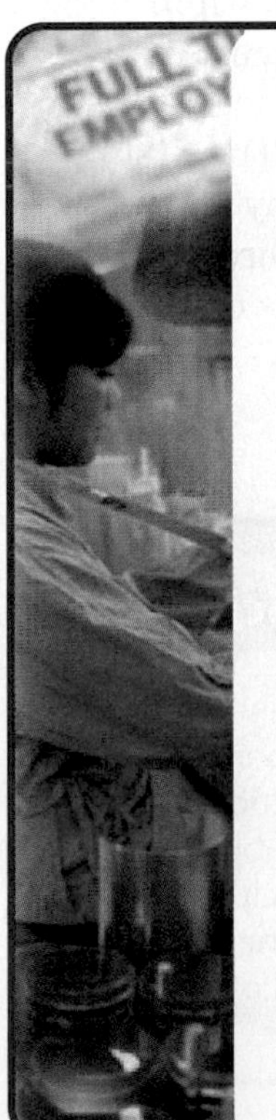

Careers in Biology

Fossil Preparer

Job Description: work for private industries, museums, or universities to expose fossils covered by rock or soil or to construct missing fossil parts

Education: a college degree in biology or geology, knowledge about information concerning the fossils being worked on

Skills: be knowledgeable about many areas of science, ability to use fine tools under a microscope, self-motivated, patient, ability to handle very fragile specimens for long periods

Highlights: work with fossils; collaborate with many types of people—from amateur fossil collectors to professional paleontologists

Go Online
PHSchool.com

For: Career links
Visit: PHSchool.com
Web Code: cbb-5173

▶ **Figure 17–20** During the Quaternary Period, Earth's climate cooled, producing a series of ice ages. Among the characteristic animals of the time were these huge mammoths. **Inferring** *How might the change to a colder climate have affected different types of organisms?*

Quaternary Period Mammals that had evolved during the Tertiary Period eventually faced a changing environment during the Quaternary Period. During this time, Earth's climate cooled, causing a series of ice ages. Repeatedly, thick continental glaciers advanced and retreated over parts of Europe and North America. So much of Earth's water was frozen in continental glaciers that the level of the oceans fell by more than 100 meters. Then, about 20,000 years ago, Earth's climate began to warm. Over the course of thousands of years, the continental glaciers melted. This caused sea levels to rise again.

In the oceans, algae, coral, mollusks, fishes, and mammals thrived. Insects and birds shared the skies. On land, mammals—such as bats, cats, dogs, cattle, and the mammoths shown in **Figure 17–20**—became common. The fossil record suggests that the early ancestors of our species appeared about 4.5 million years ago but that they did not look entirely human. The first fossils assigned to our own species, *Homo sapiens,* may have appeared as early as 200,000 years ago in Africa. According to one hypothesis, members of our species began a series of migrations from Africa that ultimately colonized the world.

17–3 Section Assessment

1. **Key Concept** Where did life exist during the early Paleozoic Era?
2. **Key Concept** What evolutionary milestone involving animals occurred during the Devonian Period?
3. **Key Concept** What are two key events from the Mesozoic Era?
4. **Critical Thinking Inferring** If you were a paleontologist investigating fossils from the Cenozoic Era, what fossils might you find?

Writing in Science

Creative Writing
Choose one of the periods described in this section. Then, write a story about life during that time. Include information about the life forms, weather, and other characteristics.

17–4 Patterns of Evolution

1-S3.1 Interpreting data
4-3.1 Evolutionary changes
LS- Analyze results

Biologists often use the term **macroevolution** to refer to large-scale evolutionary patterns and processes that occur over long periods of time. **Six important topics in macroevolution are extinction, adaptive radiation, convergent evolution, coevolution, punctuated equilibrium, and changes in developmental genes.**

Guide for Reading

Key Concept
- What are six important patterns of macroevolution?

Vocabulary
macroevolution
adaptive radiation
convergent evolution
coevolution
punctuated equilibrium

Reading Strategy: Summarizing
List the six patterns of macroevolution described in this section. As you read, write a statement describing each pattern.

Extinction

More than 99 percent of all species that have ever lived are now extinct. Usually, extinctions happen for the reasons that Darwin proposed. Species compete for resources, and environments change. Some species adapt and survive. Others gradually become extinct in ways that are often caused by natural selection.

Several times in Earth's history, however, mass extinctions wiped out entire ecosystems. Food webs collapsed, and this disrupted energy flow through the biosphere. During these events, some biologists propose, many species became extinct because their environment was collapsing around them, rather than because they were unable to compete. Under these environmental pressures, extinction is not necessarily related to ordinary natural selection.

Until recently, most researchers looked for a single, major cause for each mass extinction. For example, one hypothesis suggests that at the end of the Cretaceous Period, the impact of a huge asteroid, as shown in **Figure 17–21,** wiped out the dinosaurs and many other organisms. Scientific evidence confirms that an asteroid did strike Earth at that time. The impact threw huge amounts of dust and water vapor into the atmosphere and probably caused global climate change. It is reasonable to assume that this kind of event played a role in the end of the dinosaurs.

Many paleontologists, however, think that most mass extinctions were caused by several factors. During several mass extinctions, many large volcanoes were erupting, continents were moving, and sea levels were changing. Researchers have not yet determined the precise causes of mass extinctions.

What effects have mass extinctions had on the history of life? Each disappearance of so many species left habitats open and provided ecological opportunities for those organisms that survived. The result was often a burst of evolution that produced many new species. The extinction of the dinosaurs, for example, cleared the way for the evolution of modern mammals and birds.

▼ **Figure 17–21 Mass extinctions are one pattern of macroevolution.** A huge asteroid hitting Earth may have caused the extinction of the dinosaurs at the end of the Cretaceous Period. This illustration shows an artist's conception of that event.

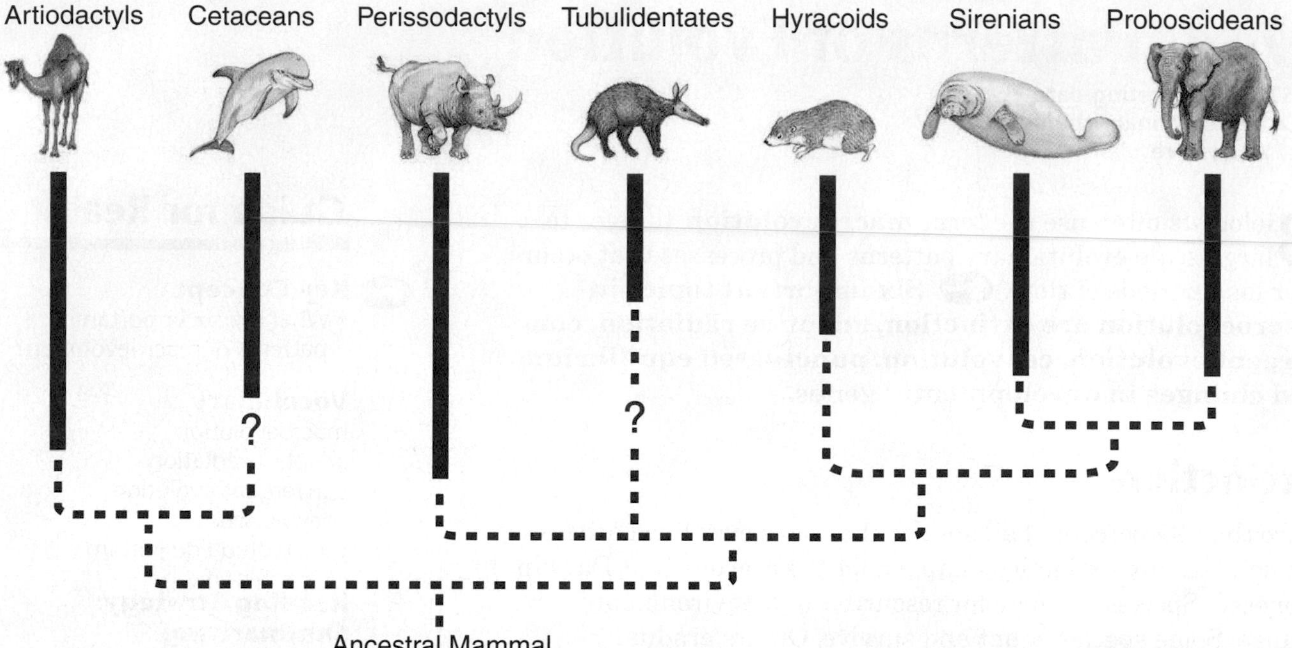

▲ **Figure 17–22** This diagram shows part of the adaptive radiation of mammals, emphasizing current hypotheses about how a group of ancestral mammals diversified over millions of years into several related living orders. Note that the dotted lines and question marks in this diagram indicate a combination of gaps in the fossil record and uncertainties about the timing of evolutionary branching. **Interpreting Graphics** *According to this diagram, which mammal group is the most closely related to elephants?*

Adaptive Radiation

Often, studies of fossils or of living organisms show that a single species or a small group of species has evolved, through natural selection and other processes, into diverse forms that live in different ways. This process is known as **adaptive radiation.** In the adaptive radiation of Darwin's finches, more than a dozen species evolved from a single species.

Adaptive radiations can also occur on a much larger scale. Dinosaurs, for example, were the products of a spectacular adaptive radiation among ancient reptiles. The first dinosaurs and the earliest mammals evolved at about the same time. Dinosaurs and other ancient reptiles, however, underwent an adaptive radiation first and "ruled" Earth for about 150 million years. During that time, mammals remained small and relatively scarce. But the disappearance of the dinosaurs cleared the way for the great adaptive radiation of mammals. This radiation, part of which is shown in **Figure 17–22,** produced the great diversity of mammals of the Cenozoic.

Convergent Evolution

Adaptive radiations can have an interesting evolutionary "side effect." They can produce unrelated organisms that look remarkably similar to one another. How does that happen? Sometimes, groups of different organisms, such as mammals and dinosaurs, undergo adaptive radiation in different places or at different times but in ecologically similar environments. These organisms start out with different "raw material" for natural selection to work on, but they face similar environmental demands, such as moving through air, moving through water, or eating similar foods.

For: Links on extinction
Visit: www.SciLinks.org
Web Code: cbn-5174

Shark

Figure 17–23 Each of these animals has a streamlined body and various appendages that enable it to move rapidly through water. Yet, the shark (above) is a fish, the penguin (center) is a bird, and the dolphin (bottom) is a mammal. **Applying Concepts** *How did these different animals come to resemble one another?*

Penguins

Dolphin

In these situations, natural selection may mold different body structures, such as arms and legs, into modified forms, such as wings or flippers. The wings or flippers function in the same way and look very similar. This process, by which unrelated organisms come to resemble one another, is called **convergent evolution.** Convergent evolution has occurred time and time again in both animals and plants.

Consider swimming animals, for example. An animal can move through the water rapidly with the least amount of energy if its body is streamlined and if it has body parts that can be used like paddles. That is why convergent evolution involving fishes, two different groups of aquatic mammals, and swimming birds has resulted in sharks, dolphins, seals, and penguins whose streamlined bodies and swimming appendages look a lot alike, as shown in **Figure 17–23.** Structures such as a dolphin's flukes and a fish's tail fin, which look and function similarly but are made up of parts that do not share a common evolutionary history, are called analogous structures. There are a surprising number of animals (including one of Darwin's finches) that have evolved adaptations analogous to those of woodpeckers for feeding on insects living beneath the bark of trees and in rotted wood.

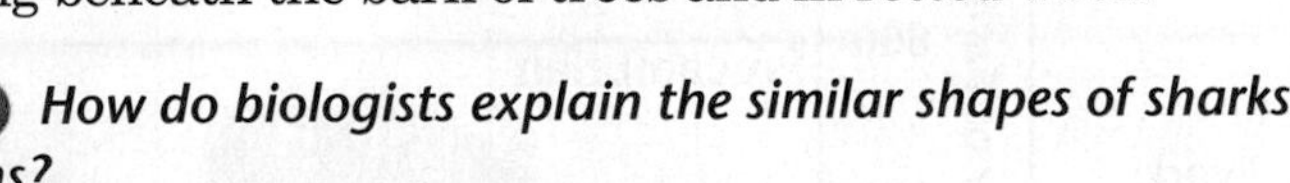

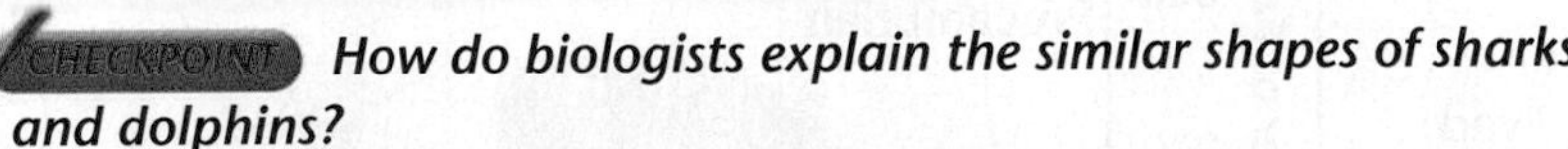

CHECKPOINT *How do biologists explain the similar shapes of sharks and dolphins?*

Coevolution

Sometimes organisms that are closely connected to one another by ecological interactions evolve together. Many flowering plants, for example, can reproduce only if the shape, color, and odor of their flowers attract a specific type of pollinator. Not surprisingly, these kinds of relationships can change over time. An evolutionary change in one organism may also be followed by a corresponding change in another organism. The process by which two species evolve in response to changes in each other over time is called **coevolution.**

◀ **Figure 17–24** This orchid has an unusually long spur containing a supply of nectar within its tip. The hawk moth has an equally long feeding tube that enables it to feed on the nectar. The flower spur and the feeding tube are an example of coevolution. **Inferring** *How might natural selection bring about the evolution of this orchid and the moth?*

The pattern of coevolution involving flowers and insects is so common that biologists in the field often discover additional examples. When Charles Darwin saw an orchid like the one in **Figure 17–24,** he closely examined the long structure called a spur. Inside the tip of that 40-centimeter spur is a supply of nectar, which serves as food for many insects. Darwin predicted the discovery of a pollinating insect with a 40-centimeter structure that could reach the orchid's nectar. About fifty years later, researchers discovered a moth that matched Darwin's prediction.

Consider another example, the relationships between plants and plant-eating insects. Insects have been feeding on flowering plants since both groups emerged during the Mesozoic. Over time, a number of plants have evolved poisonous compounds that prevent insects from feeding on them. In fact, some of the most powerful poisons known in nature are plant compounds that have evolved in response to insect attacks. But once plants began to produce poisons, natural selection in herbivorous insects began to favor any variants that could alter, inactivate, or eliminate those poisons. In a few cases, coevolutionary relationships can be traced back over millions of years.

What happens during coevolution?

Analyzing Data

Changing Number of Marine Families

Using fossil evidence, scientists make inferences about the kinds and number of organisms that lived at different times in the past. Further, they classify those organisms in ways that facilitate comparisons between past and present types. The graph on the right gives an estimate of the number of ocean-dwelling families over time. In biology, a family consists of several groups of related species.

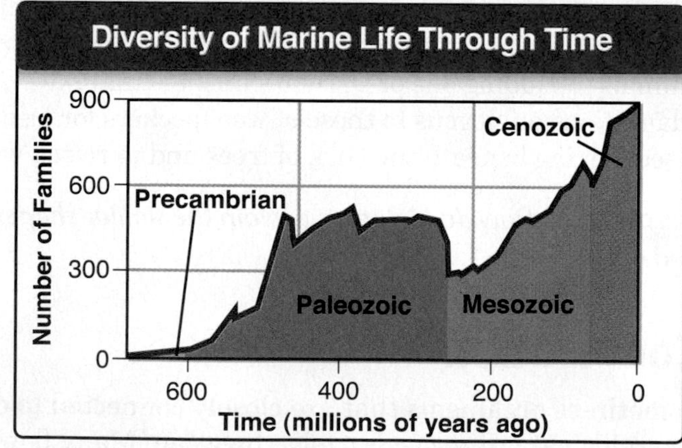

1. **Using Tables and Graphs** What overall trend does this graph show?
2. **Calculating** What was the change in the number of marine families at the end of the Paleozoic Era? At the end of the Mesozoic?
3. **Inferring** What kind of event(s) might explain the changes at the end of the Paleozoic and Mesozoic eras?
4. **Predicting** What factors might cause this graph to change in the next 1000 years? The next 10,000,000 years? Explain.

Punctuated Equilibrium

How quickly does evolution operate? Does it always occur at the same speed? These are questions on which some modern biologists would disagree with Darwin. Recall that Darwin was enormously impressed by the way Hutton and Lyell discussed the slow and steady nature of geologic change. Darwin, in turn, felt that biological change also needed to be slow and steady, an idea known as gradualism. In many cases, the fossil record confirms that populations of organisms did, indeed, change gradually over time.

But there is also evidence that this pattern does not always hold. Some species, such as horseshoe crabs, have changed little from the time they first appeared in the fossil record. In other words, much of the time these species are in a state of equilibrium, which means they do not change very much. Every now and then, however, something happens to upset the equilibrium. At several points in the fossil record, changes in animals and plants occurred over relatively short periods of time. Some biologists suggest that most new species are produced by periods of rapid change. (Remember that "short" and "rapid" are relative to the geologic time scale. Short periods of time for geologists can be hundreds of thousands—even millions—of years!)

Rapid evolution after long periods of equilibrium can occur for several reasons. It may occur when a small population becomes isolated from the main part of the population. This small population can then evolve more rapidly than the larger one because genetic changes can spread more quickly among fewer individuals. Or it may occur when a small group of organisms migrates to a new environment. That's what happened with the Galápagos finches, for example. Organisms evolve rapidly to fill available niches. In addition, mass extinctions can open many ecological niches and provide new opportunities to those organisms that survive. Thus, it is not surprising that some groups of organisms have evolved rapidly following mass extinctions.

Scientists use the term **punctuated equilibrium** to describe this pattern of long, stable periods interrupted by brief periods of more rapid change. The concept of punctuated equilibrium, illustrated in **Figure 17–25,** has generated much debate and is still somewhat controversial among biologists today. It is clear, however, that evolution has often proceeded at different rates for different organisms at different times during the long history of life on Earth.

▲ **Figure 17–25** Biologists have considered two different explanations for the rate of evolution, as illustrated in these diagrams. Gradualism involves a slow, steady change in a particular line of descent. Punctuated equilibrium involves stable periods interrupted by rapid changes involving many different lines of descent. **Interpreting Graphics** *How do the diagrams illustrate these explanations?*

Ancient Insect

Pairs of wings on many segments

Two Types of Modern Insects

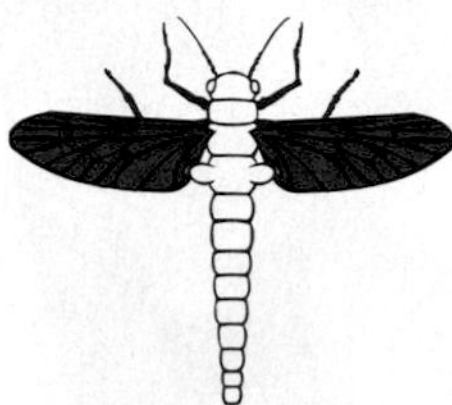

One pair of wings

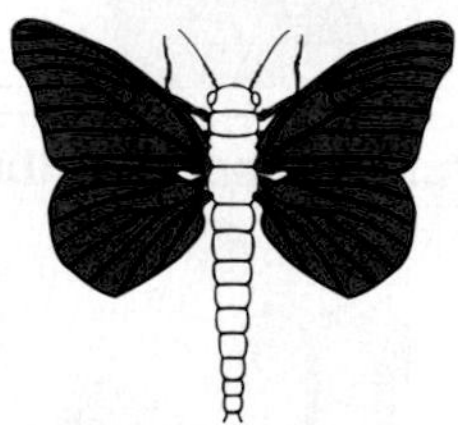

Two pairs of wings

▲ **Figure 17–26** Some ancient insects, such as the mayfly nymph (top), had winglike structures on many body segments. Modern insects have only four wings or two wings. **Changes in the expression of developmental genes may explain how these differences evolved.**

Developmental Genes and Body Plans

Biologists have long suspected that changes in the genes for growth and differentiation during embryological development could produce transformations in body shape and size. Until recently, however, researchers had only limited ability to affect gene activity in embryos. Therefore, they couldn't develop many of those hunches into testable scientific hypotheses. Molecular tools have changed all that. We can now perform experiments with gene expression by turning genes on or off and examining the results. These studies shed new light on how genetic change can produce major evolutionary transformations.

For example, as you saw in Chapter 12, "master control genes," called hox genes, guide development of major body structures in animals. Some determine which parts of an embryo become front and rear, or top and bottom. Others control the size and shape of arms, legs, or wings. Homologous control genes serve similar functions in animals as different as insects and humans—even though those animals haven't shared a common ancestor in at least 700 million years!

Small changes in the activity of control genes can affect many other genes to produce large changes in adult animals. If one gene, called "wingless," is turned on in an insect body segment, that segment grows no wings. This is interesting because some ancient insects, shown in **Figure 17–26,** had winglike structures on all body segments. Yet modern insects have wings on only one or two segments. Changes in the activation of this gene could have enabled many-winged ancestors of modern insects to evolve into four-winged and two-winged forms.

Small changes in the timing of cell differentiation and gene expression can make the difference between long legs and short ones, between long, slender fingers or short, stubby toes. In fact, recent studies suggest that differences in gene expression may cause many of the differences between chimpanzee brains and human brains. Small wonder that this new field is one of the hottest areas in all of evolutionary biology!

17–4 Section Assessment

1. **Key Concept** What is macroevolution? Describe two patterns of macroevolution.
2. What role have mass extinctions played in the history of life?
3. What is convergent evolution? Describe an example.
4. How might hox genes contribute to variation?
5. **Critical Thinking Comparing and Contrasting** Compare and contrast the hypotheses of gradualism and punctuated equilibrium.

Thinking Visually

Making a Table
Create a table that lists each of the six patterns of macroevolution, explains each pattern, and gives one example for each. Add a title to your table.

Exploration

Modeling Coevolution

Flowering plants and the animals that pollinate their flowers include many examples of coevolving species. In this investigation, you will model how these plants and animals evolve in response to one another.

Problem **How do flowering plants and their pollinators coevolve?**

Materials

- long forceps
- spoon
- dried peas
- 3 25-mL graduated cylinders
- 3 100-mL beakers
- watch or clock with second hand

Skills Using Models, Inferring

Procedure

1. Work in groups of three. Each group member represents a different bird species. To represent the birds' beaks, one group member will use forceps, the second group member will use a spoon, and the third will use two fingertips.
2. On a separate sheet of paper, make a copy of the data table shown. The beakers represent short, open flowers and the graduated cylinders represent long, narrow flowers. The dried peas represent the flowers' nectar, which is the birds' food. Fill the beakers and the graduated cylinders halfway with dried peas. **CAUTION:** *Handle the beakers and graduated cylinders carefully. If one breaks, tell your teacher immediately.*
3. For 1 minute, use the method you chose in step 1 to remove the peas. Remove them one at a time from your beaker. Do not move or tip the beaker as you do this.
4. Record the number of peas you removed in your data table.
5. To produce seeds, a flower must be pollinated by a member of its own species. Assume that 1 flower was pollinated for every 5 peas removed. Record the number of pollinations for each bird.
6. Repeat steps 3 through 5, using the graduated cylinders instead of the beakers.
7. **Calculating** Exchange data with your classmates and record the class averages for each bird species in your data table.

Data Table

Beak Type	Individual Data		Class Average	
	Peas	Pollinations	Peas	Pollinations
Forceps				
Spoon				
Fingers				

Analyze and Conclude

1. **Analyzing Data** Which bird species obtained the most nectar from the beakers? From the graduated cylinders?
2. **Analyzing Data** From which type of flower was each bird most successful in obtaining food?
3. **Inferring** What is the benefit to a plant of short, open flowers?
4. **Inferring** What is the benefit to a bird of a long, narrow beak?
5. **Drawing Conclusions** Which type of bird is the best pollinator for long, narrow flowers?
6. **Evaluating and Revising** How does this model represent coevolution? How could you improve this model?

Go Further

Using Models Construct an alternative model of coevolution between flowering plants and birds that feed on their nectar. Then, compare your model to the one you used in this lab. Analyze the strengths and weaknesses of each model.

Chapter 17 Study Guide

17–1 The Fossil Record

Key Concepts

- The fossil record provides evidence about the history of life on Earth. It also shows how different groups of organisms, including species, have changed over time.
- Relative dating allows paleontologists to estimate a fossil's age compared with that of other fossils.
- In radioactive dating, scientists calculate the age of a sample based on the amount of remaining radioactive isotopes it contains.
- After Precambrian Time, the basic divisions of the geologic time scale are eras and periods.

Vocabulary

paleontologist, p. 417
fossil record, p. 417
extinct, p. 417
relative dating, p. 419
index fossil, p. 419
half-life, p. 420
radioactive dating, p. 420
geologic time scale, p. 421
era, p. 421
period, p. 422

17–2 Earth's Early History

Key Concepts

- Earth's early atmosphere probably contained hydrogen cyanide, carbon dioxide, carbon monoxide, nitrogen, hydrogen sulfide, and water.
- Miller and Urey's experiments suggested how mixtures of the organic compounds necessary for life could have arisen from simpler compounds present on a primitive Earth.
- The rise of oxygen in the atmosphere drove some life forms to extinction, while other life forms evolved new, more efficient metabolic pathways that used oxygen for respiration.
- The endosymbiotic theory proposes that eukaryotic cells arose from living communities formed by prokaryotic organisms.

Vocabulary

proteinoid microsphere, p. 425
microfossil, p. 426
endosymbiotic theory, p. 427

17–3 Evolution of Multicellular Life

Key Concepts

- Rich fossil evidence shows that early in the Paleozoic Era, there was a diversity of marine life.
- During the Devonian, vertebrates began to invade the land.
- The mass extinction at the end of the Paleozoic affected both plants and animals on land and in the seas. As much as 95 percent of the complex life in the oceans disappeared.
- Events during the Mesozoic include the increasing dominance of dinosaurs. The Mesozoic is marked by the appearance of flowering plants.
- During the Cenozoic, mammals evolved adaptations that allowed them to live in various environments—on land, in water, and even in the air.

Vocabulary

mass extinction, p. 431

17–4 Patterns of Evolution

Key Concept

- Six important topics in macroevolution are extinctions, adaptive radiation, convergent evolution, coevolution, punctuated equilibrium, and changes in developmental genes.

Vocabulary

macroevolution, p. 435
adaptive radiation, p. 436
convergent evolution, p. 437
coevolution, p. 437
punctuated equilibrium, p. 439

Thinking Visually

Use information from the chapter to create a flowchart that illustrates how natural selection can lead to the extinction of a species.

Preparing for the Living Environment Exam

Blue questions emphasize Regents Exam content

Chapter 17

Part A

Multiple Choice

For each statement or question, select the number of the word or expression that, of those given, best completes the statement or answers the question.

1 Radioactive dating of rock samples
(1) is a method of absolute dating
(2) is a method of relative dating
(3) provides no information about the age in years of the rock samples
(4) relies on the use of index fossils

2 Half-life is the length of time required for half the atoms in a radioactive sample to
(1) decay (3) double
(2) expand (4) be created

3 Earth's first atmosphere contained little or no
(1) oxygen (3) hydrogen sulfide
(2) nitrogen (4) hydrogen cyanide

4 In Miller and Urey's experiment, electric sparks were passed through a mixture of gases to
(1) increase temperature
(2) simulate sunlight
(3) sterilize the gases
(4) simulate lightning

5 Evolution is the study of the
(1) development of fish from mammals
(2) change from simpler to more complex forms of life
(3) development of modern transportation
(4) energy flow in food webs

6 Throughout the history of life on Earth, which factor has probably been the chief cause of the extinction of species?
(1) human interference with the natural environment
(2) failure to adapt to environmental change
(3) competition within species
(4) volcanic eruptions

7 Outlines of ancient cells that are preserved well enough to identify them as prokaryotes are
(1) microfossils
(2) endosymbiotic organisms
(3) aerobic bacteria
(4) photosynthethic bacteria

8 Which event occurred at the end of the Paleozoic Era?
(1) first appearance of flowering plants
(2) mass extinction of many types of organisms
(3) evolution of dinosaurs
(4) extinction of mammals

9 The process that produces a similar appearance among unrelated groups of organisms is
(1) adaptive radiation
(2) convergent evolution
(3) coevolution
(4) changes in hox genes

10 Evolution is often represented with a tree diagram like the one below.

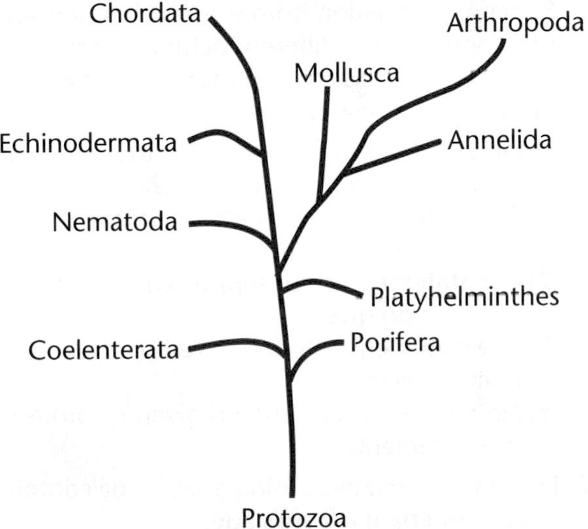

The diagram suggests that different groups of organisms, such as Nematoda and Mollusca, have similar characteristics because they
(1) share a common ancestor
(2) evolved at the same time
(3) share the same environment
(4) evolved at the same rate

Test-Taking Tip If you find particular questions difficult, put a light mark beside them and keep working. (Do not write in this book.) As you answer later questions, you may find information that helps you find the answers you still need.

Preparing for the Living Environment Exam

Part B

Multiple Choice and Extended Response

For those questions that ask you to select a response, choose the one that best completes the statement or answers the question. For all others follow the directions given.

11 The Galápagos Islands in the Pacific Ocean were probably never connected to South America. However, in the various habitats on the islands, there are about 14 species of finches that appear to be related to the finches on the South American mainland. Although the Galápagos finches vary in beak structure, there is a close resemblance among them in plumage, calls, nests, and eggs. These species do not interbreed or compete for food.

Statement: Isolation from the South American mainland and the different habitats on the Galápagos Islands are important factors in the production of new species.

What is the relationship between the statement and the information given above?

(1) The statement is supported by the information given.
(2) The statement is not supported by the information given.
(3) The statement is contradicted by the information given.
(4) No relevant information is given regarding the statement.

12 Explain how relative dating enables paleontologists to estimate a fossil's age.

13 Geologic changes often accompany mass extinctions of life forms. Explain why this is true.

14 Explain how proteinoid microspheres are like living cells.

15 Evolutionary biologists say that there is good reason for gaps in the fossil record. Explain why some extinct animals and plants were probably never fossilized.

16 State one connection between sexual reproduction and evolution.

17 Explain the process of adaptive radiation, and give an example of the process.

18 Explain the pattern known as punctuated equilibrium.

Base your answers to questions 19 and 20 on the graph below and on your knowledge of biology.

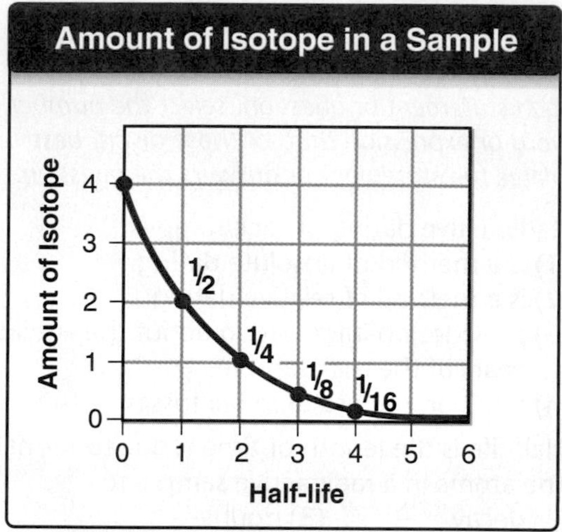

19 The half-life of thorium-230 is 75,000 years. How long will it take for $\frac{7}{8}$ of the original amount of thorium-230 in a sample to decay?

(1) 25,000 years
(2) 70,000 years
(3) 75,000 years
(4) 225,000 years

20 The half-life of potassium-40 is about 1300 million years. The age of a fossil that contains only one half of its original potassium-40 is about

(1) 1300 million years
(2) 2600 million years
(3) 650 million years
(4) 32.5 million years

Base your answers to questions 21 through 22 on the passage below and on your knowledge of biology.

Biologist Lynn Margulis championed the endosymbiotic theory, which states that the first eukaryotes formed as the result of symbiosis, or interdependence, among several prokaryotes. According to the theory, some prokaryotes lived inside of bacteria and algae as endosymbionts, using the bacteria and algae as hosts. Eventually, the hosts and the endosymbionts formed such an effective team that the endosymbionts lost the ability to survive on their own. In this way, they evolved into the organelles of eukaryotic cells. In support of the theory, Margulis noted that some of the organelles of eukaryotic cells are similar in structure to prokaryotes. For example, mitochondria closely resemble bacteria, chloroplasts closely resemble blue-green algae, and the flagella of many eukaryotic cells are very similar to a group of bacteria known as spirochetes. In addition, both mitochondria and chloroplasts contain DNA.

21 The endosymbiotic theory includes all of the following *except*
(1) photosynthetic prokaryotes evolved into chloroplasts
(2) eukaryotic cells arose from the merging of different prokaryotic organisms
(3) all organelles evolved from specialized enfoldings of the plasma membrane
(4) eukaryotic cells are the result of an interdependent relationship among different organisms

22 The passage states that some prokaryotes lived inside bacteria. Explain how this might have proved valuable to both the bacteria and the prokaryotes.

Base your answers to questions 23 and 24 on the graph below and on your knowledge of biology.

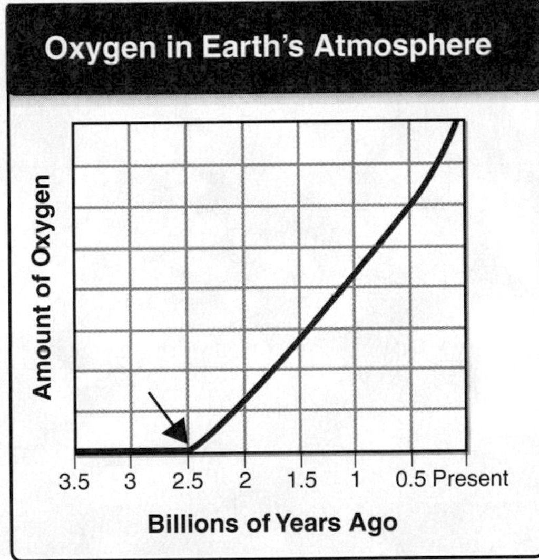

23 The graph shows an approximation of the amount of oxygen in the atmosphere since life began. State what event occurred at the point indicated by the arrow.

24 Explain how the addition of oxygen to Earth's atmosphere affected the evolution of life.

Part C

Extended Response

Answer the questions or follow the directions given.

25 Describe the sequence of events scientists hypothesize to have occurred in the formation of Earth's early atmosphere and oceans. In your description, be sure to include:
- the gases making up the early atmosphere
- the sources of the atmospheric gases
- how the gases changed over time
- the significance of temperature and lightning storms

26 Use the diagram below to explain the significance of Miller and Urey's experiment.

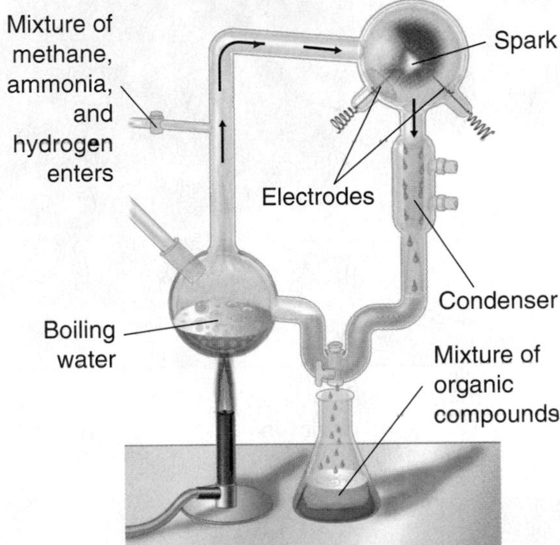

In your explanation be sure to include
- the purpose of the mixture of methane, ammonia, and hydrogen
- the reason boiling water was used
- what the electrodes and spark simulated
- the source of the organic compounds

For: An interactive self-test
Visit: PHSchool.com
Web Code: cba-5170

CHAPTER 18

Classification

Each person might divide these shells into different categories. Scientists often group and name, or classify, organisms using certain guidelines. This makes it easier to discuss the types and characteristics of living things.

Inquiry Activity

How can you classify fruits?

Procedure  

1. Obtain five different fruits. Use a paring knife to cut each fruit open and examine its structure. **CAUTION:** *Use caution with sharp instruments. Do not eat any of the fruit.*
2. Construct a table with five rows and four columns. Label each row with the name of a different fruit.
3. Observe each fruit and choose four characteristics by which you can tell the fruits apart. Label the columns in your table with these four characteristics.
4. Record a description of each fruit in your table.

Think About It

1. **Observing** What characteristics did you use to describe the fruits?
2. **Classifying** Based on your table, which fruits are most closely related? Explain.

18–1 Finding Order in Diversity

1-S1.1 Historical development of ideas in science
LS- Follow safety rules
LS- Make observations
LS- Organize data in tables/graphs

For more than 3.5 billion years, life on Earth has been constantly changing. Natural selection and other processes have led to a staggering diversity of organisms. A tropical rain forest, for example, may support thousands of species per acre. Recall that a species is a population of organisms that share similar characteristics and can breed with one another and produce fertile offspring. Biologists have identified and named about 1.5 million species so far. They estimate that anywhere between 2 and 100 million additional species have yet to be discovered.

Guide for Reading

Key Concepts
- How are living things organized for study?
- What is binomial nomenclature?
- What is Linnaeus's system of classification?

Vocabulary
taxonomy
binomial nomenclature
genus
taxon
family
order
class
phylum
kingdom

Reading Strategy: Building Vocabulary
As you read about the seven categories established by Linnaeus, list those categories in order, starting with the smallest group. Then, create a memory aid to help you remember them.

Why Classify?

To study this great diversity of organisms, biologists must give each organism a name. Biologists must also attempt to organize living things into groups that have biological meaning.  **To study the diversity of life, biologists use a classification system to name organisms and group them in a logical manner.**

In the discipline known as **taxonomy,** scientists classify organisms and assign each organism a universally accepted name. One example appears in **Figure 18–1.** By using a scientific name, biologists can be certain that everyone is discussing the same organism. When taxonomists classify organisms, they organize them into groups that have biological significance. When you hear the word "bird," for example, you immediately form a mental picture of the organism being discussed—a flying animal that has feathers. But science often requires smaller categories as well as larger, more general categories. In a good system of classification, organisms placed into a particular group are more similar to each other than they are to organisms in other groups.

You use classification systems also, for example, when you refer to "teachers" or "mechanics," or more specifically, "biology teachers" or "auto mechanics." Such a process, like scientific classification, uses accepted names and common criteria to group things.

▶ **Figure 18–1** Depending on where you live, you might recognize this as a mountain lion, a puma, a cougar, or a panther—all of which are common names for the same animal. The scientific name for this animal is *Felis concolor.* **To avoid the confusion caused by regional names, biologists use a classification system to group organisms in a logical manner and to assign names.**

Assigning Scientific Names

▲ **Figure 18–2** The problem of naming organisms efficiently continues to challenge biologists as they discover new species. This barking deer was recently discovered near the border of Laos and Vietnam. Its scientific name, which is based on Latin, is *Muntiacus muntjak.* **In binomial nomenclature, each animal is assigned a two-part scientific name.**

By the eighteenth century, European scientists recognized that referring to organisms by common names was confusing. Common names vary among languages and even among regions within a single country. The animal you saw in **Figure 18–1,** for example, can be called a cougar, a puma, a panther, or a mountain lion. Furthermore, different species sometimes share a single common name. In the United Kingdom, the word *buzzard* refers to a hawk, whereas in many parts of the United States, *buzzard* refers to a vulture. To eliminate such confusion, scientists agreed to use a single name for each species. Because eighteenth-century scientists understood Latin and Greek, they used those languages for scientific names. This practice is still followed today in naming newly discovered species, such as the barking deer in **Figure 18–2.**

Early Efforts at Naming Organisms The first attempts at standard scientific names often described the physical characteristics of a species in great detail. As a result, these names could be twenty words long! For example, the English translation of the scientific name of a particular tree might be "Oak with deeply divided leaves that have no hairs on their undersides and no teeth around their edges." This system of naming had another major drawback. It was difficult to standardize the names of organisms because different scientists described different characteristics.

Binomial Nomenclature A major step was taken by Carolus Linnaeus, shown in **Figure 18–3,** a Swedish botanist who lived during the eighteenth century. He developed a two-word naming system called **binomial nomenclature** (by-NOH-mee-ul NOH-mun-klay-chur). This system is still in use today. **In binomial nomenclature, each species is assigned a two-part scientific name.** The scientific name is always written in italics. The first word is capitalized, and the second word is lowercased.

For example, the grizzly bear shown in **Figure 18–4** is called *Ursus arctos.* The first part of the scientific name—in this case, *Ursus*—is the genus to which the organism belongs. A **genus** (JEE-nus; plural: genera, JEN-ur-uh) is a group of closely related species. The genus *Ursus* contains five other kinds of bears, including *Ursus maritimus,* the polar bear.

The second part of a scientific name—in this case, *arctos* or *maritimus*—is unique to each species within the genus. Often, this part of the name is a Latinized description of some important trait of the organism or an indication of where the organism lives. The Latin word *maritimus,* referring to the sea, comes from the fact that polar bears often live on pack ice that floats in the sea.

CHECKPOINT *Do* Ursus arctos *and* Ursus maritimus *belong to the same species? To the same genus?*

For: Links on classification
Visit: www.SciLinks.org
Web Code: cbn-5181

Word Origins

Binomial and *nomenclature* are built from some familiar roots. *Bi-* is Latin for "two." *Nomen-* is Latin for "name." So *binomial nomenclature* means a two-name system of assigning names. **If *pedis* is Latin for "of the foot," how many feet does a *biped* have?**

Linnaeus's System of Classification

Linnaeus's classification system is hierarchical; that is, it consists of levels. **Linnaeus's hierarchical system of classification includes seven levels. They are—from smallest to largest—species, genus, family, order, class, phylum, and kingdom.** In taxonomic nomenclature, or naming system, each of those levels is called a **taxon** (plural: taxa), or taxonomic category.

The two smallest categories, genus and species, were discussed in the example of the bears. The giant panda, shown in **Figure 18–4,** resembles the grizzly bear and the polar bear. However, it differs enough from them and other species in the genus *Ursus* that it is placed in its own genus, *Ailuropoda*.

Genera that share many characteristics, such as *Ursus* and *Ailuropoda,* are grouped in a larger category, the **family**—in this case, Ursidae. These bears, together with six other families of animals, such as dogs (Canidae) and cats (Felidae), are grouped together in the order Carnivora. An **order** is a broad taxonomic category composed of similar families. The next larger category, the **class,** is composed of similar orders. For example, order Carnivora is placed in the class Mammalia, which includes animals that are warm-blooded, have body hair, and produce milk for their young.

Several different classes make up a **phylum** (FY-lum; plural: phyla). A phylum includes many different organisms that nevertheless share important characteristics. The class Mammalia is grouped with birds (class Aves), reptiles (class Reptilia), amphibians (class Amphibia), and all classes of fishes into the phylum Chordata. All these organisms share important features of their body plan and internal functions. Finally, all animals are placed in the kingdom Animalia. The **kingdom** is the largest and most inclusive of Linnaeus's taxonomic categories. Linnaeus named two kingdoms, Animalia and Plantae. You can see the seven taxonomic levels in **Figure 18–5** on the next page.

▲ **Figure 18–3** Carolus Linnaeus (1707–1778) brought order to the process of naming species and classifying them into groups. **Evaluating** *Why do biologists consider Linnaeus's system an improvement over earlier systems?*

Figure 18–4 The grizzly bear, *Ursus arctos,* and the polar bear, *Ursus maritimus,* are classified as different species in the same genus, *Ursus.* The giant panda is placed in a separate genus. **Inferring** *What do the scientific names of the polar and grizzly bears tell you about their similarity to each other?*

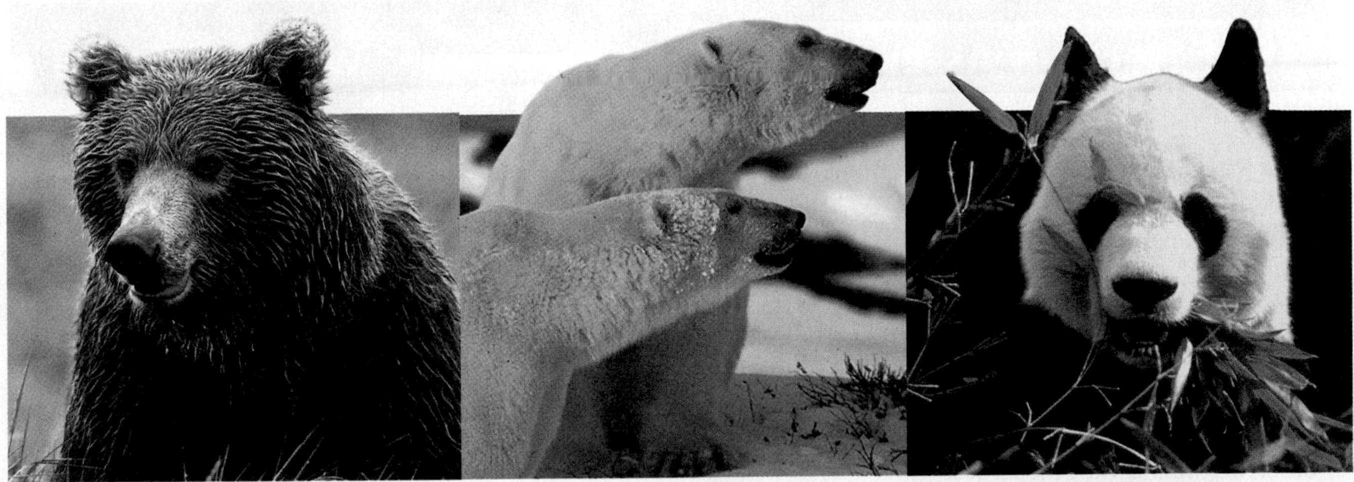

Grizzly Bear *Ursus arctos*

Polar Bear *Ursus maritimus*

Giant Panda *Ailuropoda melanoleuca*

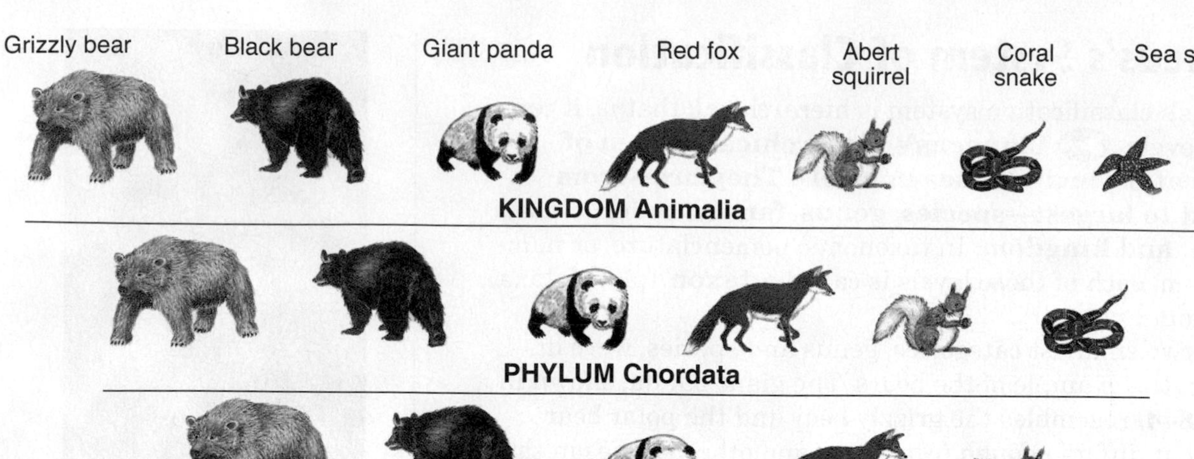

▶ **Figure 18–5 Linnaeus's hierarchical system of classification uses seven taxonomic categories.** This illustration shows how a grizzly bear, *Ursus arctos,* is grouped within each taxonomic category. Only some representative species are illustrated for each category above the species level.

18–1 Section Assessment

1. **Key Concept** How are living things organized for study?
2. **Key Concept** Describe the system for naming species that Linnaeus developed.
3. **Key Concept** What are the seven taxonomic categories of Linnaeus's classification system? Rank these taxa in hierarchical order, beginning with the largest level and ending with the smallest.
4. Why do scientists avoid using common names when discussing organisms?
5. What is binomial nomenclature?
6. **Critical Thinking Applying Concepts** Look at **Figure 18–5** above. Are foxes more closely related to sea stars or to snakes? Explain.

Writing in Science

Explanatory Paragraph

Think of a classification system that you use in everyday life, and then write a paragraph explaining how the classification system organizes objects or other things. *Hint:* Before you write, make a diagram that shows the organization of the classification system.

18–2 Modern Evolutionary Classification

4-3.1 Natural selection and evolution
4-3.1 Evolutionary changes
LS- Make observations and analyze results

In a sense, organisms determine who belongs to their species by choosing with whom they will mate! Taxonomic groups above the level of species are "invented" by researchers who decide how to distinguish between one genus, family, or phylum, and another. Linnaeus and other taxonomists have always tried to group organisms according to biologically important characteristics. Like any taxonomic system, however, Linnaeus's system had limitations and problems.

Guide for Reading

Key Concepts
- How are evolutionary relationships important in classification?
- How can DNA and RNA help scientists determine evolutionary relationships?

Vocabulary
phylogeny
evolutionary classification
derived character
cladogram
molecular clock

Reading Strategy: Predicting Before you read, preview **Figure 18–7.** Predict how the field of taxonomy has changed since Linnaeus's time. As you read, note whether or not your prediction was correct.

Which Similarities Are Most Important?

Linnaeus grouped species into larger taxa, such as genus and family, mainly according to visible similarities and differences. But which similarities and differences are most important? If you lived in Linneaus's time, for example, how would you have classified dolphins? Would you have called them fishes because they live in water and have finlike limbs? Or would you call them mammals because they breathe air and feed their young with milk? How about the animals shown in **Figure 18–6**? Adult barnacles and limpets live attached to rocks and have similarly shaped shells with holes in the center. Crabs, on the other hand, have body shapes unlike those of barnacles or limpets. Based on these features, would you place limpets and barnacles together, and crabs in a different group?

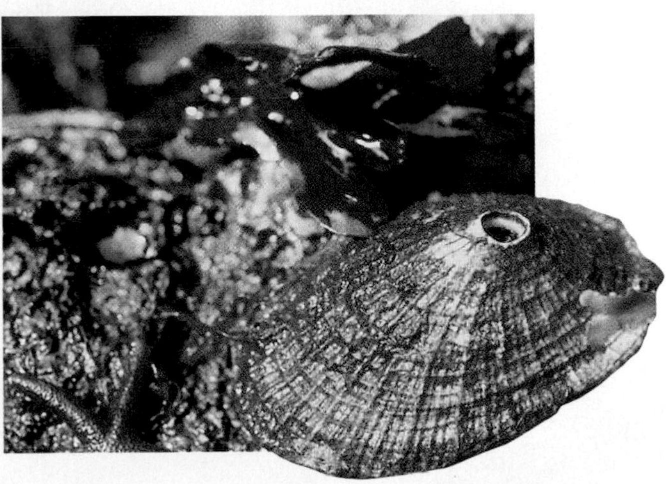

Figure 18–6 Classifying species based on easily observed adult traits can pose problems. Observe the crab (top left), barnacles (bottom left), and limpet (right). Which seem most alike? **Asking Questions** *What additional information might you gather to help inform your decision?*

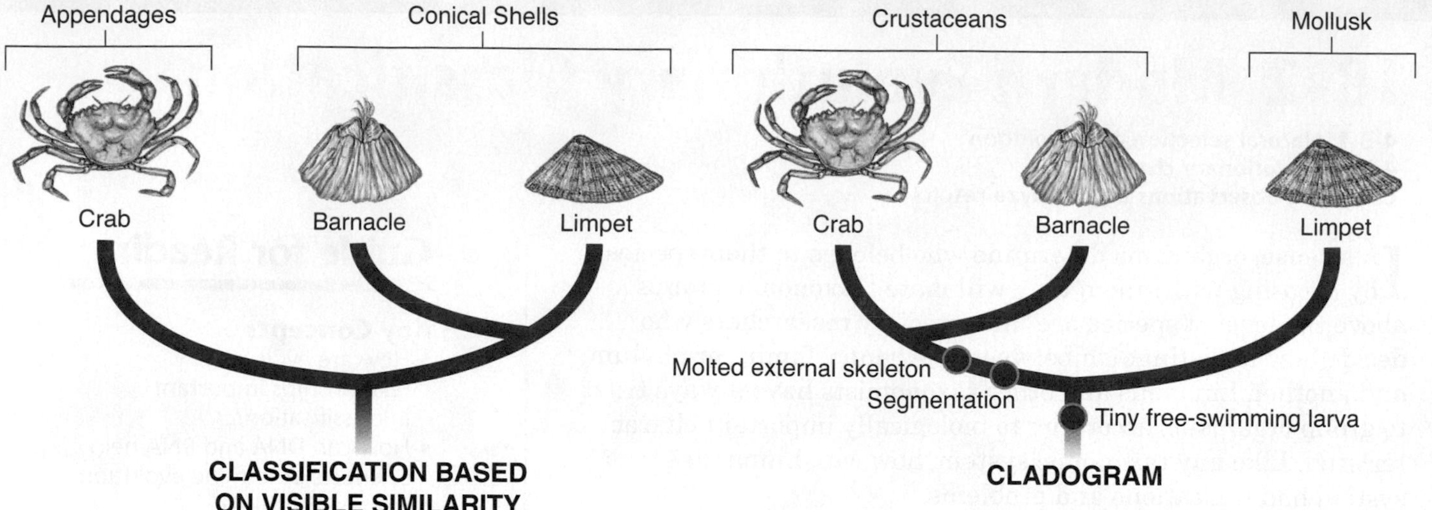

Figure 18–7 Early systems of classification grouped organisms together based on visible similarities. That approach might result in classifying limpets and barnacles together (left). **Biologists now group organisms into categories that represent lines of evolutionary descent, or phylogeny, not just physical similarities.** Crabs and barnacles are now grouped together (right) because they share several characteristics that indicate that they are more closely related to each other than either is to limpets. These characteristics include segmented bodies, jointed limbs, and an external skeleton that is shed during growth.

Evolutionary Classification

Darwin's ideas about descent with modification have given rise to the study of **phylogeny,** or evolutionary relationships among organisms. **Biologists now group organisms into categories that represent lines of evolutionary descent, or phylogeny, not just physical similarities.** The strategy of grouping organisms together based on their evolutionary history is called **evolutionary classification.**

Species within a genus are more closely related to each another than to species in another genus. According to evolutionary classification, that is because all members of a genus share a recent common ancestor. Similarly, all genera in a family share a common ancestor. This ancestor is further in the past than the ancestor of any genus in the family but more recent than the ancestor of the entire order. The higher the level of the taxon, the farther back in time is the common ancestor of all the organisms in the taxon.

Organisms that appear very similar may not share a recent common ancestor. Natural selection, operating on species in similar ecological environments, has often caused convergent evolution. For example, superficial similarities once led barnacles and limpets to be grouped together, as shown on the left in **Figure 18–7.**

However, barnacles and limpets are different in important ways. For example, their free-swimming larvae, or immature forms, are unlike one another. Certain adult characteristics are different too. Adult barnacles have jointed limbs and a body divided into segments. Barnacles periodically shed, or molt, their external skeleton. These characteristics make barnacles more similar to crabs than to limpets. Limpets, in turn, have an internal anatomy that is closer to that of snails, which are mollusks. And like mollusks, limpets do not shed their shells. Because of such characteristics, taxonomists infer that barnacles are more closely related to crabs than to mollusks. In other words, barnacles and crabs share an evolutionary ancestor that is more recent than the ancestor that barnacles share with limpets. Thus, both barnacles and crabs are classified as crustaceans, and limpets are mollusks.

Classification Using Cladograms

To refine the process of evolutionary classification, many biologists now prefer a method called cladistic analysis. Cladistic analysis identifies and considers only those characteristics of organisms that are evolutionary innovations—new characteristics that arise as lineages evolve over time. Characteristics that appear in recent parts of a lineage but not in its older members are called **derived characters.**

Derived characters can be used to construct a **cladogram,** a diagram that shows the evolutionary relationships among a group of organisms. You can see an example of a cladogram on the right-hand side of **Figure 18–7.** Notice how derived characters, such as "free-swimming larva" and "segmentation," appear at certain locations along the branches of the cladogram. These locations are the points at which these characteristics first arose. You can see that crabs and barnacles share some derived characters that barnacles and limpets do not. One such shared derived character is a segmented body. Another is a molted external skeleton. Thus, this cladogram groups crabs and barnacles together as crustaceans and separates them from limpets, which are classified as a type of mollusk.

Cladograms are useful tools that help scientists understand how one lineage branched from another in the course of evolution. Just as a family tree shows the relationships among different lineages within a family, a cladogram represents a type of evolutionary tree, showing evolutionary relationships among a group of organisms.

What is a cladogram?

Quick Lab

How is a cladogram constructed?

Procedure

1. Identify the organism in the table that is least closely related to the others.
2. Use the information in the table to construct a cladogram of these animals.

Derived Characters in Organisms

Organism	Derived Character		
	Backbone	Legs	Hair
Earthworm	Absent	Absent	Absent
Trout	Present	Absent	Absent
Lizard	Present	Present	Absent
Human	Present	Present	Present

Analyze and Conclude

1. **Using Tables and Graphs** What trait separates the least closely related organism from the other animals?
2. **Classifying** List the animals in your cladogram in order of distance from the least closely related organism.
3. **Drawing Conclusions** Does your cladogram indicate that lizards and humans share a more recent common ancestor than either does with an earthworm? Explain.
4. **Inferring** Where would you insert a frog if you added it to the cladogram? Explain your answer.

▲ **Figure 18–8** **Similarities at the DNA level in the genes of organisms can be used to help determine classification.** Traditionally, African vultures (top) and American vultures (center) were classified together in the falcon family. But DNA analysis has revealed that American vultures are actually more closely related to storks (bottom).

Similarities in DNA and RNA

All of the classification methods discussed so far are based primarily on physical similarities and differences. But even organisms with very different anatomies have common traits. For example, all organisms use DNA and RNA to pass on information and to control growth and development. Hidden in the genetic code of all organisms are remarkably similar genes. Because DNA and RNA are so similar across all forms of life, these molecules provide an excellent way of comparing organisms at their most basic level—their genes.

The genes of many organisms show important similarities at the molecular level. Similarities in DNA can be used to help determine classification and evolutionary relationships. Now that scientists can sequence, or "read," the information coded in DNA, they can compare the DNA of different organisms to trace the history of genes over millions of years.

Similar Genes Even the genes of diverse organisms such as humans and yeasts show many surprising similarities. For example, humans have a gene that codes for myosin, a protein found in our muscles. Researchers have found a gene in yeast that codes for a myosin protein. As it turns out, myosin in yeast helps enable internal cell parts to move. Myosin is just one example of similarities at the molecular level—an indicator that humans and yeasts share a common ancestry.

DNA Evidence DNA evidence can also help show the evolutionary relationships of species and how species have changed. The more similar the DNA sequences of two species, the more recently they shared a common ancestor, and the more closely they are related in evolutionary terms. And the more two species have diverged from one another, or changed in comparison to one another during evolution, the less similar their DNA will be.

Consider the birds in **Figure 18–8.** The bird in the top photograph looks a lot like the bird in the middle photograph. Both birds have traditionally been classified together as "vultures." One group of birds inhabits Africa and Asia, and the other, the Americas. But American vultures have a peculiar behavior: When they get overheated, they urinate on their legs, and evaporative cooling removes some body heat. The only other birds known to behave this way are storks, which look quite different and have always been put in a separate family. Does this similarity in behavior indicate a close evolutionary relationship?

Scientists analyzed the DNA of these three birds. The analysis showed that the DNA sequences of the American vulture and the stork were more similar than those of the American vulture and the African vulture. This similarity in DNA sequences indicates that the American vulture and the stork share a more recent common ancestor than do the American vulture and the African vulture. Therefore, the American vulture is more closely related to storks than to other vultures.

Molecular Clocks

Comparisons of DNA can also be used to mark the passage of evolutionary time. A model known as a **molecular clock** uses DNA comparisons to estimate the length of time that two species have been evolving independently. To understand molecular clocks, think about a pendulum clock. It marks time with a periodically swinging pendulum. A molecular clock also relies on a repeating process to mark time—mutation.

Simple mutations occur all the time, causing slight changes in the structure of DNA, as shown in **Figure 18–9.** Some mutations have a major positive or negative effect on an organism's phenotype. These mutations are under powerful pressure from natural selection. Other mutations have no effects on phenotype. These neutral mutations accumulate in the DNA of different species at about the same rate. A comparison of such DNA sequences in two species can reveal how dissimilar the genes are. The degree of dissimilarity is, in turn, an indication of how long ago the two species shared a common ancestor.

The use of molecular clocks is not simple, however, because there is not just one molecular clock in a genome. Instead, there are many, each of which "ticks" at a different rate. This is because some genes accumulate mutations faster than others. These different clocks allow researchers to time different kinds of evolutionary events. Think of a conventional clock. If you want to time a brief event, you pay attention to the second hand. To time an event that lasts longer, you use the minute hand or the hour hand. In the same way, researchers would use a different molecular clock to compare modern bird species than they would to estimate the age of the common ancestor of yeasts and humans.

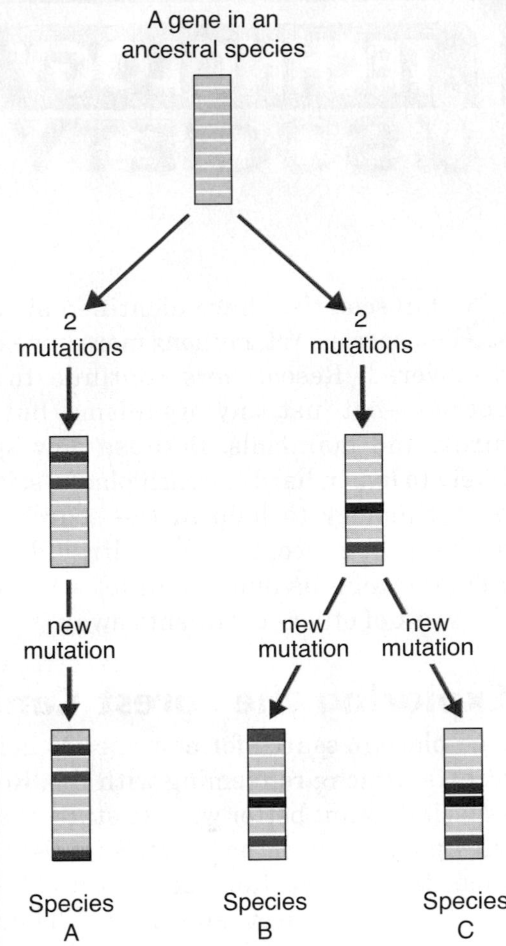

▲ **Figure 18–9** By comparing the DNA sequences of two or more species, biologists estimate how long the species have been separated. **Analyzing Data** ***What evidence indicates that species C is more closely related to species B than to species A?***

18–2 Section Assessment

1. **Key Concept** How is information about evolutionary, or phylogenetic, relationships useful in classification?
2. **Key Concept** How are genes used to help scientists classify organisms?
3. What is the principle behind cladistic analysis?
4. What gene indicates that yeasts and humans share a common ancestor?
5. Describe the relationship between evolutionary time and the similarity of genes in two species.
6. **Critical Thinking Inferring** Would a barnacle's DNA be more similar to the DNA of a crab or that of a limpet? Explain.

Thinking Visually

Constructing a Chart
Draw a cladogram of a manufactured item, such as an automobile or a household item, that has changed over the years. Label derived characters that appeared as new models arose. For example, automobiles came to have electronic fuel injection and antilock brakes.

TECHNOLOGY & SOCIETY

The Search for New Species in Tropical Forests

So far, scientists have identified about 1.5 million species. Yet, millions more have never been discovered. Researchers continue to find new species—not just tiny organisms, but also fish, birds, and mammals. Because new species are likely to live in hard-to-reach places, scientists call on technology to help in the search, including scuba gear, helicopters, and ultralight airplanes. Remote cameras and e-mail let scientists follow the work of others continents away.

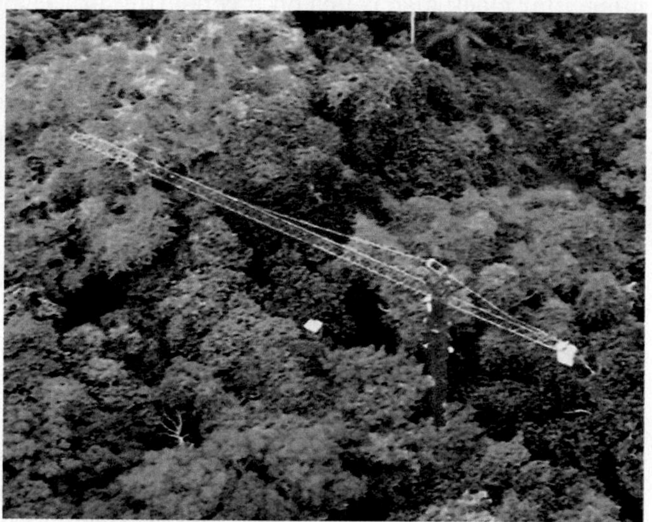

Exploring the Forest Canopy

One place to search for new species is in tropical forests, which are teeming with life. Researchers especially want better ways to study the canopy—the upper layers of the forest. Scientists have used ropes to climb the tall trees, but it is hard to stay up long or collect specimens. Then, French researchers invented an unusual "raft" suspended from a hot-air balloon that floats over the tops of the trees. Scientists on the raft could work together for longer periods of time, collecting many more species.

One canopy explorer, biologist Margaret Lowman, worked with a structural engineer to design and build a canopy walkway as her "green laboratory." The walkway looks like a huge treehouse 75 feet above the forest floor, with platforms on which researchers can work. Another new and dramatic route into the canopy is a huge construction crane like those used in building skyscrapers. Scientists on the arm of the crane get a close-up look at trees. Today there is a worldwide network of forest sites.

New Species or Not?

When researchers spot an unfamiliar organism, they may use simple observation to classify it. How many petals are on the flower? How many toes are on the animal? If the organism does not match known categories, the species may be new. Unusual antlers, for instance, were a major clue in identifying a new deer species in Vietnam.

External appearances can fool you, however. X-rays and electron microscopes may reveal differences that set one species apart from another. The most exciting advances have come with studies of DNA. By analyzing DNA, scientists can demonstrate how two organisms are—or are not—related.

Research and Decide

Use library or Internet resources to learn more about the search for new species. Then, describe and sketch your own ideas for an invention that would help scientists search in a forest canopy or other location that is hard to reach.

For: Links from the authors
Visit: PHSchool.com
Web Code: cbe-5182

18–3 Kingdoms and Domains

4-3.1 Evolutionary changes

As in all areas of science, systems of classification adapt to new discoveries. Ideas and models change as new information arises. Some explanations have been discarded altogether, whereas others, such as Darwin's theory of evolution by natural selection, have been upheld and refined through years of research. So, it should not be surprising that early attempts at drawing life's universal tree were based on some misguided assumptions. Some of the earliest trees of life were dominated by humans. These models represented vertebrates as the most important and abundant animals. They also implied that "higher" animals evolved from "lower" animals that were identical to modern forms. Biologists now know these notions are incorrect.

Guide for Reading

Key Concepts

- What are the six kingdoms of life as they are now identified?
- What is the three-domain system of classification?

Vocabulary

domain
Bacteria
Eubacteria
Archaea
Archaebacteria
Eukarya
Protista
Fungi
Plantae
Animalia

Reading Strategy: Classifying As you read, write the names of the six kingdoms recognized by biologists. Label each group as either prokaryotes or eukaryotes.

The Tree of Life Evolves

The scientific view of life was simpler in Linnaeus's time. The only known differences among living things were the fundamental traits that separated animals from plants. Animals were mobile organisms that used food for energy. Plants were green, photosynthetic organisms that used energy from the sun.

Five Kingdoms As biologists learned more about the natural world, they realized that Linnaeus's two kingdoms, Animalia and Plantae, did not adequately represent the full diversity of life. First, microorganisms, such as the protist and bacterium in **Figure 18–10,** were recognized as being significantly different from plants and animals. Scientists soon agreed that microorganisms merited their own kingdom, which was named Protista. Then, the mushrooms, yeasts, and molds were placed in their own kingdom, Fungi. Later still, scientists realized that bacteria lack the nuclei, mitochondria, and chloroplasts found in other forms of life. Therefore, they were placed in another new kingdom, Monera. This process produced five kingdoms—Monera, Protista, Fungi, Plantae, and Animalia.

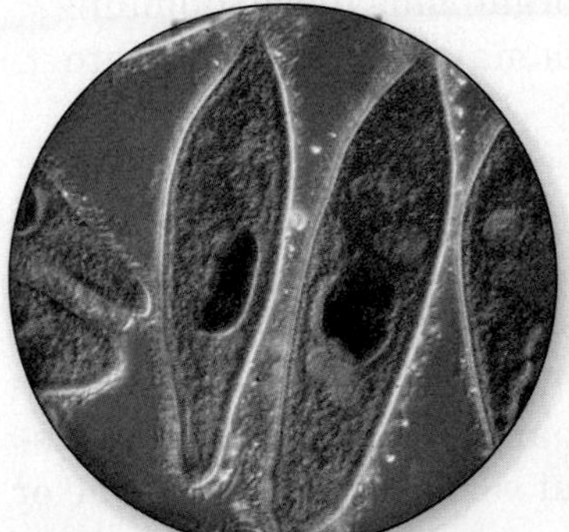

Paramecium caudatum
(magnification: about 1000×)

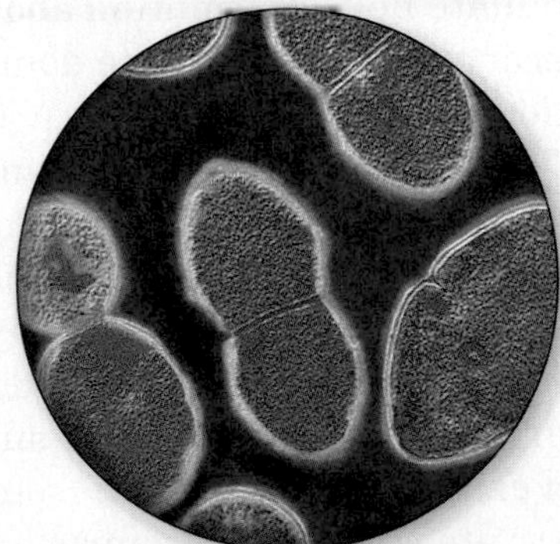

Streptococcus faecalis
(magnification: 26,000×)

Figure 18–10 The paramecium (left) is a single-celled organism that is eukaryotic, or has a nucleus. *Streptococcus faecalis* (right) is a bacterium that evolved long before eukaryotic cells. Bacteria are prokaryotes—they do not have nuclei. The classification of these two organisms has changed greatly over the years. **Classifying** *List reasons that these two organisms should be classified in separate kingdoms.*

<table>
<tr><th colspan="7">Changing Number of Kingdoms</th></tr>
<tr><th>First Introduced</th><th colspan="6">Names of Kingdoms</th></tr>
<tr><td>1700s</td><td colspan="5">Plantae</td><td>Animalia</td></tr>
<tr><td>Late 1800s</td><td colspan="3">Protista</td><td colspan="2">Plantae</td><td>Animalia</td></tr>
<tr><td>1950s</td><td colspan="2">Monera</td><td>Protista</td><td>Fungi</td><td>Plantae</td><td>Animalia</td></tr>
<tr><td>1990s</td><td>Eubacteria</td><td>Archaebacteria</td><td>Protista</td><td>Fungi</td><td>Plantae</td><td>Animalia</td></tr>
</table>

▲ **Figure 18–11** This diagram shows some of the ways organisms have been classified into kingdoms over the years. **The six-kingdom system includes the following kingdoms: Eubacteria, Archaebacteria, Protista, Fungi, Plantae, and Animalia.**

Six Kingdoms In recent years, as evidence about microorganisms continued to accumulate, biologists came to recognize that the Monera were composed of two distinct groups. Some biologists consider the differences between these two groups to be as great as those between animals and plants. As a result, the Monera have been separated into two kingdoms, Eubacteria and Archaebacteria, bringing the total number of kingdoms to six.

The six-kingdom system of classification includes the kingdoms Eubacteria, Archaebacteria, Protista, Fungi, Plantae, and Animalia. This system of classification is shown in the bottom row of **Figure 18–11.**

The Three-Domain System

Some of the most recent evolutionary trees have been produced using comparative studies of a small subunit of ribosomal RNA that occurs in all living things. Using a molecular clock model, scientists have grouped modern organisms according to how long they have been evolving independently.

Molecular analyses have given rise to a new taxonomic category that is now recognized by many scientists. The **domain** is a more inclusive category than any other—larger than a kingdom. **The three domains are the domain Eukarya, which is composed of protists, fungi, plants, and animals; the domain Bacteria, which corresponds to the kingdom Eubacteria; and the domain Archaea, which corresponds to the kingdom Archaebacteria.** As scientists continue to accumulate new information about organisms in the domains Bacteria and Archaea, these domains may be subdivided into additional kingdoms.

Clearly, modern classification is a rapidly changing science, and we must pick a convention to classify life's diversity for the purposes of this book. In this book, we recognize the three domains and also refer frequently to the six kingdoms. The relationship between the three domains and the six kingdoms is shown in **Figure 18–12.** It also summarizes the key characteristics of each kingdom. You can see that some groups share one or more traits with other groups.

For: Link on domains of life
Visit: www.SciLinks.org
Web Code: cbn-5183

What are the three domains?

Domain Bacteria

The members of the domain **Bacteria** are unicellular and prokaryotic. Their cells have thick, rigid cell walls that surround a cell membrane. The cell walls contain a substance known as peptidoglycan. The domain Bacteria corresponds to the kingdom **Eubacteria.** These bacteria are ecologically diverse, ranging from free-living soil organisms to deadly parasites. Some photosynthesize, while others do not. Some need oxygen to survive, while others are killed by oxygen.

Domain Archaea

Also unicellular and prokaryotic, members of the domain **Archaea** live in some of the most extreme environments you can imagine—volcanic hot springs, brine pools, and black organic mud totally devoid of oxygen. Indeed, many of these bacteria can survive only in the absence of oxygen. Their cell walls lack peptidoglycan, and their cell membranes contain unusual lipids that are not found in any other organism. The domain Archaea corresponds to the kingdom **Archaebacteria.**

CHECKPOINT ***What characteristics distinguish members of the domain Bacteria from members of the domain Archaea?***

▼ **Figure 18–12 Organisms are grouped in three domains. There is a simple relationship between the three domains and the six kingdoms.** This table summarizes key evidence used in classifying organisms into these major taxonomic groups.

Classification of Living Things

DOMAIN	Bacteria	Archaea	Eukarya			
KINGDOM	Eubacteria	Archaebacteria	Protista	Fungi	Plantae	Animalia
CELL TYPE	Prokaryote	Prokaryote	Eukaryote	Eukaryote	Eukaryote	Eukaryote
CELL STRUCTURES	Cell walls with peptidoglycan	Cell walls without peptidoglycan	Cell walls of cellulose in some; some have chloroplasts	Cell walls of chitin	Cell walls of cellulose; chloroplasts	No cell walls or chloroplasts
NUMBER OF CELLS	Unicellular	Unicellular	Most unicellular; some colonial; some multicellular	Most multicellular; some unicellular	Multicellular	Multicellular
MODE OF NUTRITION	Autotroph or heterotroph	Autotroph or heterotroph	Autotroph or heterotroph	Heterotroph	Autotroph	Heterotroph
EXAMPLES	*Streptococcus, Escherichia coli*	Methanogens, halophiles	*Amoeba, Paramecium,* slime molds, giant kelp	Mushrooms, yeasts	Mosses, ferns, flowering plants	Sponges, worms, insects, fishes, mammals

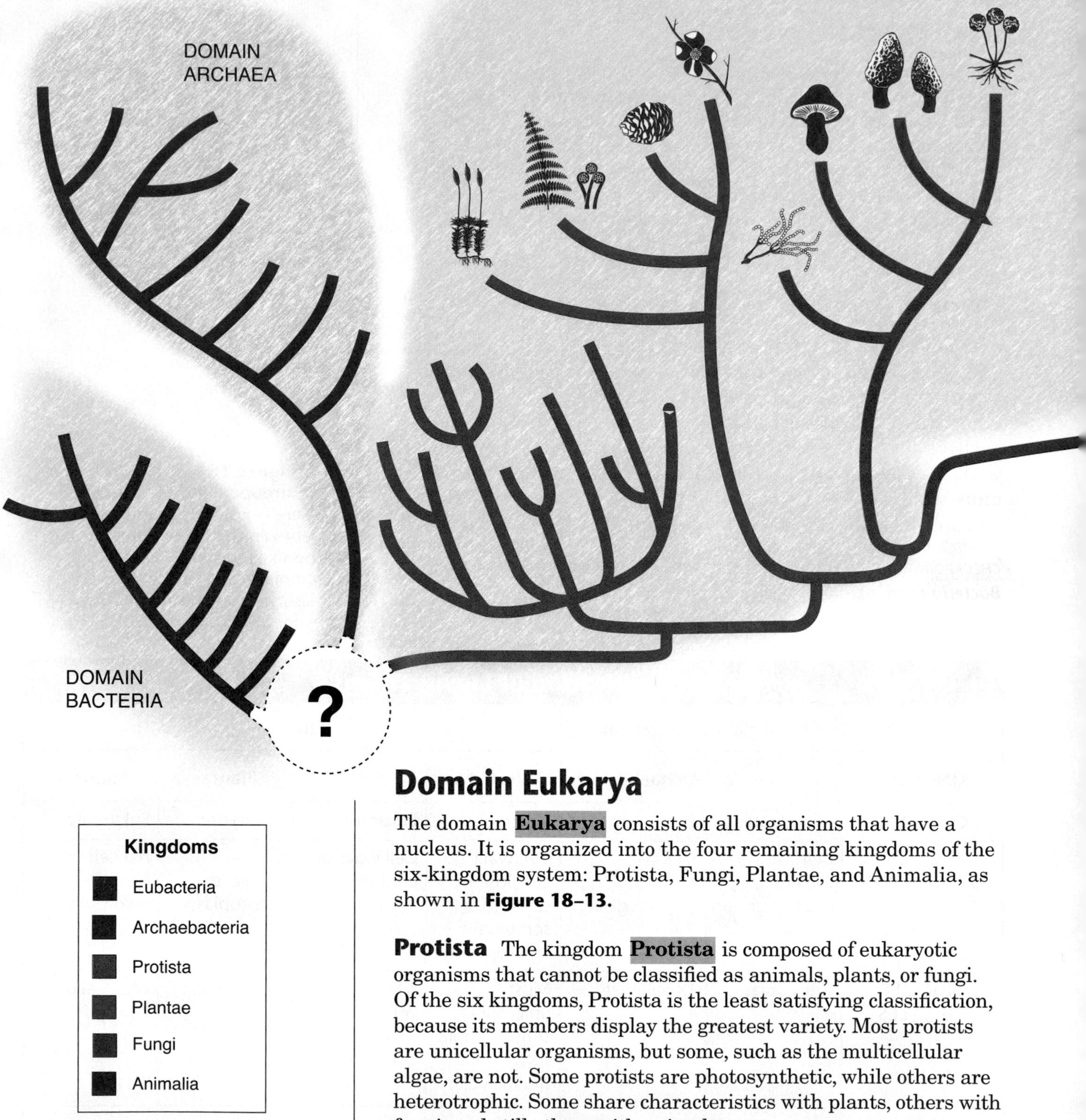

DOMAIN ARCHAEA

DOMAIN BACTERIA

?

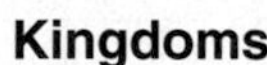

Domain Eukarya

The domain **Eukarya** consists of all organisms that have a nucleus. It is organized into the four remaining kingdoms of the six-kingdom system: Protista, Fungi, Plantae, and Animalia, as shown in **Figure 18–13.**

Protista The kingdom **Protista** is composed of eukaryotic organisms that cannot be classified as animals, plants, or fungi. Of the six kingdoms, Protista is the least satisfying classification, because its members display the greatest variety. Most protists are unicellular organisms, but some, such as the multicellular algae, are not. Some protists are photosynthetic, while others are heterotrophic. Some share characteristics with plants, others with fungi, and still others with animals.

Fungi Members of the kingdom **Fungi** are heterotrophs. Most feed on dead or decaying organic matter. Unlike other heterotrophs, these fungi secrete digestive enzymes into their food source. They then absorb the smaller food molecules into their bodies. The most recognizable fungi, including mushrooms, are multicellular. Some fungi, such as yeasts, are unicellular.

▲ **Figure 18–13** The domains Bacteria and Archaea include the same organisms that are in the kingdoms Eubacteria and Archaebacteria. The domain Eukarya includes the protists, fungi, plants, and animals. Biologists continue to investigate how these three large groups originated. **Interpreting Graphics** ***Which domain includes organisms from more than one kingdom?***

Plantae Members of the kingdom **Plantae** are multicellular organisms that are photosynthetic autotrophs. In other words, they carry out photosynthesis. Plants are nonmotile—they cannot move from place to place. They also have cell walls that contain cellulose. The plant kingdom includes cone-bearing and flowering plants as well as mosses and ferns. Although older classification systems regard multicellular algae as plants, in this book we group algae with the protists.

Animalia Members of the kingdom **Animalia** are multicellular and heterotrophic. The cells of animals do not have cell walls. Most animals can move about, at least for some part of their life cycle. As you will see in later chapters, there is incredible diversity within the animal kingdom, and many species of animals exist in nearly every part of the planet.

18–3 Section Assessment

1. **Key Concept** What are the six kingdoms of life as they are now identified?
2. **Key Concept** What are the three domains of life?
3. Why was the kingdom Monera divided into two separate kingdoms?
4. Why might kingdom Protista be thought of as the "odds and ends" kingdom?
5. How are members of the kingdom Fungi different from members of the kingdom Plantae? How are members of the two kingdoms similar?
6. **Critical Thinking Classifying** Which kingdoms include only prokaryotes? Which kingdoms include only heterotrophs?

Connecting Concepts

Write a Riddle

Review what you learned in Chapter 7 about how the cells of various organisms differ. Then, write a riddle (What kingdom am I?) describing the characteristics of members of a particular kingdom. Exchange your riddle with a classmate, and see if you can guess the kingdom being described.

Real-World Lab

Classifying Organisms Using Dichotomous Keys

One tool used to identify unfamiliar organisms is a dichotomous key. A dichotomous key is a series of paired statements that describe physical characteristics of different organisms. In this activity, you will use a dichotomous key to identify tree leaves.

Problem

How are dichotomous keys used and made?

Materials

- 6–8 writing implements or other group of common items

Skills

Observing, Classifying, Forming Operational Definitions

Procedure

Part A: Using a Dichotomous Key

1. To use the dichotomous key for leaves, begin by reading paired statements 1a and 1b. Notice that the statements are opposites.
2. Carefully observe the leaf labeled I on the next page. Decide which statement, 1a or 1b, applies to this leaf. Then, follow the direction at the end of the statement. In other words, because the leaf is a simple leaf, go to statement 4.
3. Continue reading the paired statements and following the direction at the end of the applicable statement until you determine the identity of leaf I.
4. Repeat steps 2 and 3 for leaves II through VII.

Part B: Constructing a Dichotomous Key

5. Examine the group of items your teacher gives you. List some characteristics you could use to classify these items into groups.
6. Using the dichotomous key from Part A as a model, construct a dichotomous key for your group of items. You may wish to use some of the characteristics you listed in step 5 to construct your key. Make sure that each of the paired statements in your key are opposites.
7. Once your dichotomous key is complete, test it with each item and revise your key, if necessary.
8. Exchange keys and items with a classmate. Use your classmate's key to identify his or her items. Then, suggest ways to improve that key.

Dichotomous Key for Leaves

1. Compound or simple leaf
   1a) Compound leaf (leaf divided into leaflets) ....go to step 2
   1b) Simple leaf (leaf not divided into leaflets) ....go to step 4
2. Arrangement of leaflets
   2a) Palmate arrangement of leaflets (leaflets all attached at one central point) ....*Aesculus* (buckeye)
   2b) Pinnate arrangement of leaflets (leaflets attached at several points) ....go to step 3
3. Leaflet shape
   3a) Leaflets taper to pointed tips ....*Carya* (pecan)
   3b) Oval leaflets with rounded tips ....*Robinia* (locust)
4. Arrangement of leaf veins
   4a) Veins branch out from one central point ....go to step 5
   4b) Veins branch off main vein in the middle of the leaf ....go to step 6
5. Overall shape of leaf
   5a) Leaf is heart shaped..........*Cercis* (redbud)
   5b) Leaf is star shaped ....*Liquidambar* (sweet gum)
6. Appearance of leaf edge
   6a) Leaf has toothed (jagged) edge ....*Betula* (birch)
   6b) Leaf has untoothed (smooth) edge ....*Magnolia* (magnolia)

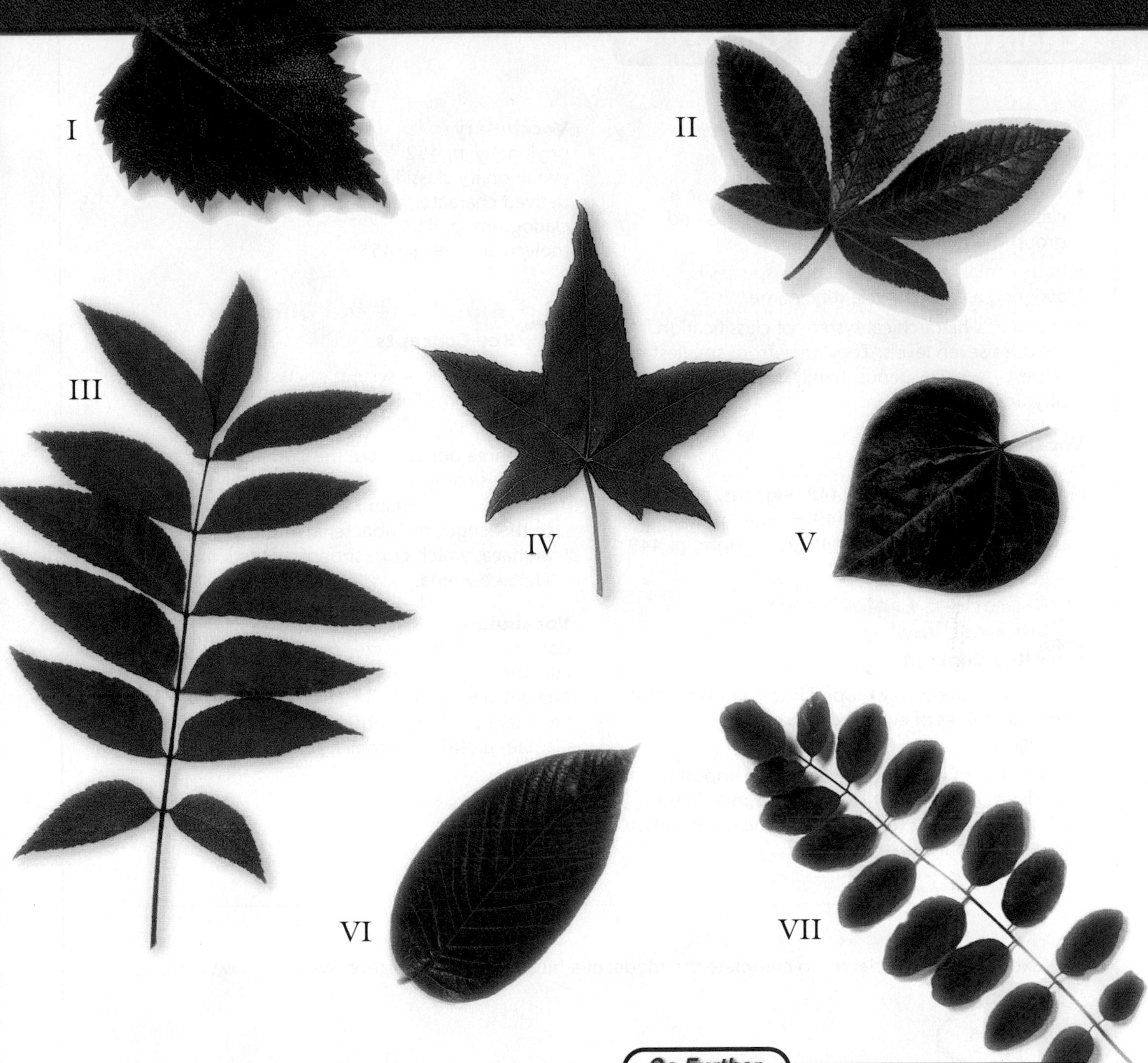

Analyze and Conclude

1. **Classifying** In Part A, identify leaves I through VII.
2. **Applying Concepts** In Part B, how did you choose the characteristics for your key? How did you decide on the key's order?
3. **Evaluating and Revising** Based on your classmate's feedback, does the key you developed in Part B need to be revised? If so, how?
4. **Inferring** Why is it important that the paired statements in a dichotomous key be opposites?

Go Further

Classifying Develop a model of a hierarchical classification system for a group of small objects, such as nuts, bolts, and screws. Your classification should be based on observable similarities and differences. Invent your own taxonomic nomenclature for the levels of your classification system. Then, develop a dichotomous key that someone can use to identify the items in your classification system. Use the dichotomous key in this lab as a model.

Chapter 18 Study Guide

18–1 Finding Order in Diversity

Key Concepts

- To study the diversity of life, biologists use a classification system to name organisms and group them in a logical manner.
- In binomial nomenclature, each species is assigned a two-part scientific name.
- Linnaeus's hierarchical system of classification includes seven levels. They are—from smallest to largest—species, genus, family, order, class, phylum, and kingdom.

Vocabulary
taxonomy, p. 447
binomial nomenclature, p. 448 • genus, p. 448
taxon, p. 449 • family, p. 449 • order, p. 449
class, p. 449 • phylum, p. 449 • kingdom, p. 449

18–2 Modern Evolutionary Classification

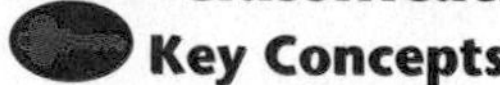

Key Concepts

- Organisms are now grouped into categories that represent lines of evolutionary descent, or phylogeny.
- The genes of many organisms show important similarities at the molecular level. Similarities in DNA can be used to help determine classification and evolutionary relationships.

Vocabulary
phylogeny, p. 452
evolutionary classification, p. 452
derived character, p. 453
cladogram, p. 453
molecular clock, p. 455

18–3 Kingdoms and Domains

Key Concepts

- The six-kingdom system of classification includes the kingdoms Eubacteria, Archaebacteria, Protista, Fungi, Plantae, and Animalia.
- The three domains are the domain Eukarya, which is composed of protists, fungi, plants, and animals; the domain Bacteria, which corresponds to the kingdom Eubacteria; and the domain Archaea, which corresponds to the kingdom Archaebacteria.

Vocabulary
domain, p. 458 • Bacteria, p. 459
Eubacteria, p. 459 • Archaea, p. 459
Archaebacteria, p. 459 • Eukarya, p. 460
Protista, p. 460 • Fungi, p. 460
Plantae, p. 461 • Animalia, p. 461

Thinking Visually

Use taxonomic nomenclature to complete the model of a hierarchical classification system below.

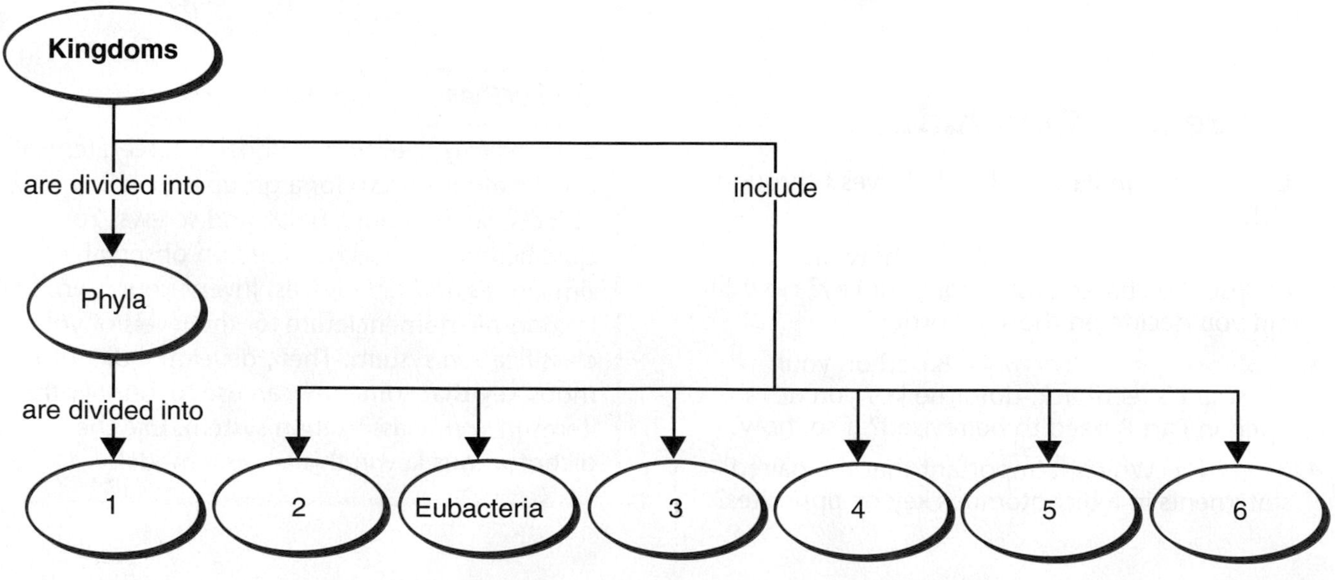

Preparing for the Living Environment Exam

NEW YORK LIVING ENVIRONMENT

Blue questions emphasize Regents Exam content

Chapter 18

Part A

Multiple Choice

For each statement or question, select the number of the word or expression that, of those given, best completes the statement or answers the question.

1 The discipline that specializes in the classification of organisms is
(1) anatomy (3) botany
(2) taxonomy (4) paleontology

2 Modern taxonomists classify organisms according to
(1) evolutionary relationships
(2) kind of environment
(3) age and size
(4) seasonal variation

3 Of the following, *Rana catesbiana* is most closely related to
(1) *Rana pipiens* (3) *Xenopus catesbiana*
(2) *Felis domesticus* (4) *Homo erectus*

4 The largest and most inclusive of Linnaeus's taxonomic categories is the
(1) kingdom (3) phylum
(2) order (4) species

5 Which is *not* a characteristic of Linnaeus's system for naming organisms?
(1) a multi-part name describing several traits
(2) a name that identifies the organism's genus
(3) a name that includes the organism's species identifier
(4) a name unique to a single species

6 Which term shows the evolutionary relationships among a group of organisms?
(1) taxon (3) binomial nomenclature
(2) cladogram (4) molecular clock

7 The three domains are
(1) Animalia, Plantae, Archaebacteria
(2) Plantae, Fungi, Eubacteria
(3) Bacteria, Archaea, Eukarya
(4) Protista, Bacteria, Animalia

8 A new organism has been discovered that cannot produce its own food. Based on this information, it should *not* be placed into the kingdom
(1) Protista (3) Plantae
(2) Fungi (4) Eubacteria

9 What is true about using similarities or dissimilarities to classify different species?
(1) Only similar species, such as two species of rabbits, can be meaningfully compared.
(2) Genetic similarities are no indication of the relationship between two species.
(3) Even dissimilar species can be compared at the level of certain genes.
(4) It is impossible to compare dissimilar species because they have no traits in common.

10 Which organism belongs in the kingdom Animalia?
(1) tree (3) mollusk
(2) protozoan (4) bacterium

11 If species A and B have very similar genes and proteins, which statement is probably true?
(1) Species A and B shared a relatively recent common ancestor.
(2) Species A evolved independently of species B for a long period.
(3) Species A and B are the same species.
(4) Species A is older than species B.

12 The length of time that two taxa have been evolving separately can be estimated using a model called a
(1) phylogenetic tree (3) molecular clock
(2) cladogram (4) six-kingdom system

13 In the six-kingdom system of classifying living things, the kingdom(s) that contain(s) microscopic organisms is (are)
(1) Eubacteria, only
(2) Archaebacteria, only
(3) Eubacteria and Archaebacteria, only
(4) Eubacteria, Archaebacteria, and Protista

14 *Ursus maritimus* is to scientific name as polar bear is to
(1) Latin name (3) genus name
(2) common name (4) phylum name

Test-Taking Tip When you open your test booklet, reassure yourself that the question format is similar to the ones that you have seen in these practice tests. Notice that the directions and the number of choices are similar to those with which you have experience.

Preparing for the Living Environment Exam

Part B

Multiple Choice and Extended Response
For those questions that ask you to select a response, choose the one that best completes the statement or answers the question. For all others follow the directions given.

15 The diagram below shows changes over time in the DNA of related species.

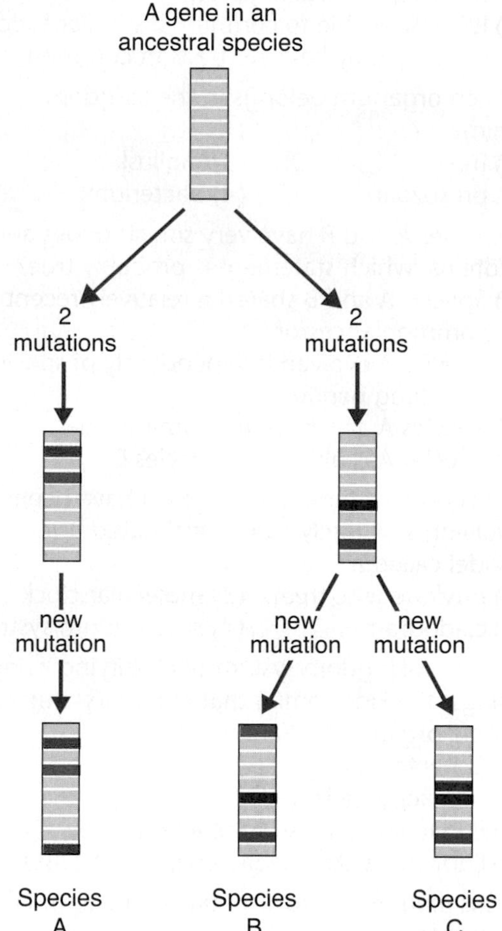

The mutations were most likely
(1) not harmful enough to affect survival
(2) life threatening for species A but not species B and C
(3) life threatening to species B and C but not to species A
(4) life threatening to species A, B, and C

16 State which *two* of the species named below are most closely related. Support your answer with an explanation. The species are: *Entamoeba histolytica, Escherichia coli,* and *Entamoeba coli.*

17 Species 1 is a multicellular, photosynthetic autotroph with cell walls that contain cellulose. Species 2 has cell walls that lack peptidoglycan and cell membranes that contain lipids not found in other organisms. Many individuals of species 2 live in extreme environments and can survive only in the absence of oxygen. Species 3 is a single-celled eukaryotic organism that has chloroplasts. Place each of these three species in the correct kingdom.

18 Venn diagrams can be used to model classification schemes. In the Venn diagram below, each circular region, labeled A, B, C, or D, represents a collection of organisms at the same taxonomic level. Regions that overlap share common members. Regions that do not overlap do not share common members. Match the following terms to the four regions: All Animals, Animals that Have Backbones, Insects, and Mammals. (Do not write in this book.)

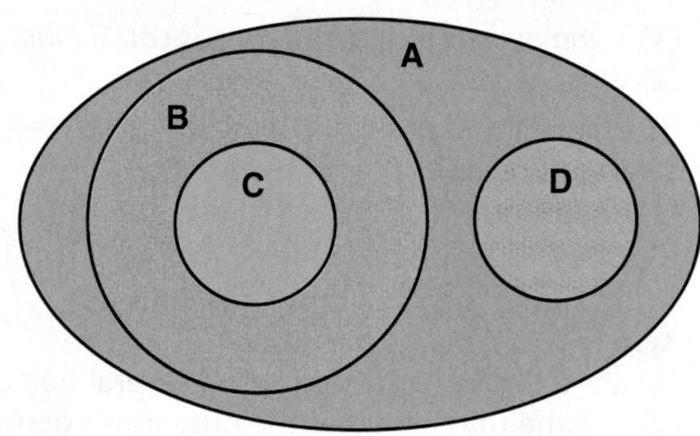

19 The chart below compares some characteristics of fungi and plants.

Kingdom	Plantae	Fungi
Cell Type	Eukaryote	(a)
Cell Structures	(b)	Cell walls of chitin
Number of Cells	(c)	Most unicellular; some multicellular
Mode of Nutrition	Autotroph	(d)

a Complete the chart by filling in the missing information. (Do not write in this book.)
b Explain why mushrooms are *not* placed in the same kingdom as vegetables such as carrots and lettuce.

20 The figure below shows the presumed relationships among three insect taxa.

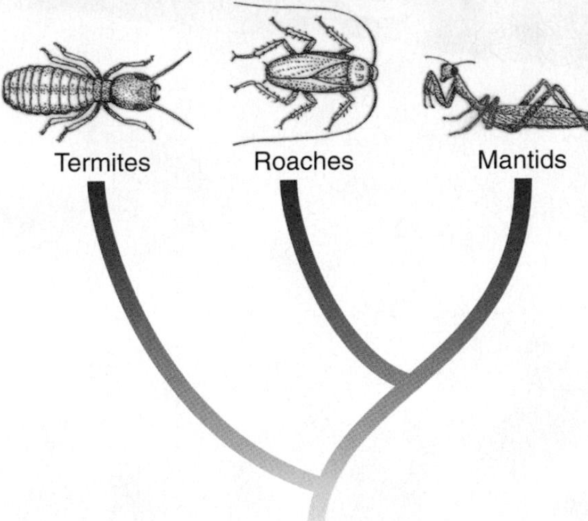

Which statements are true about these three taxa?

A Roaches and mantids share a more recent common ancestor than do roaches and termites.

B Roaches and mantids share a more recent common ancestor than do mantids and termites.

C Termites, roaches, and mantids share a common ancestor.

(1) A and B, only **(3)** B and C, only
(2) A and C, only **(4)** A, B, and C

Part C

Extended Response

Answer the questions or follow the directions given.

Base your answers to questions 21 and 22 on the information below and on your knowledge of biology.

The family Felidae is made up of three genera: *Felis,* which includes pumas, ocelots, and the domestic cat; *Panthera,* which includes jaguars, lions, and tigers; *Lynx,* which includes lynx and bobcats. Some cats, such as the puma and house cat, purr. Some cats, such as the tiger and lion, roar. Some cats are adapted for running at great speeds on land, and others for moving quickly through treetops.

21 Bobcats were originally classified in the genus *Felis*. What can be inferred from the fact that the bobcat has been reclassified?

22 Describe how a molecular clock can be used to estimate the length of time that the bobcat and domestic cat have been evolving independently.

Base your answers to questions 23 through 25 on the reading passage below and on your knowledge of biology.

Wealth of the Rain Forests

It has been estimated that there are more unknown species in tropical rain forests than there are known species in the world. Scientists are concerned that the rain forests might be destroyed before the species in them can be discovered and classified.

During his voyage on the *HMS Beagle* in the 1830s, Charles Darwin spent many months collecting different species. Much of that time was spent in and around tropical rain forests. When Darwin returned to England, he classified the organisms he found. Scientists working in tropical rain forests today use some of the same techniques Darwin used to collect and classify organisms. They also use many techniques Darwin would never have thought of.

23 Compare Darwin's methods of gathering organisms with those used by modern scientists.

24 What instruments could Darwin use for observing organisms? Contrast these with the instruments modern scientists can use.

25 Compare the way Darwin gathered and shared information about organisms with the way modern scientists do these research tasks.

For: An interactive self-test
Visit: PHSchool.com
Web Code: cba-5180

UNIT 6

Microorganisms and Fungi

Chapters

▶ These scarlet waxy cap mushrooms, a type of fungus, were photographed growing among the leaves and debris on a forest floor in Tennessee.

From the Author

Zero. A big, red zero was at the top of my essay, and I couldn't believe my eyes. I had described algae as "simple microorganisms," and Mr. Zong marked the whole essay wrong. After class, he called me aside and asked me to look at a drop of pond water under the microscope. "Can you explain how these organisms swim? How they find food and mates? How their eyespots work?" "No," I admitted. I couldn't answer any of his questions. "Then, will you ever call these organisms 'simple' again, Mr. Miller?" "No," I promised him. And since that day, I never have.

Ken Miller

What discoveries lie ahead?

- Can we learn enough about viruses to develop cures for viral diseases?
- Will we be able to fully grasp the role that microorganisms play in maintaining the natural environment?

Go Online
PHSchool.com

For: Latest discoveries
Visit: PHSchool.com
Web Code: cbe-6000

CHAPTER 19

Bacteria and Viruses

The beautiful colors in this sulfur spring are caused by the bacteria that live in it. Bacteria can survive in extreme habitats.

Inquiry Activity

Where are bacteria found?

Procedure   

1. Label 2 sterile agar plates "control" and "exposed."
2. Tape closed the cover of the control plate. Remove the cover of the exposed plate. Leave both plates on the table for 5 minutes. Do not touch or breathe on the agar.
3. After 5 minutes, tape closed the lid of the exposed plate. Store both plates upside down in a warm place.
4. After 2 days, record the number of bacterial colonies on each plate. **CAUTION:** *Do not open the plates. Give them to your teacher for disposal.*

Think About It

1. **Observing** Which plate had more colonies?
2. **Drawing Conclusions** Where did the bacteria on your plates come from? Explain your answer.
3. **Asking Questions** Write three questions you could investigate using yo[illegible] observations and results.

19–1 Bacteria

4-2.1 Asexual reproduction
4-6.1 The atoms and molecules on Earth cycle
4-6.1 Organism's interactions
LS- Follow safety rules
LS- Make observations and analyze results
LS- Identify control group
LS- Differentiate between variables
LS- Formulate a conclusion

Imagine living all your life as a member of the only family on your street. Then, one morning, you open the front door and discover houses all around you. You see neighbors tending their gardens and children walking to school. Where did all the people come from? What if the answer turned out to be that they had always been there—you just hadn't seen them? In fact, they had lived on your street for years and years before your house was even built. How would your view of the world change? What would it be like to go, almost overnight, from thinking that you and your family were the only folks on the block to just one family in a crowded community? A bit of a shock!

Humans once had just such a shock. Suddenly, the street was very crowded! Thanks to Robert Hooke and Anton van Leeuwenhoek, the invention of the microscope opened our eyes to the hidden, living world around us.

Microscopic life covers nearly every square centimeter of Earth. There are microorganisms of many different sizes and shapes, even in a single drop of pond water. The smallest and most common microorganisms are **prokaryotes**—unicellular organisms that lack a nucleus. For many years, most prokaryotes were called "bacteria." The word *bacteria* is so familiar that we will use it as a common term to describe prokaryotes.

Prokaryotes typically range in size from 1 to 5 micrometers, making them much smaller than most eukaryotic cells, which generally range from 10 to 100 micrometers in diameter. There are exceptions to this, of course. One example is *Epulopiscium fisheloni,* a gigantic prokaryote, shown in **Figure 19–1,** that is about 500 micrometers long.

Guide for Reading

Key Concepts

- How do the two groups of prokaryotes differ?
- What factors are used to identify prokaryotes?
- What is the importance of bacteria?

Vocabulary

prokaryote • bacillus
coccus • spirillum
chemoheterotroph
photoheterotroph
photoautotroph
chemoautotroph
obligate aerobe
obligate anaerobe
facultative anaerobe
binary fission
conjugation • endospore
nitrogen fixation

Reading Strategy: Finding Main Ideas Before you read this section, write down the major headings of the section. Then, as you read the section, list the important information under each heading.

Classifying Prokaryotes

Until fairly recently, all prokaryotes were placed in a single kingdom—Monera. More recently, however, biologists have begun to appreciate that prokaryotes can be divided into two very different groups: the eubacteria (yoo-bak-TEER-ee-uh) and the archaebacteria (ahr-kee-bak-TEER-ee-uh). Each group is now considered to be a separate kingdom. Some biologists think that the split between these two groups is so ancient and so fundamental that they should be called domains, a level of classification even higher than kingdom.

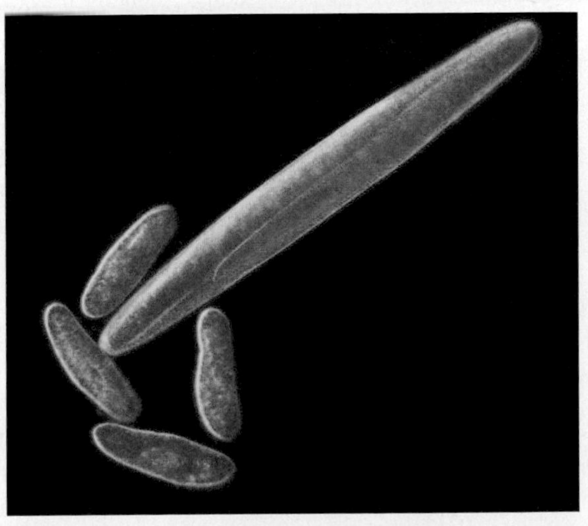

(magnification: 100×)

▶ **Figure 19–1** The large cell in this photograph is *Epulopiscium fisheloni,* one of the largest prokaryotes. Notice its size in relation to the neighboring cells, which are eukaryotic paramecia.

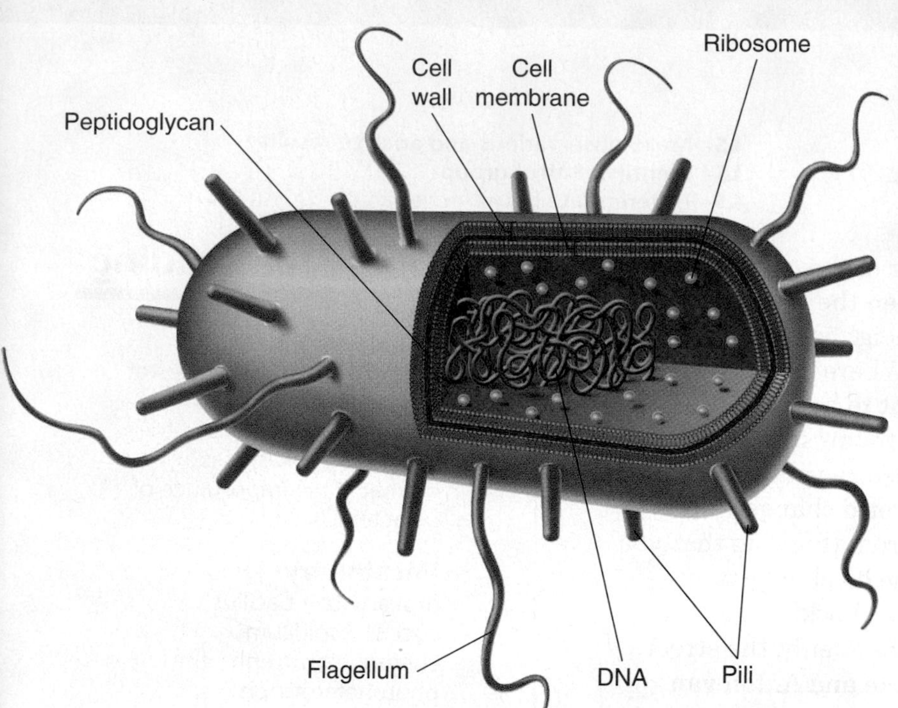

(magnification: 32,300×)

Figure 19–2 A bacterium such as *E. coli* has the basic structure typical of most prokaryotes: cell wall, cell membrane, and cytoplasm. Some prokaryotes have flagella that they use for movement. The pili are involved in cell-to-cell contact. **The cell walls of eubacteria contain peptidoglycan.**

Eubacteria The larger of the two kingdoms of prokaryotes is the eubacteria. Eubacteria include a wide range of organisms with different lifestyles. The variety is so great, in fact, that biologists do not agree on exactly how many phyla are needed to classify this group. Eubacteria live almost everywhere. They live in fresh water, salt water, on land, and on and within the human body. **Figure 19–2** shows a diagram of *Escherichia coli,* a typical eubacterium that lives in human intestines.

Eubacteria are usually surrounded by a cell wall that protects the cell from injury and determines its shape. The cell walls of eubacteria contain peptidoglycan, a carbohydrate. Inside the cell wall is a cell membrane that surrounds the cytoplasm. Some eubacteria have a second membrane, outside the cell membrane, that makes them especially resistant to damage.

Archaebacteria Under a microscope, archaebacteria look very similar to eubacteria. They are equally small, lack nuclei, have cell walls, but chemically archaebacteria are quite different. **Archaebacteria lack the peptidoglycan of eubacteria and also have different membrane lipids. Also, the DNA sequences of key archaebacterial genes are more like those of eukaryotes than those of eubacteria.** Based on this and other data, scientists reason that archaebacteria may be the ancestors of eukaryotes.

Many archaebacteria live in extremely harsh environments. One group of archaebacteria is the methanogens, prokaryotes that produce methane gas. Methanogens live in oxygen-free environments, such as thick mud and the digestive tracts of animals. Other archaebacteria live in extremely salty environments, such as Utah's Great Salt Lake, or in hot springs where temperatures approach the boiling point of water.

CHECKPOINT *Where do archaebacteria live?*

Identifying Prokaryotes

Because prokaryotes are so small, it may seem difficult to tell one type of prokaryote from another. **Prokaryotes are identified by characteristics such as shape, the chemical nature of their cell walls, the way they move, and the way they obtain energy.**

Shapes Look at the different shapes of the prokaryotes shown in **Figure 19–3.** Rod-shaped prokaryotes are called **bacilli** (buh-SIL-eye; singular: bacillus). Spherical prokaryotes are called **cocci** (KAHK-sy; singular: coccus). Spiral and corkscrew-shaped prokaryotes are called **spirilla** (spy-RIL-uh; singular: spirillum).

Cell Walls Two different types of cell walls are found in eubacteria. A method called Gram staining is used to tell them apart. The Gram stain consists of two dyes—one violet (the primary stain) and the other red (the counterstain). The violet stain, applied first, stains peptidoglycan cell walls. This is followed by an alcohol treatment that tends to wash out the stain. Gram-positive bacteria have thick peptidoglycan walls that retain the dark color of the violet stain even after the alcohol wash. Gram-negative bacteria have much thinner walls inside an outer lipid layer. Alcohol dissolves the lipid and removes the dye from the walls of these bacteria. The counterstain then makes these bacteria appear pink or light red.

Movement You can also identify prokaryotes by whether they move and how they move. Some prokaryotes do not move at all. Others are propelled by flagella, whiplike structures used for movement. Other prokaryotes lash, snake, or spiral forward. Still others glide slowly along a layer of slimelike material they secrete.

Metabolic Diversity

No characteristic of prokaryotes illustrates their diversity better than the ways in which they obtain energy. Depending on their source of energy and whether or not they use oxygen for cellular respiration, prokaryotes can be divided into two main groups. Most prokaryotes are heterotrophs, meaning that they get their energy by consuming organic molecules made by other organisms. Other prokaryotes are autotrophs and make their own food from inorganic molecules.

Heterotrophs Most heterotrophic prokaryotes must take in organic molecules for both energy and a supply of carbon. These prokaryotes are called **chemoheterotrophs** (kee-moh-HET-ur-oh-trohfs). Most animals, including humans, are chemoheterotrophs. A smaller group of heterotrophic prokaryotes are called **photoheterotrophs** (foh-toh-HET-ur-oh-trohfs). These organisms are photosynthetic, using sunlight for energy, but they also need to take in organic compounds as a carbon source.

Figure 19–3 **Prokaryotes can be identified by their shapes.** Prokaryotes usually have one of three basic shapes: rods (bacilli), spheres (cocci), or spirals (spirilla).

Bacilli
(magnification: 3738×)

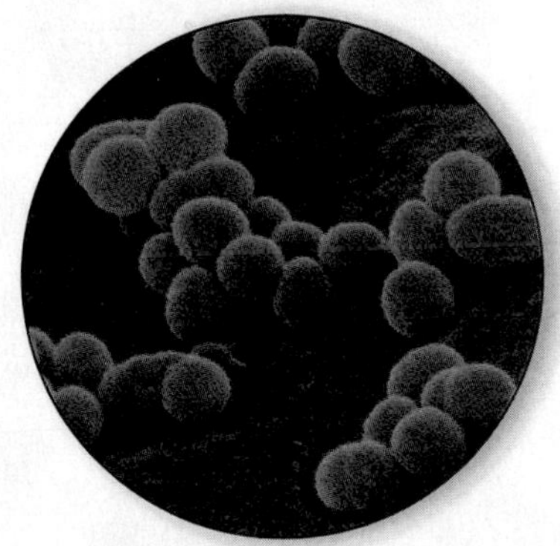

Cocci
(magnification: 30,000×)

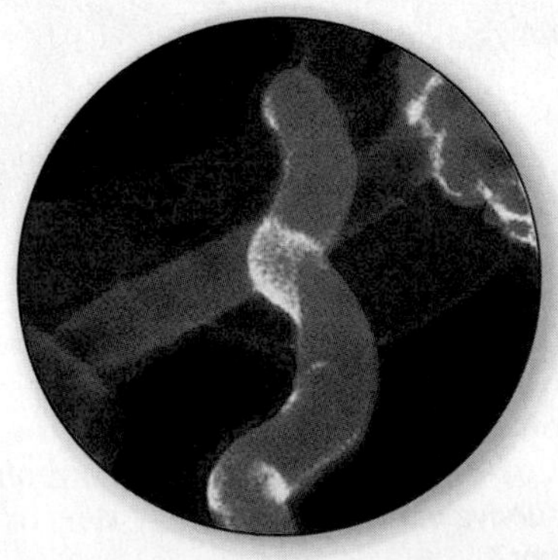

Spirilla
(magnification: about 7000×)

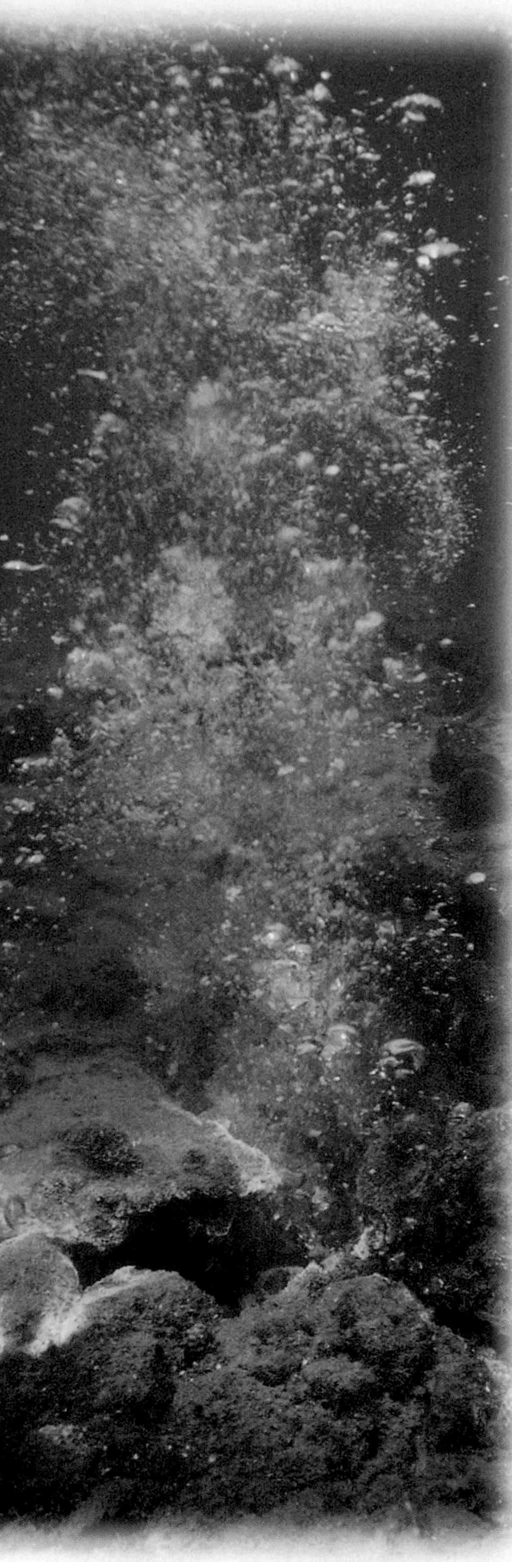

▲ **Figure 19–4** Ocean vents, such as this one, are often home to a variety of organisms, including tube worms and other exotic organisms. **Applying Concepts** *Would photoautotrophs survive in this environment? Why or why not?*

Autotrophs Other groups of prokaryotes are autotrophs. Some autotrophs, the **photoautotrophs** (foh-toh-AW-toh-trohfs), use light energy to convert carbon dioxide and water to carbon compounds and oxygen in a process similar to that used by green plants. As you might expect, these organisms are found where light is plentiful, such as near the surfaces of lakes, streams, and oceans. One group, the cyanobacteria (sy-uh-noh-bak-TEER-ee-uh), contains a bluish pigment and chlorophyll *a*, the key pigment in photosynthesis. Cyanobacteria are found throughout the world—in fresh water, salt water, and even on land. In fact, cyanobacteria are often the very first species to recolonize the site of a natural disaster such as a volcanic eruption.

Other prokaryotes can perform chemosynthesis and are called **chemoautotrophs** (kee-moh-AW-toh-trohfs). Like photoautotrophs, chemoautotrophs make organic carbon molecules from carbon dioxide. Unlike photoautotrophs, however, they do not require light as a source of energy. Instead, they use energy directly from chemical reactions involving ammonia, hydrogen sulfide, nitrites, sulfur, or iron. Some chemoautotrophs live deep in the darkness of the ocean. They obtain energy from hydrogen sulfide gas that flows from hydrothermal vents on the ocean floor, such as the one shown in **Figure 19–4.**

CHECKPOINT *What are the two groups of autotrophs found in prokaryotes?*

Releasing Energy Like all organisms, bacteria need a constant supply of energy. This energy is released by the processes of cellular respiration or fermentation or both. Organisms that require a constant supply of oxygen in order to live are called **obligate aerobes.** (*Obligate* means that the organisms are obliged, or required, by their life processes to live only in that particular way.) *Mycobacterium tuberculosis,* the bacterium that causes tuberculosis, is an obligate aerobe.

Some bacteria, however, do not require oxygen and, in fact, may be killed by it! These bacteria are called **obligate anaerobes,** and they must live in the absence of oxygen. *Clostridium botulinum* is an obligate anaerobe found in soil. Because of its ability to grow without oxygen, it can grow in canned food that has not been properly sterilized.

A third group of bacteria can survive with or without oxygen and are known as **facultative anaerobes.** (*Facultative* means that the organisms are able to function in different ways, depending on their environment.) Facultative anaerobes do not require oxygen, but neither are they killed by its presence. Their ability to switch between the processes of cellular respiration and fermentation means that facultative anaerobes are able to live just about anywhere. *E. coli* is a facultative anaerobe that lives anaerobically in the large intestine and aerobically in sewage or contaminated water.

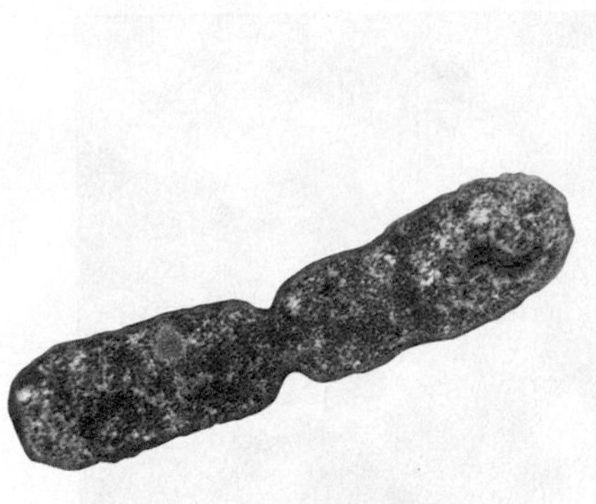

Binary Fission
(magnification: 26,500×)

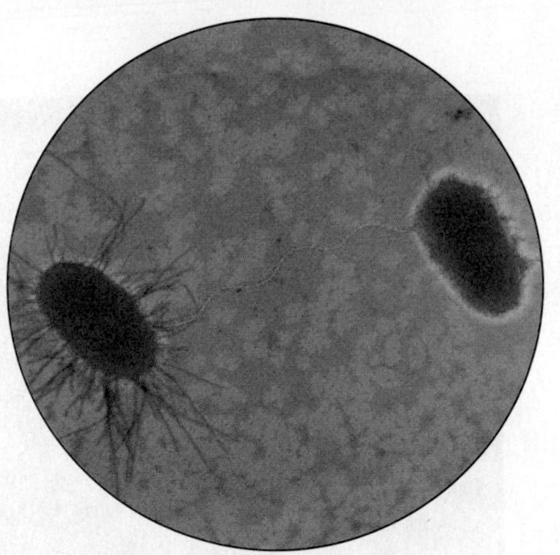

Conjugation
(magnification: 7000×)

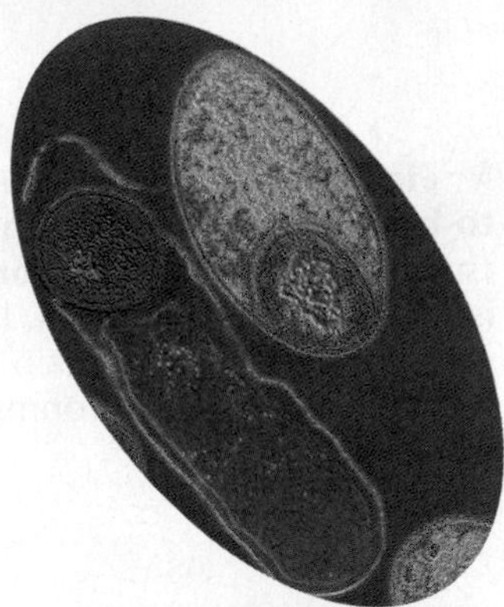

Spore Formation
(magnification: 7800×)

Figure 19–5 Most prokaryotes reproduce by binary fission, producing two identical "daughter" cells. Some prokaryotes take part in conjugation, in which genetic information is transferred from one cell to another by way of a hollow bridge. Other prokaryotes produce endospores, which allow them to withstand harsh conditions. **Comparing and Contrasting** *Compare the process of conjugation to binary fission.*

Growth and Reproduction

When conditions are favorable, bacteria can grow and divide at astonishing rates. Some divide as often as every 20 minutes! If unlimited space and food were available to a single bacterium and if all of its offspring divided every 20 minutes, in just 48 hours they would reach a mass approximately 4000 times the mass of Earth! Fortunately, this does not happen. In nature, growth is held in check by the availability of food and the production of waste products.

Binary Fission When a bacterium has grown so that it has nearly doubled in size, it replicates its DNA and divides in half, producing two identical "daughter" cells, as in **Figure 19–5** (left). This type of reproduction is known as **binary fission.** Because binary fission does not involve the exchange or recombination of genetic information, it is an asexual form of reproduction.

Conjugation Many bacteria are also able to exchange genetic information by a process called conjugation. During **conjugation,** a hollow bridge forms between two bacterial cells, as shown in **Figure 19–5** (center), and genes move from one cell to the other. This transfer of genetic information increases genetic diversity in populations of bacteria.

Spore Formation When growth conditions become unfavorable, many bacteria form structures called spores, the objects that appear red in **Figure 19–5** (right). One type of spore, called an **endospore,** is formed when a bacterium produces a thick internal wall that encloses its DNA and a portion of its cytoplasm. Spores can remain dormant for months or even years while waiting for more favorable growth conditions. When conditions improve, the endospore will germinate and the bacterium will begin to grow again. The ability to form spores makes it possible for some bacteria to survive harsh conditions—such as extreme heat, dryness, or lack of nutrients—that might otherwise kill them.

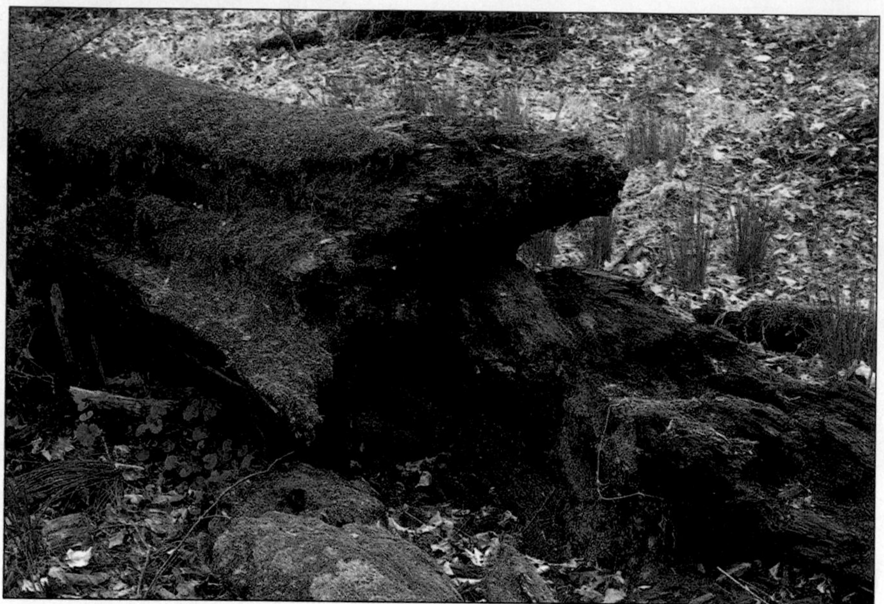

▶ **Figure 19–6** **Bacteria help to break down the nutrients in this tree, allowing other organisms to use the nutrients.** In this way, bacteria help maintain equilibrium in the environment.

Importance of Bacteria

You probably remember the principal actors in the last film you saw. You might even recall some of the supporting actors. Have you ever thought that there would be no film at all without the hundreds of workers who are never seen on screen? Bacteria are just like those unseen workers. **Bacteria are vital to maintaining the living world. Some are producers that capture energy by photosynthesis. Others are decomposers that break down the nutrients in dead matter and the atmosphere. Still other bacteria have human uses.**

Decomposers Every living thing depends directly or indirectly on a supply of raw materials. If these materials were lost when an organism died, life could not continue. Before long, plants would drain the soil of minerals and die, and animals that depend on plants for food would starve. As decomposers, bacteria help the ecosystem recycle nutrients, therefore maintaining equilibrium in the environment. When a tree dies, such as the one in **Figure 19–6,** armies of bacteria attack and digest the dead tissue, breaking it down into simpler materials, which are released into the soil. Other organisms, including insects and fungi, also play important roles in breaking down dead matter.

Bacteria also help in sewage treatment. Sewage contains human waste, discarded food, and chemical waste. Bacteria break down complex compounds in the sewage into simpler ones. This process produces purified water, nitrogen and carbon dioxide gases, and leftover products that can be used as fertilizers.

Nitrogen Fixers Plants and animals depend on bacteria for nitrogen. You may recall that plants need nitrogen to make amino acids, the building blocks of proteins. Nitrogen gas (N_2) makes up approximately 80 percent of Earth's atmosphere.

For: Links on bacteria
Visit: www.SciLinks.org
Web Code: cbn-6191

However, plants cannot use nitrogen gas directly. Nitrogen must first be changed chemically to ammonia (NH_3) or other nitrogen compounds. Expensive synthetic fertilizers contain these nitrogen compounds, but certain bacteria in the soil produce them naturally. The process of converting nitrogen gas into a form plants can use is known as **nitrogen fixation.** Nitrogen fixation allows nitrogen atoms to continually cycle through the biosphere.

Many plants have symbiotic relationships with nitrogen-fixing bacteria. For example, soybeans and other legumes host the bacterium *Rhizobium. Rhizobium* grows in nodules, or knobs, on the roots of the soybean plant, as shown in **Figure 19–7.** The plant provides a source of nutrients for *Rhizobium*, which converts nitrogen in the air into ammonia, helping the plant. Thus, soybeans have their own fertilizer factories in their roots!

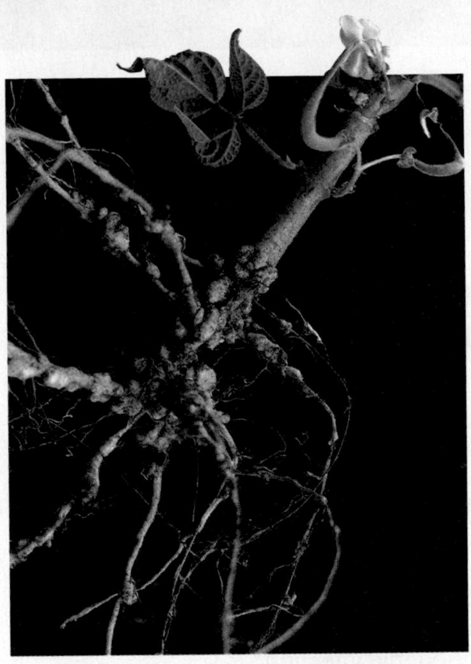

▲ **Figure 19–7** The knoblike structures on the roots of this soybean plant are called nodules. Within these nodules are populations of the nitrogen-fixing bacteria *Rhizobium*. **Applying Concepts** ***What is the name of the relationship between*** **Rhizobium** ***and soybean plants?***

Human Uses of Bacteria Many of the remarkable properties of bacteria provide us with products we depend on every day. For example, bacteria are used in the production of a wide variety of foods and beverages. Bacteria can also be used in industry. One type of bacteria can digest petroleum, making it very helpful in cleaning up small oil spills. Some bacteria remove waste products and poisons from water. Others can even help to mine minerals from the ground. Still others are used to synthesize drugs and chemicals through the techniques of genetic engineering.

Our intestines are inhabited by large numbers of bacteria, including *E. coli*. The term *coli* was derived from the fact that these bacteria were discovered in the human colon, or large intestine. In the intestines, the bacteria are provided with a warm and safe home, plenty of food, and free transportation. These bacteria also make a number of vitamins that the body cannot produce by itself. So both we and the bacteria benefit from this symbiotic relationship.

Biologists continue to discover new uses for bacteria. For example, biotechnology companies have begun to realize that bacteria adapted to extreme environments may be a rich source of heat-stable enzymes. These enzymes can be used in medicine, food production, and industrial chemistry.

19–1 Section Assessment

1. **Key Concept** Describe the characteristics of the two kingdoms of prokaryotes.
2. **Key Concept** What factors can be used to identify prokaryotes?
3. **Key Concept** Give one example of how bacteria maintain equilibrium in the environment.
4. Identify the parts of a prokaryote.
5. What are some ways that prokaryotes obtain energy?
6. **Critical Thinking Inferring** Why might an infection by Gram-negative bacteria be more difficult to treat than a Gram-positive bacterial infection?

Thinking Visually

Making a Venn Diagram
Create a Venn diagram that illustrates the similarities and differences between eubacteria and archaebacteria. *Hint*: Before you start, you may want to list the similarities and differences.

19–2 Viruses

4-5.2 Viruses
4-6.1 Relationships and interactions between organisms

Guide for Reading

Key Concepts
- What is the structure of a virus?
- How do viruses cause infection?

Vocabulary
virus
capsid
bacteriophage
lytic infection
lysogenic infection
prophage
retrovirus

Reading Strategy: Using Visuals As you read about viral replication in this section, trace each step in **Figure 19–10.** Then, list the steps, and write a few sentences to describe each step.

Imagine that you have been presented with a great puzzle. Farmers have begun to lose a valuable crop to a plant disease. The disease produces large pale spots on the leaves of plants similar to those shown in **Figure 19–8.** The diseased leaves look like mosaics of yellow and green. As the disease progresses, the leaves turn completely yellow, wither, and fall off, killing the plant.

To determine what is causing the disease, you take leaves from a diseased plant and extract a juice. You place a few drops of the juice on the leaves of healthy plants. A few days later, the mosaic pattern appears where you put the drops. Could the source of the disease be in the juice?

You use a light microscope to look for a germ that might cause the disease, but none can be seen. Even when the tiniest of cells are filtered out of the juice, it still causes the disease. You hypothesize that the juice must contain disease-causing agents so small that they are not visible under the microscope. Although you cannot see the disease-causing particles, you're sure they are there. You give them the name *virus*, from the Latin word for "poison."

If you think you could have carried out this investigation, congratulations! You're walking in the footsteps of a 28-year-old Russian biologist, Dmitri Ivanovski. In 1892, Ivanovski identified the cause of tobacco mosaic disease as juice extracted from infected plants. In 1897, Dutch scientist Martinus Beijerinck suggested that tiny particles in the juice caused the disease, and he named these particles viruses.

What Is a Virus?

In 1935, the American biochemist Wendell Stanley obtained crystals of tobacco mosaic virus. Living organisms do not crystallize, so Stanley inferred that viruses were not alive. **Viruses** are particles of nucleic acid, protein, and in some cases, lipids. Viruses can reproduce only by infecting living cells. Viruses differ widely in terms of size and structure, as you can see in **Figure 19–9.** As different as they are, all viruses have one thing in common: They enter living cells and, once inside, use the machinery of the infected cell to produce more viruses.

Most viruses are so small they can be seen only with the aid of a powerful electron microscope. **A typical virus is composed of a core of DNA or RNA surrounded by a protein coat.** The simplest viruses contain only a few genes, whereas the most complex may have more than a hundred genes.

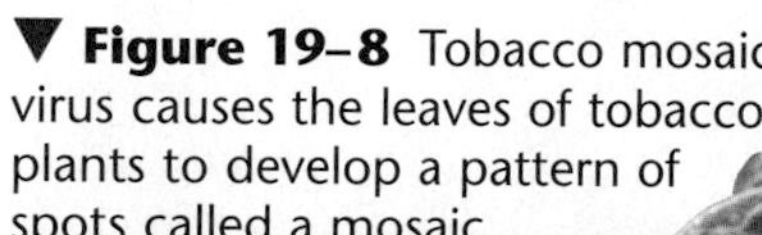

▼ **Figure 19–8** Tobacco mosaic virus causes the leaves of tobacco plants to develop a pattern of spots called a mosaic.

Figure 19–9 Virus Structures

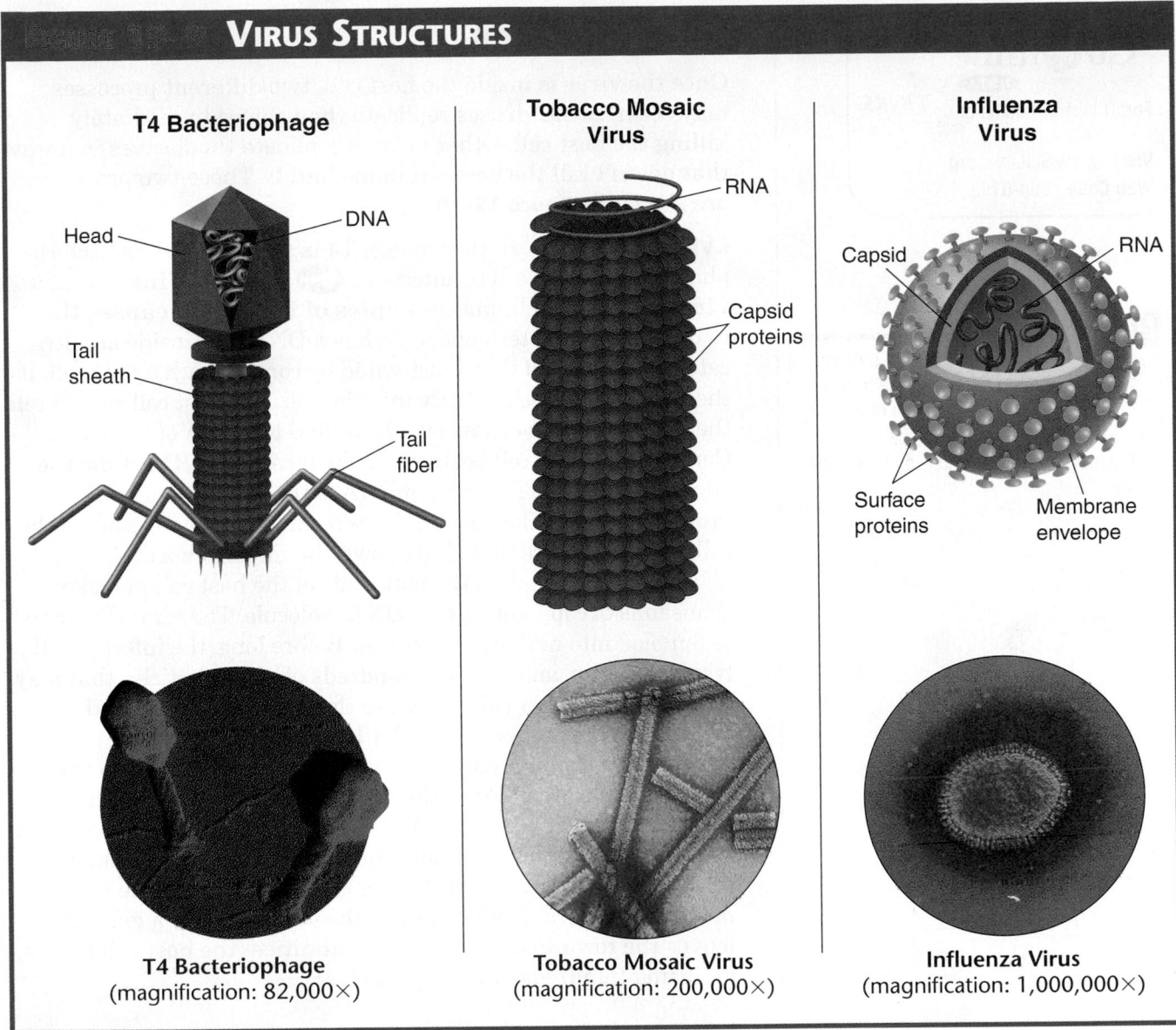

T4 Bacteriophage

Head
DNA
Tail sheath
Tail fiber

Tobacco Mosaic Virus

RNA
Capsid proteins

Influenza Virus

Capsid
RNA
Surface proteins
Membrane envelope

T4 Bacteriophage
(magnification: 82,000×)

Tobacco Mosaic Virus
(magnification: 200,000×)

Influenza Virus
(magnification: 1,000,000×)

▲ **Figure 19–9** Viruses come in a wide variety of sizes and shapes. **A typical virus is composed of a core of either DNA or RNA, which is surrounded by a protein coat, or capsid.**

A virus's protein coat is called its **capsid.** The capsid includes proteins that enable a virus to enter a host cell. The capsid proteins of a typical virus bind to receptors on the surface of a cell and "trick" the cell into allowing it inside. Once inside, the viral genes are expressed. The cell transcribes and translates the viral genetic information into viral capsid proteins. Sometimes that genetic program causes the host cell to make copies of the virus, and in the process the host cell is destroyed.

Because viruses must bind precisely to proteins on the cell surface and then use a host's genetic system, most viruses are highly specific to the cells they infect. Plant viruses infect plant cells; most animal viruses infect only certain related species of animals; and bacterial viruses infect only certain types of bacteria. Viruses that infect bacteria are called **bacteriophages.**

 ***What happens when a cell transcribes a viral gene?***

For: Links on the lytic cycle
Visit: www.SciLinks.org
Web Code: cbn-6192

To find out more about the transmission of a virus, view the segment "Influenza: Tracking a Virus," on Videotape Three.

Viral Infection

Once the virus is inside the host cell, two different processes may occur. Some viruses replicate themselves immediately, killing the host cell. Other viruses replicate themselves in a way that doesn't kill the host cell immediately. These two processes are shown in **Figure 19–10.**

Lytic Infection Bacteriophage T4 is an example of a bacteriophage that causes a lytic infection. **In a lytic infection, a virus enters a cell, makes copies of itself, and causes the cell to burst.** Bacteriophage T4 has a DNA core inside an intricate protein capsid that is activated by contact with a host cell. It then injects its DNA directly into the cell. The host cell cannot tell the difference between its own DNA and the DNA of the virus. Consequently, the cell begins to make messenger RNA from the genes of the virus. This viral mRNA is translated into viral proteins that act like a molecular wrecking crew, chopping up the cell DNA, a process that shuts down the infected host cell.

The virus then uses the materials of the host cell to make thousands of copies of its own DNA molecule. The viral DNA gets assembled into new virus particles. Before long, the infected cell lyses, or bursts, and releases hundreds of virus particles that may go on to infect other cells. Because the host cell is lysed and destroyed, this process is called a **lytic infection.**

In its own way, a lytic virus is similar to an outlaw in the American Old West. First, the outlaw eliminates the town's existing authority (host cell DNA). Then, the outlaw demands to be outfitted with new weapons, horses, and riding equipment by terrorizing the local people (using the host cell to make viral proteins and viral DNA). Finally, the outlaw forms a gang that leaves the town to attack new communities (the host cell bursts, releasing hundreds of virus particles).

Lysogenic Infection Other viruses, including the bacteriophage lambda, cause **lysogenic infections** in which a host cell makes copies of the virus indefinitely. **In a lysogenic infection, a virus integrates its DNA into the DNA of the host cell, and the viral genetic information replicates along with the host cell's DNA.** Unlike lytic viruses, lysogenic viruses do not lyse the host cell right away. Instead, a lysogenic virus remains inactive for a period of time.

The viral DNA that is embedded in the host's DNA is called a **prophage.** The prophage may remain part of the DNA of the host cell for many generations before becoming active. A virus may not stay in the prophage form indefinitely. Eventually, any one of a number of factors may activate the DNA of a prophage, which will then remove itself from the host cell DNA and direct the synthesis of new virus particles.

The steps of lytic and lysogenic infections may be different from those of other viruses when they attack eukaryotic cells. Most animal viruses, however, show patterns of infection similar to either the lytic or lysogenic patterns of infection of bacteria.

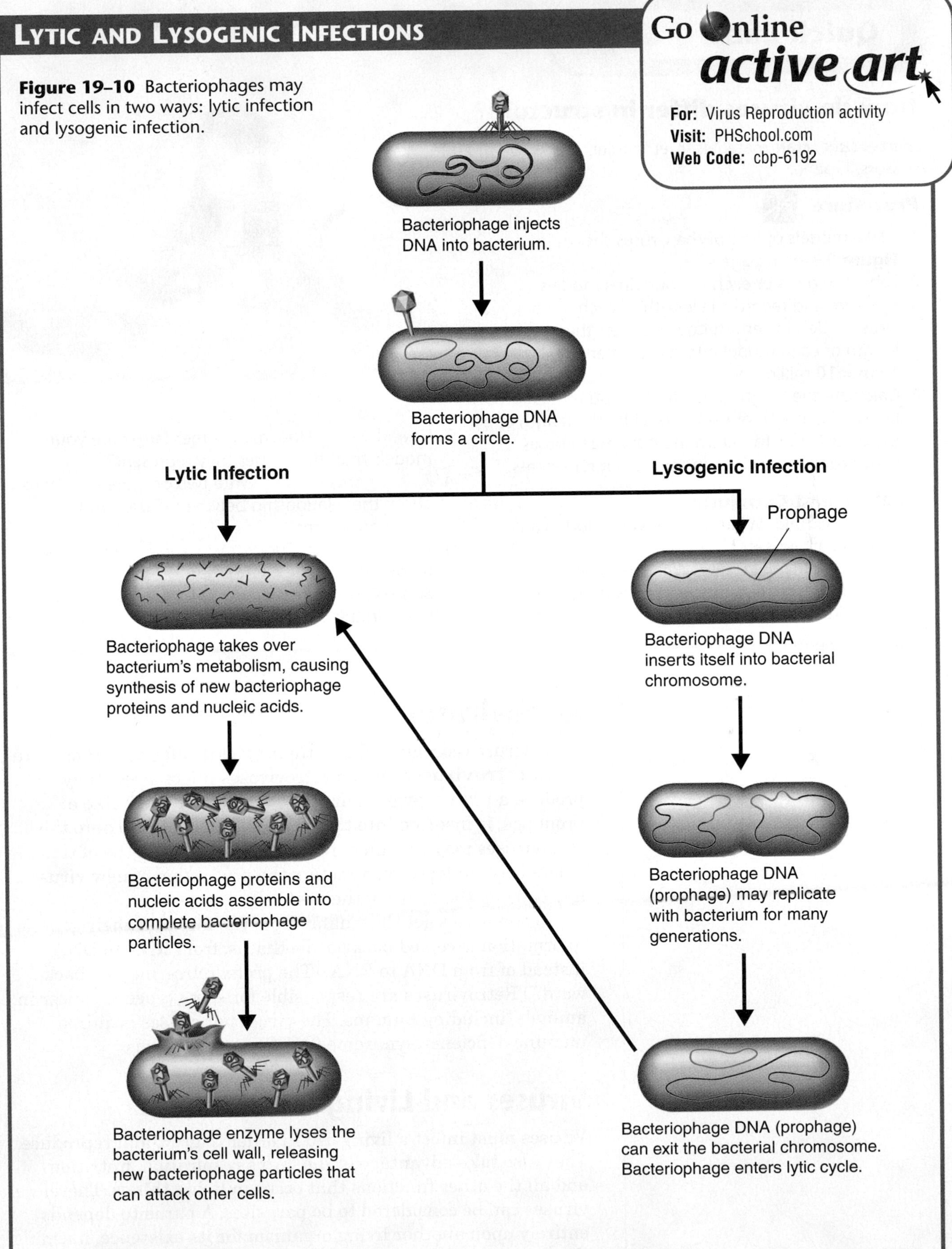
LYTIC AND LYSOGENIC INFECTIONS
Go Online
active art
For: Virus Reproduction activity
Visit: PHSchool.com
Web Code: cbp-6192
Bacteriophage injects DNA into bacterium.
Bacteriophage DNA forms a circle.
Lytic Infection
Lysogenic Infection
Prophage
Bacteriophage takes over bacterium's metabolism, causing synthesis of new bacteriophage proteins and nucleic acids.
Bacteriophage proteins and nucleic acids assemble into complete bacteriophage particles.
Bacteriophage enzyme lyses the bacterium's cell wall, releasing new bacteriophage particles that can attack other cells.
Bacteriophage DNA inserts itself into bacterial chromosome.
Bacteriophage DNA (prophage) may replicate with bacterium for many generations.
Bacteriophage DNA (prophage) can exit the bacterial chromosome. Bacteriophage enters lytic cycle.

Figure 19–10 Bacteriophages may infect cells in two ways: lytic infection and lysogenic infection.

Quick Lab

How do viruses differ in structure?

Materials craft materials, metric ruler, scissors, tape

Procedure 

1. Make models of two of the viruses shown in **Figure 19–9** on page 479.
2. Label the parts of each of your virus models.
3. Measure and record the length of each of your virus models in centimeters. Convert the length of each model into nanometers: 1 cm = 10 million nm.
4. Calculate the length of each virus you modeled. Divide the length of each model by the length of the actual virus to determine how many times larger each model is than the virus it represents.

Analyze and Conclude

1. **Using Models** What parts of your models are found in all viruses?
2. **Drawing Conclusions** What parts do one or both of your models include that are found in only some viruses?
3. **Calculating** How many times larger are your models than the viruses they represent?
4. **Asking Questions** Write two or more questions about the relationship between viruses and single-celled organisms.
5. **Using Models** Suggest ways you can use models to investigate one of your questions in question 4. Suggest an alternative for the virus model you made in this activity.

Retroviruses

Some viruses contain RNA as their genetic information and are called **retroviruses.** When retroviruses infect a cell, they produce a DNA copy of their RNA. This DNA, much like a prophage, is inserted into the DNA of the host cell. There the retroviruses may remain dormant for varying lengths of time before becoming active, directing the production of new viruses, and causing the death of the host cell.

Retroviruses get their name from the fact that their genetic information is copied backward—that is, from RNA to DNA instead of from DNA to RNA. (The prefix *retro-* means "backward.") Retroviruses are responsible for some types of cancer in animals, including humans. The virus that causes acquired immune deficiency syndrome (AIDS) is a retrovirus.

Viruses and Living Cells

Viruses must infect a living cell in order to grow and reproduce. They also take advantage of the host's respiration, nutrition, and all the other functions that occur in living things. Therefore, viruses can be considered to be parasites. A parasite depends entirely upon another living organism for its existence, harming that organism in the process.

Viruses and Cells		
Characteristic	**Virus**	**Cell**
Structure	DNA or RNA core, capsid	Cell membrane, cytoplasm; eukaryotes also contain nucleus and organelles
Reproduction	only within a host cell	independent cell division either asexually or sexually
Genetic Code	DNA or RNA	DNA
Growth and Development	no	yes; in multicellular organisms, cells increase in number and differentiate
Obtain and Use Energy	no	yes
Response to Environment	no	yes
Change Over Time	yes	yes

▲ **Figure 19–11** The differences between viruses and cells are listed in this chart. **Applying Concepts** ***Based on this information, would you classify viruses as living or nonliving? Explain.***

Are viruses alive? If we require that living things be made up of cells and be able to live independently, then viruses are not alive. Yet, viruses have many of the characteristics of living things. After infecting living cells, viruses can reproduce, regulate gene expression, and even evolve. Some of the main differences between cells and viruses are summarized in **Figure 19–11.** Viruses are at the borderline of living and nonliving things.

Although viruses are smaller and simpler than the smallest cells, it is not likely that they could have been the first living things. Because viruses are completely dependent upon living things, it seems more likely that viruses developed after living cells. In fact, the first viruses may have evolved from the genetic material of living cells. Once established, however, viruses have continued to evolve, along with the cells they infect, over billions of years.

19–2 Section Assessment

1. **Key Concept** What are the parts of a virus?
2. **Key Concept** Describe the two ways that viruses cause infection.
3. What is the difference between a bacteriophage and a prophage?
4. What is a retrovirus?
5. **Critical Thinking Making Judgments** Do you think viruses should be considered a form of life? Describe the reasons for your opinion.
6. **Critical Thinking Evaluating** What are the strengths and weaknesses of the tobacco mosaic virus hypothesis?

Connecting Concepts

Structure and Function
Viruses and cells are similar yet different. Compare the structure of a virus to the structure of a eukaryotic cell. Organize your information in a table. You may wish to refer to Chapter 7, which discusses the structures of cells in detail.

Should Mass Vaccinations Be Required?

Smallpox is a deadly disease that produces pustules like those shown in the photograph. Smallpox had been brought under control by a worldwide vaccination program. It appeared that vaccination had eradicated every trace of smallpox in nature. As a result, the routine vaccination of children against smallpox was ended in the United States in 1971. No new smallpox cases have been reported anywhere since 1978. Only two laboratories, one in Atlanta, Georgia, and the other in Russia, are known to have samples of the virus.

Today there is concern that certain infectious diseases, such as smallpox, will be used as a biological weapon. This has led authorities in the United States and other countries to order the production of new stocks of certain vaccines. Preparing millions of doses of a vaccine as a precaution against attack certainly seems like a good idea. But it also raises an important social and scientific question—should a nation require its citizens to be vaccinated against a particular disease, or should we wait until there is evidence of an outbreak of a disease in a given area?

The Viewpoints

Require Vaccinations

Human history shows just how deadly certain infectious diseases can be. Therefore, it makes sense to preempt an outbreak by requiring vaccinations as soon as enough doses of the vaccine are available. The benefits of immunity would outweigh any possible adverse reactions to the vaccine. In addition, it is cheaper to vaccinate everyone, rather than to treat infectious diseases on an individual basis.

Hold the Vaccine in Reserve

As serious as the threat from certain infectious diseases may be, we should keep in mind the rule of medicine that is taught to all doctors: First, do no harm. We already know, unfortunately, that administering vaccines to an entire population will indeed do harm. For example, U. S. health statistics

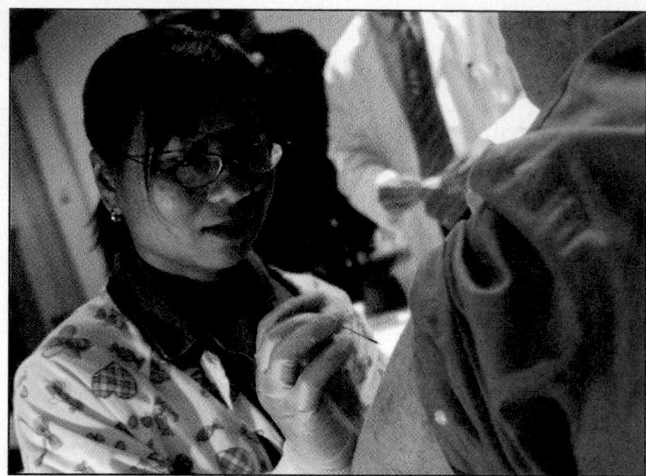

show that for every 1 million infants vaccinated for smallpox, as many as 5 may have died from reactions to the vaccine. The exact number of deaths that will result from a nationwide vaccination program is not certain, but any number of deaths is too many when the risk of infection is only hypothetical.

Research and Decide

1. **Analyzing the Viewpoints** To make an informed decision, learn more about this issue by consulting library or Internet resources. Then, list both the risks and benefits of nationwide vaccination.
2. **Forming Your Opinion** How do you balance the risks and benefits of vaccination now against the risks and benefits of stockpiling the vaccine? What factors should you consider?
3. **Role-Playing** You are a researcher for the Centers for Disease Control in Atlanta. You have been offered the chance to be inoculated with a vaccine such as smallpox. Would you get the vaccination? Explain your answer and support it with facts from your research.

For: Links from the authors
Visit: PHSchool.com
Web Code: cbe-6194

19–3 Diseases Caused by Bacteria and Viruses

4-5.2 Bacteria may infect and interfere with organisms
4-5.2 Biological research
4-5.2 Vaccinations

Have you ever heard a teacher say that when a few people misbehave, they ruin it for everybody? In a way, that saying could be applied to bacteria and viruses. Bacteria and viruses are everywhere in nature, but only a few cause disease. However, these **pathogens,** or disease-causing agents, get all the attention.

Disease can be considered a conflict between the pathogen and the host. All viruses reproduce by infecting living cells, and disease results when the infection causes harm to the host. All bacteria require nutrients and energy; however, disease results when bacteria interfere with the host's ability to obtain enough of those elements to function properly.

Guide for Reading

Key Concepts

- How do bacteria cause disease?
- How can bacterial growth be controlled?
- How do viruses cause disease?

Vocabulary

pathogen
vaccine
antibiotic
viroid
prion

Reading Strategy: Outlining Before you read, use the headings of this section to make an outline about disease. As you read, fill in subtopics. Then, add phrases or a sentence after each to provide key information.

Bacterial Disease in Humans

Many bacteria live on and within our bodies, and some bacteria even help us to perform essential functions, such as digesting our food. The growth of pathogenic bacteria, on the other hand, disrupts the body's equilibrium by interfering with its normal activities and producing disease.

The French chemist Louis Pasteur, shown in **Figure 19–12,** was the first person to show convincingly that bacteria cause disease. Pasteur helped to establish what has become known as the germ theory of disease when he showed that bacteria were responsible for a number of human and animal diseases.

Bacteria produce disease in one of two general ways. Some bacteria damage the cells and tissues of the infected organism directly by breaking down the cells for food. Other bacteria release toxins (poisons) that travel throughout the body interfering with the normal activity of the host.

Using Cells for Food The bacterium *Mycobacterium tuberculosis*, which causes tuberculosis, is inhaled into the lungs, where it destroys the lung tissue. The bacterium also may enter a blood vessel and travel to new sites in the body where it destroys more tissue.

Releasing Toxins Bacterial toxins can travel throughout the body. For example, the *Streptococcus* bacterium that causes strep throat can release toxins into the bloodstream. These toxins can cause scarlet fever. A red rash appears on the skin of someone infected with scarlet fever. Diphtheria, another disease caused by the *Corynebacterium diphtheriae* bacterium, infects the tissues of the throat. *C. diphtheriae* releases toxins into the bloodstream, where they destroy tissues. Diphtheria can lead to breathing problems, heart failure, paralysis, and death.

▲ **Figure 19–12** By testing multiple hypotheses, Louis Pasteur was able to show that bacteria cause disease.

Word Origins

Pathogen comes from the Greek words *pathos,* meaning "suffering," and *-genes,* meaning "born" or "produced." So a pathogen is something that produces suffering. **The Greek word *karkinos* means "cancer." What do you think a carcinogen is?**

Preventing Bacterial Disease **Figure 19–13** shows some common bacterial diseases, the pathogens that cause them, and their effects on the body. Many bacterial diseases can be prevented by stimulating the body's immune system with vaccines. A **vaccine** is a preparation of weakened or killed pathogens. When injected into the body, a vaccine sometimes prompts the body to produce immunity to the disease. Immunity is the body's ability to destroy new pathogens. You will learn more about immunity in Chapter 40.

If a bacterial infection does occur, a number of drugs can be used to attack and destroy the invading bacteria. These drugs include antibiotics, such as penicillin and tetracycline. **Antibiotics** are compounds that block the growth and reproduction of bacteria. They can be used to cure many bacterial diseases. One of the major reasons for the dramatic increase in human life expectancy during the past two centuries is an increased understanding of how to prevent and cure bacterial infections.

What is the effect of antibiotics on bacteria?

Bacterial Disease in Animals

Animals are also affected by bacterial diseases, requiring farmers and ranchers to take precautions to protect their livestock from infection. Adding to the danger is the fact that many bacteria can affect both humans and animals. One example of such a bacterium is *Bacillus anthracis*, which causes the disease known as anthrax. Anthrax infections are often found in sheep, sometimes spreading to farmers and wool workers who have contact with the animals. Anthrax can be fatal to both humans and animals. The bacterium produces tough, resistant spores that can last for years. These properties have led some groups to develop anthrax as a biological warfare agent.

The deadly nature of anthrax as a biological weapon is clear. Hundreds of people died in the city of Sverdlovski when anthrax was accidentally released from a Soviet research facility in 1979. About 20 years later, letters laced with anthrax caused several deaths in the United States.

▼ **Figure 19–13** **Bacteria cause disease in the body.** Some of the diseases caused by pathogenic bacteria are listed in the table.

Diseases Caused by Bacteria

Disease	Bacterium	Effect on Body
Lyme disease	*Borrelia burgdorferi*	"Bulls-eye" rash at site of tick bite, fever, fatigue, headaches, muscle aches, joint aches
Tetanus	*Clostridium tetani*	Severe muscle spasms, paralysis, death
Tuberculosis	*Mycobacterium tuberculosis*	Fatigue, weight loss, mild fever, night sweats, chronic cough
Diphtheria	*Corynebacterium diphtheria*	Sore throat, low-grade fever
Bacterial meningitis	*Neisseria meningitidis*	High fever, headache, stiff neck, nausea, fatigue
Strep throat	*Streptococcus pyogenes*	Fever, sore throat, swollen glands
Tooth decay	*Streptococcus mutans*	Destruction of tooth enamel

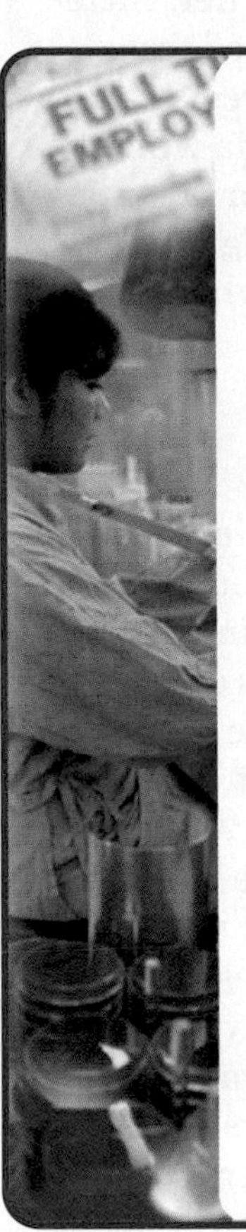

Careers in Biology

Epidemiologist

Job Description: work for a university, health department, research or health organization, or medical corporation to identify and track diseases and develop programs that prevent or control the spread of disease

Education: master's or doctoral degree in epidemiology, including course work in statistics, demography, research design, and public health

Skills: good communication skills, strong computer skills, knowledge of health and medical conditions

Highlights: You get to ask lots of questions and travel. You can work on infectious diseases such as tuberculosis. Some epidemiologists work on specific issues such as tobacco addiction.

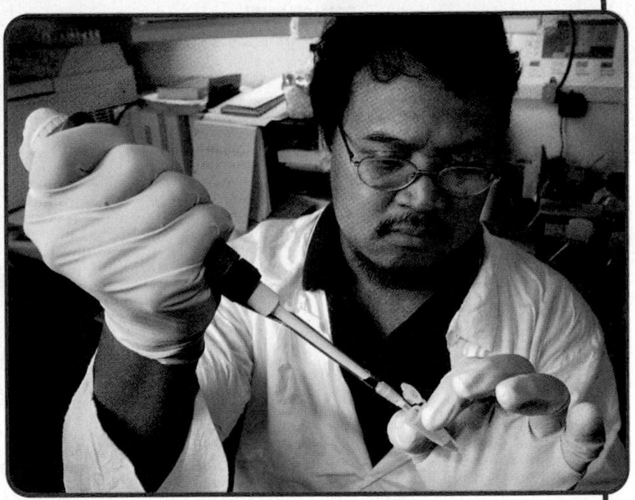

For: Career links
Visit: PHSchool.com
Web Code: cbb-6195

Controlling Bacteria

Although most bacteria are harmless, and many are beneficial, the risks of bacterial infection are great enough to warrant efforts to control bacterial growth. **There are various methods used to control bacterial growth, including sterilization, disinfectants, and food processing.**

Sterilization by Heat One method used to control the growth of potentially dangerous bacteria is sterilization. Sterilization destroys all bacteria by subjecting them to great heat. Most bacteria cannot survive high temperatures for a long time, so most can be killed by exposure to high heat.

Disinfectants Another method of controlling bacteria is by using disinfectants—chemical solutions that kill pathogenic bacteria. Disinfectants are used in the home to clean bathrooms, kitchens, and other rooms where bacteria may flourish.

Today, some manufacturers of soaps, cleansers, and even kitchen utensils have added antibacterial chemicals to their products. If you wash your hands properly, ordinary soaps do a good job of removing bacteria. Overuse of antibacterial compounds increases the likelihood that common bacteria will eventually evolve to become resistant to them—and therefore much more dangerous and difficult to kill.

For: Articles on bacteria and viruses
Visit: PHSchool.com
Web Code: cbe-6193

Food Storage and Processing As you read earlier, bacteria can cause food to spoil. One method of stopping food from spoiling is storing it in a refrigerator. Food that is stored at a low temperature will stay fresh longer because the bacteria will take much longer to multiply. In addition, boiling, frying, or steaming can sterilize many kinds of food. Each of these cooking techniques raises the temperature of the food to a point where the bacteria are killed.

Viral Disease in Humans

Like bacteria, viruses produce disease by disrupting the body's normal equilibrium. In many viral infections, viruses attack and destroy certain cells in the body, causing the symptoms of the disease. Poliovirus infects and kills cells of the nervous system, producing paralysis. Other viruses cause infected cells to change their patterns of growth and development. Some common diseases caused by viruses are listed in **Figure 19–14.**

Unlike bacterial diseases, viral diseases cannot be treated with antibiotics. The best way to protect against most viral diseases lies in prevention, often by the use of vaccines. Several decades of childhood vaccination against smallpox have virtually eliminated this disease. Most vaccines provide protection only if they are used before an infection begins. Once a viral disease has been contracted, it may be too late to control the infection. However, sometimes the symptoms of the infection can be treated.

▼ **Figure 19–14** **Viruses produce disease by disrupting the body's normal equilibrium.** Some common human diseases caused by viruses are listed in this table.

Diseases Caused by Viruses

Disease	Effect on Body	Transmission
Common cold	Sneezing, sore throat, fever, headache, muscle aches	Contact with contaminated objects; droplet inhalation
Influenza	Body aches, fever, sore throat, nasal congestion, headache, dry cough, fatigue	Contact with contaminated objects; droplet inhalation
Smallpox	High fever, fatigue, head and back aches, rash	Contact with contaminated objects; droplet inhalation
AIDS	Helper T cells, which are needed for normal immune system function, are destroyed	Contact with contaminated blood or bodily fluids; pregnant women to babies during delivery or during breastfeeding
Chickenpox	Fever and weakness, red, itchy rash	Contact with rash; droplet inhalation
Measles	High fever, sore throat, cough, rash, sneezing, swollen eyelids, white spots on cheek lining	Droplet inhalation
Hepatitis A	Jaundice, fatigue, abdominal pain, appetite loss, nausea, diarrhea, fever	Human wastes, contaminated water and food
Hepatitis B, Hepatitis C	Jaundice, fatigue, abdominal pain, appetite loss, nausea, diarrhea, joint pain	Contact with contaminated blood or bodily fluids
West Nile	Fever, headache, body ache	Bite from an infected mosquito

Viral Disease in Animals

Viruses produce serious animal diseases as well. An epidemic of foot-and-mouth disease, caused by a virus that infects livestock, swept through parts of Europe in the late 1990s. Thousands of cattle were destroyed in efforts to control the disease. American authorities took special precautions to guard against the spread of the foot-and-mouth virus to North America.

Some animal viruses can even cause cancer. An example of these oncogenic, or tumor-causing, viruses is the Rous sarcoma virus, which infects chickens. Scientists have learned a great deal about cancer by studying the genes of these oncogenic viruses, which disrupt normal controls over cell growth and division.

Viral Disease in Plants

Many viruses, including tobacco mosaic virus, infect plants. These viruses pose a serious threat to many agricultural crops. Farmers in many countries, including the United States, struggle to control them. Like other viruses, plant viruses contain a core of nucleic acid and a protein coat.

Unlike animal viruses, most plant viruses have a difficult time entering the cells they infect. This is partly because plant cells are surrounded by tough cell walls that viruses alone cannot break through. As a result, most plant viruses are adapted to take advantage of breaks in the cell wall caused by even minor damage to plant tissues. Viruses can enter through tears in leaf tissue, breaks in stems or roots, or simply through microscopic cell wall damage caused by human or animal contact with the plant.

Many plant viruses are spread by insects. The feeding action of an insect pest often provides a perfect opportunity for viral infections to spread. Potato yellow dwarf virus is spread by an insect known as the leafhopper. Leafhoppers feed on potato leaves, and they also carry the virus in their tissues. As leafhoppers move from plant to plant, they spread the infection, threatening an entire crop if they are not controlled.

Once inside the plant, many viruses spread rapidly, causing severe tissue damage, mottled leaves, and wilting, and sometimes killing the infected plant as shown in **Figure 19–15.** Plant viruses infect many valuable fruit trees, including apples and peaches, and have caused serious losses in the potato crop.

▶ **Figure 19–15** The potato plants on the left have been infected with a potato virus, while those on the right are healthy. **Inferring** *How might farmers prevent the spread of plant viruses?*

Viroids and Prions

Scientists have discovered two other viruslike particles that also cause disease: viroids and prions. Viroids cause disease in plants. Prions cause disease in animals.

Viroids Many plants, including potatoes, tomatoes, apples, and citrus fruits, can be infected by viroids. **Viroids** are single-stranded RNA molecules that have no surrounding capsids. It is believed that viroids enter an infected cell and direct the synthesis of new viroids. The viroids then disrupt the metabolism of the plant cell and stunt the growth of the entire plant.

▲ **Figure 19–16** Prions may cause several infectious diseases, including mad cow disease. This cow was killed by mad cow disease. **Comparing and Contrasting** How are prions similar to viruses? How are they different?

Prions In 1972, American Stanley Prusiner became interested in scrapie, an infectious disease in sheep for which the exact cause was unknown. Although he first suspected a virus, experiments suggested the disease might actually be caused by tiny particles found in the brains of infected sheep. Unlike viruses, these particles contained no DNA or RNA, only protein. Prusiner called these particles **prions,** short for "protein infectious particles." Although prions were first discovered in sheep, many animals, including humans, can become infected with prions.

There is some evidence that prions cause disease by forming protein clumps. These clumps induce normal protein molecules to become prions. Eventually, there are so many prions in the nerve tissue that cells become damaged. There is strong evidence that mad cow disease and Creutzfeldt-Jakob disease, a similar disease in humans, may be caused by prions.

19–3 Section Assessment

1. **Key Concept** What are the two ways that bacteria cause disease?
2. **Key Concept** Describe the three methods of preventing bacterial growth in food.
3. **Key Concept** Describe how viruses cause disease.
4. What are viroids?
5. **Critical Thinking Applying Concepts** You think you might have a bacterial infection. Would you ask for a vaccination against the bacteria? Why or why not?
6. **Critical Thinking Applying Concepts** How might epidemiologists collaborate with scientists who study viruses as they investigate viral diseases?

Writing in Science

Creative Writing

In *War of the Worlds,* Earth is invaded by aliens. No weapons can kill the invaders. Earth is saved when the invaders die from diseases they contract. Write a summary of a story about people from Earth voyaging to another planet. Include information on how the people from Earth might protect themselves from possible new diseases.

Exploration

Identifying Limits to the Growth of Bacteria

In this investigation, you will determine whether an environmental factor such as temperature can control the growth and reproduction of bacteria.

Problem

Does temperature limit the growth and reproduction of bacteria?

Materials

- glass-marking pencil
- 3 sterile agar plates
- sterile cotton swabs
- bacterial culture
- transparent tape
- hand lens

Skills

Analyzing Data, Drawing Conclusions

Procedure

1. **Asking Questions** Read the investigation; then, write three questions about how temperature might affect the growth of bacteria.
2. **Predicting** Predict how temperature will affect the growth rate of bacterial colonies.
3. Put on your plastic gloves. Use a glass-marking pencil to label the edges of the agar plates "3°C," "20°C," and "37°C." Also, write your name on each plate.
4. Dip a sterile swab in the bacterial culture and wipe it back and forth in a zigzag pattern over the entire surface of the agar on one plate. Cover the plate and seal it with transparent tape. **CAUTION:** *Do not open the plates once they have been exposed to the air.*
5. Repeat step 4 with each plate, using a new sterile swab for each plate.
6. Place the plate labeled "3°C" in a refrigerator. Leave the plate labeled "20°C" in a place designated by your teacher. Place the plate labeled "37°C" in an incubator. Be sure to store each plate upside down.
7. Make a copy of the data table. After 24 hours, examine each plate with a hand lens. Bacterial colonies look like small white or colored dots on the agar surface. In your data table, record the number of bacterial colonies on each agar plate. Return each plate to its location.
8. After a second period of 24 hours, record in your data table the number of bacterial colonies on each agar plate. Return your agar plates to your teacher for safe disposal.

Data Table

Temperature	Number of Colonies	
	24 hours	48 hours
3°C		
20°C		
37°C		

9. Make a graph of the results in your data table. Plot time on the *x*-axis and number of bacterial colonies on the *y*-axis. Use a different symbol to represent data from each day. After you have plotted all your data on your graph, draw a straight line or smooth curve as close as possible to all the points that represent observations after 24 hours. Draw a second curve or line through the points that represent observations after 48 hours.

Analyze and Conclude

1. **Analyzing Data** At what temperature were the most bacterial colonies visible after 24 hours? At what temperature were the fewest bacterial colonies visible after 24 hours?
2. **Analyzing Data** Did the same plate have the most bacteria after 48 hours? The fewest?
3. **Analyzing Data** Describe the effect of temperature on the growth of bacteria.
4. **Evaluating** Do you consider your data reliable? Explain. Did the results of your experiment confirm your prediction?

Go Further

Formulating Hypotheses Propose a hypothesis about the effects of another variable on the growth of bacteria. Design an experiment that could test your hypothesis.

Chapter 19 Study Guide

19–1 Bacteria

Key Concepts

- Eubacteria, the larger of the two kingdoms of prokaryotes, have cell walls made up of peptidoglycan.
- Archaebacteria do not contain peptidoglycan. The DNA sequences of key archaebacterial genes are more like those of eukaryotes than those of eubacteria.
- Prokaryotes are identified by their shapes, the chemical natures of their cell walls, the ways they move, and the way they obtain energy.
- Some bacteria are producers that capture energy by photosynthesis. Others break down the nutrients in dead matter and the atmosphere. Still other bacteria have human uses.

Vocabulary

prokaryote, p. 471 • bacillus, p. 473
coccus, p. 473 • spirillum, p. 473
chemoheterotroph, p. 473
photoheterotroph, p. 474
photoautotroph, p. 474
chemoautotroph, p. 474
obligate aerobe, p. 474
obligate anaerobe, p. 474
facultative anaerobe, p. 474
binary fission, p. 475
conjugation, p. 475
endospore, p. 475
nitrogen fixation, p. 477

19–2 Viruses

Key Concepts

- A typical virus is composed of a core of DNA or RNA surrounded by a protein coat.
- In a lytic infection, a virus enters a cell, makes copies of itself, and causes the cell to burst.
- In a lysogenic infection, a virus integrates its DNA into the DNA of the host cell and the viral genetic information replicates along with the host cell's DNA.

Vocabulary

virus, p. 478 • capsid, p. 479
bacteriophage, p. 479
lytic infection, p. 480
lysogenic infection, p. 480
prophage, p. 480
retrovirus, p. 482

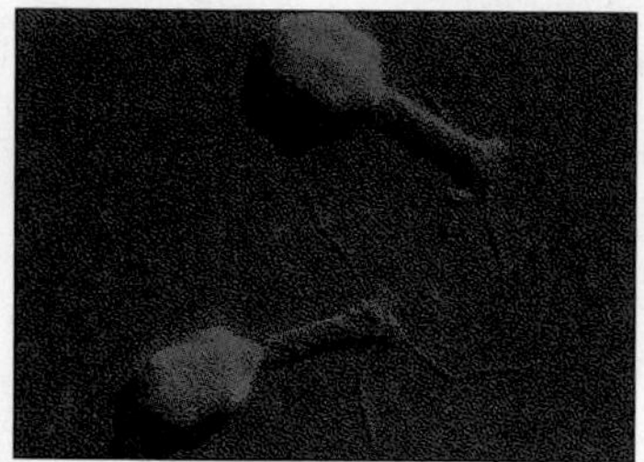

19–3 Diseases Caused by Bacteria and Viruses

Key Concepts

- Bacteria produce disease in one of two general ways. Some bacteria damage the cells and tissues of the infected organism directly by breaking down the cells for food. Other bacteria release toxins (poisons) that travel throughout the body interfering with the normal activity of the host.
- There are various methods used to control bacterial growth, including sterilization, disinfectants, and food processing.
- Viruses produce disease by disrupting the body's normal equilibrium.

Vocabulary

pathogen, p. 485
vaccine, p. 486
antibiotic, p. 486
viroid, p. 490
prion, p. 490

Thinking Visually

Complete this concept map about prokaryotes.

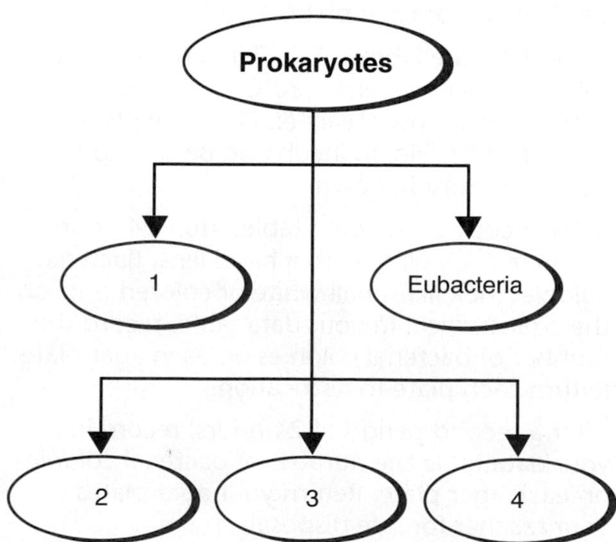

Preparing for the Living Environment Exam

Blue questions emphasize Regents Exam content

Chapter 19

Part A

Multiple Choice

For each statement or question, select the number of the word or expression that, of those given, best completes the statement or answers the question.

1 Prokaryotes are unlike all other organisms in that their cells
(1) lack nuclei (3) have cell walls
(2) have organelles (4) lack nucleic acids

2 Which photograph shows bacillus bacteria?

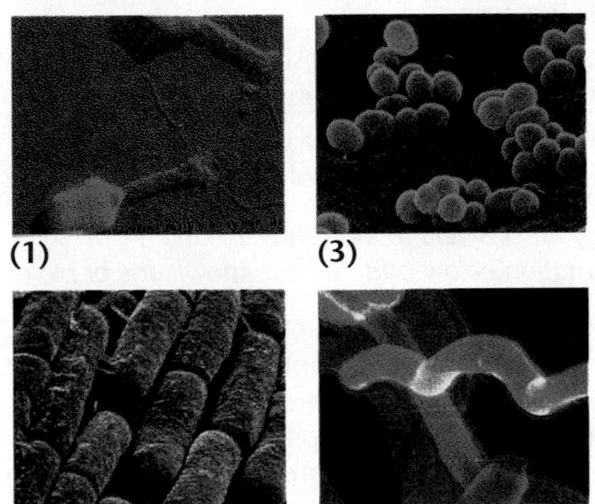

3 Which group includes the bacteria that contain chlorophyll *a*?
(1) archaebacteria (3) chemoautotrophs
(2) cyanobacteria (4) pathogens

4 Bacteria reproduce asexually by
(1) binary fission (3) conjugation
(2) spores (4) external fertilization

5 The process of converting nitrogen into a form plants can use is known as nitrogen
(1) conjugation (3) decomposition
(2) transfer (4) fixation

6 Organisms that infect plants and animals and interfere with normal life functions may be classified as
(1) pathogens and bacteria
(2) foreign substances and enzymes
(3) parasites and hosts
(4) toxins and viruses

7 The outer protein coat of a virus is a
(1) core of DNA (3) capsid
(2) core of RNA (4) membrane envelope

8 Which illness is caused by a virus?
(1) Lyme disease (3) tetanus
(2) measles (4) food poisoning

9 Which characteristic is *not* used to identify specific prokaryotes?
(1) cell size (3) cell movement
(2) cell shape (4) cell energy source

10 One group of viruses that contain RNA as their genetic information is
(1) oncogenic (3) capsids
(2) retroviruses (4) prophages

11 Which method is *not* used to protect food against microorganisms?
(1) salting (3) vaccination
(2) freezing (4) sterilization

12 Archaebacteria that live in oxygen-free environments include
(1) protists (3) retroviruses
(2) methanogens (4) bacteriophages

13 Which process is used for the exchange of genetic information between two bacterial cells?
(1) lytic cycle (3) binary fission
(2) conjugation (4) immunization

14 Spherical prokaryotes are called
(1) cocci (3) spirilla
(2) eubacteria (4) archaebacteria

15 Bacterial cells do NOT contain a
(1) cell membrane (3) nucleus
(2) cell wall (4) chromosome

For question 16, complete the analogy by selecting the correct number. In analogies, A : B :: C : means "A is to B as C is to ___?___."

16 Cell : cell membrane :: virus :
(1) cell wall (3) bacteriophage
(2) capsid (4) DNA core

Test-Taking Tip For questions containing the word *not*, begin by jotting down items that do fit the characteristic in question. Then, compare your notes with the answer choices and eliminate those that correspond to your list. Finally, check to see that your answer is correct by confirming that it does not fit the characteristic in question.

Preparing for the Living Environment Exam

Part B

Multiple Choice and Extended Response

For those questions that ask you to select a response, choose the one that best completes the statement or answers the question. For all others follow the directions given.

Base your answers to questions 17 and 18 on the graph below and on your knowledge of biology.

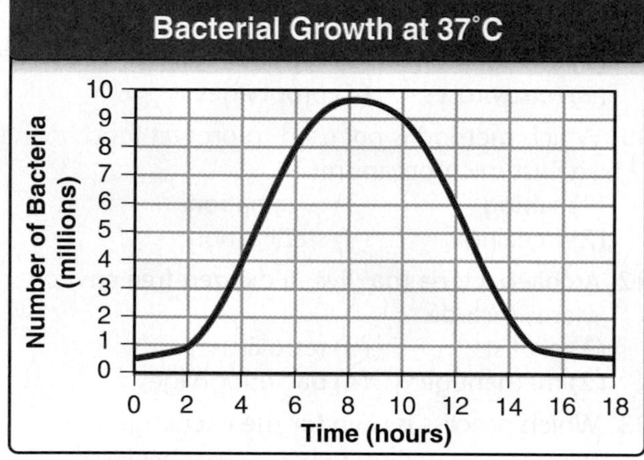

17 At which point in the graph does the number of living bacteria increase at the greatest rate?

(1) between hours 2 and 4

(2) between hours 4 and 6

(3) between hours 6 and 8

(4) between hours 10 and 14

18 Which is the most likely reason for the decrease in population shown?

(1) The temperature of the bacteria culture was too high after 8 hours

(2) The bacteria ceased mating after 8 hours

(3) More nutrients were added to the culture at regular intervals

(4) Waste products from the bacteria accumulated in the nutrient solution

19 State *two* distinguishing characteristics of prokaryotes.

20 Describe the *three* main cell shapes of prokaryotes.

21 State *two* methods by which prokaryotes move.

22 State one way in which photoautotrophs are similar to chemoautotrophs and one way in which they are different.

23 State one way in which photoheterotrophs are similar to ordinary heterotrophs and one way in which they are different.

24 State one way to distinguish between an obligate aerobe and an obligate anaerobe.

25 Facultative anaerobes can survive with or without oxygen. Explain how this is advantageous to them.

26 State the role of certain bacteria in the conversion of atmospheric nitrogen into a form that is usable by plants.

27 State the one thing that all viruses have in common concerning their interactions with living cells.

28 State one way the capsid protein is important to the functioning of a virus.

29 Describe the sequence of events that occurs during the lytic cycle of a T4 bacteriophage.

Base your answers to questions 30 and 31 on the information below and on your knowledge of biology.

An experiment was conducted to determine the effectiveness of different antibiotics against a certain strain of bacteria. Four disks, each soaked in a different antibiotic, were placed in a petri dish where the bacteria were growing. The results are summarized below.

Effects of Antibiotics

Antibiotic	Observation After One Week
A	No growth for 6 mm from disk edge
B	Growth all around disk edge
C	Growth all around disk edge
D	No growth for 2 mm from disk edge

30 State which antibiotics were the least effective at retarding the growth of the bacteria. Support your answer with data from the experiment.

31 State which of these antibiotics would most likely be effective for treating an infection caused by this strain of bacteria. Support your answer with data from the experiment.

32 Describe what happens to a bacterial cell when the bacteriophage DNA exits from the bacterial chromosome.

33 What is the most commonly used method to protect humans against most viral diseases?

34 Explain how other organisms would be affected if bacteria lost the ability to function in the recycling of nitrogen compounds.

35 Bacteria and viruses can be cultured (grown) in the laboratory. Bacteria are typically cultured on synthetic media. Viruses are not. Many viruses are grown on cultures of bacteria. Explain why viruses must be grown on bacteria and not synthetic media.

Base your answers to questions 36 and 37 on the information below and on your knowledge of biology.

The data table shows the results of an experiment conducted with one species of bacterium. The bacteria were grown for 24 hours in five dishes with nutrient media at several different pH levels, all at a temperature of 37°C.

pH of the Nutrient Medium	Number of Bacterial Colonies on the Nutrient Medium
5	10
6	50
7	60
8	70
9	5

36 The most appropriate title for this data table is
(1) The Effect of pH of Bacteria on Nutrient Media at 37°C
(2) The Effect of pH on Bacterial Population Growth
(3) The Effect of Bacterial Population Growth on pH
(4) The Effect of Bacteria at 37°C for 24 Hours

37 State an appropriate conclusion that could be drawn from the data reported in the table.

Part C

Extended Response

Answer the questions or follow the directions given.

38 Bacteria and viruses are often considered together because they have some things in common. Yet, they also differ in many significant ways. Compare the features and impact of both bacteria and viruses on humans and the environment. In your answer, be sure to
- compare the overall structure of a bacterial cell with the structure of a virus
- compare the genetic material of bacteria with the genetic material of viruses
- state one specific way each can be harmful to humans
- state one specific way each has been used by humans in a positive way
- state one specific way each has an impact on the environment

39 Describe the design of an experiment to test the hypothesis that contact of an agar plate with a finger results in more bacterial growth than the exposure of the plate to classroom air.

40 Scientists use stains to distinguish between Gram-positive and Gram-negative bacteria. Explain how these stains work to distinguish between the two. In your answer be sure to include:
- the number of dyes used in Gram staining
- the colors that indicate the presence of Gram-positive and Gram-negative bacteria
- the structural differences in the bacteria that result in the color difference

For: An interactive self-test
Visit: PHSchool.com
Web Code: cba-6190

CHAPTER 20

Protists

These diatoms, with their beautiful glasslike walls, make up a small part of the diverse group known as protists.

Inquiry Activity

What are protists?

Procedure

1. Place a drop of water containing a variety of microorganisms on a microscope slide. Add a drop of methyl cellulose and a coverslip. Observe the slide under the microscope at low and high magnifications.
2. Record your observations. Draw and label each type of organism.
3. Draw a chart listing each type of organism that you observed and its characteristics.

Think About It

1. **Classifying** Are any of these organisms bacteria, animals, or plants? Explain your answer.
2. **Forming Operational Definitions** The organisms you observed are members of a group called protists. Write a definition of *protist*.

20–1 The Kingdom Protista

4-1.3 Organelles in single-celled organisms
LS- Compare sizes of cells/organelles
LS- Identify/compare cell parts or types
LS- Make observations
LS- Prepare wet mount slides
LS- Use of compound microscope

Guide for Reading

Key Concept
• What are protists?

Vocabulary
protist

Reading Strategy: Summarizing As you read, find the main ideas for each blue heading. Write down a few key words from each main idea. Then, use the key words in your summary. Reread and revise your summary, keeping only the most important ideas.

On a dark, quiet night you sit at the stern of a tiny sailboat as it glides through the calm waters of a coastal inlet. Suddenly, the boat's wake sparkles with its own light. As the stern cuts through the water, glimmering points of light leave a ghostly trail into the darkness. What's responsible for this eerie display? You've just had a close encounter with one group of some of the most remarkable organisms in the world—the protists.

What Is a Protist?

The kingdom Protista is a diverse group that may include more than 200,000 species. Biologists have argued for years over the best way to classify protists, and the issue may never be settled. In fact, protists are defined less by what they are and more by what they are not: A **protist** is any organism that is not a plant, an animal, a fungus, or a prokaryote. **Protists are eukaryotes that are not members of the kingdoms Plantae, Animalia, or Fungi.** Recall that a eukaryote has a nucleus and other membrane-bound organelles. Although most protists are unicellular, quite a few are not, as you can see in **Figure 20–1**. A few protists actually consist of hundreds or even thousands of cells but are still considered protists because they are so similar to other protists that are truly unicellular.

CHECKPOINT *What is the classification of an organism that is not a plant, an animal, a fungus, or a prokaryote?*

Figure 20–1 **Protists are a diverse group of mainly single-celled eukaryotes.** Examples of protists include freshwater ciliates, radiolarians, and *Spirogyra*. *Spirogyra* may form slimy floating masses in fresh water. The organism's name refers to the helical arrangement of its ribbonlike chloroplasts.

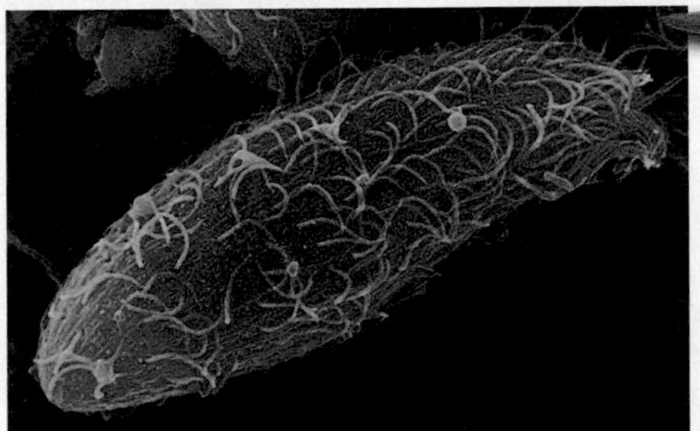

Euplotes **(a freshwater ciliate)**
(magnification: about 140×)

Radiolarian
(magnification: 3400×)

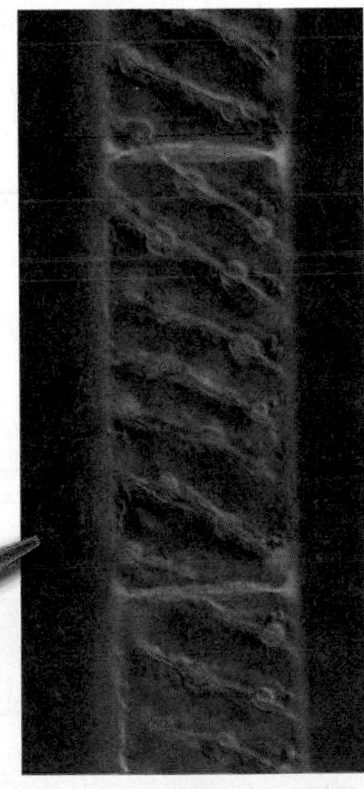

Spirogyra
(magnification: 400×)

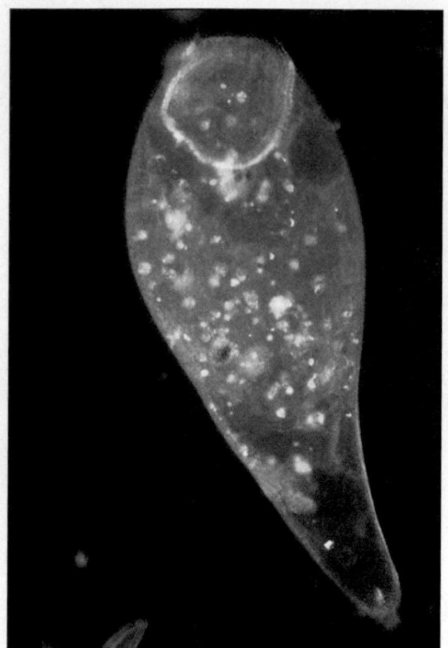

Stentor (magnification: 350×)

▲ **Figure 20–2** According to one hypothesis, some organelles in eukaryotic cells were once symbiotic prokaryotes that lived inside other cells. For example, the mitochondria found in this *Stentor* may be descended from early prokaryotes. **Applying Concepts** ***What other organelle may originally have been symbiotic cells?***

Go Online NSTA SciLinks

For: Links on protists
Visit: www.SciLinks.org
Web Code: cbn-6201

Evolution of Protists

Protists are members of a kingdom whose formal name, *Protista,* comes from Greek words meaning "the very first." The name is appropriate. The first eukaryotic organisms on Earth, which appeared nearly 1.5 billion years ago, were protists.

Where did the first protists come from? Biologist Lynn Margulis has hypothesized that the first eukaryotes evolved from a symbiosis of several cells. Mitochondria and chloroplasts found in eukaryotic cells may be descended from aerobic and photosynthetic prokaryotes that began to live inside larger cells. **Figure 20–2** shows a representative protist.

Classification of Protists

Protists are so diverse that many biologists suggest that they should be broken up into several kingdoms. This idea is supported by recent studies of protist DNA indicating that different groups of protists evolved independently from archaebacteria. Unfortunately, at present, biologists don't agree on how to classify the protists. Therefore, we will take the traditional approach of considering the protists as a single kingdom.

One way to classify protists is according to the way they obtain nutrition. Thus, many protists that are heterotrophs are called animallike protists. Those that produce their own food by photosynthesis are called plantlike protists. Finally, those that obtain their food by external digestion—either as decomposers or parasites—are called funguslike protists. This is the way in which we will organize our investigation of the protists.

It is important to understand that these categories are an artificial way to organize a very diverse group of organisms. Categories based on the way protists obtain food do not reflect the evolutionary history of these organisms. For example, all animallike protists did not necessarily share a relatively recent ancestor. The protistan family tree is likely to be redrawn many times as the genes of the many species of protists are analyzed and compared using the powerful tools of molecular biology.

20–1 Section Assessment

1. **Key Concept** What is a protist?
2. Describe Margulis's theory about the evolution of protists.
3. Are most protists unicellular or multicellular?
4. What are the three methods that protists use to obtain food?
5. Identify the characteristics of organisms belonging to the kingdom Protista.
6. **Critical Thinking Using Analogies** In what way is the kingdom Protista similar to a group of people who do not belong to a political party?

Writing in Science

Creative Writing
Write and illustrate a brief newspaper story explaining the hypothesis that eukaryotic cells evolved from a symbiosis of several prokaryotes with larger cells. *Hint:* Begin with a draft and then revise that draft, looking at organization and word choice.

20–2 Animallike Protists: Protozoans

4-1.3 Organelles in single-celled organisms
4-6.1 Relationships and interactions between organisms
4-5.2 Parasites may infect and interfere with normal functioning of organisms
LS- Make observations and state an appropriate hypothesis
LS- Use a compound microscope and prepare wet mount slides

Guide for Reading

Key Concepts
- What are the distinguishing features of the major phyla of animallike protists?
- How do animallike protists harm other living things?

Vocabulary
pseudopod
amoeboid movement
food vacuole • cilium
trichocyst • macronucleus
micronucleus • gullet
anal pore • contractile vacuole
conjugation

Reading Strategy: Building Vocabulary
Before you read, preview new vocabulary by skimming the section and making a list of the highlighted, boldface terms. Leave space to make notes as you read.

At one time, animallike protists were called protozoa, which means "first animals," and were classified separately from more plantlike protists. Like animals, these organisms are heterotrophs. The four phyla of animallike protists are distinguished from one another by their means of movement. As you will read, zooflagellates swim with flagella, sarcodines move by extensions of their cytoplasm, ciliates move by means of cilia, and sporozoans do not move on their own at all.

Zooflagellates

Many protists easily move through their aquatic environments propelled by flagella. Flagella are long, whiplike projections that allow a cell to move. **Animallike protists that swim using flagella are classified in the phylum Zoomastigina and are often referred to as zooflagellates.** Most zooflagellates (zoh-oh-FLAJ-uh-lits) have either one or two flagella, although a few species have many flagella. Two representative zooflagellates are shown in **Figure 20–3.**

Zooflagellates are generally able to absorb food through their cell membranes. Many live in lakes and streams, where they absorb nutrients from decaying organic material. Others live within the bodies of other organisms, taking advantage of the food that the larger organism provides.

Most zooflagellates reproduce asexually by mitosis and cytokinesis. Mitosis followed by cytokinesis results in two cells that are genetically identical. Some zooflagellates, however, have a sexual life cycle as well. During sexual reproduction, gamete cells are produced by meiosis. When gametes from two organisms fuse, an organism with a new combination of genetic information is formed.

Figure 20–3 **Zooflagellates are animallike protists that swim using flagella.** Most zooflagellates live as solitary cells. Some form colonies of cells.

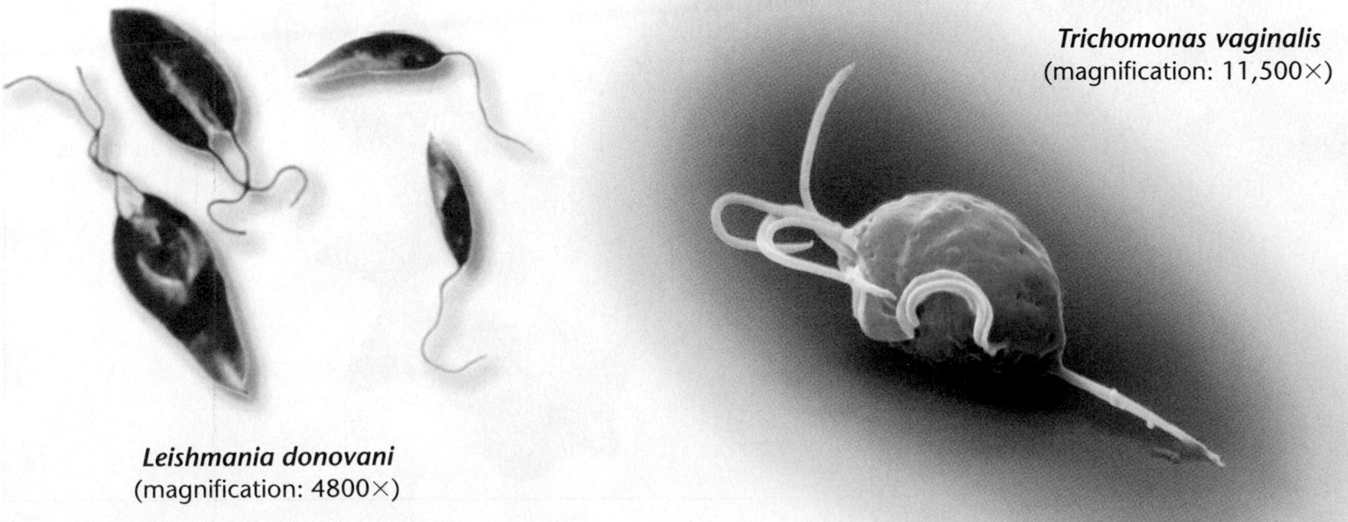

Leishmania donovani (magnification: 4800×)

Trichomonas vaginalis (magnification: 11,500×)

Word Origins

Pseudopod comes from the Greek words *pseudes,* meaning "false," and *-pous,* meaning "foot." So *pseudopod* means "false foot." The suffix *-onym* comes from the Greek word *onama,* meaning "name." **What do you think the word *pseudonym* means?**

Sarcodines

Members of the phylum Sarcodina, or sarcodines, move via temporary cytoplasmic projections known as **pseudopods** (SOO-doh-pahdz). **Sarcodines are animallike protists that use pseudopods for feeding and movement.** The best-known sarcodines are the amoebas, shown in **Figure 20–4.** Amoebas are flexible, active cells with thick pseudopods that extend out of the central mass of the cell. The cytoplasm of the cell streams into the pseudopod, and the rest of the cell follows. This type of locomotion is known as **amoeboid movement.**

Amoebas can capture and digest particles of food and even other cells. They do this by surrounding their meal, then taking it inside themselves to form a food vacuole. A **food vacuole** is a small cavity in the cytoplasm that temporarily stores food. Once inside the cell, the material is digested rapidly and the nutrients are passed along to the rest of the cell. Undigestible waste material remains inside the vacuole until its contents are eliminated by releasing them outside the cell. Amoebas reproduce by mitosis and cytokinesis.

Foraminiferans, another member of Sarcodina, are abundant in the warmer regions of the oceans. Foraminiferans secrete shells of calcium carbonate ($CaCO_3$). As they die, the calcium carbonate from their shells accumulates on the bottom of the ocean. In some regions, thick deposits of foraminiferan shells have formed on the ocean floor. The white chalk cliffs of Dover, England, are huge deposits of foraminiferan skeletons that were raised above sea level by geological processes.

Heliozoans comprise another group of sarcodines. The name *heliozoa* means "sun animal." Thin spikes of cytoplasm, supported by microtubules, project from their silica (SiO_2) shells, making heliozoans look like the sun's rays.

▼ **Figure 20–4 Sarcodines use pseudopods for feeding and movement.** The amoeba, a common sarcodine, moves by first extending a pseudopod away from its body. The organism's cytoplasm then streams into the pseudopod. Amoebas also use pseudopods to surround and ingest prey.

Amoeba proteus (magnification: 330×)

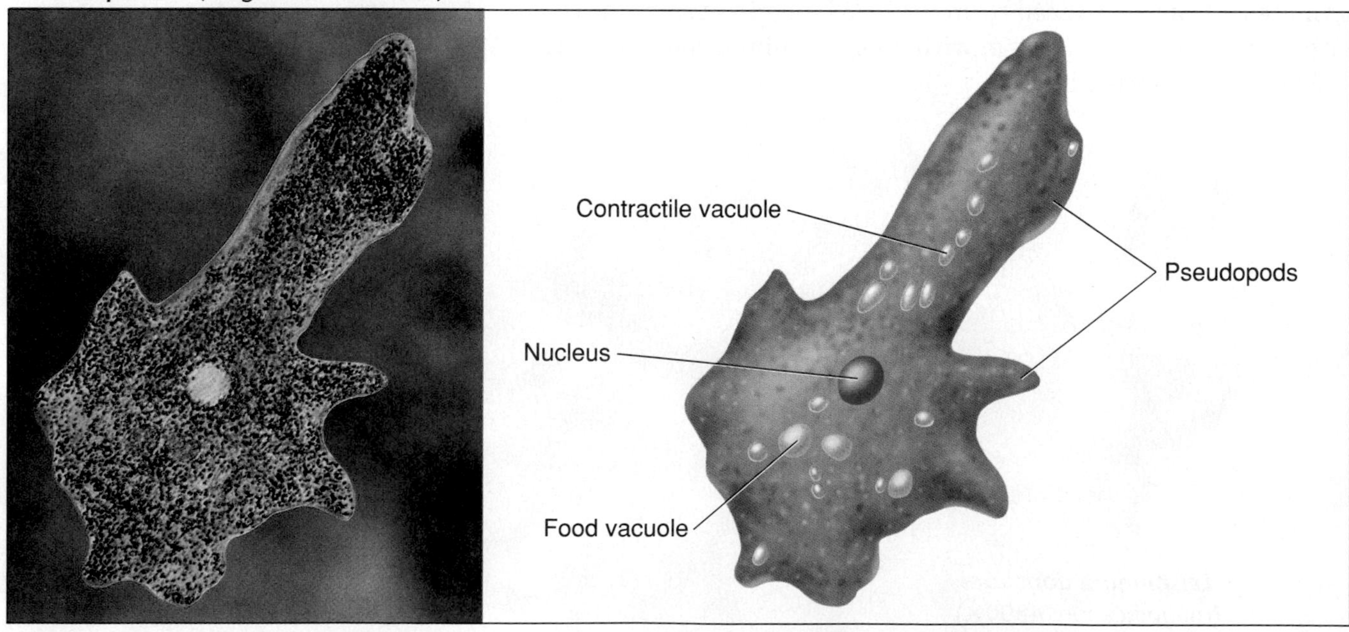

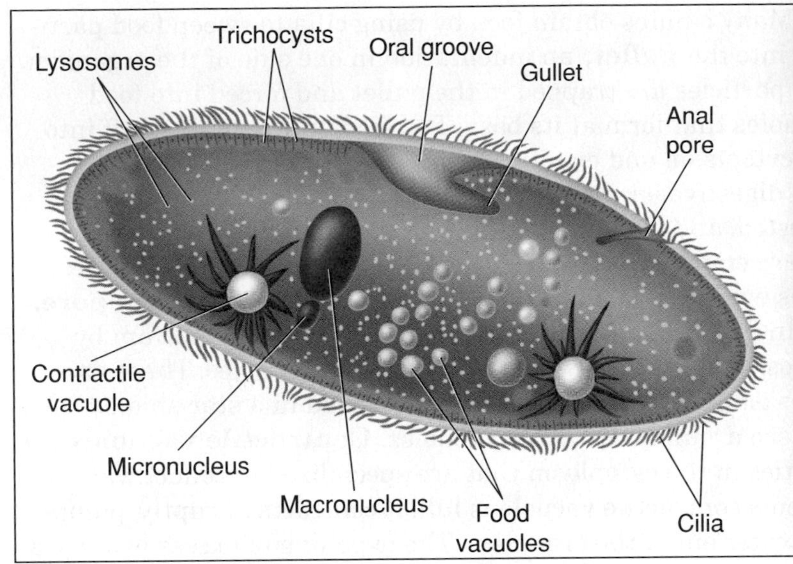

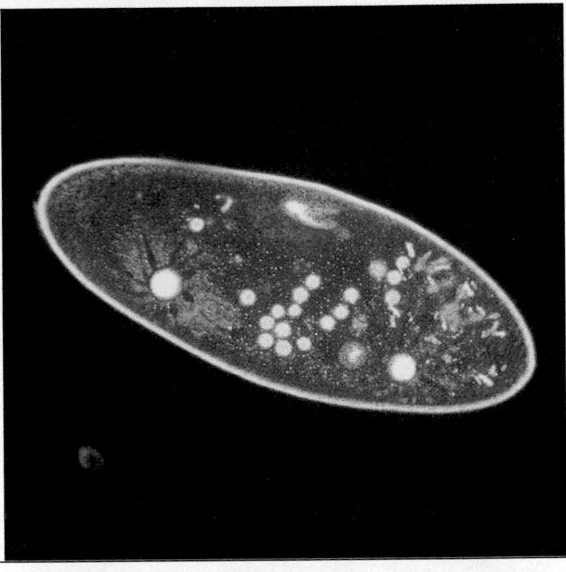

Paramecium caudatum (magnification: 2500×)

▲ **Figure 20–5** **Ciliates use hairlike projections called cilia for feeding and movement.** Ciliates, including this paramecium, are covered with short, hairlike cilia that propel them through the water. Cilia also line the organism's gullet and move its food—usually bacteria—to the organism's interior. There, the food particles are engulfed, forming food vacuoles. The contractile vacuoles collect and remove excess water, thereby helping to achieve homeostasis, a stable internal environment.

Ciliates

The phylum Ciliophora is named for **cilia** (singular: cilium), short hairlike projections similar to flagella. **Members of the phylum Ciliophora, known as ciliates, use cilia for feeding and movement.** The internal structure of cilia and flagella are identical. The beating of cilia, like the pull of hundreds of oars in an ancient ship, propels a cell rapidly through water.

Ciliates are found in both fresh and salt water. In fact, a lake or stream near your home might contain many different ciliates. Most ciliates are free living, which means that they do not exist as parasites or symbionts.

 *What are cilia, and how do ciliates use them?*

Internal Anatomy Some of the best-known ciliates belong to the genus *Paramecium.* A paramecium can be as long as 350 micrometers. Its cilia, which are organized into evenly spaced rows and bundles, beat in a regular, efficient pattern. The cell membrane of a paramecium is highly structured and has trichocysts just below its surface. **Trichocysts** (TRY-koh-sists) are very small, bottle-shaped structures used for defense. When a paramecium is confronted by danger, such as a predator, the trichocysts release stiff projections that protect the cell.

A paramecium's internal anatomy is shown in **Figure 20–5.** Like most ciliates, a paramecium possesses two types of nuclei: a macronucleus and one or more smaller micronuclei. Why does a ciliate need two types of nuclei? The **macronucleus** is a "working library" of genetic information—a site for keeping multiple copies of most of the genes that the cell needs in its day-to-day existence. The **micronucleus,** by contrast, contains a "reserve copy" of all of the cell's genes.

For: Amoeba and Paramecium activity
Visit: PHSchool.com
Web Code: cbp-6202

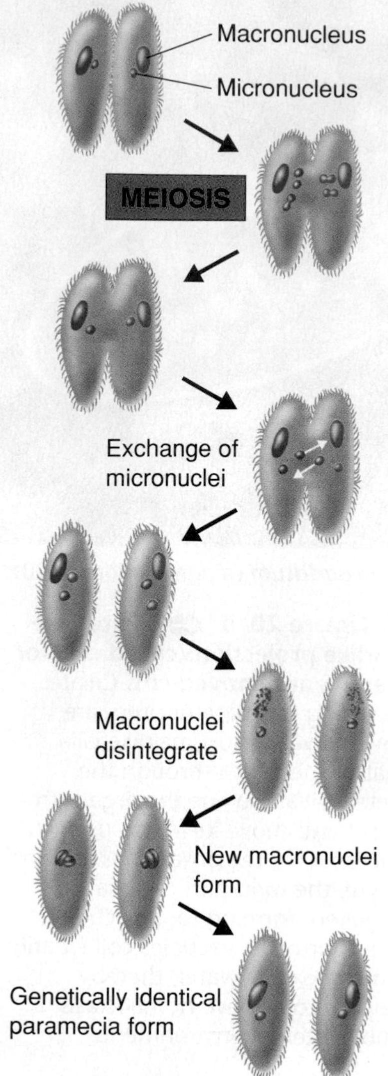

▲ **Figure 20–6** During conjugation, two paramecia attach themselves to each other and exchange genetic information. The process is not reproduction because no new individuals are formed. Conjugation is a sexual process, however, and it results in an increase in genetic diversity. **Interpreting Graphics** ***What structures do paramecia exchange during conjugation?***

Many ciliates obtain food by using cilia to sweep food particles into the **gullet,** an indentation in one side of the organism. The particles are trapped in the gullet and forced into food vacuoles that form at its base. The food vacuoles pinch off into the cytoplasm and eventually fuse with lysosomes, which contain digestive enzymes. The material in the food vacuoles is digested, and the organism obtains nourishment. Waste materials are emptied into the environment when the food vacuole fuses with a region of the cell membrane called the **anal pore.**

In fresh water, water may move into the paramecium by osmosis. This excess water is collected in vacuoles. These vacuoles empty into canals that are arranged in a star-shaped pattern around contractile vacuoles. **Contractile vacuoles** are cavities in the cytoplasm that are specialized to collect water. When a contractile vacuole is full, it contracts abruptly, pumping water out of the organism. The expelling of excess water via the contractile vacuole is one of the ways the paramecium maintains homeostasis.

Conjugation Under most conditions, ciliates reproduce asexually by mitosis and cytokinesis. When placed under stress, paramecia may engage in a process known as **conjugation** that allows them to exchange genetic material with other individuals. The process of conjugation is shown in **Figure 20–6.**

Conjugation begins when two paramecia attach themselves to each other. Meiosis of their diploid micronuclei produces four haploid micronuclei, three of which disintegrate. The remaining micronucleus in each cell divides mitotically, forming a pair of identical micronuclei. The two cells then exchange one micronucleus from each pair. The macronuclei disintegrate, and each cell forms a new macronucleus from its micronucleus. The two paramecia that leave conjugation are genetically identical to each other, but both have been changed by the exchange of genetic information.

Conjugation is not a form of reproduction, because no new individuals are formed. It is, however, a sexual process—because it uses meiosis to produce new combinations of genetic information. In a large population, conjugation helps to produce and maintain genetic diversity.

Sporozoans

While many animallike protists are free living, some are parasites. **Members of the phylum Sporozoa do not move on their own and are parasitic.** Sporozoans are parasites of a wide variety of organisms, including worms, fish, birds, and humans. Many sporozoans have complex life cycles that involve more than one host. Sporozoans reproduce by sporozoites. Under the right conditions, a sporozoite can attach itself to a host cell, penetrate it, and then live within it as a parasite.

 ***How do sporozoans reproduce?***

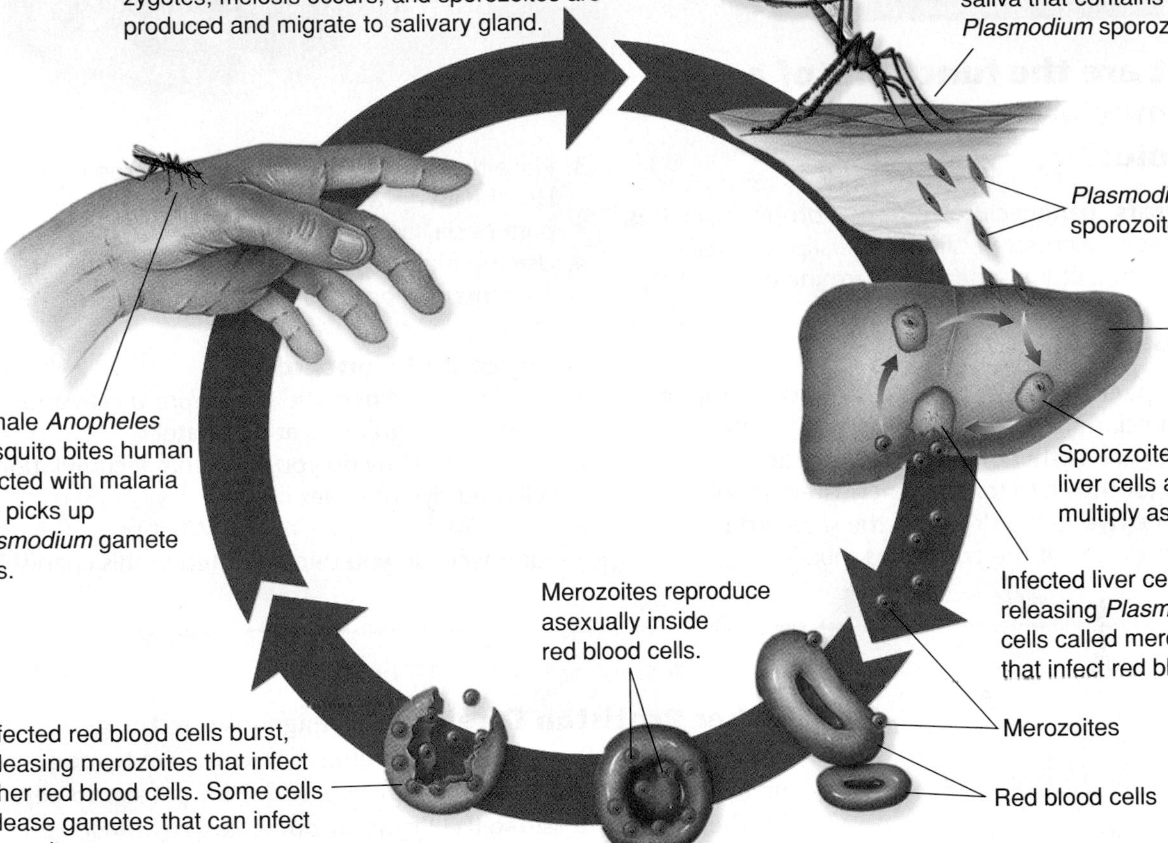

Sexual phase of *Plasmodium* life cycle takes place inside mosquito: Gametes fuse to form zygotes, meiosis occurs, and sporozoites are produced and migrate to salivary gland.

Infected mosquito bites another human, injecting saliva that contains *Plasmodium* sporozoites.

Plasmodium sporozoites

Liver

Sporozoites infect liver cells and multiply asexually.

Infected liver cells burst, releasing *Plasmodium* cells called merozoites that infect red blood cells.

Merozoites

Red blood cells

Merozoites reproduce asexually inside red blood cells.

Infected red blood cells burst, releasing merozoites that infect other red blood cells. Some cells release gametes that can infect mosquitoes.

Female *Anopheles* mosquito bites human infected with malaria and picks up *Plasmodium* gamete cells.

Animallike Protists and Disease

Unfortunately for humans and for other organisms, many protists are disease-causing parasites. **Some animallike protists cause serious diseases, including malaria and African sleeping sickness.**

Malaria Malaria is one of the world's most serious infectious diseases. As many as 2 million people still die from malaria every year. The sporozoan *Plasmodium,* which causes malaria, is carried by the female *Anopheles* mosquito.

The cycle of malarial infection is shown in **Figure 20–7.** When an infected mosquito bites a human, the mosquito's saliva, which contains sporozoites, enters the human's bloodstream. Once inside the blood, *Plasmodium* infects liver cells and then red blood cells, where it multiplies rapidly. When the red blood cells burst, the release of the parasites into the bloodstream produces severe chills and fever, symptoms of malaria.

Although drugs such as chloroquinine are effective against some forms of the disease, many strains of *Plasmodium* are resistant to these drugs. Scientists have developed a number of vaccines against malaria, but to date most are only partially effective. For the immediate future, the best means of controlling malaria involve controlling the mosquitoes that carry it.

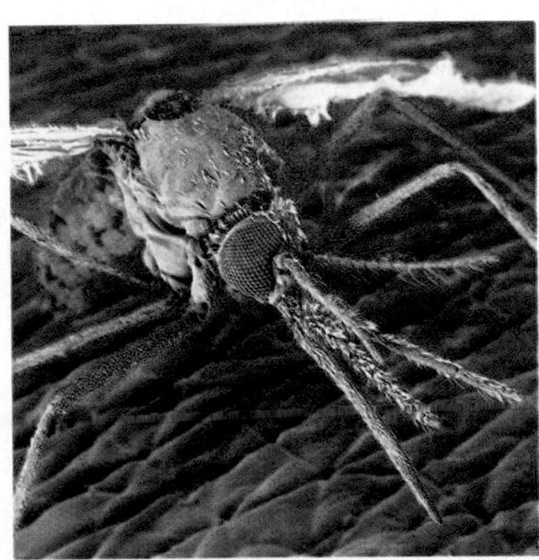

Figure 20–7 Animallike protists can cause serious diseases, including malaria. The bite of an *Anopheles* mosquito can transmit *Plasmodium* sporozoites. Once in the human body, *Plasmodium* infects liver cells and red blood cells and multiplies.

Quick Lab

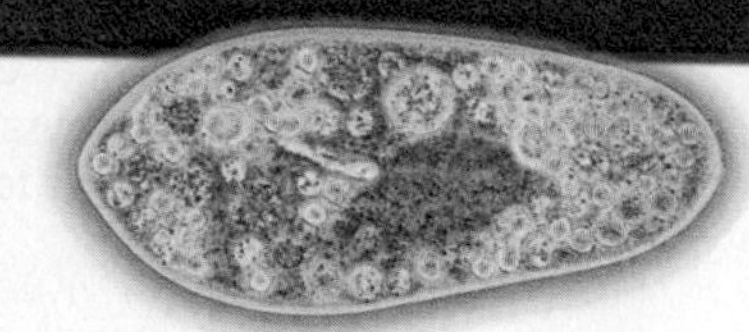

What are the functions of a paramecium's gullet and food vacuoles?

Materials paramecium culture, 2 dropper pipettes, microscope, microscope slide, coverslip, *Chlorella* (green alga) culture, toothpick, carmine dye

Procedure 

1. Use separate dropper pipettes to place a drop of paramecium culture and a drop of *Chlorella* culture next to each other on a microscope slide.
2. Use a toothpick to transfer a few granules of carmine dye to the drops on the slide. Add a coverslip so that the two drops mix.
3. Place the slide on the stage of a microscope. Use the low-power objective to locate several paramecia.
4. Use the high-power objective to observe the contents and behavior of the paramecia.

Analyze and Conclude

1. **Observing** Where did the *Chlorella* cells and carmine dye granules accumulate?
2. **Inferring** How do you think this accumulation of cells and dye granules occurs?
3. **Formulating Hypotheses** What process in the paramecia do you think resulted in this change?

Other Protistan Diseases Zooflagellates of the genus *Trypanosoma* cause African sleeping sickness. The trypanosomes that cause this disease are spread from person to person by the bite of the tsetse fly. Trypanosomes destroy blood cells and infect other tissues in the body. Symptoms of infection include fever, chills, and rashes. Trypanosomes also infect nerve cells. Severe damage to the nervous system causes some individuals to lose consciousness, lapsing into a deep and sometimes fatal sleep from which the disease gets its name. The control of the tsetse fly and the protist pathogens that it spreads is a major goal of health workers in Africa.

In certain regions of the world, many people are infected with species of *Entamoeba.* The parasitic protist *Entamoeba* causes a disease known as amebic dysentery. The parasitic amoebas that cause this disease live in the intestines, where they absorb food from the host. They also attack the wall of the intestine itself, destroying parts of it in the process and causing severe bleeding. These amoebas are passed out of the body in feces. In places where sanitation is poor, the amoebas may then find their way into supplies of food and water. In some areas of the world, amebic dysentery is a major health problem, weakening the human population and contributing to the spread of other diseases.

Amebic dysentery is common in areas with poor sanitation, but even crystal-clear streams may be contaminated with the flagellated pathogen, *Giardia. Giardia* produces tough, microscopic cysts that can be killed only by boiling water thoroughly or by adding iodine to the water. Infection by *Giardia* can cause severe diarrhea and digestive system problems.

For: Articles on protozoans
Visit: PHSchool.com
Web Code: cbe-6202

What is one method for controlling amebic dysentery?

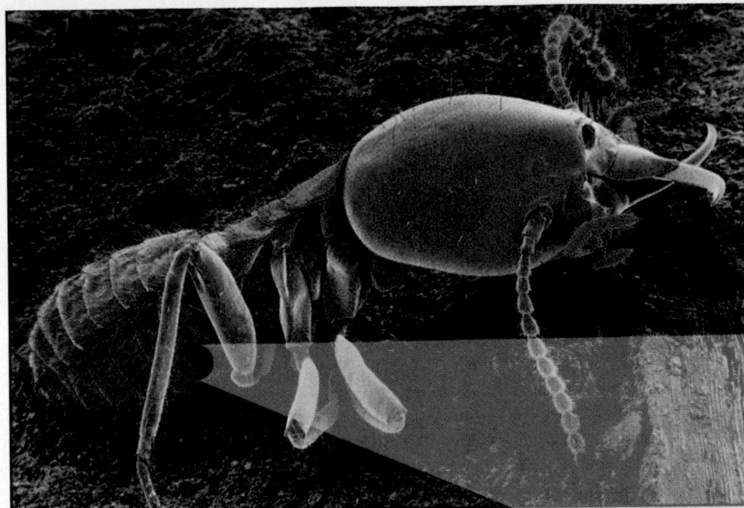

(magnification: 10×)

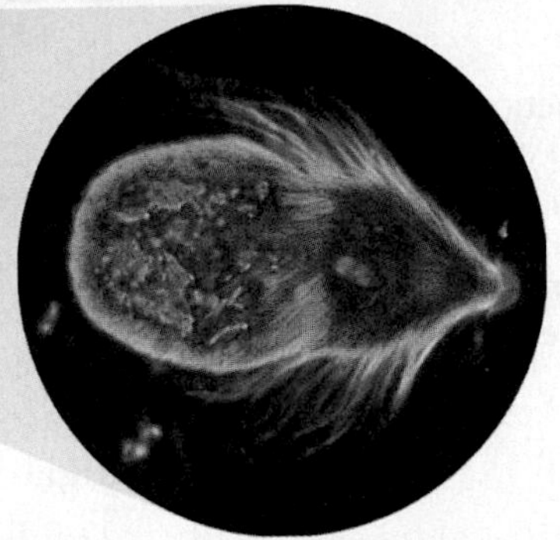

(magnification: about 250×)

Trichonympha

Figure 20–8 *Trichonympha* (below), a wood-digesting protist, lives in the digestive systems of insects such as a termite (left). Digestive enzymes produced by the protist break down the particles of wood, which you can see inside the protist's body. **Predicting** ***What would happen to a termite if its*** Trichonympha ***colony died?***

Ecology of Animallike Protists

Many animallike protists play essential roles in the living world. Some live symbiotically within other organisms. Others recycle nutrients by breaking down dead organic matter. Many animallike protists live in seas and lakes, where they are eaten by tiny animals, which in turn serve as food for larger animals.

Some animallike protists are beneficial to other organisms. *Trichonympha,* shown in **Figure 20–8,** is a zooflagellate that lives within the digestive systems of termites. This protist makes it possible for the termites to eat wood. Termites do not have enzymes to break down the cellulose in wood. (Incidentally, neither do humans, so it does us little good to nibble on a piece of wood.) How, then, does a termite digest cellulose? In a sense, it doesn't. *Trichonympha* does.

Trichonympha and other organisms in the termite's gut manufacture cellulase. Cellulase is an enzyme that breaks the chemical bonds in cellulose and makes it possible for termites to digest wood. Thus, with the help of their protist partners, termites can munch away, busily digesting all the wood they can eat.

20–2 Section Assessment

1. **Key Concept** What are the four major phyla of animallike protists? How do members of each of these groups move?
2. **Key Concept** What animallike protists cause disease?
3. How does a macronucleus differ in function from a micronucleus?
4. Describe the role of animallike protists in the environment.
5. **Critical Thinking Comparing and Contrasting** Compare animallike protists that have flagella to those that have cilia.
6. **Critical Thinking Making Judgments** Summarize how *Plasmodium* can cause a major disruption in the equilibrium of a human population.

Connecting Concepts

Comparing and Contrasting

Compare asexual and sexual processes in paramecia. Include the terms *mitosis* and *meiosis* in your answer. You may wish to refer back to Chapters 10 and 11 to review mitosis and meiosis.

20–3 Plantlike Protists: Unicellular Algae

4-1.3 Organelles in single-celled organisms
4-5.1 Chloroplasts
4-6.1 Relationships and interactions between organisms
LS- Analyze, formulate, and identify the control group

Guide for Reading

Key Concepts

- What is the function of chlorophyll and accessory pigments in algae?
- What are the distinguishing features of the major phyla of unicellular algae?

Vocabulary

accessory pigment
eyespot
pellicle
phytoplankton

Reading Strategy: Summarizing As you read, make a list of the types of unicellular algae. Write a sentence about each type.

Many protists contain the green pigment chlorophyll and carry out photosynthesis. Many of these organisms are highly motile, or able to move about freely. Despite this, the fact that they perform photosynthesis is so important that we group these protists in a separate category, the plantlike protists. Plantlike protists are commonly called "algae."

Some scientists place those algae that are more closely related to plants in the kingdom Plantae. In this textbook, we will consider all forms of algae, including those most closely related to plants, to be protists. There are seven major phyla of algae classified according to a variety of cellular characteristics. The first four phyla, which contain unicellular organisms, are discussed in this section. These four phyla are the euglenophytes, the chrysophytes, the diatoms, and the dinoflagellates. The last three phyla include many multicellular organisms and will be discussed in the next section.

Chlorophyll and Accessory Pigments

One of the key traits used to classify algae is the type of photosynthetic pigments they contain. As you will remember, light is necessary for photosynthesis, and it is chlorophyll and the accessory pigments that trap the energy of sunlight.

Life in deep water poses a major difficulty for algae—a shortage of light. As sunlight passes through water, much of the light's energy is absorbed by the water. In particular, sea water absorbs large amounts of the red and violet wavelengths. Thus, light becomes dimmer and bluer, in deeper water. Because chlorophyll *a* is most efficient at capturing red and violet light, the dim blue light that penetrates into deep water contains very little light energy that chlorophyll *a* can use.

In adapting to conditions of limited light, various groups of algae have evolved different forms of chlorophyll. Each form of chlorophyll—chlorophyll *a,* chlorophyll *b,* and chlorophyll *c*—absorbs different wavelengths of light. The result of this evolution is that algae can use more of the energy of sunlight than just the red and violet wavelengths.

Many algae also have compounds called **accessory pigments** that absorb light at different wavelengths than chlorophyll. Accessory pigments pass the energy they absorb to the algae's photosynthetic machinery. **Chlorophyll and accessory pigments allow algae to harvest and use the energy from sunlight.** Because accessory pigments reflect different wavelengths of light than chlorophyll, they give algae a wide range of colors.

▼ **Figure 20–9 Chlorophyll and other pigments allow algae to collect and use energy from sunlight.** These green algae of the species *Acetabularia calyculus* live on the roots of mangrove trees in Florida.

Euglenophytes

Members of the phylum Euglenophyta (yoo-GLEE-nuh-fyt-uh), or euglenophytes, are closely related to the animallike flagellates. **Euglenophytes are plantlike protists that have two flagella but no cell wall.** Although euglenophytes have chloroplasts, in most other ways they are like zooflagellates.

The phylum takes its name from the genus *Euglena*. Euglenas are found in ponds and lakes throughout the world. A typical euglena, such as the one shown in **Figure 20–10,** is about 50 micrometers in length. Euglenas are excellent swimmers. Two flagella emerge from a gullet at one end of the cell, and the longer of these two flagella spins in a pattern that pulls the organism rapidly through the water. Near the gullet end of the cell is a cluster of reddish pigment known as the **eyespot,** which helps the organism find sunlight to power photosynthesis. If sunlight is not available, euglenas can also live as heterotrophs, absorbing the nutrients available in decayed organic material. Euglenas store carbohydrates in small storage bodies.

Euglenas do not have cell walls, but they do have an intricate cell membrane called a **pellicle.** The pellicle is folded into ribbonlike ridges, each ridge supported by microtubules. The pellicle is tough and flexible, letting euglenas crawl through mud when there is not enough water for them to swim. Euglenas reproduce asexually by binary fission.

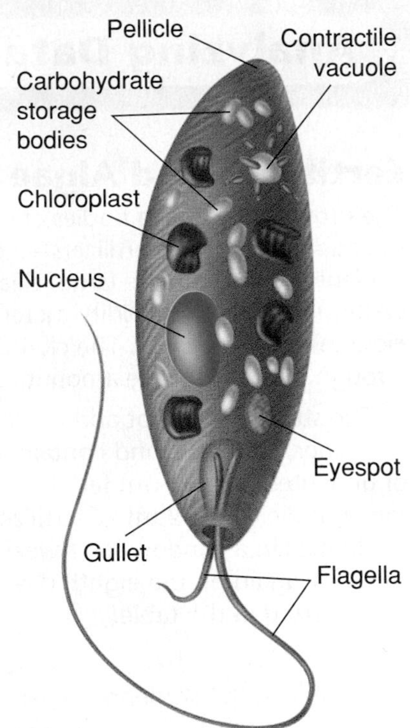

▲ **Figure 20–10** **Euglenophytes are plantlike protists that have two flagella but no cell wall.** The green structures inside the euglena shown are chloroplasts, which allow the organism to carry on photosynthesis. Like paramecia, euglenas expel excess water through a contractile vacuole.

Chrysophytes

The phylum Chrysophyta (KRIS-oh-fyt-uh) includes the yellow-green algae and the golden-brown algae. The chloroplasts of these organisms contain bright yellow pigments that give the phylum its name. Chrysophyta means "golden plants." **Members of the phylum Chrysophyta are a diverse group of plantlike protists that have gold-colored chloroplasts.**

The cell walls of some chrysophytes contain the carbohydrate pectin rather than cellulose, and others contain both pectin and cellulose. Chrysophytes generally store food in the form of oil rather than starch. They reproduce both asexually and sexually. Most are solitary, but some form threadlike colonies.

Diatoms

Members of the phylum Bacillariophyta (buh-sil-LAHR-ee-oh-fyt-uh), or diatoms, are among the most abundant and beautiful organisms on Earth. **Diatoms produce thin, delicate cell walls rich in silicon (Si)—the main component of glass.** These walls are shaped like the two sides of a petri dish or flat pillbox, with one side fitted snugly into the other. The cell walls have fine lines and patterns that almost seem to be etched into their glasslike brilliance, as shown in **Figure 20–11.**

▼ **Figure 20–11** **Tiny jewellike diatoms such as this centric diatom have cell walls rich in silicon.**

(magnification: 2200×)

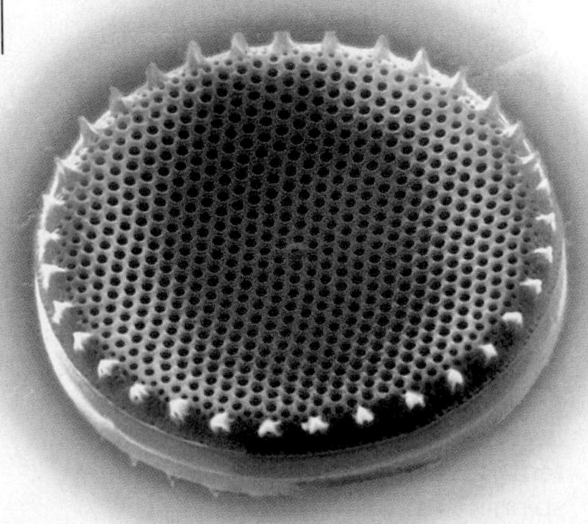

How are diatoms and glass alike?

Analyzing Data

Fertilizers and Algae

The growth of algae in bodies of water is affected by the addition of plant fertilizers—a pollutant. A group of students collected three large, clear containers of pond water. They used a turbidity meter to measure the cloudiness of the water. The cloudiness, or turbidity, is a rough indicator of the amount of algae present.

The students did not add anything to the first container. To the second container, they added 1 mL of undiluted liquid plant fertilizer. To the third container, they added 2 mL of fertilizer. They then left the containers in a window for 1 week and measured the turbidity again on the eighth day. Their data are summarized in the table.

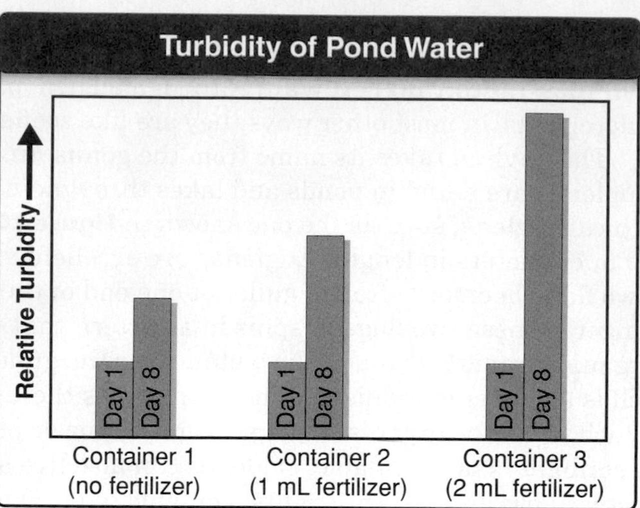

1. **Controlling Variables** What is the responding variable in the students' experiment?
2. **Designing Experiments** What is the role of the first container of water, to which no fertilizer was added?
3. **Using Tables and Graphs** In which container did the algae grow the most?
4. **Drawing Conclusions** What can you conclude about the effect of fertilizers on the growth of algae?

(magnification: 1280×)

▲ **Figure 20–12** **Some dinoflagellates are photosynthetic, whereas others are heterotrophs.** The paired flagella of a dinoflagellate lie in grooves around its circumference, shown here in red. The flagella propel the organism, spinning, through the water.

Dinoflagellates

Dinoflagellates are members of the phylum Pyrrophyta (PIR-oh-fyt-uh). **About half of the dinoflagellates are photosynthetic; the other half live as heterotrophs.** Dinoflagellates generally have two flagella, and these often wrap around the organism in grooves between two thick plates of cellulose that protect the cell, as shown in **Figure 20–12.** Most dinoflagellates reproduce asexually by binary fission.

Many dinoflagellate species are luminescent, and when agitated by sudden movement in the water, give off light. Some areas of the ocean are so filled with dinoflagellates that the movement of a boat's hull will cause the dark water to shimmer with a ghostly blue light. This luminescent property gives the phylum its name, *Pyrrophyta*, which means "fire plants."

Ecology of Unicellular Algae

Plantlike protists are common in both fresh and salt water, and thus are an important part of freshwater and marine ecosystems. A few species of algae, however, can cause serious problems.

Plantlike protists play a major ecological role on Earth. They are important organisms whose position at the base of the food chain makes much of the diversity of aquatic life possible. They make up a considerable part of the phytoplankton.

Phytoplankton (fyt-oh-PLANK-tun) constitute the population of small, photosynthetic organisms found near the surface of the ocean. About half of the photosynthesis that occurs on Earth is carried out by phytoplankton, which provide a direct source of nourishment for organisms as diverse as shrimp and whales. Even such land animals as humans get nourishment indirectly from phytoplankton. When you eat tuna fish, you are eating fish that fed on smaller fish that fed on still smaller animals that fed on plantlike protists.

Algal Blooms Many protists grow rapidly in regions where sewage is discharged. These protists play a vital role in recycling sewage and other waste materials. When the amount of waste is excessive, however, populations of euglenophytes and other algae may grow into enormous masses known as blooms. These algal blooms deplete the water of nutrients, and the cells die in great numbers. The decomposition of these dead algae can rob water of its oxygen, choking its resident fish and invertebrate life. As a result, these microorganisms disrupt the equilibrium of the aquatic ecosystem.

Great blooms of the dinoflagellates *Gonyaulax* and *Karenia* have occurred in recent years on the east coast of the United States, although scientists are not sure of the reason. These blooms, such as the one shown in **Figure 20–13,** are known as "red tides." These species produce a potentially dangerous toxin. Filter-feeding shellfish such as clams can trap *Gonyaulax* and *Karenia* for food and become filled with the toxin. Eating shellfish from water infected with red tide can cause serious illness, paralysis, and even death in humans and fish.

Figure 20–13 Blooms of the dinoflagellate *Karenia brevis* (inset) can produce red tides. *Karenia* contains a toxin that becomes concentrated in the tissue of filter feeders such as clams and oysters. **Inferring** *How can red tides be harmful to humans?*

20–3 Section Assessment

1. **Key Concept** What do chlorophyll and accessory pigments do in algae?
2. **Key Concept** What are the four phyla of unicellular plantlike protists?
3. How do most unicellular algae get food? How does this differ from the way most animallike protists get food?
4. What is the role of unicellular algae in the environment?
5. **Critical Thinking Problem Solving** Identify two ways to reduce the problem of algal blooms in fresh water.
6. **Critical Thinking Problem Solving** Summarize the role of a red tide in disrupting an ecosystem.

Writing in Science

Comparing and Contrasting

Four of the seven phyla of unicellular algae are described in this section. Write one or more paragraphs that compare and contrast the distinguishing features of these phyla. *Hint:* You may wish to develop a table or an outline before you begin writing.

20–4 Plantlike Protists: Red, Brown, and Green Algae

Guide for Reading

Key Concepts
- What are the distinguishing features of the major phyla of multicellular algae?
- How do multicellular algae reproduce?

Vocabulary
phycobilin
filament
alternation of generations
gametophyte
spore
sporophyte

Reading Strategy: Outlining Before you read, use the blue and the green headings to make an outline about multicellular algae. As you read, add phrases or a sentence after each heading to provide key information.

Have you ever taken a walk along a rocky beach at low tide? As the water recedes, in many places it reveals a damp forest of green and brown "plants" clinging to the rocks. These seaweeds have the size, color, and appearance of plants, but they are not plants. They are actually algae. Unlike the algae in the previous section, most of these algae are multicellular, like plants. They also have reproductive cycles that are sometimes very similar to those of plants. Many of them have cell walls and photosynthetic pigments that are identical to those of plants. Many of these algae also possess highly specialized tissues.

The three phyla of algae that are largely multicellular are commonly known as red algae, brown algae, and green algae. The most important differences among these phyla involve their photosynthetic pigments.

Red Algae

Red algae are members of the phylum Rhodophyta (roh-duh-FYT-uh), meaning "red plants." **Red algae are able to live at great depths due to their efficiency in harvesting light energy. Red algae contain chlorophyll *a* and reddish accessory pigments called phycobilins.** **Phycobilins** (fy-koh-BIL-inz) are especially good at absorbing blue light, enabling red algae to live deeper in the ocean than many other photosynthetic algae. Many red algae are actually green, purple, or reddish black, depending upon the other pigments they contain. Red algae are an important group of marine algae that can be found in waters from the polar regions to the tropics. The highly efficient light-harvesting pigments in these algae enable them to grow anywhere from the ocean's surface to depths of up to 260 meters.

Most species of red algae are multicellular, and all species have complex life cycles. Red algae lack flagella and centrioles. Red algae also play an important role in the formation of coral reefs, as shown in **Figure 20–14.** These microorganisms help to maintain the equilibrium of the coral ecosystem, providing nutrients from photosynthesis that nourish coral animals. Coralline red algae provide much of the calcium carbonate that helps to stabilize the growing coral reef.

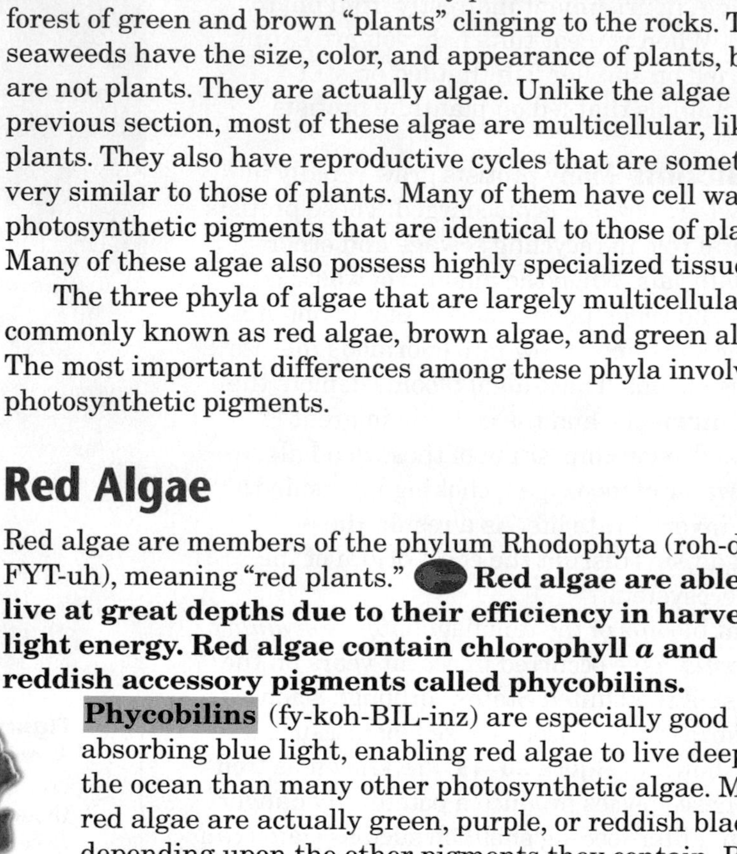

◀ **Figure 20–14** **Red algae contain chlorophyll *a* and reddish pigments called phycobilins.** Coralline algae, a type of red alga, collect calcium carbonate in their cell walls, giving them a tough, stony texture.

Brown Algae

Brown algae belong to the phylum Phaeophyta (fay-uh-FYT-uh), meaning "dusky plants." **Brown algae contain chlorophyll *a* and *c*, as well as a brown accessory pigment, fucoxanthin.** The combination of fucoxanthin (fyoo-koh-ZAN-thin) and chlorophyll *c* gives most of these algae a dark, yellow-brown color. Brown algae are the largest and most complex of the algae. All brown algae are multicellular and most are marine, commonly found in cool, shallow coastal waters of temperate or arctic areas.

The largest known alga is giant kelp, a brown alga that can grow to more than 60 meters in length. Another brown alga called *Sargassum* forms huge floating mats many kilometers long in an area of the Atlantic Ocean near Bermuda known as the Sargasso Sea. Bunches of *Sargassum* often drift on currents to beaches in the Caribbean and southern United States.

One of the most common brown alga is *Fucus*, or rockweed, found along the rocky coast of the eastern United States. Each *Fucus* alga has a holdfast, a structure that attaches the alga to the bottom. The body of the alga consists of flattened stemlike structures called stipes, leaflike structures called blades, and gas-filled swellings called bladders, which float and keep the alga upright in the water. **Figure 20–15** shows the structures of a brown alga.

What does a holdfast do?

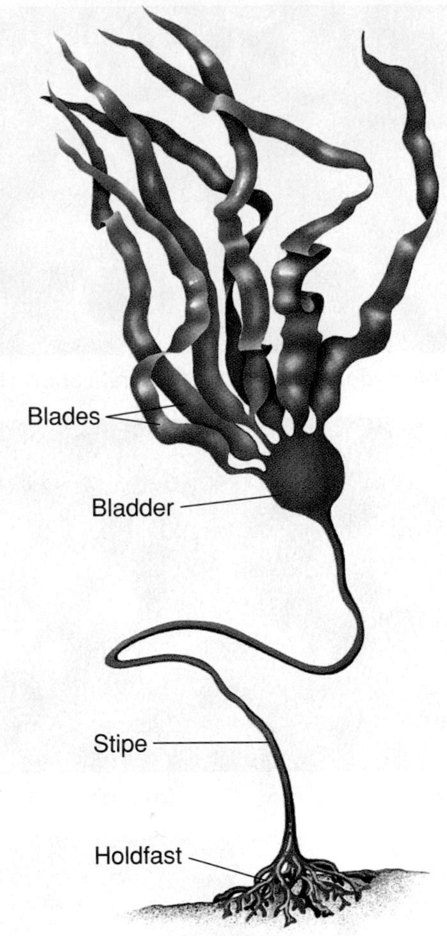

▲ **Figure 20–15 Brown algae contain chlorophyll *a* and *c*, plus fucoxanthin, a brown pigment.**

Green Algae

Green algae are members of the phylum Chlorophyta (klawr-uh-FYT-uh), which means "green plants" in Greek. **Green algae share many characteristics with plants, including their photosynthetic pigments and cell wall composition.** Green algae have cellulose in their cell walls, contain chlorophyll *a* and *b*, and store food in the form of starch, just like land plants. One stage in the life cycle of mosses—small land plants you will learn about in the next unit—looks remarkably like a tangled mass of green algae strands. All these characteristics lead scientists to hypothesize that the ancestors of modern land plants looked a lot like certain species of living green algae. Unfortunately, algae rarely form fossils, so there is no single specific fossil that scientists can call an ancestor of both living algae and mosses. However, scientists think that mosses and green algae shared such a common algalike ancestor millions of years ago.

Green algae are found in fresh and salt water, and even in moist areas on land. Many species live most of their lives as single cells. Others form colonies, groups of similar cells that are joined together but show few specialized structures. A few green algae are multicellular and have well-developed specialized structures.

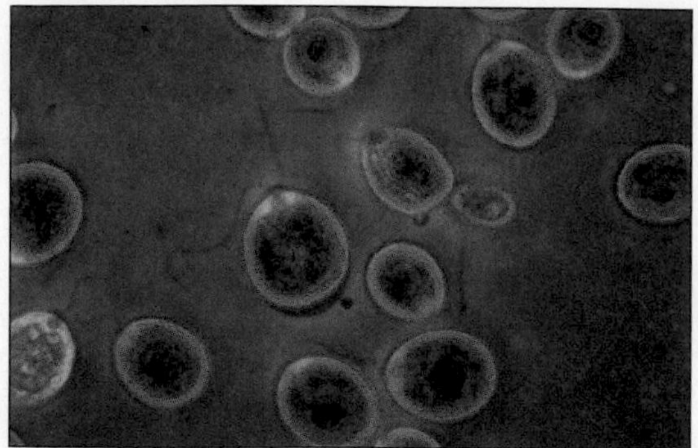

Chlamydomonas (magnification: 1000×)

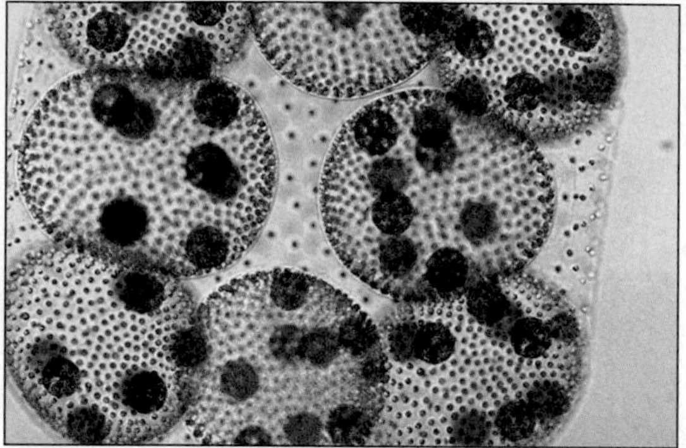

Volvox (magnification: 450×)

Ulva

Figure 20–16 Green algae have the same photosynthetic pigments and cell wall compositions as green plants. *Chlamydomonas* is a unicellular green alga that lives in ponds. Delicate spherical colonies of the green alga *Volvox* live in fresh water. New colonies can develop within existing colonies and are released when an older colony ruptures. *Ulva* is a multicellular green alga that lives along seacoasts.

Unicellular Green Algae *Chlamydomonas* (kluh-mid-uh-MOHN-uz), a typical single-celled green alga, grows in ponds, ditches, and wet soil. *Chlamydomonas* is a small egg-shaped cell with two flagella and a single large, cup-shaped chloroplast. Within the base of the chloroplast is a region that synthesizes and stores starch. *Chlamydomonas* lacks the large vacuoles found in the cells of land plants. Instead, it has two small contractile vacuoles. *Chlamydomonas* and two other green algae are shown in **Figure 20–16.**

Colonial Green Algae Several species of green algae live in multicellular colonies. The freshwater alga *Spirogyra,* shown in **Figure 20–1,** forms long threadlike colonies called **filaments,** in which the cells are stacked almost like aluminum cans placed end to end. *Volvox* colonies are more elaborate, consisting of as few as 500 to as many as 50,000 cells arranged to form hollow spheres. The cells in a *Volvox* colony are connected to one another by strands of cytoplasm, enabling them to coordinate movement. When the colony moves, cells on one side of the colony "pull" with their flagella, and the cells on the other side of the colony have to "push." Although most cells in a *Volvox* colony are identical, a few gamete-producing cells are specialized for reproduction. Because it shows some cell specialization, *Volvox* straddles the fence between colonial and multicellular life.

Multicellular Green Algae *Ulva*, or "sea lettuce," is a bright-green marine alga that is commonly found along rocky seacoasts. *Ulva* is a true multicellular organism, containing several specialized cell types. Although the body of *Ulva* is only two cells thick, it is tough enough to survive the pounding of waves on the shores where it lives. A group of cells at its base forms holdfasts that attach *Ulva* to the rocks.

Reproduction in Green Algae

The life cycles of many algae include both a diploid and a haploid generation. Recall from Chapter 11 that diploid cells have two sets of chromosomes, whereas haploid cells have a single set. Many algae switch back and forth between haploid and diploid stages during their life cycles, in a process known as **alternation of generations.** Many species also shift back and forth between sexual and asexual forms of reproduction.

Reproduction in *Chlamydomonas* The single-celled *Chlamydomonas* spends most of its life in the haploid stage. As long as its living conditions are suitable, this haploid cell reproduces asexually, producing cells called zoospores by mitosis. Reproduction by mitosis is asexual. The two haploid daughter cells produced by mitosis are genetically identical to the single haploid cell that entered mitosis.

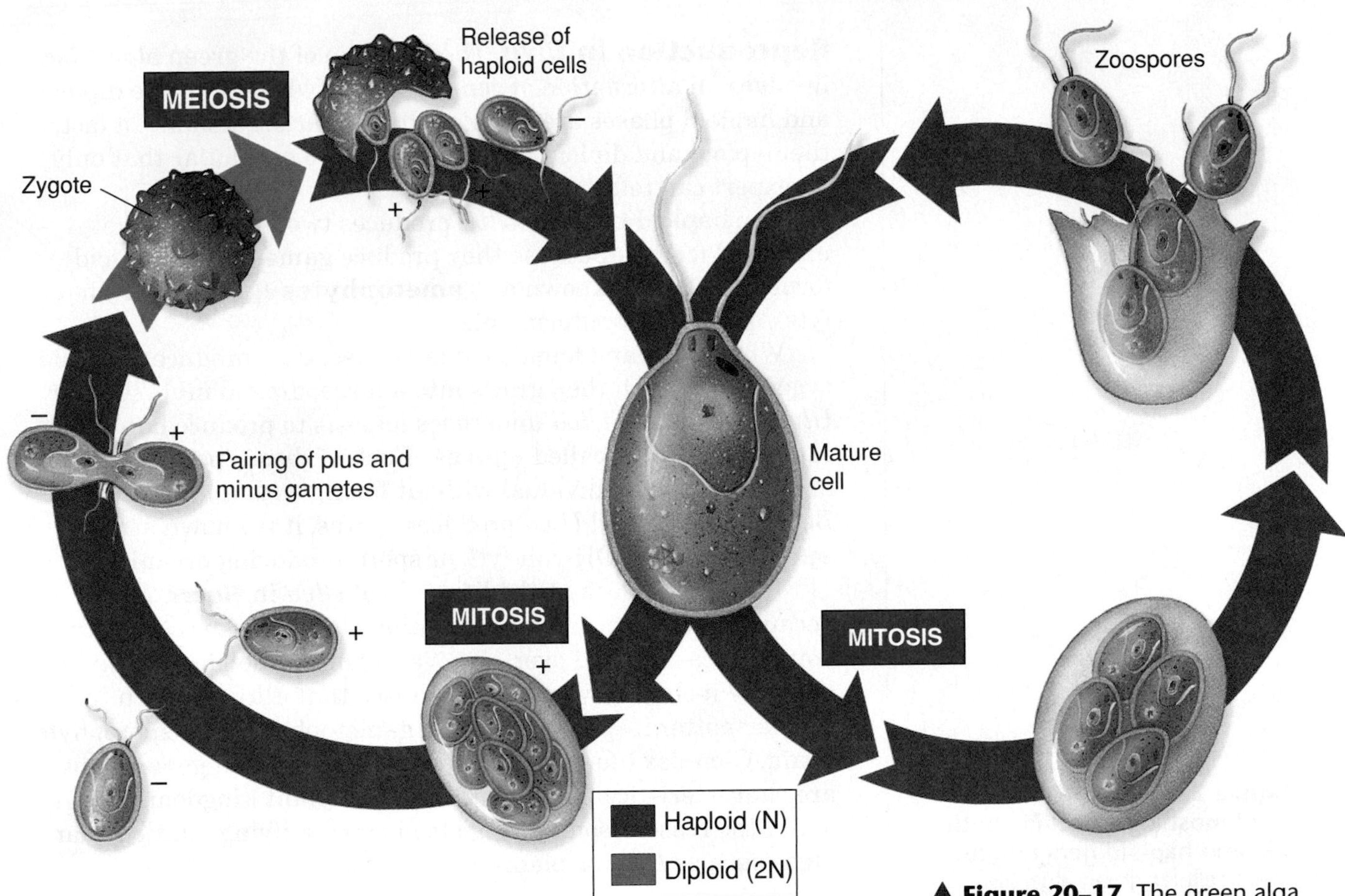

▲ **Figure 20–17** The green alga *Chlamydomonas* reproduces asexually by producing zoospores and sexually by producing zygotes, which release haploid gametes. **Interpreting Graphics** ***Which form of reproduction includes a diploid organism that can survive adverse conditions?***

If conditions become unfavorable, *Chlamydomonas* can also reproduce sexually. The life cycle of *Chlamydomonas* is shown in **Figure 20–17.** The haploid cells continue to undergo mitosis, but instead of releasing zoospores, the cells release gametes. The gametes, which look identical, are of two opposite mating types, + (plus) and – (minus). During sexual reproduction, the gametes gather in large groups. Then + and – gametes form pairs that soon move away from the group. The paired gametes join flagella and spin around in the water. Both members of the pair then shed their cell walls and fuse, forming a diploid zygote.

The zygote sinks to the bottom of the pond and grows a thick protective wall. Within this protective wall, *Chlamydomonas* can survive freezing or drying conditions that otherwise would kill it. When conditions once again become favorable, the zygote begins to grow. It divides by meiosis to produce four flagellated haploid cells. These haploid cells can swim away, mature, and reproduce asexually. Thus, during its life cycle, *Chlamydomonas* alternates between a haploid stage, in which it spends most of its life, and a brief diploid stage, represented by the zygote cell.

CHECKPOINT ***What two types of gametes does*** **Chlamydomonas** ***produce?***

Reproduction in *Ulva* The life cycle of the green alga *Ulva* involves an alternation of generations in which both the diploid and haploid phases are large, multicellular organisms. In fact, the haploid and diploid phases of *Ulva* are so similar that only an expert can tell them apart!

The haploid phase of *Ulva* produces two forms of gametes—male and female. Because they produce gametes, the haploid forms of *Ulva* are known as **gametophytes** (guh-MEET-uh-fyts), or gamete-producing plants.

When male and female gametes fuse, they produce a diploid zygote cell, which then grows into a large, diploid multicellular *Ulva*. The diploid *Ulva* undergoes meiosis to produce haploid reproductive cells called **spores.** Each of these spores is able to grow into a new individual without fusing with another cell. Because the diploid *Ulva* produces spores, it is known as a **sporophyte** (SPOH-ruh-fyt), or spore-producing organism.

Take a close look at the life cycle of *Ulva* in **Figure 20–18,** because the alternation of generations it displays is a pattern you will see repeated over and over again in the plants. *Ulva*'s life cycle includes two separate phases that alternate in a regular pattern: sporophyte, then gametophyte, then sporophyte again. Complex life cycles involving alternation of generations are characteristic of the members of the plant kingdom. This is one of the reasons some biologists favor classifying multicellular algae such as *Ulva* as plants.

▼ **Figure 20–18** **The life cycles of most algae include both diploid and haploid generations.** The multicellular green alga *Ulva* exhibits alternation of generations. The haploid generation produces a diploid generation. Then, the diploid generation produces a haploid generation. The two generations are multicellular and virtually indistinguishable from each other.

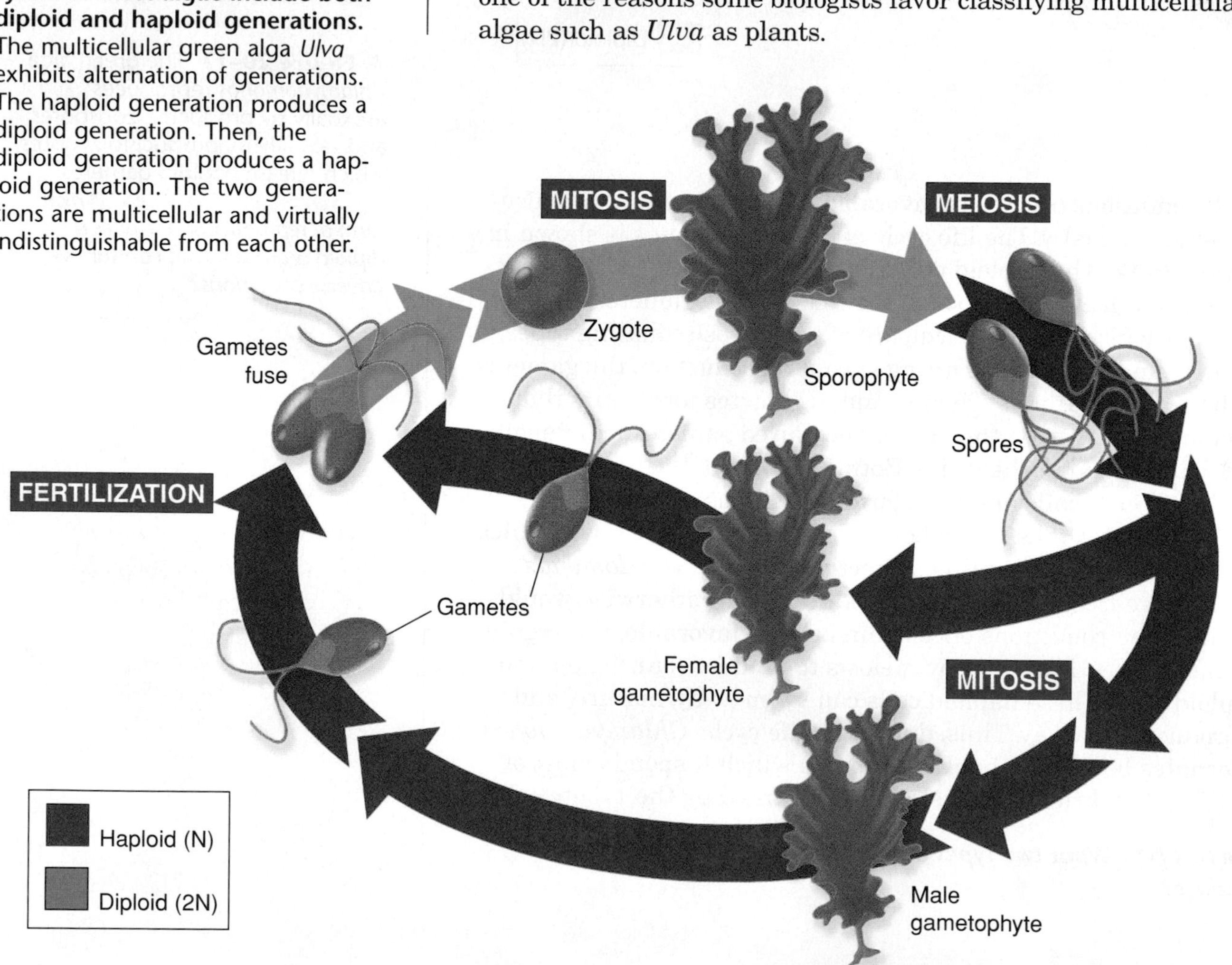

Human Uses of Algae

Algae are a major food source for life in the oceans. Algae have even been called the "grasses" of the seas, because they make up much of the base of the food chain upon which sea animals "graze." The enormous brown kelp forests off the coasts of North America are home to many animal species.

Algae produce much of Earth's oxygen through photosynthesis. Scientists calculate that about half of all the photosynthesis that occurs on Earth is performed by algae. This fact alone makes algae one of the most important groups of organisms on the entire planet.

Over the years, people have learned to use algae—and the chemicals produced by algae—in many different ways. Many species of algae are rich in vitamin C and iron. Chemicals in algae are used to treat stomach ulcers, high blood pressure, arthritis, and other health problems.

Have you ever eaten algae? Almost certainly, your answer should be yes. In Japan, the red alga *Porphyra* is grown on special marine farms. Dried *Porphyra*—called *nori* in Japanese—is dark green and paper-thin. Nori is used to wrap portions of rice, fish, and vegetables to make sushi, as shown in **Figure 20–19.** You say you've never had sushi? Well, you've probably eaten ice cream, salad dressing, pudding, or a candy bar. Other products from algae are used in pancake syrups and eggnog.

Industry has even more uses for algae. Chemicals from algae are used to make plastics, waxes, transistors, deodorants, paints, lubricants, and even artificial wood. Algae even have an important use in scientific laboratories. The compound agar, derived from certain seaweeds, thickens the nutrient mixtures scientists use to grow bacteria and other microorganisms.

▲ **Figure 20–19** People have found many different uses for algae. The red alga *Porphyra* is used as a wrapper in Japanese sushi rolls. Ice cream often contains algin, a thickener made from brown algae. **Predicting** ***How would your life be different without products made from algae?***

20–4 Section Assessment

1. **Key Concept** Describe the main features of the major phyla of multicellular algae.
2. **Key Concept** What is alternation of generations?
3. How are multicellular algae important at a global level?
4. Why can red algae live in deeper water than green algae?
5. **Critical Thinking Comparing and Contrasting** Choose a green alga and illustrate its life cycle. Identify which parts are haploid and which are diploid. Show where meiosis and mitosis occur. Illustrate which part of the life cycle involves sexual reproduction and which involves asexual reproduction.

Thinking Visually

Organizing Information
Make a poster illustrating three types of multicellular algae. Your poster should have detailed drawings or photographs of each group. Each illustration should show the correct classification and list two written characteristics of each group.

20–5 Funguslike Protists

4-6.1 Relationships and interactions between organisms
4-6.1 Organisms interact in various ways
4-5.2 Fungi and other parasites infect other organisms

Guide for Reading

Key Concepts
- What are the similarities and differences between funguslike protists and fungi?
- What are the defining characteristics of the slime molds and water molds?

Vocabulary
cellular slime mold
acellular slime mold
fruiting body
plasmodium
hypha
zoosporangium
antheridium
oogonium

Reading Strategy: Predicting Before you read, preview the life cycles in **Figure 20–22** and **Figure 20–23.** Predict how these life cycles are similar and how they are different.

▼ **Figure 20–20 Funguslike protists absorb nutrients from dead organic matter.** Slime molds like this red raspberry slime mold are often found in the damp, shaded environments preferred by many fungi.

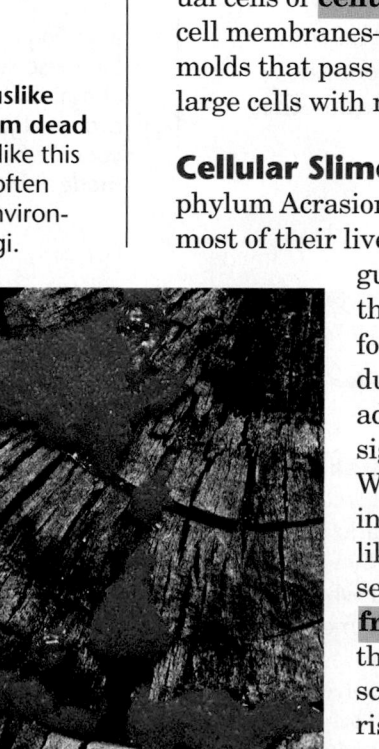

If you look closely at the debris-laden floor of a forest after several days of rain, you may see patches of what looks like brightly colored mold. Funguslike protists, such as in **Figure 20–20** and **Figure 20–21,** grow in damp, nutrient-rich environments and absorb food through their cell membranes, much like fungi. These organisms have sometimes been classified as fungi, even though their cellular structure more closely resembles that of the protists. **Like fungi, the funguslike protists are heterotrophs that absorb nutrients from dead or decaying organic matter. But unlike most true fungi, funguslike protists have centrioles. They also lack the chitin cell walls of true fungi.** The funguslike protists include the cellular slime molds, the acellular slime molds, and the water molds.

Slime Molds

Slime molds are found in places that are damp and rich in organic matter, such as the floor of a forest or a backyard compost pile. **Slime molds are funguslike protists that play key roles in recycling organic material.** At one stage of their life cycle, slime molds look just like amoebas. At other stages, they form moldlike clumps that produce spores, almost like fungi.

Two broad groups of slime molds are recognized. The individual cells of **cellular slime molds** remain distinct—separated by cell membranes—during every phase of the mold's life cycle. Slime molds that pass through a stage in which their cells fuse to form large cells with many nuclei are called **acellular slime molds.**

Cellular Slime Molds Cellular slime molds belong to the phylum Acrasiomycota (ak-ruh-see-oh-my-KOH-tuh). They spend most of their lives as free-living cells that are not easily distinguishable from soil amoebas. In nutrient-rich soils, these amoeboid cells reproduce rapidly. When their food supply is exhausted, they go through a reproductive process to produce spores that can survive adverse conditions. First, they send out chemical signals that attract other cells of the same species. Within a few days, thousands of cells aggregate into a large sluglike colony that begins to function like a single organism. The colony migrates for several centimeters, then stops and produces a **fruiting body,** a slender reproductive structure that produces spores. Eventually, the spores are scattered from the fruiting body. Each spore gives rise to a single amoeba-like cell that starts the cycle all over again, as shown in **Figure 20–22.**

Figure 20–21 Slime molds help recycle organic matter. The bright yellow acellular slime mold shown here, *Fuligo septica,* is often found growing in gardens on damp, rich soil.

In many ways, these remarkable organisms challenge our understanding of what it means to be multicellular. During much of their life cycle, cellular slime molds are unicellular organisms that look and behave like animallike protists. When they aggregate, however, they act very much like multicellular organisms. Slime molds have been especially interesting to biologists who study how cells send signals and regulate development. They have kept biologists busy for decades, but their secrets are still not fully understood.

CHECKPOINT *Why is it difficult to classify cellular slime molds as unicellular or multicellular?*

Figure 20–22 Cellular slime molds reproduce asexually and sexually. **Interpreting Graphics** *Is most of the cellular slime mold life cycle haploid or diploid?*

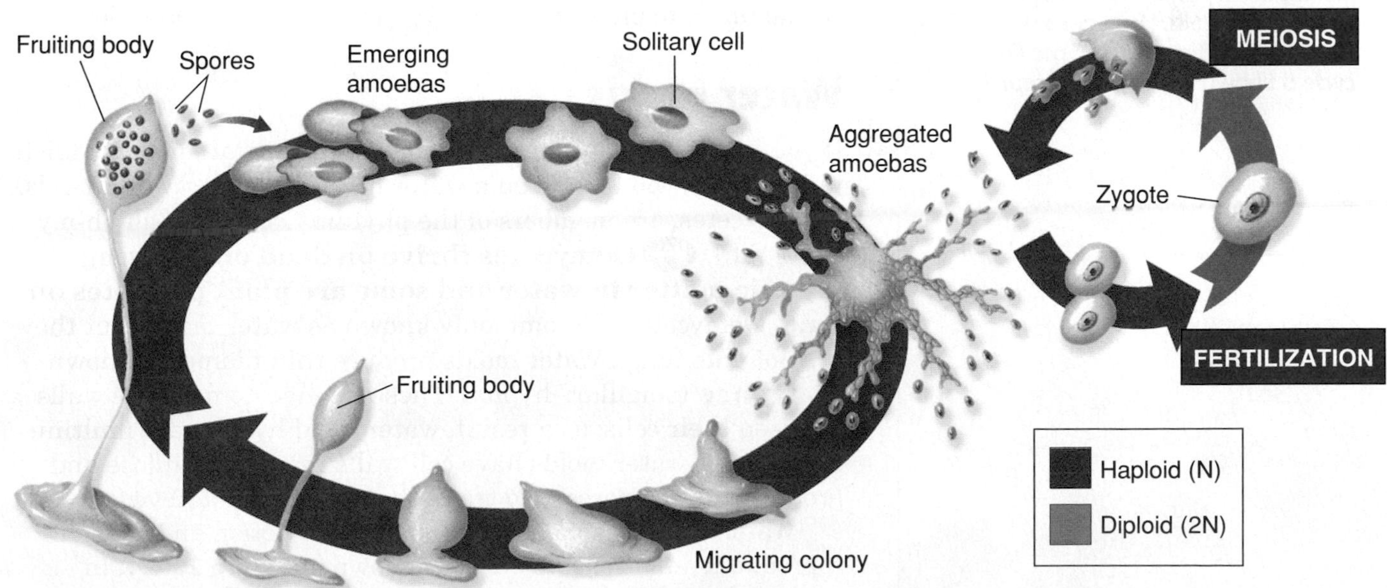

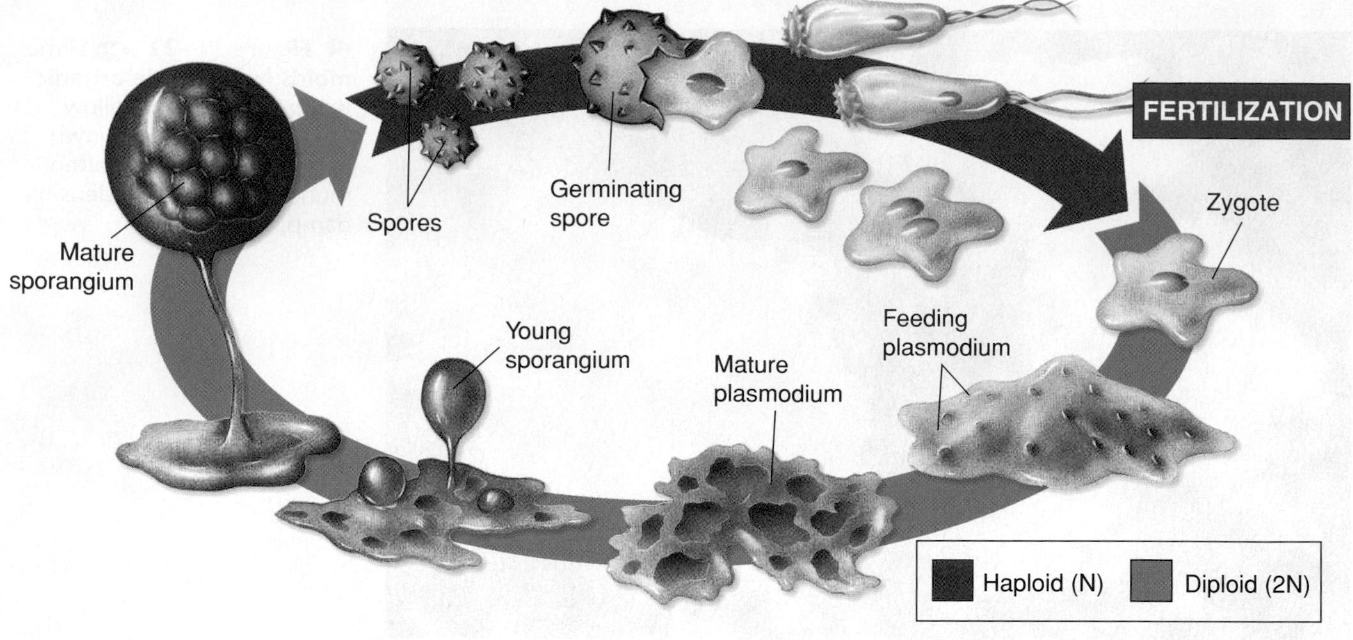

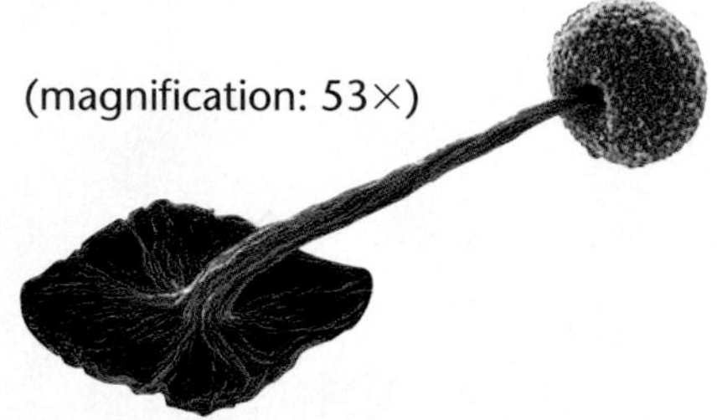

Figure 20–23 The plasmodium of an acellular slime mold is the collection of many amoeba-like organisms contained in a single cell membrane. The plasmodium will eventually produce sporangia, which in turn will undergo meiosis and produce haploid spores. Upon pairing up and fusing, these result in new diploid amoeba-like cells. **Interpreting Graphics** *What stage of the life cycle is shown in the photograph?*

Acellular Slime Molds Acellular slime molds belong to the phylum Myxomycota (myk-suh-my-KOH-tuh). Like cellular slime molds, acellular slime molds begin their life cycles as amoeba-like cells. However, when they aggregate, their cells fuse to produce structures with many nuclei.

These structures are known as **plasmodia** (singular: plasmodium). The large plasmodium of an acellular slime mold, such as the one shown in **Figure 20–23,** is actually a single structure with many nuclei. A plasmodium may grow as large as several meters in diameter!

Eventually, small fruiting bodies, or sporangia, spring up from the plasmodium. The sporangia produce haploid spores by meiosis. These spores scatter to the ground where they germinate into amoeba-like or flagellated cells. The flagellated cells then fuse in a sexual union to produce diploid zygotes that repeat the cycle.

Water Molds

If you have seen white fuzz growing on the surface of a dead fish in the water, you have seen a water mold in action. Water molds, or oomycetes, are members of the phylum Oomycota (oh-oh-my-KOH-tuh). **Oomycetes thrive on dead or decaying organic matter in water and some are plant parasites on land.** Oomycetes are commonly known as water molds, but they are not true fungi. Water molds produce thin filaments known as **hyphae** (singular: hypha). These hyphae do not have walls between their cells; as a result, water mold hyphae are multinucleate. Also, water molds have cell walls made of cellulose and produce motile spores, two traits that fungi do not have.

Water molds display both sexual reproduction and asexual reproduction in their life cycle, as shown in **Figure 20–24.** In asexual reproduction, portions of the hyphae develop into **zoosporangia** (singular: zoosporangium), which are spore cases.

Each zoosporangium produces flagellated spores that swim away in search of food. When they find food, the spores develop into hyphae, which then grow into new organisms.

Sexual reproduction takes place in specialized structures that are formed by the hyphae. One structure, the **antheridium** (an-thur-ID-ee-um), produces male nuclei. The other structure, the **oogonium** (oh-oh-GOH-nee-um), produces female nuclei. Fertilization, or sexual fusion, occurs within the oogonium, and the spores that form develop into new organisms.

CHECKPOINT *Where does sexual reproduction in water molds take place?*

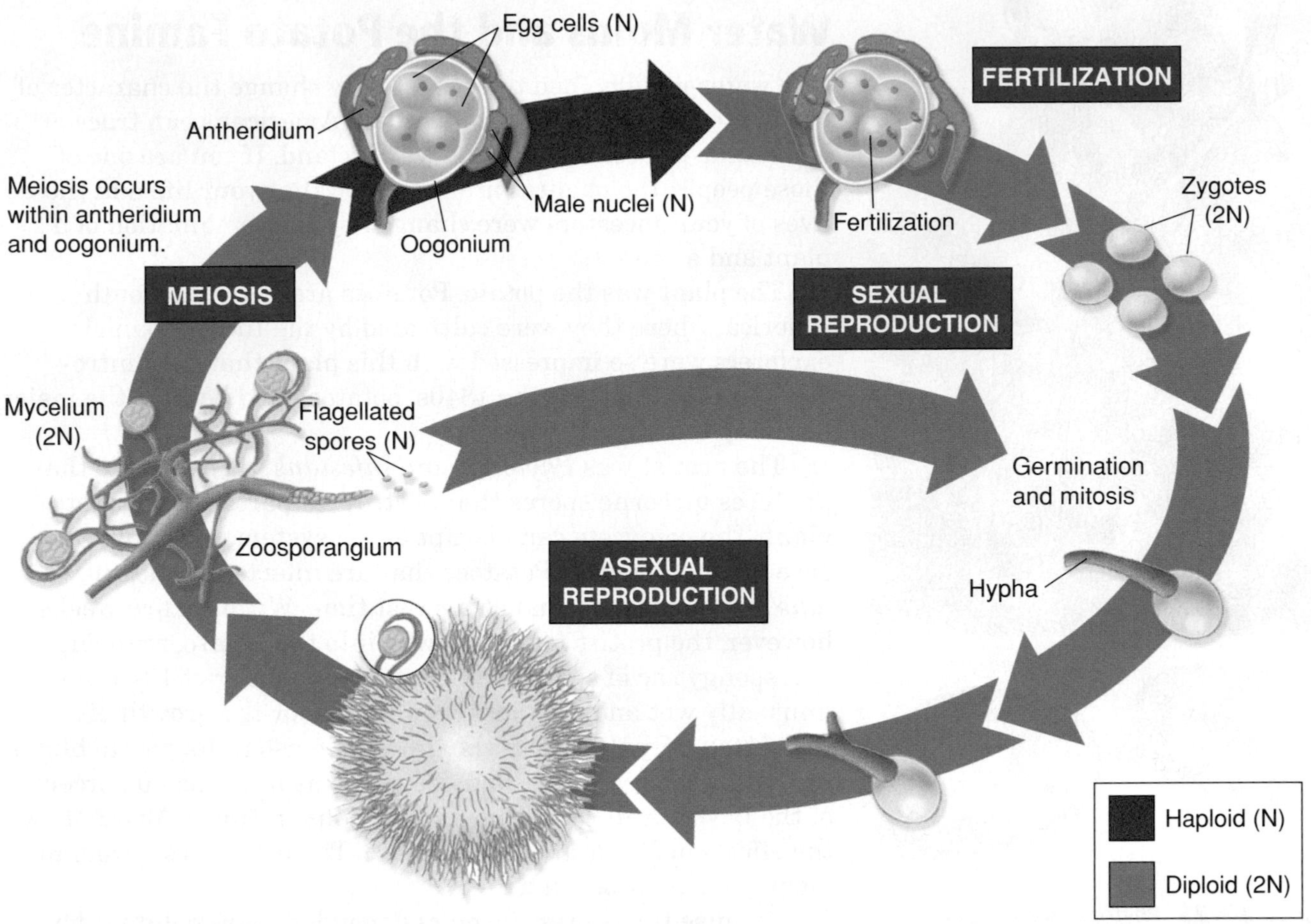

▲ **Figure 20–24 Water molds live on decaying organic matter in water.** Water molds reproduce both asexually and sexually. During asexual reproduction, flagellated spores are produced by the diploid (2N) mycelium. These spores grow into new mycelia. During sexual reproduction, a male nucleus fuses with a female nucleus.

Ecology of Funguslike Protists

Slime molds and water molds are important as recyclers of organic material. In other words, they help things rot. A walk through woods or grassland shows that the ground is not littered with the bodies of dead animals and plants. After these organisms die, their tissues are broken down by slime molds, water molds, and other decomposers. The dark, rich topsoil that provides plants with nutrients results from this decomposition.

Some funguslike protists can harm living things. In addition to their beneficial function as decomposers, land-dwelling water molds cause a number of important plant diseases. These diseases include mildews and blights of grapes and tomatoes.

Go Online
PHSchool.com
For: Links on funguslike protists
Visit: PHSchool.com
Web Code: cbe-6205

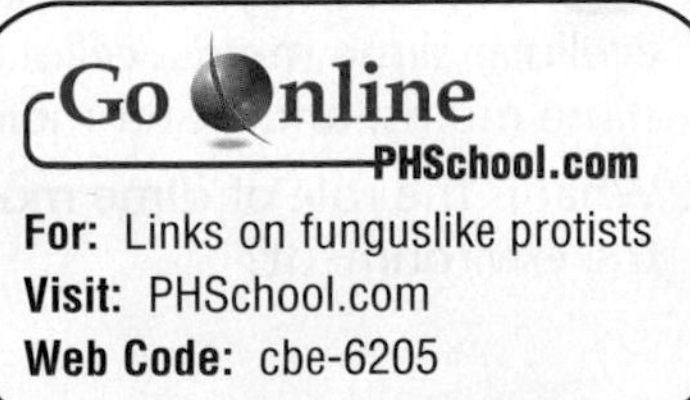

Figure 20–25 *Phytophthora infestans* is an oomycete that attacks potatoes (bottom right). In the summer of 1846, *P. infestans* destroyed nearly the entire potato crop of Ireland within weeks, leading to the Great Potato Famine. **Applying Concepts** *How did the famine affect the United States?*

Water Molds and the Potato Famine

One water mold helped to permanently change the character of the United States. Roughly 40 million Americans can trace at least some part of their ancestry to Ireland. If you are one of those people, the chances are very good that your life and the lives of your ancestors were changed by the combination of a plant and a protist.

The plant was the potato. Potatoes are native to South America, where they were cultivated by the Incas. Spanish explorers were so impressed with this plant that they introduced it to Europe. By the 1840s, potatoes had become the major food crop of Ireland.

The protist was *Phytophthora infestans*, an oomycete that produces airborne spores that destroy all parts of the potato plant. The oomycete can disrupt an ecosystem and cause disease in a potato crop. Potatoes that are infected with *P. infestans* may appear normal at harvest time. Within a few weeks, however, the protist makes its way into the potato, reducing it to a spongy sac of spores and dust. The summer of 1845 was unusually wet and cool, ideal conditions for the growth of *P. infestans*. By the end of the growing season, the potato blight caused by this pathogen had destroyed as much as 60 percent of the Irish potato crop. The photographs in **Figure 20–25** show the effects of *P. infestans* on a potato. The art shows a woman digging for potatoes in a field.

Because the poorest farmers depended upon potatoes for their food, the effects were tragic. In 1846, nearly the entire potato crop was lost, leading to mass starvation. Between 1845 and 1851, at least 1 million Irish people died of starvation or disease. During this same period, more than 1 million people emigrated from Ireland to the United States and other countries. The Great Potato Famine, as this tragic event was known, changed the ethnic and social character of many American cities, the new home of so many Irish immigrants.

20–5 Section Assessment

1. **Key Concept** How are funguslike protists and fungi similar? How are they different?
2. **Key Concept** Compare acellular slime molds, cellular slime molds, and water molds.
3. What is the role of slime molds in the environment?
4. How can water molds affect other living things?
5. **Critical Thinking Comparing and Contrasting** How is the sluglike mass of cellular slime molds similar to the plasmodium of acellular slime molds? How do they differ?

Thinking Visually

Constructing a Flowchart
Draw two flowcharts—one showing the steps from unicellular existence through multicellular existence and reproduction in cellular slime molds and one showing those steps in acellular slime molds.

Investigating Contractile Vacuoles

Most freshwater protists have contractile vacuoles. The function of these organelles is to regulate the concentration of water in the cytoplasm, thereby maintaining homeostasis within the organism. In this investigation, you will observe how this structure works under various conditions.

Problem

How do the salt concentration and temperature of the environment affect the action of contractile vacuoles?

Materials

- 3 *Paramecium caudatum* cultures at room temperature, 25°C (fresh water, 0.5% salt solution, 1.0% salt solution)
- *Paramecium caudatum* culture at 2°C in fresh water
- dropper pipette
- 4 microscope slides
- coverslips
- microscope
- cotton ball
- forceps
- clock with second hand

Skills

Designing Experiments, Observing

Design Your Experiment

1. Use a dropper pipette to put one drop of *Paramecium caudatum* culture in fresh water at 25°C on a microscope slide.
2. Use forceps to pull apart a cotton ball and put a few threads in the drop of water. Cover the drop with a coverslip.
3. Use the low-power objective to locate and focus on one paramecium. If necessary, increase the magnification to observe the alternating contractions of the two contractile vacuoles.
4. Record how long a contractile vacuole takes to contract and refill.
5. **Formulating Hypotheses** Formulate a hypothesis about how salt concentration and temperature will affect the rate of expansion and contraction of a contractile vacuole.
6. **Designing Experiments** Design an experiment to test your hypothesis. As you plan your procedures, refer to the Lab Tips box on page 55 for ways to demonstrate safe practices, make wise choices in the use of materials, and select equipment and technology.
7. Construct a data table to record your observations. With your teacher's approval, carry out your experiment.

Analyze and Conclude

1. **Observing** How did an increase in the concentration of salt in its environment affect the paramecium's contractile vacuoles?
2. **Inferring** What can you infer from this result about the rate at which water enters the paramecium in salt solutions? Explain your answer.
3. **Inferring** What can you infer about the relationship between the contractile vacuole and homeostasis?
4. **Observing** How did temperature affect the contractile vacuoles?
5. **Drawing Conclusions** What can you conclude about the paramecium's use of energy from the effect of temperature on the contractile vacuole?

Go Further

Designing Experiments Does temperature affect paramecia in other ways? Design an experiment to investigate the effects of temperature on movement or feeding. With your teacher's approval, carry out your experiment.

Chapter 20 Study Guide

20–1 The Kingdom Protista

Key Concept

- Protists are eukaryotes that are not members of the kingdoms Plantae, Animalia, or Fungi.

Vocabulary
protist, p. 497

20–2 Animallike Protists: Protozoans

Key Concepts

- Animallike protists that swim using flagella are classified in the phylum Zoomastigina and are often referred to as zooflagellates.
- Sarcodines are animallike protists that use pseudopods for feeding and movement.
- Members of the phylum Ciliophora, known as ciliates, use cilia for feeding and movement.
- Members of the phylum Sporozoa do not move on their own and are parasitic.
- Some animallike protists cause serious diseases, including malaria and African sleeping sickness.

Vocabulary
pseudopod, p. 500
amoeboid movement, p. 500
food vacuole, p. 500 • cilium, p. 501
trichocyst, p. 501 • macronucleus, p. 501
micronucleus, p. 501 • gullet, p. 502
anal pore, p. 502 • contractile vacuole, p. 502
conjugation, p. 502

20–3 Plantlike Protists: Unicellular Algae

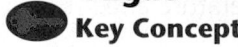

Key Concepts

- Chlorophyll and accessory pigments allow algae to harvest and use the energy from sunlight.
- Euglenophytes are plantlike protists that have two flagella but no cell wall.
- Members of the phylum Chrysophyta are a diverse group of plantlike protists that have gold-colored chloroplasts.
- Diatoms produce thin, delicate cell walls rich in silicon (Si)—the main ingredient in glass.
- About half of dinoflagellates are photosynthetic; the other half live as heterotrophs.

Vocabulary
accessory pigment, p. 506 • eyespot, p. 507
pellicle, p. 507 • phytoplankton, p. 509

20–4 Plantlike Protists: Red, Brown, and Green Algae

Key Concepts

- Red algae are able to live at great depths due to their efficiency in harvesting light energy. Red algae contain chlorophyll *a* and reddish accessory pigments called phycobilins.
- Brown algae contain chlorophyll *a* and *c*, as well as a brown accessory pigment, fucoxanthin.
- Green algae share many characteristics with plants, including their photosynthetic pigments and cell wall composition.
- The life cycles of most algae include both a diploid and a haploid generation.

Vocabulary
phycobilin, p. 510
filament, p. 512
alternation of generations, p. 512
gametophyte, p. 514
spore, p. 514
sporophyte, p. 514

20–5 Funguslike Protists

Key Concepts

- Funguslike protists lack chlorophyll and absorb nutrients from dead or decaying organic matter. But unlike most true fungi, funguslike protists have centrioles. They also lack the chitin cell walls of true fungi.
- Slime molds are funguslike protists that play key roles in recycling organic material.
- Oomycetes thrive on dead or decaying organic matter in water and are plant parasites on land.

Vocabulary
cellular slime mold, p. 516
acellular slime mold, p. 516
fruiting body, p. 516
plasmodium, p. 518
hypha, p. 518
zoosporangium, p. 518
antheridium, p. 519
oogonium, p. 519

Thinking Visually

Make a table that compares the means of feeding and movement of the four main groups of protists.

Preparing for the Living Environment Exam

NEW YORK LIVING ENVIRONMENT

Blue questions emphasize Regents Exam content

Chapter 20

Part A

Multiple Choice

For each statement or question, select the number of the word or expression that, of those given, best completes the statement or answers the question.

1 Which description applies to most protists?
(1) unicellular prokaryotes
(2) multicellular prokaryotes
(3) unicellular eukaryotes
(4) multicellular eukaryotes

2 For defense, a paramecium uses small, bottle-shaped structures known as
(1) cilia (3) trichocysts
(2) pseudopodia (4) micronuclei

3 Which of the diagrams below shows the process of conjugation?

(1) 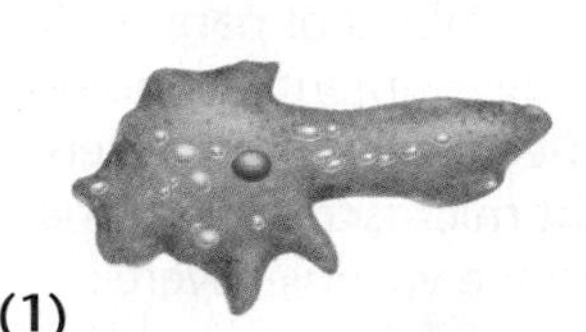

(3) 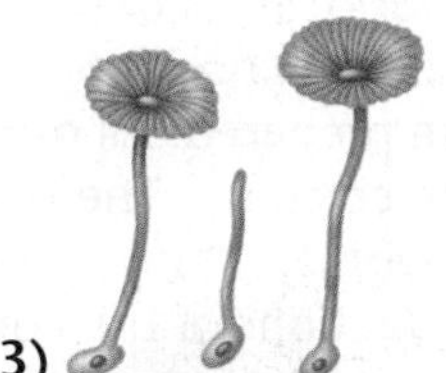

(2) 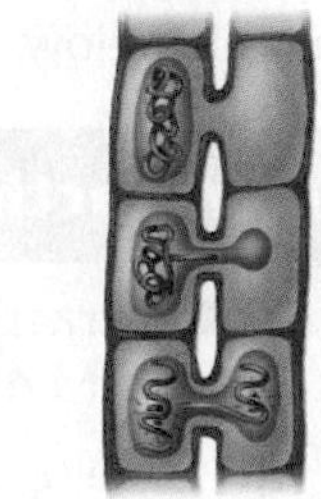

(4) 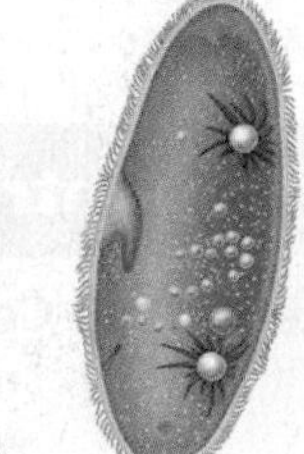

4 The population of small, photosynthetic organisms found near the ocean surface is called
(1) euglenophytes
(2) chrysophytes
(3) phytoplankton
(4) dinoflagellates

5 Which organisms are chiefly involved in the recycling of dead matter?
(1) fungi (3) carnivores
(2) algae (4) autotrophs

6 The thin filaments produced by water molds are known as
(1) oogonia (3) antheridia
(2) zoosporangia (4) hyphae

7 Slime molds are found primarily in
(1) oceans
(2) rotting wood or compost piles
(3) fast-moving streams
(4) deserts

8 Which structure in a unicellular organism corresponds in function with human lungs?
(1) vacuole (3) cell membrane
(2) nucleus (4) mitochondrion

9 Because the relative concentration of water in the pond in which a paramecium lives is greater than the concentration of water in its cytoplasm, water molecules constantly move from the pond into the organism. The best long-term solution to the problem of maintaining a stable internal environment is for the paramecium to
(1) change the water into carbon dioxide and excrete it
(2) store water molecules
(3) incorporate water molecules into its structure
(4) actively transport water molecules out of the cell

10 The cilia of paramecia are tiny hairlike structures that help paramecia to move from one location to another. Which of the following best describes the importance of cilia to paramecia?
(1) Cilia help in maintaining homeostasis.
(2) Cilia are useful in the process of diffusion.
(3) The ability to decompose other organisms is made possible by cilia action.
(4) Asexual reproduction is made possible directly through the activities of cilia.

11 All one-celled organisms are able to continue living because of their ability to
(1) produce food
(2) excrete wastes
(3) produce offspring
(4) produce hormones

Test-Taking Tip As you briefly scan the questions, mark those that may be pure guesswork on your part and save them for last. (Do not write in this book.) Use your time on those questions that you can reason through and for which you can eliminate answers.

Preparing for the Living Environment Exam

Part B

Multiple Choice and Extended Response
For those questions that ask you to select a response, choose the one that best completes the statement or answers the question. For all others follow the directions given.

12 Explain how the terms *animallike, plantlike,* and *funguslike* are useful in classifying protists.

13 Describe the *two* methods euglenophytes can use to obtain energy.

14 Explain the connection between water pollution and the occurrence of a red tide.

15 All freshwater protozoans have contractile vacuoles to get rid of excess water. Describe the process responsible for this excess water.

16 Explain the role of plantlike protists in aquatic food chains.

Base your answers to questions 17 through 19 on the graph below and on your knowledge of biology.

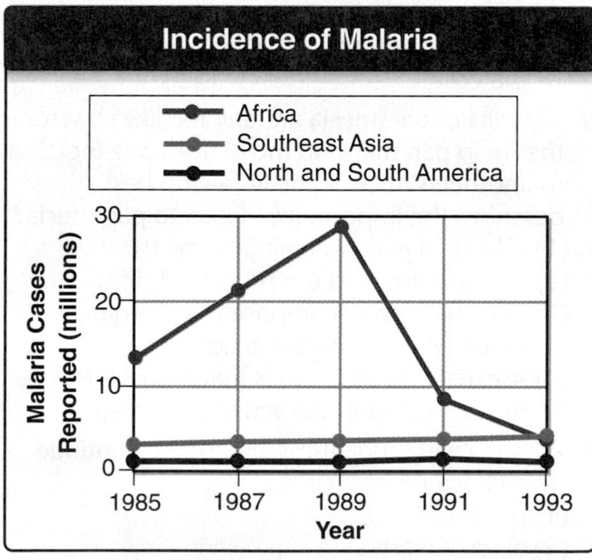

17 Based on the data in the graph, the incidence of malaria is
(1) decreasing in Southeast Asia and increasing in South America
(2) increasing in Africa and decreasing in Southeast Asia
(3) decreasing in Africa and increasing in Southeast Asia
(4) increasing in Southeast Asia and in North and South America

18 It is estimated that there are at least ten actual cases of malaria for every one reported and shown in the graph. Based on this estimate, how many cases of malaria were there in Africa in 1991?

19 Note the rapid change in malaria cases in Africa after 1989. Many question that the number of actual cases of malaria changed so rapidly. Explain what other factors could have affected the number of cases reported.

Base your answers to questions 20 through 22 on the information and chart below and on your knowledge of biology.

A study was done to determine the effect of different salt concentrations on the number of contractions per minute of contractile vacuoles of paramecia.

Four beakers of water containing different salt concentrations and equal numbers of paramecia were prepared. All other environmental conditions were constant. The paramecia were then observed through a compound light microscope, and the contractions of the contractile vacuoles were counted. Whenever a contractile vacuole contracts, it is pumping water out of a paramecium. The results were recorded in the data table below.

Salt Concentration vs. Contractions

Beaker	Salt Concentration (mg/mL)	Contractions per Minute
A	0.000	5.5
B	0.001	4.0
C	0.010	2.5
D	0.100	1.5

20 Using the information in the data table, construct a line graph on your own sheet of graph paper. Be sure that you
- label and scale the two axes appropriately
- plot the data, surround each point with a small circle, and connect the points

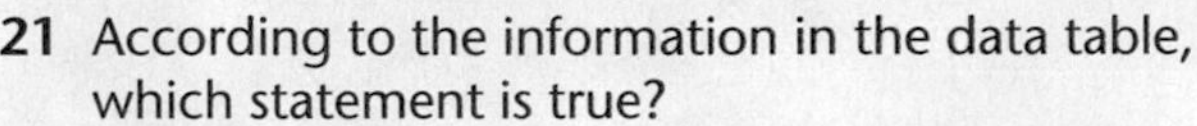

NEW YORK LIVING ENVIRONMENT

21 According to the information in the data table, which statement is true?
(1) Beaker B has a lower salt concentration than Beaker A.
(2) Beaker C has a lower salt concentration than Beaker D.
(3) The paramecia in Beaker A respond the least to the water concentration in the beaker.
(4) The paramecia in Beaker D have nonfunctioning contractile vacuoles.

22 According to the data, as the salt concentration increases, the number of contractions per minute changes. What most likely accounts for this change?
(1) a decrease in water concentration outside the paramecium
(2) a decrease in salt concentration outside the paramecium
(3) an increased diffusion of salt out of the paramecium
(4) an increased percentage of water inside the paramecium

For questions 23 through 26, select the structure, chosen from the list below, that is most closely associated with the statement. Then, record the number on your paper. A choice may be used once, more than once, or not at all.

(1) Contractile vacuole
(2) Gullet
(3) Trichocyst
(4) Food vacuole
(5) Anal pore

23 Where food particles in a unicellular organism's body are digested

24 Indentation where food particles are trapped

25 Collects and gets rid of excess water

26 Site where waste is released into the environment

Base your answers to questions 27 through 29 on the information below and on your knowledge of biology.

Algae are the foundation of most aquatic food chains in both marine and freshwater ecosystems. Through the process of photosynthesis, algae are able to combine inorganic raw materials into energy-rich organic compounds.

27 List the reactants and products of photosynthesis.

28 State the organelle that serves as the site of photosynthesis in algal cells.

29 Explain where algae obtain the raw materials needed to carry out photosynthesis.

Part C

Extended Response

Answer the questions or follow the directions given.

30 Describe the events that occur during the process of alternation of generations and explain its significance. In you answer be sure to include:
- an example of an organism that carries out the process
- the role of meiosis
- the role of the haploid and diploid forms of the organism during its life cycle
- the advantage of this type of life cycle

31 Ever growing "holes" in Earth's ozone shield may increase the amount of ultraviolet radiation that reaches the surface of the ocean. If this radiation were to affect the growth of phytoplankton (single-celled photosynthetic organisms), what long-term consequences might this have on Earth's atmosphere? In your answer be sure to describe:
- the significance of the ozone shield
- the impact of increased ultraviolet radiation reaching Earth's surface
- the role of phytoplankton in maintaining the present composition of atmospheric gases

For: An interactive self-test
Visit: PHSchool.com
Web Code: cba-6200

CHAPTER 21

Fungi

These morels are a type of fungus prized by many people for their distinctive flavor. Unlike the violets, fungi are not plants and do not produce their own food.

Inquiry Activity

What are mushrooms made of?

Procedure 

1. Examine a mushroom without damaging it. Record your observations, and include a sketch.
2. Carefully separate the stalk and cap of the mushroom. Try to break the stalk across and lengthwise.
3. Crumble a piece of the stalk. Describe the shape of the parts that make up the stalk.
4. Break the cap in two, and examine the thin sheets on the underside of the cap. Record your observations.

Think About It

1. **Observing** Was the stalk made up of parts with specific shapes? If so, what are the shapes of those parts?
2. **Comparing and Contrasting** Compare a mushroom to a plant. How are they similar? Different?

21–1 The Kingdom Fungi

4-5.2 Fungi and other parasites infect other organisms
4-6.1 Organisms may interact
4-6.1 Relationships and interactions between organisms
LS- Make observations and identify the control group

In spring, if you know where to look, you can find one of the most prized of all foods—the common morel—growing wild in woodlands throughout the United States. Its ridged cap is often camouflaged by dead leaves that collect in abandoned orchards or underneath old oaks or tulip poplars. Some morels grow alone, but others grow in groups. They appear suddenly, often overnight, and live for only a few days. What are these mysterious organisms? How do they grow so quickly?

Guide for Reading

Key Concepts
- What are the defining characteristics of fungi?
- What is the internal structure of a fungus?
- How do fungi reproduce?

Vocabulary
chitin
hypha
mycelium
fruiting body
sporangium
sporangiophore

Reading Strategy: Asking Questions
Before you read, preview **Figures 21–1** and **21–2.** Make a list of questions you have about the structure of fungi. As you read, look for answers to your questions.

What Are Fungi?

Like mushrooms and molds, morels are fungi. The way in which many fungi grow from the ground once led scientists to classify them as nonphotosynthetic plants. But they aren't plants at all. In fact, fungi are very different from plants.

Fungi are eukaryotic heterotrophs that have cell walls. The cell walls of fungi are made up of **chitin,** a complex carbohydrate that is also found in the external skeletons of insects. Recall that heterotrophs depend on other organisms for food. Unlike animals, fungi do not ingest their food. Instead, they digest food outside of their bodies and then absorb it. Many fungi feed by absorbing nutrients from decaying matter in the soil. Others live as parasites, absorbing nutrients from the bodies of their hosts.

Structure and Function of Fungi

Except for yeasts, all fungi are multicellular. Multicellular fungi are composed of thin filaments called **hyphae** (HY-fee; singular: hypha). Each hypha is only one cell thick. In some fungi, cross walls divide the hyphae into cells containing one or two nuclei, as shown in **Figure 21–1.** In the cross walls, there are tiny openings through which the cytoplasm and nuclei can move. Other hyphae lack cross walls and contain many nuclei.

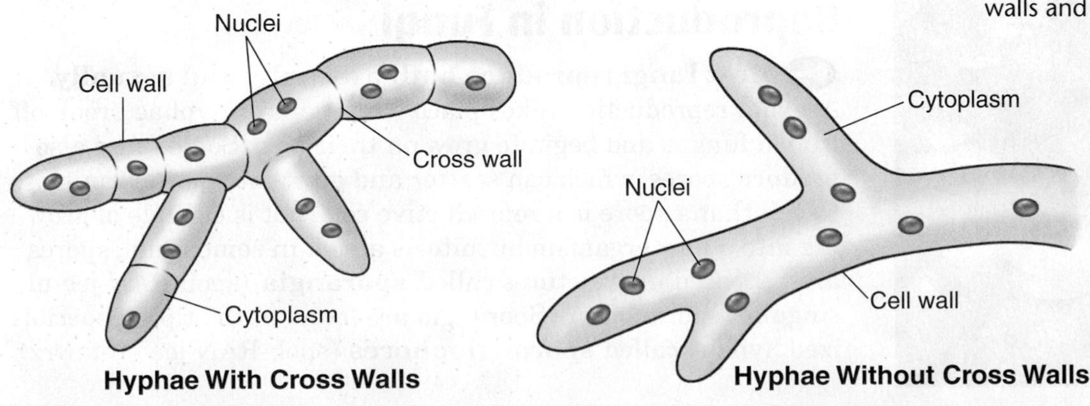

▼ **Figure 21–1 Fungi are eukaryotes that have cell walls made of chitin.** Most fungi are made up of filaments called hyphae. In some fungi, the hyphae are divided by cross walls. These cells may contain one or two nuclei. In other fungi, the hyphae lack cross walls and contain many nuclei.

Figure 21–2 **The body of a mushroom is part of a mycelium formed from many tangled hyphae.** The major portion of the mycelium grows below ground. The visible portion of the mycelium is the reproductive structure, or fruiting body, of the mushroom.

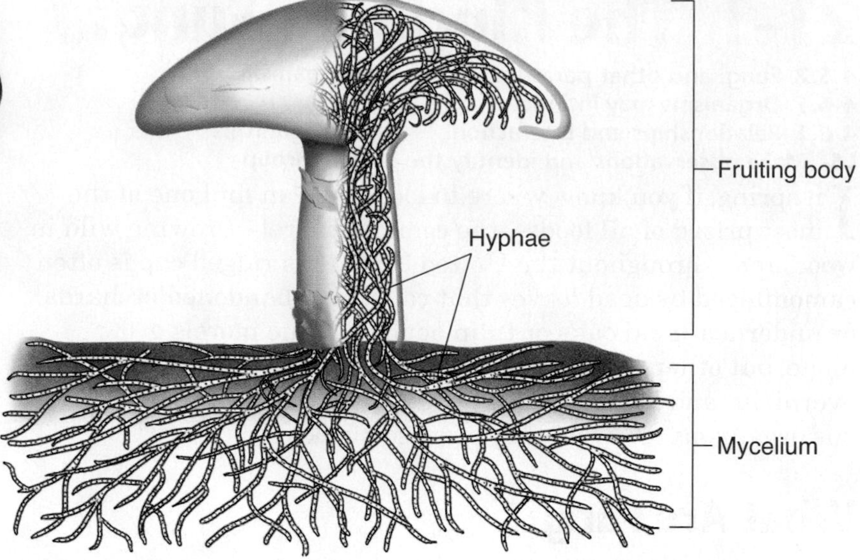

Fungus Structure **Figure 21–2** shows the structure of a multicellular fungus. **The bodies of multicellular fungi are composed of many hyphae tangled together into a thick mass called a mycelium.** The **mycelium** (my-SEE-lee-um; plural: mycelia) is well suited to absorb food because it permits a large surface area to come in contact with the food source through which it grows.

What you recognize as a mushroom is actually the fruiting body of a fungus. A **fruiting body** is a reproductive structure growing from the mycelium in the soil beneath it. Clusters of mushrooms are often part of the same mycelium, which means that they are part of the same organism.

Fairy Rings Some mycelia can live for many years. As time goes by, soil nutrients near the center of the mycelium become depleted. As a result, new mushrooms sprout only at the edges of the mycelium, producing a ring like the one in **Figure 21–3.** People once thought fairies dancing in circles during warm nights produced these rings, so they were called "fairy rings." Over many years, fairy rings can become enormous—from 10 to 30 meters in diameter.

▼ **Figure 21–3** This fairy ring is composed of the fruiting bodies of mushrooms that developed at the outer edges of a single mycelium. **Predicting** *How will the size of the fairy ring change in future years?*

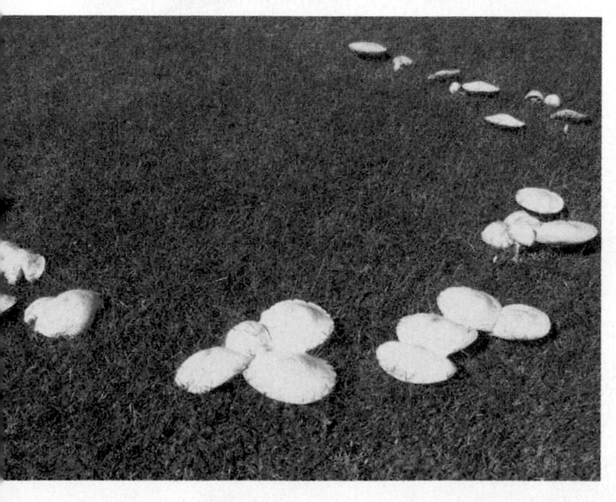

Reproduction in Fungi

Most fungi reproduce both asexually and sexually. Asexual reproduction takes place when cells or hyphae break off from a fungus and begin to grow on their own. Some fungi also produce spores, which can scatter and grow into new organisms. Recall that a spore is a reproductive cell that is capable of growing into a new organism by mitosis alone. In some fungi, spores are produced in structures called **sporangia** (spoh-RAN-jee-uh; singular: sporangium). Sporangia are found at the tips of specialized hyphae called **sporangiophores** (spoh-RAN-jee-oh-fawrz).

Sexual reproduction in fungi usually involves two different mating types. Because gametes of both mating types are about the same size, they are not called male and female. Rather, one mating type is called "+" (plus) and the other "–" (minus). When hyphae of opposite mating types meet, they start the process of sexual reproduction by fusing, bringing plus and minus nuclei together in the same cell. After a period of growth and development, these nuclei form a diploid zygote nucleus. In most fungi, the diploid zygote then enters meiosis, completing the sexual phase of its life cycle by producing haploid spores. Like the spores produced asexually, these spores are also capable of growing, by repeated rounds of mitosis, into new organisms.

How Fungi Spread

Fungal spores are found in almost every environment. This is why molds seem to spring up in any location that has the right combination of moisture and food. Many fungi produce dry, almost weightless spores, as shown in **Figure 21–4.** These spores scatter easily in the wind. On a clear day, a few liters of fresh air may contain hundreds of spores from many species of fungi.

If these spores are to germinate, they must land in a favorable environment. There must be the proper combination of temperature, moisture, and food so that the spores can grow. Even under the best of circumstances, the probability that a spore will produce a mature organism can be less than one in a billion.

Other fungi are specialized to lure animals, which disperse fungal spores over long distances. Stinkhorns smell like rotting meat, which attracts flies. When they land on the stinkhorn, the flies ingest the sticky, smelly fluid on the surface of the fungus. The spore-containing fluid will pass unharmed out of the flies' digestive systems, depositing spores over many kilometers.

▲ **Figure 21–4 Most fungi reproduce both sexually and asexually.** One form of asexual reproduction is spore formation. Here, an earthstar puffball *(Geastrum saccatum)* that has been struck by a raindrop expels a cloud of spores.

21–1 Section Assessment

1. **Key Concept** Identify the characteristics all fungi have in common.
2. **Key Concept** Describe the structure of the body of a typical fungus.
3. **Key Concept** Briefly describe asexual and sexual reproduction in fungi.
4. By what means are fungal spores spread to new locations?
5. **Critical Thinking Applying Concepts** Tissue from several mushrooms gathered near the base of a tree were tested and found to be genetically identical. How might you explain this?

Writing in Science

Writing a Proposal

A house may become uninhabitable because of the presence of mold spores. Research how to detect and identify mold allergens in the home. Assume you are a contractor. Write a proposal for how you will assess this problem in preparation for a cleanup. *Hint:* Write a draft of your proposal.

21–2 Classification of Fungi

LS- Make observations
LS- State an appropriate hypothesis
LS- Analyze results

Guide for Reading

Key Concept
- What are the characteristics of the four main phyla of fungi?

Vocabulary
zygospore
rhizoid
stolon
gametangium
conidium
ascus
ascospore
budding
basidium
basidiospore

Reading Strategy: Finding Main Ideas Before you read, skim the section to identify the four main groups of fungi. Write the name of each group on a notecard. As you read, make note of the characteristics of each group.

For: Links on fungi
Visit: www.SciLinks.org
Web Code: cbn-6211

The kingdom Fungi has over 100,000 species. Fungi are classified according to their structure and method of reproduction. The methods by which fungi reproduce are unlike those of any other kingdom. The four main groups of fungi are the common molds (Zygomycota), the sac fungi (Ascomycota), the club fungi (Basidiomycota), and the imperfect fungi (Deuteromycota).

The Common Molds

The familiar molds that grow on meat, cheese, and bread are members of the phylum Zygomycota, also called zygomycetes. **Zygomycetes have life cycles that include a zygospore.** A **zygospore** (ZY-goh-spawr) is a resting spore that contains zygotes formed during the sexual phase of the mold's life cycle. The hyphae of zygomycetes generally lack cross walls, although the cells of their reproductive structures do have cross walls.

Structure and Function of Bread Mold

Black bread mold, *Rhizopus stolonifer,* is a familiar zygomycete. Expose preservative-free bread to dust, and you can grow the mold. Keep the bread warm and moist in a covered jar, and in a few days dark fuzz will appear. With a hand lens, you can see delicate hyphae on moldy bread. There are two different kinds of hyphae. The rootlike hyphae that penetrate the bread's surface are **rhizoids** (RY-zoydz). Rhizoids anchor the fungus to the bread, release digestive enzymes, and absorb digested organic material. The stemlike hyphae that run along the surface of the bread are **stolons.** The hyphae that push up into the air are the sporangiophores, which form sporangia at their tips. A single sporangium may contain up to 40,000 spores.

What is a zygospore?

Life Cycle of Molds

The life cycle of black bread mold is shown in **Figure 21–5.** Its sexual phase begins when hyphae from different mating types fuse to produce gamete-forming structures known as **gametangia** (gam-uh-TAN-jee-uh; singular: gametangium). Haploid (N) gametes produced in the gametangia fuse with gametes of the opposite mating type to form diploid (2N) zygotes. These zygotes develop into thick-walled zygospores, which may remain dormant for months. When conditions become favorable, the zygospore germinates, then undergoes meiosis, and new haploid spores are released. The significance of this sexual process—zygote formation followed by meiosis—is that it produces new combinations of genetic information that may help the organism meet changing environmental conditions.

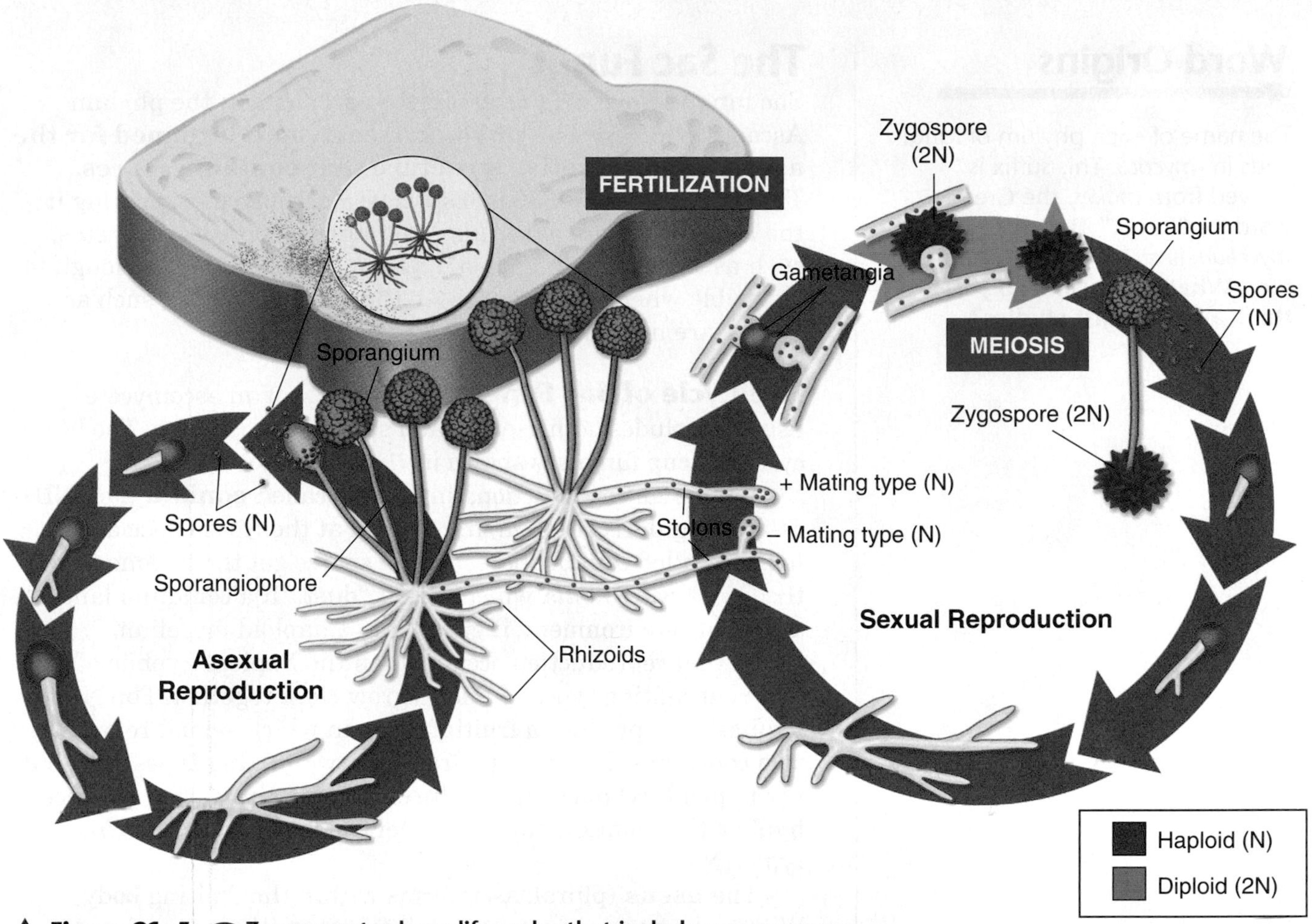

▲ **Figure 21–5** **Zygomycetes have life cycles that include a zygospore.** During sexual reproduction in the bread mold *Rhizopus stolonifer,* hyphae from two different mating types form gametangia. The gametangia fuse, and zygotes form within a zygospore. The zygospore develops a thick wall and can remain dormant for long periods. The zygospore eventually germinates, and a sporangium emerges. The sporangium reproduces asexually by releasing haploid spores produced by meiosis.

Quick Lab

What is the structure of bread mold?

Materials transparent tape, moldy bread, microscope slide, microscope

Procedure  

1. Touch the sticky side of a 2-cm piece of transparent tape to the black "fuzzy" area of a bread mold.
2. Gently stick the tape to a glass slide. Observe the slide under the compound microscope. Make a sketch of your observations.
3. Return all slides to your teacher for proper disposal. Wash your hands before leaving the laboratory.

Analyze and Conclude

1. **Observing** Describe the structures you observed in the bread mold.
2. **Formulating Hypotheses** What do you think the function of the round structures is? Why might it be advantageous for a single mass of bread mold to produce so many of the round structures?
3. **Inferring** How can your observations help explain the ability of molds to appear on foods even in very clean kitchens?

Word Origins

The name of each phylum of fungi ends in *-mycota.* This suffix is derived from *mukes,* the Greek word for "fungi." The term *mycelium* is also derived from this root. **What organisms do you think a mycologist studies?**

The Sac Fungi

Sac fungi, also known as ascomycetes, belong to the phylum Ascomycota. **The phylum Ascomycota is named for the ascus, a reproductive structure that contains spores.** There are more than 30,000 species of ascomycetes, making it the largest phylum of the kingdom Fungi. Some ascomycetes, such as the cup fungi shown in **Figure 21–6,** are large enough to be visible when they grow above the ground. Others, such as yeasts, are microscopic.

Life Cycle of Sac Fungi The life cycle of an ascomycete usually includes both asexual and sexual reproduction. The life cycle of a cup fungus is shown in **Figure 21–7.**

In asexual reproduction, tiny spores called **conidia** (koh-NID-ee-uh; singular: conidium) are formed at the tips of specialized hyphae called conidiophores. These spores get their name from the Greek word *konis,* which means "dust." If a conidium lands in a suitable environment, it grows into a haploid mycelium.

Sexual reproduction occurs when the haploid hyphae of two different mating types (+ and –) grow close together. The N + N hyphae then produce a fruiting body in which sexual reproduction continues. Gametangia from the two mating types fuse, but the haploid (N) nuclei do not fuse. Instead, this fusion produces hyphae that contain haploid nuclei from each of the mating types (N + N).

The **ascus** (plural: asci) forms within the fruiting body. Within the ascus, two nuclei of different mating types fuse to form a diploid zygote (2N). The zygote soon divides by meiosis, producing four haploid cells. In most ascomycetes, meiosis is followed by a cycle of mitosis, so that eight cells known as **ascospores** are produced. In a favorable environment, an ascospore can germinate and grow into a haploid mycelium.

CHECKPOINT *Where are ascospores formed? Are they haploid or diploid?*

▼ **Figure 21–6** These cup fungi are members of the phylum Ascomycota. In cup fungi, asci lie on the interior surface of the cup. At maturity, the spore-filled asci burst, releasing the spores into the air. **Applying Concepts** *What type of spores are formed by the cup fungi?*

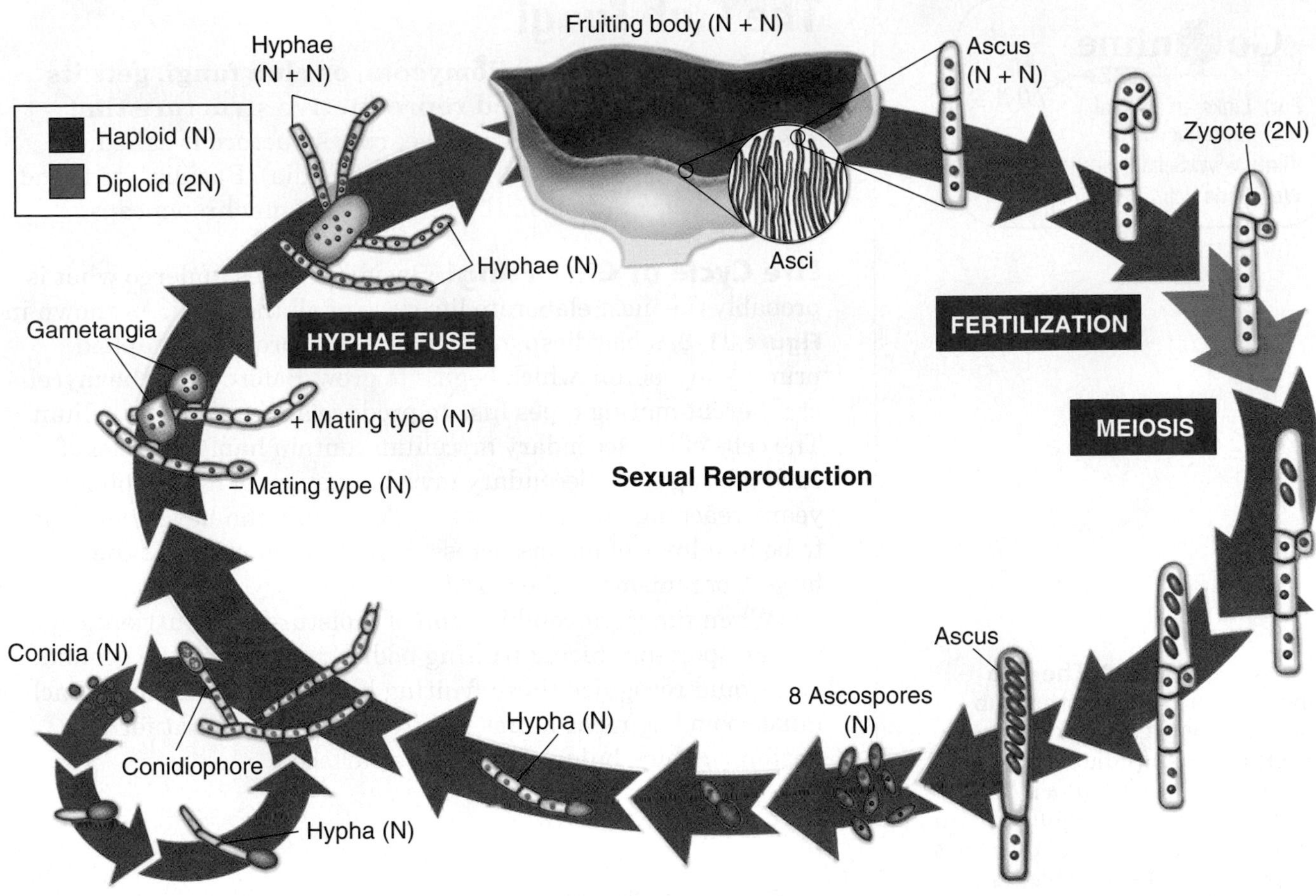

▲ Figure 21–7 The life cycle of ascomycetes includes both asexual and sexual reproduction. During asexual reproduction, spores called conidia are formed at the tips of specialized hyphae called conidiophores. During sexual reproduction, hyphae of two mating types fuse to form hyphae with two haploid nuclei (N + N). The N + N hyphae then form a fruiting body, which eventually releases ascospores. **Ascomycetes are named for the ascus, the reproductive structure that contains ascospores.**

Yeasts Yeasts are unicellular fungi. The yeasts used by humans for baking and brewing are classified as ascomycetes because they form asci with ascospores during the sexual phase of their life cycle.

You might think of yeast as a lifeless, dry powder that is used to make bread. Actually, the dry granules contain ascospores, which become active in a moist environment. To see this for yourself, add a spoonful of dry yeast to half a cup of warm water that contains some sugar. In about 20 minutes, when you examine a drop of this mixture under a microscope, you will be able to see cell division in the rapidly growing yeast cells. The process of asexual reproduction you are observing is called **budding.**

The common yeasts used for baking and brewing are members of the genus *Saccharomyces,* which means "sugar fungi." These yeasts are grown in a rich nutrient mixture containing very little oxygen. Prior to baking, the nutrient mixture is a mound of thick dough. Lacking oxygen, the yeasts within the mixture use the process of alcoholic fermentation to obtain energy. The byproducts of alcoholic fermentation are carbon dioxide and alcohol. The carbon dioxide gas makes beverages bubble and bread rise (by producing bubbles within the dough). The alcohol in bread dough evaporates during baking. In brewing, alcohol remains in the resulting alcoholic beverages.

Go Online NSTA SCiLINKS
For: Links on asexual reproduction
Visit: www.SciLinks.org
Web Code: cbn-6212

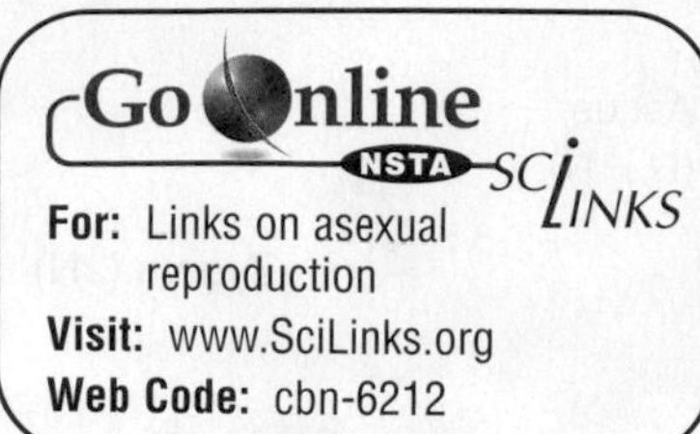

The Club Fungi

The phylum Basidiomycota, or club fungi, gets its name from a specialized reproductive structure that resembles a club. The spore-bearing structure is called the **basidium** (buh-SID-ee-um; plural: basidia). Basidia are found on the gills that grow on the underside of mushroom caps.

Life Cycle of Club Fungi Basidiomycetes undergo what is probably the most elaborate life cycle of all the fungi. As shown in **Figure 21–8,** a basidiospore germinates to produce a haploid primary mycelium, which begins to grow. Before long, the mycelia of different mating types fuse to produce a secondary mycelium. The cells of the secondary mycelium contain haploid nuclei of each mating type. Secondary mycelia may grow in the soil for years, reaching an enormous size. A few mycelia have been found to be hundreds of meters across, making them perhaps the largest organisms in the world.

When the right combination of moisture and nutrients occurs, spore-producing fruiting bodies push above the ground. You would recognize these fruiting bodies as mushrooms. Each mushroom begins as a mass of growing hyphae that forms a button, or thick bulge, at the soil's surface.

▼ **Figure 21–8** **The club fungi are named after the club shape of their reproductive structure, the basidium.** The cap of a basidiomycete such as a mushroom is composed of tightly packed hyphae. The lower side of the cap is composed of gills—thin blades of tissue lined with basidia that produce basidiospores.

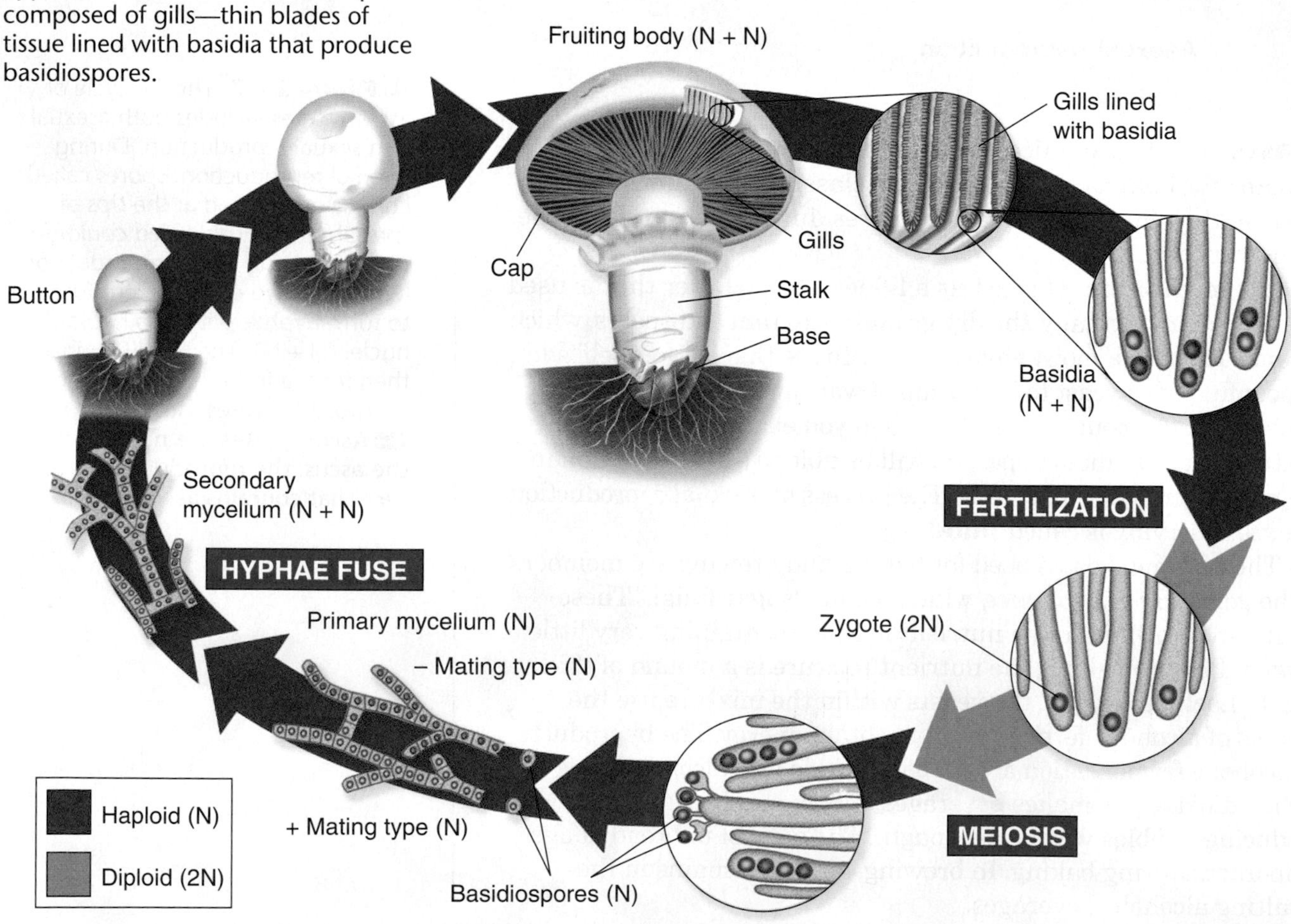

▲ The club fungi are a very diverse group. These fungi are all decomposers, but other kinds of club fungi are parasites of plants and animals. At least two of these fungi, the pigskin poison puffball and the fly agaric, are poisonous. **Inferring** ***Can you tell by looking at a fungus whether or not it is poisonous?***

Fruiting bodies expand with astonishing speed, sometimes producing fully developed mushrooms overnight. This remarkable growth rate is caused by cell enlargement, not cell division. The cells of the hyphae enlarge by rapidly taking in water.

When the mushroom cap opens, it exposes hundreds of tiny gills on its underside. Each gill is lined with basidia. The two nuclei in each basidium fuse to form a diploid (2N) zygote cell, which then undergoes meiosis, forming clusters of haploid **basidiospores.** The basidiospores form at the edge of each basidium and, within a few hours, are ready to be scattered. Mushrooms are truly amazing reproductive structures—a single mushroom can produce billions of spores, and giant puffballs can produce trillions.

Diversity of Club Fungi In addition to mushrooms, basidiomycetes include shelf fungi, which grow near the surfaces of dead or decaying trees. The visible bracketlike structure that forms is a reproductive structure, and it, too, is a prolific producer of spores. Puffballs, earthstars, jelly fungi, and plant parasites known as rusts are other examples of basidiomycetes. **Figure 21–9** shows some examples of basidiomycetes.

✔ ***On which part of a mushroom would you find basidia?***

Edible and Inedible Mushrooms Many types of fungi have long been considered delicacies, and several different species of mushrooms are cultivated for food. You may have already tasted sliced mushrooms on pizza, feasted on delicious sautéed portobello mushrooms, or eaten shiitake mushrooms. When properly cooked and prepared, domestic mushrooms are tasty and nutritious.

Wild mushrooms are a different story: Although some are edible, many are poisonous. Because many species of poisonous mushrooms look almost identical to edible mushrooms, you should never pick or eat any mushrooms found in the wild. Instead, mushroom gathering should be left to experts who can positively identify each mushroom they collect. The result of eating a poisonous mushroom can be severe illness, or even death.

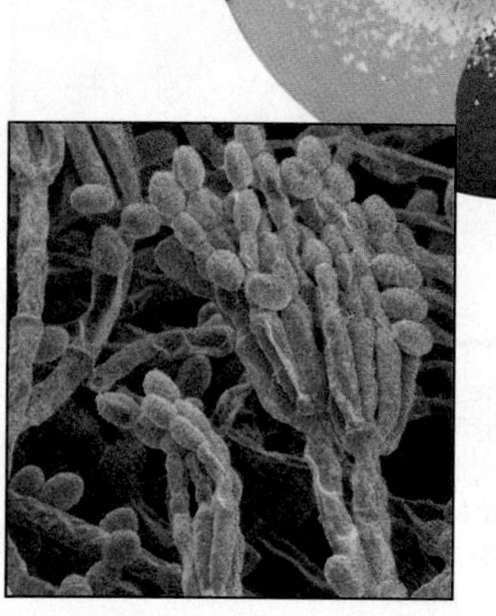

Figure 21–10 **The phylum Deuteromycota is made up of fungi that cannot be classified in any other phylum.** Under the microscope, the brushlike clusters of many small, spherical conidia characterize *Penicillium notatum.* This organism was the first of the *Penicillium* fungi used to produce the antibiotic penicillin.

(magnification: 930×)

The Imperfect Fungi

Fungi are usually classified by the sexual phase of their life cycle. So, what do biologists do when they discover a fungus that does not seem to have a sexual phase? Until a sexual phase is discovered, scientists place it in the phylum called Deuteromycota, or imperfect fungi. The term *imperfect*, by the way, doesn't mean that there's anything wrong with these organisms. It simply means that *our* understanding of their life cycles may not be perfect. **The Deuteromycota are fungi that cannot be placed in other phyla because researchers have never been able to observe a sexual phase in their life cycles.** A majority of the imperfect fungi closely resemble ascomycetes. Others are similar to basidiomycetes, and a few resemble the zygomycetes.

One of the best-known genera of the imperfect fungi is *Penicillium.* The species *Penicillium notatum,* shown in **Figure 21–10,** is a mold that frequently grows on fruit and is the source of the antibiotic penicillin. Like the ascomycetes, *Penicillium* reproduces asexually by means of conidia, leading many biologists to conclude that *Penicillium* evolved from an ascomycete that lost the sexual phase of its life cycle.

21–2 Section Assessment

1. **Key Concept** List the four phyla of fungi, and identify the main characteristics of the members of each phylum.
2. How do conidia form? What is their function?
3. Which fungal phylum contains the largest number of species?
4. **Critical Thinking Comparing and Contrasting** Compare the structure and function of an ascus and a basidium.
5. **Critical Thinking Comparing and Contrasting** Compare asexual and sexual reproduction in bread mold. At what stage does meiosis occur?

You & Your Community

Exploring Your Community

Visit a local supermarket to find out how fungi are used in the cuisines of different cultures. Select a particular fungus, research recipes in which it is used, and try one of the recipes. You may also want to find the scientific name of the fungus you have selected.

21–3 Ecology of Fungi

1-S2.1, S2.3 Scientists experiment
4-6.1 Relationships and interactions between organisms
4-6.1 Materials are recycled by the action of decomposers
4-5.2 Fungi and other parasites infect other organisms

Fungi have been around since life first moved onto land. In fact, the oldest known fossils of fungi, shown in **Figure 21–11,** were formed about 460 million years ago. At that time, the largest land plants were small organisms similar to mosses. Paleontologists think that fungi helped early plants to obtain nutrients from the ground. Their early appearance suggests that fungi may have been essential to plants' successful colonization of the land, one of the key events in the history of life.

Over time, fungi have become an important part of virtually all ecosystems, adapting to conditions in every corner of Earth. Because most fungi live their lives out of our sight, people often overlook them. But without fungi, the world would be a very different place.

Guide for Reading

Key Concepts
- What is the main role of fungi in natural ecosystems?
- What problems do parasitic fungi cause?
- What kinds of symbiotic relationships do fungi form with other organisms?

Vocabulary
saprobe
lichen
mycorrhiza

Reading Strategy: Using Prior Knowledge Before you read this section, write down all the different ways that you think fungi interact in the environment. As you read, add to or revise your list as necessary.

All Fungi Are Heterotrophs

As heterotrophs, fungi cannot manufacture their own food. Instead, they must rely on other organisms for their energy. Unlike animals, fungi cannot move to capture food, but their mycelia can grow very rapidly into the tissues and cells of plants and other organisms. Many fungi are **saprobes,** organisms that obtain food from decaying organic matter. Others are parasites, which harm other organisms while living directly on or within them. Still other fungi are symbionts that live in close and mutually beneficial association with other species.

Although most fungi feed on decaying matter, a few feed by capturing live animals. *Pleurotus ostreatus* is a carnivorous fungus that lives on the sides of trees. As roundworms crawl into the fungus to feed, they are exposed to a fungal chemical that makes them become sluggish. As the worms slow to a stop, fungal hyphae penetrate their bodies, trapping them in place and then digesting them.

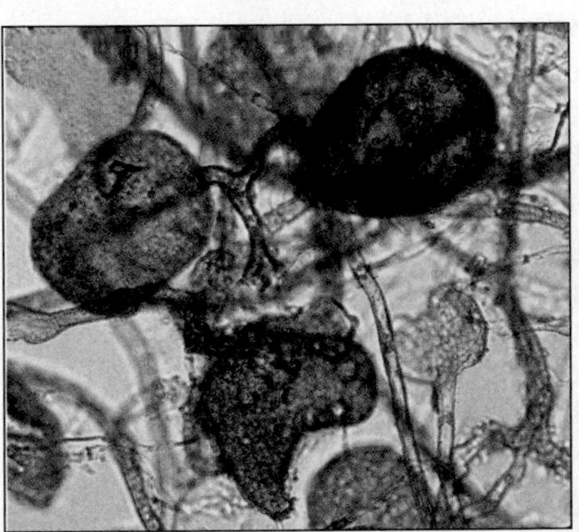

(magnification: 280×)

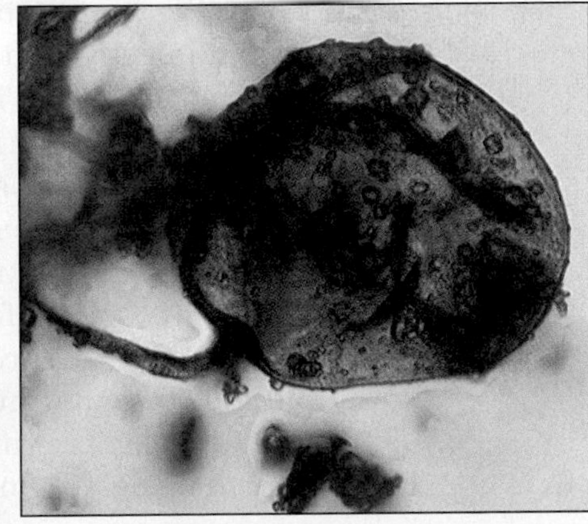

(magnification: 560×)

Figure 21–11 These microscopic images show fossils of the earliest known fungi, zygomycetes that lived about 460 million years ago. An overview of fossilized hyphae with spores is shown on the left. The close-up of hyphae growing out of a spore is shown on the right. **Observing** *Can you identify structures similar to those of modern molds?*

▲ **Figure 21–12** **Many fungi are decomposers that recycle nutrients by breaking down the bodies of other organisms.** The mycelia of these mushrooms have released enzymes that are breaking down the wood tissues of the decaying tree stump.

Fungi as Decomposers

Fungi play an essential role in maintaining equilibrium in nearly every ecosystem, where they recycle nutrients by breaking down the bodies and wastes of other organisms. Like the fungi in **Figure 21–12,** many fungi feed by releasing digestive enzymes that break down leaves, fruit, and other organic material into simple molecules. These molecules then diffuse into the fungus. The mycelia of fungi produce digestive enzymes that speed the breakdown of wastes and dead organisms. In so doing, they promote the recycling of nutrients and essential chemicals, helping to maintain ecosystem equilibrium.

Imagine a world without decomposers. Without decay, the energy-rich compounds that organisms accumulate during their lifetimes would be lost forever. Many organisms, especially plants, remove important trace elements and nutrients from the soil. If these materials were not returned, the soil would quickly be depleted, and Earth would become lifeless and barren.

Fungi as Parasites

As useful as many fungi are, others can infect both animals and plants, disrupting their internal equilibrium and causing disease. **Parasitic fungi cause serious plant and animal diseases. A few cause diseases in humans.**

Plant Diseases Fungi cause diseases such as corn smut, which destroys the corn kernels, as shown in **Figure 21–13.** Mildews, which infect a wide variety of fruits, are also fungi. Fungal diseases are responsible for the loss of approximately 15 percent of the crops grown in temperate regions of the world. In tropical areas, where high humidity favors fungal growth, the loss of crops is sometimes as high as 50 percent. Fungi are in direct competition with humans for food. Unfortunately for us, sometimes fungi win that competition.

One fungal disease—wheat rust—affects one of the most important crops grown in North America. Rusts are caused by a type of basidiomycete that needs two different plants to complete its life cycle. Spores produced by rust in barberry plants are carried by the wind into wheat fields. There, the spores germinate and infect wheat plants. The patches of rust produce a second type of spore that infects other wheat plants, allowing the disease to spread through the field like wildfire.

Later in the growing season, a new variety of spore is produced by the rust. These tough black spores easily survive through the winter. In spring, they go through a sexual phase and produce spores that infect barberry plants. Once on the barberry leaves, the rust produces the spores that infect wheat plants, and the cycle continues. Fortunately, once agricultural scientists understood the life cycle of the rust, they were able to slow its spread by destroying barberry plants.

 *What are two examples of plant diseases caused by fungi?*

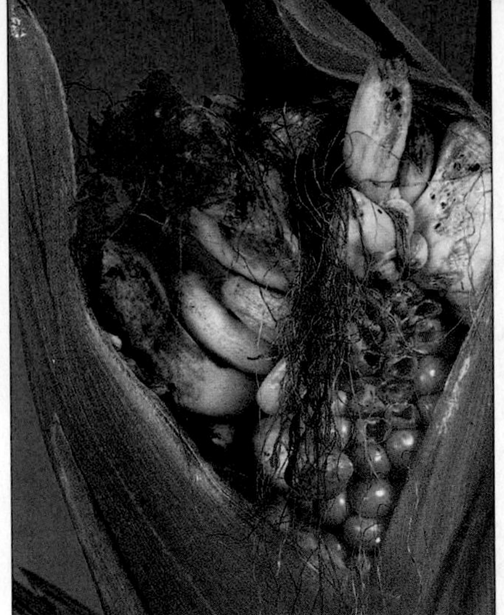

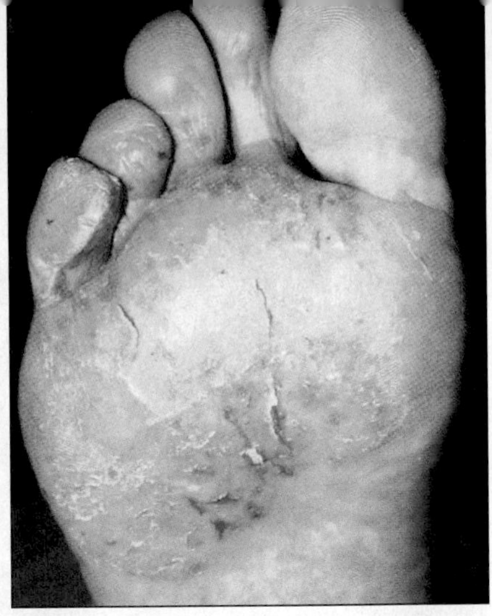

Figure 21–13 **Parasitic fungi cause serious diseases in plants and animals.** Corn smut (left) grows on a corn plant, harming it. The fungus releases millions of spores that survive in the soil during the winter and begin their life cycle again in the spring. Wheat rust (center) is a basidiomycete that infects both wheat and barberry plants. Athlete's foot (right) infects the outer layers of human skin.

Human Diseases Fungal parasites can also infect humans. One deuteromycete can infect the areas between the toes, causing the infection known as athlete's foot. The fungus forms a mycelium directly within the outer layers of the skin. This produces a red, inflamed sore from which the spores can easily spread from person to person. When the same fungus infects other areas, such as the skin of the scalp, it produces a red scaling sore known as ringworm, which is not a worm at all.

The microorganism *Candida albicans,* a yeast, can disrupt the equilibrium within the human body, causing fungal disease. *Candida,* which grows in moist regions of the body, is usually kept in check by competition from bacteria that grow in the body and by the body's immune system. This normal balance can be upset by many factors, including the use of antibiotics, which kill bacteria, or by damage to the immune system. When this happens, *Candida* may produce thrush, a painful mouth infection. Yeast infections of the female reproductive tract usually are due to overgrowth of *Candida.*

Other Animal Diseases As problematic as human fungal diseases can be, few fungal diseases are as deadly as the infection by one fungus from the genus *Cordyceps.* This fungus infects grasshoppers in rain forests in Costa Rica. Microscopic spores become lodged in the grasshopper, where they germinate and produce enzymes that slowly penetrate the insect's tough external skeleton. The spores multiply in the insect's body, digesting all its cells and tissues until the insect dies. To complete the process of digestion, hyphae develop, cloaking the decaying exoskeleton in a web of fungal material. Reproductive structures, which will produce more spores that will spread the infection, then emerge from the grasshopper's remains, as shown in **Figure 21–14.**

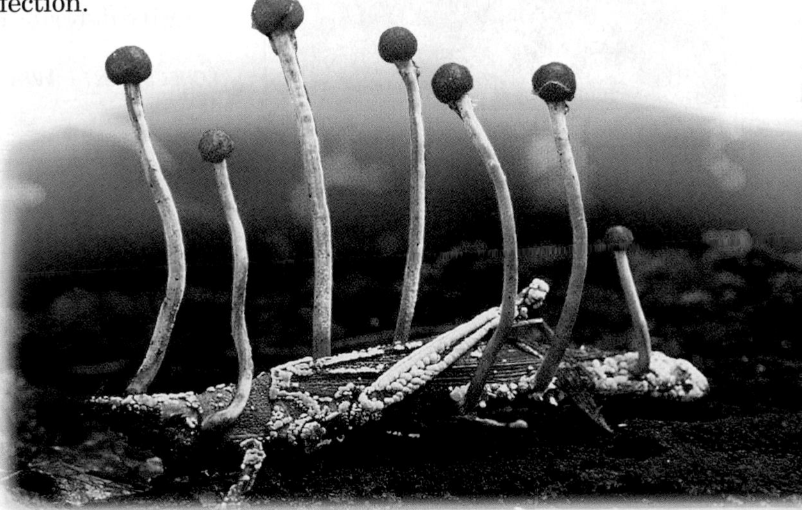

▲ **Figure 21–14** This grasshopper is the victim of *Cordyceps,* a fungus. Once the fungus's tiny spore enters the insect's body, it multiplies rapidly and digests body tissues. The structures growing out of the grasshopper's body are the fungus's fruiting bodies. **Comparing and Contrasting** ***Some pathogens rely on their host to spread them to other potential hosts. How does this fungus spread?***

Symbiotic Relationships

Fungi often grow in close association with members of other species in symbiotic relationships. Although fungi are parasites in many of these relationships, that is not always the case. **Some fungi form symbiotic relationships in which both partners benefit. Two such mutualistic associations, lichens and mycorrhizae, are essential to many ecosystems.** Lichens are shown in **Figure 21–15.**

Lichens **Lichens** (LY-kunz) are not single organisms. Rather, they are symbiotic associations between a fungus and a photosynthetic organism. The fungi in lichens are usually ascomycetes, although a few are basidiomycetes. The photosynthetic organism is either a green alga or a cyanobacterium, or both. **Figure 21–16** shows the structure of a lichen.

Lichens are extremely resistant to drought and cold. Therefore, they can grow in places where few other organisms can survive—on dry, bare rock in deserts and on the tops of mountains. Lichens are able to survive in these harsh environments because of the relationship between the two partner organisms. The algae or cyanobacteria carry out photosynthesis, providing the fungus with a source of energy. The fungus, in turn, provides the algae or bacteria with water and minerals that it collects and protects the delicate green cells from intense sunlight.

Lichens are often the first organisms to enter barren environments, gradually breaking down the rocks on which they grow. In this way, lichens help in the early stages of soil formation. Lichens are also remarkably sensitive to air pollution, and they are among the first organisms to be affected when air quality deteriorates.

What two groups of organisms grow together in lichens?

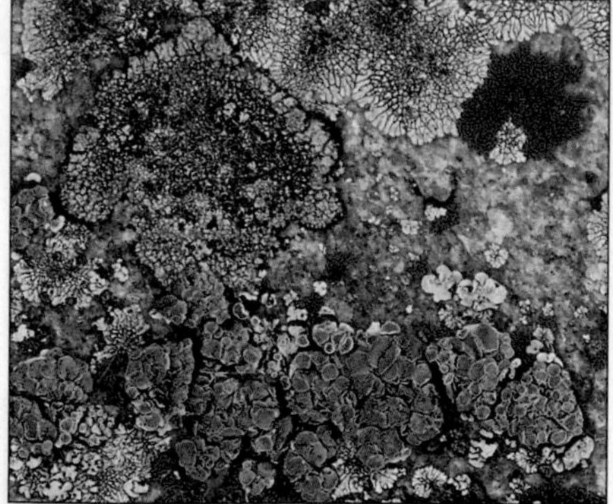

Figure 21–15 Lichens grow in one of three forms. Crustose lichens (top) are flat; foliose lichens (middle) resemble leaves; and fruticose lichens (bottom) grow upright. **Inferring** *How do lichens assist in soil formation?*

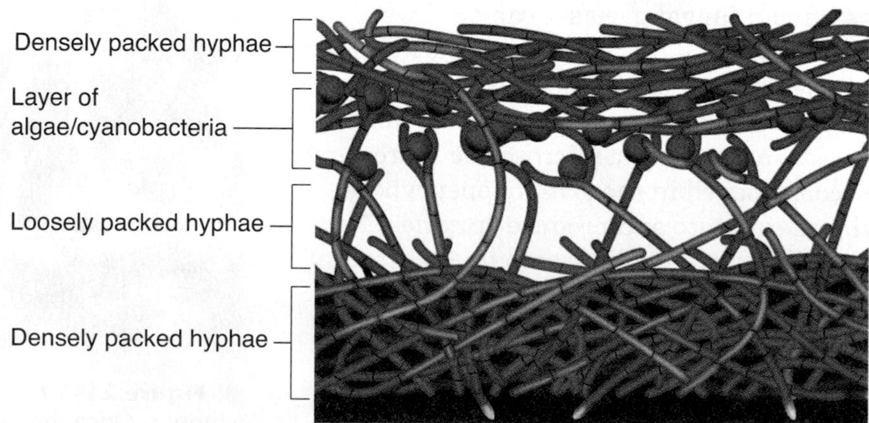

▲ **Figure 21–16** **Lichens are a mutualistic relationship between a fungus and an alga or a cyanobacterium, or both.** The protective upper surface of a lichen is composed of fungal hyphae. Below this is the layer of cyanobacteria or algae with loosely woven hyphae. The third layer consists of loosely packed hyphae. The bottom layer is a protective surface covered by small projections that attach the lichen to a rock or tree.

Problem Solving

Repotting Orchids

You are working in a greenhouse that has just begun to grow orchids. The plants arrive in small pots from a nursery. When they outgrow the pots, your supervisor asks you to place them in larger pots with fresh soil, just as you have done with other plants. However, every time you follow the greenhouse procedure for repotting, which includes carefully washing off the "old" soil and placing the roots into a sterilized soil mix, the plants soon wither and die.

Defining the Problem In your own words, what is the problem the greenhouse faces?

Organizing Information What problems could sterile, microbe-free soil present to a plant? Are there microorganisms in soil that might be essential to orchids? Might the loss of such organisms cause problems for the plants? What kinds of problems?

Creating a Solution Describe an experiment that you could use to find out if the use of sterile soil is causing the problems with repotting. Be sure to devise controls that might determine whether the mechanical stress of repotting, rather than the soil mixture, is causing the problems.

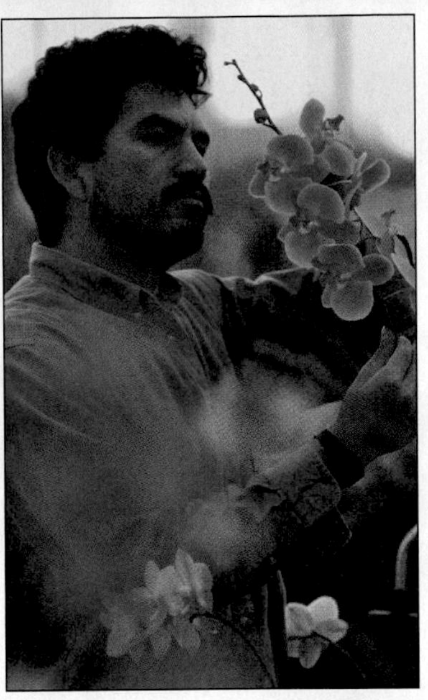

Presenting Your Plan Make a poster showing the steps and procedures in your proposed experiment, and explain it to the class.

Mycorrhizae Fungi also form mutualistic relationships with plants. Almost half of the tissues of trees are hidden beneath the ground in masses of tangled roots. These roots are woven into a partnership with an even larger web of fungal mycelia. These associations of plant roots and fungi are **mycorrhizae** (my-koh-RY-zee; singular: mycorrhiza).

Scientists have known about this partnership for years, but recent research shows that it is more common and more important than was previously thought. Researchers now estimate that 80 percent of all plant species form mycorrhizae with fungi.

How do plants and fungi benefit from each other? The tiny hyphae of the fungi aid plants in absorbing water and minerals. They do this by producing a network that covers the roots of the plants and increases the effective surface area of the root system. This allows the roots to absorb more water and minerals from the soil. In addition, the fungi release enzymes that free nutrients in the soil. The plants, in turn, provide the fungi with the products of photosynthesis.

The presence of mycorrhizae is essential for the growth of many plants. The seeds of some plants, such as orchids, cannot germinate in the absence of mycorrhizal fungi. Many trees are unable to survive without fungal symbionts. Mycorrhizal associations have even been cited as an adaptation that was critical in the evolution of land plants from more-aquatic ancestors.

For: Articles on fungi
Visit: PHSchool.com
Web Code: cbe-6213

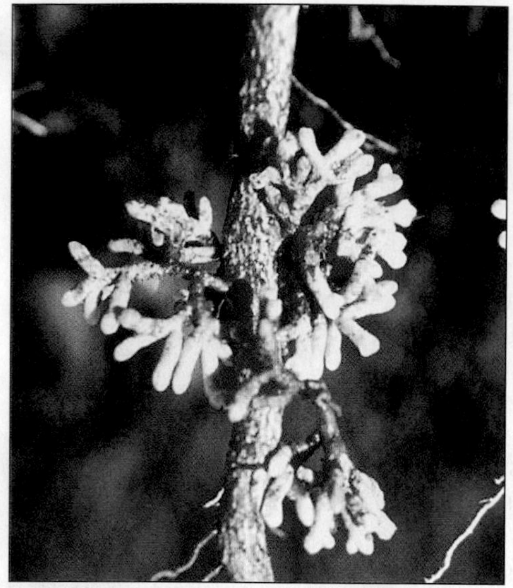

Figure 21–17 Plants and fungi often form associations called mycorrhizae (top photograph). The fungi in the mycorrhizae allow the host plant to absorb more water and nutrients. In the bottom photograph, the lemon seedlings on the left were grown without mycorrhizae. Those on the right, of the same age, were grown with mycorrhizae. **Applying Concepts** *What type of symbiotic relationship is illustrated by mycorrhizae?*

Mycorrhizal relationships are often very specialized. For example, the Douglas fir forests of the Pacific Northwest are dependent on the presence of a particular species of white truffle. In Europe, black truffles are found growing with oak and beech trees. The fly agaric grows mostly with birch and pine trees. **Figure 21–17** shows how mycorrhizae affect the growth of young lemon trees.

Why is this networking relationship so important? The partnership between plant and fungus does not end with a single plant. The roots of each plant are plugged into mycorrhizal networks that connect many plants. What's more astounding is that these networks appear to connect plants of different species.

A recent experiment showed that carbon atoms from one tree often end up in another nearby tree. In an experiment using carbon isotopes to track the movement of carbon, ecologist Suzanne Simard found that mycorrhizal fungi transferred carbon from paper birch trees growing in the sun to Douglas fir trees growing in the shade. As a result, the sun-starved fir trees thrived, basically by being "fed" carbon from the birches.

Simard's findings suggest that plants are far from being isolated individuals, as was previously thought. Instead, plants—and their associated fungi—may be evolving as part of an ecological partnership.

21–3 Section Assessment

1. **Key Concept** What is the major role of fungi in an ecosystem?
2. **Key Concept** Explain the roles of fungi in causing disease in humans and in other living things.
3. **Key Concept** Describe two mutualistic relationships that fungi form with other organisms.
4. Describe the life cycle of wheat rust.
5. **Critical Thinking Applying Concepts** What might happen to a garden if it were sprayed with a long-acting fungicide?
6. **Critical Thinking Applying Concepts** Summarize the role of fungi in disrupting the equilibrium in an ecosystem. Give one specific example.

Connecting Concepts

Structure and Function
Both bacteria and fungi are decomposers. What characteristics do these two groups share that allow them to function in this ecological role? Use the information in Chapter 19 to help answer this question.

Real-World Lab

Examining Seeds for Fungi

The fungi that you are probably most familiar with are mushrooms and the molds that attack stored foods. In this investigation, you will examine how storage conditions affect the growth of fungi on seeds.

Problem
What storage conditions best protect seeds from fungi?

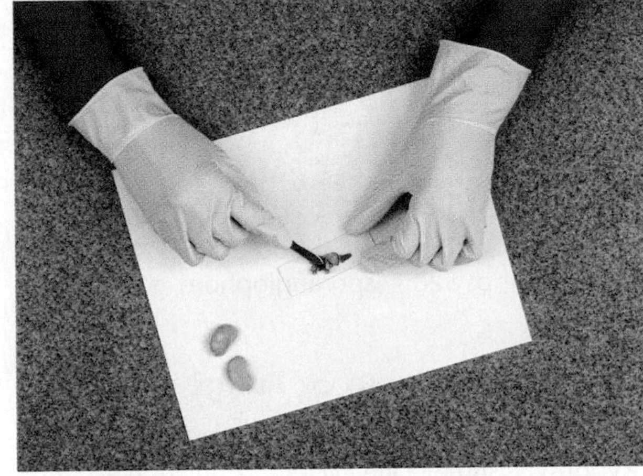

Materials
- seeds stored in cold, dry conditions
- seeds stored in warm, moist conditions
- forceps
- microscope slide
- coverslip
- microscope
- aniline blue stain
- dropper pipette
- paper towels

Skill
Formulating Hypotheses

Procedure

1. **Formulating Hypotheses** Develop a hypothesis about the effect of temperature and moisture on the growth of a seed-destroying fungus. Predict whether you will find more hyphae in seeds stored in cold, dry conditions or in seeds stored in warm, moist conditions.
2. Use a dropper pipette to place a drop of aniline blue stain on a microscope slide. **CAUTION:** *Avoid getting the stain on your hands or clothing.*
3. Use forceps to carefully remove the outer seed coat from a seed stored in cool, dry conditions. Place the seed in the drop of aniline blue stain.
4. Use the flat side of the forceps to gently mash and flatten the seed in the drop of stain. Place a coverslip on top of the mashed seed. Leave the seed in the stain for 1 minute.
5. Use a dropper pipette to place a drop of water on the slide, touching one edge of the coverslip.
6. Touch a paper towel to the edge of the coverslip opposite the drop of water to draw the water under the coverslip. Repeat steps 4 and 5 until you have removed the drop of stain.
7. Use the high-power objective of the microscope to examine the stained seed. Any hyphae that are present will be stained blue. Record your observations as notes and sketches.
8. Repeat steps 2 through 7 with a seed stored in warm, moist conditions.

Analyze and Conclude

1. **Observing** Which seeds had more hyphae?
2. **Analyzing Data** What conditions favor the growth of fungi? What conditions are better for storing seeds?
3. **Drawing Conclusions** Did your observations support your hypothesis? Are the environmental requirements of this fungus typical of most fungi?
4. **Inferring** Aniline blue stains the cell walls of fungi more easily than plant cell walls. What substance in fungi do you think aniline blue binds to? Explain your answer.
5. **SAFETY** Explain how you demonstrated safe practices as you carried out this investigation.

Go Further

Designing Experiments Plan an experiment to compare the growth of plants from both healthy and fungus-infected seeds. Define your controlled and manipulated variables. Obtain your teacher's permission before carrying out your experiment.

Chapter 21 Study Guide

21–1 The Kingdom Fungi

Key Concepts

- Fungi are eukaryotic heterotrophs that have cell walls made of chitin.
- The bodies of multicellular fungi are composed of many hyphae tangled together into a thick mass called a mycelium.
- Most fungi reproduce both asexually and sexually.

Vocabulary

chitin, p. 527 • hypha, p. 527
mycelium, p. 528 • fruiting body, p. 528
sporangium, p. 528 • sporangiophore, p. 528

21–2 Classification of Fungi

Key Concepts

- Zygomycetes have life cycles that include a zygospore.
- The phylum Ascomycota is named for the ascus, a reproductive structure that contains spores.
- The phylum Basidiomycota, or club fungi, gets its name from the basidium, a specialized reproductive structure that resembles a club.
- Deuteromycota are fungi that cannot be placed in other phyla because researchers have never been able to observe a sexual phase in their life cycles.

Vocabulary

zygospore, p. 530 • rhizoid, p. 530
stolon, p. 530 • gametangium, p. 530
conidium, p. 532 • ascus, p. 532
ascospore, p. 532 • budding, p. 533
basidium, p. 534 • basidiospore, p. 535

21–3 Ecology of Fungi

Key Concepts

- Fungi play an essential role in maintaining equilibrium in nearly every ecosystem, where they recycle nutrients by breaking down the bodies and wastes of other organisms.
- Parasitic fungi cause serious plant and animal diseases. A few fungi cause diseases in humans.
- Some fungi form symbiotic relationships in which both partners benefit. Two such mutualistic associations, lichens and mycorrhizae, are essential to many ecosystems.

Vocabulary

saprobe, p. 537
lichen, p. 540
mycorrhiza, p. 541

Thinking Visually

Use the information in Section 21–2 to complete the following compare-and-contrast table about the different phyla of Fungi:

Four Phyla of Fungi

Phylum	Examples	Characteristics	Reproduction	
			Asexual	Sexual
Zygomycota (common molds)	*Rhizopus stolonifer* (black bread mold)	1	Spores in sporangiophores	2
Ascomycota (sac fungi)	3	Long stage in which cells have two nuclei; yeasts are unicellular	4	5
Basidiomycota (club fungi)	Mushrooms, puffballs, earthstars, shelf fungi, jelly fungi, rusts	Extremely variable; long stage in which cells have two nuclei	None or conidia on conidiophores	6
Deuteromycota (imperfect fungi)	*Penicillium,* ringworm, and athlete's foot fungus	7	Conidia on conidiophores	8

Preparing for the Living Environment Exam

NEW YORK LIVING ENVIRONMENT

Blue questions emphasize Regents Exam content

Chapter 21

Part A

Multiple Choice

For each statement or question, select the number of the word or expression that, of those given, best completes the statement or answers the question.

1 Decomposition and decay of organic matter are accomplished by the action of
(1) green plants (3) viruses and algae
(2) bacteria and fungi (4) scavengers

2 The body of a typical fungus consists of a tangled mass of filaments called a(an)
(1) basidium (3) hypha
(2) mycelium (4) antheridium

3 When hyphae of opposite mating types of fungi meet, each hypha forms a
(1) sporangium (3) gametangium
(2) zygospore (4) zoospore

4 In the diagram of bread mold shown below, X is pointing to what structure?

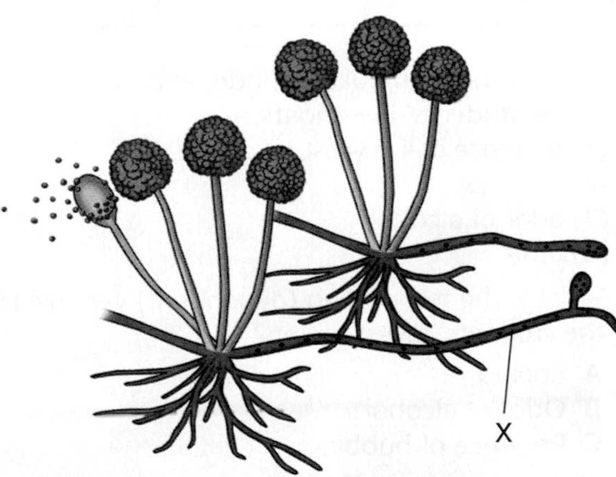

(1) stolon (3) basidium
(2) rhizoid (4) ascus

5 The asexual spores of ascomycetes are called
(1) zygospores (3) ascospores
(2) conidia (4) zoospores

6 In both baking and brewing, yeast cells bud and obtain their energy from the process of
(1) lactic acid fermentation
(2) aerobic respiration
(3) alcoholic fermentation
(4) digestion

7 A mushroom that you see above the ground is actually a
(1) basidiospore (3) fruiting body
(2) gametangium (4) basidium

8 Sexual reproduction has never been observed in
(1) zygomycetes (3) basidiomycetes
(2) ascomycetes (4) deuteromycetes

9 Organisms that obtain food from decaying organic matter are called
(1) mutualists (3) parasites
(2) autotrophs (4) saprobes

10 An example of a symbiotic association between a fungus and a photosynthetic organism is a
(1) mycorrhiza (3) lichen
(2) fruiting body (4) mushroom

11 Which organism is *not* a fungus?
(1) mushroom (3) bread mold
(2) water mold (4) yeast

12 Which is (are) characteristic of some types of fungi?
A Decomposition
B Parasitism
C Mutualism
(1) A and B, only (3) C and A, only
(2) B and C, only (4) A, B, and C

For questions 13 and 14, complete each analogy by selecting the correct number. In analogies, A : B :: C : means "A is to B as C is to ___?___."

13 Sac fungus : morel :: club fungus :
(1) mushroom (3) bread mold
(2) yeast (4) lichen

14 Plant : root :: mold :
(1) gametangium
(2) zygospore
(3) rhizoid
(4) stolon

Test-Taking Tip Before you begin answering questions, determine the total number of questions on the test and how much time, on average, you have to answer each question. Try to partition your time accordingly.

Part B

Multiple Choice and Extended Response

For those questions that ask you to select a response, choose the one that best completes the statement or answers the question. For all others follow the directions given.

15 State *two* conditions other than the presence of food, that are necessary for fungal spores to germinate.

16 State *two* factors that serve as the basis of classification for different groups of fungi.

Base your answers to questions 17 and 18 on the information and graph below and on your knowledge of biology.

The graph below illustrates the growth rates of three species of trees—two individuals of each. One tree of each species grew with mycorrhizae, and one grew without mycorrhizae.

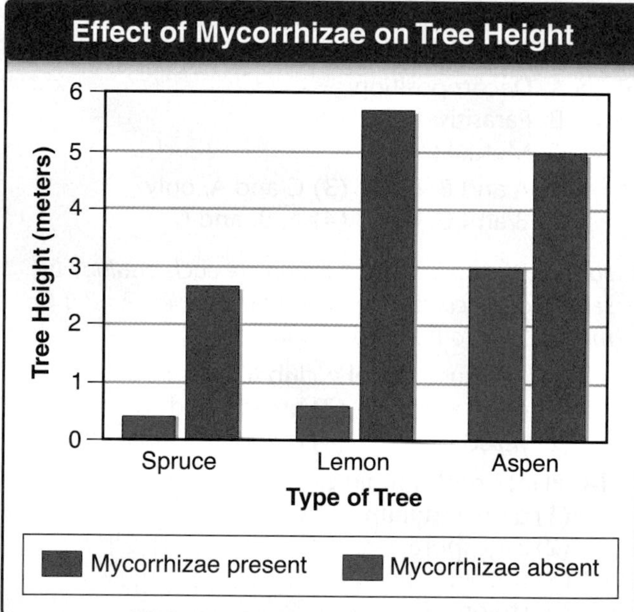

17 For each species, state how the growth of the two plants compare.

18 State a generalization about the affect of mycorrhizae on the rate of plant growth.

Base your answers to questions 19 through 21 on the information below and on your knowledge of biology.

Ripe grapes are covered with a grayish film called "bloom," which contains yeasts and sometimes other microorganisms. A group of students prepared three test tubes of fresh, mashed grapes. They heated two of the test tubes to the boiling point and then cooled them. They inoculated one of these test tubes with live yeast. They incubated all three test tubes at 30°C for 48 hours and then examined the test tubes for signs of fermentation—the presence of bubbles and alcohol. Their data are summarized in the table below.

Evidence of Fermentation

Test-Tube Contents	Alcohol Odor (yes or no)	Bubbles (yes or no)
Unheated grape mash	yes	yes
Boiled grape mash	no	no
Boiled grape mash inoculated with yeast	yes	yes

19 What is the manipulated (independent) variable in the students' investigation?
(1) presence of live yeast
(2) bubbles
(3) odor of alcohol
(4) time

20 What is the responding (dependent) variable in the students' investigation?
A Boiling
B Odor of alcohol
C Presence of bubbles
(1) A, only
(2) B, only
(3) B and C, only
(4) A, B, and C

21 What is an appropriate conclusion, based on the students' results?
A Uninoculated, boiled grape mash does not seem to ferment over a 48-hour period.
B Boiled grape mash that contains live yeast undergoes fermentation.
C Grape mash does not ferment unless live yeast is added.
(1) A and B, only
(2) A and C, only
(3) B and C, only
(4) A, B, and C

For each phrase in questions 22 through 25, select the numbered term that is most closely associated with that phrase. A term may be used once, more than one, or not at all.

(1) Lichen (4) Mycelium
(2) Mycorrhiza (5) Chitin
(3) Penicillium

22 Cell wall carbohydrate

23 Tangled mass of hyphae

24 Plant/fungus symbiont

25 Fungal source of antibiotic

26 State the name of the carbohydrate found in the cell walls of both insects and fungi.

27 Explain how a sporangiophore functions in the reproduction of fungi.

28 Explain how the method by which fungi obtain food helps in the recycling of nutrients and essential chemicals.

29 Explain the significance of mycorrhizae in the evolution of plants.

30 State one reason why it is dangerous to eat wild mushrooms.

31 Heavily polluted fresh water contains few fungi. Explain how this would affect life in a polluted lake.

Part C

Extended Response

Base your answers to questions 32 through 36 on the information below and on your knowledge of biology.

The ABC Drug Company is developing a new, anti-fungal lotion for the treatment of athlete's foot. Tests were conducted to determine how effective the medicine is. The company studied two groups of athlete's foot sufferers. One group consisted of 200 men. The other group consisted of 200 women. Members of each group applied the lotion twice a day for two weeks. After the two week period, 75 percent of the men and 83 percent of the women had no trace of the fungus on their feet.

32 Identify the manipulated (independent) variable in this study.

33 Two groups of subjects were in this study.
a In order for the results to be valid, state what other group(s) should be added.
b What treatment should that group(s) receive?

34 Fungi that cause athlete's foot belong to the phylum Deuteromycota. What is a characteristic of that group of fungi that might affect this study?

35 State *two* additional kinds of information that would be needed for other scientists to be able to duplicate this study.

36 Consider the conditions necessary for fungal spores to germinate and explain why athlete's foot can be such a problem to cure.

37 Most fungi are heterotrophic, multicellular, organisms that reproduce both sexually and asexually. Explain how common molds (zygomycetes) reproduce. In your explanation be sure to include the following terms:
- hyphae
- spores
- zygospores
- haploid and diploid

38 Saprobes and parasites fill very different niches in the ecosystem.
a Explain the difference between a saprobe and a parasite.
b Provide an example of each type of organism.

39 Compare the structure and function of rhizoids and stolons. In your explanation be sure to include:
- how these two forms of hyphae differ in structure and function
- the life process each structure is associated with

For: An interactive self-test
Visit: PHSchool.com
Web Code: cba-6210

UNIT

7 Plants

Chapters

These colorful poppies, found growing on the Kenai Peninsula in Alaska, are only one example of the thousands of species of flowering plants that inhabit Earth.

From the Author

Every spring I dig up a patch of soil in my backyard. I scatter a handful of impossibly tiny seeds in a few rows near the back of the garden and just wait. By midsummer, vines grown from those seeds are heavy with ripe red tomatoes. How do the tomatoes taste? Every time I bite into one, I'm reminded of the best line of a song I once heard in a coffeehouse, "There's only two things that money can't buy—true love and home-grown tomatoes." To my way of thinking, that's about as magical as life can get.

Ken Miller

What discoveries lie ahead?

- Will studies of plants reveal new compounds that can be effective in treating human disease?
- Can we learn enough from studies of plant genetics to produce new crops that will feed more people around the world and place less stress on the environment?

Go Online
PHSchool.com
For: Latest discoveries
Visit: PHSchool.com
Web Code: cbe-7000

CHAPTER 22

Plant Diversity

A great diversity of plants can be found in the Hoh Rain Forest of Olympic National Park in Washington.

Inquiry Activity

Are all plants the same?

Procedure 

1. Obtain three plants, a metric ruler, and a hand lens.
2. Construct a table for recording your data.
3. Identify the major parts of each plant. Measure the heights of the plants and the sizes of their parts.
4. Use the hand lens to examine the plants. Record your observations.

Think About It

1. **Comparing and Contrasting** How are the three plants alike? How do they differ?
2. **Inferring** What are the functions of the major parts of each plant?
3. **Classifying** Use your observations to classify the three plants into two groups. Explain your reasons for classifying them in these groups.

22–1 Introduction to Plants

4-3.1 Earth's species developed from earlier species
4-3.1 Fossils indicate many organisms have become extinct
4-5.1 Chloroplasts in plant cells are the site of photosynthesis
4-5.1 Photosynthesis uses solar energy
LS- Make observations, measure, and organize data in a table

Guide for Reading

Key Concepts
- What is a plant?
- What do plants need to survive?
- How did the first plants evolve?

Vocabulary
sporophyte
gametophyte

Reading Strategy: Using Prior Knowledge
Before you read the chapter, make a list of the different groups of plants that you know. As you read, revise your list to include new information about plant groups.

What color is life? That's a silly question, of course, because living things can be just about any color. But consider it in a different way. Imagine yourself in a place on Earth where the sounds and scents of life are all around you. The place is so abundant with life that when you stand on the ground, living things blot out the sun. Now, what color do you see? If you have imagined a thick forest or a teeming jungle, then one color will fill the landscape of your mind—green—the color of plants.

Plants dominate the landscape. Where plants are plentiful, other organisms, such as animals, fungi, and microorganisms, take hold and thrive. Plants provide the base for food chains on land. They also provide shade, shelter, and oxygen for animals of every size and kind. The oldest fossil evidence of plants dates from about 470 million years ago. Since then, plants have colonized and transformed nearly every corner of Earth.

What Is a Plant?

Plants are members of the kingdom Plantae. **Plants are multicellular eukaryotes that have cell walls made of cellulose. They develop from multicellular embryos and carry out photosynthesis using the green pigments chlorophyll *a* and *b*.** Plants include trees, shrubs, and grasses, as well as other organisms, such as mosses and ferns. Most plants, including the one in **Figure 22–1,** are autotrophs, although a few are parasites or saprobes that live on decaying materials.

Plants are so different from animals that sometimes there is a tendency to think of them as not being alive. With few exceptions, plants do not gather food nor do they move about or struggle directly with their predators. Plants can neither run away from danger nor strike blows against an adversary. But as different as they are from animals, plants are everywhere. How have they managed to be so successful?

That question has many answers. In the next few chapters, we will explore some of them. For now, it might help to think of plants as a well-known botanist once described them—as "stationary animals that eat sunlight"!

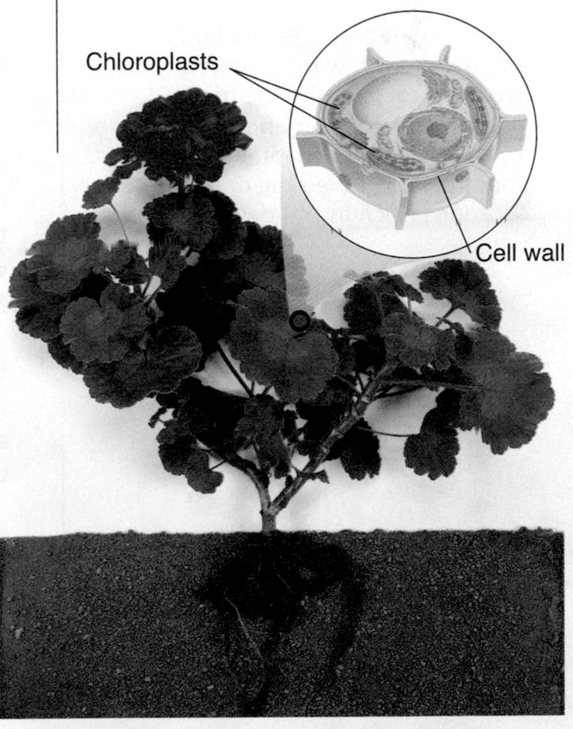

▶ **Figure 22–1 All plants are multicellular eukaryotes that have cell walls made of cellulose.** Their leaves appear green because of the photosynthetic pigments chlorophyll *a* and *b*, which are located in chloroplasts.

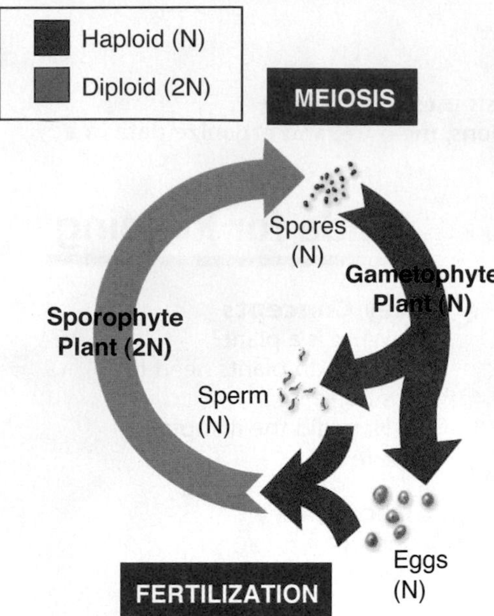

▲ **Figure 22–2** All plants have a life cycle with alternation of generations, in which the haploid gametophyte phase alternates with the diploid sporophyte phase. **Interpreting Graphics** *What stage in the life cycle is produced by fertilization?*

▼ **Figure 22–3** **All plants need sunlight, water, minerals, oxygen, carbon dioxide, and a way to move water and nutrients to all their cells.** Adaptations allow them to live in even the driest locations, such as this desert.

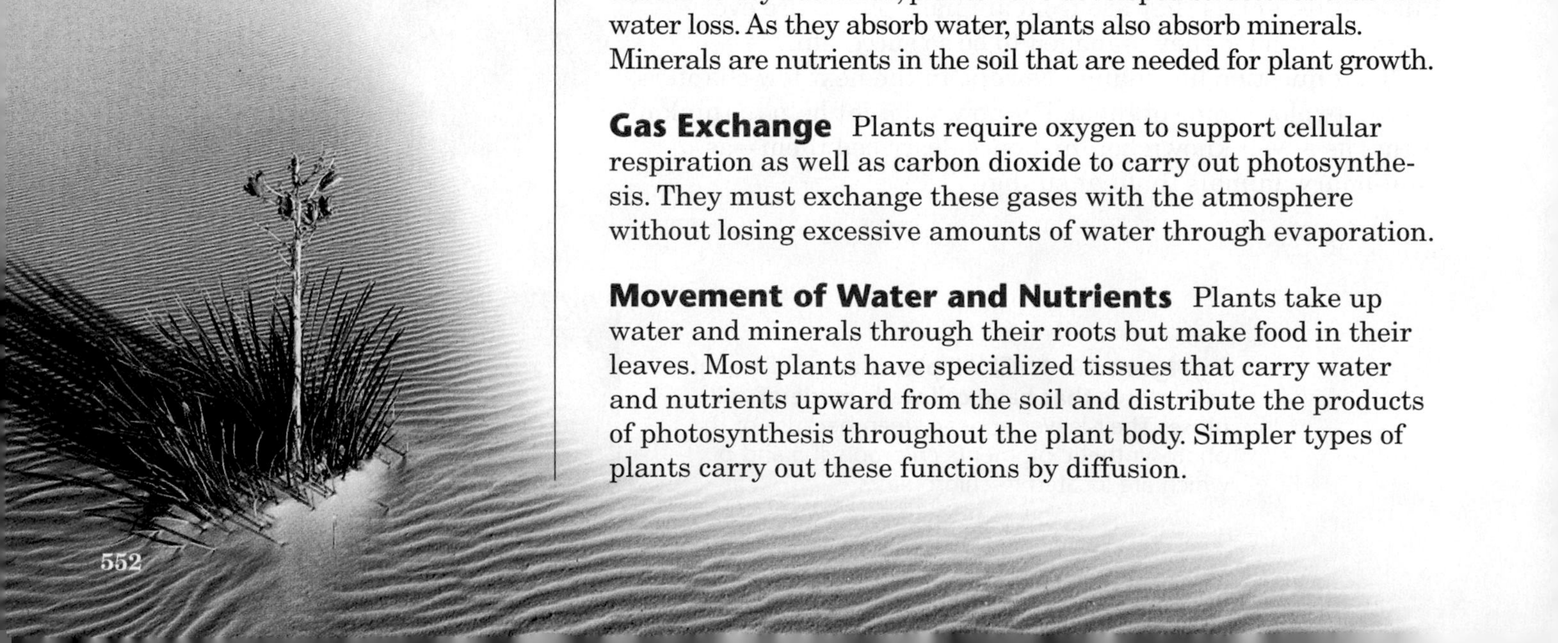

The Plant Life Cycle

Plant life cycles have two alternating phases, a diploid (2N) phase and a haploid (N) phase, known as alternation of generations. During the two phases of the life cycle, shown in **Figure 22–2,** mitosis and meiosis alternate to produce the two types of reproductive cells—gametes and spores. The diploid (2N) phase is known as the **sporophyte,** or spore-producing plant. The haploid (N) phase is known as the **gametophyte,** or gamete-producing plant. Plant spores are haploid (N) reproductive cells formed in the sporophyte plant by meiosis that can grow into new individuals. The new individual is the gametophyte. A gamete is a reproductive cell that is produced by mitosis and fuses during fertilization with another gamete to produce a new individual, the diploid sporophyte.

The earliest plants, mosses and ferns, require water to reproduce. Seed plants, which appeared more recently, have reproductive cycles that can be carried out without water. Many plants also have forms of vegetative, or asexual, reproduction.

What Plants Need to Survive

Surviving as stationary organisms on land is a difficult task, but plants have developed a number of adaptations that enable them to succeed. **The lives of plants center on the need for sunlight, water and minerals, gas exchange, and the transport of water and nutrients throughout the plant body.**

Sunlight Plants use the energy from sunlight to carry out photosynthesis. As a result, every plant displays adaptations shaped by the need to gather sunlight. Photosynthetic organs such as leaves are typically broad and flat and are arranged on the stem so as to maximize light absorption.

Water and Minerals All cells require a constant supply of water. For this reason, plants must obtain and deliver water to all their cells—even those that grow aboveground in the dry air. Water is one of the raw materials of photosynthesis, so it is used up quickly when the sun is shining. Sunny conditions can cause living tissues to dry out. Thus, plants have developed structures that limit water loss. As they absorb water, plants also absorb minerals. Minerals are nutrients in the soil that are needed for plant growth.

Gas Exchange Plants require oxygen to support cellular respiration as well as carbon dioxide to carry out photosynthesis. They must exchange these gases with the atmosphere without losing excessive amounts of water through evaporation.

Movement of Water and Nutrients Plants take up water and minerals through their roots but make food in their leaves. Most plants have specialized tissues that carry water and nutrients upward from the soil and distribute the products of photosynthesis throughout the plant body. Simpler types of plants carry out these functions by diffusion.

Problem Solving

"Plantastic" Voyage

You are part of a team that is planning a space mission that will send astronauts into space for two years. As part of their food, the astronauts will be growing yam plants, *Dioscorea composita*. Your job is to develop a plan to help plants grow on the spacecraft.

Defining the Problem In your own words, state the problem at hand.

Organizing Information Research the types of conditions these plants would need. What requirements would the plants have for moisture? Soil conditions? Light intensity? Day length?

Creating a Solution Make a detailed scale drawing of a container for growing 10 of these plants. (*Dioscorea* plants are vines; assume that each is 10 cm long and 0.5 cm wide.) Determine what material(s) you will use for your container. As you devise your plan, be sure to keep a journal in which you record your team's ideas, drawings, data, and other information.

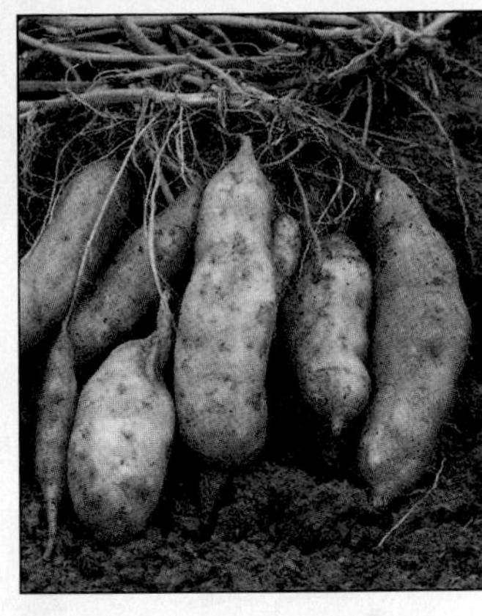

Presenting Your Plan Prepare a multimedia presentation for your classmates as if they were the managers of the space mission. Describe how your team solved the problem, the sources of information you used, the design itself, and what you learned during the project.

Early Plants

For most of Earth's history, plants did not exist. Life was concentrated in oceans, lakes, and streams. Algae and photosynthetic prokaryotes added the oxygen to our planet's atmosphere and provided food for animals and microorganisms.

When plants appeared, much of the existing life on Earth changed. As these new photosynthetic organisms colonized the land, they changed the environment in ways that made it possible for other organisms to develop. New ecosystems emerged, and organic matter began to form soil. How did plants adapt to the conditions of life on land? How plants evolved structures that acquire, transport, and conserve water is the key to answering this question.

Origins in the Water You may recall from Chapter 20 that green algae, shown in **Figure 22–4,** are photosynthetic, plantlike protists. Many of these algae are multicellular. **The first plants evolved from an organism much like the multicellular green algae living today.** Multicellular green algae have the size, color, and appearance of plants. But the resemblance of many green algae to plants is more than superficial. They have reproductive cycles that are similar to those of plants. In addition, green algae have cell walls and photosynthetic pigments that are identical to those of plants.

CHECKPOINT *What was the greatest "challenge" to plants as they began to live on land?*

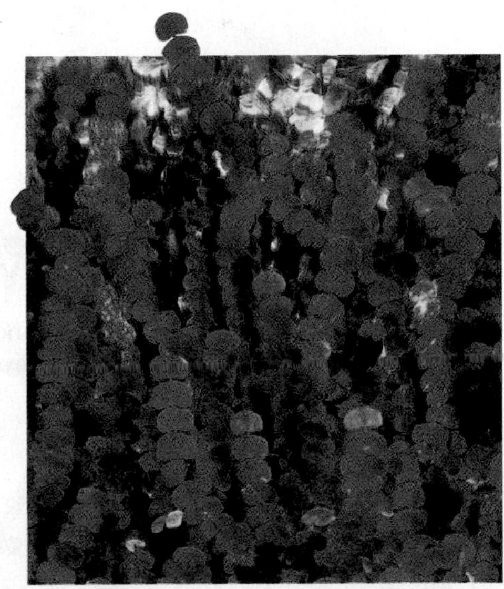

▲ **Figure 22–4** **The first plants evolved from an organism much like the modern multicellular green algae.** The alga *Halimeda* is found in Honduras in Central America. It has many cellular features in common with plants.

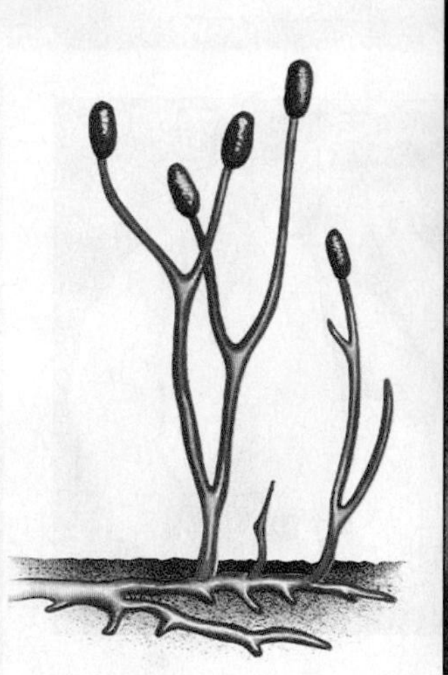

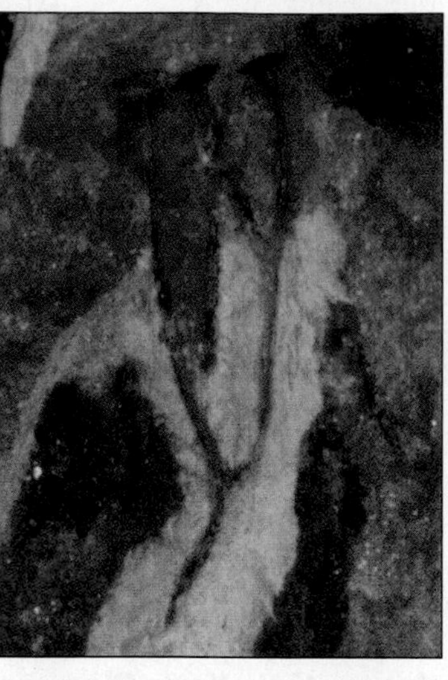

▲ **Figure 22–5** One of the earliest fossil vascular plants was *Cooksonia,* which looked similar to mosses living today. *Cooksonia* had simple branched stalks that bore reproductive structures at their tips. The figure above shows an artist's drawing of *Cooksonia* and a photograph of the fossil. **Inferring** ***Which structures of this early plant might have carried out photosynthesis? Obtained water and minerals?***

The First Plants Plants share many characteristics with the green algae described in Chapter 20, including their photosynthetic pigments and the composition of their cell walls. DNA sequences confirm that plants are closely related to certain groups of green algae, further suggesting that the ancestors of the first plants were indeed algae. The oldest known fossils of plants, nearly 450 million years old, show that the earliest plants were similar to today's mosses. As shown in **Figure 22–5,** they had a simple structure and grew close to the damp ground. The fossils also suggest that the first true plants were still dependent on water to complete their life cycles. Over time, the demands of life on land favored the evolution of plants more resistant to the drying rays of the sun, more capable of conserving water, and more capable of reproducing without water.

From these plant pioneers, several major groups of plants evolved. One group developed into the mosses and their relatives. Another lineage gave rise to all the other plants on Earth today—ferns, cone-bearing plants, and flowering plants. All of these groups of plants are now successful in living on dry land, but they have evolved very different adaptations for a wide range of terrestrial environments.

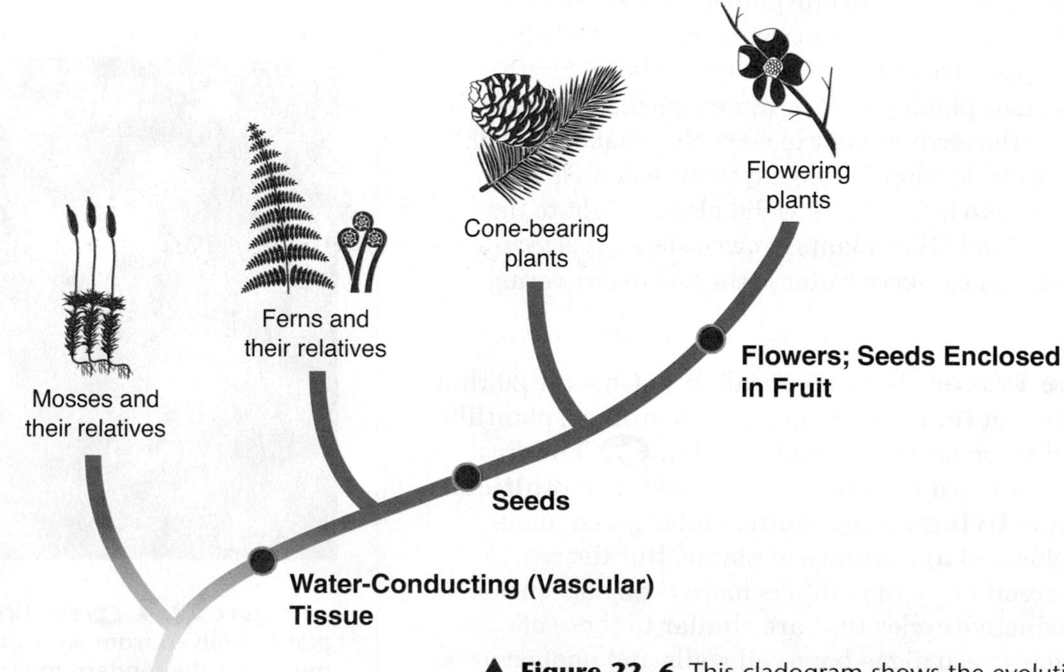

▲ **Figure 22–6** This cladogram shows the evolutionary relationships among the various groups of plants. The four main groups of living plants are mosses and their relatives, ferns and their relatives, cone-bearing plants, and flowering plants. **Interpreting Graphics** ***Which two groups of plants contain seeds?***

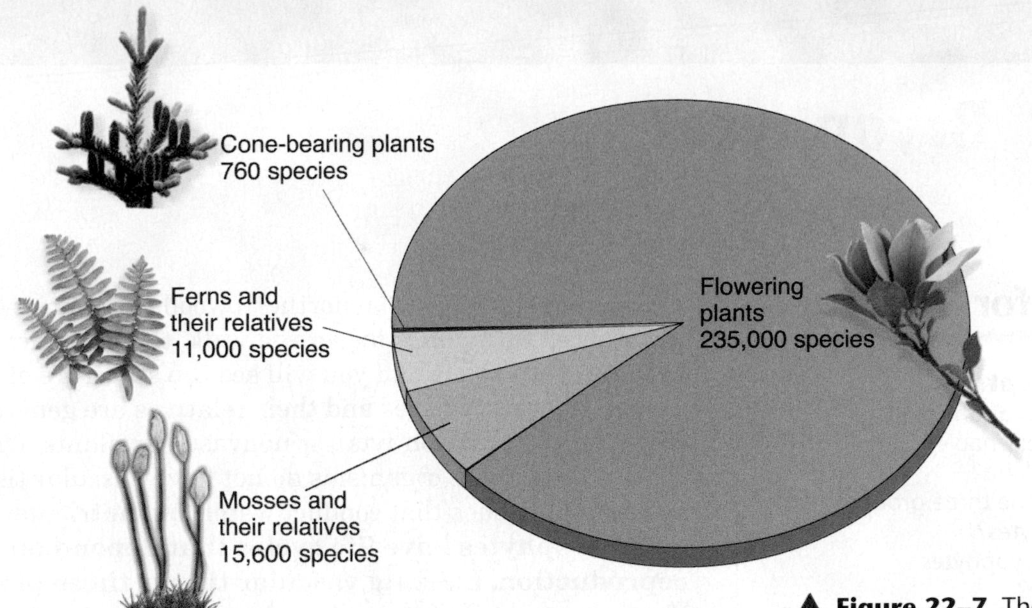

▲ **Figure 22–7** The great majority of plants alive today are angiosperms, which are also known as flowering plants. **Interpreting Graphics** *What is the second largest group of plants?*

Overview of the Plant Kingdom

Botanists divide the plant kingdom into four groups based on three important features: water-conducting tissues, seeds, and flowers. The relationship of these groups is shown in **Figure 22–6.** There are, of course, many other features by which plants are classified, including reproductive structures and body plan.

Today, plant scientists can classify plants more precisely by comparing the DNA sequences of various species. Since 1994, a team of biologists from twelve nations has begun to change our view of plant relationships. Their project, Deep Green, has provided strong evidence that the first plants evolved from green algae living in fresh water, not in the sea as had been thought.

In the rest of this chapter, we will explore how important plant traits evolved over the course of millions of years. In particular, we will examine the success of the flowering plants. As shown in **Figure 22–7,** flowering plants consist of 235,000 species—almost 90 percent of all living species of plants.

For: Links on classifying plants
Visit: www.SciLinks.org
Web Code: cbn-7221

22–1 Section Assessment

1. **Key Concept** Identify the characteristics of the plant kingdom.
2. **Key Concept** To live successfully on land, what substances must plants obtain from their environment?
3. **Key Concept** From which group of protists did the first plants evolve? How are plants similar to these protists?
4. **Critical Thinking Comparing and Contrasting** Compare the gametophyte and sporophyte stages of the plant life cycle. Which is haploid? Which is diploid?
5. **Critical Thinking Comparing and Contrasting** Compare the roles of mitosis and meiosis in a plant life cycle. Which of these processes is related to sexual reproduction? To asexual reproduction?

Connecting Concepts

Cell Structure
How do the cells of plants differ from those of animals? How are they different from those of fungi? You may wish to use labeled diagrams or a table to present your comparison. Refer to Chapters 7 and 21 for help in answering these questions.

22–2 Bryophytes

Guide for Reading

Key Concepts

- What adaptations of bryophytes enable them to live on land?
- What are the three groups of bryophytes?
- How do bryophytes reproduce?

Vocabulary

bryophyte
rhizoid
gemma
protonema
antheridium
archegonium

Reading Strategy: Using Visuals
Before you read, preview **Figure 22–11,** which shows the life cycle of a moss. In your own words, describe the basic process of reproduction shown. As you read the section, add information that you learn about reproduction in bryophytes.

In the cool forests of the northern woods, the moist ground is carpeted with green. When you walk, this soft carpet feels spongy. Look closely and you will see the structure of this carpet—mosses. Mosses and their relatives are generally called **bryophytes** (BRY-oh-fyts), or nonvascular plants. Unlike all other plants, these organisms do not have vascular tissues, or specialized tissues that conduct water and nutrients. **Bryophytes have life cycles that depend on water for reproduction. Lacking vascular tissue, these plants can draw up water by osmosis only a few centimeters above the ground.** This method of development keeps them relatively small. During at least one stage of their life cycle, bryophytes produce sperm that must swim through water to reach the eggs of other individuals. Therefore, they must live in places where there is rainfall or dew for at least part of the year.

Groups of Bryophytes

The most recognizable feature of bryophytes is that they are low-growing plants that can be found in moist, shaded areas. Where water is in regular supply—in habitats from the polar regions to the tropics—these plants thrive. **Bryophytes include mosses, liverworts, and hornworts.** Today, most botanists classify these groups of plants in three separate phyla.

Mosses The most common bryophytes are mosses, which are members of the phylum Bryophyta (bry-oh-FYT-uh). Mosses grow most abundantly in areas with water—in swamps and bogs, near streams, and in rain forests. Bryophytes are well adapted to life in wet habitats and nutrient-poor soils. Many mosses can tolerate low temperatures, allowing them to grow in harsh environments where other plants cannot. In fact, mosses are the most abundant plants in the polar regions.

Mosses vary in appearance from miniature evergreen trees to small, filamentous plants that together form a threadlike carpet of green, as shown in **Figure 22–8.** The moss plants that you might have observed on a walk through the woods are actually clumps of gametophytes growing close together. Each moss plant has a thin, upright shoot that looks like a stem with tiny leaves. These are not true stems or leaves, however, because they do not contain vascular tissue. When mosses reproduce, they produce thin stalks, each containing a capsule. This is the sporophyte stage, as shown in **Figure 22–9.**

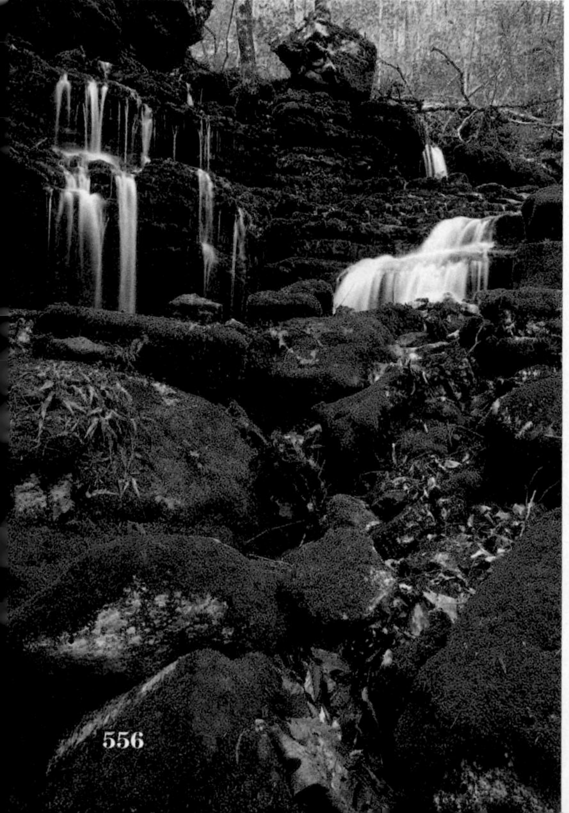

◀ **Figure 22–8** Mosses grow best in moist environments, such as on the rocks by this waterfall. **Like all bryophytes, mosses have life cycles that depend on water for reproduction.**

Because the "leaves" of mosses are only one cell thick, these plants lose water quickly if the surrounding air is dry. The lack of vascular tissues also means that mosses do not have true roots. Instead, they have **rhizoids,** which are long, thin cells that anchor them in the ground and absorb water and minerals from the surrounding soil. Water moves from cell to cell through the rhizoids and into the rest of the plant.

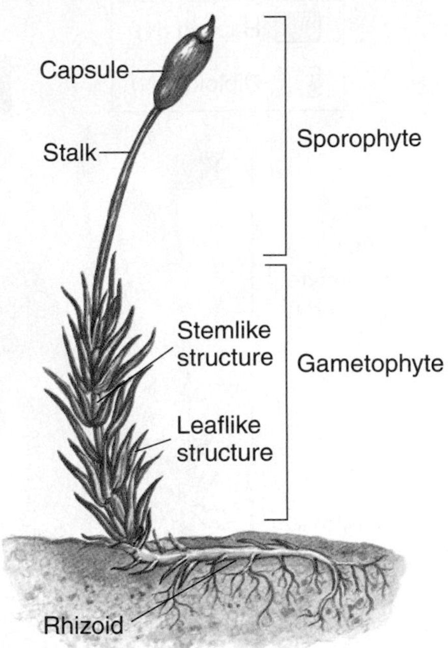

▲ **Figure 22–9** This illustration shows the structure of a typical moss plant. The green photosynthetic portion is the gametophyte. The brown structure on the tip of the gametophyte is the sporophyte. **Applying Concepts** ***Which stage of the moss plant provides nutrients for the other stage?***

Liverworts If you have come across odd little plants that look almost like flat leaves attached to the ground, you have probably seen a liverwort, shown in **Figure 22–10.** These plants belong to the phylum Hepaticophyta (hih-PAT-ik-oh-fy-tuh) and get their name from the fact that some species resemble the shape of a liver. In their method of development, the liverwort gametophytes form broad and thin structures that draw up moisture directly from the surface of the soil. When the plants mature, the gametophytes produce structures that look like tiny green umbrellas. These "umbrellas" carry the structures that produce eggs and sperm.

Some liverworts can also reproduce asexually by means of gemmae. **Gemmae** (JEM-ee; singular: gemma) are small multicellular reproductive structures. In some species of liverworts, gemmae are produced in cuplike structures called gemma cups. When washed out of the gemma cup, the gemmae can divide by mitosis to produce a new individual.

Hornworts Hornworts are members of the phylum Anthocerophyta (an-tho-SEHR-oh-fy-tuh). Like the liverworts, hornworts are generally found only in soil that is damp nearly year-round. Their gametophytes look very much like those of liverworts. The hornwort sporophyte, however, looks like a tiny green horn.

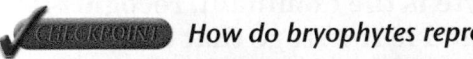

How do bryophytes reproduce asexually?

Liverworts

Hornworts

◀ **Figure 22–10** **Bryophytes include liverworts and hornworts.** The liverworts produce gametes in structures that look like little green umbrellas. The tiny cuplike structures on the liverworts are gemma cups. The hornworts have sporophytes that look like tiny green horns.

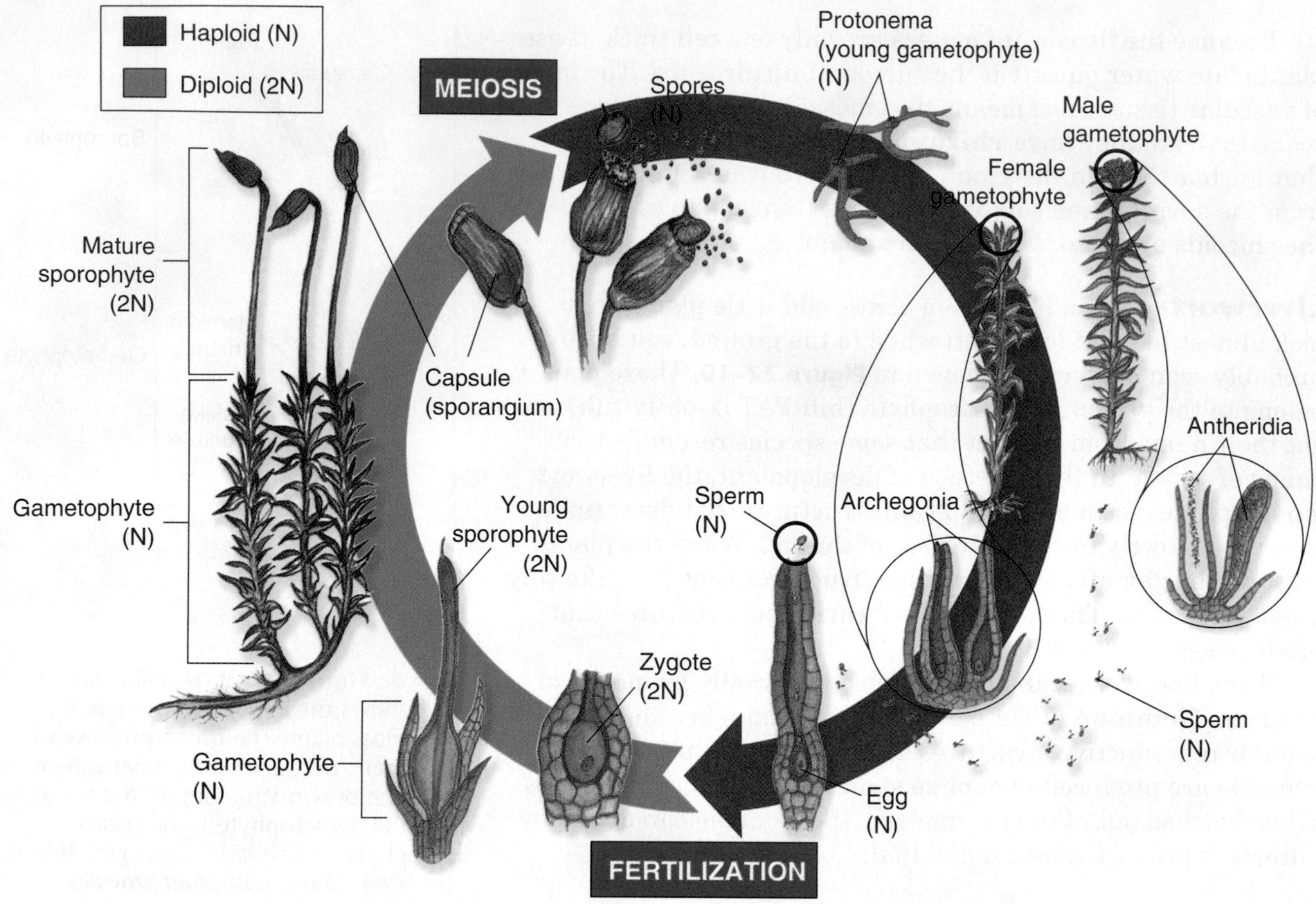

▲ **Figure 22–11** **In bryophytes, the gametophyte is the dominant, recognizable stage of the life cycle and is the form that carries out photosynthesis.** Sporophytes, which produce haploid spores, grow at the top of the gametophyte plant. When the spores are ripe, they are shed from the capsule like pepper from a shaker. In some species, gametes (sperm and eggs) are produced on separate male and female gametophyte plants.

Life Cycle of Bryophytes

Like all plants, bryophytes display a method of reproduction and development involving alternation of generations. **In bryophytes, the gametophyte is the dominant, recognizable stage of the life cycle and is the stage that carries out most of the plant's photosynthesis.** The sporophyte is dependent on the gametophyte for supplying water and nutrients.

Dependence on Water For fertilization to occur, the sperm of a bryophyte must swim to an egg. Because of this dependence on water for reproduction, bryophytes must live in habitats where water is available at least part of the year.

Life Cycle of a Moss The life cycle of a moss, shown in **Figure 22–11,** helps illustrate how bryophytes reproduce and develop. When a moss spore lands in a moist place, it germinates and grows into a mass of tangled green filaments called a **protonema** (proh-toh-NEE-muh). As the protonema grows, it forms rhizoids that grow into the ground and shoots that grow into the air. These shoots grow into the familiar green moss plants, which are the gametophyte stage of its life cycle.

 *What is a protonema?*

For: Bryophyte activity
Visit: PHSchool.com
Web Code: cbd-7222

Gametes are formed in reproductive structures at the tips of the gametophytes. Sperm with whiplike tails are produced in **antheridia** (an-thur-ID-ee-uh; singular: antheridium), and egg cells are produced in **archegonia** (ahr-kuh-GOH-nee-uh; singular: archegonium). Some species produce both sperm and eggs on the same plant, whereas other species produce sperm and eggs on separate plants. Once sperm are released and reach egg cells, fertilization produces a diploid zygote. This zygote is the beginning of the sporophyte stage of the life cycle. It grows directly out of the body of the gametophyte and actually depends on it for water and nutrients. The mature sporophyte is a long stalk ending in a capsule that looks like a saltshaker. Inside the capsule, haploid spores are produced by meiosis. When the capsule ripens, it opens and haploid spores are scattered to the wind to start the cycle again.

▼ **Figure 22–12** The compacted remains of sphagnum moss may eventually form thick deposits of peat. When it is cut and dried, it can be burned to produce heat. Peat has been used as a form of fuel in Ireland for many centuries. **Inferring** ***What can you infer about the climate of an area where sphagnum moss grows abundantly in peat bogs?***

Human Use of Mosses

Sphagnum (SFAG-num) mosses are a group of mosses that thrive in the acidic water of bogs. Dried sphagnum moss absorbs many times its own weight in water and thus acts as a sort of natural sponge. In certain environments the dead remains of sphagnum accumulate to form thick deposits of peat. Peat can be cut from the ground, as shown in **Figure 22–12**, and then burned as a fuel.

Peat moss is also used in gardening. Gardeners add peat moss to the soil because it improves the soil's ability to retain water. Peat moss also has a low pH, so when added to the soil it increases the soil's acidity. Some plants, such as azaleas, grow well only if they are planted in acidic soil.

22–2 Section Assessment

1. **Key Concept** How is water essential in the life cycle of a bryophyte?
2. **Key Concept** List the three groups of bryophytes. In what type of habitat do they live?
3. **Key Concept** What is the relationship between the gametophyte and the sporophyte in mosses and other bryophytes?
4. What is an archegonium? An antheridium? How are these structures important in the life cycle of a moss?
5. **Critical Thinking Inferring** What characteristic of bryophytes is responsible for their small size? Explain.

Writing in Science

Descriptive Writing

You are writing a pocket field guide about plants and are working on the bryophytes chapter. Develop several paragraphs to help your readers distinguish among the mosses, hornworts, and liverworts. *Hint:* Do additional library or Internet research to find examples of bryophytes in your locality.

22–3 Seedless Vascular Plants

Guide for Reading

Key Concepts
- How is vascular tissue important to ferns and their relatives?
- What are the characteristics of the three phyla of seedless vascular plants?
- What are the stages in the life cycle of ferns?

Vocabulary
vascular tissue • tracheid
xylem • phloem • lignin
root • leaf • vein • stem
rhizome • frond
sporangium • sorus

Reading Strategy: Building Vocabulary
Before you read, preview new vocabulary by skimming the section and making a list of the highlighted, boldface terms. Leave space to make notes about each term as you read.

Bryophytes have only one way to transport water—from cell to cell by osmosis. This fact limits their height to just a few centimeters; for millions of years, plants grew no larger. About 420 million years ago, something remarkable happened. The small, mosslike plants on land were suddenly joined by some plants more than a meter tall and others as large as small trees. Fossil evidence shows that these new plants were the first to have a transport system with **vascular tissue,** which is specialized to conduct water and nutrients throughout the plant.

Evolution of Vascular Tissue: A Transport System

The first vascular plants had a new type of cell that was specialized to conduct water. **Tracheids** (TRAY-kee-idz), shown in **Figure 22–13,** were one of the great evolutionary innovations of the plant kingdom. They are the key cells in **xylem** (ZY-lum), a transport subsystem that carries water upward from the roots to every part of a plant. Tracheids are hollow cells with thick cell walls that resist pressure. They are connected end to end like a series of drinking straws. Tracheids allow water to move through a plant more efficiently than by diffusion alone.

Vascular plants have a second transport subsystem composed of vascular tissue called phloem. **Phloem** (FLOH-um) transports solutions of nutrients and carbohydrates produced by photosynthesis. Like xylem, the main cells of phloem are long and specialized to move fluids throughout the plant body. **Both forms of vascular tissue—xylem and phloem—can move fluids through the plant body, even against the force of gravity**. Together, xylem and phloem form an integrated transport system that moves water, nutrients, and other dissolved materials from one end of the plant to the other. In many plants, the combination of the thick walls of xylem and **lignin,** a substance that makes cell walls rigid, enables vascular plants to grow upright and reach great heights.

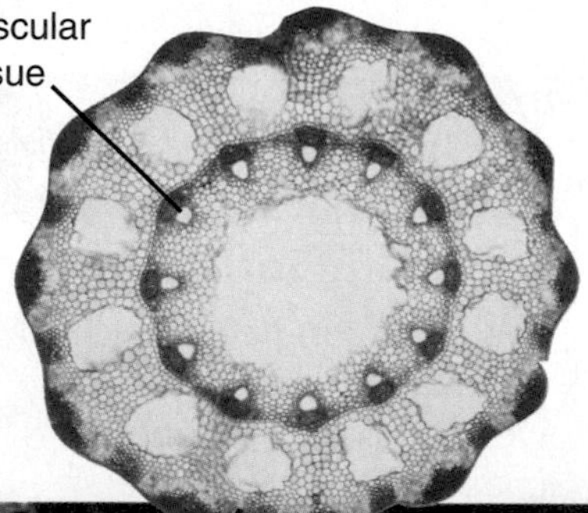

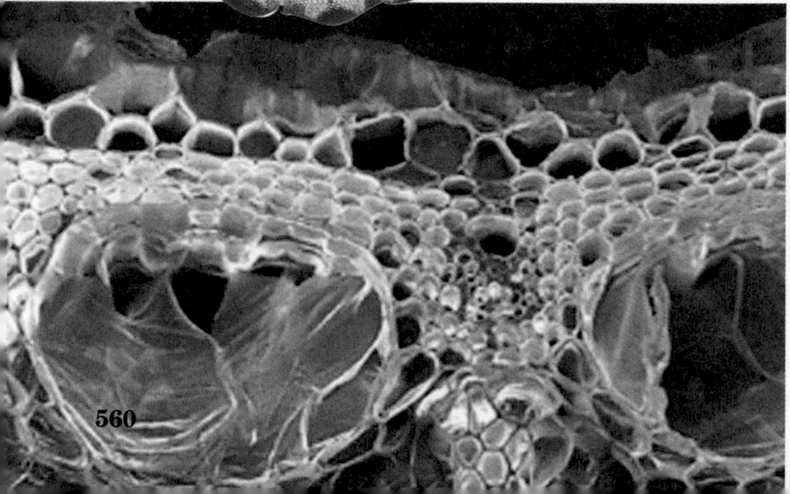

◀ **Figure 22–13** **Vascular tissue conducts water and nutrients throughout the plant body.** It also provides support for the leaves and other organs of the plant. The two types of vascular tissue are xylem, which conducts water, and phloem, which conducts solutions of nutrients. The cross section (top) shows the vascular tissue of the horsetail stem. The bottom photo shows a much-magnified view of tracheids from the xylem of the horsetail.

Ferns and Their Relatives

Seedless vascular plants include club mosses, horsetails, and ferns. The most numerous phylum of these is the ferns. Like other vascular plants, ferns and their relatives have true roots, leaves, and stems. **Roots** are underground organs that absorb water and minerals. Water-conducting tissues are located in the center of the root. **Leaves** are photosynthetic organs that contain one or more bundles of vascular tissue. This vascular tissue is gathered into **veins** made of xylem and phloem. **Stems** are supporting structures that connect roots and leaves, carrying water and nutrients between them.

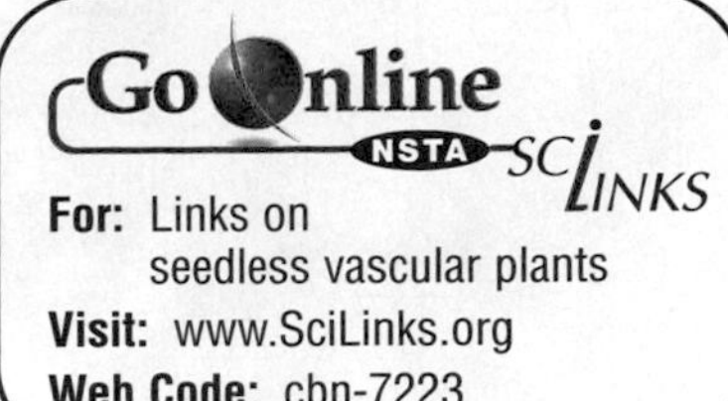

For: Links on seedless vascular plants
Visit: www.SciLinks.org
Web Code: cbn-7223

Club Mosses What was once a large and ancient group of land plants—phylum Lycophyta (LY-koh-fy-tuh)—exists now as a much smaller group that includes the club mosses. Once, ancient club mosses grew into huge trees—up to 35 meters tall—and some produced Earth's first forests. The fossilized remains of these forests exist today as huge beds of coal.

Today, club mosses are small plants that live in moist woodlands. Members of the genus *Lycopodium,* the common club mosses shown in **Figure 22–14,** look like miniature pine trees. For this reason they are also called "ground pines."

Horsetails The only living genus of Arthrophyta (AHR-throh-fy-tuh) is *Equisetum,* which is a plant that usually grows about a meter tall. Like the club mosses, *Equisetum* has true leaves, stems, and roots. Its nonphotosynthetic, scalelike leaves are arranged in distinctive whorls at joints along the stem. *Equisetum* is called horsetail, or scouring rush, because its stems look similar to horses' tails and contain crystals of abrasive silica. During Colonial times, horsetails were commonly used to scour pots and pans.

What chemical makes the stems of* Equisetum *abrasive?

Figure 22–14 Club mosses and horsetails are seedless vascular plants. The club moss *Lycopodium* (left) looks like a tiny pine tree growing on the forest floor. The only living genus of Arthrophyta is *Equisetum,* or horsetail (above).

▲ **Figure 22–15** Ferns are easily recognized because of their delicate leaves, which are called fronds. Fronds grow from a rhizome, which grows horizontally through the soil. **Applying Concepts** *Is the plant shown a sporophyte or a gametophyte?*

Ferns Ferns, members of phylum Pterophyta (TEHR-oh-fy-tuh), probably evolved about 350 million years ago, when great club moss forests covered ancient Earth. Ferns have survived during Earth's long history in numbers greater than any other group of spore-bearing vascular plants. More than 11,000 species of ferns are living today.

Ferns have true vascular tissues, strong roots, creeping or underground stems called **rhizomes,** and large leaves called **fronds,** shown in **Figure 22–15.** Ferns can thrive in areas with little light. They are most abundant in wet, or at least seasonally wet, habitats around the world. They are often found living in the shadows of forest trees, where direct sunlight hardly penetrates the forest's leafy umbrella. Ferns are found in great numbers in the rain forests of the Pacific Northwest. In tropical forests, some species grow as large as small trees.

Life Cycle of Ferns

The large plants we recognize as ferns are actually diploid sporophytes. **Ferns and other vascular plants have a life cycle in which the diploid sporophyte is the dominant stage.** Fern sporophytes develop haploid spores on the underside of their fronds in tiny containers called **sporangia** (spoh-RAN-jee-uh; singular: sporangium). Sporangia are grouped into clusters called **sori** (SOH-ry; singular: sorus), shown in **Figure 22–16.** The life cycle and method of development of a typical fern are shown in **Figure 22–17.**

When the spores germinate, they develop into haploid gametophytes. The small gametophyte first grows a set of rootlike rhizoids. It then flattens into a thin, heart-shaped, green structure that is the mature gametophyte. Although it is tiny, the gametophyte grows independently of the sporophyte.

The antheridia and archegonia are found on the underside of the gametophyte. As in bryophytes, fertilization requires at least a thin film of water, allowing the sperm to swim to the eggs. The diploid zygote produced by fertilization immediately begins to develop into a new sporophyte plant. As the sporophyte grows, the gametophyte withers away. Fern sporophytes often live for many years. In some species, the fronds produced in the spring die in the fall, but the rhizomes live through the winter and produce new leaves again the following spring.

▶ **Figure 22–16** Many clusters of sporangia form on the underside of fern leaves—each cluster is called a sorus. In each sporangium, cells undergo meiosis to produce spores. **Inferring** *Are these spores haploid or diploid?*

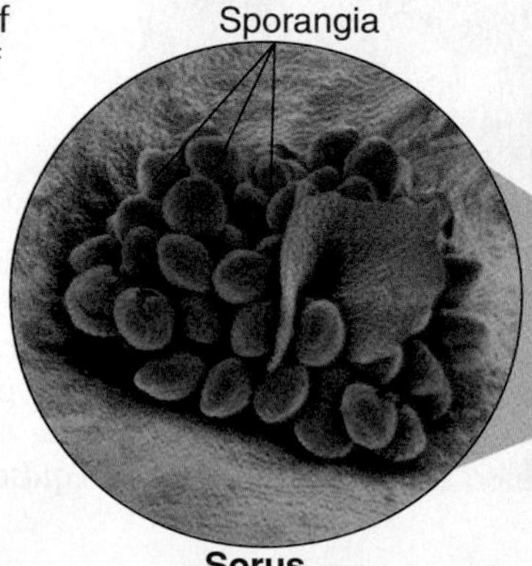

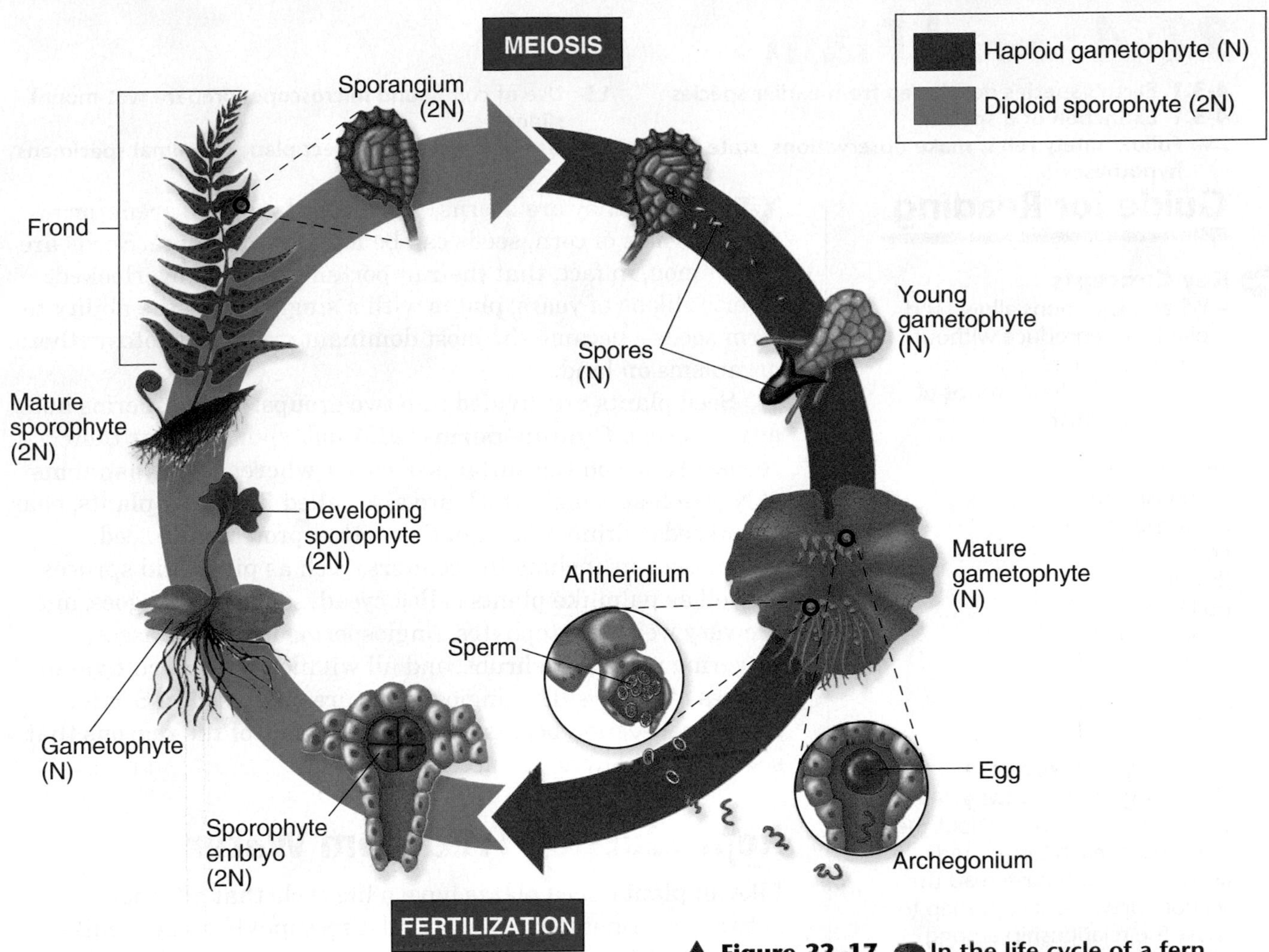

▲ **Figure 22–17** **In the life cycle of a fern, the dominant and recognizable stage is the diploid sporophyte.** The tiny, heart-shaped gametophyte grows close to the ground and relies on dampness for the sperm it produces to fertilize an egg. The young sporophyte grows from the gametophyte.

22–3 Section Assessment

1. **Key Concept** What are the two types of vascular tissue? Describe the function of each.
2. **Key Concept** What are the three phyla of seedless vascular plants? Give an example of each.
3. **Key Concept** What is the dominant stage of the fern life cycle? What is the relationship of the fern gametophyte and sporophyte?
4. **Critical Thinking Inferring** The size of plants increased dramatically with the evolution of vascular tissue. How might these two events be related?
5. **Critical Thinking Applying Concepts** Explain why xylem and phloem together can be considered to be a transport system.

Thinking Visually

Making a Visual Essay
Find out more about club mosses, horsetails, and ferns. Research information such as description, method of development, ecology, and scientific name. Use this information along with photographs or drawings of these plants to create a two-page photo essay about seedless vascular plants.

22–4 Seed Plants

4-3.1 Earth's species developed from earlier species
4-3.1 Extinction of a species
LS- Follow safety rules, make observations, state hypotheses
LS- Use of compound microscope, prepare wet mount slides
LS- Use of indicators, dissect plant or animal specimens

Guide for Reading

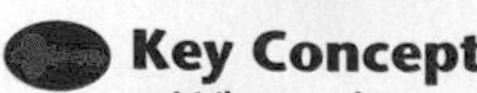

Key Concepts
- What adaptations allow seed plants to reproduce without standing water?
- What are the four groups of gymnosperms?

Vocabulary
gymnosperm
angiosperm
cone
flower
pollen grain
pollination
seed
embryo
seed coat

Reading Strategy: Building Vocabulary As you read, make notes about the meaning of each term listed above. After you have read the section, draw a concept map to show the relationship among these terms.

Whether they are acorns, pine nuts, dandelion seeds, or kernels of corn, seeds can be found everywhere. Seeds are so common, in fact, that their importance may be overlooked. Over millions of years, plants with a single trait—the ability to form seeds—became the most dominant group of photosynthetic organisms on land.

Seed plants are divided into two groups: gymnosperms and angiosperms. **Gymnosperms** (JIM-noh-spurmz) bear their seeds directly on the surfaces of cones, whereas **angiosperms** (AN-jee-oh-spurmz), which are also called flowering plants, bear their seeds within a layer of tissue that protects the seed. Gymnosperms include the conifers, such as pines and spruces, as well as palmlike plants called cycads, ancient ginkgoes, and the very weird gnetophytes. Angiosperms include grasses, flowering trees and shrubs, and all wildflowers and cultivated species of flowers. The angiosperms are discussed in Section 22–5. This section begins by exploring some of the reasons that seed plants became so successful.

Reproduction Free From Water

Like all plants, seed plants have a life cycle that alternates between a gametophyte stage and a sporophyte stage. Unlike mosses and ferns, however, seed plants do not require water for fertilization of gametes. Because of this method of development, seed plants can live just about anywhere—from moist habitats that are often dominated by seedless plants, to dry and cold habitats where most seedless plants cannot survive. **Adaptations that allow seed plants to reproduce without water include flowers or cones, the transfer of sperm by pollination, and the protection of embryos in seeds.**

Cones and Flowers The gametophytes of seed plants grow and mature within sporophyte structures called **cones,** which are the seed-bearing structures of gymnosperms, and **flowers,** which are the seed-bearing structures of angiosperms. The cones of a common gymnosperm are shown in **Figure 22–18.** The gametophyte generations of seed plants live inside these reproductive structures.

◀ **Figure 22–18** **Adaptations that allow seed plants to reproduce without water include reproduction in flowers or cones, the transfer of sperm by pollination, and the protection of embryos in seeds.** Gymnosperms, such as this spruce tree, bear their seeds on the scales of cones.

Pollen In seed plants, the entire male gametophyte is contained in a tiny structure called a **pollen grain.** Sperm produced by this gametophyte do not swim through water to fertilize the eggs. Instead, the pollen grain is carried to the female reproductive structure by wind, insects, or small animals. The transfer of pollen from the male reproductive structure to the female reproductive structure is called **pollination.**

Seeds A **seed** is an embryo of a plant that is encased in a protective covering and surrounded by a food supply. An **embryo** is an organism in its early stage of development. A plant embryo is diploid and is the early developmental stage of the sporophyte plant. The seed's food supply provides nutrients to the embryo as it grows. The **seed coat** surrounds and protects the embryo and keeps the contents of the seed from drying out. Seeds may also have special tissues or structures that aid in their dispersal to other habitats. Some seed coats are textured so that they stick to the fur or feathers of animals. Other seeds are contained in fleshy tissues that are eaten and dispersed by animals.

After fertilization, the zygote contained within a seed grows into a tiny plant—the embryo. The embryo often stops growing while it is still small and contained within the seed. The embryo can remain in this condition for weeks, months, or even years. When the embryo begins to grow again, it uses nutrients from the stored food supply. Seeds can survive long periods of bitter cold, extreme heat, or drought—beginning to grow only when conditions are once again right.

What is a pollen grain?

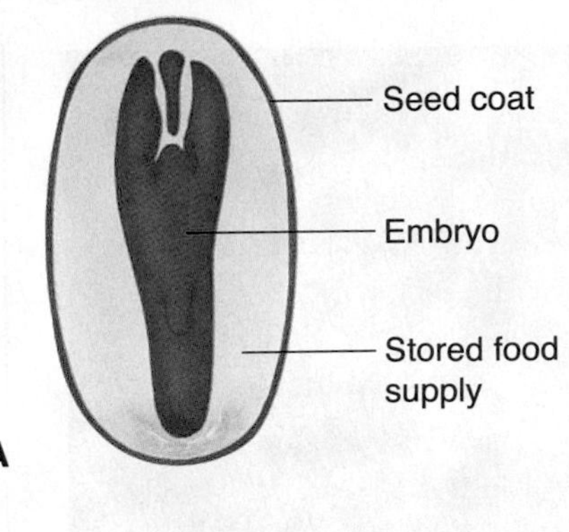

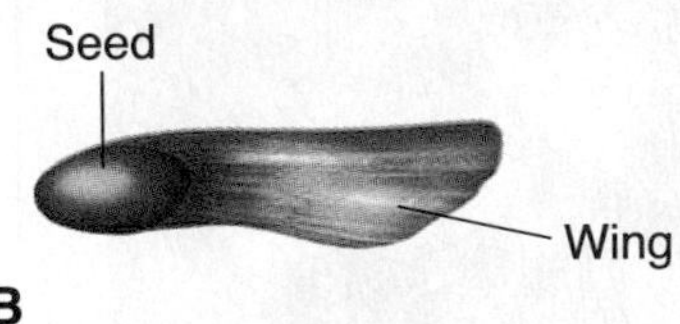

▲ **Figure 22–19** (A) This longitudinal section shows the internal structure of the seed of a pine tree. (B) The pine tree seed, found on the scale of a cone, is winged. **Predicting** *How might the food stored in the seed affect the reproductive success of the pine tree?*

Quick Lab

How do seeds differ from spores?

Materials Fern frond with sori, microscope, scalpel, microscope slide, coverslip, dropper pipette, sunflower seeds in shells, brown paper bag, hand lens

Procedure 

1. Use a scalpel to scrape sporangia from the underside of a fern frond onto a microscope slide. Add a drop of water and a coverslip and examine the slide under low power. Sketch a few spores. **CAUTION:** *Use care with the scalpel.*
2. **CAUTION:** *Do not perform steps 2 and 3 if you are allergic to sunflower seeds. Do not eat the sunflower seeds.* Open a sunflower seed. With a hand lens, examine the nutlike kernel of the seed and sketch the embryo.
3. Rub the seed on brown paper and hold the paper up to the light. A bright spot indicates lipids. Wash your hands.

Analyze and Conclude

1. **Observing** What evidence do you have that nutrients are stored in sunflower seeds?
2. **Predicting** A spore and a seed are deposited in an area where the soil is poor in nutrients. Which is more likely to survive in a nutrient-poor environment? Explain.
3. **Formulating Hypotheses** Consider two populations of ferns and seed plants. How might their reproductive strategies, or methods of reproduction, have an impact on their survival? Over time, how might these events affect the overall diversity of plants?

▲ **Figure 22–20** Seed ferns are part of the fossil record. They represent a link between ferns, which do not form seeds, and seed plants. This ancient plant had leaves that resemble the leaves of modern ferns. **Comparing and Contrasting** *If this plant were alive, what structures would distinguish it from a fern?*

Evolution of Seed Plants

The fossil record indicates that ancestors of seed plants evolved new adaptations that enabled them to survive in many places where most mosses and ferns could not—from frigid mountains to scorching deserts. The most important of these adaptations was the seed itself, which can survive dry conditions and extreme temperatures.

Mosses and ferns underwent major adaptive radiations during the Carboniferous and Devonian periods, 300 to 400 million years ago. During these periods, land environments were much wetter than they are today. Tree ferns and other seedless plants flourished and developed into forests that covered much of Earth. Over millions of years, however, continents became much drier, making it harder for seedless plants to survive and reproduce. Many moss and fern species became extinct, replaced by seed plants adapted to live in drier conditions. Similarities in DNA sequences from modern plants provide evidence that today's seed plants are all descended from common ancestors.

Fossils of seed-bearing plants exist from almost 360 million years ago. As shown in **Figure 22–20**, some of these early seed plants outwardly resembled ferns. Seed fern fossils document several evolutionary stages in the development of the seed.

The early seed plants reached every landmass on Earth. Together with now-extinct seed ferns and other seedless vascular plants, seed plants formed dense forests and swamps that spread over much of what is now the eastern United States. Their remains now exist in the form of coal deposits.

Gymnosperms—Cone Bearers

The most ancient surviving seed plants are the gymnosperms. **Gymnosperms include gnetophytes, cycads, ginkgoes, and conifers.** These plants all reproduce with seeds that are exposed—gymnosperm means "naked seed."

Gnetophytes About 70 present-day species of the phylum Gnetophyta (NEE-toh-fy-tuh) are known, placed in just three genera. The reproductive scales of these plants are clustered into cones. *Welwitschia,* an inhabitant of the Namibian desert in southwestern Africa, is one of the most remarkable gnetophytes. It has only two huge leathery leaves, shown in **Figure 22–21**, which grow continuously and spread across the ground.

▼ **Figure 22–21** The *Welwitschia* plant (below), a type of gnetophyte, is an odd desert plant that produces only two leaves during its entire life. Cones are produced at the bases of the two leaves. **Classifying** *In what phylum is this plant classified?*

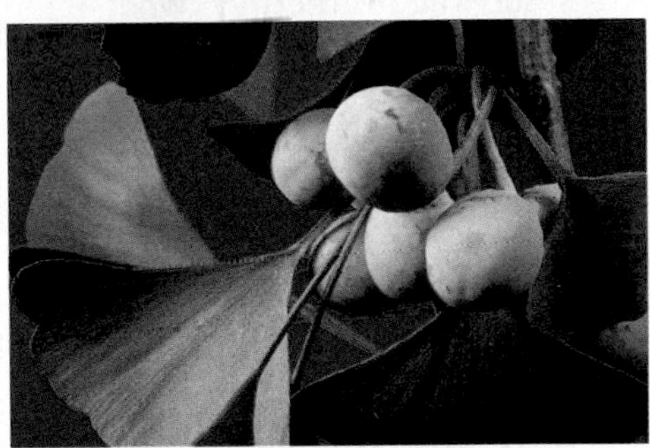

Figure 22–22 **Cycads, ginkgoes, and conifers are gymnosperms.** Some cycads (top left) produce seeds in reproductive structures that look like giant pine cones. The bristlecone pine (top right) is a conifer that can live for thousands of years. The ginkgo tree (bottom) is sometimes called a "living fossil" because it has changed little over millions of years.

Cycads Cycads, shown in **Figure 22–22** (top left), members of the phylum Cycadophyta (SY-kad-oh-fy-tuh), are beautiful palm-like plants that reproduce with large cones. Cycads first appeared in the fossil record during the Triassic Period, 225 million years ago. Huge forests of cycads thrived when dinosaurs roamed Earth. Today, only nine genera of cycads exist. Cycads can be found growing naturally in tropical and subtropical places such as Mexico, the West Indies, Florida, and parts of Asia, Africa, and Australia.

Ginkgoes Ginkgoes were common when dinosaurs were alive, but today the phylum Ginkgophyta (GING-koh-fy-tuh) contains only one species, *Ginkgo biloba.* The living *Ginkgo* species looks similar to its fossil ancestors, so it is truly a living fossil. In fact, *G. biloba,* also shown in **Figure 22–22,** may be one of the oldest seed plant species alive today. Ginkgo trees were carefully cultivated in China, where they were often planted around temples. Ginkgoes are now often planted in urban settings in the United States, where their toughness and resistance to air pollution make them popular shade trees.

How many different species of ginkgoes exist?

Conifers By far the most common gymnosperms, with more than 500 known species, are the conifers. The phylum Coniferophyta (koh-nif-ur-oh-FYT-uh) includes pines, spruces, firs, cedars, sequoias, redwoods, junipers, and yews. Some conifers, such as the bristlecone pine tree at right, can live for more than 4000 years. Other species, such as giant redwoods, can grow to more than 100 meters in height.

Figure 22–23 These longleaf pines in North Carolina grow in an area that receives abundant rainfall. Yet water sinks quickly through the sandy soil, limiting the availability of water to tree roots. In this environment, the pines' water-conserving needles (inset) are an adaptation that contributes to the trees' survival. **Predicting** *What might happen to a tree with large, flat leaves planted in this environment? Explain.*

Ecology of Conifers Today, conifers thrive in a wide variety of habitats in several biomes: on mountains, in sandy soil, and in cool, moist areas such as the temperate rain forest of the Pacific Northwest. Surprisingly, conifer leaves have specific adaptations to dry conditions. How did these adaptations develop? Scientists have hypothesized that more than 250 million years ago, when conifers evolved, climate conditions were dry and cool. In response to these conditions, most conifers developed leaves that are long and thin, like the pine needles in **Figure 22–23.** This shape reduces the surface area from which water can be lost by evaporation. Another water-conserving adaptation is the thick, waxy layer that covers conifer leaves. In addition, the openings of leaves that allow for gas exchange are located in cavities below the surface of the leaves, also reducing water loss.

Most conifers are "evergreens"—that is, they retain their leaves throughout the year. The needles of most conifer species remain on the plant for 2 to 14 years. Older needles are gradually replaced by new needles, so the trees never become bare. However, not all species are evergreen. Larches and bald-cypresses, for example, lose their needles every fall.

For: Links on seed plants
Visit: www.SciLinks.org
Web Code: cbn-7224

22–4 Section Assessment

1. **Key Concept** Identify the main characteristics of seed plants.
2. **Key Concept** What are the different groups of gymnosperms?
3. What major change in Earth's climate favored the evolution of seed plants?
4. **Critical Thinking Applying Concepts** Pollination is a process that occurs only in seed plants. What process in seedless plants is analogous to pollination?

Sharpen Your Skills

Comparing and Contrasting
Compare reproduction in non-seed plants and seed plants. Then, explain how the evolution of the seed was critical to the success of gymnosperms and angiosperms.

22–5 Angiosperms—Flowering Plants

Flowering plants, or angiosperms, are members of the phylum Anthophyta (AN-tho-fy-tuh). They first appeared during the Cretaceous Period, about 135 million years ago, making their origin the most recent of all plant phyla. Flowering plants originated on land and soon came to dominate Earth's plant life. The vast majority of living plant species have a method of reproduction and development involving flowers and fruits.

Guide for Reading

Key Concepts
- What are the characteristics of angiosperms?
- What are monocots and dicots?
- What are the three categories of plant life spans?

Vocabulary
fruit
monocot
dicot
cotyledon
annual
biennial
perennial

Reading Strategy: Finding Main Ideas
Angiosperms are the most diverse group of plants. As you read, take notes on the ways by which their diversity can be organized.

Flowers and Fruits

Angiosperms develop unique reproductive organs known as flowers. In general, flowers are an evolutionary advantage to plants because they attract animals such as bees, moths, or hummingbirds, which then transport pollen from flower to flower. This means of pollination is much more efficient than the wind pollination of most gymnosperms.

Flowers contain ovaries, which surround and protect the seeds. The presence of an ovary gives angiosperms their name: Angiosperm means "enclosed seed." After pollination, the ovary develops into a fruit, which protects the seed and aids in its dispersal.

The unique angiosperm **fruit**—a wall of tissue surrounding the seed—is another reason for the success of these plants. When an animal eats a fruit, seeds from the core of the fruit generally enter the animal's digestive system. By the time these seeds leave the digestive system—ready to sprout—the animal may have traveled many kilometers. By using fruit to attract animals, flowering plants increase the ranges they inhabit, spreading seeds over hundreds of square kilometers.

◀ **Figure 22–24** **Angiosperms develop unique reproductive structures known as flowers, which contain ovaries that surround and protect the seeds.** Apple flowers (left) produce seeds inside ovaries, which mature into fruits (right).

Diversity of Angiosperms

The angiosperms are an incredibly diverse group. There are many different ways of categorizing them. These include monocots and dicots; woody and herbaceous plants; and annuals, biennials, and perennials. Keep in mind that the categories can overlap. An iris, for example, is a monocot plant that is also an herbaceous perennial. These categories simply provide a way of organizing the diversity of angiosperms.

Monocots and Dicots There are two classes within the angiosperms: the Monocotyledonae, or **monocots,** and the Dicotyledonae, or **dicots.** The general characteristics of both groups are shown in **Figure 22–25.** **Monocots and dicots are named for the number of seed leaves, or cotyledons, in the plant embryo. Monocots have one seed leaf, and dicots have two.** A **cotyledon** is the first leaf or the first pair of leaves produced by the embryo of a seed plant. Other differences include the distribution of vascular tissue in stems, roots, and leaves, and the number of petals per flower. Monocots include corn, wheat, lilies, orchids, and palms. Dicots include roses, clover, tomatoes, oaks, and daisies.

Figure 22–25 **Monocots and dicots are named for the number of seed leaves, or cotyledons, in the plant embryo.** The table compares the characteristics of monocots and dicots.

Characteristics of Monocots and Dicots

	Monocots	Dicots
Seeds	Single cotyledon 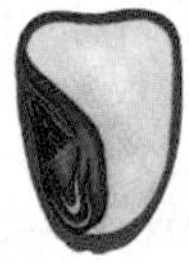	Two cotyledons 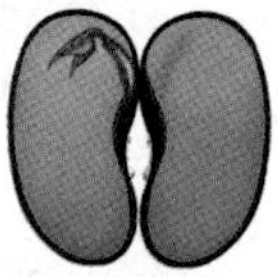
Leaves	Parallel veins 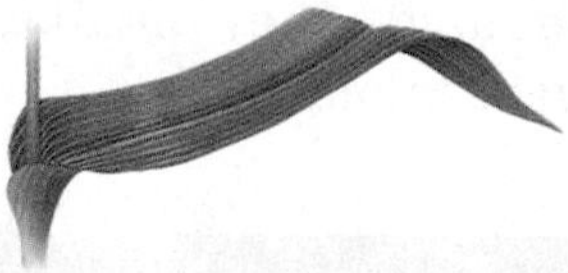	Branched veins 
Flowers	Floral parts often in multiples of 3 	Floral parts often in multiples of 4 or 5 
Stems	Vascular bundles scattered throughout stem 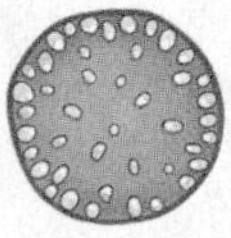	Vascular bundles arranged in a ring 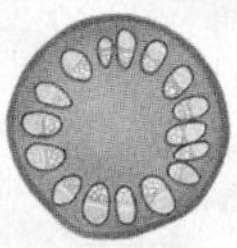
Roots	Fibrous roots 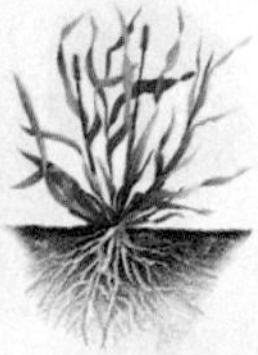	Taproot 

Careers in Biology

Botanical Illustrator

Job Description: work in a museum, outdoors, in a botanical garden, or at home to illustrate plants and organisms related to the plants

Education: two- or four-year college degree in an art school or other school noted for its art and design department

Skills: ability to observe nature; artistic talent; knowledge of biology; detail oriented; knowledge of the Internet, library, and museum research sources

Highlights: You provide illustrations that help people understand and appreciate biology. You have the pleasure of taking people of all ages on exciting visual adventures into the world of plants.

For: Career links
Visit: PHSchool.com
Web Code: cbb-7225

Woody and Herbaceous Plants The flowering plants can be subdivided into various groups according to the characteristics of their stems. One of the most important and noticeable stem characteristics is woodiness. Woody plants are made primarily of cells with thick cell walls that support the plant body. Woody plants include trees, shrubs, and vines. Shrubs are typically smaller than trees, and vines have stems that are long and flexible. Examples of woody vines are grapes and ivy. Examples of shrubs include blueberries, rhododendrons, and roses.

Plant stems that are smooth and nonwoody are characteristic of herbaceous plants. Herbaceous plants do not produce wood as they grow. Examples of herbaceous plants include dandelions, zinnias, petunias, and sunflowers.

What is one example of a woody plant? One example of a herbaceous plant?

Annuals, Biennials, and Perennials If you've ever planted a garden, you know that many flowering plants grow, flower, and die in a single year. Other types of plants continue to grow from year to year. The life span of plants is determined by a combination of genetic and environmental factors. Many long-lived plants continue growing despite yearly environmental fluctuations. However, harsh environmental conditions can shorten the life of other plants. **There are three categories of plant life spans: annual, biennial, and perennial.**

Word Origins

Annual comes from the Latin word *annus,* which means "year." The Latin prefix *bi-* means "two." **Based on the characteristics of perennials, what do you think the Latin prefix *per-* means?**

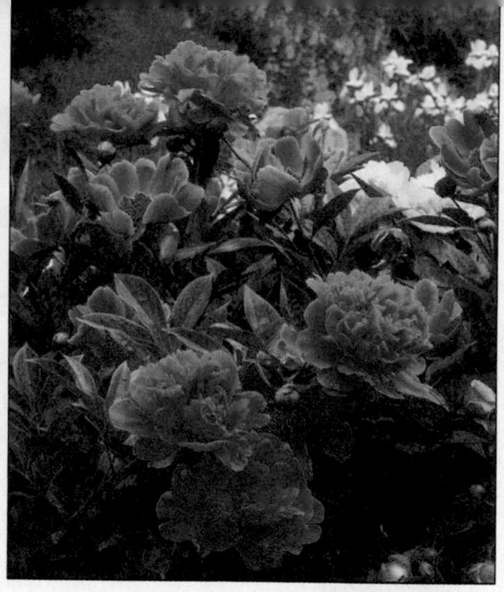

Figure 22–26 **Categories of plant life spans include annuals, biennials, and perennials.** Zinnias (left) are annual plants, which germinate, grow to maturity, set seed, and die in one growing season. Biennials such as the evening primrose (middle) grow roots, stems, and leaves in their first year, then produce flowers and seeds in their second year. Perennials such as peonies (right) live through many years.

Some plants grow from seed to maturity, flower, produce seeds, and die all in the course of one growing season. Flowering plants that complete a life cycle within one growing season are called **annuals.** Annuals include many garden plants, such as marigolds, petunias, pansies, and the zinnias in **Figure 22–26.** Wheat and cucumbers are also annuals.

Angiosperms that complete their life cycle in two years are called **biennials** (by-EN-ee-ulz). In the first year, biennials germinate and grow roots, very short stems, and sometimes leaves. During their second year, biennials grow new stems and leaves and then produce flowers and seeds. Once the flowers produce seeds, the plant dies. Evening primrose, parsley, celery, and foxglove are biennials.

Flowering plants that live for more than two years are called **perennials.** Perennials usually live through many years. Some perennials, such as peonies, asparagus, and many grasses, have herbaceous stems that die each winter and are replaced in the spring. Most perennials, however, have woody stems. Palm trees, sagebrush, maple trees, and honeysuckle are examples of woody perennials.

22–5 Section Assessment

1. **Key Concept** What reproductive structures are unique to angiosperms? Briefly describe the function of each.
2. **Key Concept** What are monocots and dicots?
3. **Key Concept** How do annuals, biennials, and perennials differ?
4. Compare the growth forms of plants with woody stems and those with herbaceous stems.
5. **Critical Thinking Forming Hypotheses** Which are more likely to be dispersed by animals—the seeds of an angiosperm or the spores of a fern? Explain your reasoning.

Thinking Visually

Creating a Display

Prepare a display comparing two specific plants, one monocot and one dicot. On this display, show photographs or drawings of the plants and write a brief summary of the basic differences between these two types of angiosperms.

Exploration

Comparing Adaptations of Mosses and Ferns

As plants evolved from their aquatic ancestors, they adapted to increasingly drier environments. In this investigation, you will compare a moss and a fern to determine which plant is better adapted for life in a dry environment.

Problem Are ferns or mosses better adapted for life in a dry environment?

Materials

- fern plant
- clump of moss plants
- hand lens
- forceps
- scalpel
- microscope slide
- dropper pipette
- coverslip
- compound microscope

Skills Observing, Comparing and Contrasting

Procedure

1. Make a copy of the data table on a separate sheet of paper. Record all your observations in the table.

Data Table

Characteristic	Fern	Moss
Appearance of surface		
Flexibility		
Presence or absence of veins		

2. Remove a single moss plant from the clump of plants. Examine the plant. Record whether its leaf surface is dull or shiny. Examine a fern frond. Record whether its surface is dull or shiny.
3. Gently bend the leafy moss plant and the fern frond back and forth. Record the flexibility (ability to bend) of the moss and the fern.
4. Use a forceps to gently transfer a single moss "leaf" to the center of a clean microscope slide. Use a dropper pipette to place a drop of water on top of it, and cover the drop with a coverslip.
5. Examine the slide under the low-power objective of your microscope. Note whether you find veins in the moss. Record your observations.
6. Use a scalpel to cut a thin slice of a fern frond. Using the slice of fern as your specimen, follow the procedure in steps 4 and 5.

Analyze and Conclude

1. **Inferring** Describe the surface of the moss leaf and the fern leaf. What substance did you find on the surface of the fern? How does this substance help ferns live on dry land?
2. **Comparing and Contrasting** Which plant was firmer—the fern or the moss? How can you explain this difference?
3. **Observing** Did you observe veins in the fern? In the moss?
4. **Formulating Hypotheses** Why do you think the fern is able to grow larger than the moss?
5. **Drawing Conclusions** Which plant has structural adaptations that make it better able to survive in a dry environment? Explain.

Go Further

Observing Use a microscope to examine prepared slides of cross sections of mosses and ferns. Where do you see vascular tissue? Explain how these variations in traits might impact the survival of moss and fern species.

Chapter 22 Study Guide

22–1 Introduction to Plants

Key Concepts

- Plants are multicellular eukaryotes that have cell walls made of cellulose. They develop from multicellular embryos and carry out photosynthesis using the green pigments chlorophyll *a* and *b*.
- The lives of plants revolve around the need for sunlight, water and minerals, gas exchange, and the movement of water and nutrients throughout the plant body.
- The first plants evolved from an organism much like the multicellular green algae living today.

Vocabulary

sporophyte, p. 552
gametophyte, p. 552

22–2 Bryophytes

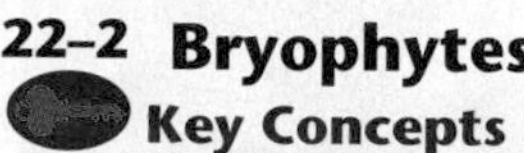

Key Concepts

- Bryophytes have life cycles that depend on water for reproduction. Lacking vascular tissue, these plants can draw up water by osmosis only a few centimeters above the ground.
- Bryophytes include mosses, liverworts, and hornworts.
- In bryophytes, the gametophyte is the dominant, recognizable stage of the life cycle and is the stage that carries out most of the plant's photosynthesis.

Vocabulary

bryophyte, p. 556 • rhizoid, p. 557
gemma, p. 557 • protonema, p. 558
antheridium, p. 559 • archegonium, p. 559

22–3 Seedless Vascular Plants

Key Concepts

- Both forms of vascular tissue—xylem and phloem—can move fluids throughout the plant body, even against the force of gravity.
- Seedless vascular plants include club mosses, horsetails, and ferns.
- Ferns and other vascular plants have a life cycle in which the diploid sporophyte is the dominant stage.

Vocabulary

vascular tissue, p. 560 • tracheid, p. 560
xylem, p. 560 • phloem, p. 560
lignin, p. 560 • root, p. 561
leaf, p. 561 • vein, p. 561 • stem, p. 561
rhizome, p. 562 • frond, p. 562
sporangium, p. 562 • sorus, p. 562

22–4 Seed Plants

Key Concepts

- Adaptations that allow seed plants to reproduce in areas without water include flowers or cones, the transfer of sperm by pollination, and the protection of embryos in seeds.
- Gymnosperms include gnetophytes, cycads, ginkgoes, and conifers.

Vocabulary

gymnosperm, p. 564 • angiosperm, p. 564
cone, p. 564 • flower, p. 564
pollen grain, p. 565 • pollination, p. 565
seed, p. 565 • embryo, p. 565
seed coat, p. 565

22–5 Angiosperms—Flowering Plants

Key Concepts

- Angiosperms develop unique reproductive organs known as flowers. Flowers contain ovaries, which surround and protect the seeds.
- Monocots and dicots are named for the number of seed leaves, or cotyledons, in the plant embryo. Monocots have one seed leaf, and dicots have two.
- There are three categories of plant life spans: annual, biennial, and perennial.

Vocabulary

fruit, p. 569 • monocot, p. 570 • dicot, p. 570
cotyledon, p. 570 • annual, p. 572
biennial, p. 572 • perennial, p. 572

Thinking Visually

Using the information in this chapter, make a compare-and-contrast table comparing bryophytes, ferns, gymnosperms, and angiosperms. Compare these groups of plants in terms of reproduction (seeds or seedless), tissues (vascular or nonvascular), typical size, and type of habitat.

Preparing for the Living Environment Exam

Blue questions emphasize Regents Exam content

Chapter 22

Part A

Multiple Choice

For each statement or question, select the number of the word or expression that, of those given, best completes the statement or answers the question.

1 Which is *not* a characteristic of plants?
(1) eukaryotic
(2) cell walls contain chitin
(3) multicellular
(4) contain chlorophyll

2 The first plants evolved from
(1) brown algae
(2) green algae
(3) red algae
(4) golden algae

3 The most recognizable stage of a moss is the
(1) sporophyte (3) archegonium
(2) protonema (4) gametophyte

4 Water is carried upward from the roots to every part of a plant by
(1) cell walls (3) cuticle
(2) phloem (4) xylem

5 To which group does the plant shown below belong?
(1) bryophytes (3) gymnosperms
(2) ferns (4) angiosperms

6 In angiosperms, the mature seed is surrounded by a
(1) cone (3) fruit
(2) flower (4) cotyledon

7 Parsley is an herb that has a life cycle that lasts two years. It is called a
(1) bryophyte (3) biennial
(2) monocot (4) perennial

8 Which term is most closely associated with ferns and other plants that are seedless and possess vascular tissue?
(1) Bryophytes (3) Gymnosperms
(2) Angiosperms (4) Fungi

9 The tissue that conducts sugars throughout a vascular plant is composed of
(1) tracheids (3) phloem
(2) xylem (4) epidermal cells

10 Cones contain which of these structures?
A gametophytes
B spores
C seeds
(1) A, only (3) A and B
(2) B, only (4) A and C

11 During the life cycle of a moss, what environmental condition is necessary before fertilization can occur?
(1) sunlight (3) high temperature
(2) water (4) wind

For questions 12 and 13, complete each analogy by selecting the correct number. In analogies, A : B :: C : means "A is to B as C is to ___?___."

12 Gymnosperms : cones :: angiosperms :
(1) seeds (3) leaves
(2) stems (4) flowers

13 Monocots : grasses :: dicots :
(1) day lilies
(2) two seed leaves
(3) oak trees
(4) flowers

Test-Taking Tip If you find particular questions difficult, put a light pencil mark beside them and keep working. (Do not write in this book.) As you answer later questions, you may find information that helps you answer the difficult questions.

Preparing for the
Living Environment Exam

Part B

Multiple Choice and Extended Response

For those questions that ask you to select a response, choose the one that best completes the statement or answers the question. For all others follow the directions given.

Base your answers to questions 14 and 15 on the information and photograph below and on your knowledge of biology.

14 A photographer was looking for good examples of monocots and dicots to photograph for a science text. He selected the plant shown because it has leaves with parallel veins and flowers with six petals. Is this plant an example of a monocot or a dicot? Support your answer with an explanation.

15 To illustrate the other class of Angiosperm, state *two* characteristics of the plant that the photographs should exhibit.

Base your answers to questions 16 through 18 on the information and graph below and on your knowledge of biology.

A group of students placed a sprig of the pondweed, *Elodea,* in a beaker of water. They measured the amount of oxygen given off during a set period of time to determine the rate of photosynthesis. They changed the temperature of the beaker using an ice bucket and a hot plate. Their data are summarized in the following graph.

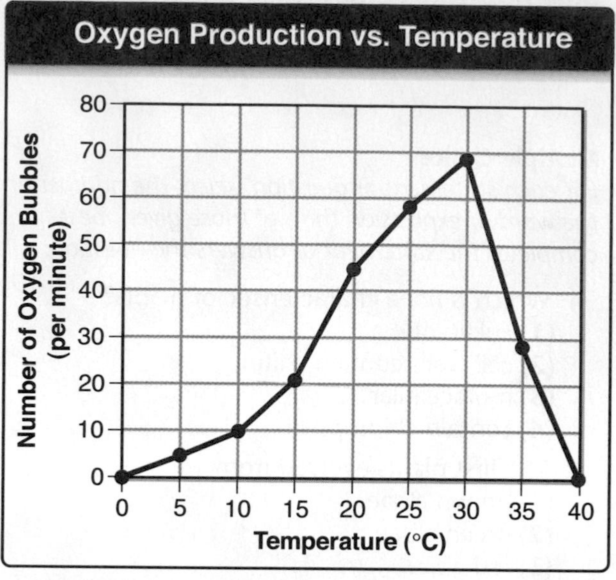

16 What is the manipulated (independent) variable in the students' investigation?
(1) light intensity
(2) temperature
(3) oxygen bubbles
(4) photosynthesis rate

17 Which variables should the students have held constant?
A Plant type
B Temperature
C Light intensity
(1) A, only
(2) B, only
(3) A and C, only
(4) A, B, and C

18 What is an appropriate conclusion based on the graph?
(1) The higher the temperature, the more oxygen bubbles are released.
(2) There is an optimum temperature for photosynthesis in this species of *Elodea.*
(3) All plants are most efficient at 30°C.
(4) Temperature has no effect on photosynthesis.

19 Moss plants are small. Ferns can grow as tall as a small tree. Explain why this is so.

20 A friend of yours lives in a desert area of New Mexico. She wants to grow a garden of mosses and liverworts. List the environmental conditions she would need to maintain for her garden to be successful.

21 List *three* adaptations that allow conifers to live in dry habitats.

22 List *two* adaptations that allow seed plants to reproduce without water.

NEW YORK LIVING ENVIRONMENT

23 Explain how the ability to produce lignin is significant in the evolution of plants.

24 Propose a hypothesis to explain why angiosperms have become the dominant type of plant on Earth.

25 During World War I, the British army used sterilized sphagnum moss to bandage millions of wounds. List *two* properties of sphagnum moss that make it suitable for use in bandages.

Part C

Extended Response

Answer the questions or follow the directions given.

Base your answers to questions 26 through 28 on the information below and on your knowledge of biology.

Recently taxonomists have added several kingdoms to the classification system of living things. Mostly these additions have come about as scientists try to organize different types of unicellular organisms. Overall, there have not been many changes in the classification system for the plant kingdom.

26 Explain how plants are classified. In your answer be sure to:
- identify the four groups of plants
- describe the important features used to organize these groups
- state the role of DNA in the classification of plants

27 Taxonomists often use fossil evidence to help them classify organisms. Explain what this evidence shows about the origin of the earliest plants.

28 A cladogram is a graphic representation of evolutionary relationships. Draw a cladogram to show the evolution of water-conducting tissue, seeds, and flowers from a green algae ancestor.

29 One botanist described a seed as "a ship that carries a plant on a voyage to colonize new land."

a Describe the role of each part of a seed in this voyage. Your answer should identify the role of each of the following structures:
- embryo
- endosperm
- seed coat

b Several adaptations have evolved that assist plants in the dispersal of their seeds. Fruits are one of these. Explain the importance of fruits in seed dispersal.

30 The plant below is called *Cooksonia.* At one time, scientists thought it was the ancestor of all land plants. Describe how this plant was likely similar to, yet different from, a modern flowering plant such as a maple tree. In your answer be sure to compare the two plants in terms of their:
- method of nutrition
- method of reproduction
- relative size
- presence of vascular tissue

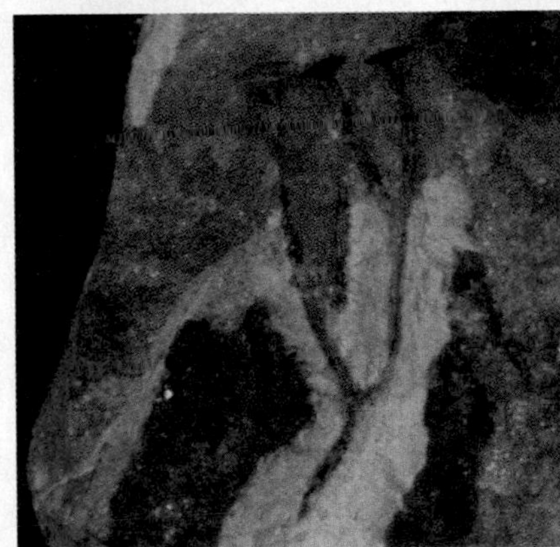

For: An interactive self-test
Visit: PHSchool.com
Web Code: cba-7220

CHAPTER 23

Roots, Stems, and Leaves

Cacti leaves are modified into thin, sharp spines. The reduced-leaf surface area prevents excess water loss.

Inquiry Activity

What parts of plants do we eat?

Procedure 

1. Examine an onion, a potato, and an artichoke. Record your observations as notes and labeled sketches.
2. Use your observations to classify each vegetable as a root, stem, leaf, or other plant part.

Think About It

1. **Classifying** How did you classify the onion? Explain what characteristics you used to make this decision.
2. **Inferring** How did you classify the potato? How is its structure related to its function?
3. **Inferring** How did you classify the artichoke? What does its inner structure tell you about its function?

23–1 Specialized Tissues in Plants

LS- Make observations

Have you ever wondered if plants were really alive? Compared to animals, plants don't seem to do much. Yet, in one sense, plants have been more successful than animals. Individual plants outnumber animals and also make up far more of Earth's biomass. So, it's only fair to admit that plants must be doing something right. And so they are.

If you look deep inside a living plant, that first impression of inactivity vanishes. Instead, you will find a busy and complex organism packed with specialized systems and subsystems. Materials move throughout the plant, and growth and repair take place continuously. Plants may act at a pace that seems slow to us, but their cells work together in remarkably effective ways to ensure the plant's survival.

Guide for Reading

Key Concepts
- What are the three principal organs and tissues of seed plants?
- What are the three main tissue systems of plants?
- What specialized cells make up vascular tissue?
- How does meristematic tissue differ from other plant tissue?

Vocabulary
epidermal cell
vessel element
sieve tube element
companion cell
parenchyma
collenchyma
sclerenchyma
meristem
meristematic tissue
apical meristem
differentiation

Reading Strategy: Building Vocabulary Before you read, preview new vocabulary by skimming the section and making a list of the highlighted, boldface terms. Leave space to make notes of definitions as you read.

Seed Plant Structure

The cells of a seed plant are organized into different tissues and organs, as shown in **Figure 23–1** on page 580.  **Three of the principal organs of seed plants are roots, stems, and leaves.** These organs are linked together by systems and subsystems that run the length of the plant, performing functions such as transport and protection and coordinating plant activities.

Roots The root system of a plant absorbs water and dissolved nutrients. Roots anchor plants in the ground, holding soil in place and preventing erosion. Root systems also protect the plant from harmful soil bacteria and fungi, transport water and nutrients to the rest of the plant, and hold plants upright against forces such as wind and rain.

Stems A stem has a support system for the plant body, a transport system that carries nutrients, and a defense system that protects the plant against predators and disease. Stems can be as short as a few millimeters or as tall as 100 meters. Whatever its size, the support system of a stem must be strong enough to hold up its leaves and branches. Similarly, the stem's transport system must contain subsystems that can lift water from roots up to the leaves and carry the products of photosynthesis from the leaves back down to the roots.

Leaves Leaves are the plant's main photosynthetic systems. The broad, flat surfaces of many leaves help increase the amount of sunlight plants absorb. Leaves also expose a great deal of tissue to the dryness of the air and, therefore, must contain subsystems to protect against water loss. Adjustable pores in leaves help conserve water while letting oxygen and carbon dioxide enter and exit the leaf.

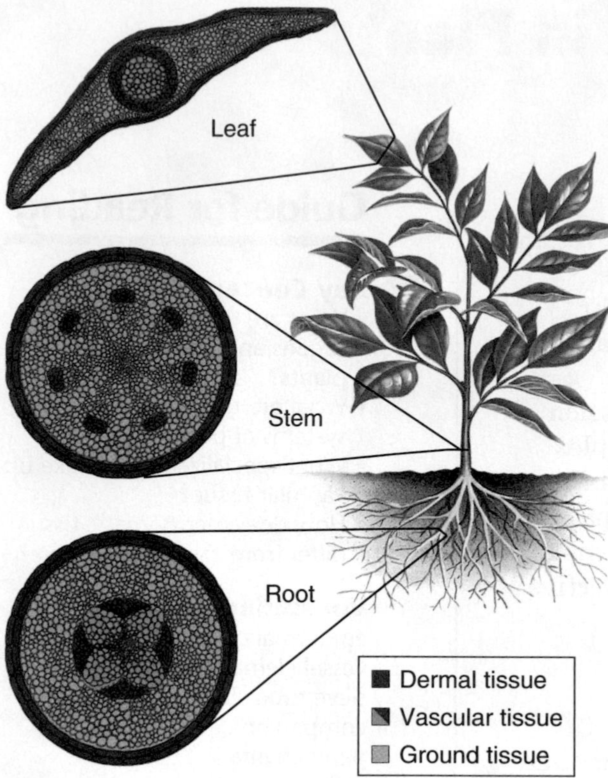

◀ **Figure 23–1** **Vascular plants consist of roots, stems, and leaves.** Each of these organs contains dermal tissue, vascular tissue, and ground tissue, as shown by the cross sections of the leaf, stem, and root. **Interpreting Graphics** ***Which tissue is found in the center of a plant stem?***

Plant Tissue Systems

Within the roots, stems, and leaves of plants are specialized tissue systems. **Plants consist of three main tissue systems: dermal tissue, vascular tissue, and ground tissue.** Dermal tissue is like the "skin" of a plant in that it is the outmost layer of cells. Vascular tissue is like the plant's "bloodstream," transporting water and nutrients throughout the plant; and ground tissue is everything else. On this and the following page, you will see how the cells in these systems compare to one another.

Dermal Tissue

The outer covering of a plant consists of dermal tissue, which typically consists of a single layer of **epidermal cells,** shown in **Figure 23–2.** The outer surfaces of these are often covered with a thick waxy layer that protects against water loss and injury. The thick waxy coating of the epidermal cells is known as the cuticle. Some epidermal cells have tiny projections known as trichomes (TRY-kohmz), which help protect the leaf and also give it a fuzzy appearance. In roots, dermal tissue includes root hair cells that provide a large amount of surface area and aid in water absorption. On the underside of leaves, dermal tissue contains guard cells, which regulate water loss and gas exchange.

▼ **Figure 23–2** This scanning electron micrograph shows the specialized cells of the epidermis of a rosebud. The epidermis is covered with thin, unicellular trichomes as well as large, bulbous trichomes that secrete chemicals that protect the plant against insect attack (magnification: 150×). **Formulating Hypotheses** ***Develop a hypothesis to explain how natural selection might have led to the development of plants with large trichomes.***

Vascular Tissue

Vascular tissue forms a transport system that moves water and nutrients throughout the plant. The principal subsystems in vascular tissue are xylem, a water-conducting tissue, and phloem, a food-conducting tissue. **Vascular tissue contains several types of specialized cells. Xylem consists of tracheids and vessel elements. Phloem consists of sieve tube elements and companion cells.** As you can see in **Figure 23–3,** both xylem and phloem are made up of networks of hollow connected cells that carry fluids throughout the plant.

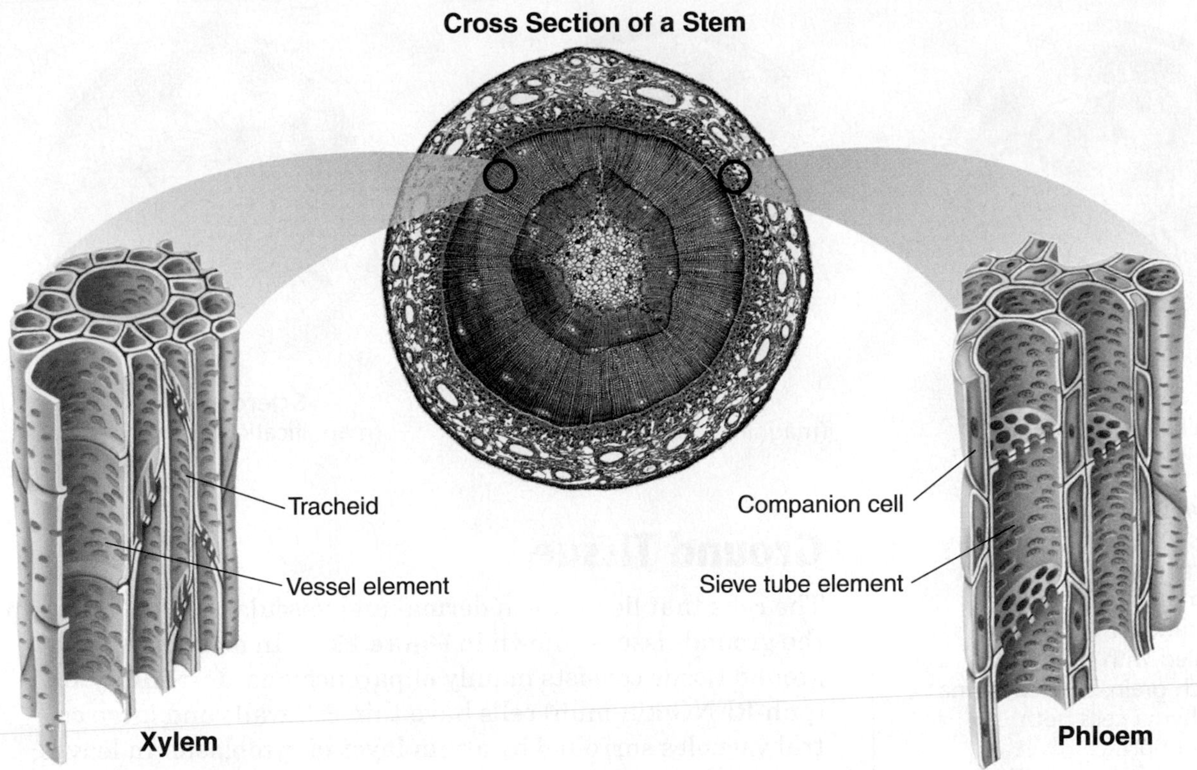

▲ Figure 23–3 Vascular tissue is made up of xylem and phloem. Xylem tissue (left) conducts water from the roots to the rest of the plant. Phloem tissue (right) conducts a variety of materials, mostly carbohydrates, throughout a plant.

Xylem All seed plants have a type of xylem cell called a tracheid. Recall that tracheids are long, narrow cells with walls that are impermeable to water. These walls, however, are pierced by openings that connect neighboring cells to one another. When tracheids mature, they die, and their cytoplasm disintegrates.

Angiosperms have another kind of xylem cell that is called a **vessel element.** Vessel elements are much wider than tracheids. Like tracheids, they mature and die before they conduct water. Vessel elements are arranged end to end on top of one another like a stack of tin cans. The cell walls at both ends are lost when the cells die, transforming the stack of vessel elements into a continuous tube through which water can move freely.

Phloem The main phloem cells are **sieve tube elements.** These cells are arranged end to end, like vessel elements, to form sieve tubes. The end walls of sieve tube elements have many small holes in them. Materials can move through these holes from one adjacent cell to another. As sieve tube elements mature, they lose their nuclei and most of the other organelles in their cytoplasm. The remaining organelles hug the inside of the cell wall. The rest of the space is a pipeline through which sugars and other foods are carried in a watery stream.

Companion cells are phloem cells that surround sieve tube elements. Companion cells keep their nuclei and other organelles through their lifetime. Companion cells support the phloem cells and aid in the movement of substances in and out of the phloem.

CHECKPOINT *What are the three main tissue systems?*

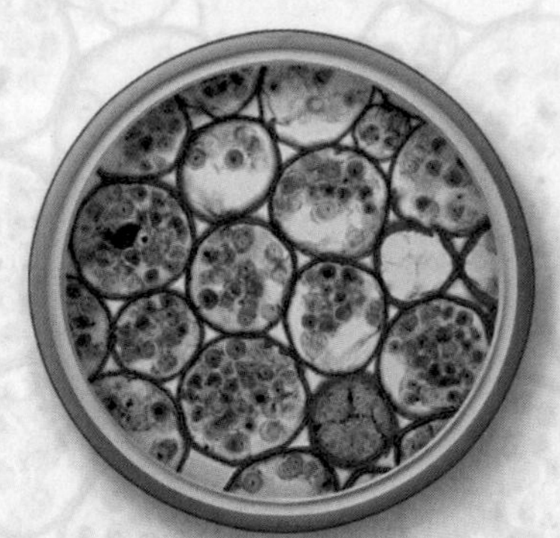
Parenchyma
(magnification: about 50×)

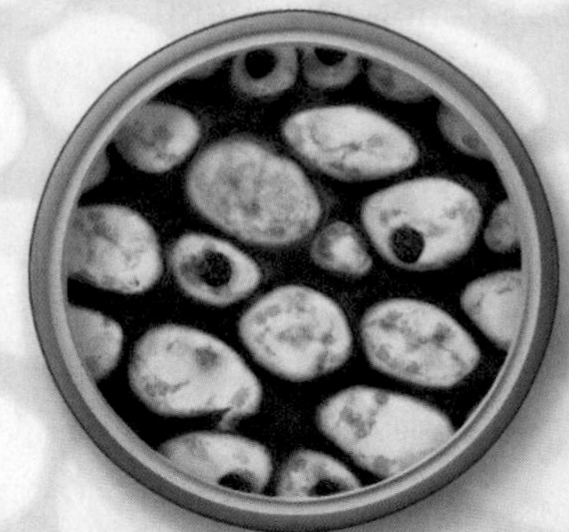
Collenchyma
(magnification: about 150×)

Sclerenchyma
(magnification: about 200×)

Figure 23–4 Ground tissue is made of cells whose cell walls have different thicknesses. Parenchyma cells function mainly in storage and photosynthesis. The root cells shown are filled with purple-staining starch grains. Collenchyma and sclerenchyma cells both function in support. **Predicting** ***Where would you expect to find more sclerenchyma—in the leaves or the stem of a plant?***

Ground Tissue

The cells that lie between dermal and vascular tissues make up the ground tissues, shown in **Figure 23–4.** In most plants, ground tissue consists mainly of parenchyma. **Parenchyma** (puh-RENG-kih-muh) cells have thin cell walls and large central vacuoles surround by a thin layer of cytoplasm. In leaves, these cells are packed with chloroplasts and are the site of most of a plant's photosynthesis. Ground tissue may also contain two types of cells with thicker cell walls. **Collenchyma** (kuh-LENG-kih-muh) cells have strong, flexible cell walls that help support larger plants. Collenchyma cells make up the familiar "strings" of a stalk of celery. **Sclerenchyma** (sklih-RENG-kih-muh) cells have extremely thick, rigid cell walls that make ground tissue tough and strong.

CHECKPOINT *How do the cells of the three kinds of ground tissue compare with one another?*

Plant Growth and Meristematic Tissue

Most plants have a method of development that involves an open, or indeterminate, type of growth. Indeterminate growth means that they grow and produce new cells at the tips of their roots and stems for as long as they live. These cells are produced in **meristems** (MEHR-uh-stems), clusters of tissue that are responsible for continuing growth throughout a plant's lifetime. The new cells produced in **meristematic tissue** are undifferentiated—that is, they have not yet become specialized for specific functions, such as transport.

Near the end, or tip, of each growing stem and root is an apical meristem. An **apical meristem** is a group of undifferentiated cells that divide to produce increased length of stems and roots. **Figure 23–5** shows examples of root and shoot apical meristems. **Meristematic tissue is the only plant tissue that produces new cells by mitosis.**

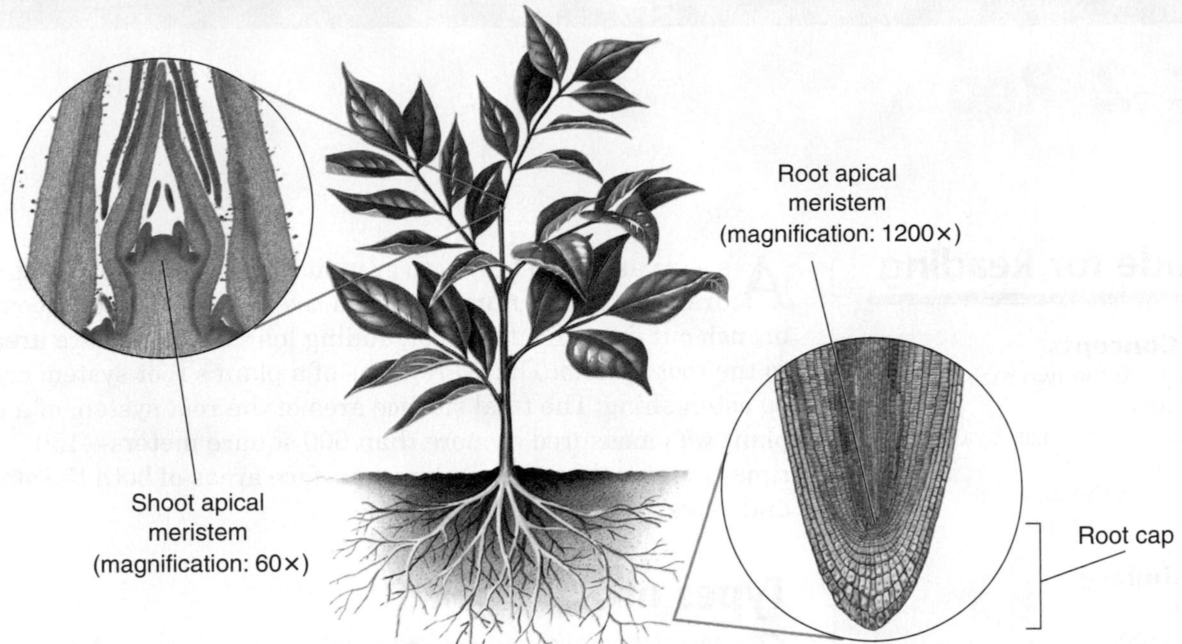

▲ **Figure 23–5 Meristematic tissue produces new cells by mitosis.** Apical meristems, which consist of many actively dividing cells, are located at the tips of shoots (left) and roots (right). The apical meristem of a root is surrounded by a root cap that protects the root as it grows through the soil.

At first, the cells that originate in meristems look very much alike: They divide rapidly and have thin cell walls. Gradually, these cells develop into mature cells with specialized structures and functions, a process called **differentiation.** As these cells differentiate, they produce each of the tissue systems of the plant, including dermal, ground, and vascular tissue.

The highly specialized cells found in flowers, which make up the reproductive systems of flowering plants, are also produced in meristems. Flower development begins when certain genes are turned on in a shoot apical meristem. The actions of these genes transform the apical meristem into a floral meristem, producing the modified leaves that become the flower's colorful petals, as well as the reproductive tissues of the flower. Many plants also grow in width as a result of meristematic tissue that lines the stems and roots of a plant. Later in the chapter, you will learn how this method of growth and development takes place.

23–1 Section Assessment

1. **Key Concept** What are the three main organs of seed plants? Describe the structure of each.
2. **Key Concept** List the three tissue systems of plants. Describe how each tissue is distributed in stems, tissues, and leaves.
3. **Key Concept** What two cell types make up xylem? Phloem?
4. **Key Concept** What is the function of meristematic tissue in a plant?
5. In a stem that needs to support heavy leaves, what type of ground tissue might you expect to find?
6. **Critical Thinking Comparing and Contrasting** Choose a group of cells making up vascular tissue in the root, the stem, and the leaf. Compare these cells, showing how they are alike and different.

Writing in Science

Comparing and Contrasting

You probably have some knowledge of the human circulatory system. Based on this knowledge, write a paragraph comparing and contrasting the vascular system of a plant to the human circulatory system. *Hint:* Show how the systems are alike and different.

23–2 Roots

Guide for Reading

Key Concepts

- What are the two main types of roots?
- What are the main tissues in a mature root?
- What are the different functions of roots?

Vocabulary

taproot
fibrous root
root hair
cortex
endodermis
vascular cylinder
root cap
Casparian strip

Reading Strategy: Outlining Before you read, use the headings of the section to make an outline about plant roots. As you read, fill in phrases or a sentence after each heading to provide key information.

As soon as a seed begins to grow, it puts out its first root to draw water and nutrients from the soil. Other roots soon branch out from this first root, adding length and surface area to the root system. The overall size of a plant's root system can be astonishing: The total surface area of the root system of a rye plant was measured at more than 600 square meters—130 times greater than the combined surface areas of both the stems and leaves.

Types of Roots

The two main types of roots are taproots, which are found mainly in dicots, and fibrous roots, which are found mainly in monocots. In some plants, the primary root grows long and thick while the secondary roots remain small. This type of primary root is called a **taproot,** shown in **Figure 23–6.** Taproots of oak and hickory trees grow so long that they can reach water far below Earth's surface. Carrots, dandelions, beets, and radishes have short, thick taproots that store sugars or starches.

In other plants, such as grasses, **fibrous roots** branch to such an extent that no single root grows larger than the rest. The extensive fibrous root systems produced by many plants help prevent topsoil from being washed away by heavy rain.

How do roots help prevent erosion?

▼ **Figure 23–6** **Plants have taproots, fibrous roots, or both.** Taproots have a central primary root and generally grow deep into the soil. Fibrous roots are usually shallow and consist of many thin roots.

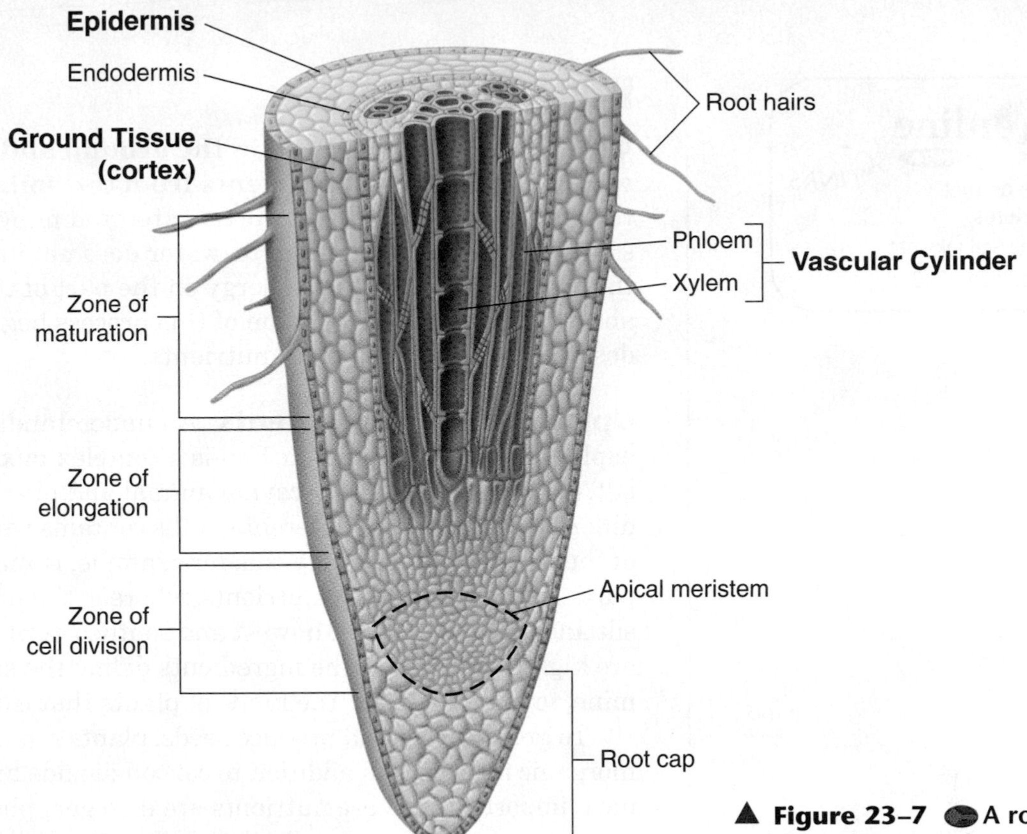

▲ **Figure 23–7** **A root consists of a central vascular cylinder surrounded by ground tissue and the epidermis.** Root hairs along the surface of the root aid in water absorption. Only the cells in the root tip divide. In the area just behind the root tip, the newly divided cells increase in length, pushing the root tip farther into the soil. The root cap, located just ahead of the root tip, protects the dividing cells as they are pushed forward. Dicot roots, such as the one shown in the cross section, have a central column of xylem cells arranged in a radiating pattern.

Root Structure and Growth

Roots contain cells from the three tissue systems—dermal, vascular, and ground tissue. **A mature root has an outside layer, the epidermis, and a central cylinder of vascular tissue. Between these two tissues lies a large area of ground tissue.** The root system plays a key role in water and mineral transport. Its cells and tissues, as shown in **Figure 23–7,** contain a number of subsystems that carry out these functions. The root's epidermal subsystem performs the dual functions of protection and absorption. Its surface is covered with tiny cellular projections called **root hairs.** These hairs penetrate the spaces between soil particles and produce a large surface area through which water can enter the plant. Just inside the epidermis is a spongy layer of ground tissue called the **cortex.** This layer extends to another layer of cells, the **endodermis.** The endodermis completely encloses the root's vascular subsystem in a region called the **vascular cylinder.**

Roots grow in length as their apical meristem produces new cells near the root tip. These fragile new cells are covered by a tough **root cap** that protects the root as it forces its way through the soil. As the root grows, the root cap secretes a slippery substance that lubricates the progress of the root through the soil. Cells at the very tip of the root cap are constantly being scraped away, and new root cap cells are continually added by the meristem. Most of the increase in root length occurs immediately behind the meristem, where cells are growing longer. At a later stage, these cells mature and take on specialized functions. The process by which unspecialized cells change to become specialized in structure and function is known as cell differentiation.

For: Links on root structures
Visit: www.SciLinks.org
Web Code: cbn-7232

Root Functions

Roots anchor a plant in the ground and absorb water and dissolved nutrients from the soil. How does a root go about the job of absorbing water and minerals from the soil? Although it might seem to, water does not just "soak" into the root from soil. It takes energy on the part of the plant to absorb water. Our explanation of this process begins with a description of soil and plant nutrients.

Uptake of Plant Nutrients An understanding of soil helps explain how plants function. Soil is a complex mixture of sand, silt, clay, air, and bits of decaying animal and plant tissue. Soil in different places and at different depths contains varying amounts of these ingredients. Sandy soil, for example, is made of large particles that retain few nutrients, whereas the finely textured silt and clay soils of the Midwest and southeastern United States are high in nutrients. The ingredients define the soil and determine, to a large extent, the kinds of plants that can grow in it.

To grow, flower, and produce seeds, plants require a variety of inorganic nutrients in addition to carbon dioxide and water. The most important of these nutrients are nitrogen, phosphorus, potassium, magnesium, and calcium. The functions of these essential nutrients within a plant are described in **Figure 23–8.** These nutrients are located in varying amounts in the soil and are drawn up by the roots of a plant. In addition to these essential nutrients, trace elements are required in small quantities to maintain proper plant growth. Trace elements include sulfur, iron, zinc, molybdenum, boron, copper, manganese, and chlorine. Large amounts of trace elements in the soil can be poisonous.

What are essential nutrients and trace nutrients?

▼ **Figure 23–8** Soil contains several nutrients that are essential for plant growth. Each nutrient plays a different role in plant functioning and development, and produces distinct effects when deficient in the soil. **Interpreting Graphics** *If you notice that a plant is becoming paler and more yellow, what nutrient might need to be added?*

Essential Plant Nutrients

Nutrient	Role in Plant	Result of Deficiency
Nitrogen	Proper leaf growth and color; synthesis of amino acids, proteins, nucleic acids, and chlorophyll	Stunted plant growth; pale yellow leaves
Phosphorus	Synthesis of DNA; development of roots, stems, flowers, and seeds	Poor flowering; stunted growth
Potassium	Synthesis of proteins and carbohydrates; development of roots, stems, and flowers; resistance to cold and disease	Weak stems and stunted roots; edges of leaves turn brown
Magnesium	Synthesis of chlorophyll	Thin stems; mottled, pale leaves
Calcium	Cell growth and division; cell wall structure; cellular transport; enzyme action	Stunted growth; curled leaves

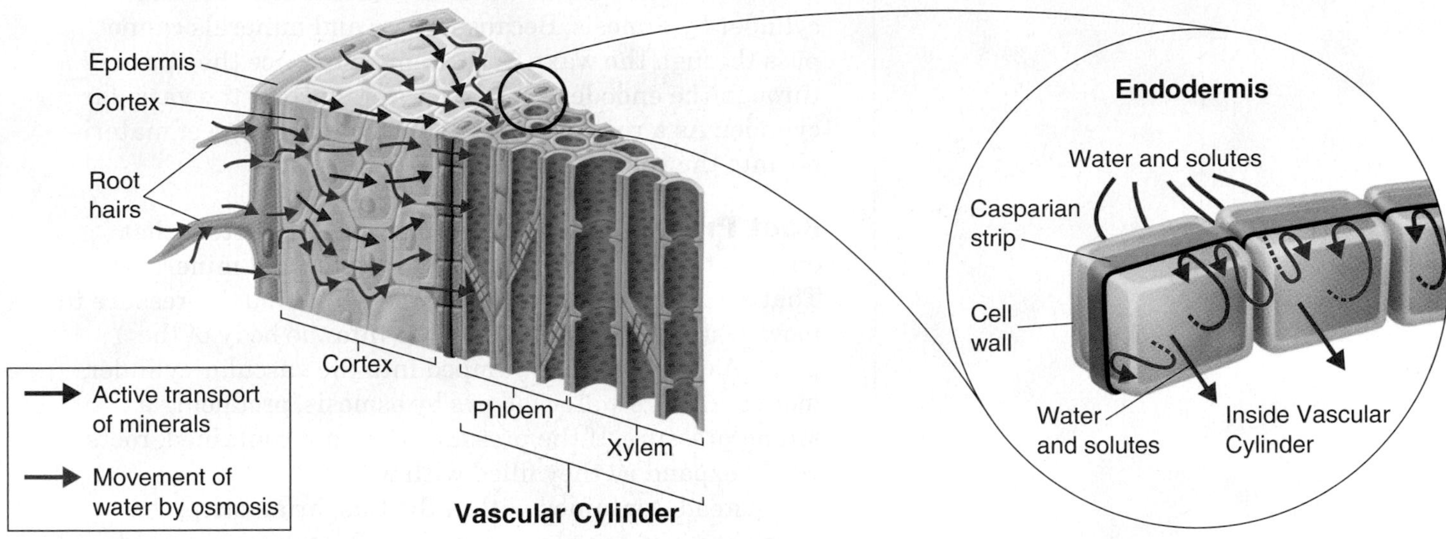

▲ **Figure 23–9** **Roots absorb water and dissolved nutrients from the soil.** Most water and minerals enter a plant through the tiny root hairs. Water moves into the cortex, through the cells of the endodermis, and into the vascular cylinder. Finally, water reaches the xylem, where it is transported throughout the plant. Cells in the endodermis are made waterproof by the Casparian strip. The Casparian strip is another example of how cells are specialized to perform a particular function—in this case, preventing the backflow of water out of the vascular cylinder into the root cortex.

Active Transport of Minerals The cell membranes of root hairs and other cells in the root epidermis contain active transport proteins. These proteins use ATP (an energy source) to pump mineral ions from the soil into the plant. The high concentration of mineral ions in the plant cells causes water molecules to move into the plant by osmosis, as shown in **Figure 23–9.**

You may recall that osmosis is the movement of water across a membrane toward an area where the concentration of dissolved material is higher. By using active transport to accumulate ions from the soil, cells of the root epidermis create conditions under which osmosis causes water to "follow" those ions and flow into the root. Note that the root does not actually pump water. But by pumping dissolved minerals into its own cells, the end result is almost the same—the water moves from the epidermis through the cortex into the vascular cylinder.

Movement Into the Vascular Cylinder Both osmosis and active transport cause water and minerals to move from the root epidermis into the cortex. From there, the water and dissolved minerals pass the inner boundary of the cortex and enter the endodermis. This process is shown in **Figure 23–9.**

The endodermis encloses the vascular cylinder and stretches up and down the entire length of the root, like a cylinder. It is composed of many individual cells, each shaped a bit like a brick. Each of these cells is surrounded on four sides by a waterproof strip called a **Casparian strip.** To imagine what the Casparian strip looks like, think of a brick with a thick rubber band stretched around it. The rubber bands stick together like mortar between the bricks. Imagine many of these bricks placed edge to edge to build a cylinder. When a root is viewed in cross section, the endodermis forms a circle.

Osmosis Recall that water moves into the vascular cylinder by osmosis. Because water and minerals cannot pass through the waxy Casparian strip, once they pass through the endodermis, they are trapped in the vascular cylinder. As a result, there is a one-way passage of materials into the vascular cylinder in plant roots.

Root Pressure Why do plants "need" a system that ensures the one-way movement of water and minerals? That system is how the plant generates enough pressure to move water out of the soil and up into the body of the plant. As minerals are pumped into the vascular cylinder, more and more water follows by osmosis, producing a strong pressure. If the pressure were not contained, roots would expand as they filled with water.

Instead, contained within the Casparian strip, the water has just one place to go—up. Root pressure, produced within the cylinder by active transport, forces water through the vascular cylinder and into the xylem. As more water moves from the cortex into the vascular cylinder, more water in the xylem is forced upward through the root into the stem. In **Figure 23–10,** you can see a demonstration of root pressure in a carrot root. Root pressure is the starting point for the movement of water through the vascular system of the entire plant. But it is just the beginning. Once you have learned about stems and leaves, you will see how water and other materials are transported within an entire plant.

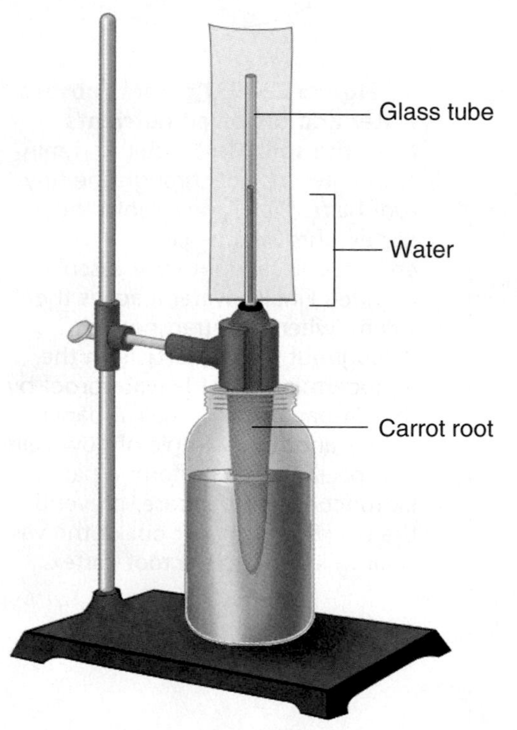

◀ **Figure 23–10** As a carrot root absorbs water, root pressure forces water upward into the glass tube, which takes the place of the stem and leaves of the carrot in this demonstration. **Applying Concepts** ***Would you expect root pressure to be higher in the leaves or in the roots? Explain your answer.***

23–2 Section Assessment

1. **Key Concept** Compare a taproot and a fibrous root.
2. **Key Concept** How are tissues distributed in a plant root?
3. **Key Concept** Describe the two main functions of roots.
4. How is osmosis involved in the absorption of water and nutrients?
5. Analyze how a root is part of a plant's transport system. Which parts of a root may be thought of as a subsystem?
6. **Critical Thinking Inferring** Why is it important that the root endodermis permit only a one-way passage of materials?

Thinking Visually

Making a Diagram

Make two diagrams, one showing a root's structure and growth, the other showing how roots absorb water and nutrients. Label the diagrams and write brief descriptions of the processes shown in each.

23–3 Stems

LS- Analyze results

What do a barrel cactus, a tree trunk, a dandelion stem, and a potato have in common? They are all types of stems. Stems vary in size, shape, and method of development. Some grow entirely underground; others reach high into the air. Stems also vary in structure and internal arrangement of cells.

Guide for Reading

Key Concepts

- What are the three main functions of stems?
- How do monocot and dicot stems differ?
- How do primary growth and secondary growth occur in stems?

Vocabulary

node • internode • bud
vascular bundle • pith
primary growth
secondary growth
vascular cambium
cork cambium • heartwood
sapwood • bark

Reading Strategy: Using Visuals Before you read, preview the art in **Figure 23–15.** As you read the section, refer to this art to learn about the structure of mature woody stems.

Stem Structure and Function

In general, stems have three important functions: They produce leaves, branches, and flowers; they hold leaves up to the sunlight; and they transport substances between roots and leaves. Stems make up an essential part of the water and mineral transport systems of the plant. The vascular tissue in stems conducts water, nutrients, and other compounds throughout the plant. Xylem and phloem, the major subsystems of the transport system, form continuous tubes from the roots through the stems to the leaves. These vascular tissues link all parts of the plant, allowing water and nutrients to be carried throughout the plant. In many plants, stems also function as storage systems and in the process of photosynthesis.

Like the rest of the plant, the stem is composed of three tissue systems: dermal, vascular, and ground tissue. Stems are surrounded by a layer of epidermal cells that have thick cell walls and a waxy protective coating.

In most plants, stems contain distinct **nodes,** where leaves are attached, and **internode** regions between the nodes, as shown in **Figure 23–11.** Small buds are found where leaves attach to the nodes. **Buds** contain undeveloped tissue that can produce new stems and leaves. In larger plants, stems develop woody tissue that helps support leaves and flowers.

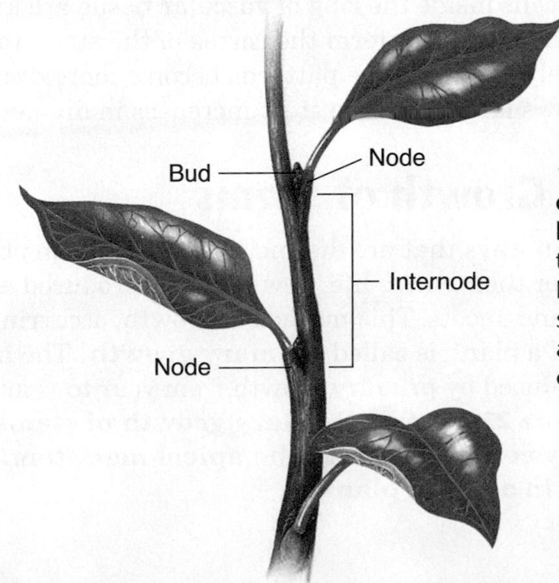

Figure 23–11 **Stems produce leaves and branches and hold leaves up to the sunlight, where they carry out photosynthesis.** Leaves are attached to a stem at structures called nodes. These nodes are separated by regions of the stem called internodes.

▶ **Figure 23–12** The arrangement of vascular bundles in the stem of a monocot differs from that in the stem of a dicot. **In a monocot, vascular bundles are scattered throughout the stem. In a dicot, vascular bundles are arranged in a ring.**

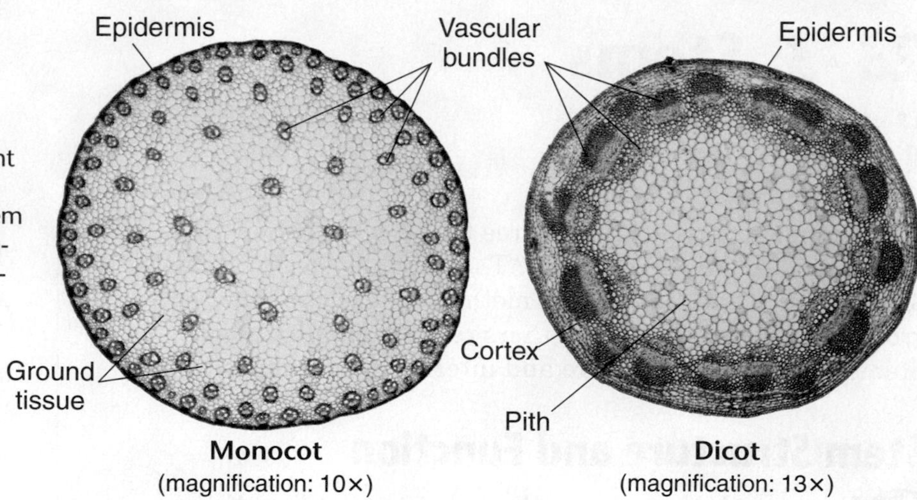

Monocot and Dicot Stems

The arrangement of tissues in a stem differs among seed plants. **In monocots, vascular bundles are scattered throughout the stem. In dicots and most gymnosperms, vascular bundles are arranged in a cylinder.** Recall that monocots and dicots are two types of flowering plants, or angiosperms. For a comparison of monocot and dicot stems, look at **Figure 23–12.**

Monocot Stems The cross section of a young monocot stem shows all three tissue systems clearly. The stem has a distinct epidermis, which encloses a series of **vascular bundles,** each of which contains xylem and phloem tissue. Phloem faces the outside of the stem, and xylem faces the center. In monocots, these bundles are scattered throughout the ground tissue. The ground tissue is fairly uniform, consisting mainly of parenchyma cells.

Dicot Stems Young dicot stems have vascular bundles, but they are generally arranged in an organized, ringlike pattern. The parenchyma cells inside the ring of vascular tissue are known as **pith,** while those outside form the cortex of the stem. In dicots, these relatively simple tissue patterns become more complex as the plant grows larger and the stem increases in diameter.

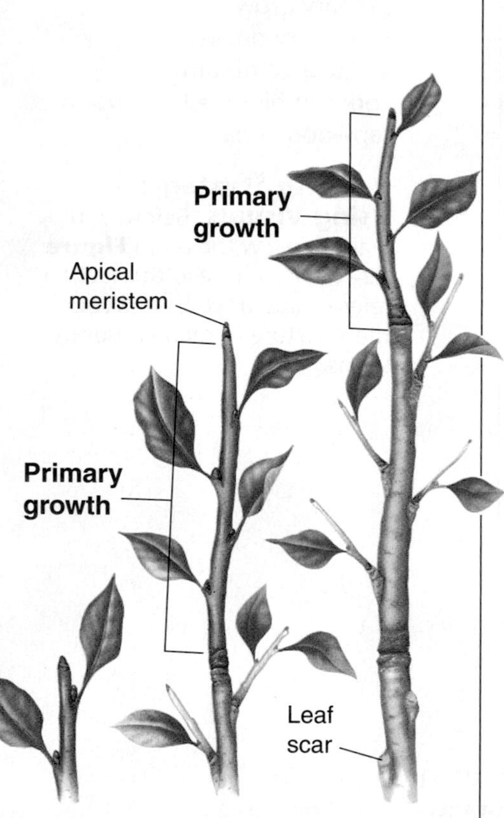

▲ **Figure 23–13** **All seed plants undergo primary growth, which is an increase in length.** Every year, apical meristems, shown in red, divide to produce new growth. The primary growth for one season consists of a stem and several leaves.

Primary Growth of Stems

Plants grow in ways that are distinctly different from other organisms. For their entire life, new cells are produced at the tips of roots and shoots. This method of growth, occurring only at the ends of a plant, is called **primary growth.** The increase in length produced by primary growth from year to year is shown in **Figure 23–13.** **Primary growth of stems is produced by cell divisions in the apical meristem. It takes place in all seed plants.**

Secondary Growth of Stems

If a plant is to grow larger year after year, its stems must increase in thickness as well as in length. They have more mass to support and more fluid to move through their vascular tissues. Yet, only meristematic tissue can produce new cells for growth. Some monocots, such as palm trees, produce thick stems from a meristem that becomes wider as the plant grows. However, most monocots, such as grasses, produce only fleshy growth and do not grow very tall. Many dicots grow extremely tall and also grow in width to support this extra weight. This growth occurs as a result of meristems other than the apical meristem.

The method of growth in which stems increase in width is called **secondary growth.** In **Figure 23–14** you can see the pattern of secondary growth in a dicot stem. **In conifers and dicots, secondary growth takes place in lateral meristematic tissues called the vascular cambium and cork cambium.** The type of lateral meristematic tissue called **vascular cambium** produces vascular tissues and increases the thickness of stems over time. **Cork cambium** produces the outer covering of stems. Another kind of cambium enables roots to grow thicker and branch. The addition of new tissue in these cambium layers increases the thickness of the stem.

Formation of the Vascular Cambium

In a young dicot stem produced by primary growth, bundles of xylem and phloem are arranged in a ring. Once secondary growth begins, the vascular cambium appears as a thin layer situated between clusters of vascular tissue. This new meristematic tissue forms between the xylem and phloem of each vascular bundle. Divisions in the vascular cambium give rise to new layers of xylem and phloem. As a result, the stem becomes wider. The cambium continues to produce new layers of vascular tissue, causing the stem to become thicker and thicker.

What tissue divides to produce secondary growth in dicots?

▼ **Figure 23–14** **Dicots produce secondary growth from meristematic tissue called vascular cambium.** This tissue forms between the xylem and phloem of the individual vascular bundles, as shown in A. Once the tissue forms, as shown in B, it divides to produce xylem cells toward the center of the stem and phloem cells toward the outside. These different tissues form the bark and wood of a mature stem, shown in C.

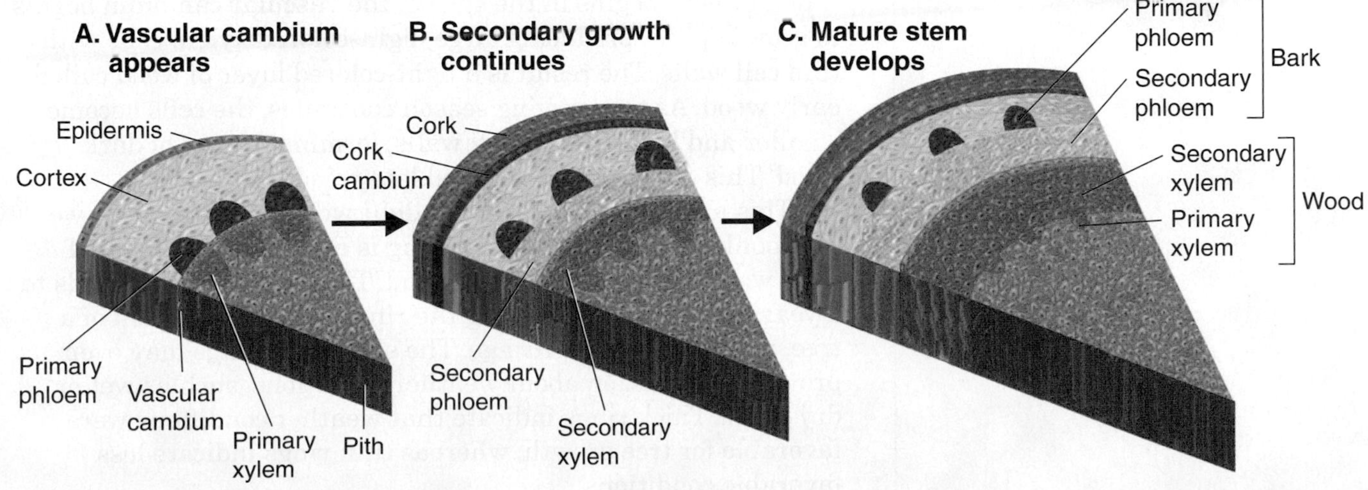

Analyzing Data

Reading a Tree's History

The field of dendrochronology (*dendron* means "tree"; *chronos* means "time") analyzes tree rings to determine information about a tree and the environment in which it grew. A tree's age, for example, can be measured by counting its growth rings—each produced by a year of growth. The specific environmental conditions can be inferred for each year of its growth by examining the relative width and color of each ring. Use the photograph below to answer each question.

1. **Interpreting Graphics** Approximately how old was this tree when it was cut down?
2. **Inferring** Areas A and B were both produced by four years of growth, yet they are different widths. What climatic conditions might account for this difference?
3. **Interpreting Graphics** The area at C is blackened from a fire that apparently affected only one side of the tree. Describe how the tree grew after this fire.
4. **Comparing and Contrasting** Areas D and E are two types of wood. Give their names, and explain how they differ.
5. **Applying Concepts** On a separate sheet of paper, draw a simple sketch of the tree, indicating where the xylem and phloem are located. Where are the youngest xylem cells located? The youngest phloem cells? What tissue produces both of these cells?

Formation of Wood Most of what we call "wood" is actually layers of xylem. These cells build up year after year, layer on layer. As woody stems grow thicker, the older xylem near the center of the stem no longer conducts water and instead becomes what is known as **heartwood.** Heartwood usually darkens with age because it accumulates impurities that cannot be removed. Heartwood is surrounded by **sapwood,** which is active in fluid transport and therefore usually lighter in color. Both heartwood and sapwood are shown in **Figure 23–15.**

In most of the temperate zone, tree growth is seasonal. When growth begins in the spring, the vascular cambium begins to grow rapidly, producing large, light-colored xylem cells with thin cell walls. The result is a light-colored layer of wood called early wood. As the growing season continues, the cells become smaller and have thicker cell walls, forming a layer of dark wood. This darker wood is called late wood.

This alternation of dark and light wood produces what we commonly call tree rings. Each ring is composed of a band of light wood and a band of dark wood. Thus, a ring corresponds to a year of growth. By counting the rings in a cross section of a tree, you can estimate its age. The size of the rings may even provide information about weather conditions, such as wet or dry years. Thick rings indicate that weather conditions were favorable for tree growth, whereas thin rings indicate less favorable conditions.

Formation of Bark On most trees, **bark** includes all of the tissues outside the vascular cambium, as shown in **Figure 23–15.** These tissues include phloem, the cork cambium, and cork. How does bark form? Picture a tree as new xylem is being laid down. It is expanding in width, or girth. Recall that the phloem tissue lies to the outside of this xylem. Phloem must grow to accommodate the larger size of the tree. As the vascular cambium increases in diameter, it forces the phloem tissue outward. This expansion causes the oldest tissues to split and fragment as they are stretched by the expanding stem. Were this expansion left unchecked, the outer covering of the stem might eventually split and break.

Another layer of growing tissue, the cork cambium, solves this potential problem. The cork cambium surrounds the cortex and produces a thick protective layer of cork. Cork consists of cells that have thick walls and usually contain fats, oils, or waxes. These waterproof substances help prevent the loss of water from the stem. The outermost cork cells are usually dead. As the stem increases in size, this dead bark often cracks and flakes off in strips or patches.

CHECKPOINT *What is heartwood?*

Go Online
SCIENCE NEWS

For: Articles on plants
Visit: PHSchool.com
Web Code: cbe-7233

▼ **Figure 23–15** In a mature tree that has undergone several years of secondary growth, the vascular cambium lies between layers of xylem to the inside, and layers of phloem to the outside. The youngest xylem, called sapwood, transports water and minerals. **Classifying** *Which layer contains meristematic cells?*

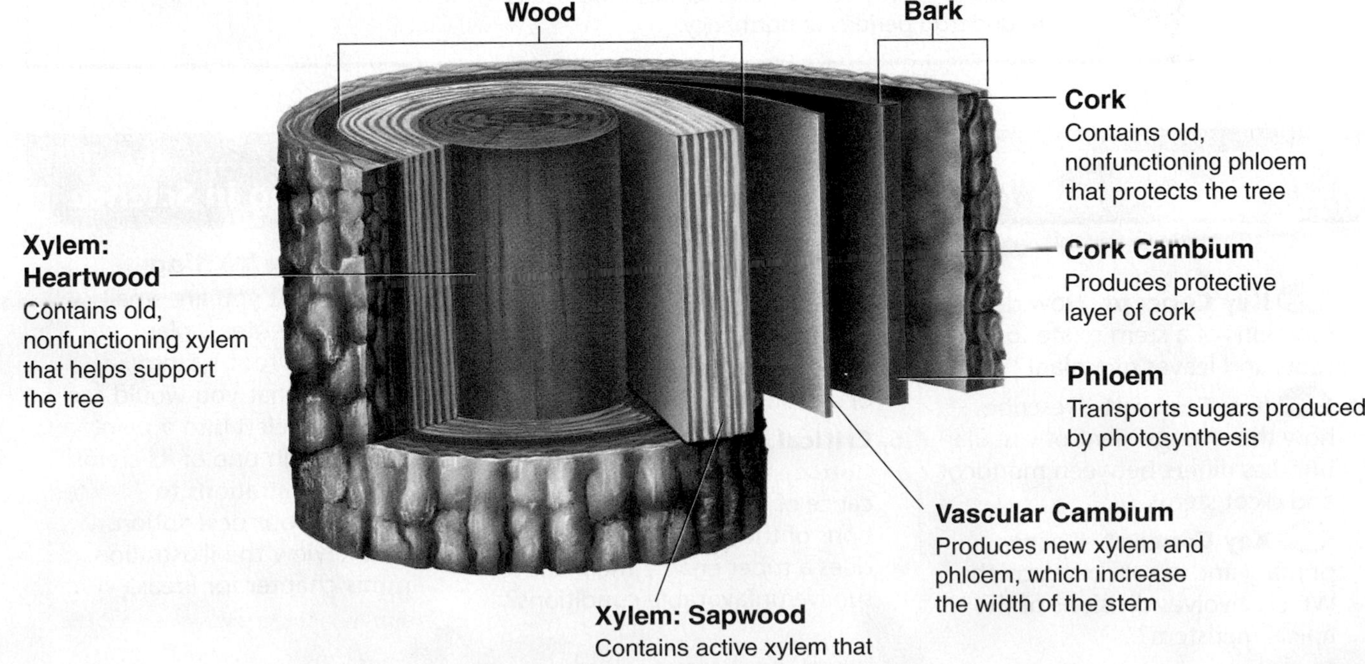
Wood
Bark
Cork
Contains old, nonfunctioning phloem that protects the tree
Cork Cambium
Produces protective layer of cork
Phloem
Transports sugars produced by photosynthesis
Vascular Cambium
Produces new xylem and phloem, which increase the width of the stem
Xylem: Sapwood
Contains active xylem that transports water and minerals
Xylem: Heartwood
Contains old, nonfunctioning xylem that helps support the tree

Figure 23–16 Stems Adapted for Storage and Dormancy

Many kinds of plants have modified stems that store food. Tubers, rhizomes, bulbs, and corms can remain dormant during cold or dry periods until favorable conditions for growth return.

Tuber
A tuber is a stem, usually growing underground, that stores food. In potato plants grown from cuttings (shown here), the tubers form at the end of underground stems. In potato plants grown from seed, tubers form at the tips of stems that grow along the ground surface.

Potato

Bulb
A bulb is made up of a central stem surrounded by short, thick leaves. As in the amaryllis bulb shown here, the leaves wrap around and protect the stem and also store food. A bulb may remain dormant for a long time, yet still grow into a plant.

Amaryllis

Corm
A corm looks similar to a bulb, but is a thickened stem that stores food. A corm has an outer covering that consists of layers of thin leaves. Plants such as the gladiolus (shown here) and the crocus form corms.

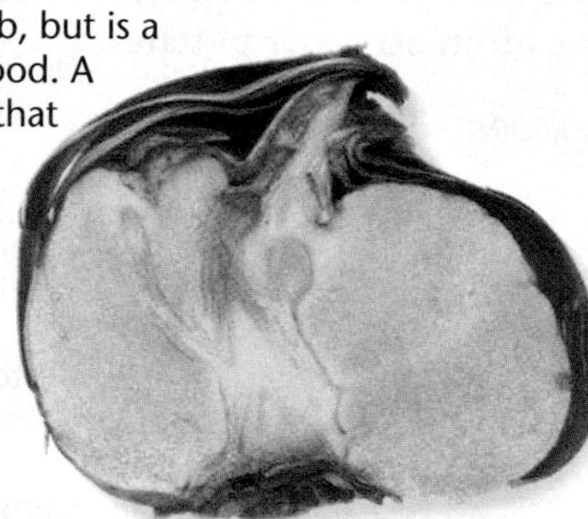

Gladiolus

Ginger

Rhizome
The stem of a ginger is a rhizome, which is a horizontal, underground stem. As shown in the ginger, new shoots can form from a rhizome, allowing plants to undergo periods of dormancy.

23–3 Section Assessment

1. **Key Concept** How do the functions of a stem relate to the roots and leaves of a plant?
2. **Key Concept** Describe how the arrangement of vascular bundles differs between monocot and dicot stems.
3. **Key Concept** Define primary and secondary growth. Which involves divisions of the apical meristem?
4. How do heartwood and sapwood differ?
5. Analyze how a stem is part of a plant's transport system. Which parts of a stem may be thought of as a subsystem?
6. **Critical Thinking Applying Concepts** Evaluate the significance of the structural adaptations of the white potato. How does a tuber enable the plant to survive unfavorable conditions?

Writing in Science

Descriptive Writing
Pretend that you are small enough to enter a plant through its root system. Describe what you would see as you traveled into a plant and through one of its stems. Include illustrations to enhance your description. *Hint:* Review the illustrations in this chapter for ideas.

23–4 Leaves

4-5.1 Photosynthesis
4-5.1 Chloroplasts in plant cells are the site of photosynthesis
4-5.3 Feedback mechanisms that maintain homeostasis

Guide for Reading

Key Concepts

- How does the structure of a leaf enable it to carry out photosynthesis?
- How does gas exchange take place in a leaf?

Vocabulary

blade
petiole
mesophyll
palisade mesophyll
spongy mesophyll
stoma
guard cell
transpiration

Reading Strategy: Monitoring Your Understanding Make a table with three columns, labeled K, W, and L. Before you read, write what you already know about leaves in the first column (K). Under the next heading, write down what you want to learn about leaves (W). After you read, write down what you learned about leaves in the last column (L).

The leaves of a plant are its main organs of photosynthesis. In a sense, plant leaves are the world's most important manufacturers of food. Sugars, starches, and oils manufactured by plants in their leaves are sources of food for virtually all land animals.

Recall from Chapter 8 that photosynthesis uses carbon dioxide and water to produce sugars and oxygen. Leaves, therefore, must have a way of obtaining the materials needed for photosynthesis as well as distributing its end products. Much of the internal structure of leaves can be understood in terms of their functions in carrying out photosynthesis.

Leaf Structure

The structure of a leaf is optimized for absorbing light and carrying out photosynthesis. As you can see in **Figure 23–17**, leaves may differ greatly in shape, yet share certain structural features. To collect sunlight, most leaves have thin, flattened sections called **blades.** The blade is attached to the stem by a thin stalk called a **petiole.** Like roots and stems, leaves have an outer covering of dermal tissue and inner regions of ground and vascular tissues. As shown in **Figure 23–18** on page 596, leaves are covered on the top and bottom by epidermis made of a layer of tough, irregularly shaped cells. The epidermis of many leaves is also covered by the cuticle. Together, the cuticle and epidermal cells form a waterproof barrier that protects tissues and limits the loss of water through evaporation.

The vascular tissues of leaves are connected directly to the vascular tissues of stems, making them part of the plant's transport system. In leaves, xylem and phloem tissues are gathered together into bundles that run from the stem into the petiole. Once they are in the leaf blade, the vascular bundles are surrounded by parenchyma and sclerenchyma cells.

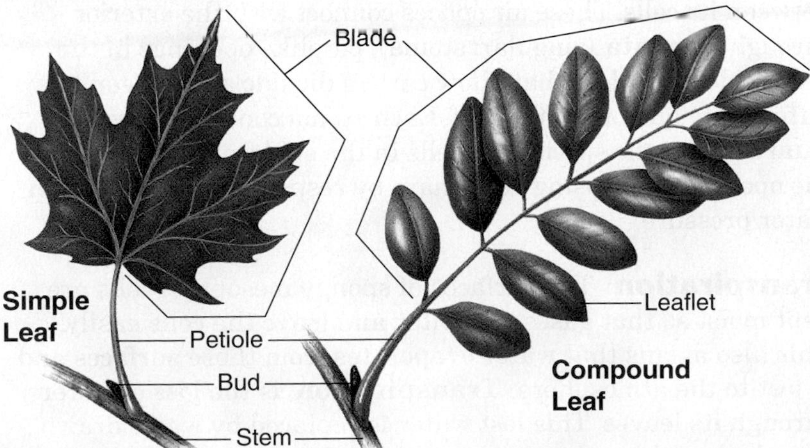

Figure 23–17 Most of a leaf consists of a blade attached to the stem by a petiole. The blade of a simple leaf (left) can be different shapes. In a compound leaf (right), the blade is divided into many separate leaflets.

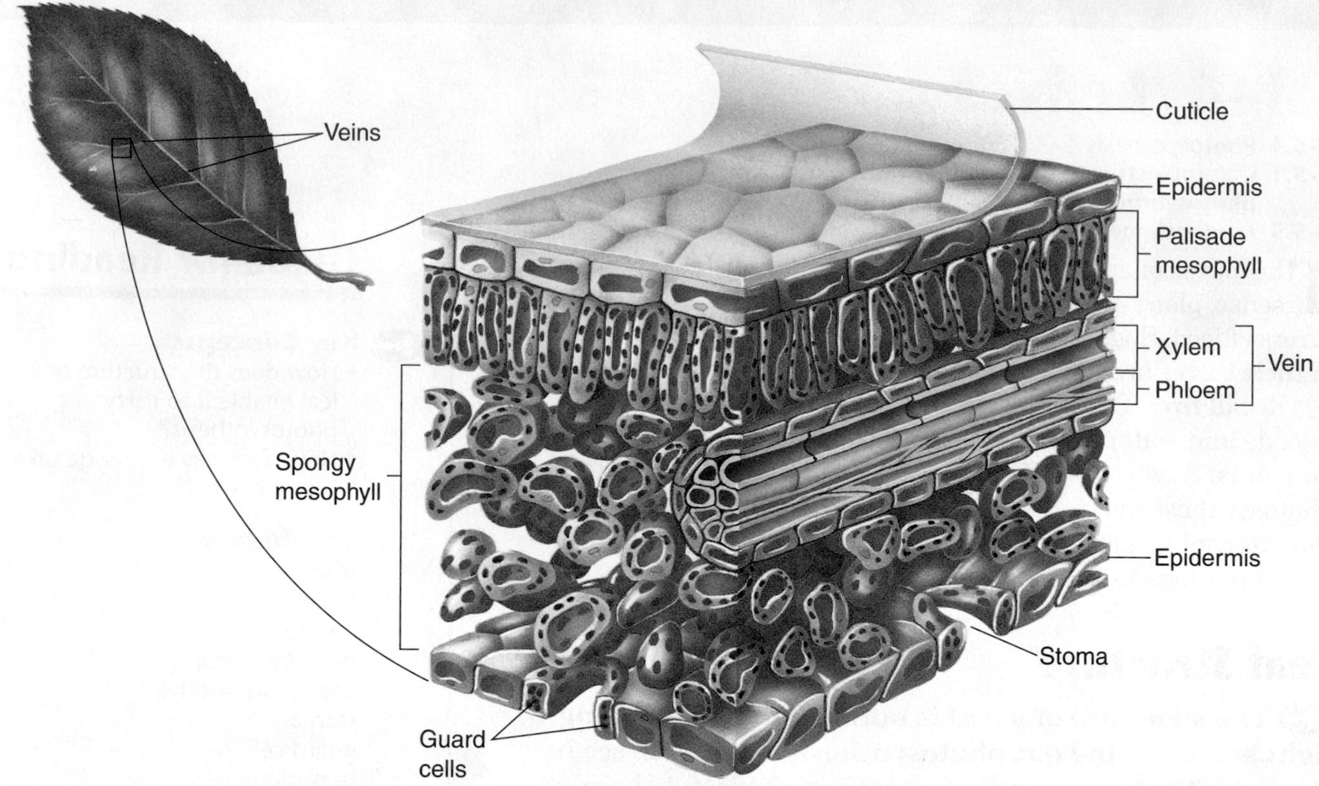

▲ **Figure 23–18** **Leaves absorb light and carry out most of the photosynthesis in a plant.** Some of the most important manufacturing sites on Earth are found in the leaves of plants. The cells in plant leaves are able to use light energy to make carbohydrates. Compare the structure of the different kinds of cells in a leaf.

Leaf Functions

A leaf can be considered a system specialized for photosynthesis. Subsystems of the leaf include tissues that bring gases, water, and nutrients to the cells that carry out photosynthesis.

Photosynthesis The bulk of most leaves consists of a specialized ground tissue known as **mesophyll,** shown in **Figure 23–18.** Photosynthesis in most plants occurs in the mesophyll. The carbohydrates produced move into phloem vessels of the transport system, which carry them to the rest of the plant.

A leaf has specialized cells that enable it to carry out photosynthesis. Under the epidermis is a layer of mesophyll cells called the **palisade mesophyll.** These closely packed cells absorb light that enters the leaf. Beneath the palisade layer is the **spongy mesophyll,** a loose tissue with many air spaces between its cells. These air spaces connect with the exterior through **stomata** (singular: stoma), porelike openings in the underside of the leaf that allow carbon dioxide and oxygen to diffuse into and out of the leaf. Each stoma consists of two **guard cells,** the specialized cells in the epidermis that control the opening and closing of stomata by responding to changes in water pressure.

Transpiration The surfaces of spongy mesophyll cells are kept moist so that gases can enter and leave the cells easily. This also means that water evaporates from these surfaces and is lost to the atmosphere. **Transpiration** is the loss of water through its leaves. This lost water is replaced by water drawn into the leaf through xylem vessels in the vascular tissue.

Word Origins

Mesophyll comes from two Greek words: *meso,* meaning "middle," and *phyllon,* meaning "leaf." **If the Greek word *chloro* means "green," what does the term *chlorophyll* mean?**

Gas Exchange Leaves take in carbon dioxide and give off oxygen during photosynthesis. When plant cells use the food they make, the cells respire, taking in oxygen and giving off carbon dioxide (just as animals do). Plant leaves allow gas exchange between air spaces in the spongy mesophyll and the exterior by opening their stomata.

It might seem that stomata should be open all the time, allowing gas exchange to take place and photosynthesis to occur at top speed. This is not what happens! If stomata were kept open all the time, water loss due to transpiration would be so great that few plants would be able to take in enough water to survive. So, plants maintain a kind of balance. **Plants keep their stomata open just enough to allow photosynthesis to take place but not so much that they lose an excessive amount of water.**

Guard cells are epidermal cells found on the undersides of leaves. They are structurally specialized to control stomata and thus regulate the movement of gases, especially water vapor, into and out of leaf tissues. The stomata open and close in response to changes in water pressure within the guard cells, as shown in **Figure 23–19.** When water pressure within the guard cells is high, the thin outer walls of the cells are forced into a curved shape. This pulls the thick inner walls of the guard cells away from one another, opening the stoma. When water pressure within the guard cells decreases, the inner walls pull together and the stoma closes. Guard cells respond to conditions in the environment, such as wind and temperature, helping to maintain homeostasis within a leaf. Notice how the structure of guard cells, which is quite different from the structure of other epidermal cells, helps them to carry out this task.

In general, stomata are open during the daytime, when photosynthesis is active, and closed at night, when open stomata would only lead to water loss. However, stomata may be closed even in bright sunlight under hot, dry conditions in which water conservation is a matter of life and death.

CHECKPOINT *What factor regulates the opening and closing of stomata?*

Figure 23–19 Plants regulate the opening and closing of their stomata to balance water loss with rates of photosynthesis. A stoma opens or closes in response to the changes in pressure within the guard cells that surround the opening. When the guard cells are swollen with water (bottom, left), the stoma is open. When the guard cells lose water (bottom, right), the opening closes, limiting further water loss from the leaf.

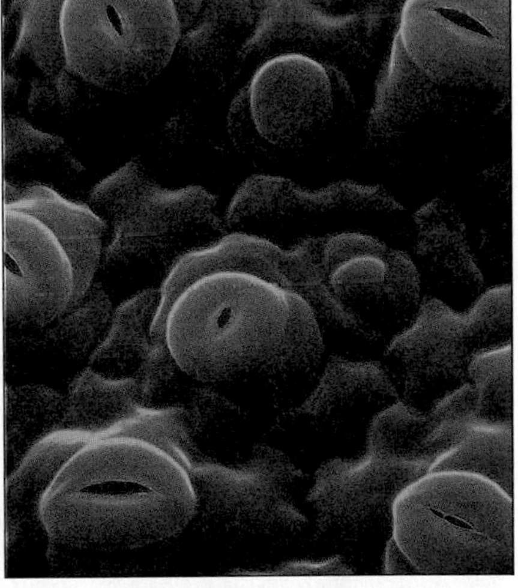

(magnification: 420×)

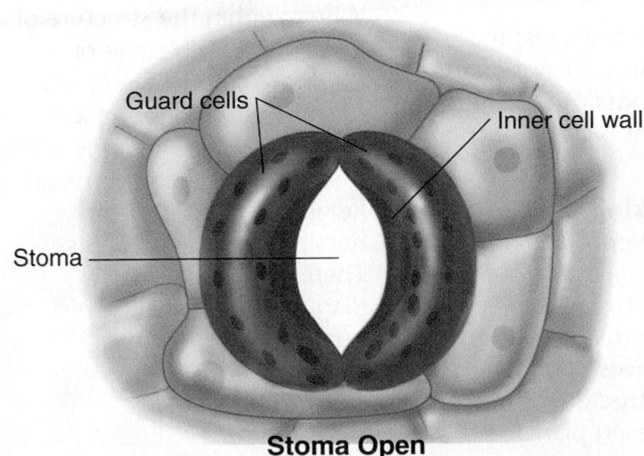

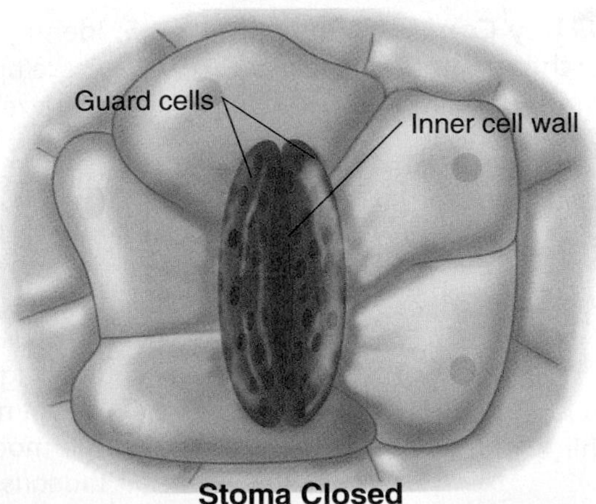

FIGURE 23–20 ADAPTATIONS OF LEAVES

The plants shown here grow in different biomes. The leaves of these plants show variations and adaptations to the dry or low-nutrient conditions in which they live.

Pitcher plant
The leaf of a pitcher plant is modified to attract and then digest insects and other small prey. Such plants typically live in nutrient-poor soils and rely on insects as their source of nitrogen.

Cactus
Cactus leaves are actually nonphotosynthetic thorns that protect against herbivores. Most of the plant's photosynthesis is carried out in its stem.

Pine
The narrow leaves of a pine tree contain a waxy epidermis as well as stomata that are sunken below the surface of the leaf. This arrangement reduces water loss from the leaf.

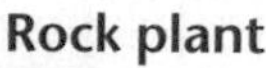

Rock plant
The leaves of a rock plant are adapted for hot, dry conditions. They are round, with few stomata, and often have clear tissue that allows light to penetrate into the leaf.

23–4 Section Assessment

1. **Key Concept** Describe how the structure of a leaf is optimized for light absorption.
2. **Key Concept** What factors regulate the opening and closing of guard cells?
3. Are stomata more likely to be open or closed on a hot day? Explain your answer.
4. Describe the cell types found within a typical leaf.
5. Identify the parts of a leaf that make up its transport system. Analyze how some of these parts may be thought of as a transport subsystem.
6. **Critical Thinking Inferring** The leaves of desert plants often have two or more layers of palisade mesophyll, rather than the single layer that is characteristic of most leaves. How might this modified structure be advantageous to a desert plant?

Connecting Concepts

Leaf Structure
Where within the structure of a leaf does each stage of photosynthesis occur? How does the structure of a leaf allow it to obtain energy and materials for photosynthesis? Refer to Section 8–3 for details on photosynthesis. Then, draw and label a diagram that answers the questions asked above.

23–5 Transport in Plants

4-5.3 Feedback mechanisms that maintain homeostasis **LS-** Make observations
LS- Follow safety rules
LS- Formulate a conclusion
LS- Identify control group

The pressure created by water entering the tissues of a root can push water upward in a plant stem. This creates more than enough pressure to force water into the vascular system and out of the root. However, root pressure does not exert enough pressure to lift water up into trees, such as the topmost needles of a redwood tree 90 meters above the ground. To draw water to such great heights, plants take advantage of some of water's most interesting physical properties.

Guide for Reading

Key Concepts
- How is water transported throughout a plant?
- How are the products of photosynthesis transported throughout a plant?

Vocabulary
adhesion
capillary action
pressure-flow hypothesis

Reading Strategy: Making Comparisons This section describes how xylem and phloem function in transport. As you read, write down statements about similarities and differences between the functions of these two tissues.

Water Transport

Recall that xylem tissue forms a continuous set of tubes that stretch from roots through stems and out into the spongy mesophyll of leaves. This set of tubes forms a complex transport system within a plant. The transport is carried out by a subsystem of cells and tissues. Active transport and root pressure cause water to move from soil into plant roots. Root pressure alone, however, cannot account for the movement of water and dissolved materials throughout an entire plant. Obviously, other forces are at work. These include capillary action and transpiration. **The combination of root pressure, capillary action, and transpiration provides enough force to move water through the xylem tissue of even the tallest plant.** As you will learn, transpiration is the most powerful of these forces.

Capillary Action Water molecules are attracted to one another by a force called cohesion. Recall from Chapter 2 that cohesion is the attraction of molecules of the same substance to each other. Because of cohesion, water molecules have a tendency to form hydrogen bonds with each other. Water molecules can also form hydrogen bonds with other substances.This results from a force called **adhesion,** which is attraction between unlike molecules. Place empty glass tubes of various widths into a dish of water, as shown in **Figure 23–21,** and you will see both forces at work. The tendency of water to rise in a thin tube is called **capillary action.** Water is attracted to the walls of the tube, and water molecules are attracted to one another. The thinner the tube, the higher the water will rise inside it.

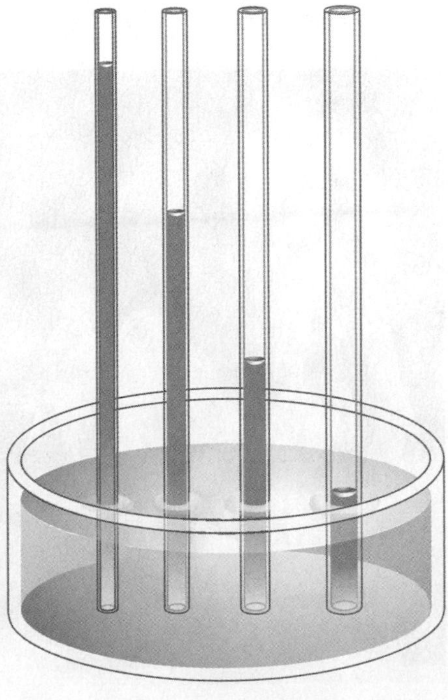

▶ **Figure 23–21** Capillary action—the result of water molecules' ability to stick to one another and to the walls of a tube—contributes to the movement of water up the cells of xylem tissue. As shown here, capillary action causes water to move much higher in a narrow tube than in a wide tube. **Applying Concepts** *Which force—adhesion or cohesion—causes the water to stick to the walls of the glass tube?*

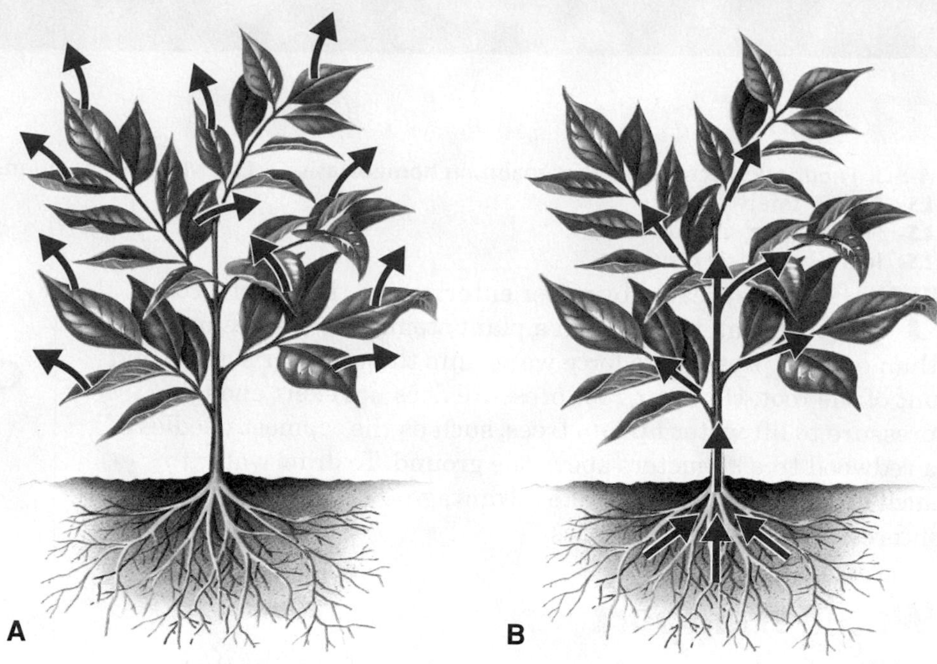

▶ **Figure 23–22** **Root pressure, capillary action, and transpiration contribute to the movement of water within a plant.** Transpiration is the movement of water molecules out of leaves. The faster water evaporates from a plant, shown in A, the stronger the pull of water upward from the roots, shown in B.

What does capillary action have to do with water movement through xylem? Recall that there are two main types of xylem tissue in flowering plants: tracheids and vessel elements. Both tracheids and vessel elements form hollow connected tubes similar to a thin, glass capillary tube. Capillary action in the tubelike structures formed by both types of cells causes water to rise well above the level of the ground.

Transpiration For trees and other tall plants, the combination of root pressure and capillary action does not provide enough force to lift water to the topmost branches and leaves. The major force in water transport is provided by the evaporation of water from leaves during transpiration. When water is lost through transpiration, osmotic pressure moves water out of the vascular tissue of the leaf, as shown in **Figure 23–22.** Then, like a locomotive pulling a train with hundreds of cars, the movement of water out of the leaf "pulls" water upward through the vascular system all the way from the roots. This process is known as transpirational pull.

How important is transpirational pull? On a hot day, even a small tree may lose as much as 100 liters of water to transpiration. The hotter and drier the air, and the windier the day, the greater the amount of water lost. As a result of this water loss, the plant draws up even more water from the roots.

Controlling Transpiration The leaf's gas exchange subsystem helps to maintain homeostasis by keeping the water content of the leaf relatively constant. For example, when water is abundant, it flows into the leaf, raising water pressure in the guard cells, which then open the stomata. Excess water is then lost through the open stomata by transpiration. When water is scarce, the opposite occurs. Water pressure in the leaf falls, and the guard cells respond by closing the stomata. This reduces further water loss by limiting transpiration.

▼ **Figure 23–23** In hot, dry conditions, transpiration can lead to water loss that is severe enough to cause wilting. High transpiration rates can cause a loss of osmotic pressure in a plant's cells. In leaves, this loss of pressure causes guard cells to close, thereby slowing down the rate of transpiration. **Inferring** *Why do hot, dry conditions cause transpiration rates to increase?*

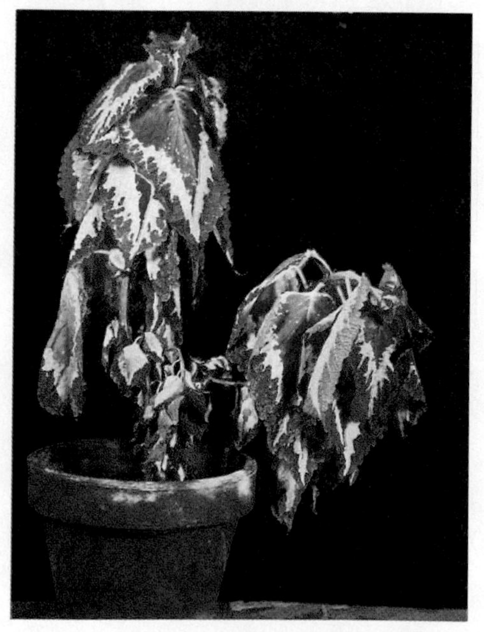

Quick Lab

What is the role of leaves in transpiration?

Materials 3 stalks of celery with leaves, plastic container, food coloring, petroleum jelly, cotton swab, scalpel, metric ruler

Procedure 

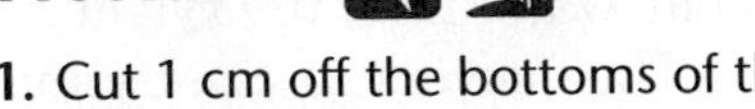

1. Cut 1 cm off the bottoms of the celery stalks. **CAUTION:** *Use the scalpel with care.*
2. Remove the leaves from one stalk. Use a cotton swab to apply petroleum jelly to both sides of all the leaves on another stalk. Place all three stalks into a plastic container containing about 200 mL of water and food coloring.
3. Place the plastic container in a sunny location. Observe the celery at the end of the class and the next day. Record your observations each day.

Analyze and Conclude

1. **Observing** In which stalk did the colored water rise the most? The least?
2. **Inferring** What effect did the petroleum jelly have on transpiration? What part of the leaf did the petroleum jelly affect?
3. **Drawing Conclusions** How are leaves involved in transpiration?

Transpiration and Wilting Osmotic pressure keeps a plant's leaves and stems rigid, or stiff. High transpiration rates can lead to wilting, shown in **Figure 23–23.** Wilting results from the loss of water—and therefore of the pressure in a plant's cells. Without this internal pressure to support them, the plant's cell walls bend inward, and the plant's leaves and stems wilt. When a leaf wilts, its stomata close. As a result, transpiration slows down significantly. Thus, wilting helps a plant to conserve water.

What happens when a plant wilts?

Nutrient Transport

You have learned how transpiration *pulls* water upward through a plant. But most plant nutrients, including sugars, minerals, and complex organic compounds, are *pushed* through phloem.

Functions of Phloem Many plants pump sugars into their fruits. This action often requires moving sugars out of leaves or roots into stems, and then through stems to the fruits. All of this movement takes place in the phloem. In cold climates, many plants pump food down into their roots for winter storage. This stored food must be moved back into the trunk and branches of the plant before growth begins again in the spring. Phloem carries out this seasonal movement of sugars within a plant.

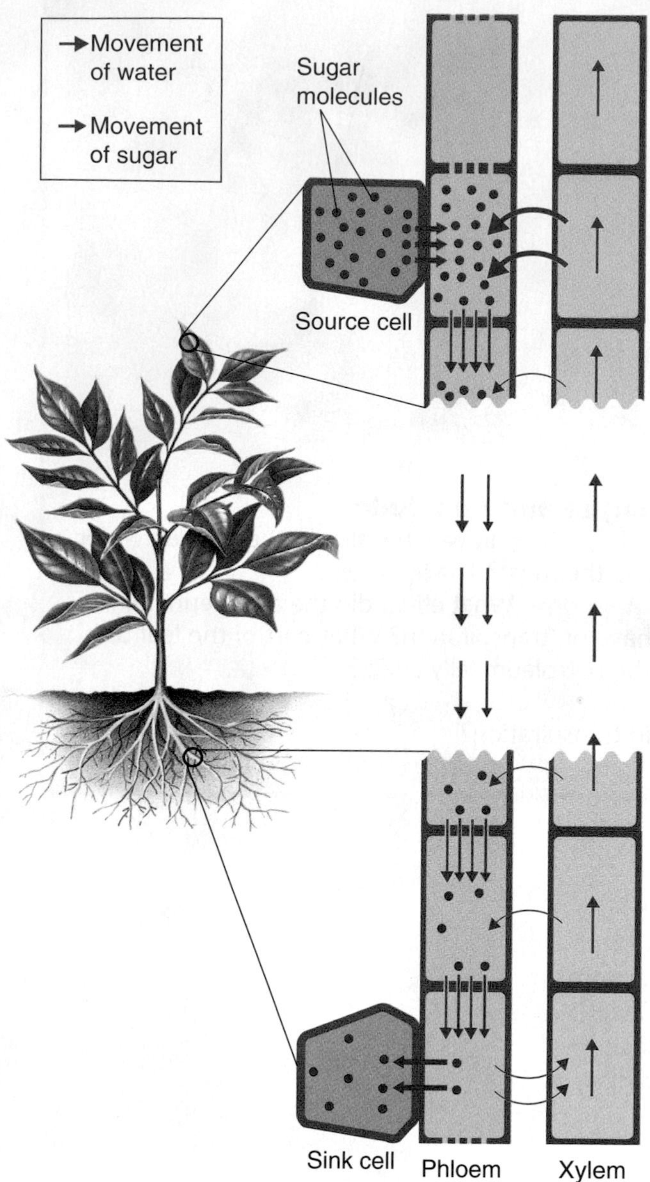

Movement From Source to Sink A process of phloem transport moves sugars through a plant from a source to a sink. The source can be any cell in which sugars are produced by photosynthesis. The sink is a cell where the sugars are used or stored. How does phloem transport take place?

One idea put forward by many plant scientists is called the **pressure-flow hypothesis.** As you can see in **Figure 23–24,** sugars are pumped into the phloem at one point, called the source. For example, sugars produced by photosynthesis may move from a leaf. As concentrations of sugar increase in the phloem, water from the xylem moves in by osmosis. This movement causes an increase in pressure at that point, forcing nutrient-rich fluid to move through the phloem away from nutrient-producing regions and toward a region that uses these nutrients, called the sink.

Conversely, if part of a plant actively absorbs nutrients from the phloem, osmosis causes water to follow. This movement of water decreases pressure and causes a movement of fluid in the phloem toward the sink. **When nutrients are pumped into or removed from the phloem system, the change in concentration causes a movement of fluid in that same direction. As a result, phloem is able to move nutrients in either direction to meet the nutritional needs of the plant.**

◀ **Figure 23–24** The diagram shows the movement of sugars and water throughout the phloem and xylem as explained by the pressure-flow hypothesis. Materials move from a source cell, where photosynthesis produces a high concentration of sugars, to a sink cell, where sugars are lower in concentration. **Interpreting Graphics** *What is the source of the water that forces nutrients through phloem tissue?*

23–5 Section Assessment

1. **Key Concept** What three processes work together to cause water to flow upward through a plant?
2. **Key Concept** How does the pressure-flow hypothesis explain the function of phloem?
3. Why is capillary action insufficient to move water through a plant?
4. **Critical Thinking Predicting** If a plant's stomata close on a hot, dry day, how could this affect the plant's rate of photosynthesis?

Sharpen Your Skills

Designing Experiments
Devise an experiment to measure the rate of transpiration from a plant cutting. Describe results you would expect with changes in temperature, humidity, and light.

Exploration

Identifying the Growth Zones in a Plant

Do roots grow at the tips or do existing root tissues grow longer? In this investigation, you will answer this question by examining root growth.

Problem In which part of a root does most growth occur?

Materials

- 150-mL beaker
- metric ruler
- paper towels
- India ink
- 4 large seeds
- toothpick
- petri dish

Skills Measuring, Analyzing Data

Procedure

1. Fill a 150-mL beaker loosely with crumpled paper towels. Wet the towels with water.
2. Place 4 seeds between the towels and the sides of the beaker. Cover the beaker with a petri dish. Keep the paper towels damp.
3. On a separate sheet of paper, make a copy of the data table shown.
4. When the roots appear, gently place one seedling on a wet paper towel. Use a ruler to measure the length of the root. Record this length in your copy of the data table. Use another sprout if this one becomes damaged.
5. Pick up a very small drop of India ink on the tip of a toothpick. Use the toothpick to mark the root with small dots of ink 3, 10, 15, and 20 mm from the root tip. **CAUTION:** *India ink stains skin and clothing.*
6. Allow the ink dots to dry. Return the sprout to the beaker and replace the cover. Keep the paper towels in the beaker moist.
7. **Predicting** Record your prediction of which part of the root will grow the most over the next 3 days. Wash your hands before you leave the lab.
8. **Measuring** Measure precisely and record the length of the root and the positions of the dots in your data table each day for 3 days. Wash your hands.

Data Table

Days	Position of Mark (mm from root tip)				Root Length (mm)
	3	10	15	20	
1					
2					
3					

Analyze and Conclude

1. **Observing** Did most of the growth occur at the tip of the root (0–3 mm) or farther up?
2. **Analyzing Data** Which part of the root grew the most?
3. **Drawing Conclusions** Do your data support the idea that roots grow mostly at their tips or that growth farther up the root pushes the root tip through the soil?

Go Further

Designing Experiments Design a similar experiment to determine where most stem growth occurs. With your teacher's permission, perform your experiment.

For: Data sharing
Visit: PHSchool.com
Web Code: cbd-7235

Share Your Data Online Enter your data on the growth of the roots. Then, look at the data entered by other students. Based on the available data, which part of the root grew the most? Which grew the least? Why might your data differ from those of other students?

Chapter 23 Study Guide

23–1 Specialized Tissues in Plants

Key Concepts

- Three of the principal organs of seed plants are roots, stems, and leaves.
- Plants consist of three tissue systems: dermal tissue, vascular tissue, and ground tissue.
- Vascular tissue contains several different cell types. Xylem consists of tracheids and vessel elements, and phloem consists of sieve tube elements and companion cells.
- Meristematic tissue is the only plant tissue that produces new cells by mitosis.

Vocabulary

epidermal cell, p. 580 • vessel element, p. 581
sieve tube element, p. 581
companion cell, p. 581 • parenchyma, p. 582
collenchyma, p. 582 • sclerenchyma, p. 582
meristem, p. 582 • meristematic tissue, p. 582
apical meristem, p. 582 • differentiation, p. 583

23–2 Roots

Key Concepts

- The two main types of roots are taproots, found mainly in dicots, and fibrous roots, found mainly in monocots.
- A mature root has an outside layer of epidermal cells and a central cylinder of vascular tissue separated by a large area of ground tissue called the cortex.
- Roots anchor a plant in the ground and absorb water and dissolved nutrients from the soil.

Vocabulary

taproot, p. 584 • fibrous root, p. 584
root hair, p. 585 • cortex, p. 585
endodermis, p. 585 • vascular cylinder, p. 585
root cap, p. 585 • Casparian strip, p. 587

23–3 Stems

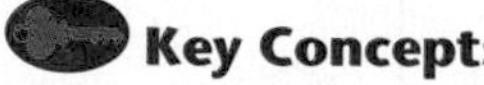

Key Concepts

- Stems have three important functions: They produce leaves, branches, and flowers; they hold leaves up in the sunlight; and they transport various substances between roots and leaves.
- In monocots, vascular bundles are scattered throughout the stem. In dicots and most gymnosperms, vascular bundles are arranged in a cylinder.
- In all seed plants, primary growth of stems is produced by cell divisions in the apical meristem.
- In conifers and dicots, secondary growth takes place in lateral meristematic tissues called the vascular cambium and cork cambium.

Vocabulary

node, p. 589 • internode, p. 589
bud, p. 589 • vascular bundle, p. 590
pith, p. 590 • primary growth, p. 590
secondary growth, p. 591
vascular cambium, p. 591 • cork cambium, p. 591
heartwood, p. 592 • sapwood, p. 592 • bark, p. 593

23–4 Leaves

Key Concepts

- The structure of a leaf is optimized for absorbing light and carrying out photosynthesis.
- Plants keep their stomata open just enough to allow photosynthesis to take place but not so much that they lose an excessive amount of water.

Vocabulary

blade, p. 595 • petiole, p. 595
mesophyll, p. 596 • palisade mesophyll, p. 596
spongy mesophyll, p. 596 • stoma, p. 596
guard cell, p. 596 • transpiration, p. 596

23–5 Transport in Plants

Key Concepts

- Root pressure, capillary action, and transpiration work together to move water through the xylem tissue of even the tallest plant.
- When nutrients are pumped into or removed from the phloem system, the change in concentration causes a movement of fluid in that same direction. As a result, phloem is able to move nutrients in either direction to meet the nutritional needs of the plant.

Vocabulary

adhesion, p. 599 • capillary action, p. 599
pressure-flow hypothesis, p. 602

Thinking Visually

Make a flowchart of the tissues through which water passes, from when it enters a plant at the root until it escapes from the plant through the leaves. Use the following terms in your flowchart: *spongy mesophyll, root epidermis, stomata, cortex, endodermis, xylem.*

Preparing for the Living Environment Exam

Blue questions emphasize Regents Exam content

Chapter 23

Part A

Multiple Choice

For each statement or question, select the number of the word or expression that, of those given, best completes the statement or answers the question.

1 The plant structure that is responsible for support of the plant and for carrying nutrients between different parts of the plant is the
(1) root (3) stem
(2) leaf (4) flower

2 Which type of plant tissue would be found only in the circled areas of the plant shown below?
(1) meristematic tissue
(2) vascular tissue
(3) dermal tissue
(4) ground tissue

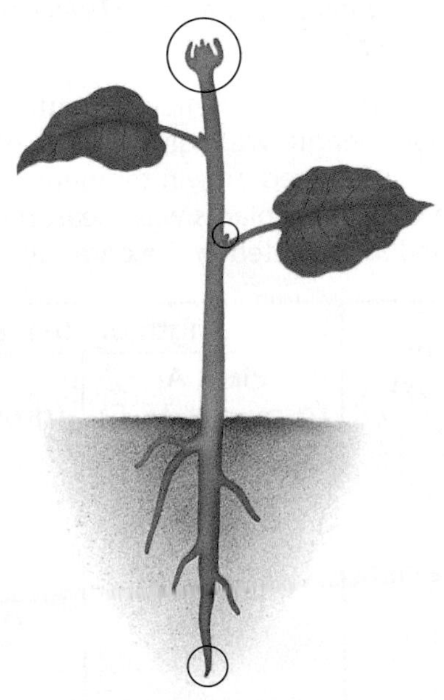

3 The dissolved sugars produced in the leaves of a maple tree move to the tree's roots through the
(1) xylem (3) phloem
(2) guard cells (4) epidermal cells

4 Tracheids and vessel elements make up
(1) phloem (3) trichomes
(2) xylem (4) meristem

5 Within a leaf, there are many air spaces between the cells of the
(1) palisade layer (3) spongy mesophyll
(2) meristem (4) cuticle

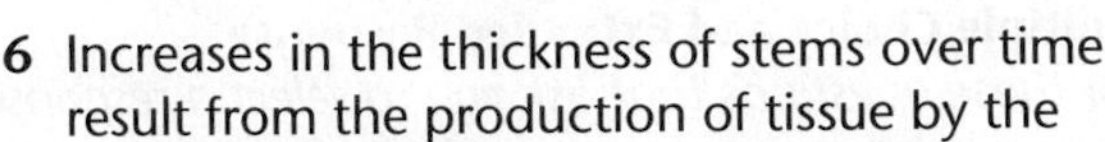

6 Increases in the thickness of stems over time result from the production of tissue by the
(1) vascular cambium
(2) cortex
(3) apical meristem
(4) pith

7 Guard cells open and close pores in leaves to regulate
(1) water loss and gas exchange
(2) growth of the apical meristem
(3) the uptake of plant nutrients from the soil
(4) the number of chloroplasts present in the leaf

8 The rise of water in a tall plant depends on root pressure and
(1) osmosis
(2) evaporation
(3) capillary action
(4) transpiration pull

9 Tree bark is made of which tissues?
(1) xylem and phloem, only
(2) cork and vascular cambium, only
(3) heartwood and sapwood
(4) phloem, cork, and cork cambium

10 Where does most of the photosynthesis occur in a plant?
(1) stomata
(2) guard cells
(3) vascular cambium
(4) mesophyll tissue

For questions 11 and 12, complete each analogy by selecting the correct letter. In analogies, A : B :: C : means "A is to B as C is to ___?___."

11 Ground tissue : sclerenchyma :: vascular tissue :
(1) cuticle (3) apical meristem
(2) xylem (4) collenchyma

12 Taproot : carrot :: fibrous root :
(1) dandelion (3) beet
(2) grass (4) radish

Test-Taking Tip When presented with questions that are related to data in a table, study each column and row of the table for the information you need to answer the questions.

Preparing for the Living Environment Exam

Part B

Multiple Choice and Extended Response
For those questions that ask you to select a response, choose the one that best completes the statement or answers the question. For all others follow the directions given.

13 List *two* different kinds of vascular tissue found in plants and state one function of each.

Base your answers to questions 14 through 16 on the information below and on your knowledge of biology.

A student compared the average number of stomata (pores regulated by guard cells) on the top side and the underside of leaves obtained from different plant species growing in the same area. His data are summarized in the table below.

Average Number of Stomata (per square mm)

Plant	Top Surfaces of Leaves	Bottom Surfaces of Leaves
Pumpkin	29	275
Tomato	12	122
Bean	40	288

14 What generalization can be made based on the data?
(1) All plants have more stomata on the top side of their leaves than on the bottom side.
(2) Plants have fewer stomata on the top side of their leaves than on the bottom side.
(3) Some plants have more stomata on the top side of their leaves than on the bottom side.
(4) The number of stomata varies greatly from plant to plant.

15 Pumpkins, tomatoes, and beans grow in direct sunlight. Assuming the plants receive plenty of water, stomata on the lower surface of their leaves would be regulated by guard cells to
(1) be always closed
(2) close only during daylight hours
(3) never close at night
(4) stay open during daylight hours

16 Describe *three* steps the student should follow when preparing a wet mount slide of the leaf tissue being examined.

17 A classmate gave you two slides that had no labels. She told you that one is a dicot root cross section and the other a dicot stem cross section. Explain how you would be able to distinguish the root from the stem.

18 State *two* ways root hairs are important to plants.

19 Describe the function of the vascular cambium in the secondary growth of stems.

20 List the *three* main functions of leaves.

21 Cork is a lightweight, spongy material made from the outer bark of a type of oak tree. Explain how cork must be removed to avoid killing the tree.

22 Explain why maple trees are tapped for their sugar in the early spring rather than in the summer or autumn.

Base your answers to questions 23 through 25 on the information and data table below and on your knowledge of biology.

For nine days, two genetically identical plants of the same stem length were grown in identical environments that differed only in temperature. The stem length of the two plants was measured and recorded as indicated in the data table below.

Time (days)	Length of Stem (mm)	
	Plant A (grown at 15°C)	Plant B (grown at 25°C)
1	15	21
3	30	50
5	44	78
7	53	96
9	54	99

23 Use the information in the data table to construct a line graph on your own graph paper.
- Label each axis, including units. Place time on the horizontal axis and length on the vertical axis.
- Mark an appropriate scale on each axis.
- Plot the data for Plant A (grown at 15°C) on the graph. Surround each point with a small circle and connect the points.

- Plot the data for Plant B (grown at 25°C) on the graph. Surround each of the points with a small triangle and connect the points.

24 Which conclusion can be made from your graph and the information given in the data table?

(1) The growth rate of plant A was greater than the growth rate of plant B.
(2) The growth rate of plant B was greater than the growth rate of plant A.
(3) The growth rate of plant A was equal to the growth rate of plant B.
(4) Not enough information was obtained to make inferences about comparable growth rates.

25 Which plant would most likely survive if the environmental temperature decreased over time to 15°C? Explain your answer using data from the table.

Base your answers to questions 26 through 29 on the graph below and on your knowledge of biology.

During transpiration, water evaporates from the leaves of plants into the air.

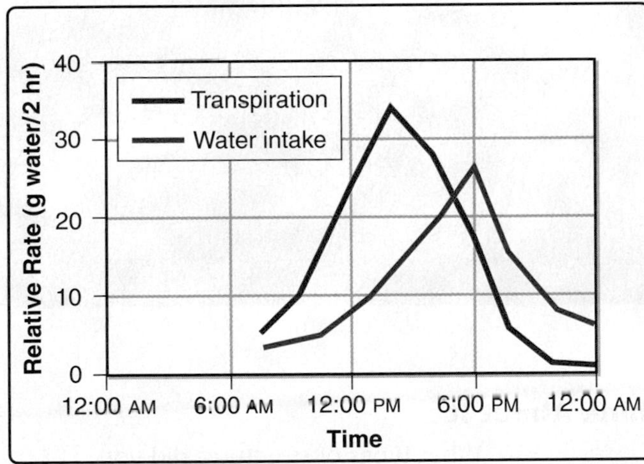

26 What does the graph illustrate?

27 During which span of time is the greatest amount of water lost through transpiration?

28 About how many grams of water are lost every two hours when the transpiration curve is at its highest peak?

29 Describe the relationship between transpiration and water intake.

30 The two main types of root systems found in plants are taproots and fibrous. Both are designed to anchor a plant in the ground and absorb water and dissolved nutrients. Compare taproots with fibrous roots. In your answer be sure to

- describe the advantages and disadvantages provided by each type of root
- identify a plant that has a taproot
- identify a plant that has a fibrous root system

Part C

Extended Response

Answer the questions or follow the directions given.

31 Explain how adhesion and cohesion are properties of water that are important in its movement up a plant.

32 During the nineteenth century, people often raised ferns and delicate plants in enclosed glass containers called Wardian cases. Although these types of plants normally required a great deal of water, plants grown in Wardian cases did not have to be watered for years. What is the most logical explanation for this? In your answer be sure to:

- explain how water in the Wardian cases could be recycled by the plants
- describe how evaporation and condensation would be involved

For: An interactive self-test
Visit: PHSchool.com
Web Code: cba-7230

CHAPTER 24

Reproduction of Seed Plants

Red nodding thistle flowers show a dramatic change as they undergo fertilization and seed development. At maturity, the seeds—each attached to long, white threads—detach from the flowers and are dispersed by wind.

Inquiry Activity

How do seeds and fruits vary?

Procedure  

1. Use a hand lens to examine a variety of seeds and fruits. (*Hint:* Review the material on seeds in Section 22–4.) Record your observations.
2. Place each seed in a petri dish and use a scalpel to cut the seed lengthwise. **CAUTION:** *Use care with sharp instruments.* Use a hand lens to examine the inside of each seed. Draw and label the structures you observe. Label the embryo of each seed.

Think About It

1. **Observing** What types of structures did you observe in all the seeds?
2. **Formulating Hypotheses** A seed contains stored nutrients that nourish the new plant until it becomes autotrophic. Which part of the seed might contain these nutrients?
3. **Predicting** What structures did you observe that could help spread the offspring of a plant over a larger area? Explain your answer.

24–1 Reproduction With Cones and Flowers

4-2.1 Sexual reproduction involves two parents
4-4.1 Meiosis
LS- Make observations and state an appropriate hypothesis
LS- Dissection, use of compound microscope
LS- Prepare wet mount slides, follow safety rules

Guide for Reading

Key Concepts
- What are the reproductive structures of gymnosperms and angiosperms?
- How does pollination differ between angiosperms and gymnosperms?

Vocabulary
pollen cone • seed cone ovule • pollen tube sepal • petal • stamen filament • anther • carpel ovary • style • stigma embryo sac • endosperm double fertilization

Reading Strategy: Making Comparisons
Before you read, preview **Figure 24–4** and **Figure 24–7.** As you read, compare the life cycles of gymnosperms and angiosperms.

Seed plants are well adapted to the demands of life on land, especially in how they reproduce. The gametes of seedless plants, such as ferns and mosses, need water for fertilization to be successful. Water allows gametes to move from plant to plant. The gametes of seed plants, however, can achieve fertilization even when the plants are not wet from rain or dew. So, they can reproduce nearly anywhere. The way in which seed plants reproduce has allowed them to survive the dry conditions on land.

Alternation of Generations

All plants have a life cycle in which a diploid sporophyte generation alternates with a haploid gametophyte generation. Gametophyte plants produce male and female gametes—sperm and eggs. When the gametes join, they form a zygote that begins the next sporophyte generation. In some plants, the two stages of the life cycle are distinct, independent plants. In most ferns, for instance, the gametophyte is a small, heart-shaped plant that grows close to the ground. The sporophyte is the familiar fern plant itself made up of graceful fronds.

Where are these two generations in seed plants? You may remember from Mendel's work on peas that such plants are diploid. Therefore, in seed plants, the familiar, recognizable form of the plant is the diploid sporophyte.

If the sporophyte is what we recognize as the plant, then where is the gametophyte? The answer may surprise you. As shown in **Figure 24–1,** the gametophytes of seed plants are actually hidden deep within tissues of the sporophyte plant. In gymnosperms they are found inside cones, and in angiosperms they are found inside flowers. Cones and flowers represent two different methods of reproduction.

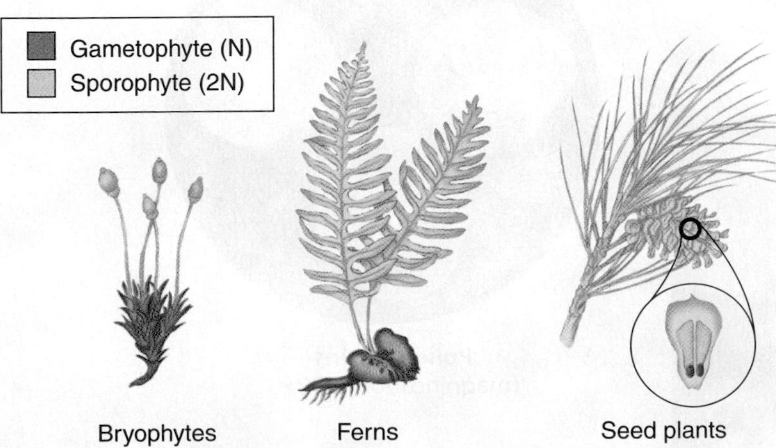

◀ **Figure 24–1** An important trend in plant evolution is the reduction of the gametophyte and the increasing size of the sporophyte. Bryophytes consist of a relatively large gametophyte and smaller sporophytes, which include a capsule and stalk. Seedless vascular plants, such as ferns, have a small gametophyte and a larger sporophyte. Seed plants have an even smaller gametophyte that is contained within sporophyte tissues. **Interpreting Graphics** *How does the relative size of the haploid and diploid stages of plants differ between bryophytes and seed plants?*

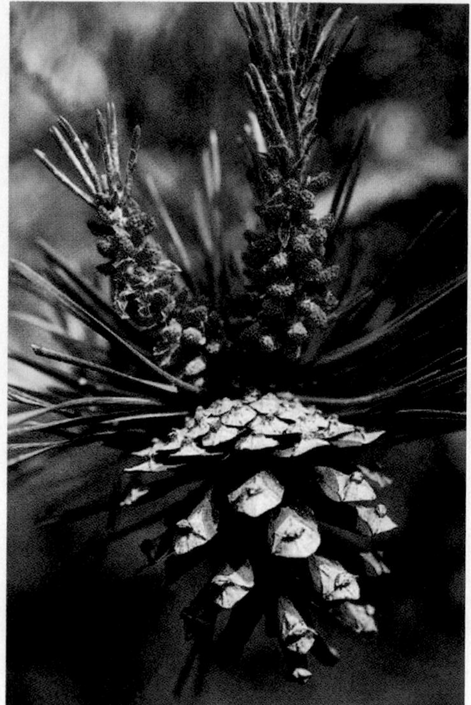

▲ **Figure 24–2** **Reproduction in gymnosperms takes place in structures called cones.** In this pine tree, pollen cones, shown on the top, produce male gametophytes, which are pollen grains. Seed cones, such as the one shown on the bottom, produce female gametophytes that develop into a new embryo following fertilization.

Life Cycle of Gymnosperms

Pine trees and other gymnosperms are diploid sporophytes. As you will see, this sporophyte develops from a zygote that is contained within a seed. How and where is this seed produced? **Reproduction in gymnosperms takes place in cones, which are produced by a mature sporophyte plant.** Gymnosperms produce two types of cones: pollen cones and seed cones.

Pollen Cones and Seed Cones **Pollen cones,** shown in **Figure 24–2,** are also called male cones. Pollen cones produce the male gametophytes, which are called pollen grains. As tiny as it is, the pollen grain makes up the entire male gametophyte stage of the gymnosperm life cycle. One of the haploid nuclei in the pollen grain will divide later to produce two sperm nuclei.

The more familiar **seed cones,** which produce female gametophytes, are generally much larger than pollen cones. Near the base of each scale are two **ovules** in which the female gametophytes develop. Within the ovules, meiosis produces haploid cells that grow and divide to produce female gametophytes. These gametophytes may contain hundreds or thousands of cells. When mature, each gametophyte contains a few large egg cells, each ready for fertilization by sperm nuclei.

Pollination The gymnosperm life cycle typically takes two years to complete. The cycle begins in the spring as male cones release enormous numbers of pollen grains. This pollen is carried by the wind, as shown in **Figure 24–3.** Some of these pollen grains reach female cones. There, some pollen grains are caught in a sticky secretion on one of the scales of the female cone. This sticky material, known as a pollination drop, ensures that pollen grains stay on the female cone.

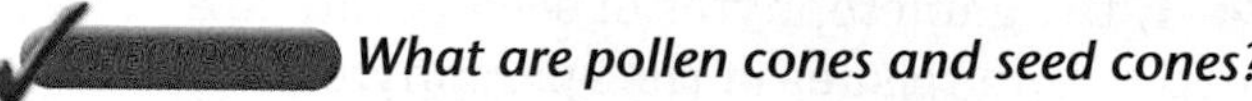

What are pollen cones and seed cones?

Figure 24–3 Pollen grains are male gametophytes. Pollen is carried by the wind until it reaches a female cone. **Inferring** *Male and female cones are distributed on a plant such that pollen usually lands on a different plant from where it started. Why might this strategy have evolved?*

Pollen Grains
(magnification: 750×)

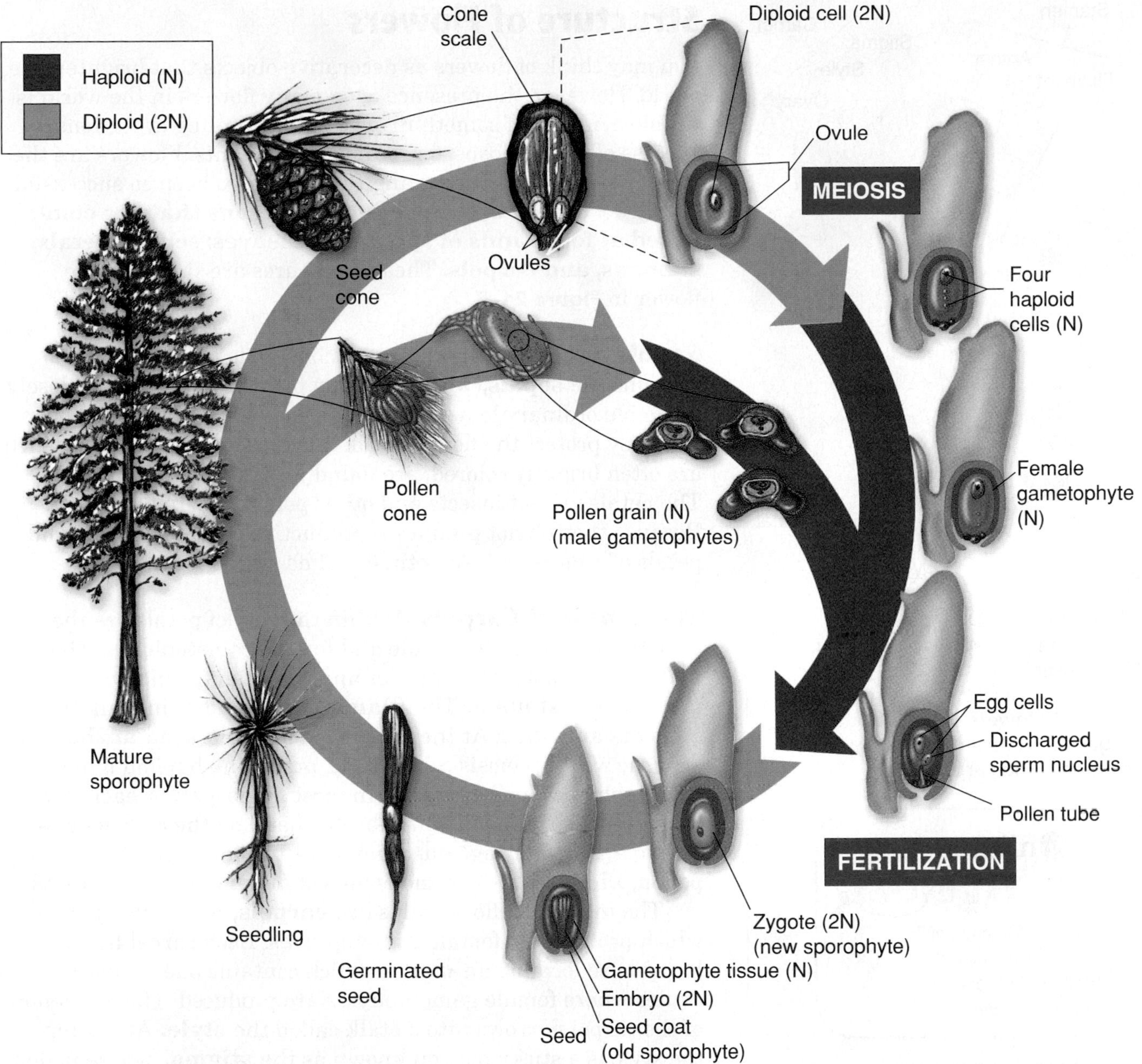

▲ Figure 24–4 This illustration shows the life cycle of a typical gymnosperm. A pine tree—the mature sporophyte—produces male and female cones. Male cones produce pollen, and female cones produce ovules located on cone scales. If an egg is fertilized by the sperm, it becomes a zygote that is nourished by the female cone. In time, the zygote develops into a new sporophyte plant. **Classifying** ***Classify each of the following terms as to whether they belong to the haploid or diploid stage of the pine tree's life cycle: pollen tube, seed cone, embryo, ovule, seedling.***

Fertilization and Development If a pollen grain lands near an ovule, the grain splits open and begins to grow a structure called a **pollen tube,** which contains two haploid sperm nuclei. Once the pollen tube reaches the female gametophyte, one sperm nucleus disintegrates, and the other fertilizes the egg contained within the female gametophyte. If sperm from another pollen tube reaches the female gametophyte, more than one egg cell may be fertilized, but just one embryo develops. As shown in **Figure 24–4**, fertilization produces a diploid zygote—the new sporophyte plant. This zygote grows into an embryo. During this time, it is encased within what will soon develop into a seed. The seed consists of three generations of the life cycle. The outer seed coat is part of the old sporophyte generation, the haploid cells surrounding the embryo are part of the female gametophyte, and the embryo is the new sporophyte plant.

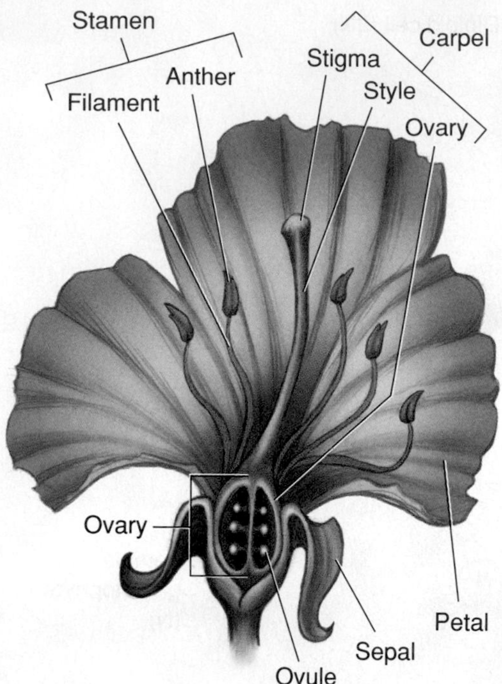

▲ **Figure 24–5** This diagram shows the parts of a typical flower. The flowers of some species, however, may not have all the parts shown here. **Flowers are reproductive organs that include sepals, petals, stamens, and carpels.**

Go Online
active art
For: The Structure of a Flower activity
Visit: PHSchool.com
Web Code: cbp-7241

Structure of Flowers

You may think of flowers as decorative objects that brighten the world. However, the presence of so many flowers in the world is visible evidence of something else—the stunning evolutionary success of the angiosperms, or flowering plants. Flowers are the key to understanding why angiosperms have been so successful.

Flowers are reproductive organs that are composed of four kinds of specialized leaves: sepals, petals, stamens, and carpels. These structures are shown in the flower in **Figure 24–5.**

Sepals and Petals The outermost circle of floral parts contains the **sepals,** which in many plants are green and closely resemble ordinary leaves. Sepals enclose the bud before it opens, and they protect the flower while it is developing. **Petals,** which are often brightly colored, are found just inside the sepals. The petals attract insects and other pollinators to the flower. Because they do not produce reproductive cells, the sepals and petals of a flower are sometimes called sterile leaves.

Stamens and Carpels Within the ring of petals are the structures that produce male and female gametophytes. The male parts consist of an anther and a filament, which together make up the **stamen.** The **filament** is a long, thin stalk that supports an anther. At the tip of each filament is an **anther,** an oval sac where meiosis takes place, producing haploid male gametophytes—pollen grains. In most angiosperms, each flower has several stamens. If you rub your hand on the anthers of a flower, a yellow-orange dust may stick to your skin. This is pollen, which consists of thousands of individual pollen grains.

The innermost floral parts are **carpels,** also called pistils, which produce the female gametophytes. Each carpel has a broad base forming an **ovary,** which contains one or more ovules where female gametophytes are produced. The diameter of the carpel narrows into a stalk called the **style.** At the top of the style is a sticky portion known as the **stigma,** where pollen grains frequently land. Some flowers have several carpels fused together to form a single reproductive structure called a compound carpel.

Quick Lab

What is the structure of a flower?

Materials flower, forceps, scalpel, microscope slide, dropper pipette, coverslips, microscope

Procedure  

1. Examine a flower carefully. Make a detailed drawing of the flower and label as many parts as you can. Note whether the anthers are above or below the stigma.
2. Remove an anther and place it on a slide. While holding the anther with forceps, use the scalpel to cut one or more thin slices across the anther. **CAUTION:** *Be careful with sharp tools.*
3. Lay the slices flat on the microscope slide and add a drop of water and a coverslip. Observe the slices with the microscope at low power. Make a labeled drawing of your observations.
4. Repeat steps 2 and 3 with the ovary.

Analyze and Conclude

1. **Observing** Are the anthers in this flower located above or below the stigma? How could this affect what happens to the pollen produced by the anthers? Explain your answer.
2. **Applying Concepts** What structures did you identify in the anther? What is the function of these structures?
3. **Applying Concepts** What structures did you identify in the ovary? What is the function of these structures?
4. **Drawing Conclusions** Which parts of the flower will become the seeds? The fruit?

Flowers vary greatly in shape, color, and size, as shown in **Figure 24–6.** A typical flower produces both male and female gametophytes. In some plants, however, male and female gametophytes are produced in separate flowers on the same individual. Corn, for example, has separate male and female flowers on the same plant. The tassel is a flower that produces male gametophytes, and the silk is the style of a flower that contains the female gametophyte. In other cases, many flowers grow together to form a composite structure that looks like a single flower, as shown in the sunflower.

CHECKPOINT *What are the male structures in a typical flower? The female structures?*

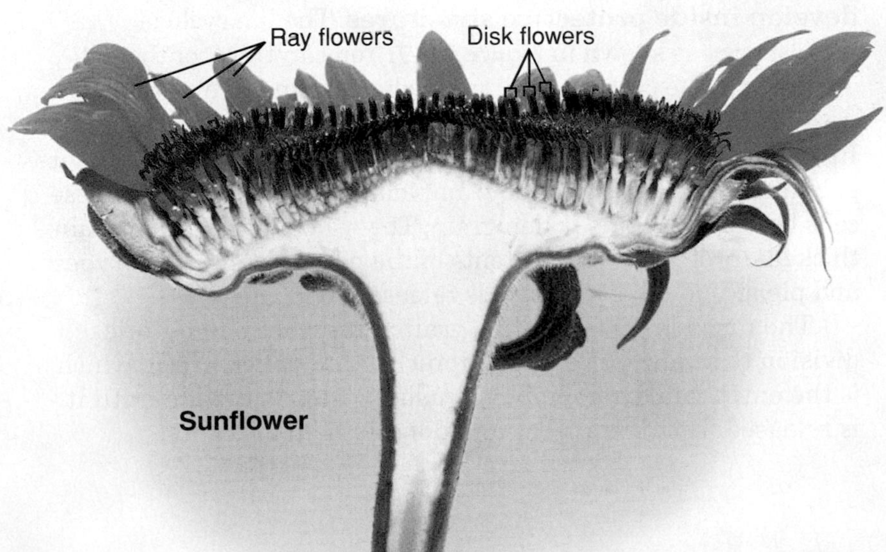

Figure 24–6 Flowers vary enormously in structure. The tulip has only a single carpel, whereas the wild rose has many carpels. Some flowerlike structures are actually clusters of many individual flowers. In the sunflower, disk flowers toward the inside of the cluster are reproductive, whereas ray flowers toward the outside are nonreproductive and form what look like petals. **Formulating Hypotheses** ***How might it be an advantage for a plant to have many flowers together in a single structure?***

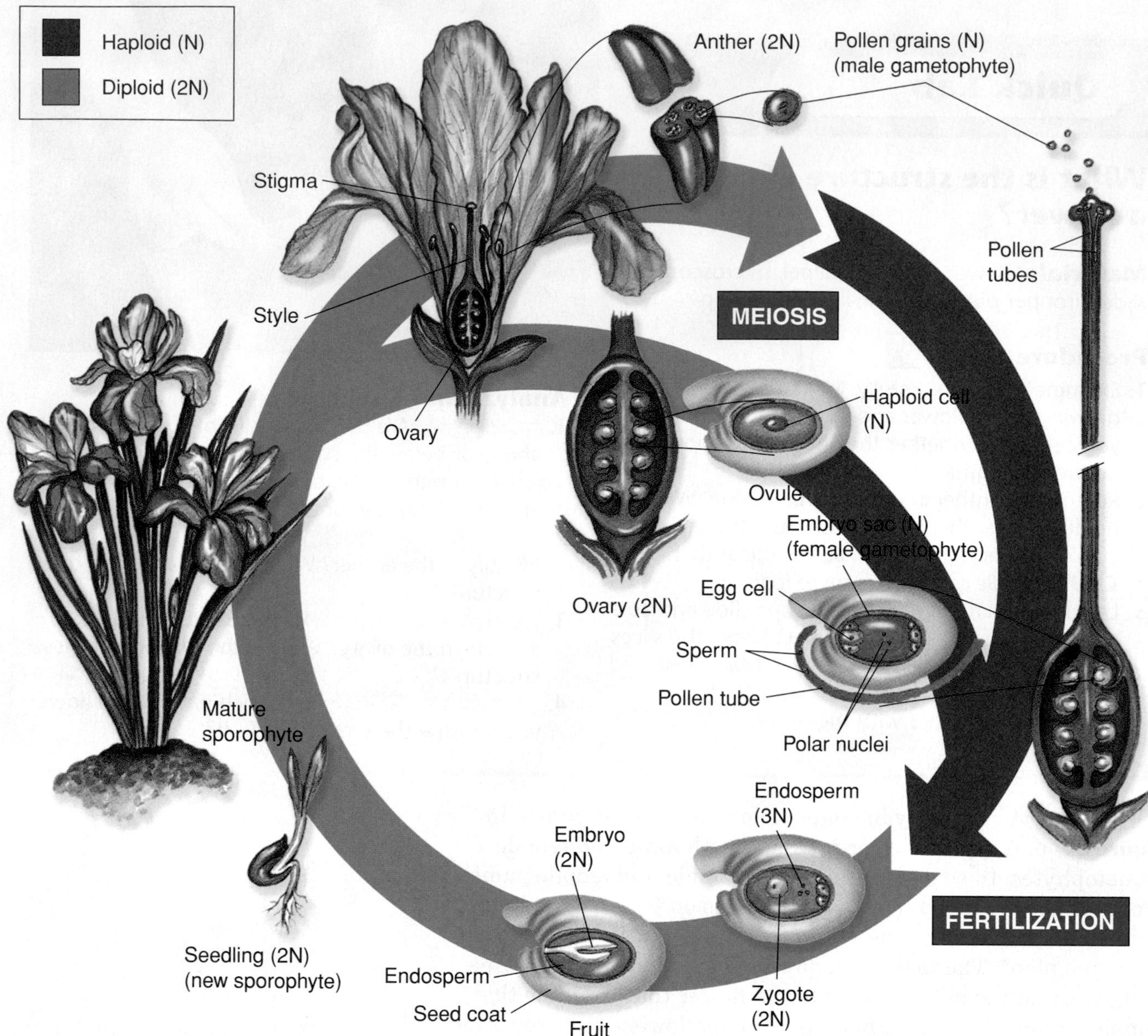

▲ **Figure 24–7** This illustration shows the life cycle of a typical angiosperm—an iris. The developing seeds of a flowering plant are protected and nourished inside the ovary, which is located at the base of the flower. **Reproduction in angiosperms takes place within the flower. After pollination, the seeds of angiosperms develop inside protective structures.**

Life Cycle of Angiosperms

Reproduction in angiosperms takes place within the flower. Following pollination and fertilization, the seeds develop inside protective structures. The life cycle of angiosperms is shown in **Figure 24–7.** You can think of the angiosperm life cycle as beginning when the mature sporophyte produces flowers. Each flower contains anthers and an ovary. Inside the anthers—the male part of the flower—each cell undergoes meiosis and produces four haploid spore cells. Each of these cells becomes a single pollen grain. The wall of each pollen grain thickens, protecting the contents of the pollen grain from dryness and physical damage when it is released from the anther.

The nucleus of each pollen grain undergoes one mitotic division to produce two haploid nuclei. The pollen grain, which is the entire male gametophyte, usually stops growing until it is released from the anther and deposited on a stigma.

The ovary of the flower contains the ovules, in which the female gametophyte develops. A single diploid cell goes through meiosis to produce four haploid cells, three of which disintegrate. The remaining cell undergoes mitosis to produce eight nuclei. These eight nuclei and the surrounding membrane are called the **embryo sac.** The embryo sac, contained within the ovule, is the female gametophyte of a flowering plant. One of the eight nuclei, near the base of the gametophyte, is the egg nucleus—the female gamete. If fertilization takes place, this cell will become the zygote that grows into a new sporophyte plant. Inside the ovary, the cells of the growing embryo begin to differentiate. That is, they begin to specialize, developing from a ball of cells into an embryonic sporophyte. The new sporophyte, or seedling, is shown in **Figure 24–7.**

CHECKPOINT *Where does the female gametophyte develop?*

Pollination

Once the gametophytes have developed inside the flower, pollination takes place. **Most gymnosperms and some angiosperms are wind pollinated, whereas most angiosperms are pollinated by animals.** These animals, mainly insects, birds, and bats, carry pollen from one flower to another. Because wind pollination is less efficient than animal pollination, wind-pollinated plants, such as the oak tree in **Figure 24–8,** rely on favorable weather and sheer numbers to get pollen from one plant to another. Animal-pollinated plants have a variety of adaptations, such as bright colors and sweet nectar, to attract animals. Animals have evolved body shapes that enable them to reach nectar deep within certain flowers.

Insect pollination is beneficial to insects and other animals because it provides a dependable source of food—pollen and nectar. Plants also benefit because the insects take the pollen directly from flower to flower. Insect pollination is more efficient than wind pollination, giving insect-pollinated plants a greater chance of reproductive success. Botanists suggest that insect pollination is the factor largely responsible for the displacement of gymnosperms by angiosperms during the past 100 million years.

Figure 24–8 Most angiosperms are pollinated by animals, although some are pollinated by wind. The shape of a flower often indicates how it is pollinated. The flowers of an oak tree (A) are typical of wind-pollinated flowers in that they are small, are not brightly colored, and produce vast amounts of pollen. To attract insects and other animals, many animal-pollinated flowers are large and brightly colored. The rose flower (B) is pollinated by a variety of insects, whereas the trumpet creeper flower (C) has a tube shape that is adapted specifically to the long beak of a hummingbird.

Fertilization in Angiosperms

If a pollen grain lands on the stigma of an appropriate flower of the same species, it begins to grow a pollen tube. The generative nucleus within the pollen grain divides and forms two sperm nuclei. The pollen tube now contains a tube nucleus and two sperm nuclei. The pollen tube grows into the style. There, it eventually reaches the ovary and enters the ovule.

Inside the embryo sac, two distinct fertilizations take place. First, one of the sperm nuclei fuses with the egg nucleus to produce a diploid zygote. The zygote will grow into the new plant embryo. Second, the other sperm nucleus does something truly remarkable—it fuses with two polar nuclei in the embryo sac to form a triploid (3N) cell. This cell will grow into a food-rich tissue known as **endosperm,** which nourishes the seedling as it grows.

As shown in **Figure 24–9**, a seed of corn, a monocot, contains a rich supply of endosperm. In many dicots, including garden beans, the cotyledons absorb the endosperm as the seed develops. The cotyledons then serve as the stored food supply for the embryo when it begins to grow.

Because two fertilization events take place between the male and female gametophytes, this process is known as **double fertilization.** Double fertilization may be one of the reasons why the angiosperms have been so successful. Recall that in gymnosperms, the food reserve built up in seeds is produced before fertilization takes place. As a result, if an ovule is not fertilized, those resources are wasted. In angiosperms, if an ovule is not fertilized, the endosperm does not form, and food is not wasted by preparing for a nonexistent zygote.

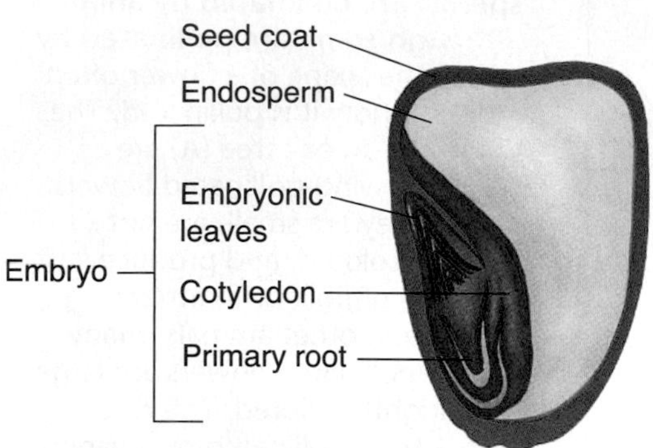

▲ **Figure 24–9** The endosperm of a corn seed develops through the process of double fertilization. After one sperm nucleus fertilizes the egg cell, the zygote forms. Then the other sperm nucleus fuses with the two polar nuclei to form a triploid cell, which develops into the endosperm. **Predicting** ***What will happen to the endosperm when the seed begins to grow?***

24–1 Section Assessment

1. **Key Concept** What are the reproductive structures of gymnosperms?
2. **Key Concept** Describe the flower and how it is involved in reproduction.
3. **Key Concept** Are angiosperms typically wind pollinated or animal pollinated? How does this process occur?
4. What is endosperm? Where does it form in a flowering plant?
5. **Critical Thinking Inferring** Many flowers have bright patterns of coloration that directly surround the reproductive structures. How might this type of coloration be advantageous to the plant?

Connecting Concepts

Alternation of Generations

Review the life cycle of the green alga *Chlamydomonas* in Section 20–4. Make a compare-and-contrast table comparing alternation of generations in seed plants and *Chlamydomonas*. Include which stage (haploid or diploid) of each organism's life cycle is dominant, the process by which zygotes form, and when meiosis occurs.

TECHNOLOGY & SOCIETY

Using Technology to Design Flowers

What's your favorite flower? Perhaps your answer was "the rose." Roses are the world's most popular ornamental flowers. They come in many colors. Chances are you've seen red, white, pink, or even yellow roses. But have you ever seen a blue rose? Probably not! Roses do not have the enzymes to produce blue pigments, so even the best efforts of plant breeders have not produced a blue rose.

What Makes a Flower?

Botanists have discovered that flower development is controlled by a series of genes. By manipulating these genes, scientists have produced plants that will flower earlier and much faster than normal.

Changing the color of a flower, however, has proved a little more difficult. Knowing that petunias often produce blue flowers, in 1991 Australian researchers isolated the gene for the enzyme that produces blue pigment. Then, they transferred this "blue gene" to a rose. To their disappointment, however, the new roses were just as red as ever. Apparently, flower color is a tricky and unpredictable business—particularly in roses—that involves complex interactions with other genes and pigments.

Violet Carnations?

When the Australian scientists turned from roses to carnations, they produced a carnation with unique violet flowers. Again, they inserted the gene from the blue petunias into a carnation plant. The result, shown in the photos, was a deep violet carnation unlike any ever seen in nature. In 1999, these genetically modified carnation plants were introduced for sale in Europe and the United States. A number of biotech companies are hoping to master the intricacies of color genetics in flowers. Someday, one of these companies may have what they've all been seeking—a blue rose.

Research and Decide

1. Use library or Internet resources to learn more about the relationship between genetics and new flower varieties. Then, choose a common food crop and find out how breeders have modified the plants to give the crop specific traits.
2. Suppose you are a plant geneticist and you want to create a new color of lily. Decide which flower color you would like to produce. Then, write down the scientific steps that you would take to produce the new flower color.

For: Links from the authors
Visit: PHSchool.com
Web Code: cbe-7241

24–2 Seed Development and Germination

Guide for Reading

Key Concepts
- How do fruits form?
- How are seeds dispersed?
- What factors influence the dormancy and germination of seeds?

Vocabulary
dormancy
germination

Reading Strategy: Summarizing As you read, take notes on the development, dispersal, dormancy, and germination of seeds. Write a few sentences summarizing each of these processes.

The development of the seed, which provides protection and nutrition for the embryo, was a major factor in the success of plants on land. The angiosperm seed, encased within a fruit formed by the ovary wall, offers even more. As you will see, by helping a seed get into the best possible location to start its new life, angiosperm seeds were immediately favored by natural selection.

Seed and Fruit Development

Once fertilization is complete, nutrients flow into the flower tissue and support the development of the growing embryo within the seed. **As angiosperm seeds mature, the ovary walls thicken to form a fruit that encloses the developing seeds.** A fruit is a ripened ovary that contains angiosperm seeds. Examples of fruits are shown in **Figure 24–10.** Parts of the ovule toughen to form a seed coat, which is the outer layer that protects the delicate embryo and its tiny food supply. The ovary wall then thickens and may join with other parts of the flower stem. These structures together form a fruit that encloses the seeds.

The term *fruit,* biologically speaking, applies to any seed that is enclosed within its embryo wall. The term applies to the things we usually think of as fruits, such as apples, grapes, and strawberries. However, foods such as peas, corn, beans, rice, cucumbers, and tomatoes, which we commonly call vegetables, are also fruits. Whether it tastes sweet or not, if it contains a seed enclosed inside the ovary wall, it is a fruit.

The ovary wall surrounding a simple fruit may be fleshy, as it is in grapes and tomatoes, or tough, like the pod of a bean. In some fruits, such as peaches and cherries, the inner wall of the ovary is attached rigidly to the surface of the seed. In others, such as the maple, the dry fruit forms an aerodynamic shape that helps the seed whirl gracefully down when it is released from the parent plant.

What is a fruit?

Figure 24–10 As seeds mature, the ovary walls thicken to form a fruit that encloses the developing seeds. Like the flowers from which they develop, fruits vary in structure. They can contain one seed, as in the lychee nut, or several, as in the apple. Fruits also have different amounts of tissue, which often relates to the mode of seed dispersal.

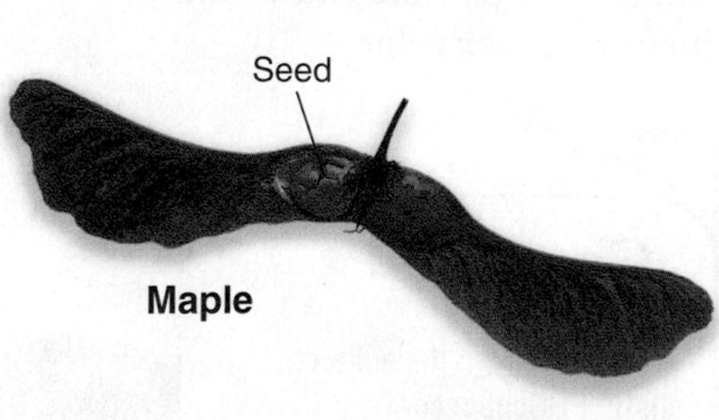

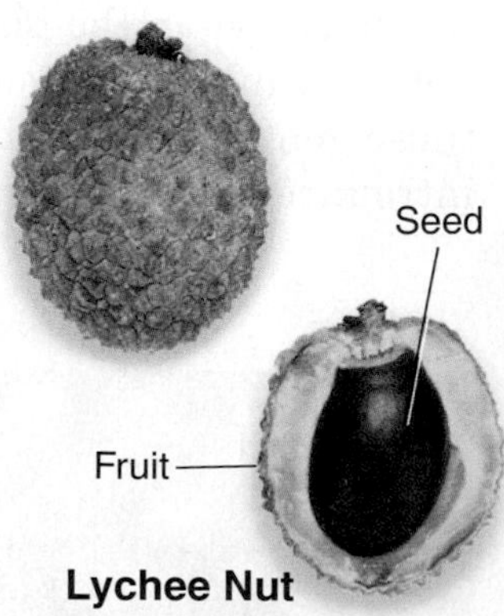

Seed Dispersal

What are fruits for, and why have they been favored by natural selection? They are not there to nourish the seedling—the endosperm does that. Why should an entire phylum of plants have seeds that are wrapped in an additional layer of nutrient-packed tissue—tissue that is later discarded when the fruit is released from the plant? It seems pointless, but in evolutionary terms, it makes all the sense in the world.

Think of the blackberries that grow wild in the forests of North America. Each seed is enclosed in a sweet, juicy fruit, making it a tasty treat for all kinds of birds and mammals. What good does all that sweetness do the fruit? All it does is get the seed eaten! Well, believe it or not, that's exactly the point.

Dispersal by Animals The seeds of many plants, especially those with sweet, fleshy fruits, are eaten by animals, as shown in **Figure 24–11.** The seeds are covered with tough coatings that protect them from digestive chemicals, enabling them to pass through an animal's digestive system unharmed. The seeds then sprout in the feces eliminated from the animal. **Seeds dispersed by animals are typically contained in fleshy, nutritious fruits.** These fruits provide nutrition for the animal and also help the plant disperse its seeds—often to areas where there is less competition with the parent plants.

▲ **Figure 24–11 Seeds that are dispersed by animals typically contain fleshy, sweet tissue.** A cedar waxwing feasts on mountain ash berries. Berries are enclosed in sugary tissue that is eaten by birds or other animals. Berries contain seeds that pass through the animal and are dispersed away from the parent plant.

Dispersal by Wind and Water Animals are not the only means by which plants can scatter their seeds. Seeds are also adapted for dispersal by wind and water. **Seeds dispersed by wind or water are typically lightweight, allowing them to be carried in the air or to float on the surface of the water.** The seeds of ash and maple trees are encased in winglike structures that spin and twirl as they are released, helping them glide considerable distances from their parent plants. Westerners are familiar with tumbleweed plants, shown in **Figure 24–12.** These plants break off at their roots and tumble along the dry plains, scattering their seeds as they are blown by the wind. An example of a seed that is dispersed by water is the coconut. This seed contains a liquid endosperm layer (the "milk" of the coconut). A coconut is buoyant enough to float in sea water within its protective coating for many weeks. Water dispersal is one reason for the success of this species in reaching remote islands.

▶ **Figure 24–12 Wind-dispersed seeds are typically lightweight.** Tumbleweed plants, which live in a hot, dry, and windy environment, release small seeds as the plants are blown along open stretches of land. **Inferring** *How do the structural adaptations of tumbleweeds enable them to survive?*

Analyzing Data

Temperature and Seed Germination

Arisaema dracontium—"green dragon"—is a plant that grows from the southern United States to Canada. The graph shows germination properties of *Arisaema* seeds gathered from Clinton, Ontario, and from Baton Rouge, Louisiana. Seeds from both locations were stored at two different temperatures: 3°C and 24°C. The graph indicates the rate of seed germination following storage at these different temperatures.

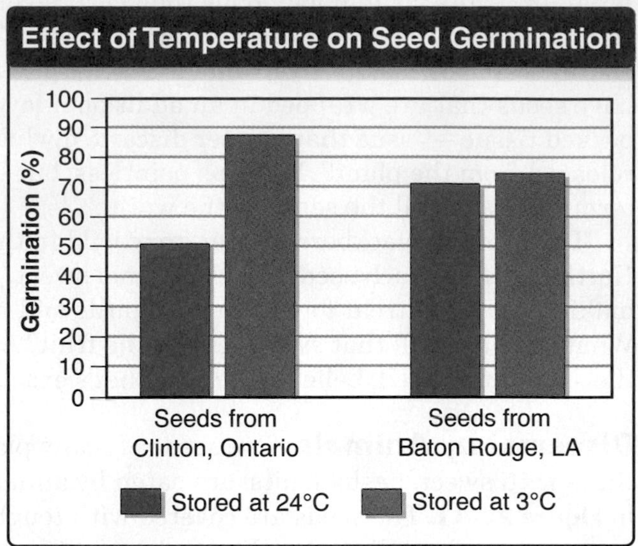

1. **Interpreting Graphics** What effect does chilling have on germination of seeds from Ontario? How does chilling affect the seeds from Louisiana?
2. **Formulating Hypotheses** Keeping in mind that annual temperatures are much lower in Ontario than in Louisiana, describe how the different rates of seed germination might be explained in terms of adaptation to the local climate.

Seed Dormancy

Some seeds sprout so rapidly that they are practically instant plants. Bean seeds are a good example. With proper amounts of water and warmth, a newly planted mature bean seed rapidly develops into a bean plant. But many seeds will not grow when they first mature. Instead, these seeds enter a period of **dormancy,** during which the embryo is alive but not growing. The length of dormancy varies in different plant species. 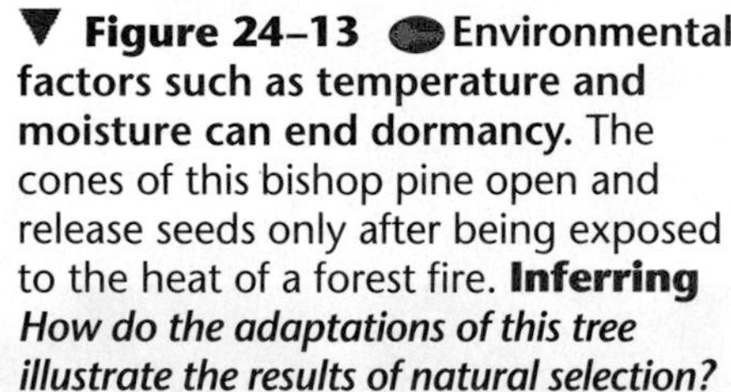 **Environmental factors such as temperature and moisture can cause a seed to end dormancy and germinate.**

Seed dormancy can be adaptive in several ways. It can allow for long-distance dispersal, as in a coconut that floats across the sea for weeks or even months until it washes ashore. It may also allow seeds to germinate under ideal growth conditions. The seeds of many temperate plants do not germinate during the summer or winter, since the extremes of temperature would make it impossible for seedlings to survive. Instead, most seeds germinate in the spring, when conditions are best for growth. The long period of cold temperatures during which the seeds are dormant is required before growth can begin.

Other environmental conditions can end seed dormancy. Some pine trees, for example, produce seeds in sealed cones. These seeds remain dormant until the high temperatures generated by forest fires cause the cones to open, as shown in **Figure 24–13.** This process activates the seeds, allowing the plants to reclaim the forest floor quickly after a fire.

▼ Figure 24–13 Environmental factors such as temperature and moisture can end dormancy. The cones of this bishop pine open and release seeds only after being exposed to the heat of a forest fire. **Inferring** ***How do the adaptations of this tree illustrate the results of natural selection?***

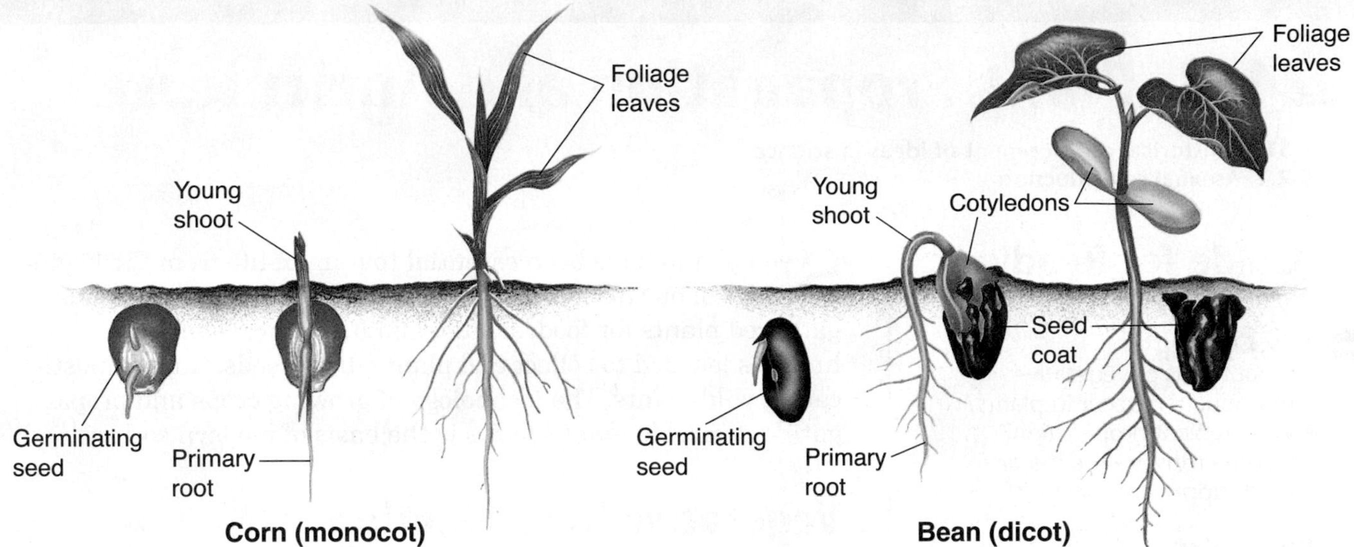

Seed Germination

Seed **germination** is the early growth stage of the plant embryo. **Figure 24–14** shows germination in monocots and dicots. When seeds germinate, they absorb water. The absorbed water causes food-storing tissues to swell, cracking open the seed coat. Through the cracked seed coat, the young root emerges and begins to grow.

Recall that monocots have a single cotyledon, or seed leaf. In most monocots, the single cotyledon remains underground. The growing shoot emerges while protected by a sheath. In dicots, which have two cotyledons, germination takes place in one of two ways. In some species, the cotyledons emerge aboveground, protecting the stem and first foliage leaves. The cotyledons may then wither and drop off the plant, such as in the bean shown in **Figure 24–14,** or become photosynthetic, such as in the pumpkin. In other species, such as the garden pea, the cotyledons stay underground and provide a food source for the growing seedling. In this case, the young stem grows longer and forms an arch that protects the delicate shoot tip.

▲ **Figure 24–14** The corn seedling (left) is a monocot in which the shoot grows directly upward, protected by its sheath. The garden bean (right) is a dicot in which the cotyledons emerge aboveground. **Applying Concepts** *What roles do cotyledons play in the early growth of plants?*

For: Links on seed structure and function
Visit: www.SciLinks.org
Web Code: cbn-7242

24–2 Section Assessment

1. **Key Concept** Describe what happens as fertilized angiosperm seeds mature.
2. **Key Concept** Compare the typical structure of seeds that are dispersed by animals to those dispersed by wind and water.
3. **Key Concept** Why is it adaptive for some seeds to remain dormant before they germinate?
4. **Critical Thinking Applying Concepts** The seeds of a bishop pine germinate only after they have undergone a forest fire. Evaluate the significance of this structural adaptation.
5. **Critical Thinking Applying Concepts** Describe which adaptations of a seed would enable it to germinate in a vacant lot where a building once stood.

Writing in Science

Writing a Book
Imagine that you are writing a children's book on seeds and that you are working on the chapter on dispersal. Write from one to three paragraphs on seed dispersal by wind. *Hint*: Try to include details that you would have found appealing when you were about 8 years old.

24–3 Plant Propagation and Agriculture

1-S1.1 Historical development of ideas in science
4-2.1 Asexual reproduction

Guide for Reading

Key Concepts
- What forms of vegetative reproduction occur in plants?
- What is plant propagation?
- Which crops are the major food supply for humans?

Vocabulary
vegetative reproduction
stolon
grafting
budding

Reading Strategy: Using Prior Knowledge Before you read the section, make a list of methods that humans use to grow food plants such as fruit trees and grains. As you read, add new information to your list.

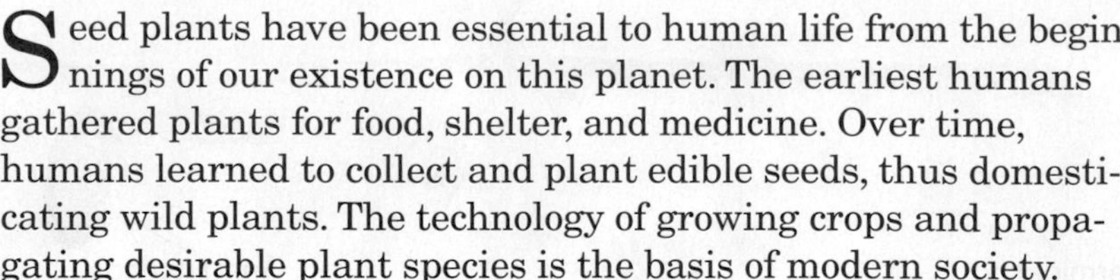

Seed plants have been essential to human life from the beginnings of our existence on this planet. The earliest humans gathered plants for food, shelter, and medicine. Over time, humans learned to collect and plant edible seeds, thus domesticating wild plants. The technology of growing crops and propagating desirable plant species is the basis of modern society.

Vegetative Reproduction

Although the chapter so far has concentrated on patterns of sexual reproduction, this section deals with the many flowering plants that reproduce asexually by **vegetative reproduction.** Growing a new plant by mitosis alone, vegetative reproduction enables a single plant to produce many offspring genetically identical to itself. This process takes place naturally in many plants, and it is also used as a technique by horticulturalists who want to produce many copies of an individual plant. **Vegetative reproduction includes the production of new plants from horizontal stems, from plantlets, and from underground roots.**

Because vegetative reproduction does not involve pollination or seed formation, it can enable plants to reproduce very quickly. Several species of angiosperms, such as the spider plant shown in **Figure 24–15,** produce tiny plants, or plantlets, at the tips of elongated stems. If the parent plant is knocked over or if plantlets fall to the soil, they can take root and grow into new plants. New plants can also grow from the leaves of a parent plant if the leaves fall to the ground under conditions that allow them to root.

Another way in which plants reproduce vegetatively is by growing horizontal stems. Strawberry plants, shown in **Figure 24–16,** send out long trailing stems called **stolons** that produce roots when they touch the ground. Once the roots are well established, each stolon may be broken, forming a new plant that is truly independent of its parent. Bamboo plants grow long underground stems that can send up new shoots in several places. In fact, bamboo forests that cover huge areas are often the descendants of a single bamboo plant that reproduced asexually.

◀ **Figure 24–15 The production of plantlets is a form of asexual reproduction.** The spider plant produces plantlets at the tips of elongated stems. When a plantlet reaches the soil, it can develop roots and grow into a new spider plant.

◀ **Figure 24–16** The strawberry plant reproduces vegetatively by producing thin, horizontal stems called stolons. Each node along the stolon produces roots that anchor the plant into the ground. **Applying Concepts** *Describe how asexual reproduction might allow a plant to become established rapidly in a new area.*

Plant Propagation

Sometimes the characteristics of a particular plant are so attractive or beneficial that horticulturists want to make many exact copies of the plant. But the growers also want to avoid the variation that would result if the plant reproduced sexually by seeds. In addition, new varieties of some plants, such as grapefruits and navel oranges, do not produce seeds. **In plant propagation, horticulturists use cuttings, grafting, or budding to make many identical copies of a plant or to produce offspring from seedless plants.**

Cuttings One of the simplest ways to reproduce plants vegetatively is by cuttings. A grower "cuts" from the plant a length of stem that includes a number of buds containing meristematic tissue. That stem is then partially buried in soil or in a special rooting mixture. Some common plants, such as coleus, root so easily that no other treatment is necessary. The cuttings of many woody plants, however, do not develop roots easily. To help cuttings of these plants form roots, growers use mixtures of plant hormones called rooting powders.

Grafting and Budding Grafting and budding are used to reproduce seedless plants and varieties of woody plants that do not produce strong root systems. In both of these techniques, new plants are grown on plants that have strong root systems. To do this, a piece of stem or a lateral bud is cut from the parent plant and attached to another plant. The cut piece is called the scion, and the plant to which it is attached is called the stock. When stems are used as scions, the process is called **grafting,** shown in **Figure 24–17.** When buds are used as scions, the process is called **budding.**

Grafting usually works best when plants are dormant because the wounds created can heal before new growth starts. In all cases, grafts are successful only if the vascular cambiums of scion and stock are firmly connected to each other.

What are the different techniques used to propagate woody plants?

▼ **Figure 24–17** **Plant propagation uses a variety of techniques to make identical copies of a single plant.** Here, a scion of a commercial orange tree is being grafted to a larger, established tree.

▲ **Figure 24–18** **Most of the world's food supply comes from a few crop plants.** Rice, here being planted by hand, is a staple crop in China and many nations of Southeast Asia.

Agriculture

The importance of agriculture—the systematic cultivation of plants—should be obvious, even to those of us who live in urban areas and seldom visit a farm. Modern farming is the foundation on which human society is built. North America has some of the richest, most productive cropland in the world. As a result, farmers in the United States and Canada produce so much food that they are able to feed millions of people around the world as well as their own citizens.

Worldwide Patterns of Agriculture Many scholars now trace the beginnings of human civilization to the cultivation of crop plants. Evidence suggests that agriculture developed separately in many parts of the world about 10,000 to 12,000 years ago. Once people discovered how to grow plants for food, the planting and harvesting of crops tended to keep them in one place for much of the year, leading directly to the establishment of social institutions. Even today, agriculture, shown in **Figure 24–18,** is the principal occupation of more human beings than any other activity.

Thousands of different plants—nearly all of which are angiosperms—are raised for food in various parts of the world. **Most of the people of the world depend on a few crop plants, such as wheat, rice, and corn, for the bulk of their food supply.** The same crops are also used to feed livestock.

Biology and History

The Evolution of Agrigulture

More than 10,000 years ago, humans began a gradual transition from hunter-gatherer societies to civilizations that were reliant on cultivated crops—many of which are still cultivated today.

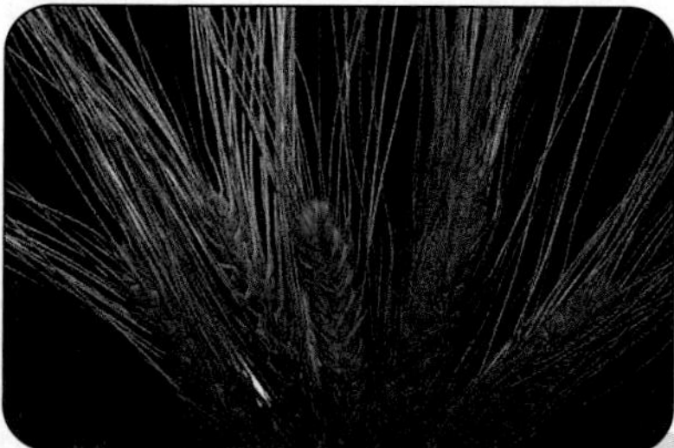

8000 BC
Inhabitants of the Middle East begin to cultivate wheat. The change from gathering a crop in the wild to farming it eventually contributes to the rise of one of the earliest Middle Eastern civilizations.

7000 BC
Chilies and avocados are cultivated as important additions to the diets of Mesoamerican people. Chilies are used for flavoring foods, and avocados provide vitamins and oils.

5500 BC
Barley is cultivated in the Nile Valley of Egypt. About 2000 years later, farming settlements are united throughout the Nile Valley, and Egyptian culture flourishes.

8000

7000

6000

You may not have thought of it this way, but the food we eat from most crop plants is taken from their seeds. In monocots, nearly all of this food is stored in the endosperm. Worldwide, most of humanity depends for food on the endosperm of only a few carefully cultivated species of grass. The pattern in the United States is similar. Roughly 80 percent of all U.S. cropland is used to grow just four crops: wheat, corn, soybeans, and hay. Of these crops, three—wheat, corn, and hay—are derived from grasses.

What is agriculture?

For: Articles on agriculture
Visit: PHSchool.com
Web Code: cbe-7243

Changes in Agriculture The discovery and introduction of new plants has changed human history. Before they were discovered in the Americas, many important crops—including corn, peanuts, beans, and potatoes—were unknown in Europe. The introduction of these plants changed European agriculture rapidly. Within a century, many of these foods had become important parts of the European diet. We think of boiled potatoes, for example, as traditional staples of German and Irish cooking, but 400 years ago they were new items in the diets of Europeans.

The efficiency of agriculture has been improved through the selective breeding of crop plants and improvements in farming techniques. The corn grown by Native Americans, for example, was developed more than 8000 years ago from teosinte (tee-oh-SIN-tee), a wild grass found in Mexico.

Writing in Science

The domestication of all major crops had a huge impact on the growth of civilizations. Choose one of the crops discussed below and research how that crop contributed to the rise of civilization and culture in that region.

5000 BC
People in central Mexico domesticate corn, also called maize. Early corncobs are only about an inch long and have a few dozen kernels. The ancestor of corn was probably a wild grass called teosinte.

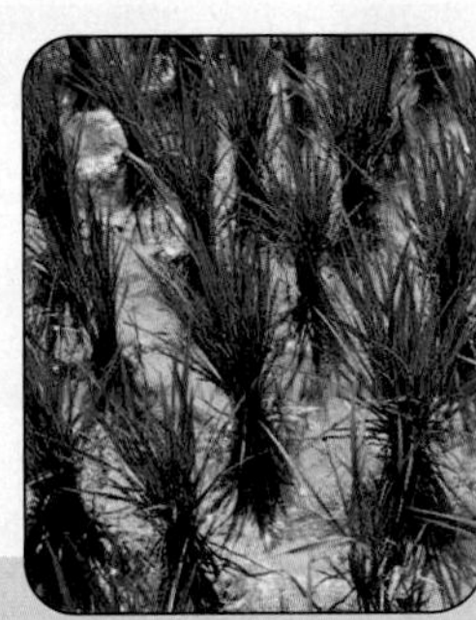

4500 BC
Rice cultivation becomes well established in southern China, southeast Asia, and northern India. Rice farming spreads widely from these regions, and rice later becomes a major Chinese export.

3500 BC
The potato is domesticated in the Andes Mountains of South America. Early Andean farmers eventually produce 700 varieties of potatoes by cultivating them on irrigated terraces built on mountain slopes.

5000 4000 3000

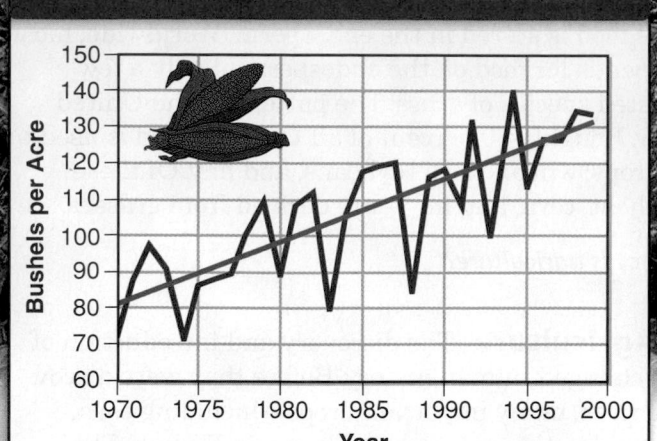

▲ **Figure 24–19** Between 1970 and 2000, the amount of corn grown per acre in the United States increased more than 60 percent. A field of corn, also called *Zea mays*, is shown in the photograph. **Interpreting Graphics** *Describe the trend shown in the graph for the years 1983 and 1988.*

Recall from Chapter 13 that selective breeding is a method for improving a species by allowing only organisms with certain traits to produce the next generation. In more recent times, other familiar crops have been the product of selective breeding. Sugar beets, the source of most refined sugar from the United States, were produced from the ordinary garden beet using selective breeding. Plants as different as cabbage, broccoli, and Brussels sprouts have been developed from a single species of wild mustard.

Improvements in farming techniques have contributed to dramatic improvements in crop yields, as shown in **Figure 24–19.** Some of the most important techniques have been the use of pesticides and fertilizers. These improvements have lowered the price of food and enabled farmers to feed many more people without any expansion of the amount of land under cultivation.

24–3 Section Assessment

1. **Key Concept** Define vegetative reproduction. How do the offspring produced compare to the parent plant?
2. **Key Concept** What is the purpose of plant propagation?
3. **Key Concept** What are the main food crops? What techniques have improved crop yields during recent decades?
4. Compare grafting and budding. Why are these techniques preferable to sexual propagation of woody plants?
5. **Critical Thinking Inferring** Dandelions employ an unusual form of reproduction that produces seeds but does not involve meiosis and the production of haploid gametes. The pollen produced within flowers is sterile and produces seeds without fertilization. What advantages might this system have over sexual reproduction of viable seeds?

Sharpen Your Skills

Predicting

Imagine that you are growing a *Coleus* plant by using a cutting. You place the cutting in a beaker of water and leave the plant in a sunny place. Draw and label a picture of the way you think the cutting will look on Day 1. Then, draw and label a picture of the way you think it will look on Day 8. Write a list of the changes you think will occur in the cutting.

Design an Experiment

Investigating Pollen Tube Growth

In this investigation, you will design an experiment to test a hypothesis about the chemical signals that steer the growth of pollen tubes toward the ovary.

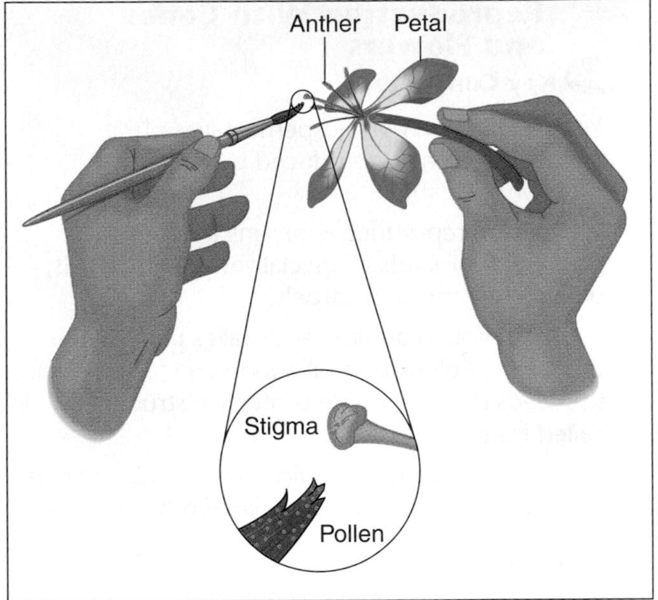

Problem

What controls the direction of pollen tube growth?

Materials

- flowering plants, such as beans or *Brassicas*
- hand lens
- small paintbrush
- forceps
- pollen nutrient solution
- pollen nutrient solution without calcium
- concentrated calcium chloride solution
- dissecting probe
- microscope slides
- coverslips
- dropper pipette

Skills Designing Experiments, Controlling Variables

Design Your Experiment

1. Use a hand lens to observe the flowers of a flowering plant. Identify the anthers and stigma of a flower.
2. Use a small paintbrush to transfer pollen from several flowers to the stigmas of other flowers.
3. Use forceps to transfer several anthers to a microscope slide. Add a drop of pollen nutrient solution. Gently tap the anthers with the tip of a dissecting probe to release pollen.
4. Discard the anthers and add a coverslip. Observe the pollen with the microscope at low power. Make a labeled drawing of your observations.
5. Your teacher will provide slides containing pollen that has been in pollen nutrient solution for several hours. Observe these slides with the microscope. Record your observations.
6. Pollen tubes have been found to grow toward calcium or pieces of ovaries. Design an experiment to test the hypothesis that calcium is the chemical signal that guides the growing pollen tube toward the ovary.
7. As you plan your investigative procedures, refer to the Lab Tips box on page 55 for information on demonstrating safe practices, making wise choices in the use of materials, and selecting equipment and technology.
8. In your plan, also be sure to define and control all important variables. If observing pollen tube growth in a flower directly is too difficult, you will need to choose some other method to test the hypothesis. Have your teacher check your plan before you begin your experiment.

Analyze and Conclude

1. **Applying Concepts** The pollen of most plants will not germinate in pure water. What function of the stigma and style did the pollen nutrient solution replace?
2. **Observing** Did the pollen tubes grow toward a source of calcium? Toward ovary tissue?
3. **Drawing Conclusions** In many experiments, pollen tubes grow toward either calcium or ovary tissue. From these results, could you conclude that calcium directs pollen tube growth toward the ovary in flowers? Explain.

Go Further

Formulating Hypotheses Use scientific literature to form a hypothesis on the effect of light on pollen tube growth.

Chapter 24 Study Guide

24–1 Reproduction With Cones and Flowers

Key Concepts

- Reproduction in gymnosperms takes place in cones, which are produced by a mature sporophyte plant.
- Flowers are reproductive organs that are composed of four kinds of specialized leaves: sepals, petals, stamens, and carpels.
- Reproduction in angiosperms takes place within the flower. Following pollination and fertilization, the seeds develop inside protective structures called fruits.
- Most gymnosperms are wind pollinated, whereas most flowering plants are pollinated by animals.

Vocabulary
pollen cone, p. 610 • seed cone, p. 610
ovule, p. 610 • pollen tube, p. 611
sepal, p. 612 • petal, p. 612
stamen, p. 612 • filament, p. 612
anther, p. 612 • carpel, p. 612
ovary, p. 612 • style, p. 612
stigma, p. 612 • embryo sac, p. 615
endosperm, p. 616 • double fertilization, p. 616

24–2 Seed Development and Germination

Key Concepts

- As angiosperm seeds mature, the ovary walls thicken to form a fruit that encloses the developing seeds.
- Seeds dispersed by animals are typically contained in fleshy, nutritious fruits.
- Seeds dispersed by wind or water are typically lightweight, allowing them to be carried in the air or to float on the surface of the water.
- Environmental factors such as temperature and moisture can cause a seed to end dormancy and germinate.

Vocabulary
dormancy, p. 620
germination, p. 621

24–3 Plant Propagation and Agriculture

Key Concepts

- Vegetative reproduction includes the production of new plants from horizontal stems, cuttings, leaves, plantlets, and underground roots.
- Horticulturists use plant propagation to make many identical copies of a plant or to produce offspring from seedless plants.
- Most of the people of the world depend on a few crop plants, such as wheat, rice, and corn, for the bulk of their food supply.

Vocabulary
vegetative reproduction, p. 622
stolon, p. 622 • grafting, p. 623
budding, p. 623

Thinking Visually

Use the following terms to complete the flowchart about reproduction in gymnosperms: *female gametophyte, seed, pollen cone, mature sporophyte, seed cone, zygote, pollen grains.*

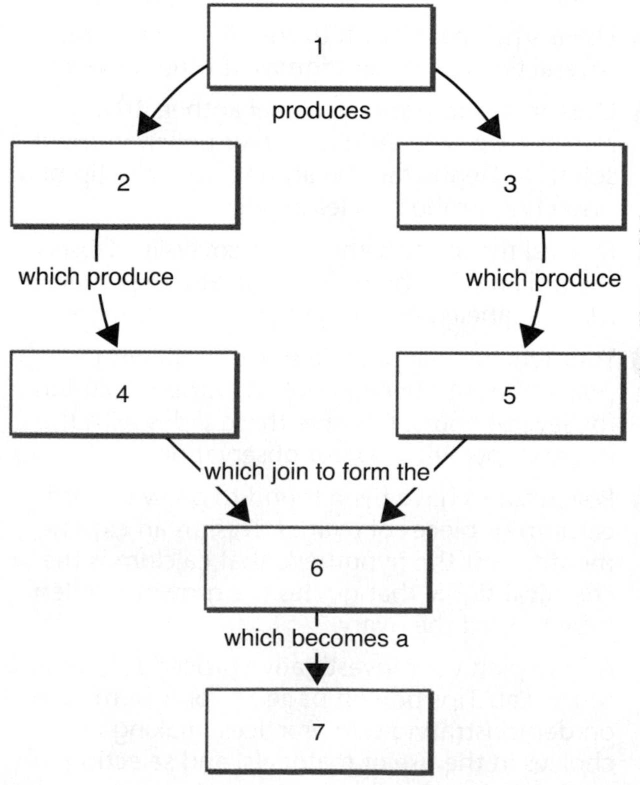

Preparing for the Living Environment Exam

Blue questions emphasize Regents Exam content

Chapter 24

Part A

Multiple Choice

For each statement or question, select the number of the word or expression that, of those given, best completes the statement or answers the question.

1 Two structures specialized for reproduction in seed plants are
(1) cones and flowers
(2) cones and lateral buds
(3) lateral and terminal buds
(4) meristems and flowers

2 Which statement is *not* true of reproduction in a pine tree?
(1) The pollen tube contains two diploid sperm.
(2) One sperm fertilizes the egg.
(3) One sperm disintegrates.
(4) The zygote grows into an embryo.

3 In angiosperms, the structures that produce the male gametophyte are called the
(1) anthers (3) pollen tubes
(2) sepals (4) stigmas

4 Pollination occurs when pollen lands on the
(1) style (3) filament
(2) stigma (4) anther

5 The thickened ovary wall of a plant joins with other parts of the flower stem to become the
(1) fruit (3) endosperm
(2) seed (4) cotyledon

6 The food-rich tissue that nourishes seedlings as they grow is known as
(1) endosperm (3) radicles
(2) carpels (4) cotyledons

7 In seed plants, the structure that encloses the male gametophyte and transports it to another plant is called a
(1) pollen grain (3) flower
(2) seed (4) pollinator

8 The period during which the embryo is alive but not growing is called
(1) fertilization (3) dormancy
(2) germination (4) vegetative growth

9 A scientist wants to artificially pollinate a flower. Where would he find the pollen grains?
(1) sepal (3) anther
(2) carpel (4) ovary

10 The process in which a single plant produces many offspring genetically identical to itself is called
(1) sexual reproduction
(2) agriculture
(3) dormancy
(4) vegetative reproduction

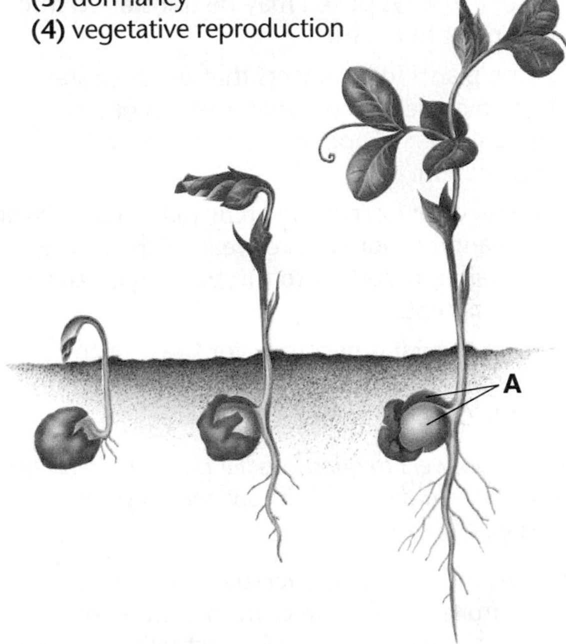

11 The illustration above shows the germination of a pea plant. The feature labeled A is a(an)
(1) anther (3) cotyledon
(2) seed coat (4) root

12 Which part of a flower develops into a fruit?
(1) pollen tube (3) anther
(2) carpel (4) ovary

13 Which flower structure below includes all of the others listed?
(1) style (3) ovary
(2) stigma (4) carpel

14 All of the following are fruits *except*
(1) tomatoes (3) beets
(2) corn (4) cucumbers

Test-Taking Tip When answering questions pertaining to experimental situations, read all of the questions first. Then, read the passage carefully and examine any accompanying data, looking for the specific information required to answer the questions.

Preparing for the Living Environment Exam

Part B

Multiple Choice and Extended Response

For those questions that ask you to select a response, choose the one that best completes the statement or answers the question. For all others follow the directions given.

15 State *two* ways pollen may be transferred from one plant to another.

16 Some plants form flowers that produce stamens but no carpels. Could fruit form on one of these flowers? Support your answer with an explanation.

17 The seeds of lupines, an arctic plant, can remain dormant for thousands of years. Explain why this trait is important to this plant in an arctic environment.

18 Explain why it is necessary for the root to emerge from a germinating seed before the shoot.

Base your answers to questions 19 through 21 on the information and data table below and on your knowledge of biology.

A scientist measured the average time it took different fruits to fall 1 meter from the parent tree. Assume that for every second a fruit falls, it is carried 1.5 meters away from the parent tree.

Relationship Between Fruit Type and Dispersal Time

Type of Tree	Average Time (sec) for Seed to Fall 1 m
Norway maple	0.98
Silver maple	0.64
White ash	0.30
Shagbark hickory	0.16
Red oak	0.16

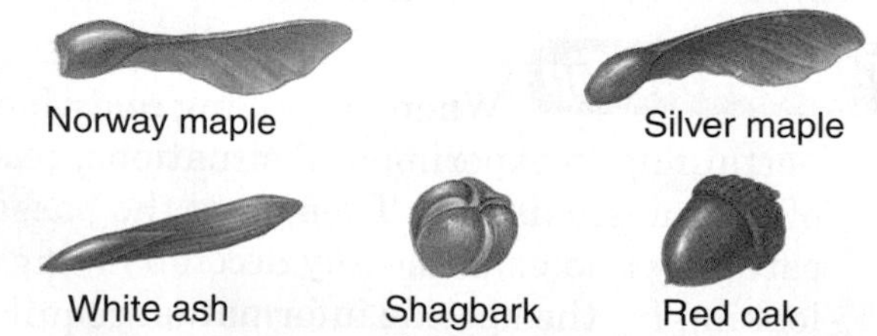

19 Which fruit was carried the farthest from the parent tree?
(1) Norway maple (3) white ash
(2) silver maple (4) shagbark hickory

20 According to these data, what benefit does a winged fruit have over an acorn?
A It is lighter.
B It is heavier.
C It will travel farther.
(1) A, only (3) C, only
(2) B, only (4) A and C

21 The fruit of the oak and hickory is very different from the fruit of the maples and ash. Other than dropping from the tree, what means of seed dispersal might the oak and hickory rely upon?

Base your answers to questions 22 and 23 on the diagram below and on your knowledge of biology.

The diagram below shows the parts of a typical flower.

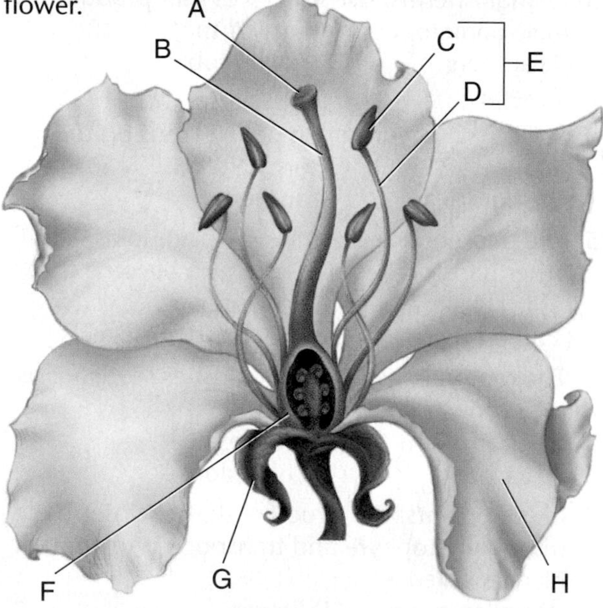

22 Identify structure A. Explain its role in pollination and fertilization.

23 Identify structure H. Explain its role in pollination and fertilization.

24 List *two* advantages of seed dormancy.

Part C

Extended Response

Answer the questions or follow the directions given.

25 Vegetative reproduction allows a single plant that is well adapted to a particular environment to produce many offspring. Explain the advantages of vegetative reproduction to a plant compared with sexual reproduction. In your explanations be sure to include:
- *two* examples of plant structures used in vegetative reproduction
- the relative amount of time it takes to produce offspring compared to sexual reproduction
- how the offspring compare to the parent genetically
- *two* reasons plant growers would use vegetative reproduction instead of sexual

26 Seed germination is the early growth stages of the plant embryo. In both monocots and dicots, absorbed water initiates the germination process. What happens next? Compare the events of germination in monocots and dicots. In your answer be sure to identify the:
- role of the endosperm
- first structure to emerge from the seed
- relationship of the cotyledon in monocots to the shoot
- relationship of the cotyledons in dicots to the first foliage leaves

27 Female cones secrete a sticky substance.
a State one way this trait is advantageous to gymnosperms.
b Explain how this trait might have evolved.

28 A friend suggests that seeds do not need cotyledons to grow. You argue that cotyledons are important to seeds. Design an experiment that shows the effect that removing cotyledons has on seed growth. Be sure to identify
- the importance of cotyledons
- your hypothesis
- the procedures you will follow
- the type of data you will collect

29 The graph below shows the increase in the annual yield of corn in the U.S. over a 30-year period. The yield of corn has nearly doubled in that time span. Much of this increase is due to the use of improved fertilizers and pesticides. In addition, farmers have used selective breeding methods to improve production.

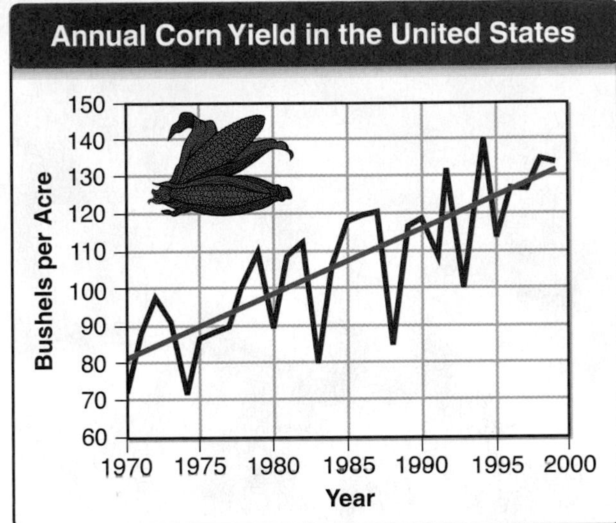

Some individuals are concerned that the increased yield is not worth the potential risks associated with increased pesticide and fertilizer use. Some claim that selective breeding is the only way to improve production. Explain why these issues must be seriously considered. In your answer be sure to include:
- the environmental consequences of fertilizers
- the effect of pesticides on the food chain
- the traits a farmer would choose in a selective breeding program

30 It is important to store seeds in a dry, dark place. Predict what might happen if water were to drip onto packages of seeds. Support your prediction with an explanation.

For: An interactive self-test
Visit: PHSchool.com
Web Code: cba-7240

CHAPTER 25 Plant Responses and Adaptations

In what may be its last moments, an ant peers down into a pitcher plant's specialized leaf. The leaf is lined with slippery hairs and is filled with digestive enzymes that will extract nutrients from any unsuspecting prey.

Inquiry Activity

How are plants adapted to their environments?

Procedure 

1. Examine several desert plants and several rain forest plants. Note any differences between these two groups of plants. Record your observations.
2. List the characteristics that vary between desert plants and rain forest plants. List any characteristics that you observed in both types of plants.

Think About It

1. **Classifying** What variations did you identify that distinguish desert plants and rain forest plants?
2. **Formulating Hypotheses** How could these variations help desert and rain forest plants survive in their environments?
3. **Predicting** Draw a real or an imaginary plant that is adapted for warm, dry summers and rainy, cold winters. Write a paragraph describing the adaptations of your plant.

25–1 Hormones and Plant Growth

4-5.1 Hormones and receptor molecules
4-5.3 Dynamic equilibrium
4-5.3 Feedback mechanisms
LS- Analyze results and formulate a conclusion
LS- Make observations and state an appropriate hypothesis

Unlike most animals, plants do not have a rigidly set organization to their bodies. Cows have four legs, ants have six, and spiders have eight; but tomato plants do not have a predetermined number of leaves or branches. However, plants such as the baobab tree in **Figure 25–1** show distinct patterns of growth. As a result, you can easily tell the difference between a tomato plant and a corn plant, between an oak tree and a pine tree.

Guide for Reading

Key Concepts
- What are plant hormones?
- How do auxins, cytokinins, gibberellins, and ethylene affect plant growth?

Vocabulary
hormone
target cell
phototropism
auxin
gravitropism
lateral bud
apical dominance
herbicide
cytokinin
gibberellin
ethylene

Reading Strategy: Finding Main Ideas Before you read, skim the section to identify the key ideas about plant hormones. Then, read the section carefully, making a list of supporting details for each main idea.

Patterns of Plant Growth

Although plant growth is not determined precisely, it still follows general patterns that differ among species. What controls these patterns of development? Biologists have discovered that plant cells send signals to one another that indicate when to divide and when not to divide, and when to develop into a new kind of cell.

There is another difference between growth in plants and animals. Once most animals reach adulthood, they stop growing. In contrast, even plants that are thousands of years old continue to grow new needles, add new wood, and produce cones or new flowers, almost as if parts of their bodies remained "forever young." As you have learned, the secrets of plant growth are found in meristems, regions of tissue that can produce cells that later develop into specialized tissues. Meristems are found at places where plants grow rapidly—the tips of growing stems and roots, and along the outer edges of woody tissues that produce new growth every year.

If meristems are the source of plant growth, how is that growth controlled and regulated? Plants grow in response to environmental factors such as light, moisture, temperature, and gravity. But how do roots "know" to grow down, and how do stems "know" to grow up toward light? How do the tissues of a plant determine the right time of year to produce flowers? How do plants ensure that their growth is evenly balanced—that the trunk of a tree grows large enough to support the weight of its leaves and branches? The answers to these questions involve the actions of chemicals that direct, control, and regulate plant growth.

▶ **Figure 25–1** All plants follow a highly regulated pattern of growth that continues throughout the life of the plant. This pattern of growth leads to distinct shapes, such as the thick trunk and widely spaced branches of this baobab tree. **Applying Concepts** *In which plant tissue does growth occur?*

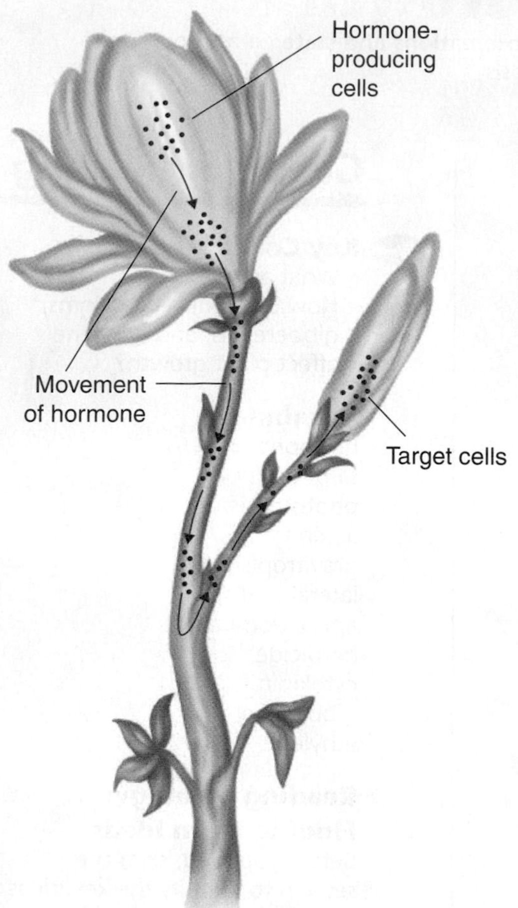

▲ **Figure 25–2** **Plant hormones are chemical substances that control patterns of development as well as plant responses to the environment.** Hormones are produced in apical meristems, in young leaves, in roots, and in growing flowers and fruits. From their place of origin, hormones move to other parts of the plant, where target cells respond in a way that is specific to the hormone.

Plant Hormones

In plants, the division, growth, maturation, and development of cells are controlled by a group of chemicals called hormones. A **hormone** is a substance that is produced in one part of an organism and affects another part of the same individual. **Plant hormones are chemical substances that control a plant's patterns of growth and development, and the plant's responses to environmental conditions.**

The general mechanism of hormone action in plants is shown in **Figure 25–2.** As you can see, the hormone moves through the plant from the place where it is produced to the place where it triggers its response. The portion of an organism affected by a particular hormone is known as its **target cell** or target tissue. To respond to a hormone, the target cell must contain a hormone receptor—usually a protein—to which the hormone binds. If the appropriate receptor is present, the hormone can exert an influence on the target cell by changing its metabolism, affecting its growth rate, or activating the transcription of certain genes. Cells that do not contain receptors are generally unaffected by hormones.

Different kinds of cells may have different receptors for the same hormone. As a result, a single hormone may affect two different tissues in different ways. For example, a particular hormone may stimulate growth in stem tissues but inhibit growth in root tissues.

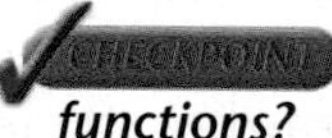 *In which cells do hormones carry out their functions?*

Auxins

The experiment that led to the discovery of the first plant hormone was carried out by Charles Darwin. In 1880, Darwin and his son Francis published a book called *The Power of Movement in Plants.* In this book, they described an experiment in which oat seedlings demonstrated a response known as phototropism. **Phototropism** is the tendency of a plant to grow toward a source of light.

Figure 25–3 shows an experiment similar to the one carried out by the Darwins. Notice that the tip of one of the oat seedlings was covered with an opaque cap. This plant did not bend toward the light, even though the rest of the plant was uncovered. However, if an opaque shield was placed a few centimeters below the tip, the plant would bend toward the light as if the shield were not there. Clearly, something was taking place at the tip of the seedling.

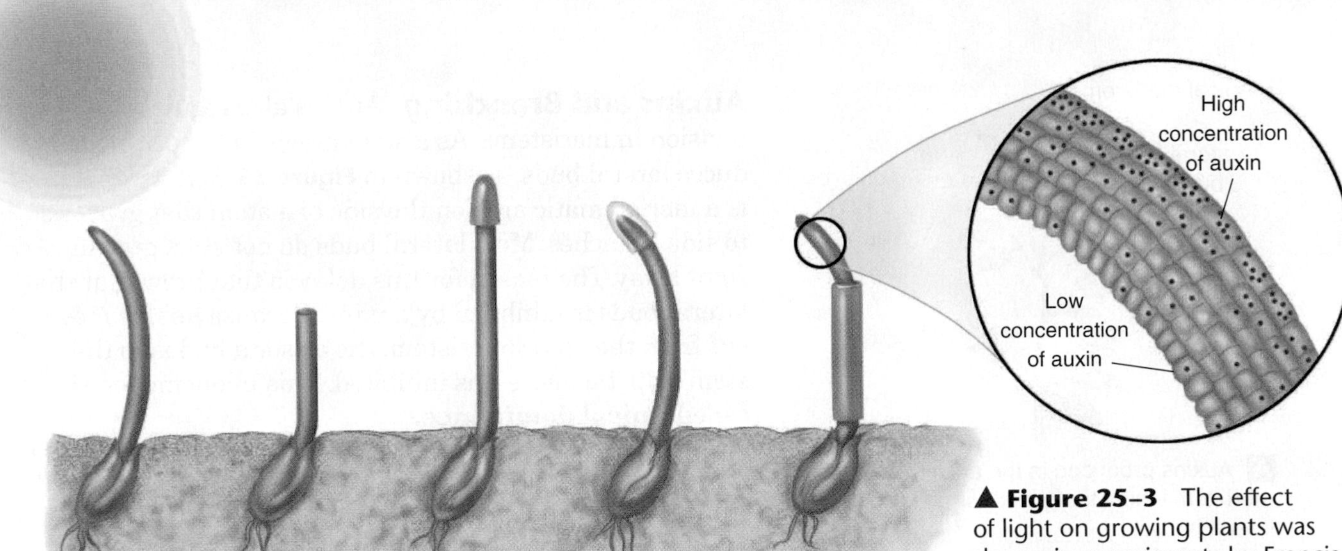

▲ **Figure 25–3** The effect of light on growing plants was shown in experiments by Francis and Charles Darwin and other scientists. They demonstrated that chemical substances are produced in the growing tip of a plant. **Auxins stimulate cell elongation.** A higher concentration of auxins accumulate in the shaded part of a stem and cause the plant to bend toward a light source.

Auxins and Phototropism The Darwins suspected that the tip of each seedling produced substances that regulated cell growth. Forty years later, these substances were identified and named **auxins.** **Auxins are produced in the apical meristem and are transported downward into the rest of the plant. They stimulate cell elongation.** When light hits one side of the stem, a higher concentration of auxins develops in the shaded part of the stem. This change in concentration stimulates cells on the dark side to elongate. As a result, the stem bends away from the shaded side and toward the light. Recent experiments have shown that auxins migrate toward the shaded side of the stem, possibly due to changes in membrane permeability in response to light.

Auxins and Gravitropism Auxins are also responsible for **gravitropism,** which is the response of a plant to the force of gravity. By mechanisms that are still not understood, auxins build up on the lower sides of roots and stems. In stems, auxins stimulate cell elongation, helping turn the trunk upright, as shown in **Figure 25–4.** In roots, however, the effects of auxins are exactly the opposite. There, auxins inhibit cell growth and elongation, causing the roots to grow downward.

Auxins are also involved in the way roots grow around objects in the soil. If a growing root is forced sideways by an obstacle such as a rock, auxins accumulate on the lower side of the root. Once again, high concentrations of auxins inhibit the elongation of root cells. The uninhibited cells on the top elongate more than the auxin-inhibited cells on the bottom of the root. As a result, the root grows downward.

▶ **Figure 25–4** Auxins are responsible for the plant response called gravitropism. Auxins caused the tip of this tree stem to grow upright. **Comparing and Contrasting** *Compare how auxins affect the growth of stems and roots.*

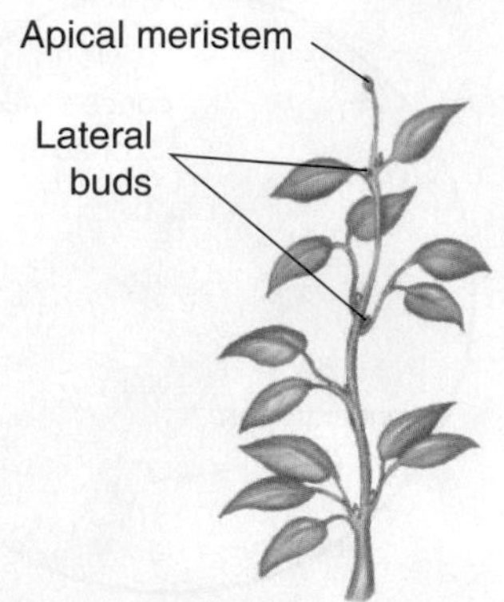

A Auxins produced in the apical meristem inhibit the growth of lateral buds.

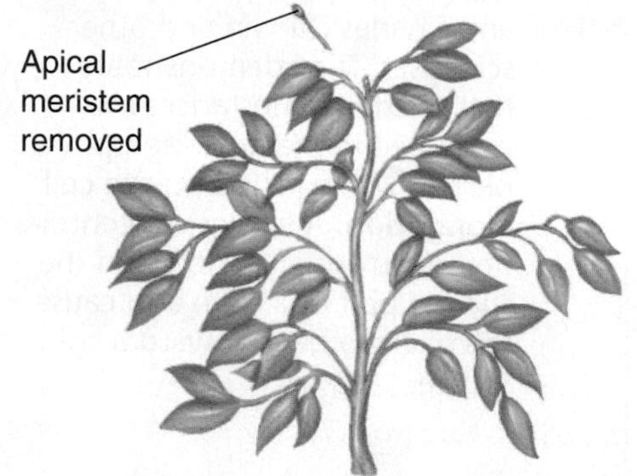

B Without the inhibiting effect of auxins from the apical meristem, lateral buds produce many branches.

▲ **Figure 25–5** Apical dominance, shown here, is controlled by the relative amounts of auxins and cytokinins. During normal growth (A), lateral buds are kept dormant because of the production of auxins in the apical meristem. If the apical meristem is removed (B), the concentration of auxins drops. **Applying Concepts How can a gardener use this knowledge of hormones to produce fuller, bushier plants?**

Auxins and Branching Auxins also regulate cell division in meristems. As a stem grows in length, it produces lateral buds, as shown in **Figure 25–5.** A **lateral bud** is a meristematic area on the side of a stem that gives rise to side branches. Most lateral buds do not start growing right away. The reason for this delay is that growth at the lateral buds is inhibited by auxins. Because auxins move out from the apical meristem, the closer a bud is to the stem's tip, the more it is inhibited. This phenomenon is called **apical dominance.**

Although not all gardeners have heard of auxins, most of them know how to overcome apical dominance. If you snip off the tip of a plant, the side branches begin to grow more quickly, resulting in a rounder, fuller plant. Why does this happen? When the tip is removed, the apical meristem—the source of the growth-inhibiting auxins—goes with it. Without the influence of auxins, meristems in the side branches grow more rapidly, changing the overall shape of the plant.

Auxinlike Weed Killers Chemists have produced many compounds that mimic the effects of auxins. Because high concentrations of auxins inhibit growth, many of these compounds are used as **herbicides,** which are compounds that are toxic to plants. Herbicides include a chemical known as 2,4-D (2,4-dichlorophenoxyacetic acid), which is used to kill weeds. A mixture containing 2,4-D was used as Agent Orange, a chemical defoliant sprayed during the Vietnam War.

What role do auxins play in apical dominance?

Cytokinins

Cytokinins are plant hormones that are produced in growing roots and in developing fruits and seeds. **In plants, cytokinins stimulate cell division and the growth of lateral buds, and cause dormant seeds to sprout.** Cytokinins also delay the aging of leaves and play important roles in the early stages of plant growth.

Cytokinins often produce effects opposite to those of auxins. For example, auxins stimulate cell elongation, whereas cytokinins inhibit elongation and cause cells to grow thicker. Auxins inhibit the growth of lateral buds, whereas cytokinins stimulate lateral bud growth. Recent experiments show that the rate of cell growth in most plants is determined by the ratio of the concentration of auxins to cytokinins. In growing plants, therefore, the relative concentrations of auxins, cytokinins, and other hormones determine how the plant grows.

Analyzing Data

Auxins and Plant Growth

Auxins affect plant growth in a variety of ways. This graph shows the results of experiments in which carrot cells were grown in the presence of varying concentrations of auxins. The orange line on the graph shows the growth pattern of the carrot plants' roots. The green line shows the growth pattern of the carrot plants' stems.

1. **Using Tables and Graphs** At what auxin concentration are the stems stimulated to grow the most?
2. **Using Tables and Graphs** How is the growth of the roots affected by the auxin concentration at which stems grow the most?
3. **Drawing Conclusions** Use the data in the graph to describe the relationship between the concentration of auxins and the growth of carrot plant stems.
4. **Inferring** If you were a carrot farmer, what concentration of auxin should you apply to your fields to produce the largest-sized carrots?

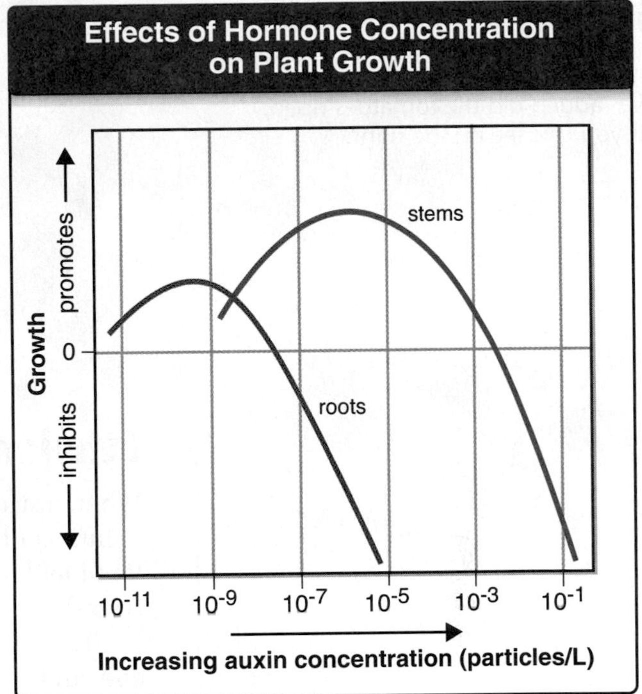

Gibberellins

For years, farmers in Japan knew of a disease that weakened rice plants by causing them to grow unusually tall. They called the disease the "foolish seedling" disease. In 1926, Japanese biologist Eiichi Kurosawa discovered that this extraordinary growth was caused by a fungus: *Gibberella fujikuroi.* His experiments showed that the fungus produced a growth-promoting substance that was named **gibberellin.**

Before long, other researchers had learned that plants themselves produce more than 60 similar compounds, all of which are now known as gibberellins. **Gibberellins produce dramatic increases in size, particularly in stems and fruit.** Their effects on a flower are shown in **Figure 25–6.** Gibberellins are also produced by seed tissue and are responsible for the rapid early growth of many plants.

How were gibberellins discovered?

▼ **Figure 25–6** **Gibberellins cause an increase in the overall size of plants and individual plant structures.** Their effect can be seen in the difference between an untreated geranium plant (left) and a geranium plant treated with gibberellin (right).

▶ Figure 25–7 Ethylene is a plant hormone that causes fruits to ripen. The tomatoes on the left were allowed to ripen naturally, whereas those in the middle were genetically altered to prevent transcription of the gene that produces ethylene. Only when ethylene gas was added did the tomatoes ripen, as you can see on the right.

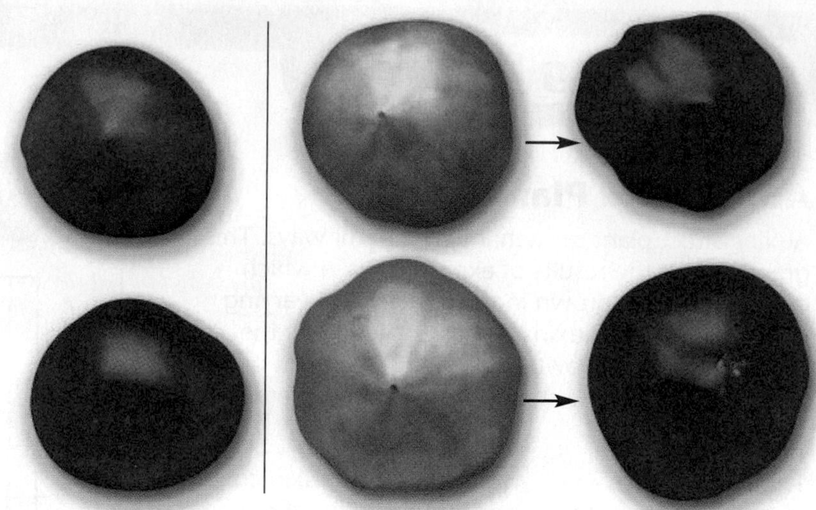

Ethylene

When natural gas was used in city street lamps in the nineteenth century, people noticed that trees along the street suffered leaf loss and stunted growth. This effect was eventually traced to **ethylene,** one of the minor components of natural gas.

Today, scientists know that plants produce their own ethylene, and that it affects plants in a number of ways. **In response to auxins, fruit tissues release small amounts of the hormone ethylene. Ethylene then stimulates fruits to ripen.**

Commercial producers of fruit sometimes use this hormone to control the ripening process. Many crops, including lemons and tomatoes, shown in **Figure 25–7,** are picked before they ripen so that they can be handled without damage to the fruit. Just before they are delivered to market, the fruits are treated with synthetic ethylene to produce a ripe color quickly. This trick does not always produce a ripe flavor, which is one reason why naturally ripened fruits often taste much better.

25–1 Section Assessment

1. **Key Concept** What effects do hormones have within a growing plant?
2. **Key Concept** Identify the four main types of hormones. What parts of the plant does each hormone affect?
3. Compare the effects of auxins and cytokinins on plant growth.
4. **Critical Thinking Inferring** A person who trims trees for a living must know the effect of apical dominance on the shape of trees. Explain.
5. **Critical Thinking Interpreting Graphics** Using **Figure 25–3,** describe the experiment by Francis and Charles Darwin. Explain why the seedling at the far right is curved.

Connecting Concepts

Scientific Method
Using the Darwins' experiment as an example, develop a flowchart that shows the scientific process. Be sure to identify each process. (*Hint:* You may wish to review Chapter 1, which describes the scientific method.)

25–2 Plant Responses

4-5.3 Dynamic equilibrium
LS- Follow safety rules
LS- Make observations

Guide for Reading

 **Key Concepts**
- What are plant tropisms?
- What is photoperiodism?
- How do deciduous plants prepare for winter?

Vocabulary
tropism
thigmotropism
short-day plant
long-day plant
photoperiodism
phytochrome
dormancy
abscission layer

Reading Strategy: Using Visuals Before you read, preview **Figure 25–10.** From this figure, what can you conclude about the topic of photoperiodism?

Like all living things, plants respond to changes in their environments. Some biologists call these responses "plant behavior," which is a useful way of thinking about them. Plants generally do not respond as quickly as animals do, but that does not make their responses any less effective. Some plant responses are so fast that even animals cannot keep up with them!

Tropisms

Plants change their patterns and directions of growth in response to a multitude of cues. The responses of plants to external stimuli are called **tropisms,** from a Greek word that means "turning." **Plant tropisms include gravitropism, phototropism, and thigmotropism. Each of these responses demonstrates the ability of plants to respond effectively to external stimuli, such as gravity, light, and touch.**

Gravitropism and Phototropism You have already read about gravitropism, the response of a plant to gravity, and phototropism, the response of a plant to light. Both of these responses are controlled by the hormone auxin. Gravitropism causes the shoot of a germinating seed to grow out of the soil—against the force of gravity. It also causes the roots of a plant to grow with the force of gravity and into the soil.

Phototropism causes a plant to grow toward a light source. This response can be so quick that young seedlings reorient themselves in a matter of hours.

Thigmotropism The response of plants to touch is called **thigmotropism** (thig-MAH-troh-piz-um). A plant that is touched regularly, for example, may be stunted in its growth—sometimes quite dramatically. Another example of thigmotropism is the growth of vines and climbing plants. The stems of these plants do not grow straight up. Rather, the growing tip of each stem points sideways and twists in circles as the shoot grows. When the tip encounters an object, it quickly wraps around it. Some climbing plants have long, twisting leaf tips or petioles that wrap tightly around small objects. Other plants, such as the grapes in **Figure 25–8,** have extra growths called tendrils that emerge near the base of the leaf and wrap tightly around any object they encounter.

▶ **Figure 25–8** **Plant tropisms include gravitropism, phototropism, and thigmotropism.** One effect of thigmotropism is that plants curl and twist around objects, as shown by the stems of this grapevine.

Figure 25–9 The mimosa plant responds to touch by folding in its leaves quickly. This response is produced by decreased osmotic pressure in cells near the base of each leaflet. **Inferring** ***What adaptive value might rapid responses have for a plant?***

Rapid Responses

Some plant responses do not involve growth. In fact, they are so rapid that it would be a mistake to call them tropisms. **Figure 25–9** shows what happens if you touch a leaf of *Mimosa pudica,* appropriately called the "sensitive plant." Within only two or three seconds, its two leaflets fold together completely. The secret to this movement is changes in osmotic pressure. Recall that osmotic pressure is caused by the diffusion of water into cells. The leaves are held apart due to osmotic pressure where the two leaflets join. When the leaf is touched, cells near the center of the leaflet pump out ions and lose water due to osmosis. Pressure from cells on the underside of the leaf, which do not lose water, force the leaflets together.

The carnivorous Venus' flytrap also demonstrates rapid responses. When a fly triggers sensory cells on the inside of the flytrap's leaf, electrical signals are sent from cell to cell. A combination of changes in osmotic pressure and cell wall expansion causes the leaf to snap shut, trapping the insect inside.

Quick Lab

Can a plant find its way through a maze?

Materials scissors, masking tape, cardboard box, cardboard dividers, 4 bean seeds, small flowerpot containing soil

Procedure  

1. Make a maze by taping cardboard dividers upright inside a cardboard box as shown. Cut a hole in the side of the box at the end of the maze. **CAUTION:** *Use care when handling scissors.*
2. Plant 4 bean seeds in a small flowerpot of soil. Water the flowerpot.
3. Place the flowerpot in the box at the beginning of the maze. Close the box so that the only light in the box comes from the hole that you cut. **CAUTION:** *Wash your hands with soap and warm water after handling soil or plants.*

4. Over the next 2 weeks, open the box every 2 to 3 days to water the seeds and observe the seedlings. Record your observations each day.

Analyze and Conclude

1. **Observing** Summarize what happened to the seedlings.
2. **Inferring** What caused the plants to grow the way they did?

Photoperiodism

"To every thing there is a season." Nowhere is this more evident than in the regular cycles of plant growth. Year after year, some plants flower in the spring, others in summer, and still others in the fall. Plants such as chrysanthemums and poinsettias flower when days are short and are therefore called **short-day plants.** Plants such as spinach and irises flower when days are long and are therefore known as **long-day plants.**

How do all these plants manage to time their flowering so precisely? In the early 1920s, scientists discovered that tobacco plants flower according to the number of hours of light and darkness they receive. Additional research showed that many other plants also respond to periods of light and darkness, a response called **photoperiodism.** This type of response is summarized in **Figure 25–10.** **Photoperiodism in plants is responsible for the timing of seasonal activities such as flowering and growth.**

It was later discovered that a plant pigment called **phytochrome** (FYT-oh-krohm) is responsible for photoperiodism. Phytochrome absorbs red light and activates a number of signaling pathways within plant cells. By mechanisms that are still not understood completely, plants respond to regular changes in these pathways. These changes determine the patterns of a variety of plant responses.

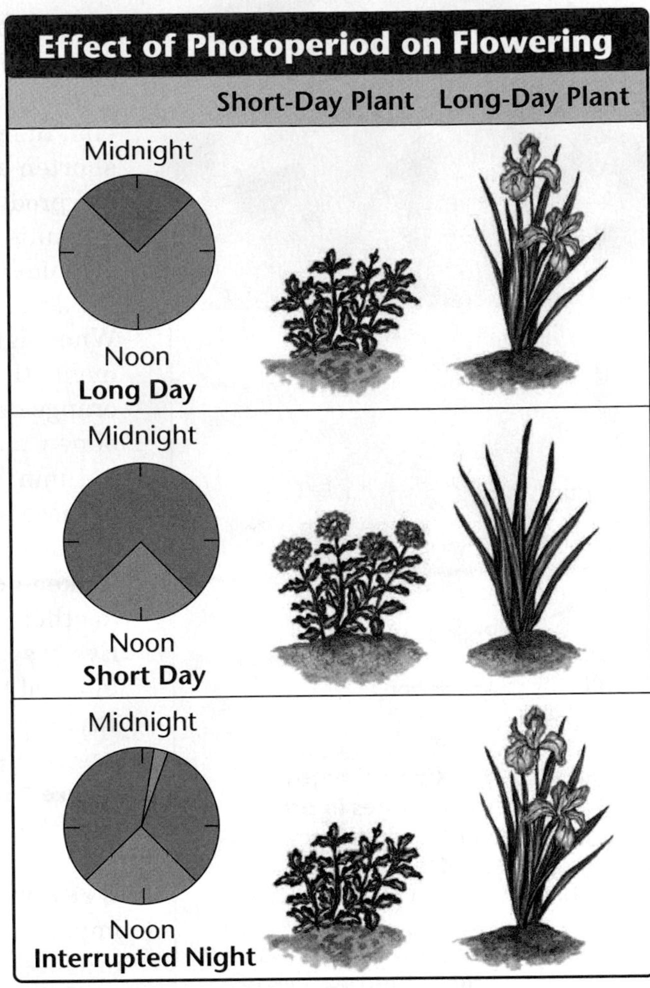

▲ **Figure 25–10** **Photoperiodism controls the timing of flowering and seasonal growth.** The response of flowering, shown here, is controlled by the amount of darkness plants receive. Short-day plants, such as chrysanthemums, flower only when exposed to an extended period of darkness every night—and thus a short period of light during the day. Long-day plants, such as irises, flower when exposed to a short period of darkness or to a long period of darkness interrupted by a brief period of light.

Winter Dormancy

Phytochrome also regulates the changes in activity that prepare many plants for dormancy as winter approaches. **Dormancy** is the period during which an organism's growth and activity decrease or stop.

The changes that prepare a plant for dormancy are important adaptations that protect plants over the cold winter months. **As cold weather approaches, deciduous plants turn off photosynthetic pathways, transport materials from leaves to roots, and seal leaves off from the rest of the plant.** In early autumn, the shorter days and lower temperatures gradually reduce the efficiency of photosynthesis. With these changing conditions, the plant gains very little by keeping its leaves alive. In fact, the thin, delicate leaves produced by most flowering plants would have little chance of surviving a tough winter, and their continued presence would be costly in terms of water loss.

CHECKPOINT *What is dormancy? What changes do plants undergo as colder weather approaches?*

Figure 25–11 **Deciduous plants undergo changes in preparation for winter dormancy.** Photosynthetic pathways in leaves shut down (top). An abscission layer of cells forms at the petiole to seal the leaf off from the rest of the plant (bottom). Eventually, the leaf falls off.

Leaf Abscission In temperate regions, most flowering plants lose their leaves during the colder months. During the warm growing season, auxins are produced in leaves. At summer's end, the phytochrome in leaves absorbs less light as days shorten and nights become longer. Auxin production drops, but the production of ethylene increases. The change in the relative amounts of these two hormones starts a series of events that gradually shut down the leaf.

The chemical pathways for chlorophyll synthesis stop first. When light destroys the remaining green pigment, other pigments that have been present all along—including yellow and orange carotenoids—become visible for the first time. Production of new plant pigments—the reddish anthocyanins—begins in the autumn. The brilliant colors of autumn leaves are a direct result of these processes.

Behind the scenes, enzymes extract nutrients from the broken-down chlorophyll. These nutrients are then transported to other parts of the plant, where they are stored until spring. Every available carbohydrate is transported out of the leaf, and much of the leaf's water is extracted. Finally, an **abscission layer** of cells at the petiole seals the leaf off from the plant's vascular system. The location of the abscission layer is shown in **Figure 25–11.** Before long, the leaf falls to the ground, a sign that the tree is fully prepared for winter.

Overwintering of Meristems Hormones also produce important changes in apical meristems. Instead of continuing to produce leaves, meristems produce thick, waxy scales that form a protective layer around new leaf buds. Enclosed in its coat of scales, a terminal bud can survive the coldest winter days. At the onset of winter, xylem and phloem tissues pump themselves full of ions and organic compounds. These molecules act like antifreeze in a car, preventing the tree's sap from freezing, thus making it possible to survive the bitter cold.

25–2 Section Assessment

1. **Key Concept** Identify three types of plant tropisms that show how plants respond to external stimuli.
2. **Key Concept** Compare short-day and long-day plants. Which type of plant is likely to bloom in the summer?
3. **Key Concept** What changes occur in plants before winter? How do these changes help the plant to survive?
4. Describe the process of leaf abscission.
5. **Critical Thinking Designing Experiments** How could a garden-store owner determine what light conditions are needed for a particular flowering plant to bloom? Design a controlled experiment to find out.

Connecting Concepts

Evolution
Review what you learned about evolution by natural selection in Chapter 15. Then, using what you know about natural selection, describe how plant adaptations for dormancy may have developed over time.

25–3 Plant Adaptations

4-6.2 Diversity of organisms
4-6.2 Biodiversity lost
4-6.2 Biodiversity provides a rich variety of genetic material

Flowering plants grow in a variety of biomes—in deserts, savannas, and tundras—to name a few. They also grow in various aquatic ecosystems, such as ponds and streams. Angiosperms can survive in many different locations. How is this possible? Through natural selection they have evolved tolerances and structural and physiological adaptations to meet the conditions of each biome. In this section, we explore how plants have become adapted to various environments through evolutionary change.

Guide for Reading

 **Key Concepts**

- How are plants adapted to different environments?
- How do plants obtain nutrients from sources other than photosynthesis?
- How do plants defend themselves from insects?

Vocabulary
xerophyte
epiphyte

Reading Strategy: Using Prior Knowledge
Before you read, list the different environments in which plants grow. Next to each environment listed, describe adaptations you might expect to find in plants. As you read, compare your predictions with information about different plant adaptations.

Aquatic Plants

Aquatic plants are able to tolerate mud that is saturated with water and nearly devoid of oxygen. **To take in sufficient oxygen, many aquatic plants have tissues with large air-filled spaces through which oxygen can diffuse.** In waterlilies, shown in **Figure 25–12,** there are large open spaces in the long petioles that reach from the leaves down to the roots at the bottom. Oxygen diffuses from these open spaces into the roots.

Many other plants show similar adaptations. Several species of mangrove trees grow in shallow water along tropical seacoasts. Mangroves tolerate this environment by means of specialized air roots with air spaces in them, just like waterlily stems. These spaces conduct air down to the buried roots, allowing the root tissues to respire normally. Stately bald cypress trees thrive in freshwater swamps in the southern United States. These trees grow structures called knees, which protrude above the water. The knees bring oxygen-rich air down to the roots.

The reproductive adaptations of aquatic plants include seeds that float in water and delay germination for long periods. Many aquatic plants grow quickly after germination, extending the growing shoot above the water's surface.

▼ **Figure 25–12** **Aquatic plants have air-filled spaces in their tissues that allow for the uptake and diffusion of oxygen.** These waterlilies transport oxygen from the air to their roots through large spaces in their petioles.

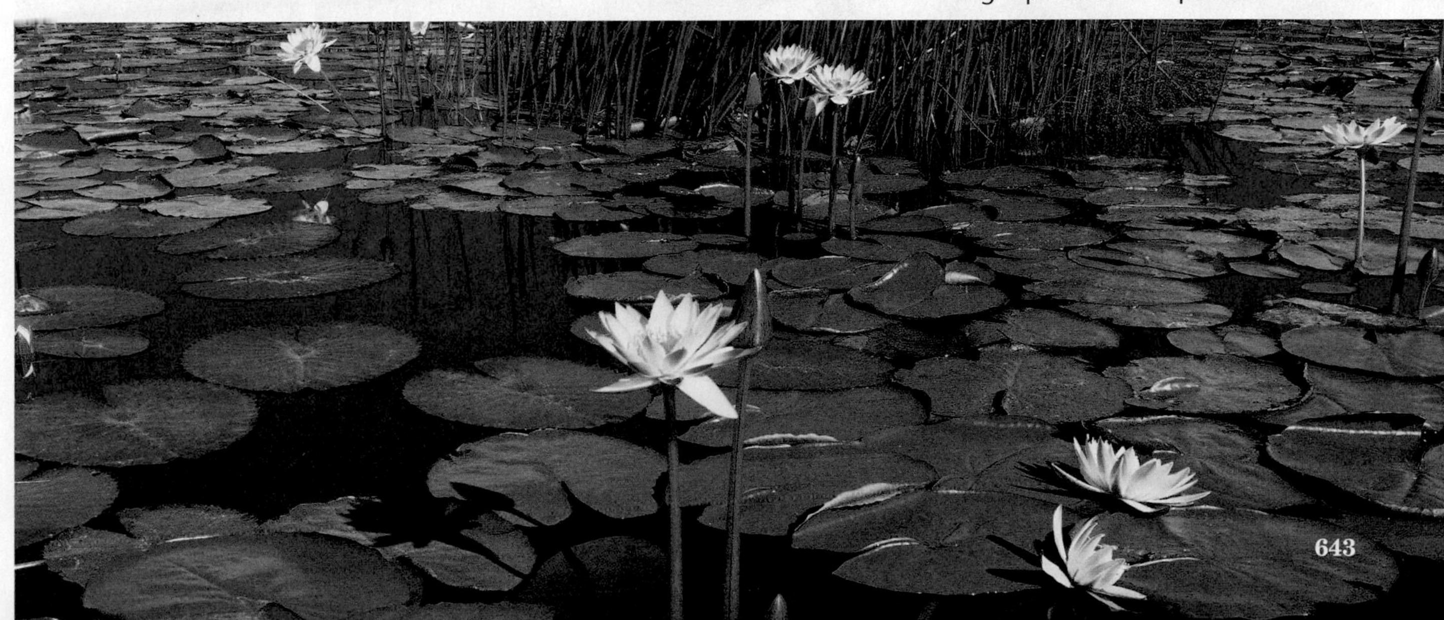

Word Origins

Xerophyte comes from the Greek words *xeros,* meaning "dry," and *phyton,* meaning "plant." **Where do you think hydrophytes live?**

Salt-Tolerant Plants

When plant roots take in dissolved minerals, a difference in the concentration of water molecules is created between the root cells and the surrounding soil. This concentration difference causes water to enter the root cells by osmosis. For plants that grow in salt water, such as mangroves, this means taking in much more salt than the plant can use. The roots of salt-tolerant plants are adapted to salt concentrations that would quickly destroy the root hairs on most plants. The leaves of these plants have specialized cells that pump salt out of the plant tissues and onto the leaf surfaces, where it is washed off by rain.

Desert Plants

Plants that live in the desert biome are called **xerophytes.** Xerophytes must tolerate a variety of extreme conditions, including strong winds, daytime heat, sandy soil, and infrequent rain. Rainwater sinks rapidly through desert soils instead of staying near the surface. The hot, dry air quickly removes moisture from any wet surface, making life difficult for plants. **Plant adaptations to a desert climate include extensive roots, reduced leaves, and thick stems that can store water.**

One familiar group of desert plants is the cactus (family Cactaceae), shown in **Figure 25–13.** Cactuses have root systems that either spread out for long distances just beneath the soil surface or that reach deep down into the soil. In addition, the roots have many hairs that quickly absorb water after a rainstorm, before the water sinks too deeply into the soil.

To reduce water loss due to transpiration, cactus leaves have been reduced to thin, sharp spines. Cactuses also have thick green stems that carry out photosynthesis and are adapted to store water. The stems of cactuses swell during rainy periods and shrivel during dry spells, when the plants are forced to use up their water reserves.

▼ **Figure 25–13** **Desert plants have evolved different adaptations to survive desert conditions.** For example, the shallow root systems of cactuses allow them to pick up surface water. The deep taproots of the mesquite tree and the sagebrush collect underground water. Spines, which are found on many desert plants, are actually reduced leaves that carry out little or no photosynthesis and, as a result, lose little water. Most of a plant's photosynthesis is carried out in its fleshy stem.

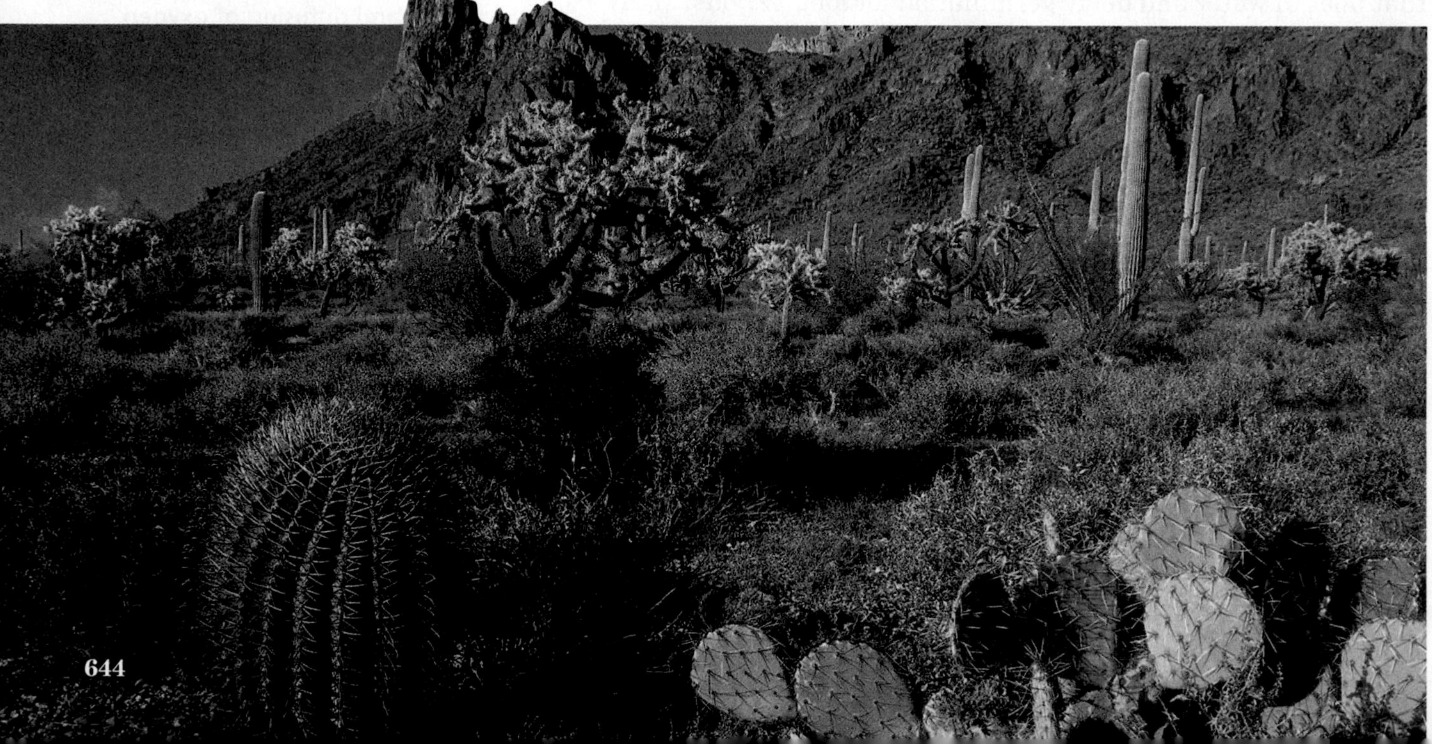

Seeds of many desert plants can remain dormant for years, germinating only when sufficient moisture guarantees them a chance for survival. Other desert plants have bulbs, tubers, or other specialized stems that can remain dormant for years. When rain does come, the plants mature, flower, and set seed in a matter of weeks or even days, before the water disappears.

CHECKPOINT *How are the roots and leaves of desert plants specialized for the environment in which they live?*

Nutritional Specialists

Some plants grow in environments that have low concentrations of nutrients in the soil. **Plants that have specialized features for obtaining nutrients include carnivorous plants and parasites.**

Carnivorous Plants Some plants live in bogs, wet and acidic environments where there is very little or no nitrogen present. Because conditions are too wet and too acidic, bacteria that cause decay cannot survive. Without these bacteria, neither plant nor animal material is broken down into the nutrients plants can use.

A number of plants that live in these habitats obtain nutrients using specialized leaves that trap and digest insects. Pitcher plants drown their prey in pitcher-shaped leaves that hold rainwater and digestive enzymes. Sundews trap insects on leaf hairs tipped with sticky secretions. The best known of the carnivorous plants is the Venus' flytrap, shown in **Figure 25–14.** This plant has leaf blades that are hinged at the middle. If an insect touches the trigger hairs on the leaf, the leaf folds up suddenly, trapping the animal inside. Over a period of several days, the leaf secretes enzymes that digest the insect and release nitrogen for the plant to use.

Parasites Some plants extract water and nutrients directly from a host plant. Like all parasites, these plants harm their host organisms and sometimes even pose a serious threat to other species. The dodder plant *Cuscuta* is a parasitic plant that has no chlorophyll and thus does not produce its own food. The plant grows directly into the vascular tissue of its host. There, it extracts nutrients and water. Mistletoe grows as a parasite on many plants, including conifers in the western United States.

Epiphytes

Epiphytes are plants that are not rooted in soil but instead grow directly on the bodies of other plants. Most epiphytes are found in the tropical rain forest biome, but they grow in other moist biomes as well. Epiphytes are not parasites. They gather their own moisture, generally from rainfall, and produce their own food. One of the most common epiphytes is Spanish moss. This plant is actually not a moss at all but a member of the bromeliad family. Over half the species of orchids are epiphytes.

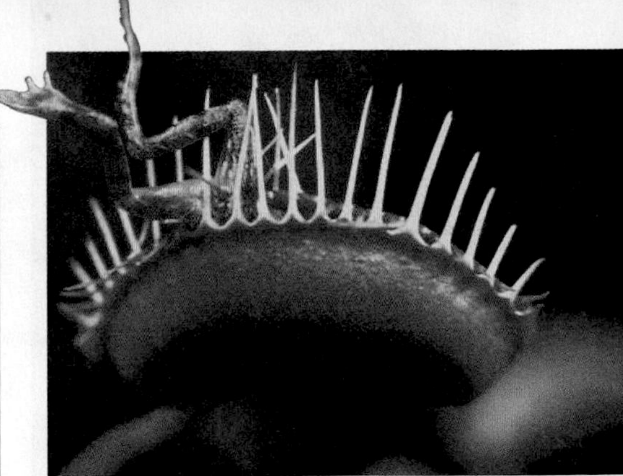

Carnivorous Plant: Venus' flytrap

Parasite: Mistletoe

Figure 25–14 Plants that have specialized features for obtaining nutrients include carnivorous plants and parasites. Carnivorous plants, such as the Venus' flytrap, digest insects—and occasionally frogs—as a source of nutrients. Parasites grow into the tissues of their host plant and extract water and nutrients, causing harm to the host.

Figure 25–15 **Many plants produce chemical compounds that ward off potential predators.** *Digitalis* (left), which is also called foxglove, is poisonous when eaten. The monarch caterpillar (right) can eat milkweed—which is toxic to most animals—because it can store the toxic compounds in its body.

Chemical Defenses

Seed plants and insects have had such a long relationship that each has had plenty of time to adapt to the other. The beginnings of the relationship are obvious—plants represent an important source of food for insects, as shown in **Figure 25–15.** Plants, therefore, fall prey to a host of plant-eating insects. Because plants cannot run away, you might think that they are defenseless against insects that are armed with biting and sucking structures. But plants have their own defenses.

Many plants defend themselves against insect attack by manufacturing compounds that have powerful effects on animals. Some of these chemicals are poisons that can be lethal when eaten. Other chemicals act as insect hormones, disrupting normal growth and development and preventing insects from reproducing. These chemicals include those used in aspirin, codeine, and scores of other drugs that humans use as medicines.

As you may know, nicotine is a chemical that is found in tobacco plants. When a person smokes tobacco in the form of cigarettes, the nicotine in the tobacco affects the human nervous system. Biologists hypothesize that nicotine is a natural insecticide that disrupts the nervous system of many insects, protecting tobacco plants from potential predators.

25–3 Section Assessment

1. **Key Concept** Compare the variations and adaptations of aquatic plants and desert plants. Which plants have adaptations for obtaining sufficient oxygen?
2. **Key Concept** Describe how carnivorous plants and parasites obtain their nutrients.
3. **Key Concept** How do some plants defend themselves from insect predators?
4. How are salt-tolerant plants adapted to their environment?
5. **Critical Thinking Predicting** Suppose a temperate region underwent a drought. Predict which structural and physiological adaptations would enable some plants to survive. Give at least two examples.
6. **Critical Thinking Comparing and Contrasting** Choose two different biomes and then compare adaptations of two different groups of plants in those biomes.

Thinking Visually

Creating Artwork
Choose one of the plants discussed in this section. Then, create a piece of artwork that shows how the plant is adapted to live in its natural environment. Label the particular adaptation you are illustrating.

Should Herbal Remedies Be Regulated?

Natural herbal medicines and dietary supplements can be found in the medicine cabinets of millions of Americans. Annually, Americans spend about $2 billion on herbal remedies. These remedies include St. John's wort, for treatment of depression; *Echinacea,* for colds and flu; and *Ephedra,* for weight loss.

Because these preparations are made from plants and plant extracts, they are considered to be foods and food supplements, not drugs. As a result, the Food and Drug Administration (FDA) cannot require studies to determine the safety and effectiveness of herbal substances. Advocates for herbal products say that additional regulations are not needed. Critics worry that many of these products are as powerful and as dangerous as drugs.

SNEEZING? CHILLS? FLU?

Try Echinacea to **RELIEVE** your cold and flu symptoms!

Echinacea will boost your immune system to fight upper respiratory tract infections!

Warning: Do not use Echinacea if you are pregnant, intend to become pregnant, have an autoimmune disease, liver disease, or are allergic to daisies, chrysanthemums, or ragweed. Consult with your physician or pharmacist before beginning any self-medication.

The Viewpoints

Are Herbal Remedies Safe?

Natural herbal products have been used for thousands of years by people of every culture. *Ephedra,* for example, comes from the Chinese herb *ma huang* and has been used to treat asthma and nasal congestion for centuries. Remedies using *Echinacea* were developed long ago by Native Americans. Such substances should continue to be exempt from new FDA regulations and available without a prescription. Herbal substances present consumers with increased health benefits combined with low risks.

Are Herbal Remedies Dangerous?

Just because a product is "natural" does not mean that it is safe. Plants produce many substances that are more powerful and dangerous than synthetic drugs. *Ephedra,* sometimes used for weight loss, is itself a powerful stimulant that can cause hypertension, stroke, and perhaps death. St. John's wort interferes with the functions of many drugs, including medications for AIDS, epilepsy, and heart disease. As with other drugs, the FDA should regulate and test herbal substances for safety and effectiveness.

Research and Decide

1. **Analyzing the Viewpoints** To make an informed decision, learn more about this issue by consulting library or Internet sources. Write why some people prefer herbal remedies to drugs. Explain why some people think that herbal remedies should be better regulated.
2. **Forming Your Opinion** If an extract of an herb such as *Echinacea* produces effects as powerful as those of synthetic drugs, should it be regulated in the same way? What principles should shape government policies regarding these substances?
3. **Persuasive Writing** Write an e-mail to a friend who is thinking about taking *Echinacea.* Provide guidelines for evaluating labels and ads for *Echinacea* so that your friend can discuss this topic with an adult family member.

For: Links from the authors
Visit: PHSchool.com
Web Code: cbe-7253

Using Hormones to Control Plant Development

Plant hormones have many practical uses. Growers spray gibberellins on sugar cane and fruits to promote their growth. Orchid growers use cytokinins when they clone orchids. Auxins are used to keep potatoes from sprouting and apples from falling from trees before they are ripe. Auxins are also used to stimulate pineapples to flower and develop fruits. In this investigation, you will use auxins to identify the locations of meristems that can be forced to form roots on leaf and stem cuttings.

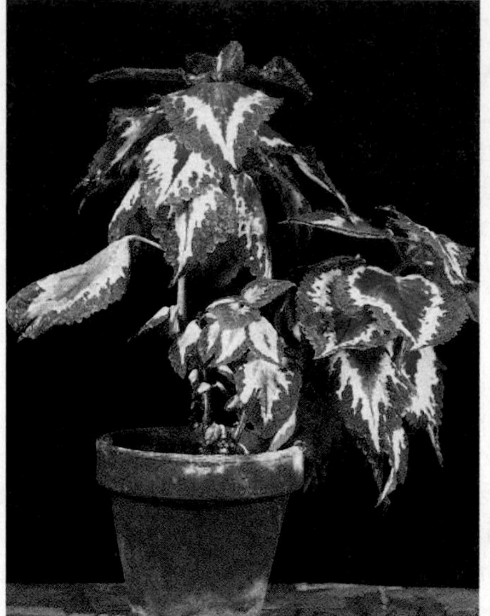

Problem How do auxins affect plant development?

Materials

- large coleus plants (total of at least 4 branches)
- dissecting pin
- scalpel
- metric ruler
- rooting compound (auxin powder)
- commercial potting soil
- 12 paper cups
- flat, wooden toothpick

Skills Observing, Formulating Hypotheses, Comparing and Contrasting

Procedure 

Part A: Observing the Effects of Auxins on Root and Leaf Development

1. Use a scalpel to cut a piece containing a stem tip from a coleus plant as shown. The stem-tip cutting should include a stem tip and 2 nodes that are at least 1 cm from the tip of the stem. Cut the stem tip 3 mm below these 2 nodes. Cut 3 more stem-tip cuttings. **CAUTION:** *Be careful with sharp instruments.*
2. Cut off the petioles growing from the bottom node of each stem-tip cutting. Make sure the cut is 3 mm from the stem. See the illustration.
3. Put on plastic gloves. Cut the top from each stem-tip cutting, 3 mm above the top node. Using a toothpick, apply only enough rooting compound to coat the cut surfaces on the tops of 2 stem-tip cuttings.
4. Cut 8 pieces from the lower stems of each plant as shown. As in step 1, each stem cutting should contain at least 2 nodes and be cut 3 mm below the lower node.
5. Dip the stem-tip cuttings and 6 of the lower stem cuttings into powdered rooting hormone (an auxin) so that the bottom nodes are covered with powder. Leave 2 stem cuttings untreated.
6. Use a dissecting pin to punch several small drainage holes in the bottoms of the paper cups. Fill each paper cup with potting soil. Push the bottom of each cutting into the potting soil in a paper cup so that the bottom nodes are buried. Keep the soil moist but not wet. Label the paper cups to indicate what type of cutting each cup contains.
7. After 1 week, carefully pull 1 treated and 1 untreated stem cutting from the potting soil. Gently wash the soil off the roots and observe the differences. Record your observations and discard the cuttings you removed. Repeat this procedure after 2 weeks.
8. Allow the stem-tip cuttings to grow for 3 weeks. Observe, measure with precision, and record any differences in leaf growth between the treated and untreated plants.

Stem-Tip Cutting

At least 1 cm
Nodes
Petioles
3 mm
Cut here
Step 1

Cut here
Cut here
3 mm
Step 2

Cut here
3 mm
Step 3

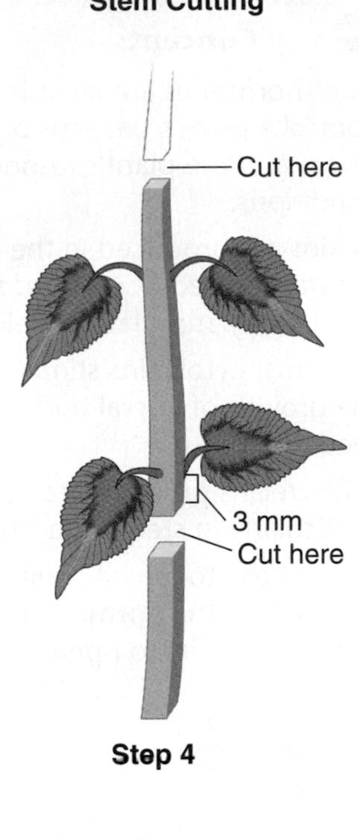

Part B: Using the Effects of Auxins

9. **Formulating Hypotheses** Because auxins stimulate meristems to produce new roots and other plant parts, auxins can be used to locate meristems. Record a hypothesis about whether there are meristems in stems between nodes and in the veins on the bottoms of leaves.

10. **Designing Experiments** Design an experiment to test your hypothesis. You may need to nick the leaf veins slightly with a scalpel to expose any meristems in the veins to the rooting compound and moist soil. With your teacher's approval, carry out your experiment.

Analyze and Conclude

1. **Comparing and Contrasting** What differences did you see between the roots of the auxin-treated and untreated cuttings after 1 week? How can you explain these differences?
2. **Comparing and Contrasting** Was there more difference between roots of treated cuttings and untreated cuttings after 1 week or 2 weeks? How can you explain this result?
3. **Inferring** In step 8, what differences did you observe between the leaves of the treated and untreated stem-tip cuttings? Explain your observations.
4. **Drawing Conclusions** Did the results of your experiment in step 10 show that there are meristem cells in the stem between nodes? In the veins on the underside of the leaves? Explain your conclusions.
5. **Evaluating** Do you consider your conclusions in step 4 to be valid? Explain your answer.

Go Further

Designing Experiments Examine a coleus plant and list questions about the effect of ethylene gas on the development of flowers and new leaves. Design an experiment to answer one of your questions. Use a bruised apple as a source of ethylene gas.

Chapter 25 Study Guide

25–1 Hormones and Plant Growth

Key Concepts

- Plant hormones are chemical substances that control a plant's patterns of growth and development, and the plant's responses to environmental conditions.
- Auxins are produced in the apical meristem and are transported downward into the rest of the plant. They stimulate cell elongation.
- In plants, cytokinins stimulate cell division and the growth of lateral buds, and cause dormant seeds to sprout.
- Gibberellins produce dramatic increases in size, particularly in stems and fruit.
- In response to auxins, fruit tissues release small amounts of the hormone ethylene. Ethylene then stimulates fruits to ripen.

Vocabulary

hormone, p. 634 • target cell, p. 634
phototropism, p. 634 • auxin, p. 635
gravitropism, p. 635 • lateral bud, p. 636
apical dominance, p. 636 • herbicide, p. 636
cytokinin, p. 636 • gibberellin, p. 637
ethylene, p. 638

25–2 Plant Responses

Key Concepts

- Plant tropisms include gravitropism, phototropism, and thigmotropism. Each of these responses demonstrates the ability of plants to respond effectively to external stimuli, such as gravity, light, and touch.
- Photoperiodism in plants is responsible for the timing of seasonal activities such as flowering and growth.
- As cold weather approaches, deciduous plants turn off photosynthetic pathways, transport materials from leaves to roots, and seal leaves off from the rest of the plant.

Vocabulary

tropism, p. 639
thigmotropism, p. 639
short-day plant, p. 641
long-day plant, p. 641
photoperiodism, p. 641
phytochrome, p. 641
dormancy, p. 641
abscission layer, p. 642

25–3 Plant Adaptations

Key Concepts

- To take in sufficient oxygen, many aquatic plants have tissues with large air-filled spaces through which oxygen can diffuse.
- Plant adaptations to a desert climate include extensive roots, reduced leaves, and thick stems that can store water.
- Plants that have specialized features for obtaining nutrients include carnivorous plants and parasites.
- Many plants defend themselves against insect attack by manufacturing compounds that have powerful effects on animals.

Vocabulary

xerophyte, p. 644
epiphyte, p. 645

Thinking Visually

Using the information in this chapter, complete the following flowchart about leaf abscission.

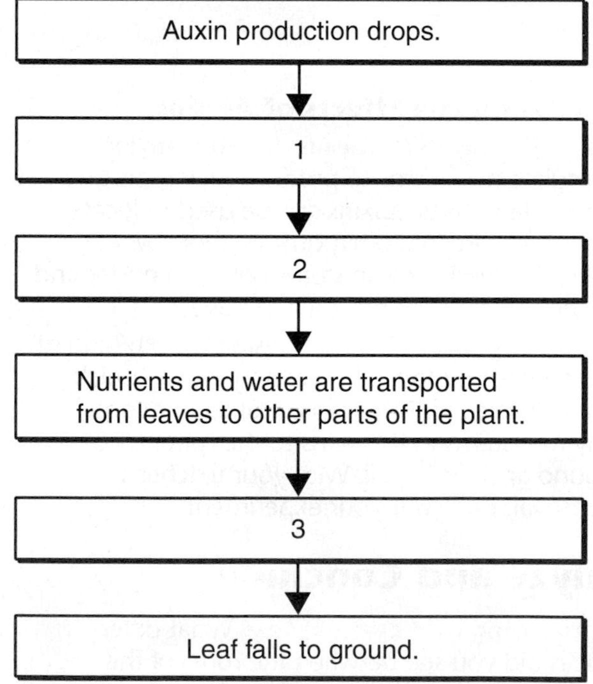

Auxin production drops.
1
2
Nutrients and water are transported from leaves to other parts of the plant.
3
Leaf falls to ground.

Preparing for the Living Environment Exam

Blue questions emphasize Regents Exam content

Chapter 25

Part A

Multiple Choice

For each statement or question, select the number of the word or expression that, of those given, best completes the statement or answers the question.

1 A substance produced in one part of a plant that is able to affect target cells in another part of the plant is
(1) an enzyme (3) a hormone
(2) a herbicide (4) a phytochrome

2 Substances that stimulate cell division and cause dormant seeds to sprout are
(1) gibberellins (3) cytokinins
(2) auxins (4) xerophytes

3 In the illustration below, what phenomenon is responsible for the shape of the plant on the left?
(1) gravitropism (3) phytochromes
(2) dormancy (4) apical dominance

4 A high concentration of auxins can inhibit plant growth. Compounds containing such high concentrations are commercially produced and sold as
(1) fruit ripeners (3) pesticides
(2) growth stimulants (4) herbicides

5 Japanese scientists found that a fungus causes a disease that resultes in the extraordinary growth of certain rice plants. This led to the discovery of a growth-promoting chemical called
(1) auxin (3) cytokinin
(2) gibberellin (4) ethylene

6 The period during which an organism's growth and activity decreases or stops is called
(1) abscission (3) thigmotropism
(2) dormancy (4) gravitropism

7 Plants that have air-filled spaces in their tissues are likely to be
(1) desert plants (3) epiphytes
(2) aquatic plants (4) parasites

8 Plants that grow directly on the bodies of other plants but manufacture their own food are
(1) epiphytes (3) carnivorous plants
(2) aquatic plants (4) parasites

9 The ripening of fruit is most closely associated with
(1) auxins (3) ethylene
(2) cytokinins (4) gibberellins

10 Which choice best illustrates a thigmotropism?
(1) leaf abscission
(2) climbing vines
(3) branching stems
(4) blooming period

11 Which statement best describes a short-day plant?
(1) It will bloom if the dark period is long enough.
(2) It will bloom if the light period is long enough.
(3) It will not bloom when days are short.
(4) It will not bloom when nights are long.

12 Scientists have learned that growth patterns in plants result from hormone signals sent through plant tissues. This suggests that
(1) homeostasis in plants is disrupted when target cells receive hormone signals
(2) homeostatic mechanisms involving hormones have evolved in many plants
(3) plants use the same hormones as animals to maintain homeostasis
(4) plants do not need to maintain homeostasis when their hormones are functioning correctly

Test-Taking Tip Take the time to read each question completely, including all the answer choices. Consider each possible choice before determining which answer is correct.

Part B

Multiple Choice and Extended Response
For those questions that ask you to select a response, choose the one that best completes the statement or answers the question. For all others follow the directions given.

Base your answers to questions 13 through 15 on the information below, which summarizes an experiment with oat seedlings, and on your knowledge of biology.

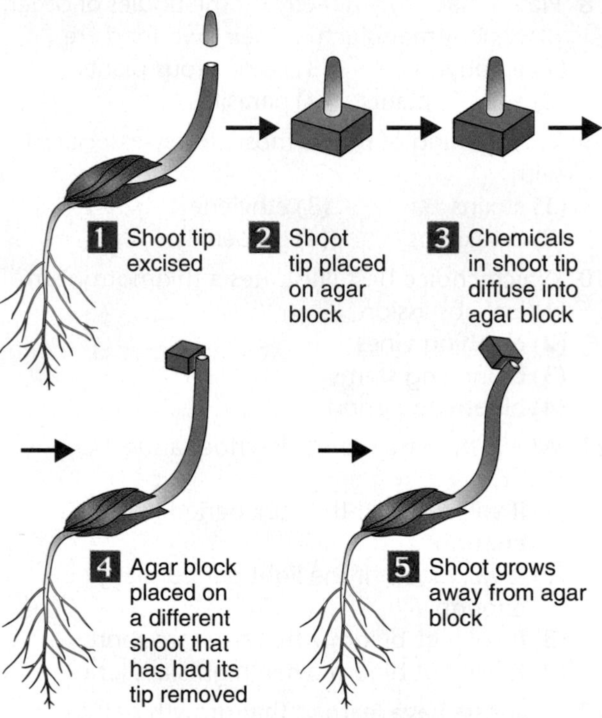

1 Shoot tip excised
2 Shoot tip placed on agar block
3 Chemicals in shoot tip diffuse into agar block
4 Agar block placed on a different shoot that has had its tip removed
5 Shoot grows away from agar block

13 Which is the best conclusion that can be made from the results of this experiment?
(1) Hormones are produced in the growing tips of plants.
(2) Oat plants grow toward the sun because of compounds produced in their stems.
(3) Chemicals produced in plant stems stimulate plant growth.
(4) Compounds produced in shoot tips can cause oat seedlings to bend.

14 If the cells of the stem near the agar block were examined with a compound light microscope, they would not all look the same. Make a sketch to illustrate the difference between the cells nearest the block and those on the other side of the stem.

15 To make these experimental results more valid, the experimenter should have
(1) used a smaller agar block to soak up the chemicals
(2) tested a second seedling with its tip removed and used an untreated agar block
(3) left the shoot tip on the agar block when it was placed on the seedling
(4) used a seedling from a different plant species

Base your answers to questions 16 through 18 on the information below and on your knowledge of biology.

A scientist used the following experimental setup to study the effects of gibberellic acid on plant growth. He measured and recorded the change in height of each plant at the same time every day for one week.

Effects of Gibberellic Acid on Plant Growth

Container	Type of Plant	Volume of Solution in Flask	Percent Gibberellic Acid
Flask 1	Bean seedling	200 mL	0.0
Flask 2	Bean seeding	200 mL	0.1
Flask 3	Bean seedling	200 mL	1.0
Flask 4	Bean seedling	200 mL	10.0

16 Identify the manipulated (independent) variable in this investigation.

17 State one possible hypothesis that could be tested with this experimental setup.

18 Which column headings would be most appropriate in a table that summarizes the data obtained from this experiment?
(1) Percent Gibberellic Acid and Total Growth After 7 Days
(2) Container Number and Percent Gibberellic Acid
(3) Day Number and Total Growth After 7 Days
(4) Container Number and Daily Growth for 7 Days

Base your answers to questions 19 and 20 on the information and illustration below and on your knowledge of biology.

The experiment shown below was intended to test the effect of gravitropism on plant growth. The conclusion drawn from the experiment was that plant stems grow upward because they are growing away from the force of gravity.

19 State the probable hypothesis for this experiment.

20 Explain why this experiment may not have successfully tested the effect of gravity on plant growth.

21 A student wanted to investigate the effect of gibberellin on the average diameter of flowers produced by a particular plant species. Seven groups were tested, each consisting of 10 plants. All groups were treated in the same manner, except for the concentration of gibberellin solution applied to the developing flower buds. The results of the experiment are shown in the table below.

Micrograms of Gibberellin in a Constant Volume of Water	Average Diameter of Flowers (in mm)
0.00	110
0.05	230
0.10	305
0.25	365
0.50	395
1.00	410
2.00	410

How do the flowers of this plant species respond to varying amounts of gibberellin treatment? In your answer be sure to
- state the effect of low concentrations of gibberellin on flower diameter
- state the effect that higher concentrations of gibberellin have on flower diameter
- explain how flowers of this species would most likely respond to a treatment of 4 mg of gibberellin in the same volume of water

Part C

Extended Response

Answer the questions or follow the directions given.

22 Tropisms are important adaptations common to many species of plants. Explain how some plants rely on tropisms for survival. In your answer, be sure to:
- explain what a tropism is
- identify one tropism that affects plant stems
- identify one tropism that affects plant roots
- explain why each tropism you identify is important for plant survival

23 During the autumn, deciduous trees and shrubs prepare for the coming winter. Describe what happens to the leaves and buds of these plants as they prepare for winter dormancy. In your answer, be sure to explain:
- what happens to the rate of photosynthesis
- how the plant prevents water loss
- what is done to protect leaf buds
- where nutrients located in leaves are stored

For: An interactive self-test
Visit: PHSchool.com
Web Code: cba-7250

UNIT 8

Invertebrates

Chapters

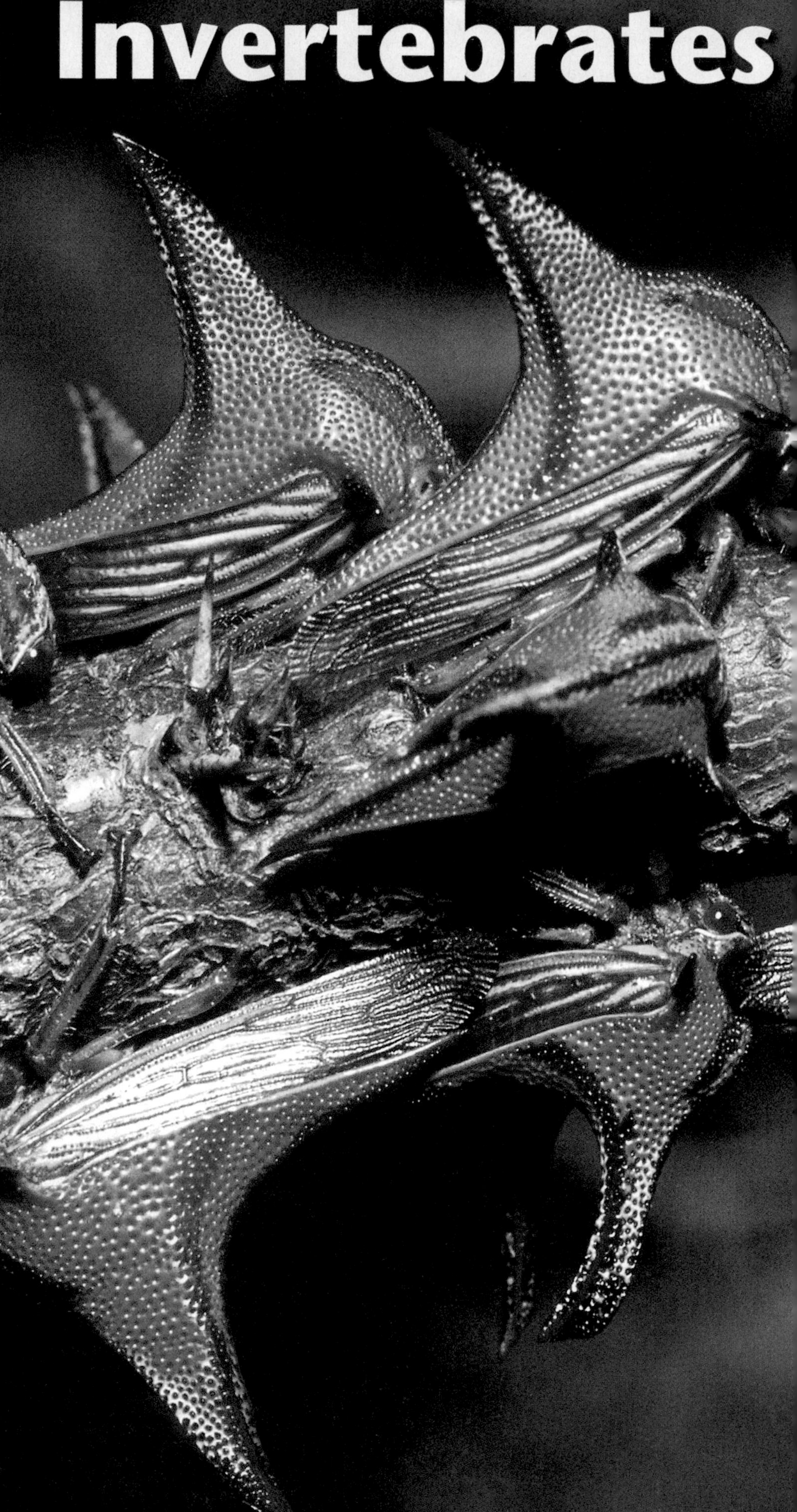

Thorn bugs got their name from the fact that they look like thorns, thus scaring away any predators. The close resemblance of an organism such as these thorn bugs to an object in its environment—in this case thorns—is known as mimicry.

From the Author

I never really liked hydras. They were small, didn't do much, and were usually half dead by the time I got one under my microscope. "What good are all these creepy-crawlies?" I'd ask myself. "Why should I care about them?" Years later, during a marine biology course, I saw a coral reef for the first time. Nothing prepared me for the beauty and fascination of that place—built and inhabited mostly by invertebrates. After that, I would never belittle animals without backbones again.

What discoveries lie ahead?

- Can a better understanding of insects help protect farms from insect pests and protect humans from insect-borne diseases?
- What will paleontology and molecular genetics tell us about how major groups of invertebrates are related to one another—and to us?

Go Online
PHSchool.com

For: Latest discoveries
Visit: PHSchool.com
Web Code: cbe-8000

CHAPTER 26

Sponges and Cnidarians

Tube sponges (pink objects) are the most common variety of sponge. Water is constantly filtered through the sponge's body and ejected through the large hole at the top. The golden yellow objects and red objects are crinoids (a type of echinoderms).

Inquiry Activity

What makes an animal an animal?

Procedure 

1. Observe the specimens or photographs of organisms provided by your teacher. Some of the organisms are animals, whereas others are not. Examine each organism carefully.
2. Make a list of each organism's characteristics.

Think About It

1. **Classifying** Classify the organisms into two groups: animals and nonanimals. Give your reasons for putting each organism into a particular group.
2. **Forming Operational Definitions** List at least three characteristics shared by each of the organisms you classified as animals. Describe how these characteristics separate them from the nonanimals.

26–1 Introduction to the Animal Kingdom

4-2.1 Genetic instructions
4-3.1 Earth's species developed from earlier species
4-3.1 Natural selection and evolution
4-6.1 Relationships and interactions between organisms

Of all the kingdoms of organisms, the animal kingdom is the most diverse in appearance. Some animals are so small that they live on or inside the bodies of other animals. Others are many meters long and live in the depths of the sea. They may walk, swim, crawl, burrow, or fly—or not move at all. As you will see, each major group, or phylum, has its own typical body plan.

Guide for Reading

Key Concepts
- What characteristics do all animals share?
- What essential functions do animals carry out?
- What are the important trends in animal evolution?

Vocabulary
invertebrate • vertebrate
feedback inhibition
blastula • protostome
deuterostome • anus
endoderm • mesoderm
ectoderm • radial symmetry
bilateral symmetry
cephalization

Reading Strategy: Monitoring Your Understanding Before you read, write down what you already know about animals. After you have read this section, write down what you learned about animals.

What Is an Animal?

All members of the animal kingdom share certain characteristics. Animals are all heterotrophs, meaning that they obtain nutrients and energy by feeding on organic compounds from other organisms. Animals are multicellular, or composed of many cells. The cells that make up animal bodies are eukaryotic, meaning that they contain a nucleus and membrane-bound organelles. Unlike the cells of algae, fungi, and plants, animal cells do not have cell walls.  **Animals, members of the kingdom Animalia, are multicellular, eukaryotic heterotrophs whose cells lack cell walls.**

The bodies of most animals contain tissues. Recall that a tissue is a group of cells that perform a similar function. Animals have epithelial, muscular, connective, and nervous tissues. Epithelial tissues cover body surfaces. The epithelial cells that line lung surfaces, for example, have thin, flat structures through which gases move in and out easily. The cells of muscle tissue contain proteins that enable the cells to contract, moving parts of animals' bodies. Connective tissue, such as bone and blood, support an animal's body and connect its parts. Cells embedded in bone tissue produce minerals that give strength and hardness to bone. Nervous tissue is composed of nerve cells, which have threadlike projections that act like telephone wires to carry information throughout the body.

Over 95 percent of all animal species are often grouped in a single, informal category: invertebrates. This group is defined in an odd way—by describing a characteristic that its members do *not* have. **Invertebrates** are animals that do not have a backbone, or vertebral column. They range in size from microscopic dust mites to the giant squid, which is more than 20 meters in length. They include groups as diverse as sea stars, worms, jellyfishes, and insects. The other 5 percent of animals, including fishes, amphibians, reptiles, birds, and mammals, are called **vertebrates,** because they have a backbone.

▶ **Figure 26–1** The animal kingdom includes an incredible diversity of forms and lifestyles. **Despite their differences in appearance, both the collared lizard and the grasshopper are eukaryotic heterotrophs whose cells lack cell walls.**

What Animals Do to Survive

Animals carry out the following essential functions: feeding, respiration, circulation, excretion, response, movement, and reproduction. Over millions of years, animals have evolved in a variety of ways that enable them to do this. The study of the functions of organisms is called physiology. The structure, or anatomy, of an animal's body enables it to carry out physiological processes.

Many body functions help animals maintain homeostasis, or a relatively stable internal environment. Homeostasis is often maintained by internal feedback mechanisms. Most of these mechanisms involve **feedback inhibition,** in which the product or result of a process stops or limits the process. For example, when a dog becomes too hot, it pants. Panting releases heat, and the animal's body temperature decreases.

Feeding

Feeding Most animals cannot absorb food; instead, they ingest (or eat) it. Animals have evolved a variety of ways to feed. Herbivores eat plants; carnivores eat other animals; and omnivores feed on both plants and animals. Detritivores feed on decaying plant and animal material. Filter feeders are aquatic animals that strain tiny floating organisms from water.

Animals can also form symbiotic relationships, in which two species live in close association with each other. A parasite, for example, is a type of symbiont that lives within or on another organism, the host. The parasite feeds on the host, harming it.

Respiration

Respiration Whether they live in water or on land, all animals respire, which means that they take in oxygen and give off carbon dioxide. Because of their very simple, thin-walled bodies, some animals can rely on the diffusion of these substances through their skin. Most other animals, however, have evolved complex tissues and organ systems for respiration.

Circulation Many small aquatic animals, such as some aquatic worms, rely solely on diffusion to transport oxygen, nutrient molecules, and waste products among all their cells. Diffusion is sufficient because these animals are only a few cell layers thick. Larger animals, however, have some kind of circulatory system to move materials around within their bodies.

Circulation

Excretion

Excretion A primary waste product of cells is ammonia, a poisonous substance that contains nitrogen. A buildup of ammonia and other waste products would kill an animal. Most animals have an excretory system that either eliminates ammonia quickly or converts it into a less toxic substance that is removed from the body. By eliminating metabolic wastes, excretory systems help maintain homeostasis.

Response Animals respond to events in their environment using specialized cells called nerve cells. In most animals, nerve cells hook up together to form a nervous system. Some cells, called receptors, respond to sound, light, and other external stimuli. Other nerve cells process information and determine how the animal responds. The arrangement of nerve cells in the body changes dramatically from phylum to phylum.

Movement Some adult animals stay attached to a single spot. Most animals, however, are motile, meaning they can move. But both stick-in-the-muds and jet-setters usually have either muscles or musclelike tissues that generate force by becoming shorter. Muscle contraction enables motile animals to move around, usually by working in combination with a support structure called a skeleton. Muscles also help even sedentary animals feed and pump water and fluids through their bodies.

Reproduction Most animals reproduce sexually by producing haploid gametes. Sexual reproduction helps create and maintain genetic diversity in populations. It therefore helps improve species' abilities to evolve when the environment changes. Many invertebrates can also reproduce asexually. Asexual reproduction produces offspring that are genetically identical to the parent. It allows animals to increase their numbers rapidly.

CHECKPOINT *How do sexual and asexual reproduction differ?*

Figure 26–2 Animals carry out seven essential functions: feeding, respiration, circulation, excretion, response, movement, and reproduction. Some snakes feed by constricting, or squeezing, their prey. Humans respire by breathing oxygenated air into lungs. A rabbit's circulatory system pumps blood through closed vessels, which are visible in its ears. Crabs rid their bodies of metabolic wastes by excreting fluid. Like many insects, moths respond to stimuli that they detect from the environment using specialized sense organs such as antennae. Herons move using a system of muscles attached to a low-density skeleton. Animals reproduce either sexually or asexually; lions reproduce sexually and have only a few offspring per litter.

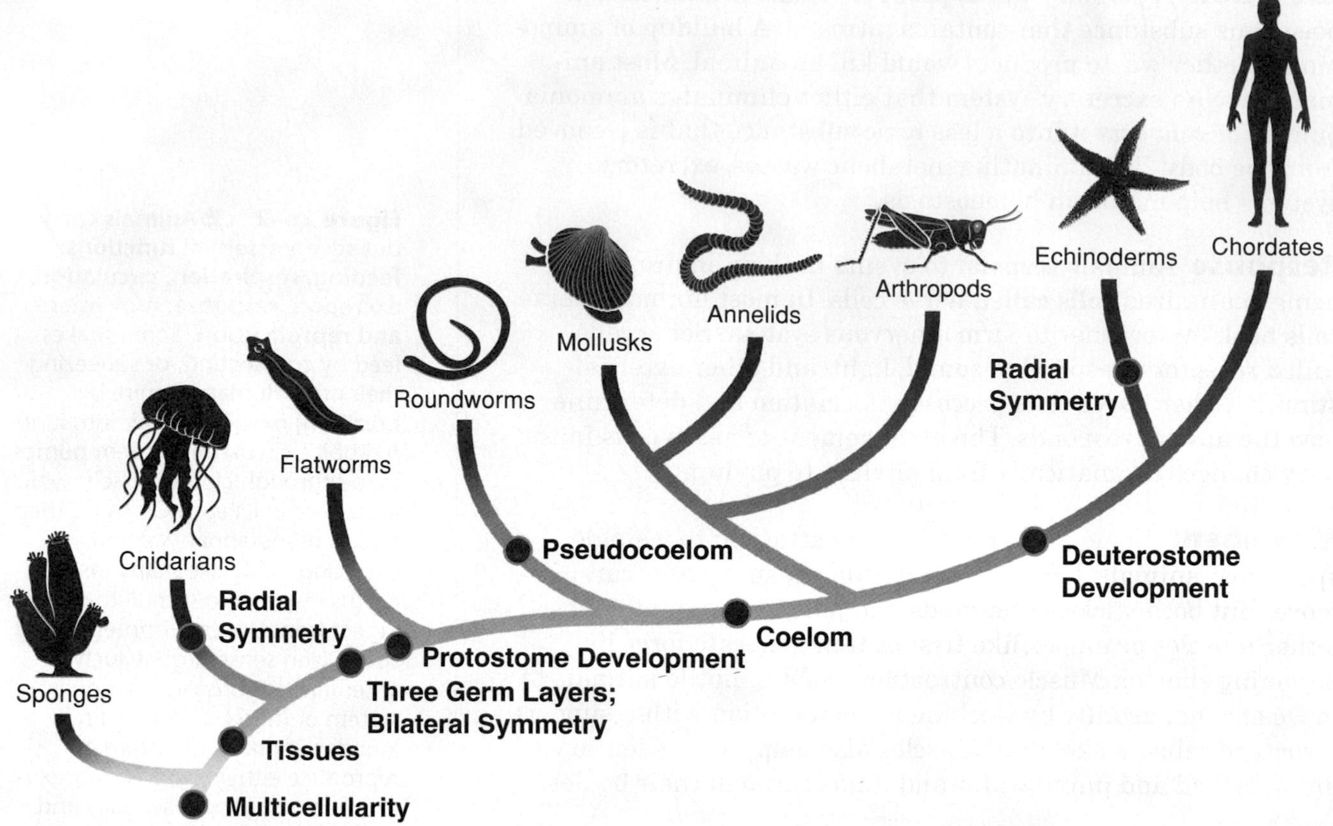

▲ **Figure 26–3** This diagram illustrates phylogenetic, or evolutionary, relationships among major groups of animals. Groups shown close together, such as echinoderms and chordates, are more closely related than groups that are shown farther apart, such as echinoderms and cnidarians. During the course of evolution that produced these different groups, important traits evolved. **Animals that are more complex typically have specialized cells, bilateral body symmetry, cephalization, and a body cavity.**

Trends in Animal Evolution

Your survey of the animal kingdom will begin with simple forms and move through more complicated ones. These different phyla are related to one another by a common evolutionary heritage. The diagram in **Figure 26–3** shows our most current understanding of phylogenetic relationships among groups of living animals. A comparison of the groups in the diagram shows important trends in animal evolution. **Complex animals tend to have high levels of cell specialization and internal body organization, bilateral body symmetry, a front end or head with sense organs, and a body cavity.** In addition, the embryos of complex animals develop in layers.

Cell Specialization and Levels of Organization As animals have evolved, by natural selection and other evolutionary processes, their cells have become specialized to carry out different functions, such as movement and response. Large animals need greater efficiency in body processes than do very small animals. Unicellular organisms, such as amoebas, move nutrients and waste products directly across their cell membranes. In multicellular organisms such as animals, however, each cell type has a structure and chemical composition that enable it to perform a specialized function. Groups of specialized cells form tissues. Tissues join together to form organs and organ systems—all of which work together to carry out a variety of complex functions.

Early Development Animals that reproduce sexually begin life as a zygote, or fertilized egg. **Figure 26–4** shows patterns of embryology, or development of the embryo after fertilization. The zygote undergoes a series of divisions to form a **blastula** (BLAS-tyoo-luh), which is a hollow ball of cells. The blastula folds in on itself, forming a single opening called a blastopore. The process of blastopore formation changes a simple ball of cells—similar to an inflated balloon—into an elongated structure with a tube inside, as if you were holding the balloon and pushing your thumbs toward the center.

The blastopore leads into a central tube that runs the length of the developing embryo. This tube becomes the digestive tract and is formed in one of two ways. A **protostome** (PROH-tuh-stohm) is an animal whose mouth is formed from the blastopore. Most invertebrate animals are protostomes. A **deuterostome** (DOO-tur-uh-stohm) is an animal whose anus is formed from the blastopore. The **anus** is the opening through which wastes leave the digestive tract. The mouth is formed second, after the anus (*deuterostome* means "second mouth"). Echinoderms and all vertebrates are deuterostomes. This similarity in embryology may indicate that vertebrates have a closer evolutionary relationship to echinoderms than to other invertebrates.

During early development, the cells of most animal embryos differentiate into three layers called germ layers. The cells of the **endoderm,** or innermost germ layer, develop into the linings of the digestive tract and much of the respiratory system. The cells of the **mesoderm,** or middle layer, give rise to muscles and much of the circulatory, reproductive, and excretory organ systems. The **ectoderm,** or outermost layer, gives rise to sense organs, nerves, and the outer layer of the skin.

CHECKPOINT *Which germ layer gives rise to the muscles?*

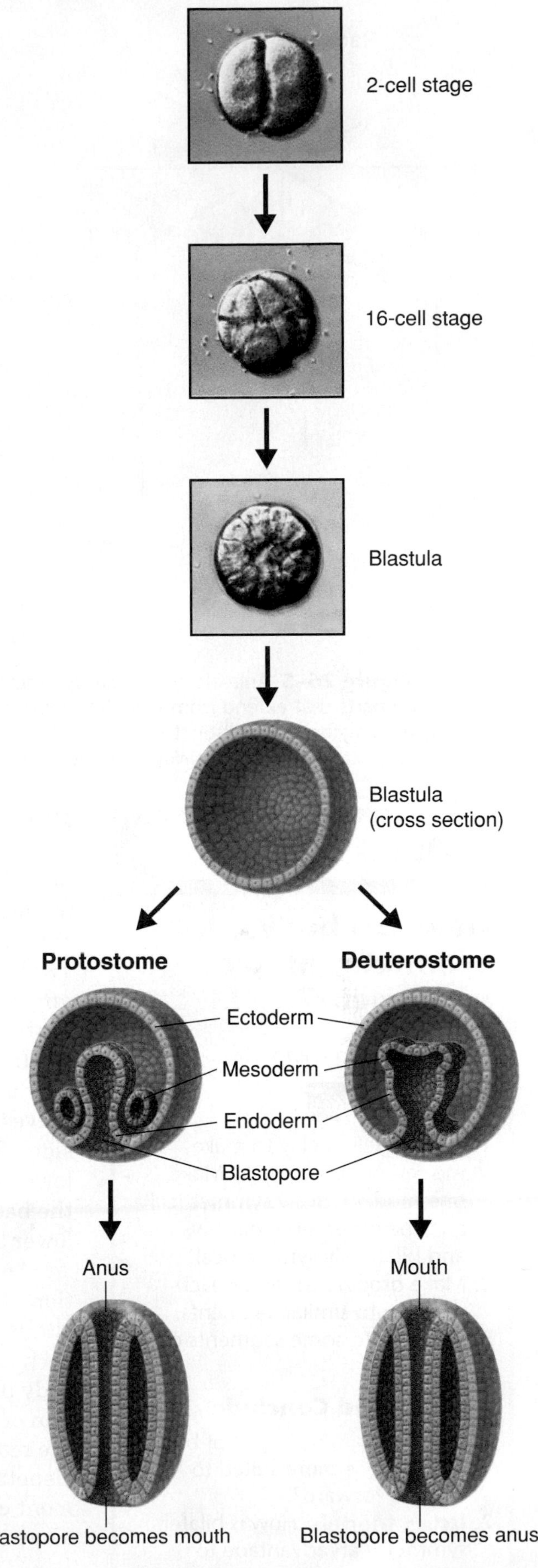

▶ **Figure 26–4** During the early development of animal embryos, cells divide to produce a hollow ball of cells called a blastula. An opening called a blastopore forms in this ball. In protostomes, the blastopore develops into the mouth. In deuterostomes, the blastopore forms an anus. **Interpreting Graphics** ***Which cell layer lines the digestive tract in both protostomes and deuterostomes?***

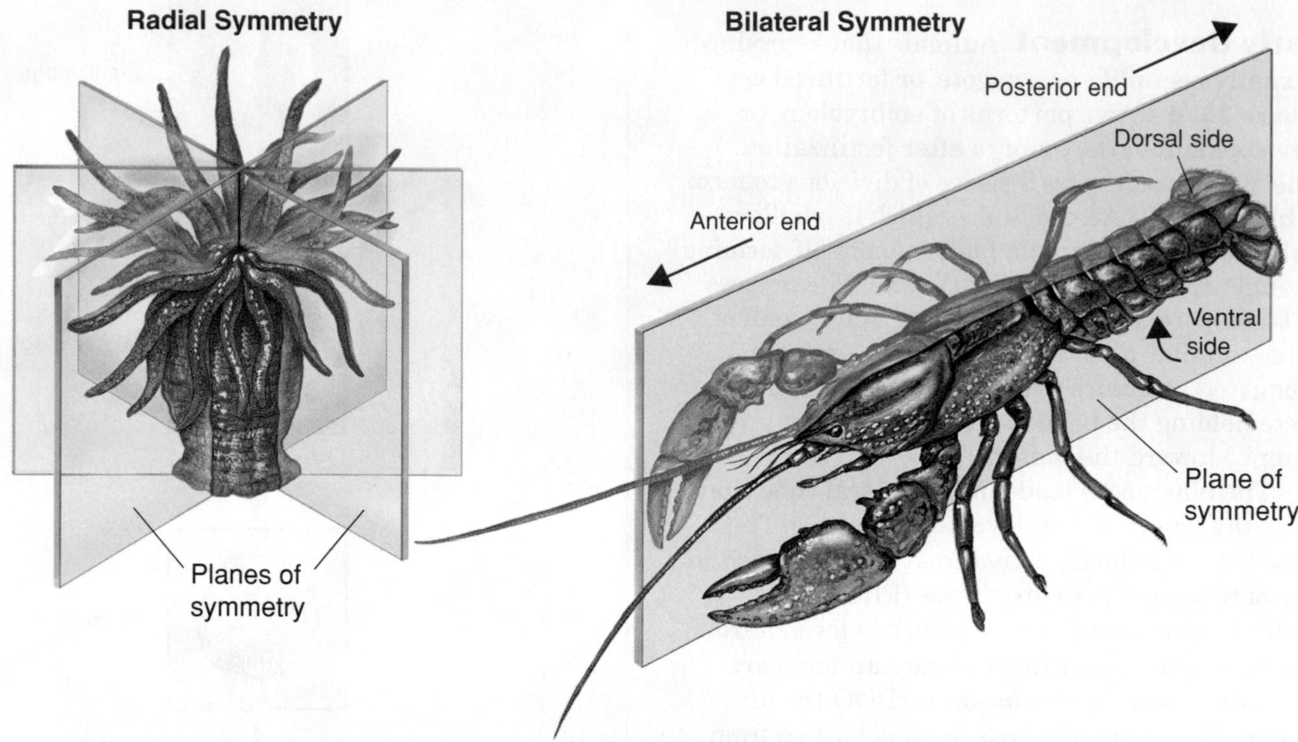

▲ **Figure 26–5** Animals with radial symmetry, such as the sea anemone, have body parts that extend from a central point. Animals with bilateral symmetry, such as the crayfish, have distinct anterior and posterior ends and right and left sides. **Interpreting Graphics** *How many planes of symmetry does the crayfish have?*

Quick Lab

How can body symmetry affect movement?

Material modeling clay

Procedure 

1. Use modeling clay to make models of two animals. Make one model radially symmetrical and the other long, narrow, and bilaterally symmetrical.
2. Make grooves to divide each model into similar segments.
3. Add legs to some segments of your models.

Analyze and Conclude

1. **Inferring** Which type of body symmetry is more suited to walking forward?
2. **Using Models** How is bilateral symmetry an advantage to animals that walk or run?

Body Symmetry With the exception of sponges, every kind of animal exhibits some type of body symmetry in its anatomy, or body structure. Many simple animals, such as the sea anemone shown on the left in **Figure 26–5,** have body parts that repeat around the center of the body. These animals exhibit **radial symmetry,** similar to that of a bicycle wheel, in which any number of imaginary planes can be drawn through the center, each dividing the body into equal halves.

In animals with **bilateral symmetry,** such as the crayfish, only a single imaginary plane can divide the body into two equal halves. Animals with bilateral symmetry have left and right sides. They also usually have front and back ends and upper and lower sides. The anterior is the front end, and the posterior is the back end. The dorsal is the upper side, and the ventral is the lower side.

An anatomy with bilateral symmetry allows for segmentation, in which the body is constructed of many repeated and similar parts, or segments. Animals with bilateral symmetry, such as worms, insects, and vertebrates, typically have external body parts that repeat on either side of the body. The combination of bilateral symmetry and segmentation is found in two of the most successful animal groups—arthropods and vertebrates. Geneticists are learning how gene interactions during development control the growth and form of segments. Amazingly, the same controls are found in humans and insects!

CHECKPOINT *How do radial symmetry and bilateral symmetry differ?*

◀ **Figure 26–6** Animals with cephalization, such as this dragonfly, have the brain and other sense organs toward the front of the body. This end of the body comes into contact with the environment first, allowing animals to respond effectively to stimuli. **Inferring** *How might cephalization help animals to move quickly?*

Cephalization Animals with bilateral symmetry usually exhibit the anatomical characteristic called cephalization (sef-uh-lih-ZAY-shun). **Cephalization** is the concentration of sense organs and nerve cells at the front end of the body. Animals with cephalization, such as the dragonfly in **Figure 26–6,** respond to the environment more quickly and in more complex ways than simpler animals can. Animals with bilateral symmetry usually move with the anterior end forward, so this end comes in contact with new parts of the environment first. As sense organs such as eyes have evolved, they have tended to gather at the anterior end, as have nerve cells that process information and "decide" what the animal should do. In general, the more complex animals become, the more pronounced their cephalization. The anterior end is often different enough from the rest of the body that it is called a head.

Body Cavity Formation Most animals have a body cavity, which is a fluid-filled space that lies between the digestive tract and the body wall. A body cavity is important because it provides a space in which internal organs can be suspended so that they are not pressed on by muscles or twisted out of shape by body movements. Body cavities also allow for specialized regions to develop, and they provide room for internal organs to grow and expand. In some animals, body cavities contain fluids that are involved in circulation, feeding, and excretion.

For: Links on classifying animals
Visit: www.SciLinks.org
Web Code: cbn-8261

26–1 Section Assessment

1. **Key Concept** What are the characteristics of members of the animal kingdom?
2. **Key Concept** Describe the seven essential functions performed by all animals.
3. **Key Concept** In what ways are complex animals different from simple animals?
4. How is the embryology of echinoderms similar to that of vertebrates? What might this similarity indicate about their evolutionary relationship?
5. How are body symmetry and cephalization related?
6. **Critical Thinking Applying Concepts** How is hunger an internal feedback mechanism for maintaining homeostasis?

Thinking Visually

Constructing a Chart
Make a two-column chart of the different functions that enable animals to survive and respond to the environment. In the first column, list each function. In the second column, include a drawing, photograph, or magazine clipping that illustrates an example of that function.

26–2 Sponges

Guide for Reading

Key Concepts
- Why are sponges classified as animals?
- How do sponges carry out essential functions?

Vocabulary
choanocyte
osculum
spicule
archaeocyte
internal fertilization
larva
gemmule

Reading Strategy: Using Visuals Before you read, preview **Figure 26–8** and **Figure 26–9.** For each figure, write a brief statement that summarizes the content of the illustration. Once you have read the section, explain how each illustration reinforces or enhances the content of the section.

Sponges are the simplest and probably the most unusual animals. Living on Earth for at least 540 million years, sponges are also the most ancient animals. Today, most sponges live in the ocean, from the Arctic and Antarctic regions to the tropics, and from shallow water to depths of several hundred meters. To humans, however, they are probably best known in their dried form—the natural sponges used for bathing.

What Is a Sponge?

Sponges are placed in the phylum Porifera (poh-RIF-ur-uh), which means "pore-bearers." This name is appropriate because sponges have tiny openings, or pores, all over their bodies, as shown in **Figure 26–7.** Sponges are sessile, meaning that they live their entire adult life attached to a single spot.

Given these unusual features, why are sponges considered animals?  **Sponges are classified as animals because they are multicellular, heterotrophic, have no cell walls, and contain a few specialized cells.** Because sponges are so different from other animals, some scientists think that they evolved independently from all other animals. Other evidence suggests that sponges share a common ancestor with other animals but that they separated from this ancestor long before the other groups did.

CHECKPOINT *Why is the phylum name Porifera appropriate for sponges?*

Form and Function in Sponges

Sponges have nothing resembling a mouth or gut, and they have no tissues or organ systems. Simple physiological processes are carried out by a few specialized cells.

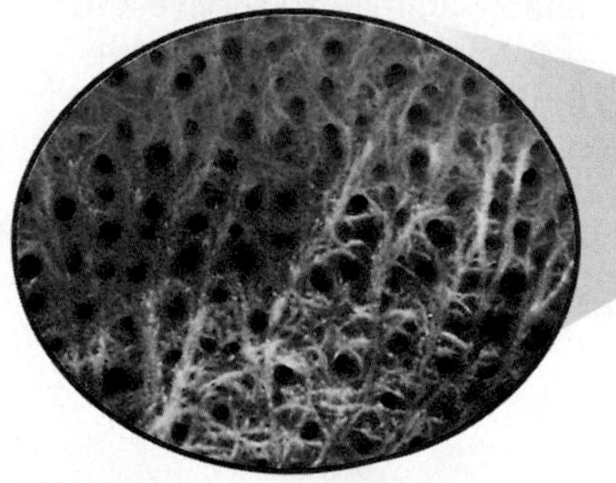

▼ **Figure 26–7** **Sponges are animals because they are heterotrophic and have specialized cells.** Sponges are probably the least typical of what we think of as animals. They grow in irregular shapes and live attached to the floor of oceans and freshwater bodies. Water enters the body of a sponge through small holes called pores (inset photo).

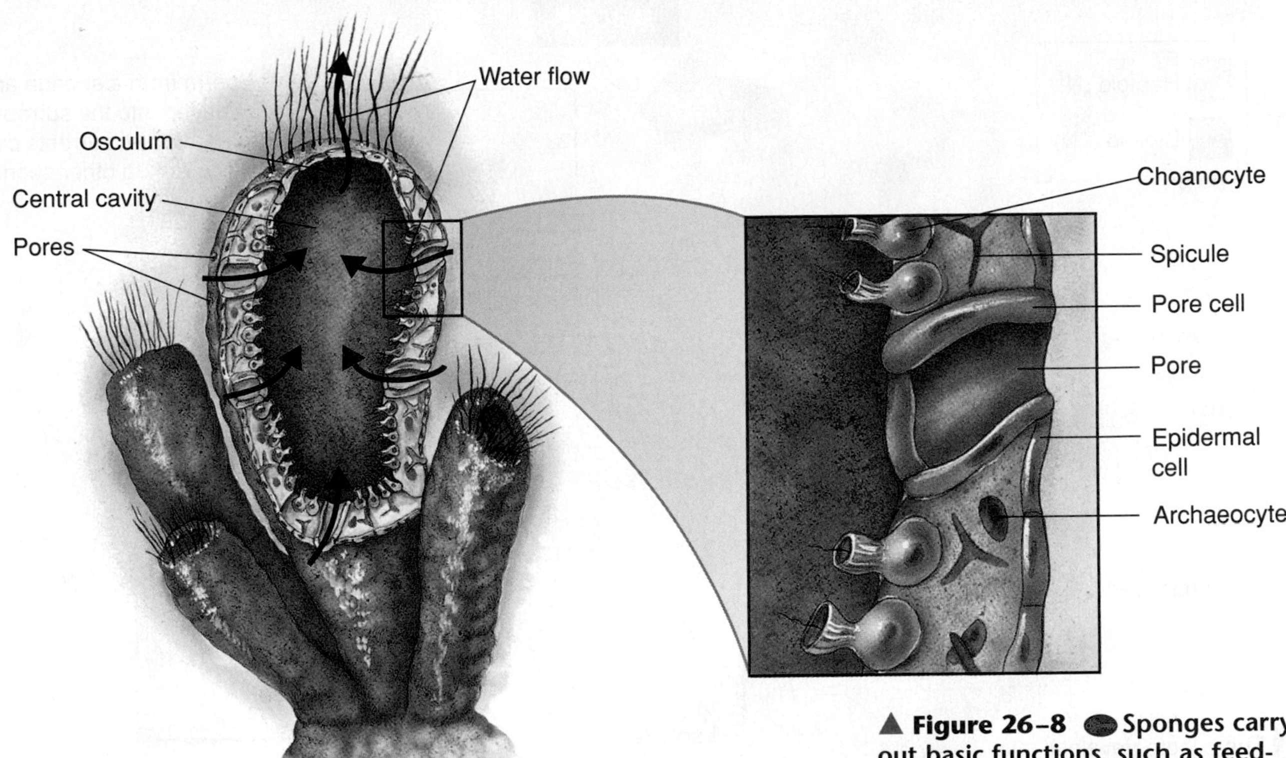

▲ **Figure 26–8** **Sponges carry out basic functions, such as feeding and circulation, by moving water through their bodies.** Choanocytes use flagella to move water through pores In the wall of the sponge and out through the osculum. As water moves through the sponge, food particles are filtered from the water, and wastes are removed from the sponge.

Body Plan Sponges are asymmetrical; they have no front or back ends, and no left or right sides. A sponge can be thought of as a large, cylindrical water pump. The body of a sponge, shown in **Figure 26–8,** forms a wall around a large central cavity through which water is circulated continually. **Choanocytes** (koh-AN-uh-sytz) are specialized cells that use flagella to move a steady current of water through the sponge. This water enters through pores located in the body wall. Water then leaves through the **osculum** (AHS-kyoo-lum), a large hole at the top of the sponge. **The movement of water through the sponge provides a simple mechanism for feeding, respiration, circulation, and excretion.**

Sponges have a simple skeleton. In harder sponges, the skeleton is made of spiny spicules. A **spicule** is a spike-shaped structure made of chalklike calcium carbonate or glasslike silica. Spicules are made by **archaeocytes** (ARK-ee-uh-sytz), which are specialized cells that move around within the walls of the sponge. Softer sponges have an internal skeleton made of spongin, a network of flexible protein fibers. These are the sponges that are harvested and used as natural bath sponges.

Feeding Sponges are filter feeders that sift microscopic food particles from the water. Digestion is intracellular, meaning that it takes place inside cells. As water moves through the sponge, food particles are trapped and engulfed by choanocytes that line the body cavity. These particles are then digested or passed on to archaeocytes. The archaeocytes complete the digestive process and transport digested food throughout the sponge.

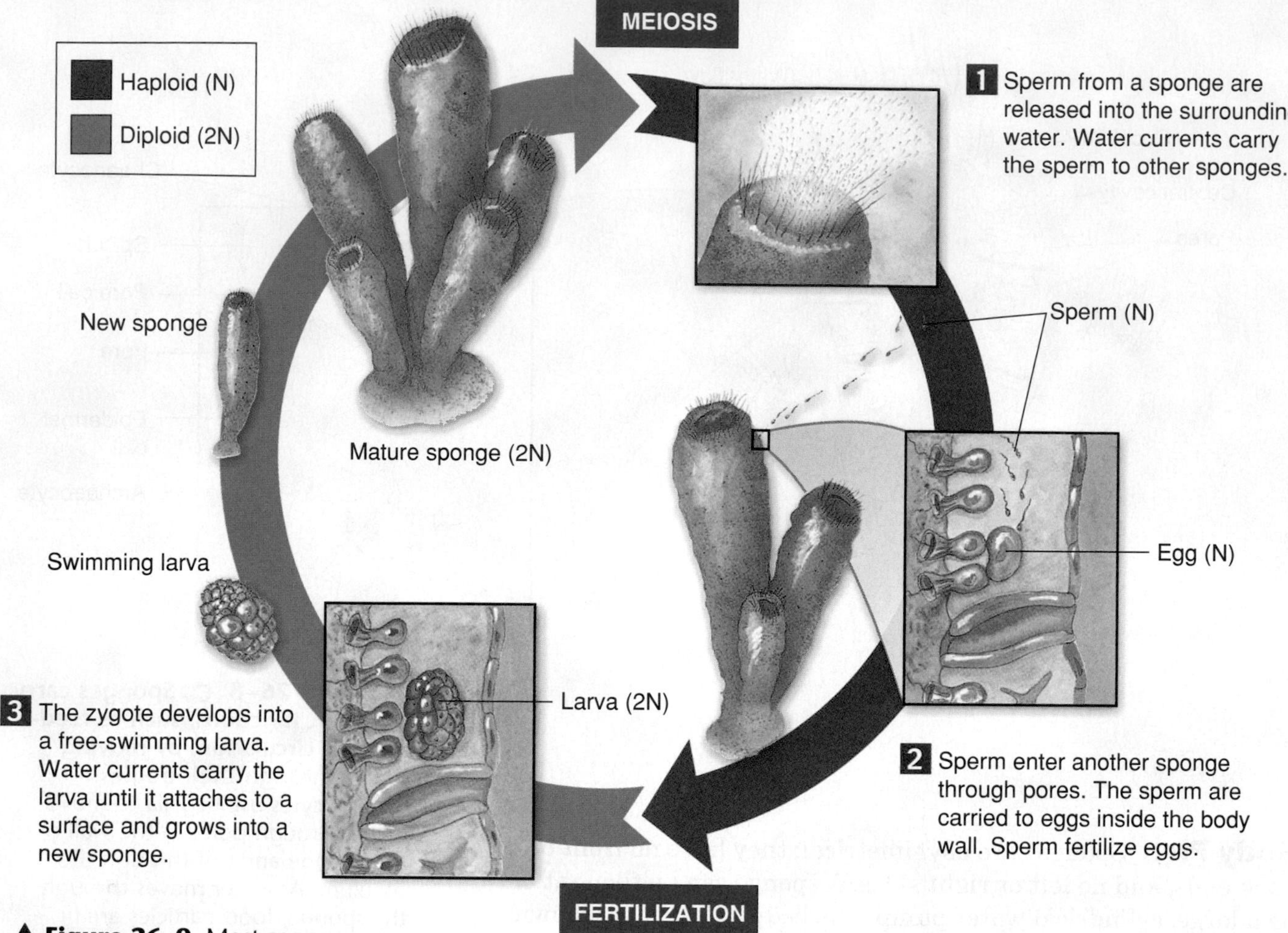
MEIOSIS
Haploid (N)
Diploid (2N)
1 Sperm from a sponge are released into the surrounding water. Water currents carry the sperm to other sponges.
Sperm (N)
New sponge
Mature sponge (2N)
Egg (N)
Swimming larva
Larva (2N)
3 The zygote develops into a free-swimming larva. Water currents carry the larva until it attaches to a surface and grows into a new sponge.
2 Sperm enter another sponge through pores. The sperm are carried to eggs inside the body wall. Sperm fertilize eggs.
FERTILIZATION

▲ **Figure 26–9** Most sponges reproduce sexually, and many have internal fertilization. **Interpreting Graphics** *Is an adult sponge haploid or diploid?*

Respiration, Circulation, and Excretion Sponges rely on the movement of water through their bodies to carry out body functions. As water moves through the body cavity, oxygen dissolved in the water diffuses into the surrounding cells. At the same time, carbon dioxide and other wastes, such as ammonia, diffuse into the water and are carried away.

Response Sponges do not have nervous systems that would allow them to respond to changes in their environment. However, many sponges protect themselves by producing toxins that make them unpalatable or poisonous to potential predators.

Reproduction Sponges can reproduce either sexually or asexually. The steps in sexual reproduction are diagrammed in **Figure 26–9.** In most sponge species, a single sponge forms both eggs and sperm by meiosis. The eggs are fertilized inside the sponge's body, in a process called **internal fertilization.** Sperm are released from one sponge and are carried by water currents until they enter the pores of another sponge. Archaeocytes carry the sperm to an egg. After fertilization, the zygote develops into a larva. A **larva** is an immature stage of an organism that looks different from the adult form. The larvae of sponges are motile and are usually carried by currents before they settle to the sea floor.

Sponges can reproduce asexually by budding or by producing gemmules. In budding, part of a sponge breaks off of the parent sponge, settles to the sea floor, and grows into a new sponge. When faced with difficult environmental conditions, some sponges produce **gemmules** (JEM-yoolz), which are groups of archaeocytes surrounded by a tough layer of spicules. Gemmules can survive freezing temperatures and drought. When conditions become favorable, a gemmule grows into a new sponge.

Sexual reproduction—in sponges and other organisms—involves the joining of haploid gametes that have been produced by meiosis. Since the zygote contains genes from both parents, the new sponge is not genetically identical to either parent. Asexual reproduction, in contrast, does not involve meiosis or the joining of haploid gametes. Instead, the cells of the bud or gemmule, which are diploid, divide repeatedly by mitosis, producing growth. Asexual reproduction produces offspring that are genetically identical to the parent.

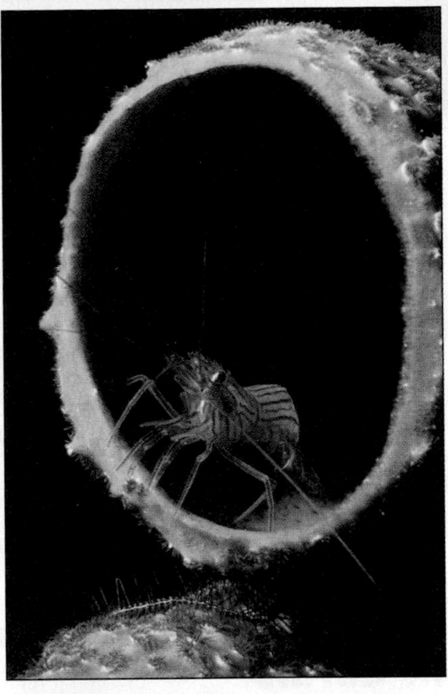

▲ **Figure 26–10** Sponges often provide habitats for other organisms. Observe how the sponge provides shelter for this snapping shrimp. **Inferring** *How might the sponge protect the shrimp from predators?*

Ecology of Sponges

Sponges are important in aquatic ecology. Sponges have irregular shapes and many are large. Therefore, they provide habitats for marine animals such as snails, sea stars, and the shrimp in **Figure 26–10.** These are examples of commensalism. Sponges also form partnerships with photosynthetic bacteria, algae, and plantlike protists. These photosynthetic organisms provide food and oxygen to the sponge, while the sponge provides a protected area where these organisms can thrive. This relationship is an example of mutualism, since both partners benefit. Sponges containing photosynthetic organisms play an important role in the ecology and primary productivity of coral reefs.

Sponges usually live attached to the sea floor, where they often receive only low levels of filtered sunlight. Recently, scientists have found clues to the mystery of how organisms within the sponge get enough light to carry out photosynthesis. The spicules of some sponges look like cross-shaped antennae. Like a lens or magnifying glass, they focus and direct incoming sunlight to cells lying below the surface of the sponge—where symbiotic organisms carry out photosynthesis. This adaptation may allow sponges to survive in a wider range of habitats.

26–2 Section Assessment

1. **Key Concept** What features do sponges share with all other animals?
2. **Key Concept** How do sponges use water to carry out essential functions?
3. Describe the different types of sponge skeletons.
4. **Critical Thinking Drawing Conclusions** Why would sponges be unable to live on land?

Connecting Concepts

Symbiosis

In Chapter 4, you learned about mutualism, commensalism, and other symbiotic relationships. Compare and contrast mutualism and commensalism, and explain how each is important in the life of a sponge.

TECHNOLOGY & SOCIETY

Using Nature to Produce Sunscreen

One way of generating new medicines is to look for them in nature. Organisms of all kinds have been battling one another and their physical environment since life began. So, researchers can search for molecules that have been assembled and tested by the oldest process for generating new compounds on Earth—natural selection.

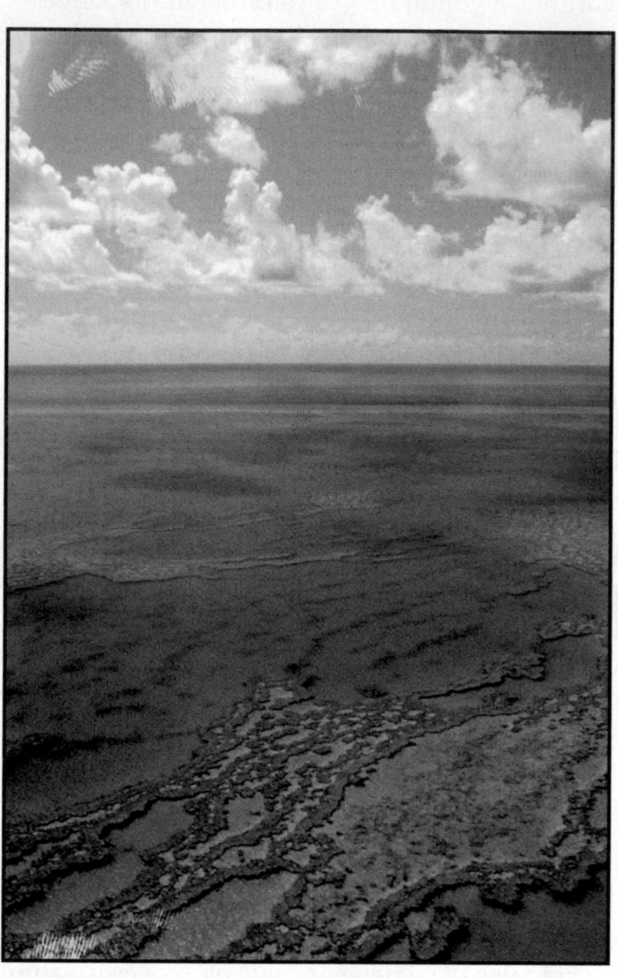

Natural UV Protection in Corals

One of these "new" molecules may be the world's first naturally produced sunscreen. Known as Sunscreen 855, this compound was discovered by researchers studying corals that live in shallow waters along Australia's Great Barrier Reef. During the low tide, these corals are exposed to the air and full sunlight. Investigators reasoned that these corals might have evolved some sort of protection against the damaging ultraviolet (UV) radiation of intense sunlight. Sure enough, their search turned up a UV-blocking compound in the tissues of these corals.

From Natural to Synthetic

After isolating and analyzing the compound in Sunscreen 855, the researchers learned that it was structurally different from the compounds used in synthetic sunscreens. They devised a way to produce it in the laboratory so that corals would not need to be harvested to make the sunscreen. Preliminary tests have shown that the sunscreen is highly efficient in absorbing radiation in the damaging UV-B region of the spectrum.

But Sunscreen 855 is not sold in any drugstore—nor will it be for several years. Researchers are working with investors, lawyers, and businesspeople to test the new product for safety and effectiveness. If it passes final tests, Sunscreen 855 could be the best—and most natural—protection yet against the harmful effects of the sun.

Research and Decide

Use library or Internet resources to learn more about Sunscreen 855. Then, suppose that Sunscreen 855 were made into a product that people could buy. Make a list of things that the product should do. Make another list of things it should not do (such as harmful side effects it might cause). Describe how you would test these different claims.

For: Links from the authors
Visit: PHSchool.com
Web Code: cbe-8262

26–3 Cnidarians

4-7.1 Human beings can alter ecosystems
4-7.1 Human destruction of habitats
4-7.2 Human activities can degrade ecosystems
LS- Analyze results

Imagine that you are swimming in warm, tropical waters. Far away, delicate jellyfishes float in the ocean currents. Within arm's reach, sea fans sway in the shallow currents. Brightly colored sea anemones cling to rocks, looking more like underwater flowers than animals. All these creatures are animals in the phylum Cnidaria (ny-DAYR-ee-uh), a group that includes hydras, jellyfishes, sea anemones, and corals. These fascinating animals are found in waters all over the world. Some cnidarians live as individuals. Others live in colonies composed of dozens or even thousands of connected individuals.

Guide for Reading

Key Concepts
- What is a cnidarian?
- What two body plans exist in the cnidarian life cycle?
- What are the three groups of cnidarians?

Vocabulary
cnidocyte
nematocyst
polyp
medusa
gastrovascular cavity
nerve net
hydrostatic skeleton
external fertilization

Reading Strategy: Finding Main Ideas Before you read, skim the section to identify the key concepts. Read the section carefully, then write down the information that supports each key concept.

What Is a Cnidarian?

A few important features unite the cnidarians as a group. **Cnidarians are soft-bodied, carnivorous animals that have stinging tentacles arranged in circles around their mouths. They are the simplest animals to have body symmetry and specialized tissues.** Cnidarians get their name from the **cnidocytes** (NY-duh-syts), or stinging cells, that are located along their tentacles. **Figure 26–11** shows the structure of cnidocytes. Cnidarians use these cells for defense and to capture prey. Within each cnidocyte is a nematocyst (NEM-uh-toh-sist). A **nematocyst** is a poison-filled, stinging structure that contains a tightly coiled dart. When an unsuspecting shrimp or small fish brushes up against the tentacles, thousands of nematocysts explode into the animal, releasing enough poison to paralyze or kill the prey.

What is the function of cnidocytes?

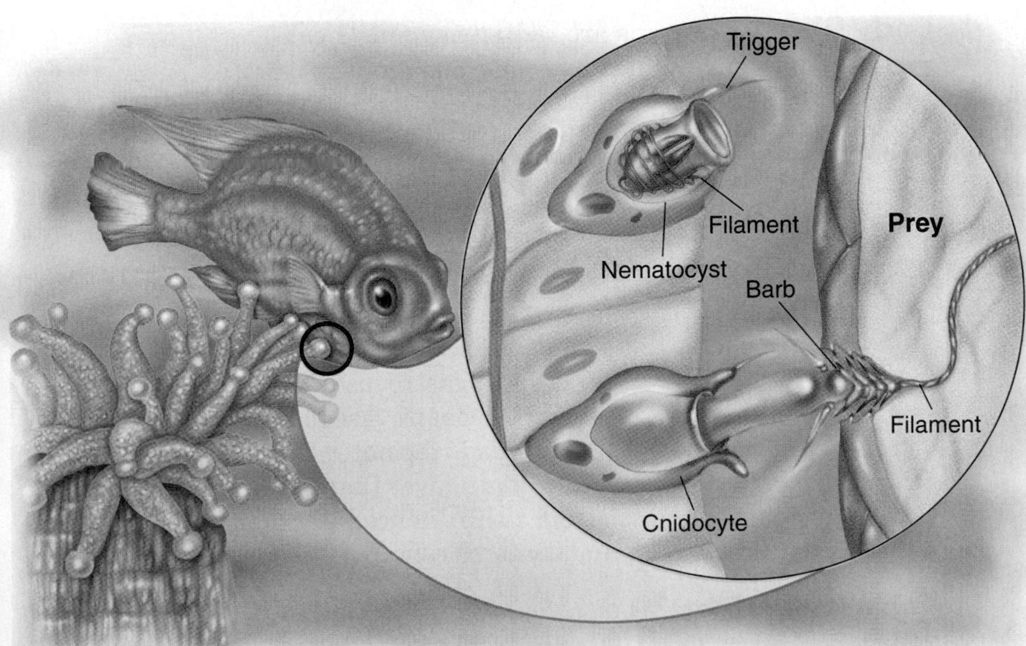

◀ Figure 26–11 **Cnidarians are carnivorous animals that have stinging tentacles arranged around their mouths. Stinging cells called cnidocytes are used to capture and paralyze prey.** Within each cnidocyte is a stinging structure called a nematocyst. Here, a sea anemone captures a fish that has brushed the trigger of the nematocyst. When an animal touches the trigger of a nematocyst, the filament inside uncoils and shoots a barb into the animal.

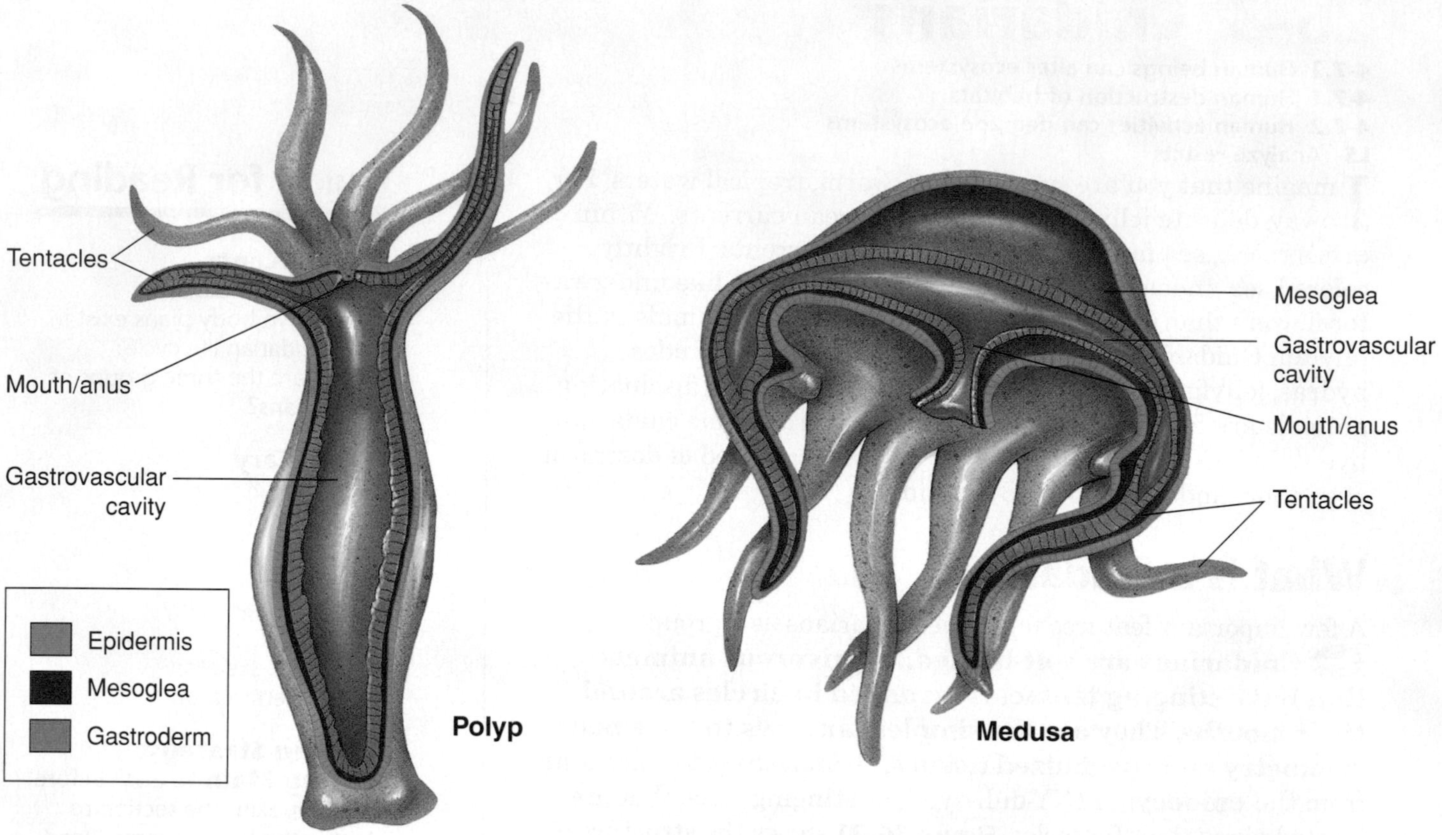

▲ **Figure 26–12** **Many cnidarians have both a polyp stage and a medusa stage.** Both stages have an outer epidermal tissue; a gastroderm tissue, which lines the gastrovascular cavity; and a mesoglea layer, which lies between the two tissues. (Note that a medusa's tentacles are much narrower than in the illustration.)

Form and Function in Cnidarians

Cnidarians are only a few cells thick and have simple body systems. Most of their responses to the environment are carried out by specialized cells and tissues. These tissues function in physiological processes such as feeding and movement.

Body Plan Cnidarians are radially symmetrical. They have a central mouth surrounded by numerous tentacles that extend outward from the body. **Cnidarians typically have a life cycle that includes two different-looking stages: a polyp and a medusa.** Both forms are shown in **Figure 26–12.** A **polyp** (PAHL-ip) is a cylindrical body with armlike tentacles. In a polyp, the mouth points upward. Polyps are usually sessile. A **medusa** (muh-DOO-suh) has a motile, bell-shaped body with the mouth on the bottom.

Cnidarian polyps and medusas each have a body wall that surrounds an internal space called a gastrovascular cavity. The gastroderm is the inner lining of the gastrovascular cavity, where digestion takes place. The epidermis is the outer layer of cells. The mesoglea (mez-uh-GLEE-uh) is a layer that lies between these two tissues. It varies from a thin, noncellular membrane to a thick, jellylike material that contains cells.

 *What are the three layers in cnidarians?*

Word Origins

Medusa is the name of a monster in Greek mythology. In the myth, Medusa was once a beautiful woman, but she bragged about her beauty, causing a jealous goddess to change her into a hideous monster. Medusa had long, twisting snakes for hair. **In what way are cnidarian medusas similar to the monster named Medusa?**

Before

After

Figure 26–13 Cnidarians have nerve nets that consist of many individual nerve cells, as shown in the hydra below. Many cnidarians respond to touch by pulling their tentacles inside their bodies. This response, shown at left in cup corals, is cued by nerve cells located in the tentacles. **Formulating Hypotheses** ***How might a nerve net differ between motile and sessile cnidarians?***

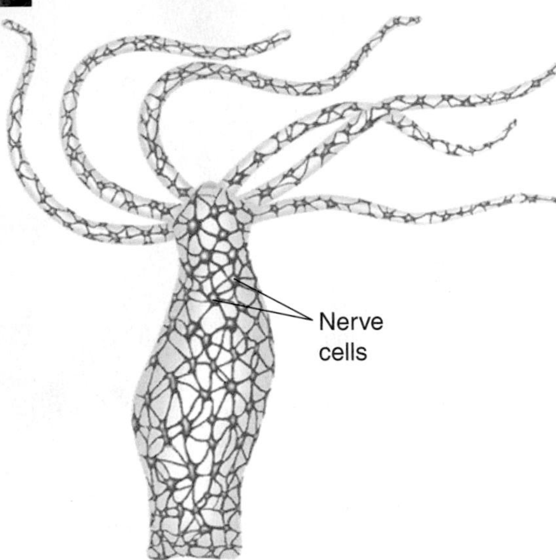

Feeding After paralyzing its prey, a cnidarian pulls the prey through its mouth and into its **gastrovascular cavity,** a digestive chamber with one opening. Food enters and wastes leave the body through that opening. Digestion—the breakdown of food—begins in the gastrovascular cavity. The digestion that occurs in the gastrovascular cavity is extracellular, meaning that it takes place outside of cells. Partially digested food is absorbed by the gastroderm. Digestion is completed intracellularly, within cells in the gastroderm. Any materials that cannot be digested are passed out of the body through the mouth.

Respiration, Circulation, and Excretion Following digestion, nutrients are usually transported throughout the body by diffusion. Cnidarians respire and eliminate the wastes of cellular metabolism by diffusion through their body walls.

Response Cnidarians gather information from their environment using specialized sensory cells. Both polyps and medusas have a nerve net, shown in **Figure 26–13.** A **nerve net** is a loosely organized network of nerve cells that together allow cnidarians to detect stimuli such as the touch of a foreign object. The nerve net is usually distributed uniformly throughout the body, although in some species it is concentrated around the mouth or in rings around the body. Cnidarians also have statocysts, which are groups of sensory cells that help determine the direction of gravity. Ocelli (oh-SEL-eye; singular: ocellus) are eyespots made of cells that detect light.

Movement Different cnidarians move in different ways. Some cnidarians, such as sea anemones, have a hydrostatic skeleton. The **hydrostatic skeleton** consists of a layer of circular muscles and a layer of longitudinal muscles that, together with the water in the gastrovascular cavity, enable the cnidarian to move. For example, if the anemone's circular muscles contract when the anemone's mouth is closed, the water inside the cavity can't escape. The pressure of the water makes the body become taller. In contrast, medusas move by jet propulsion. Muscle contractions cause the bell-shaped body to close like a folding umbrella. This action pushes water out of the bell, moving the medusa forward, as shown in **Figure 26–14.**

▲ **Figure 26–14** Jellyfishes move by means of jet propulsion. The body contracts to force water out, moving the jellyfish in the opposite direction. **Applying Concepts** ***Is the body plan of this jellyfish a medusa or a polyp?***

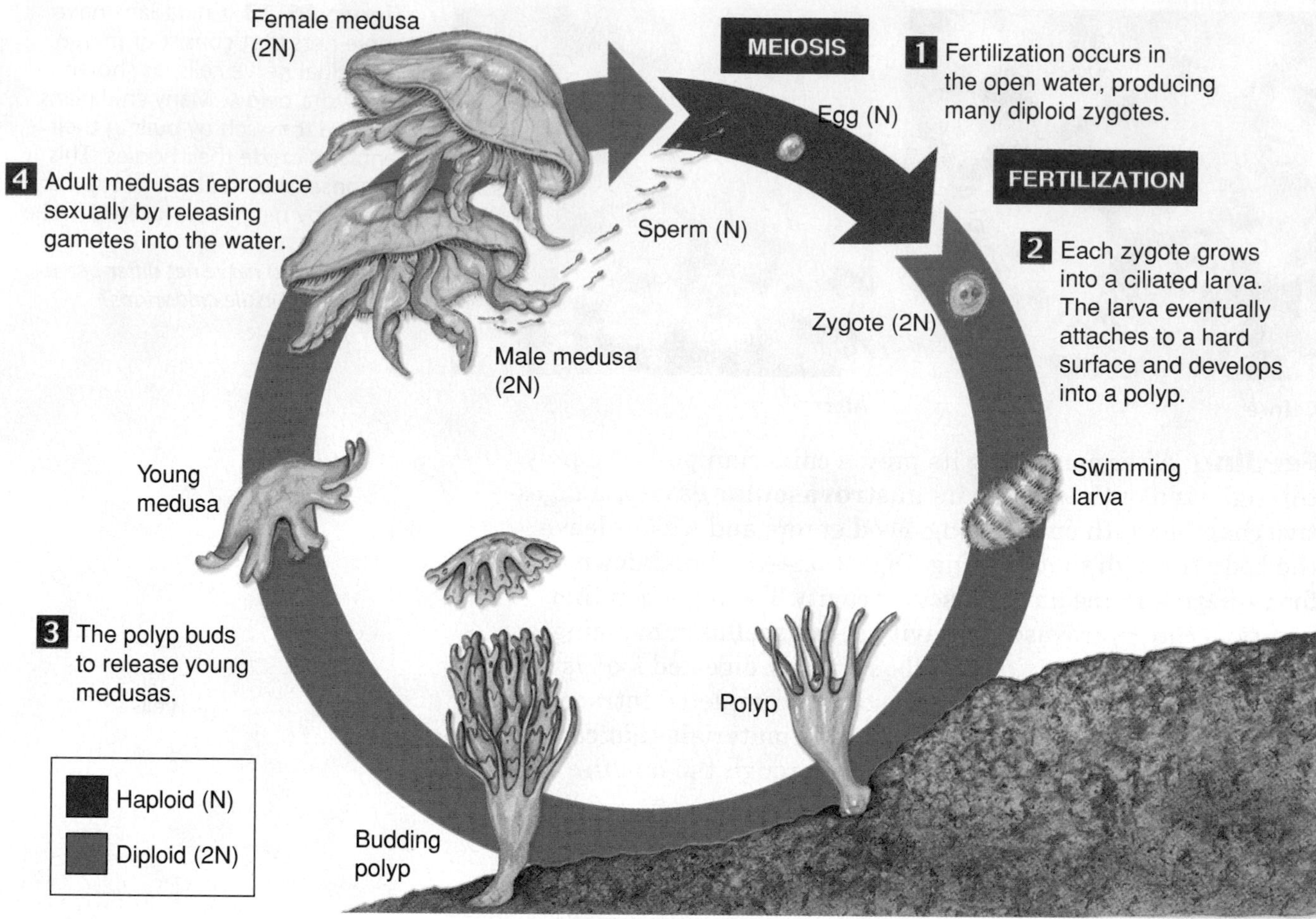
Female medusa
(2N)
MEIOSIS
1 Fertilization occurs in the open water, producing many diploid zygotes.
Egg (N)
FERTILIZATION
4 Adult medusas reproduce sexually by releasing gametes into the water.
Sperm (N)
2 Each zygote grows into a ciliated larva. The larva eventually attaches to a hard surface and develops into a polyp.
Zygote (2N)
Male medusa
(2N)
Young
medusa
Swimming
larva
3 The polyp buds to release young medusas.
Polyp
Haploid (N)
Diploid (2N)
Budding
polyp

▲ **Figure 26–15** Jellyfishes reproduce sexually by producing eggs and sperm. Depending on the species, fertilization is either internal or external. In *Aurelia,* shown here, fertilization is external, occurring after eggs and sperm are released into the water. **Interpreting Graphics** *What cells are formed by the process of meiosis?*

Reproduction Most cnidarians reproduce both sexually and asexually. Polyps can reproduce asexually by budding. The new animal is genetically identical to the parent animal. One type of budding begins with a swelling on the side of an existing polyp. This swelling grows into a new polyp. In another type of budding, polyps produce tiny medusas that separate and become new individuals.

In most cnidarians, sexual reproduction takes place with external fertilization in water. **External fertilization** takes place outside the female's body. The sexes are often separate—each individual is either male or female. The female releases eggs into the water, and the male releases sperm. The life cycle of *Aurelia,* a common jellyfish, is shown in **Figure 26–15.** Observe that the zygote grows into a free-swimming larva. The larva eventually attaches to a hard surface and develops into a polyp. Then, the polyp buds and releases a medusa that begins the cycle again.

Groups of Cnidarians

All cnidarians live under water, and nearly all live in the ocean. **Cnidarians include jellyfishes, hydras and their relatives, and sea anemones and corals.** Some of the most familiar cnidarians are the jellyfishes.

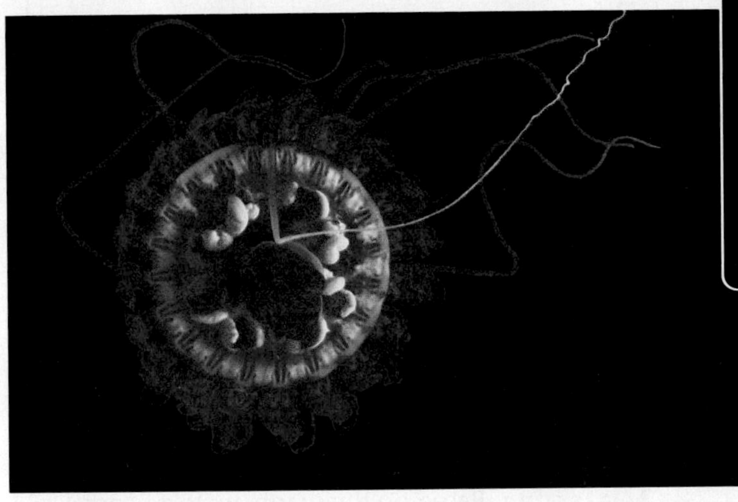

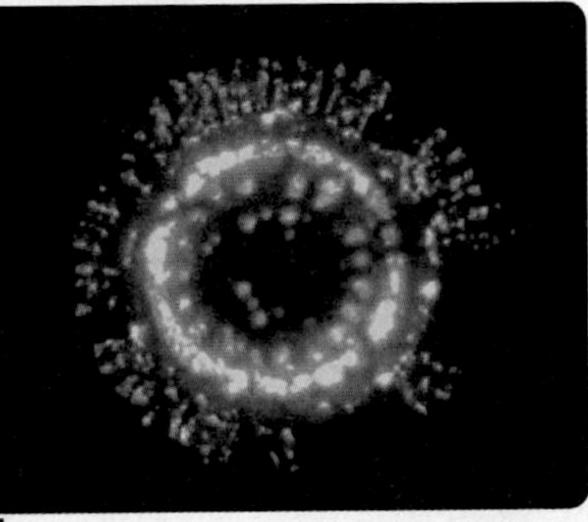

Figure 26–16 Like many marine organisms, jellyfishes use bioluminescence, or the production of light by an organism, to ward off predators. The entire body of this jellyfish becomes bioluminescent when it is threatened (inset). **Formulating Hypotheses** ***How might bioluminescence discourage potential predators?***

Jellyfishes The class Scyphozoa (sy-fuh-ZOH-uh) contains the jellyfishes, such as the jellyfish shown in **Figure 26–16.** Scyphozoans, which means "cup animals," live their lives primarily as medusas. The polyp form of jellyfishes is restricted to a small larval stage, and no elaborate colonies ever form. Jellyfishes can be quite large—the largest jellyfish ever found was almost 4 meters in diameter and had tentacles more than 30 meters long. Jellyfishes reproduce sexually.

Hydras and Their Relatives The class Hydrozoa (hy-druh-ZOH-uh) contains hydras and other related animals. The polyps of most hydrozoans grow in branching colonies that sometimes extend more than a meter. Within the colony, polyps are specialized to perform different functions. In the Portuguese man-of-war, shown in **Figure 26–17,** one polyp forms a balloonlike float that keeps the entire colony afloat. Other polyps in the colony produce long tentacles that hang several meters under water and sting prey (and humans!) using nematocysts. Some polyps digest food held by the tentacles, while others make eggs and sperm.

The most common freshwater hydrozoans are hydras. Hydras differ from other cnidarians in this class because they lack a medusa stage. Instead, they live only as solitary polyps. Hydras reproduce asexually, by budding, or sexually, by producing eggs and sperm in the body wall. Many hydras get their nutrition from capturing, stinging, and digesting small prey. Some hydras, however, get their nutrition from symbiotic photosynthetic protists that live in their tissues.

How do hydras reproduce?

▶ **Figure 26–17** **Jellyfishes, hydrozoans, sea anemones, and corals are all cnidarians.** The Portuguese man-of-war, shown here, is a colonial hydrozoan that is composed of many specialized polyps. A single polyp that is enlarged and full of air helps keep the animal afloat, while other specialized polyps below water function in feeding and reproduction.

Analyzing Data

Coral Vanishing Act

The World Resources Institute, an organization that examines global environmental problems, has announced that 58 percent of the world's coral reefs are in danger of dying. Threats to coral reefs fall into four broad categories shown in the graph. The graph indicates the percentage of reefs that are threatened by each of these categories. It also rates the threat as medium or high, based on the distance between the coral reef and the source of the threat. Use the information in the graph to answer the following questions.

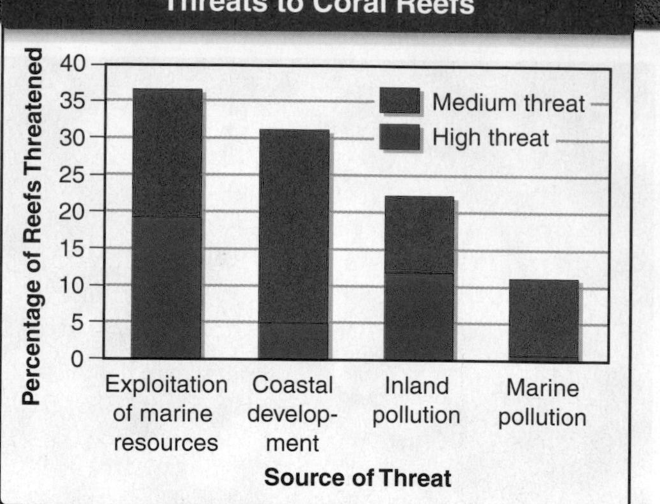

1. **Classifying** Place the four categories of risk in order from greatest high threat to least high threat.
2. **Using Tables and Graphs** Approximately how much greater is the high threat of overexploitation than the high threat of coastal development?
3. **Inferring** Based on the graph, write a generalization about the effect of human activities on the destruction of coral reefs.
4. **Making Judgments** Assume that you are a legislator drafting a law to protect coral reefs. Choose one of the threats shown in the graph, and outline a law that you would propose to counter the threat.

▼ **Figure 26–18** Coral reefs are home to many types of organisms and are rivaled only by rain forests in their biological diversity. Each flowerlike form shown in this photograph is an entire colony made of thousands of individual coral polyps. **Observing** *How would you describe the symmetry of individual coral polyps?*

Sea Anemones and Corals The class Anthozoa (an-thuh-ZOH-uh) contains sea anemones and corals, animals that have only the polyp stage in their life cycle. Anthozoans all have a central body surrounded by tentacles—a form that gave them their name, *anthozoa,* which means "flower animal." Many species are colonial, or composed of many individual polyps. The appearance of an entire reef can include varied forms, as shown in **Figure 26–18.**

Sea anemones are solitary polyps that live at all depths of the ocean. Using nematocysts, they catch a variety of marine organisms. Many shallow-water species also depend on nutrition from photosynthetic symbionts.

Individual coral polyps look like miniature sea anemones. But most corals are colonial, and their polyps grow together in large numbers. Hard coral colonies are usually founded when a motile larva settles onto a hard surface and develops into a single polyp. New polyps are produced by budding, and as the colonies grow, they secrete an underlying skeleton of calcium carbonate, or limestone. These colonies grow slowly and may live for hundreds or even thousands of years. Many coral colonies growing near one another produce the magnificent structures known as coral reefs.

Anthozoans reproduce sexually by producing eggs and sperm that are released into the water. The zygote grows into a ciliated larva that becomes a new polyp. Some species can also reproduce asexually by budding or splitting into two halves.

Ecology of Corals

The worldwide distribution of corals is determined by a few variables: temperature, water depth, and light intensity. The "stony" or "hard" corals that build coral reefs require high levels of light. Why should light be a requirement for an animal? Light is necessary because these corals rely on mutualistic relationships with algae that capture solar energy, recycle nutrients, and help corals lay down their calcium carbonate skeletons. Symbionts provide as much as 60 percent of the energy that corals need. This arrangement allows coral reefs to live in water that carries few nutrients.

Many coral reefs are now suffering from human activity. For example, recreational divers sometimes damage coral reefs. Silt and other sediments from logging, farming, mining, and construction can wash onto reefs and smother corals. Chemical fertilizers, insecticides, and industrial pollutants can poison the corals. Overfishing can upset the ecological balance of coral reefs. Even when human-caused problems do not kill corals, they can cause stress that makes the coral reefs susceptible to other threats.

Meanwhile, a problem called coral bleaching has become common. High temperatures can kill the algae that usually live in the tissues of corals, leaving behind only transparent cells atop ghostly white skeletons. The results of coral bleaching are shown in **Figure 26–19.** In the past, bleaching was a rare and short-term event from which many corals recovered. Over the last 20 years, however, bleaching has become more common and more severe, causing many corals to die. Researchers fear that rising ocean temperatures, produced by global warming, may be contributing to this problem. If this is the case, many reefs around the world could soon be in serious danger.

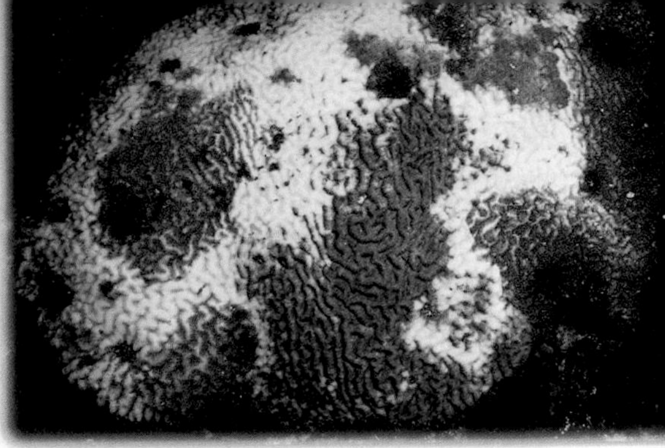

▲ **Figure 26–19** Under normal conditions, algae live within coral tissues, carrying out photosynthesis and giving the coral its green appearance. However, when stressed by pollutants or increasing temperatures, these algae can die, so only the clear cells of the coral remain. **Inferring** ***What effect might the loss of symbiotic algae have on the coral?***

26–3 Section Assessment

1. **Key Concept** Describe three characteristics that all cnidarians share.
2. **Key Concept** How do the two body plans of cnidarians differ?
3. **Key Concept** Describe the three groups of cnidarians and give an example from each.
4. Describe how the digestion and absorption of food take place in cnidarians.
5. How has human activity affected coral reefs?
6. **Critical Thinking Inferring** A medusa typically has more specialized organs for movement and response than a polyp does. Why might this be the case? *Hint:* How does the lifestyle of a medusa differ from that of most polyps?

Writing in Science

Descriptive Writing

Write a paragraph describing the body of a hydra. Assume that your readers know nothing about hydras. *Hint*: First, list all the details you want to include in your paragraph. Then, decide how you want to organize those details—for example, from the outside of the hydra to the inside.

Exploration

Investigating the Responses of Hydras to External Stimuli

Hydras, a type of cnidarian, are some of the simplest known animals to have a nervous system. What kinds of behavior can their simple nerve nets produce? Can they detect food and move toward it? Can they detect predators and move away from them? How do they respond to light, temperature, and other external stimuli? How do these responses help them to survive? In this investigation, you will observe and try to explain the behavior of hydras.

Problem

How do hydras respond to light?

Materials

- 6 test tubes with screw caps
- test-tube rack
- green hydras
- brown hydras
- aluminum foil
- pond or spring water
- glass-marking pencil
- dropper pipette
- transparent tape

Skills

Inferring, Drawing Conclusions

Procedure   

1. Make a copy of the data table shown. Number 6 test tubes 1 through 6 near the top of each tube. Fill the test tubes with pond water or spring water to within 2 cm of the top. **CAUTION:** *Handle the test tubes carefully. Do not drink the water.*
2. Use a dropper pipette to gently place 3 brown hydras in the bottoms of the test tubes labeled 1 through 3, and place 3 green hydras in the bottoms of the test tubes labeled 4 through 6.
3. Wrap the bottom half of each test tube in aluminum foil.
4. Tightly cap all 6 test tubes. Place test tubes 1 and 4 right side up in the test-tube rack and test tubes 2 and 5 upside down.
5. Label the test-tube rack with your name and place it in a brightly lit place.
6. Lay test tubes 3 and 6 on their sides next to the test-tube rack so that all 6 test tubes are equally well lit. Tape test tubes 3 and 6 in place. Place the tape over the foil and caps so that it does not block the light.
7. **Predicting** Record the time that you completed step 6. Make a prediction of how each type of hydra will respond to the external stimulus—either moving away from or toward the light. Record your prediction of any other behavior that you expect to see, along with the reasons for your predictions.

Data Table

Tube	Hydras	Source of Light	Number of Hydras		Class Total	
			In light	In dark	In light	In dark
1	brown	above				
2	brown	below				
3	brown	side				
4	green	above				
5	green	below				
6	green	side				

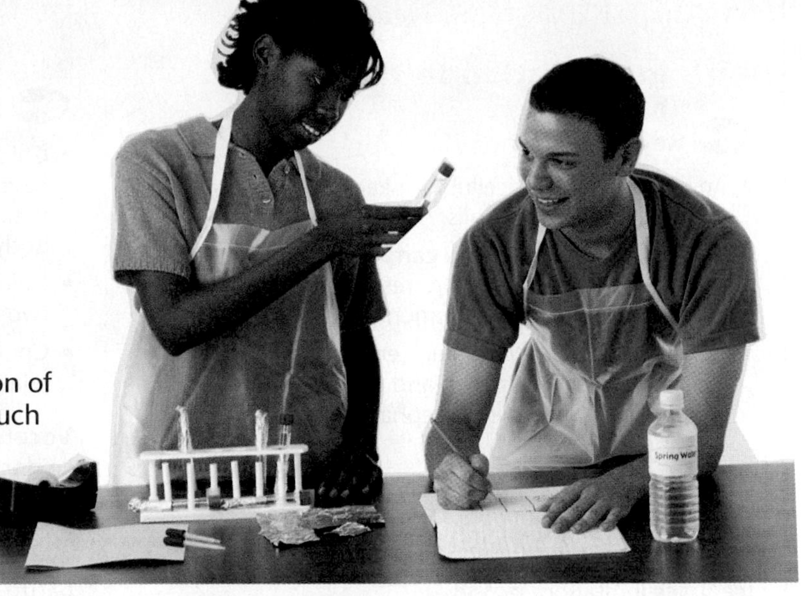

8 Observe the test tubes. Record a description of any hydra behavior you observe. Include such information as when the behavior occurred, how many hydras you saw, what they did, and any other observations you made. Leave the test tubes overnight. Be sure to wash your hands before leaving the lab.

9 The next day, observe the test tubes and again record any hydra behavior you observe. Count the number of hydras in the light and in the dark in each test tube. Record these observations in your data table.

10 **Communicating Results** Share your observations with the class to complete the Class Total columns of your data table.

Analyze and Conclude

1. **Observing** Which type of hydra moved toward the light? Which type avoided light?
2. **Observing** How did the hydras move? Were their movements random or in a specific direction?
3. **Observing** What differences did you observe between the behavior of green and brown hydras?
4. **Inferring** Green hydras are green because of the presence of green algae in their bodies. What seems to be the relationship between the presence of algae and the behavior of green hydras?
5. **Drawing Conclusions** How might their response to light help green hydras survive?
6. **Comparing and Contrasting** The nervous system directs animal behavior. Compare the behavior of hydras to the behavior of animals with more complex nervous systems that you have observed, such as dogs and insects.
7. **SAFETY** Explain how you demonstrated safe practices as you handled the test tubes.

Go Further

Designing Experiments What are some other behaviors that hydras exhibit? For example, do they react to changes in temperature, differences in prey behavior, or the presence of predators? Can they learn? Consult scientific literature about the behavior of hydras. Then, design an experiment to investigate a specific hypothesis about hydra behavior. Formulate your hypothesis on the basis of what you have read and your own observations. Have your teacher approve your plan before you perform your experiment.

For: Data sharing
Visit: PHSchool.com
Web Code: cbd-8263

Share Your Data Online Communicate your results by entering your data on the behavior of the two types of hydra. Then, look at the data entered by other students. Based on the available data, which type of hydra moved toward the light? Which avoided light? Why might your data differ from those of other students? Does this larger set of data support your results and indicate that your conclusions are valid?

Chapter 26 Study Guide

26–1 Introduction to the Animal Kingdom

Key Concepts

- An animal is a multicellular, eukaryotic heterotroph whose cells lack cell walls.
- Animals are specialized to carry out the following essential functions: feeding, respiration, circulation, excretion, response, movement, and reproduction.
- In general, complex animals tend to have high levels of cell specialization and internal organization, bilateral body symmetry, cephalization, and a body cavity.

Vocabulary
invertebrate, p. 657
vertebrate, p. 657
feedback inhibition, p. 658
blastula, p. 661
protostome, p. 661
deuterostome, p. 661
anus, p. 661
endoderm, p. 661
mesoderm, p. 661
ectoderm, p. 661
radial symmetry, p. 662
bilateral symmetry, p. 662
cephalization, p. 663

26–2 Sponges

Key Concepts

- Sponges are classified as animals because they are multicellular, heterotrophic, have no cell walls, and contain a few specialized cells.
- The movement of water through a sponge provides a simple mechanism for feeding, respiration, circulation, and excretion.

Vocabulary
choanocyte, p. 665
osculum, p. 665
spicule, p. 665
archaeocyte, p. 665
internal fertilization, p. 666
larva, p. 666
gemmule, p. 667

26–3 Cnidarians

Key Concepts

- Cnidarians are soft-bodied, carnivorous animals that have stinging tentacles arranged in circles around their mouth. They are the simplest animals to have body symmetry and specialized tissues.
- Cnidarians typically have a life cycle that includes two different-looking stages, a polyp and a medusa.
- Cnidarians include jellyfishes, hydras and their relatives, and sea anemones and corals.

Vocabulary
cnidocyte, p. 669
nematocyst, p. 669
polyp, p. 670
medusa, p. 670
gastrovascular cavity, p. 671
nerve net, p. 671
hydrostatic skeleton, p. 671
external fertilization, p. 672

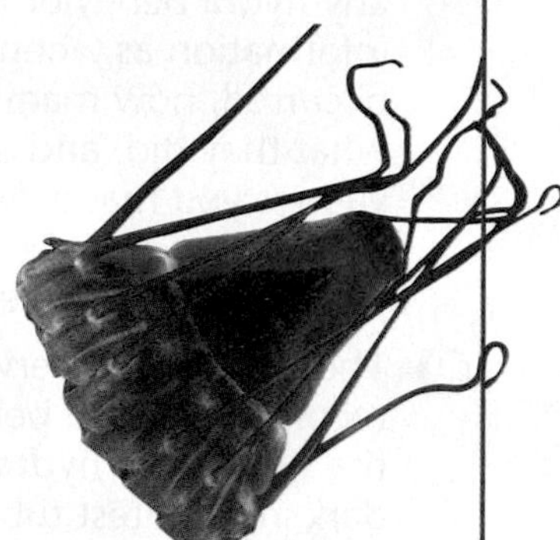

Thinking Visually

Complete the following concept map using information from the chapter:

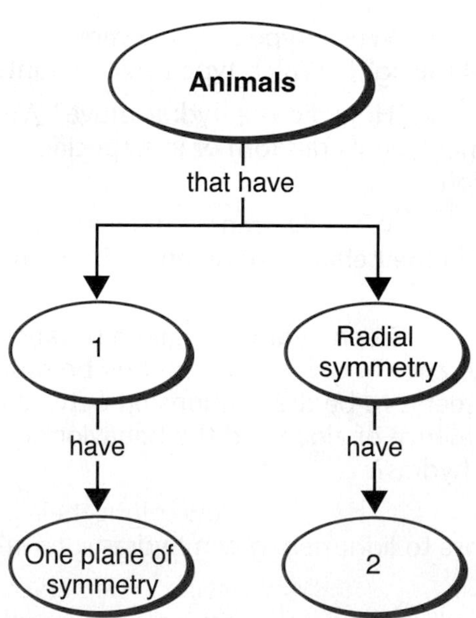

Preparing for the Living Environment Exam

Blue questions emphasize Regents Exam content

Chapter 26

Part A

Multiple Choice

For each statement or question, select the number of the word or expression that, of those given, best completes the statement or answers the question.

1 The process by which animals take in oxygen and give off carbon dioxide is known as
(1) circulation (3) reproduction
(2) respiration (4) response

2 Animals that have a backbone, also called a vertebral column, are known as
(1) vertebrates (3) deuterostomes
(2) prokaryotes (4) invertebrates

3 Symmetry with distinct front and back ends is called
(1) radial (3) circular
(2) bilateral (4) dorsal

4 Which pairing of terms most closely applies to the developing embryo shown below?

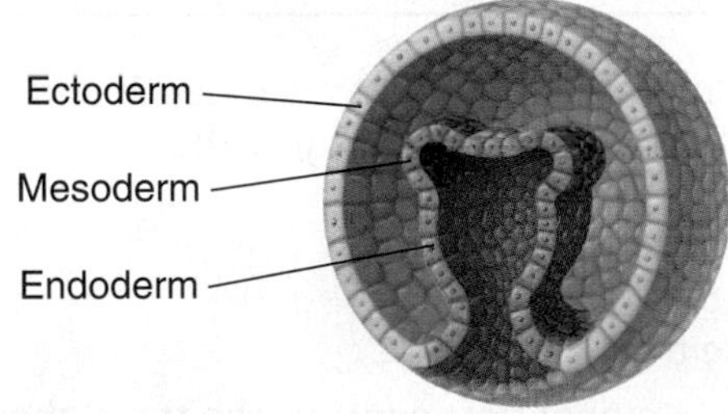

(1) protostome; simple invertebrates
(2) protostome; vertebrates
(3) deuterostome; echinoderms and chordates
(4) deuterostome; invertebrates

5 An animal whose mouth is formed from the blastopore is a
(1) deuterostome (3) protostome
(2) detritivore (4) carnivore

6 Animals in the phylum Porifera include
(1) chordates (3) sponges
(2) sea stars (4) sea anemones

7 A concentration of sense organs and nerve cells at the anterior end of the body is known as
(1) fertilization (3) symmetry
(2) cephalization (4) anteriorization

8 The sessile body form of a cnidarian is a
(1) polyp (3) planula
(2) medusa (4) nematocyst

9 A soft-bodied animal with stinging tentacles arranged around its mouth is a
(1) spicule (3) vertebrate
(2) cnidarian (4) choanocyte

10 Which are the three germ layers that arise in the early development of most animal embryos?
(1) endoderm, gastrula, and blastula
(2) ectoderm, mesoderm, and blastula
(3) mesoderm, gastrula, and ectoderm
(4) endoderm, mesoderm, and ectoderm

11 In hydra and other cnidarians, gas exchange occurs by diffusion across membranes of
(1) the cells of the tentacles, only
(2) the outer layer of cells, only
(3) the inner layer of cells, only
(4) all the cells of the organism

12 Respiratory gases are exchanged between a hydra and its environment primarily by the process of
(1) mitosis
(2) diffusion
(3) active transport
(4) hormone signals

13 An adult sponge has all the characteristics below *except*
(1) body symmetry
(2) the inability to move from place to place
(3) cells without cell walls
(4) a central cavity

For questions 14 and 15, complete each analogy by selecting the correct number. In analogies, A : B :: C : means "A is to B as C is to ___?___."

14 Radial symmetry : jellyfish :: asymmetry :
(1) medusa (3) polyp
(2) coral (4) sponge

15 Hard sponge : spicule :: soft sponge :
(1) nematocyst (3) hydrostatic skeleton
(2) spongin (4) calcium carbonate

Test-Taking Tip When evaluating multiple-choice answers, read all the answer choices, even if the first choice seems to be the correct one. By doing so, you can make sure that the answer you choose is the best one.

Preparing for the Living Environment Exam

Part B

Multiple Choice and Extended Response

For those questions that ask you to select a response, choose the one that best completes the statement or answers the question. For all others follow the directions given.

16 Most cnidarians do not swim toward their prey. Instead, they capture prey carried by water currents. Explain how this behavior is related to their body plan.

17 State *three* ways sponges are similar to other animals. State *two* ways they are different.

18 Describe the process of feeding in cnidarians.

19 Describe the life cycle of *Aurelia,* a common jellyfish. Be sure to include how the polyp form alternates with the medusa form.

20 State the function of statocysts.

21 The characteristics below are associated with some organisms in the animal kingdom.

1 anterior end
2 posterior end
3 bilateral symmetry
4 radial symmetry
5 dorsal surface
6 ventral surface
7 lateral surface
8 sessile
9 motile

Make a chart similar to the one shown below on your answer paper. Fill in the *number* of each characteristic that applies to each organism in the chart.

Organism	Characteristics (list numbers only)
Sponge	
Jellyfish	
Fish	

22 Describe what is meant by cephalization, then explain how this characteristic is an advantage to animals that have it.

23 Distinguish between a protostome and a deuterostome.

24 Describe the mutually beneficial relationship that exists between many sponges and certain photosynthetic organisms.

25 Describe the *two* methods of asexual reproduction that occur in cnidarian polyps.

Base your answers to questions 26 through 28 on the graph below, which shows the growth rate of a hypothetical coral species under different conditions, and on your knowledge of biology.

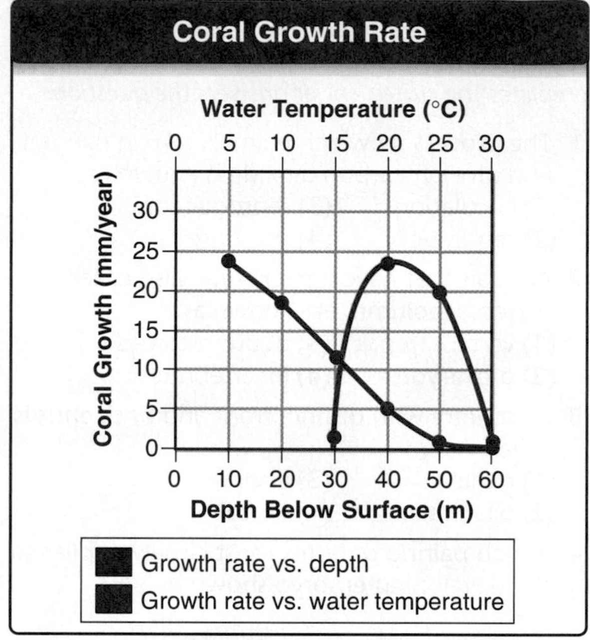

26 According to the graph, at what depth and temperature does the coral grow best?
(1) 0–10 m; 20°C
(2) less than 10 m; 15°C
(3) less than 10 m; 28°C
(4) more than 10 m; 21°C

27 Which statement best explains the trend shown in the graph?
(1) The growth rate of the coral increases as the depth below the water surface increases.
(2) At temperatures of 15°C or above, the growth rate depends only on temperature.
(3) Corals cannot grow below 30 m.
(4) This coral grows best from 18° to 21°C.

28 State the responding (dependent) variable shown on this graph.

Base your answers to questions 29 through 31 on the reading passage below and on your knowledge of biology.

Coral Reefs in Peril

Coral reefs are the "rain forests" of the ocean. Life is abundant and varied. Coral reefs are in trouble for many reasons. Some reefs are being damaged as a result of exploitation by humans for resources. Coastal development damages other reefs.

Inland pollution is an issue in reef destruction. As chemicals and sediment wash downstream to the ocean, these materials wash out into the ocean and damage coral reefs. Pollution of the ocean by tankers, the oil industry, and the dumping of wastes is also a huge problem.

Global warming poses a large threat in the form of coral bleaching. High temperatures kill the algae that live in the tissues of corals.

29 Explain why killing the algae living in coral tissues is harmful to coral.

30 Choose one human activity that can harm coral reefs. Then, describe one measure people can take to reduce the damage.

31 Evaluate the impact that the measure you described in your answer to question 30 might have on human society.

Part C

Extended Response

Answer the questions or follow the directions given.

32 Some claim that the life cycle of most cnidarians is more complex than the life cycle of sponges. Others claim exactly the opposite. Compare the life cycles of these two groups. In your comparison, be sure to:
- state *two* ways the life cycles are similar
- state *two* ways the life cycles are different
- state one reason why a scientist would consider the cnidarian life cycle more complex than the sponge life cycle

33 Cnidaria use a nerve net, cnidocytes, statocysts, and ocelli to detect changes in and/or respond to their environment. Describe how each of these structures plays a role in the survival of cnidaria. In your answer, be sure to:
- describe the structure and composition of the nerve net
- identify the specific stimulus that each of the other three structures respond to
- explain how the cnidocytes help the animal survive

34 Animals that reproduce sexually begin life as a zygote. The zygote undergoes a series of divisions to form a hollow ball of cells. During the early development of most animal embryos, the cells differentiate into three germ layers. These layers give rise to various tissues. Describe these layers and their significance. In your answer be sure to
- identify the *three* germ layers
- identify *two* body structures that develop from each layer

35 The gemmules of some sponges are an adaptation that can help them survive periods of severe drought or freezlng temperatures. Describe the design of an experiment to investigate the effect of freezing on the survival of gemmules. In your description, be sure to:
- state one specific question that the experiment could be designed to answer
- state one possible hypothesis that could be formulated based on the question you propose
- briefly describe the procedure to follow in conducting a controlled experiment to test the hypothesis

For: An interactive self-test
Visit: PHSchool.com
Web Code: cba-8260

CHAPTER 27

Worms and Mollusks

The tips of the beautiful, tentacle-like structures of this nudibranch, *Flavella affinis*, contain stinging cells that defend against predators. A nudibranch is a kind of mollusk.

Inquiry Activity

Does a planarian have a head?

Procedure

1. Put on plastic gloves. Cover half of the outside of a petri dish with black paper. Place a white sheet of paper under the other half. Place a planarian in the center of the dish, and add spring water to keep it moist. Observe the planarian for 2 minutes. Record how long it stays on each side of the dish.
2. Where did the planarian spend more time? Hypothesize why the planarian preferred this side.
3. Tape a 4-cm piece of rubber band to a pencil so that 1 cm of the rubber band hangs freely. Use the tip of the rubber band to gently prod each end of the planarian. Observe its behavior. Wash your hands with soap and warm water before leaving the lab.

Think About It

1. **Observing** When the planarian moved, did one end always go first?
2. **Drawing Conclusions** How might the behaviors that you observed help the planarian survive?

27–1 Flatworms

4-5.2 Parasites infect other organisms
4-6.1 Relationships and interactions between organisms
LS- Make observations
LS- State an appropriate hypothesis

When most people think of worms, they think of long, squiggly earthworms. But there are many other kinds of worms. Some are the length of your body or as thick as your arm. Others look like glowing, furry blobs. Worms can flutter and glide, or climb around with paddlelike bristles. Still others are very small and live in tubes cemented to rocks.

How is their body shape beneficial to worms? A long, slender body allows an animal to move about more rapidly than a radially symmetrical body, like that of a cnidarian. Worms can move forward in a single direction rather than remaining stationary or drifting in currents. In addition, the mouth, sense organs, and brain (if there is one) are usually located at the anterior end, or head, of the body. This arrangement allows worms to locate food and respond to stimuli as they move. Many groups of organisms have worm-shaped bodies. The familiar earthworm is a segmented worm, which you will read about later in this chapter. The unsegmented worms include flatworms and roundworms. The simplest of these are the flatworms.

Guide for Reading

Key Concepts

- What are the defining features of flatworms?
- What are the characteristics of the three groups of flatworms?

Vocabulary

acoelomate • coelom
pharynx • flame cell
ganglion • eyespot
hermaphrodite
fission • scolex
proglottid • testis

Reading Strategy: Outlining Before you read, use the headings of the section to make an outline about the characteristics of flatworms. As you read, fill in subtopics where they apply in the outline. Add phrases after each subtopic to provide key information.

What Is a Flatworm?

The phylum Platyhelminthes (plat-ih-hel-MIN-theez) consists of the flatworms. Most flatworms are no more than a few millimeters thick. **Flatworms are soft, flattened worms that have tissues and internal organ systems. They are the simplest animals to have three embryonic germ layers, bilateral symmetry, and cephalization.**

Flatworms are known as **acoelomates** (ay-SEE-luh-mayts), meaning "without coelom." A **coelom** (SEE-lum) is a fluid-filled body cavity that is lined with tissue derived from mesoderm. No coelom forms between the tissues of flatworms. **Figure 27–1** shows that the digestive cavity, which is lined with tissue derived from endoderm, is the only body cavity. Flatworms also have bilateral symmetry. This means that the animal has two well-formed sides that can be identified as left and right. Most flatworms exhibit enough cephalization to have what is called a head.

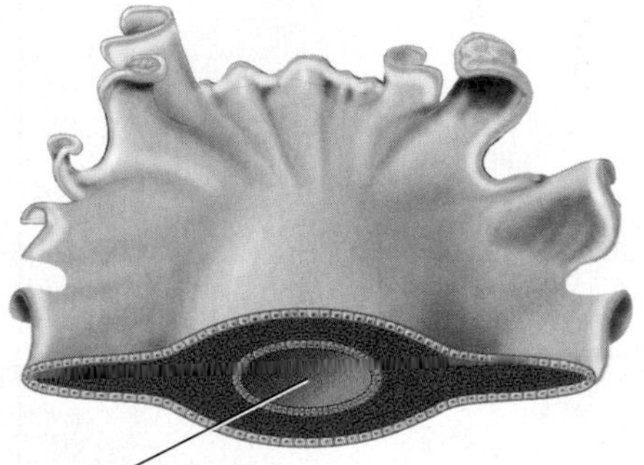

Figure 27–1 Flatworms are the simplest animals to have three embryonic germ layers—ectoderm, endoderm, and mesoderm. Shown here is the tropical, free-living flatworm *Pseudobiceros gloriosus.*

Form and Function in Flatworms

Because flatworms are thin and most of their cells are close to the external environment, materials can pass easily into and out of their bodies. All flatworms rely on diffusion for some essential body functions, such as respiration, excretion, and circulation. Other processes are carried out in different ways in different species. Free-living flatworms have organ systems for digestion, excretion, response, and reproduction.

Parasitic species of flatworms, such as the fluke in **Figure 27–2,** probably evolved from free-living ancestors. As the worms evolved into parasites, internal organs and other structures were modified or even lost. As a result, parasitic species are typically simpler in structure than their free-living relatives.

▲ **Figure 27–2** Blood flukes are parasitic flatworms that mature in the blood vessels of humans. Unlike free-living flatworms, parasitic worms take in nutrients from another organism. **Comparing and Contrasting** *How do the internal structures of parasitic flatworms compare to those of free-living flatworms?*

Feeding Free-living flatworms can be carnivores that feed on tiny aquatic animals, or they can be scavengers that feed on recently dead animals. Like cnidarians, flatworms have a digestive cavity with a single opening, or mouth, through which food and wastes pass. Near the mouth is a muscular tube called a **pharynx** (FAR-inks). Flatworms extend the pharynx out of the mouth. The pharynx then pumps food into the digestive cavity, or gut. Once inside, food is digested by cells of the gut, where digestion and nutrient absorption take place. Digested food diffuses from the digestive cavity into all other body tissues.

Parasitic worms feed on blood, tissue fluids, or pieces of cells within the host's body. Many parasitic worms obtain nutrients from foods that have already been digested by their host. Therefore, most parasitic worms do not need a complex digestive system. Many parasitic species have a digestive tract that is simpler than that of free-living forms. Some species have a pharynx that pumps food into a pair of dead-end intestinal sacs for digestion. Tapeworms, on the other hand, have no digestive tract at all. They live within the intestine of their host, such as a cow or a human, and simply absorb digested nutrients that are in their host's intestine.

Respiration, Circulation, and Excretion Because their bodies are so flat and thin, many flatworms do not need a circulatory system to transport materials. Instead, flatworms rely on diffusion to transport oxygen and nutrients to their internal tissues, and to remove carbon dioxide and other wastes from their bodies. Flatworms have no gills or other respiratory organs, and no heart, blood vessels, or blood.

Some flatworms have flame cells that function in excretion. **Flame cells** are specialized cells that remove excess water from the body. They may also filter and remove metabolic wastes such as ammonia and urea. Many flame cells are joined together to form a network of tubes that empties into the outside environment through tiny pores in the animal's skin.

What is the function of flame cells?

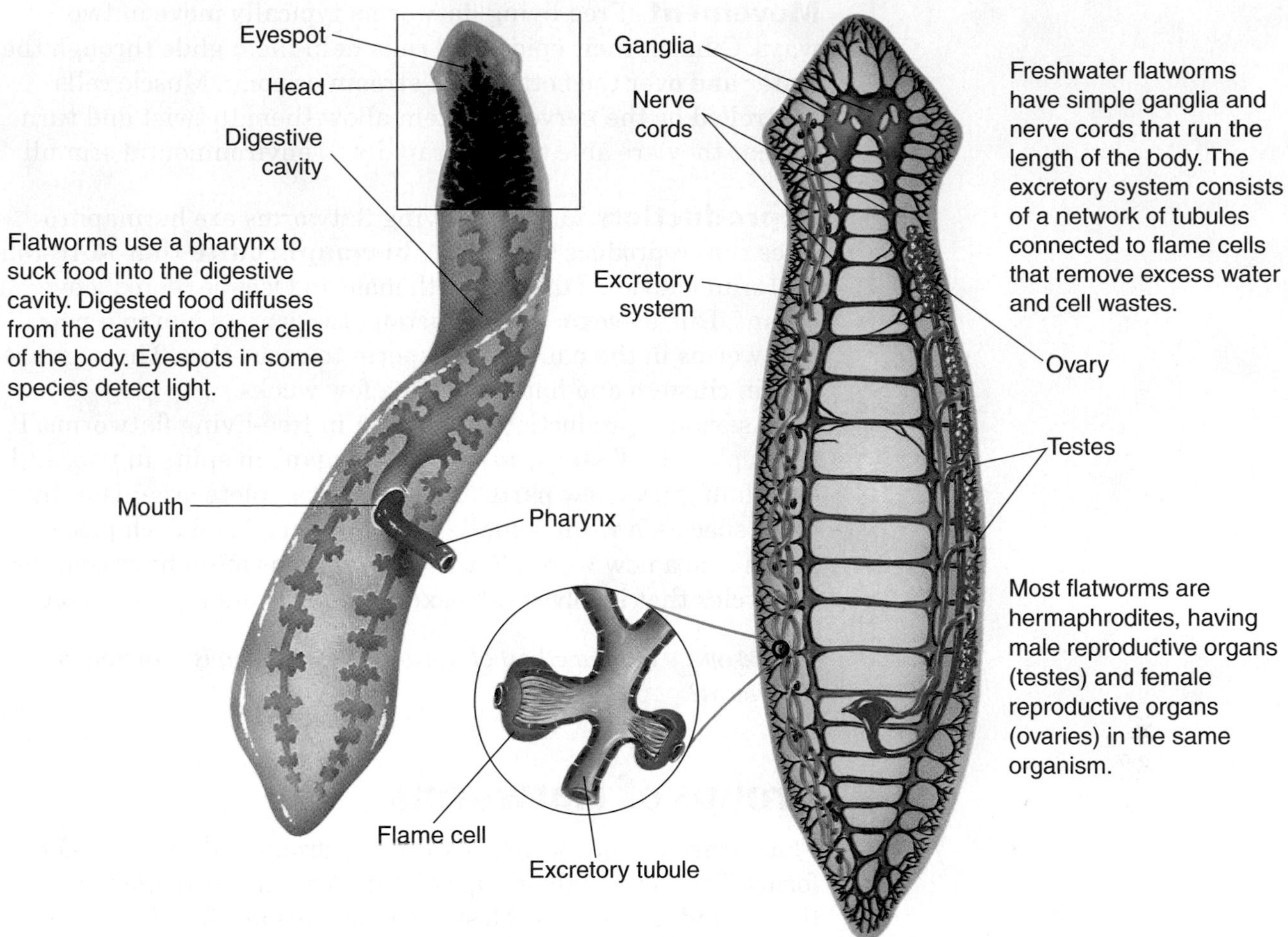
Eyespot
Head
Digestive cavity
Flatworms use a pharynx to suck food into the digestive cavity. Digested food diffuses from the cavity into other cells of the body. Eyespots in some species detect light.
Mouth
Pharynx
Flame cell
Excretory tubule
Ganglia
Nerve cords
Excretory system
Freshwater flatworms have simple ganglia and nerve cords that run the length of the body. The excretory system consists of a network of tubules connected to flame cells that remove excess water and cell wastes.
Ovary
Testes
Most flatworms are hermaphrodites, having male reproductive organs (testes) and female reproductive organs (ovaries) in the same organism.

▲ **Figure 27–3** All flatworms, including this planarian, have organ systems that perform essential life functions. The digestive cavity (left) is branched throughout the body and opens to the outside through the pharynx. The diagram on the right shows the excretory system, nervous system, and reproductive system. The excretory system (in purple) consists of many flame cells (in red) that maintain water balance and may remove waste. The nervous system (in dark gray) consists of ganglia and two nerve cords that run the length of the body. The reproductive system (in green) has testes and ovaries, or male and female reproductive organs, along both sides of the body. **Inferring** ***How is a branched digestive cavity advantageous to a flatworm?***

Response Most flatworms have more complex structures for detecting and responding to external stimuli than those of cnidarians or sponges. In free-living flatworms, a head encloses several **ganglia** (singular: ganglion), or groups of nerve cells, that control the nervous system. These ganglia are not complex enough to be called a brain. Two long nerve cords run from the ganglia along both sides of the body. Locate these nerve cords in **Figure 27–3.** Observe that shorter nerve cords run across the body, like the rungs of a ladder. Parasitic flatworms interact little with their external environment and typically have a less complex nervous system.

Many free-living flatworms have what look like eyes near the anterior end of their body. Each "eye" is actually an **eyespot,** or group of cells that can detect changes in the amount of light in their environment. In addition to having eyespots, most flatworms have specialized cells that detect external stimuli, such as chemicals found in food or the direction in which water is flowing. These cells are usually scattered throughout the body.

The nervous systems of free-living flatworms allow them to gather information from their environment. They use this information to locate food and to find dark hiding places beneath stones and logs during the day.

Movement Free-living flatworms typically move in two ways. Cilia on their epidermal cells help them glide through the water and over the bottom of a stream or pond. Muscle cells controlled by the nervous system allow them to twist and turn so that they are able to react rapidly to environmental stimuli.

Reproduction Most free-living flatworms are hermaphrodites that reproduce sexually. A **hermaphrodite** (hur-MAF-roh-dyt) is an individual that has both male and female reproductive organs. During sexual reproduction, two worms join in a pair. The worms in the pair deliver sperm to each other. The eggs are laid in clusters and hatch within a few weeks.

Asexual reproduction is common in free-living flatworms. It takes place by **fission,** in which an organism splits in two, and each half grows new parts to become a complete organism. In some species, a worm simply "falls to pieces," and each piece grows into a new worm. Parasitic flatworms often have complex life cycles that involve both sexual and asexual reproduction.

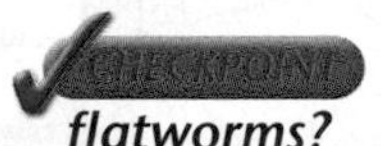
What method of asexual reproduction is common in flatworms?

Groups of Flatworms

Flatworms are an enormously diverse group with many different forms. The three main groups of flatworms are turbellarians, flukes, and tapeworms. Most turbellarians are free-living. Most other flatworm species are parasites.

Turbellarians Free-living flatworms belong to the class Turbellaria (tur-buh-LAYR-ee-uh). **Turbellarians are free-living flatworms. Most live in marine or fresh water.** Most species are bottom dwellers, living in the sand or mud under stones and shells. The most familiar flatworms of this group are the planarians, the "cross-eyed" freshwater worms. Turbellarians can vary greatly in color, form, and size, as shown in **Figure 27–4.**

Figure 27–4 **Free-living flatworms are called turbellarians.** Turbellarians vary in size, shape, coloration, and habitat. The species at left is feeding on a coral reef, and the species at right lives in the leaf litter in a tropical forest.

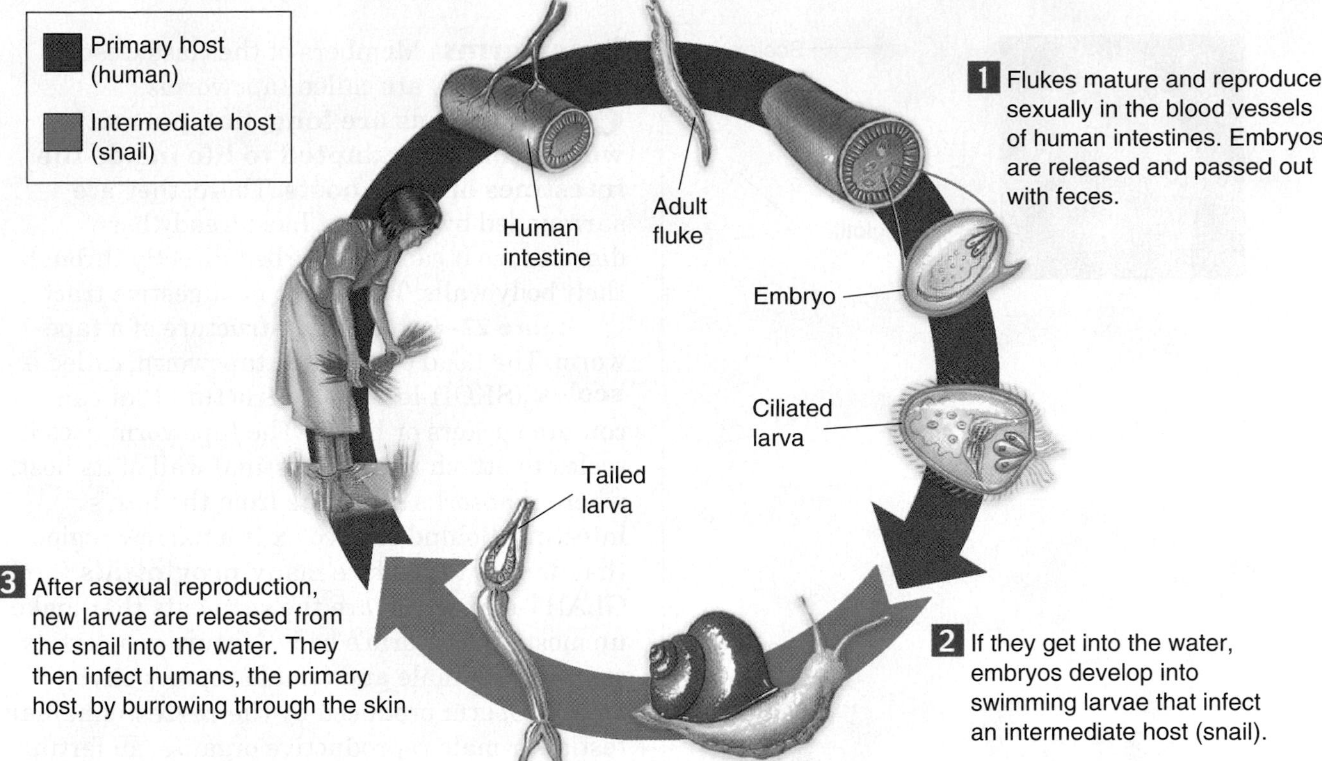

Primary host (human)
Intermediate host (snail)
Human intestine
Adult fluke
Embryo
Ciliated larva
Tailed larva
1 Flukes mature and reproduce sexually in the blood vessels of human intestines. Embryos are released and passed out with feces.
2 If they get into the water, embryos develop into swimming larvae that infect an intermediate host (snail).
3 After asexual reproduction, new larvae are released from the snail into the water. They then infect humans, the primary host, by burrowing through the skin.

▲ **Figure 27–5** **Flukes usually infect the internal organs of their host.** The life cycle of the blood fluke *Schistosoma mansoni* involves two hosts: humans and snails.

Flukes Members of the class Trematoda (trem-uh-TOH-duh) are known as flukes. **Flukes are parasitic flatworms. Most flukes infect the internal organs of their host.** They can infect the blood or virtually any internal organ of the host. Some flukes are external parasites that live on the skin, mouth, gills, or other outside parts of a host.

The blood fluke *Schistosoma mansoni* has a life cycle that is typical of parasitic flukes and of many parasites in general. As shown in **Figure 27–5,** the fluke lives in multiple hosts. Its primary host, the organism in which it reproduces sexually, is a human. Blood flukes infect humans by burrowing through exposed skin. Once inside, they are carried to the tiny blood vessels of the intestine. There, the flukes mature into adults, reproduce sexually, and release embryos into the intestine. The embryos are passed out of the body in feces.

If the embryos reach water, they develop into swimming larvae and infect freshwater snails, the intermediate host. An intermediate host is an organism in which a parasite reproduces asexually. Larvae that result from asexual reproduction are eventually released to begin the cycle again.

The *Schistosoma* fluke causes schistosomiasis (shis-tuh-soh-MY-uh-sis) in humans. Schistosomiasis is a serious disease in which the *Schistosoma* eggs clog blood vessels, causing swelling and tissue decay in the lungs, liver, spleen, or intestines. Schistosomiasis affects millions of people worldwide. It is particularly widespread in tropical areas that lack proper sewage systems, where human wastes are tossed into streams or used as fertilizer. There, the parasites are transmitted to intermediate hosts and back to humans with deadly efficiency.

For: Links on flukes
Visit: www.SciLinks.org
Web Code: cbn-8271

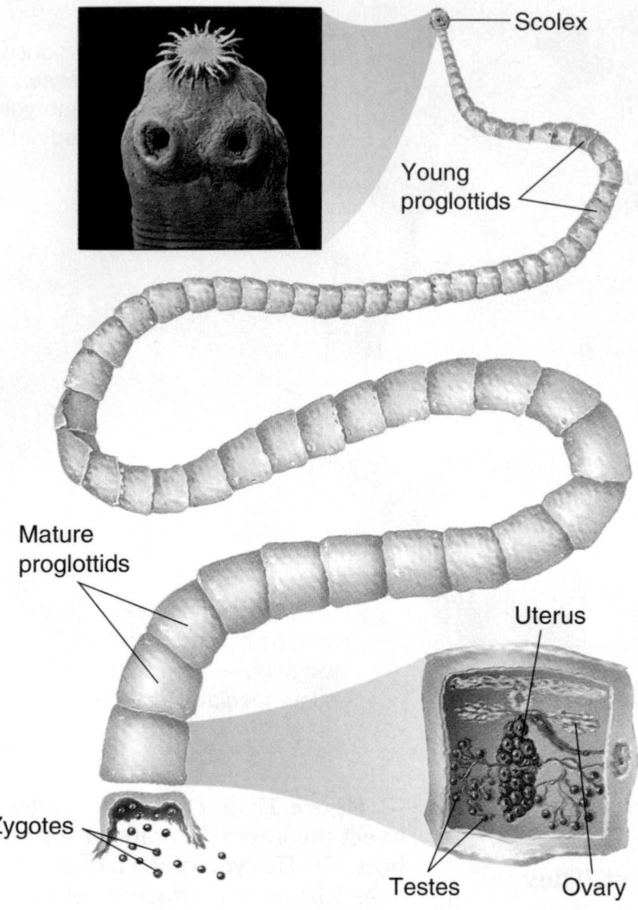

▲ **Figure 27–6 Tapeworms are parasitic flatworms that live in the intestines of their host.** A tapeworm attaches to the host using hooks or suckers on its scolex. A single tapeworm is made of many proglottids. The youngest proglottids are at the anterior (head) end, and the largest and most mature proglottids are at the posterior (tail) end. After eggs have been fertilized, proglottids break off and release zygotes that are then passed out of the host in feces.

Tapeworms Members of the class Cestoda (ses-TOHD-uh) are called tapeworms. **Tapeworms are long, flat, parasitic worms that are adapted to life inside the intestines of their hosts.** There, they are surrounded by food that has already been digested, so it can be absorbed directly through their body walls. They have no digestive tract.

Figure 27–6 shows the structure of a tapeworm. The head of an adult tapeworm, called a **scolex** (SKOH-leks), is a structure that can contain suckers or hooks. The tapeworm uses its scolex to attach to the intestinal wall of its host, where it absorbs nutrients from the host's intestine. Behind the scolex is a narrow region that divides to produce many **proglottids** (proh-GLAHT-idz), which are the segments that make up most of the worm's body. Mature proglottids contain both male and female reproductive organs. Sperm produced by the **testes** (singular: testis), or male reproductive organs, can fertilize eggs of other tapeworms or of the same individual. After the eggs are fertilized, proglottids break off and burst to release the fertilized eggs, or zygotes. These zygotes are passed out of the host in feces.

If food or water contaminated with tapeworm zygotes is consumed by cows, fishes, or other intermediate hosts, the eggs enter the host and hatch into larvae. These larvae grow and then burrow into the muscle tissue of the intermediate host. There they form a dormant protective stage called a cyst. If a human eats incompletely cooked meat containing these cysts, the larvae become active and grow into adult worms within the human's intestines, beginning the cycle again.

27–1 Section Assessment

1. **Key Concept** What is a flatworm?
2. **Key Concept** List the three groups of flatworms and give an example of each.
3. How do the feeding methods of parasitic and free-living flatworms relate to their specific environments?
4. Describe the life cycle of the blood fluke, *Schistosoma mansoni.*
5. **Critical Thinking Applying Concepts** How do a turbellarian's nervous system and digestive system work together to provide the food that the worm's body needs?

Writing in Science

Compare-Contrast Paragraph

Write a paragraph comparing free-living and parasitic flatworms. Be sure to explain how these worms are alike as well as how they are different. *Hint:* Before you write, construct a Venn diagram to organize your ideas.

27–2 Roundworms

4-5.2 Parasites infect other organisms
4-6.1 Relationships and interactions between organisms

Members of the phylum Nematoda, also known as roundworms, are among the most numerous of all animals. It is difficult to imagine how many live around us. A single rotting apple can contain as many as 90,000 roundworms. A cubic meter of garden soil can be home to more than a million!

Guide for Reading

Key Concepts
- What are the defining features of roundworms?
- What roundworms are important in human disease?

Vocabulary
pseudocoelom
anus

Reading Strategy: Using Visuals As you read, write a statement explaining how each illustration or photograph reinforces or enhances the content of the section.

What Is a Roundworm?

Roundworms are slender, unsegmented worms with tapering ends. They range in size from microscopic to a meter in length. Most species of roundworms are free-living, inhabiting soil, salt flats, aquatic sediments, and water, from polar regions to the tropics. Many others are parasitic and live in hosts that include almost every kind of plant and animal.

Like flatworms, roundworms develop from three germ layers. However, roundworms have a body cavity between the endoderm and mesoderm tissues. Because this cavity is lined only partially with tissue derived from the mesoderm, it is called a **pseudocoelom** (soo-doh-SEE-lum), which means "false coelom." Observe the pseudocoelom in **Figure 27–7.**

Also, unlike most flatworms, roundworms have a digestive tract with two openings. This body plan is often called a tube-within-a-tube. The inner tube is the digestive tract, and the outer tube is the body wall. This arrangement makes digestion in roundworms very different from that in flatworms because food moves in one direction through the digestive tract. Any material in the food that cannot be digested leaves through the anus. The **anus** is the posterior opening of the digestive tract. **Roundworms are unsegmented worms that have pseudocoeloms and digestive systems with two openings—a mouth and an anus.**

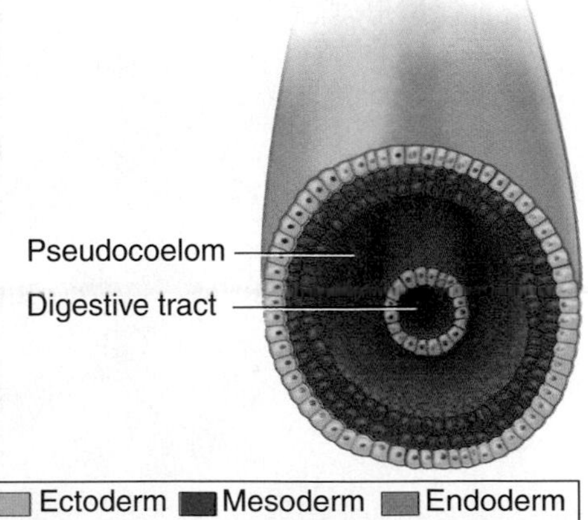

Figure 27–7 Roundworms such as hookworms are unsegmented worms that have a pseudocoelom and a digestive system with a mouth and an anus. Roundworms develop from three germ layers, and a pseudocoelom forms between the endoderm and mesoderm layers.

Figure 27–8 **Parasitic roundworms include trichinosis-causing *Trichinella* worms (top) and hookworms (inset).** *Trichinella* worms reproduce in the intestines of their host and then form cysts in the muscle tissue. Hookworms affect as many as one quarter of the world's population. They suck the host's blood from inside the intestines, weakening the host.

Form and Function in Roundworms

Roundworms have specialized tissues and organ systems that carry out essential physiological functions. In general, the body systems of free-living roundworms tend to be more complex than those of parasitic forms.

Feeding Many free-living roundworms are predators that use grasping mouthparts and spines to catch and eat other small animals. Some soil-dwelling and aquatic forms eat algae, fungi, or pieces of decaying organic matter. Others digest the bacteria and fungi that break down dead animals and plants.

Respiration, Circulation, and Excretion Like flatworms, roundworms exchange gases and excrete metabolic waste through their body walls. They have no internal transport system. Therefore, they depend on diffusion to carry nutrients and waste through their bodies.

Response Roundworms have simple nervous systems, consisting of several ganglia. Several nerves extend from ganglia in the head and run the length of the body. These nerves transmit sensory information and control movement. Roundworms have several types of sense organs. Some include simple structures that detect chemicals given off by prey or hosts.

Movement The muscles of roundworms extend the length of their bodies. Together with the fluid in the pseudocoelom, these muscles function as a hydrostatic skeleton. Aquatic roundworms contract these muscles to move like snakes through the water. Soil-dwelling roundworms simply push their way through the soil by thrashing around.

Reproduction Roundworms reproduce sexually, and most species have separate sexes—an individual is either male or female. Roundworms reproduce using internal fertilization. Usually, the male deposits sperm inside the female's reproductive tract. Parasitic roundworms often have life cycles that involve two or three different hosts or several organs within a single host.

CHECKPOINT *How do free-living roundworms that are predators obtain their food?*

Roundworms and Human Disease

Although most roundworms are free-living, the phylum is better known for species that parasitize their hosts, including humans. Parasitic roundworms, such as those in **Figure 27–8,** have been evolving relationships with other organisms for hundreds of millions of years. Unfortunately, this process has produced worms that cause a great deal of pain and suffering in humans. **Parasitic roundworms include trichinosis-causing worms, filarial worms, ascarid worms, and hookworms.**

Careers in Biology

Meat Inspector

Job Description: work with farms and meat-processing plants to ensure that all meat and poultry products use healthy animals, are processed in a sanitary manner, and are labeled truthfully with no harmful ingredients added; enforce government regulations to ensure that proper safety, sanitation, preservation, disposal, and packaging procedures are followed

Education: college courses in sanitation and public health; USDA certification

Skills: knowledge of food-borne illnesses, proper sanitation practices, and regulations; public relations skills for dealing with different people in the industry; patience and communication skills for educating the public; ability to work independently and with a team

Highlights: You help protect the safety of the public by working to eliminate food-borne illnesses. You inspect farms to make sure that sanitary procedures are followed.

For: Career links
Visit: PHSchool.com
Web Code: cbb-8272

Trichinosis-Causing Worms Trichinosis (trik-ih-NOH-sis) is a terrible disease caused by the roundworm *Trichinella*. Adult worms live and mate in the intestines of their hosts. Female worms carrying fertilized eggs burrow into the intestinal wall and then release larvae. These larvae travel through the bloodstream and burrow into organs and tissues, causing terrible pain for the host. The larvae form cysts and become inactive in the host's muscle tissue.

Trichinella completes its life cycle only when another animal eats muscle tissue containing these cysts. Two common hosts for *Trichinella* are rats and pigs. Humans get trichinosis almost exclusively by eating raw or incompletely cooked pork.

Filarial Worms Filarial worms, which are found primarily in tropical regions of Asia, are threadlike worms that live in the blood and lymph vessels of birds and mammals, including humans. They are transmitted from one primary host to another through biting insects, especially mosquitoes. In severe infections, large numbers of filarial worms may block the passage of fluids within the lymph vessels. This causes elephantiasis, shown in **Figure 27–9**, a condition in which the affected part of the body swells enormously.

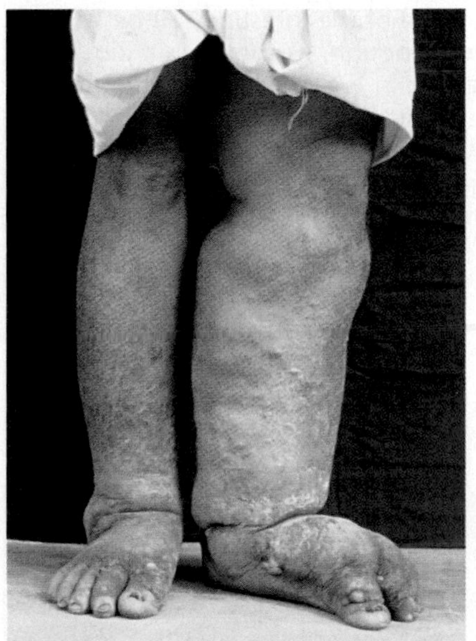

▲ **Figure 27–9 Filarial worms are one kind of parasitic roundworm.** Elephantiasis, shown here in an advanced stage, is a disease caused by filarial worms.

Describe the cause of elephantiasis.

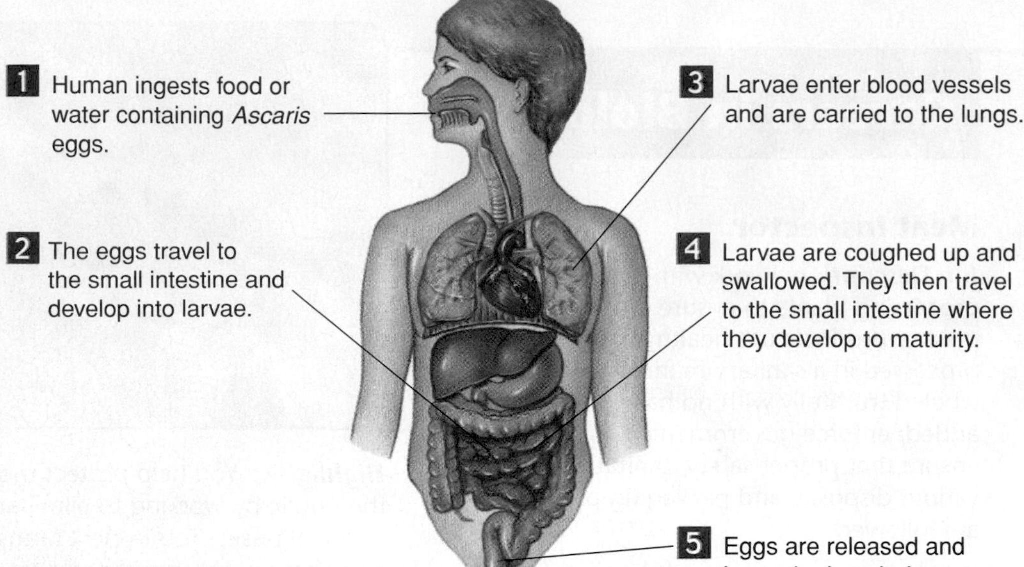
1 Human ingests food or water containing Ascaris eggs.
2 The eggs travel to the small intestine and develop into larvae.
3 Larvae enter blood vessels and are carried to the lungs.
4 Larvae are coughed up and swallowed. They then travel to the small intestine where they develop to maturity.
5 Eggs are released and leave the host in feces.

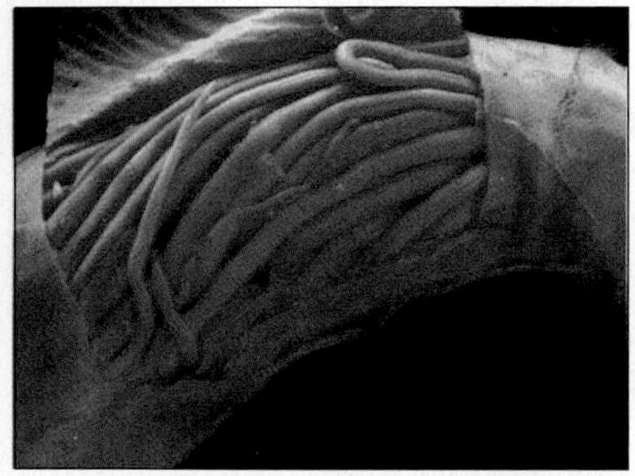

Figure 27–10 *Ascaris lumbricoides* fill the host's intestine. These worms absorb the host's digested food and can cause severe malnutrition. Blockage of the intestine can be severe enough, as shown in a pig intestine in the photograph, that it causes death. **Interpreting Graphics** *What is the sequence of organs that* Ascaris *travels through in humans?*

Ascarid Worms *Ascaris lumbricoides* is a serious parasite of humans and many other vertebrate animals. It causes malnutrition in more than 1 billion people worldwide. It does this by absorbing digested food from the host's small intestine. *Ascaris lumbricoides* is commonly spread by eating vegetables or other foods that are not washed properly.

The life cycle of *Ascaris* is summarized in **Figure 27–10** above. *Ascaris* matures in the intestines of its host, such as a human, and can reach a length of almost 50 cm. In the intestine, the ascarid worms produce a large number of fertilized eggs, which leave the body in the feces. If food or water contaminated with these feces is eaten by another host, then the eggs hatch in the small intestine of the new host. The young worms burrow into the walls of the intestines and enter the surrounding blood vessels. The worms are carried in the blood until they reach the lungs. There, they spread into air passages and into the throat, where they are swallowed. Carried back into the intestines, they mature, and the cycle repeats itself.

Species that are closely related to *Ascaris* affect horses, cattle, pigs, chickens, dogs, cats, and many other animals. *Ascaris* and its relatives, which are collectively known as ascarids, have life cycles that are similar to one another. One of the reasons puppies are wormed while they are young is to rid them of the ascarid worms that affect dogs.

Hookworms Today, as many as one quarter of the people in the world are infected with hookworms. Hookworm eggs hatch outside the body of the host and develop in the soil. If they find an unprotected foot, they use sharp toothlike plates and hooks to burrow into the skin and enter the bloodstream. Hookworms travel through the blood of their host to the lungs and down to the intestines. There, they suck the host's blood, causing weakness and poor growth.

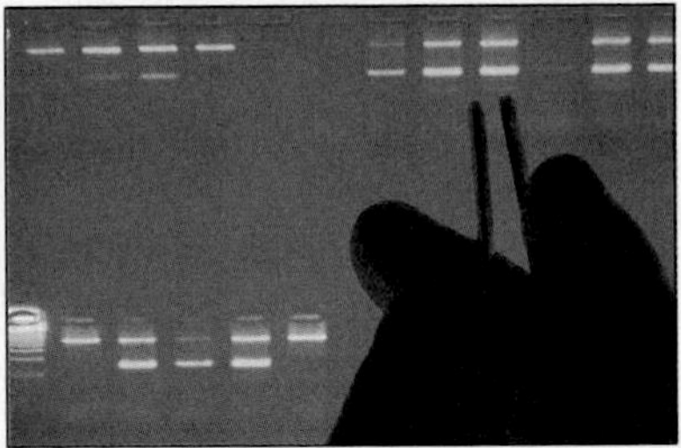

Figure 27–11 The DNA of *C. elegans,* a free-living roundworm, was the first genome of any multicellular animal to be sequenced completely. Biologists used techniques such as gel electrophoresis, shown above, to determine the exact sequence of base pairs in each chromosome. **Predicting** ***How might these results be important to our understanding of human development?***

Research on C. *elegans*

Roundworms have recently been making headlines in scientific research. The free-living roundworm *Caenorhabditis elegans*, or *C. elegans*, is shown in **Figure 27–11,** above left. This worm lives a modest existence feeding on rotting vegetation. However, this species is extraordinary because its DNA was the first of any multicellular animal's to be sequenced completely.

Scientists now have the sequence of all 97 million base pairs of *C. elegans* DNA. This is roughly one thirtieth the number of base pairs in human DNA. They have also traced the differentiation and development of each body cell of *C. elegans*, starting from a single fertilized egg. Researchers are still learning how this differentiation is controlled by the animal's DNA. This research will lead to a better understanding of how eukaryotes became multicellular. Information from *C. elegans* may also shed light on how genes make multicellular organisms both similar to and different from one another.

27 2 Section Assessment

1. **Key Concept** What is a roundworm?
2. **Key Concept** What are the parasitic roundworms?
3. Describe how humans become infected with the parasitic roundworm *Ascaris lumbricoides*.
4. How do hookworms enter the human body?
5. What have scientists already learned about *Caenorhabditis elegans*? What do they hope to learn in the future?
6. **Critical Thinking Problem Solving** What steps might individual people and governments take to reduce the spread of elephantiasis?

Thinking Visually

Creating a Poster
Choose a type of roundworm that can cause disease in humans. Design an educational poster that promotes prevention of the disease. Be sure to include information about how the roundworm infects humans.

27–3 Annelids

4-6.1 Relationships and interactions between organisms
LS- Make observations
LS- Use of compound microscope

Guide for Reading

Key Concepts

- What are the defining features of annelids?
- What are the characteristics of the three classes of annelids?

Vocabulary
septum • seta
crop • gizzard
closed circulatory system
gill • nephridium
clitellum

Reading Strategy: Using Visuals Before you read, preview **Figure 27–16.** How does this animal seem to differ from the other worms you have already studied? Briefly summarize any differences you notice.

If you have ever dug in a garden in the spring, you have probably seen earthworms wriggling through the soil. Earthworms are annelids, members of the phylum Annelida. Other annelids include exotic seafloor worms and parasitic, blood-sucking leeches. Because their bodies are long and narrow, some annelids look a bit like flatworms or roundworms. However, the annelids are a distinct group that is probably more closely related to clams and snails. One piece of evidence for this relationship is the fact that annelids, clams, and snails all share a similar larval stage.

What Is an Annelid?

The name Annelida (uh-NEL-ih-duh) is derived from the Latin word *annellus*, which means "little ring." The name refers to the ringlike appearance of annelids' body segments. The body of an annelid is divided into segments that are separated by **septa** (singular: septum), which are internal walls between each segment. Most segments are similar to one another, although they may be modified to perform special functions. Some body segments may carry one or more pairs of eyes, several pairs of antennae, and other sense organs. Other segments may be specialized for functions such as respiration. In many annelids, bristles called **setae** (SEE-tee; singular: seta) are attached to each segment.

Annelids are worms with segmented bodies. They have a true coelom that is lined with tissue derived from mesoderm. These structures are shown in **Figure 27–12.** Recall that flatworms have no coelom, whereas roundworms have a pseudocoelom. Like the roundworms, annelids have a tube-within-a-tube digestive tract that food passes through from the mouth to the anus.

CHECKPOINT *What are some functions performed by specialized segments?*

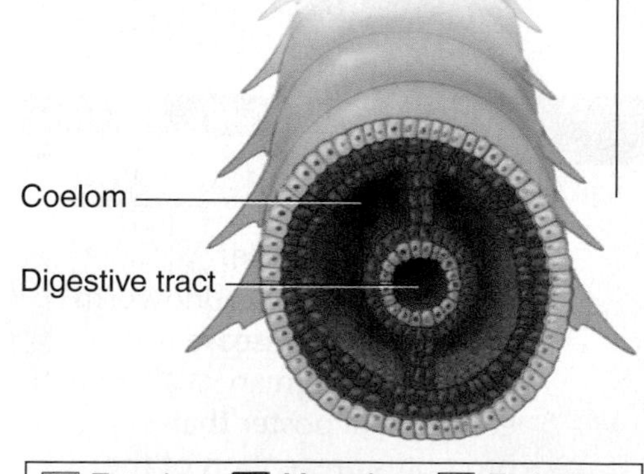

Figure 27–12 Annelids are among the simplest animals to have a true coelom that is lined with mesoderm. Annelids are also called segmented worms because the body is divided into many similar segments. The photo shows a marine annelid.

Quick Lab

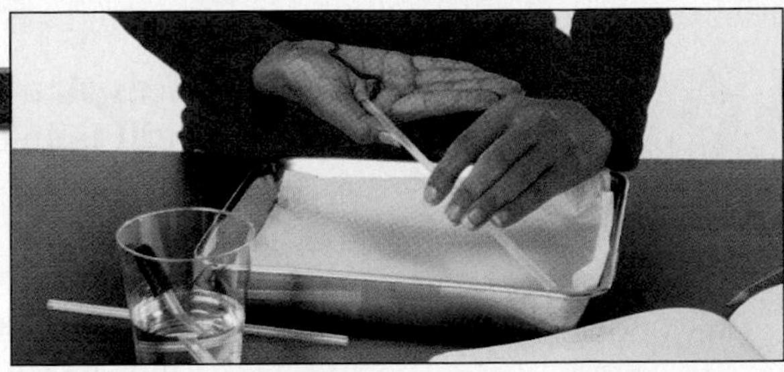

How does an earthworm pump blood?

Materials earthworm; dropper pipette; nonchlorinated water; large, clear plastic soda straw; dissecting microscope; clock or watch with second hand

Procedure 

1. Carefully insert an earthworm into a clear plastic straw. Do not force the worm into the straw. **CAUTION:** *Handle the earthworm carefully to avoid harming it. Wash your hands after handling the worm.*
2. Use a dropper pipette to add a drop or two of nonchlorinated water into the straw.
3. Examine the straw using a microscope. Direct light through the straw from below. Look near the front of the worm for the large ring blood vessels. Count how often these organs beat during a one minute period. Observe the rest of the circulatory system.

Analyze and Conclude

1. **Inferring** Did you see the worm breathing? Explain your answer. Why must the earthworm's skin be kept moist? How do your answers relate to how earthworms live in their environment?
2. **Observing** Is an earthworm's circulatory system open or closed? Explain your answer.

Form and Function in Annelids

Annelids have complex organ systems. Many of these systems are unique because of the segmented body plan of this group.

Feeding and Digestion Annelids range from filter feeders to predators. Many annelids get their food using a pharynx. In carnivorous species, such as the *Nereis* in **Figure 27–13,** the pharynx usually holds two or more sharp jaws that are used to attack prey. In annelids that feed on decaying vegetation, the pharynx is covered with sticky mucus. The worm collects food particles by extending its pharynx and pressing it against the surrounding sediments. Other annelids obtain nutrients by filter feeding. They fan water through tubelike burrows and catch food particles in a mucus bag.

In earthworms, the pharynx pumps food and soil into a tube called the esophagus. The food then moves through the **crop,** where it can be stored, and through the **gizzard,** where it is ground into smaller pieces. The food is absorbed farther along in the digestive tract, in an organ called the intestine.

Circulation Annelids typically have a **closed circulatory system,** in which blood is contained within a network of blood vessels. An earthworm's blood circulates through two major blood vessels that run from head to tail. Blood in the dorsal (top) vessel moves toward the head of the worm. Blood in the ventral (bottom) vessel runs from head to tail. In each body segment, a pair of smaller blood vessels connect the dorsal and ventral blood vessels and supply blood to the internal organs. The dorsal blood vessel functions like a heart because it contracts rhythmically and helps pump blood.

▲ **Figure 27–13** The annelid *Nereis* uses jaws to capture prey. When prey approaches, the worm lunges forward, rapidly extends its pharynx, and grabs the prey using its jaws. **Inferring** *How is the structure of a* Nereis*'s jaws related to their function?*

▲ **Figure 27–14** These feather-duster worms exchange gases underwater using feathery gills. **Applying Concepts** *How do land-dwelling annelids exchange gases?*

Respiration Aquatic annelids often breathe through gills. A **gill** is an organ specialized for the exchange of gases underwater. In feather-duster worms, shown in **Figure 27–14,** feathery structures that function as gills protrude from the opening of the worm's burrow or tube. Land-dwelling annelids, such as earthworms, take in oxygen and give off carbon dioxide through their moist skin. These annelids secrete a thin protective coating of mucus, which keeps their skins moist.

Excretion Like other animals, annelids produce two kinds of waste. Digestive waste passes out through the anus at the end of the digestive tract. Cellular waste containing nitrogen is eliminated by **nephridia** (nee-FRID-ee-uh; singular: nephridium), which are excretory organs that filter fluid in the coelom.

Response Most annelids have a well-developed nervous system consisting of a brain and several nerve cords. However, the sense organs are best developed in free-living marine annelids. Many of these species have a variety of adaptations for detecting stimuli: sensory tentacles, chemical receptors, statocysts that help detect gravity, and two or more pairs of eyes.

Movement Annelids have two major groups of body muscles that function as part of a hydrostatic skeleton. Longitudinal muscles run from the front of the worm to the rear and can contract to make the worm shorter and fatter. Circular muscles wrap around each body segment and can contract to make the worm longer and thinner. The earthworm moves by alternately contracting these two sets of muscles, using its setae to prevent slipping. Burrowing annelids use their muscles to force their way through heavy sediment. Marine annelids have paddlelike appendages, or parapodia (singular: parapodium), on each segment, which they use for swimming and crawling.

Reproduction Most annelids reproduce sexually. Some species use external fertilization and have separate sexes. Other annelids are hermaphrodites. Individuals rarely fertilize their own eggs. Instead, two worms attach to each other, as shown in **Figure 27–15,** exchange sperm, and then store the sperm in special sacs. When eggs are ready for fertilization, a **clitellum** (kly-TEL-um), or band of thickened, specialized segments, secretes a mucus ring into which eggs and sperm are released. Fertilization takes place within this ring. The ring then slips off the worm's body and forms a protective cocoon. Young worms hatch weeks later.

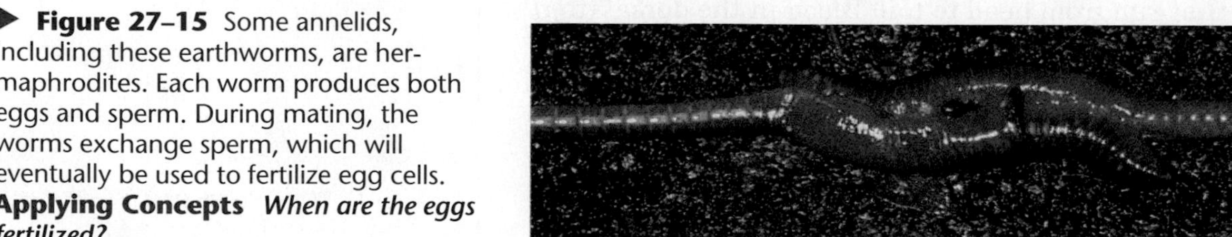

▶ **Figure 27–15** Some annelids, including these earthworms, are hermaphrodites. Each worm produces both eggs and sperm. During mating, the worms exchange sperm, which will eventually be used to fertilize egg cells. **Applying Concepts** *When are the eggs fertilized?*

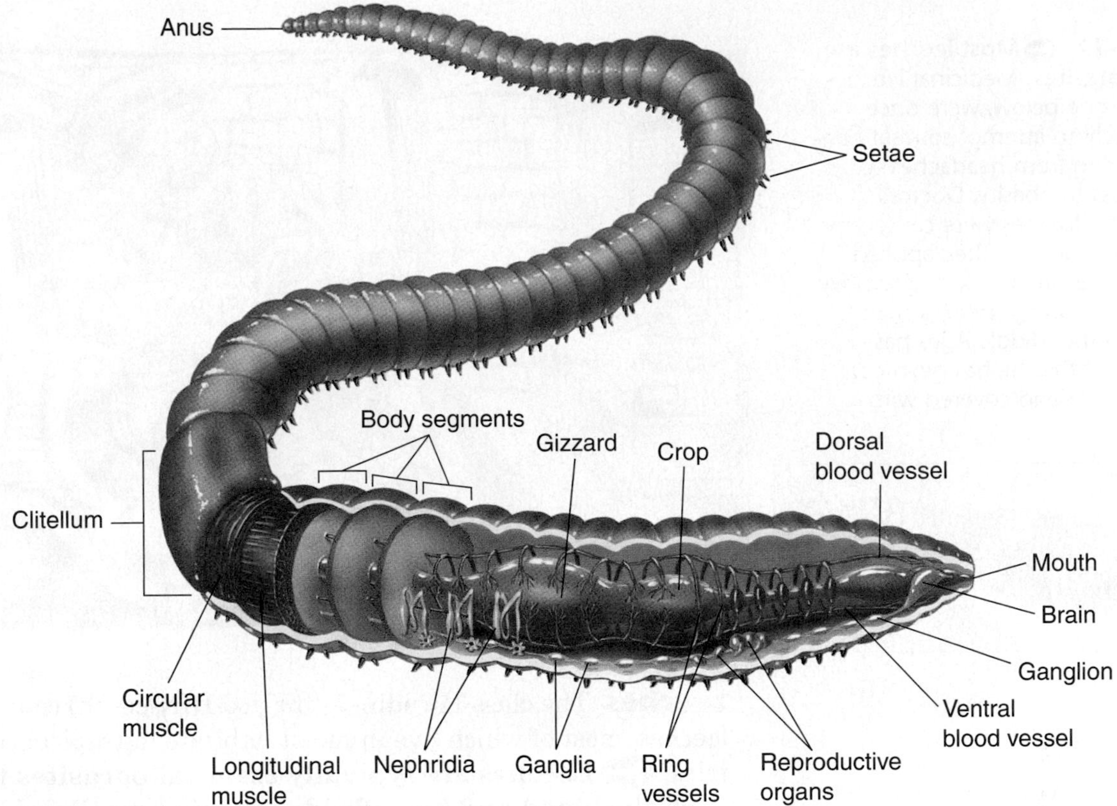

▲ **Figure 27–16** **Earthworms are oligochaetes that live in soil.** Earthworms carry out essential functions using digestive, circulatory, excretory, nervous, and reproductive systems. Many organs, including nephridia and blood vessels, repeat in nearly every body segment.

Groups of Annelids

Because of their visible segmentation, all annelids show a basic similarity. Annelids are divided into three classes—oligochaetes, leeches, and polychaetes.

Oligochaetes The class Oligochaeta, or oligochaetes (AHL-ih-goh-keets), contains earthworms and their relatives. **Oligochaetes are annelids that typically have streamlined bodies and relatively few setae compared to polychaetes. Most oligochaetes live in soil or fresh water.** Earthworms, such as the one shown in **Figure 27–16,** are long, pinkish-brown worms that are common in woods, fields, and gardens. Tubifex worms—another common oligochaete—are red, threadlike aquatic worms that are sold in pet stores as food for tropical fish.

Although earthworms spend most of their lives hidden underground, you may find evidence of their presence above ground in the form of squiggles of mud known as castings. Recall that an earthworm—which swallows just about anything it can get into its mouth—uses its pharynx to suck a mixture of detritus and soil particles into its mouth. As the mixture of food and soil passes through the intestine, part of it is digested and absorbed. Sand grains, clay particles, and indigestible organic matter pass out through the anus in large quantities, producing castings. Some tropical earthworms produce enormous castings—as large as 18 centimeters long and 2 centimeters in diameter!

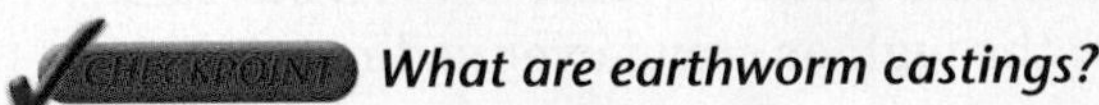
What are earthworm castings?

Word Origins

Oligochaete comes from the Greek words *oligos,* meaning "few" or "small," and *chaite,* meaning "hair." **If *poly-* means "many," what is a characteristic of the group of annelids known as polychaetes?**

Figure 27–17 **Most leeches are external parasites.** Medicinal leeches, such as the one below, were once used routinely to attempt to treat conditions ranging from headaches to mental illness to obesity. Doctors believed that diseases were caused by an excess of blood, so they applied leeches to the patient's skin to remove blood from the body. Here, a man who lived in the Middle Ages has become so fat that he has been confined to a room and covered with leeches.

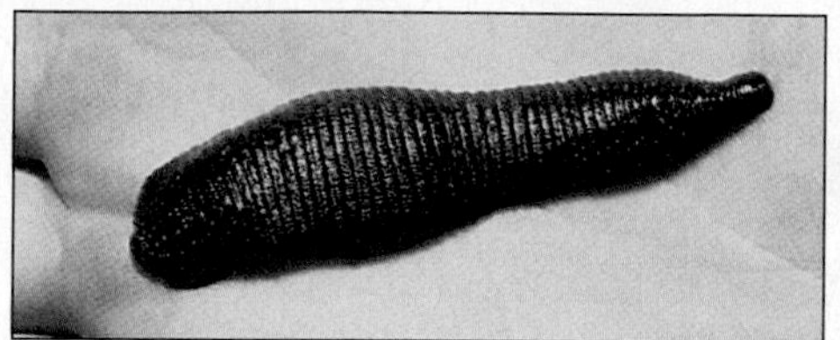

Leeches The class Hirudinea (hir-yoo-DIN-ee-uh) contains the leeches, most of which live in moist habitats in tropical countries. **Leeches are typically external parasites that suck the blood and body fluids of their host.** Roughly one fourth of all leeches are carnivores that feed on soft-bodied invertebrates such as snails, worms, and insect larvae.

Leeches have powerful suckers at both ends of their bodies that help them cling to their hosts. The posterior sucker can also anchor a leech to rocks or leaves as it waits for a host to pass. Some leeches force a muscular extension called a proboscis (proh-BAHS-is) into the tissue of their host. Others slice into the skin with a razor-sharp pair of jaws. Once a wound has been made, the leech uses its pharynx to suck blood from the area. Some leeches also release a substance that anesthetizes the wound—keeping the host from knowing it has been bitten!

Leeches were once commonly used to treat medical conditions. Today the use of medicinal leeches is undergoing a revival of sorts. Doctors are finding that leeches can reduce swelling after surgery. After surgeries in which a body part is reattached, hungry leeches are applied to the area. These leeches can suck several milliliters of blood at a time—up to five times their own weight! They also secrete a fluid that prevents blood from clotting. This anti-clotting mechanism helps relieve pressure and congestion in the healing tissues.

▼ **Figure 27–18** **Polychaetes are marine annelids.** The bearded fireworm is a polychaete that lives in coral reefs. It is best known for its method of defense—its setae, or bristles, break off when touched and cause irritation and burning.

Polychaetes The class Polychaeta, or polychaetes (PAHL-ih-keets), contains sandworms, bloodworms, and their relatives. **Polychaetes are marine annelids that have paired, paddlelike appendages tipped with setae.** The setae are the brushlike structures on the worm shown in **Figure 27–18.** Polychaetes live in cracks and crevices in coral reefs; in sand, mud, and piles of rocks; or even out in the open water. Some burrow through or crawl over sediment.

Ecology of Annelids

▲ **Figure 27–19** Some annelids, including this earthworm, burrow through soil, mixing it as they go. **Predicting** ***What might happen to a garden if all the annelids in the soil were killed?***

The importance of earthworms in nature was noted as far back as ancient Greece, when Aristotle called them "the intestines of the earth." Charles Darwin was impressed enough with earthworms that he devoted years—and an entire book—to their study. Earthworms, like the one shown in **Figure 27–19,** and many other annelids spend their lives burrowing through soil, aerating it, and mixing it to depths of 2 meters or more. Their tunnels provide passageways for plant roots and water and allow the growth of beneficial, oxygen-requiring soil bacteria. Earthworms pull plant matter down into the soil and pass it through the gut. There, they grind it, partially digest it, and mix it with bacteria that help the plant matter decompose. Worms also "mine" minerals from deeper soil layers, bringing them up to the surface. Earthworm feces (castings) are rich in nitrogen, phosphorus, potassium, micronutrients, and beneficial bacteria.

You've probably seen a bird struggling to pull an earthworm out of the ground. Earthworms are an important part of the diet of many birds, such as robins. Moles, skunks, toads, and snakes also prey on earthworms.

In the sea, annelids participate in a wide range of food chains. Many marine annelids have free-swimming larvae that are part of the animal plankton that is consumed by fishes and other plankton feeders. As adults, some marine annelids are mud-dwelling filter feeders that are common in areas where sediment is disturbed or large amounts of organic material are present. These worms are especially numerous where pollution from sewage promotes the growth of bacteria and algae. As any fisher knows, many bottom-dwelling polychaetes are important in the diets of fishes. Crustaceans, such as crabs and lobsters, also include annelids in their diets.

27–3 Section Assessment

1. **Key Concept** What features distinguish annelids from roundworms?
2. **Key Concept** List the defining characteristics for each class of annelid.
3. Describe the feeding strategies of earthworms and leeches.
4. **Critical Thinking Inferring** An earthworm has more light-sensitive cells in its anterior and posterior segments than in other parts of its body. Explain how this is advantageous for the worm.

Connecting Concepts

Food Chains and Annelids
Review what you learned about food chains in Chapter 3. Then, draw a possible food chain involving an annelid. The food chain should include at least three levels.

What Can Be Done About the Zebra Mussel?

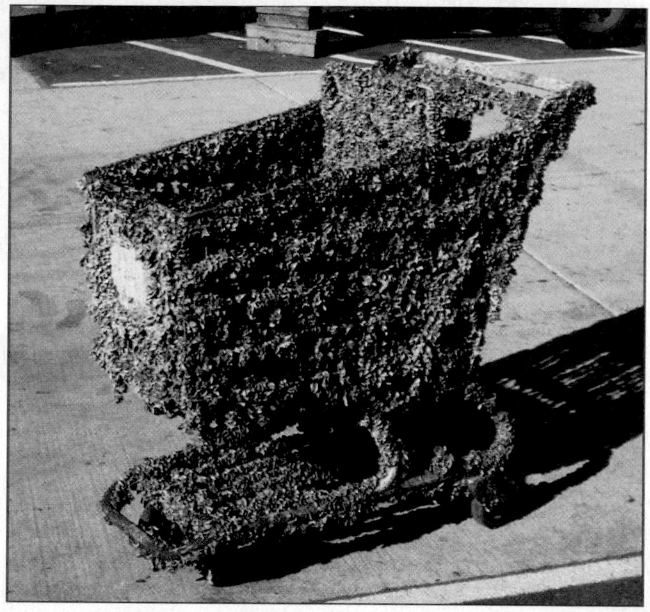

Zebra mussels *(Dreissena polymorpha)* were introduced into the United States from Eastern Europe and Asia when ships from the areas emptied their ballast tanks. They were first spotted in the Great Lakes in the mid-1980s. Zebra mussels have few natural enemies here and reproduce very rapidly. They have already colonized the entire Great Lakes region and have spread to rivers in more than ten states.

Zebra mussels live attached to almost any surface—from shopping carts to fiberglass boats—and can form layers up to 20 centimeters thick. They have caused serious structural damage and have clogged water supply lines to power plants and water treatment facilities. One paper company, for example, spent over a million dollars to remove zebra mussels that were clogging its cooling pipes.

Zebra mussels also threaten the ecology of aquatic communities. They can tolerate a wide range of temperatures and light intensities. In some habitats, they have displaced native mollusks, almost making them extinct. Zebra mussels have also depleted the food of many fish species. What can be done to control zebra mussels and other exotic (nonnative) species and prevent new ones from arriving?

The Viewpoints

Control and Prevention

Many scientists believe that there is no way to remove zebra mussels and many other established exotic species. Instead, these scientists attempt to control the growth of populations and prevent the transfer of exotic species to new areas. One regulation, for example, could require boaters to filter and chemically clean all ballast water. Another approach would be to find beneficial uses for zebra mussels. Scientists are already exploring the ability of zebra mussels to filter large volumes of waste water.

Eradication

Other groups contend that zebra mussels should be eradicated. Engineers, for example, are developing robotic submarines that can remove mussels from pipelines. Chemists are testing chemicals for the potential to destroy or disrupt the life cycle of zebra mussels. Other scientists are adding chemicals to paints and plastics to prevent mussels from attaching to new surfaces.

Research and Decide

1. **Analyzing the Viewpoints** To make an informed decision, learn more about this issue by consulting library or Internet resources. Then, determine the advantages and disadvantages of each proposed solution to the problems caused by zebra mussels.
2. **Forming Your Opinion** What measures do you think would be most effective in dealing with exotic species?

For: Links from the authors
Visit: PHSchool.com
Web Code: cbe-8273

27–4 Mollusks

4-6.1 Relationships and interactions between organisms
4-7.1 Human beings can alter ecosystems
4-7.2 Human beings alter ecosystems
LS- Analyze results and state an appropriate hypothesis

They climb trees in tropical rain forests and float over coral reefs. They crawl into garbage cans, eat their way through farm crops, and speed through the deep ocean. Some are so small that you can hardly see them with the unaided eye, while others are 20 meters long! They are the mollusks—one of the oldest and most diverse phyla. Mollusks come in so many sizes, shapes, and forms that you might wonder why they are classified in the same phylum. To learn the answer, read on.

Guide for Reading

Key Concepts
- What are the defining features of mollusks?
- What is the basic body plan of mollusks?
- What are the characteristics of the three main classes of mollusks?

Vocabulary
trochophore • foot
mantle • shell • visceral mass
radula • siphon
open circulatory system

Reading Strategy: Building Vocabulary
As you read, make notes about the meaning of each term in the list above. After you read the section, make a table listing the different types of mollusks on the left and the vocabulary words that apply on the right.

What Is a Mollusk?

Members of the phylum Mollusca, known as mollusks, are named from the Latin word *molluscus*, which means "soft." **Mollusks are soft-bodied animals that usually have an internal or external shell.** Mollusks include snails, slugs, clams, squids, and octopi. But a snail looks very different from a squid, which looks very different from a clam. So why are these animals all placed in the same phylum? One reason is that many mollusks share similar developmental stages. Many aquatic mollusks have a free-swimming larval stage called a **trochophore** (TRAHK-oh-fawr). The trochophore larva, which is shown in **Figure 27–20,** is also characteristic of annelids, indicating that these two groups may be closely related. Molecular studies suggest that a common ancestor of annelids and mollusks lived more than 550 million years ago.

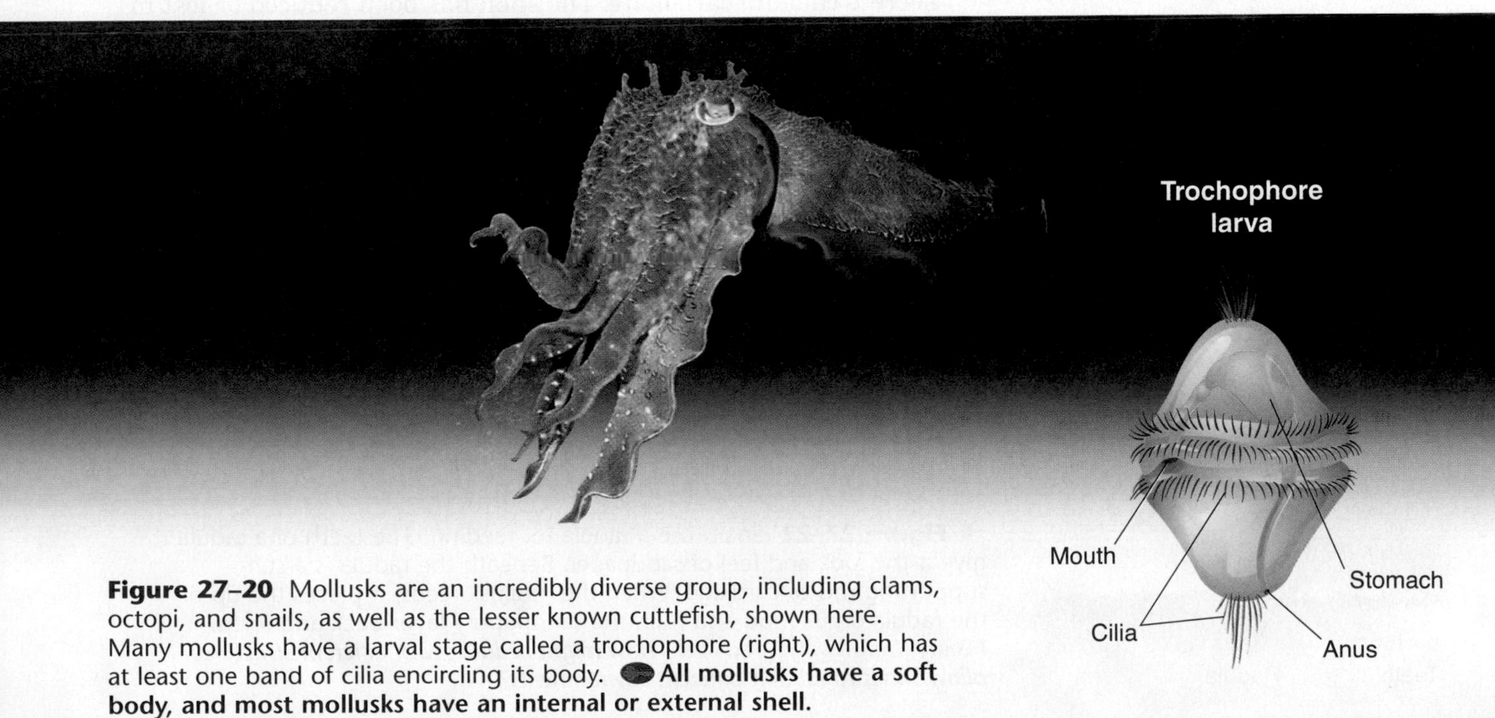

Figure 27–20 Mollusks are an incredibly diverse group, including clams, octopi, and snails, as well as the lesser known cuttlefish, shown here. Many mollusks have a larval stage called a trochophore (right), which has at least one band of cilia encircling its body. **All mollusks have a soft body, and most mollusks have an internal or external shell.**

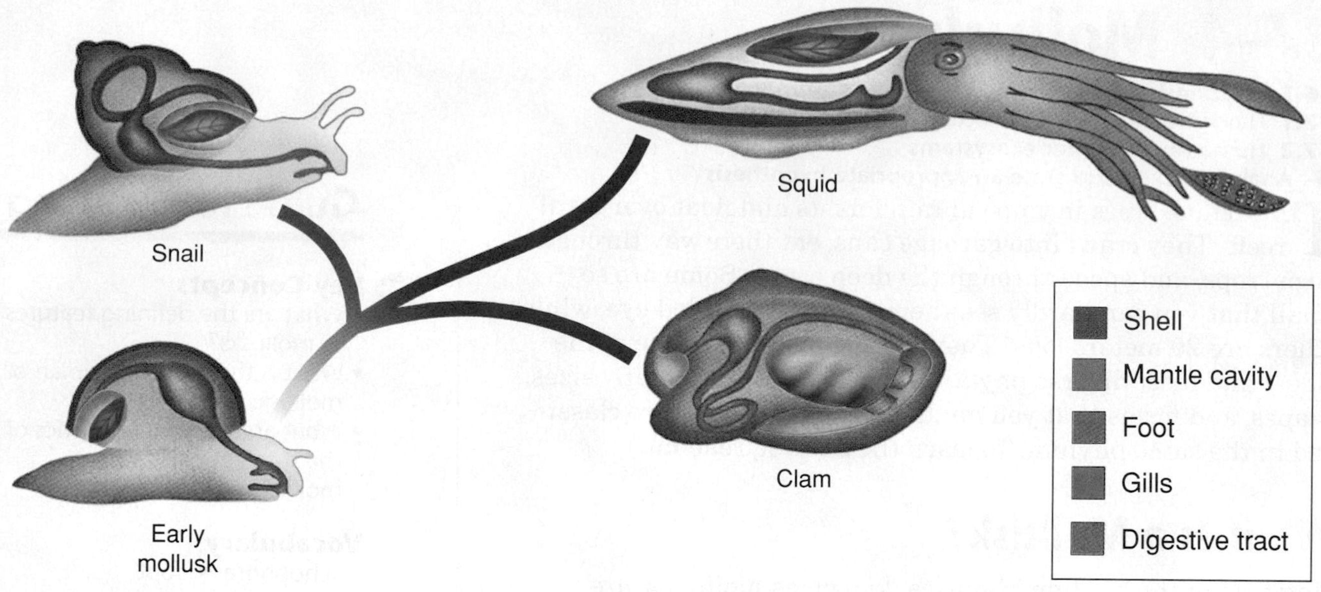

▲ **Figure 27–21** **The body plan of most mollusks includes a foot, mantle, shell, and visceral mass.** Early mollusks may have looked like the animal shown at the bottom. As they evolved, their body parts became adapted for different functions.

Form and Function in Mollusks

Like the annelids, mollusks have true coeloms surrounded by mesoderm tissue. They also have complex, interrelated organ systems that function together to maintain the body as a whole.

Body Plan The different body shapes of mollusks are variations on a single body plan, shown in **Figure 27–21.** **The body plan of most mollusks has four parts: foot, mantle, shell, and visceral mass.** The muscular **foot** takes many forms, including flat structures for crawling, spade-shaped structures for burrowing, and tentacles for capturing prey. The **mantle** is a thin layer of tissue that covers most of the mollusk's body, much like a cloak. The **shell** is made by glands in the mantle that secrete calcium carbonate. The shell has been reduced or lost in slugs and some other mollusk groups. Just beneath the mantle is the **visceral mass,** which consists of the internal organs.

Feeding Mollusks can be herbivores, carnivores, filter feeders, detritivores, or parasites. Snails and slugs feed using a flexible, tongue-shaped structure known as a **radula** (RAJ-oo-luh; plural: radulae), shown in **Figure 27–22,** to which hundreds of tiny teeth are attached. Herbivorous mollusks use their radula to scrape algae off rocks or to eat the soft tissues of plants. Carnivorous mollusks use their radula to drill through shells of other animals and to tear up and swallow the prey's soft tissue.

CHECKPOINT *How is a mollusk's shell made?*

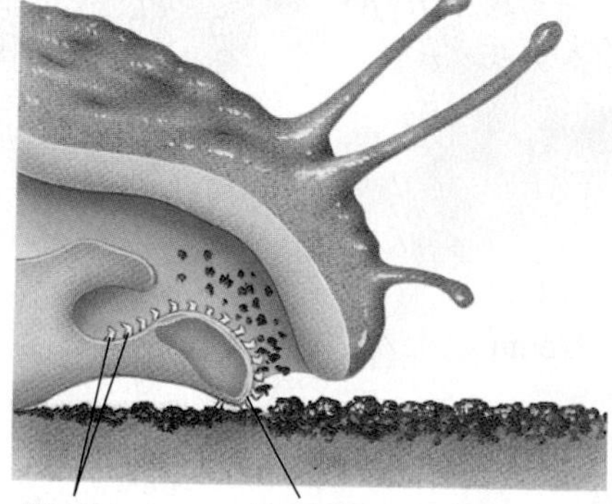

◀ **Figure 27–22** Snails use a radula for feeding. The teeth of a radula give it the look and feel of sandpaper. Beneath the radula is a stiff supporting rod of cartilage. When the mollusk feeds, it places the tip of the radula on its food and pulls the sandpapery layer back and forth. **Formulating Hypotheses** *How might radulae with different structures allow snails to inhabit different environments?*

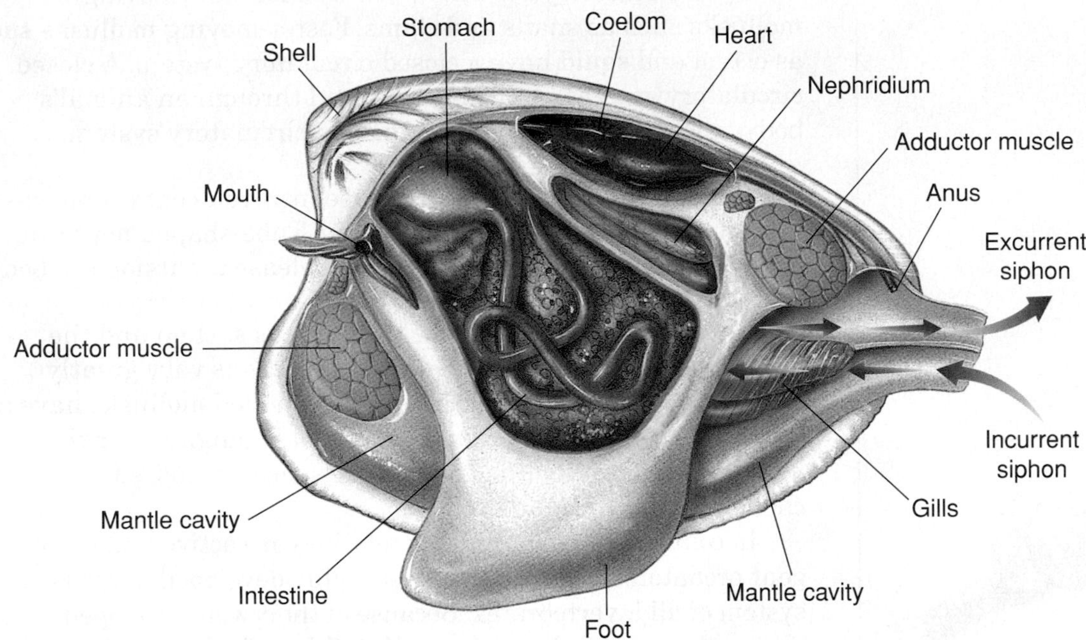

▲ **Figure 27–23** The anatomy of a clam is typical of bivalves, or two-shelled mollusks. The mantle and part of the foot have been cut away to show internal organs. The adductor muscles are used to open and shut the two exterior shells. The gills exchange oxygen and carbon dioxide between the body and the surrounding water. The arrows show the path of water over the gills. **Predicting** ***What might happen if a clam's incurrent siphon became blocked?***

Octopi and certain sea slugs use their sharp jaws to eat their prey. To subdue their prey, some octopi also produce poisons. Clams, oysters, and scallops lead a quieter existence by filter feeding using feathery gills. Food is carried by water, which enters through the incurrent siphon, shown on the right in **Figure 27–23.** A **siphon** is a tubelike structure through which water enters and leaves the body. The water flows over the gills and then leaves by the excurrent siphon. As water passes over the gills, plankton become trapped in sticky mucus. Cilia on the gills move the mixture of mucus and food into the mouth.

Respiration Aquatic mollusks such as snails, clams, and octopi typically breathe using gills inside their mantle cavity. As water passes through the mantle cavity, oxygen in the water moves into blood flowing through the gills. At the same time, carbon dioxide moves in the opposite direction—from the blood into the water. Land snails and slugs do not have gills. Instead, they respire using a mantle cavity that has a large surface area lined with blood vessels. Because this lining must be kept moist so that oxygen can diffuse across its surface, land snails and slugs typically live in moist places.

Circulation Oxygen and nutrients are carried to all parts of a mollusk's body by a circulatory system. The circulatory system of mollusks is either open or closed. "Open" does not mean that blood can spill to the outside of the animal! In an **open circulatory system,** blood is pumped through vessels by a simple heart. Blood eventually leaves the vessels and works its way through different sinuses. A sinus is a large saclike space. The blood passes from the sinuses to the gills, where oxygen and carbon dioxide are exchanged, and then back to the heart.

Open circulatory systems work well for slow-moving mollusks such as snails and clams. Faster-moving mollusks such as octopi and squid have a closed circulatory system. A closed circulatory system can transport blood through an animal's body much more quickly than an open circulatory system.

Excretion Cells of the body release nitrogen-containing waste into the blood in the form of ammonia. Tube-shaped nephridia remove ammonia from the blood and release it outside the body.

Response The complexity of the nervous system and the ability to respond to environmental conditions vary greatly among mollusks. Clams and other two-shelled mollusks have a simple nervous system consisting of small ganglia near the mouth, a few nerve cords, and simple sense organs, such as chemical receptors and eyespots.

In contrast, octopi and their relatives are active and intelligent predators that have the most highly developed nervous system of all invertebrates. Because of their well-developed brains, these animals can remember things for long periods and may be more intelligent than some vertebrates. Octopi are capable of complex behavior, such as opening a jar to get food inside, and they have been trained to perform different tasks for a reward or to avoid punishment.

Movement Mollusks move in many different ways. Snails secrete mucus along the base of the foot, and then move over surfaces using a rippling motion of the foot. The fast-moving octopus uses a form of jet propulsion. It draws water into the mantle cavity and then forces the water out through a siphon. Water leaving the body propels the octopus in the opposite direction.

Reproduction Mollusks reproduce in a variety of ways. Many snails and two-shelled mollusks reproduce sexually by external fertilization. They release enormous numbers of eggs and sperm into the open water. The eggs are fertilized in the water and then develop into free-swimming larvae. In tentacled mollusks and certain snails, fertilization takes place inside the body of the female. Some mollusks are hermaphrodites, having both male and female reproductive organs. Individuals of these species usually fertilize eggs from another individual.

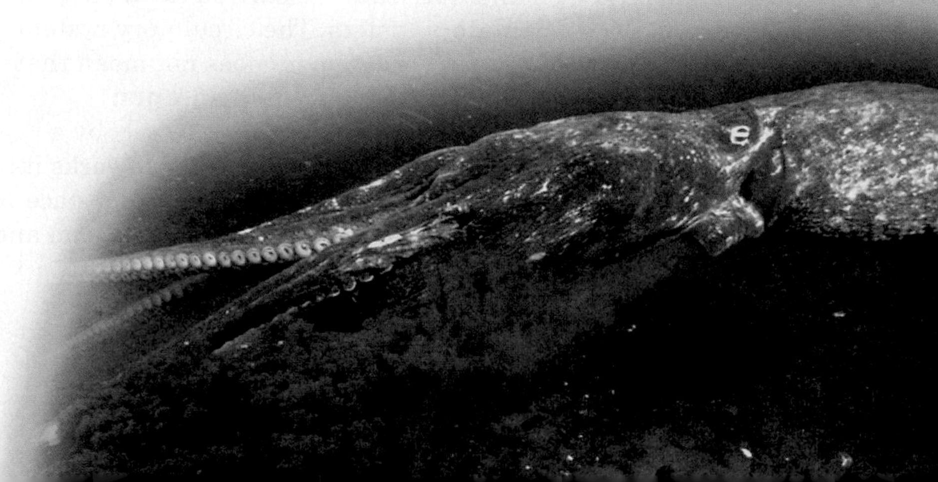

Figure 27–24 Mollusks have evolved a variety of ways of responding to potential danger. Snails (above) protect themselves by withdrawing into their shells in a matter of seconds. In some snails, a hard plate blocks the entrance to the shell, protecting the snail inside. Once the danger has passed, the snail reemerges and moves forward on its muscular foot. Octopi (right) and squids squirt ink from inside their digestive tracts. The ink startles predators and may also cause temporary numbness. **Predicting** ***How might the hard plate protect snails during a period of drought?***

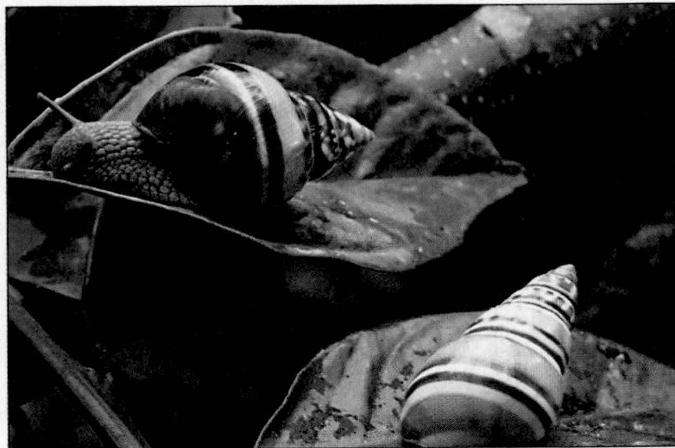

Figure 27–25 **Gastropods move by using a large, muscular foot located on the ventral side.** They can be shell-less, such as the nudibranch or sea slug (top left), or have a single shell, such as the tree snail (top right). Many sea hares (bottom) have a reduced shell covered by the mantle. The sea hare defends itself by "inking"—squirting ink at potential predators.

Groups of Mollusks

Mollusks are divided into several classes according to characteristics of the foot and the shell. The three major classes of mollusks are gastropods, bivalves, and cephalopods.

Gastropods Members of the class Gastropoda, or gastropods (GAS-truh-pahdz), include pond snails, land slugs, sea butterflies, sea hares, limpets, and nudibranchs (NOO-duh-branks). **Gastropods are shell-less or single-shelled mollusks that move by using a muscular foot located on the ventral side.**

Many gastropods, such as the snails shown on the top right in **Figure 27–25,** have a single shell that protects their bodies. When threatened, they can pull completely into their coiled shells. Some snails are also protected by a hard disk on the foot that forms a solid "door" at the mouth of their shell when they withdraw.

Land slugs and nudibranchs have no shell but protect themselves in other ways. Most land slugs spend daylight hours hiding under rocks and logs, hidden from birds and other potential predators. Some sea hares, when threatened, can squirt ink into the surrounding water, producing a "smoke screen" that confuses predators.

Some nudibranchs have chemicals in their bodies that taste bad or are poisonous. When a predator bites one of these nudibranchs, the predator becomes ill. Many nudibranchs are able to recycle the nematocysts from cnidarians they eat, using them to sting predators. These "booby-trapped" nudibranchs are usually brightly colored. The bright coloring serves as a warning to potential predators.

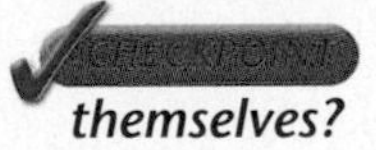

How do shell-less gastropods protect themselves?

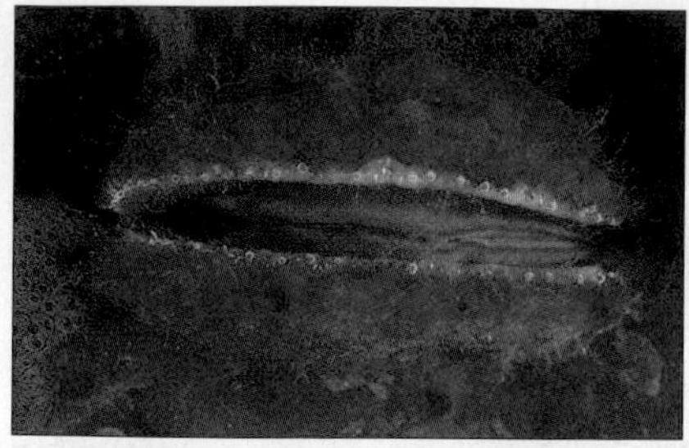

▲ **Figure 27–26** **Bivalves are two-shelled mollusks that include clams, mussels, oysters, and scallops like the one above.** Observe the tiny blue eyespots along the open edges of the shell.

Bivalves **Members of the class Bivalvia have two shells that are held together by one or two powerful muscles.** Common bivalves include clams, oysters, mussels, and scallops. Most bivalves stay in one place for much of the time. Clams burrow in mud or sand, whereas mussels use sticky threads to attach themselves to rocks. Scallops, such as the one shown in **Figure 27–26,** are the least sedentary bivalves and can move around rapidly by flapping their shells when threatened.

Currents created by cilia on the gills circulate water through the body cavities of bivalves. Once water is inside the body, filter-feeding bivalves use mucus and cilia on their gills to trap food particles in the water. Some bivalves feed on material deposited in sand or mud. They use long, muscular extensions of tissue that surround the mouth to collect food particles from the surrounding sediments. The indigestible sand or mud particles are expelled from the mantle cavity.

 *What are some common bivalves?*

Word Origins

Cephalopod comes from the Greek *kephale,* meaning "head," and *podos,* meaning "foot." **Pseudopods** are structures found in some single-celled organisms. **If *pseudo-* means "false," what does *pseudopod* mean?**

Cephalopods Cephalopods (SEF-uh-luh-pahdz)—members of the class Cephalopoda—are the most active of the mollusks. This class includes octopi, squids, cuttlefishes, and nautiluses. **Cephalopods are typically soft-bodied mollusks in which the head is attached to a single foot. The foot is divided into tentacles or arms.** Cephalopods have eight or more tentacles equipped with sucking disks that grab and hold prey. Nautiluses have many more tentacles than other cephalopods—in some cases up to 90! Their tentacles lack suckers but have a sticky, mucuslike covering.

As with some of the gastropods, most modern cephalopods have only small internal shells or no shells at all. The only present-day cephalopods with external shells are nautiluses, such as the one shown in **Figure 27–27.** These animals can control their depth in the water by regulating the amount of gas in their shells. Ancestors of the nautilus dominated the seas more then 500 million years ago.

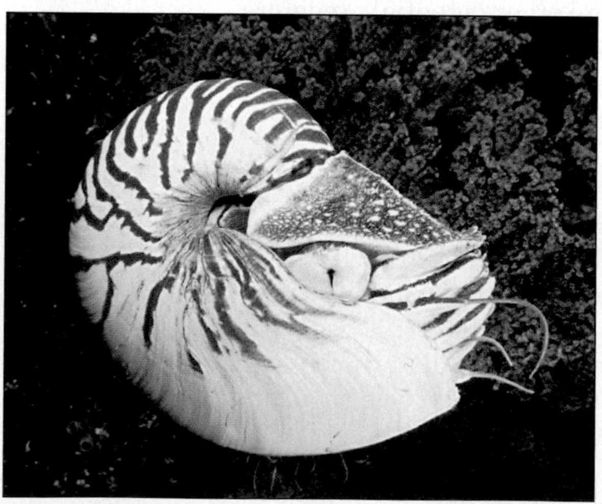

Figure 27–27 Nautiluses like the one shown here are the most primitive group of cephalopods. **Comparing and Contrasting** *How does this nautilus differ from most cephalopods?*

Analyzing Data

Raising Clams

Aquaculture is the growth of aquatic animals and plants for use by humans. In one example of aquaculture, hard clams are first grown in commercial hatcheries under very favorable conditions. The young clams are then removed from the hatcheries and placed into the mud beds of creeks, where they develop into adults. At that time, the size of the young clams is around 40 millimeters.

Because Georgian clams grow so quickly, they are ideal for aquaculture. Unlike the hard clams in the northeastern United States that grow only during the warm months, Georgian hard clams grow year-round. As a result, the Georgian clams grow to market size in less than half the time that the northeastern clams need to grow. The graph shows how clam shells grow over a period of 10 years.

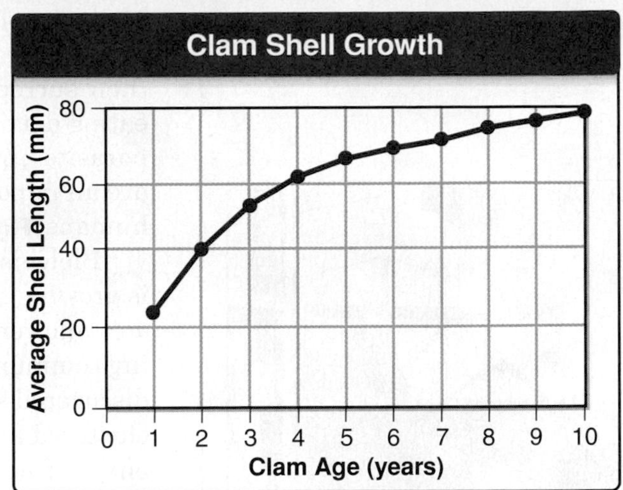

1. **Using Tables and Graphs** Approximately how many years does it take clams to reach a size at which they can be removed from hatcheries and put in creeks?
2. **Applying Concepts** How does climate affect the growth of most clams?
3. **Using Tables and Graphs** How much did the clams grow during the first 5 years? The next 5?
4. **Formulating Hypotheses** Formulate a hypothesis to explain the slower growth rate from years 5 to 10.
5. **Drawing Conclusions** What general trends do you observe about growth from the graph?

Cuttlefishes have small shells inside their bodies. These are the cuttlebones given to pet birds to condition their beaks. A squid's internal shell has evolved into a thin supporting rod known as a pen. Octopi have lost their shells completely.

Cephalopods also have numerous complex sense organs that help them detect and respond to external stimuli. Cephalopods distinguish shapes by sight and texture by touch. The eyes of many cephalopods, such as the squid shown in **Figure 27–28,** are as complex as those of some vertebrates, such as fishes and humans. Cephalopod eyes can be large—the size of a dinner plate in some species—and can distinguish objects as small as 0.5 centimeters from a meter away, allowing squids to locate a wide variety of prey. Though cephalopod eyes may look something like vertebrate eyes from the outside, their internal structures are quite different.

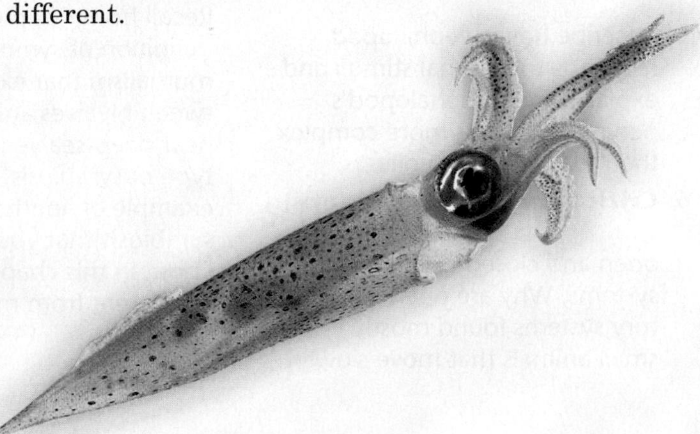

◀ **Figure 27–28** **Most cephalopods are mollusks in which the head is attached to a single foot that is divided into tentacles or arms.** They have the most complex nervous system of all the mollusks, with a highly developed brain and sense organs, such as the eye of this common squid.

Ecology of Mollusks

▲ **Figure 27–29** These clams will find their way to many people's dinner tables. **Applying Concepts** *Besides providing food for humans and other animals, what are some other roles that mollusks play in ecosystems?*

Mollusks play many different roles in living systems. For example, they feed on plants, prey on animals, and "clean up" their surroundings by filtering algae out of the water or by eating detritus. Some of them are hosts to symbiotic algae or to parasites; others are themselves parasites. In addition, mollusks are an important source of food for many organisms, including humans. **Figure 27–29** shows clams caught for human use.

Biologists' understanding of molluskan diversity and ecology is growing all the time. Recent explorations around deep-sea volcanic vents called "black smokers" have revealed a fascinating community that includes several bivalves. Researchers have discovered symbiotic bacteria within the foot-long bivalves clustered around these vents. These bacteria extract chemical energy from simple compounds released in the superheated water. From this energy, the bacteria produce food molecules that the mollusks can use. Without this mutualistic relationship with the bacteria, these mollusks would be unable to inhabit this extreme environment. Other research has discovered a similar symbiosis between related bacteria and bivalves that live in the mud of salt marshes and mangrove swamps.

Scientists have found some new uses for mollusks. Because filter-feeding bivalves concentrate dangerous pollutants and microorganisms in their tissues, they can be used to monitor water quality. Careful checks of bivalves can warn biologists and public health officials of health problems long before scientists can detect these dangers in the open water. Besides acting as environmental monitors, mollusks also serve as subjects in biological research. Some current investigations are based on the observation that snails and other mollusks never seem to develop any form of cancer. If scientists can determine what protects the cells of these animals from cancer, they will gain valuable insights into how to fight cancer in humans.

27–4 Section Assessment

1. **Key Concept** What is a mollusk?
2. **Key Concept** List and describe the four parts of the mollusk body plan.
3. **Key Concept** Describe the main characteristics of the three major classes of mollusks.
4. Why are land snails restricted to moist environments?
5. Describe how a cephalopod responds to external stimuli and explain how a cephalopod's nervous system is more complex than that of other mollusks.
6. **Critical Thinking Comparing and Contrasting** Compare open and closed circulatory systems. Why are open circulatory systems found mostly in small animals that move slowly?

Connecting Concepts

Symbiosis
Recall from Chapter 4 the definition of symbiosis. The mutualism that exists between bivalves and bacteria near deep-sea vents is one type of symbiosis. Describe an example of another type of symbiosis that you have read about in this chapter. How is it different from mutualism?

Exploration

Investigating Land Snails

Although most mollusks are aquatic, some snails live on land. In this investigation, you will explore how land snails are adapted to survive in this environment.

Problem **How do land snails move and react to various external stimuli?**

Materials

- land snail
- glass slides
- dropper pipette
- dissecting tray
- black construction paper
- paper towels
- 40-watt desk lamp
- metric ruler
- dissecting microscope
- petri dish
- clock with second hand

Skills Observing, Calculating, Using Tables and Graphs

Procedure    

1. Using a clean pipette, put a drop of water in the center of a glass slide. Gently place the snail in the water drop. Look for the mucus trail as the snail begins to move.
2. Gently turn the slide over and place it on top of a petri dish. Place the petri dish under the dissecting microscope and observe the movement of the muscular foot under low power. Look for the radula as it scrapes the slide.
3. Copy the data table onto a separate sheet of paper. Line each half of a dissecting tray with a separate piece of paper towel. Place a sheet of black construction paper above one half of the tray. Shine the desk lamp on the other half of the tray from a distance of 30 cm. **CAUTION:** *Do not touch the lamp, because it may be hot.*
4. Place the snail in the center of the tray and observe how it responds to the external stimulus of bright light. Measure and record the number of seconds in each minute that the snail spends in the dark.
5. **Calculating** Exchange data with the class and determine class averages.
6. Return the snail to its habitat, clean up your materials, and wash your hands.

Data Table

Time (minutes)	Time in Dark (seconds)	
	Group	Class Average
0–1		
1–2		
2–3		
3–4		
4–5		

Analyze and Conclude

1. **Drawing Conclusions** Describe the movement of the snail across the glass slide. Name one advantage and one limitation of this type of movement.
2. **Using Tables and Graphs** Make a bar graph of the class average data that shows the time the snails spent in the dark for each of the five minutes. What trend do you see in your data? How can you explain this result?
3. **Drawing Conclusions** Do snails prefer dark places or bright places? Refer to the class average data to explain why your conclusion is valid. Communicate your conclusion by writing a short paragraph describing your results.

For: Data sharing
Visit: PHSchool.com
Web Code: cbd-8274

Share Your Data Online Enter your data on the behavior of the land snails. Then, look at the data entered by other students. Based on the available data, do snails prefer dark places or light places? Why might your data differ from those of other students? Does this larger set of data support your results and indicate that your conclusions are valid?

Chapter 27 Study Guide

27–1 Flatworms

Key Concepts

- Flatworms are soft, flattened worms that have tissues and internal organ systems. They are the simplest animals to have three embryonic germ layers, bilateral symmetry, and cephalization.
- Turbellarians are free-living marine or freshwater flatworms.
- Flukes are parasitic flatworms that usually infect the internal organs of their hosts.
- Tapeworms are long, flat, parasitic worms that are adapted to life inside the intestines of their hosts.

Vocabulary

acoelomate, p. 683 • coelom, p. 683
pharynx, p. 684
flame cell, p. 684
ganglion, p. 685
eyespot, p. 685
hermaphrodite, p. 686
fission, p. 686
scolex, p. 688
proglottid, p. 688
testis, p. 688

27–2 Roundworms

Key Concepts

- Roundworms are unsegmented worms that have pseudocoeloms and digestive systems with two openings—a mouth and an anus.
- Parasitic roundworms include trichinosis-causing worms, filarial worms, ascarid worms, and hookworms.

Vocabulary

pseudocoelom, p. 689
anus, p. 689

27–3 Annelids

Key Concepts

- Annelids are worms with segmented bodies. They have a true coelom that is completely lined with mesoderm.
- Oligochaetes are annelids that typically have streamlined bodies and relatively few setae compared to polychaetes. Most oligochaetes live in soil or fresh water.
- Leeches are typically external parasites that suck the blood and body fluids of their host.
- Polychaetes are marine annelids that have paired, paddlelike appendages tipped with setae.

Vocabulary

septum, p. 694 • seta, p. 694
crop, p. 695 • gizzard, p. 695
closed circulatory system, p. 695
gill, p. 696 • nephridium, p. 696
clitellum, p. 696

27–4 Mollusks

Key Concepts

- Mollusks are soft-bodied animals that usually have an internal or external shell.
- The typical mollusk body plan has four parts: foot, mantle, shell, and visceral mass.
- Gastropods are shell-less or single-shelled mollusks that move by using a muscular foot located on the ventral side.
- Bivalves have two shells that are held together by one or two powerful muscles.
- Cephalopods are typically soft-bodied mollusks in which the head is attached to a single foot. The foot is divided into tentacles or arms.

Vocabulary

trochophore, p. 701
foot, p. 702
mantle, p. 702 • shell, p. 702
visceral mass, p. 702
radula, p. 702
siphon, p. 703
open circulatory system, p. 703

Thinking Visually

Create a concept map that shows the classes and main characteristics of mollusks. Include at least two examples of types of mollusks within each class.

Preparing for the Living Environment Exam

NEW YORK LIVING ENVIRONMENT

Blue questions emphasize Regents Exam content

Chapter 27

Part A

Multiple Choice

For each statement or question, select the number of the word or expression that, of those given, best completes the statement or answers the question.

1 The muscular tube found near the mouth of the gastrovascular cavity in flatworms is called a(an)
(1) proglottid (3) anus
(2) scolex (4) pharynx

2 The head of an adult tapeworm is called a
(1) flame cell (3) cuticle
(2) scolex (4) mantle

3 Waste products are excreted from the body of a planarian by
(1) nephridia (3) proglottids
(2) flame cells (4) cilia

4 The body cavity of a roundworm is called a
(1) coelom (3) gizzard
(2) pseudocoelom (4) crop

5 Which term best describes the clusters of nerve cells in roundworms?
(1) flame cells (3) proglottids
(2) ganglia (4) radulae

6 In the earthworm, waste created by cellular metabolism is eliminated by the
(1) crop (3) gizzard
(2) nephridia (4) flame cell

7 Segmented bodies are characteristic of
(1) flatworms (3) roundworms
(2) annelids (4) flukes

8 The digestive organ in which an earthworm stores food is indicated by the letter

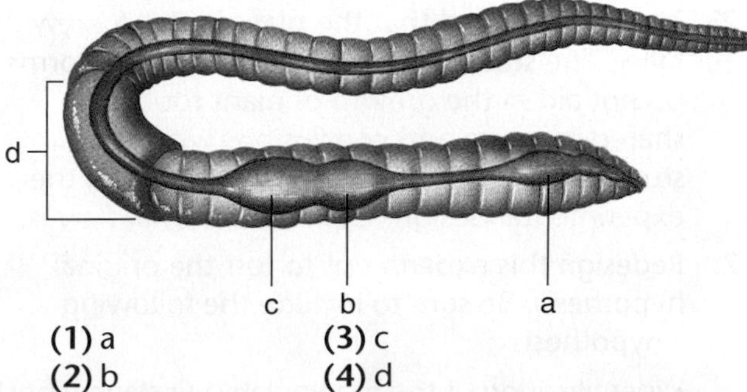

(1) a (3) c
(2) b (4) d

9 In earthworms, the clitellum is used in
(1) digestion (3) reproduction
(2) excretion (4) respiration

10 The tongue-shaped structure that some mollusks use for feeding is the
(1) sinus (3) mantle
(2) radula (4) proglottid

11 Mollusks eliminate nitrogen-containing wastes through simple tube-shaped organs called
(1) gills (3) radulae
(2) nephridia (4) nephrons

12 A mollusk with a shell consisting of two parts is a member of the class
(1) Cephalopoda (3) Bivalvia
(2) Annelida (4) Gastropoda

13 All of these animals are mollusks *except*
(1) leeches (3) octopi
(2) squids (4) snails

14 Which organisms are *not* parasitic roundworms?
(1) hookworms (3) ascarid worms
(2) filarial worms (4) tapeworms

15 The body cavity in annelids is called a(an)
(1) coelom (3) pseudocoelom
(2) trochophore (4) acoelom

16 The figure below shows an animal with three germ layers.

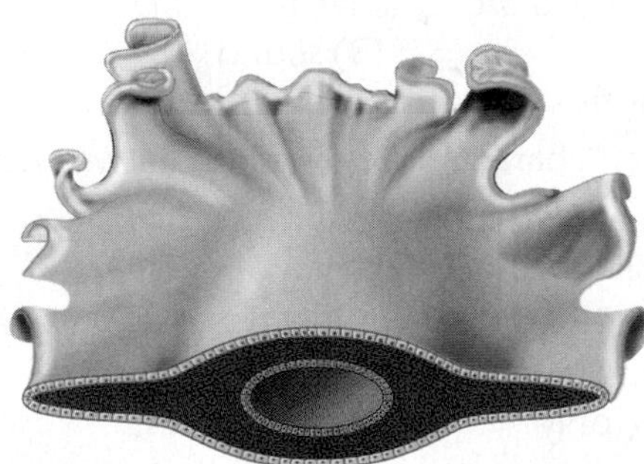

The simplest animal to develop from three germ layers belongs in the phylum
(1) Mollusca (3) Annelida
(2) Nematoda (4) Platyhelminthes

Test-Taking Tip For questions containing the words *not*, *except*, and so on, begin by eliminating each answer choice that does fit the characteristic in question. After eliminating three choices, check to see that your answer is correct by confirming that it does not fit the characteristic in question.

Preparing for the Living Environment Exam

Part B

Multiple Choice and Extended Response

For those questions that ask you to select a response, choose the one that best completes the statement or answers the question. For all others follow the directions given.

Base your answers to questions 17 through 19 on the information and illustration below and on your knowledge of biology.

This two-headed planarian was produced by a procedure that began with cutting the original head in half lengthwise and keeping the two halves separated for several days.

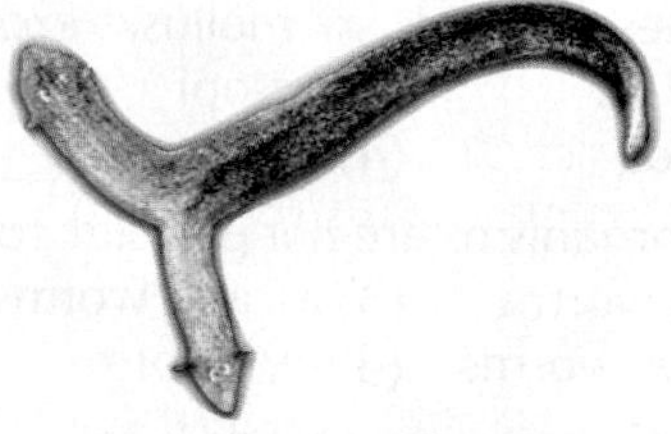

17 The process illustrated in the diagram is known as
(1) fission (3) sexual reproduction
(2) regeneration (4) hermaphroditism

18 The two light ovals located near the center of each head are sensitive to
(1) heat (3) sound
(2) light (4) chemicals

19 Which characteristics apply to flatworms?
A Cephalization
B Bilateral symmetry
C Segmented bodies
(1) A, only (3) A and B, only
(2) B, only (4) A, B, and C

Use the lettered choices below to answer questions 20 through 24. Select the best lettered choice. A choice may be used once, more than once, or not at all.

A Flatworms
B Roundworms
C Annelids
D Snails
E Mollusks

20 Include gastropods, bivalves, and cephalopods

21 Have internal walls, or septa, between body segments

22 Usually have an internal or external shell

23 Have a pseudocoelom

24 Include turbellarians, flukes, and tapeworms

25 Describe how feeding and digestion occur in planarians.

26 Describe the process by which earthworms move.

Part C

Extended Response

Answer the questions or follow the directions given.

Base your answers to questions 27 through 30 on the information below and on your knowledge of biology.

A student conducts an experiment to test the hypothesis that earthworms aid in the growth of plant roots. She grows two identical plants in Pots A and B but adds earthworms only to Pot B. Over a three-week period, she waters and fertilizes both pots the same. Every third day, she measures the height of each plant, collecting the following data.

Day	Pot A	Pot B
1	5 cm	5 cm
3	5 cm	5 cm
6	6.5 cm	8 cm
9	8 cm	8 cm
12	9.5 cm	10.5 cm
15	12 cm	11 cm
18	14 cm	12 cm
21	15.5 cm	13 cm

27 Identify the manipulated (independent) variable and the responding (dependent) variable in this experiment.

28 The data showed that the plant in Pot A grew taller. The student determined that earthworms do not aid in the growth of plant roots. She shared her data and conclusions with another student. Her friend found a serious flaw in the experimental design. Explain what that flaw is.

29 Redesign this experiment to test the original hypothesis. Be sure to include the following
- hypothesis
- identification of the manipulated (independent) and responding (dependent) variable
- procedure and data-collection methods

30 Interpret the data from the student's original experiment. Summarize what it appears to show and suggest possible modifications. In your summary, be sure to
- state what effect the earthworms had on the growth of these plants
- state one possible explanation for this result
- explain why the use of only two plants limits the validity of any conclusion that may come from the experiment.

Base your answers to questions 31 through 33 on the data table and reading passage below and on your knowledge of biology.

Survival Rate of *Dirofilaria* sp.

Temperature in °C	Number of Microfilariae/100
0	0
5	0
10	0
15	19
40	48
41	65
30	86
40	82
41	85
45	74

Heartworms

Dirofilaria immitis, the dog heartworm, is a large, whitish roundworm found circulating around the heart in dogs. After reproduction, the females produce tiny embryos called microfilariae, which are found circulating throughout the dog's body. The microfilariae are spread by mosquitoes. A mosquito picks up blood when it bites an infected dog. The heartworm embryo grows inside the mosquito and is deposited into the next dog when the mosquito has its next meal. The microfilariae move through the dog's blood vessels until they get to the right side of the dog's heart. They settle there and in the pulmonary arteries, where they can reproduce and remain for many years.

Some scientists wanted to determine if the development of the microfilariae in the mosquito is dependent on temperature. To do this, they kept 100 microfilariae at various temperatures for a two-week period and then counted the surviving organisms. Their data are shown in the table, Survival Rate of *Dirofilaria*.

31 Describe the appearance of a line graph of this data. In your description:
- identify the data represented by the line
- identify the variable that would be scaled on the *x*-axis (the horizontal axis)
- describe the shape of the line on the graph, including where it would begin, end, and how it would vary between these two points.

32 Based on the data shown, make an inference about temperature and the development of microfilariae. Be sure to refer to the entire range of temperatures used in the study.

33 Describe the effect of climate on the transmission of heartworm disease in North America. In your answer, be sure to explain:
- how transmission of the disease would be affected by seasonal changes in North America
- how transmission of the disease would differ between northern and southern regions of North America

For: An interactive self-test
Visit: PHSchool.com
Web Code: cba-8270

CHAPTER 28

Arthropods and Echinoderms

The zebra swallowtail butterfly is one of more than 750,000 species of arthropods—the largest phylum of animals.

Inquiry Activity

What is an arthropod?

Procedure  

1. Put on plastic gloves. Examine a variety of specimens or photographs of arthropods. Make a list of features that all of these organisms have in common.
2. Look at some animals that are not arthropods. Make a list of features that all of these organisms have in common. Compare the two lists.
3. Wash your hands with soap and warm water.

Think About It

1. **Forming Operational Definitions** Write a definition of the term *arthropod.* Include in your definition at least two characteristics that all arthropods share but most other animals do not.
2. **Classifying** Classify the arthropods you observed into two or more groups. Which characteristics did you use to distinguish the groups?

28–1 Introduction to the Arthropods

4-3.1 Fossils indicate extinctions
LS- Analyze results
LS- Make observations
LS- Organize data in tables/graphs

If you have ever admired a spider's web, watched the flight of a butterfly, or eaten shrimp, you have had close encounters with members of the phylum Arthropoda (ahr-THRAHP-oh-duh). In terms of evolutionary success, which can be measured as the number of living species, arthropods are the most diverse and successful animals of all time. At least three quarters of a million species have been identified—more than three times the number of all other animal species combined!

What Is an Arthropod?

Arthropods include animals such as insects, crabs, centipedes, and spiders. **Arthropods have a segmented body, a tough exoskeleton, and jointed appendages.** Like annelids, arthropods have bodies that are divided into segments. The number of these segments varies among groups of arthropods.

Arthropods are also surrounded by a tough external covering, or **exoskeleton.** The exoskeleton is like a suit of armor that protects and supports the body. It is made from protein and a carbohydrate called **chitin** (KY-tun). Exoskeletons vary greatly in size, shape, and toughness. The exoskeletons of caterpillars are firm and leathery, whereas those of crabs and lobsters are so tough and hard that they are almost impossible to crush by hand. The exoskeletons of many terrestrial, or land-dwelling, species have a waxy covering that helps prevent the loss of body water. Terrestrial arthropods, like all animals that live entirely on land, need adaptations that hold water inside their bodies.

All arthropods have jointed appendages. **Appendages** are structures such as legs and antennae that extend from the body wall. Jointed appendages are so distinctive of arthropods that the phylum is named for them: *arthron* means "joint" in Greek, and *podos* means "foot."

Guide for Reading

Key Concepts
- What are the main features of arthropods?
- What are the important trends in arthropod evolution?
- What happens when an arthropod outgrows its exoskeleton?

Vocabulary
exoskeleton
chitin
appendage
tracheal tube
spiracle
book lung
Malpighian tubule
molting

Reading Strategy: Finding Main Ideas Before you read, skim the section to find the three boldface sentences. Copy each sentence onto a notecard. As you read, make notes of supporting details.

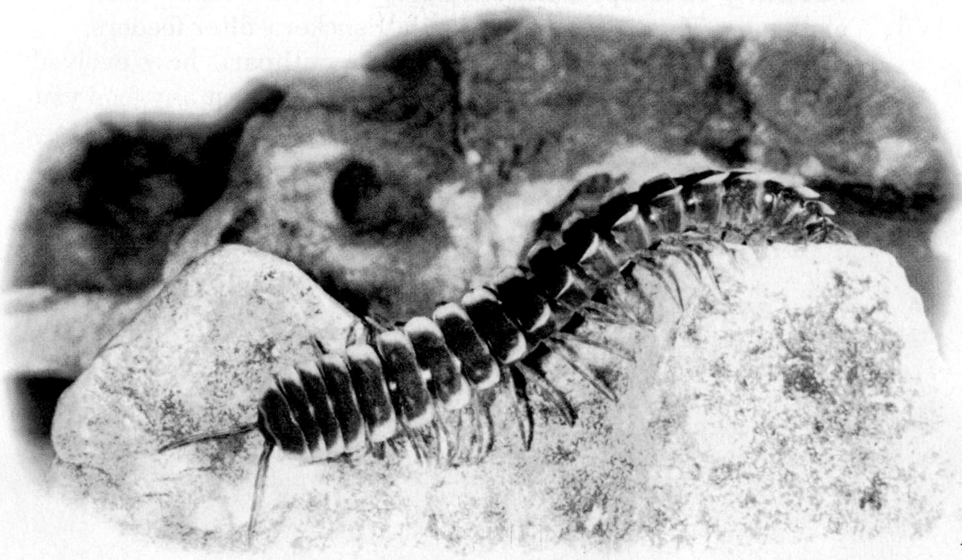

◀ **Figure 28–1** **Arthropods such as the cave millipede have a body usually composed of segments, a tough exoskeleton, and jointed appendages.** Observe the millipede's legs, which are adapted for walking.

▲ **Figure 28–2** Trilobites, such as the fossilized one shown above, were marine arthropods that were abundant more than 500 million years ago. They were divided into many body segments, each with a walking leg. Trilobites became extinct some 200 million years ago. **Living arthropods generally have fewer body segments and more specialized appendages than ancestral arthropods.**

Evolution of Arthropods

The first arthropods appeared in the sea more than 600 million years ago. Since then, arthropods have moved into all parts of the sea, most freshwater habitats, the land, and the air. **The evolution of arthropods, by natural selection and other processes, has led to fewer body segments and highly specialized appendages for feeding, movement, and other functions.**

A typical primitive arthropod was composed of many identical segments, each carrying a pair of appendages. Its body probably closely resembled that of a trilobite (TRY-loh-byt), shown in **Figure 28–2.** This early body plan was modified gradually. Body segments were lost or fused over time. Most living arthropods, such as spiders and insects, have only two or three body segments. Arthropod appendages also evolved into different forms that are adapted in ways that enable them to perform different functions. These appendages include antennae, claws, walking legs, wings, flippers, mouthparts, tails, and other specialized structures.

These gradual changes in arthropods are similar to the changes in modern cars since the Model T, the first mass-produced automobile. The Model T had all the basic components, such as an internal combustion engine, wheels, and a frame. Over time, the design and style of each component changed, producing cars as different as off-road vehicles, sedans, and sports cars. Similarly, modifications to the arthropod body plan have produced creatures as different as a tick and a lobster.

Form and Function in Arthropods

Arthropods use complex organ systems to carry out different essential functions. As with all animals, organ systems are interrelated; the functioning of one system depends on that of other systems. For example, the digestive system breaks food into nutrient molecules, which then move into blood in the circulatory system. The blood carries the nutrients to body cells.

Feeding Arthropods include herbivores, carnivores, and omnivores. There are arthropod bloodsuckers, filter feeders, detritivores, and parasites. Arthropod mouthparts have evolved in ways that enable different species to eat almost any food you can imagine. Their mouthparts range from pincers or fangs to sickle-shaped jaws that can cut through the tissues of captured prey. The mouthparts of a nut weevil are shown in **Figure 28–3.**

◀ **Figure 28–3** This photo of a nut weevil illustrates how its mouthparts are adapted in ways that enable it to bore into and eat nuts. **Applying Concepts** *Do you think a nut weevil would be able to capture and eat other arthropods? Explain your answer.*

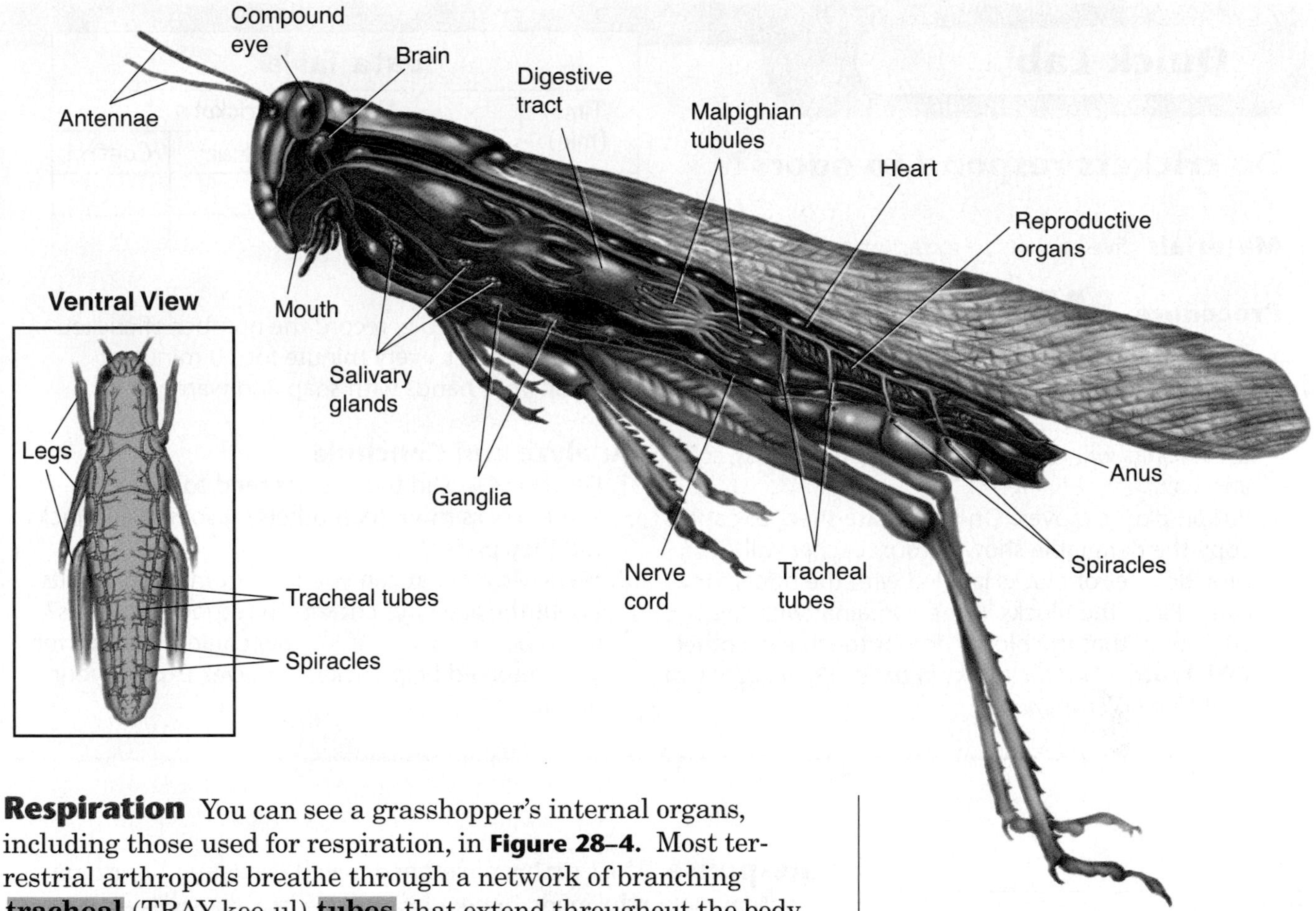

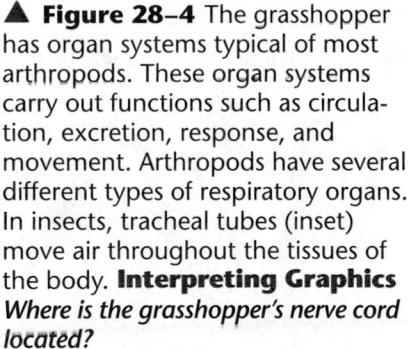

Compound eye
Brain
Antennae
Digestive tract
Malpighian tubules
Heart
Reproductive organs
Ventral View
Mouth
Salivary glands
Legs
Ganglia
Anus
Nerve cord
Tracheal tubes
Spiracles
Tracheal tubes
Spiracles

▲ **Figure 28–4** The grasshopper has organ systems typical of most arthropods. These organ systems carry out functions such as circulation, excretion, response, and movement. Arthropods have several different types of respiratory organs. In insects, tracheal tubes (inset) move air throughout the tissues of the body. **Interpreting Graphics** ***Where is the grasshopper's nerve cord located?***

Respiration You can see a grasshopper's internal organs, including those used for respiration, in **Figure 28–4.** Most terrestrial arthropods breathe through a network of branching **tracheal** (TRAY-kee-ul) **tubes** that extend throughout the body. Air enters and leaves the tracheal tubes through **spiracles** (SPEER-uh-kulz), which are small openings located along the side of the body. Other terrestrial arthropods, such as spiders, respire using book lungs. **Book lungs** are organs that have layers of respiratory tissue stacked like the pages of a book. Most aquatic arthropods, such as lobsters and crabs, respire through featherlike gills. The horseshoe crabs, however, respire through organs called book gills.

Circulation Arthropods have an open circulatory system. A well-developed heart pumps blood through arteries that branch and enter the tissues. Blood leaves the blood vessels and moves through sinuses, or cavities. The blood then collects in a large sinus surrounding the heart. From there, it re-enters the heart and is again pumped through the body.

Excretion Most terrestrial arthropods, such as insects and spiders, dispose of nitrogenous wastes using Malpighian (mal-PIG-ee-un) tubules. **Malpighian tubules** are saclike organs that extract wastes from the blood and then add them to feces, or digestive wastes, that move through the gut. In aquatic arthropods, diffusion moves cellular wastes from the arthropod's body into the surrounding water.

CHECKPOINT ***What is the function of Malpighian tubules?***

Go Online NSTA SCI LINKS
For: Links on arthropods
Visit: www.SciLinks.org
Web Code: cbn-8281

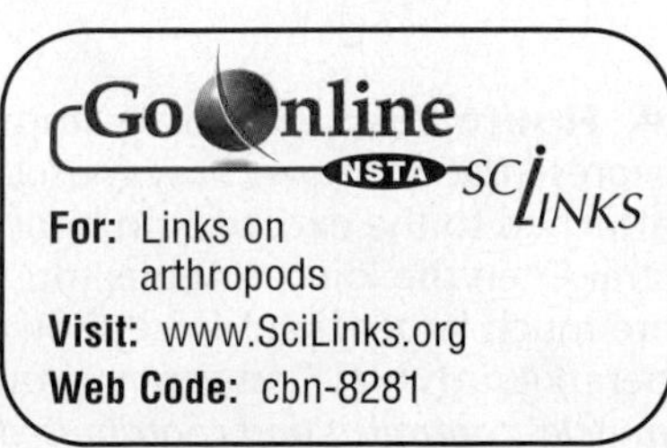

Quick Lab

Do crickets respond to odors?

Materials live crickets in terrarium, wooden blocks

Procedure 

1. **Predicting** Crickets are common in grassy areas. They eat leaves and are eaten by mice, some birds, and other animals. Record a prediction of how the crickets will respond to the odors of grass, soil, and hair.
2. Put on plastic gloves. On a separate sheet of paper, copy the data table shown. Your teacher will provide a set of blocks labeled with the odors they carry. Place the blocks in the container with the crickets so that the blocks do not touch each other. **CAUTION:** *Place the blocks in the container gently to avoid injuring the crickets.*
3. In your data table, record the number of crickets on each block every minute for 10 minutes.
4. Wash your hands with soap and warm water.

Data Table

Time (min)	Number of Crickets			
	Grass	Soil	Hair	Control
1				
2				

Analyze and Conclude

1. **Observing** Did the crickets tend to climb on some blocks more than others? If so, which blocks did they prefer?
2. **Inferring** What can you infer from these results about the ability of crickets to respond to odors?
3. **Drawing Conclusions** How could the behavior you observed help crickets survive? Explain your answer.

Response Most arthropods have a well-developed nervous system. All arthropods have a brain. The brain serves as a central switchboard that receives incoming information and then sends outgoing instructions to muscles. Two nerves that encircle the esophagus connect the brain to a ventral nerve cord. Along this nerve cord are several ganglia, or groups of nerve cells. These ganglia coordinate the movements of individual legs and wings. Most arthropods have sophisticated sense organs, such as compound eyes for gathering information from the environment. Compound eyes may have more than 2000 separate lenses and can detect color and motion very well.

Movement Arthropods move using well-developed groups of muscles that are coordinated and controlled by the nervous system. In arthropods and other animals, muscles are made up of individual muscle cells. Muscle cells can contract, or become shorter, when stimulated by nerves. Other cells in animals' bodies do not have this ability. Muscles generate force by contracting and then pulling on the exoskeleton.

At each body joint, different muscles either flex (bend) or extend (straighten) the joint. This process is diagrammed in **Figure 28–5.** The pull of muscles against the exoskeleton allows arthropods to beat their wings against the air to fly, push their legs against the ground to walk, or beat their flippers against the water to swim.

CHECKPOINT *How do arthropods move?*

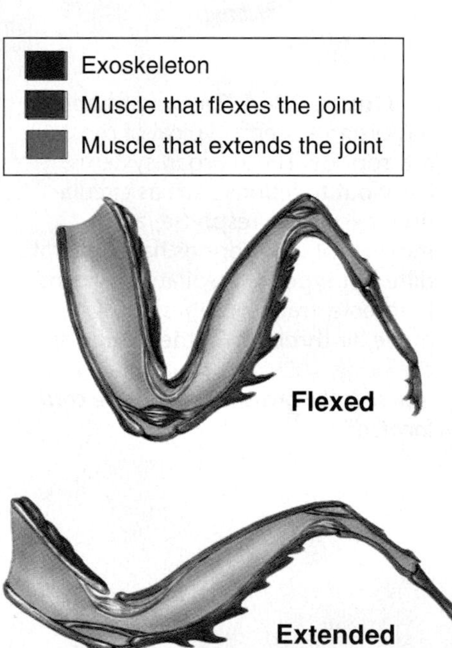

▲ **Figure 28–5** This diagrammatic representation shows how muscles attached to the exoskeleton bend and straighten the joints. (Actual muscles are much larger than those shown here.) **Applying Concepts** *How are muscles controlled and coordinated?*

Reproduction Terrestrial arthropods have internal fertilization. In some species, males have a reproductive organ that places sperm inside females. In other species, the males deposit a sperm packet that is picked up by the females. Aquatic arthropods may have internal or external fertilization. External fertilization takes place outside the female's body. It occurs when females release eggs into the external environment and males shed sperm around the eggs.

▲ **Figure 28–6** **When they become too large for their exoskeletons, arthropods undergo periods of molting.** This cicada has just molted and is climbing out of its old exoskeleton.

Growth and Development in Arthropods

An exoskeleton does not grow as the animal grows. Imagine that you are wearing a suit of armor fitted exactly to your measurements. Think of it not only as skintight but as part of your skin. What would happen when you grew taller and wider? Arthropods have this same difficulty. **When they outgrow their exoskeletons, arthropods undergo periods of molting.** During **molting,** an arthropod sheds its entire exoskeleton and manufactures a larger one to take its place. Molting is controlled by the arthropod's endocrine system. An animal's endocrine system regulates body processes by means of chemicals called hormones.

As the time for molting approaches, skin glands digest the inner part of the exoskeleton, and other glands secrete a new skeleton. When the new exoskeleton is ready, the animal pulls itself out of what remains of the original skeleton, as shown in **Figure 28–6.** This process can take several hours. While the new exoskeleton is still soft, the animal fills with air or fluids to allow room for growth before the next molting. Most arthropods molt several times between hatching and adulthood. This process is dangerous to the animal because it is vulnerable to predators while its shell is soft. To protect themselves, arthropods typically hide during the molting period or molt at night.

28–1 Section Assessment

1. **Key Concept** What are the main features of arthropods?
2. **Key Concept** What is the evolutionary trend for segmentation in arthropods?
3. **Key Concept** How is the process of molting related to growth in arthropods?
4. What body system controls molting?
5. How are both the circulatory and excretory systems involved in removing nitrogenous wastes from an arthropod's body?
6. **Critical Thinking Comparing and Contrasting** How are the muscle cells of arthropods and other animals different from other body cells? How does this difference enable movement?

Connecting Concepts

Cellular Respiration

Use what you learned about cellular respiration in Chapter 9 to explain why every cell in an arthropod's body needs oxygen. Then describe how the respiratory system delivers the needed oxygen.

28–2 Groups of Arthropods

1-S3.1 Interpreting data
LS- Analyze results
LS- State an appropriate hypothesis

Guide for Reading

Key Concepts
- How are arthropods classified?
- What are the distinguishing features of the three major groups of arthropods?

Vocabulary
cephalothorax
thorax
abdomen
carapace
mandible
cheliped
swimmeret
chelicera
pedipalp
spinneret

Reading Strategy: Building Vocabulary
Before you read, preview new vocabulary by skimming the section and making a list of the highlighted, boldface terms. Leave space to make notes as you read.

For: Links on crustaceans
Visit: www.SciLinks.org
Web Code: cbn-8282

You are a naturalist sent to the rain forests of Brazil to bring back a representative sample of arthropods from the region. As you search the forest, your collection grows to include an astonishing array of arthropods—butterflies several centimeters across, armored wormlike animals that move about using dozens of legs, and beetles that defend themselves by shooting out a stream of poisonous liquid. You must organize your collection before you return home, but you do not know how all these arthropod species are related to one another. Where to begin?

This is the challenge that has faced biologists for many decades—how to catalogue all the world's arthropods. The diversity of arthropods is daunting to any biologist interested in understanding the relationships among organisms. As you will see, however, arthropod classification is based on a few important characteristics. **Arthropods are classified based on the number and structure of their body segments and appendages—particularly their mouthparts.** The three major groups of arthropods are crustaceans, spiders and their relatives, and insects and their relatives.

Crustaceans

Animals in subphylum Crustacea, or crustaceans (krus-TAY-shunz), are primarily aquatic. This subphylum includes organisms such as crabs, shrimps, lobsters, crayfishes, and barnacles. Crustaceans range in size from small terrestrial pill bugs to enormous spider crabs that have masses around 20 kilograms. **Crustaceans typically have two pairs of antennae, two or three body sections, and chewing mouthparts called mandibles.** An example of a crustacean is shown in **Figure 28–7.**

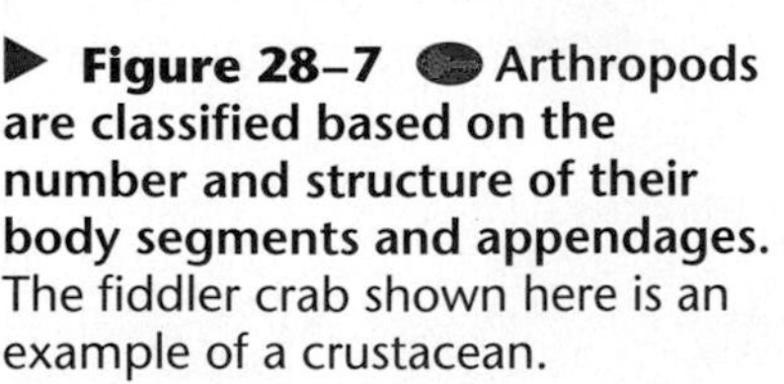

▶ **Figure 28–7** **Arthropods are classified based on the number and structure of their body segments and appendages.** The fiddler crab shown here is an example of a crustacean.

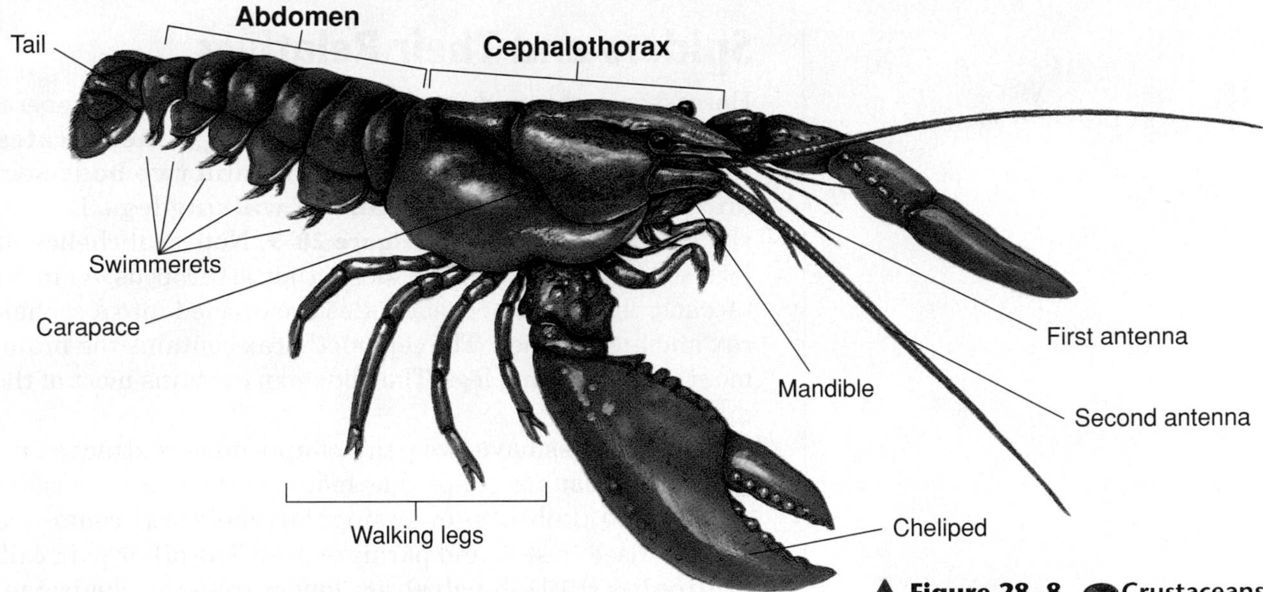

▲ **Figure 28–8** **Crustaceans typically have two pairs of antennae, two or three body sections, and chewing mouthparts called mandibles.** Notice these structures in this illustration of a crayfish, an aquatic crustacean. Each of the smaller antennae has two branches.

The crayfish, shown in **Figure 28–8,** has a body plan that is typical of many crustaceans. Its body is divided into a cephalothorax (sef-uh-loh-THAWR-aks) and an abdomen. The anterior **cephalothorax** is formed by fusion of the head with the **thorax,** which lies just behind the head and houses most of the internal organs. The **abdomen** is the posterior part of the body. The **carapace** is the part of the exoskeleton that covers the cephalothorax.

Crustacean appendages vary in form and function. The first two pairs of appendages are antennae, which bear many sensory hairs. In crayfish, antennae are primarily sense organs. In other crustaceans, they are used for filter feeding or swimming. The third pair of appendages are the mandibles. A **mandible** is a mouthpart adapted for biting and grinding food. Gills are attached to the appendages associated with the cephalothorax.

Crayfishes, lobsters, and crabs are members of the largest group of crustaceans: the decapods. The decapods have five pairs of legs. In crayfishes, the first pair of legs, called **chelipeds,** bear large claws that are modified to catch, pick up, crush, and cut food. Behind these legs are four pairs of walking legs. Along the abdomen are several pairs of **swimmerets,** which are flipperlike appendages used for swimming. The final abdominal segment is fused with a pair of paddlelike appendages to form a large, flat tail. When the abdominal muscles contract, the crayfish's tail snaps beneath its body. This pushes the animal backward.

The barnacles are another group of crustaceans. Unlike the decapods, barnacles are sessile, or attached to a single spot. Barnacles are crustaceans that have lost their abdominal segments and no longer use mandibles. Because of their outer shell-like coverings, barnacles were once classified as mollusks. Barnacles attach themselves to rocks along the shore and in tide pools. They even attach to the surface of marine animals such as whales. Barnacles use their appendages to capture and draw food particles into their mouths.

✔ CHECKPOINT *What are the body sections of a crayfish?*

Word Origins

Decapod comes from the Greek word *deka,* meaning "ten," and the Greek word *podos,* meaning "foot." So, *decapod* means "ten-footed." **If *cephalo* means "head," what do you think the term *cephalopod* means?**

Spiders and Their Relatives

Horseshoe crabs, spiders, ticks, and scorpions are members of subphylum Chelicerata, or chelicerates. **Chelicerates have mouthparts called chelicerae and two body sections, and nearly all have four pairs of walking legs.** Locate these structures in the spider in **Figure 28–9.** Note that chelicerates lack the antennae found on most other arthropods. As in crustaceans, the bodies of chelicerates are divided into a cephalothorax and an abdomen. The cephalothorax contains the brain, eyes, mouth, and walking legs. The abdomen contains most of the internal organs.

Chelicerates have two pairs of appendages attached near the mouth that are adapted as mouthparts. One pair, called **chelicerae** (kuh-LIS-ur-ee; singular: chelicera), contain fangs and are used to stab and paralyze prey. The other pair, called **pedipalps** (PED-ih-palps), are longer than the chelicerae and are usually modified to grab prey. Chelicerates respire using either book gills or book lungs. Horseshoe crabs, which are aquatic, move water across the membranes of book gills. In spiders, which are terrestrial, air enters through spiracles and then circulates across the surfaces of the book lung.

Chelicerates are divided into two main classes: Merostomata and Arachnida. Class Merostomata includes horseshoe crabs and class Arachnida, or arachnids, includes spiders, mites, ticks, and scorpions.

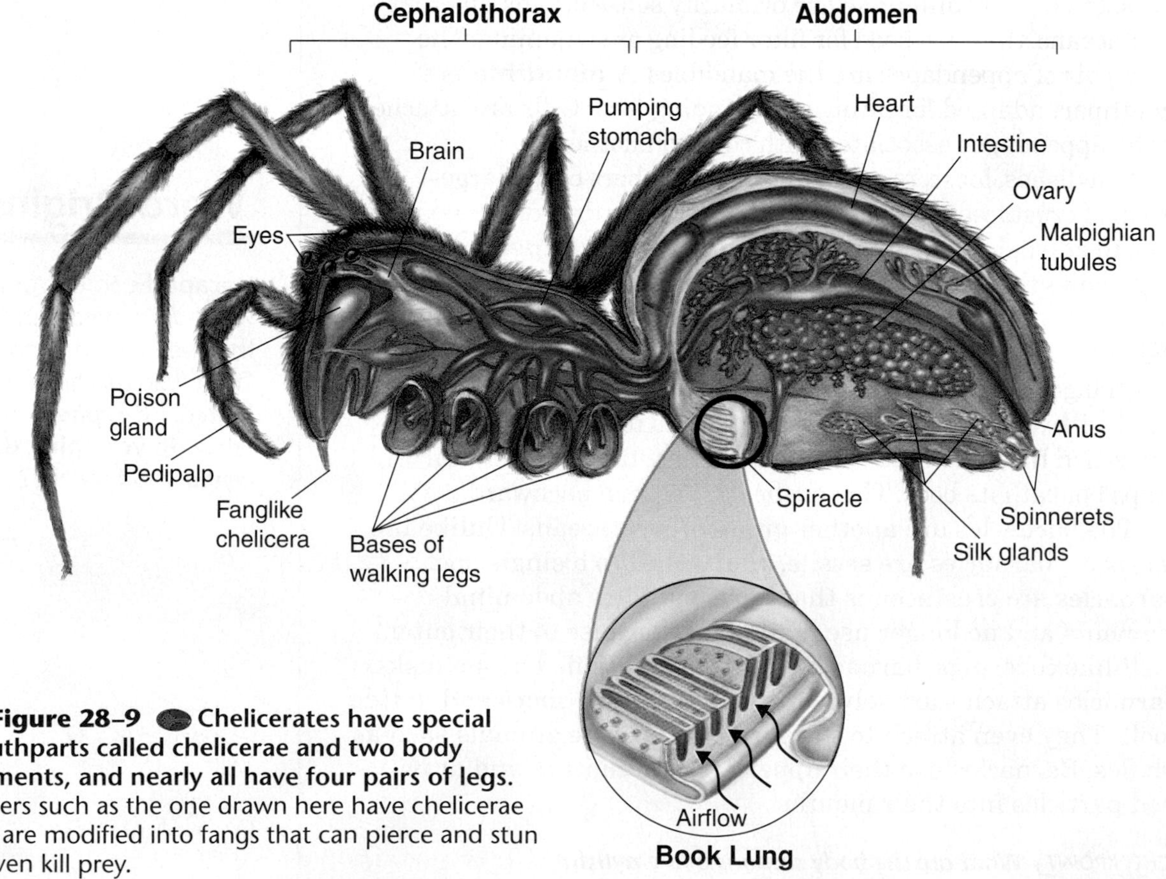

▶ **Figure 28–9 Chelicerates have special mouthparts called chelicerae and two body segments, and nearly all have four pairs of legs.** Spiders such as the one drawn here have chelicerae that are modified into fangs that can pierce and stun or even kill prey.

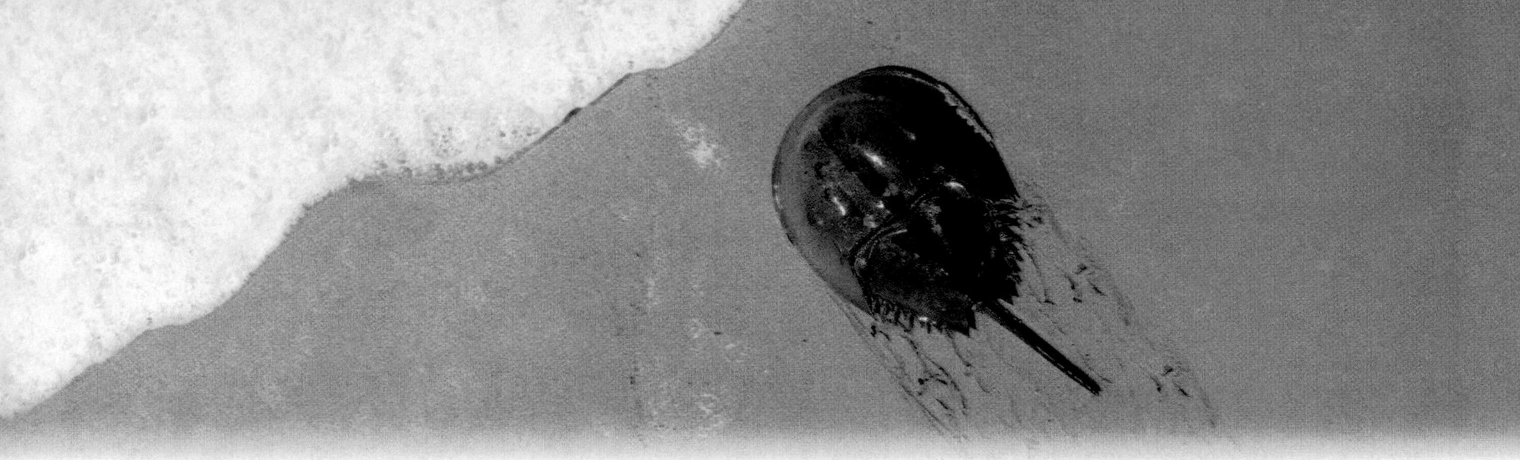

Horseshoe Crabs Horseshoe crabs, such as the one shown in **Figure 28–10,** are among the oldest living arthropods. They first appeared more than 500 million years ago and have changed little since that time. Despite their name, horseshoe crabs are not true crabs at all. They are heavily armor-plated, like crabs, but have an anatomy closer to that of spiders. They have chelicerae, five pairs of walking legs, and a long spikelike tail that is used for movement. Horseshoe crabs grow to about the size—and shape—of a large frying pan. They are common along the marshes and shallow bays of the eastern United States seacoast.

▲ **Figure 28–10** Horseshoe crabs look a bit like true crabs, but their bodies more closely resemble those of spiders and other chelicerates. The abdomen and cephalothorax of these animals are encased in a hard shell. **Inferring** *From this photograph, what can you infer about the habitat of horseshoe crabs?*

Spiders Spiders, the largest group of arachnids, capture and feed on animals ranging from other arthropods to small birds. They catch their prey in a variety of ways. Some spin webs of a strong, flexible protein called silk, which they use to catch flying prey. Others, including the tarantula shown in **Figure 28–11,** stalk and then pounce on their prey. Other spiders lie in wait beneath a camouflaged burrow, leaping out to grab insects that venture too near.

Because spiders do not have jaws for chewing, they must liquefy their food to swallow it. Once a spider captures its prey, it uses fanglike chelicerae to inject paralyzing venom into it. When the prey is paralyzed, the spider injects digestive enzymes into the wounds. These enzymes break down the prey's tissues, enabling the spider to suck the tissues into a specialized pumping stomach. The stomach forces the liquefied food through the rest of the spider's digestive system. In the digestive system, enzymes break food molecules into smaller molecules that can be absorbed.

Whether or not they spin webs, all spiders produce silk. Spider silk is much stronger than steel! Spiders spin silk into webs, cocoons for eggs, and wrappings for prey. They do this by forcing liquid silk through **spinnerets,** which are organs that contain silk glands. As the silk is pulled out of the spinnerets, it hardens into a single strand. Web-spinning spiders can spin webs almost as soon as they hatch; the complicated procedure seems to be preprogrammed behavior.

CHECKPOINT *How do chelicerates respire?*

▲ **Figure 28–11** The tarantula shown here is an example of a chelicerate. The chelicerae, or specialized mouthparts, can inject poison by way of a painful bite. **Applying Concepts** *How might this action be useful to tarantulas?*

Analyzing Data

Ticks and Lyme Disease

Lyme disease is caused by a bacterium found in two species of small ticks, the deer tick (*Ixodes scapularis*) and the western black-legged tick (*Ixodes pacificus*). Both species are most common in humid, wooded areas. They feed by sucking blood from deer, mice, birds, or humans. In warmer climates where reptiles such as lizards and snakes are most common, deer ticks prefer to feed on reptiles. The disease-causing bacteria are transmitted to the host by the bite of an infected tick. In humans the bacteria can cause a rash, fever, fatigue, joint and muscle pain, and damage to the nervous system. The bacteria do not survive well in reptiles.

The map shows the distribution of the two tick species and areas where there is a high incidence of Lyme disease. Use the map to help you answer the questions that follow.

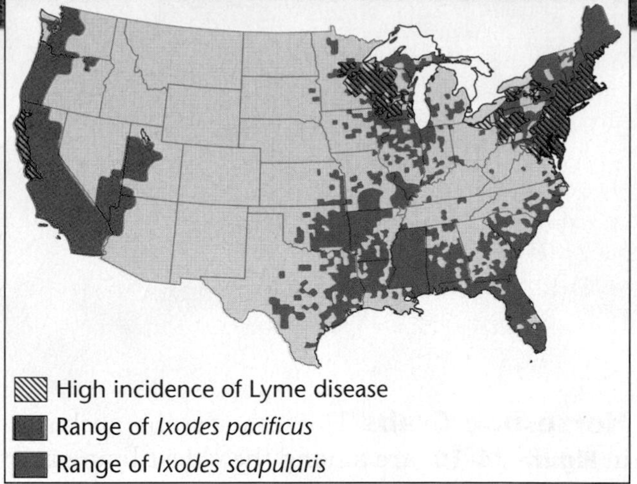

1. **Interpreting Graphics** How can you explain the differences in the incidence of Lyme disease within the range of deer ticks?
2. **Formulating Hypotheses** What are two possible reasons that Lyme disease is not common in the parts of the dry southwest where western black-legged ticks are found?

▼ **Figure 28–12** Scorpions are easily recognized by their clawlike pedipalps and curved abdomen that bears a stinger at its tip. Although scorpions inflict stings on humans—usually causing as much pain as a wasp sting—they typically prey on other invertebrates, such as insects. **Comparing and Contrasting** *How do scorpions and spiders capture their prey?*

Mites and Ticks Mites and ticks are small arachnids that are often parasitic. Their chelicerae and pedipalps are specialized for digging into a host's tissues and sucking out blood or plant fluids. In many species, the chelicerae are needlelike structures that are used to pierce the skin of the host. The pedipalps are often equipped with claws for attaching to the host. These mouthparts are so strong that if a tick begins to feed on you and you try to pull it off, its cephalothorax may separate from its abdomen and remain in your skin!

Mites and ticks parasitize a variety of organisms. Spider mites damage houseplants and are major agricultural pests on crops such as cotton. Others—including chiggers, mange, and scabies mites—cause itching or painful rashes in humans and other mammals. Ticks can transmit bacteria that cause serious diseases, such as Rocky Mountain spotted fever and Lyme disease.

Scorpions Scorpions are widespread in warm areas around the world, including the southern United States. Scorpions have pedipalps that are enlarged into claws, as shown in **Figure 28–12.** The long, segmented abdomen of a scorpion carries a venomous stinger that can kill or paralyze prey. Unlike spiders, scorpions chew their prey, using their chelicerae.

CHECKPOINT *Where are scorpions usually found?*

Insects and Their Relatives

Centipedes, millipedes, and insects all belong to the subphylum Uniramia, or uniramians (yoo-nuh-RAY-mee-unz). This subphylum contains more species than all other groups of animals alive today. **Uniramians have jaws, one pair of antennae, and unbranched appendages.** They also have widely varying forms and lifestyles. Centipedes and millipedes have long, wormlike bodies composed of many leg-bearing segments, as shown in **Figure 28–13.** Insects have compact, three-part bodies, and most are adapted for flight. The insects are so diverse and important that they are discussed separately, in the next section.

Figure 28–13 **Uniramians such as centipedes and millipedes have jaws, one pair of antennae, and unbranched appendages.** A centipede (top) is a carnivore that feeds on earthworms and other small animals. A millipede (bottom) is a herbivore that feeds on rotting vegetation.

Centipedes Centipedes belong to class Chilopoda. They have from a few to more than 100 pairs of legs, depending on the species. Most body segments bear one pair of legs each. Centipedes are carnivores whose mouthparts include venomous claws. They use these claws to catch and stun or kill their prey—including other arthropods, earthworms, toads, small snakes, and even mice. Centipedes usually live beneath rocks or in the soil. Their spiracles cannot close, and their exoskeleton is not waterproof. As a result, their bodies lose water easily. This characteristic restricts centipedes to moist or humid areas.

Millipedes Millipedes form class Diplopoda. Like the centipedes, millipedes have a highly segmented body. However, each millipede segment bears two, not one, pairs of legs. These two pairs of legs per segment develop from the fusion of two segments in the millipede embryo. Millipedes live under rocks and in decaying logs. They feed on dead and decaying plant material. Unlike centipedes, they are timid creatures. When disturbed, many millipedes roll up into a ball. This behavior protects their softer undersides. Millipedes may also defend themselves by secreting unpleasant or toxic chemicals.

28–2 Section Assessment

1. **Key Concept** What characteristics are used to classify arthropods?
2. **Key Concept** How do the three largest groups of arthropods differ?
3. Describe the process of digestion in spiders.
4. What characteristic of horseshoe crabs is different from most other chelicerates?
5. Compare and contrast the body plans and feeding habits of millipedes and centipedes.
6. **Critical Thinking Applying Concepts** Are insects more closely related to spiders or to centipedes? Explain.

Sharpen Your Skills

Problem Solving

Use information from this section to design a new type of arthropod. Make sure that the arthropod has all the characteristics described in this section. Draw the arthropod and give it a name. Include a brief description of what it eats and where it lives.

28–3 Insects

1-S1.1 Historical development of ideas in science

Guide for Reading

Key Concepts
- What are the distinguishing features of insects?
- What two types of development can insects undergo?
- What types of insects form societies?

Vocabulary
incomplete metamorphosis
nymph
complete metamorphosis
pupa
pheromone
society
caste

Reading Strategy: Summarizing As you read, find the most important concepts in each paragraph. Then, use the important concepts to write a summary of what you have read.

What animals other than humans have the greatest impact on the activities of this planet? If you said "insects," you would be correct. From bees that flit from flower to flower to weevils that feed on crops, insects seem to be everywhere. As **Figure 28–14** shows, class Insecta contains more species than any other group of animals. Ants and termites alone account for nearly one third of all the animal biomass in the Amazon basin.

Many characteristics of insects have contributed to their evolutionary success. These include different ways of responding to stimuli; the evolution of flight, which allowed insects to disperse long distances and colonize new habitats; and a life cycle in which the young differ from adults in appearance and feeding methods. These features have allowed insects to thrive in almost every terrestrial habitat on Earth, as well as in many freshwater and some marine environments.

The insects cover an incredible variety of life forms—from stunning, iridescent beetles and butterflies to the less attractive fleas, weevils, cockroaches, and termites. Biologists sometimes disagree on how to classify insects, and the number of living orders ranges from 26 to more than 30.

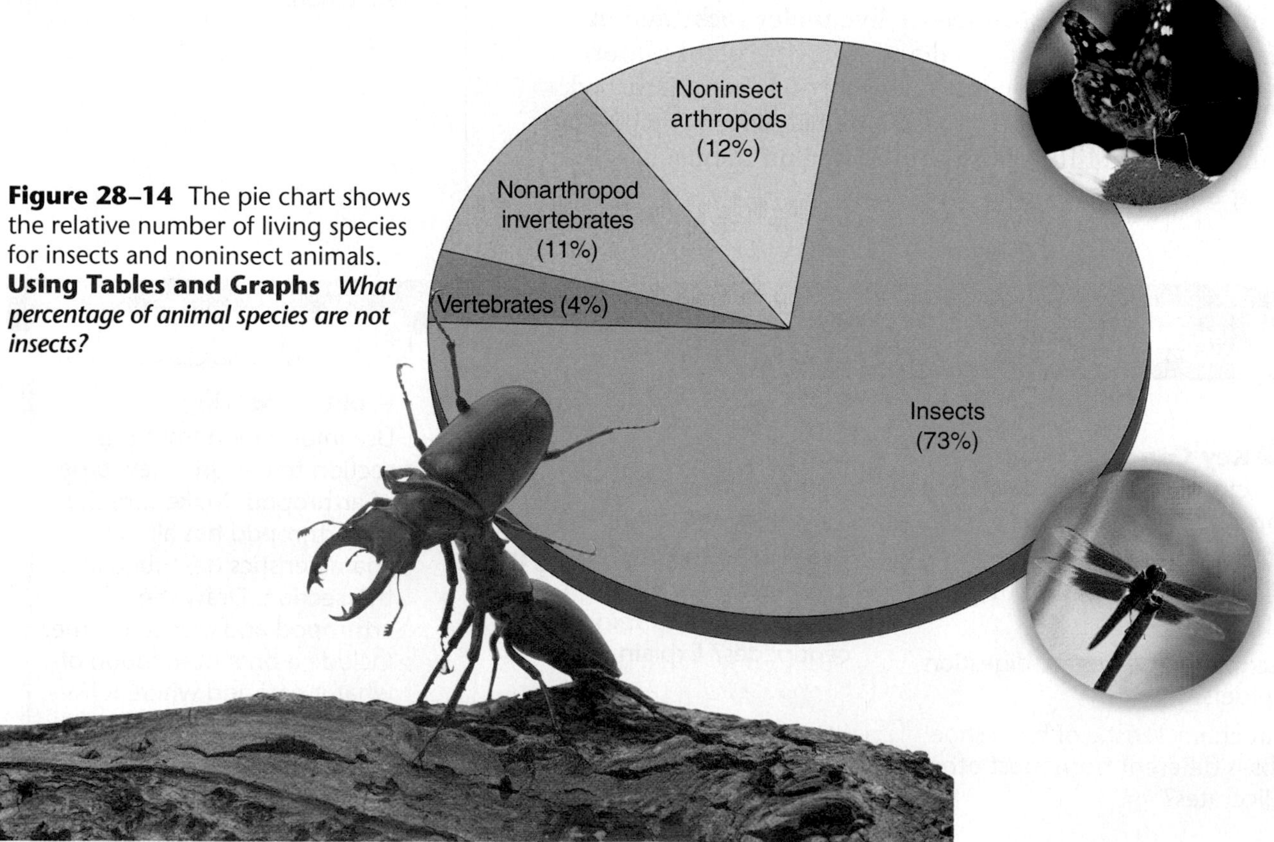

Figure 28–14 The pie chart shows the relative number of living species for insects and noninsect animals. **Using Tables and Graphs** *What percentage of animal species are not insects?*

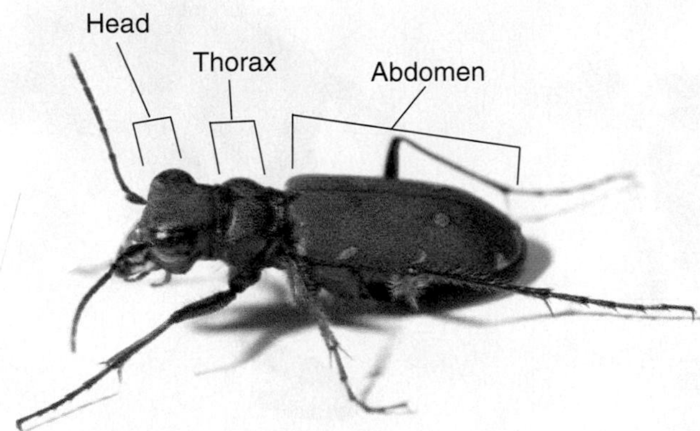

◀ **Figure 28–15** **Insects have a body divided into three parts—head, thorax, and abdomen. Three pairs of legs are attached to the thorax.** In addition to these features, this green tiger beetle has other characteristics of a typical insect—wings, antennae, compound eyes, and tracheal tubes for respiration.

What Is an Insect?

Like all arthropods, insects have a segmented body, an exoskeleton, and jointed appendages. They also have several features that are specific to insects. **Insects have a body divided into three parts—head, thorax, and abdomen. Three pairs of legs are attached to the thorax.** The beetle in **Figure 28–15** exhibits these characteristics. In many insects, such as ants, the body parts are clearly separated from each other by narrow connections. In other insects, such as grasshoppers, the divisions between the three body parts are not as sharply defined. A typical insect also has a pair of antennae and a pair of compound eyes on the head, two pairs of wings on the thorax, and tracheal tubes that are used for respiration.

Insects carry out life functions in basically the same ways as other arthropods. However, insects have a variety of adaptations that deserve a closer look.

What are the three main parts of an insect's body?

Responses to Stimuli Insects use many sense organs to detect external stimuli. Compound eyes are made of many lenses that detect minute changes in color and movement. The brain assembles this information into a single image and directs the insect's response. Compound eyes produce an image that is less detailed than what we see. However, eyes with multiple lenses are far better at detecting movement—one reason it is so hard to swat a fly!

Insects have chemical receptors for taste and smell on their mouthparts, as might be expected, and also on their antennae and legs. When a fly steps in a drop of water, it knows immediately whether the water contains salt or sugar. Insects also have sensory hairs that detect slight movements in the surrounding air or water. As objects move toward insects, the insects can feel the movement of the displaced air or water and respond appropriately. Many insects also have well-developed ears that hear sounds far above the human range. These organs are located in what we would consider odd places—behind the legs in grasshoppers, for example.

For: Articles on insects and other invertebrates
Visit: PHSchool.com
Web Code: cbe-8283

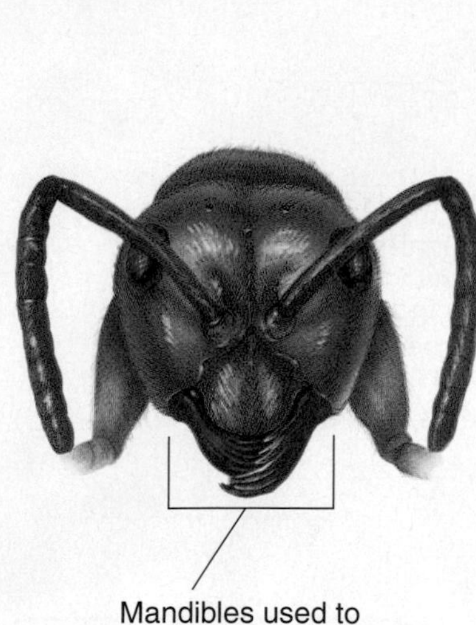

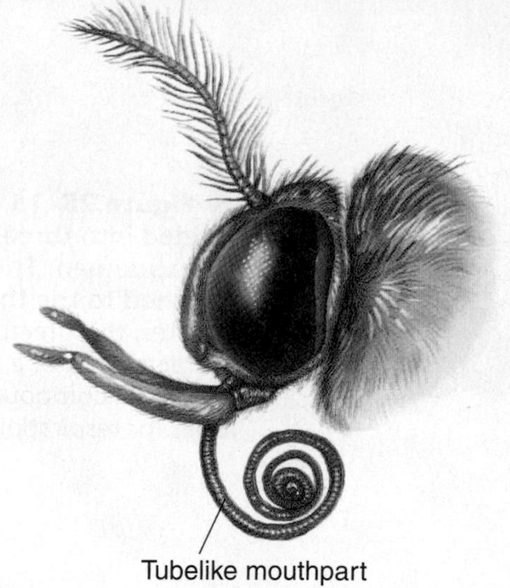

▲ **Figure 28–16** Insect mouthparts are specialized for a variety of functions. An ant's mouthparts can saw through and then grind food into a fine pulp. The mouthpart of a moth consists of a long tube that can be uncoiled to sip nectar from a flower. Flies have a spongy mouthpart that is used to stir saliva into food and then lap up the food. **Applying Concepts** *What is the function of saliva?*

Adaptations for Feeding Insects have three pairs of appendages that are used as mouthparts, including a pair of mandibles. These mouthparts can take on a variety of shapes, as shown in **Figure 28–16.**

Insect adaptations for feeding are not restricted to their mouthparts. Many insects produce saliva containing digestive enzymes that help break down food. The chemicals in bee saliva, for example, help change nectar into a more digestible form—honey. Glands on the abdomen of bees secrete wax, which is used to build storage chambers for food and other structures within a beehive.

Movement and Flight Insects have three pairs of legs, which in different species are used for walking, jumping, or capturing and holding prey. In many insects, the legs have spines and hooks that are used for grasping and defense.

Many insects can fly, as shown in **Figure 28–17.** Flying insects typically have two pairs of wings made of chitin—the same substance that makes up an insect's exoskeleton.

The evolution of flight has allowed insects to disperse long distances and to colonize a wide variety of habitats. Flying abilities and styles vary greatly among the insects. Butterflies usually fly slowly. Flies, bees, and moths, however, can hover, change direction rapidly, and dart off at great speed. Dragonflies can reach speeds of 50 kilometers per hour.

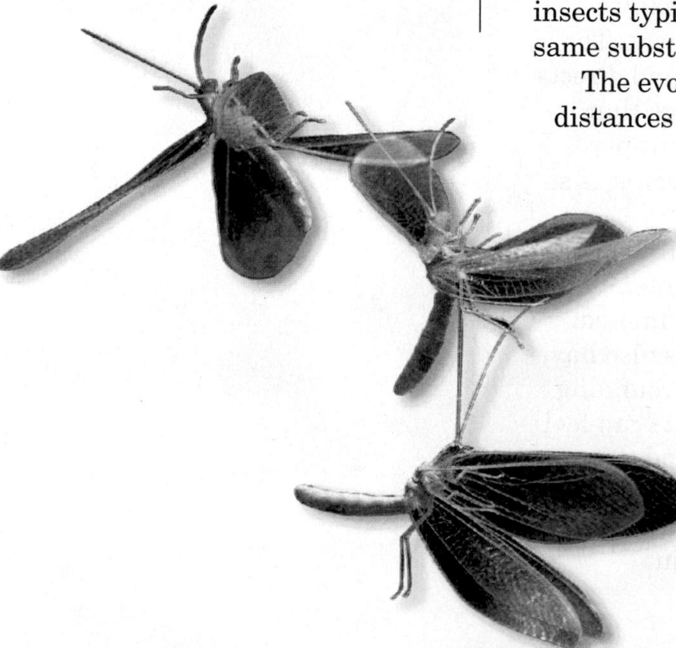

◀ **Figure 28–17** Flying insects, such as this lacewing, move their wings using two sets of muscles. The muscles contract to change the shape of the thorax, alternately pushing the wings down and lifting them up and back. In some small insects, these muscles can produce wing speeds of up to 1000 beats per second! **Drawing Conclusions** *How might the evolution of flight change an animal's habitat?*

Metamorphosis **The growth and development of insects usually involve metamorphosis, which is a process of changing shape and form. Insects undergo either incomplete metamorphosis or complete metamorphosis.** Both complete and incomplete metamorphosis are shown in **Figure 28–18.** The immature forms of insects that undergo gradual or **incomplete metamorphosis,** such as the chinch bug, look very much like the adults. These immature forms are called **nymphs** (NIMFS). Nymphs lack functional sexual organs and other adult structures, such as wings. As they molt several times and grow, the nymphs gradually acquire adult structures. This type of development is characterized by a similar appearance throughout all stages of the life cycle.

Many insects, such as bees, moths, and beetles, undergo a more dramatic change in body form during a process called **complete metamorphosis.** These animals hatch into larvae that look and act nothing like their parents. They also feed in completely different ways from adult insects. The larvae typically feed voraciously and grow rapidly. They molt a few times and grow larger but change little in appearance. Then they undergo a final molt and change into a **pupa** (PYOO-puh; plural: pupae)—the stage in which an insect changes from larva to adult. During the pupal stage, the body is completely remodeled inside and out. The adult that emerges seems like a completely different animal. Unlike the larva, the adult typically can fly and is specialized for reproduction. **Figure 28–18** shows the complete metamorphosis of a ladybug beetle.

CHECKPOINT *What is a pupa?*

To find out how insect metamorphosis plays a part in forensic science, view the segment "Insect Clues: The Smallest Witnesses," on Videotape Three.

Figure 28–18 **The growth and development of insects usually involve metamorphosis, which is a process of changing shape and form.** The chinch bug (left) undergoes incomplete metamorphosis, in which the developing nymphs look similar to the adult. The ladybug (right) undergoes complete metamorphosis. During the early stages, the developing larva and pupa look completely different from the adult.

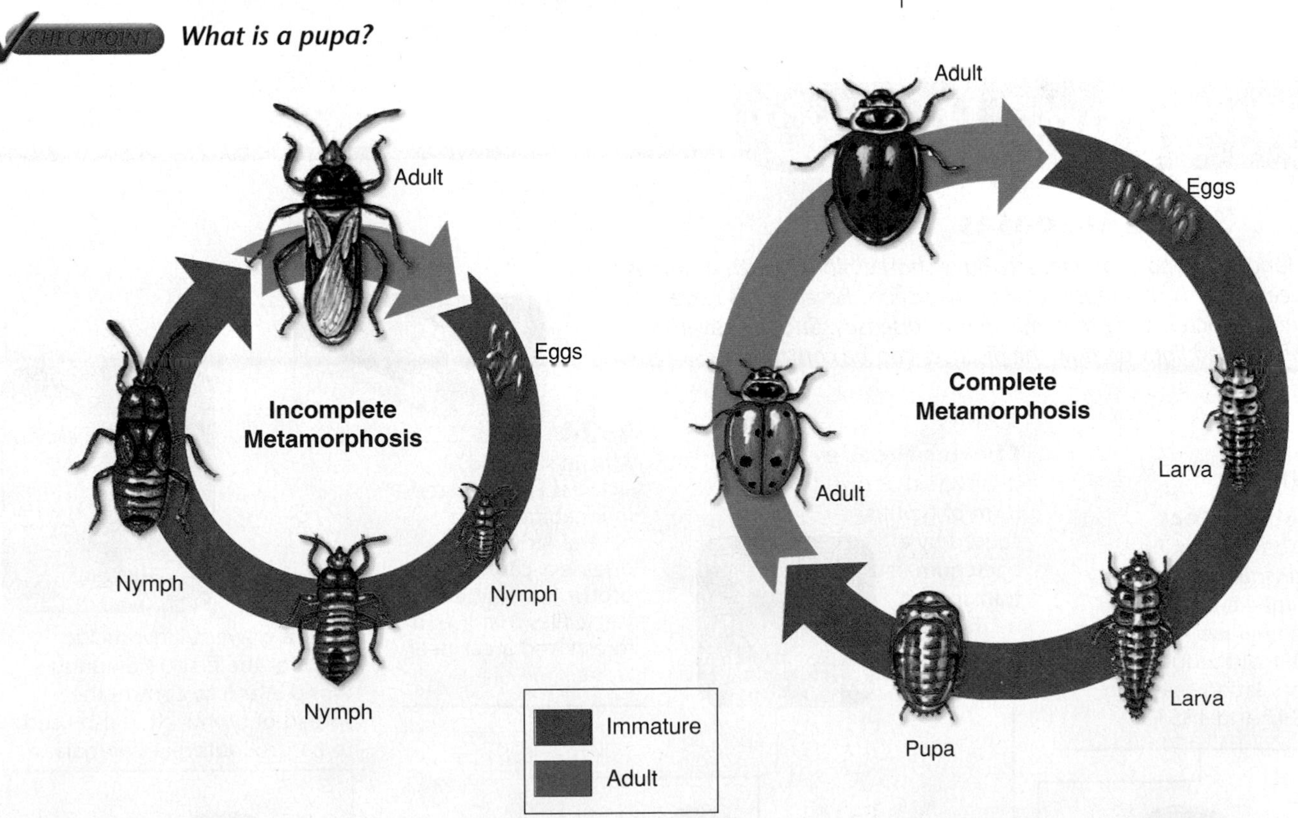

Insects and Humans

Many insects are known for their negative effects. Termites destroy wood structures, moths eat their way through wool clothing and carpets, and bees and wasps produce painful stings. Insects such as desert locusts cause billions of dollars in damage each year to livestock and crops. Boll weevils are notorious for the trouble they cause cotton farmers in the South. Mosquitoes are annoying and have been known to spoil many a leisurely outdoor activity. Only female mosquitoes bite humans and other animals to get a blood meal for their developing eggs. Male mosquitoes, on the other hand, do not bite; they feed on nectar. Many insects, including mosquitoes, cause far more serious damage than itchy bites. Their bites can infect humans with microorganisms that cause devastating diseases such as malaria, yellow fever, and bubonic plague.

Despite their association with destruction and disease, insects also contribute enormously to the richness of human life. Agriculture would be very different without the bees, butterflies, wasps, moths, and flies that pollinate many crops. One third of the food you eat depends on plants pollinated by animals, including insects. Insects also produce commercially valuable products such as silk, wax, and honey. They are even considered a food delicacy in certain countries of Africa and Asia.

How do insects affect humans negatively? Positively?

Biology and History

Insect-Borne Diseases

For as long as humans and insects have shared planet Earth, humans have been victims of diseases carried by insects. Researchers have discovered which insects transmit specific diseases. Such discoveries have often shed light on how the diseases can be controlled.

1906
Robert Koch discovers that fleas transmit the bubonic-plague bacterium. The plague killed 25% of Europe's population between 1347 and 1351.

1909
Charles Nicolle discovers that one form of typhus, caused by a bacterium, is transmitted by the body louse.

1924
African sleeping sickness is discovered in inhabitants of central Africa. The disease is caused by a protist transmitted by tsetse flies that live in forests and areas near water.

1943
DDT, a powerful insecticide, is used for the first time during World War II to control the spread of typhus. It is also used to control outbreaks of malaria.

Insect Communication

Insects communicate using sound, visual, chemical, and other types of signals. Much of their communication involves finding a mate. To attract females, male crickets chirp by rubbing their forewings together, and male cicadas buzz by vibrating special membranes on the abdomen.

Visual Cues Male fireflies use visual cues to communicate with potential mates. As shown in **Figure 28–19**, a light-producing organ in the abdomen is used to produce a distinct series of flashes. When female fireflies see the signal, they flash back a signal of their own, inducing the males to fly to them. This interaction is sometimes more complicated, however, because the carnivorous females of one genus of fireflies can mimic the signal of another genus—and then lure unsuspecting males to their death!

Chemical Signals Many insects communicate using chemical signals. These chemicals are called **pheromones** (FEHR-uh-mohnz), which are specific chemical messengers that affect the behavior or development of other individuals of the same species. Some pheromones function to signal alarm or alert other insects. Other pheromones enable males and females to communicate during courtship and mating.

▲ **Figure 28–19** Fireflies use light to communicate with other individuals of their species. They are programmed to respond to specific patterns of light. **Applying Concepts** *What are some other ways in which insects communicate?*

Writing in Science

Some insect-borne diseases have an intermediate host in which the parasite reproduces asexually. Conduct research on the bubonic plague to identify its intermediate host. Write a report on how this host was discovered and how the discovery affected control of the disease.

1972
Use of DDT is severely restricted in the United States because it is found to be toxic to fishes, birds, and possibly humans.

1974
The World Health Organization begins to get rid of the black fly population of West Africa. Black flies transmit river blindness, which is caused by a roundworm.

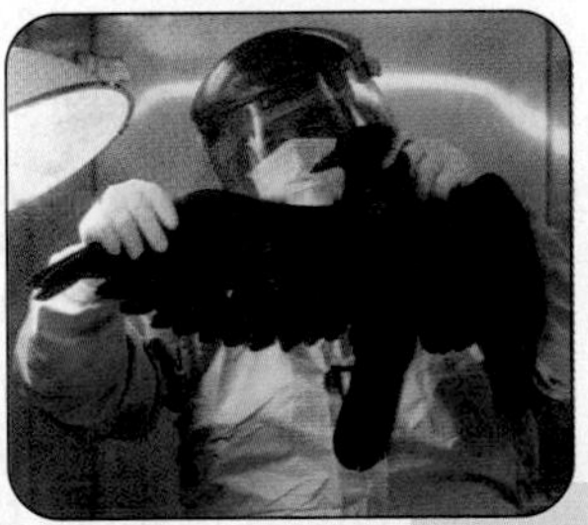

1999
An outbreak of West Nile virus occurs in New York City and its suburbs. The disease is carried by mosquitoes and can affect humans as well as birds and livestock. Officials order spraying of insecticides near bodies of water in which mosquitoes might breed.

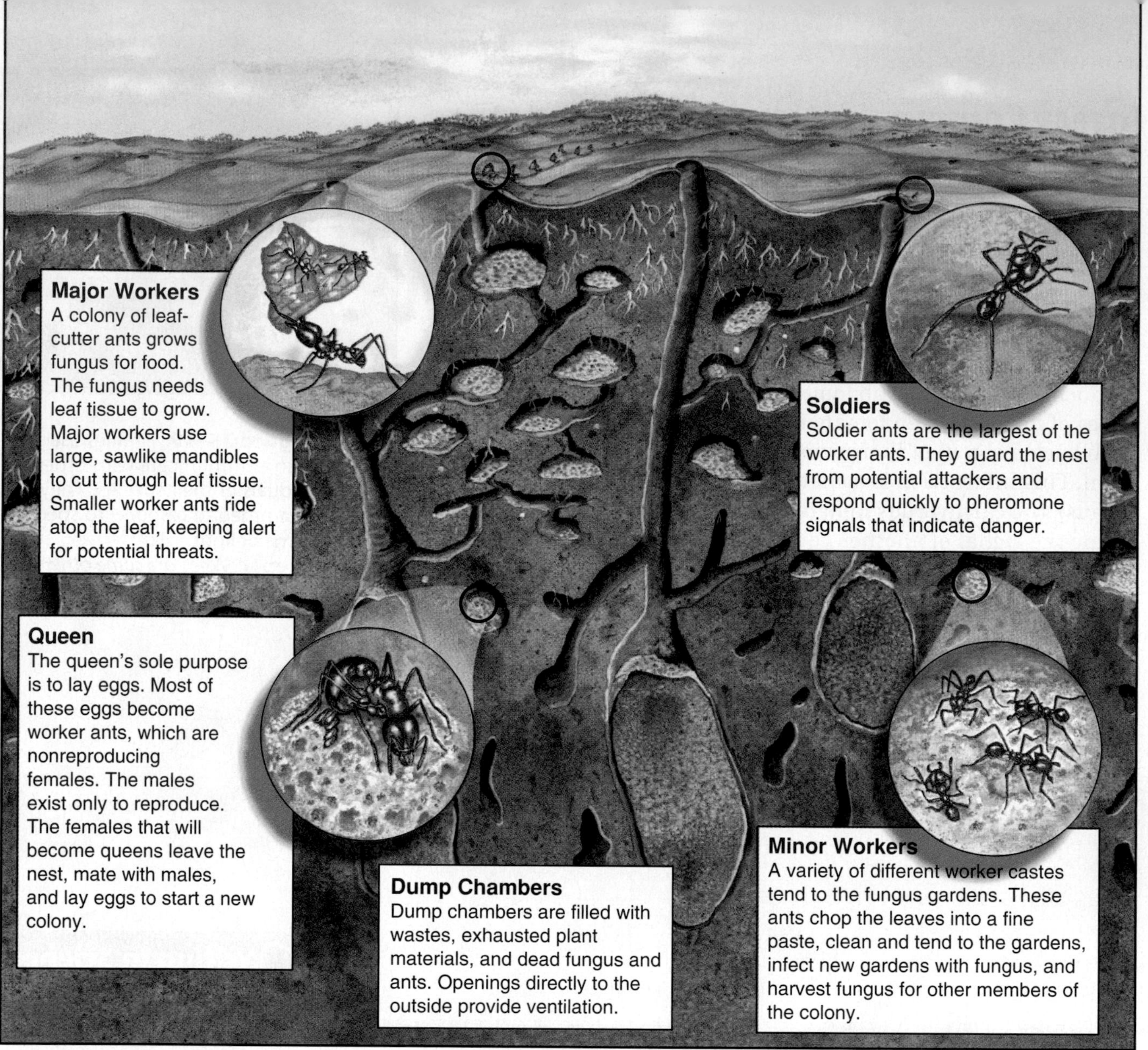

Major Workers
A colony of leaf-cutter ants grows fungus for food. The fungus needs leaf tissue to grow. Major workers use large, sawlike mandibles to cut through leaf tissue. Smaller worker ants ride atop the leaf, keeping alert for potential threats.
Soldiers
Soldier ants are the largest of the worker ants. They guard the nest from potential attackers and respond quickly to pheromone signals that indicate danger.
Queen
The queen's sole purpose is to lay eggs. Most of these eggs become worker ants, which are nonreproducing females. The males exist only to reproduce. The females that will become queens leave the nest, mate with males, and lay eggs to start a new colony.
Dump Chambers
Dump chambers are filled with wastes, exhausted plant materials, and dead fungus and ants. Openings directly to the outside provide ventilation.
Minor Workers
A variety of different worker castes tend to the fungus gardens. These ants chop the leaves into a fine paste, clean and tend to the gardens, infect new gardens with fungus, and harvest fungus for other members of the colony.

▲ **Figure 28–20** **Some insects, such as these tropical leaf-cutter ants, form societies.** In a tropical leaf-cutter society, only a single queen reproduces. The queen can produce thousands of eggs in a single day. Several different castes of leaf-cutter ants perform all other tasks within the colony. They care for the queen and her eggs and young; they grow fungus for food; and they build, maintain, and defend the colony's home. One group of workers even cultivates bacteria that produce antibiotics! These antibiotics prevent the growth of parasitic molds on the fungus that the ants use for food.

Insect Societies

Just as people form teams that work together toward a common goal, some insects live and work together in groups. Unlike people, however, insects act instinctively rather than voluntarily. **Ants, bees, termites, and some of their relatives form complex associations called societies.** A **society** is a group of closely related animals of the same species that work together for the benefit of the whole group. Insect societies may consist of more than 7 million individuals. A tropical leaf-cutter ant colony is shown in **Figure 28–20.**

Castes Within an insect society, individuals may be specialized to perform particular tasks, or roles. These are performed by groups of individuals called **castes.** Each caste has a body form specialized for its role. The basic castes are reproductive females called queens (which lay eggs), reproductive males, and workers. Most insect societies have only one queen, which is typically the largest individual in the colony.

Communication in Societies A sophisticated system of communication is necessary for the functioning of a society. Each species of social insect has its own "language" of visual, touch, sound, and chemical signals that convey information among members of the colony. When a worker ant finds food, for example, she leaves behind a trail of a special pheromone as she heads back to the nest. Her nest mates can then detect her trail to the food by using sensory hairs on their antennae.

Honeybees communicate with complex movements as well as with pheromones. Worker bees are able to convey information about the type, quality, direction, and distance of a food source by "dancing." As shown in **Figure 28–21,** bees have two basic dances: a round dance and a waggle dance. In the round dance, the bee that has found food circles first one way and then the other, over and over again. This dance tells the other bees that there is food within a relatively short distance from the hive. The frequency with which the dancing bee changes direction indicates the quality of the food source: The more frequent the changes in direction, the greater the energy value of the food.

In the waggle dance, the bee that has found food runs forward in a straight line while waggling her abdomen. She circles around one way, runs in a straight line again, and circles around the other way. The waggle dance tells the other bees that the food is a longer distance away. The longer the bee takes to perform the straight run and the greater the number of waggles, the farther away the food. The straight run also indicates in which direction the food is to be found. The angle of the straight run in relation to the vertical surface of the honeycomb indicates the angle of the food in relation to the sun. For example, if the dancer runs straight up the vertical part of the honeycomb, the food is in the same direction as the sun. In contrast, if the straight run is 10° to the right of the vertical, the food is 10° to the right of the sun.

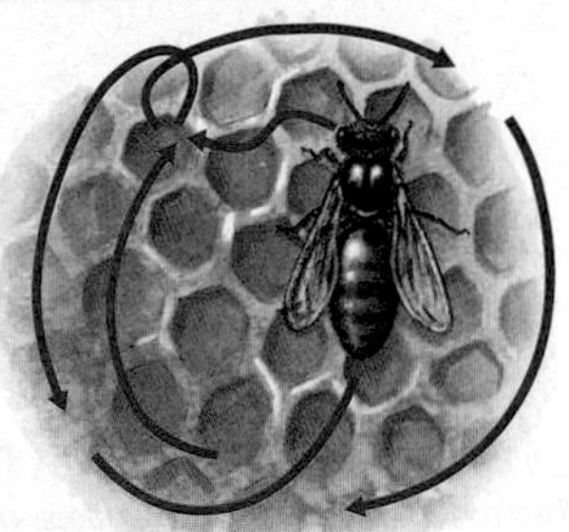

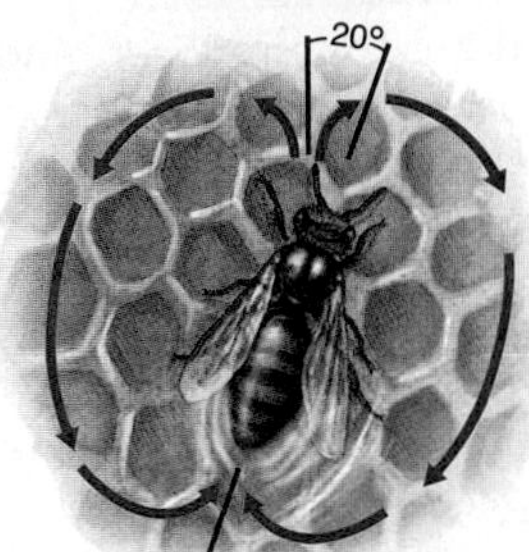

▲ **Figure 28–21** Bees use dances to communicate information about food sources. The round dance indicates that food is fairly close to the hive. The waggle dance indicates that food is farther away. It also indicates the direction of the food. **Interpreting Graphics** ***In what direction does the food lie, according to this bee's waggle dance?***

28–3 Section Assessment

1. **Key Concept** Describe the basic body plan of an insect.
2. **Key Concept** Compare the processes of incomplete and complete metamorphosis. Which involves a dramatic change in form?
3. **Key Concept** Describe the organization of a leaf-cutter ant society. What are the roles of the different castes?
4. What are pheromones? Identify two functions of pheromones.
5. What information is passed on by the dances of honeybees? Compare the messages of both types of dances.
6. **Critical Thinking Drawing Conclusions** The compound eyes of insects are better at detecting movement than the fine details of an image. Why might the ability to detect movement be important to insects?

Writing in Science

Explanatory Paragraph

Write a paragraph in which you briefly explain how insects communicate. *Hints:* In the first sentence in your paragraph, identify the different ways in which insects communicate. Then, in the sentences that follow, explain these ways. Use specific examples to clarify the points you make.

28–4 Echinoderms

Guide for Reading

Key Concepts

- What are the distinguishing features of echinoderms?
- What functions are carried out by the water vascular system of echinoderms?
- What are the different classes of echinoderms?

Vocabulary
endoskeleton
water vascular system
madreporite
tube foot

Reading Strategy: Using Visuals Before you read, preview **Figure 28–23.** As you read, notice where in the sea star each function occurs.

One of the most unusual sights along the seashore might be the sea stars, sea urchins, and sand dollars that have washed up on the beach. These animals look like stars, pin-cushions, and coins. They are all echinoderms (ee-KY-noh-durmz), members of the phylum Echinodermata. *Echino-* means "spiny," and *dermis* means "skin." If you have ever touched a sea star, you will know why this name is appropriate. The skin of echinoderms is stretched over an internal skeleton, or **endoskeleton,** that is formed of hardened plates of calcium carbonate. These plates give the animal a bumpy and irregular texture. Echinoderms live only in the sea. Some are delicate, brightly colored, feathery-armed creatures. Others look like mud-brown half-rotten cucumbers!

What Is an Echinoderm?

The body plan of echinoderms is like no other in the animal kingdom. Adult echinoderms typically have no anterior or posterior end and lack cephalization. However, the bodies of most echinoderms are two-sided. The side in which the mouth is located is called the oral surface, and the opposite side is called the aboral surface.

Echinoderms are characterized by spiny skin, an internal skeleton, a water vascular system, and suction-cuplike structures called tube feet. Most adult echinoderms exhibit five-part radial symmetry. The body parts, which usually occur in multiples of five, are arranged around the central body like the spokes of a wheel. The brittle star in **Figure 28–22** exhibits this kind of symmetry. Although radial symmetry is characteristic of simpler animals such as cnidarians, echinoderms are actually more closely related to humans and other vertebrates. The larvae of echinoderms are bilaterally symmetrical, indicating that body symmetry evolved differently in this group than in simpler animals. Also, echinoderms are deuterostomes, animals in which the blastopore develops into an anus. This type of development is found in echinoderms and vertebrates, indicating that these groups are closely related.

◀ **Figure 28–22** **Echinoderms such as this brittle star have spiny skin, five-part radial symmetry, an internal skeleton, a water vascular system, and suction-cuplike structures called tube feet.** Observe that the brittle star has five arms. The bodies of most echinoderms are divided into parts that are multiples of five.

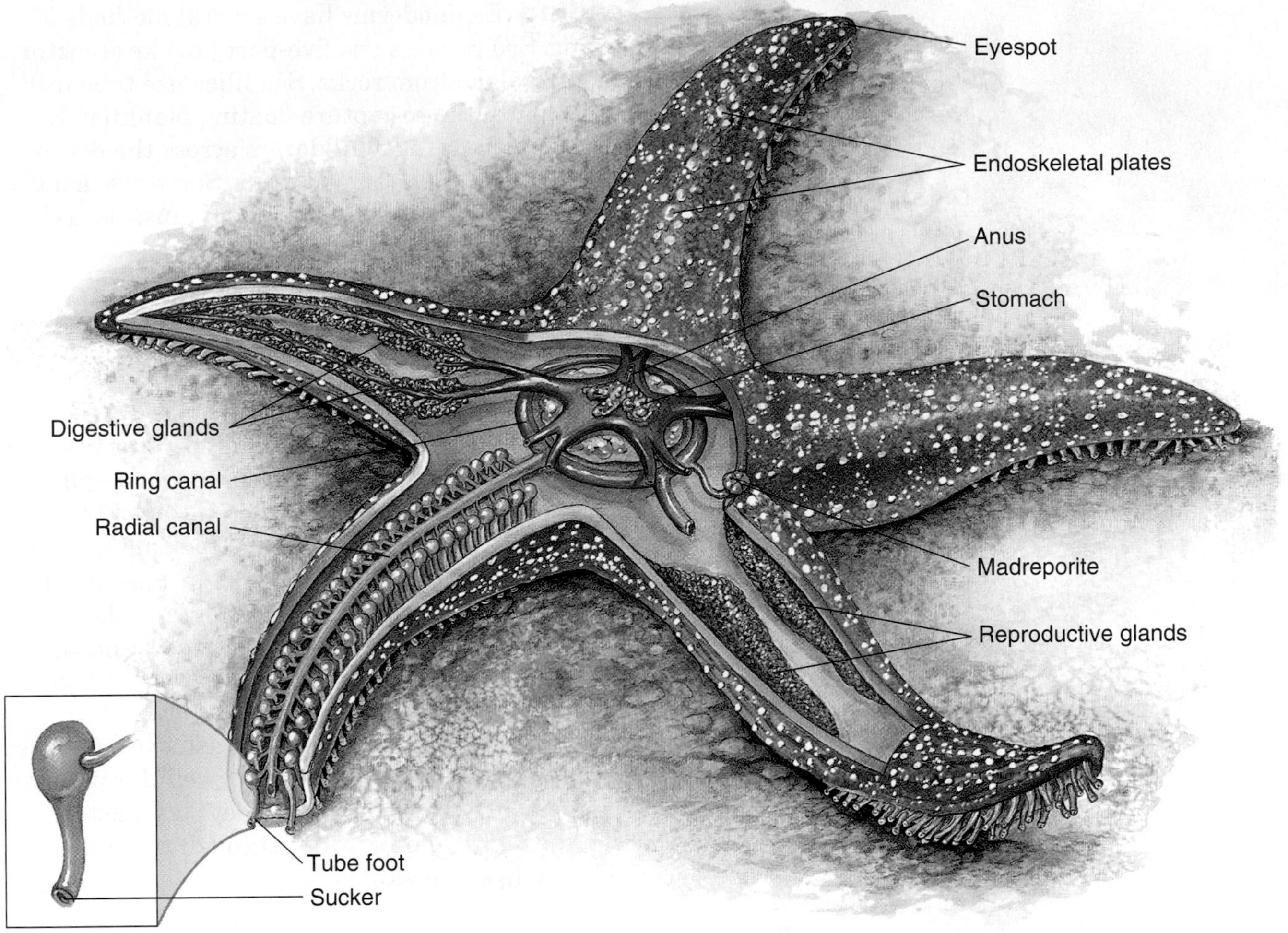

Eyespot

Endoskeletal plates

Anus

Stomach

Digestive glands

Ring canal

Radial canal

Madreporite

Reproductive glands

Tube foot

Sucker

▲ **Figure 28–23** The most distinctive system of echinoderms is the water vascular system, shown here in a sea star. **The water vascular system, which extends throughout the body, functions in respiration, circulation, and movement.**

Form and Function in Echinoderms

A unique feature of echinoderms is a system of internal tubes called a **water vascular system,** which is shown in **Figure 28–23.** **The water vascular system, which is filled with fluid, carries out many essential body functions in echinoderms, including respiration, circulation, and movement.** It opens to the outside through a sievelike structure called a **madreporite** (MAD-ruh-pawr-yt). In sea stars, the madreporite connects to a ring canal that forms a circle around the animal's mouth. From the ring canal, five radial canals extend along body segments.

Attached to each radial canal are hundreds of tube feet. A **tube foot** is a structure that operates much like a suction cup. Each tube foot has a sucker on the end. Muscles pull the center of the sucker upwards, forming a cup shape. This action creates suction on the surface to which the foot is attached, so the tube foot pulls on the surface. Hundreds of tube feet acting together create enormous force, allowing echinoderms to "walk" and even to pull open shelled prey such as clams.

What is the system of internal tubes in echinoderms?

For: Water Vascular System activity
Visit: PHSchool.com
Web Code: cbp-8284

▲ **Figure 28–24** Echinoderms use all types of feeding methods. Sea stars, like the one shown above, are carnivores that typically feed on mussels and other bivalves. **Comparing and Contrasting** *How do other groups of echinoderms feed?*

Feeding Echinoderms have several methods of feeding. Sea urchins use five-part jawlike structures to scrape algae from rocks. Sea lilies use tube feet along their arms to capture floating plankton. Sea cucumbers move like bulldozers across the ocean floor, taking in sand and detritus. Sea stars usually feed on mollusks such as clams and mussels, as shown in **Figure 28–24.** Once the prey's shell is open, the sea star pushes its stomach out through its mouth, pours out enzymes, and digests the mollusk in its own shell. Then, the sea star pulls its stomach and the partially digested prey into its mouth.

Respiration and Circulation Other than the water vascular system, echinoderms have few adaptations to carry out respiration or circulation. In most species, the thin-walled tissue of the tube feet provides the main surface for respiration. In some species, small outgrowths called skin gills also function in gas exchange.

Circulation of needed materials and wastes takes place throughout the water vascular system. Oxygen, food, and wastes are carried by the water vascular system.

Excretion In most echinoderms, digestive wastes are released as feces through the anus. Nitrogen-containing cellular wastes are excreted primarily in the form of ammonia. This waste product is passed into surrounding water through the thin-walled tissues of tube feet and skin gills.

Response Echinoderms do not have a highly developed nervous system. Most have a nerve ring that surrounds the mouth, and radial nerves that connect the ring with the body sections. Most echinoderms also have scattered sensory cells that detect light, gravity, and chemicals released by potential prey.

Movement Most echinoderms move using tube feet. An echinoderm's mobility is determined in part by the structure of its endoskeleton. Sand dollars and sea urchins have movable spines attached to the endoskeleton. Sea stars and brittle stars have flexible joints that enable them to use their arms for locomotion. In sea cucumbers, the plates of the endoskeleton are reduced and contained inside a soft, muscular body wall. These echinoderms crawl along the ocean floor by the combined action of tube feet and the muscles of the body wall.

Reproduction Echinoderms reproduce by external fertilization. Sperm are produced in testes, and eggs are produced in ovaries. Both types of gametes are shed into open water, where fertilization takes place. The larvae, which have bilateral symmetry, swim around for some time and then swim to the ocean bottom, where they develop into adults that have radial symmetry.

How do echinoderms move?

For: Links on echinoderms
Visit: www.SciLinks.org
Web Code: cbn-8284

Groups of Echinoderms

There are roughly 7000 species of echinoderms—all of which live in the world's oceans. **Classes of echinoderms include sea urchins and sand dollars; brittle stars; sea cucumbers; sea stars; sea lilies and feather stars.** Some of these echinoderms are shown in **Figure 28–25.**

Sea Urchins and Sand Dollars This class includes sea urchins and disk-shaped sand dollars. These echinoderms are unique in having large, solid plates that form a box around their internal organs. Many are detritivores or grazers that eat large quantities of algae. They defend themselves in different ways. Sand dollars often burrow under layers of sand or mud. Some sea urchins wedge themselves in rock crevices during the day, whereas others defend themselves using long, sharp spines.

Brittle Stars Brittle stars are common in many parts of the sea, especially on coral reefs. They have slender, flexible arms and can scuttle around quite rapidly to escape predators. In addition to using speed for protection, brittle stars shed one or more arms when attacked. The detached arm keeps moving, distracting the predator while the brittle star escapes. Brittle stars are filter feeders and detritivores that hide by day and wander around under cover of darkness.

Sea Cucumbers Sea cucumbers look like warty, moving pickles. Most sea cucumbers are detritus feeders that move along the sea floor while sucking up organic matter and the remains of other animals and plants. Herds containing hundreds of thousands of sea cucumbers roam across the deep-sea floor.

Sea Stars Sea stars are probably the best-known group of echinoderms. They move by creeping slowly along the ocean floor. Most are carnivorous, preying on bivalves that they encounter. Many sea stars have incredible abilities to repair themselves when damaged. If a sea star is pulled into pieces, each piece will grow into a new animal, as long as it contains a portion of the central part of the body.

Figure 28–25 **Sea urchins, brittle stars, sea cucumbers, and sea stars represent different classes of echinoderms.** Observe the characteristics of these representatives of each class.

Long-Spined Sea Urchin

Brittle Star

Red-Lined Sea Cucumber

Sun Star

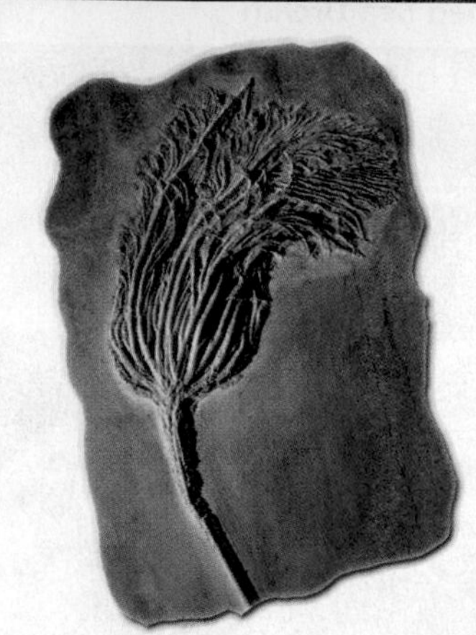

Figure 28–26 Sea lilies belong to the most ancient class of echinoderms, known as crinoids. The red crinoid (top) is one of the few species of this class that are alive today. This stalked crinoid fossil (bottom) is an example of the types of crinoids that dominated Earth during the Paleozoic Era. **Comparing and Contrasting** *How are sea lilies different from other echinoderms?*

Sea Lilies and Feather Stars These filter feeders, which have long, feathery arms, make up the oldest class of echinoderms. Sea lilies and feather stars are common in tropical oceans today, and a rich fossil record shows that they were distributed widely throughout ancient seas. Like modern sea lilies, their fossilized ancestors lived attached to the ocean bottom by a long, stemlike stalk, as seen in **Figure 28–26.** Many modern feather stars live on coral reefs, where they perch on top of rocks and use their tube feet to catch floating plankton.

Ecology of Echinoderms

Echinoderms are common in a variety of marine habitats. In many areas, a sudden rise or fall in the number of echinoderms can cause major changes to populations of other marine organisms. Sea urchins help control the distribution of algae and other forms of marine life. Sea stars are important predators that help control the numbers of other organisms such as clams and corals.

A major threat to coral reefs is one kind of sea star called the crown-of-thorns. This echinoderm is named for the rows of poisonous spines located along its arms. It feeds almost exclusively on coral. In the Great Barrier Reef of Australia—one of the largest reef systems in the world—this organism has destroyed extensive areas of coral.

28–4 Section Assessment

1. **Key Concept** What is an echinoderm?
2. **Key Concept** What is the water vascular system? How is it important to echinoderms?
3. **Key Concept** List the major classes of echinoderms and describe their characteristics.
4. What are tube feet? What functions do they perform, and how do they perform them?
5. Echinoderms are deuterostomes. What does this indicate about their relationship to other animals?
6. **Critical Thinking Inferring** Why is tearing a sea star apart and throwing it back into the water an ineffective way of trying to reduce sea star populations?

Connecting Concepts

Body Symmetry
In Chapter 26, you learned about the kinds of body symmetry exhibited by animals. What kind of body symmetry do adult sea stars have? How is this kind of symmetry similar to that of a cnidarian? How is it different?

Design an Experiment

Observing Ant Behavior

In this investigation, you will design experiments to determine how ants respond to members of other colonies and other species.

Problem How do ants respond to members of other colonies and other species?

Materials

- covered petri dish containing 10 ants of species A from the same colony (**CAUTION:** *Do not use stinging species of ants such as fire ants or harvester ants, or destructive species such as carpenter ants.*)
- hand lens or dissecting microscope
- field guide (for identifying ants)
- watch or clock with a second hand
- 3 covered petri dishes, each containing 5 ants of species A from different colonies
- covered petri dish containing 5 ants from species B (**CAUTION:** *Do not use stinging species of ants such as fire ants or harvester ants, or destructive species such as carpenter ants.*)

Skills Predicting, Drawing Conclusions

Design Your Experiment 

Part A: Observing Ants That Are Related

1. Obtain a petri dish containing 10 ants from the same colony. Look at the ants under a hand lens or dissecting microscope. Use a field guide to identify the species to which they belong.
2. For 30 seconds, count the number of ants that are fighting with one another. Record this number on a sheet of paper. If the ants are not fighting, write "0."
3. **Predicting** Record your prediction of whether ants from separate colonies of the same species will fight, and whether ants of two different species will fight.

Part B: Observing Ants That Are Not Related

4. **Designing Experiments** Design experiments to test your predictions. As you plan your investigative procedures, refer to the Lab Tips box on page 55 for information on planning safe investigations, planning wise use of materials, and selecting equipment and technology.
5. Write a hypothesis for each experiment and control all variables except the one you are testing. **CAUTION:** *Ants are delicate, and some can produce painful stings. Do not try to pick them up.* Have your teacher check your plan before you begin to perform your experiment.

Analyze and Conclude

1. **Observing** Did most of the ants fight in step 2? How would you explain the behavior you observed?
2. **Observing** What happened when you put ants from two different colonies of the same species together? When you put ants from two different species together? Were your predictions correct?
3. **Drawing Conclusions** How do you think the behavior you observed helps the ants survive?

Go Further

Asking Questions Think of some other aspects of ants and their behavior that you would like to learn about. For example, you might be curious about how different environmental conditions affect an ant colony, or which foods individual ants prefer. Write your ideas as a series of questions. Choose one of your questions and find an answer to it, either by finding information in reference materials or designing an experiment. Before performing any experiments, obtain your teacher's approval.

Chapter 28 Study Guide

28–1 Introduction to the Arthropods

Key Concepts

- Arthropods have a segmented body, a tough exoskeleton, and jointed appendages.
- The evolution of arthropods, by natural selection and other evolutionary processes, has led to fewer body segments and highly specialized appendages for feeding, movement, and other functions.
- When they outgrow their exoskeletons, arthropods undergo periods of molting.

Vocabulary

exoskeleton, p. 715
chitin, p. 715
appendage, p. 715
tracheal tube, p. 717
spiracle, p. 717
book lung, p. 717
Malpighian tubule, p. 717
molting, p. 719

28–2 Groups of Arthropods

Key Concepts

- Arthropods are classified based on the number and structure of their body segments and appendages, particularly their mouthparts.
- Crustaceans typically have two pairs of antennae, two or three body sections, and chewing mouthparts called mandibles.
- Chelicerates have mouthparts called chelicerae and two body sections, and nearly all have four pairs of walking legs.
- Uniramians have jaws, one pair of antennae, and unbranched appendages.

Vocabulary

cephalothorax, p. 721
thorax, p. 721
abdomen, p. 721
carapace, p. 721
mandible, p. 721
cheliped, p. 721
swimmeret, p. 721
chelicera, p. 722
pedipalp, p. 722
spinneret, p. 723

28–3 Insects

Key Concepts

- Insects have a body divided into three parts—head, thorax, and abdomen. Three pairs of legs are attached to the thorax.
- The growth and development of insects usually involve metamorphosis, which is a process of changing shape and form. Insects undergo either incomplete metamorphosis or complete metamorphosis.
- Ants, bees, termites, and some of their relatives form complex associations called societies.

Vocabulary

incomplete metamorphosis, p. 729
nymph, p. 729
complete metamorphosis, p. 729
pupa, p. 729
pheromone, p. 731
society, p. 732
caste, p. 732

28–4 Echinoderms

Key Concepts

- Echinoderms are characterized by spiny skin, an internal skeleton, a water vascular system, and suction-cuplike structures called tube feet. Most adults have five-part radial symmetry.
- The water vascular system carries out many essential body functions in echinoderms, including respiration, circulation, and movement.
- Classes of echinoderms include sea urchins and sand dollars; brittle stars; sea cucumbers; sea stars; sea lilies and feather stars.

Vocabulary

endoskeleton, p. 734
water vascular system, p. 735
madreporite, p. 735
tube foot, p. 735

Thinking Visually

Construct a diagram that models the classification of the phylum Arthropoda. Your classification system should be based on similarities and differences. It should show a hierarchy, or the arrangement of the subgroups within the phylum. Be sure to use taxonomic nomenclature (phylum, subphylum, and so forth).

Preparing for the Living Environment Exam

Blue questions emphasize Regents Exam content

Chapter 28

Part A

Multiple Choice

For each statement or question, select the number of the word or expression that, of those given, best completes the statement or answers the question.

1 One body feature that all arthropods have in common is
(1) gills (3) jointed appendages
(2) antennae (4) chelicerae

2 Most terrestrial arthropods breath using branched, air-filled structures called
(1) gills (3) tracheal tubes
(2) book gills (4) book lungs

3 Transport of materials in most arthropods is accomplished with
(1) no circulatory system
(2) an open circulatory system
(3) a closed circulatory system
(4) a four-chambered circulatory system

4 Crustaceans are the only arthropods that have
(1) three pairs of legs
(2) two pairs of antennae
(3) chitin in their exoskeleton
(4) chelicerae

5 Which of the organisms below belongs in the subphylum Chelicerata?

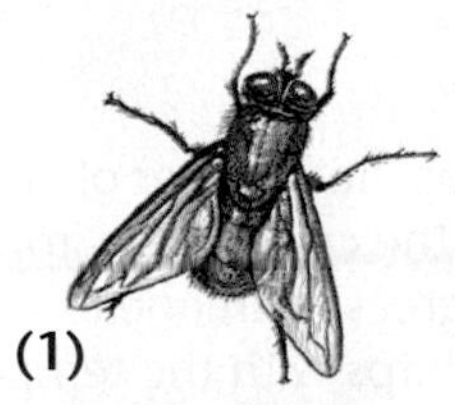
(1)

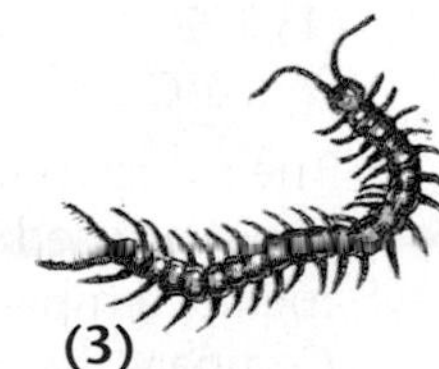
(3)

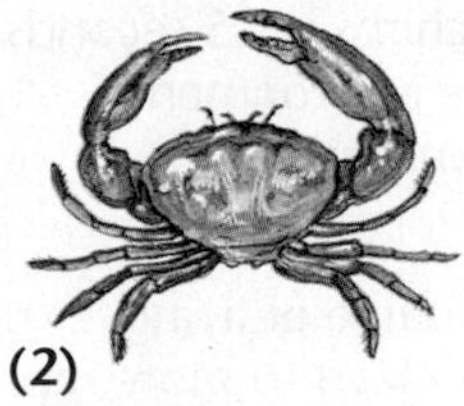
(2)

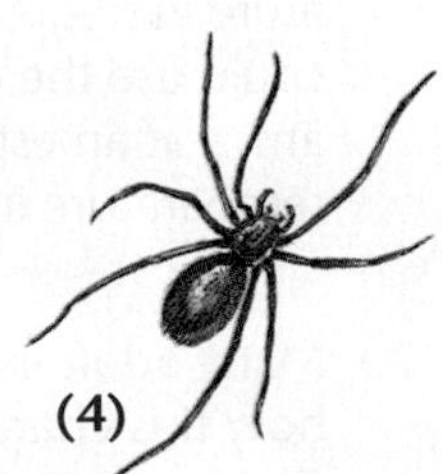
(4)

6 All insects have
(1) two pairs of legs
(2) three antennae
(3) three pairs of wings
(4) three body sections

7 The type of symmetry exhibited by most adult echinoderms is
(1) bilateral (3) top and bottom
(2) radial (4) no symmetry

8 Oxygen is transported throughout the body of a sea star in its
(1) madreporite stalk
(2) Malpighian tubules
(3) water vascular system
(4) open circulatory system

9 Mites and ticks are example of
(1) crustaceans
(2) uniramians
(3) arachnids
(4) chelicerae

10 Which combination correctly pairs the structure with its function?
(1) spiracle—digestion of food
(2) madreporite—muscle coordination
(3) spinnerets—molting
(4) mandible—feeding

11 Which characteristic is *not* found in echinoderms?
(1) an internal skeleton
(2) a pair of antennae
(3) tube feet
(4) a water vascular system

12 Which animal has four pairs of walking legs?
(1) centipede (3) ant
(2) insect (4) arachnid

13 Chemical messengers that affect the behavior or development of other individuals of the same species are called
(1) trilobites (3) chitins
(2) pheromones (4) chelicerae

14 An extinct group of marine arthropods that were abundant more than 500 million years ago were the
(1) arachnids (3) pheromones
(2) trilobites (4) brittle stars

Test-Taking Tip If you are taking a long time to answer a question, consider coming back to it later. As you answer the other questions, you may remember the information you need to answer the skipped question.

Part B

Multiple Choice and Extended Response
For those questions that ask you to select a response, choose the one that best completes the statement or answers the question. For all others follow the directions given.

15 In many insect species, insect adults and larvae feed on different substances. Explain how this characteristic might help members of those species survive.

Base your answers to questions 16 through 19 on the information below and on your knowledge of biology.

A biology student is investigating the relationship between cricket chirps and temperature. He catches a cricket and places it in a jar. He leaves the jar outside, and each day he measures the number of chirps during a 15-second period. At the same time, he records the outside temperature near the cricket. His data are shown in the data table below.

Relationship Between Temperature and Cricket Chirping

Day	Number of Chirps in 15 Seconds	Outside Temperature (°C)
Monday	31	23
Tuesday	20	16
Wednesday	12	11
Thursday	29	21
Friday	25	19

16 Make a copy of the following data table on your answer paper and complete it according to these directions.
- Arrange the number of chirps in order from least to most, then fill in the appropriate temperatures in degrees Celsius.
- Calculate the temperature in degrees Fahrenheit by multiplying the Celsius temperature by 1.8 and then adding 32. Round off to the nearest degree.
- Fill in the Fahrenheit temperatures you calculate in the appropriate places in the table.

Relationship Between Temperature and Cricket Chirping

Chirps in 15 Seconds	Outside Temperature (°C)	Outside Temperature (°F) (°C x 1.8) + 32 = °F

17 The student obtained 20 more crickets and repeated his procedure with each of them. Nearly identical results were obtained each time. The most valid conclusion that can be drawn from this experiment is
(1) Crickets cannot chirp more than 31 times in 15 seconds.
(2) The number of chirps decreases when the temperature decreases.
(3) Crickets cannot chirp less than 12 times every 11 seconds.
(4) The number of chirps increases when the temperature decreases.

18 At which temperature would a cricket be most likely to chirp 9 times in 15 seconds?
(1) 2°C (3) 18°C
(2) 10°C (4) 25°C

19 The student concluded that the number of chirps could be used to estimate the cricket's environmental temperature in degrees Fahrenheit. Compare the number of chirps with the temperature in degrees Fahrenheit. Then, state how you could use the number of chirps in 15 seconds to arrive at an estimate of the environmental temperature in degrees Fahrenheit.

---

20 Many adult insects are capable of flying. Explain how this characteristic can lead to more reproductive success for a species.

21 Explain how the structural variations among the insects that make up an anthill are of value to the insect society of which they are a part. Support your explanation with an example.

22 The legs and bodies of honeybees are covered with hairs that collect pollen and other materials. Explain how this adaptation is helpful to both flowering plants and honeybees.

23 Blue crabs usually have hard shells. During certain times of the year some of the blue crabs have thin, papery shells. State one reason why these blue crabs would have soft shells.

24 An animal is discovered that has an exoskeleton, sucking mouthparts, head fused with thorax, no wings, and four pairs of walking legs. It is decided that this animal is not an insect. Identify the *two* features of this animal that would lead to the decision that it could not be an insect, and explain how insects would differ in these two features.

Base your answers to questions 25 and 26 on the information and graph below and on your knowledge of biology.

The graph below shows the effect of water temperature on the time it takes for brine shrimp eggs to hatch. Brine shrimp are small crustaceans found in salty lakes and ponds.

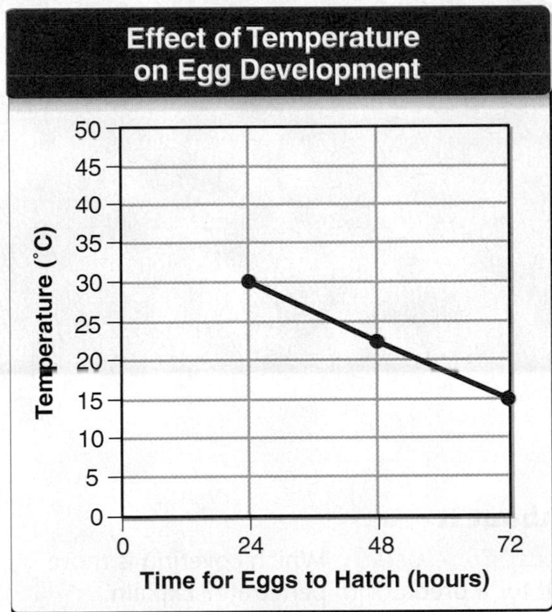

25 Based on the graph, state a valid conclusion about the relationship between water temperature and hatching time.

26 Predict how many hours it would take for eggs to hatch at 10°C, 18°C, and 25°C.

27 In a stagnant pool of water, a crayfish may spend much of its time lying on its side near the surface moving its walking legs on that side back and forth. State one life activity that this behavior is likely to aid and explain how it may help the animal's survival.

Part C

Extended Response

Answer the questions or follow the directions given.

28 Compare incomplete metamorphosis with complete metamorphosis. In your answer be sure to
- describe the stages of each process
- state one way a nymph differs from a pupa
- state one example of an organism that undergoes each process

29 Female insects release certain pheromones into the air to attract males for mating. Some companies have produced devices that use pheromones to attract specific insects and trap them. Compare the usefulness of pheromones and insect poisons, which are often used in the control of pest insects. In your answer be sure to state
- one environmental benefit of using pheromones instead of the usual insect poisons
- one way that using a trap that releases pheromones may not be as effective as expected in reducing the pest insect population

For: An interactive self-test
Visit: PHSchool.com
Web Code: cba-8280

CHAPTER 29

Comparing Invertebrates

The spotted cleaner shrimp lives among, and cleans, the tentacles of this anemone. The anemone protects the shrimp from predators.

Inquiry Activity

Which protective covering is better?

Procedure  

1. Examine some arthropod exoskeletons and mollusk shells. Observe as many differences as you can between these two types of protective coverings.
2. List the differences you observed. Next to each item, note how that difference in protective covering is adaptive to the organism in its own particular niche and habitat.

Think About It

1. **Drawing Conclusions** Which covering is more difficult for a predator to penetrate? Explain.
2. **Predicting** Animals must use energy to move. Which type of covering is more useful to an active, motile animal? Explain your answer.
3. **Drawing Conclusions** How can your observations help explain the fact that most mollusks are slow-moving animals, whereas many arthropods are more active?

29–1 Invertebrate Evolution

4-3.1 Earth's species developed from earlier species
4-3.1 Some individuals are better adapted to survive
4-3.1 Fossils indicate extinctions
LS- Make observations and formulate a conclusion

Until recently, the origins of invertebrates were shrouded in mystery. This was because few fossils old enough to shed light on this period in Earth's history had been found. But ongoing discoveries around the world are shedding new light on the origins of invertebrates. Treasure troves of beautifully preserved invertebrate fossils, dating between 575 and 543 million years ago, have been discovered in the Ediacara Hills of Australia and in Chengjiang, China. These fossils join those known from the Burgess Shale deposits in the Canadian Rockies to show a fascinating history of early multicellular life.

Guide for Reading

Key Concept
- What are the major trends in invertebrate evolution?

Vocabulary
radial symmetry
bilateral symmetry
cephalization
coelom

Reading Strategy: Using Visuals Before you read, preview **Figure 29–4.** As you read, notice how the evolutionary trends in the cladogram are discussed in the text.

Origin of the Invertebrates

The Ediacaran fossils brought to light a strange group of ancient invertebrates. These peculiar fossils puzzled paleontologists for years because they seemed quite different from any modern invertebrates. More recently, paleontologists have identified beautifully preserved, microscopic fossils, between 610 and 570 million years old, that seem to be the developing embryos of early multicellular animals. From the same time period, they also identified what are called trace fossils. Trace fossils are tracks and burrows made by soft-bodied animals whose bodies were not fossilized.

Molecular biologists and paleontologists have also created a new field called molecular paleontology. This research uses cutting-edge studies in genetics to understand how different animal body plans evolved. DNA comparisons among living invertebrates help determine which phyla are most closely related. In addition, geneticists are studying how small changes in certain genes can cause major changes in body structures.

The First Multicellular Animals The Ediacaran fossils include some of the earliest and most primitive animals known. Most, like the animal shown in **Figure 29–1,** were flat and plate-shaped and lived on the bottom of shallow seas. They were made of soft tissues that absorbed nutrients from the surrounding water. Some may have had photosynthetic algae living within their bodies. These animals were segmented and had bilateral symmetry. However, they show little evidence of cell specialization or organization into a front and back end. Some of these early animals may have been related to soft-bodied invertebrates such as jellyfishes and worms. Their body plan, however, is distinct from anything alive today. Regardless of their relationships to other organisms, these animals were probably simple and had little internal specialization.

▼ **Figure 29–1** The drawing is an artist's conception of what an early invertebrate might have looked like. **Applying Concepts** *In what environment did most early invertebrates live?*

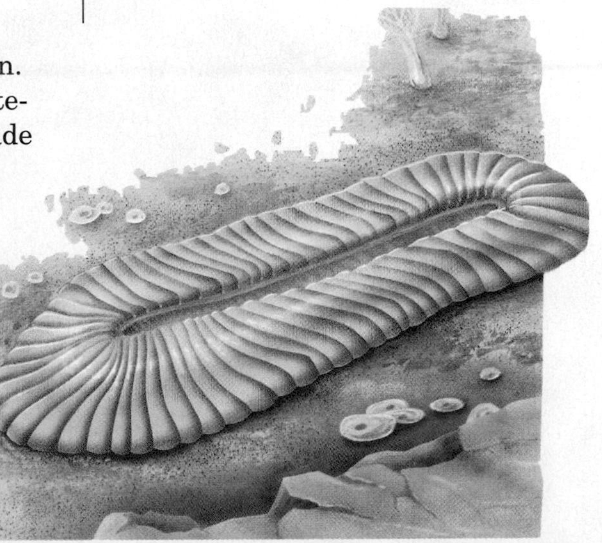

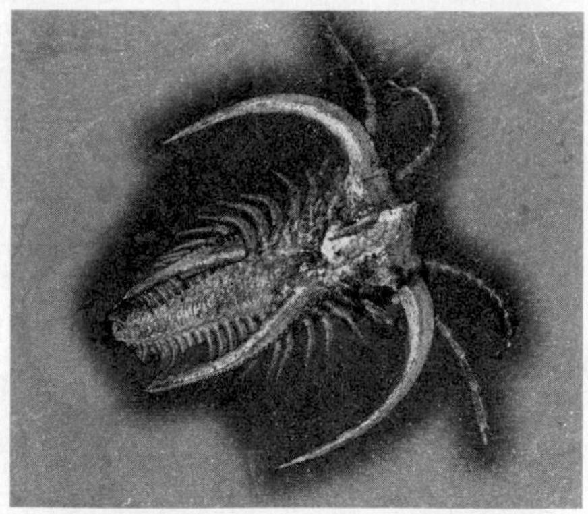

▲ **Figure 29–2** The fossilized arthropod *Marrella splendens* had body symmetry, segmentation, a skeleton, a front and a back end, and appendages adapted for many functions. **Applying Concepts** ***What type of symmetry does this fossil exhibit?***

Beginnings of Invertebrate Diversity Fossils from a few million years later—a short period in geological time—paint a radically different picture of invertebrate life. The Cambrian Period, which began 544 million years ago, is marked by an abundance of different fossils. Why the difference from earlier periods? By the Cambrian Period, some animals had evolved shells, skeletons, and other hard body parts—all of which are readily preserved in fossils. Suddenly, the fossil record provided a wealth of information about animal diversity, body plans, and adaptations to life. One of the best-known sites of Cambrian fossils is the Burgess Shale of Canada. A fossil from the Burgess Shale is shown in **Figure 29–2.**

You can see what some of the Burgess Shale animals may have looked like in **Figure 29–3.** Trilobites such as *Olenoides* moved along the ocean floor. *Wiwaxia* had two rows of long, pointed spikes. The annelid *Canadia,* like many annelids today, had prominent setae. *Anomalocaris,* the largest Burgess Shale fossil, had fearsome-looking forelimbs that were probably used to grasp prey. The animals of the Burgess Shale are far more numerous and diverse than anything that lived earlier.

In just a few million years, animals had evolved complex body plans. They acquired specialized cells, tissues, and organs. Because of the extraordinary growth in animal diversity, events of the early Cambrian Period are called the Cambrian Explosion. During that time, the ancestors of most modern animal phyla first appeared in the fossil record.

▼ **Figure 29–3** This illustration shows what some of the Cambrian organisms found in the Burgess Shale may have looked like. Note the wide variety of body shapes and appendages. **Observing** ***What body features of these animals are similar to those of modern invertebrates?***

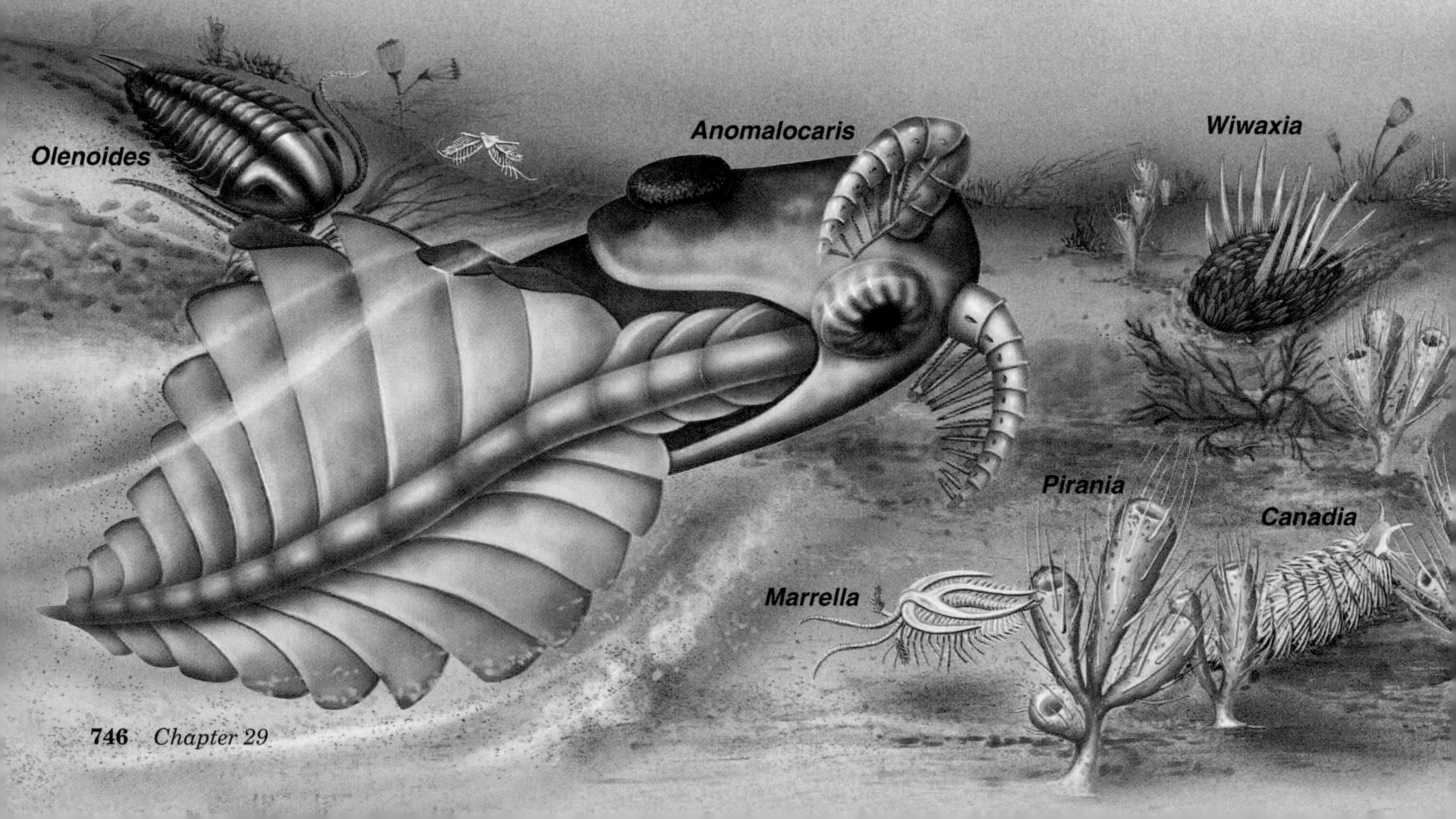

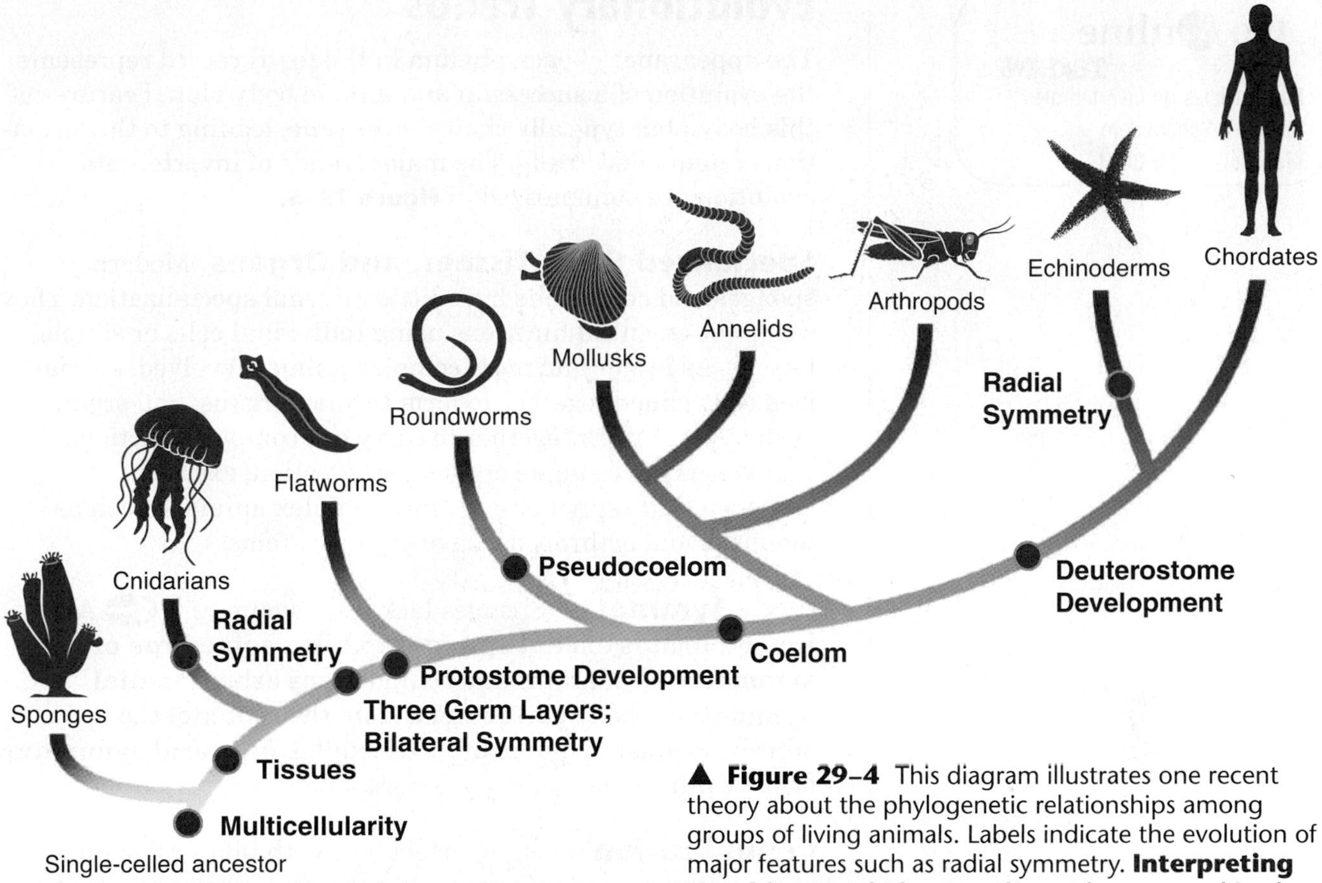

▲ **Figure 29–4** This diagram illustrates one recent theory about the phylogenetic relationships among groups of living animals. Labels indicate the evolution of major features such as radial symmetry. **Interpreting Graphics** *To which group of invertebrates are echinoderms least closely related?*

What features of the Cambrian animals made them so successful? One way of determining this is to find their common features—especially those that are present in animals today. The anatomies of Burgess Shale animals typically had body symmetry, segmentation, some type of skeleton, a front and a back end, and appendages adapted for many functions. These features are characteristic of most invertebrates living today.

Invertebrate Phylogeny

The diagram in **Figure 29–4** shows the evolutionary relationships among major groups of living invertebrates. It also indicates the sequence in which some important features evolved. These features include tissues and organs, patterns of early development, body symmetry, cephalization, segmentation, and the formation of three germ layers and a coelom. Many of these features, which have persisted up to modern times, evolved in animals of the Cambrian Period. As you review the major trends in invertebrate evolution, consider how each feature might have contributed to the evolutionary success of animals.

Word Origins

The word *germ* in the term *germ layers* comes from the Latin word *germen,* which means "embryo" or "sprout." **If the suffix *-ate* means "to become," what happens to a seed when it germinates?**

What groups of animals are deuterostomes?

For: Articles on invertebrates
Visit: PHSchool.com
Web Code: cbe-8291

Evolutionary Trends

The appearance of each phylum in the fossil record represents the evolution of a successful and unique body plan. Features of this body plan typically change over time, leading to the formation of many new traits. The major trends of invertebrate evolution are summarized in **Figure 29–5.**

Specialized Cells, Tissues, and Organs Modern sponges and cnidarians have little internal specialization. They carry out essential functions using individual cells or simple tissues. As larger and more complex animals evolved, specialized cells joined together to form tissues, organs, and organ systems that work together to carry out complex functions. Flatworms have simple organs for digestion, excretion, response, and reproduction. More complex animals, such as mollusks and arthropods, have organ systems.

Body Symmetry Sponges lack body symmetry. **All invertebrates except sponges exhibit some type of body symmetry.** Cnidarians and echinoderms exhibit **radial symmetry** —body parts extend from the center of the body. Worms, mollusks, and arthropods exhibit **bilateral symmetry,** or have mirror-image left and right sides.

Cephalization Most invertebrates with bilateral symmetry rely on movement for feeding, defense, and other important functions. The evolution of this body plan and lifestyle was accompanied by the trend toward **cephalization,** which is the concentration of sense organs and nerve cells in the front of the body. **Invertebrates with cephalization can respond to the environment in more sophisticated ways than can simpler invertebrates.** In most worms and arthropods, nerve cells are arranged in structures called ganglia. In more complex invertebrates, nerve cells form an organ called a brain.

How does cephalization benefit an animal?

Comparing Invertebrates

	Sponges	Cnidarians	Flatworms
Germ Layers	Absent	Two	Three
Body Symmetry	Absent	Radial	Bilateral
Cephalization	Absent	Absent	Present
Coelom	Absent	Absent	Absent
Early Development	——	——	Protostome

▶ **Figure 29–5** This table shows the major characteristics of the main groups of invertebrates. **Germ layers, body symmetry, cephalization, and development of a coelom are more common in complex invertebrates than in simple ones.** Mollusks, for example, have all of these features, but sponges have none of them.

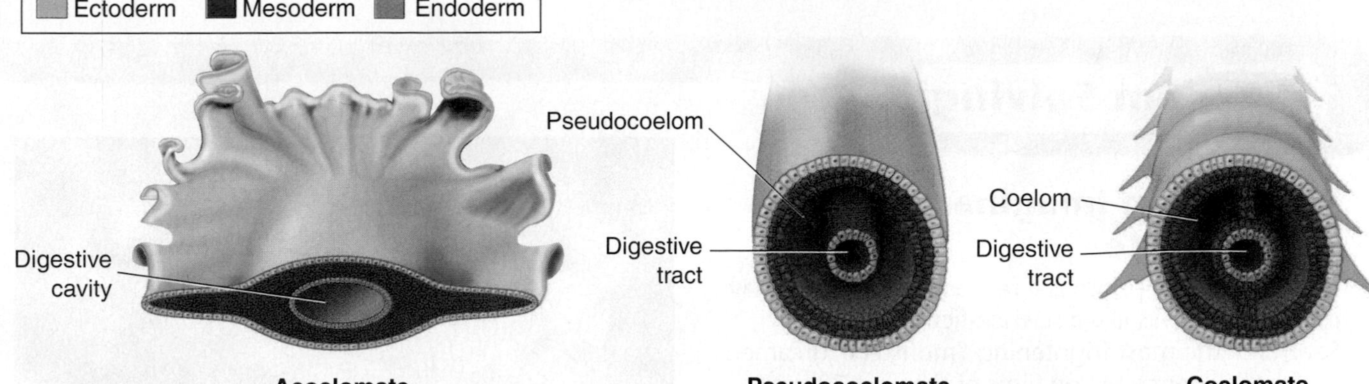

▲ **Figure 29–6** Acoelomates do not have a coelom, or body cavity, between their body wall and digestive cavity. Pseudocoelomates have body cavities that are partially lined with tissues from mesoderm. **Most complex animal phyla are coelomates, meaning that they have a true coelom that is lined completely with tissues from mesoderm.**

Segmentation Most invertebrates with bilateral symmetry also have segmented bodies. Over the course of evolution, different segments have often become specialized for specific functions. Because the same structures are repeated in each body segment, segmentation also allows an animal to increase in body size with a minimum of new genetic material.

Coelom Formation Cnidarians have a simple construction in which a jellylike layer lies between ectoderm and endoderm tissues. Other invertebrates develop from three germ layers, the endoderm, mesoderm, and ectoderm, as shown in **Figure 29–6.** Flatworms are acoelomates, meaning that no **coelom,** or body cavity, forms between the germ layers. Pseudocoelomates, such as roundworms, have a body cavity lined partially with mesoderm. **Most complex animal phyla have a true coelom that is lined completely with tissue derived from mesoderm.**

Embryological Development In most invertebrates, the zygote divides repeatedly to form a blastula—a hollow ball of cells. In protostomes, the blastopore, or the opening of the blastula, develops into a mouth. In deuterostomes, the blastopore forms an anus. Worms, arthropods, and mollusks are protostomes, and echinoderms (and chordates) are deuterostomes.

Roundworms	Annelids	Mollusks	Arthropods	Echinoderms
Three	Three	Three	Three	Three
Bilateral	Bilateral	Bilateral	Bilateral	Radial (adults)
Present	Present	Present	Present	Absent (adults)
Pseudocoelom	True coelom	True coelom	True coelom	True coelom
Protostome	Protostome	Protostome	Protostome	Deuterostome

Problem Solving

Creating an Imaginary Invertebrate

The moth in the photo is a real animal, but you may think that it looks like a science-fiction monster. Several of the most frightening "monsters" dreamed up for the science-fiction films of the past 20 years have actually been based on bits and pieces of anatomy and behavior of real invertebrates. Now that you have studied all the invertebrate phyla, try to create the "perfect invertebrate" for a habitat of your choice.

Defining the Problem First, choose a habitat: a temperate zone desert, a tropical coral reef, or inside the body of a mammal. Depending on which habitat you chose, define the environmental challenges (such as heat, cold, or lack of water) and the biological needs (such as food and oxygen) that your organism must meet.

Organizing Information Once you have defined the problem, look back over the characteristics of all the invertebrate groups you have studied, and pick the kind of body systems that you think would work best in your chosen habitat.

Creating a Solution Assemble the body systems you have chosen into an imaginary animal. Make sure that the systems you use can work in harmony. You could not, for example, expect an animal to breathe through its skin if it had an impermeable exoskeleton covering its entire body! Make sure that you have considered all the organism's needs. Give your animal an appropriate name.

Presenting Your Plan Create external and cutaway diagrams of your animal, including any larval stages. Label the diagrams, including the name of the real-life invertebrate system that fulfills each essential function. Conclude by describing the complete life cycle of your organism.

29–1 Section Assessment

1. **Key Concept** Describe three major trends in the evolution of invertebrates.
2. Compare the first multicellular animals with those of the Burgess Shale.
3. How was the evolution of internal specialization important to invertebrate form and function?
4. Compare the body structures and other characteristics of cnidarians and mollusks.
5. **Critical Thinking Observing** Observe the fossil of *Marrella splendens* in **Figure 29–2.** What evidence does the fossil exhibit of anatomical (structural) characteristics similar to those of present-day arthropods?

Writing in Science

Creative Writing

Imagine that you are one of the first paleontologists to find fossils in the Burgess Shale. Suppose that you have studied the fossils and compared them with earlier animal fossils such as the one in **Figure 29–1.** Write a report for a scientific journal about your discovery and its significance.

29–2 Form and Function in Invertebrates

4-2.1 Asexual reproduction
4-4.1 Sexual reproduction
LS- Make observations
LS- Follow safety rules

To survive, all animals perform the same essential tasks: feeding and digestion, respiration, circulation, excretion, response, movement, and reproduction. In many ways, each animal phylum represents an "experiment" in the adaptation of body structures to carry out these tasks. The appearance of each phylum in the fossil record, therefore, represents the evolutionary development of a unique body plan. The continued history of each phylum is the story of further evolutionary changes to that plan.

Biologists can learn a great deal about the nature of life by comparing body systems among groups of living invertebrates. Body systems that perform the essential tasks of life have taken many different forms in different phyla. Each phylum has a particular type of breathing device, a certain type of body support system, and numerous variations on other physiological functions. More complicated systems are not necessarily better than simpler ones. The fact that any system is found in living animals testifies to its success in performing functions. This section reviews the basic evolutionary trends in each body system, using examples from a variety of invertebrate groups.

Guide for Reading

Key Concept
- How do different invertebrate phyla carry out life functions?

Vocabulary
intracellular digestion
extracellular digestion
open circulatory system
closed circulatory system
hydrostatic skeleton
exoskeleton
endoskeleton
external fertilization
internal fertilization

Reading Strategy: Finding Main Ideas Before you read, skim the section to identify the key ideas. Then, carefully read the section, making a list of supporting details for each main idea.

Feeding and Digestion

Invertebrates have evolved many different ways of obtaining food. The spider in **Figure 29–7,** for example, is feeding on a caterpillar after killing it with venom. Before food can be used for energy, the food must be broken down, or digested. The digested food must then be absorbed into the animal's body. Complex animals accomplish the physiological process of digestion in different ways than simpler animals.

Intracellular and Extracellular Digestion Invertebrates have evolved different ways of digesting food. **The simplest animals break down food primarily through intracellular digestion, but more complex animals use extracellular digestion.** Sponges digest their food inside archaeocytes, which pass nutrients to other cells by diffusion. Because food is digested inside cells, this process is known as **intracellular digestion.** In contrast, mollusks, annelids, arthropods, and echinoderms rely almost entirely on extracellular digestion. In **extracellular digestion,** food is broken down outside the cells in a digestive cavity or tract and then absorbed into the body. Flatworms and cnidarians use both intracellular and extracellular digestion.

▶ **Figure 29–7** **Complex animals break down food using extracellular digestion.** The spider's venom is breaking down the tissues of the caterpillar. Later, the broken-down food molecules will be absorbed into the spider's digestive tract.

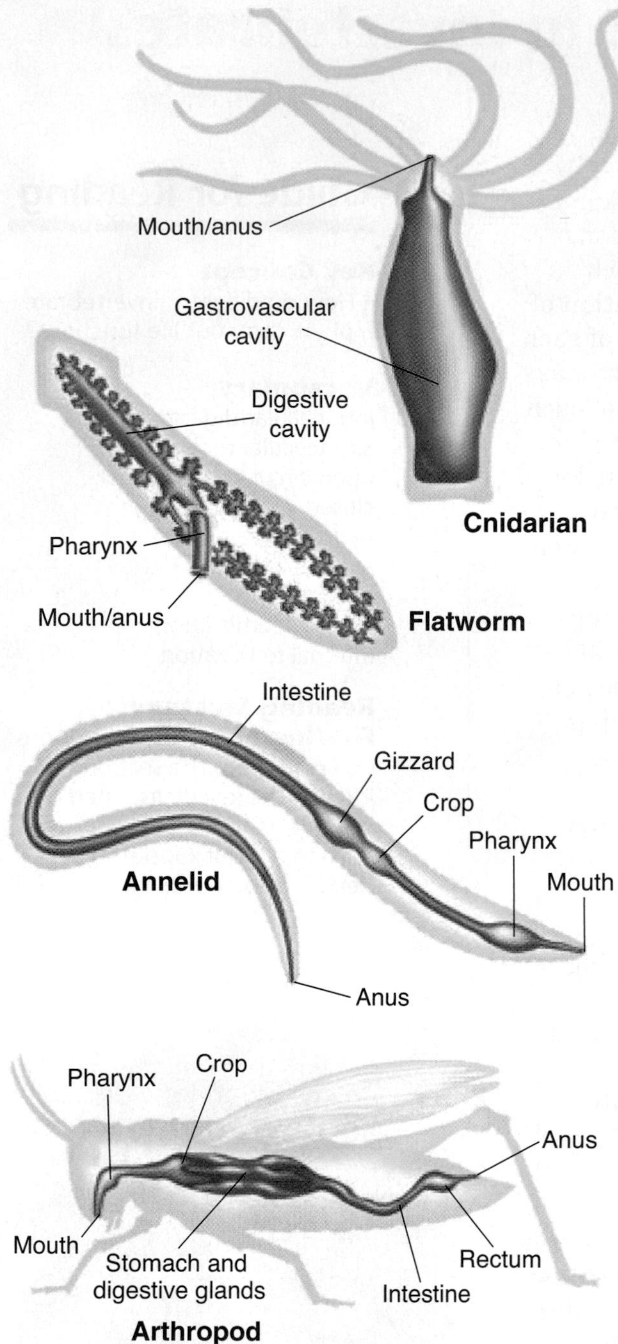

▲ **Figure 29–8** Cidarians and flatworms have a digestive system with only one opening. In more complex animals, the digestive system has two openings. In addition, the digestive organs have become more specialized. **Interpreting Graphics** *Which of these animals has the least specialized digestive system?*

Patterns of Extracellular Digestion

Invertebrates have a variety of digestive systems, as shown in **Figure 29–8.** Simple animals such as cnidarians and most flatworms ingest food and expel wastes through a single opening. Food is digested in a cavity through both extracellular and intracellular means. Some cells of the gastrovascular cavity secrete enzymes and absorb the digested food. Other cells surround food particles and digest them in vacuoles. Digested food then diffuses to cells throughout the body.

More-complex animals digest food in a tube called the digestive tract. Food enters the body through the mouth, and wastes leave through the anus. A one-way digestive tract (which is characteristic of roundworms, annelids, mollusks, arthropods, and echinoderms) often has specialized regions, such as a stomach and intestines. Specialization of the digestive tract allows food to be processed more efficiently, because each step in the process takes place in order, at a specific place along the digestive tract.

CHECKPOINT *What is the difference between intracellular digestion and extracellular digestion?*

Respiration

All animals must exchange oxygen and carbon dioxide with the environment. The more surface area that is exposed to the environment, the greater the amount of gas exchange that can occur. In addition, gases diffuse most efficiently across a thin, moist membrane. Given these principles, all respiratory systems share two basic features. **Respiratory organs have large surface areas that are in contact with the air or water. Also, for diffusion to occur the respiratory surfaces must be moist.**

Aquatic Invertebrates Aquatic animals, such as cnidarians and some flatworms, naturally have moist respiratory surfaces. Many animals even respire through their skins. However, for most active animals larger than worms, skin respiration alone is not sufficient. Aquatic mollusks, arthropods, and many annelids exchange gases through gills. Gills are feathery structures that expose a large surface area to the water. Gills are rich in blood vessels that bring blood close to the surface for gas exchange.

Quick Lab

How do clams and crayfishes breathe?

Materials live clam, food coloring, crayfish, small container of water

Procedure 

1. Do not touch the clam or crayfish. Put a drop of food coloring in the water near a clam's siphons. Observe what happens to the coloring.
2. Put a drop of food coloring in the water near the middle of a crayfish's carapace. **CAUTION:** *Keep your fingers away from the crayfish's pincers.* Observe what happens to the coloring.

Analyze and Conclude

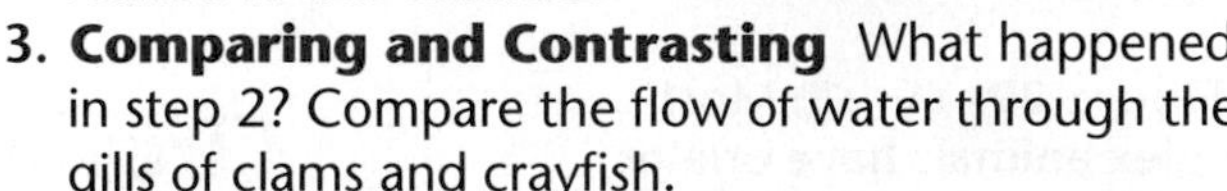

1. **Observing** Describe what happened to the coloring in step 1. How does water move through a clam's gills?
2. **Inferring** What is the clam's main defense? How is the location of the clam's siphons related to this defense?
3. **Comparing and Contrasting** What happened in step 2? Compare the flow of water through the gills of clams and crayfish.
4. **Inferring** Why do you think the crayfish has gills rather than spiracles, as some other arthropods do?

Terrestrial Invertebrates In terrestrial animals, respiratory surfaces are covered with water or mucus, thereby minimizing water loss. In addition, air is moistened as it travels through the body to the respiratory surface.

Terrestrial invertebrates have several types of respiratory surfaces. The mantle cavity of a land snail is a moist tissue that has an extensive surface area lined with blood vessels. Spiders respire using organs called book lungs, such as the one shown in **Figure 29–9.** Book lungs are made of parallel, sheetlike layers of thin tissues that contain blood vessels. In insects, air enters the body through openings called spiracles. It then enters a network of tracheal tubes, where gases diffuse in and out of surrounding body fluids.

CHECKPOINT ***How does respiration in aquatic invertebrates differ from respiration in terrestrial invertebrates?***

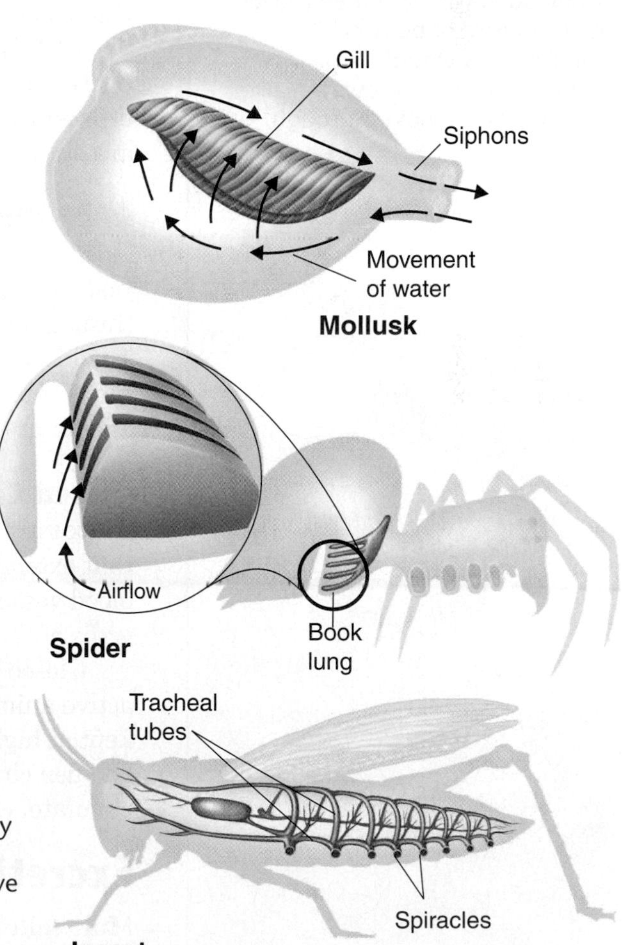

▶ **Figure 29–9** Invertebrates have a variety of respiratory structures. Clams and other aquatic mollusks have gills. Many spiders have book lungs. Grasshoppers and other insects have spiracles and tracheal tubes. **All respiratory organs have large, moist surface areas in contact with air or water.**

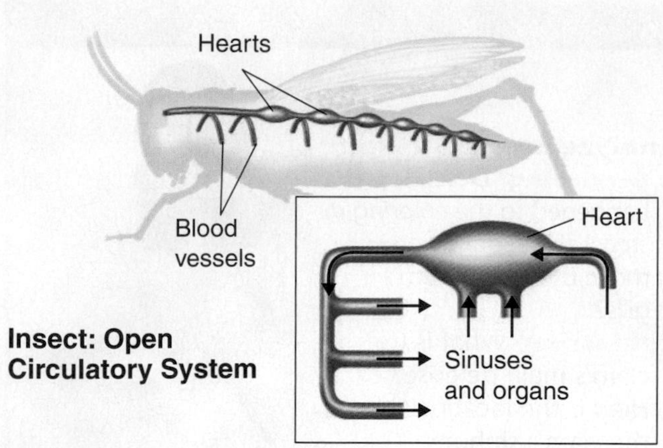

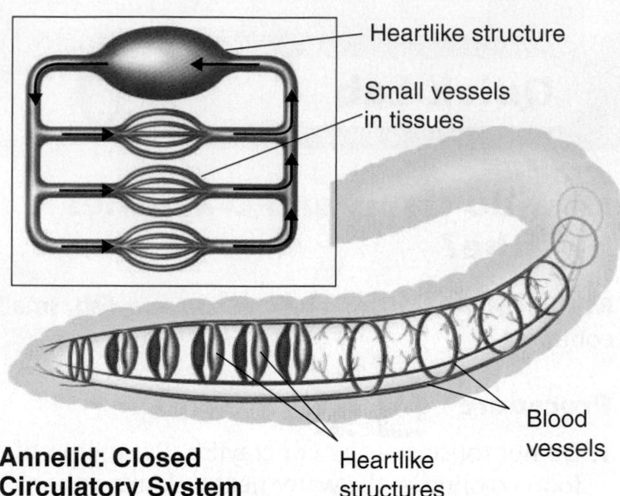

▲ **Figure 29–10** **Most complex animals have one or more hearts to move fluid through their bodies in either an open or a closed circulatory system.** An insect has an open circulatory system in which blood leaves blood vessels and then moves through sinuses, or body cavities. An annelid has a closed circulatory system in which blood stays in blood vessels as it moves through the body.

Circulation

All cells of multicellular animals require a constant supply of oxygen and nutrients, and cells must also remove metabolic wastes. The smallest and thinnest animals meet this requirement by simple diffusion between their body surface and the environment. But this system is usually insufficient for more complex animals. **Most complex animals move blood through their bodies using one or more hearts and either an open or a closed circulatory system.** Both types of circulatory systems are shown in **Figure 29–10.**

Open Circulatory Systems In an **open circulatory system,** blood is only partially contained within a system of blood vessels. Instead, one or more hearts or heartlike organs pump blood through blood vessels into a system of sinuses, or spongy cavities. The blood comes into direct contact with the tissues, collects in body sinuses, and eventually makes its way back to the heart. Open circulatory systems are found in arthropods and most mollusks.

Closed Circulatory Systems In a **closed circulatory system,** a heart or heartlike organ forces blood through vessels that extend throughout the body. The blood stays within these blood vessels. Materials reach body tissues by diffusing across the walls of the blood vessels.

Closed circulatory systems are characteristic of larger, more active animals. Because blood trapped within the blood vessels is kept at high pressure, it can be circulated more efficiently than in an open circulatory system. Among the invertebrates, closed circulatory systems are found in annelids and some mollusks.

Excretion

Multicellular animals must control the amount of water in their tissues. At the same time, all animals must get rid of ammonia. The excretory systems of invertebrates carry out these functions in a variety of ways as shown in **Figure 29–11.**

Most animals have an excretory system that rids the body of metabolic wastes while controlling the amount of water in the tissues.

In aquatic invertebrates, ammonia diffuses from their body tissues into the surrounding water. The water immediately dilutes the ammonia and carries it away. Flatworms use a network of flame cells to eliminate excess water. Fluid travels through execretory tubules and leaves the body through tiny pores in the animal's skin.

Terrestrial invertebrates must conserve water while removing nitrogenous wastes. To do this, many animals convert ammonia into a compound called urea. Urea is eliminated from the body in urine. Urine is highly concentrated, so little water is lost. In annelids and mollusks, urine forms in tubelike structures called nephridia. Fluid enters the nephridia through openings called nephrostomes. Urine leaves the body through excretory pores.

Some insects and arachnids have Malpighian tubules, saclike organs that convert ammonia into uric acid. Both uric acid and digestive wastes combine to form a thick paste that leaves the body through a structure called the rectum. Because the paste contains little water, this process also reduces water loss.

Go Online NSTA SCILINKS
For: Links on invertebrates
Visit: www.SciLinks.org
Web Code: cbn-8292

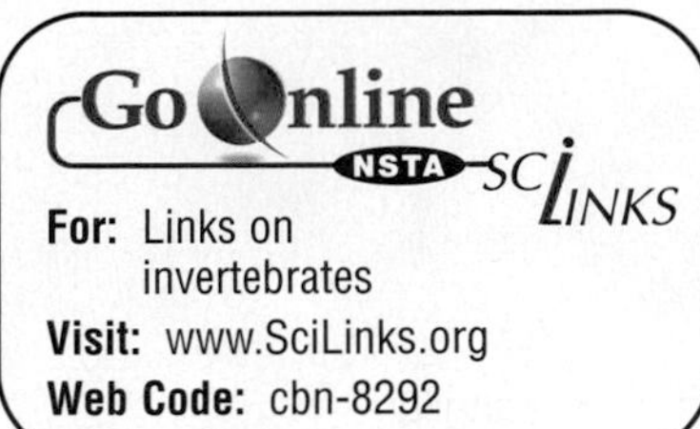

▼ Figure 29–11 Most animals dispose of wastes through excretory systems. Excretory systems also control an organism's water levels. Flatworms excrete ammonia directly into the water and use flame cells to remove excess water. Annelids use nephridia to convert ammonia into urea and to concentrate it in urine. Some arthropods have Malpighian tubules, which convert ammonia into uric acid. Uric acid is eliminated from the body in a paste.

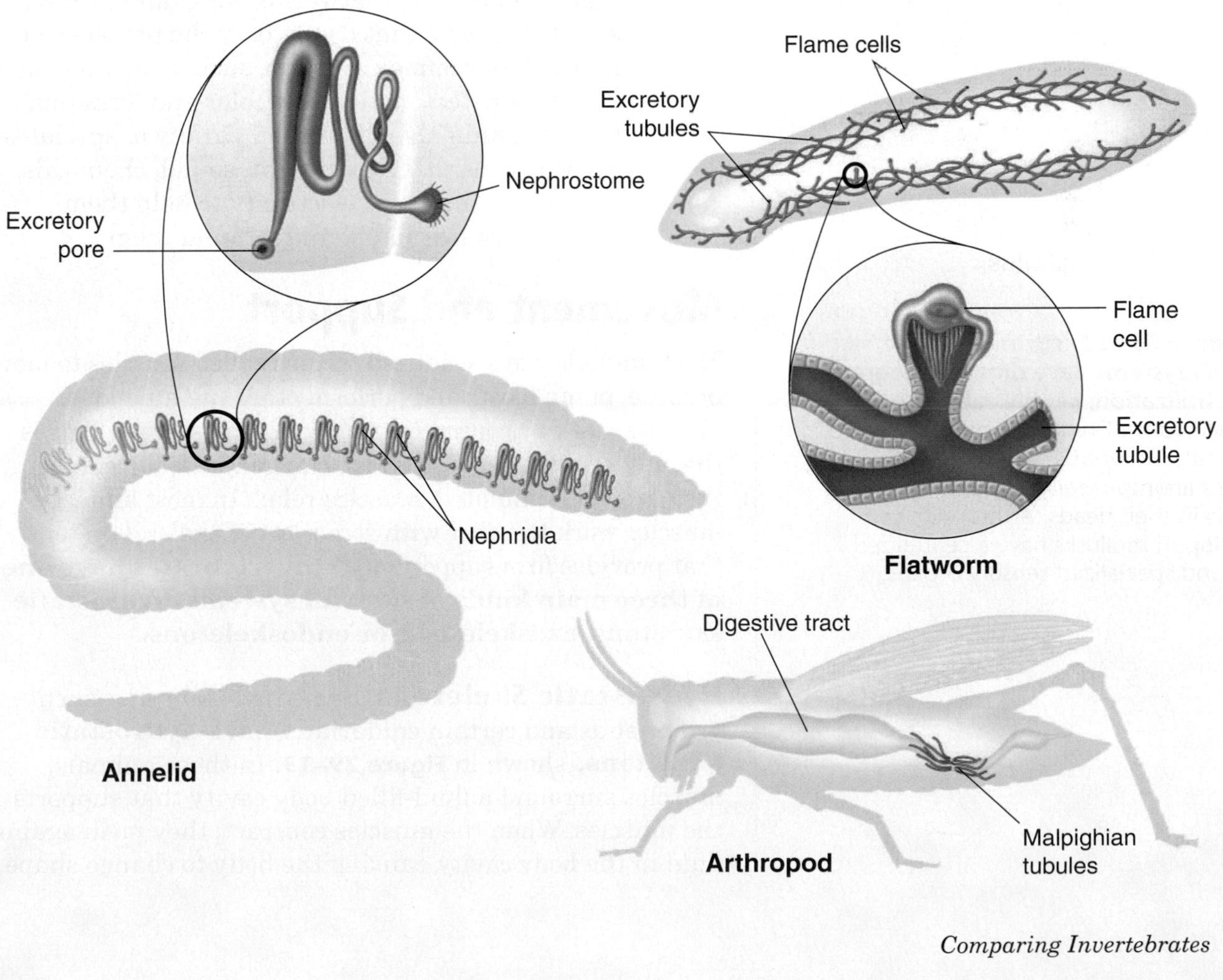

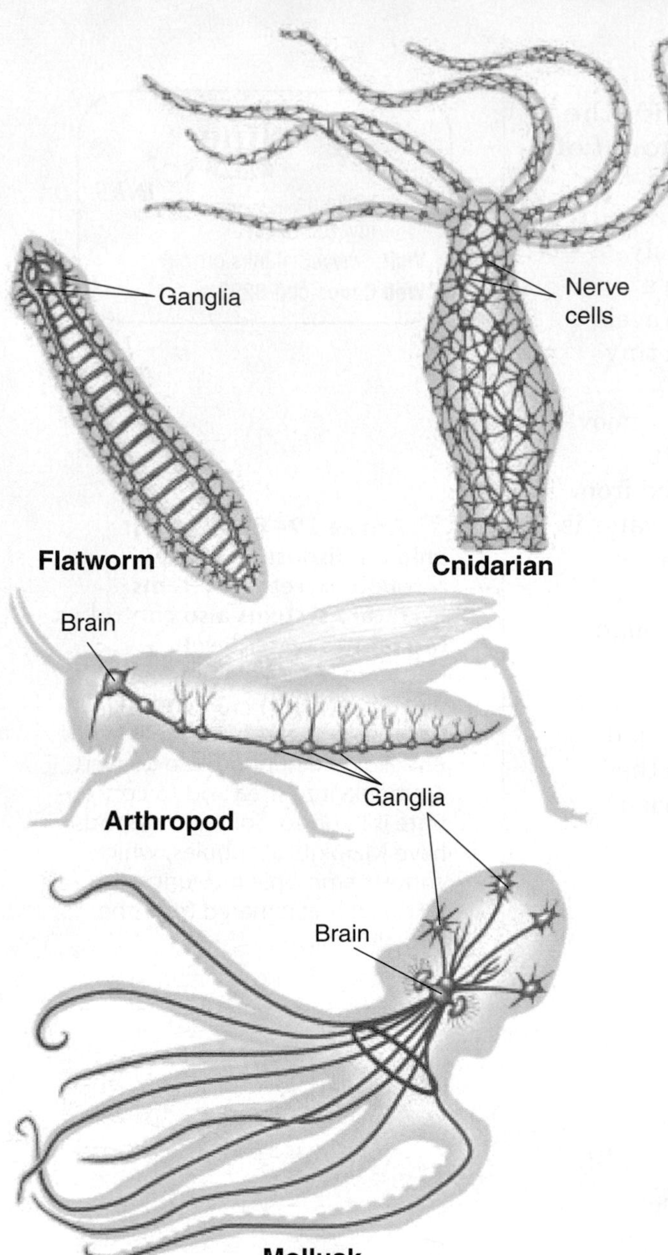

▲ **Figure 29–12** **Invertebrate nervous systems have different degrees of centralization, cephalization, and specialization.** Cnidarians have a simple nerve net. Flatworms, whose nervous systems are more centralized, have small ganglia in their heads. Arthropods and cephalopod mollusks have a centralized brain and specialized sensory organs.

Response

Nervous systems gather and process information from the environment and allow animals to respond appropriately. **Figure 29–12** shows the nervous system of four invertebrates. **Invertebrates show three trends in the evolution of the nervous system: centralization, cephalization, and specialization.** Different nervous systems have various degrees of each of these characteristics.

Centralization and Cephalization The simplest nervous systems, found in cnidarians, are called nerve nets. Nerve nets consist of individual nerve cells that form a netlike arrangement throughout the animal's body. In flatworms and roundworms, the nerve cells are more concentrated, or centralized. There are a few small clumps of nerve tissue, or ganglia, in the head. In cephalopod mollusks and arthropods, ganglia are organized into a brain that controls and coordinates the nervous system. This concentration of nerve tissue and organs in one end of the body is called cephalization.

Specialization The more complex an animal's nervous system is, the more developed its sense organs tend to be. Flatworms, for example, have simple eyespots that detect only the presence of light. More complex animals, such as insects, have eyes that detect motion and color and form images. Complex animals may have a variety of specialized sense organs that detect light, sound, chemicals, movement, and even electricity to help them discover what is happening around them.

Movement and Support

Most animals use specialized tissues called muscles to move, breathe, pump blood, and perform other life functions. Muscles work by contracting, or becoming shorter. This is the only way that muscle tissue can generate force. When they are not stimulated, muscles relax. In most animals, muscles work together with some sort of skeletal system that provides firm support. **Invertebrates have one of three main kinds of skeletal systems: hydrostatic skeletons, exoskeletons, or endoskeletons.**

Hydrostatic Skeletons Some invertebrates, such as annelids and certain cnidarians, have **hydrostatic skeletons,** shown in **Figure 29–13.** In these animals, muscles surround a fluid-filled body cavity that supports the muscles. When the muscles contract, they push against fluid in the body cavity, causing the body to change shape.

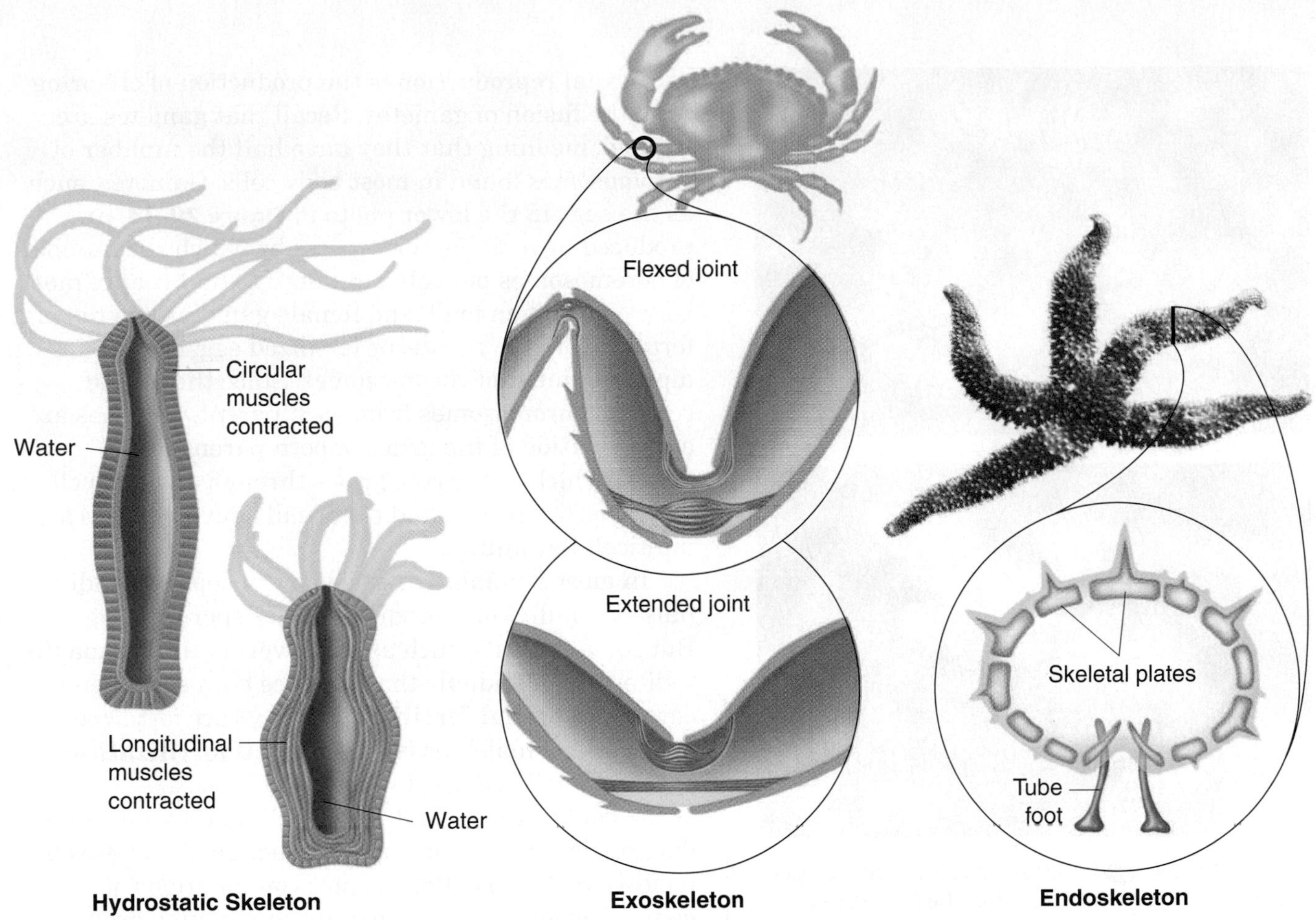

Exoskeletons In arthropods, the **exoskeleton,** or external skeleton, is a hard body covering made of chitin. Arthropods move by using muscles that are attached to the inside of the exoskeleton. These muscles bend and straighten different joints. The shells of some mollusks can also be considered exoskeletons. Muscles attached to the shell make it possible for snails to withdraw into their shells and for bivalves to close their shells.

Endoskeletons An **endoskeleton** is a structural support located inside the body. Sea stars and other echinoderms have an endoskeleton made of calcified plates. These plates function in support and protection, and also give these animals a bumpy and irregular texture. Vertebrates also have endoskeletons.

▲ **Figure 29–13** **The three main types of invertebrate skeletons are hydrostatic skeletons, exoskeletons, and endoskeletons.** In animals with hydrostatic skeletons, muscles contract against a fluid-filled body cavity. In animals with exoskeletons, the muscles pull against the insides of the exoskeleton. Echinoderms and some sponges have endoskeletons.

Sexual and Asexual Reproduction

Most invertebrates reproduce sexually during at least part of their life cycle. Depending on environmental conditions, however, many invertebrates may also reproduce asexually. Each form of reproduction has advantages and disadvantages. Asexual reproduction allows animals to reproduce rapidly and take advantage of favorable conditions in the environment. Sexual reproduction, in contrast, maintains genetic diversity in a population by creating individuals with new combinations of genes.

Figure 29–14 **Invertebrates may reproduce asexually or sexually.** Note that the largest sea anemone in this group is undergoing asexual reproduction by splitting into two parts (top). The *Acorpora* coral (bottom) is releasing brown eggs into the water. The eggs will be fertilized externally. This is an example of sexual reproduction.

Sexual reproduction is the production of offspring from the fusion of gametes. Recall that gametes are haploid, meaning that they have half the number of chromosomes found in most body cells. Gametes, such as the eggs in the lower photo in **Figure 29–14,** are produced by meiosis, the process by which the number of chromosomes per cell is reduced to half that of most body cells. When male and female gametes join during fertilization, the zygote, or fertilized egg, has the diploid number of chromosomes. Since the zygote received chromosomes from each parent, its genes are a combination of the genes of both parents. The zygote, which is one cell, grows through ongoing cell divisions, or mitosis, and eventually develops into a multicellular animal.

In most animals, the sexes are in separate individuals—an individual produces either sperm or eggs. But some animals, such as earthworms, are hermaphrodites, or individuals that produce both sperm and eggs. In **external fertilization,** eggs are fertilized outside the female's body. In **internal fertilization,** eggs are fertilized inside the female's body.

In contrast to sexual reproduction, asexual reproduction does not involve the production of gametes by meiosis or the formation of new combinations of genes. The offspring of asexual reproduction grow into multicellular organisms by mitosis of diploid cells. In asexual reproduction, all the offspring are genetically identical to the parent. Asexual reproduction sometimes occurs through budding, in which new individuals are produced by outgrowths of the body wall. Some animals reproduce asexually by dividing in two.

29–2 Section Assessment

1. **Key Concept** In your own words, describe the evolution of three different body systems of invertebrates.
2. **Key Concept** Compare asexual and sexual reproduction. What are the advantages and disadvantages of each?
3. Compare circulation in annelids and arthropods.
4. What are the three main kinds of skeletal systems in invertebrates?
5. **Critical Thinking Applying Concepts** List the three forms of nitrogenous wastes excreted by animals. How are the ways in which animals dispose of these wastes related to each animal's environment?

Thinking Visually

Creating a Venn Diagram

Create a Venn diagram that compares and contrasts open and closed circulatory systems. Be sure to include similarities as well as differences. In your Venn diagram, identify some kinds of animals that have each type of circulatory system.

Investigating Invertebrate Responses to External Stimuli

The responses of animals to external stimuli depend on their nervous systems. In this investigation, you will design experiments to test the responses of three invertebrates to touch and food.

Problem

How do the responses of invertebrates to external stimuli relate to the structures of their nervous systems?

Materials

- dropper pipette
- hydra culture
- watch glass
- dissecting microscope
- blunt metal probe
- planarian
- petri dish
- crayfish
- brine shrimp
- cooked egg yolk
- slice of bologna

Skills

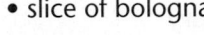

Formulating Hypotheses, Observing

Design Your Experiment

1. Use a dropper pipette to transfer a hydra and some water to the center of a watch glass or petri dish. Do not touch the hydra.
2. Place the watch glass or petri dish on the stage of a dissecting microscope and observe the hydra's movements for a few minutes.
3. With a blunt metal probe, gently touch one of the hydra's tentacles from several directions. Observe and record the hydra's responses to this stimulus. Return the hydra to its culture.
4. Design experiments to determine how a planarian and a crayfish respond to touch. Refer to the Lab Tips box on page 55. Include touching both ends of each animal in your plan.
5. Now design another set of experiments to determine how each animal will respond to food. Hydras will consume brine shrimp, planarians will eat cooked egg yolk, and crayfish will eat small pieces of bologna.
6. **Predicting** For each experiment you plan, write your prediction of the result. After your teacher approves your plan, carry out the experiments you have designed. Wear plastic gloves while handling the animals, and handle them gently. Record your observations. Wash your hands with soap and warm water before leaving the lab.

Analyze and Conclude

1. **Comparing and Contrasting** Describe how each animal responded to touch. How were the responses of the animals related to the direction from which they were touched? What, if any, were the differences among the animals?
2. **Drawing Conclusions** Which animal displayed the most specific response to touch? Explain your answer in terms of the animals' nervous systems.
3. **Comparing and Contrasting** Describe how each animal responded to its food. Did your results support your hypothesis? How do each animal's responses relate to the structure of its nervous system?
4. **Drawing Conclusions** Which of these animals shows cephalization? Relate your answer to each animal's behavior.

Go Further

Designing Experiments Design similar experiments using other invertebrates such as sponges or earthworms. Obtain your teacher's permission before carrying out the experiments.

Chapter 29 Study Guide

29–1 Invertebrate Evolution

Key Concepts

- As animals became larger and more complex, specialized cells joined together to form tissues, organs, and organ systems that work together to carry out complex functions.
- All invertebrates except sponges exhibit some type of body symmetry—either radial symmetry or bilateral symmetry.
- Invertebrates with cephalization can respond to the environment in more sophisticated ways than can simpler invertebrates.
- Most invertebrates with bilateral symmetry also have segmented bodies. Over the course of evolution, different segments have often become specialized for specific functions.
- Most animal phyla have a true coelom that is lined completely with tissue derived from mesoderm.
- Worms, arthropods, and mollusks are protostomes, and echinoderms are deuterostomes.

Vocabulary
radial symmetry, p. 748
bilateral symmetry, p. 748
cephalization, p. 748
coelom, p. 749

29–2 Form and Function in Invertebrates

Key Concepts

- The simplest animals break down food primarily through intracellular digestion, but more complex animals use extracellular digestion.
- Respiratory organs have large surface areas that are in contact with the air or water. In order for diffusion to occur, these respiratory surfaces must be kept moist.
- Most complex animals move blood through their bodies using one or more hearts and either an open or a closed circulatory system.
- Most animals have an excretory system that rids the body of metabolic wastes and controls the amount of water in their tissues.
- Invertebrates show three trends in the evolution of the nervous system: centralization, cephalization, and specialization.
- Invertebrates have one of three main kinds of skeletal systems: hydrostatic skeletons, exoskeletons, or endoskeletons.
- Most invertebrates reproduce sexually during at least part of their life cycle. Depending on environmental conditions, however, many invertebrates also reproduce asexually.

Vocabulary
intracellular digestion, p. 751
extracellular digestion, p. 751
open circulatory system, p. 754
closed circulatory system, p. 754
hydrostatic skeleton, p. 756
exoskeleton, p. 757
endoskeleton, p. 757
external fertilization, p. 758
internal fertilization, p. 758

Thinking Visually

Create two flowcharts describing the steps in the digestion of food. One flowchart should describe digestion in a hydra. The second flowchart should describe digestion in an earthworm.

Preparing for the Living Environment Exam

Blue questions emphasize Regents Exam content

Chapter 29

Part A

Multiple Choice

For each statement or question, select the number of the word or expression that, of those given, best completes the statement or answers the question.

1 Roundworms are classified as
(1) acoelomates (3) deuterostomes
(2) coelomates (4) pseudocoelomates

2 Which animal relies primarily on intracellular digestion?
(1) sponge (3) dragonfly
(2) clam (4) earthworm

3 Grasshoppers possess several organ systems that help them effectively perform the same essential tasks as all other animals. Which organ system is shown in the illustration below?

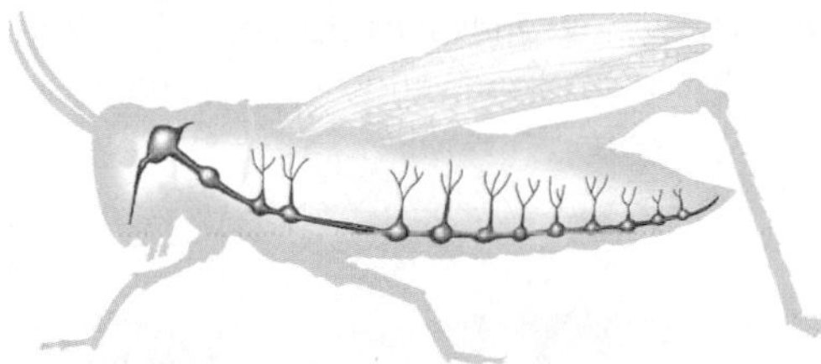

(1) digestive (3) excretory
(2) circulatory (4) nervous

4 In order for the exchange of oxygen and carbon dioxide to take place, an animal's respiratory surfaces must be
(1) thin and moist
(2) thick and dry
(3) thick and moist
(4) thin and dry

5 Which statement best describes a closed circulatory system?
(1) The blood comes in direct contact with tissues.
(2) The blood remains within blood vessels.
(3) The blood empties into body cavities called sinuses.
(4) The blood does not transport oxygen.

6 Malpighian tubules convert nitrogenous wastes into
(1) urine (3) uric acid
(2) ammonia (4) urea

7 The simplest type of nervous system is found in cnidarians. This system is called
(1) nerve net (3) ganglia network
(2) motor neurons (4) sensory neurons

8 Which term best describes an individual animal that produces both sperm and eggs?
(1) gamete
(2) hermaphrodite
(3) bud
(4) fragment

9 During invertebrate evolution, which trend did *not* occur?
(1) specialization of cells
(2) loss of a true coelom
(3) segmentation of bodies
(4) cephalization

10 All animals have some form of body symmetry *except* the
(1) sponges (3) worms
(2) jellyfishes (4) arthropods

11 Which activity is most closely associated with the excretory system?
(1) supplying cells with oxygen and nutrients
(2) ridding the body of metabolic wastes
(3) exchanging oxygen and carbon dioxide with the environment
(4) gathering information from the environment

12 The concentration of nerve tissue and organs in one end of an animal's body is called
(1) cephalization (3) body symmetry
(2) segmentation (4) diffusion

13 Which groups of invertebrates have a mesoderm?
(1) jellyfishes and arthropods
(2) earthworms and echinoderms
(3) echinoderms and jellyfishes
(4) sponges and roundworms

Test-Taking Tip Before taking a standardized test, it helps to become familiar with the format of the test, including the different question types. One method for this is to complete practice tests, such as this one. Even if you have practiced for a standardized test, be sure to read the direction lines carefully before you begin.

Preparing for the Living Environment Exam

Part B

Multiple Choice and Extended Response

For those questions that ask you to select a response, choose the one that best completes the statement or answers the question. For all others follow the directions given.

Base your answers to questions 14 and 15 on the information and diagram below and on your knowledge of biology.

A biology student wanted to find out if changing the temperature of an earthworm's environment would result in a corresponding change in heart rate. The student decided to set up two containers of worms kept at different temperatures, as shown below. To determine the number of heartbeats per minute, the student removed one worm at a time from each container and counted heartbeats through a stereomicroscope.

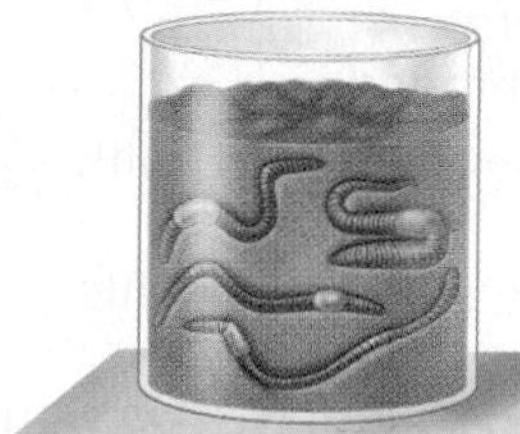

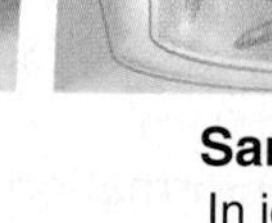

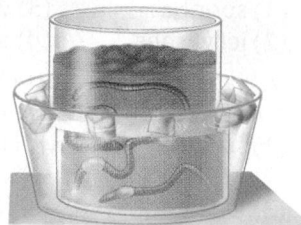

Sample A:
At temperature of worms' soil environment

Sample B:
In ice water

14 After examining the two containers of worms, it can be concluded that
(1) Sample A is the control
(2) Sample B is the control
(3) either sample can serve as the control
(4) this is not a controlled experiment

15 The student found that the worms in Sample A have a faster heart rate than the worms in Sample B. Based on this observation, an appropriate conclusion would be that
(1) the worms in Sample A are healthier than the worms in Sample B
(2) there is no relationship between body temperature and heart rate
(3) with a decrease in body temperature, there is a corresponding increase in heart rate
(4) with a decrease in body temperature, there is a corresponding decrease in heart rate

16 Describe the *two* types of circulatory systems. Give an example of an animal that has each type.

17 State the *three* major trends observed in the evolution of invertebrate nervous systems.

18 Compare and contrast internal and external fertilization.

19 The excretory systems of terrestrial invertebrates, such as earthworms, convert ammonia into less toxic components. State why this conversion is unnecessary in small aquatic invertebrates, such as planarians.

20 The external surface of slugs is slimy. Identify *two* adaptive advantages of this characteristic.

21 Animals with cephalization have sense organs concentrated in the anterior end. State *two* actions that animals with cephalization are capable of that would be difficult or even impossible for animals without cephalization.

Base your answers to questions 22 and 23 on the illustration below and your knowledge of biology.

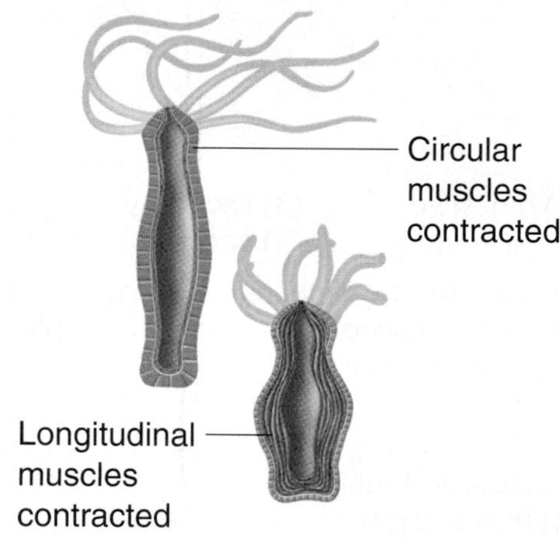

22 Identify the type of skeleton illustrated in the diagrams.

23 Explain how this type of skeleton functions.

24 State the effect on a flatworm if its flame cells were damaged. Support your answer with an explanation.

Part C

Multiple Choice and Extended Response
Answer the questions or follow the directions given.

25 Compare asexual reproduction with sexual reproduction. In the comparison, you should:
- state one way that both methods are similar
- state *two* ways that the two methods are different
- identify one organism that uses asexual reproduction
- identify one organism that uses sexual reproduction

26 Almost all animals exhibit some type of body symmetry. Describe the *two* major forms of body symmetry seen in invertebrates. In your description, be sure to include
- the name used for each type of symmetry
- a description of the advantages provided by each type of symmetry
- an example of an organism exhibiting each type of symmetry

27 A specific organ system of the grasshopper is shown in the diagram below.

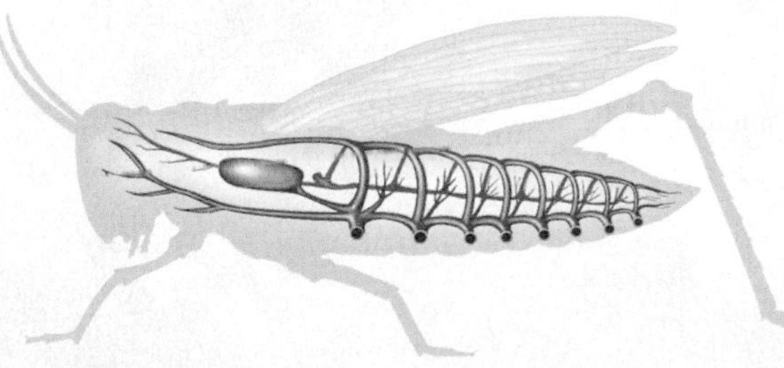

Explain the functioning of this organ system. In your answer, be sure to:
- identify the life function carried out by this organ system
- identify *two* specific structures that are part of this organ system
- explain the function of each of the two structures you identify

28 The terms *acoelomate, pseudocoelomate,* and *coelomate* represent three different body plans of organisms. Compare these *three* body plans. In your comparison, be sure to
- describe how the three body plans differ, including the location of the mesoderm
- provide an example of a group of organisms that exhibits each body plan

29 Gills and book lungs are two types of respiratory structures used by invertebrates for gas exchange. Describe how these respiratory structures function in the process of gas exchange. In your answer, be sure to:
- state the *two* main features common to all respiratory organs
- explain how gills function in gas exchange, and identify one organism that uses gills for its respiration
- explain how book lungs function in gas exchange, and identify one organism that uses book lungs for respiration

30 Digestive systems in animals vary in structure from the gastrovascular cavity of cnidaria and flatworms to the digestive tract of annelids and arthropods. Compare the functioning of these *two* types of digestive system. In your answer, be sure to:
- compare how food moves into and out of the two types of digestive system
- compare the processes of intracellular digestion and extracellular digestion
- explain how the system found in the more complex animals is more efficient in digesting food

For: An interactive self-test
Visit: PHSchool.com
Web Code: cba-8290

UNIT 9

Chordates

Chapters

The greater bulldog bat (*Noctilio leporinus*), which is found in Mexico, Argentina, Brazil, and the Bahamas, is one of only a few bat species that catch and eat fish.

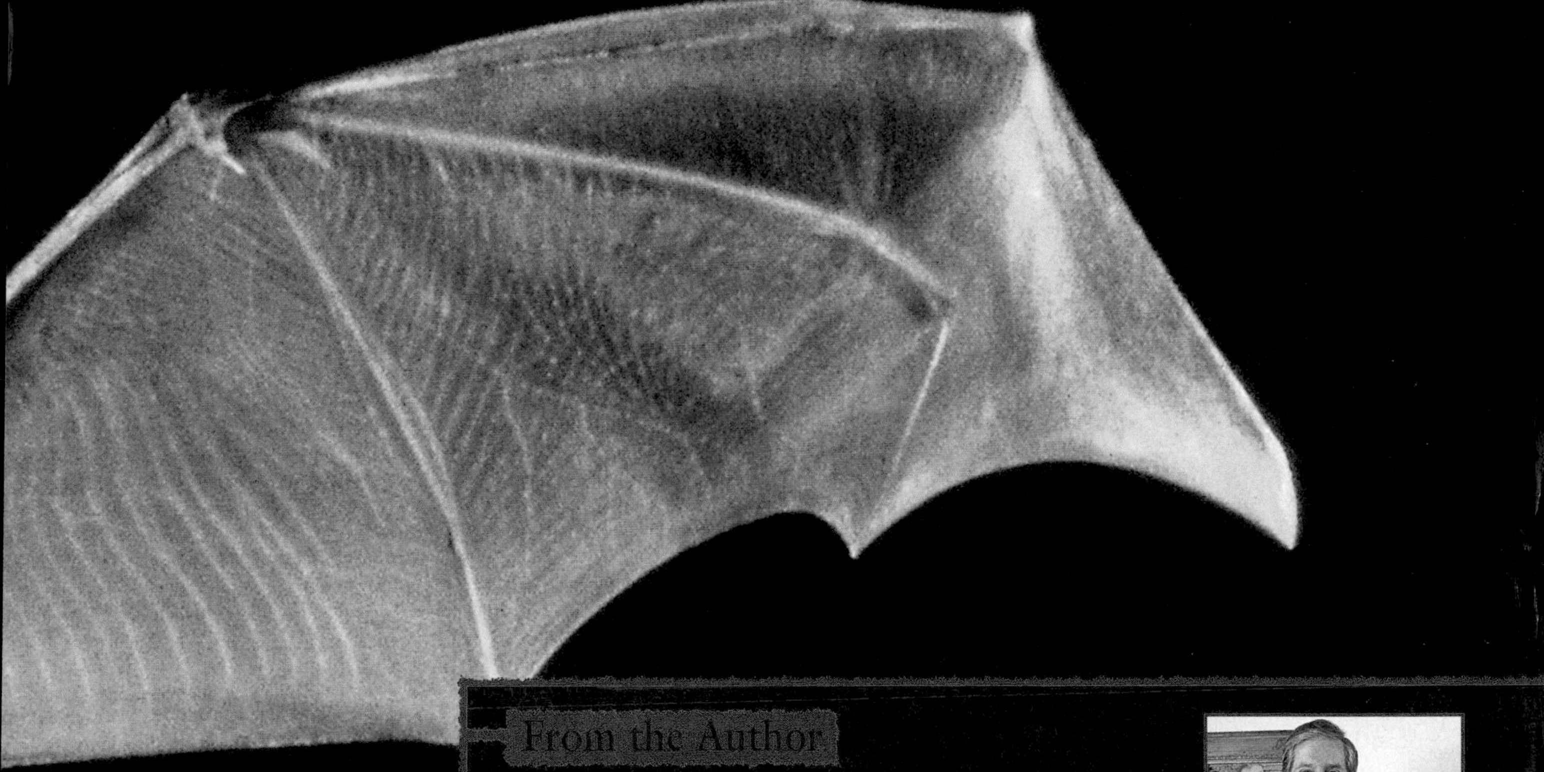

From the Author

What are my favorite animals? Fishes! It started when I won a goldfish at a county fair when I was nine years old—and my parents let me keep him. We lived in an apartment building that didn't allow other pets, so I couldn't have a dog, cat, or bird. I ended up falling for fishes. Years later, when my folks sent me off to college, they thought I was headed for medical school. But, after finally earning my PhD, I chose to work in the Fish Department at Harvard University! And "fish people" are still my favorite scientists!

Joe Levine

What discoveries lie ahead?

- What environmental factors are causing declines in amphibian populations—and what do those declines mean for the health of ecosystems?
- Just how and when did the first four-limbed vertebrates leave the water for land?

For: Latest discoveries
Visit: PHSchool.com
Web Code: cbe-9000

CHAPTER 30

Nonvertebrate Chordates, Fishes, and Amphibians

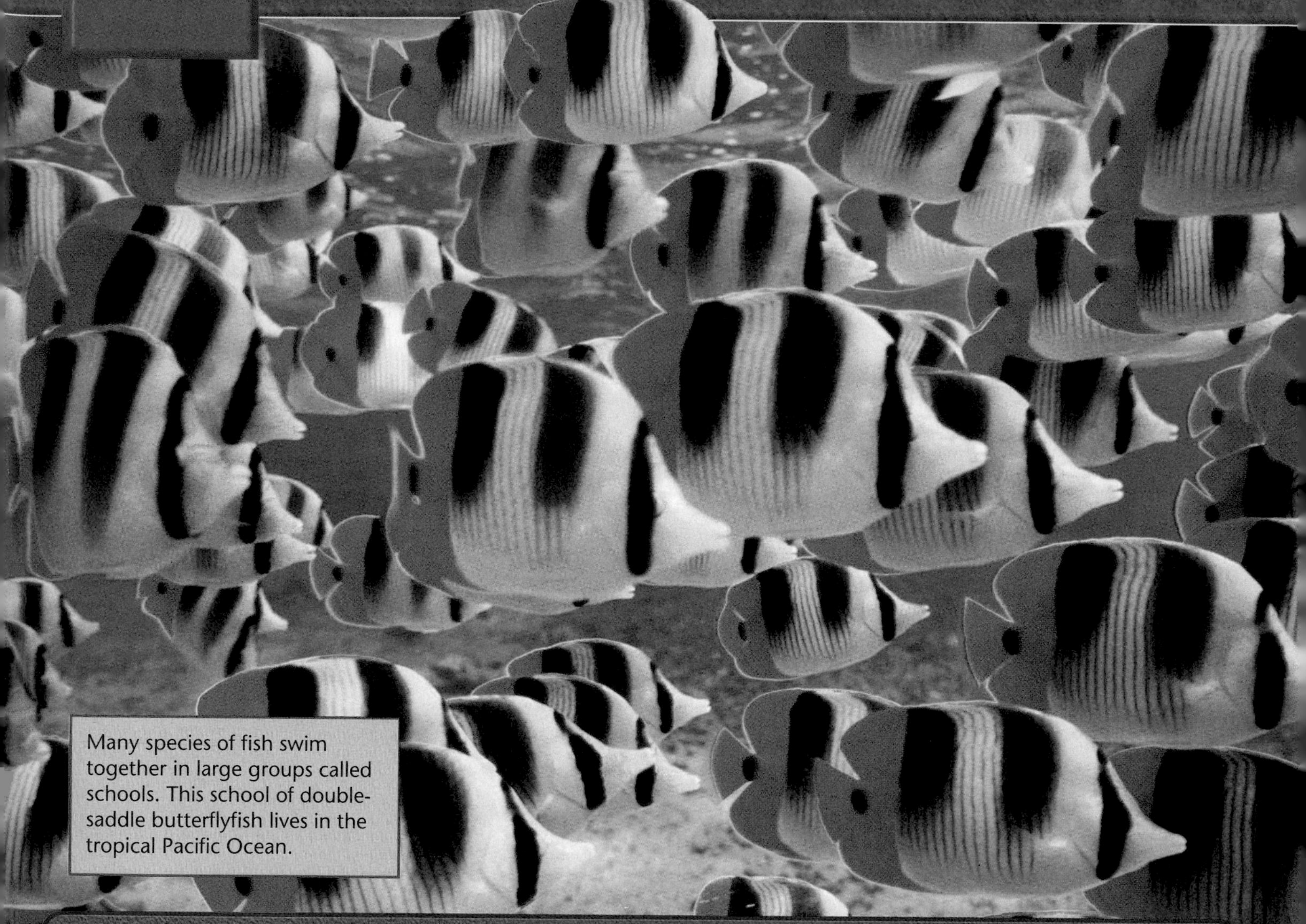

Many species of fish swim together in large groups called schools. This school of double-saddle butterflyfish lives in the tropical Pacific Ocean.

Inquiry Activity

Is a lancelet a fish?

Procedure  

1. Put on plastic gloves. Closely examine a fish, using a hand lens if you like. Also look at a dissected fish. List the main characteristics of fishes.
2. Now, closely examine a preserved lancelet and a dissected lancelet. List the characteristics of lancelets. Wash your hands with soap and warm water.

Think About It

1. **Comparing and Contrasting** How are the fish and the lancelet similar? How are they different from each other?
2. **Classifying** Not all fishes have jaws or scales. Given this information, do you think the lancelet is a type of fish? Explain your answer.

30–1 The Chordates

4-3.1 Earth's species developed from earlier species
4-3.1 Natural selection and evolution
4-3.1 Evolutionary changes
LS- Make observations

Guide for Reading

 **Key Concepts**

- What characteristics do all chordates share?
- What are the two groups of nonvertebrate chordates?

Vocabulary
chordate
notochord
pharyngeal pouch
vertebra

Reading Strategy: Building Vocabulary
Before you read, preview new vocabulary by skimming the section and making a list of the highlighted, boldface terms. As you read, make notes next to each term.

At first glance, fishes, amphibians, reptiles, birds, and mammals appear to be very different from one another. Some have feathers; others have fins. Some fly; others swim or crawl. These variations are some of the characteristics that biologists use to separate these animals into different classes, yet all are members of the phylum Chordata (kawr-DAHT-uh).

What Is a Chordate?

Members of the phylum Chordata are called **chordates** (KAWR-dayts). To be classified as a chordate, an animal must have four key characteristics, although these characteristics need not be present during the entire life cycle. **A chordate is an animal that has, for at least some stage of its life, a dorsal, hollow nerve cord; a notochord; pharyngeal (fuh-RIN-jee-ul) pouches; and a tail that extends beyond the anus.** Refer to **Figure 30–1** as you read about each of these characteristics.

The hollow nerve cord runs along the dorsal (back) part of the body. Nerves branch from this cord at regular intervals and connect to internal organs, muscles, and sense organs.

The **notochord** is a long supporting rod that runs through the body just below the nerve cord. Most chordates have a notochord only when they are embryos.

Pharyngeal pouches are paired structures in the throat (pharynx) region. In some chordates—such as fishes and amphibians—slits develop that connect the pharyngeal pouches to the outside of the body. These slits may then develop gills that are used for gas exchange.

At some point in their lives, all chordates have a tail that extends beyond the anus. The tail can contain bone and muscle and is used in swimming by many aquatic species.

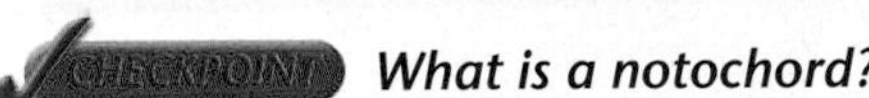

What is a notochord?

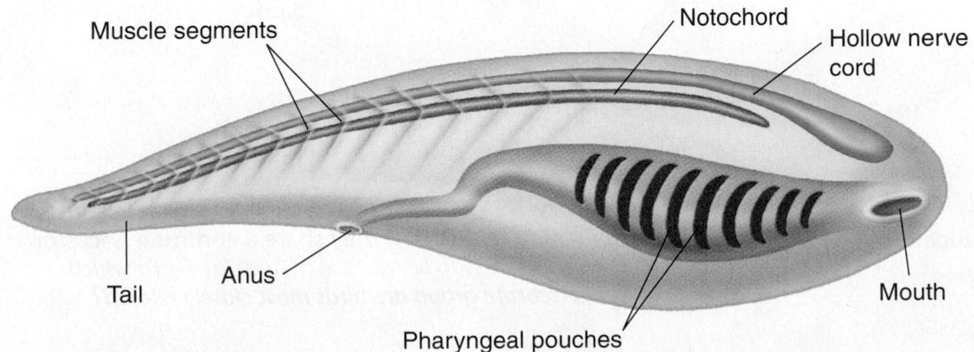

◀ **Figure 30–1 All chordates share four characteristics: a dorsal, hollow nerve cord; a notochord; pharyngeal pouches; and a tail that extends beyond the anus.** Some chordates possess all these characteristics as adults; others possess them only as embryos.

Most Chordates Are Vertebrates

The diagram in **Figure 30–2** shows the current understanding of the phylogeny, or evolutionary relationships, of chordates. About 96 percent of all chordate species are placed in the subphylum Vertebrata and are called vertebrates. Most vertebrates have a strong supporting structure known as the vertebral column, or backbone. In vertebrates, the dorsal, hollow nerve cord is called the spinal cord. As a vertebrate embryo develops, the front end of the spinal cord grows into a brain. The backbone, which replaces the notochord in most developing vertebrates, is made of individual segments called **vertebrae** (singular: vertebra). In addition to providing support, vertebrae enclose and protect the spinal cord.

A vertebrate's backbone is part of an endoskeleton, or internal skeleton. Like an arthropod's exoskeleton, a vertebrate's endoskeleton supports and protects the animal's body and gives muscles a place to attach. However, unlike an arthropod's exoskeleton, a vertebrate's skeleton grows as the animal grows and does not need to be shed periodically. In addition, whereas an arthropod's skeleton is made entirely of nonliving material, a vertebrate's skeleton contains living cells as well as nonliving material. The cells produce the nonliving material in the skeleton.

CHECKPOINT ***What is the function of the vertebral column?***

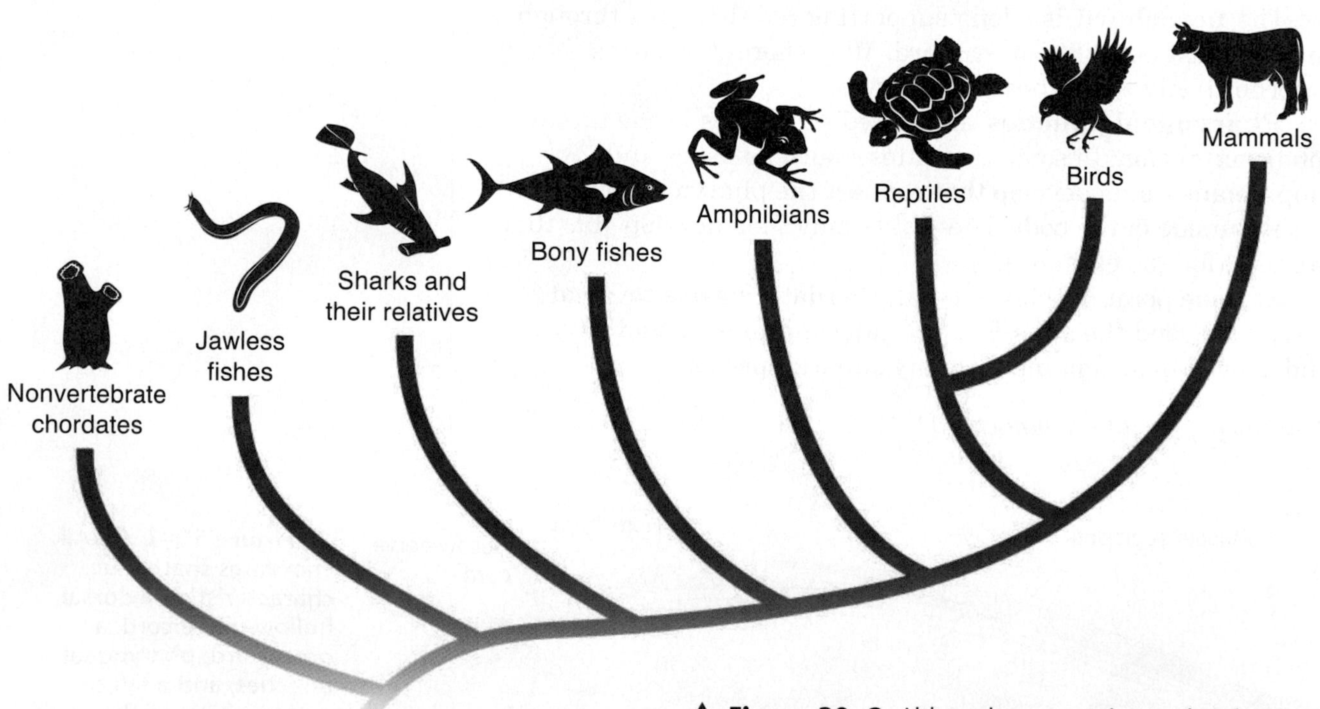

▲ **Figure 30–2** Although nonvertebrate chordates lack a vertebral column, they share a common ancestor with vertebrates. **Interpreting Graphics** *To which other vertebrate group are birds most closely related?*

▼ **Figure 30–3** **Tunicates are one of two groups of nonvertebrate chordates.** The tadpole-shaped tunicate larva (left) has all four chordate characteristics. When most tunicate larvae grow into adults, they lose their tails and attach to a solid surface. Adult tunicates (right) look nothing like the larvae, or even like other adult chordates. Both larvae and adults are filter feeders. The blue arrows show where water enters and leaves the tunicate's body.

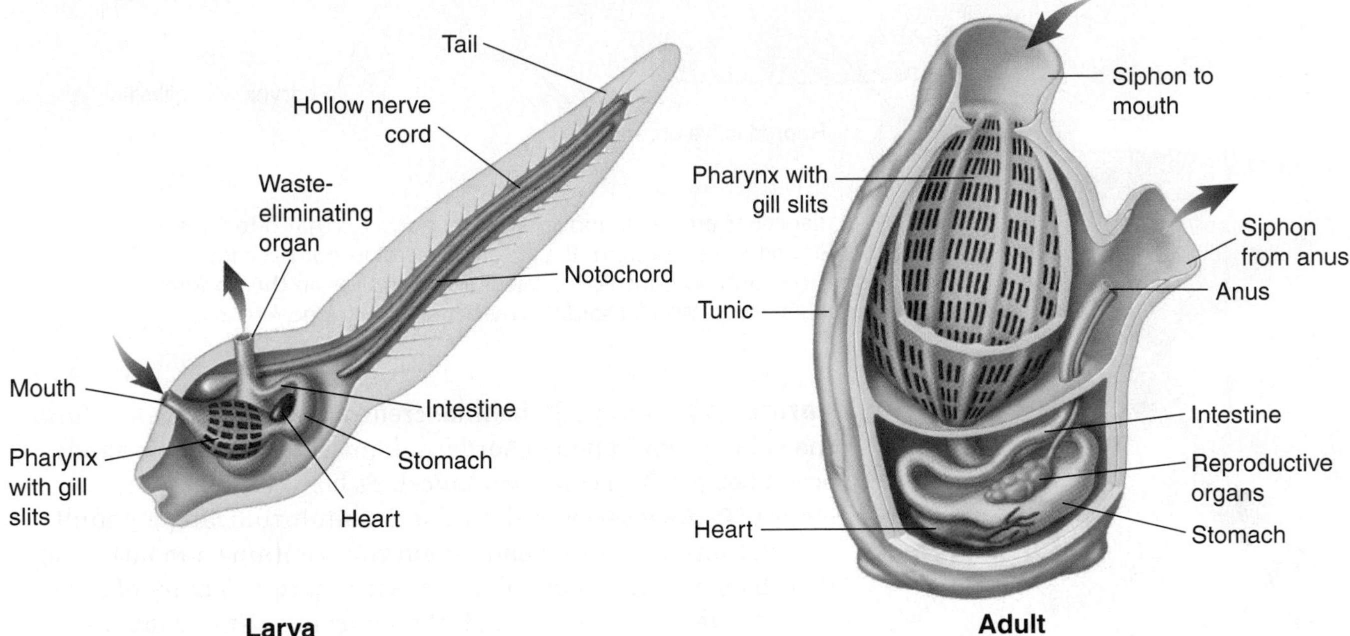

Nonvertebrate Chordates

There are two subphyla of chordates that do not have backbones. **The two groups of nonvertebrate chordates are tunicates and lancelets.** Both are soft-bodied marine organisms. Like all chordates, these animals have a hollow nerve cord, a notochord, pharyngeal pouches, and a tail at some stage of their life cycle.

In some ways, studying nonvertebrate chordates is like using a time machine to investigate the ancestors of our own subphylum, Vertebrata. Similarities in anatomy and embryological development indicate that vertebrates and nonvertebrate chordates evolved from a common ancestor. Fossil evidence from the Cambrian Period places this divergence at more than 550 million years ago. Although they seem to be simple animals, tunicates and lancelets are relatives of ours—very distant ones.

Tunicates Filter-feeding tunicates (subphylum Urochordata) certainly do not look as if they are related to us. **Figure 30–3** shows the body structure of a tunicate larva and an adult. Observe that the larval form has all of the chordate characteristics. In contrast, adult tunicates, like the ones in **Figure 30–4,** have neither a notochord nor a tail.

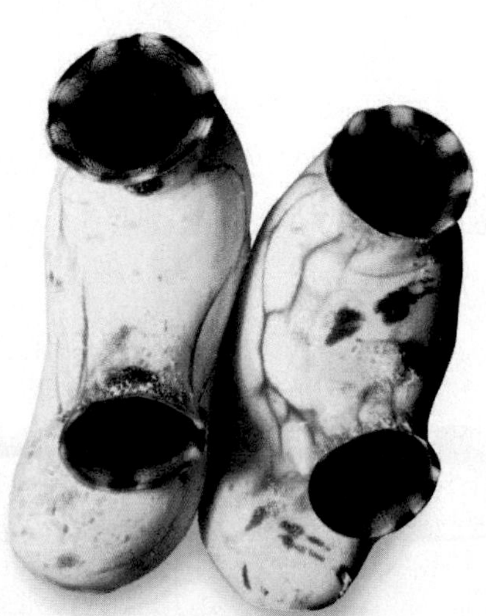

▲ **Figure 30–4** Tunicates get their name from the adult's body covering—the tough, nonliving tunic. Most tunicates are commonly known as sea squirts, because of the stream of water they sometimes eject. **Inferring** ***In what kind of ecosystem are you likely to find tunicates?***

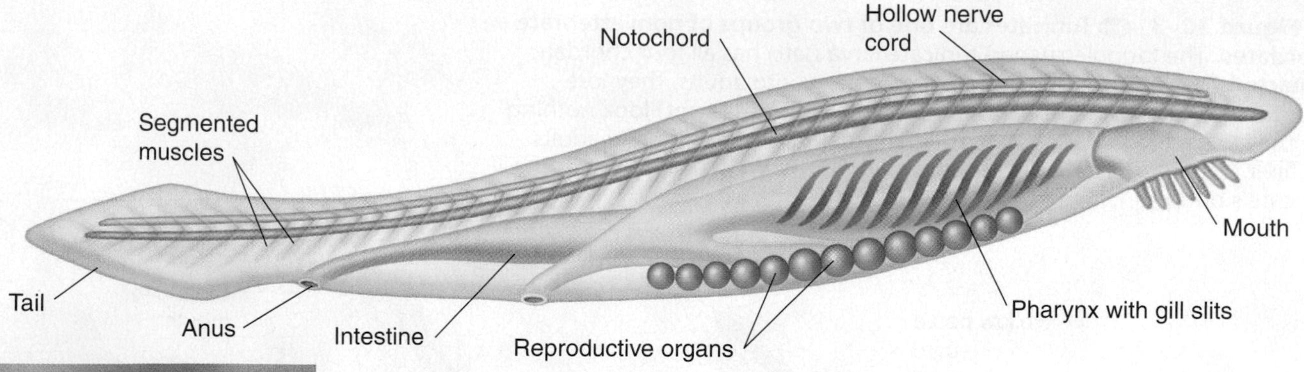

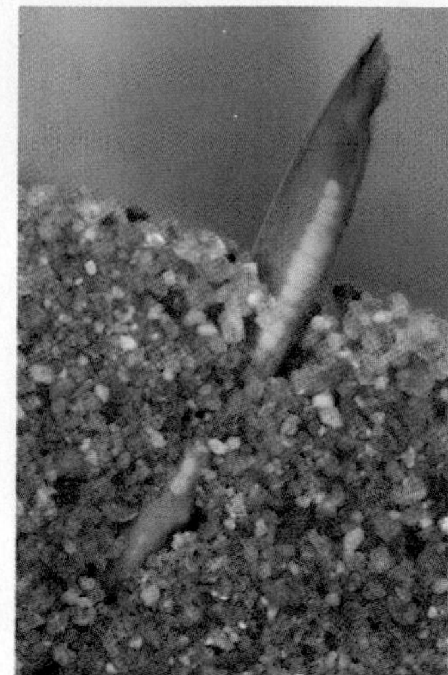

Figure 30–5 Lancelets are small nonvertebrate chordates that often live with their bodies half buried in sand. Because lancelets do not have fins or legs, they can move only by contracting the paired muscles on their bodies. **Interpreting Graphics** *Which chordate characteristics do lancelets have?*

Lancelets The small, fishlike creatures called lancelets form the subphylum Cephalochordata. Lancelets live on the sandy ocean bottom. You can see a lancelet's body structure in **Figure 30–5.** Observe that, unlike an adult tunicate, an adult lancelet has a definite head region that contains a mouth. The mouth opens into a long pharynx with up to 100 pairs of gill slits. As water passes through the pharynx, a sticky mucus catches food particles. The lancelet then swallows the mucus into the digestive tract. Lancelets use the pharynx for gas exchange. In addition, lancelets are thin enough to exchange gases through their body surface.

Lancelets have a closed circulatory system. They do not have a true heart. Instead, the walls of the major blood vessels contract to push blood through the body. The fishlike motion of lancelets results from contracting muscles that are organized into V-shaped units. The muscle units are paired on either side of the body.

30–1 Section Assessment

1. **Key Concept** Describe four characteristics of chordates.
2. **Key Concept** How do lancelets and tunicates differ?
3. What one characteristic distinguishes most vertebrates from the other chordates?
4. How is a vertebrate's skeleton similar to that of an arthropod? How is it different?
5. Describe two ways in which lancelets obtain oxygen.
6. **Critical Thinking Inferring** How would a free-swimming larval stage be an advantage for tunicates?

Writing in Science

Creative Writing

Imagine that a scientist has just discovered the existence of one of the nonvertebrate chordate groups. Write a short newspaper article describing what the scientist has discovered. *Hint:* Before you write, list the characteristics of the chordate group. Then, identify these characteristics in the article.

30–2 Fishes

4-3.1 Earth's species developed from earlier species
4-3.1 The variability of offspring
4-3.1 Fossils indicate extinction
LS- Make observations

If you think of Earth as land, then the name "Earth" is not particularly appropriate for the planet on which you live, for more than two thirds of its surface is water. And almost anywhere there is water—fresh or salt—there are fishes. At the edge of the ocean, blennies jump from rock to rock and occasionally dunk themselves in tide pools. Beneath the Arctic ice live fishes whose bodies contain a biological antifreeze that keeps them from freezing solid. In some shallow desert streams, pupfishes tolerate temperatures that would cook almost any other animal. Evolution by natural selection and other processes has resulted in a great diversity of fishes.

Guide for Reading

Key Concepts
- What are the basic characteristics of fishes?
- What were the important developments during the evolution of fishes?
- How are fishes adapted for life in water?
- What are the three main groups of fishes?

Vocabulary
cartilage • atrium • ventricle
cerebrum • cerebellum
medulla oblongata
lateral line system
swim bladder • oviparous
ovoviviparous • viviparous

Reading Strategy: Using Prior Knowledge
Before you read, make a list of the things you already know about fishes. After you have finished reading, check the list. Correct any errors and add new facts.

What Is a Fish?

You might think that with such extreme variations in habitat, fishes would be difficult to characterize. However, describing a fish is a rather simple task. **Fishes are aquatic vertebrates; most fishes have paired fins, scales, and gills.** Fins are used for movement, scales for protection, and gills for exchanging gases. You can observe most of those characteristics in **Figure 30–6.**

Fishes are so varied, however, that for almost every general statement there are exceptions. For example, some fishes, such as catfish, do not have scales. One reason for the enormous diversity among living fishes is that these chordates belong to very different classes. Thus, many fishes—sharks, lampreys, and perch, for example—are no more similar to one another than humans are to frogs!

What are the basic functions of fins, scales, and gills?

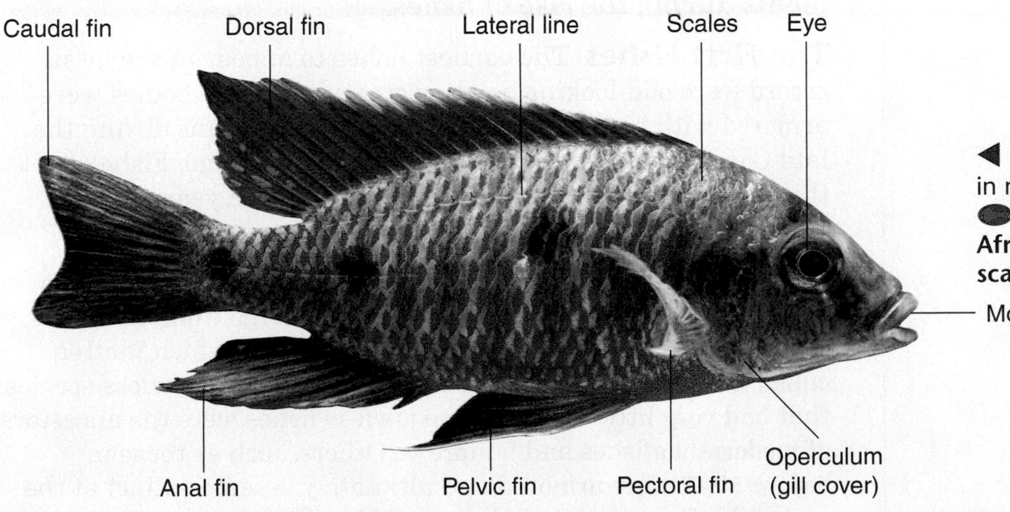

◀ **Figure 30–6** Fishes come in many shapes and sizes. **Like most fishes, this African cichlid has paired fins, scales, and gills.**

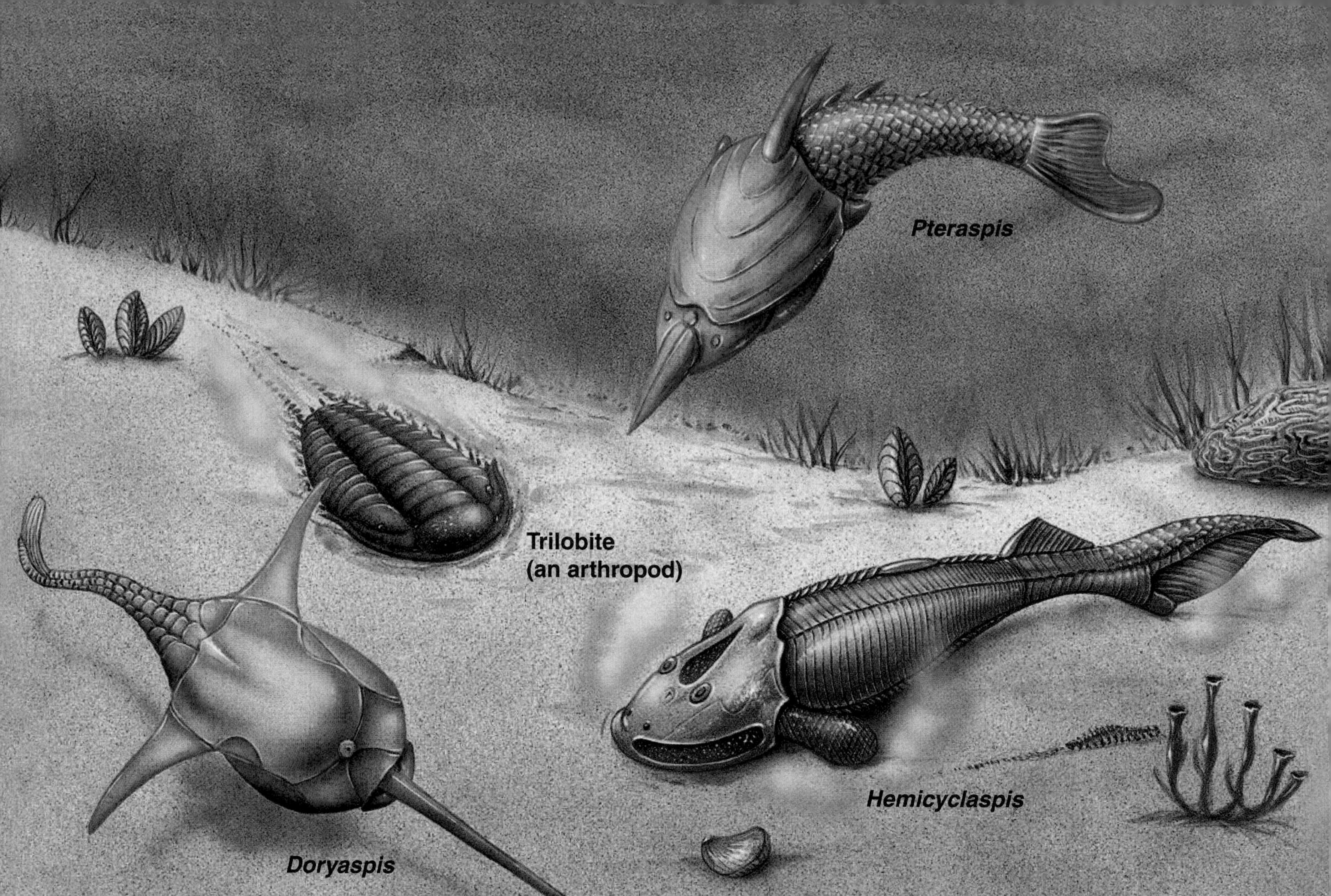

▲ **Figure 30–7** Ancient jawless fishes swam in shallow seas during the early Devonian Period, about 400 million years ago. Lacking jaws, early jawless fishes were limited in their ability to feed and to defend themselves against predators. **The evolution of paired fins, however, gave these fishes more control over their movement in the water.**

Evolution of Fishes

Fishes were the first vertebrates to evolve. They did not arise directly from tunicates or lancelets, but fishes and nonvertebrate chordates probably did evolve from common invertebrate ancestors. During the course of their evolution, fishes underwent several important changes. **The evolution of jaws and the evolution of paired fins were important developments during the rise of fishes.**

The First Fishes The earliest fishes to appear in the fossil record were odd-looking, jawless creatures whose bodies were armored with bony plates. They lived in the oceans during the late Cambrian Period, about 510 million years ago. Fishes kept this armored, jawless body plan for 100 million years.

The Age of Fishes During the Ordovician and Silurian Periods, about 505 to 410 million years ago, fishes underwent a major adaptive radiation. The species to emerge from the radiation ruled the seas during the Devonian Period, which is often called the Age of Fishes. Some of these fishes were jawless species that had very little armor. These jawless fishes were the ancestors of modern hagfishes and lampreys. Others, such as those in **Figure 30–7,** were armored and ultimately became extinct at the end of the Devonian Period, about 360 million years ago.

The Arrival of Jaws and Paired Fins Still other ancient fishes kept their bony armor and possessed a feeding adaptation that would revolutionize vertebrate evolution: These fishes had jaws. Observe the powerful jaws of the ancient fish in **Figure 30–8.** Jaws are an extremely useful adaptation. Jawless fishes are limited to eating small particles of food that they filter out of the water or suck up like a vacuum cleaner. Because jaws can hold teeth and muscles, jaws make it possible for vertebrates to nibble on plants and munch on other animals. Thus, animals with jaws can eat a much wider variety of food. They can also defend themselves by biting.

The evolution of jaws in early fishes accompanied the evolution of paired pectoral (anterior) and pelvic (posterior) fins. These fins were attached to girdles—structures of cartilage or bone that support the fins. **Cartilage** is a strong tissue that supports the body and is softer and more flexible than bone. **Figure 30–9** shows the fins and fin girdles in one ancient fish species.

Paired fins gave fishes more control of body movement. In addition, tail fins and powerful muscles gave fishes greater thrust when swimming. The combination of accuracy and speed enabled fishes to move in new and varied patterns. This ability, in turn, helped fishes use their jaws in complex ways.

The Rise of Modern Fishes Although the early jawed fishes soon disappeared, they left behind two major groups that continued to evolve and still survive today. One group—the ancestors of modern sharks and rays—evolved a skeleton made of strong, resilient cartilage. The other group evolved skeletons made of true bone. A subgroup of bony fishes, called lobe-finned fishes, had fleshy fins from which the limbs of chordates would later evolve.

CHECKPOINT *Which two groups of early jawed fishes still survive today?*

▲ **Figure 30–8** This photograph shows a reconstruction of an ancient armored fish called *Dunkleosteus,* an enormous predator that lived in the inland seas of North America during the late Devonian Period. **Drawing Conclusions** *What feature made this fish a successful predator in its time?*

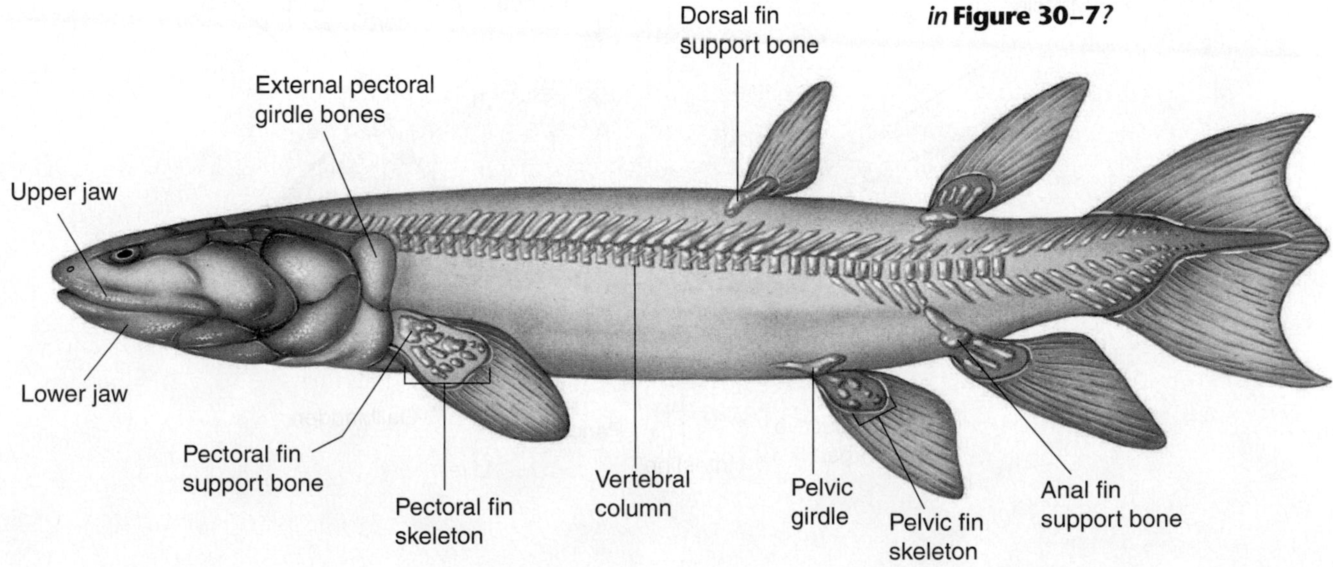

▼ **Figure 30–9** This ancient Devonian fish is called *Eusthenopteron.* Although its skeleton differs from those of most modern fishes, its basic features—vertebral column, fins, and fin girdles—have been retained in many species. **Comparing and Contrasting** *How does this fish differ from the fishes in* ***Figure 30–7****?*

▲ **Figure 30–10** **Adaptations to aquatic life include various modes of feeding.** This deep-sea anglerfish has a built-in "fishing pole" that it uses to attract prey.

Form and Function in Fishes

Over time, fishes have evolved to survive in a tremendous range of aquatic environments. **Adaptations to aquatic life include various modes of feeding, specialized structures for gas exchange, and paired fins for locomotion.** Fishes have other types of adaptations, too, as you will learn.

Feeding Every mode of feeding is seen in fishes. There are herbivores, carnivores, parasites, filter feeders, and detritus feeders. In fact, a single fish may exhibit several modes of feeding, depending on what type of food happens to be available. Certain carp, for example, eat algae, aquatic plants, worms, mollusks, arthropods, dead fish, and detritus. Other fishes, such as barracuda, are highly specialized carnivores. A few fishes, such as some lampreys, are parasites. **Figure 30–10** shows a fish that even uses a fleshy bait to catch its meals!

Use **Figure 30–11** to locate the internal organs that are important during the fish's digestion of its food. From the fish's mouth, food passes through a short tube called the esophagus to the stomach, where it is partially broken down. In many fishes, the food is further processed in fingerlike pouches called pyloric ceca (py-LAWR-ik SEE-kuh; singular: cecum). The pyloric ceca secrete digestive enzymes and absorb nutrients from the digested food. Other organs, including the liver and pancreas, add enzymes and other digestive chemicals to the food as it moves through the digestive tract. The intestine completes the process of digestion and nutrient absorption. Any undigested material is eliminated through the anus.

▼ **Figure 30–11** The internal organs of a typical bony fish are shown here. **Applying Concepts** *What is the function of the pyloric cecum?*

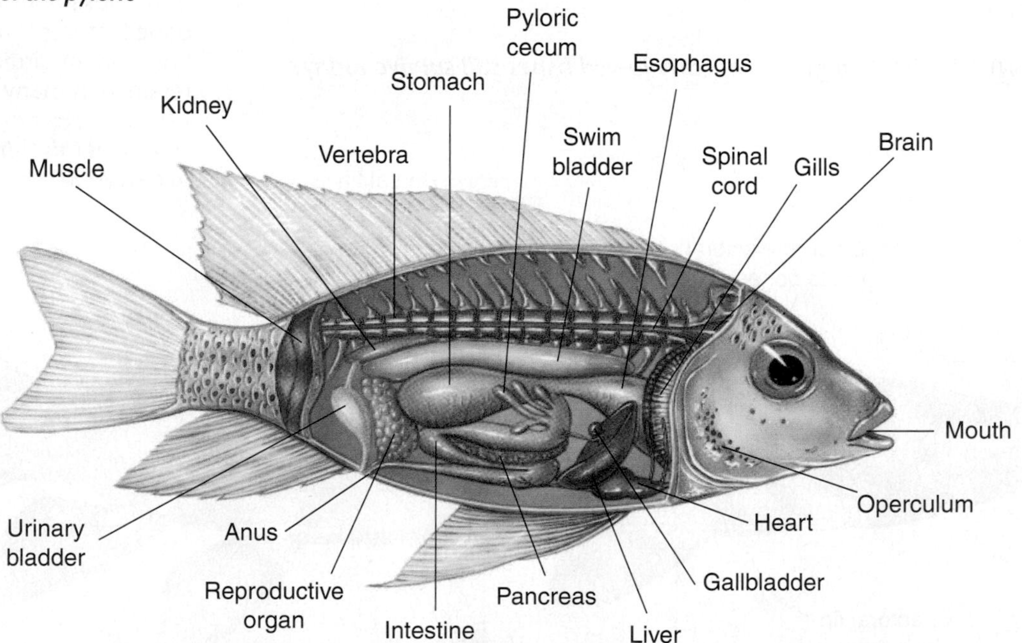

Quick Lab

How do fishes use gills?

Materials fish food, food coloring, plastic cup, dropper pipette, live fish in an aquarium

Procedure  

1. Mix some fish food and food coloring in a small volume of aquarium water in a plastic cup.
2. Use a dropper pipette to release the mixture near a fish in an aquarium. Release the mixture gently so that it does not scatter.
3. Observe what happens when the fish approaches the mixture. Watch the fish's gills especially closely.

Analyze and Conclude

1. **Drawing Conclusions** Describe what happened to the food coloring. What does this tell you about how water moves through a fish's body?
2. **Inferring** Why do most fishes seem to move or swallow continuously? What might happen if a fish were not able to move or stopped "swallowing"?

Respiration Most fishes exchange gases using gills located on either side of the pharynx. The gills are made up of feathery, threadlike structures called filaments. Each filament contains a network of fine capillaries that provides a large surface area for the exchange of oxygen and carbon dioxide. Fishes that exchange gases using gills do so by pulling oxygen-rich water in through their mouths, pumping it over their gill filaments, and then pushing oxygen-poor water out through openings in the sides of the pharynx.

Some fishes, such as lampreys and sharks, have several gill openings. Most fishes, however, have a single gill opening on each side of the body through which water is pumped out. This opening is hidden beneath a protective bony cover called the operculum.

A number of fishes have an adaptation that allows them to survive in oxygen-poor water or in areas where bodies of water often dry up. These fishes have specialized organs that serve as lungs. A tube brings air containing oxygen to this organ through the fish's mouth. Some lungfishes are so dependent on getting oxygen from the air that they will suffocate if prevented from reaching the surface of the water.

What structures do fishes use for gas exchange?

▶ **Figure 30–12** This African lungfish has a breathing adaptation that allows it to survive in shallow waters that are subject to drought. It burrows into mud, covers itself with mucus, and becomes dormant. For several months until the rains fall, the lungfish breathes through its mouth and lungs. **Drawing Conclusions** *How is it an advantage for this lungfish to cover itself with mucus?*

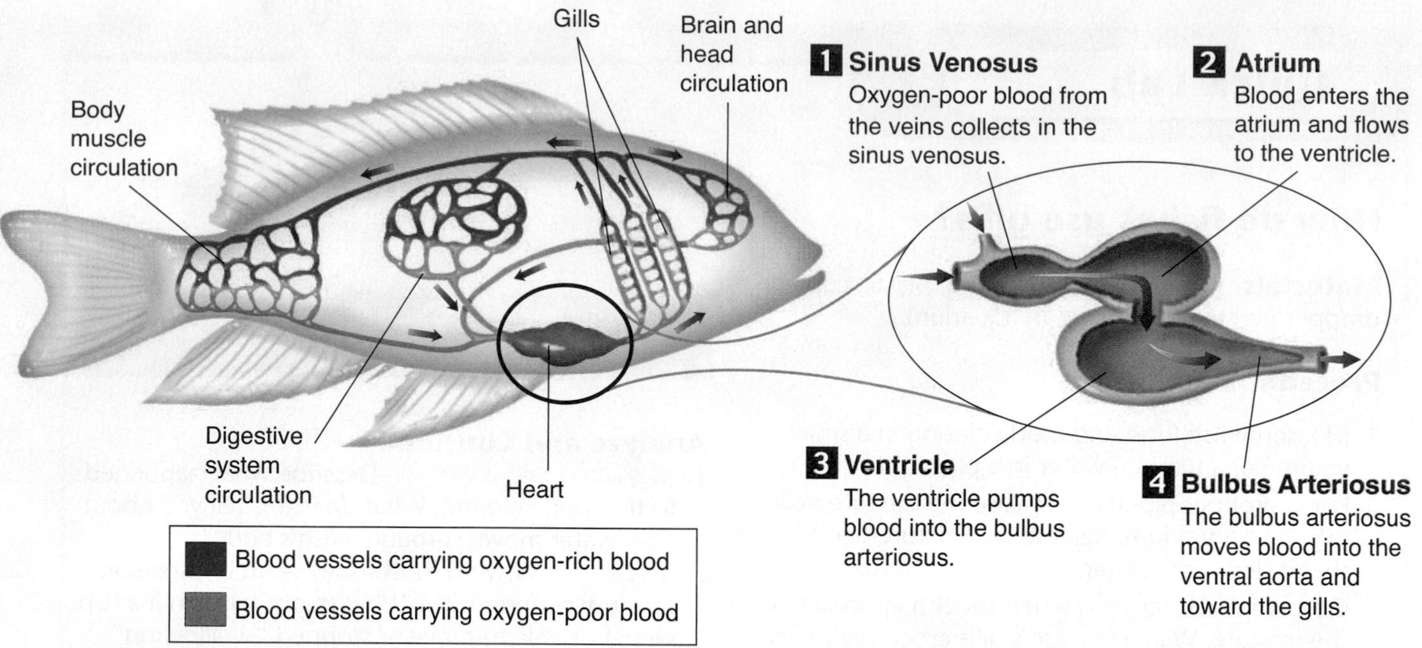

▲ **Figure 30–13** Blood circulates through a fish's body in a single loop—from the heart to the gills to the rest of the body, and then back to the heart again. (Note that in diagrams of animals' circulatory systems, blood vessels carrying oxygen-rich blood are red, while blood vessels carrying oxygen-poor blood are blue.) **Interpreting Graphics** ***Is the blood that flows from the heart to the gills rich in oxygen or does it lack oxygen?***

Circulation Fishes have closed circulatory systems with a heart that pumps blood around the body in a single loop—from the heart to the gills, from the gills to the rest of the body, and back to the heart. **Figure 30–13** shows the path of blood and the structure of the heart.

In most fishes, the heart consists of four parts: the sinus venosus (SYN-us vuh-NOH-sus), atrium, ventricle, and bulbus arteriosus (BUL-bus ahr-teer-ee-OH-sus). The sinus venosus is a thin-walled sac that collects blood from the fish's veins before it flows to the **atrium,** a large muscular chamber that serves as a one-way compartment for blood that is about to enter the ventricle. The **ventricle,** a thick-walled, muscular chamber, is the actual pumping portion of the heart. It pumps blood to a large, muscular tube called the bulbus arteriosus. At its front end, the bulbus arteriosus connects to a large blood vessel called the aorta, through which blood moves to the fish's gills.

Excretion Like many other aquatic animals, most fishes rid themselves of nitrogenous wastes in the form of ammonia. Some wastes diffuse through the gills into the surrounding water. Others are removed by kidneys, which are excretory organs that filter wastes from the blood.

Kidneys help fishes control the amount of water in their bodies. Fishes in salt water tend to lose water by osmosis. To solve this problem, the kidneys of marine fishes concentrate wastes and return as much water as possible to the body. In contrast, a great deal of water continually enters the bodies of freshwater fishes. The kidneys of freshwater fishes pump out plenty of dilute urine. Some fishes are able to move from fresh to salt water by adjusting their kidney function.

Response Fishes have well-developed nervous systems organized around a brain, which has several parts, as shown in **Figure 30–14.** The most anterior parts of a fish's brain are the olfactory bulbs, which are involved with the sense of smell, or olfaction. They are connected to the two lobes of the cerebrum. In most vertebrates, the **cerebrum** is responsible for all voluntary activities of the body. However, in fishes, the cerebrum primarily processes the sense of smell. The optic lobes process information from the eyes. The **cerebellum** coordinates body movements. The **medulla oblongata** controls the functioning of many internal organs.

Most fishes have highly developed sense organs. Almost all fishes that are active in daylight have well-developed eyes and color vision that is at least as good as yours. Many fishes have specialized cells called chemoreceptors that are responsible for their extraordinary senses of taste and smell. Although most fishes have ears inside their head, they may not hear sounds well. Most fishes can, however, detect gentle currents and vibrations in the water with sensitive receptors that form the **lateral line system.** Fishes use this system to sense the motion of other fishes or prey swimming nearby. In addition to detecting motion, some fishes, such as catfish and sharks, have evolved sense organs that can detect low levels of electric current. Some fishes, such as the electric eel shown in **Figure 30–15,** can even generate their own electricity!

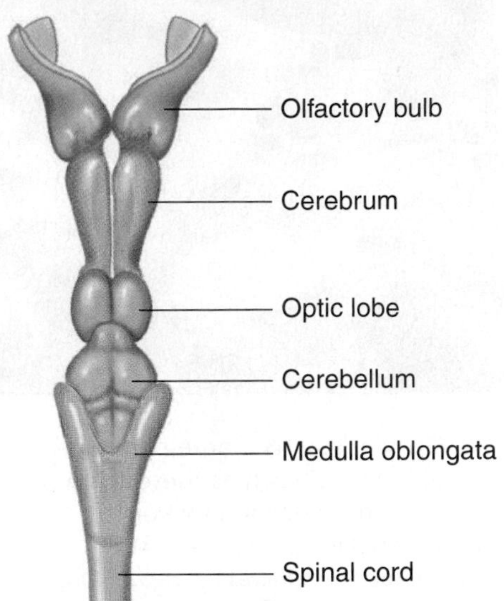

▲ **Figure 30–14** The brain of a fish, like all vertebrate brains, is situated at the anterior end of the spinal cord and has several different parts. **Inferring** *How might the size of the various parts of the brain differ in a blind cave fish that relies primarily on its sense of smell?*

What are the parts of a fish's brain?

Movement Most fishes move by alternately contracting paired sets of muscles on either side of the backbone. This creates a series of S-shaped curves that move down the fish's body. As each curve travels from the head toward the tail fin, it creates backward force on the surrounding water. This force, along with the action of the fins, propels the fish forward. The fins of fishes are also used in much the same way that airplanes use stabilizers, flaps, and rudders—to keep on course and adjust direction. Fins also increase the surface area of the tail, providing an extra boost of speed. The streamlined body shapes of most fishes help reduce the amount of drag (friction) as they move through the water.

Because their body tissues are more dense than the water they swim in, sinking is an issue for fishes. Many bony fishes have an internal, gas-filled organ called a **swim bladder** that adjusts their buoyancy. The swim bladder lies just beneath the backbone.

▶ **Figure 30–15** The electric eel, *Electrophorus electricus,* can produce several hundred volts of electricity in brief bursts. **Formulating Hypotheses** *What function might such powerful electric bursts serve?*

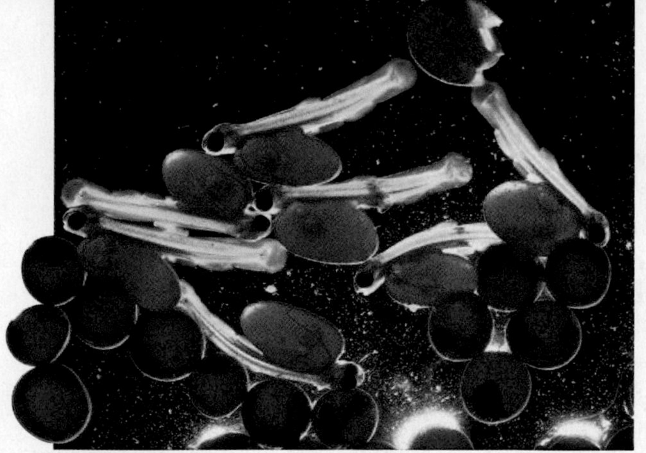

▲ **Figure 30–16** Some newly hatched fishes, such as these coho salmon, are nourished by yolk sacs on their bellies. **Inferring** *What are the orange spheres at the bottom of the photograph?*

Reproduction The eggs of fishes are fertilized either externally or internally, depending on the species. In many fish species, the female lays the eggs and the embryos in the eggs develop and hatch outside her body. Fishes whose eggs hatch outside the mother's body are **oviparous** (oh-VIP-uh-rus). As the embryos of oviparous fishes develop, they obtain food from the yolk in the egg. The salmon in **Figure 30–16** are oviparous. In contrast, in **ovoviviparous** (oh-voh-vy-VIP-uh-rus) species, such as guppies, the eggs stay in the mother's body after internal fertilization. Each embryo develops inside its egg, using the yolk for nourishment. The young are then "born alive," like the young of most mammals. A few fish species, including several sharks, are viviparous. In **viviparous** (vy-VIP-uh-rus) animals, the embryos stay in the mother's body after internal fertilization, as they do in ovoviviparous species. However, these embryos obtain the substances they need from the mother's body, not from material in an egg. The young of viviparous species are also born alive.

What are the three different modes of fish reproduction?

Groups of Fishes

With over 24,000 living species, fishes are an extremely diverse group of chordates. These diverse species can be grouped according to body structure. **When you consider their basic internal structure, all living fishes can be classified into three groups: jawless fishes, cartilaginous fishes, and bony fishes.**

Figure 30–17 **Jawless fishes make up one of three major groups of living fishes.** Modern jawless fishes are divided into two classes: lampreys (top) and hagfishes (bottom).

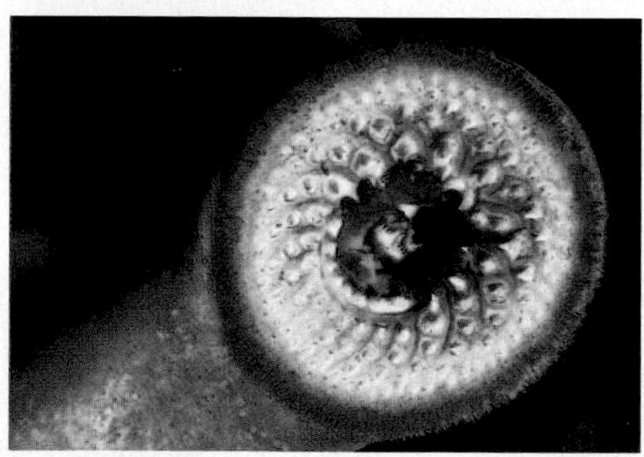

Jawless Fishes As their name implies, jawless fishes have no true teeth or jaws. Their skeletons are made of fibers and cartilage. They lack vertebrae, and instead keep their notochords as adults. Modern jawless fishes are divided into two classes: lampreys and hagfishes.

Lampreys are typically filter feeders as larvae and parasites as adults. An adult lamprey's head is taken up almost completely by a circular sucking disk with a round mouth in the center, which you can see in **Figure 30–17.** Adult lampreys attach themselves to fishes, and occasionally to whales and dolphins. There, they scrape away at the skin with small toothlike structures that surround the mouth and with a strong, rasping tongue. The lamprey then sucks up the tissues and body fluids of its host.

Hagfishes have pinkish gray, wormlike bodies and four or six short tentacles around their mouths. Hagfishes lack eyes, although they do have light-detecting sensors scattered around their bodies. They feed on dead and dying fish by using a toothed tongue to scrape a hole into the fish's side. Hagfishes have other peculiar traits: They secrete incredible amounts of slime, have six hearts, possess an open circulatory system, and regularly tie themselves into knots!

Sharks and Their Relatives The class Chondrichthyes (kahn-DRIK-theez) contains sharks, rays, skates, and a few uncommon fishes such as sawfishes and chimaeras. Some chondrichthyes are shown in **Figure 30–18.** *Chondros* is the Greek word for cartilage, so the name of this class tells you that the skeletons of these fishes are built entirely of cartilage, not bone. The cartilage of these animals is similar to the flexible tissue that supports your nose and your external ears. Most cartilaginous fishes also have toothlike scales covering their skin. These scales make shark skin so rough that it can be used as sandpaper.

Most of the 350 or so living shark species have large curved tails, torpedo-shaped bodies, and pointed snouts with the mouth underneath. One of the most noticeable characteristics of sharks is their enormous number of teeth. Many sharks have thousands of teeth arranged in several rows. As teeth in the front rows are worn out or lost, new teeth are continually replacing them. A shark goes through about 20,000 teeth in its lifetime!

Not all sharks have such fierce-looking teeth, however. Some, like the basking shark, are filter feeders with specialized feeding structures. Their teeth are so small they are virtually useless. Other sharks have flat teeth adapted for crushing the shells of mollusks and crustaceans. Although there are a number of carnivorous sharks large enough to prey on humans, most sharks do not attack people.

Skates and rays are even more diverse in their feeding habits than their shark relatives. Some feed on bottom-dwelling invertebrates by using their mouths as powerful vacuums. However, the largest rays, like the largest sharks, are filter feeders that eat floating plankton. Skates and rays often glide through the sea with flapping motions of their large, winglike pectoral fins. When they are not feeding or swimming, many skates and rays cover themselves with a thin layer of sand and spend hours resting on the ocean floor.

▼ **Figure 30–18** Sharks and rays have skeletons that are made of cartilage. The large jaws and teeth of many sharks make them top predators in the world's oceans. **Applying Concepts** ***How is the structure of a basking shark's mouth related to its diet?***

Basking shark

FIGURE 30–19 DIVERSITY OF RAY-FINNED FISHES

Combtooth Blenny

Emperor Angelfish

Flying Fish

Peacock Flounder

Nearly all bony fishes belong to an enormous and diverse group called ray-finned fishes. These fishes have thin, bony spines that form the fins. **Observing** *What unusual adaptations do you see in each of these fishes?*

Leafy Sea Dragon

Bony Fishes Bony fishes make up the class Osteichthyes (ahs-tee-IK-theez). The skeletons of these fishes are made of hard, calcified tissue called bone. Almost all living bony fishes belong to a huge group called ray-finned fishes, some of which are shown in **Figure 30–19.** The name "ray-finned" refers to the slender bony spines, or rays, that are connected by a thin layer of skin to form the fins. The fin rays support the skin much as the thin rods in a handheld folding fan hold together the webbing of the fan.

Only seven living species of bony fishes are not classified as ray-finned fishes. These are the lobe-finned fishes, a subclass that includes lungfishes and the coelacanth (SEE-luh-kanth). Lungfishes live in fresh water, but the coelacanth lives in salt water. The fleshy fins of lobe-finned fishes have support bones that are more substantial than the rays of ray-finned fishes. Some of these bones are jointed, like the arms and legs of land vertebrates.

Ecology of Fishes

Most fishes spend all their lives either in fresh water or in the ocean. Most freshwater fishes cannot tolerate the high salt concentration in saltwater ecosystems, because their kidneys cannot maintain internal water balance in this environment. Since freshwater fishes cannot maintain homeostasis in salt water, they cannot survive in the ocean. In contrast, ocean fishes cannot tolerate the low salt concentration in freshwater ecosystems.

However, some fish species can move from saltwater ecosystems to fresh water, and vice versa. Lampreys, sturgeons, and salmon, for example, spend most of their lives in the ocean but migrate to fresh water to breed. Fishes with this type of behavior are called anadromous (uh-NAH-druh-mus). Salmon, for example, begin their lives in rivers or streams but soon migrate to the sea. After one to four years at sea, mature salmon return to the place of their birth to reproduce. This trip can take several months, covering as much as 3200 kilometers, and can involve incredible feats of strength, as shown in **Figure 30–20.** The adult salmon recognize their home stream using their sense of smell.

In contrast to anadromous fishes, some fishes live their lives in fresh water but migrate to the ocean to breed. These fishes are said to be catadromous (kuh-TAD-ruh-mus). European eels, for instance, live and feed in the rivers of North America and Europe. They travel up to 4800 kilometers to lay their eggs in the Sargasso Sea, in the North Atlantic Ocean. The eggs are carried by currents to shallow coastal waters. As they grow into young fish, the eels find their way to fresh water and migrate upstream.

▲ **Figure 30–20** Adult salmon return from the sea to reproduce in the stream or river in which they were born. Their journey is often long and strenuous. The salmon must swim upstream against the current and may even leap up waterfalls! **Applying Concepts** *What sense do the salmon use to find their home stream?*

30–2 Section Assessment

1. **Key Concept** Identify the main characteristics of fishes.
2. **Key Concept** What adaptive advantages do jaws and fins provide for fishes?
3. **Key Concept** List four specific ways in which fishes are adapted for aquatic life.
4. **Key Concept** Name the three main groups of fishes and give an example for each group.
5. **Critical Thinking Applying Concepts** For fishes to survive in an aquarium, the water must be kept clean and well oxygenated. Explain why water quality is so important to a fish's survival.

Connecting Concepts

Comparing Circulatory Systems

In Chapter 27, you learned about the circulatory system of annelids. Create a Venn diagram comparing the circulatory system of an annelid with that of a fish. How are the two circulatory systems similar and different?

30–3 Amphibians

1-S3.4 Questioning claims
4-3.1 Earth's species developed from earlier species
4-7.2 Human activities can degrade ecosystems
LS- Analyze results

Guide for Reading

Key Concepts
- What is an amphibian?
- How are amphibians adapted for life on land?
- What are the main groups of living amphibians?

Vocabulary
cloaca
nictitating membrane
tympanic membrane

Reading Strategy: Making Comparisons As you read, write down similarities and differences between fishes and amphibians. Consider such characteristics as body structure, habitat, and method of reproduction.

Amphibians have survived for hundreds of millions of years, typically living in places where fresh water is plentiful. With over 4000 living species, amphibians are the only modern descendants of an ancient group that gave rise to all other land vertebrates.

What Is an Amphibian?

The word *amphibian* means "double life," emphasizing that these animals live both in water and on land. The larvae are fishlike aquatic animals that respire using gills. In contrast, the adults of most species of amphibians are terrestrial animals that respire using lungs and skin.

An amphibian is a vertebrate that, with some exceptions, lives in water as a larva and on land as an adult, breathes with lungs as an adult, has moist skin that contains mucous glands, and lacks scales and claws. In a sense, amphibians are to the animal kingdom what mosses and ferns are to the plant kingdom: They are descendants of ancestral organisms that evolved some—but not all—of the adaptations necessary for living entirely on land.

Evolution of Amphibians

The first amphibians to climb onto land probably resembled lobe-finned fishes similar to the modern coelacanth. However, the amphibians had legs, as in **Figure 30–21.** They appeared in the late Devonian Period, about 360 million years ago.

The transition from water to land involved more than just having legs and clambering out of the water. Vertebrates colonizing land habitats faced the same challenges that had to be overcome by invertebrates. Terrestrial vertebrates have to breathe air, protect themselves and their eggs from drying out, and support themselves against the pull of gravity.

◀ **Figure 30–21** Evolving in the swamplike tropical ecosystems of the Devonian Period, amphibians were the first chordates to live at least part of their lives on land. **Most amphibians live in water as larvae and on land as adults.**

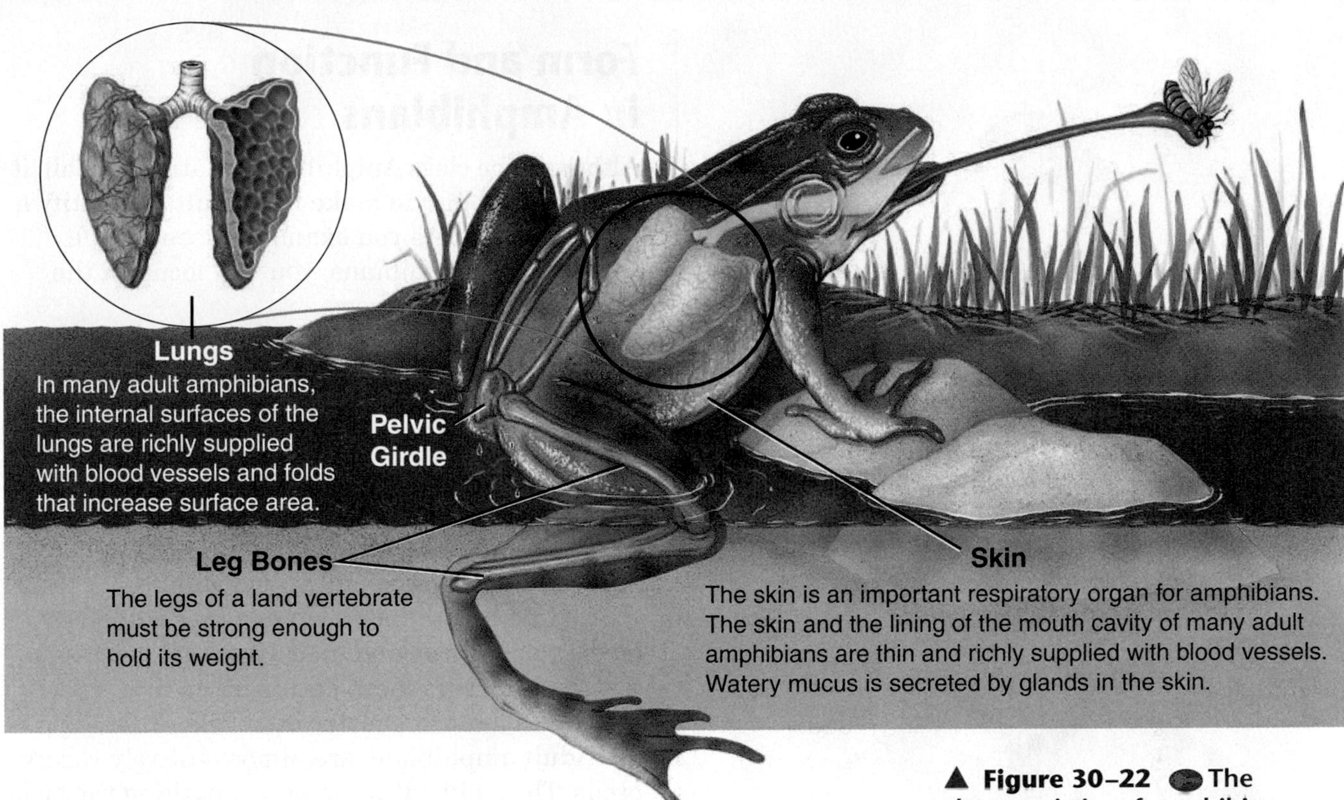

Lungs
In many adult amphibians, the internal surfaces of the lungs are richly supplied with blood vessels and folds that increase surface area.
Pelvic Girdle
Leg Bones
The legs of a land vertebrate must be strong enough to hold its weight.
Skin
The skin is an important respiratory organ for amphibians. The skin and the lining of the mouth cavity of many adult amphibians are thin and richly supplied with blood vessels. Watery mucus is secreted by glands in the skin.

▲ **Figure 30–22** **The characteristics of amphibians include adaptations for living partially on land.** For example, lungs enable adult amphibians to obtain oxygen from air.

Early amphibians evolved several adaptations that helped them live at least part of their lives out of water. Bones in the limbs and limb girdles of amphibians became stronger, permitting more efficient movement. Lungs and breathing tubes enabled amphibians to breathe air. The sternum, or breastbone, formed a bony shield to support and protect internal organs, especially the lungs. Some of these adaptations are shown in **Figure 30–22.**

Soon after they first appeared, amphibians underwent a major adaptive radiation. Some of these ancient amphibians were huge. One early amphibian, *Eogyrinus,* is thought to have been about 5 meters long. Amphibians became the dominant form of animal life in the warm, swampy fern forests of the Carboniferous Period, about 360 to 290 million years ago. In fact, they were so numerous that the Carboniferous Period is sometimes called the Age of Amphibians. These animals gave rise to the ancestors of living amphibians and of vertebrates that live completely on land.

The great success of amphibians didn't last, however. Climate changes caused many of their low, swampy habitats to disappear. Most amphibian groups became extinct by the end of the Permian Period, about 245 million years ago. Only three orders of small amphibians survive today—frogs and toads, salamanders, and caecilians (see-SIL-ee-unz).

✓ ***Which geological period is called the Age of Amphibians?***

Word Origins

Carboniferous is a combination of two root words—*carbone* and *fer. Carbone* is a French word for coal; *fer* is a Latin suffix meaning "bearing or producing." *Carboniferous* is an adjective describing the coal-making period of the Paleozoic Era. **If *cone* refers to a reproductive structure of a tree, what do you think the word *coniferous* means?**

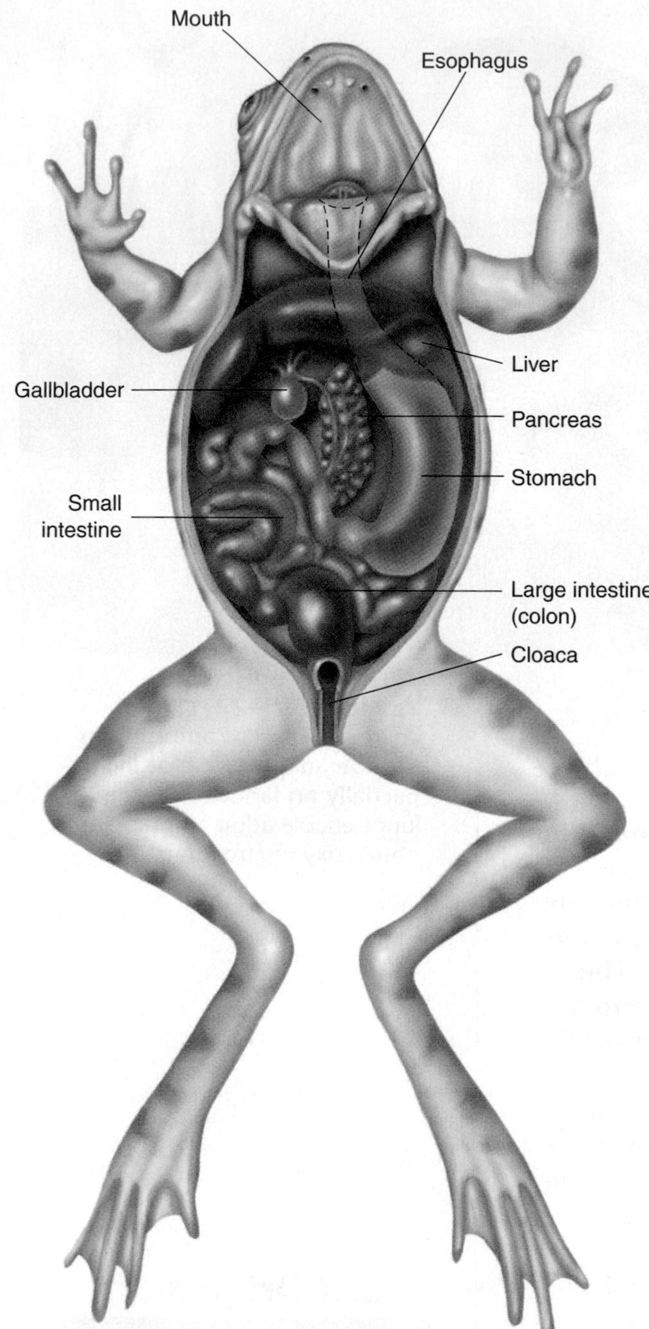

▲ **Figure 30–23** This illustration shows the organs of a frog's digestive system. **Comparing and Contrasting** ***Which digestive organs are found in both frogs and fishes?***

Form and Function in Amphibians

Although the class Amphibia is relatively small, it is diverse enough to make it difficult to identify a typical species. As you examine essential life functions in amphibians, you will focus on the structures found in frogs.

Feeding The double lives of amphibians are reflected in the feeding habits of frogs. Tadpoles are typically filter feeders or herbivores that graze on algae. Like other herbivores, the tadpoles eat almost constantly. Their intestines, whose long, coiled structure helps break down hard-to-digest plant material, are usually filled with food. However, when tadpoles change into adults, their feeding apparatus and digestive tract are transformed to strictly meat-eating structures, complete with a much shorter intestine.

Adult amphibians are almost entirely carnivorous. They will eat practically anything they can catch and swallow. Legless amphibians can only snap their jaws open and shut to catch prey. In contrast, many salamanders and frogs have long, sticky tongues specialized to capture insects.

Trace the path of food in a frog's digestive system in **Figure 30–23.** From the mouth, food slides down the esophagus into the stomach. The breakdown of food begins in the stomach and continues in the small intestine, where digestive enzymes are manufactured and food is absorbed. Tubes connect the intestine with organs such as the liver, pancreas, and gallbladder that secrete substances that aid in digestion. The small intestine leads to the large intestine, or colon. At the end of the large intestine is a muscular cavity called the **cloaca** (kloh-AY-kuh), through which digestive wastes, urine, and eggs or sperm leave the body.

Respiration In most larval amphibians, gas exchange occurs through the skin as well as the gills. Lungs typically replace gills when an amphibian becomes an adult, although some gas exchange continues through the skin and the lining of the mouth cavity. In frogs, toads, and many other adult amphibians, the lungs are reasonably well developed. In other amphibians, such as salamanders, the lungs are not as well developed. In fact, many terrestrial salamanders have no lungs at all! Lungless salamanders exchange gases through the thin lining of the mouth cavity as well as through the skin.

Circulation In frogs and other adult amphibians, the circulatory system forms what is known as a double loop. The first loop carries oxygen-poor blood from the heart to the lungs and skin, and takes oxygen-rich blood from the lungs and skin back to the heart. The second loop transports oxygen-rich blood from the heart to the rest of the body and then carries oxygen-poor blood from the body back to the heart.

The amphibian heart, shown in **Figure 30–24,** has three separate chambers: left atrium, right atrium, and ventricle. Oxygen-poor blood circulates from the body into the right atrium. At the same time, oxygen-rich blood from the lungs and skin enters the left atrium. When the atria contract, they empty their blood into the ventricle. The ventricle then contracts, pumping blood out to a single, large blood vessel that divides and branches off into smaller blood vessels. Because of the pattern in which the blood vessels branch, most oxygen-poor blood goes to the lungs, and most oxygen-rich blood goes to the rest of the body. However, there is some mixing of oxygen-rich and oxygen-poor blood.

CHECKPOINT *How many chambers are in an amphibian's heart?*

Excretion Amphibians have kidneys that filter wastes from the blood. The excretory product of the kidneys—urine—travels through tubes called ureters into the cloaca. From there, urine can be passed directly to the outside, or it may be temporarily stored in a small urinary bladder just above the cloaca.

▼ **Figure 30–24** Like all vertebrates, amphibians have a circulatory system and an excretory system. An amphibian's heart has three chambers—two atria and one ventricle. Although some wastes diffuse across the skin, kidneys remove most wastes from the bloodstream. **Applying Concepts** ***What excretory product do the kidneys produce?***

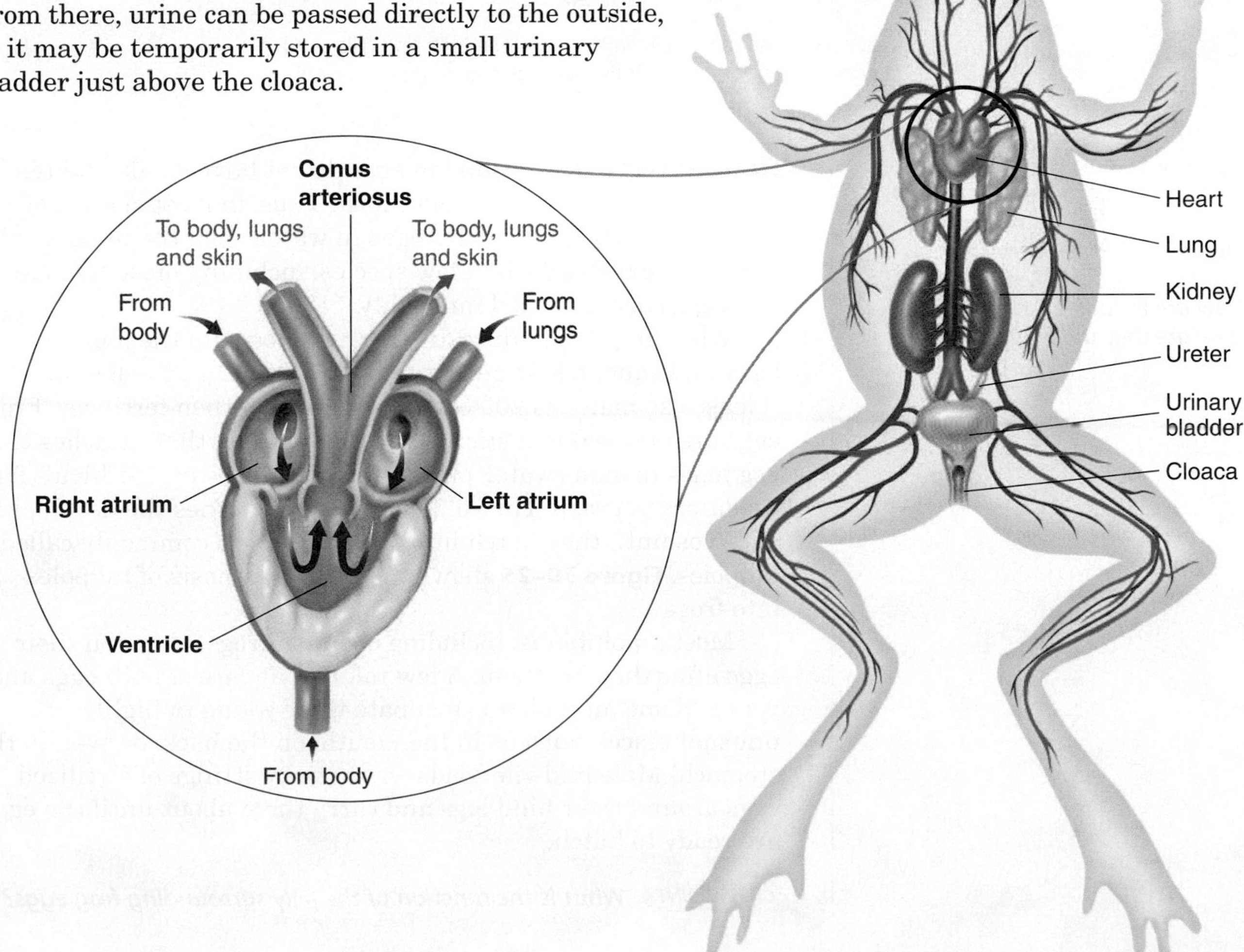

Adult Frog
Adults are typically ready to breed in about one to two years.
Young Frog
Frog eggs are laid in water and undergo external fertilization.
Fertilized Eggs
The eggs hatch into tadpoles a few days to several weeks later.
Tadpoles
Tadpoles gradually grow limbs, lose their tails and gills, and become meat-eaters as they develop into terrestrial adults.

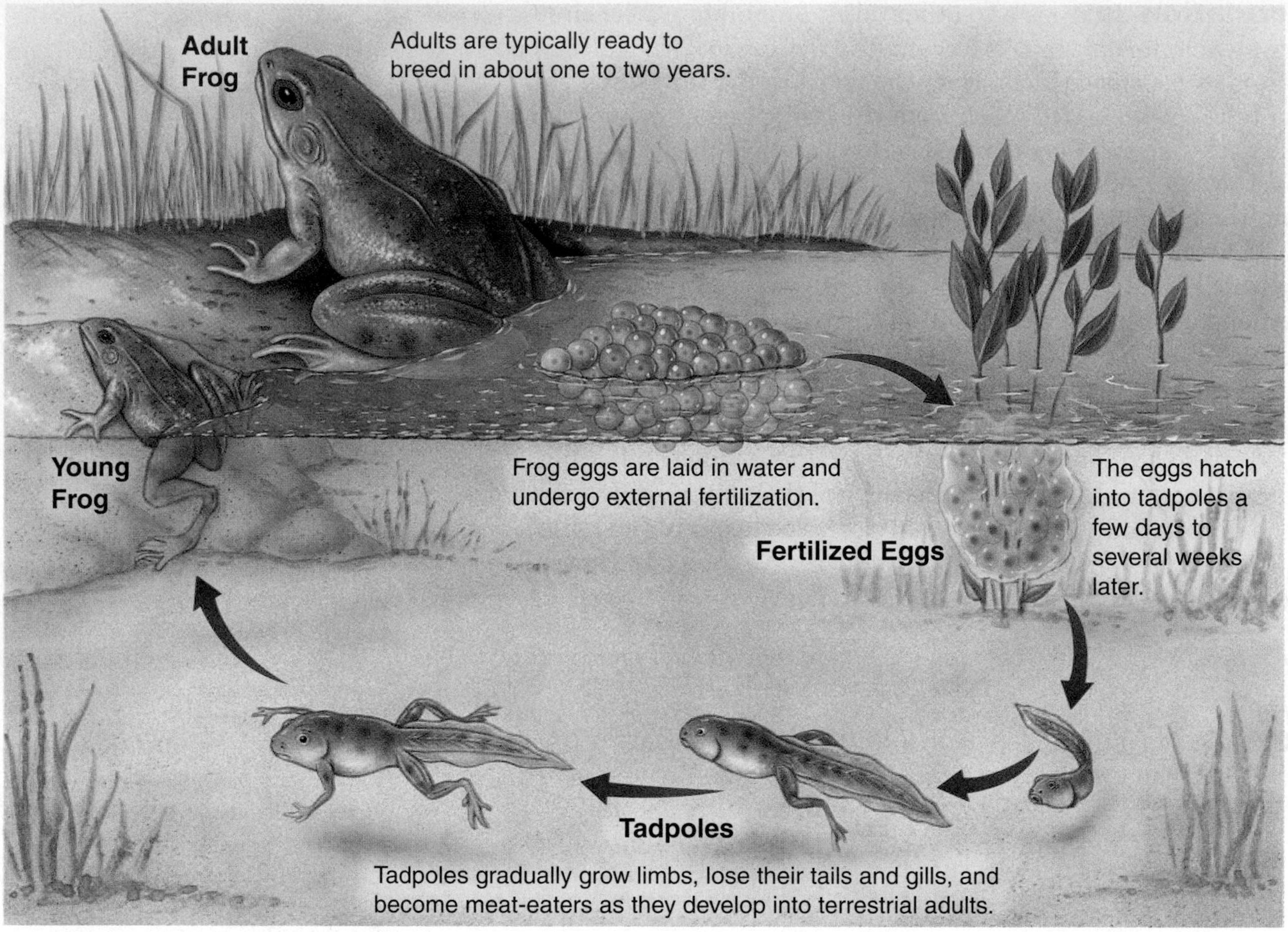

▲ **Figure 30–25** An amphibian typically begins its life in the water, then moves onto land as an adult. This diagram shows the process of metamorphosis in a frog. **Comparing and Contrasting** *How are tadpoles similar to fish? How are they different?*

Reproduction Amphibian eggs do not have shells and tend to dry out if they are not kept moist. Thus, in most species of amphibians, the female lays eggs in water, then the male fertilizes them externally. In a few species, including most salamanders, eggs are fertilized internally.

When frogs reproduce, the male climbs onto the female's back and squeezes. In response to this stimulus, the female releases as many as 200 eggs that the male then fertilizes. Frog eggs are encased in a sticky, transparent jelly that attaches the egg mass to underwater plants and makes the eggs difficult for predators to grasp. The yolk of the egg nourishes the developing embryos until they hatch into larvae that are commonly called tadpoles. **Figure 30–25** shows the metamorphosis of tadpoles into frogs.

Most amphibians, including common frogs, abandon their eggs after they lay them. A few take great care of both eggs and young. Some amphibians incubate their young in highly unusual places, such as in the mouth, on the back, or even in the stomach! Male midwife toads wrap sticky strings of fertilized eggs around their hind legs and carry them about until the eggs are ready to hatch.

CHECKPOINT
What is the function of the jelly surrounding frog eggs?

Movement Amphibian larvae often move very much like fishes, by wiggling their bodies and using a flattened tail for propulsion. Most adult amphibians, like other four-limbed vertebrates, use their front and back legs to move in a variety of ways. Adult salamanders have legs that stick out sideways. These animals walk—or, in some cases, run—by throwing their bodies into S-shaped curves and using their legs to push backward against the ground. Other amphibians, including frogs and toads, have well-developed hind limbs that enable them to jump long distances. Some amphibians, such as tree frogs, have disks on their toes that serve as suction cups for climbing.

Response The brain of an amphibian has the same basic parts as that of a fish. Like fishes, amphibians have well-developed nervous and sensory systems. **Figure 30–26** points out some sense organs in a typical frog. An amphibian's eyes are large and can move around in their sockets. The surface of the eye is protected from damage under water and kept moist on land by a transparent **nictitating** (NIK-tuh-tayt-ing) **membrane.** This movable membrane is located inside the regular eyelid, which can also be closed over the eye. Frogs have keen vision that enables them to spot and respond to moving insects. However, frogs probably do not see color as well as fishes do.

Amphibians hear through **tympanic** (tim-PAN-ik) **membranes,** or eardrums, located on each side of the head. In response to the external stimulus of sound, a tympanic membrane vibrates, sending sound waves deeper within the skull to the middle and inner ear. Many amphibian larvae and adults also have lateral line systems, like those of fishes, that detect water movement.

▼ **Figure 30–26** A frog's eyes and ears are among its most important sensory organs. Transparent eyelids called nictitating membranes protect the eyes underwater and keep them moist in air. Tympanic membranes receive sound vibrations from air as well as water. **Inferring** *What functions does hearing serve in frogs?*

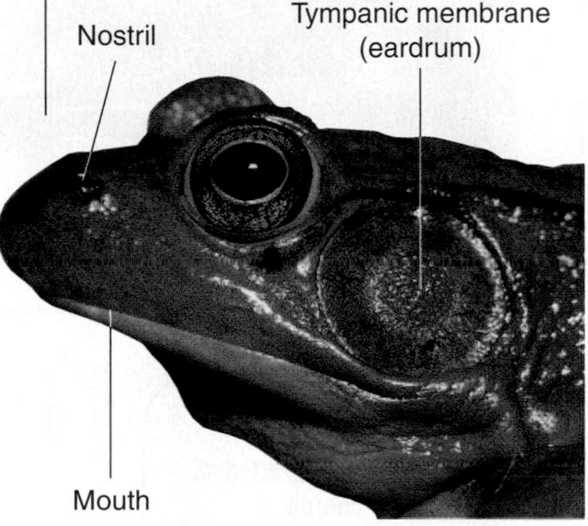

Analyzing Data

Amphibian Population Trends

Over the past several decades, scientists have reported changes in amphibian populations worldwide. In 2000, a team of researchers analyzed data sets contributed by various amphibian population studies conducted in 37 different countries. The results of this analysis are shown in the table. Study the data table and answer the questions.

Numbers of Amphibian Populations

Region	Declining	Increasing	No Trend
Western Europe	309	248	29
North America	130	96	14
South America	31	19	1
Australia/NZ	17	6	1
Asia	10	10	1
Eastern Europe	4	5	0
Africa/Middle East	2	2	1

1. **Using Tables and Graphs** How many amphibian populations were studied?
2. **Predicting** If the trends presented in the data table continue, how do you expect amphibian populations in North America to change in the next two decades?
3. **Calculating** What percentage of worldwide amphibian populations is decreasing?
4. **Evaluating** Do you think that regional population data can be used to predict global population trends? Explain your answer.

Figure 30–27 Diversity of Amphibians

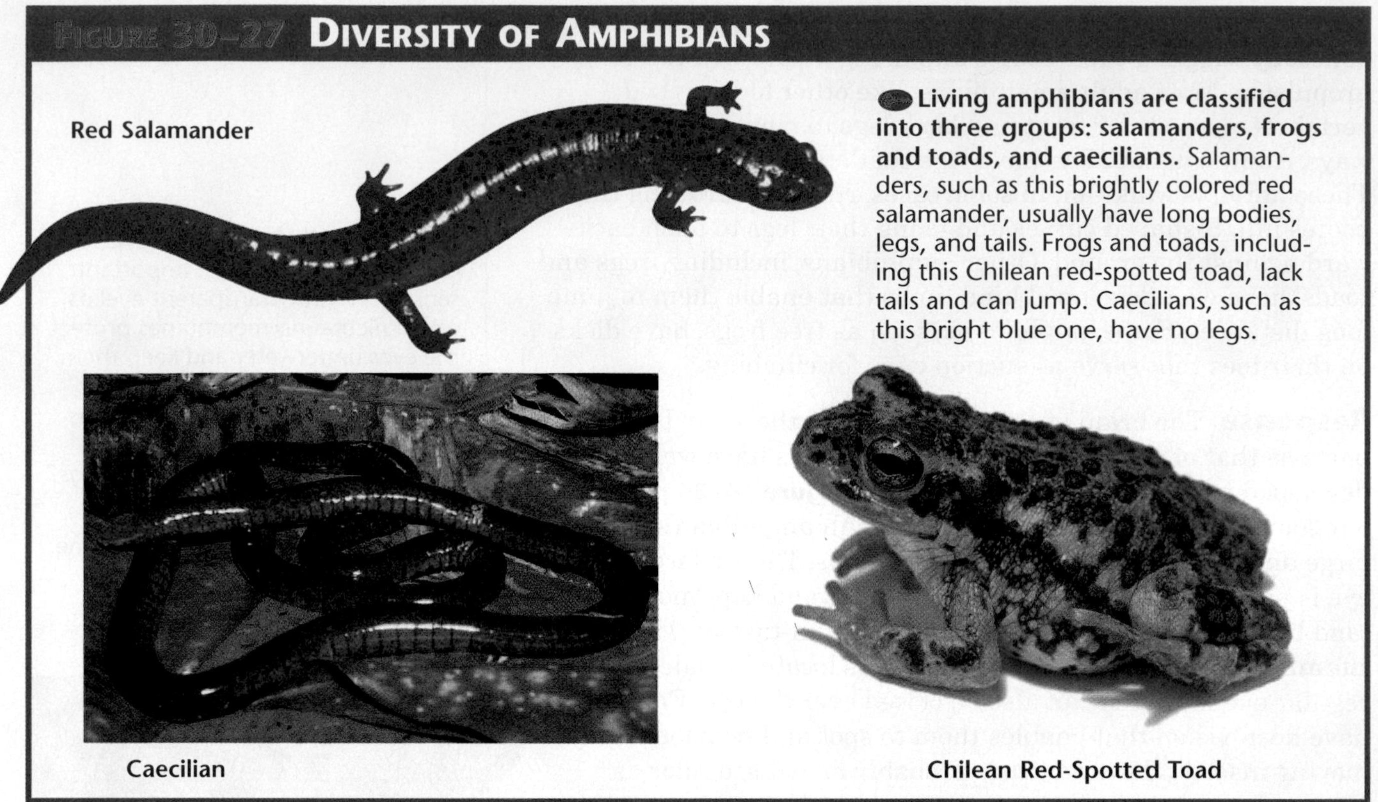

Living amphibians are classified into three groups: salamanders, frogs and toads, and caecilians. Salamanders, such as this brightly colored red salamander, usually have long bodies, legs, and tails. Frogs and toads, including this Chilean red-spotted toad, lack tails and can jump. Caecilians, such as this bright blue one, have no legs.

SCIENCE NEWS®
For: Articles on chordates and vertebrates
Visit: PHSchool.com
Web Code: cbe-9303

Groups of Amphibians

Modern amphibians can be classified into three categories. **The three groups of amphibians alive today are salamanders, frogs and toads, and caecilians.** Representative members are shown in **Figure 30–27.**

Salamanders Members of the order Urodela (yoor-oh-DEE-luh), including salamanders and newts, have long bodies and tails. Most also have four legs. Both adults and larvae are carnivores. The adults usually live in moist woods, where they tunnel under rocks and rotting logs. Some salamanders, such as the mud puppy, keep their gills and live in water all their lives.

Frogs and Toads The most obvious feature that members of the order Anura (uh-NOOR-uh) share is their ability to jump. Frogs tend to have long legs and make lengthy jumps, whereas the relatively short legs of toads limit them to short hops. Frogs are generally more closely tied to water—including ponds and streams—than toads, which often live in moist woods and even in deserts. Adult frogs and toads lack tails.

Caecilians The least known of the amphibians are the caecilians, members of the order Apoda (ay-POH-duh). Caecilians are legless animals that live in water or burrow in moist soil or sediment, feeding on small invertebrates such as termites. Many have fishlike scales embedded in their skin—which demonstrates that some amphibians don't fit the general definition.

Ecology of Amphibians

Amphibians must live near water, and they are common in moist, warm places such as tropical rain forest biomes. In contrast, because most amphibians cannot tolerate dry conditions, comparatively few live in desert biomes. Desert amphibians have adaptations that enable them to take advantage of water when it is available. For example, some toads stay inactive in sealed burrows for months, then emerge when a heavy rain falls.

Many amphibians make an ideal meal for predators such as birds and mammals. However, amphibians have adaptations that protect them from predators. For example, many species have skin colors and markings that enable them to blend in with their surroundings. Most adult amphibians, such as the toad in **Figure 30–28,** have skin glands that ooze an unpleasant-tasting and poisonous substance, or toxin.

Recently, scientists have noticed an alarming trend in amphibian populations worldwide. For the past several decades, the numbers of living species have been decreasing. The golden toad of Costa Rica, for example, seems to be extinct. In North America, the numbers of boreal toads have dwindled. Even the leopard frog and its relatives, once common worldwide, are getting harder to find.

Scientists do not yet know what is causing the global amphibian population to decline. It is possible that amphibians are susceptible to a wide variety of environmental threats, such as decreasing habitat, depletion of the ozone layer, acid rain, water pollution, fungal infections, introduced aquatic predators, and an increasing human population.

To better understand this phenomenon, biologists worldwide have been focusing their efforts and sharing data about amphibian populations. In the late 1990s, a group of scientists set up monitoring programs that cover the entire area of North America. One such program relies mostly on the efforts of volunteers, who are trained to recognize the specific call of various species such as cricket frogs, bullfrogs, or spring peepers.

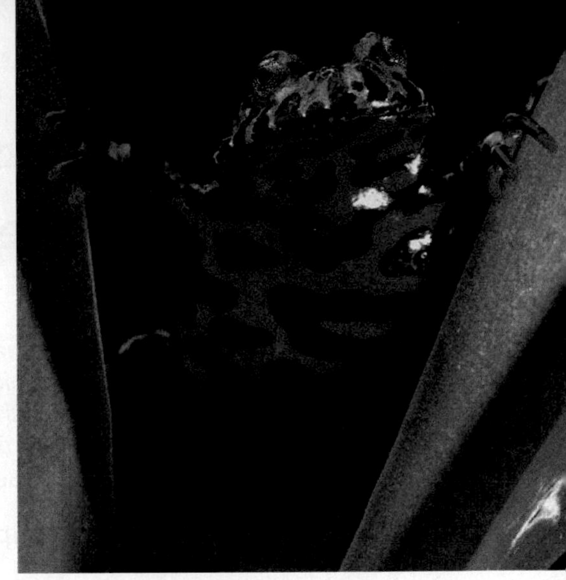

▲ **Figure 30–28** Some amphibians that release toxins, such as this European fire-bellied toad, have bodies that are brightly colored and have bold patterns. The colors and patterns serve as a warning to potential predators. **Using Analogies** ***How is the underside of this frog comparable to a dog showing its teeth?***

30–3 Section Assessment

1. **Key Concept** List the characteristics of amphibians.
2. **Key Concept** What adaptations helped amphibians evolve into land animals?
3. **Key Concept** List the three groups of amphibians.
4. What characteristics usually restrict amphibian reproduction to moist environments?
5. How are scientists attempting to deal with the problem of declining amphibian populations?
6. **Critical Thinking Formulating Hypotheses** Most caecilian species are totally blind as adults. How do you think this characteristic has evolved?

Thinking Visually

Making a Cycle Diagram

Construct a cycle diagram that identifies and describes the stages in the life cycle of a typical amphibian. For information about cycle diagrams, see Appendix A at the back of the book.

Exploration

Investigating Homeostasis in Fishes and Amphibians

All living organisms must maintain homeostasis, or a controlled internal environment. Fishes are adapted to avoid gaining or losing excessive amounts of water or salts due to osmosis. Amphibians need to maintain a surface that can absorb oxygen from air and release carbon dioxide. In this investigation, you will examine these adaptations.

Problem How do fishes and amphibians maintain homeostasis?

Materials

- 5 g saltwater fish
- 5 g freshwater fish
- balance
- 4 test tubes
- test tube rack
- paper towels
- 2 glass rods
- 10-mL graduated cylinder
- 2 funnels
- 2 filter-paper circles
- silver nitrate solution
- 1000-mL beaker
- vinegar
- distilled water
- string
- scissors
- transparent tape
- blue litmus paper
- sodium bicarbonate (baking soda)
- glass-marking pencil

Skills Evaluating and Revising, Using Models

Procedure      

Part A: Osmotic Homeostasis in Fishes

1. **Predicting** Predict whether saltwater fishes or freshwater fishes will have saltier flesh.
2. Put on your safety goggles, plastic gloves, and lab apron. Obtain 5-g samples of freshwater fish and saltwater fish. Label 2 test tubes "salt" and "fresh" with a glass-marking pencil. Place each sample into the corresponding test tube and add 10 mL of distilled water. Put the test tubes in the rack.
3. Fold 2 paper towels in half 3 times to make 2 cushions. Place a paper towel cushion under each test tube. To make an extract of each fish sample, gently mash the sample with a glass rod until it becomes pasty. Use a separate glass rod for each sample. **CAUTION:** *Be careful not to break the rods or the test tubes.*
4. Label 2 more test tubes "salt filtered" and "fresh filtered." Put the test tubes in a rack and place a funnel in each of these test tubes. Fold 2 filter-paper circles in half, and then in half again. Open one layer of each folded filter paper to form a cone as shown. Insert a paper cone into each funnel.

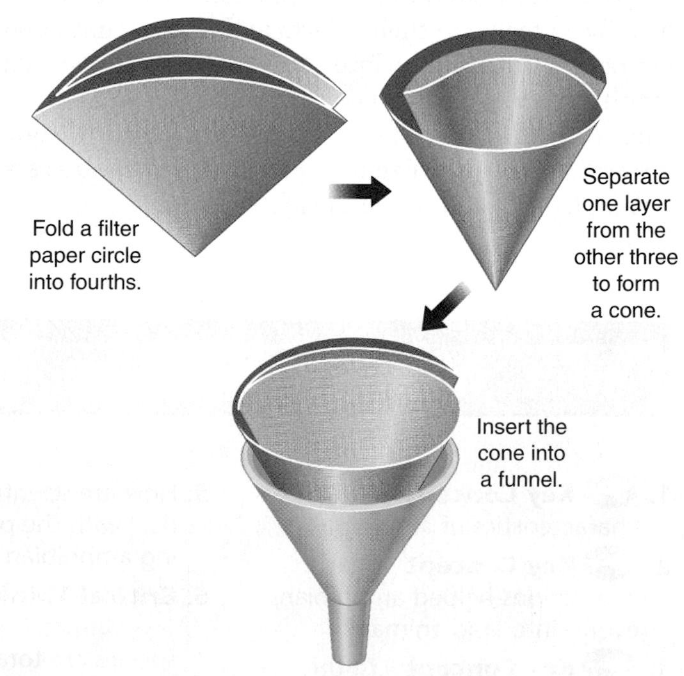

Fold a filter paper circle into fourths.
Separate one layer from the other three to form a cone.
Insert the cone into a funnel.

5. Pour the contents of the saltwater fish test tube into the funnel in the "salt filtered" test tube. Pour the contents of the freshwater fish test tube into the funnel in the "fresh filtered" test tube. Allow the liquid to filter through, and then remove the funnels.

6. Silver nitrate is a chemical that is used to detect salt. A drop of silver nitrate turns cloudy when it is added to a solution that contains salt. **CAUTION:** *Silver nitrate is toxic and will stain your skin and clothing.* Observe each filtered sample as you add 1 drop of silver nitrate solution. Then record your observations.

Part B: Gas Exchange in Air

7. **Predicting** Amphibians need to exchange oxygen and carbon dioxide with the air around them. Record your prediction of whether gases will enter a dry surface or a moist surface more quickly.

8. Place 100 mL of vinegar in a 1000-mL beaker. Cut a piece of paper large enough to cover the beaker and extend approximately 3 cm beyond the sides of the beaker.

9. Near the center of the paper, tape two 5-cm pieces of string approximately 3 cm apart. Then, tape a piece of blue litmus paper to the end of each string.

10. Use a drop of distilled water to moisten one of the strips of litmus paper, being sure to keep the other strip dry. The moist litmus paper is a model that represents an amphibian's skin. The color of the litmus paper will change to red In the presence of carbon dioxide gas, which acts as an acid. The reaction between vinegar and sodium bicarbonate produces this gas.

11. Add 5 g of sodium bicarbonate to the beaker of vinegar. Quickly cover the beaker with the paper lid so that the filter strips hang down into the beaker as shown in the photograph. Record the time required for each strip of litmus paper to change color.

12. Wash your hands thoroughly with soap and warm water before leaving the lab.

Analyze and Conclude

1. **Comparing and Contrasting** Compare the appearance of the saltwater and freshwater fish extracts after adding the silver nitrate.
2. **Inferring** What can you infer from this result about the ability of freshwater and saltwater fishes to maintain homeostasis?
3. **Drawing Conclusions** What must a freshwater fish do to maintain homeostasis? How would these activities differ in a saltwater fish?
4. **Inferring** What do your results in Part B indicate about the ability of gases to enter moist and dry surfaces?
5. **Inferring** Explain why it is important for amphibians to maintain a moist surface for gas exchange.

Go Further

Constructing an Alternative Model
In Part B, you created a model of how an amphibian's skin absorbs a gas. Construct an alternative model that shows a different characteristic of an amphibian's skin. (*Hint:* Recall that an amphibian's skin is thin, moist, and covered with mucus.) Analyze your new model by comparing it to the model in Part B. What does each model show that the other does not?

Chapter 30 Study Guide

30–1 The Chordates

Key Concepts

- A chordate is an animal that has, for at least some stage of its life, a dorsal, hollow nerve cord; a notochord; pharyngeal pouches; and a tail that extends beyond the anus.
- The two groups of nonvertebrate chordates are tunicates and lancelets.

Vocabulary
chordate, p. 767
notochord, p. 767
pharyngeal pouch, p. 767
vertebra, p. 768

30–2 Fishes

Key Concepts

- Fishes are aquatic vertebrates; most fishes have paired fins, scales, and gills.
- The evolution of jaws and the evolution of paired fins were important developments during the rise of fishes.
- Fishes' adaptations to aquatic life include various modes of feeding, specialized structures for gas exchange, and paired fins for locomotion.
- On the basis of their basic internal structure, all living fishes can be classified into three groups: jawless fishes, cartilaginous fishes, and bony fishes.

Vocabulary
cartilage, p. 773
atrium, p. 776
ventricle, p. 776
cerebrum, p. 777
cerebellum, p. 777
medulla oblongata, p. 777
lateral line system, p. 777
swim bladder, p. 777
oviparous, p. 778
ovoviviparous, p. 778
viviparous, p. 778

30–3 Amphibians

Key Concepts

- An amphibian is a vertebrate that, with some exceptions, lives in water as a larva and on land as an adult, breathes with lungs as an adult, has moist skin that contains mucous glands, and lacks scales and claws.
- Early amphibians evolved several adaptations that helped them live at least part of their lives out of water. Bones in the limbs and limb girdles of amphibians became stronger, permitting more-efficient movement. A set of lungs and breathing tubes enabled them to breathe air. Their sternum formed a bony shield that supports and protects the internal organs, especially the lungs.
- The three groups of living amphibians are salamanders, frogs and toads, and caecilians.

Vocabulary
cloaca, p. 784
nictitating membrane, p. 787
tympanic membrane, p. 787

Thinking Visually

Using information from this chapter, complete the following concept map:

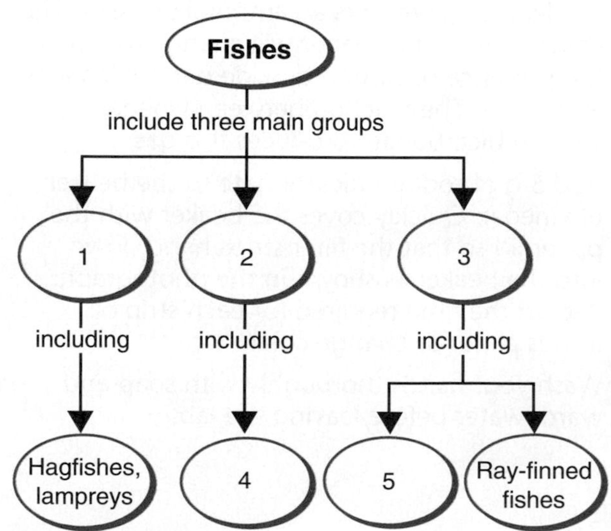

Preparing for the Living Environment Exam

NEW YORK LIVING ENVIRONMENT

Blue questions emphasize Regents Exam content

Chapter 30

Part A

Multiple Choice

For each statement or question, select the number of the word or expression that, of those given, best completes the statement or answers the question.

1 A characteristic not present in all chordates is
(1) hollow nerve cord
(2) pharyngeal pouches
(3) fins
(4) notochord

2 The term that is *least* closely related to the others is
(1) chordate (3) nonvertebrate
(2) cerebrum (4) lancelet

3 The evolution of jaws and paired fins was an important development during the rise of
(1) tunicates (3) fishes
(2) lancelets (4) amphibians

4 Most fishes exchange gases by pumping water from their mouths
(1) over the gill filaments
(2) through the pyloric ceca
(3) over the atrium
(4) through the esophagus

5 A fish's body movements would be affected if which part of the brain were damaged?
(1) olfactory lobe (3) cerebrum
(2) optic lobe (4) cerebellum

6 Examine the diagrams below. Which of these is a jawed cartilaginous fish?

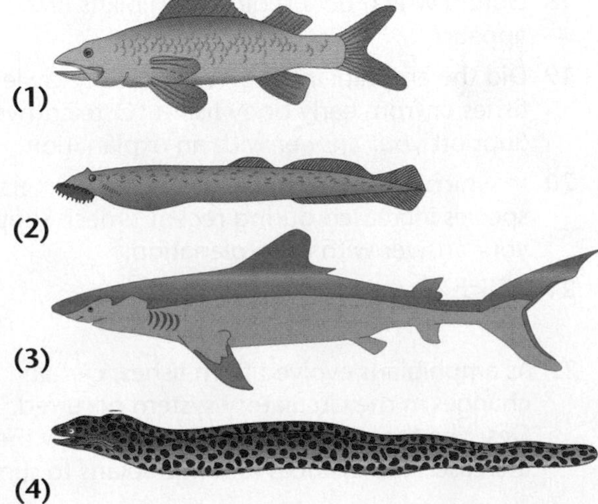

7 At the end of the large intestine of a frog is a muscular cavity called the
(1) cloaca (3) gallbladder
(2) pancreas (4) esophagus

8 An adult amphibian's heart typically has
(1) one chamber (3) three chambers
(2) two chambers (4) four chambers

9 Into which group can nonvertebrate chordates be classified?
A Lancelets
B Tunicates
C Fishes
(1) A, only (3) A and C, only
(2) A and B, only (4) A, B, and C

10 Each organ serves as an organ of gas exchange in frogs *except* the
(1) skin (3) lungs
(2) mouth cavity (4) nictitating membrane

11 Which statement is *never* true of oviparous fishes?
(1) Their eggs are fertilized externally.
(2) Their eggs hatch outside the mother's body.
(3) They have paired fins.
(4) The embryos receive nourishment directly from the mother's body.

12 Most amphibian larvae are
(1) carnivores
(2) producers
(3) filter feeders and herbivores
(4) parasites and omnivores

13 Organisms that feed through the mouth with no jaws and breathe through thin skin are
(1) lancelets (3) salamanders
(2) fishes (4) caecilians

Complete the following analogy by selecting the correct number. In analogies, A : B :: C : means "A is to B as C is to ___?___."

14 Tadpole: gills :: frog :
(1) atrium (3) scales
(2) lungs (4) stomach

Test-Taking Tip If a test question seems confusing, try rephrasing it in your own words. Often, rephrasing a question will allow you to better understand it.

Preparing for the Living Environment Exam

Part B

Multiple Choice and Extended Response
For those questions that ask you to select a response, choose the one that best completes the statement or answers the question. For all others follow the directions given.

Base your answers to questions 15 through 17 on the information and data table below and on your knowledge of biology.

An ecologist collected data about the number of frogs that inhabit a certain pond each year. In addition, he collected data about the total amount of rainfall in that area each spring. The data are shown in the table below.

Rainfall and Frog Population in Pond

Year	Amount of Rainfall (centimeters)	Number of Frogs
1995	13	45
1996	20	61
1997	8	33
1998	5	20
1999	23	63

15 In what year were the most frogs observed?
(1) 1996 (3) 1998
(2) 1997 (4) 1999

16 Which statement is best supported by the data?
(1) The number of frogs increased each year.
(2) The number of frogs decreased each year.
(3) The number of frogs in the pond increased as the amount of rainfall increased.
(4) The number of frogs in the pond decreased as the amount of rainfall increased.

17 Based on the data and your knowledge of the frog's life cycle, explain why the amount of rainfall might affect the number of frogs.

Base your answers to questions 18 through 21 on the information and chart below and on your knowledge of biology.

The chart below shows changes in five groups of vertebrates over the past 500 million years. The thickness of each band indicates changes in the relative number of species over geologic time.

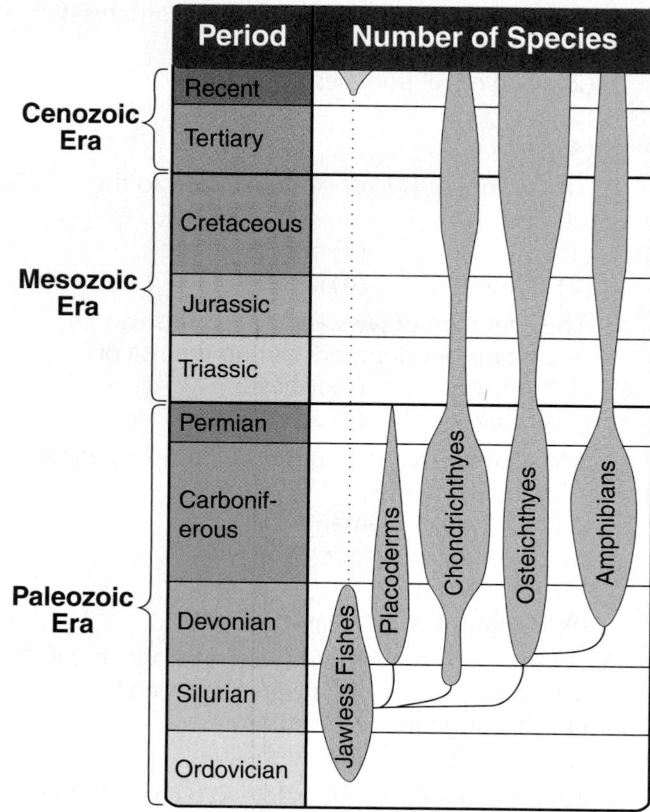

18 During which period did amphibians first appear?

19 Did the amphibians evolve from early jawless fishes or from early bony fishes (Osteichthyes)? Support your answer with an explanation.

20 In which groups of fishes have the numbers of species increased during recent times? Support your answer with an explanation.

21 Which group of fishes is extinct?

22 As amphibians evolved from fishes, certain changes in the circulatory system occurred. Describe these changes and explain how they increased the chances for amphibians to survive.

Part C

Extended Response

Answer the questions or follow the directions given.

Base your answers to questions 23 through 25 on the reading passage below and on your knowledge of biology.

Farm Ponds

Throughout New York state, there are many farm ponds on private land. The Department of Environmental Conservation provides guidelines for people interested in stocking a pond on their land.

Before beginning the process, individuals must obtain a stocking permit in order to have accurate records of what species of fish are being stocked. They must also determine whether the pond is "cold water" (the temperature stays below 72°F) or "warm water" (the temperature is above 72°F for long periods during summer). Coldwater ponds are generally stocked with trout. Warmwater ponds are stocked with largemouth bass.

Warmwater species can reproduce in the pond, whereas trout must be re-stocked every two years. A combination of largemouth bass/bluegill or bass/golden shiner is generally recommended for stocking.

Bluegills reproduce rapidly. If they are used to stock the pond, they must be heavily fished. Also, only 11 bass per acre should be caught annually in the average bass/bluegill pond.

23 From an ecological point of view, why is it important for wildlife managers to have a record of the species of fish in a stocked pond?

24 When stocking ponds, people must understand the flow of energy in a pond ecosystem. Using information provided in the passage, construct a food chain that illustrates the flow of energy through three or four different organisms.

25 Populations of organisms living in a pond must remain at certain levels for the ecosystem to remain in balance.

a Explain why it is important to heavily fish bluegills in order to maintain a balanced pond ecosystem. Support your answer with an explanation.

b Explain why is it important to *not* heavily fish bass each year. Support your answer with an explanation.

Base your answer to question 26 on the information below and on your knowledge of biology.

There are 18 salamander species in New York. A five-year survey was recently completed to document the distribution of these species throughout the state. Of particular interest is the eastern tiger salamander, which is on New York's endangered species list. Currently, the eastern tiger salamander lives only on Long Island, where most of its breeding colonies are in the eastern Pine Barrens. Heavy development on western Long Island has destroyed the salamander's habitat.The reproductive cycle of the tiger salamander begins with a brief courtship in the spring. The female lays a mass of eggs, which are fertilized by the male underwater. Larvae (young salamanders) hatch after about four weeks and remain in the pond until midsummer. They transform into air-breathing adults, leaving the pond and moving to land for their underground life.

It is interesting that the eastern tiger salamander spends most of its life underground and is often called the "mole salamander." Unlike many salamanders, this species does not spend its adult life in lakes or ponds. Yet, pesticides and other contaminants that enter pond ecosystems are a major threat to the eastern tiger salamanders' existence.

26 Wildlife managers have suggested constructing "salamander tunnels" under roadways separating salamander habitat from breeding ponds. Describe what will be likely to happen to the species diversity that exists in the eastern salamander population if these tunnels are not constructed. Support your answer with an explanation.

For: An interactive self-test
Visit: PHSchool.com
Web Code: cba-9300

CHAPTER 31

Reptiles and Birds

A spur-thighed tortoise hatches from its egg, ready to face life as a young reptile.

Inquiry Activity

How are bird eggs adapted for life on land?

Procedure  

1. Put on plastic gloves. Examine a frog egg. Describe the characteristics of the egg.
2. Examine a chicken egg. Open the egg on a disposable plate. Describe the structures inside. **CAUTION:** *Do not eat raw egg.*
3. Wash your hands with soap and warm water after completing this activity.

Think About It

1. **Inferring** What conditions do frog eggs require to develop? How does this affect which types of habitats these animals can live in?
2. **Formulating Hypotheses** How do the characteristics of bird eggs affect which types of habitats birds can live in?

31–1 Reptiles

4-3.1 Earth's species developed from earlier species
4-3.1 Fossils indicate extinction
LS- Make observations and state an appropriate hypothesis

Humans have always been fascinated by—and sometimes frightened of—reptiles. Some people fear snakes because of their venomous bites or the way they crawl. Explorers' encounters with lizards and crocodiles inspired images of dragons in European folk tales. Turtles, too, are the subject of many a fable. The truth about reptiles is that they are as astonishing as any creatures of human imagination.

Guide for Reading

Key Concepts
- What are the characteristics of reptiles?
- How are reptiles adapted to life on land?
- What are the four living orders of reptiles?

Vocabulary
ectotherm
amniotic egg
carapace
plastron

Reading Strategy: Outlining Before you read, use the headings in this section to make an outline about reptiles. As you read, add phrases or a sentence about each topic and subtopic in your outline.

What Is a Reptile?

The basic body plan of a reptile is typical of land vertebrates: a well-developed skull, a backbone and tail, two limb girdles, and four limbs. The iguana in **Figure 31–1** exhibits this body plan. Two types of reptiles have slightly different body plans. Snakes are mostly limbless, while turtles have hard shells that are fused to their vertebrae.

What characteristics do snakes, turtles, and other reptiles share? **A reptile is a vertebrate that has dry, scaly skin, lungs, and terrestrial eggs with several membranes.** These characteristics enable reptiles to live their entire lives out of water, unlike their amphibious relatives.

Reptilian skin is dry and often covered with thick, protective scales. These scales may be smooth or rough. A reptile's body covering helps prevent the loss of body water in dry environments. But dry, waterproof skin can also be a disadvantage to reptiles. Because the tough, scaly layer of skin does not grow when the rest of a reptile grows, it must be shed periodically as the reptile increases in size.

Today, reptiles are widely distributed on Earth. Temperate and tropical areas contain populations of reptiles that are remarkably diverse in appearance and lifestyle. The only places on Earth that most reptiles cannot live in are very cold areas. The reason for this will soon be apparent.

CHECKPOINT *What are the advantages of dry, scaly skin for reptiles?*

▶ **Figure 31–1** **Like all reptiles, this green iguana has lungs and dry, scaly skin.** These characteristics help the iguana live on land.

Word Origins

Dinosaur is a combination of two Greek words: *deinos,* meaning "terrible," and *sauros,* meaning "lizard." The suffix *-ian* is used to turn a noun into an adjective. The adjective *dinosaurian,* for example, describes a dinosaurlike animal. **What do you think the adjective *saurian* describes?**

Evolution of Reptiles

To colonize dry habitats, animals needed a way to reproduce that did not require depositing eggs into water. Reptiles, which evolved from amphibianlike ancestors, were the first vertebrates to develop this adaptation. The fossil of the first known reptile dates back to the Carboniferous Period, some 350 million years ago. As the Carboniferous Period came to a close and the Permian Period began, Earth's climate became cooler and less humid. Many lakes and swamps dried up, reducing the available habitat for water-dependent amphibians. Under these drier conditions, the first great adaptive radiation of reptiles began. These environmental pressures had a negative impact on the survival of many amphibian populations.

Mammal-like Reptiles By the end of the Permian Period, about 245 million years ago, a great variety of reptiles roamed Earth. One early group was the mammal-like reptiles, which displayed a mix of reptilian and mammalian characteristics. These chordates eventually came to dominate many land habitats. Toward the end of the Triassic Period, about 215 million years ago, another group of reptiles—the dinosaurs—became dominant.

Enter the Dinosaurs During the late Triassic and Jurassic periods, a great adaptive radiation of reptiles took place. The vast diversity and abundance of reptiles during that time are the main reasons why the Mesozoic Era is often called the Age of Reptiles. Two separate groups of large aquatic reptiles swam in the seas. Ancestors of modern turtles, crocodiles, lizards, and snakes populated many land habitats. And dinosaurs were everywhere. **Figure 31–2** shows two dinosaurs, *Plateosauras* and *Coelophysis.* The illustration also shows another kind of reptile, *Teratosaurus.*

▼ **Figure 31–2** In the Triassic Period, reptiles such as these lived in the forests. The herbivorous *Plateosaurus* (left), nibbling on leaves, was a dinosaur, as were the group of carnivorous *Coelophysis* (center). The large carnivorous *Teratosaurus* (right) was a reptile but not a dinosaur. **Observing** ***What characteristics did these reptiles have in common with modern reptiles?***

Problem Solving

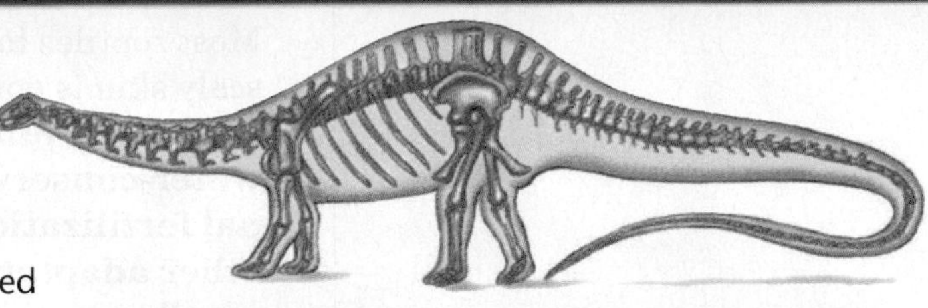

A Massive Controversy

Dinosaurs were the largest animals ever to walk on Earth. The plant-eating dinosaur *Brachiosaurus* reached lengths greater than 22 meters and had a mass of about 50,000 kilograms. It would take about 10 elephants to match the mass of one *Brachiosaurus.* How could the skeleton of such an animal support its immense mass? Imagine that you are a paleontologist searching for an answer to this question. Your job is to examine fossil skeletons of large dinosaurs for clues.

Defining the Problem Use your own words to describe the problem you face.

Organizing Information List the kinds of skeletal adaptations that would help a dinosaur support its mass.

Creating a Solution Carefully study the above illustration of a large dinosaur. Make a model of the part of the spinal column that is supported by the animal's legs. Include the legs in the model. Make another model of an alternative shape for the spinal column, one that is not curved.

Presenting Your Plan Describe what you might do to each model to discover which would support a greater mass. Show how you would test the models. Next to the models, place a card describing the steps in your test.

Dinosaurs ranged in size from small to enormous. They ran on two legs or lumbered along on four. Some, like *Plateosaurus,* ate leafy plants. *Coelophysis* and other hunters traveled in herds. Others, such as duckbilled *Maiasaura,* lived in small family groups, caring for their eggs and young in carefully constructed nests. Certain dinosaurs may even have had feathers, which may have evolved as a means of regulating body temperature. All of the dinosaurs, however, belonged to one of two major groups: the Ornithischia (awr-nuh-THISH-ee-uh), or "bird-hipped" dinosaurs, and the Saurischia (saw-RISH-ee-uh), or "lizard-hipped" dinosaurs. From one of these two branches of dinosaurs, probably the Saurischia, came the earliest members of evolutionary lines that would lead to modern birds.

Exit the Dinosaurs At the end of the Cretaceous Period, about 65 million years ago, a mass extinction occurred worldwide. This extinction was caused by a dramatic series of natural disasters. These disasters probably included a string of massive volcanic eruptions and lava flows, the dropping of sea level, and a huge asteroid or comet smashing into what is now the Yucatán Peninsula in Mexico. The asteroid or comet collision produced major forest fires and enormous dust clouds. After these events, dinosaurs, along with many other animal and plant groups, became extinct. The disappearance of these organisms during the late Cretaceous Period provided opportunities for other kinds of organisms to evolve on land and in the seas.

CHECKPOINT ***How did the extinction of the dinosaurs pave the way for modern reptiles?***

For: Links on dinosaur extinction
Visit: www.SciLinks.org
Web Code: cbn-9311

Form and Function in Reptiles

Most reptiles have adapted to a fully terrestrial life. Tough, scaly skin is one adaptation to this type of life. **Well-developed lungs; a double-loop circulatory system; a water-conserving excretory system; strong limbs; internal fertilization; and shelled, terrestrial eggs are the other adaptations that have contributed to the success of reptiles on land.** In addition, reptiles can control their body temperature by moving to a different place.

Body Temperature Control The ability to control their body temperature is an enormous asset for active animals. All the animals that you have read about so far are ectotherms (EK-toh-thurmz). **Ectotherms** rely on behavior to help control body temperature. Turtles, snakes, and other modern reptiles are all ectotherms. To warm up, they bask in the sun during the day or stay under water at night. To cool down, they move to the shade, go for a swim, or take shelter in underground burrows.

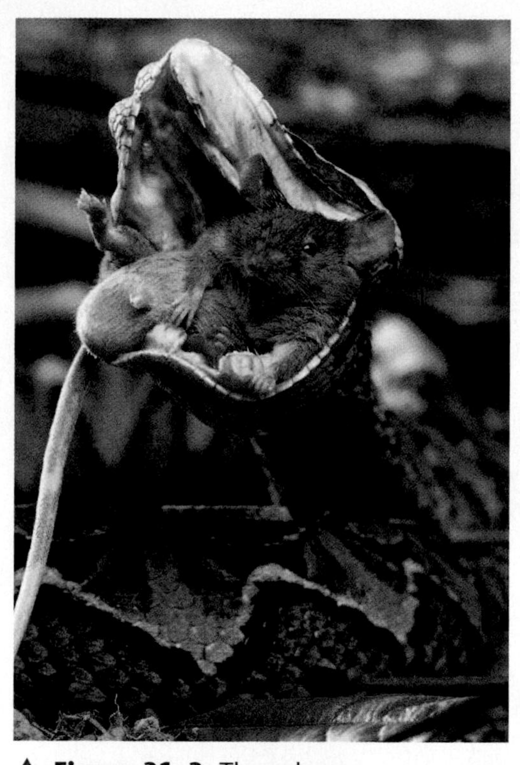

▲ **Figure 31–3** The gaboon viper, like all snakes, is entirely carnivorous. It eats mice and other small mammals by stretching its jaws wide and swallowing its prey whole. **Inferring** ***Besides feeding, what other function might fangs serve in snakes?***

Feeding Reptiles eat a wide range of foods. Iguanas, which are herbivores, tear plants into shreds and swallow the tough, fibrous chunks. Their long digestive systems enable them to break down plant material. Many other reptiles are carnivores. Snakes, for example, prey on small animals, bird eggs, or even other snakes, grabbing them with their jaws and swallowing them whole as shown in **Figure 31–3.** Crocodiles and alligators eat fish and even land animals when they can catch them. Most reptiles eat insects. Chameleons have sticky tongues as long as their bodies that flip out to catch insects.

Respiration The lungs of reptiles are spongy, providing more gas-exchange area than those of amphibians. This isn't surprising, because most reptiles cannot exchange gases through their skin the way many moist-skinned amphibians do. Many reptiles have muscles around their ribs that expand the chest cavity to inhale and collapse the cavity to force air out. Several species of crocodiles also have flaps of skin that can separate the mouth from the nasal passages, allowing these crocodiles to breathe through their nostrils while their mouth remains open. To exchange gases with the environment, reptiles have two efficient lungs or, in the case of certain species of snakes, one lung.

Circulation Reptiles have an efficient double-loop circulatory system. One of the loops brings blood to and from the lungs, and the other loop brings blood to and from the rest of the body. The heart diagram in **Figure 31–4** shows how blood flows through a turtle's heart. Reptile hearts contain two atria and either one or two ventricles. Most reptiles have a single ventricle with a partial septum, or wall, that helps separate oxygen-rich and oxygen-poor blood during the pumping cycle. Crocodiles and alligators, however, have the most developed hearts of living reptiles. The heart consists of two atria and two ventricles—an arrangement that is also found in birds and mammals.

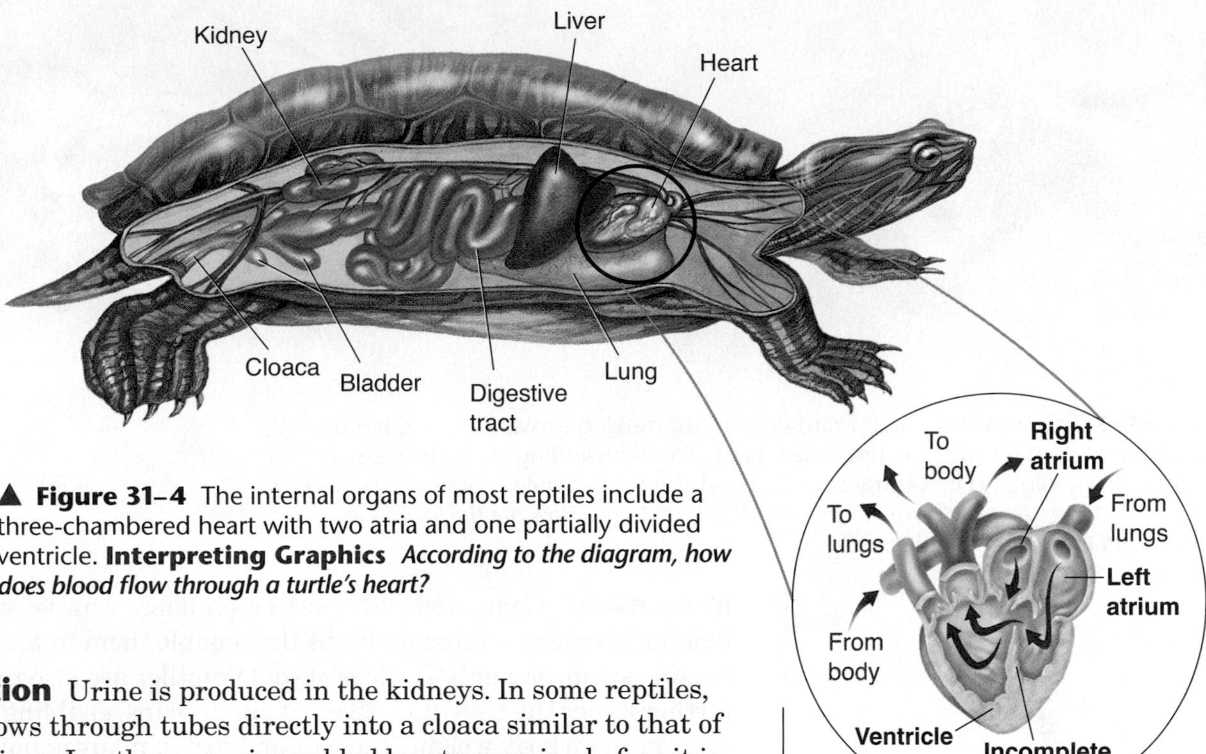

▲ **Figure 31–4** The internal organs of most reptiles include a three-chambered heart with two atria and one partially divided ventricle. **Interpreting Graphics** ***According to the diagram, how does blood flow through a turtle's heart?***

Excretion Urine is produced in the kidneys. In some reptiles, urine flows through tubes directly into a cloaca similar to that of amphibians. In others, a urinary bladder stores urine before it is expelled from the cloaca.

Reptiles' urine contains either ammonia or uric acid. Reptiles that live mainly in water, such as crocodiles and alligators, excrete most of their nitrogenous wastes in the form of ammonia, a toxic compound. Crocodiles and alligators drink a large amount of water, which dilutes the ammonia in the urine and helps carry it away. In contrast, many other reptiles—especially those that live entirely on land—do not excrete ammonia directly. Instead, they convert ammonia into a compound called uric acid. Uric acid is much less toxic than ammonia, so it does not have to be diluted as much. In these reptiles, excess water is absorbed in the cloaca, reducing urine to crystals of uric acid that form a pasty white solid. By eliminating wastes that contain little water, a reptile can conserve water.

Response The basic pattern of a reptile's brain is similar to that of an amphibian, although the cerebrum and cerebellum are considerably larger compared to the rest of the brain. Reptiles that are active during the day tend to have complex eyes and can see color well. Many snakes also have an extremely good sense of smell. In addition to a pair of nostrils, most reptiles have a pair of sensory organs in the roof of the mouth that can detect chemicals when the reptiles flick their tongues. Reptiles have simple ears with an external eardrum and a single bone that conducts sound to the inner ear. Snakes can also pick up vibrations in the ground through bones in their skulls. Some snakes, such as the viper in **Figure 31–5,** have the extraordinary ability to detect the body heat of their prey.

✓ ***How does a reptile's brain compare to an amphibian's?***

▼ **Figure 31–5** The heat-sensitive pits above this eyelash viper's mouth enable it to locate prey, even in total darkness. Snakes that have these pits are commonly called pit vipers. **Inferring** ***How would these organs give pit vipers an advantage over other reptiles?***

Figure 31–6 The shovel-snouted lizard (left) is not moving forward; rather, it lifts its feet to limit contact with the hot desert sand. The sidewinding adder propels itself forward by digging its ventral scales against the dunes while pushing its body into long curving waves. **Comparing and Contrasting** *How are the lizard's legs different from those of an amphibian?*

Movement Compared with most amphibians, reptiles with legs tend to have larger, stronger limbs that enable them to walk, run, burrow, swim, or climb. The legs of some reptiles are also rotated further under the body than those of amphibians, enabling reptiles to carry more body weight. The legs and feet of many aquatic turtles have developed into flippers. **Figure 31–6** shows some ways that reptiles can move. As with amphibians, the backbones of reptiles help accomplish much of their movement.

▼ **Figure 31–7** After a female box turtle digs a hole in the ground for her nest, she lays her eggs, dropping them one by one and gently lowering them into the hole with her hind feet. When she finishes, she will cover up her nest and leave without a backward glance. **Inferring** *Why would it be an advantage for turtles to lay a large number of eggs?*

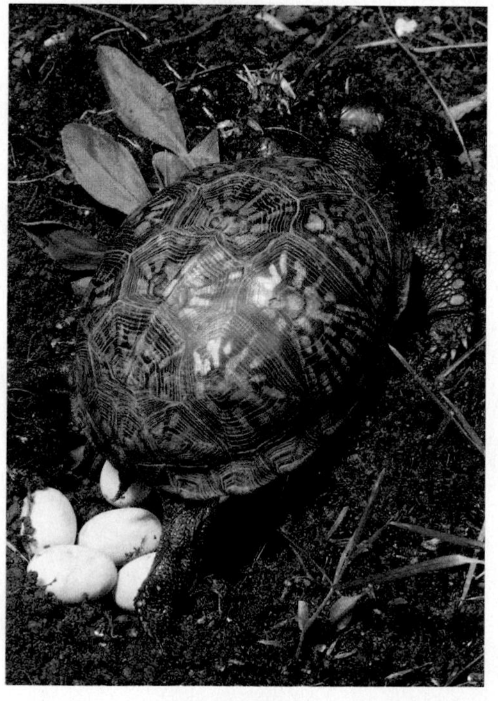

Reproduction All reptiles reproduce by internal fertilization, in which the male deposits sperm inside the body of the female. Most male reptiles have a penislike organ that allows them to deliver sperm into the female's cloaca. After fertilization has occurred, the female's reproductive system covers the embryos with several membranes and a leathery shell.

Most reptiles are oviparous, laying eggs that develop outside the mother's body. Some species, such as the box turtle in **Figure 31–7,** lay their eggs in carefully prepared nests, then abandon them. Alligators also lay their eggs in nests, but they guard the eggs until they hatch, and provide some care after hatching. Some snakes and lizards are ovoviviparous, and the young are born alive. By carrying her eggs within her body, the female can protect the eggs and keep them warm.

Unlike an amphibian egg, which almost always needs to develop in water, the shell and membranes of a reptilian egg create a protected environment in which the embryo can develop without drying out. This type of egg is called an **amniotic** (am-nee-AHT-ik) **egg,** named after the amnion, one of the four membranes that surrounds the developing embryo. The other three membranes are the yolk sac, the chorion, and the allantois. Find each of these membranes in **Figure 31–8** and learn about their functions. The amniotic egg, also seen in birds, is one of the most important adaptations to life on land.

CHECKPOINT *What are the four parts of an amniotic egg?*

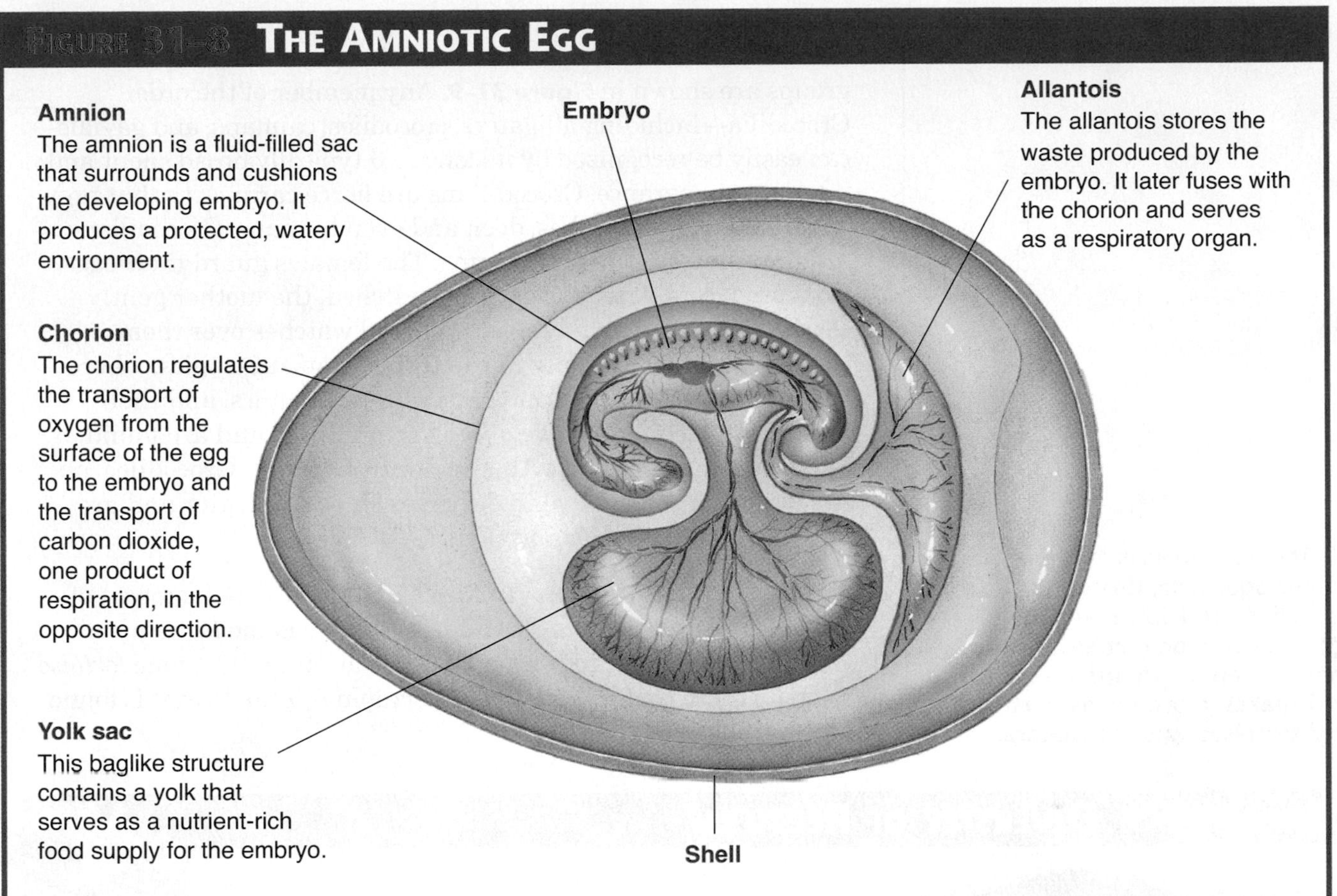

Figure 31–8 The Amniotic Egg
Amnion
The amnion is a fluid-filled sac that surrounds and cushions the developing embryo. It produces a protected, watery environment.
Embryo
Allantois
The allantois stores the waste produced by the embryo. It later fuses with the chorion and serves as a respiratory organ.
Chorion
The chorion regulates the transport of oxygen from the surface of the egg to the embryo and the transport of carbon dioxide, one product of respiration, in the opposite direction.
Yolk sac
This baglike structure contains a yolk that serves as a nutrient-rich food supply for the embryo.
Shell

▲ An amniotic egg contains several membranes and an external shell. Although it is waterproof, the egg shell is porous, allowing gases to pass through. The shell of reptile eggs is usually soft and leathery. **The amniotic egg is one of the most important adaptations to life on dry land.**

Groups of Reptiles

Since the dinosaurs disappeared, modern reptiles have had plenty of time and space to diversify. **The four surviving groups of reptiles are lizards and snakes, crocodilians, turtles and tortoises, and the tuatara (too-uh-TAH-ruh).**

Lizards and Snakes Modern lizards and snakes belong to the order Squamata (skwa-MAH-tuh), or scaly reptiles. Most lizards have legs, clawed toes, external ears, and movable eyelids. Some lizards have evolved into highly specialized forms. For example, Gila (HEE-luh) monsters—large, stocky lizards that live in the southwestern United States and Mexico—have glands in the lower jaw that produce venom for defense against predators.

Snakes have lost both pairs of legs during the course of their evolution. Although they are legless, snakes are highly efficient predators, even in the ocean. Some snakes are so small that they resemble earthworms. Others, such as some species of python, can grow to more than 8 meters in length. The ability of certain snakes to produce venom has caused some people to harbor an unjustified fear of all snakes. More people in the United States die from bee stings than from snakebites. In fact, snakes tend to avoid people, not confront them!

Crocodilians Examples of crocodilians and other reptile groups are shown in **Figure 31–9.** Any member of the order Crocodilia—including alligators, crocodiles, caimans, and gavials—can easily be recognized by its long and typically broad snout and its squat appearance. Crocodilians are fierce carnivores that prey on animals such as fishes, deer, and even humans. Crocodilians are very protective of their young. The females guard their eggs from predators. After the eggs are hatched, the mother gently carries her young to a nursery area and watches over them.

Crocodilians live only in the tropics and subtropics, where the climate remains warm year-round. Alligators, and their relatives the caimans, live only in fresh water and are found almost exclusively in North and South America. Crocodiles, on the other hand, may live in either fresh or salt water and are native to Africa, India, and Southeast Asia.

▼ The four orders of living reptiles are the Squamata, Crocodilia, Testudines, and Sphenodonta. **The common names of these modern reptile groups are lizards and snakes, crocodilians, turtles and tortoises, and the tuatara.**

Turtles and Tortoises Turtles and tortoises are members of the order Testudines (tes-TOO-dih-neez). The name *turtle* usually refers to members of this order that live in water; the name *tortoise* refers to those that live on land. A terrapin is a turtle that is found in water that is somewhat salty.

FIGURE 31–9 DIVERSITY OF REPTILES

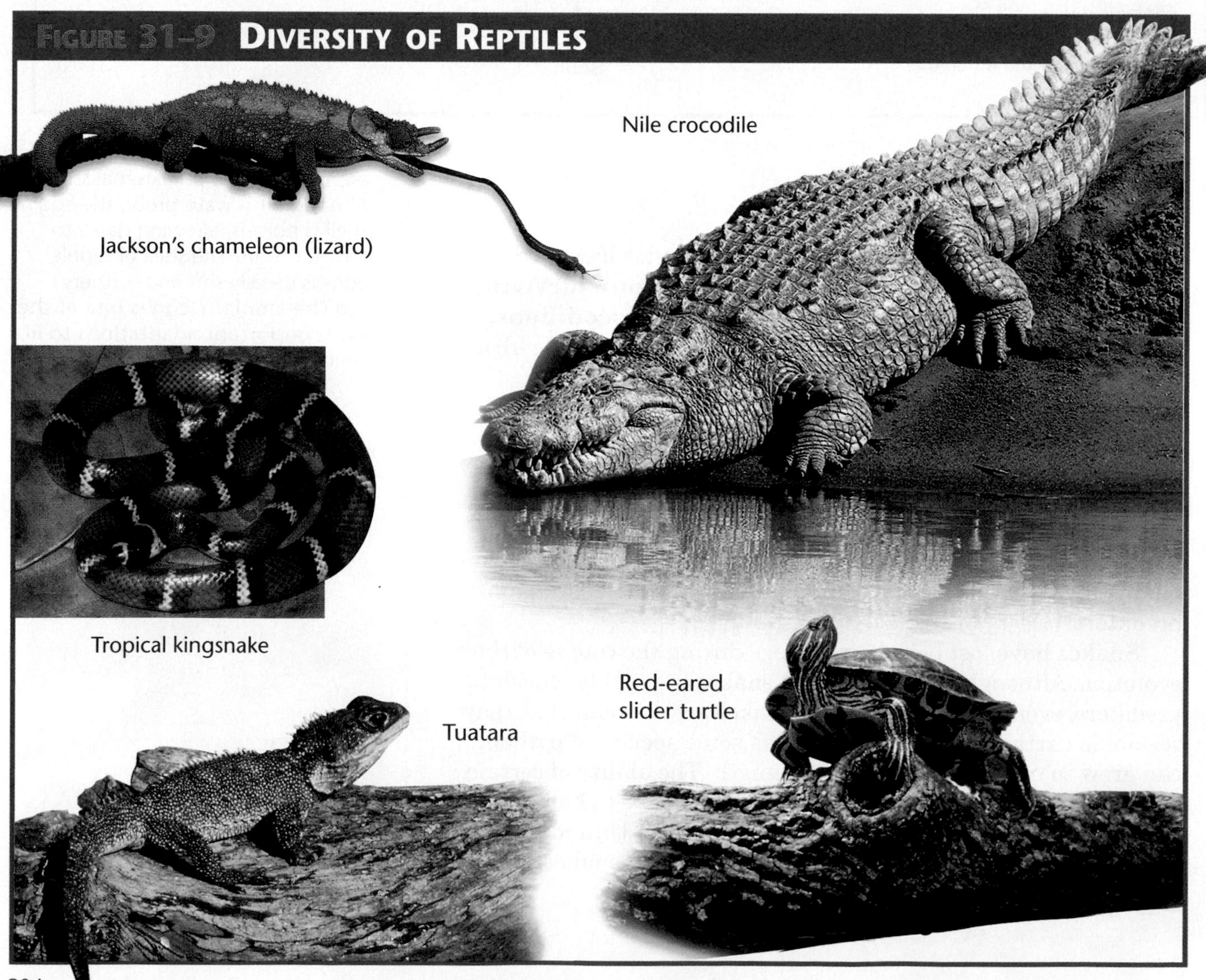

Turtles and tortoises have a shell built into the skeleton, although in a few species the shell is not very hard. The shell consists of two parts: a dorsal part, or **carapace,** and a ventral part, or **plastron.** The animal's backbone forms the center of the carapace. The head, legs, and tail stick out through holes where the carapace and plastron join. Tortoises and most turtles pull into their shells to protect themselves.

Several other adaptations allow turtles and tortoises to live in a wide range of habitats—dry, wet, and in-between. Lacking teeth, these reptiles have horny ridges that cover the upper and lower jaws. The jaws are often powerful enough to deliver a damaging bite. All possess strong limbs that lift their body off the ground when walking or, in the case of sea turtles, to drag themselves across a sandy shore to lay eggs.

Tuataras The tuatara is the only surviving member of the order Sphenodonta (sfen-uh-DONT-uh). It is found only on a few small islands off the coast of New Zealand. Tuataras resemble lizards, but they differ from lizards in many ways. For example, they lack external ears and retain primitive scales. Tuataras also have a legendary "third eye," which is part of a complex organ located on top of the brain. This eye can sense the level of sunlight, but its function is unknown.

▲ **Figure 31–10** This wildlife ranger is retrieving green sea turtle eggs on Turtle Island National Park in Borneo. He will bring the eggs to an incubation station, where they can hatch safe from harm. After hatching, the young turtles will be released to the sea. **Inferring** ***What might harm sea turtle eggs that are left on a beach to hatch?***

Ecology of Reptiles

Many reptiles are in danger because their habitats have been, and are being, destroyed. In addition, humans hunt reptiles for food, to sell as pets, and for their skins, from which bags, boots, and combs are made. Laws now protect some species, such as sea turtles, which were once numerous in both the Atlantic and Pacific oceans. Sea turtle recovery programs, such as the one shown in **Figure 31–10,** give many young turtles a head start on survival. Although there are many other programs in place that protect reptiles, more conservation efforts are needed worldwide to counteract their dwindling numbers.

31–1 Section Assessment

1. **Key Concept** List the main characteristics of reptiles.
2. **Key Concept** List five ways that reptiles are adapted to life on dry land.
3. **Key Concept** Name the four orders of modern reptiles and give an example of each.
4. How is excretion carried out in reptiles that live on land?
5. How does a lizard control its body temperature?
6. **Critical Thinking Predicting** What might happen to reptiles if conditions on Earth became permanently warmer and much damper?

Connecting Concepts

Survival in Desert Biomes
In Chapter 4, you learned about different biomes, including deserts. In Chapter 30, you learned the characteristics of amphibians. Use this knowledge to explain why more reptiles than amphibians can tolerate the hot, dry climate of deserts. *Hint:* Compare reptiles' and amphibians' adaptations to living on land.

31–2 Birds

4-3.1 Fossils indicate extinction
4-7.2 Human activities can degrade ecosystems
LS- Safety, use of instruments, make observations
LS- Organize data, design experiments, and interpret results

Guide for Reading

Key Concepts
- What characteristics do birds have in common?
- How are birds adapted for flight?

Vocabulary
feather
endotherm
crop
gizzard
air sac

Reading Strategy: Monitoring Your Understanding
As you read, make sure that you understand what you read. If you have difficulty, think of a strategy that might make the text clearer. For example, you might read the paragraph again, slowly; see whether an illustration helps you understand the printed text; or ask another student or your teacher for help.

Whether they are greeting the dawn with song or coloring the air with brilliant feathers, birds are among the most obvious and welcome of all animals. From common robins to the spectacular and rare quetzal of Central America, the nearly 10,000 modern bird species seem to live everywhere.

What Is a Bird?

In a group this diverse, it is difficult to find many characteristics that are shared by all members. But we can identify the features that most birds have in common. **Birds are reptilelike animals that maintain a constant internal body temperature. They have an outer covering of feathers; two legs that are covered with scales and are used for walking or perching; and front limbs modified into wings.** Most of these features are adaptations for flight.

The single most important characteristic that separates birds from living reptiles, and from all other living animals, is feathers. **Feathers** are made mostly of protein and develop from pits in the birds' skin. Feathers help birds fly and also keep them warm. **Figure 31–11** shows the two main types of feathers: contour feathers and down. Herons and some other birds that live on or in water also have powder down, which releases a fine powder that repels water.

▼ **Figure 31–11** Birds have different types of feathers that vary in structure and function. **An outer covering of feathers is the main characteristic that sets birds apart from other animals.**

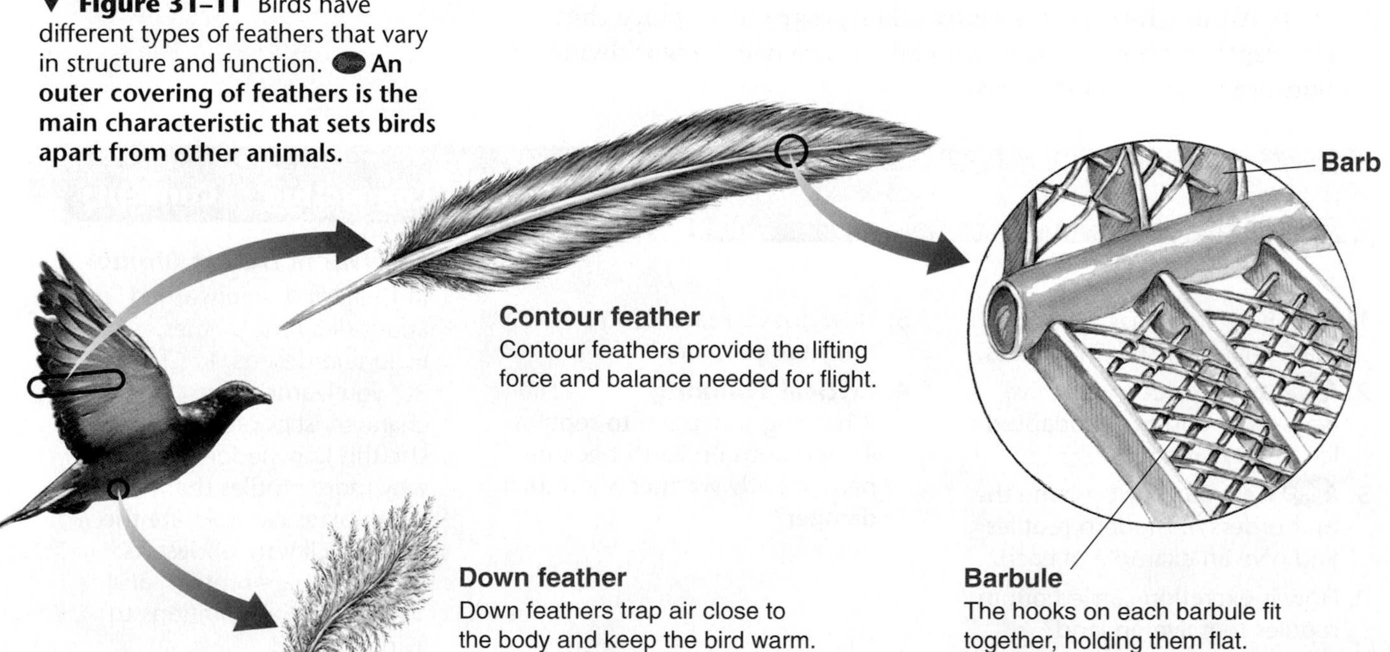
Barb
Contour feather
Contour feathers provide the lifting force and balance needed for flight.
Down feather
Down feathers trap air close to the body and keep the bird warm.
Barbule
The hooks on each barbule fit together, holding them flat.

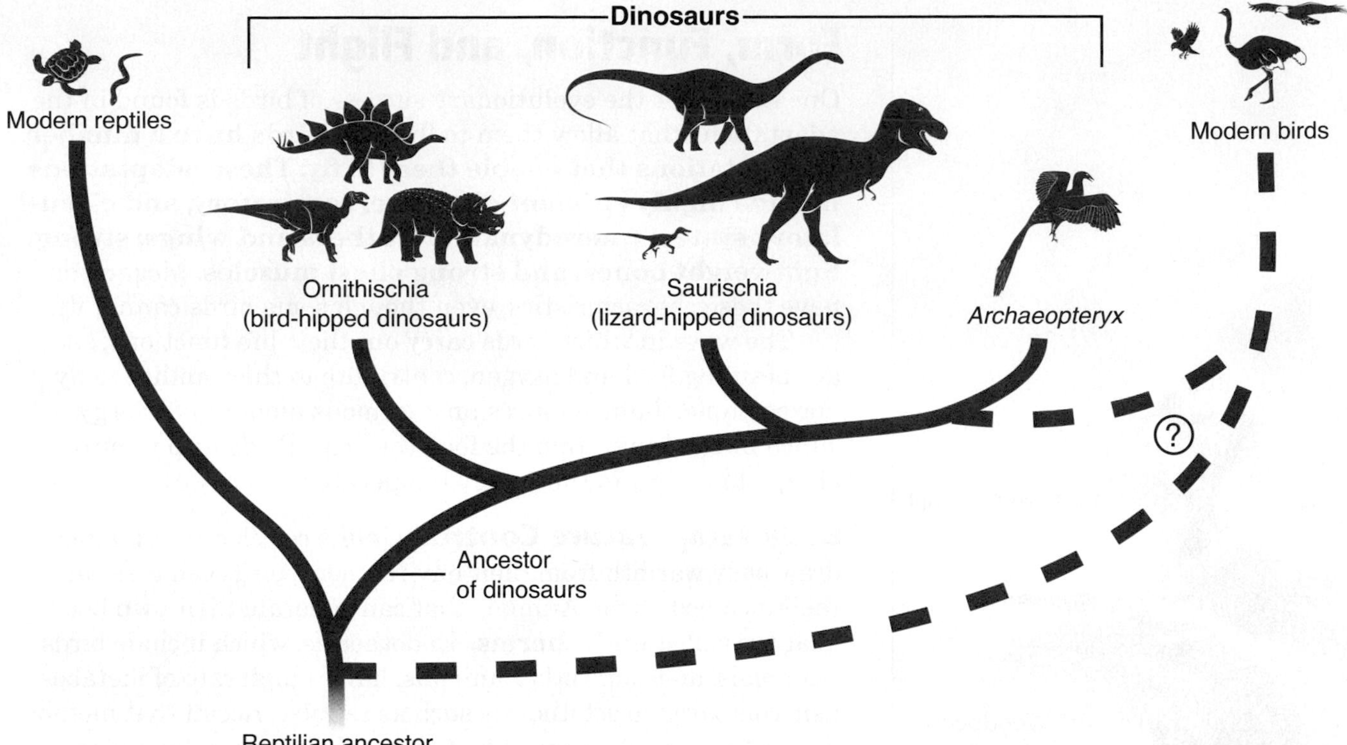

Evolution of Birds

Paleontologists agree that birds evolved from extinct reptiles. Evidence for this hypothesis is provided by many embryological, anatomical, and physiological characteristics shared by modern birds and living reptiles. For example, the embryos of birds and reptiles develop within amniotic eggs. Birds, like most reptiles, excrete nitrogenous wastes in the form of uric acid. The bones that support the front and hind limbs, and several other parts of the skeleton, are similar in both groups.

Most paleontologists think that birds evolved directly from dinosaurs. Part of the evidence consists of *Archaeopteryx* (ahr-kee-AHP-tur-iks), the first birdlike fossil discovered. This fossil dates from the late Jurassic Period, about 150 million years ago. *Archaeopteryx* looked so much like a small, running dinosaur that it would be classified as a dinosaur except for one important feature: It had well-developed feathers covering most of its body. Those feathers led to the classification of *Archaeopteryx* as an early bird. Unlike modern birds, however, this creature had teeth in its beak, a bony tail, and toes and claws on its wings. Thus, *Archaeopteryx* can be seen as a transitional species with characteristics of both dinosaurs and birds.

However, other fossil evidence leads some researchers to hypothesize that birds and dinosaurs both evolved from an earlier common ancestor. The origin of birds is still not completely resolved, as shown in **Figure 31–12.** New fossils of ancient birds are being found all the time. So watch for new discoveries and discussions on the subject!

What is Archaeopteryx*?*

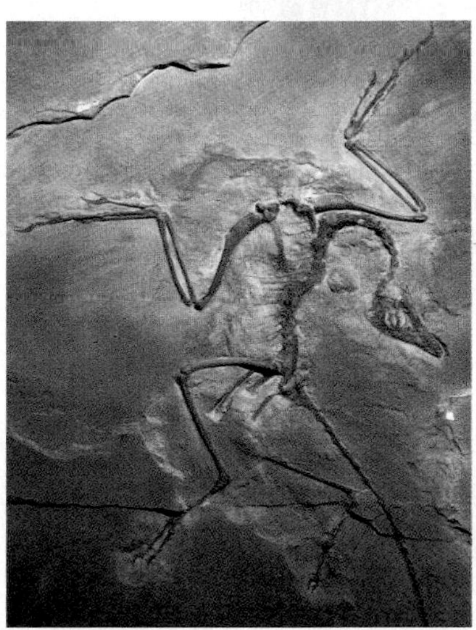

▲ **Figure 31–12** The diagram at the top shows the evolutionary tree of modern birds. None of the animals shown are direct ancestors of modern birds. But fossils such as *Archaeopteryx* (above) do show a mixture of characteristics of birds and dinosaurs. **Interpreting Graphics** ***Based on the diagram, what are the two alternative explanations for the evolution of modern birds?***

Form, Function, and Flight

One reason for the evolutionary success of birds is found in the adaptations that allow them to fly. **Birds have a number of adaptations that enable them to fly. These adaptations include highly efficient digestive, respiratory, and circulatory systems; aerodynamic feathers and wings; strong, lightweight bones; and strong chest muscles.** Most birds have these characteristics, even though some birds cannot fly.

The ways in which birds carry out their life functions, such as obtaining food and oxygen, contribute to their ability to fly. For example, flight requires an enormous amount of energy, which birds obtain from the food they eat. Birds also require energy to maintain their body temperature.

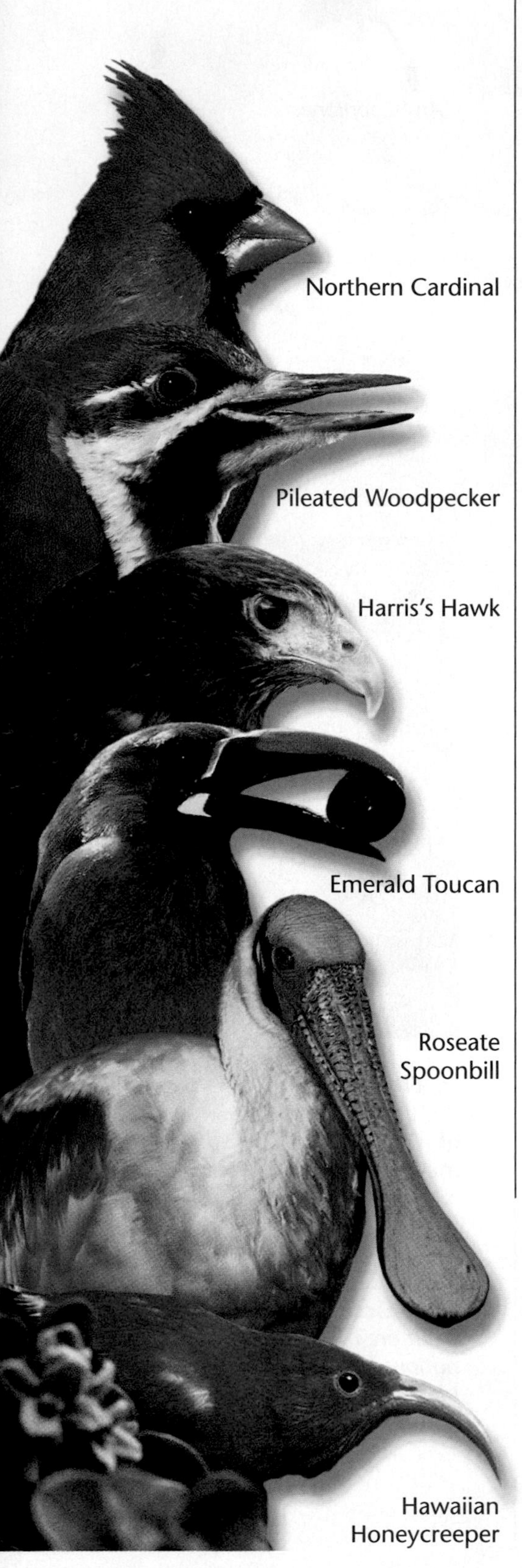

Body Temperature Control Unlike reptiles, which must draw body warmth from their environment, birds can generate their own body heat. Animals that can generate their own body heat are called **endotherms.** Endotherms, which include birds, mammals, and some other animals, have a high rate of metabolism compared to ectotherms such as reptiles. Recall that metabolism is the sum of chemical and physical processes that go on inside the body. Metabolism produces heat. A bird's feathers insulate its body enough to conserve most of its metabolic energy, allowing the bird to warm its body more efficiently. The body temperature of most birds is about 41°C even on cold winter days.

 *What is an endotherm?*

Feeding Any body heat that a bird loses must be regained by eating food. The more food a bird eats, the more heat energy its metabolism can generate. Because small birds lose heat relatively faster than large ones, small birds must eat more, relative to their body size. In fact, the phrase "eats like a bird" is quite misleading, because most birds are voracious eaters!

As you can see in **Figure 31–13,** birds' beaks, or bills, are adapted to the type of food they eat. Insect-eating birds have short, fine bills that can pick ants and other insects off leaves and branches, or can catch flying insects. Seed-eaters have short, thick bills. Carnivorous birds, such as eagles, shred their prey with strong hooked bills. Long, thin bills can be used for gathering nectar from flowers or probing soft mud for worms and shellfish. Large, long bills help birds to pick fruit from branches, while long, flat bills are used to grasp fish.

Figure 31–13 Bird bills come in a variety of shapes and sizes. You can tell a good deal about a bird's feeding habits from its bill. **Drawing Conclusions** *Based on the size and shape of its bill, what does a roseate spoonbill feed on?*

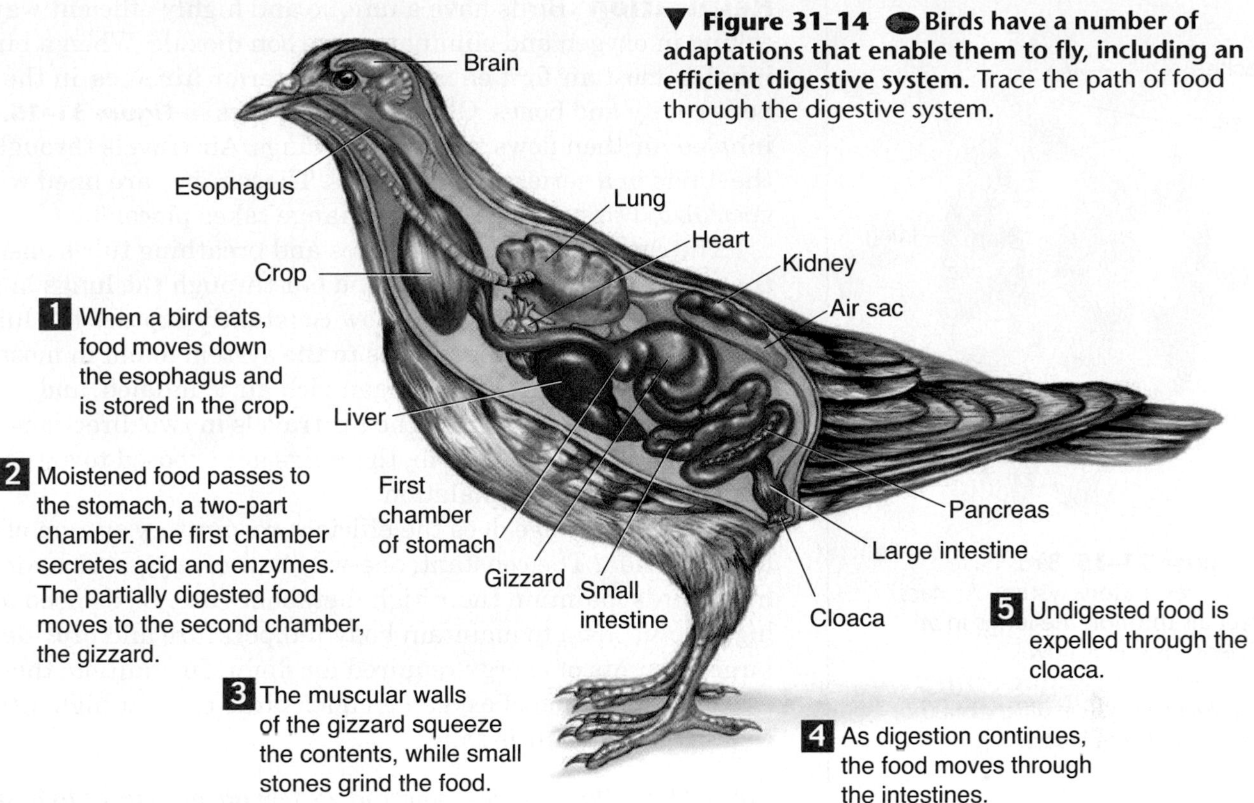
Brain
Esophagus
Lung
Heart
Kidney
Crop
Air sac
1 When a bird eats, food moves down the esophagus and is stored in the crop.
Liver
2 Moistened food passes to the stomach, a two-part chamber. The first chamber secretes acid and enzymes. The partially digested food moves to the second chamber, the gizzard.
First chamber of stomach
Pancreas
Large intestine
Gizzard
Small intestine
Cloaca
5 Undigested food is expelled through the cloaca.
3 The muscular walls of the gizzard squeeze the contents, while small stones grind the food.
4 As digestion continues, the food moves through the intestines.

▼ **Figure 31–14** **Birds have a number of adaptations that enable them to fly, including an efficient digestive system.** Trace the path of food through the digestive system.

The digestive system of a bird is shown in **Figure 31–14.** Birds lack teeth, and therefore they cannot break down food by chewing it. However, many birds have specialized structures to help digest food. One such structure is the **crop,** which is located at the lower end of the esophagus. Food is stored and moistened in the crop before it moves further in the digestive tract.

In some birds, such as pigeons, the crop has a second function. During nesting season, the breakdown of cells in the crop produces a substance that is rich in protein and fat. Parent birds regurgitate this substance and feed their newly hatched young with it. This substance provides the young birds with materials they need to grow.

From the crop, moistened food moves into the stomach. The form that a bird's stomach takes depends on the bird's feeding habits. Birds that eat meat or fish have an expandable area in which large amounts of soft food can be stored. Birds that eat insects or seeds, however, have a muscular organ called the **gizzard** that helps in the mechanical breakdown of food by grinding it. The gizzard forms part of the stomach. In many species of bird, the gizzard contains small pieces of stone and gravel that the bird has swallowed. The thick, muscular walls of the gizzard grind the gravel and food together, crushing food particles and making them easier to digest.

Food moves from the stomach to the small intestine, where the breakdown of food is completed and food is absorbed into the body. Digestive wastes leave the body through the cloaca.

Go Online
NSTA SCiLINKS

For: Links on birds
Visit: www.SciLinks.org
Web Code: cbn-9312

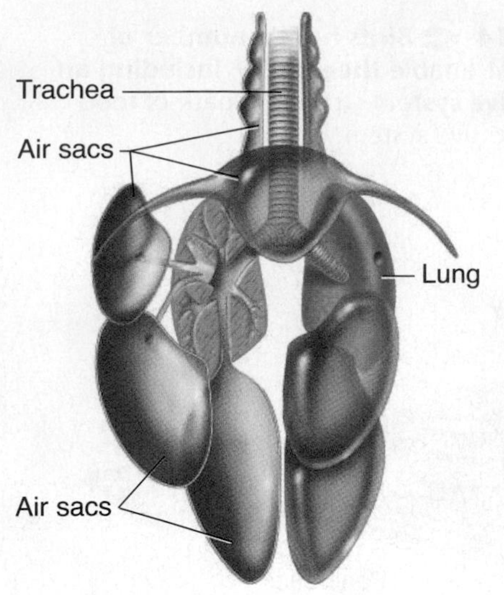

▲ **Figure 31–15** Birds have a unique respiratory system. Air sacs direct air through the lungs in an efficient, one-way flow. **Comparing and Contrasting** *How does this system differ from that of most land vertebrates?*

Respiration Birds have a unique and highly efficient way of taking in oxygen and eliminating carbon dioxide. When a bird inhales, most air first enters large posterior **air sacs** in the body cavity and bones. Observe the air sacs in **Figure 31–15.** The inhaled air then flows through the lungs. Air travels through the lungs in a series of small tubes. These tubes are lined with specialized tissue, where gas exchange takes place.

The complex system of air sacs and breathing tubes ensures that air flows into the air sacs and out through the lungs in a single direction. The one-way flow constantly exposes the lungs to oxygen-rich air. Contrast this to the system found in most land vertebrates, in which oxygen-rich air is inhaled, and oxygen-poor air is exhaled. The air travels in two directions, in and out. In an in-out system, the lungs are exposed to oxygen-rich air only during inhalation.

What advantage does the efficient respiratory system of birds provide? The constant, one-way flow of oxygen-rich air helps birds maintain their high metabolic rate. Birds need a high metabolism to maintain body temperature and provide the large amounts of energy required for flight. In addition, the efficient extraction of oxygen enables birds to fly at high altitudes where the air is thin.

CHECKPOINT *How is their respiratory system advantageous to birds?*

Circulation Birds have four-chambered hearts and two separate circulatory loops. Notice in **Figure 31–16** that a bird's heart, unlike that of amphibians and most reptiles, has two separate ventricles, the right ventricle and the left ventricle. There is complete separation of oxygen-rich and oxygen-poor blood. One half of the heart receives oxygen-poor blood from the body and pumps this blood to the lungs. Oxygen-rich blood returns to the other side of the heart to be pumped to the rest of the body. This double-loop system ensures that oxygen collected by the lungs is distributed to the body tissue with maximum efficiency.

▼ **Figure 31–16** To keep blood moving rapidly, a bird's heart beats quickly—from 150 to more than 1000 beats per minute! **Applying Concepts** *Why is it important for a bird's heart to move blood so rapidly?*

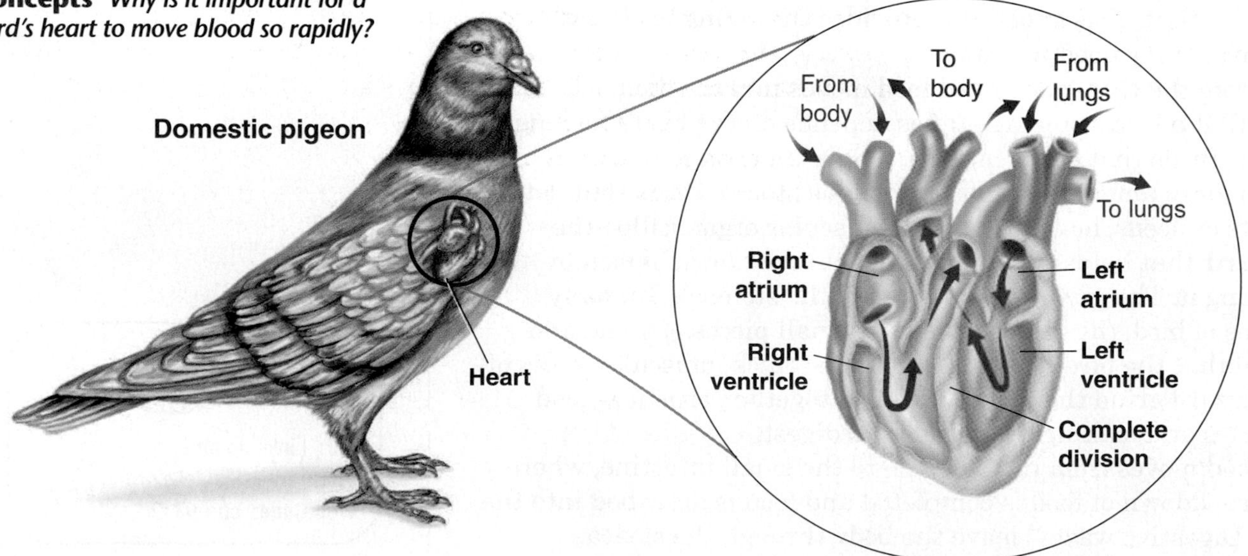

Quick Lab

How do birds breathe?

Materials 6 round balloons, hand-powered balloon pump, measuring tape, clock with second hand

Procedure

1. Work in groups of three. Make a copy of the data table at right on a blank sheet of paper. One person will inflate a balloon by mouth, while a second person inflates a balloon with a hand-powered pump. The third person is the timekeeper.
2. Begin inflating both balloons at the same time. After 10 seconds, the timer will say "stop." Stop inflating the balloons and pinch the necks of the balloons to keep the air inside. **CAUTION:** *Do not try to inflate balloons by mouth if you have a condition that would make this dangerous for you.*
3. Measure and record the circumference of each balloon in your data table. **CAUTION:** *Discard all balloons that have been inflated.*

Data Table

Name	Balloon Circumference (cm)		Difference
	Mouth	Pump	
		Average Difference	______

4. Repeat Steps 1–3 until each member of your group has inflated two balloons. In your data table, record the difference in balloon diameter for each person and the average difference for the group.

Analyze and Conclude

1. **Analyzing Data** Which method was faster? Which method required more effort?
2. **Using Models** Which method worked like reptile lungs? Which method worked like bird lungs? Explain your answers.
3. **Formulating Hypotheses** How is efficient respiration especially valuable to birds?

Excretion The excretory systems of many birds are similar to those of most living reptiles. Nitrogenous wastes are removed from the blood by the kidneys, converted to uric acid, and deposited in the cloaca. There, most of the water is reabsorbed, leaving uric acid crystals in a white, pasty form that you may recognize as bird droppings.

Response Birds have well-developed sense organs, which are adaptations that enable them to coordinate the movements required for flight. Birds also have a brain that can quickly interpret and respond to a lot of incoming signals. A bird's brain, shown in **Figure 31–17**, is relatively large for its body size. The cerebrum, which controls such behaviors as flying, nest building, care of young, courtship, and mating, is quite large. The cerebellum is also well developed, as you might expect in an animal that uses precise, coordinated movements. The medulla oblongata coordinates basic body processes, such as the heartbeat.

Birds have extraordinarily well developed eyes and sizable optic lobes in the brain. Birds see color very well—in many cases, better than humans. Most bird species can also hear quite well. The senses of taste and smell, however, are not well developed in most birds, and the olfactory bulbs in a bird's brain are small.

▼ **Figure 31–17** Compared to reptiles, birds have an enlarged cerebellum that coordinates the movements of wings and legs. **Formulating Hypotheses** ***Why would the cerebrum also be larger in birds than in reptiles?***

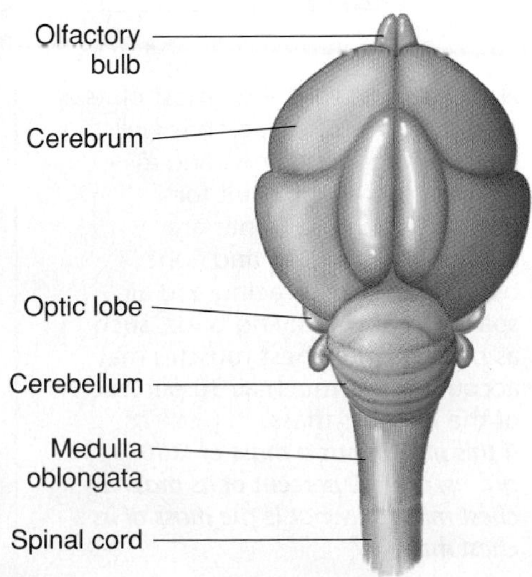

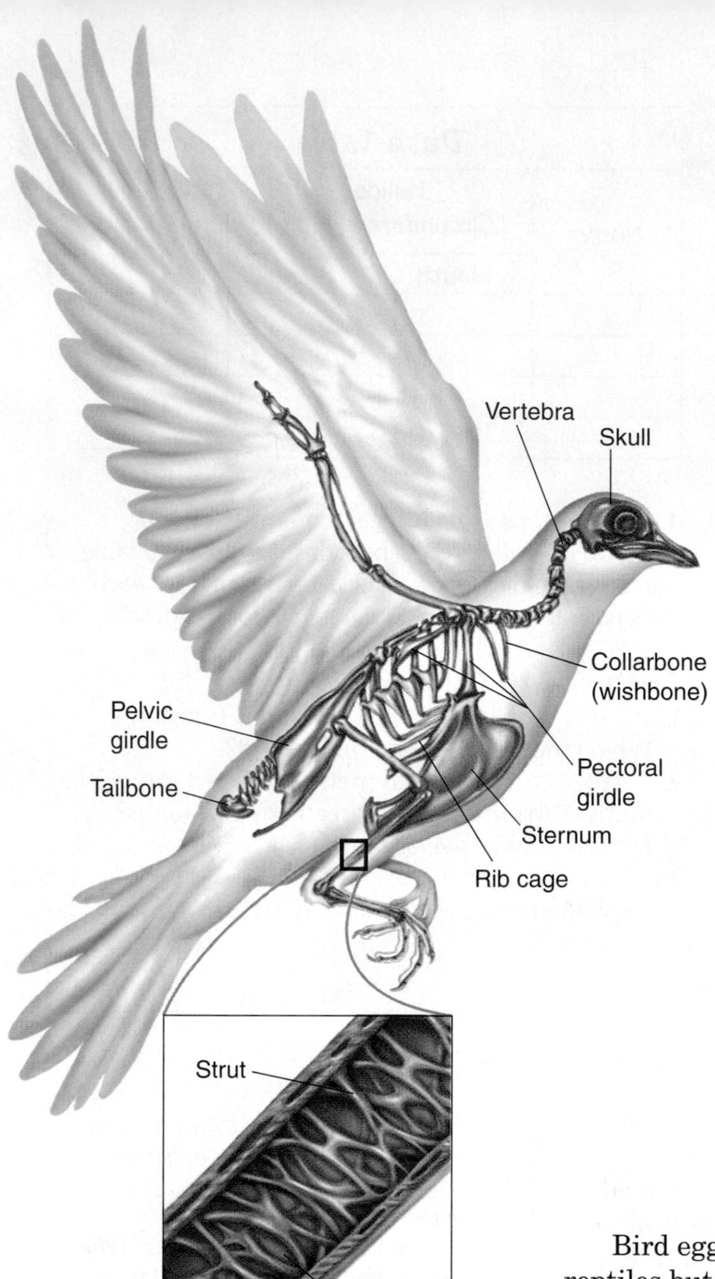

▲ **Figure 31–18** Like most of its anatomy, a bird's skeleton is well adapted for flight, providing a sturdy attachment point for muscles. The long bones are exceptionally strong and light because of cross-bracing and air spaces. In strong flying birds, such as pigeons, the chest muscles may account for as much as 30 percent of the animal's mass. **Calculating** *If this pigeon has a mass of 200 grams, and 30 percent of its mass is chest muscles, what is the mass of its chest muscles?*

Movement Some birds cannot fly. Instead, they get around mainly by walking or running, like ostriches, or by swimming, like penguins. However, the vast majority of birds can fly. The skeletal and muscular systems of flying birds exhibit adaptations that enable flight.

Observe a bird's skeletal system in **Figure 31–18.** Although the bones in a bird's wings are homologous to the bones in the front limbs of other vertebrates, they have very different shapes and structures. In flying birds, many large bones, such as the collarbone, are fused together, making a bird's skeleton more rigid than a reptile's. These bones form a sturdy frame that anchors the muscles used for flight. The bones are strengthened by internal struts similar to those used in the framework of tall buildings and bridges. Air spaces make many bones lightweight. Birds also have large chest muscles that power the upward and downward wing strokes necessary for flight. The muscles attach to a long keel that runs down the front of an enlarged breastbone, or sternum.

Reproduction In birds, both male and female reproductive tracts open into the cloaca. The sex organs often shrink in size when the birds are not breeding. As birds prepare to mate, the ovaries and testes grow larger until they reach functioning size. Mating birds press their cloacas together to transfer sperm from the male to the female. Some male birds have a penis that transfers sperm to the female's cloaca.

Bird eggs are amniotic eggs. They are similar to the eggs of reptiles but have hard outer shells. Most birds incubate their eggs until the eggs hatch. When a chick is ready to hatch, it uses a small tooth on its bill to make a hole in the shell. After much pushing, poking, and prodding by the chick, the eggshell breaks open. Once the exhausted bird has hatched, it collapses for a while and allows its feathers to dry. Both parents may be kept busy providing food for their hungry offspring.

Do birds have external or internal fertilization?

Groups of Birds

Birds fill the woods and fields with song. Imagine how dull the world would be without the color, song, and variety of birds. With nearly 30 different orders, it is impossible to present each type of bird here. Instead, **Figure 31–19** provides an overview of some better-known groups and their adaptations. By far, the largest order of birds is the passerines (pas-uh-REENZ), or perching birds. This group includes songbirds such as larks, sparrows, and finches. There are over 5000 species of perching birds.

FIGURE 31–19 DIVERSITY IN BIRDS

Birds show remarkable diversity and inhabit many different environments. Some representative groups are shown below. **Applying Concepts** ***Which group of birds is the largest?***

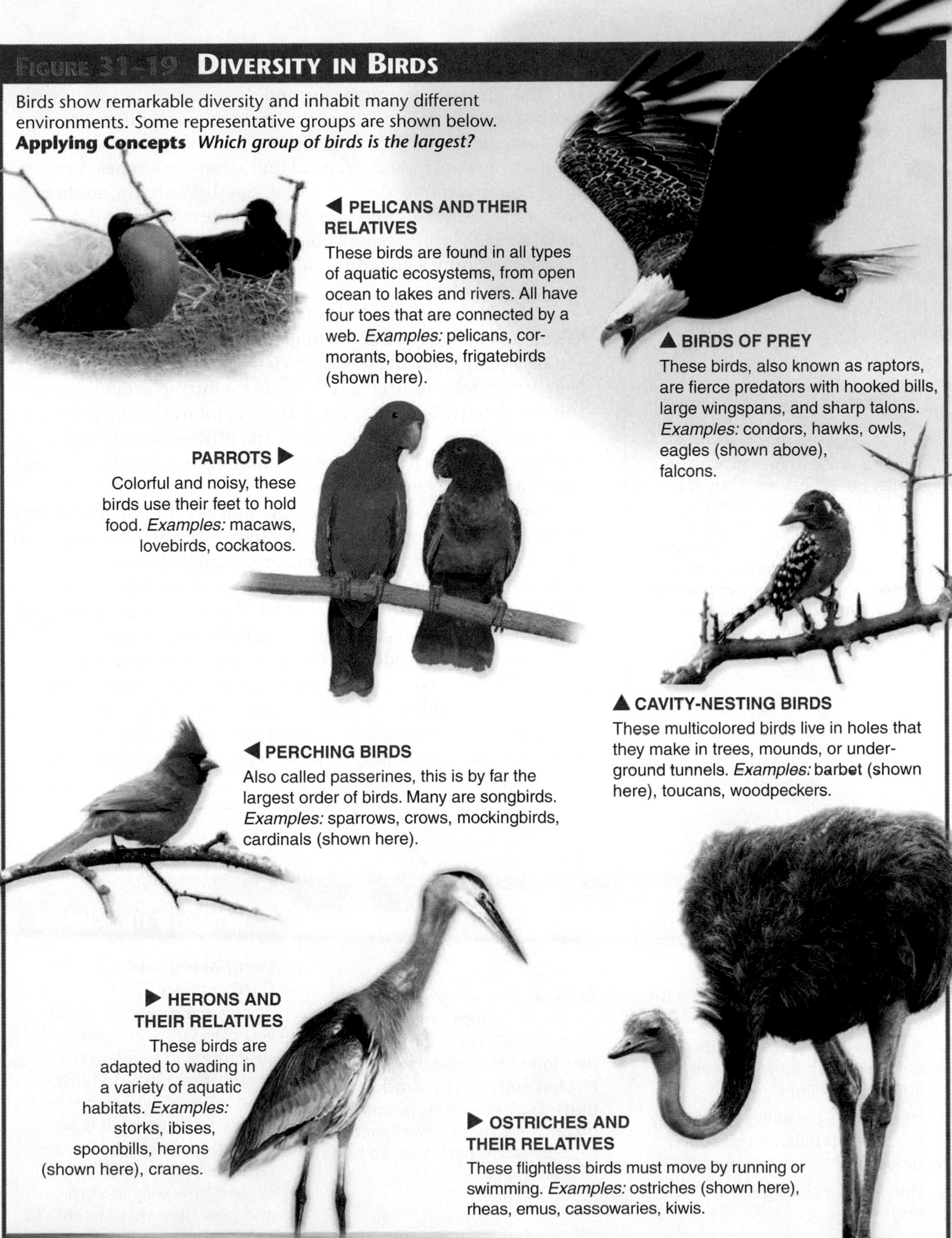

◀ **PELICANS AND THEIR RELATIVES**
These birds are found in all types of aquatic ecosystems, from open ocean to lakes and rivers. All have four toes that are connected by a web. *Examples:* pelicans, cormorants, boobies, frigatebirds (shown here).

▲ **BIRDS OF PREY**
These birds, also known as raptors, are fierce predators with hooked bills, large wingspans, and sharp talons. *Examples:* condors, hawks, owls, eagles (shown above), falcons.

PARROTS ▶
Colorful and noisy, these birds use their feet to hold food. *Examples:* macaws, lovebirds, cockatoos.

▲ **CAVITY-NESTING BIRDS**
These multicolored birds live in holes that they make in trees, mounds, or underground tunnels. *Examples:* barbet (shown here), toucans, woodpeckers.

◀ **PERCHING BIRDS**
Also called passerines, this is by far the largest order of birds. Many are songbirds. *Examples:* sparrows, crows, mockingbirds, cardinals (shown here).

▶ **HERONS AND THEIR RELATIVES**
These birds are adapted to wading in a variety of aquatic habitats. *Examples:* storks, ibises, spoonbills, herons (shown here), cranes.

▶ **OSTRICHES AND THEIR RELATIVES**
These flightless birds must move by running or swimming. *Examples:* ostriches (shown here), rheas, emus, cassowaries, kiwis.

▲ **Figure 31–20** This hummingbird uses its long, thin beak to draw nectar from a flower. While feeding, the bird may pick up pollen on its beak and carry it to the next flower it visits, thereby helping the flower to pollinate. **Applying Concepts** ***Which type of ecological relationship is represented by the hummingbird and the flower: parasitism, mutualism, or commensalism?***

Ecology of Birds

Because birds are so numerous and diverse, they interact with natural ecosystems and human society in many different ways. For example, hummingbirds, like the one in **Figure 31–20,** pollinate flowers in both tropical and temperate zones. Fruit-eating birds swallow seeds but may not digest them, so their droppings disperse seeds over great distances. Insect-eating birds, such as swallows and chimney swifts, catch great numbers of mosquitoes and other insects, and therefore help control insect populations.

Many birds migrate long distances—often over hundreds of kilometers of open sea. Such migrations are usually seasonal. It can be startling during a winter visit to a tropical country to see Northern orioles or bright red cardinals flitting around banana trees with parrots and toucans! How do migrating birds find their way? Some species use stars and other celestial bodies as guides. Other species may use a combination of landmarks and cues from Earth's magnetic field.

Because birds are highly visible and are an important part of the biosphere, they can serve as indicators of environmental health. It is no accident that conservationist Rachel Carson chose songbirds for the focus of her pioneering campaign in the 1960s against the careless use of DDT and other pesticides. In her book *Silent Spring,* Carson described to the public for the first time how pesticides that stay in the environment can accumulate in food chains and cause harm to animals they were never intended to affect. Thanks to the efforts of Carson and other conservationists, many birds—especially predators such as eagles and ospreys—have returned from the brink of extinction.

31–2 Section Assessment

1. **Key Concept** Describe the characteristics of a bird.
2. **Key Concept** List three ways in which birds are well adapted for flight.
3. What is the possible evolutionary relationship between birds and dinosaurs?
4. How does a chick get out of its eggshell?
5. **Critical Thinking Applying Concepts** Crops and gizzards are especially common and well developed in seed-eating birds but less common in carnivorous birds. Explain why crops and gizzards are more advantageous to seed-eating birds than to birds that eat meat.

Writing in Science

Comparing and Contrasting

Write a paragraph in which you compare and contrast the structure and function of the hearts of reptiles and birds. *Hint:* When you compare and contrast two items, it is not enough to describe each one separately. You need to explain how they are similar and how they are different. To help with this task, you might construct a Venn diagram or a compare-and-contrast table.

Examining Bird Bones

Birds have many adaptations that enable them to fly, including the structure and properties of their skeletons. In this investigation, you will compare bones from birds and mammals to determine how bird bones are adapted for flight.

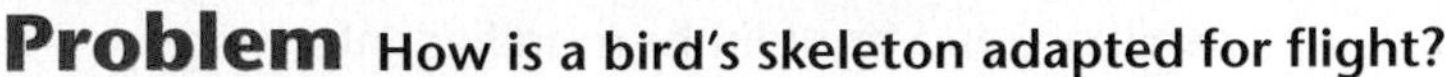

Problem **How is a bird's skeleton adapted for flight?**

Materials

- cut sections of bird and mammal bones
- bird breastbone
- hand lens
- mammal bone
- bird wing bone
- balance
- 250-mL graduated cylinder
- dissecting probe
- calculator

Skills Observing, Measuring, Calculating

Procedure

Part A: Bone Structure

1. Put on plastic gloves. Use a hand lens to examine cut sections of bird and mammal bones. Look carefully at the interiors of the bones and record your observations.
2. Look at a bird breastbone (sternum). Carefully observe its structure.

Part B: Bone Density

3. Make a copy of the data table on a separate sheet of paper. Use a balance to measure the mass of a bird wing bone.
4. Put 180 mL of water in the graduated cylinder. **CAUTION:** *Handle the graduated cylinder carefully. If it breaks, tell your teacher immediately.*
5. Use a dissecting probe to hold the bird wing bone under water in the graduated cylinder. In your data table, record the water level in the cylinder. Subtract the original water volume from this value to find the volume of the bone.
6. The density of an object is equal to its mass divided by its volume (d = m/v). Calculate the density of the bone by dividing its mass by its volume. Record the density of the bird bone in your data table.
7. Repeat steps 3 to 6 to find the density of the mammal bone. Wash your hands with soap and warm water before leaving the lab.

Data Table

Source of Bone	Mass (g)	Volume (mL)			Density of Bone (g/cm^3)
		Water	Water + Bone	Bone	
Bird					
Mammal					

Analyze and Conclude

1. **Comparing and Contrasting** How are the bird and mammal bones similar? Different? How is the bird bone adapted for flight?
2. **Applying Concepts** What is the function of the muscles that attach to a bird's sternum? How is the protruding bird sternum an adaptation for flight?
3. **Drawing Conclusions** How are the densities of bird and mammal bones related to the way these animals move?
4. **Evaluating** With your teacher's permission, determine the validity of your density data by repeating Part B. Do you obtain the same results?

Go Further

Applying Concepts In addition to specialized bones, birds' adaptations to flight include several types of feathers. Use reference materials to find out how each type of feather is an adaptation.

Chapter 31 Study Guide

31–1 Reptiles

Key Concepts

- A reptile is a vertebrate that has scaly skin, lungs, and eggs with several membranes.
- Well-developed lungs; a double-loop circulatory system; an efficient excretory system; strong limbs; internal fertilization; and shelled, terrestrial eggs are the main adaptations that have contributed to the success of reptiles on land.
- The four surviving groups of reptiles are lizards and snakes, crocodilians, turtles and tortoises, and the tuatara.

Vocabulary
ectotherm, p. 800
amniotic egg, p. 802
carapace, p. 805
plastron, p. 805

31–2 Birds

Key Concepts

- Birds are reptilelike animals that maintain a constant internal body temperature. They have an outer covering of feathers; two legs that are covered with scales and are used for walking or perching; and front limbs modified into wings.
- Birds have a number of adaptations that enable them to fly. These adaptations include highly efficient digestive, respiratory, and circulatory systems; aerodynamic feathers and wings; strong, lightweight bones; and strong chest muscles.

Vocabulary
feather, p. 806
endotherm, p. 808
crop, p. 809
gizzard, p. 809
air sac, p. 810

Thinking Visually

Using information from this chapter, complete the following concept map:

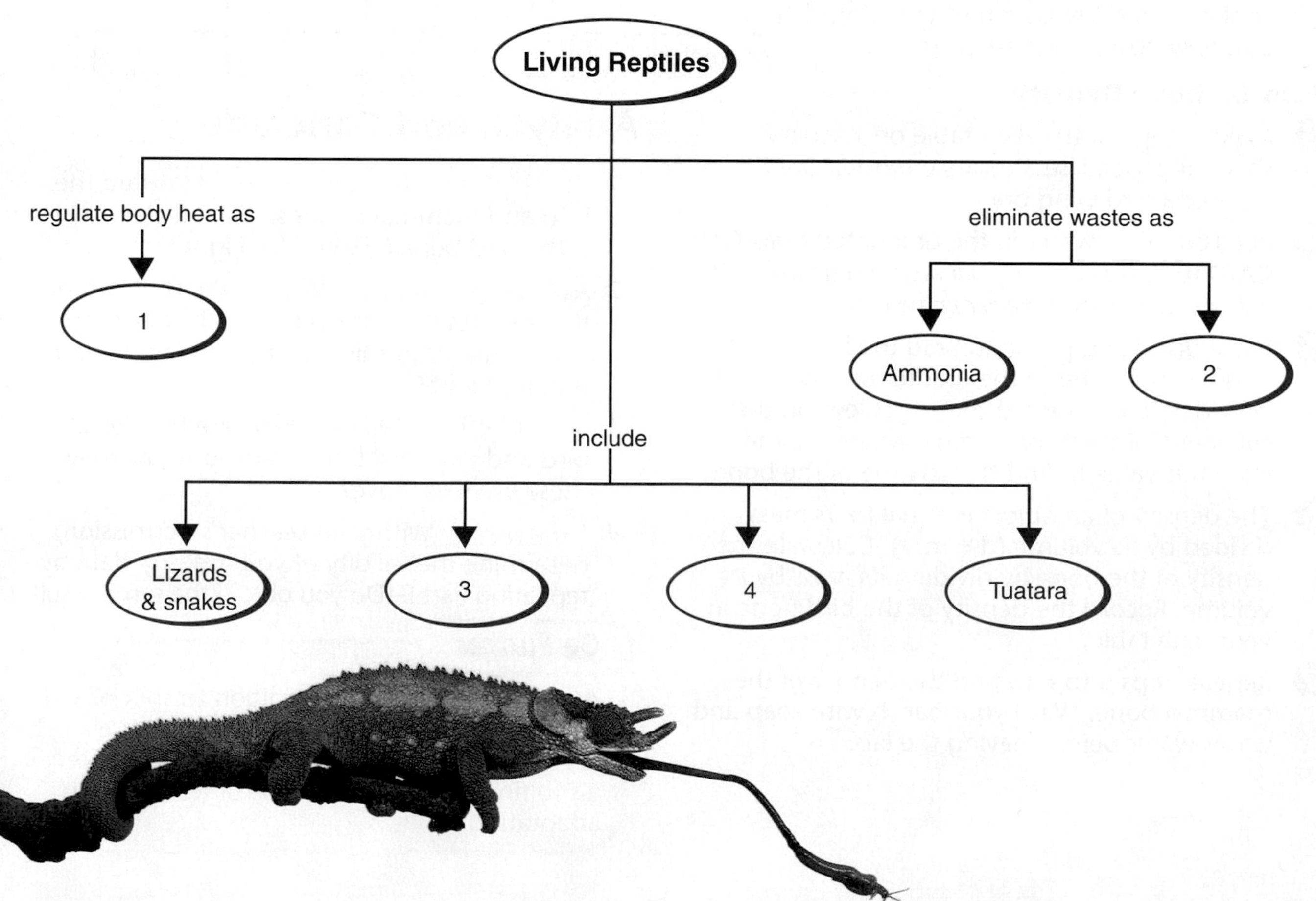

Preparing for the Living Environment Exam

NEW YORK LIVING ENVIRONMENT

Blue questions emphasize Regents Exam content

Chapter 31

Part A

Multiple Choice

For each statement or question, select the number of the word or expression that, of those given, best completes the statement or answers the question.

1 Feathers that provide lifting force and balance needed for flight are known as
(1) down feathers
(2) contour feathers
(3) powder feathers
(4) scale feathers

2 The term that best describes an animal that relies on interaction with the environment to help it control body temperature is
(1) endotherm (3) ectotherm
(2) amnion (4) endoderm

3 Which reptiles have both a carapace and a plastron for protection?
(1) lizards and snakes
(2) turtles and tortoises
(3) crocodilians
(4) tuataras

4 In the diagram below of a developing egg, the function of the structure labeled Y is to

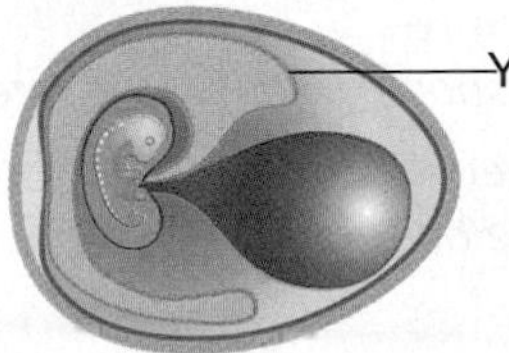

(1) store wastes produced by the embryo
(2) supply nutrients to the embryo
(3) enlarge the shell as the embryo grows
(4) cushion the embryo from shock

5 Unlike other vertebrates, birds have respiratory systems that
(1) take in oxygen and release carbon dioxide
(2) excrete nitrogenous wastes
(3) maintain a one-way flow of air
(4) lower their metabolism

6 The part of a bird's digestive tract adapted for the storage of food before digestion takes place is the
(1) esophagus (3) gizzard
(2) crop (4) cloaca

7 Which bird structure is especially adapted to support flight?
(1) muscular gizzard
(2) lightweight bill
(3) strong legs
(4) chest muscles

8 Which statement about reptiles is correct?
(1) Water-dwelling reptiles produce eggs without shells.
(2) Many reptiles have a single-loop circulatory system.
(3) Land-dwelling reptiles convert ammonia to uric acid.
(4) Most reptiles have internal mechanisms to regulate body temperature.

9 Birds are currently believed to have evolved from
(1) mammal-like reptiles
(2) flying amphibians
(3) lizards
(4) dinosaurs

10 Which group consists of organisms that are *all* reptiles?
(1) tuataras, lizards, and dinosaurs
(2) turtles, snakes, and passerines
(3) crocodilians, condors, and cormorants
(4) raptors, archaeopteryx, and tortoises

11 Amniotic eggs are a characteristic of
(1) both amphibians and reptiles
(2) both reptiles and birds
(3) birds, only
(4) reptiles, only

12 Reptiles carry on
(1) internal fertilization and only external development
(2) external fertilization and only external development
(3) internal fertilization and either internal or external development
(4) external fertilization and either internal or external development

Test-Taking Tip When presented with questions that are related to data in a table, study each column and row of the table for information you need to answer the questions.

Preparing for the Living Environment Exam

Part B

Multiple Choice and Extended Response
For those questions that ask you to select a response, choose the one that best completes the statement or answers the question. For all others follow the directions given.

13 State *two* adaptations that enable birds to live in environments that are colder than those typically supporting reptiles.

14 Explain why the amniotic egg is considered to be one of the most important adaptations to life on land.

15 Explain why a turtle cannot "crawl out of its shell."

16 Explain how a pigeon's crop helps it care for its young.

17 Birds are excellent navigators. State *two* ways migrating birds are able to find their way.

Base your answers to questions 18 through 21 on the information and data table below and on your knowledge of biology.

An experiment was conducted to see how air temperature affects a snake's ability to move. The experimenter recorded the air temperature, then placed the snake a fixed distance away from a piece of food. Then, she recorded the time it took for the snake to reach the food. She repeated the experiment four times, each time at a different air temperature. The table shows the results of the five trials.

The Effect of Temperature on Snake Movement

Temperature (°C)	Time (seconds)
4	51
10	50
15	43
21	37
27	35

18 Graph the data recorded in "The Effect of Temperature on Snake Movement" table on a separate sheet of graph paper. (Hint: Assign the manipulated, or independent, variable to the *x*-axis and the responding, or dependent, variable to the *y*-axis.)

- Label both axes, including the units used.
- Indicate an appropriate scale on both axes.
- Plot each data point. Surround each point with a circle, and then connect the points with a line.

19 At what air temperature did the snake reach the food the fastest?
(1) 27°C (3) 10°C
(2) 21°C (4) 4°C

20 State the relationship between air temperature and the time it took the snake to reach the food.

21 If this same experiment were conducted with a bird instead of a snake, would the experimenter be likely to obtain similar results? Support your answer with an explanation.

22 Predict how the ability of a bird egg to develop and hatch would be affected if the egg were coated with oil or wax. Support your prediction with information about the structures associated with bird eggs.

23 From the small size of its sternum, or breastbone, scientists infer that *Archaeopteryx* was a poor flier. Propose a hypothesis to explain how *Archaeopteryx* might have used its wings.

Part C

Extended Response
Answer the questions or follow the directions given.

Base your answers to questions 24 through 26 on the reading passage below and on your knowledge of biology.

Bird Imports

Among the 1000 established species of birds in the United States, about 97 species were introduced. Of those, only about 5 percent are considered beneficial—chickens, for example—while most are pests. Peskiest of all is the ubiquitous pigeon, which racks up an estimated $1.1 billion a year in economic costs. Add in a few other imports, such as the starling, and the total comes to $2.1 billion.

The nonnative pigeons spend their time feeding on grain and fouling buildings, statues, cars, and sometimes people in most cities of the world. One study estimated the economic impact of fouling at $9 per pigeon per year. Assuming there are 0.5 pigeons per person in urban areas, scientists estimate that common pigeons cause at least $1.1

billion in damage each year. Pigeons are also reservoirs for over 50 diseases, including parrot fever, ornithosis, histoplasmosis, and encephalitis.

The English sparrow was imported to the United States in 1853 to control the cankerworm. Like other nonindigenous species, English sparrows didn't limit themselves to the intended food source. With none of their normal predators to keep their population in check, English sparrows cause extensive damage to decorative plants; devour wheat, corn, and buds of fruit trees; and harass robins, orioles, and other native bird species. They also have displaced many native species, such as bluebirds, wrens, and cliff swallows, by driving them from their nests, and they spread about 29 diseases of humans and domestic animals. Researchers estimate their damage at $200 million a year.

24 State *three* specific problems associated with imported birds that were probably not anticipated when the birds were originally brought into this country.

25 State one reason why nonnative species are able to build up such large populations in their new environments.

26 Since the English sparrow has become a major pest species in the United States, it has been suggested that we import a population of one of the natural predators of the sparrow from England and release these predators to help control the pest species. Explain how this suggestion could add to the problem, rather than solve it.

27 Most reptiles have dry skin covered with thick scales. Explain why this is both advantageous and disadvantageous to reptiles. In your explanation, be sure to
- state one advantage of having dry skin with thick scales
- state one disadvantage of having dry skin with thick scales
- state how reptiles overcome this disadvantage

28 Explain how the climate changes that occurred at the end of the Carboniferous Period affected the evolution of reptiles. In your explanation, be sure to
- describe the climate changes that occurred
- describe how these changing conditions affected amphibians at the end of the Carboniferous Period
- state specifically why reptiles finally had a competitive advantage over amphibians

Base your answers to questions 29 and 30 on the information and data table below and on your knowledge of biology.

Reptiles rely on their environment for body warmth. Studies have shown that there is a relationship between a turtle's body temperature and the ability of digestive enzymes to break down food, as shown in the following table.

The Effect of Body Temperature on Rate of Turtle Digestion

Body Temperature of Turtle	Rate of Digestion
35°C	Normal or slightly below normal
25°C	Proceeding normally
15°C	Very slow
5°C	No digestion occurring

29 State the environmental temperature that would most likely produce the maximum rate of growth in this species of turtle. Support your answer with data from the table.

30 Explain why variations in the turtle's body temperature affect its rate of digestion.

For: An interactive self-test
Visit: PHSchool.com
Web Code: cba-9310

CHAPTER 32

Mammals

A collared anteater carries her young on her back. **Like all mammals, anteaters have hair, breathe air, and nurse their young with milk.**

Inquiry Activity

How are teeth adapted to processing different foods?

Procedure  

1. Put on plastic gloves. Examine a mammal tooth. Describe the shape of the tooth.
2. Based on the tooth's structure, try to infer whether the mammal ate mainly plants or other animals.
3. Repeat steps 1 and 2 for other mammal teeth.
4. Wash your hands with soap and warm water before leaving the lab.

Think About It

1. **Classifying** Sort the teeth into different groups based on their structure. Explain how you classified the teeth.
2. **Inferring** Describe what type of food you think each type of tooth is adapted to processing. Explain your reasoning.

32–1 Introduction to the Mammals

4-3.1 Fossils indicate extinction
4-3.1 Some individuals are better adapted to survive
1-S2.3 Research and experimental design
LS- Make observations, state hypotheses, analyze results

It is late January in the Appalachian Mountains. In a rocky den beneath the snowdrifts, a black bear has just given birth. Two tiny cubs are nursing on their mother's rich milk. It is bitterly cold outside, but the mother's dense fur and thick layer of body fat keep her and her cubs comfortably warm. When spring arrives, the hungry bears will emerge from the den. For the next two years, the cubs will follow their mother as she teaches them to search for food and defend themselves.

Bears are mammals, members of the class Mammalia. All mammals are characterized by two notable features: hair and mammary glands. In female mammals, **mammary glands**—the feature for which mammals are named—produce milk to nourish the young.  **In addition to having hair and the ability to nourish their young with milk, all mammals breathe air, have four-chambered hearts, and are endotherms that generate their body heat internally.**

Guide for Reading

Key Concepts
- What are the characteristics of mammals?
- When did mammals evolve?
- How do mammals maintain homeostasis?

Vocabulary
mammary gland
subcutaneous fat
rumen
diaphragm
cerebral cortex

Reading Strategy: Asking Questions Before you read, rewrite the headings in the section as *how, why,* or *what* questions about mammals. As you read, write brief answers to these heading questions.

Evolution of Mammals

Neither mammary glands nor hair are preserved in the fossil record. But mammals have several other characteristics that help scientists to identify mammalian fossils. These characteristics include a lower jaw consisting of a large, teeth-bearing bone connected by a joint directly to the skull; complex teeth that are replaced just once in a lifetime; and distinctive features of the limbs and the backbone.

Mammals are descended from ancient reptiles. According to the fossil record, the ancestors of modern mammals diverged from ancient reptiles during the Carboniferous Period. For millions of years, various mammal-like reptiles lived alongside other reptile groups.

The first true mammals appeared during the late Triassic Period, about 220 million years ago. These mammals were very small and probably resembled modern tree shrews, like the one in **Figure 32–1.** While dinosaurs ruled the Cretaceous Period, from about 145 to 65 million years ago, mammals were generally small and remained out of sight. These mammals were probably nocturnal, or active at night.

After the disappearance of the dinosaurs at the end of the Cretaceous Period, mammals underwent a burst of adaptive radiation. They increased in size and occupied many new niches. In fact, the Cenozoic Era, which followed the Cretaceous Period, is usually called the Age of Mammals. Three major groups of mammals had evolved by the beginning of the Cenozoic Era. Surviving members of these groups include today's monotremes, marsupials, and placental mammals.

▼ **Figure 32–1** **The first mammals appeared on Earth about 220 million years ago.** They may have resembled this tree shrew from Madagascar, shown here clutching a beetle. Like this tree shrew, early mammals probably ate insects.

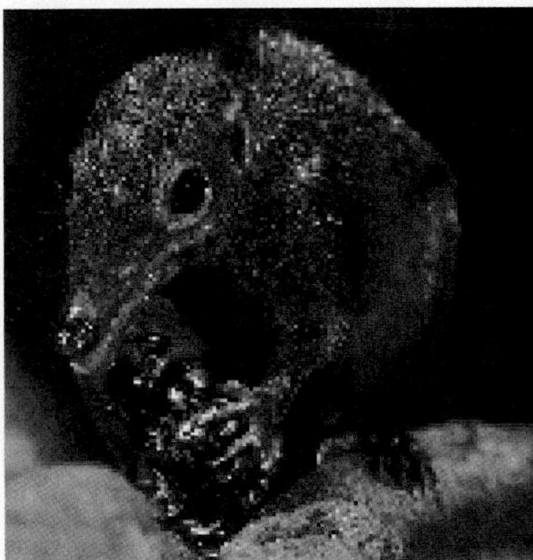

▲ **Figure 32–2** **As endotherms, mammals are capable of adjusting their body heat internally.** When they get too warm, some mammals, such as this gray wolf cub, pant to rid their bodies of excess heat.

Form and Function in Mammals

The mammalian body has adapted in varied ways to a great many habitats. As a member of this class of chordates, you may be familiar with some of these adaptations.

Body Temperature Control Like birds, mammals are endotherms; their bodies can generate heat internally. Mammals and birds—especially small ones—have a much higher metabolic rate than most other chordates. The high rate of metabolism helps mammals generate body heat. Mammals also have external body hair that helps them keep warm. Hair is part of the integumentary system, which is the outer covering of the body—the skin and all structures associated with the skin. **Subcutaneous** (sub-kyoo-TAY-nee-us) **fat,** which is a layer of fat located beneath the skin, also helps conserve body heat.

Many mammals have sweat glands that help cool the body. Sweating is regulated by an internal negative feedback mechanism, which you learned about in Chapter 26. When its internal body temperature becomes too high, the mammal begins to sweat. The evaporation of the sweat then cools the body. The mammal then stops sweating. Mammals that lack sweat glands, like the wolf in **Figure 32–2,** often pant to rid themselves of excess heat. **The ability of mammals to regulate their body heat from within is an example of homeostasis.** This ability also allows mammals to move about in the cold, while most other animals would seek shelter.

Feeding Because of its high metabolic rate, a mammal must eat nearly ten times as much food as a reptile of the same size to maintain homeostasis. Some mammals, such as rabbits and giraffes, eat only plants. Others, including cats and weasels, are meat-eaters. Bears and humans are omnivores, consuming all types of food. Certain whales, like the one in **Figure 32–3,** are filter feeders.

Early mammals ate insects. **As mammals evolved, the form and function of their jaws and teeth became adapted to eat foods other than insects.** The joint between the skull and lower jaw became stronger than that of reptiles. This joint allowed mammals to evolve larger, more powerful jaw muscles and different ways of chewing.

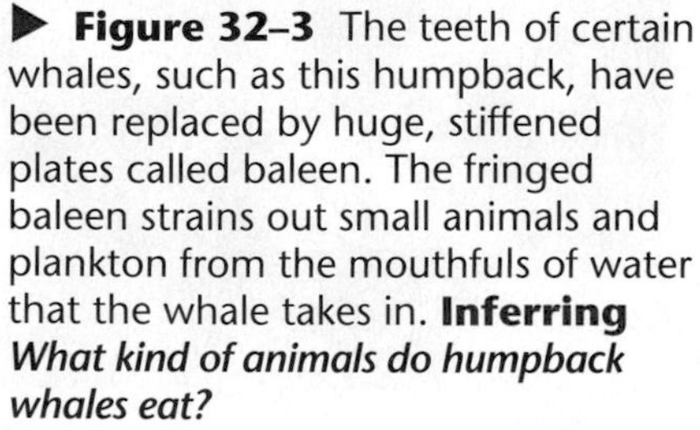

▶ **Figure 32–3** The teeth of certain whales, such as this humpback, have been replaced by huge, stiffened plates called baleen. The fringed baleen strains out small animals and plankton from the mouthfuls of water that the whale takes in. **Inferring** ***What kind of animals do humpback whales eat?***

FIGURE 32–4 JAWS AND TEETH OF MAMMALS

The specialized jaws and teeth of mammals are adapted for different diets. Carnivorous mammals use sharp canines and incisors to grip and slice flesh from their prey. Their jaws usually move up and down as they chew. Herbivorous mammals use flat-edged incisors to grasp and tear vegetation, and flattened molars to grind the food. Their jaws generally move from side to side.

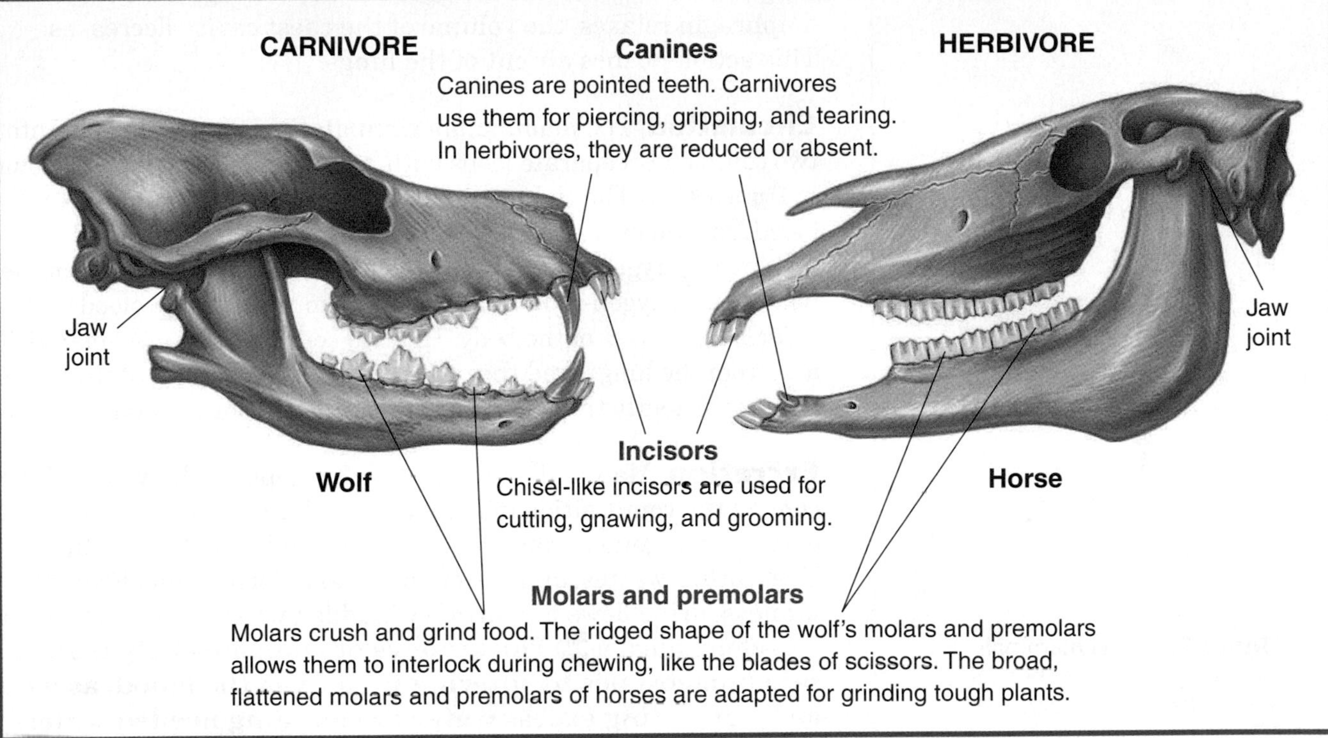

CARNIVORE
Canines
Canines are pointed teeth. Carnivores use them for piercing, gripping, and tearing. In herbivores, they are reduced or absent.
HERBIVORE
Jaw joint
Jaw joint
Incisors
Wolf
Chisel-like incisors are used for cutting, gnawing, and grooming.
Horse
Molars and premolars
Molars crush and grind food. The ridged shape of the wolf's molars and premolars allows them to interlock during chewing, like the blades of scissors. The broad, flattened molars and premolars of horses are adapted for grinding tough plants.

Modern mammals have specialized teeth—incisors, canines, molars, and premolars—which you can see in **Figure 32–4.** Observe that the structure of carnivores' teeth is different from that of herbivores' teeth. Mammals' teeth enable food to be processed efficiently. The more efficiently an animal can obtain and process its food, the more energy it can obtain.

A mammal's digestive tract breaks down and absorbs the type of food that it eats. Because digestive enzymes can quickly break down meat, carnivores have a relatively short intestine. Tough, fibrous plant tissues take much more time to digest, so most herbivores have a much longer intestine.

Many herbivores also have specialized digestive organs to break down plant matter. Cows and their relatives have a stomach chamber called the **rumen,** in which newly swallowed plant food is stored and processed. The rumen contains symbiotic bacteria that digest the cellulose of most plant tissues. After some time, the grazer regurgitates the food from the rumen into its mouth. The partially digested food is chewed and swallowed again. After several cycles, it moves through the rest of the stomach and into the intestines.

CHECKPOINT *What is the function of a rumen?*

Word Origins

The word **incisor** comes from the Latin word *incidere,* which means "to cut." **In surgery, what is an incision?**

For: Links on mammals
Visit: www.SciLinks.org
Web Code: cbn-9321

Respiration All mammals, even those that live in water, use lungs to breathe. These lungs are controlled by two sets of muscles. Mammals inhale when muscles in the chest lift the rib cage up and outward, increasing the volume of the chest cavity. At the same time, a powerful muscle called the **diaphragm** (DY-uh-fram) pulls the bottom of the chest cavity downward, which further increases its volume. As a result, air is pulled into the lungs. When the chest muscles lower the rib cage, and the diaphragm relaxes, the volume of the chest cavity decreases. This action pushes air out of the lungs.

Circulation The mammalian circulatory system is divided into two completely separate loops with a four-chambered heart, shown in **Figure 32–5.** The right side of the heart receives oxygen-poor blood from all over the body and pumps it to the lungs. After picking up oxygen in the lungs, blood returns to the left side of the heart. This oxygen-rich blood is then pumped through blood vessels to the rest of the body. The two separate circuits—one to and from the lungs, and the other to and from the rest of the body—efficiently transport materials throughout the body.

Excretion Mammals have highly developed kidneys that help control the composition of body fluids. Mammalian kidneys extract nitrogenous wastes from the blood in the form of urea. Urea, other wastes, and water combine to form urine. From the kidneys, urine flows to a urinary bladder, where it is stored until it is eliminated. **The kidneys of mammals help maintain homeostasis by filtering urea from the blood, as well as by excreting excess water or retaining needed water.** They also retain salts, sugars, and other compounds the body cannot afford to lose. Because they are so efficient at controlling and stabilizing the amount of water in the body, the kidneys enable mammals to live in many habitats, such as deserts, in which they could not otherwise survive.

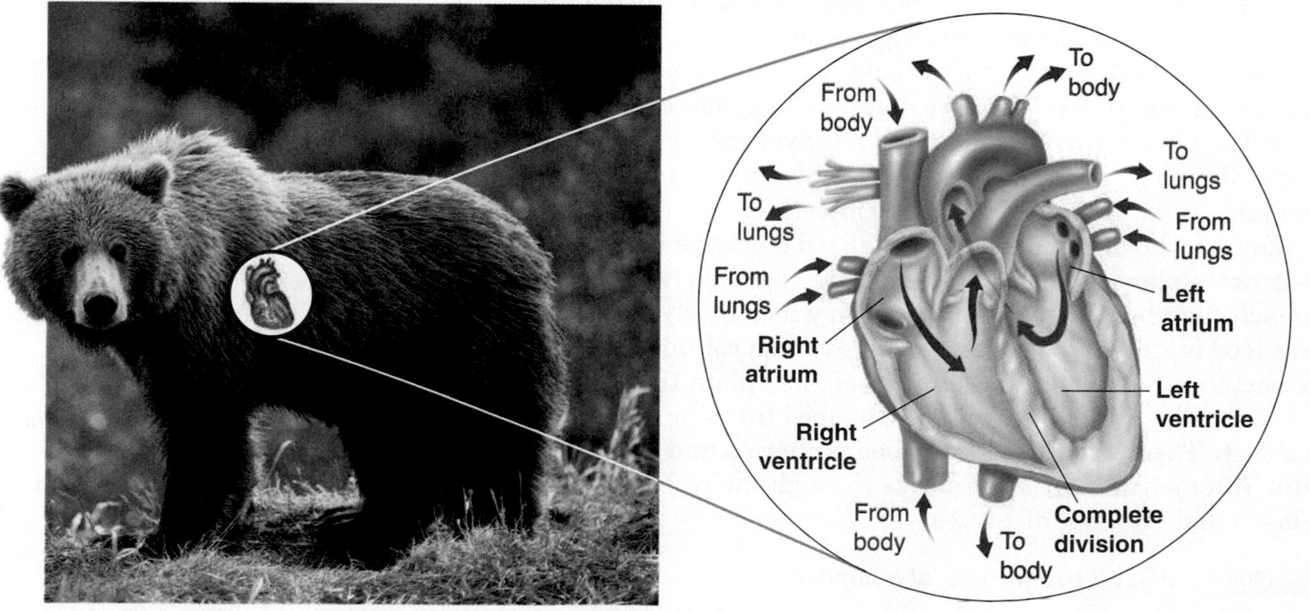

Figure 32–5 All mammals, including this brown bear, have a four-chambered heart that pumps blood in two separate circuits around the body. **Interpreting Graphics** ***According to the diagram, which chamber receives blood that is low in oxygen?***

Response Mammals have the most highly developed brains of any animals. As you can see in **Figure 32–6,** the brain consists of three main parts: the cerebrum, the cerebellum, and the medulla oblongata. The cerebrum makes possible such complicated behaviors as thinking and learning. The cerebellum controls muscular coordination. The medulla oblongata regulates involuntary body functions, or those that are not under conscious control, such as breathing and heart rate.

A mammal's cerebrum contains a well-developed outer layer called the **cerebral cortex,** which is the center of thinking and other complex behaviors. Some activities, such as reading this textbook, are possible only with the human cerebral cortex. However, mammals other than humans also exhibit complex behaviors, such as storing food for later use.

Mammals rely on highly developed senses to detect and respond to stimuli from their external environment. Many mammals have well-developed senses of smell and hearing. You probably know, for example, that dogs can easily identify people by their particular scent. Although mammalian ears all have the same basic parts, they differ in their ability to detect sound. For example, dogs, bats, and dolphins can detect sounds at much higher frequencies than humans can. In fact, bats and dolphins can find objects in their environment using the echo of their own high-frequency sounds. Other mammals, such as elephants, can detect sounds at much lower frequencies.

Many mammals have some color-sensing structures in their eyes, yet the ability to distinguish colors may vary among different species. Color vision is most useful to diurnal animals—those that are active during daylight. Although mammals such as cats can detect color, they may not see the full range of colors that humans and some other primates can.

What is the function of the cerebral cortex?

Chemical Controls The nervous system is not the only system that controls body processes. Mammals, like other vertebrates, have endocrine glands that are part of an endocrine system. Endocrine glands regulate body activities by releasing chemicals called hormones that affect other organs and tissues. Hormones produced by a gland in a mammal's neck, for example, help regulate the amount of calcium in the bones. Hormones are carried by the blood to the organs that they affect.

Fighting Disease All organisms live in an environment that contains disease-causing microorganisms, or pathogens. The immune systems of mammals and other vertebrates function to protect animals from disease. When mammals do get sick, their immune systems help them recover. Mammalian immune systems consist of barriers, such as the skin, that prevent pathogens from entering the body. In addition, specialized cells and chemicals recognize and destroy pathogens.

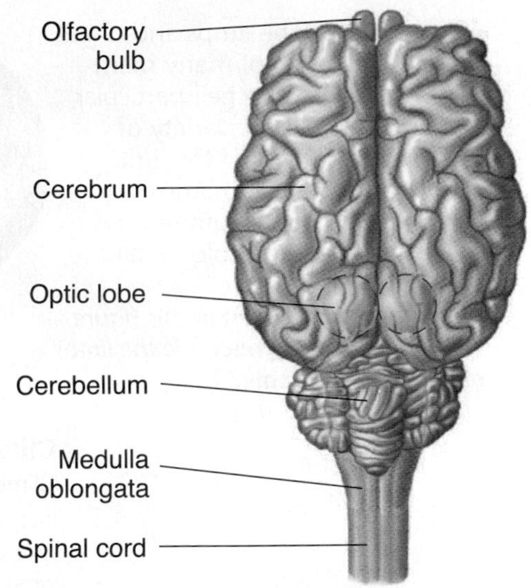

▲ **Figure 32–6** Mammals have large brains in proportion to their body size. Most of the brain is taken up by an enlarged cerebrum, which contains a well-developed cerebral cortex. **Inferring** *How would a large cerebrum be advantageous to a mammal?*

Figure 32–7 The limbs and digits (fingers and toes) of many mammals are adapted to their particular way of life. Note the variety of lengths and shapes of the limb bones that different mammals use for movement. Homologous bones are the same color in all the drawings. **Applying Concepts** ***Which structure shown in this figure would most closely resemble the limbs and digits of a whale?***

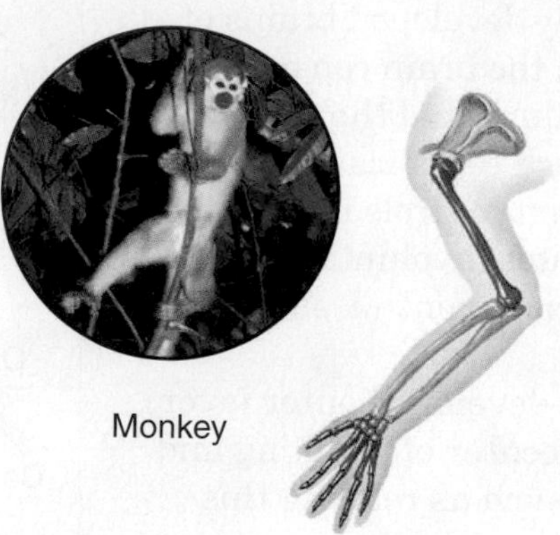

Climbers
Climbing mammals have long, flexible fingers and toes that can grasp vines and branches. They also have a flexible wrist joint.

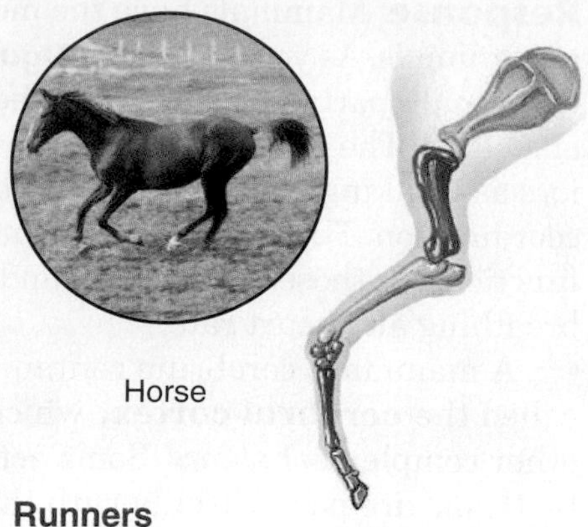

Runners
Running mammals need long limbs that can absorb shock. These animals have lost the side digits on their front and back feet. They stand on the tips of their remaining toes, which are called hooves.

Movement Mammals have evolved a variety of adaptations that aid in movement, including a backbone that flexes both vertically and side to side. This flexibility allows mammals to move with a bouncing, leaping stride. Shoulder and pelvic girdles have become more streamlined and flexible, permitting both front and hind limbs to move in a variety of ways.

Compare the adaptations of mammalian limbs shown in **Figure 32–7.** Variations in the limb bones and muscles allow mammals to run, walk, climb, burrow, hop, pounce, swing, fly, leap, and swim. Depending on their lifestyle, mammals may use any number of these methods to move about.

▼ **Figure 32–8** Still wobbly, a newborn wildebeest rises to its feet minutes after birth. Its mother will nurse and protect the calf until it is able to live on its own.

Reproduction Mammals reproduce by internal fertilization. The male deposits sperm inside the reproductive tract of the female, where fertilization occurs. As you will learn in the next section, mammals are classified into three groups, based on their modes of development and birth. Regardless of the mode of development, all newborn mammals, such as the newborn wildebeest in **Figure 32–8,** feed on their mother's milk.

Young mammals generally need care when they are born and for a long time afterward. During this period, they are cared for by one or both parents. Maternal care is an important mammalian characteristic, and the bond between mother and young is very close. Males of many species also play a role in caring for the young. Parental care helps ensure that young mammals will survive and reproduce. Mammalian parental behavior is an adaptation that is the result of natural selection and other evolutionary processes.

The duration and intensity of parental care varies among different species. Some mammals have a prolonged period when the young and the mother live together. During that period, the juvenile learns from its caregiver the behaviors it needs to survive.

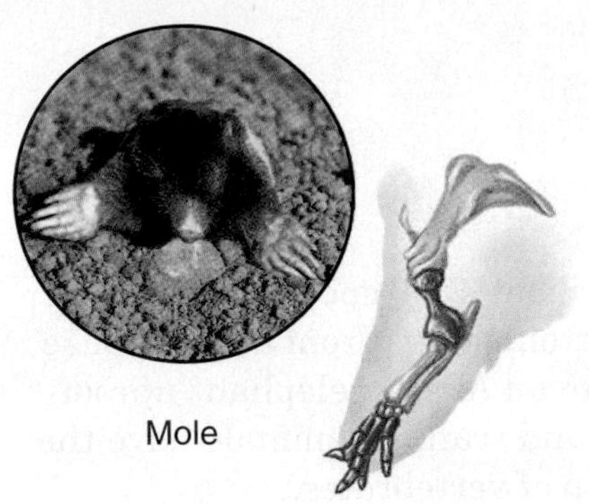

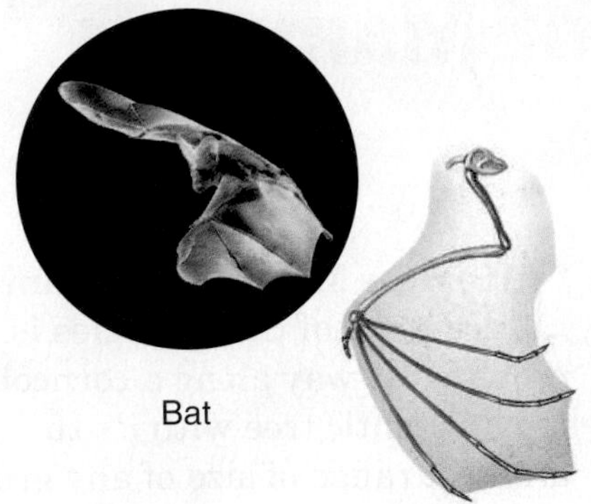

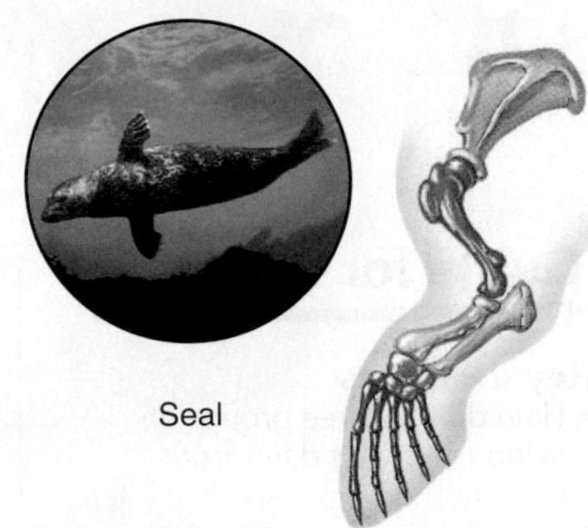

Diggers
Digging mammals have strong, thick claws, especially on their front feet. Their limbs are short and stocky, with large projections that anchor powerful muscles.

Flyers
The arms and hands of bats are modified to support flaps of skin that form wings.

Swimmers
Swimming mammals concentrate most of their movement between the arm and shoulder girdle. Their limbs are modified into broad, flat paddles, with the bones of their hands or feet extended to make a flipper.

Some mammal species, such as lions and elephants, live in groups in which the young may be cared for by adults other than the parents. Group living provides young mammals with the opportunity for complex social interaction among adults and juveniles.

Interrelationships of Organ Systems In mammals and other animals, organ systems are interdependent, as the following examples show. All body systems depend on the circulatory system to transport materials. The respiratory system, for example, ensures that oxygen enters the lungs, but the blood carries oxygen to body cells. Similarly, blood carries waste products to the kidneys, which remove the waste products from the body. Nerve impulses from cells in the nervous system carry information to and from organs in every body system. The bones of the skeletal system could not grow and maintain themselves without calcium and other materials that enter the body through the digestive system. An animal's organ systems work together to meet the needs of the body as a whole.

32–1 Section Assessment

1. **Key Concept** Name the characteristics that are common to all mammals.
2. **Key Concept** When did mammalian ancestors diverge from the other reptiles?
3. **Key Concept** List two ways in which mammals maintain homeostasis.
4. What is the function of the endocrine system?
5. **Critical Thinking Comparing and Contrasting** Compare the functions of the respiratory and circulatory systems. Then, explain how the structure of a mammal's heart helps these two systems work together to deliver oxygen to body cells.

Connecting Concepts

Brain Structure
Compare the structure of a mammal's brain to that of a fish, as shown in Chapter 30, **Figure 30–14.** What structures are more prominent in each animal's brain? How might these differences relate to the way the animals live?

32–2 Diversity of Mammals

Guide for Reading

Key Concepts
- How do the three groups of living mammals differ from one another?
- How did convergent evolution cause mammals on different continents to be similar in form and function?

Vocabulary
monotreme
marsupial
placenta

Reading Strategy: Summarizing As you read, make a list of the major groups of mammals. Write several sentences describing the characteristics of each group. Then, give an example for each.

The class Mammalia contains about 4500 species, and the diversity of these species is astonishing. From a tiny mouse nibbling its way along a corncob to an African elephant uprooting a gigantic tree with its tusks and trunk, mammals have the greatest range of size of any group of vertebrates.

As you have read, tooth structure is one characteristic that scientists use to classify mammals. Mammals are also classified by the number and kinds of bones in the head. But the most important way to categorize living mammals is by the way they reproduce and develop.

The three groups of living mammals are the monotremes (MAHN-oh-treemz), the marsupials (mahr-SOO-pee-ulz), and the placentals. These three groups differ greatly in their means of reproduction and development.

Monotremes and Marsupials

Monotremes lay eggs. Marsupials bear live young, but at a very early stage of development. All monotremes are grouped in a single order, while marsupials are split into several different orders.

Monotremes Members of the **monotremes,** or egg-laying mammals, share two notable characteristics with reptiles. In monotremes, the digestive, reproductive, and urinary systems all open into a cloaca that is similar to the cloaca of reptiles. In fact, the name *monotreme* means "single opening." Reproduction in monotremes also resembles reproduction in reptiles more than other mammals. As in reptiles, a female monotreme lays soft-shelled eggs that are incubated outside her body. The eggs hatch into young animals in about ten days. Unlike young reptiles, however, young monotremes are nourished by their mother's milk, which they lick from pores on the surface of her abdomen.

Only three species of monotremes exist today: the duckbill platypus, shown in **Figure 32–9,** and two species of spiny anteaters, or echidnas. These animals are found in Australia and New Guinea.

◀ **Figure 32–9 Like all monotremes, the platypus lays eggs that hatch outside the body but nourishes its young with milk produced in mammary glands.** The unusual snout of this duckbill platypus can sense electromagnetic signals put out by the muscles of other animals. The platypus uses its sensitive snout to locate prey, such as worms and mollusks, that burrow in the sediments.

Marsupials Kangaroos, koalas, and wombats are examples of **marsupials**—mammals bearing live young that usually complete their development in an external pouch. When marsupials reproduce, the fertilized egg develops into an embryo inside the mother's reproductive tract. The embryo is born at a very early stage of development. It crawls across its mother's fur and attaches to a nipple. In most species of marsupials, the nipples are located in a pouch called the marsupium (mahr-SOO-pee-um) on the outside of the mother's body. Marsupials are named after this structure. Once inside the marsupium, the embryo, looking much like the one in **Figure 32–10**, spends several months attached to the nipple. It will continue to drink milk in its mother's pouch until it grows large enough to survive on its own.

CHECKPOINT *How does a marsupial differ from a monotreme?*

Figure 32–10 Most marsupials, including this wallaby, are originally from Australia and New Guinea. **Marsupials bear live young that usually complete their development in a pouch.** The pink, newborn wallaby (inset) is still an embryo but will soon grow into a "joey" that resembles a small adult.

Placental Mammals

Placental mammals are the mammals with which you are most familiar. Mice, cats, dogs, whales, elephants, humans, and the sea lions in **Figure 32–11** all fall within this category. This group gets its name from an internal structure called the **placenta,** which is formed when the embryo's tissues join with tissues from within the mother's body.

In placental mammals, nutrients, oxygen, carbon dioxide, and wastes are exchanged efficiently between embryo and mother through the placenta. The placenta allows the embryo to develop for a much longer time inside the mother—from a few weeks in mice and rats to as long as two years in elephants. After birth, most placental mammals care for their young and provide them with nourishment by nursing. **Figure 32–12,** on the following pages, describes the main orders of placental mammals.

◀ **Figure 32–11** The California sea lion is an example of a placental mammal. **In placental mammals, nutrients, oxygen, carbon dioxide, and wastes are exchanged between embryo and mother through the placenta.**

FIGURE 32–12 ORDERS OF PLACENTAL MAMMALS

The 12 orders of mammals shown on these pages contain the vast majority of living placental species. **Classifying** *How are perissodactyls similar to artiodactyls? How are the two orders different?*

◀ INSECTIVORES

These insect eaters have long, narrow snouts and sharp claws that are well suited for digging. *Examples:* shrews, hedgehogs (shown here), moles.

▼ SIRENIANS

Sirenians are herbivores that live in rivers, bays, and warm coastal waters scattered throughout most of the world. These large, slow-moving mammals lead fully aquatic lives. *Examples:* manatees, dugongs (shown here).

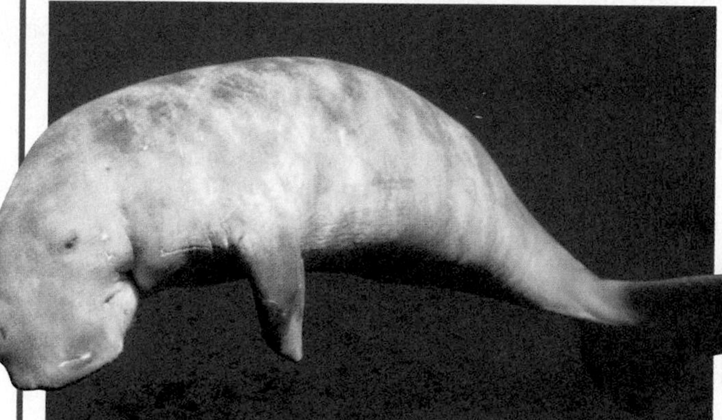

▼ CETACEANS

Like sirenians, cetaceans—the order that includes whales and dolphins—are adapted to underwater life yet must come to the surface to breathe. Most cetaceans live and breed in the ocean. *Examples:* humpback whales (shown here), narwhals, sperm whales, beluga whales, river dolphins.

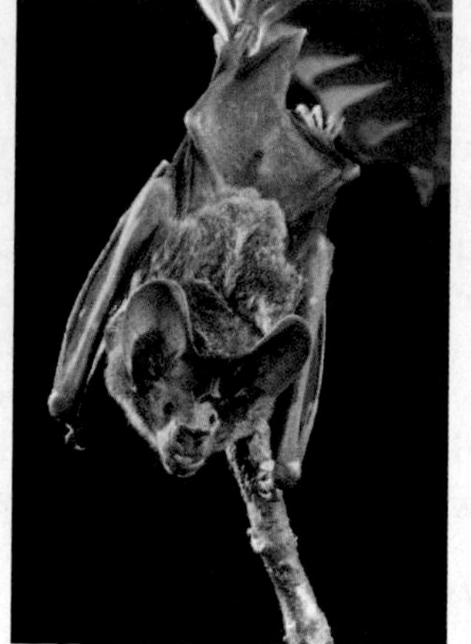

◀ CHIROPTERANS

Winged mammals—or bats—are the only mammals capable of true flight. Bats account for about one fifth of all mammalian species. They eat mostly insects or fruit and nectar, although three species feed on the blood of other vertebrates.

RODENTS ▶

Rodents have a single pair of long, curved incisor teeth in both their upper and lower jaws, which they use for gnawing wood and other tough plant material. *Examples:* mice, rats (shown here), voles, squirrels, beavers, porcupines, gophers, chipmunks, gerbils, prairie dogs, chinchillas.

▲ PERISSODACTYLS

This order contains hoofed animals with an odd number of toes on each foot. *Examples:* horses, tapirs, rhinoceroses, and zebras (shown here).

▲ **CARNIVORES**

Many mammals in this order, such as tigers and hyenas, stalk or chase their prey by running or pouncing, then kill the prey with sharp teeth and claws. Some animals in this group eat plants as well as meat. *Examples:* dogs, foxes, bears, raccoons, walruses (shown here).

▲ **XENARTHRANS**

Most of the mammals in this order have simple teeth without enamel, and a few have no teeth at all. *Examples:* sloths, anteaters, armadillos (shown here).

◀ **ARTIODACTYLS**

These hoofed mammals have an even number of toes on each foot. Like perissodactyls, this order contains mostly large, grazing animals. *Examples:* cattle, sheep, goats, pigs, ibex (shown here), giraffes, hippopotami, camels, antelope, deer, gazelles.

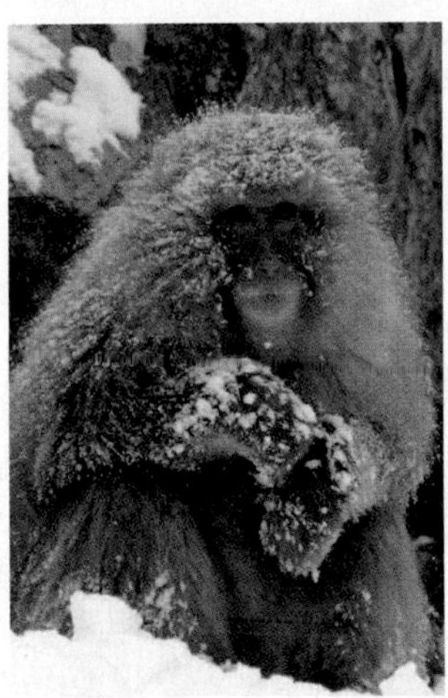

◀ **PRIMATES**

Members of this order are closely related to the ancient insectivores but have a highly developed cerebrum and complex behaviors. *Examples:* lemurs, tarsiers, apes, gibbons, macaques (shown here), humans.

▼ **PROBOSCIDEANS**

These are the mammals with trunks. Some time ago, this order went through an extensive adaptive radiation that produced many species, including mastodons and mammoths, which are now extinct. Only two species, the Asian elephant and this African elephant, survive today.

▲ **LAGOMORPHS**

Like rodents, members of this order are entirely herbivorous. They differ from rodents by having two pairs of incisors in the upper jaw. Most lagomorphs have hind legs that are adapted for leaping. *Examples:* Snowshoe hares (shown here), rabbits.

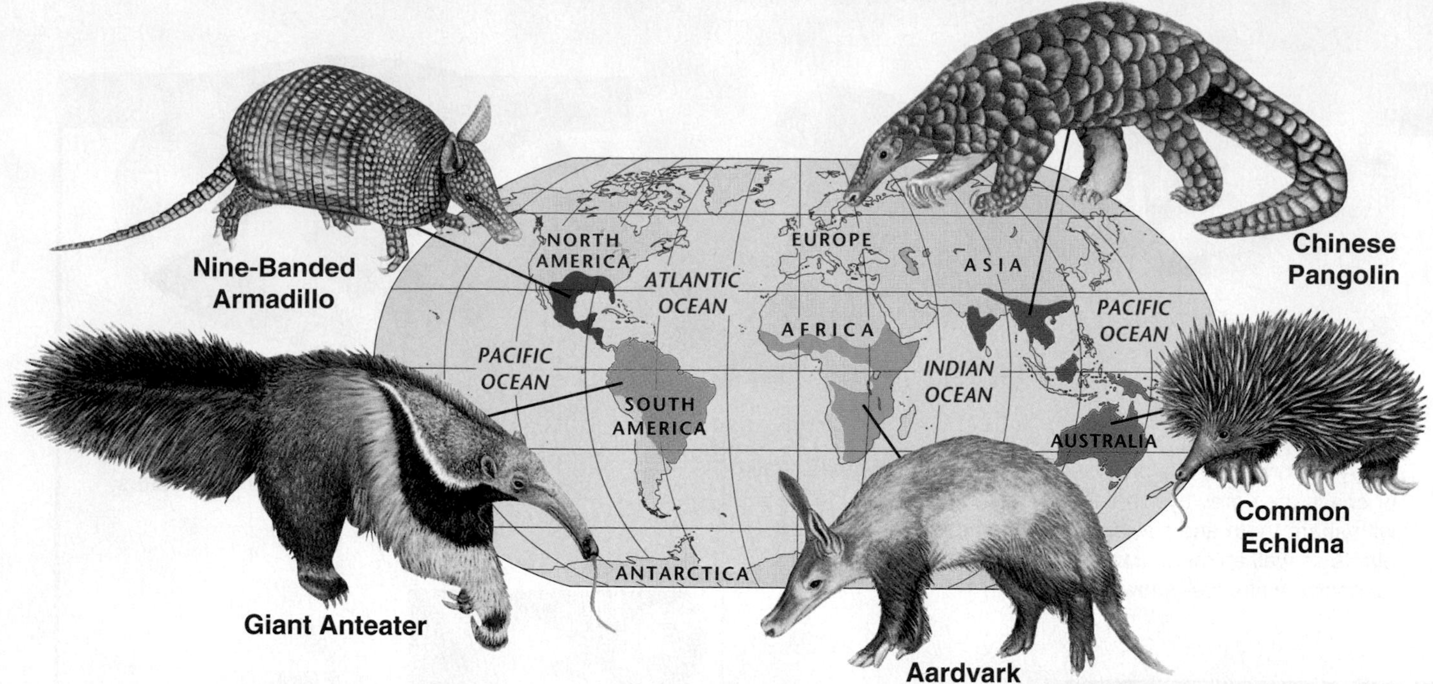

▲ **Figure 32–13** **Similar ecological opportunities on different continents have resulted in convergent evolution among these and other mammals.** Mammals that feed on ants and termites evolved not once but five times in different regions. Powerful front claws; a long, hairless snout; and a tongue covered with sticky saliva are common adaptations in these insect-eating animals.

Biogeography of Mammals

The history of Earth's geography has helped shape today's mammals. During the Paleozoic Era, the continents were one large landmass, and mammals could migrate freely across it. But as the continents drifted farther and farther apart during the Mesozoic and early Cenozoic Eras, ancestors of mammal groups were isolated from one another. Each landmass took with it a unique array of mammal groups.

Similar ecological opportunities on the different continents have produced some striking examples of convergent evolution in mammals. Thousands of kilometers apart, mammals such as those in **Figure 32–13** evolved similar adaptations in form and function. When some of the landmasses merged in the late Cenozoic Era, mammals dispersed and intermingled in new habitats. Living mammals reflect the diversity that resulted from these events.

32–2 Section Assessment

1. **Key Concept** Name the three groups of living mammals and describe the ways each develops.
2. **Key Concept** With regard to mammals, what was the result of continental drift?
3. What is the function of the placenta?
4. List the major orders of placental mammals.
5. What characteristic distinguishes lagomorphs from rodents?
6. **Critical Thinking Inferring** How are powerful front claws and sticky tongues useful adaptations in mammals that feed on ants?

Thinking Visually

Comparing and Contrasting

Create a compare-and-contrast table that describes the characteristics of monotremes, marsupials, and placental mammals. Include characteristics that they share as well as ways in which they differ.

32–3 Primates and Human Origins

1-S1.1, S1.3 Historical development of ideas
4-3.1 Evolutionary changes
4-3.1 Some individuals are better adapted to survive
4-3.1 Fossils indicate extinction

Our own species, *Homo sapiens,* belongs to the order that also includes lemurs, monkeys, and apes. Carolus Linnaeus named our order Primates, which means "first" in Latin.

Guide for Reading

 **Key Concepts**

- What characteristics do all primates share?
- What are the major evolutionary groups of primates?
- What is the current scientific thinking about hominid evolution?

Vocabulary
binocular vision
prosimian
anthropoid
prehensile
hominoid
hominid
bipedal
opposable thumb

Reading Strategy: Finding Main Ideas Before you read, draw a line down the center of a sheet of paper. On the left side, write down the main topics about primates and human origins. On the right side, note supporting details and examples.

What Is a Primate?

Just what are primates "first" in? When the first primates appeared, there was little to distinguish them from other mammals besides an increased ability to use their eyes and front limbs together to perform certain tasks. As primates evolved, however, several other characteristics became distinctive.

Primates share several important adaptations, many of which are extremely useful for a life spent mainly in trees. **In general, primates have binocular vision, a well-developed cerebrum, relatively long fingers and toes, and arms that can rotate around their shoulder joints.** The gibbon in **Figure 32–14** shows many of these characteristics.

Fingers, Toes, and Shoulders Primates normally have five flexible fingers that can curl around objects. Most also have flexible toes. Flexible digits (fingers and toes) enable many primates to run along tree limbs and swing from branch to branch with ease. Primates' arms are well adapted to climbing because they can rotate in broad circles around a strong shoulder joint. In most primates, the thumb and big toe can move against the other digits. The presence of this adaptation allows many primates to hold objects firmly in their hands or feet.

Well-Developed Cerebrum The large and intricate cerebrum of primates—including a well-developed cerebral cortex—enables them to display more complex behaviors than many other mammals. For example, many primate species have elaborate social behaviors that include adoption of orphans and even warfare between rival primate troops.

◀ **Figure 32–14** A white-handed gibbon displays several primate characteristics as it swings from tree to tree. **Like all primates, the gibbon has flexible fingers and toes and has arms that can rotate in broad circles around the shoulder joint.**

Quick Lab

Is binocular vision useful?

Material paper crumpled into a ball

Procedure

1. Throw the paper ball to your partner, who should try to catch the ball with one hand. Record whether your partner caught the ball.
2. Now have your partner close one eye. Repeat step 1.

Analyze and Conclude

1. **Using Tables and Graphs** Exchange results with other groups. Make a bar graph for the class data comparing the results with both eyes open and one eye shut.
2. **Drawing Conclusions** How is binocular vision useful to primates?

Binocular Vision Many primates have a flat face, so both eyes face forward with overlapping fields of view. This facial structure gives primates excellent binocular vision. **Binocular vision** is the ability to merge visual images from both eyes, thereby providing depth perception and a three-dimensional view of the world. This is a handy adaptation for judging the locations of tree branches, from which many primates swing.

Evolution of Primates

Humans and other primates evolved from a common ancestor that lived more than 65 million years ago. Early in their history, primates split into several groups. **Primates that evolved from two of the earliest branches look very little like typical monkeys and are called prosimians (proh-SIM-ee-unz). Members of the more familiar primate group that includes monkeys, apes, and humans are called anthropoids (AN-thruh-poydz).** Refer to **Figure 32–15** as you read about the phylogenetic relationships among these groups.

Prosimians With few exceptions, **prosimians** alive today are small, nocturnal primates with large eyes that are adapted to seeing in the dark. Many have doglike snouts. Living prosimians include the bush babies of Africa, the lemurs of Madagascar, and the lorises and tarsiers of Asia.

 *What is a prosimian?*

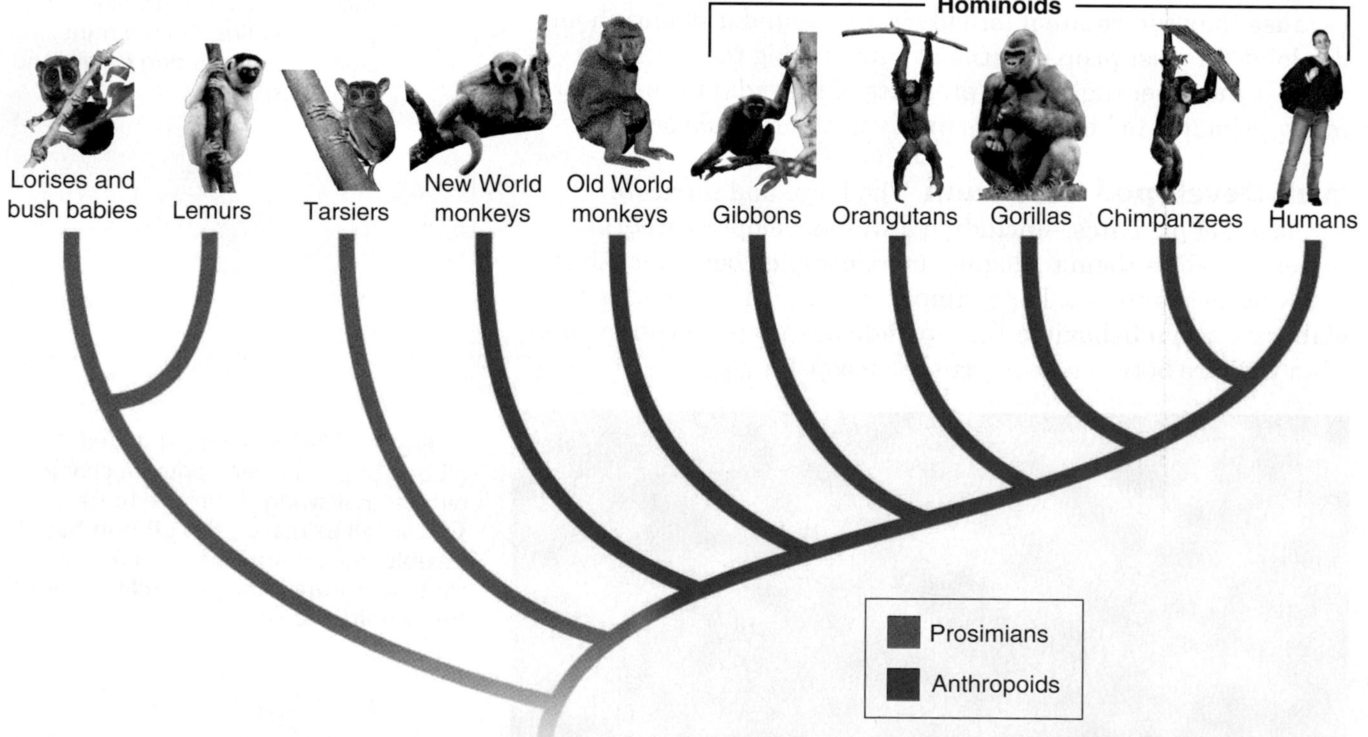

▲ **Figure 32–15** The diagram illustrates the phylogeny of modern primates. **The two main groups of primates are prosimians and anthropoids.**

Anthropoids Humans, apes, and most monkeys belong to a group called **anthropoids,** which means humanlike primates. This group split very early in its evolutionary history into two major branches. These branches became separated from each other as drifting continents moved apart. One branch, found today in Central and South America, is called the New World monkeys. (After Columbus's voyage to America, Europeans began to use the term *New World* to refer to North and South America.) New World monkeys, which include squirrel monkeys and spider monkeys, live almost entirely in trees. These monkeys have long, flexible arms that enable them to swing from branch to branch. New World monkeys also have a long, prehensile tail. A **prehensile** tail is a tail that can coil tightly enough around a branch to serve as a "fifth hand."

The other anthropoid group, which evolved in Africa and Asia, includes the Old World monkeys and great apes. Old World monkeys, such as langurs and macaques (muh-KAHKS), spend time in trees but lack prehensile tails. Great apes, also called **hominoids,** include gibbons, orangutans, gorillas, chimpanzees, and humans. Recent molecular studies confirm that chimpanzees are humans' closest relatives among the great apes. Humans and chimps share an astonishing 98 percent of their DNA!

Hominid Evolution

Between 6 and 7 million years ago, the hominoid line gave rise to a branch that ultimately led to the ancestors and closest relatives of modern humans. The **hominid** family, which includes modern humans, displayed several distinct evolutionary trends. Fossil evidence shows that as hominids evolved over millions of years, they became able to walk upright and developed thumbs adapted for grasping. They also developed large brains.

The skull, neck, spinal column, hipbones, and leg bones of early hominid species changed shape in ways that enabled later species to walk upright. **Figure 32–16** shows some ways in which the skeletons of modern humans differ from those of gorillas. The evolution of this **bipedal,** or two-foot, locomotion was very important, because it freed both hands to use tools. Meanwhile, the hominid hand evolved an **opposable thumb** that enabled grasping objects and using tools.

Comparing Human and Gorilla Skeletons

Modern Human	Modern Gorilla
Skull atop S-shaped spine	Skull atop C-shaped spine
Spinal cord exits at bottom of skull	Spinal cord exits near back of skull
Arms shorter than legs; hands do not touch ground during walking	Arms longer than legs; hands touch ground during walking
Pelvis is bowl-shaped	Pelvis is long and narrow
Thigh bones angled inward, directly below body	Thigh bones angled away from pelvis

▲ **Figure 32–16** Modern hominids walk upright on two legs; gorillas use all four limbs. **Comparing and Contrasting** ***According to the chart and illustration, what are the other differences between humans and gorillas?***

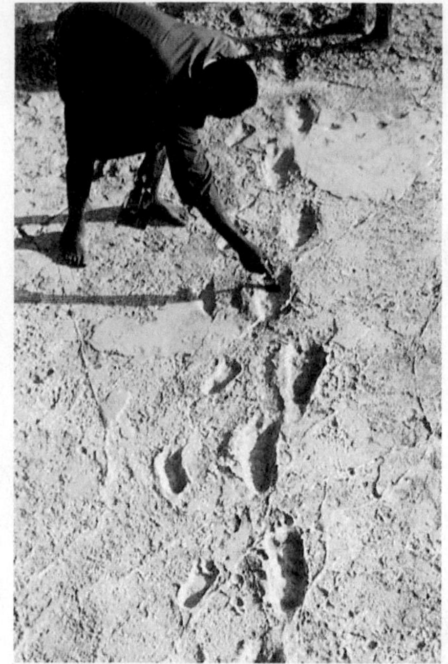

▲ **Figure 32–17** Between 3.8 and 3.6 million years ago, members of a species of *Australopithecus* made these footprints at Laetoli in Tanzania. The footprints show that hominids walked upright millions of years ago. **Applying Concepts** *What are the characteristics of* Australopithecus?

Hominids also displayed a remarkable increase in brain size. Chimpanzees, our closest living relatives among the apes, have a brain size of 280 to 450 cubic centimeters. The brain of *Homo sapiens,* on the other hand, ranges in size from 1200 to 1600 cubic centimeters! Most of the difference in brain size results from an enormously expanded cerebrum—the "thinking" area of the brain.

Early Hominids Paleontologists have unearthed a treasure trove of hominid species. At present, most paleontologists agree that the hominid fossil record includes at least these genera—*Ardipithecus, Australopithecus, Paranthropus, Kenyanthropus,* and *Homo*—and as many as 20 separate species. This diverse group of hominid fossils covers roughly 6 million years. All these species are relatives of modern humans, but not all of them are human ancestors. To understand that distinction, think of your family. Your relatives may include aunts, uncles, cousins, parents, grandparents, and great-grandparents. Of these, only your parents, grandparents, and great-grandparents are your ancestors.

Almost a third of all known hominid species have been discovered in the last 20 years. This shows how rapidly knowledge of hominid fossils is growing. It also explains why hominid evolution is both fascinating and confusing. What once looked like a simple "human family tree" now looks more like a dense, branching shrub. Many questions remain about how fossil hominids are related to one another and to humans. Let's examine a few of the most important discoveries.

Biology and History

Human-Fossil Seekers

The study of human origins is an exciting search for our past. To piece together this complicated story requires the skills of many scientists.

1812
Georges Cuvier
Cuvier, a French zoologist, rejects the idea of evolution based on a lack of evidence in the fossil record. He is noted for saying "Fossil man does not exist!" He believed species were static and unchanging.

1868
Edouard Lartet
Henry Christy
French geologist Lartet and English banker Christy unearth several ancient human skeletons in a rock shelter called Cro-Magnon in France. These hominid fossils are the first to be classified as *Homo sapiens.*

1886
Marcel de Puydt
Max Lohest
De Puydt and Lohest describe two Neanderthal skeletons found in a cave in Belgium. Their detailed description of the skeletons shows that Neanderthals were an extinct human form, not an abnormal form of modern human.

1800 1850 1900

Australopithecus One early group of hominids, members of the genus *Australopithecus,* lived from about 4 million to a million years ago. These hominids were bipedal apes that spent at least some time in trees. The structure of their teeth suggests a diet rich in fruit. Some *Australopithecus* species seem to have been human ancestors, while others formed separate branches off the main hominid line.

The best known species is *Australopithecus afarensis*—described from a remarkably complete female skeleton, nicknamed Lucy, who stood only about 1 meter tall. The humanlike footprints shown in **Figure 32–17,** which are between 3.8 and 3.6 million years old, were probably made by members of the same species as Lucy. Since *Australopithecus* fossils have small brains, the Laetoli footprints show that hominids walked bipedally long before large brains evolved.

Paranthropus Three later species, which grew to the size of well-fed football linebackers, were originally placed in the genus *Australopithecus*. However, they are now usually placed in their own genus, *Paranthropus.* The known *Paranthropus* species had huge, grinding back teeth. Their diets probably included coarse and fibrous plant foods like those eaten by modern gorillas. Most paleontologists now place *Paranthropus* on a separate, dead-end branch of our family tree.

CHECKPOINT *What are the characteristics of* Paranthropus*?*

To find out more about human history, view the segment "Mummies: Ties to the Past," on Videotape Two.

Writing in Science

You have found Mary Leakey's journal and noticed that the entry for her discovery of the footprints at Laetoli is missing. Write an entry for the journal as she would have, describing the events of the day and her initial reaction to the find.

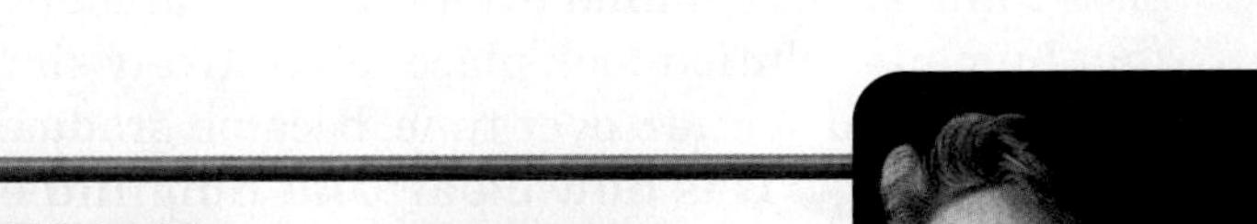

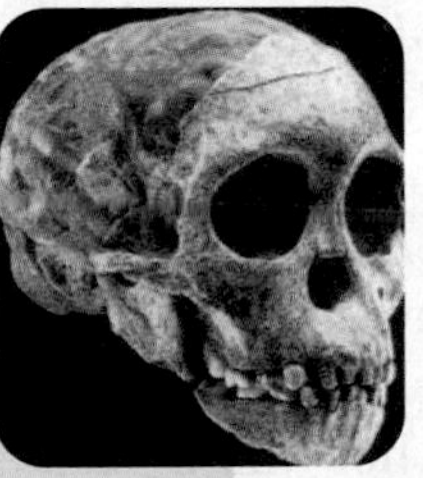

1924
Raymond Dart
Dart, an Australian anatomist, finds an early hominid fossil—a nearly complete skull of a child—in South Africa. This specimen was placed in a new genus called *Australopithecus.*

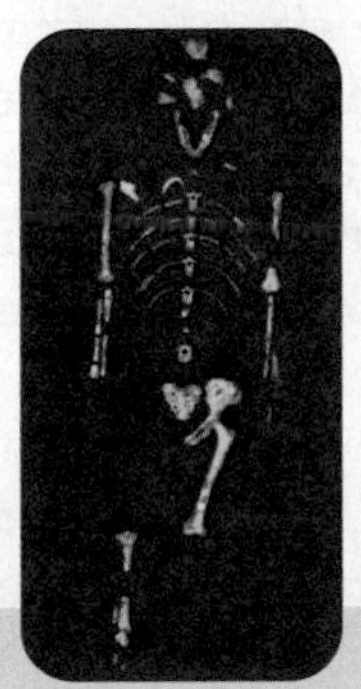

1974
Donald Johanson
An American paleontologist and his team find 40 percent of a skeleton of *Australopithecus*, which they call Lucy, in the Afar region of Ethiopia. The skeleton is about 3.2 million years old.

1978
Mary Leakey
Leakey, a British anthropologist, discovers a set of 3.6 million-year-old fossil hominid footprints at Laetoli in Tanzania. The footprints provide evidence that early hominids walked erect on two legs.

1999
Douglas Wallace
Wallace and fellow geneticists create a family tree of human evolution based on their studies of mitochondrial DNA, which is passed only from mother to child.

1900 1950 2000

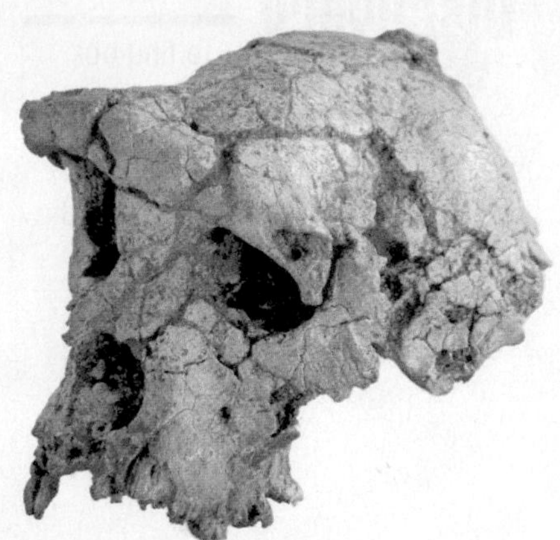

Sahelanthropus tchadensis

Kenyanthropus platyops

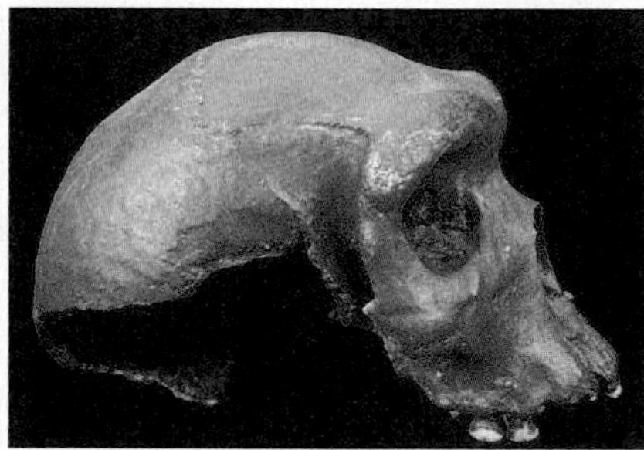

Homo erectus

▲ **Figure 32–18** Paleontologists' interpretations of hominid evolution are based on the study of fossils such as these skulls. *Sahelanthropus* may be the earliest known hominid. **Observing** *Which of these skulls most closely resembles the skull of a modern human?*

Recent Hominid Discoveries Early in 2001, a team led by paleontologist Meave Leakey announced that they had uncovered a skull in Kenya. Its ear structures resembled those of chimpanzees, and its brain was rather small. Yet some of its facial features resembled those of fossils usually placed in the genus *Homo*. Paleontologists put this skull in a new genus, *Kenyanthropus*. *Kenyanthropus* is shown in the middle in **Figure 32–18.** Evidence indicates that this species existed at the same time as *A. afarensis*.

Then, during the summer of 2002, paleontologists working in the desert in north-central Africa announced the discovery of an even more startling skull. This fossil skull, tentatively called *Sahelanthropus*, is nearly 7 million years old. If scientists agree that *Sahelanthropus* is indeed a hominid, it would be a million years older than any hominid previously known.

Sahelanthropus had a brain about the size of a modern chimp, yet its short, flat face is more like that of a human. In fact, this skull seems more humanlike in certain ways than Lucy (*A. afarensis*), who lived several million years later. While most hominid fossils have been discovered in eastern Africa, *Sahelanthropus* was discovered much farther to the west. This suggests that there may be many more fossil hominids to be found in widely separated parts of Africa.

CHECKPOINT *What is* Kenyanthropus platyops*?*

Rethinking Early Hominid Evolution Together with other recent fossil finds, the discovery of *Kenyanthropus* and *Sahelanthropus* has dramatically changed the way paleontologists think about hominid evolution. Researchers once thought that human evolution took place in relatively simple steps in which hominid species, over time, became gradually more humanlike. **It is now clear that hominid evolution did not proceed by the simple, straight-line transformation of one species into another. Rather, like the evolution of other mammalian groups, a series of complex adaptive radiations produced a large number of species whose relationships are difficult to determine.** Which hominids are true human ancestors? Which are just relatives? And how are all those species related to one another and to modern humans? At present, no one can answer these questions.

So what is known about hominid evolution? As shown in **Figure 32–19,** the hominid fossil record now dates back nearly 7 million years, close to the time that DNA studies suggest for the split between hominids and the ancestors of modern chimpanzees. In addition, there are many known fossil hominid species, several of which display a confusing mix of primitive and modern traits. It will probably take many years of work to more fully understand this fascinating and complex story.

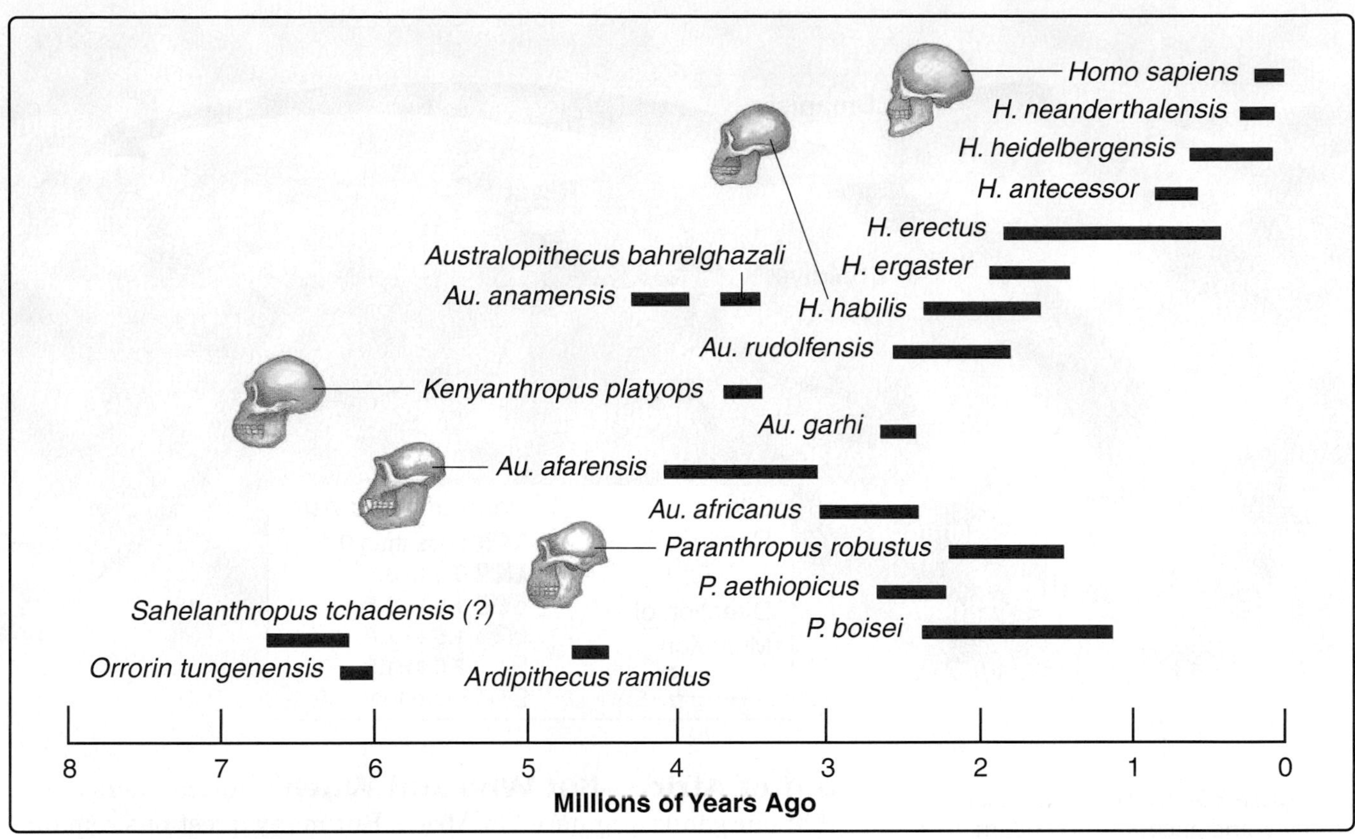

▲ **Figure 32–19** The diagram shows fossil hominids and the time ranges during which they may have existed. The time ranges are likely to change as paleontologists gather new data. The question mark after *Sahelanthropus tchadensis* indicates that scientists are not yet certain that this species is a hominid. Paleontologists do not yet have enough information to know how hominid species are related. **It is now clear that hominid evolution did not proceed by the simple, straight-line transformation of one species into another.** Current hypotheses about early stages of human evolution recognize the incompleteness of the data.

The Road to Modern Humans

The hominids that have been mentioned so far, such as *Paranthropus* and *Australopithecus,* all lived millions of years before modern humans. When did our species, *Homo sapiens,* appear? As you can see in **Figure 32–19,** other species in our genus existed before *H. sapiens,* and at least two other species in the genus *Homo* existed at the same time as early humans. As is the case with earlier hominid fossils, paleontologists still do not completely understand the history and relationships of species within our own genus.

The Genus *Homo* About 2.5 million years ago, a new kind of hominid appeared. Its fossils show that it resembled modern humans enough to be classified in the genus *Homo.* Because these fossils were found with tools made of stone and bone, researchers called the species *Homo habilis* (HAB-ih-lus), which means "handy man."

Homo habilis was the first of several species in our genus to arise in Africa. About 2 million years ago, a species larger than *H. habilis* appeared. It had a bigger brain and downward-facing nostrils that resembled those of modern humans. Today, most researchers call the African fossils of this species *Homo ergaster.* At some point, one or more species in the genus *Homo* began migrating out of Africa through what is now the Middle East. That species may have been *H. ergaster* or a closely related species named *Homo erectus*.

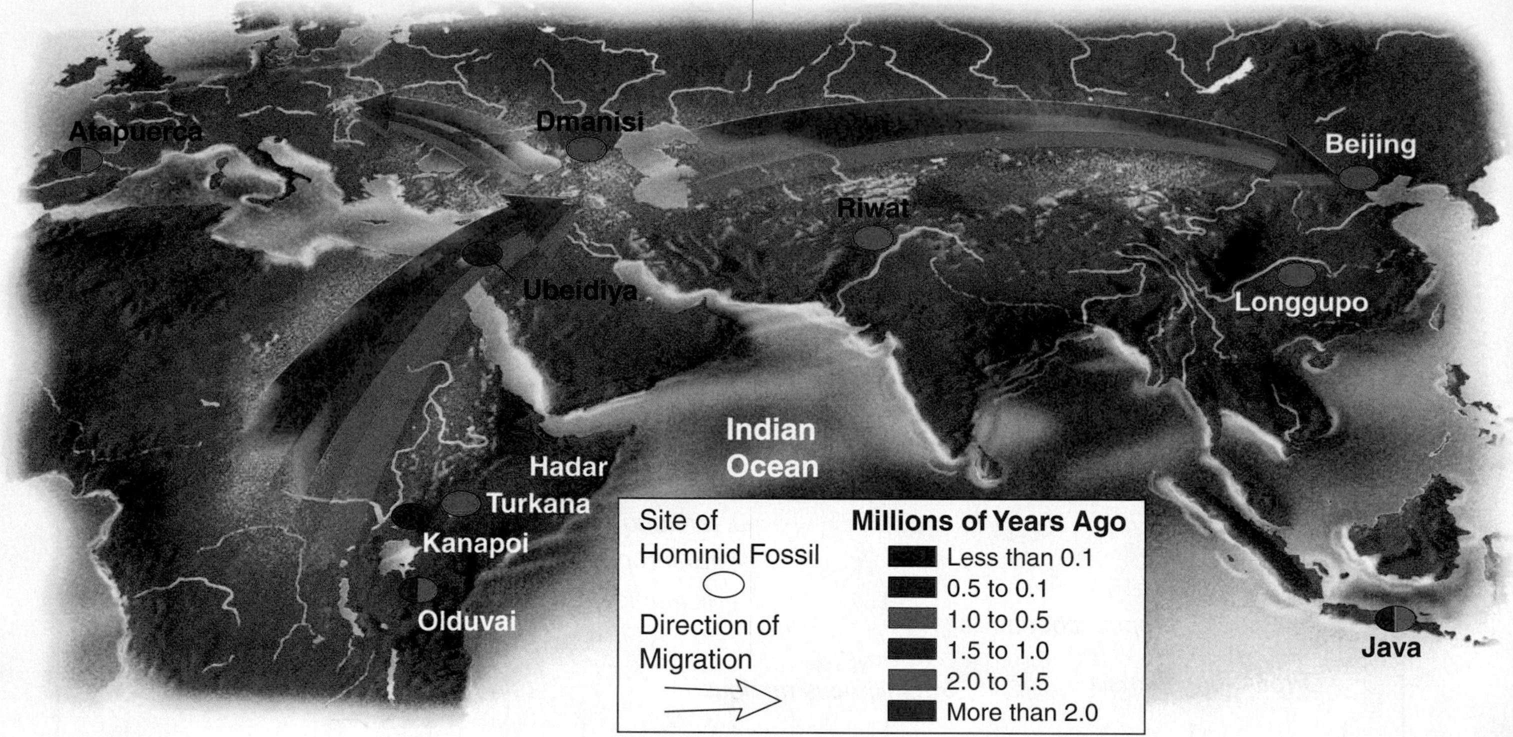

▲ **Figure 32–20** Data show that relatives and ancestors of modern humans left Africa several different times. But when did early hominids leave Africa, and how far did they travel? By comparing the mitochondrial DNA of human populations around the world, and by continuing to study the fossil record, scientists hope to improve our understanding of the complex history of *Homo sapiens.*

Out of Africa—But Who and When? Researchers agree that our genus originated in Africa. But many questions remain. When did hominids first leave Africa? Did more than one species make the trip? Which of those species were human ancestors and which were merely relatives? Fossil data and molecular evidence suggest that hominids left Africa in several waves as shown in **Figure 32–20.** By a million years ago, migrants from Africa had crossed Asia and reached China and Java, and populations of *H. erectus* were living in several places across Asia.

Many researchers have hypothesized that *H. erectus* was the first of our genus to leave Africa. Two recently discovered fossil skulls may offer additional evidence that *H. erectus* did leave Africa and migrate long distances. The skulls, which strongly resemble African *H. erectus* fossils and are about 1.75 million years old, were discovered in the country of Georgia, which is north of Turkey and far from Africa.

However, other evidence makes the situation less clear. Another 1.75-million-year-old skull found in Georgia resembles 1.9 million-year-old *Homo habilis* skulls from Kenya. Does this skull indicate that *H. habilis* left Africa before *H. erectus*? The scientific jury is still evaluating the evidence.

Paleontologists are also unsure exactly where and when *Homo sapiens* arose. One hypothesis, the multi-regional model, suggests that modern humans evolved independently in several parts of the world from widely separated populations of *H. erectus*. Another hypothesis, the out-of-Africa model, proposes that modern humans evolved in Africa between 200,000 and 150,000 years ago, migrated out to colonize the world, and replaced the descendants of earlier hominid species. Scientific debate, and the search for more data, continue.

For: Links on human evolution
Visit: www.SciLinks.org
Web Code: cbn-9323

Modern *Homo sapiens*

The story of modern humans over the past 500,000 years involves two main groups. The earliest of these species is now called *Homo neanderthalensis,* named after the Neander Valley in Germany where their remains were first found. Neanderthals, as they are commonly called, flourished from Europe through western Asia between about 200,000 and 30,000 years ago. Evidence from Neanderthal sites in Europe and the Middle East suggests that they not only made stone tools but also lived in organized social groups.

The other group is anatomically modern *Homo sapiens*—in other words, people whose skeletons look like those of modern humans. These *H. sapiens,* who probably arose in Africa, appeared in the Middle East around 100,000 years ago. They joined Neanderthals who had been living in that region for at least 100,000 years. As far as anyone can tell, Neanderthals and *Homo sapiens* lived side by side in what is now Israel, Lebanon, Syria, and Turkey for around 50,000 years, using similar tools and living in remarkably similar ways.

That situation may have changed dramatically around 50,000–40,000 years ago. According to one hypothesis, that's when some populations of *H. sapiens* seem to have fundamentally changed their way of life. They used new technology to make more sophisticated stone blades, and made elaborately worked tools from bones and antlers. They produced spectacular cave paintings, such as the one in **Figure 32–21.** These *Homo sapiens* buried their dead with elaborate rituals. In other words, these people began to behave like modern humans. About 40,000 years ago, one such group, known as Cro-Magnons (kroh-MAG-nunz), appeared in Europe.

By 30,000 years ago, Neanderthals had disappeared from Europe—and from the Middle East as well. How and why they disappeared is not yet known. But since that time, our species has been Earth's only hominid.

▲ **Figure 32–21** This ancient cave painting from France shows the remarkable artistic abilities of Cro-Magnons. **Inferring** *How might these painted images be related to the way in which these early humans lived?*

32–3 Section Assessment

1. **Key Concept** List five anatomical characteristics that most primates share.
2. **Key Concept** Describe the major primate groups and explain how they are related phylogenetically.
3. **Key Concept** Explain the way that paleontologists currently view hominid evolution.
4. Compare and contrast hominids and other hominoids. How are they similar? Different?
5. **Critical Thinking Applying Concepts** How did the separation of the continents contribute to the development of New World and Old World monkeys?

Writing in Science

Explanatory Paragraph
Write a paragraph explaining how the structure of primates' fingers, toes, and shoulders are adaptations that help with survival. *Hint:* To prepare to write, make a table that describes the structures in the left column and then lists the advantages of those structures in the right column.

To find out more about how scientists use forensic evidence, view the segment "Wrongly Accused: Science and Justice," on Videotape Three.

Using Fibers as Forensic Evidence

Hair and other fibers are often used by police as evidence that a suspect was at the scene of a crime such as a burglary. In this investigation, you will examine a variety of hairs and other fibers to match unknown fibers to known reference fibers. The two human hairs represent hairs from two people who are suspected of having been at the crime scene. The unknown fibers represent fibers found at the crime scene.

Problem

How do forensic scientists identify unknown hairs and fibers?

Materials

- reference fibers
- unknown fibers
- microscope slides
- coverslips
- dropper pipette
- microscope
- glass-marking pencil
- facial tissues
- isopropyl alcohol
- rubber cement
- forceps
- test-tube rack
- 4 test tubes of biuret reagent
- 4 glass stirring rods
- hot water bath

Skills

Observing, Inferring, Analyzing Data

Procedure

Part A: Observing Fibers

1. Place one of the reference fibers on a microscope slide. **CAUTION:** *Microscopes and slides are fragile. Handle them carefully. If you break any glass, inform your teacher immediately.* Add a drop of water and a coverslip. Label the slide with the name of the fiber. On a separate sheet of paper, make a copy of the data table shown below, with 10 blank lines.
2. Place the slide on the stage of a microscope and look at it under 100× magnification. Examine the fiber carefully, looking for features such as color, shape, texture, and whether or not a hair root is attached. Record your observations in your data table. Draw and label a sketch of the fiber.
3. Repeat steps 1 and 2 for each of the reference and unknown fibers.
4. Clean one of the reference fibers by pulling it through a folded tissue moistened with a small amount of alcohol. **CAUTION:** *Alcohol is flammable. Do not use it in the presence of an open flame or sparks.*
5. Smear a thin layer of rubber cement on the middle of a glass slide. Quickly place the fiber on the surface of the rubber cement.
6. Before the cement dries, lift the fiber off the slide with forceps. You should see an imprint of the fiber on the cement. Put the slide under a microscope and observe the surface texture of the fiber. Record your observations.
7. Repeat steps 4 to 6 for each of the other fibers.

Data Table

Fiber	General Observations	Surface Texture	Biuret Test Result

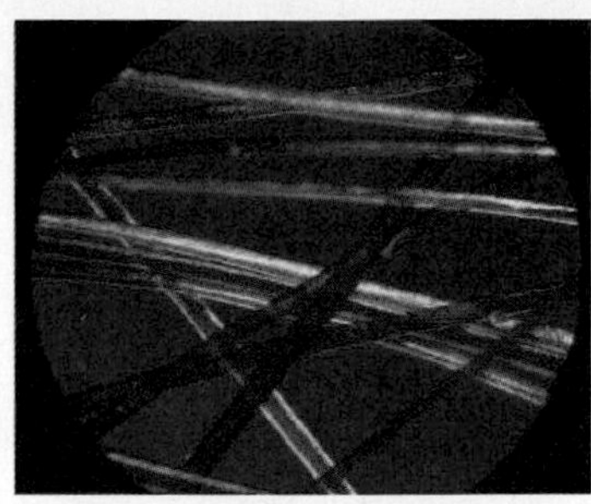

Human Hairs
(magnification: 22×)

Polyester Threads
(magnification: 70×)

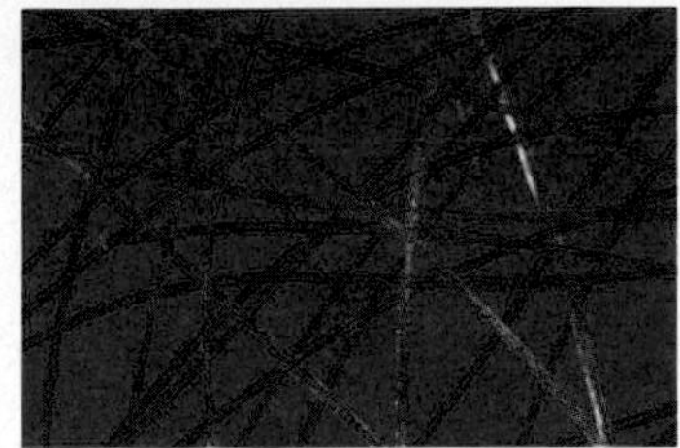

Silk Fibers
(magnification: about 50×)

Part B: Testing for Protein

8. **Formulating Hypotheses** Hair contains protein. Synthetic and plant fibers do not contain protein. On the basis of the observations you have recorded in your data table, write a hypothesis about which unknown fibers contain protein. Include the reasons for your hypothesis, explaining what evidence supports your hypothesis about each fiber.

9. Label 4 test tubes of biuret reagent solution 1 through 4. **CAUTION:** *Wear safety goggles, a lab apron, and plastic gloves when working with biuret reagent solution. If any of the solution gets on your skin or clothing, wash it off immediately and inform your teacher.* Use forceps to place several strands of each unknown fiber in the test tube with the same number. Record the time.

10. Place a glass stirring rod in each test tube. Place the test tubes in the hot water bath. Stir each test tube occasionally. **CAUTION:** *Leave the stirring rods in the test tubes. Do not place the wet stirring rods on the table.*

11. Observe the color of each test tube. A change from blue to purple or reddish-brown within 5 minutes indicates the presence of protein. Add your observations to your data table. Follow your teacher's instructions for safe disposal of the biuret reagent.

Analyze and Conclude

1. **Comparing and Contrasting** How are hairs and synthetic fibers different?
2. **Observing** Did you observe any differences between human hair and other hair? If you did, describe the differences.
3. **Drawing Conclusions** Did your observations support the idea that one or both of the suspects may have been at the crime scene? Explain your answer.
4. **Evaluating** Did your observations leave room for doubt about this conclusion? If so, what other evidence would help you decide whether your conclusion is valid? Explain your answer.

Go Further

Additional Research Forensic science is the application of scientific knowledge to questions involving law. Do research to learn more about forensic science. Some topics you might investigate include the following:

- DNA evidence
- Evidence of poisoning
- Forensic dentistry
- Forensic anthropology
- Forensic pathology
- Ballistics

Chapter 32 Study Guide

32–1 Introduction to the Mammals

Key Concepts

- In addition to having hair and the ability to nourish their young with milk, all mammals breathe air, have four-chambered hearts, and are endotherms that generate their body heat internally.
- The first true mammals appeared during the late Triassic Period, about 220 million years ago.
- The ability of mammals to regulate their body heat from within is an example of homeostasis.
- As mammals evolved to eat foods other than insects, the form and function of their jaws and teeth became adapted to their diets.
- The kidneys of mammals help maintain homeostasis by filtering urea from the blood, as well as excreting or retaining water.

Vocabulary

mammary gland, p. 821 • subcutaneous fat, p. 822
rumen, p. 823 • diaphragm, p. 824
cerebral cortex, p. 825

32–2 Diversity of Mammals

Key Concepts

- The three groups of living mammals are the monotremes, the marsupials, and the placentals. Marsupials bear live young, but at a very early stage of development. Monotremes lay eggs. In placental mammals, nutrients, oxygen, carbon dioxide, and wastes are exchanged between embryo and mother through the placenta.
- Similar ecological opportunities on the different continents have produced some striking examples of convergent evolution in mammals.

Vocabulary

monotreme, p. 828 • marsupial, p. 829
placenta, p. 829

32–3 Primates and Human Origins

Key Concepts

- In general, primates have binocular vision, a well-developed cerebrum, relatively long fingers and toes, and arms that rotate in their shoulder joints.
- Primates that evolved from two of the earliest branches look very little like typical monkeys and are called prosimians. Members of the more familiar primate group that includes monkeys, apes, and humans are called anthropoids.
- It is now clear that hominid evolution did not proceed by the simple, straight-line transformation of one species into another. Rather, like the evolution of other mammalian groups, a series of complex adaptive radiations produced a large number of species whose relationships are difficult to determine.

Vocabulary

binocular vision, p. 834
prosimian, p. 834
anthropoid, p. 835
prehensile, p. 835
hominoid, p. 835
hominid, p. 835
bipedal, p. 835
opposable thumb, p. 835

Thinking Visually

Using information from this chapter, complete the following concept map:

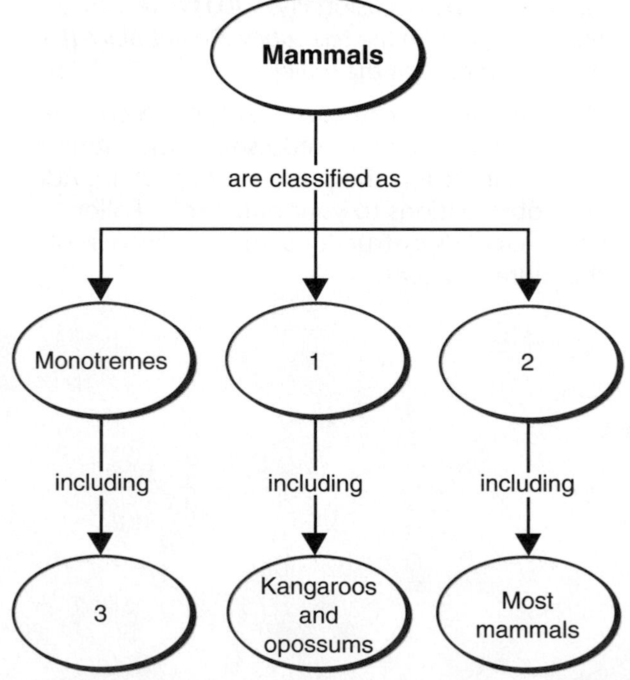

Preparing for the Living Environment Exam

Blue questions emphasize Regents Exam content

Chapter 32

Part A

Multiple Choice

For each statement or question, select the number of the word or expression that, of those given, best completes the statement or answers the question.

1 Which structure in female mammals produces milk to nourish young?
(1) kidney (3) cloaca
(2) mammary gland (4) cerebral cortex

2 The first true mammals appeared during the late
(1) Permian Period (3) Triassic Period
(2) Cretaceous Period (4) Jurassic Period

3 To determine if a vertebrate is a bird or a mammal, a biologist would need to know if it
(1) has a four-chambered heart
(2) breathes air
(3) has hair
(4) is an endotherm

4 In mammals, the powerful muscle that aids in breathing is the
(1) diaphragm (3) placenta
(2) cerebrum (4) kidney

5 The composition and levels of body fluids in mammals are controlled by the
(1) lungs (3) intestine
(2) kidneys (4) heart

6 In the mammalian circulatory system, oxygen-poor blood moves from the heart to the
(1) stomach (3) lungs
(2) diaphragm (4) brain

7 A duckbill platypus is a monotreme because it
(1) lays eggs (3) lives in Australia
(2) has only one lung (4) bears only one young

8 Which animal is *not* an example of a placental mammal?
(1) cetacean (3) rodent
(2) marsupial (4) primate

9 Primates consist of two groups, anthropoids and
(1) monotremes (3) apes
(2) hominids (4) prosimians

10 How many hominid species exist today?
(1) one (3) nine
(2) two (4) twelve

11 Which is *not* a characteristic of all mammals?
(1) the ability to nourish young with milk
(2) giving birth to live young
(3) having hair
(4) the ability to generate body heat internally

12 Humans belong to the order
(1) Chiropterans (3) Sirenians
(2) Carnivores (4) Primates

13 Each characteristic belongs to primates *except*
(1) a well-developed cerebrum
(2) binocular vision
(3) flexible digits
(4) a small brain in proportion to body size

14 How are living mammals classified into groups?
(1) method of development
(2) structure of kidneys
(3) method of respiration
(4) method of regulating body temperature

15 What is the most likely food source of the animal whose skull is shown in the diagram below?

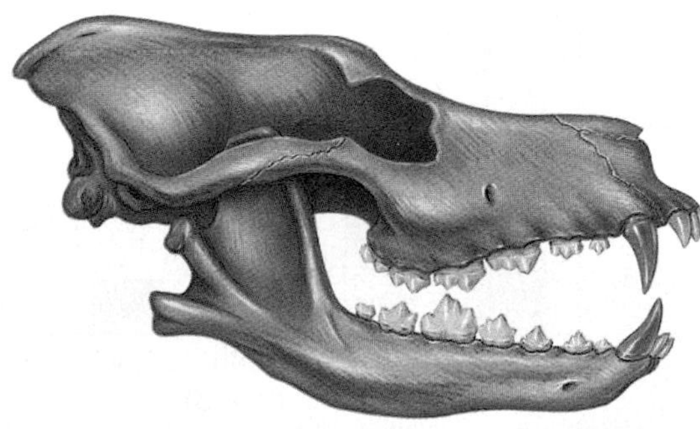

(1) grasses and vines
(2) small insects and seeds
(3) trees and shrubs
(4) deer

Test-Taking Tip Take the time to read each question completely on a standardized test, including all of the answer choices. Consider each possible choice before determining which answer is correct.

Preparing for the Living Environment Exam

Part B

Multiple Choice and Extended Response
For those questions that ask you to select a response, choose the one that best completes the statement or answers the question. For all others follow the directions given.

16 Describe three adaptations mammals have to conserve body heat.

Base your answers to questions 17 through 20 on the information and graph below and on your knowledge of biology.

Radioactive substances found in living things decay at specific rates over time. The rate at which a substance decays is measured by its half-life. A half-life is the amount of time it takes for half a radioactive sample to decay. For example, the half-life of carbon-14 is 5770 years.

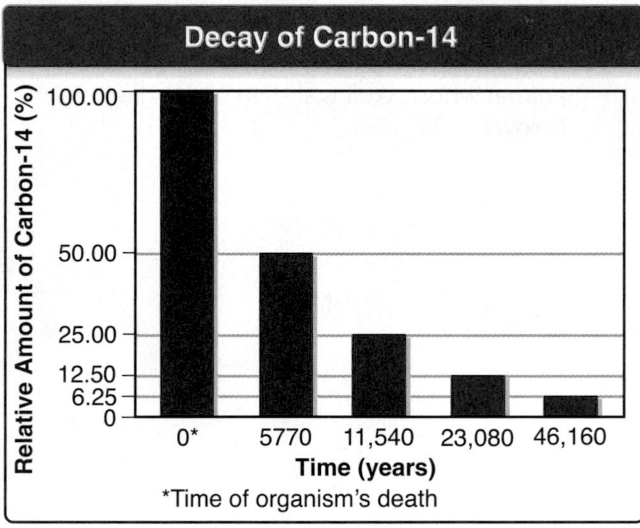

17 How much carbon-14 would remain in an 11,540-year-old fossil?
(1) 25 percent
(2) 35 percent
(3) 50 percent
(4) 60 percent

18 A paleontologist determines that a particular fossil has $\frac{1}{8}$ of the amount of carbon-14 that was present at the time the organism died. How old is the fossil estimated to be?
(1) 11,540 years
(2) 23,080 years
(3) 34,620 years
(4) 46,160 years

19 Scientists cannot accurately detect the amount of carbon-14 in a fossil when more than $\frac{1}{16}$ of the carbon-14 has decayed. Which fossils could *not* be dated accurately using carbon-14?
(1) a 5000-year-old fossil
(2) a 10,000-year-old fossil
(3) a 25,000-year-old fossil
(4) a 75,000-year-old fossil

20 Describe why carbon-14 dating is not used to provide information relative to the age of the first hominids.

21 The following flowcharts illustrate two proposed explanations for the evolution of humans. They begin with descent from *Australopithecus afarensis.*

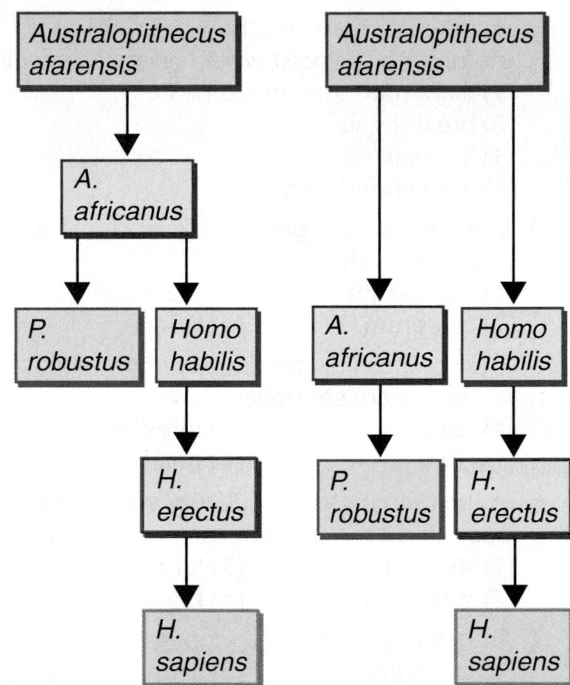

Describe how the two lines of descent are different.

For each phrase in questions 22 through 25, select the proper classification order, chosen from the list below, that is best described by that phrase. Then record its number on a separate answer paper. An order may be used once, more than once, or not at all.

Orders of Mammals
(1) Cetacean
(2) Chiropteran
(3) Rodent
(4) Xenarthrans

22 Mammal A can fly, has sharp teeth and consumes a liquid diet.

23 Mammal B has a single pair of sharp, curved incisor teeth and eats only plant material.

24 Mammal C is a filter feeder, mates and bears its young in water, but comes to the surface to breathe.

25 Select either Mammal A, B, or C and explain why you classified it as you did.

Base your answers to questions 26 through 28 on the reading passage below and on your knowledge of biology.

Neanderthal or Cro-Magnon?

A heated debate continues between archeologists as they try to determine the line of descent from ancient humans to modern humans, *Homo sapiens.* Many scientists believe that Neanderthals, whose remains were first found in the Neander Valley in Germany, should be classified as their own species because of their anatomical differences.

Neanderthals had a thick, squat body adapted to maintaining body temperature since they spent long periods in extremely cold climates. They had low, sloping foreheads and jaws that jutted forward.

Recently the skeletal remains of a four-year-old boy, buried 25,000 years ago, were discovered in a cave in Portugal. His chin, tooth size, and pelvic measurements identified him as Cro-Magnon (a group of *H. sapiens*). However, his stocky body and short legs showed that he had Neanderthal heritage. Scientists concluded that this was evidence of interbreeding between Neanderthals and Cro-Magnons.

Meanwhile, scientists in Scotland, along with their colleagues in Russia and Sweden, performed DNA analysis on the remains of a Neanderthal infant found in Russian mountains. The infant lived 30,000 years ago. By comparing regions of mitochondrial DNA that are known to evolve rapidly, they discovered that Neanderthals and modern humans diverged about 500,000 years ago. Scientists believe this discovery supports the "out-of-Africa" model of modern human evolution.

26 A species is a group of similar organisms that can breed and produce fertile offspring. State what evidence scientists have discovered that suggests Neanderthals and Cro-Magnons are not separate species.

27 Scottish scientists believe that their DNA analysis supports the "out-of-Africa model." Describe this model and explain how the Scottish DNA findings support it.

28 The findings of the Scottish and the Portuguese scientists do not agree 100%. During investigations such as these, what methods do scientists use as they analyze and report information that might seem to be conflicting?

Part C

Extended Response

Answer the questions or follow the directions given.

29 Explain why it is important for paleontologists to estimate the age of a hominid fossil along with an analysis of its structural characteristics.

30 A group of scientists working in New Guinea discovered a female mammal that no one could identify. Three methods the scientists could use to determine if the mammal is a monotreme, a marsupial, or a placental mammal are by examining its structural features, its method of reproduction, and the way it nourishes its young. Select *two* of these methods and, for each, explain how the determination of its classification would be made. For *each* method you state, be sure to:
- state the method they would be using to determine its classification
- state which characteristic(s) this animal would show if it were a monotreme, a marsupial, or a placental mammal

For: An interactive self-test
Visit: PHSchool.com
Web Code: cba-9320

CHAPTER 33

Comparing Chordates

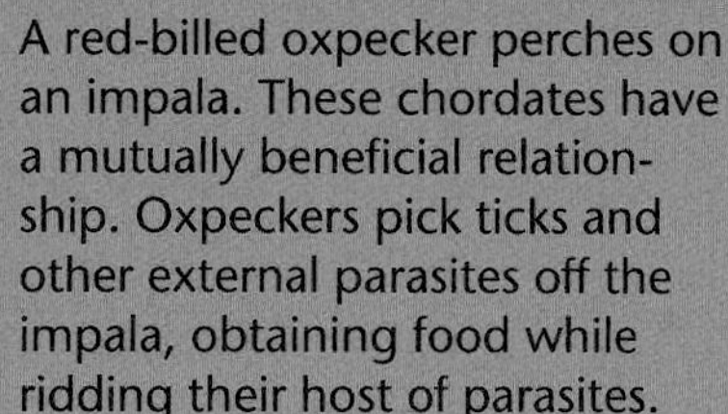

A red-billed oxpecker perches on an impala. These chordates have a mutually beneficial relationship. Oxpeckers pick ticks and other external parasites off the impala, obtaining food while ridding their host of parasites.

Inquiry Activity

What are some adaptations of vertebrae?

Procedure   

1. Put on plastic gloves. Bend a chicken neck back and forth and from side to side.
2. Insert a dissecting probe into the opening at the top of the neck. What do you observe? **CAUTION:** *Use care with sharp instruments.*

Think About It

1. **Inferring** How is the structure of the chicken's neck related to its function?
2. **Predicting** What would happen if the chicken's neck vertebrae were one bone with no central opening?
3. **Drawing Conclusions** How would you expect the vertebrae to be different in an elephant's neck? Explain your answer.

33–1 Chordate Evolution

4-3.1 Fossils indicate extinction
4-3.1 Evolutionary changes appear to be like the growth of a bush
4-3.1 Natural selection and evolution
LS- Follow safety rules, observe, and formulate conclusions

Guide for Reading

Key Concepts
- What are the roots of the chordate family tree?
- What is a main trend in the evolution of chordates?

Vocabulary
notochord
adaptive radiation

Reading Strategy: Asking Questions Before you read, study the cladogram in **Figure 33–2.** Make a list of questions about the cladogram. As you read, write down the answers to your questions.

Ever since the first chordates appeared more than 500 million years ago, they have been evolving. During this continual process, chordates developed an incredible variety of adaptations. Some of these traits—scales or hair, for example—are relatively simple. Others—such as a four-chambered heart or an amniotic egg—are far more complex. All these adaptations were tested and shaped by natural selection.

Chordate Origins

Much of what scientists know about the origins of chordates comes from studying the embryos of living organisms. Such studies suggest that the most ancient chordates were closely related to echinoderms. Do scientists know what these early chordates looked like? Surprisingly, the answer is yes.

The variety of fossilized organisms preserved in the rich Cambrian deposits of Canada's Burgess Shale includes a peculiar organism called *Pikaia* (pih-KAY-uh), shown in **Figure 33–1.** When *Pikaia* was first discovered, it was thought to be a worm. On closer inspection, scientists determined that *Pikaia* had a **notochord**—a flexible, supporting structure that is found only in chordates. *Pikaia* also had paired serial muscles that were arranged in a manner similar to those of today's nonvertebrate chordates, such as lancelets. On the basis of fossil evidence, scientists now classify *Pikaia* as an early chordate.

To better understand the early evolution of chordates, biologists study a nonvertebrate chordate that is alive today—the tunicate. The tadpolelike larvae of tunicates are the simplest living animals to have a notochord, a dorsal hollow nerve cord, a tail that extends posterior to the anus, and pharyngeal pouches—key features common to all chordates. Today, biologists are studying the genes that control the development of these features.

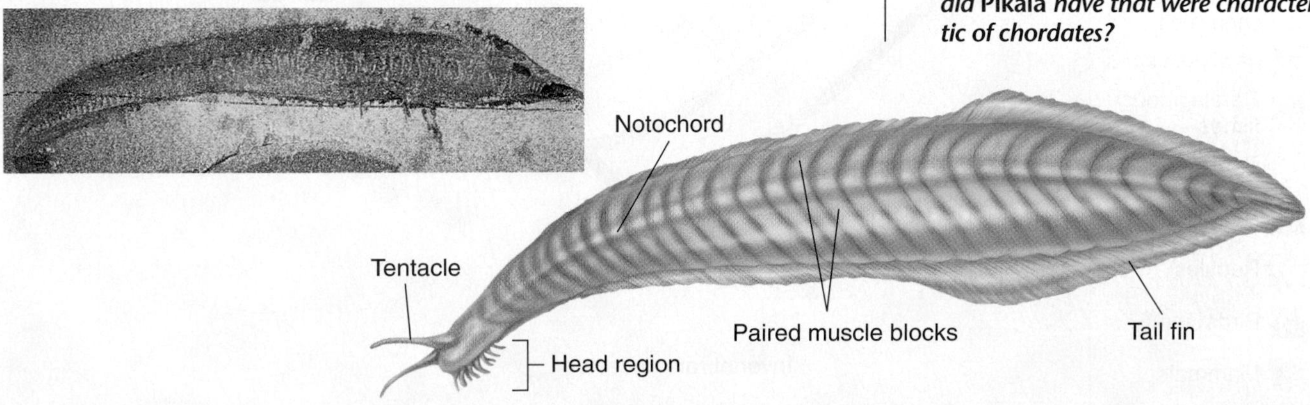

Figure 33–1 This is a reconstruction of *Pikaia,* a soft-bodied animal that lived during the Cambrian Period. **Classifying** *Which features did* Pikaia *have that were characteristic of chordates?*

The Chordate Family Tree

The chordate family tree has its roots in ancestors that vertebrates share with tunicates and lancelets. The cladogram in **Figure 33–2** shows chordate phylogeny—how the different groups of living chordates are related to one another and to their invertebrate ancestors. It also shows the evolution of distinctly vertebrate features, such as jaws and limbs. Notice that the fishes—from hagfishes to lungfishes—include six different groups with long and separate evolutionary histories. On the other hand, modern amphibians, reptiles, birds, and mammals share much more recent common ancestors. Where do extinct groups, such as dinosaurs, fit into the chordate phylum? The answer may be found in the fossil record.

CHECKPOINT *How many groups of fishes are alive today?*

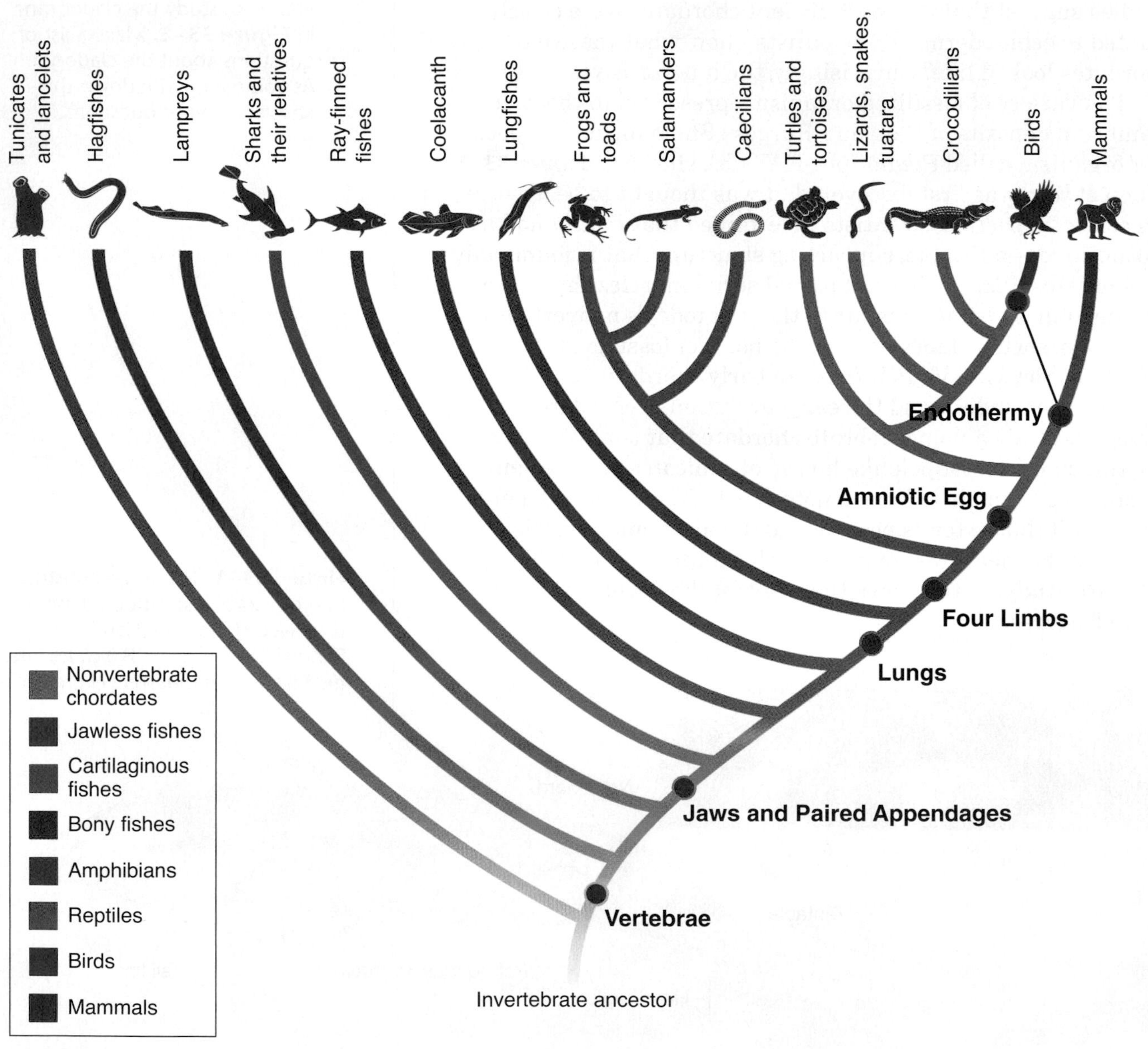

Figure 33–2 The phylum Chordata includes both vertebrates and nonvertebrate chordates. All of these subphyla share a common invertebrate ancestor. This cladogram shows the phylogenetic relationship of modern chordate groups to that common ancestor. The different colored lines represent the traditional groupings of these animals, as listed in the key. The red circles indicate some of the important chordate adaptations. Such adaptations are the results of evolutionary processes, including natural selection.

Evolutionary Trends in Vertebrates

The hard body structures of many vertebrates have left behind an excellent fossil record. As a result, scientists know a great deal about vertebrates' evolutionary history. In addition, scientists infer evolutionary trends by studying the characteristics of chordates living today.

Adaptive Radiations The number of species within each chordate group has changed over geologic time. Look at the cladogram in **Figure 33–2** again. The red circles in that figure represent the origin of certain adaptive features. For example, one notable event in chordate evolution was the development of jaws. Another event was the development of paired appendages, including pectoral and pelvic fin or limb girdles. Paired appendages allowed chordates, such as the salamander in **Figure 33–3**, to move more efficiently. **Over the course of evolution, the appearance of new adaptations—such as jaws and paired appendages—has launched adaptive radiations in chordate groups.** An **adaptive radiation** is the rapid diversification of species as they adapt to new conditions.

Convergent Evolution Adaptive radiations sometimes produce species that are similar in appearance and behavior, even though they are not closely related. This trend is called convergent evolution. Convergent evolution occurred many times during chordate evolution when unrelated species encountered similar ecological conditions and evolved similar adaptations. For example, convergent evolution has produced flying vertebrates as different as birds and bats.

Chordate Diversity

Living chordates are extremely diverse, as shown in **Figure 33–4**. Yet, the species of chordates that are alive today are a small fraction of the total number of chordate species that have existed over time. Today, vertebrates make up about 96 percent of all living chordate species and account for more than 50,000 species throughout the world. The six living groups of chordates are the nonvertebrate chordates, fishes, amphibians, reptiles, birds, and mammals. Of these, the largest group by far is the fishes.

Figure 33–3 Amphibians were the first chordates to have four limbs. Limbs allowed animals like this tiger salamander to crawl on land. **A rapid increase in the number and diversity of land vertebrates followed the evolution of four limbs.**

Figure 33–4 This pie chart shows the diversity of chordates. The area of each slice represents the relative number of living species in each group of chordates. The inner circle shows the six major chordate groups and gives the percentage of species contained in each. The outer circle breaks down each major group and shows the number of known species. **Calculating** ***Of the total number of fish species, what percentage is represented by the ray-finned fishes?***

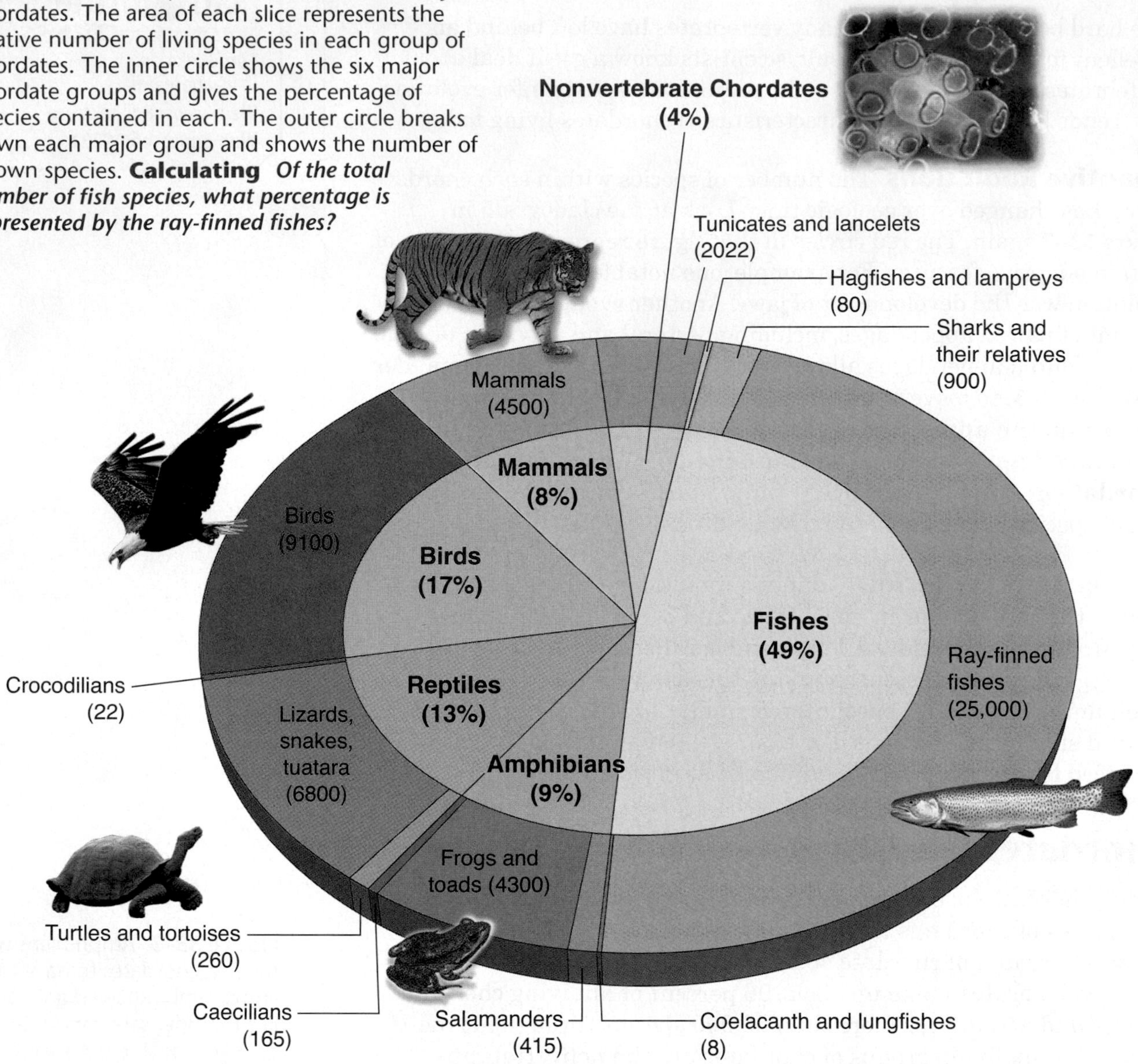

33–1 Section Assessment

1. **Key Concept** To which groups of animals are vertebrates most closely related phylogenetically?
2. **Key Concept** Describe a major trend in chordate evolution.
3. Which characteristic appeared first: four limbs or jaws?
4. What is adaptive radiation?
5. **Critical Thinking Inferring** Both frogs and ducks have webbed feet. However, ducks are more closely related to perching birds than to frogs. Explain the process that has resulted in both frogs and ducks having feet that are similar.

Connecting Concepts

Adaptations to Life on Land

Recall what you learned about plant evolution in Chapter 22. In what ways are chordate adaptations to life on land similar to plant adaptations to life on land?

Should Marine Mammals Be Kept in Captivity?

Many types of marine mammals, including dolphins, killer whales, and seals, are kept in captive display for educational, entertainment, and research purposes. Yet, there is strong debate about whether public display of such animals is ethical. Should we prohibit the capture of marine mammals for public display?

The Viewpoints

Captivity Should Be Allowed

Some people believe that we have an obligation to convey knowledge of the natural world to the public by displaying animals and educating ourselves about them. Information obtained by observing captive animals may be helpful in managing their populations in the wild. Many people argue that the adverse effects of captivity are outweighed by the benefits of conservation, an enhanced human appreciation for animals, and the advancement of scientific knowledge. There is also evidence that human interactions with captive dolphins may help people with disabilities, such as autism.

Captivity Should Be Prohibited

Other people believe that because marine mammals are naturally social, with strong family bonds, they are not suited to capture or confinement. These people are concerned that the process of capture disrupts social groups.

Those opposed to the captivity of marine mammals also argue that confinement places the animals in an unnatural situation—one that is monotonous, limited, and unhealthy. In the wild, whales and dolphins travel long distances and dive much deeper than is possible in a shallow display tank. There is also a concern that human interaction with captive marine mammals increases the risk of transmitting diseases to the animals.

Research and Decide

1. **Analyzing the Viewpoints** To make an informed decision, learn more about this issue by consulting library or Internet resources. Then, list the options for education, entertainment, and research involving marine mammals. What are the benefits? The costs?
2. **Forming Your Opinion** Should marine mammals be kept in captivity? Are there some instances when captivity is a good solution and other instances when it is not? Explain.
3. **Role Playing** Suppose you are a wildlife biologist managing a declining population of wild bottlenose dolphins. You need to learn about the lifestyle of this dolphin before you can recommend any solutions. You also want to increase public awareness to help protect the population. Write a proposal on how you will do all this.

For: Links from the authors
Visit: PHSchool.com
Web Code: cbe-9334

33–2 Controlling Body Temperature

4-5.3 Feedback mechanisms that maintain homeostasis

Guide for Reading

Key Concepts
- How is the control of body temperature an important aspect of vertebrate life?
- What is the difference between ectotherms and endotherms?

Vocabulary
ectotherm
endotherm

Reading Strategy: Finding Main Ideas Before you read, skim the section to identify the key-idea sentences about body temperature control. Then, carefully read the section, making a list of supporting details for each main idea.

On a spring morning, after a cold night, a tortoise lies on a rock basking in the sun. Nearby, a snake slides out of its burrow beneath a rotting stump. In a tree overhead, a young robin puffs up its downy feathers. As you walk out of the water after an early swim, your skin gets goose bumps and you shiver. All these activities are examples of the different ways that vertebrates control their body temperature.

Body Temperature and Homeostasis

Recall from Chapter 2 that many of the chemical reactions that are important in metabolism are influenced by temperature. For this reason, essential life functions can be carried out most efficiently when an animal's internal body temperature is within a particular "operating range." For muscles to operate quickly and efficiently, for example, their temperature can neither be too low nor too high. If muscles are too cold, they may contract slowly, making it difficult for the animal to respond quickly to events around it. If an animal gets too hot, on the other hand, its muscles may tire easily and other body systems may not function properly.

Because most chordates are vertebrates, and mechanisms for controlling body temperature are well developed among vertebrates, this section will focus exclusively on that group. **The control of body temperature is important for maintaining homeostasis in vertebrates, particularly in habitats where temperature varies widely with time of day and with season.** Vertebrates, such as the penguins in **Figure 33–5**, have a variety of ways to control their body temperature. All of these ways incorporate three important features: a source of heat for the body, a way to conserve that heat, and a method of eliminating excess heat when necessary. In terms of how they generate and control their body heat, vertebrates can be classified into two basic groups: ectotherms and endotherms.

◀ **Figure 33–5** Birds and other endotherms are able to generate their own body heat. **The internal control of body temperature allows these emperor penguins to live in cold Antarctic climates, where their feathers act as insulation.**

Analyzing Data

Comparing Ectotherms and Endotherms

Endotherms, such as humans, depend on their metabolism to maintain high body temperatures. Ectotherms, on the other hand, depend primarily on heat from the environment to regulate their body temperatures. The accompanying graph shows the internal body temperatures maintained by several ectotherms and endotherms at different environmental temperatures.

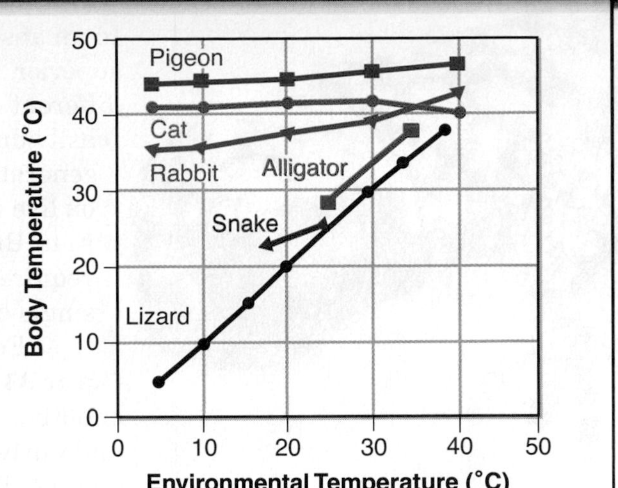

1. **Using Tables and Graphs** Which chordate has the highest body temperature when the environmental temperature is between 0° and 10°C? Which chordate has the lowest body temperature under those same conditions?
2. **Inferring** Which animals shown in the graph are ectotherms? Which are endotherms? Explain your answers.
3. **Predicting** Describe the patterns of activity you would expect for the animals shown in this graph if they lived in your local environment. Would you expect all of the animals to be equally active year-round? If not, why not?

Ectothermy On cool, sunny mornings, lizards often bask in the sun. This doesn't mean that they are lazy! A lizard is an **ectotherm,** which means that its body temperature is mainly determined by the temperature of its environment. **Most reptiles, fishes, and amphibians are ectotherms—animals whose body temperatures are controlled primarily by picking up heat from, or losing heat to, their environment.** Ectotherms often warm up by basking in the sun, and may cool down by seeking shelter in underground burrows.

Ectotherms have relatively low rates of metabolism when they are resting. Thus, their bodies do not generate much heat. When active, an ectotherm's muscles generate heat, just as your muscles do. However, because its body lacks effective insulation, the heat is lost to the environment fairly easily.

Endothermy An **endotherm** is an animal whose body temperature is controlled from within. **Birds and mammals are endotherms, which means they can generate and retain heat inside their bodies.** Endotherms have relatively high metabolic rates that generate a significant amount of heat, even when they are resting. Birds conserve body heat primarily through insulating feathers, such as down. Mammals have body fat and hair for insulation. Mammals can get rid of excess heat by panting, as dogs do, or by sweating, as humans do.

Give an example of an ectotherm and an endotherm.

Word Origins

Ectothermy and **endothermy** are both derived from the Greek word *therme*, meaning "heat." The prefix *endo-* is a Greek word meaning "within." Therefore, the word *endotherm* literally means "heat from within." **What do you think the prefix *ecto-* means?**

▲ **Figure 33–6** **Unlike birds and mammals, which can regulate their body temperature from within, lizards and other ectotherms rely on their surroundings to gain or lose body heat.** The venomous gila monster, for example, makes its home in arid regions of the southwestern United States and Mexico, most often in desert and grassland biomes. To cool down, it burrows below the ground.

Comparing Ectotherms and Endotherms

In an absolute sense, neither endothermy nor ectothermy is superior. Each strategy has advantages and disadvantages in different environments. For example, endotherms move around easily during cool nights or in cold weather because they generate and conserve their own body heat. That's how musk ox live in the tundra and killer whales swim through polar seas. But the high metabolic rate that generates that heat requires a lot of fuel. The amount of food needed to keep a single cow alive would be enough to feed ten cow-sized lizards!

Ectothermic animals, like the gila monster shown in **Figure 33–6,** need much less food than similarly sized endotherms. In environments where temperatures stay warm and fairly constant most of the time, ectothermy is a more energy-efficient strategy. But large ectotherms run into trouble in habitats where temperatures get cold at night or stay cold for long periods, such as boreal forest biomes. It takes a long time for a large animal to warm up in the sun after a cold night. Most large lizards and amphibians live in warm areas such as tropical rain forest biomes.

Evolution of Temperature Control

There is little doubt that the first land vertebrates were ectotherms. But there is some doubt as to when endothermy evolved. Although modern reptiles are ectotherms, some biologists hypothesize that at least some of the dinosaurs were endotherms. Others hypothesize that endothermy evolved a long time after the appearance of the dinosaurs, so that all the dinosaurs were ectotherms. Evidence suggests that endothermy has evolved more than one time. It developed once along the evolutionary line of reptiles that led to birds and once along the evolutionary line of reptiles that led to mammals.

33–2 Section Assessment

1. **Key Concept** What important function does the control of body temperature serve in chordates?
2. **Key Concept** Compare and contrast ectotherms and endotherms.
3. What three features are needed to control an animal's body temperature?
4. How does endothermy affect an animal's need for food?
5. **Critical Thinking Inferring** Why is it unlikely that you would find a giant lizard living in the wild in North Dakota?

Thinking Visually

Comparing and Contrasting

Construct a table that compares ectothermy and endothermy. Factors you should compare include: how body temperature is controlled; relative rates of metabolism; relative amounts of food eaten; advantages; disadvantages; and examples of animals with each method of temperature regulation.

33–3 Form and Function in Chordates

4-2.1, 4.1 Reproduction and development
4-4.1 Gametes unite to form a zygote
4-5.3 Dynamic equilibrium
LS- Use of laboratory instruments, follow safety rules
LS- Make observations, analyze results

Guide for Reading

Key Concept
- How do the organ systems of the different groups of chordates carry out essential life functions?

Vocabulary
alveolus

Reading Strategy: Using Graphic Organizers
As you read, create a table that compares and contrasts the different life functions in nonvertebrate chordates, fishes, amphibians, reptiles, birds, and mammals.

The nonvertebrate chordates that are alive today represent a simple and ancient stage in the development of chordate body systems. However, the fact that the organ systems are simple does not mean they are inferior. After all, lancelets and tunicates have survived to the present day, so their body systems are well equipped to perform the essential functions of life.

Among vertebrates, organ systems exhibit a wider range of complexity than those of nonvertebrate chordates. Many adaptive radiations of vertebrates have produced a variety of specialized organ systems that perform essential functions and maintain homeostasis. The complexity of vertebrate organ systems can be seen in the different ways that vertebrates feed, breathe, respond, move, and reproduce.

Feeding

Feeding and digestion help maintain homeostasis by providing the body with a continuing supply of needed nutrients. Most tunicates, and all lancelets, are filter feeders. These chordates remove small organisms called plankton from the water that passes through their pharynx. A few adult tunicates feed on deposited material from the surface of the sediments on which they dwell.

The skulls and teeth of vertebrates are adapted for feeding on a much wider assortment of foods, ranging from insects to large mammals, and from leaves to fruits and seeds. Some vertebrates—such as baleen whales, flamingoes, and manta rays—are filter feeders with sievelike mouth structures that enable them to strain small crustaceans and fish from the water. The long bill of the hummingbird and the narrow snout of the honey possum are both adaptations that enable them to feed on nectar. Other vertebrates, such as the crocodile in **Figure 33–7,** are adapted to eating meat. Many mammals have sharp canine teeth and incisors that they use to tear and slice their food.

▶ **Figure 33–7** The blunt, broad jaws and numerous peglike teeth of this crocodile help it catch large prey—such as zebra—even in thick vegetation. **Comparing and Contrasting** *How do the mouth structures of a filter-feeding vertebrate differ from those of a carnivore like this reptile?*

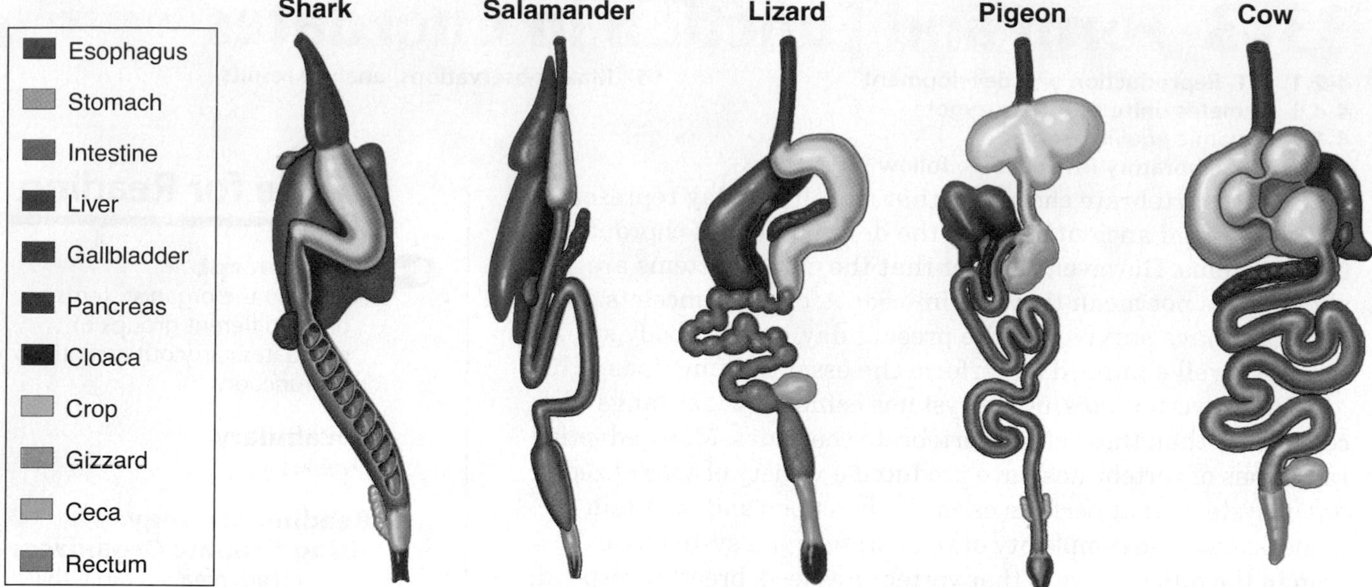

▲ **Figure 33–8** **The digestive systems of vertebrates are adapted for a variety of feeding modes.** As you can see, these systems differ in their degree of complexity.

The digestive systems of vertebrates have organs that are well adapted for different feeding habits. Such variety is shown in **Figure 33–8.** Carnivores such as sharks typically have short digestive tracts that produce fast-acting, meat-digesting enzymes. Herbivores such as cows, on the other hand, often have long intestines that harbor colonies of bacteria. These bacteria are helpful in digesting the tough cellulose fibers in plant tissues.

CHECKPOINT *Compare the digestive tracts of herbivores and carnivores.*

Respiration

Chordates typically have one of two basic structures for respiration, or gas exchange. **As a general rule, aquatic chordates—such as tunicates, fishes, and amphibian larvae—use gills for respiration. Land vertebrates, including adult amphibians, reptiles, birds, and mammals, use lungs.** However, some animals "break the rules." For example, several fishes, such as lungfishes, have both gills and lungs.

Some chordates have respiratory structures in addition to gills and lungs. Many bony fishes, for example, have accessory organs for respiration, such as simple air sacs, that are derived from the gut. All lancelets and some sea snakes respire by the diffusion of oxygen across their body surfaces. (Recall that diffusion is the process by which molecules move from an area of higher concentration to an area of lower concentration.) Many adult amphibians use their moist skins and the linings of their mouths and pharynxes to respire by diffusion.

Gills **Figure 33–9** shows how gills function in chordates. As water passes over the gill filaments, oxygen molecules diffuse into blood in tiny blood vessels called capillaries. At the same time, carbon dioxide diffuses from blood into the water.

Lungs Although the structure of the lungs varies, the basic process of breathing is the same among land vertebrates. Inhaling brings oxygen-rich air from outside the body through the trachea (TRAY-kee-uh) and into the lungs. The oxygen diffuses into the blood inside the lung capillaries. At the same time, carbon dioxide diffuses out of the capillaries into the air within the lungs. Oxygen-poor air is then exhaled.

As you move from amphibians to mammals, the surface area of the lungs increases. Observe this trend in **Figure 33–10.** The typical amphibian lung is little more than a sac with ridges. Reptilian lungs are often divided into a series of large and small chambers that increase the surface area available for gas exchange. In mammals, the lungs branch extensively, and their entire volume is filled with thousands of bubblelike structures called **alveoli** (al-VEE-uh-ly; singular: alveolus). Alveoli provide an enormous surface area for gas exchange. This lung structure enables mammals to take in the large amounts of oxygen required by their endothermic metabolism. However, because air must move in and out through the same passageways, there is always stale, oxygen-poor air trapped in the lungs of mammals and most other vertebrates.

In contrast, in the lungs of birds, air flows in only one direction. A system of tubes in a bird's lungs, plus air sacs, enables this one-way air flow. Thus, gas exchange surfaces are constantly in contact with fresh air that contains a lot of oxygen. This supply of oxygen enables birds to fly at high altitudes, where there is less oxygen in the atmosphere than at lower altitudes.

▼ **Figure 33–9** Fishes and many other aquatic chordates use gills for respiration. **Interpreting Graphics** ***Describe the path of water as it flows into and out of the fish.***

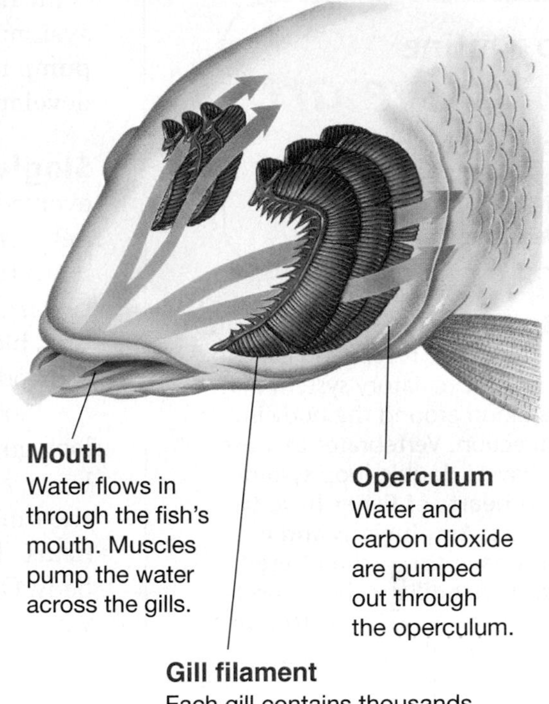
Mouth
Water flows in through the fish's mouth. Muscles pump the water across the gills.
Operculum
Water and carbon dioxide are pumped out through the operculum.
Gill filament
Each gill contains thousands of filaments that absorb oxygen from the water.

▼ **Figure 33–10** **Unlike most aquatic chordates, land vertebrates use lungs to breathe.** A few aquatic chordates, such as sea turtles and marine mammals, use lungs as well.

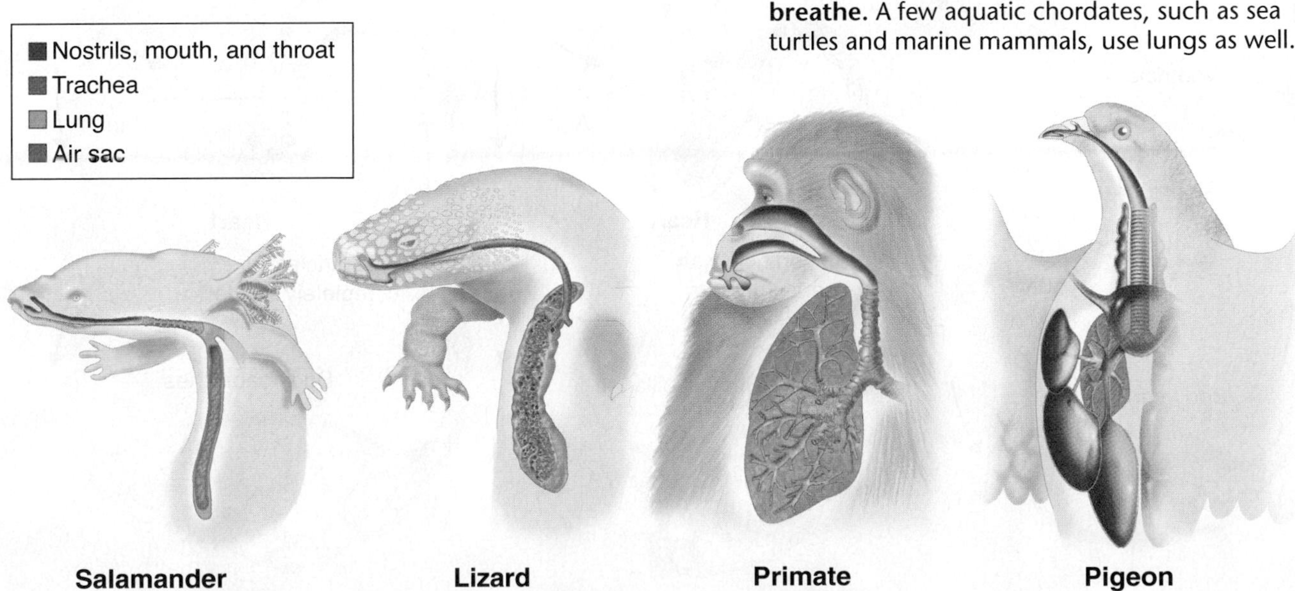
Nostrils, mouth, and throat
Trachea
Lung
Air sac
Salamander
Lizard
Primate
Pigeon

For: Vertebrate Circulatory Systems activity
Visit: PHSchool.com
Web Code: cbp-9333

▼ **Figure 33–11** Most vertebrates that use gills for respiration have a single-loop circulatory system that forces blood around the body in one direction. Vertebrates that use lungs have a double-loop system. **The hearts of fishes have two chambers. Amphibians and most reptiles have three-chambered hearts. Crocodilians, birds, and mammals have hearts with four separate chambers.**

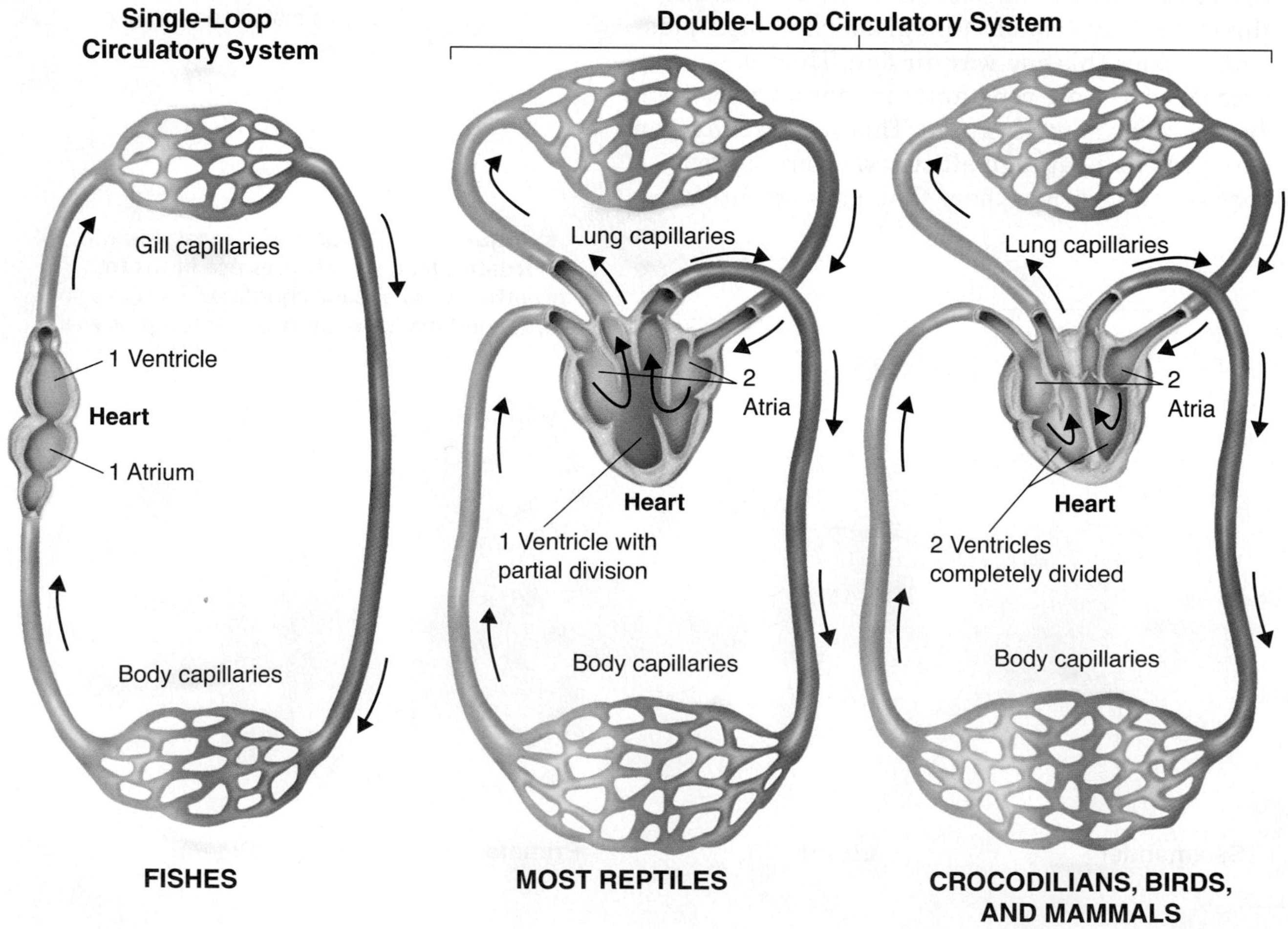

Circulation

Circulatory systems maintain homeostasis by transporting materials throughout animals' bodies. The first chordates, like tunicates and lancelets of today, probably had simple circulatory systems. Tunicates have short, tubelike hearts with a simple pump but no true chambers. Lancelets have a fairly well-developed circulatory system but no specialized heart.

Single- and Double-Loop Circulation As chordates evolved, more complex organ systems and more efficient channels for internal transport developed. **Figure 33–11** shows the main transport systems in vertebrates. Those that use gills for respiration have a single-loop circulatory system. In this system, blood travels from the heart to the gills, then to the rest of the body, and back to the heart in one circuit.

Vertebrates that use lungs for respiration have a double-loop circulatory system. The first loop carries blood between the heart and lungs. Oxygen-poor blood from the heart is pumped to the lungs, while oxygen-rich blood from the lungs returns to the heart. The second loop carries blood between the heart and the body. Oxygen-rich blood from the heart is pumped to the body, while oxygen-poor blood from the body returns to the heart.

Single-Loop Circulatory System

Gill capillaries
1 Ventricle
Heart
1 Atrium
Body capillaries
FISHES

Double-Loop Circulatory System

Lung capillaries
2 Atria
Heart
1 Ventricle with partial division
Body capillaries
MOST REPTILES

Lung capillaries
2 Atria
Heart
2 Ventricles completely divided
Body capillaries
CROCODILIANS, BIRDS, AND MAMMALS

Heart Chambers Chordate hearts are adapted to the complexity of internal transport for each of the different groups. **During the course of chordate evolution, the heart developed chambers and partitions that help separate oxygen-rich and oxygen-poor blood traveling in the circulatory system.** In vertebrates that use gills for respiration, such as fishes and larval amphibians, the heart consists of two chambers: an atrium that receives blood from the body, and a ventricle that pumps blood to the gills and then on to the rest of the body.

The hearts of most amphibians have three chambers: two atria and one ventricle. The left atrium receives oxygen-rich blood from the lungs. The right atrium receives oxygen-poor blood from the body. Both atria empty into the ventricle. There is some mixing of oxygen-rich and oxygen-poor blood in the ventricle. However, the internal structure of the ventricle directs the flow of blood so that most oxygen-poor blood goes to the lungs, and most oxygen-rich blood goes to the rest of the body.

Most reptiles have a three-chambered heart. However, unlike amphibians, most reptiles have a partial partition in their ventricle. Because of this partition, there is even less mixing of oxygen-rich and oxygen-poor blood than there is in amphibian hearts.

Birds, mammals, and crocodilians have hearts that are completely partitioned into four chambers. This type of heart is sometimes described as a double pump. One pump moves blood through the lung loop and the other moves blood through the body loop. The two loops of the circulatory system are completely separated. There is no mixing of oxygen-rich and oxygen-poor blood.

Excretion

Excretory systems eliminate nitrogenous wastes from the body. In nonvertebrate chordates and fishes, gills and gill slits play an important role in excretion. However, most vertebrates rely on kidneys—excretory organs composed of small filtering tubes that remove wastes from the blood.

Nitrogenous wastes—formed from the breakdown of proteins—are first produced in the form of ammonia. Ammonia is a highly toxic compound that must quickly be eliminated from the body or changed into a less poisonous form. In tunicates, ammonia leaves the body through the outflow siphons. Other waste byproducts, such as uric acid, are stored within the tunicate's body and released only when the animal dies.

In vertebrates, excretion is carried out mostly by the kidneys. Aquatic amphibians and most fishes also excrete ammonia directly from the gills into the surrounding water through simple diffusion. In mammals, land amphibians, and cartilaginous fishes, ammonia is changed into urea, a less-toxic compound, before it is excreted. In most reptiles and birds, ammonia is changed into uric acid. Besides filtering wastes, vertebrate kidneys help maintain homeostasis by regulating the amounts of water, salt, and other substances dissolved in body fluids.

Quick Lab

How does water affect nitrogen excretion?

Materials 2 test tubes, 2 stoppers, test-tube rack, graduated cylinder, balance, urea, uric acid, glass-marking pencil

Procedure   

1. Label one test tube "urea" and the other "uric acid." Place 2 grams of uric acid in the test tube labeled "uric acid." Place 2 grams of urea in the test tube labeled "urea."
2. Add 15 mL of water to each test tube. Stopper and shake the test tubes for 3 minutes.
3. Observe each test tube. Record your observations.

Analyze and Conclude

1. **Observing** Which substance—uric acid or urea—is most soluble? Least soluble? Explain.
2. **Inferring** Reptiles excrete nitrogenous wastes in the form of uric acid. How does this adaptation help reptiles survive on land?

Response

Compared with invertebrates, most chordates have elaborate systems that allow them to respond to stimuli in their environment. **Nonvertebrate chordates have a relatively simple nervous system with a mass of nerve cells that form a brain. Vertebrates have a more complex brain with distinct regions, each with a different function.**

Nonvertebrate chordates do not have specialized sensory organs. In tunicates, however, sensory cells in and on the siphons and other internal surfaces may help control the amount of water passing through the pharynx. Lancelets—which have a more defined head region—have a small, hollow brain with a pair of eyespots that detect light.

Vertebrates display a high degree of cephalization, or concentration of sense organs and nerve cells at the front of the body. The head contains a well-developed brain, which is situated on the anterior end of the spinal cord. The vertebrate brain is divided into several parts, including the cerebrum, cerebellum, medulla oblongata, optic lobes, and olfactory bulbs. The medulla oblongata controls the functioning of many internal organs. The optic lobes are involved in vision and the olfactory bulbs are involved in the sense of smell.

Figure 33–12 shows how the size and complexity of the cerebrum and cerebellum increase from fishes to mammals. The cerebrum is the "thinking" region of the brain. It receives, interprets, and determines the response to sensory information. The cerebrum is also involved in learning, memory, and conscious thought. In fishes, amphibians, and reptiles, the cerebrum is relatively small. In birds and mammals, especially primates, the cerebrum is greatly enlarged and may contain folds that increase its surface area. The cerebellum, which coordinates movement and controls balance, is also most developed in birds and mammals.

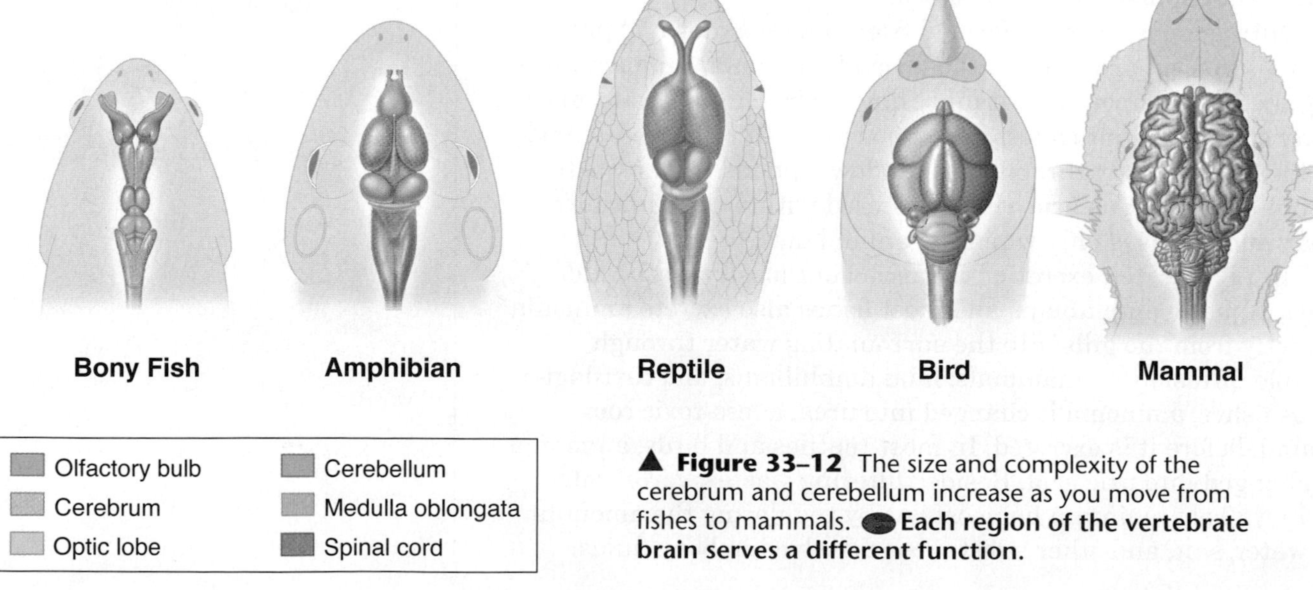

▲ **Figure 33–12** The size and complexity of the cerebrum and cerebellum increase as you move from fishes to mammals. **Each region of the vertebrate brain serves a different function.**

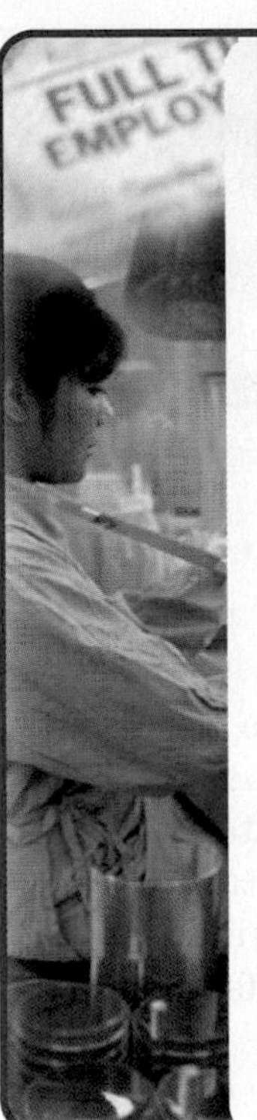

Careers in Biology

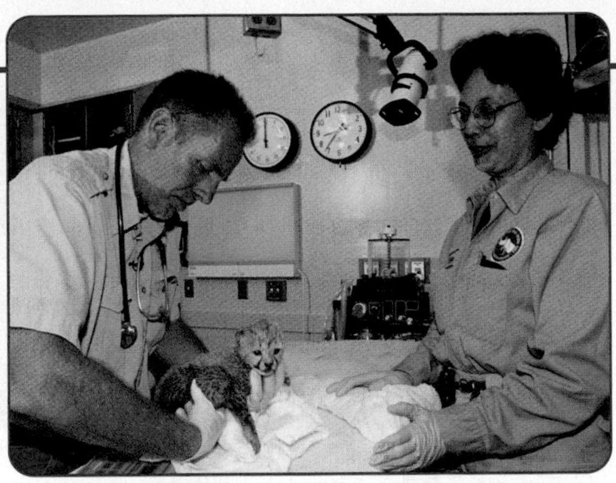

Veterinary Technician

Job Description: work in a kennel, veterinary hospital or clinic, zoo, or other setting to provide basic medical care for animals. May specialize in X-ray technology, anesthesiology, or other areas.

Education: a two-year associate or four-year bachelor's degree in Animal Health Technology. Each state has its own licensing requirements.

Skills: patient; enjoy working with animals; a good team member; effective communicator; quick thinker; excellent observer.

Highlights: You help take care of all kinds of animals in different settings. Your work can lead to medical advances that apply to humans.

For: Career links
Visit: PHSchool.com
Web Code: cbb-9333

Movement

Unlike most other chordates, nonvertebrate chordates lack bones. They do, however, have muscles. Lancelets and larval tunicates swim with a fishlike movement of their muscular tails. Some adult tunicates use their siphons to swim by jet propulsion. However, most adult tunicates lose their tails and attach to a hard surface on the ocean floor for life.

The skeletal and muscular systems support a vertebrate's body and make it possible to control movement. Vertebrates are much more mobile than nonvertebrate chordates. With the exception of hagfishes, all vertebrates have an internal skeleton of bone—as shown in **Figure 33–13**—or, in the case of certain fishes, cartilage. The skeleton includes a backbone made up of individual bones called vertebrae. In most vertebrates, tough yet flexible tissues called ligaments connect the vertebrae and allow the backbone to bend without falling apart. Most vertebrates have fin girdles or limb girdles that support the fins or limbs.

In many fishes and snakes, the main body muscles are arranged in blocks on either side of the backbone. These muscle blocks contract in waves that make the body bend back and forth, generating forward thrust. In many amphibians and reptiles, the limbs stick out sideways from the body in a position resembling a push-up. Most mammals stand with their legs straight under them, whether they walk on two legs or on four. In this position, the legs can support the body weight efficiently.

What three structures support a vertebrate's body and allow it to move?

▼ **Figure 33–13** Like the skeletons of most vertebrates, this lizard's skeleton has two pairs of appendages. **Muscles and ligaments attach the appendages to the backbone and help control movement.**

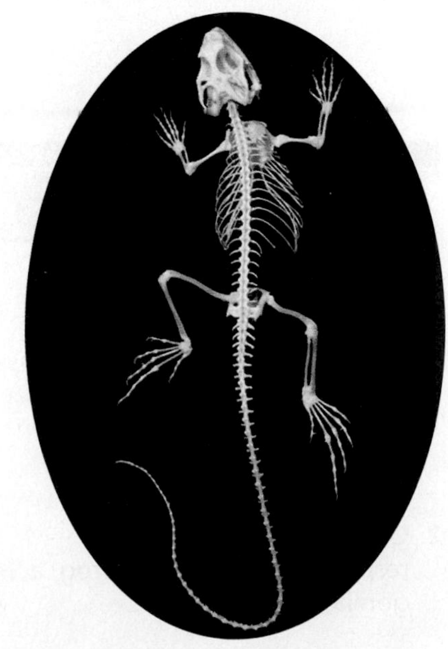

▲ **Figure 33–14** Chordates differ enormously in the way they reproduce and develop. The male band-tailed cardinalfish (left) carries externally fertilized eggs in his mouth while the eggs incubate. Like most birds, the female emperor goose (center) actively defends her nest, which contains eggs that were internally fertilized. After bearing live young, this female mountain lion (right) nurses her cubs with milk. **Applying Concepts** *Which of these animals is viviparous?*

Reproduction

Figure 33–14 shows that chordates are diverse in the ways they reproduce and develop. Almost all chordates reproduce sexually. Vertebrate evolution shows a general trend from external to internal fertilization. The eggs of most nonvertebrate chordates—and many fishes and amphibians—are fertilized externally. The eggs of reptiles, birds, and mammals are fertilized internally.

After fertilization, the development of chordates can be oviparous, ovoviviparous, or viviparous. In oviparous species, which include most fishes and amphibians and all birds, the eggs develop outside the mother's body. In ovoviviparous animals, such as sharks, the eggs develop within the mother's body and the embryos receive nutrients from the yolk in the egg. The young of ovoviviparous species are born alive. The developing embryos of viviparous species—including most mammals—obtain nutrients directly from the mother's body. As with ovoviviparous species, the young of viviparous animals are born alive.

Some vertebrates, such as most amphibians, produce many offspring but give them little or no care. This reproductive strategy is successful in circumstances favoring populations that disperse and grow rapidly. Mammals and birds, in contrast, usually care for their young but produce few of them. This helps young survive in crowded, competitive environments.

33–3 Section Assessment

1. **Key Concept** List the organ systems that chordates use to perform life functions. How does each system vary between nonvertebrate chordates and vertebrates?
2. Compare and contrast the respiratory systems of a frog, a gorilla, and a sparrow.
3. Explain the difference between oviparous, ovoviviparous, and viviparous modes of development. Give an example of each.
4. **Critical Thinking Applying Concepts** What advantage does a three-chambered heart provide that a two-chambered heart does not?

Writing in Science

Summarizing

Write a brief summary of the ways in which chordates obtain food. Your summary should contain examples of animals that use the different methods that you describe. *Hint*: Your summary should include the words *herbivore, carnivore,* and *omnivore.*

Exploration

Comparing Chordate Family Trees

Differences in the amino acid sequence of a protein can indicate how long ago two or more species diverged from a common ancestor. In this investigation, you will compare cladograms of several chordate species based on their anatomy and amino acid sequences.

Problem **How can you use anatomical and molecular evidence to determine the evolutionary relationships among chordates?**

Animal	Amino Acid Sequence of Cytochrome C											
Human	GDVEK	GKKIF	IMKCS	QCHTV	EKGGK	HKTGP	NLHGL	FGRKT	GQAPG	YSYTA	ANKNK	GIIWG
Donkey	GDVEK	GKKIF	VQKCA	QCHTV	EKGGK	HKTGP	NLHGL	FGRKT	GQAPG	FSYTD	ANKNK	GITWK
Horse	GDVEK	GKKIF	VQKCA	QCHTV	EKGGK	HKTGP	NLHGL	FGRKT	GQAPG	FTYTD	ANKNK	GITWK
Chicken	GDIED	GKKIF	VQKCS	QCHTV	EKGGK	HKTGP	NLHGL	FGRKT	GQAEG	FSYTD	ANKNK	GITWG
Turkey	GDIEK	GKKIF	VQKCS	QCHTV	EKGGK	HKTGP	NLHGL	FGRKT	GQAEG	FSYTD	ANKNK	GITWG
Rattlesnake	GDVEK	GKKIF	TMKCS	QCHTV	EKGGK	HKTGP	NLHGL	FGRKT	GQAVG	YSYTA	ANKNK	GITWG

G=glycine, A=alanine, V=valine, L=leucine, I=isoleucine, M=methionine, F=phenylalanine, W=tryptophan, P=proline, S=serine, T=threonine, C=cysteine, Y=tyrosine, N=asparagine, Q=glutamine, D=aspartate, E=glutamate, K=lysine, R=arginine, H=histidine

Skills Using Models, Analyzing Data

Procedure

1. Use your knowledge of similarities and differences in chordate anatomy to decide how to arrange humans, donkeys, horses, chickens, turkeys, and rattlesnakes in a hierarchical classification system on a cladogram. The more closely two species are related, the shorter you should make the branches that connect them.
2. Draw your cladogram in a similar way to **Figure 33–2.**
3. Write the name of each animal at the end of the appropriate branch of the cladogram.
4. Cytochrome c is a protein found in most eukaryotic cells. The table shows the first 60 amino acids that make up this protein in each animal listed in step 1.
5. Construct a data table with the headings "Donkey," "Horse," and "Chicken." Count the number of amino acids that differ in the sequences of chicken and horse cytochrome c. Record this number in your data table.
6. Complete your data table by comparing the amino acid sequences of each pair of animals.
7. Make a cladogram based on differences among animals in cytochrome c. Use taxonomic nomenclature to label the phylum, subphylum, and class of each animal.

Analyze and Conclude

1. **Comparing and Contrasting** Did your two cladograms agree? Explain your answer.
2. **Using Models** You can think of a cladogram as a visual model that shows evolutionary relationships. With which animals do horses share the most recent ancestor? Explain.
3. **Evaluating** Could a cladogram based on anatomy differ from one based on amino acid sequences? Why or why not?

Go Further

Comparing and Contrasting What advantages would comparing the DNA base sequences have over comparing amino acid sequences?

Chapter 33 Study Guide

33–1 Chordate Evolution

Key Concepts

- The chordate family tree has its roots in ancestors that vertebrates share with tunicates and lancelets.
- Over the course of evolution, the appearance of new adaptations—such as jaws and paired appendages—has launched adaptive radiations in chordate groups.

Vocabulary
notochord, p. 849
adaptive radiation, p. 851

33–2 Controlling Body Temperature

Key Concepts

- The control of body temperature is important for maintaining homeostasis in many vertebrates, particularly in habitats where temperature varies widely with time of day and with season.
- Most fishes, amphibians, and reptiles are ectotherms—organisms whose body temperatures are controlled primarily by picking up heat from, or losing heat to, their environment. Birds and mammals are endotherms, which means they can generate and retain heat inside their bodies.

Vocabulary
ectotherm, p. 855
endotherm, p. 855

33–3 Form and Function in Chordates

Key Concepts

- The digestive systems of vertebrates have organs that are well adapted for different feeding habits.
- Aquatic chordates—such as tunicates, fishes, and amphibian larvae—use gills for respiration. Land vertebrates, including adult amphibians, reptiles, birds, and mammals, use lungs.
- During the course of chordate evolution, the heart developed chambers and partitions that help separate oxygen-rich and oxygen-poor blood traveling in the circulatory system.
- Nonvertebrate chordates have a relatively simple nervous system with a mass of nerve cells that form a brain. Vertebrates have a more complex brain with distinct regions, each with a different function.
- Muscular and skeletal systems support a vertebrate's body and make it possible to control movement.

Vocabulary
alveolus, p. 859

Thinking Visually

Using information from this chapter, fill in the following concept map:

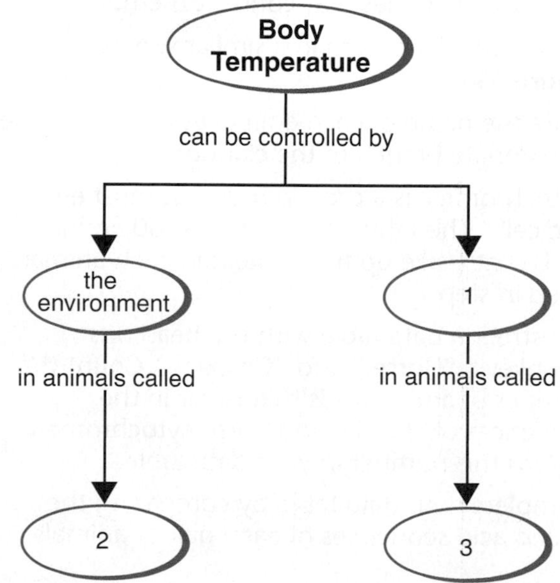

Preparing for the Living Environment Exam

NEW YORK LIVING ENVIRONMENT

Blue questions emphasize Regents Exam content

Chapter 33

Part A

Multiple Choice

For each statement or question, select the number of the word or expression that, of those given, best completes the statement or answers the question.

1 A characteristic unique to all chordates is
(1) ectothermy (3) response to light
(2) diffusion (4) a notochord

2 Which animals have an amniotic egg?
(1) birds (3) fishes
(2) tunicates (4) amphibians

3 All of the animals illustrated below can be classified as

(1) chordates (3) reptiles
(2) amphibians (4) fish

4 The main source of heat in ectotherms is their
(1) high metabolism (3) own bodies
(2) environment (4) food

5 A characteristic of endotherms is that they
(1) control body temperature through behavior
(2) control body temperature from within
(3) obtain heat from outside their bodies
(4) have relatively low rates of metabolism

6 Aquatic chordates such as tunicates, fishes, and amphibian larvae typically breathe using
(1) lungs (3) alveoli
(2) skin (4) gills

7 Most chordates that use gills for respiration have a(an)
(1) double-loop circulatory system
(2) accessory lung
(3) single-loop circulatory system
(4) four-chambered heart

8 An excretory organ composed of small tubes that filter wastes from the blood is the
(1) kidney (3) gill
(2) ureter (4) cloaca

9 The part of the chordate brain that receives, interprets, and determines the responses to sensory information is the
(1) optic lobe (3) cerebellum
(2) cerebrum (4) spinal cord

10 Most vertebrates have
(1) an inflexible backbone
(2) a flexible backbone
(3) a backbone made of cartilage
(4) no backbone

11 Rapid growth in the diversity of a group of organisms is called
(1) adaptive radiation
(2) convergent evolution
(3) evolutionary history
(4) rapid extinction

12 The sugar glider is a marsupial found in Australia. The eastern flying squirrel is a placental mammal found in North America. Both animals are nocturnal, live in trees, and can glide through the air using a flap of skin that stretches between their legs on each side of the body. The close resemblance of these two unrelated species is an example of
(1) ovovivipary (3) convergent evolution
(2) divergent traits (4) chordate diversity

13 In chordates with four-chambered hearts, there is
(1) a partial mixing of oxygen-rich and oxygen-poor blood
(2) a partial partition in the ventricle
(3) a partial partition in the atrium
(4) no mixing of oxygen-rich and oxygen-poor blood

14 In oviparous species, the eggs
(1) develop internally
(2) obtain nutrients directly from the mother's body
(3) obtain nutrients from the external environment
(4) develop outside the body

Test-Taking Tip Before you answer questions about a diagram, study the diagram and ask yourself what the diagram is about and what it tells you.

Preparing for the Living Environment Exam

Part B

Multiple Choice and Extended Response

For those questions that ask you to select a response, choose the one that best completes the statement or answers the question. For all others follow the directions given.

Base your answers to questions 15 through 17 on the cladogram below and on your knowledge of biology.

The cladogram shows the relationships that exist among chordates.

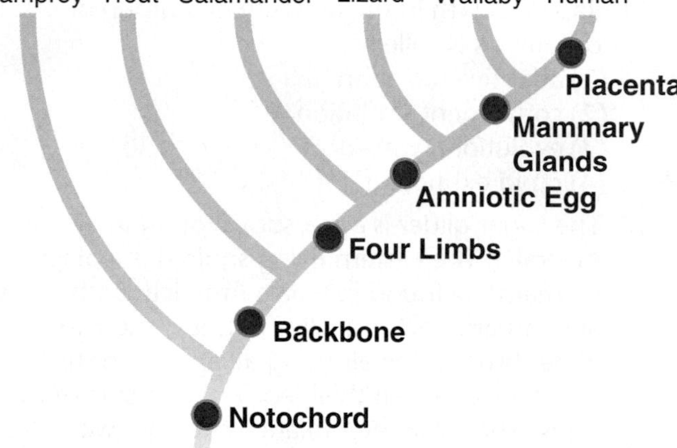

15 Which characteristic is shared by humans, wallabies, and trout?

(1) placenta
(2) notochord
(3) four limbs
(4) mammary glands

16 Which have the closest evolutionary relationship?

(1) humans and wallabies
(2) humans and lizards
(3) humans and lampreys
(4) humans and salamanders

17 A valid conclusion from this cladogram is that

(1) salamanders, trout, and lampreys all have a backbone
(2) four limbs appeared in vertebrate evolution before the notochord
(3) humans and lampreys share a common ancestor
(4) salamanders have amniotic eggs

---

18 State how the total volume of blood the right ventricle of a mammal pumps in an hour compares to the total volume of blood the left ventricle pumps in the same period of time. Support your answer with an explanation.

19 Reptiles are more commonly found in warm regions such as the southwestern U.S. rather than in cold regions such as northern Canada. State the most likely reason for this geographic distribution. Support your answer with an explanation.

For each phrase in questions 20 through 22, select the proper vertebrate order, chosen from the list below, that is best described by that phrase. Then record its number on a separate answer paper. An order may be used once, more than once, or not at all.

Vertebrate Orders

(1) Fishes
(2) Amphibians
(3) Reptiles
(4) Birds
(5) Mammals

20 Two-chambered heart; single-loop circulatory system; excrete ammonia

21 Three-chambered heart; feet not directly beneath the body when standing; larvae use gills while adults use lungs

22 Endothermic; well-developed lungs; excrete uric acid; four-chambered heart

---

23 Fishes and whales are not closely related, but share a number of similar features. Their overall body shape and the absence of legs are two examples. State how similarities such as these come about.

24 The position of the legs in mammals is different than the position of the legs in amphibians and most reptiles. Because mammals evolved from ancestral amphibians, it is assumed that the change in leg position is an adaptive advantage.

a Explain how the position of legs in mammals is different than that in amphibians.

b Explain how this characteristic is an adaptive advantage in mammals.

Base your answers to questions 25 through 27 on the reading passage below and on your knowledge of biology.

Rescue at Sea

The call came to the Coast Guard dispatch officer. The fishing boat, *RubiJewel,* was fully engulfed in flames and was losing electrical power. The lone fisherman on board was about to abandon ship. The dispatcher broadcasted a mayday relay to any vessels in the area. The *Island Transporter* radioed back. It was in the area and was on its way.

Guided by the emergency beacon on the fisherman's survival suit, the rescuers found him in the bone-chilling seawater. His suit had filled with gallons of the icy water. He had been floating for 40 minutes and was hypothermic and unresponsive. They hauled him aboard and began emergency procedures.

Evaluation of the fisherman's vital signs showed his body temperature was 32.2°C (90°F), both his pulse and respiration were very slow, and he was barely conscious. He was severely hypothermic.

In hypothermia cases, patients must be kept warm on the outside and their core body temperature must also be raised. "Inhalation re-warming therapy" is a new treatment that delivers warm, moist oxygen to the lungs of hypothermia patients. The oxygen is warmed to 43°C (normal human body temperature is 37°C).

25 Explain how the change in the fisherman's body temperature and pulse rate were attempts by the body to maintain the functioning of the internal organs.

26 Describe how the double-loop circulatory system makes it possible for inhalation re-warming therapy to save the fisherman.

27 Before his accident, the fisherman saw seabirds floating on the water and seals swimming in the sea. Explain how these animals are able to survive in the icy water when the fisherman cannot.

Part C

Extended Response

Answer the questions or follow the directions given.

Base your answers to questions 28 through 30 on the information below and on your knowledge of biology.

On cool days, a student notices that a duck sits on a sunny lawn with its wings outspread. On hot days, he sees the same duck sitting in the shade of a tree with its bill open.

28 Explain how each of these behaviors might help maintain the duck's body temperature.

29 The student thinks he sees a pattern in the duck's behavior. He decides that he would like to do a scientific study. Develop a hypothesis that the student might investigate and create the data table he would use to gather data that would prove or disprove the hypothesis.

30 Identify whether the duck is endothermic or exothermic. Explain the advantages and disadvantages of each.

31 The digestive tracts of herbivores and carnivores are adapted to efficiently process food. It is important that as many nutrients as possible enter the blood stream and unusable portions of the food be eliminated. Compare the way digestion takes place in an herbivore, such as a horse, and a carnivore, such as a wolf. Your answer must include an explanation of:

- how the digestive tract of an herbivore is specialized for a particular diet
- how the digestive tract of a carnivore is different from that of an herbivore
- the role played by bacteria and enzymes in both carnivores and herbivores

For: An interactive self-test
Visit: PHSchool.com
Web Code: cba-9330

CHAPTER 34
Animal Behavior

Male ostriches compete for females by flapping their large wings and making hissing noises.

Inquiry Activity

What is learning?

Procedure

1. Your teacher will give you a noisemaker and read a paragraph out loud. Each time your teacher reads the word *and,* sound your noisemaker once. Record a mark on a piece of paper each time you sound your noisemaker.
2. Observe when other students are sounding their noisemakers.
3. Compare the number of times that you and other students sounded the noisemakers.

Think About It

1. **Observing** Did all students sound their noisemakers the same number of times? Explain any differences.
2. **Drawing Conclusions** Communicate with your classmates about what you learned as you performed the activity, and conclude how learning affected the results. How do you know your conclusion is valid?

34–1 Elements of Behavior

1-S1.1 Historical development of ideas in science
4-3.1 Natural selection of behaviors
4-5.3 Dynamic equilibrium
LS- Analyze results
LS- Make observations
LS- Organize data in tables/graphs

Guide for Reading

Key Concepts
- What produces behavior in animals?
- What is an innate behavior?
- What are the major types of learning?

Vocabulary
behavior
stimulus
response
innate behavior
learning
habituation
classical conditioning
operant conditioning
insight learning
imprinting

Reading Strategy: Using Prior Knowledge Before you read, write a definition of behavior based on what you already know. After reading this section, use what you have learned to revise your definition and give examples to support it.

Do you wash your vegetables before you eat them? If so, you have something in common with a troop of Japanese macaque (muh-KAHK) monkeys that live on the Pacific island of Koshima. Many years ago, biologists in Koshima began leaving sweet potatoes on a sandy beach to entice the resident monkeys into the open. The monkeys ate their potatoes with sand still stuck to them. One day, a young female member of the troop dunked her potato into a nearby pool and scrubbed the sand off it with her hand. The young monkey, apparently preferring to eat a washed potato, repeated this technique each day. Soon, another monkey in the troop started to imitate her. Months later, her mother began to copy her, too. Eventually, all troop members came to wash their potatoes in the pool. To this day, the descendants of the monkeys on the island of Koshima wash their sweet potatoes before eating them.

Stimulus and Response

The macaque monkey in **Figure 34–1** is exhibiting a learned behavior. Biologists define **behavior** as the way an organism reacts to changes in its internal condition or external environment. A behavior can be simple, such as turning your head in the direction of a noise, or complex, such as washing food. Usually, behaviors are performed when an animal reacts to a stimulus. A **stimulus** (plural: stimuli) is any kind of signal that carries information and can be detected. If you are hungry, your body is providing you with an internal stimulus that might prompt you to eat. The sound of your phone ringing on a Friday night is an external stimulus that might result in your running to answer it!

A single, specific reaction to a stimulus—such as waking up when you hear an alarm—is called a **response.** A behavior may consist of more than one response. For example, a tiger shark might respond to the movements of a potential prey by swimming toward the stimulus, attacking the source of the movement, and swallowing the prey. What stimuli are you responding to right now?

▶ **Figure 34–1** On the island of Koshima, Japanese macaques like this one rinse their sweet potatoes in water. **Inferring** *How did this monkey acquire this behavior?*

▲ **Figure 34–2** **Behavior is produced by the interaction of body systems.** This frog detected a noise with its ears and is now using its brain and muscles to leap out of the water.

Types of Stimuli Animals respond to many types of external stimuli, such as light, sound, odors, and heat. However, not every animal can detect all of these stimuli. Humans perceive the world through many senses—including sight, smell, touch, taste, and hearing. Other animals have different senses and may respond to stimuli that you are not equipped to sense. The Mexican bulldog bat, for instance, uses high-pitched sounds, which humans cannot hear, to detect the ripples made by a fish breaking the surface of a lake. Some birds can detect Earth's magnetic field and use it to navigate over complex terrain.

How Animals Respond Because of the differences in animals' sensory abilities, responses can vary greatly. **When an animal responds to a stimulus, body systems—including the sense organs, nervous system, and muscles—interact to produce the resultant behavior.** Once an animal's senses have detected an external stimulus, that information is passed along nerve cells to the brain. The brain and other parts of the nervous system process the information and direct the body's response. Animals with very simple nervous systems are capable of only simple behaviors, such as moving toward a stimulus or away from it. For example, an earthworm will move away from bright light. Animals with more complex nervous systems, such as the frog in **Figure 34–2,** are better equipped to respond with more complicated and precise behaviors.

Behavior and Evolution

Animal behavior is as important to survival and reproduction as any physical characteristic, such as teeth or claws. Recall that physical traits develop according to a specific set of genetic instructions. Many behaviors are also influenced by genes. Therefore, some behaviors can be inherited by an animal's offspring. Behaviors, like physical characteristics, may evolve under the influence of natural selection. A behavior that is directed by genes may help an individual to survive and reproduce. For example, the genes that code for behavior of the moth in **Figure 34–3** may help the moth escape predators. Organisms with an adaptive behavior will survive and reproduce better than organisms that lack the behavior. After natural selection has operated for many generations, most individuals in the population will exhibit the adaptive behavior.

Figure 34–3 Moths of the genus *Automeris* normally rest with their front wings over their hind wings (left). If disturbed, the moth will move its front wings to expose a striking circular pattern on its hind wings (right). As one scientist has suggested, this behavior may scare off predators when they mistake the moth's hind-wing pattern for the eyes of predatory owls. **Inferring** *If the scientist's hypothesis is correct, how might wing-lifting behavior in this moth illustrate the results of natural selection?*

▲ **Figure 34–4 Innate behaviors appear in fully functional form the first time they are performed.** Because web building is an innate behavior, a spider weaves a web correctly the first time it performs the behavior.

Innate Behavior

Why do newly hatched birds beg for food within moments after hatching? How do spiders know how to build their first web? These animals are exhibiting an **innate behavior,** also called an instinct, or inborn behavior. **Innate behaviors appear in fully functional form the first time they are performed, even though the animal may have had no previous experience with the stimuli to which it responds.** One of the simplest innate behaviors is the suckling of a newborn mammal. Other innate behaviors, such as the weaving of a spider web like the one in **Figure 34–4,** or the building of hanging nests by weaver birds, can be quite complex. All innate behaviors depend on internal mechanisms that develop as a result of complex interactions between an animal's genes and its environment. Biologists do not yet fully understand just how these kinds of interactions occur.

 *What is innate behavior?*

Learned Behavior

Animals often live in unpredictable environments, so their behavior must be flexible enough to deal with uncertainty and change. Many animals can alter their behavior as a result of experience. Such changes are called **learning.** Acquired behavior is another name for learning, because these behaviors develop over time.

Many animals have the ability to learn. Organisms with simple nervous systems, such as most invertebrates, may learn only rarely. Among a few invertebrates, and many chordates, learning is common and occurs under a wide range of circumstances. In animals that care for their young, for example, offspring can learn behaviors from their parents or other caretakers. Scientists have identified several different ways of learning. **The four major types of learning are habituation, classical conditioning, operant conditioning, and insight learning.**

1 Before Conditioning
When a dog sees or smells food, it produces saliva. Food is the stimulus and the dog's response is salivation. Dogs do not usually salivate in response to nonfood stimuli.

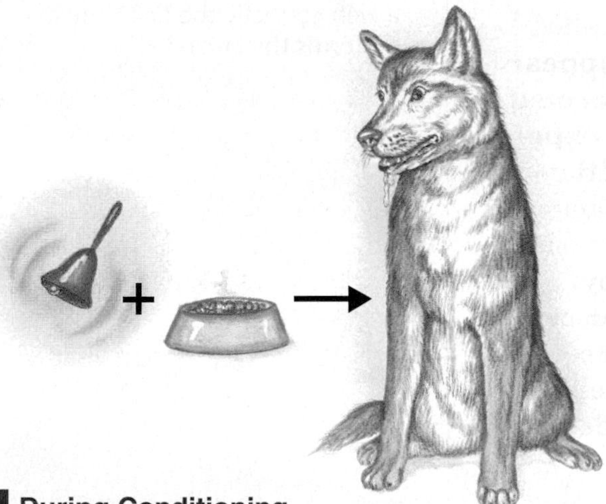

2 During Conditioning
By ringing a bell every time he fed the dog, Pavlov trained the dog to associate the sight and smell of food with the ringing bell.

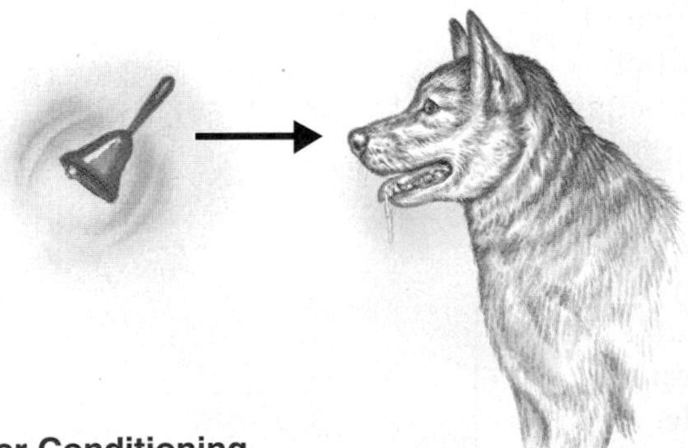

3 After Conditioning
When Pavlov rang a bell in the absence of food, the dog still salivated. The dog was conditioned to salivate in response to a stimulus that it did not normally associate with food.

Habituation The simplest type of learning is habituation. **Habituation** is a process by which an animal decreases or stops its response to a repetitive stimulus that neither rewards nor harms the animal. By ignoring a nonthreatening or unrewarding stimulus, animals can spend their time and energy more efficiently.

Consider the common shore ragworm. This animal lives in a sandy tube that it leaves only to feed. If a shadow passes overhead, the worm will instantly retreat to the safety of its burrow. Yet, if repeated shadows pass within a short time span, this response quickly subsides. When the worm has learned that the shadow is neither food nor threat, it will stop responding. At this point the worm has habituated to the stimulus.

Classical Conditioning When a dog sees its owner approaching with a leash, it may wag its tail and bark, eager to go for a walk. The dog has learned to associate the sight of the leash with a walk. Any time an animal makes a mental connection between a stimulus and some kind of reward or punishment, it has learned by **classical conditioning.** In the case of the dog and its owner, the stimulus of the leash is associated with a pleasant reward—a brisk walk. Now, think of what happens if a dog tries to attack a skunk. The skunk sprays the dog with a substance that stings and smells awful. In the future, that dog is likely to avoid skunks, because it associates the stimuli of the sight and scent of the skunk with the punishment of its foul spray.

The most famous example of classical conditioning is the work of the Russian physiologist Ivan Pavlov, around 1900. Pavlov was studying salivation—an innate behavior—in dogs. He discovered that if he always rang a bell at the same time he fed his dog, the dog would eventually begin to salivate whenever it heard a bell, even if no food was present. **Figure 34–5** shows how the dog in Pavlov's experiment learned to associate the bell (stimulus) with the arrival of food (reward).

◀ **Figure 34–5** Ivan Pavlov taught his dog to expect food whenever a bell was rung. **Pavlov's experiment is an example of classical conditioning, one of the four major types of learning.**

Operant Conditioning Conditioning is often used to train animals. **Operant conditioning** occurs when an animal learns to behave in a certain way through repeated practice, in order to receive a reward or avoid punishment. Operant conditioning is also called trial-and-error learning because it begins with a random behavior that is rewarded in an event called a trial. Most trials result in errors, but occasionally a trial will lead to a reward or punishment.

Operant conditioning was first described in the 1940s by the American psychologist B. F. Skinner. Skinner invented a testing procedure that used a certain type of box—the "Skinner box" shown in **Figure 34–6.** A Skinner box contains a colored button or lever that, when pressed, delivers a food reward. After an animal is rewarded several times, it learns that it gets food whenever it presses the button or lever. At this point, the animal has learned by operant conditioning how to obtain food.

What is operant conditioning?

Insight Learning The most complicated form of learning is **insight learning,** or reasoning. Insight learning occurs when an animal applies something it has already learned to a new situation, without a period of trial and error. For instance, if you are given a new math problem on an exam, you may apply principles you have already learned in the class in order to solve the problem. Insight learning is common among humans and other primates. In one experiment, a hungry chimpanzee used insight learning to figure out how to reach a bunch of bananas hanging overhead: it stacked some boxes on top of one another and climbed to the top of the stack. In contrast, if a dog accidentally wraps its leash around a tree, the dog is usually unable to free itself.

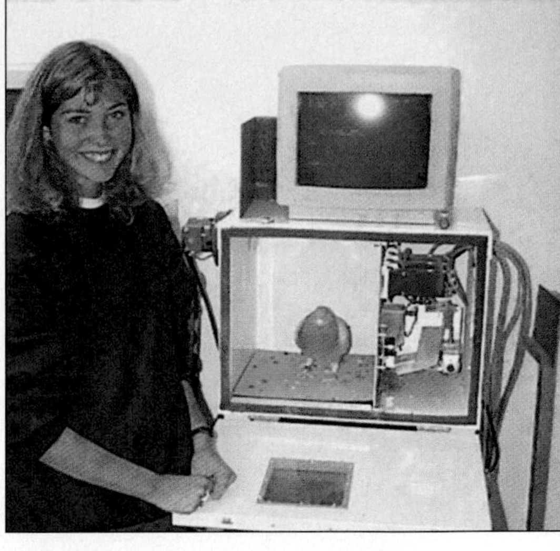

▲ **Figure 34–6** Notice the pigeon in the Skinner box. Sooner or later, a laboratory animal placed in a Skinner box will accidentally press a button or lever that delivers a food reward. In time, this pigeon will learn how to obtain food whenever it wants. **Applying Concepts** *Which type of learning occurs in a Skinner box?*

Quick Lab

What kind of learning is practice?

Materials paper, ruler, scissors

Procedure

1. Draw straight lines on a piece of paper to divide it into several sections of different sizes and shapes. Then, cut the paper into sections along those lines.
2. Shuffle the pieces and then time another student as he or she tries to reassemble the pieces. Record how long it takes the student to do this task.
3. Repeat step 2 three times. Construct a graph showing how the time needed to assemble the puzzle changed with repeated practice.

Analyze and Conclude

1. **Analyzing Data** Explain the shape of your graph. How did the time needed to reassemble the pieces change with repeated trials?
2. **Drawing Conclusions** What kind of learning was displayed in this activity? Was it classical conditioning, operant conditioning, habituation, or some other kind of learning? Explain your answer.

▲ **Figure 34–7** These young Canada geese were trained to migrate behind this ultralight aircraft in an experiment called Operation Migration. The geese followed the craft as closely as they would their own parents. This type of conditioning is now being used to help endangered species, such as whooping cranes, learn a migration route. **Inferring** *Why would these birds follow this aircraft?*

Instinct and Learning Combined

Most behaviors result from a combination of innate ability and learning. Young white-crowned sparrows, for example, have an innate ability to recognize their own species' song. To sing the complete version, however, the young birds must first hear it sung by the adults.

Some very young animals, such as ducks and geese, learn to recognize and follow the first moving object that they see during a critical time early in their lives. Usually, this object is their mother. This process is called **imprinting.** Imprinting keeps young animals close to their mother, who protects them and leads them to food sources. Once imprinting has occurred, the behavior cannot be changed.

Imprinting involves both innate and learned behavior. The young animals have an innate urge to follow the first moving object they see, but they are not born knowing what that object will look like. The young animal must learn from experience what object to follow. In fact, the object on which the young animal imprints does not have to be its mother, or even a living organism. The birds in **Figure 34–7** have imprinted on an aircraft!

Imprinting can occur through scent as well as sight. Newly hatched salmon, for example, imprint on the odor of the stream in which they hatch. Young salmon then head out to sea. Years later, when they mature, the salmon remember the odor of their home stream and return there to spawn.

34–1 Section Assessment

1. **Key Concept** Which body systems interact to produce a behavioral response?
2. **Key Concept** Compare and contrast innate and learned behavior.
3. **Key Concept** Define the four major types of learning.
4. Explain the difference between a stimulus and a response.
5. How does natural selection affect animal behavior?
6. **Critical Thinking Applying Concepts** Give an example of how humans learn through classical conditioning.

Thinking Visually

Creating a Graphic Organizer
Create a graphic organizer to compare innate behavior with the different forms of learned behavior discussed in this section. Include at least one example of each kind of behavior in your graphic organizer.

Using Remote Sensing to Study Animal Behavior

It is difficult to study animals that travel long distances, such as elephants and blue whales. Such studies once required the capture, banding, release, and recapture of individual animals. Researchers would mark or band an animal with an identification tag. If that animal was seen again or recaptured, the identification tag would be recorded and compared to the original field notes. Using this method, scientists could get an idea of the places their subjects visited. But they had few clues to the routes that animals traveled or where they went between capture points.

Remote Sensing

Today, small radio tags or transmitters are used to track the positions of some animals as they travel. As with banding, the lightweight transmitters are attached to individual animals. Satellites that orbit Earth are programmed to locate the transmitter signal and record the position—latitude, longitude, and even depth—of the animal as it moves. Some transmitters contain computer chips that can record the animal's body temperature, rate of breathing, and other physiological characteristics. These data can be made available to researchers over periods of days, weeks, or even months. This method, called satellite telemetry (tuh-LEM-uh-tree), can be expensive, but the data it provides are extremely valuable. The data may help in efforts to protect endangered species such as elephants and sea turtles.

In the Jungle

Scientists are using remote sensing techniques to track elephants through the dense jungles of Thailand and Malaysia. Preliminary data suggest that elephants can move across long distances within a home range of almost 7000 square kilometers. Such a large area would have been impossible for researchers to cover from the ground, or even by airplane or helicopter.

In the Ocean

Researchers also use remote sensing to study marine animals—particularly sea turtles. Because sea turtles spend most of their lives at sea and come ashore only during breeding season, little is known about their daily habits or migration routes. Scientists are using satellite telemetry to track the movement of sea turtles. A transmitter is glued to the back of the turtle's carapace, where it remains for up to 8 to 10 months.

Research and Decide

Use library or Internet resources to learn more about remote sensing in studies of animal behavior. Then, evaluate the advantages and disadvantages of this technology. (Consider factors such as kinds of information the technology does and does not provide, its probable cost, and what might be learned better by other methods.)

For: Links from the authors
Visit: PHSchool.com
Web Code: cbe-9341

34–2 Patterns of Behavior

4-3.1 Natural selection of behaviors
LS- Analyze results
LS- State an appropriate hypothesis

Guide for Reading

Key Concepts
- How do environmental changes affect animal behavior?
- How do courtship and social behaviors increase an animal's evolutionary fitness?
- How do animals communicate?

Vocabulary
migration
circadian rhythm
courtship
territory
aggression
communication
language

Reading Strategy: Using Visuals As you read, write a sentence explaining how each diagram or photograph reinforces or enhances the content of this section.

At this very moment, somewhere in an African grassland, elephants are calling to one another. Elephants communicate with sounds that they use to locate each other across distances more than 2 kilometers away. When they are not calling long-distance, elephants may spar with each other to test their strength or greet each other by wrapping their trunks together. These behaviors are patterns that have evolved in elephants. In this section, you will investigate some common patterns of animal behavior.

Behavioral Cycles

The environment is full of natural cycles. Night follows day, seasons change, the moon has phases, the tides rise and fall. **Many animals respond to periodic changes in the environment with daily or seasonal cycles of behavior.** For example, several species of reptiles and mammals are active during warm seasons but enter into a sleeplike state, or dormancy, during cold seasons. Dormancy allows an animal to survive periods when food and other resources may not be available.

Another type of behavior that is influenced by changing seasons is **migration,** the periodic movement from one place to another and then back again. Animals that migrate include species of birds, butterflies, and whales. **Figure 34–8** shows the migratory pattern of green sea turtles. Migration usually allows animals to take advantage of favorable environmental conditions. For example, when birds fly south for the winter, they go to regions where food is more plentiful than in northern areas.

Behavioral cycles that occur in daily patterns are called **circadian** (sur-KAY-dee-un) **rhythms.** The fact that you sleep at night and attend school during the day is an example of a circadian rhythm.

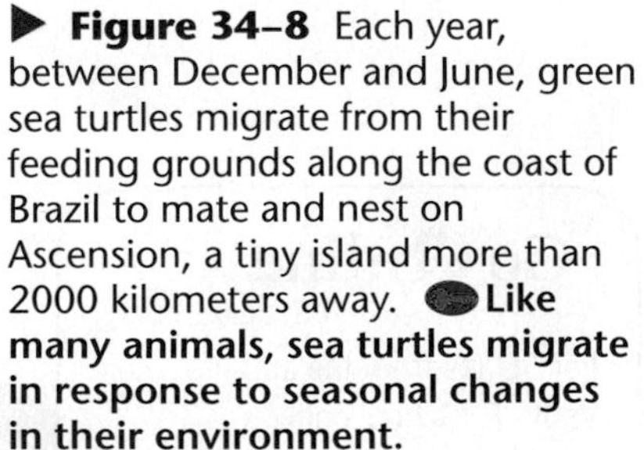

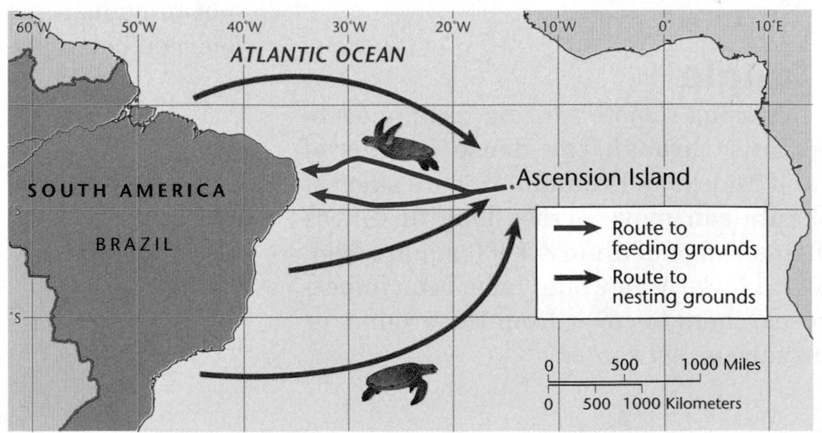

▶ **Figure 34–8** Each year, between December and June, green sea turtles migrate from their feeding grounds along the coast of Brazil to mate and nest on Ascension, a tiny island more than 2000 kilometers away. **Like many animals, sea turtles migrate in response to seasonal changes in their environment.**

Analyzing Data

Caring for Eggs

Reproduction is vital to animal survival. Humans can learn child-rearing skills. Is there evidence that other animals learn to care for their young?

The data at the right are from field studies of the short-tailed shearwater, *Puffinus tenuirostris*. Each pair of parents produces only one egg a year. If that egg breaks or if the chick dies, the egg is not replaced. The graph shows the percentage of eggs that hatch and develop into free-flying young, in relation to the number of years that the parents have been breeding. This variable is referred to as reproductive success. The purple line indicates the success rate of female parents. The green line indicates the success rate of male parents.

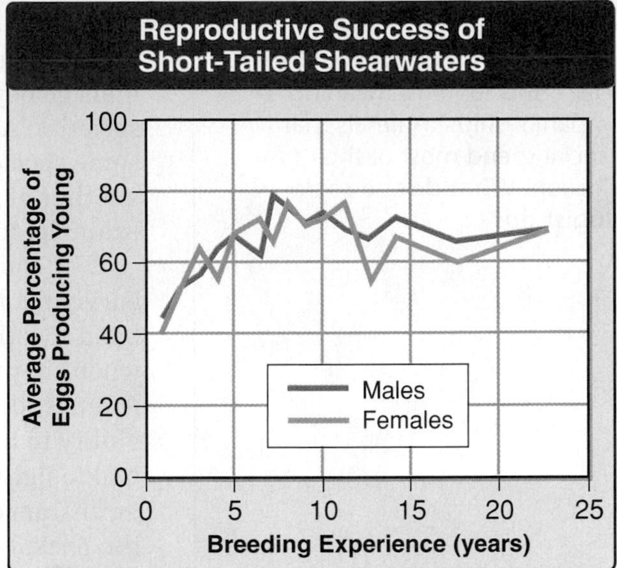

1. **Using Tables and Graphs** What is the approximate success rate of a female shearwater with 5 years of breeding experience?
2. **Using Tables and Graphs** Are there obvious differences in reproductive success between male and female shearwaters?
3. **Drawing Conclusions** Do older shearwaters have better reproductive success than younger birds? Explain your answer.
4. **Formulating Hypotheses** Do you think these birds learn to raise young more successfully over time? Is there an alternative hypothesis that could explain these data?

Courtship

Animal behavior is geared toward reproduction as well as survival. **To pass along its genes to the next generation, any animal that reproduces sexually needs to locate and mate with another member of its species at least once. Courtship behavior is part of an overall reproductive strategy that helps many animals identify healthy mates.**

In **courtship,** an individual sends out stimuli—such as sounds, visual displays, or chemicals—in order to attract a member of the opposite sex. For example, fireflies flash a distinct series of light signals to indicate their readiness to mate. The musical trill of a tree frog and the sheeplike bleat of a narrowmouth toad are among the many distinctive breeding calls of amphibians.

In some species, courtship involves an elaborate series of behaviors called rituals. A ritual is a series of behaviors performed the same way by all members of a population for the purpose of communicating. Most rituals consist of specific signals and individual responses that continue until mating occurs. For example, newly paired cranes, such as those in **Figure 34–9,** engage in intense periods of dancing before they mate.

What is the function of courtship behavior?

▼ **Figure 34–9** **Courtship behavior helps many animals identify healthy mates.** The courtship ritual of this pair of Japanese cranes consists of head bobbing, deep bows, leaps, grasping and tossing objects, short flights, and several other moves. If a potential mate does not perform the parts of this dance in the proper sequence, it will be rejected and must locate a different mate.

Word Origins

The adjective **social** is related to the Latin words *socialis,* meaning "social," and *societas,* meaning "companionship." Animals that are social spend most of their time in a group. **What does a sociobiologist do?**

Social Behavior

Whenever animals interact with members of their own species, as in courtship, they are exhibiting social behavior. Many animals go beyond courtship in their social behavior and form societies. An animal society is a group of related animals of the same species that interact closely and often cooperate with one another. It takes the cooperative work of millions of termites, for example, to build a single termite mound.

For some species, membership in a society offers great survival advantages. Zebras and other grazers, for example, band together when grazing. They are safer from predators when they are part of a group rather than when they are alone. Animal societies also use strength in numbers to improve their ability to hunt, to protect their territory, to guard their young, and to fight with rivals if necessary. In wild African dog packs, for instance, adult females take turns guarding all the pups in the pack, while the other adults hunt together for prey.

Often, members of a society are closely related to one another. Related individuals share a large proportion of each other's genes. Therefore, helping a relative survive increases the chance that the genes an individual shares with that relative will be passed along to offspring. Thus, social behavior that helps a relative survive and reproduce improves an individual's evolutionary fitness.

Primates form some of the most complex animal social groups known. Macaque, baboon, and other primate societies hunt together, travel in search of new territory, and interact with neighboring societies. A great deal of what we know about primate societies comes from the work of Jane Goodall, the animal behaviorist pictured in **Figure 34–10,** who spent thousands of hours observing chimps in their natural habitat.

For: Links on animal communication
Visit: www.SciLinks.org
Web Code: cbn-9342

What is an animal society?

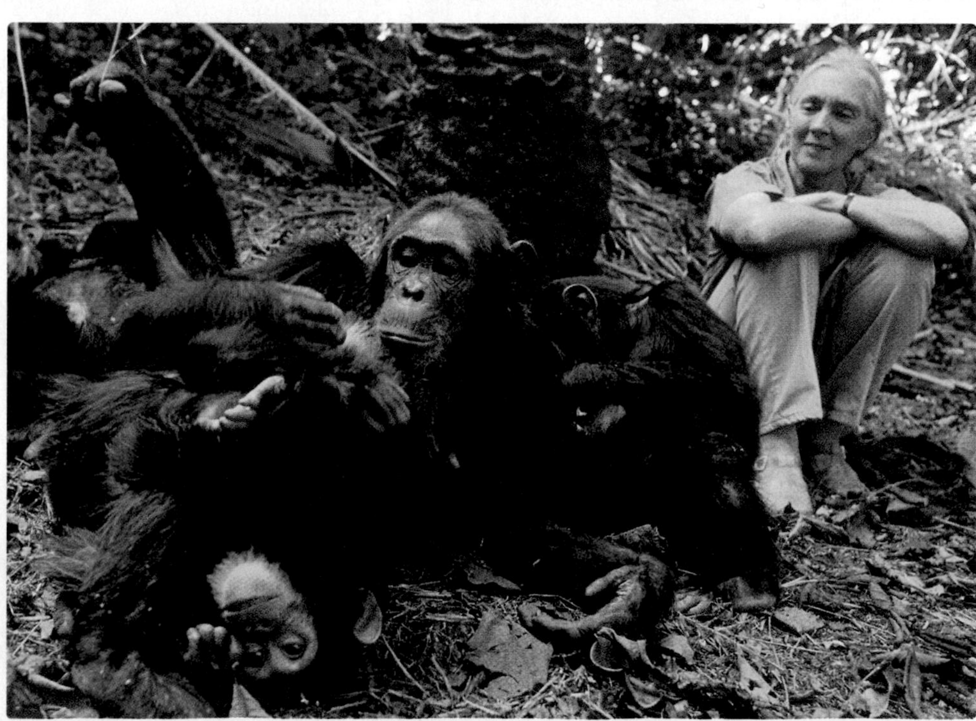

▶ **Figure 34–10** **Animal societies enhance the reproductive success of individual members.** The work of the British behaviorist Jane Goodall, at right, laid the foundation for modern primate studies. Goodall observed chimpanzees in their natural habitat, as shown here. Goodall's methodology and profound scientific discoveries revolutionized the field of animal behavior.

Competition and Aggression

Some animals have behaviors that help prevent others from using limited resources. Often, such patterns involve a specific area, or **territory,** that is occupied and protected by an animal or group of animals. Territories contain resources, such as food, water, nesting sites, shelter, and potential mates, that are necessary for an animal's survival and reproduction. By claiming a territory, an animal keeps others at a distance. If a rival enters a territory, the "owner" of the territory may attack the rival and drive it away. Algae-eating damselfish are notorious for making such attacks. An algae-eating damselfish can distinguish other algae-feeding species from species that do not eat algae. The damselfish chases the other algae-eaters away, but ignores the fish that do not eat algae.

When two or more animals try to claim limited resources, such as a territory or food, competition occurs. Many animals, such as the giraffes in **Figure 34–11,** use rituals and displays when they compete. During competition, animals may also show **aggression,** a threatening behavior that one animal uses to gain control over another. For instance, before a pride of lions settles down to eat, individuals may snap, claw, and snarl at one another. The most aggressive members will get to eat their fill of prey. The less aggressive lions will have to wait for their chance to feed.

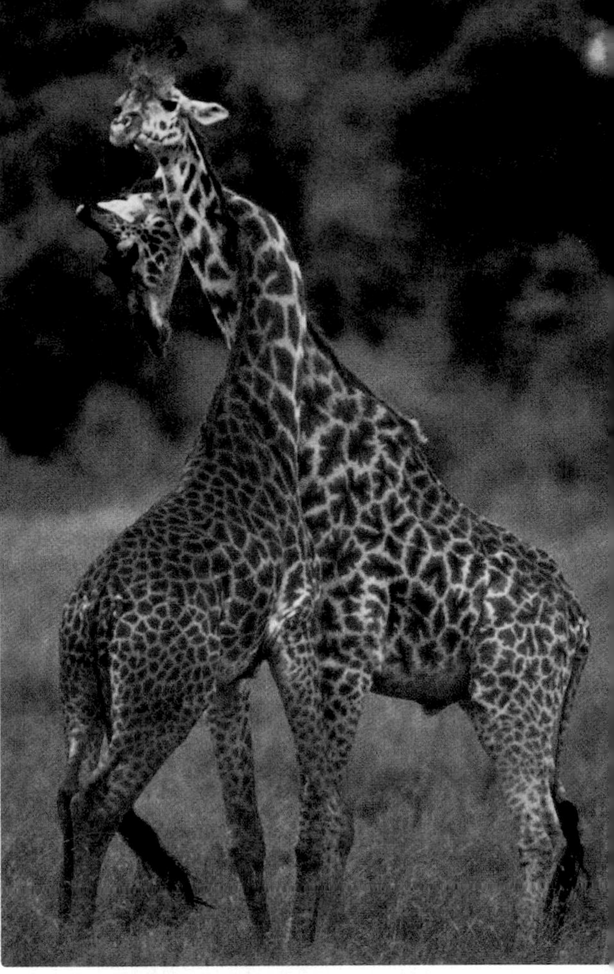

▲ **Figure 34–11** By intertwining their long necks, these two giraffes compete for resources on an African savanna. **Inferring** *What resources might these giraffes compete for?*

Communication

Often, when animal behavior involves more than one individual, some form of **communication**—the passing of information from one organism to another—is involved. **Animals may use visual, sound, touch, or chemical signals to communicate with one another.** The specific techniques that animals use depend on the types of stimuli their senses can detect.

Visual Signals Animals with good eyesight often use visual signals involving movement and color. Cuttlefish, for example, have large eyes that are as sophisticated as those of vertebrates. In a matter of seconds, a single cuttlefish, like the one in **Figure 34–12,** can undergo changes in the colors and patterns on its body. Its skin will pucker into bumps and spines, then suddenly become smooth as stone. These visual displays—as fascinating as any computer screen saver—function in defense, hunting, mating, warning, and perhaps other forms of communication that are not yet known.

▶ **Figure 34–12** **Animals use visual, sound, touch, and chemical signals to communicate.** Like many animals with good eyesight, this Pacific giant cuttlefish uses visual signals in displaying a variety of bright colors and patterns on its body.

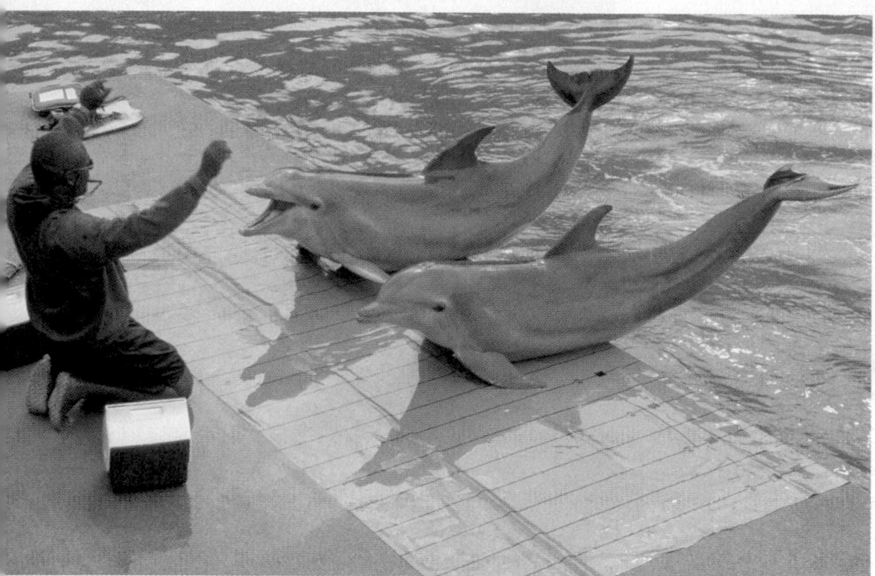

▲ **Figure 34–13** Dolphins have fairly complex ways of communicating with one another.

Chemical Signals Animals with well-developed senses of smell, including insects, fishes, and many mammals, may communicate with chemicals. For example, some animals release pheromones (FEHR-uh-mohnz), chemical messengers that affect the behavior of other individuals of the same species, to mark a territory or to signal their readiness to mate.

Sound Signals Animals with strong vocal abilities, including crickets, toads, and birds, communicate with sound. Some animals that use sound have evolved elaborate communication systems. Dolphins, for example, rely mainly on sound signals in the dark and often murky ocean depths where vision is not very useful. Scientists have discovered that bottlenose dolphins each have their own unique "signature" whistle that is used for recognition. The dolphins' whistles function something like your signature on a letter, letting others know who is sending the communication.

Language The most complicated form of communication is language. **Language** is a system of communication that combines sounds, symbols, or gestures according to sets of rules about word order and meaning, such as grammar and syntax. Many animals, like dolphins, elephants, and gorillas, have fairly complex ways of communicating. However, outside of experiments in which they were trained by humans, none of those animals have been shown to use language. Only humans are known to use language.

34–2 Section Assessment

1. **Key Concept** Name two ways in which animal behavior is related to environmental cycles.
2. **Key Concept** Explain how an animal society can contribute to the evolutionary fitness of an individual animal.
3. **Key Concept** What are the main ways in which animals communicate with one another?
4. Define "courtship ritual," and give an example of an animal's courtship ritual.
5. How do dolphins communicate with one another?
6. **Critical Thinking Inferring** Suppose you discover a new type of animal that is very different in appearance from other animals you have seen. How could observing the sense organs of this animal help you to understand if and how it communicates?

Writing in Science

Describing Migration

In your own words, write a paragraph explaining what migration is and the function it serves in an animal's life. As a way of clarifying and supporting your explanation, describe the migratory behavior of at least one animal species. *Hint:* You might use the information diagrammed in **Figure 34–8.**

Design an Experiment

Observing Behavior in Fish

Animals of the same species often use aggressive behavior to signal others to retreat, but rarely do they hurt each other. In this investigation, you will examine some stimuli that provoke aggressive behavior.

Problem **What triggers the aggressive behavior of male betta fish?**

Materials

- male betta fish
- aquarium net
- clear plastic box of aquarium water
- small mirror
- construction paper
- colored pencils or markers
- transparent tape
- popsicle sticks
- watch with a second hand

Skills Asking Questions, Designing Experiments

Design Your Experiment  

Part A: Observing Aggressive Displays

1. Use an aquarium net to transfer a male betta from the aquarium to a clear plastic box of aquarium water. **CAUTION:** *Do not touch the fish with your hands. Fish are easily injured.*
2. Observe the betta's behavior.
3. Place a mirror against the side of the box so that the fish can see its reflection. Observe and record the betta's behavior. Remove the mirror within 1 minute so that the fish does not habituate to its reflection.

Part B: Identifying the Stimulus for Aggression

4. **Formulating Hypotheses** What feature of a betta provokes aggressive behavior in other bettas? Is it color, size, movement, or something else? Record a hypothesis of what provokes aggressive displays by bettas. Base your hypothesis on your observations of bettas in Part A.
5. Design an experiment that will use paper models of bettas to test your hypothesis. You can tape the models to popsicle sticks and use colored pencils or markers to add details. Refer to the Lab Tips box on page 55. Have your teacher check your plan before you begin your experiment.
6. Carry out your experiment. Record your observations of the betta's behavior. **CAUTION:** *To avoid exhausting the betta, always allow it at least 1 minute of rest between stimuli.*

7. Wash your hands with soap and warm water before leaving the lab.

Analyze and Conclude

1. **Controlling Variables** Identify and define the manipulated and responding variables in your experiment.
2. **Observing** Did the male betta exhibit aggressive behavior? If so, how did it show aggression?
3. **Evaluating** What stimuli provoked the most aggression? Did your observations support your hypothesis?
4. **Inferring** Male bettas are more aggressive toward other males when a female betta is present. How can such behavior be an advantage to the male? How does it help the species survive?
5. **SAFETY** Explain how you demonstrated safe practices when working with live fish in this investigation.

Go Further

Designing Experiments Male bettas use aggression to defend their territory against invasion from other male bettas. Design an experiment to investigate what traits determine which male bettas will be successful in conflicts with other males.

Chapter 34 Study Guide

34–1 Elements of Behavior

Key Concepts

- When an animal responds to a stimulus, body systems—including the sense organs, nervous system, and muscles—interact to produce the resultant behavior.
- Innate behaviors appear in fully functional form the first time they are performed, even though the animal may have had no previous experience with the stimuli to which it responds.
- The four major types of learning are habituation, classical conditioning, operant conditioning, and insight learning.

Vocabulary

behavior, p. 871
stimulus, p. 871
response, p. 871
innate behavior, p. 873
learning, p. 873
habituation, p. 874
classical conditioning, p. 874
operant conditioning, p. 875
insight learning, p. 875
imprinting, p. 876

34–2 Patterns of Behavior

Key Concepts

- Many animals respond to periodic changes in the environment with daily or seasonal cycles of behavior.
- To pass along its genes to the next generation, any animal that reproduces sexually needs to locate and mate with another member of its species at least once. Courtship behavior is part of an overall reproductive strategy that helps many animals identify healthy mates.
- Often, members of a society are closely related to one another. Related individuals share a large proportion of each other's genes. Therefore, helping a relative survive increases the chance that the genes an individual shares with that relative will be passed along to offspring.
- Animals may use visual, sound, touch, or chemical signals to communicate with one another.

Vocabulary

migration, p. 878
circadian rhythm, p. 878
courtship, p. 879
territory, p. 881
aggression, p. 881
communication, p. 881
language, p. 882

Thinking Visually

Using information from this chapter, complete the following concept map:

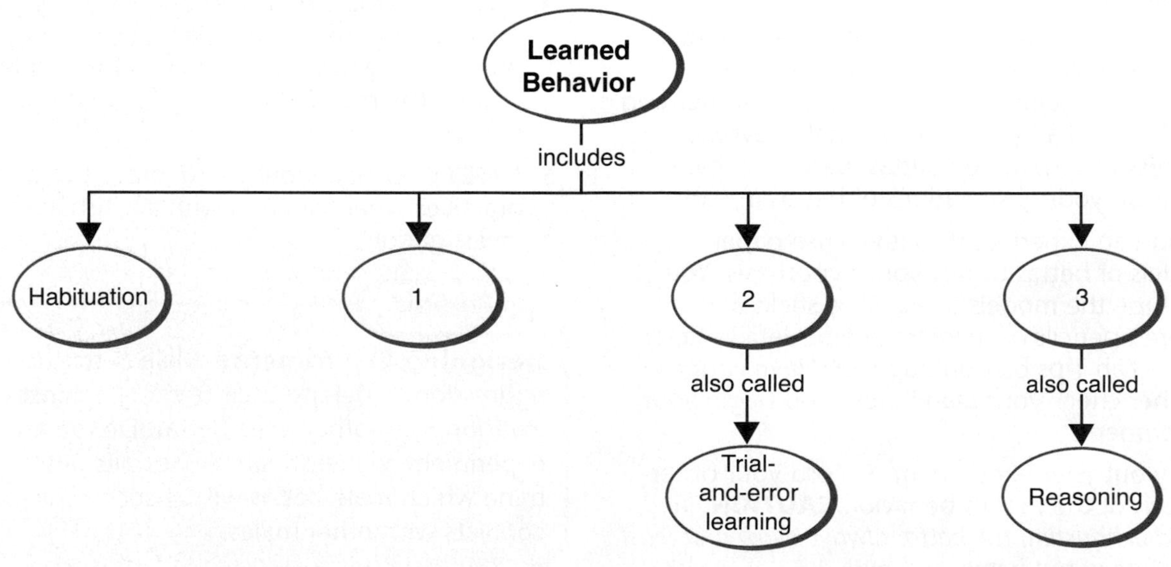

Preparing for the Living Environment Exam

NEW YORK LIVING ENVIRONMENT

Blue questions emphasize Regents Exam content

Chapter 34

Part A

Multiple Choice

For each statement or question, select the number of the word or expression that, of those given, best completes the statement or answers the question.

1 The set of reactions of an organism to changes in its internal condition or external environment is called
(1) behavior (3) learning
(2) conditioning (4) stimuli

2 Which type of behavior is demonstrated when a dog learns to expect food whenever a bell is rung?
(1) insight learning
(2) classical conditioning
(3) operant conditioning
(4) instinct habituation

3 Light, sound, and temperature are examples of
(1) responses (3) circadian rhythms
(2) stimuli (4) conditioned behaviors

4 A decrease in response to a stimulus that neither rewards nor harms an animal is called
(1) instinct
(2) operant conditioning
(3) habituation
(4) classical conditioning

5 Insight learning is common among
(1) dogs (3) insects
(2) primates (4) geese

6 What type of learning is being demonstrated by the baby birds in the illustration below?

(1) imprinting (3) classical conditioning
(2) habituation (4) operant conditioning

7 Some flowers close up at night and open during the day. This is an example of
(1) courtship
(2) a circadian rhythm
(3) conditioning
(4) a stimulus

8 Each year, a bird called the American redstart travels from its winter home in South America to its nesting area in New York. Which term best describes this behavior?
(1) migration (3) imprinting
(2) competition (4) courtship

9 A system of communication that uses meaningful sounds, symbols, or gestures according to specific rules is called
(1) competition
(2) language
(3) vision
(4) parenting

10 Which kind of behavior does *not* involve learning?
(1) habituation
(2) trial and error
(3) imprinting offspring
(4) instinct

11 A male three-spined stickleback fish will attack male red-bellied sticklebacks and models of fishes that have a red underside. It will not attack males or models that do not have a red underside. What is the best conclusion that can be drawn from the behavior of this fish?
(1) The stimulus for an attack is a fish with red fins.
(2) The stimulus for an attack is a red underside.
(3) The stickleback fish will defend its territory against all other fish.
(4) The stickleback fish will not attack red-colored fish.

For questions 12 and 13, complete each analogy by selecting the correct number. In analogies, A : B :: C : means "A is to B as C is to __?__."

12 Stimulus : cold temperatures :: response :
(1) sweating (3) shivering
(2) egg laying (4) warm weather

13 Finding a mate : courtship behavior :: protecting a territory:
(1) feeding (3) migration
(2) aggression (4) habituation

Test-Taking Tip When you are asked to analyze a graph showing experimental data, first look at the shape of the line. Identify the variables and try to determine how they are related.

Preparing for the
Living Environment Exam

Part B

Multiple Choice and Extended Response
For those questions that ask you to select a response, choose the one that best completes the statement or answers the question. For all others follow the directions given.

14 Identify each of the following as a stimulus or a response: laughter, thirst, cold air, eating, baseball being thrown at you, a sneeze, light, flying.

15 The survival of an animal often depends on making the appropriate response to a stimulus. For each of the following stimuli, state an appropriate response.
- A deer sees a predator nearby.
- A person feels something hot touching his hand.
- A female fly detects the smell of rotting meat.

16 State the brain's role in an animal's response to a stimulus.

17 The social behavior shown by some species can help them survive. Identify *two* species that demonstrate some form of social organization, and, for each species, give an example of how this behavior aids its survival.

18 Although the members of many animal species derive benefits from living in social groups, members of other species live alone. State one adaptive advantage of solitary living that would not be true for a species living in social groups.

For questions 19 through 22, select the number of the behavior chosen from the list below, that is best described by that statement. A choice may be used once, more than once, or not at all.

Behaviors
(1) Insight learning
(2) Operant conditioning
(3) Classical conditioning
(4) Habituation

19 A rat learns to press a button to get food.

20 A dog always salivates at the ringing of a bell.

21 A chimpanzee stacks boxes in order to reach a banana hanging from the ceiling.

22 A bird stops responding to a repeated warning call when it is not followed by an attack.

Base your answers to questions 23 through 25 on the information and graph below and on your knowledge of biology.

A researcher observed sedge warblers during breeding season. She charted the number of different songs each male bird sang compared to the time it took him to pair with a mate. The graph illustrates her data.

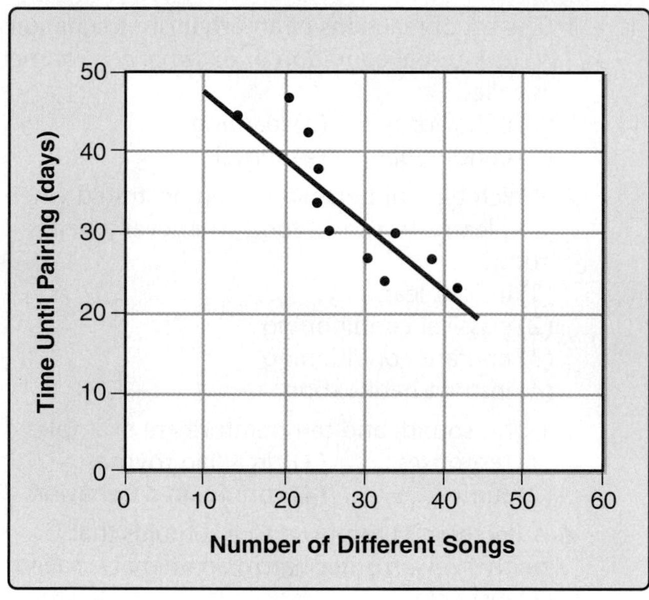

23 The graphed data show a correlation between
(1) the number of a male bird's songs and the time to sing them
(2) the number of a male bird's songs and his attractiveness to females
(3) which songs a male bird sings on different days
(4) which songs a male bird sings for each female

24 State the conclusion that would most likely be made based on the data shown in the graph. In your answer, be sure to
- name the *two* variables in the study
- explain how the two variables are related

25 Over time, natural selection could lead to changes in the courtship behavior of these birds. State one environmental condition that would favor the reproductive success of male birds that sing a greater variety of songs over those with less song variety. Support your answer with an explanation.

Part C

Extended Response

Answer the questions or follow the directions given.

26 In an effort to repopulate once-polluted rivers with salmon, scientists take fertilized salmon eggs from a clean river and place them in the once-polluted river. The salmon will hatch from the eggs, move to the ocean for several years, and then return to the river where they hatched—instead of the river from which the eggs were obtained. Explain how imprinting is specifically involved in this process.

27 State how aggression and territorial behavior are related.

28 Compare animal communication with the use of language. In your answer, be sure to include
- an explanation of the difference between communication and the use of language
- an example of an animal that communicates without language, and how it communicates
- an example of an animal that communicates with language

29 A classmate suggests that German shepherd dogs are more easily trained than poodles. Describe the steps in an experiment that would determine which breed of dog is more easily trained to respond correctly to the command "stay." In your description, be sure to include the following
- how many dogs of each breed you should attempt to train, and why it is necessary to use this many
- what procedure should be followed with each dog
- how you will know if one breed is easier to train than the other

Base your answers to questions 30 and 31 on the information below and on your knowledge of biology.

In a particular species of insect, the females each release small quantities of a certain pheromone to attract males. Once a male of the species detects the pheromone scent released by a female, it flies toward the scent to locate and mate with that particular female.

30 Predict what would happen to the ability of the males to find females in a field if a farmer released large quantities of the pheromone to form a "cloud of pheromone" over the entire area. Support your answer with an explanation.

31 Explain why this method of controlling an insect population is less damaging to other organisms in the environment than the use of pesticides to control insect pests.

32 When temperatures are low and food is scarce, some mammals enter into a state of dormancy. Dormancy is an energy-saving adaptation in which metabolism decreases, and as a result, body temperature declines. The graph below tracks a ground squirrel's body temperature over the course of a year.

Body Temperature of a Ground Squirrel

Body Temperature (°C): 0, 10, 20, 30, 40

Month: Sept. Oct. Nov. Dec. Jan. Feb. Mar. Apr. May June July Aug.

a Describe the pattern that you observe.

b Explain what can be inferred about the squirrel's behavior at different times of the year.

For: An interactive self-test
Visit: PHSchool.com
Web Code: cba-9340

UNIT

10 The Human Body

Chapters

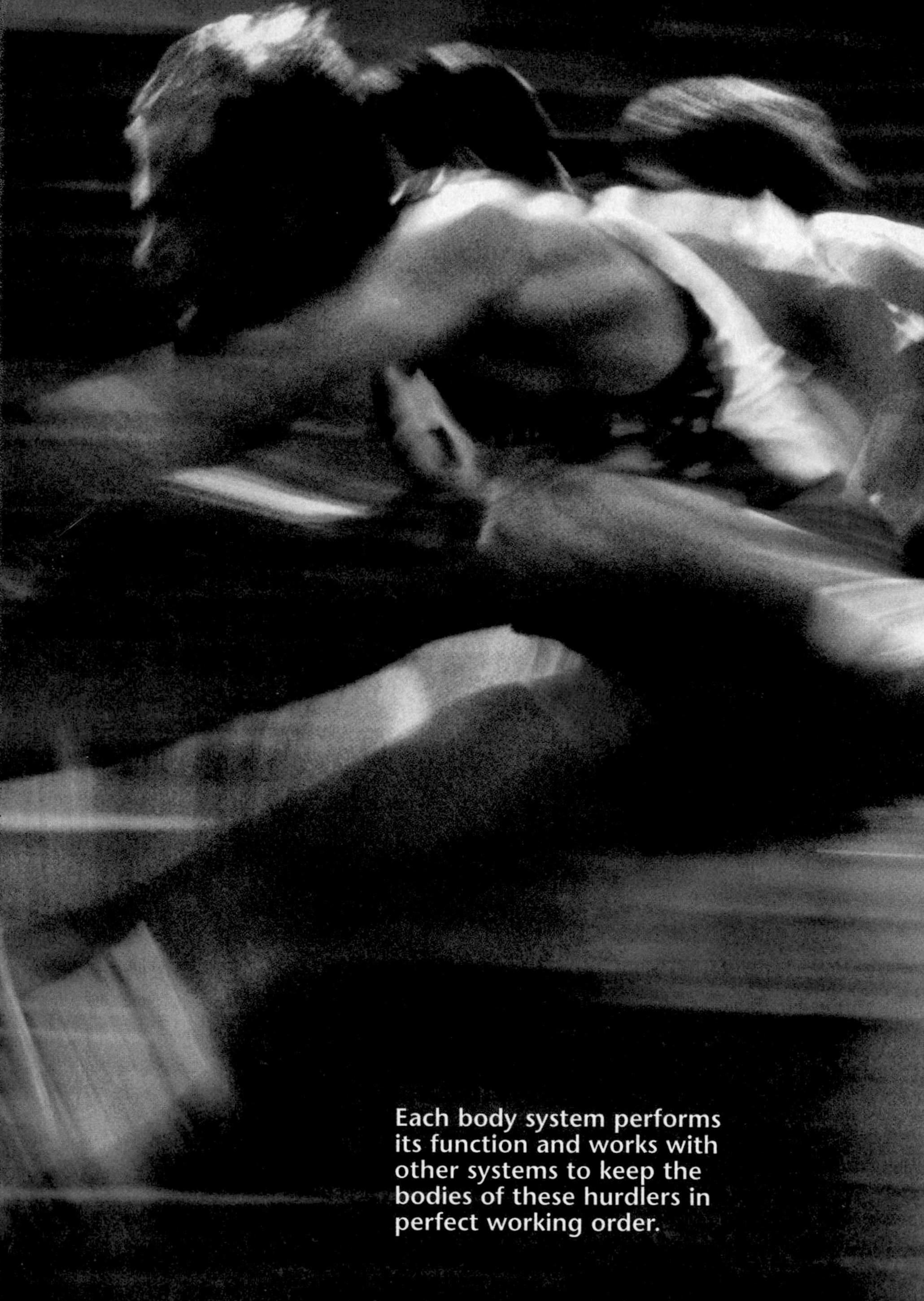

Each body system performs its function and works with other systems to keep the bodies of these hurdlers in perfect working order.

From the Author

What's the most important qualification for being an official at a sporting event? Knowing the rules of the game, of course. If you don't know the rules, you certainly can't make intelligent decisions that are based on them. In a way, the same thing is true of the human body. By understanding how the systems of the human body work, you'll not only begin to understand your own biology—you'll also become a much better player in the game of life.

Ken Miller

What discoveries lie ahead?

- Can we learn enough about the brain and nervous system to account for the subtleties of human behavior, thought, and learning?
- Will we master the immune system to the point that we can use its powerful weaponry against challenges such as cancer and AIDS?

Go Online PHSchool.com

For: Latest discoveries
Visit: PHSchool.com
Web Code: cbe-0000

CHAPTER 35

Nervous System

The agility and balance needed for fencing would not be possible without the coordination of the nervous system and the rest of the body.

Inquiry Activity

What are the organ systems?

Procedure

1. Draw an outline of the human body on a sheet of paper. Without referring to any illustrations, do your best to include the following organs on your outline: brain, stomach, kidneys, heart, and lungs. Pay attention to the shapes of the organs and their relative sizes, and to the specific body regions in which they are located.
2. Make a second drawing using **Figure 35–2** on pages 892 and 893 as a reference. Indicate which organs belong to which organ systems.

Think About It

1. **Predicting** Can an organ belong to more than one organ system? Explain.
2. **Evaluating and Revising** Compare your two drawings. Describe any misconceptions you had about the size, shape, or location of each organ.

35–1 Human Body Systems

4-1.2 Humans have complex systems
4-1.2 Cells are grouped for efficiency
4-5.3 Dynamic equilibrium

Guide for Reading

Key Concepts
- How is the human body organized?
- What is homeostasis?

Vocabulary
specialized cell
epithelial tissue
connective tissue
nervous tissue
muscle tissue
homeostasis
feedback inhibition

Reading Strategy: Predicting Before you read, use **Figure 35–2** to predict how many organ systems help to regulate body temperature. As you read, look for evidence to support your prediction.

As the missed shot bounces high in the air, one of the defenders decides to take a chance. She breaks for the other end of the court. Another defender grabs the rebound, glances upcourt, and throws a long, arching pass toward the basket. Wide open, her teammate grabs the pass, dribbles, and leaps into the air, laying the basketball carefully off the backboard and into the unguarded basket. The buzzer goes off, and the game is over.

Organization of the Body

Teamwork is a wonderful thing! Anyone watching the end of this game would be impressed at the way these two players worked together to make the winning play. But the real teamwork on this play involved a much larger number of players—the nearly one hundred trillion cells that make up the human body.

Every cell in the human body is both an independent unit and an interdependent part of a larger community—the entire organism. To make a winning basket, a basketball player has to use her eyes to watch the play and her brain to figure out how to score. With the support of her bones, her muscles propel her body up the court. As she sprints for a pass, her lungs absorb oxygen, which her blood carries to her cells. Her brain monitors the sensation of the ball on her fingertips and sends signals that guide her body into the air for the final play.

How does the body get so many individual cells to work together so beautifully? You can begin to answer this question by studying the organization of the human body. **The levels of organization in a multicellular organism include cells, tissues, organs, and organ systems.** Tissues are groups of similar cells that perform a single function, such as connecting a muscle to a bone. An organ is a group of tissues that work together to perform a complex function, such as sight. An organ system is a group of organs that perform closely related functions.

The eleven organ systems of the human body work together to maintain homeostasis in the body as a whole. The organ systems, including their main structures and functions, are shown in **Figure 35–2** on pages 892 and 893.

▶ **Figure 35–1** Each player on a basketball team has a different role, but together the team works toward a common goal—winning the game.

FIGURE 35–2 HUMAN ORGAN SYSTEMS

The levels of organization in the human body include cells, tissues, organs, and organ systems. Although each of the eleven organ systems shown here has a different set of functions, they all work together, as a whole, to maintain homeostasis.

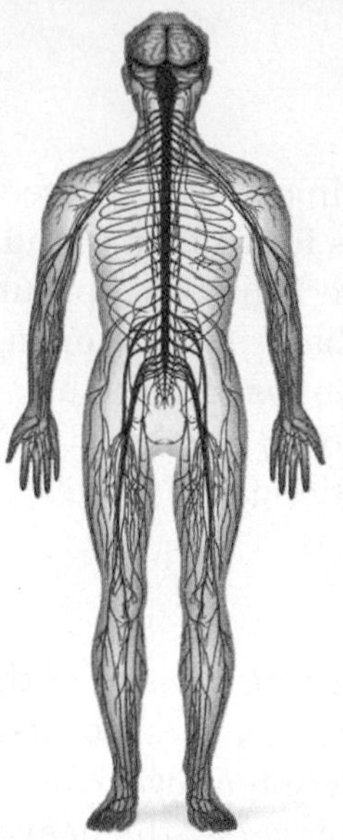

Nervous System
Structures: Brain, spinal cord, peripheral nerves
Function: Recognizes and coordinates the body's response to changes in its internal and external environments

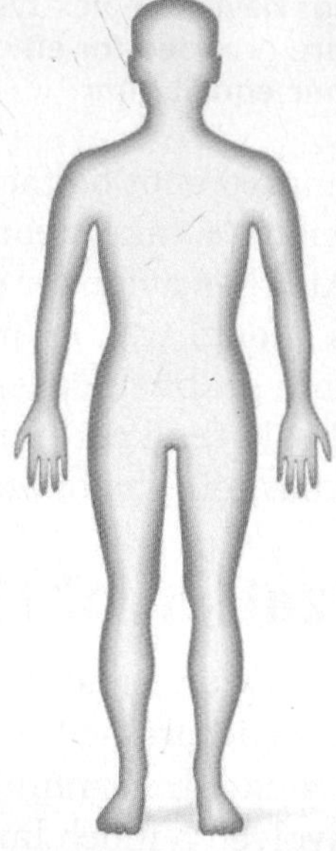

Integumentary System
Structures: Skin, hair, nails, sweat and oil glands
Function: Serves as a barrier against infection and injury; helps to regulate body temperature; provides protection against ultraviolet radiation from the sun

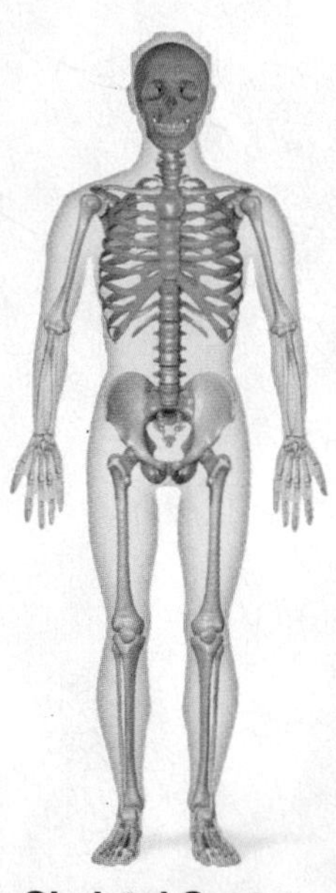

Skeletal System
Structures: Bones, cartilage, ligaments, tendons
Function: Supports the body; protects internal organs; allows movement; stores mineral reserves; provides a site for blood cell formation

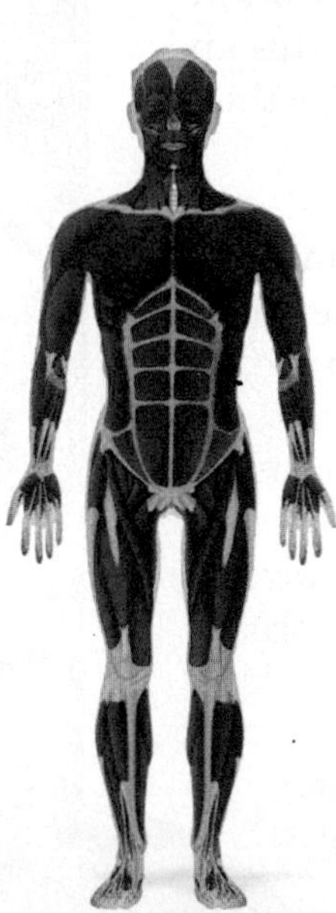

Muscular System
Structures: Skeletal muscle, smooth muscle, cardiac muscle
Function: Works with skeletal system to produce voluntary movement; helps to circulate blood and move food through the digestive system

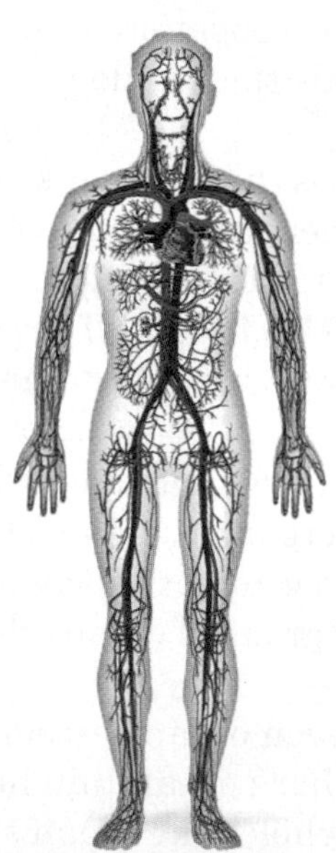

Circulatory System
Structures: Heart, blood vessels, blood
Function: Brings oxygen, nutrients, and hormones to cells; fights infection; removes cell wastes; helps to regulate body temperature

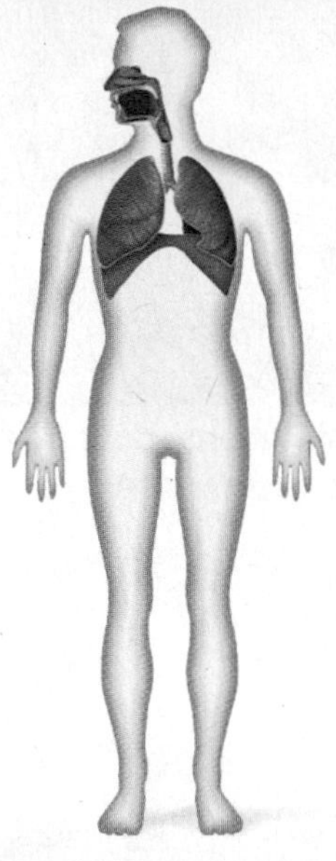

Respiratory System
Structures: Nose, pharynx, larynx, trachea, bronchi, bronchioles, lungs
Function: Provides oxygen needed for cellular respiration and removes excess carbon dioxide from the body

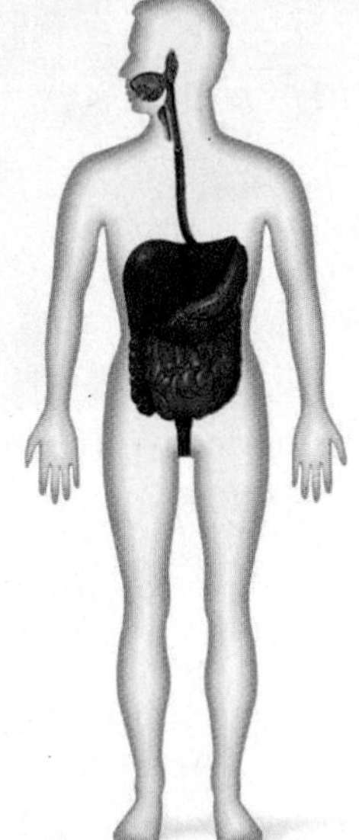

Digestive System
Structures: Mouth, pharynx, esophagus, stomach, small and large intestines, rectum
Function: Converts foods into simpler molecules that can be used by the cells of the body; absorbs food; eliminates wastes

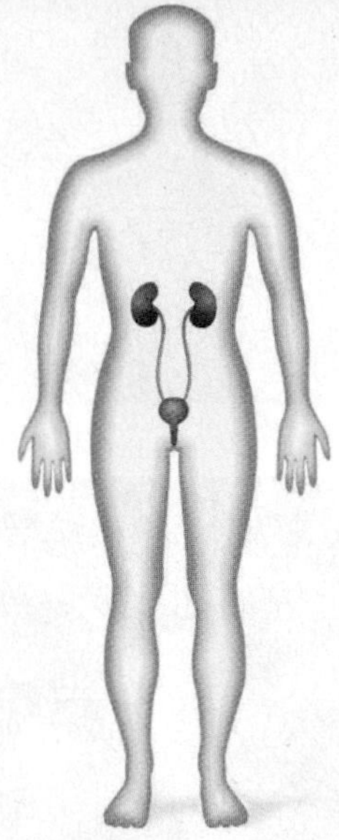

Excretory System
Structures: Skin, lungs, kidneys, ureters, urinary bladder, urethra
Function: Eliminates waste products from the body in ways that maintain homeostasis

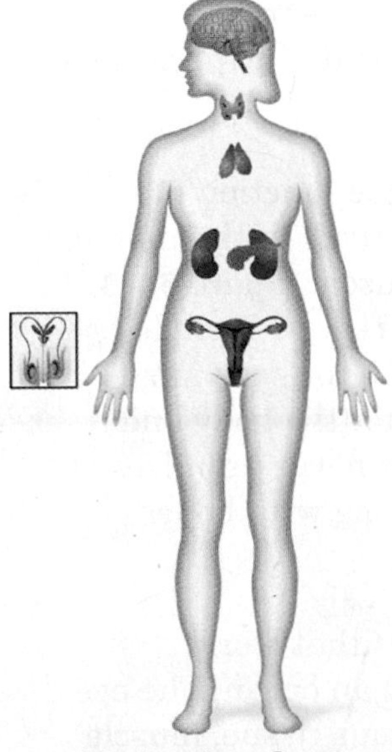

Endocrine System
Structures: Hypothalamus, pituitary, thyroid, parathyroids, adrenals, pancreas, ovaries (in females), testes (in males)
Function: Controls growth, development, and metabolism; maintains homeostasis

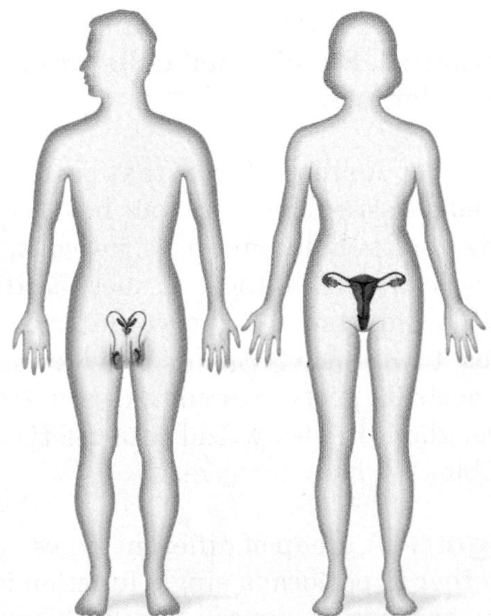

Reproductive System
Structures: Testes, epididymis, vas deferens, urethra, and penis (in males); ovaries, Fallopian tubes, uterus, vagina (in females)
Function: Produces reproductive cells; in females, nurtures and protects developing embryo

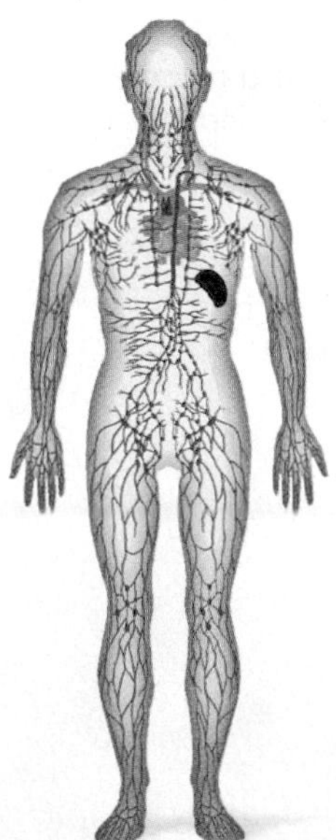

Lymphatic/Immune Systems
Structures: White blood cells, thymus, spleen, lymph nodes, lymph vessels
Function: Helps protect the body from disease; collects fluid lost from blood vessels and returns the fluid to the circulatory system

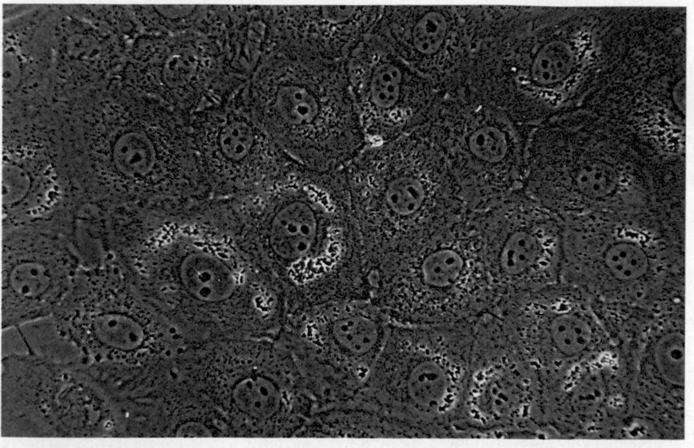

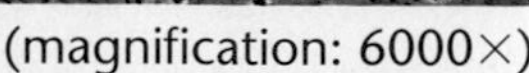

Epithelial Tissue (magnification: 6000×)

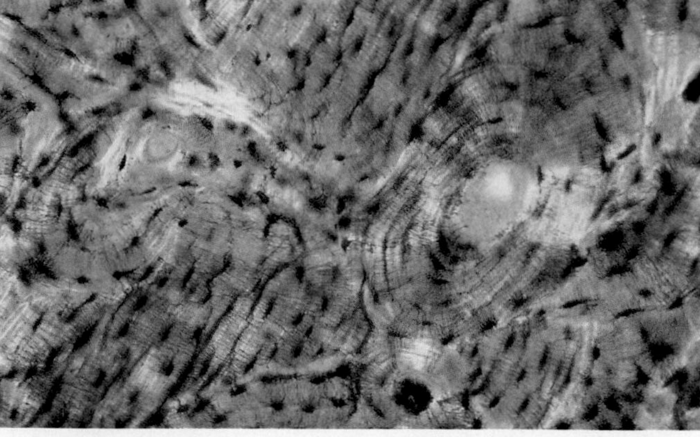

Connective Tissue (magnification: about 50×)

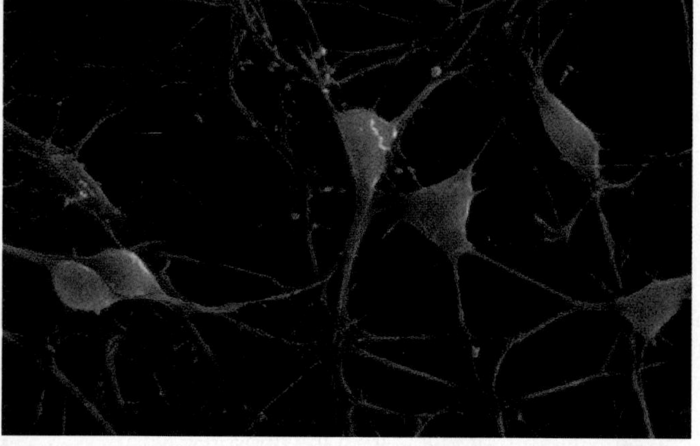

Nervous Tissue (magnification: 1100×)

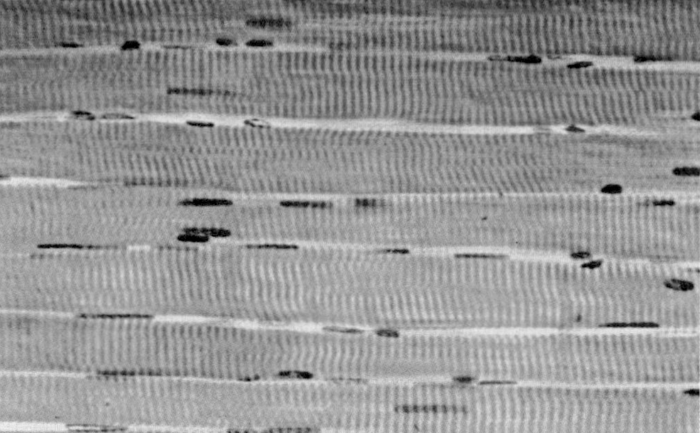

Muscle Tissue (magnification: 150×)

▲ **Figure 35–3** The four major types of tissues in the human body are epithelial tissue, connective tissue, nervous tissue, and muscle tissue. **Inferring** *What kind of tissue is bone?*

Cells A cell is the basic unit of structure and function in living things. Individual cells in multicellular organisms tend to be specialized. **Specialized cells** are uniquely suited to perform a particular function.

Tissues A group of cells that perform a single function is called a tissue. There are four basic types of tissue in the human body—epithelial, connective, nervous, and muscle. **Figure 35–3** shows examples of these tissues. **Epithelial tissue** includes glands and tissues that cover interior and exterior body surfaces. **Connective tissue** provides support for the body and connects its parts. **Nervous tissue** transmits nerve impulses throughout the body. And **muscle tissue,** along with bones, enables the body to move.

Organs A group of different types of tissues that work together to perform a single function is called an organ. The eye is an organ made up of epithelial tissue, nervous tissue, muscle tissue, and connective tissue. As different as these tissues are, they all work together for a single function—sight.

Organ Systems An organ system is a group of organs that perform closely related functions. For example, the brain is one of the organs of the nervous system, which gathers information about the outside world and coordinates the body's response.

What is the role of nervous tissue?

Maintaining Homeostasis

You can get a glimpse of the interrelationship of your body systems when you breathe deeply after climbing a steep hill or when your blood clots to seal a cut. Behind the scenes, your organ systems are working constantly to do something that few people appreciate—maintain a controlled, stable environment. This process is called **homeostasis,** which means "keeping things in balance." **Homeostasis is the process by which organisms keep internal conditions relatively constant despite changes in external environments.**

A Nonliving Example One way to understand homeostasis is to look at a nonliving system that also keeps environmental conditions within a certain range. The heating system of a house is a perfect example. In most houses, heat is supplied by a furnace that burns oil or natural gas. When the temperature within the house drops below a set point, a sensor in a device called a thermostat switches the furnace on. Heat produced by the furnace warms the house. When the temperature rises above the set point, the thermostat switches the furnace off. Because the furnace runs only when it is needed, the temperature of the house is kept within a narrow range.

A heating system like the one described is said to be controlled by feedback inhibition. **Feedback inhibition,** or negative feedback, is the process in which a stimulus produces a response that opposes the original stimulus. **Figure 35–4** summarizes the feedback inhibition process in a home heating system. When the furnace is switched on, it produces a product (heat) that changes the environment of the house (by raising the air temperature). This environmental change then "feeds back" to "inhibit" the operation of the furnace. In other words, heat from the furnace eventually raises the temperature enough to send a feedback signal to switch the furnace off. Systems controlled by feedback inhibition are generally fully automated and very stable. That is why a house with a good heating system is a comfortable place to be, even on the coldest of days.

Figure 35–4 Homeostasis is the process by which organisms keep internal conditions relatively constant despite changes in external environments. A home heating system uses a feedback mechanism to maintain a stable, comfortable environment within a house.

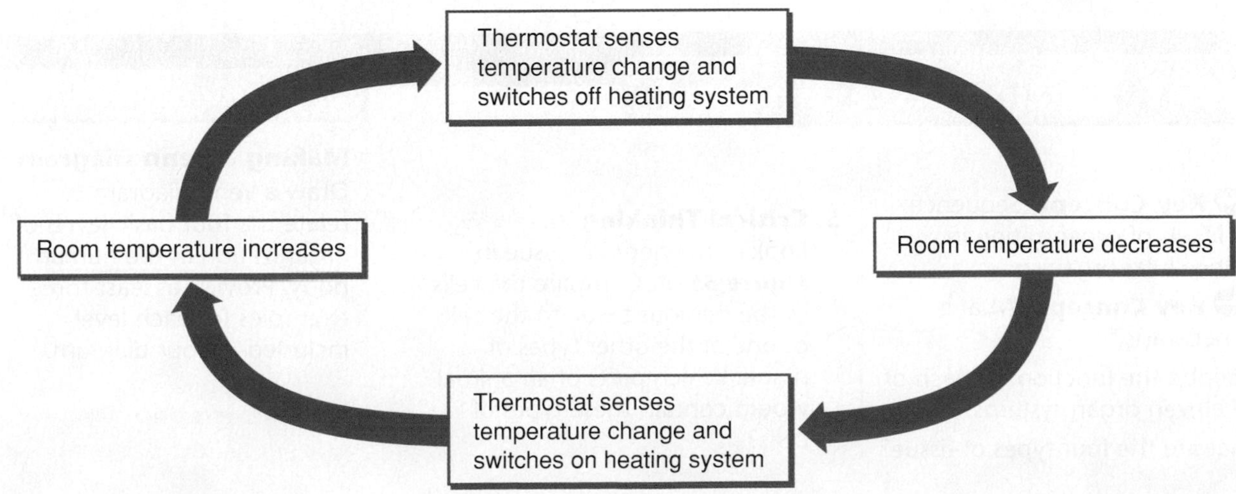
Thermostat senses temperature change and switches off heating system
Room temperature decreases
Thermostat senses temperature change and switches on heating system
Room temperature increases

For: Articles on the human body
Visit: PHSchool.com
Web Code: cbe-0351

In the Body Could biological systems achieve homeostasis through feedback inhibition? Absolutely. All that is needed is a system that regulates some aspect of the cellular environment and that can respond to feedback from its own activities by switching on or off as needed.

Maintenance of homeostasis requires the integration of all organ systems at all times. One example is the maintenance of a stable body temperature. The body regulates temperature by a mechanism that is remarkably similar to that of a home heating system. A part of the brain called the hypothalamus contains nerve cells that monitor both the temperature of the skin at the surface of the body and the temperature of organs in the body's core. The temperature of the core is generally higher than the temperature of the skin.

If the nerve cells sense that the core temperature has dropped much below 37°C, the hypothalamus produces chemicals that signal cells throughout the body to speed up their activities. Heat produced by this increase in cellular activity causes a gradual rise in body temperature, which is detected by nerve cells in the hypothalamus. This feedback inhibits the production of the chemicals that speed up cellular activity and keeps body temperature from rising to a dangerous level.

Have you ever been so cold that you began to shiver? If your body temperature drops well below its normal range, the hypothalamus releases chemicals that signal muscles just below the surface of the skin to contract involuntarily—to "shiver." These muscle contractions release heat, which helps the body temperature to rise back toward the normal range.

If body temperature rises too far above 37°C, the hypothalamus slows down cellular activities, minimizing the production of heat. This is one of the main reasons you may feel tired and sluggish on a hot day. The body also responds to high temperatures by producing sweat, which helps to cool the body surface by evaporation. Because heat from the body's core is carried by the blood to the skin, evaporation at the body surface also helps to lower the temperature of the core. When this temperature returns to its set point, the body stops producing sweat.

Word Origins

Thermometer comes from the Greek words *therme,* meaning "heat," and *metron,* meaning "measure." So, thermometer means an instrument used to measure heat. **If *hypo-* is Greek for "under," what does *hypothermia* mean?**

35–1 Section Assessment

1. **Key Concept** Sequence the levels of organization in multicellular organisms.
2. **Key Concept** What is homeostasis?
3. Describe the functions of each of the eleven organ systems.
4. What are the four types of tissue?
5. **Critical Thinking Inferring** Look at the nervous tissue in **Figure 35–3.** Compare the cells of the nervous tissue to the cells of one of the other types of tissue. Which parts of an animal would contain these types of cells?

Thinking Visually

Making a Venn Diagram
Draw a Venn diagram to relate the four basic levels of organization in the human body. Provide at least three examples for each level included in your diagram.

35–2 The Nervous System

4-1.2 Humans have complex systems
4-1.2 Cell parts, like system parts, work together
4-5.3 Dynamic equilibrium

Guide for Reading

 **Key Concepts**

- What are the functions of the nervous system?
- How is a nerve impulse transmitted?

Vocabulary
neuron
cell body
dendrite
axon
myelin sheath
resting potential
action potential
threshold
synapse
neurotransmitter

Reading Strategy: Summarizing As you read, find the main ideas for each paragraph. Write down a few key words from each main idea. Then, use the key words in your summary.

Play any team sport—basketball, softball, soccer—and you will discover that communication is one of the keys to success. Coaches call plays, players signal to one another, and the very best teams communicate in a way that enables them to play as a single unit. Communication can make the difference between winning and losing.

The same is true for living organisms. Nearly all multicellular organisms have communication systems. Specialized cells carry messages from one cell to another so that communication among all body parts is smooth and efficient. In humans, these cells include those of the nervous system. **The nervous system controls and coordinates functions throughout the body and responds to internal and external stimuli.**

Neurons

The messages carried by the nervous system are electrical signals called impulses. The cells that transmit these impulses are called **neurons.** Neurons can be classified into three types according to the direction in which an impulse travels. Sensory neurons carry impulses from the sense organs to the spinal cord and brain. Motor neurons carry impulses from the brain and the spinal cord to muscles and glands. Interneurons connect sensory and motor neurons and carry impulses between them.

Although neurons come in all shapes and sizes, they have certain features in common. **Figure 35–5** shows a typical neuron. The largest part of a typical neuron is the **cell body.** The cell body contains the nucleus and much of the cytoplasm. Most of the metabolic activity of the cell takes place in the cell body.

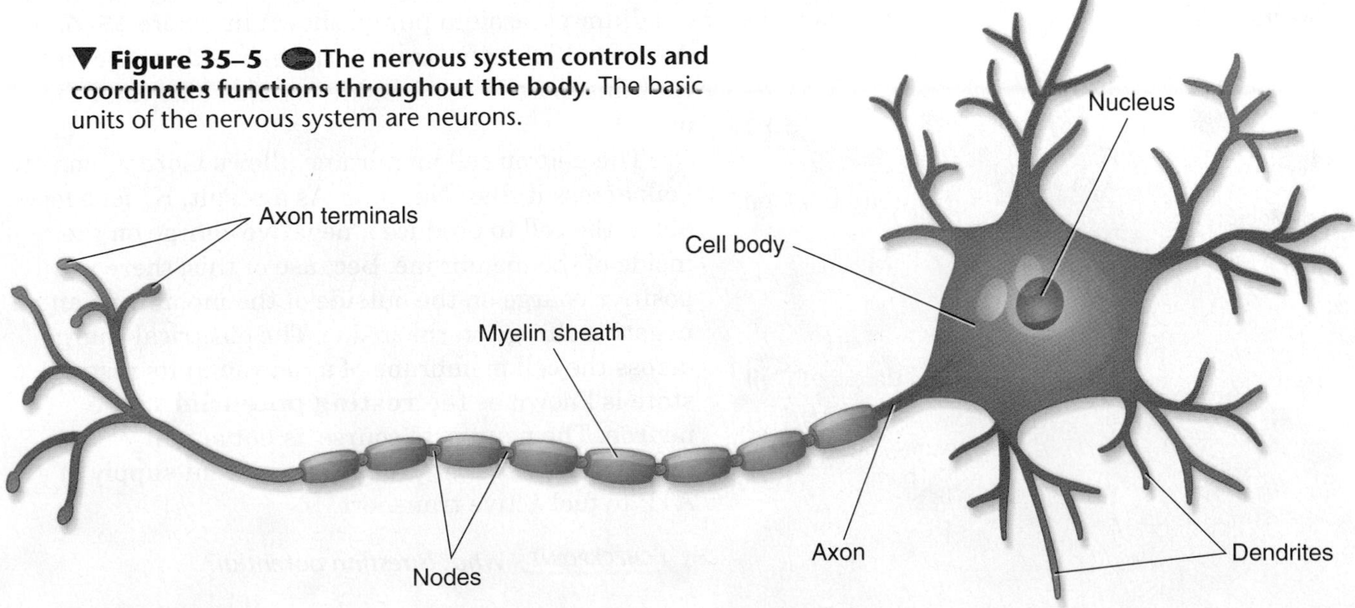

▼ **Figure 35–5** **The nervous system controls and coordinates functions throughout the body.** The basic units of the nervous system are neurons.

Spreading out from the cell body are short, branched extensions called **dendrites.** Dendrites carry impulses from the environment or from other neurons toward the cell body. The long fiber that carries impulses away from the cell body is called the **axon.** The axon ends in a series of small swellings called axon terminals, located some distance from the cell body. Neurons may have dozens of dendrites but usually have only one axon. In most animals, axons and dendrites are clustered into bundles of fibers called nerves. Some nerves contain only a few neurons, but many others have hundreds or even thousands of neurons.

In some neurons, the axon is surrounded by an insulating membrane known as the **myelin** (MY-uh-lin) **sheath.** The myelin sheath that surrounds a single long axon leaves many gaps, called nodes, where the axon membrane is exposed. As an impulse moves along the axon, it jumps from one node to the next, which increases the speed at which the impulse can travel.

The Nerve Impulse

A nerve impulse is similar to the flow of electrical current through a metal wire. The best way to understand a nerve impulse is to first look at a neuron at rest.

The Resting Neuron When a neuron is resting (not transmitting an impulse), the outside of the cell has a net positive charge, and the inside of the cell has a net negative charge. The cell membrane is said to be electrically charged because there is a difference in electrical charge between its outer and inner surfaces. Where does this difference come from? Some of the differences come from the selective permeability of the membrane. Most of the differences, however, are the result of active transport of ions across the cell membrane.

The nerve cell membrane pumps Na^+ ions out of the cell and K^+ ions into the cell by means of active transport. The active transport mechanism that performs this pumping action is called the sodium-potassium pump, shown in **Figure 35–6.** As a result of active transport, the inside of the cell contains more K^+ ions and fewer Na^+ ions than the outside.

▼ **Figure 35–6** The sodium-potassium pump in the neuron cell membrane uses the energy of ATP to pump Na^+ out of the cell and, at the same time, to pump K^+ in. This ongoing process maintains resting potential. **Applying Concepts** ***Is this process an example of diffusion or active transport?***

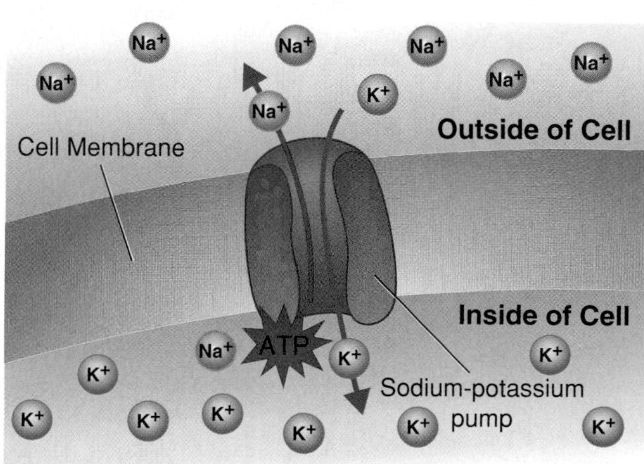

The neuron cell membrane allows more K^+ ions to leak across it than Na^+ ions. As a result, K^+ ions leak out of the cell to produce a negative charge on the inside of the membrane. Because of this, there is a positive charge on the outside of the membrane and a negative charge on the inside. The electrical charge across the cell membrane of a neuron in its resting state is known as the **resting potential** of the neuron. The neuron, of course, is not actually "resting," because it must produce a constant supply of ATP to fuel active transport.

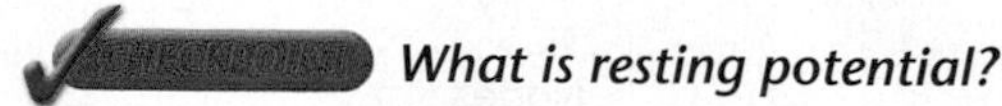 ***What is resting potential?***

The Moving Impulse A neuron remains in its resting state until it receives a stimulus large enough to start a nerve impulse. The impulse causes a movement of ions across the cell membrane. **An impulse begins when a neuron is stimulated by another neuron or by the environment.** Once it begins, the impulse travels rapidly down the axon away from the cell body and toward the axon terminals. As **Figure 35–7** shows, an impulse is a sudden reversal of the membrane potential. What causes the reversal?

The cell membrane of a neuron contains thousands of protein channels that may allow ions to pass through, depending on the state of "gates" within the channels. Generally, the gates within these channels are closed. At the leading edge of an impulse, however, gates within the sodium channels open, allowing positively charged Na^+ ions to flow inside the cell membrane. The inside of the membrane temporarily becomes more positive than the outside, reversing the resting potential. This reversal of charges, from negative to positive, is called a nerve impulse, or an **action potential.**

As the impulse passes, gates within the potassium channels open, allowing K^+ ions to flow out. This restores the resting potential so that the neuron is once again negatively charged on the inside of the cell membrane and positively charged on the outside.

A nerve impulse is self-propagating; that is, an impulse at any point on the membrane causes an impulse at the next point along the membrane. We might compare the flow of an impulse to the fall of a row of dominoes. As each domino falls, it causes the next domino to fall.

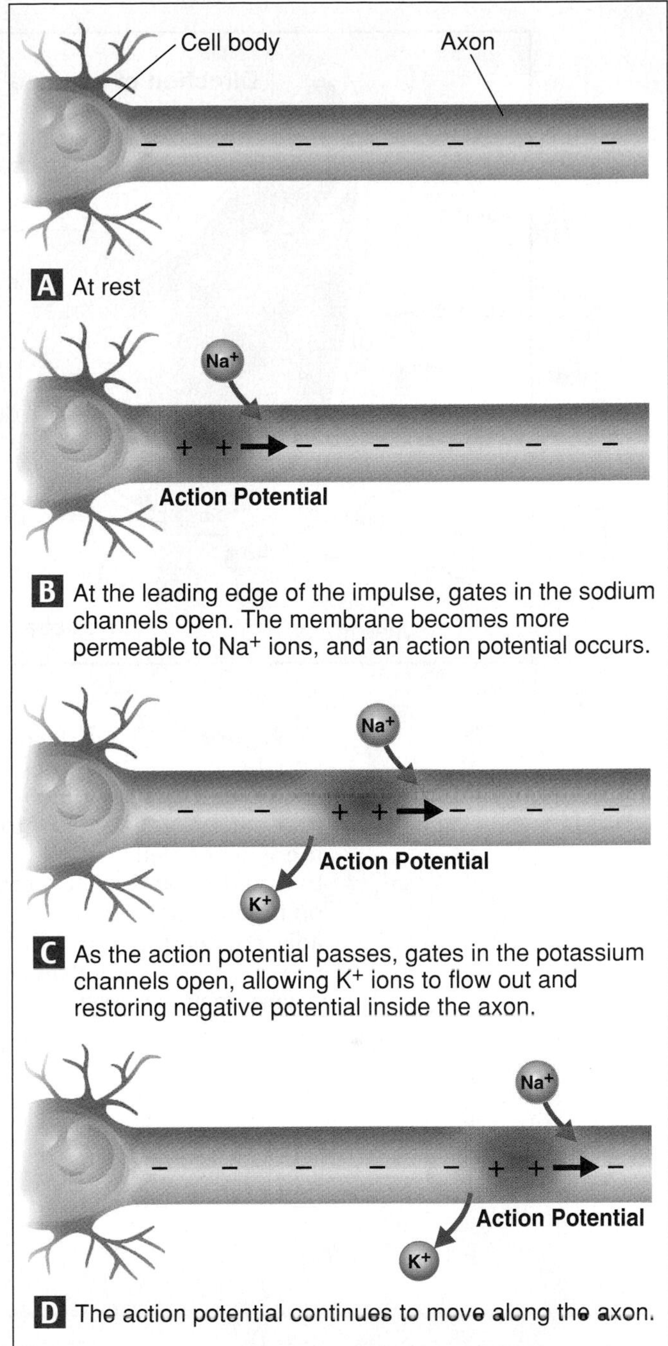

Cell body
Axon
A At rest
Na+
Action Potential
B At the leading edge of the impulse, gates in the sodium channels open. The membrane becomes more permeable to Na+ ions, and an action potential occurs.
Na+
Action Potential
K+
C As the action potential passes, gates in the potassium channels open, allowing K+ ions to flow out and restoring negative potential inside the axon.
Na+
Action Potential
K+
D The action potential continues to move along the axon.

▲ **Figure 35–7** **An impulse begins when a neuron is stimulated by another neuron.** At the leading edge of an action potential, gates in the sodium channels open, allowing Na^+ ions to flow into the cell. This flow of ions causes the action potential to move. At the trailing edge of an action potential, gates in the potassium channels open, allowing positive ions to flow out and restoring the resting potential of the neuron.

Threshold The strength of an impulse is always the same—either there is an impulse in response to a stimulus or there is not. In other words, a stimulus must be of adequate strength to cause a neuron to transmit an impulse. The minimum level of a stimulus that is required to activate a neuron is called the **threshold.** Any stimulus that is stronger than the threshold will produce an impulse. Any stimulus that is weaker than the threshold will produce no impulse. Thus, a nerve impulse follows the all-or-none principle: either the stimulus will produce an impulse, or it will not produce an impulse.

The all-or-none principle can be illustrated by using a row of dominoes. If you were to gently press the first domino in a row, it might not move at all. A slightly harder push might make the domino teeter back and forth but not fall. A slightly stronger push would cause the first domino to fall into the second. You have reached the threshold at which the row of dominoes would fall.

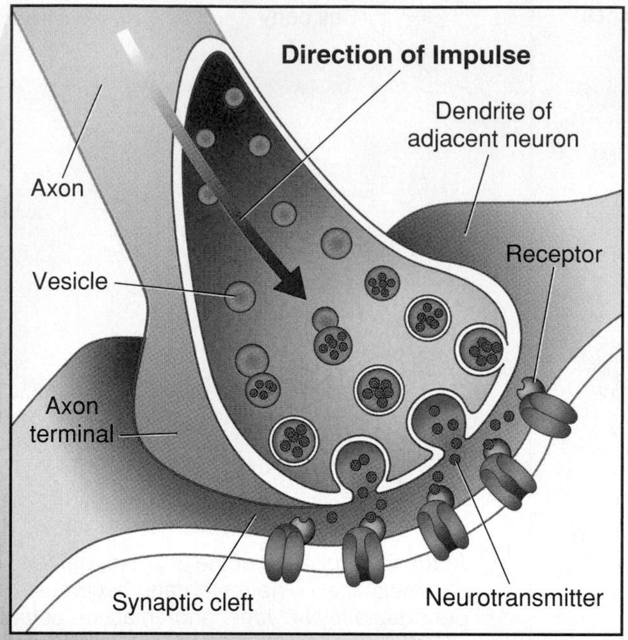

▲ **Figure 35–8** When an impulse reaches the end of the axon of one neuron, neurotransmitters are released into the synaptic cleft. The neurotransmitters bind to receptors on the membrane of an adjacent dendrite. **Applying Concepts** *Is the adjacent cell always another neuron?*

The Synapse

At the end of the neuron, the impulse reaches an axon terminal. Usually the neuron makes contact with another cell at this location. The neuron may pass the impulse along to the second cell. Motor neurons, for example, pass their impulses to muscle cells.

The location at which a neuron can transfer an impulse to another cell is called a **synapse** (SIN-aps). As shown in **Figure 35–8,** a space, called the synaptic cleft, separates the axon terminal from the dendrites of the adjacent cell, in this case a neuron. The terminals contain tiny sacs, or vesicles, filled with neurotransmitters (noo-roh-TRANZ-mit-urs). **Neurotransmitters** are chemicals used by a neuron to transmit an impulse across a synapse to another cell.

When an impulse arrives at an axon terminal, the vesicles release the neurotransmitters into the synaptic cleft. The neurotransmitter molecules diffuse across the synaptic cleft and attach themselves to receptors on the membrane of the neighboring cell. This stimulus causes positive sodium ions to rush across the cell membrane, stimulating the second cell. If the stimulation exceeds the cell's threshold, a new impulse begins.

Only a fraction of a second after binding to their receptors, the neurotransmitter molecules are released from the cell surface. They may then be broken down by enzymes, or taken up and recycled by the axon terminal.

35–2 Section Assessment

1. **Key Concept** Describe the functions of the nervous system.
2. **Key Concept** What happens when a neuron is stimulated by another neuron?
3. Name and describe the three types of neurons.
4. Describe the role of the myelin sheath.
5. **Critical Thinking Applying Concepts** How can the level of pain you feel vary if a stimulus causes an all-or-none response?

Thinking Visually

Creating a Flowchart
Create a flowchart to show the events that occur as a nerve impulse travels from one neuron to the next. Include as much detail as you can. Use your flowchart to explain the process to a classmate.

35–3 Divisions of the Nervous System

4-1.2 Humans have complex systems
4-1.2e Nerve signals affect organisms
LS- Follow safety rules, measure length, make observations
LS- Analyze results and formulate a conclusion

Guide for Reading

Key Concepts
- What are the functions of the central nervous system?
- What are the functions of the two divisions of the peripheral nervous system?

Vocabulary
meninges • cerebrospinal fluid
cerebrum • cerebellum
brain stem • thalamus
hypothalamus • reflex
reflex arc

Reading Strategy: Asking Questions Before you read, rewrite the headings in the section as *how, why,* or *what* questions about the nervous system. As you read, write down the answers to your questions.

Neurons do not act alone. Instead, they are joined together to form a complex network—the nervous system. The human nervous system is separated into two major divisions: the central nervous system and the peripheral nervous system.

The central nervous system is the control center of the body. The functions of the central nervous system are similar to those of the central processing unit of a computer.  **The central nervous system relays messages, processes information, and analyzes information.** The peripheral nervous system receives information from the environment and relays commands from the central nervous system to organs and glands.

The Central Nervous System

The central nervous system consists of the brain, shown in **Figure 35–9,** and the spinal cord. The skull and vertebrae in the spinal column protect the brain and spinal cord. Both the brain and spinal cord are wrapped in three layers of connective tissue known as **meninges** (muh-NIN-jeez). Between the meninges and the central nervous system tissue is a space filled with cerebrospinal (sehr-uh-broh-SPY-nul) fluid. **Cerebrospinal fluid** bathes the brain and spinal cord and acts as a shock absorber that protects the central nervous system. The fluid also allows for the exchange of nutrients and waste products between blood and nervous tissue.

▼ **Figure 35–9** **The brain helps to relay messages, process information, and analyze information.** The brain consists of the cerebrum, cerebellum, and brain stem.

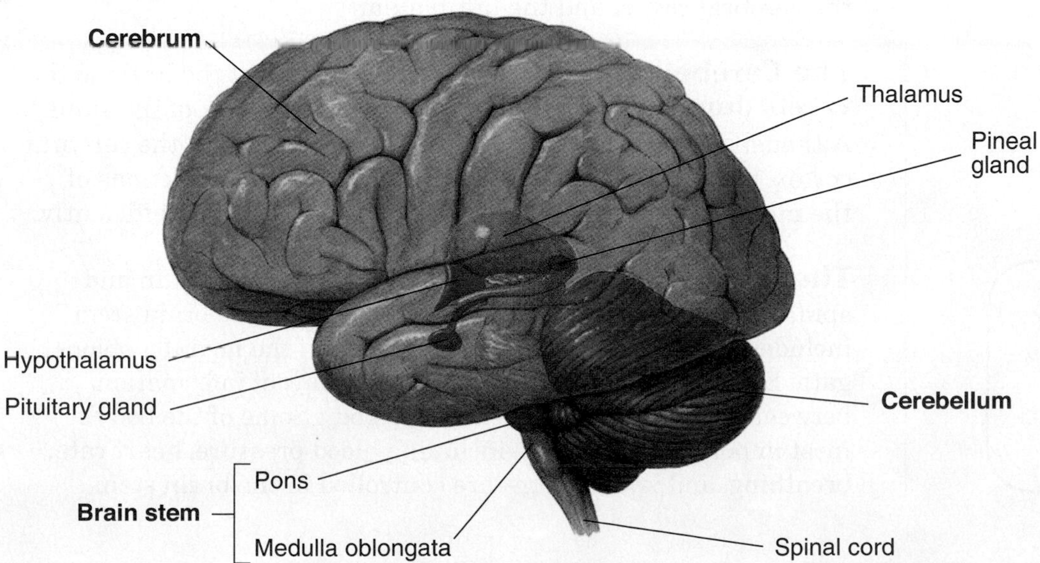

The Brain

The brain is the place to which impulses flow and from which impulses originate. The brain contains approximately 100 billion neurons, many of which are interneurons. The brain has a mass of about 1.4 kilograms.

The Cerebrum The largest and most prominent region of the human brain is the **cerebrum.** The cerebrum is responsible for the voluntary, or conscious, activities of the body. It is the site of intelligence, learning, and judgment. A deep groove divides the cerebrum into right and left hemispheres. The hemispheres are connected by a band of tissue called the corpus callosum.

Folds and grooves on the surface of each hemisphere greatly increase the surface area of the cerebrum. Each hemisphere of the cerebrum is divided into regions called lobes. The lobes are named for the skull bones that cover them. The locations of four lobes of the brain are shown in **Figure 35–10.**

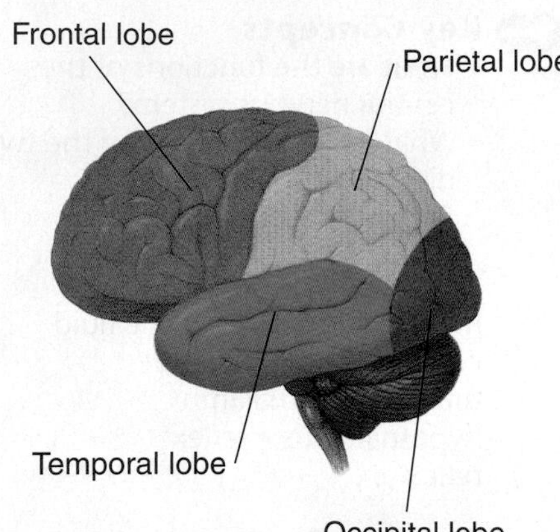

▲ **Figure 35–10** This view of the cerebrum shows the four different lobes of the brain. Different functions of the body are controlled by different lobes of the brain. **Drawing Conclusions** *The frontal lobe controls voluntary muscle movements. What might happen if this part of the brain became injured?*

Remarkably, each half of the cerebrum deals mainly with the opposite side of the body. Sensations from the left side of the body go to the right hemisphere of the cerebrum, and those from the right side of the body go to the left hemisphere. Commands to move muscles are generated in the same way. The left hemisphere controls the body's right side, and the right hemisphere controls the body's left side. Some studies have suggested that the right hemisphere may be associated with creativity and artistic ability, whereas the left hemisphere may be associated with analytical and mathematical ability.

The cerebrum consists of two layers. The outer layer of the cerebrum is called the cerebral cortex and consists of gray matter. Gray matter consists mainly of densely packed nerve cell bodies. The cerebral cortex processes information from the sense organs and controls body movements. The inner layer of the cerebrum consists of white matter, which is made up of bundles of axons with myelin sheaths. The myelin sheaths give the white matter its characteristic color. White matter connects the cerebral cortex and the brain stem.

The Cerebellum The second largest region of the brain is the **cerebellum.** The cerebellum is located at the back of the skull. Although the commands to move muscles come from the cerebral cortex, the cerebellum coordinates and balances the actions of the muscles so that the body can move gracefully and efficiently.

The Brain Stem The **brain stem** connects the brain and spinal cord. Located just below the cerebellum, the brain stem includes two regions known as the pons and the medulla oblongata. Each of these regions regulates the flow of information between the brain and the rest of the body. Some of the body's most important functions—including blood pressure, heart rate, breathing, and swallowing—are controlled in the brain stem.

The Thalamus and Hypothalamus The thalamus and hypothalamus are found between the brain stem and the cerebrum. The **thalamus** receives messages from all of the sensory receptors throughout the body and then relays the information to the proper region of the cerebrum for further processing. Just below the thalamus is the hypothalamus. The **hypothalamus** is the control center for recognition and analysis of hunger, thirst, fatigue, anger, and body temperature. The hypothalamus also controls the coordination of the nervous and endocrine systems. You will learn more about the endocrine system in a later chapter.

The Spinal Cord

Like a major telephone line that carries thousands of calls at once, the spinal cord is the main communications link between the brain and the rest of the body. Thirty-one pairs of spinal nerves branch out from the spinal cord, connecting the brain to all of the different parts of the body. Certain kinds of information, including some kinds of reflexes, are processed directly in the spinal cord.

A **reflex** is a quick, automatic response to a stimulus. Sneezing and blinking are two examples of reflexes. A reflex allows your body to respond to danger immediately, without spending time thinking about a response. Animals rely heavily on reflex behaviors for survival.

What is a reflex?

The Peripheral Nervous System

The peripheral nervous system lies outside of the central nervous system. It consists of all of the nerves and associated cells that are not part of the brain and the spinal cord. Included here are cranial nerves that pass through openings in the skull and stimulate regions of the head and neck, spinal nerves, and ganglia. Ganglia are collections of nerve cell bodies.

The peripheral nervous system can be divided into the sensory division and the motor division. **The sensory division of the peripheral nervous system transmits impulses from sense organs to the central nervous system. The motor division transmits impulses from the central nervous system to the muscles or glands.** The motor division is further divided into the somatic nervous system and the autonomic nervous system.

The Somatic Nervous System The somatic nervous system regulates activities that are under conscious control, such as the movement of the skeletal muscles. Every time you lift your finger or wiggle your toes, you are using the motor neurons of the somatic nervous system. Some somatic nerves are also involved with reflexes and can act with or without conscious control.

Quick Lab

How do you respond to an external stimulus?

Materials sheet of scrap paper

Procedure 

1. Have your partner put on safety goggles.
2. Crumple up a sheet of scrap paper into a ball.
3. Watch your partner's eyes carefully as you toss the paper ball toward his or her face. Record your partner's reaction.
4. Repeat step 3, three more times.
5. Exchange roles and repeat steps 1, 3, and 4.

Analyze and Conclude

1. **Observing** What reaction did you observe when you tossed the ball at your partner's face?
2. **Observing** Was that reaction voluntary? What kind of reaction is this?
3. **Comparing and Contrasting** Did you see any change in behavior as you repeated step 3? If so, how would you describe this change?
4. **Inferring** What is the function of the blink reflex?

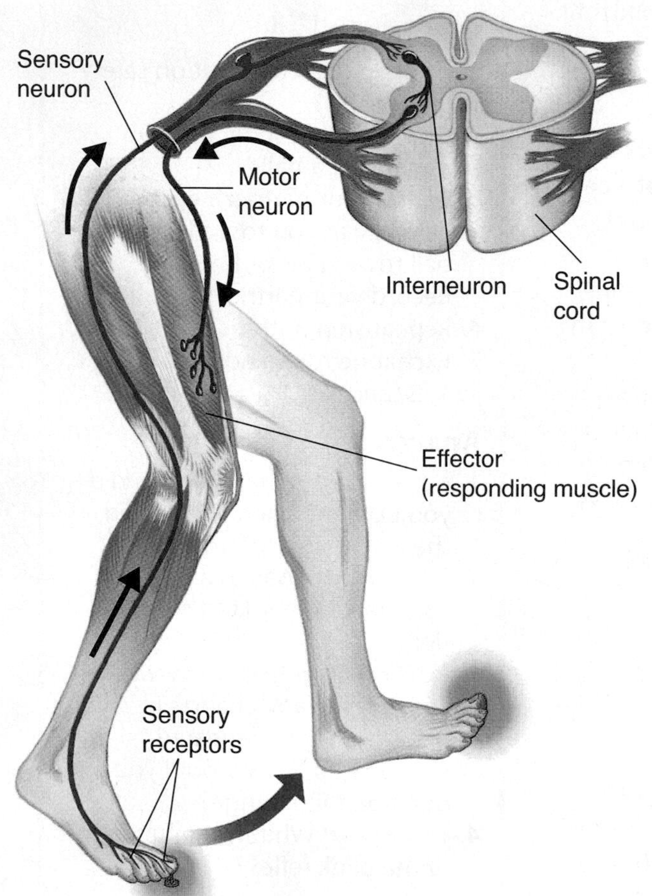

▲ **Figure 35–11** **The peripheral nervous system transmits impulses from sense organs to the central nervous system and back to muscles or glands.** When you step on a tack, sensory receptors stimulate a sensory neuron, which relays the signal to an interneuron within the spinal cord. The signal is then sent to a motor neuron, which in turn stimulates a muscle in your leg to lift your leg.

If you accidentally step on a tack with your bare foot, your leg may recoil before you are aware of the pain. This rapid response (a reflex) is possible because receptors in your skin stimulate sensory neurons, which carry the impulse to your spinal cord. Even before the information is relayed to your brain, a group of neurons in your spinal cord automatically activates the appropriate motor neurons. These motor neurons cause the muscles in your leg to contract, pulling your foot away from the tack.

The pathway that an impulse travels from your foot back to your leg is known as a reflex arc. As shown in **Figure 35–11**, a **reflex arc** includes a sensory receptor (in this case, a receptor in your toe), sensory neuron, motor neuron, and effector (leg muscle). Some reflex arcs include interneurons. In other reflex arcs, a sensory neuron communicates directly with a motor neuron.

The Autonomic Nervous System The autonomic nervous system regulates activities that are automatic, or involuntary. The nerves of the autonomic nervous system control functions of the body that are not under conscious control. The influence exerted on other body systems by the autonomic nervous system is a good example of an interrelationship that is needed between systems for the body's well-being. For instance, when you are running, the autonomic nervous system speeds up your heart rate and the blood flow to the skeletal muscles, stimulates the sweat glands and adrenal glands, and slows down the contractions of the smooth muscles in the digestive system.

The autonomic nervous system is further subdivided into two parts—the sympathetic nervous system and the parasympathetic nervous system. Most organs controlled by the autonomic nervous system are under the control of both sympathetic and parasympathetic neurons.

The sympathetic and parasympathetic nervous systems have opposite effects on the same organ system. The opposing effects of the two systems help the body maintain homeostasis. For example, heart rate is increased by the sympathetic nervous system but decreased by the parasympathetic nervous system. The process of regulating heart rate can be compared to the process of controlling the speed of a car. One system is like the gas pedal and the other is like the brake. Because there are two different sets of neurons, the autonomic nervous system can quickly speed up the activities of major organs in response to a stimulus or slam on the brakes if necessary.

Quick Lab

How do reflexes occur?

Materials string, scissors, 3 plastic mousetraps, packing tape, 30-cm ruler

Procedure  

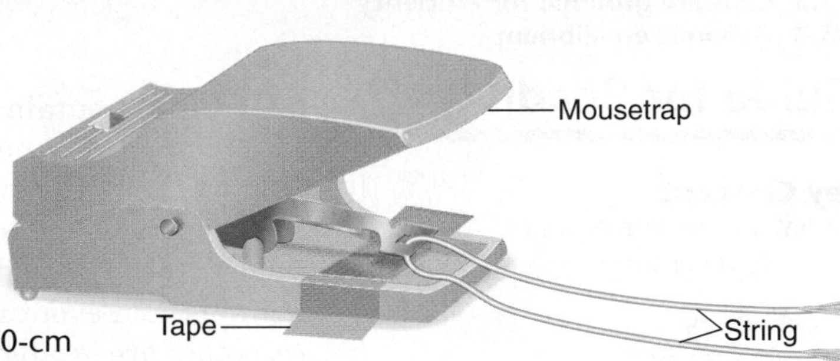

1. **Using Models** To model a synapse, cut a 30-cm piece of string. **CAUTION:** *Handle scissors carefully.*
2. Hold a mousetrap open. Pull the string through the bait platform as shown. **CAUTION:** *Do not let the mousetrap snap on your fingers.* Slide a piece of tape under the bait platform and tape the trap to the table as shown. Label the trap "sensory neuron."
3. Hold one end of the string in each hand. Gently pull one end without setting off the trap. Now gradually pull harder.
4. To model a reflex arc, cut two more 30-cm pieces of string. Tie one end of each piece of string to the bait platform of a separate trap.
5. Tape the 2 new traps to the table, 20 cm from the first trap. Label one new trap "motor neuron," and the other "brain."
6. Reset the first trap, and then set the new ones. Tape both ends of the strings attached to the new traps to the top of the first trap. Leave these strings slightly slack.
7. Pull the strings attached to the bait platform of the "sensory neuron."

Analyze and Conclude

1. **Drawing Conclusions** What was required for the trap to close in step 3? How does this behavior compare to the transmission of a nerve impulse?
2. **Applying Concepts** Does a stronger stimulus produce a stronger nerve impulse? Explain your answer.
3. **Evaluating** Do you consider this procedure an adequate model of a reflex arc? Explain your response by citing specific details. If not, propose an alternative model.
4. **SAFETY** Explain how you demonstrated safe practices as you carried out this investigation.

35–3 Section Assessment

1. **Key Concept** Discuss the overall function of the central nervous system.
2. **Key Concept** Describe the functions of the two divisions of the peripheral nervous system.
3. How is the central nervous system protected from injury?
4. What is the role of the hypothalamus?
5. Is a reflex part of the central nervous system, the peripheral nervous system, or both? Explain.
6. **Critical Thinking Inferring** Would you expect the cerebrum of a bird to be more or less developed relative to its size than the cerebrum of a human? Explain. (*Hint:* You may want to review Section 33–3.)

Connecting Concepts

Animal Behavior
Using Section 34–1, decide which parts of the nervous system are most likely to be involved with innate, or inborn, behaviors. Which parts are likely to be involved with learned behaviors? Explain your reasoning.

35–4 The Senses

4-1.2 Humans have complex systems
4-1.2 Cells are grouped for efficiency
4-5.3 Dynamic equilibrium

Guide for Reading

Key Concept
- What are the five types of sensory receptors?

Vocabulary
sensory receptor
pupil
lens
retina
rod
cone
cochlea
semicircular canal
taste bud

Reading Strategy: Outlining Before you read, use the headings of the section to make an outline about the five sense organs. As you read, fill in the subtopics and smaller topics. Then, add phrases or a sentence after each to provide key information.

The body contains millions of neurons that react directly to stimuli from the environment, including light, sound, motion, chemicals, pressure, and changes in temperature. These neurons, known as **sensory receptors,** react to a specific stimulus such as light or sound by sending impulses to other neurons, and eventually to the central nervous system. Sensory receptors are located throughout the body but are concentrated in the sense organs. These sense organs include the eyes, the inner ears, the nose, the mouth, and the skin. Sensory receptors within each organ enable it to respond to a particular stimulus.

There are five general categories of sensory receptors: pain receptors, thermoreceptors, mechanoreceptors, chemoreceptors, and photoreceptors. Pain receptors are located throughout the body except in the brain. Pain receptors respond to chemicals released by damaged cells. Pain is important to recognize because it usually indicates danger, injury, or disease. Thermoreceptors are located in the skin, body core, and hypothalamus. Thermoreceptors detect variations in temperature. Mechanoreceptors are found in the skin, skeletal muscles, and inner ears. They are sensitive to touch, pressure, stretching of muscles, sound, and motion. Chemoreceptors, located in the nose and taste buds, are sensitive to chemicals in the external environment. Photoreceptors, found in the eyes, are sensitive to light. **Figure 35–12** shows how photoreceptor cells appear under a scanning electron microscope.

Vision

The world around us is bathed in light. The sense organs that we use to sense light are the eyes. The structures of the eye are shown in **Figure 35–13.** Light enters the eye through the cornea, a tough transparent layer of cells. The cornea helps to focus the light, which then passes through a chamber filled with a fluid called aqueous (AY-kwee-uhs) humor. At the back of the chamber is a disklike structure called the iris. The iris is the colored part of the eye. In the middle of the iris is a small opening called the **pupil.** Tiny muscles in the iris adjust the size of the pupil to regulate the amount of light that enters the eye. In dim light, the pupil becomes larger so that more light can enter the eye. In bright light, the pupil becomes smaller so that less light enters the eye.

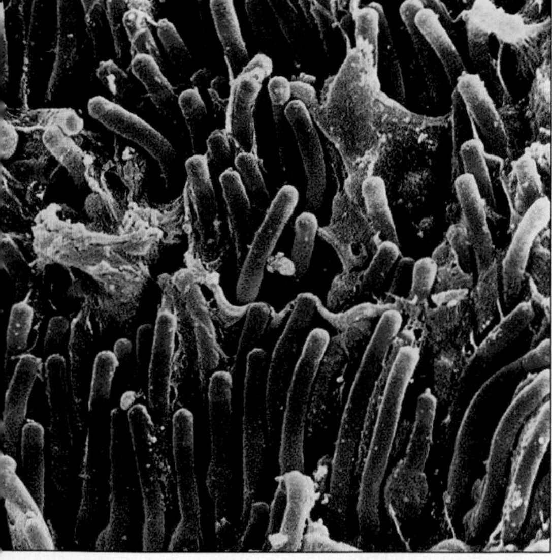

(magnification: 2000×)

◀ **Figure 35–12** **There are two types of light-sensitive photoreceptor cells in the retina—rods and cones.** This color-enhanced scanning electron micrograph shows the rod cells of an eye.

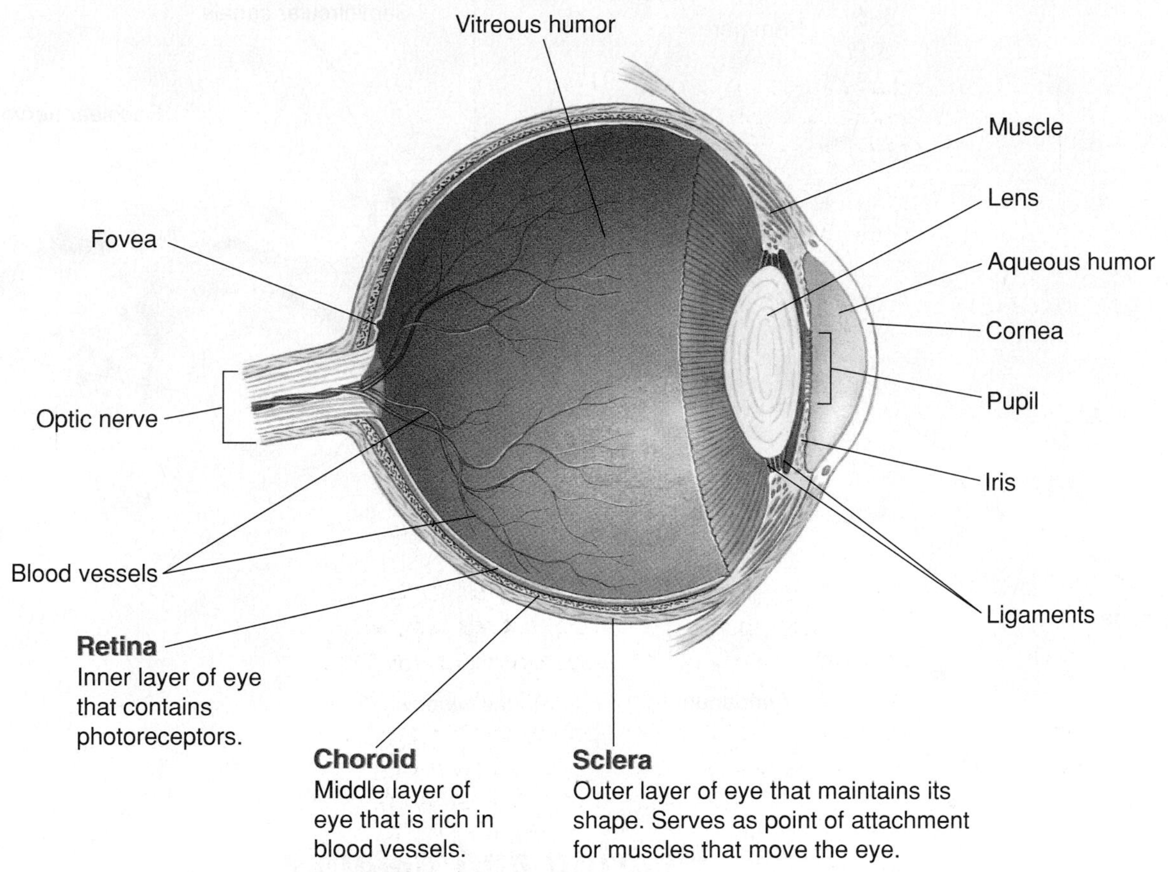

▲ **Figure 35–13** The eye is a complicated sense organ. The sclera, choroid, and retina are three layers of tissue that form the inner wall of the eyeball. **Interpreting Graphics** *What is the function of the sclera?*

Just behind the iris is the **lens.** Small muscles attached to the lens change its shape to help you adjust your eyes' focus to see near or distant objects. Behind the lens is a large chamber filled with a transparent, jellylike fluid called vitreous (VIH-tree-uhs) humor.

The lens focuses light onto the **retina.** Photoreceptors are arranged in a layer in the retina. The photoreceptors convert light energy into nerve impulses that are carried to the central nervous system. There are two types of photoreceptors: rods and cones. **Rods** are extremely sensitive to light, but they do not distinguish different colors. **Cones** are less sensitive than rods, but they do respond to light of different colors, producing color vision. Cones are concentrated in the fovea. The fovea is the site of sharpest vision. There are no photoreceptors where the optic nerve passes through the back of the eye. This place is called the blind spot.

The impulses assembled by this complicated layer of interconnected cells leave each eye by way of an optic nerve. The optic nerves then carry the impulses to the appropriate regions of the brain. The brain interprets them as visual images and provides information about the external world.

CHECKPOINT *Where are the photoreceptors located in the eye?*

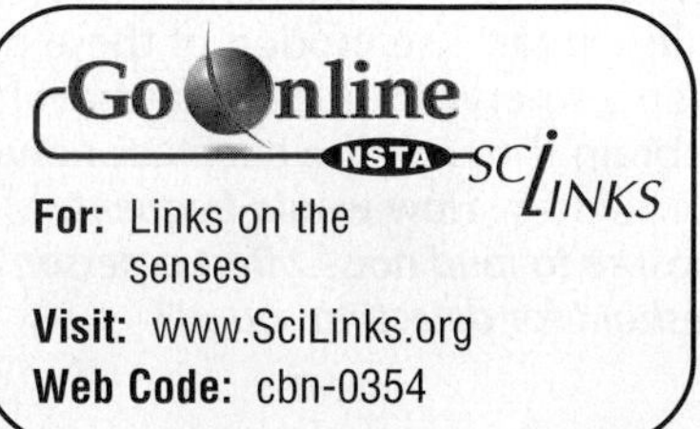

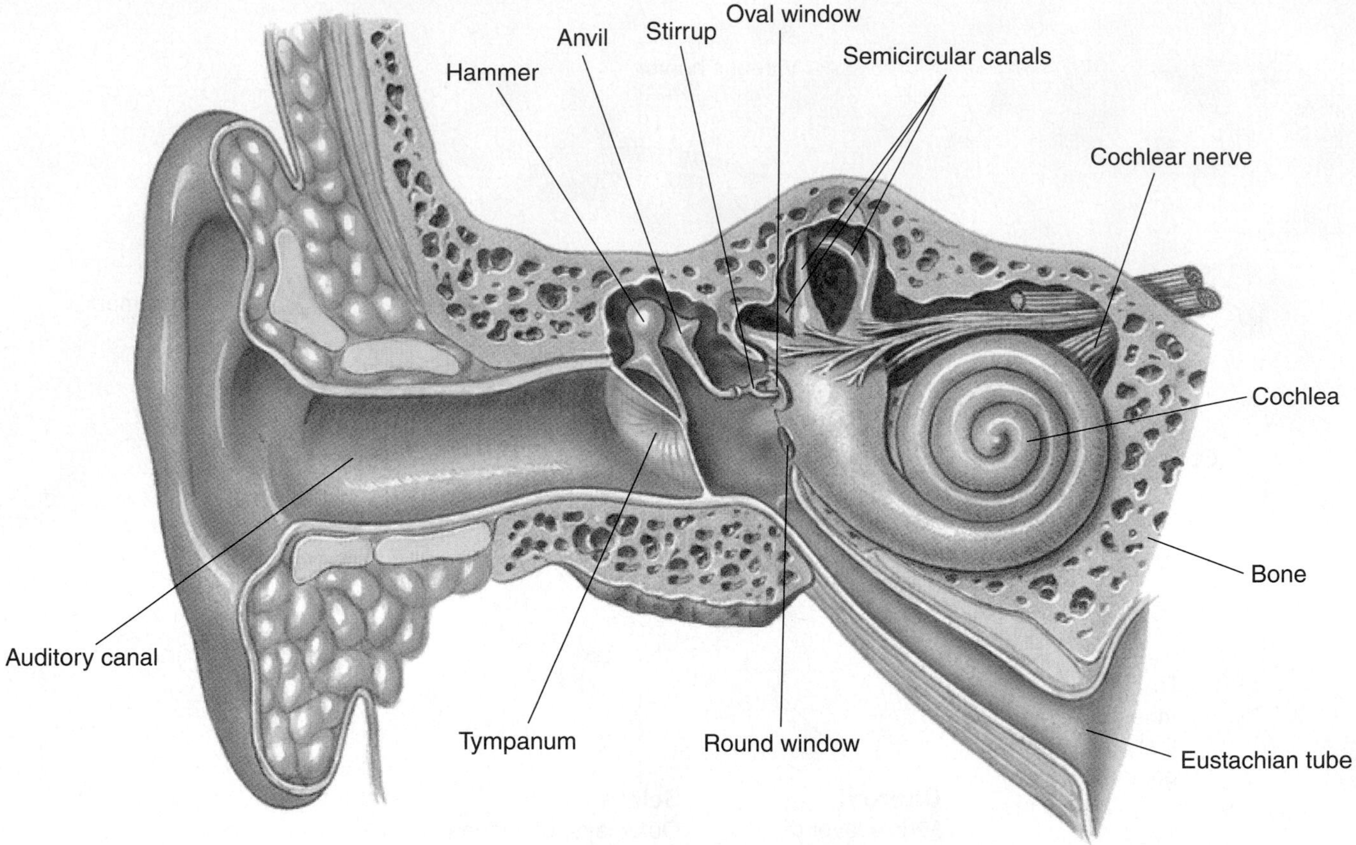

Oval window
Anvil
Stirrup
Semicircular canals
Hammer
Cochlear nerve
Cochlea
Bone
Auditory canal
Tympanum
Round window
Eustachian tube

Hearing and Balance

The human ear has two sensory functions. One of these functions is hearing. The other function is detecting positional changes associated with movement.

Hearing Sound is nothing more than vibrations in the air around us. The ears are the sensory organs that can distinguish both the pitch and loudness of those vibrations. The structure of the ear is shown in **Figure 35–14.**

Vibrations enter the ear through the auditory canal. The vibrations cause the tympanum (TIM-puh-num), or eardrum, to vibrate. These vibrations are picked up by three tiny bones, commonly called the hammer, anvil, and stirrup. The last of these bones, the stirrup, transmits the vibrations to the oval window. Vibrations of the oval window create pressure waves in the fluid-filled **cochlea** (KAHK-lee-uh) of the inner ear.

The cochlea is lined with tiny hair cells that are pushed back and forth by these pressure waves. In response to these movements, the hair cells produce nerve impulses that are sent to the brain through the cochlear nerve.

Balance Your ears contain structures that help your central nervous system maintain your balance, or equilibrium. Within the inner ear just above the cochlea are three tiny canals at right angles to one another. They are called **semicircular canals** because each forms a half circle. The semicircular canals and the two tiny sacs located behind them monitor the position of your body, especially your head, in relation to gravity.

(magnification: about 3500×)

Figure 35–14 The diagram (top) shows the structures in the ear that transmit sounds. The scanning electron micrograph shows hair cells (yellow) in the inner ear. The motion of these hairs produces nerve impulses that travel to the brain through the cochlear nerve. **Predicting** *How would frequent exposure to loud noise affect a person's threshold for detecting sound?*

The semicircular canals and the sacs are filled with fluid and lined with hair cells. As the head changes position, the fluid in the canals also changes position. This causes the hair on the hair cells to bend. This action, in turn, sends impulses to the brain that enable it to determine body motion and position.

Smell and Taste

You may never have thought of it this way, but your sense of smell is actually an ability to detect chemicals. Chemoreceptors in the lining of the nasal passageway respond to specific chemicals and send impulses to the brain through sensory nerves.

Your sense of smell is capable of producing thousands of different sensations. In fact, much of what we commonly call the "taste" of food and drink is actually smell. To prove this to yourself, eat a few bites of food while holding your nose. You'll discover that much of the taste of food disappears until you open your nose and breathe freely.

Like the sense of smell, the sense of taste is a chemical sense. The sense organs that detect taste are the **taste buds.** Most of the taste buds are on the tongue, but a few are found at other locations in the mouth. The surface of the tongue is shown in **Figure 35–15.** The tastes detected by the taste buds are classified as salty, bitter, sweet, and sour. Sensitivity to these different categories varies on different parts of the tongue.

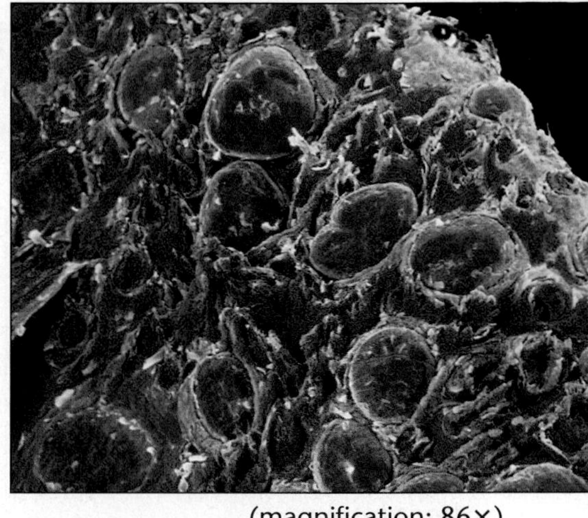

(magnification: 86×)

▲ **Figure 35–15** This color-enhanced scanning electron micrograph shows the surface of the tongue. The large pink objects are the taste buds. **Chemoreceptors found in the taste buds are sensitive to chemicals in food.**

Touch and Related Senses

The sense of touch, unlike the other senses you have just read about, is not found in one particular place. All of the regions of the skin are sensitive to touch. In this respect, your largest sense organ is your skin. Skin contains sensory receptors that respond to temperature, touch, and pain. Not all parts of the body are equally sensitive to touch, because not all parts have the same number of receptors. The greatest density of touch receptors is found on your fingers, toes, and face.

35–4 Section Assessment

1. **Key Concept** Name the five types of sensory receptors and list where they are found in the body.
2. Identify the functions of the cornea, pupil, lens, retina, and optic nerve.
3. What are the four basic tastes detected by the tongue?
4. Explain why you can't "taste" food when you have a bad cold.
5. **Critical Thinking Applying Concepts** If you spin around for a time, the fluid in your semicircular canals also moves. When you stop suddenly, you feel as though you are still moving. Why do you think you might feel dizzy?

Writing in Science

Creative Writing

Imagine that you have to do without your sense of taste for one day. How would this influence your food choices? In your journal, describe how the absence of this sense organ would affect your day.

35–5 Drugs and the Nervous System

4-1.2, 5.2 System disruptions affect homeostasis
4-4.1 Embryonic development of essential organs
1-S3.1, LS- Analyzing results and interpreting data

Guide for Reading

Key Concepts
- What are the different classes of drugs that directly affect the central nervous system?
- What is the effect of alcohol on the body?

Vocabulary
drug
stimulant
depressant
fetal alcohol syndrome
drug abuse
addiction

Reading Strategy: Using Graphic Organizers As you read, create a table that lists each of the drugs in this section and the effects that each drug has on the body.

By definition, a **drug** is any substance, other than food, that changes the structure or function of the body. Some drugs, such as cocaine and heroin, are so powerful and dangerous that their possession is illegal. Other drugs, including penicillin and codeine, are prescription drugs and can be used only under the supervision of a doctor. Still other drugs, including cough and cold medicines, are sold over the counter. All drugs, both legal and illegal, have the potential to do harm if they are used improperly or abused.

Drugs differ in the ways in which they affect the body. Some drugs kill bacteria and are useful in treating disease. Other drugs affect a particular system of the body, such as the digestive or circulatory systems. Among the most powerful drugs, however, are the ones that cause changes in the nervous system, especially to the brain and the synapses between neurons.

Drugs That Affect the Synapse

The nervous system performs its regulatory functions through the transmission of information along pathways from one part of the body to another. Synapses are key relay stations along the way. The nervous system depends on neurotransmitters to bridge the gap between neurons or between a neuron and an effector. A drug that interferes with the action of neurotransmitters can disrupt the functioning of the nervous system.

Stimulants A number of drugs, called **stimulants,** increase the actions regulated by the nervous system. **Stimulants increase heart rate, blood pressure, and breathing rate. In addition, stimulants increase the release of neurotransmitters at some synapses in the brain.** This release leads to a feeling of energy and well-being. When the effects of stimulants wear off, however, the brain's supply of neurotransmitters has been depleted. The user quickly falls into fatigue and depression. Long-term use can cause circulatory problems, hallucinations, and psychological depression.

Figure 35–16 Common stimulant drugs include amphetamines, cocaine, nicotine (found in cigarettes), and caffeine (found in coffee, tea, chocolate, and cola products). **Stimulants increase heart rate, blood pressure, and breathing rate.**

Depressants Some drugs, called **depressants,** decrease the rate of functions regulated by the brain. **Depressants slow down heart rate and breathing rate, lower blood pressure, relax muscles, and relieve tension.** Some depressants enhance the effects of neurotransmitters that prevent some nerve cells from starting action potentials. This calms parts of the brain that sense fear and relaxes the individual. As a result, the user comes to depend on the drug to relieve the anxieties of everyday life, which may seem unbearable without the drug. When depressants are used with alcohol, the results are often fatal because that combination can depress the activity of the central nervous system until breathing stops.

CHECKPOINT *What is the general function of a depressant?*

Cocaine Even stronger effects are produced by drugs that act on neurons in what are known as the pleasure centers of the brain. The effects of cocaine are so strong that they produce an uncontrollable craving for more of the drug. Cocaine is obtained from the leaves of coca plants. **Cocaine causes the sudden release in the brain of a neurotransmitter called dopamine.** Normally, this compound is released when a basic need, such as hunger or thirst, is fulfilled. By fooling the brain into releasing dopamine, cocaine produces intense feelings of pleasure and satisfaction. So much dopamine is released when the drug is used that the supply of dopamine is depleted when the drug wears off. Users quickly discover that they feel sad and depressed without the drug. The psychological dependence that cocaine produces is difficult to break.

Cocaine also acts as a powerful stimulant, increasing heart rate and blood pressure. The stimulation can be so powerful that the heart is damaged. Sometimes, even a first-time user may experience a heart attack after using cocaine.

A particularly potent and dangerous form of cocaine is crack. Crack becomes addictive after only a few doses. The intense "high" produced by crack wears off quickly and leaves the brain with too little dopamine. As a result, the user suddenly feels sad and depressed, and quickly seeks another dose of the drug. In time, the urge to seek this drug can be so strong that it leads users to commit serious crimes and to abandon their families and children.

Opiates The opium poppy, like the one shown in **Figure 35–17,** produces a powerful class of pain-killing drugs called opiates. **Opiates mimic natural chemicals in the brain known as endorphins, which normally help to overcome sensations of pain.** The first doses of these drugs produce strong feelings of pleasure and security, but the body quickly adjusts to the higher levels of endorphins. Once this happens, the body cannot do without the drug. A user who tries to stop taking these drugs will suffer from uncontrollable pain and sickness because the body cannot produce enough of the natural endorphins.

Figure 35–17 Many illegal drugs are found in nature. Cocaine comes from the South American *Erythroxylum coca* plant (top). The centers of opium poppies (below) contain pods from which opiate drugs are derived. **Opiates mimic endorphins, which help overcome pain.** For this reason, opiates are often used medically as painkillers.

Commonly Abused Drugs			
Drug Type	**Medical Use**	**Examples**	**Effects on the Body**
Stimulants	Used to increase alertness, relieve fatigue	Amphetamines	Increases heart and respiratory rates, elevates blood pressure, dilates pupils, and decreases appetite
Depressants	Used to relieve anxiety, irritability, tension	Barbiturates Tranquilizers	Slows down the actions of the central nervous system; small amounts cause calmness and relaxation; larger amounts cause slurred speech and impaired judgment
Opiates	Used to relieve pain	Morphine Codeine	Acts as a depressant; causes drowsiness, restlessness, nausea

▲ **Figure 35–18** Legal drugs that are used for medical purposes can also be abused. **Applying Concepts** *Do you think a person can become addicted to a legal drug?*

Marijuana Statistically, the most widely abused illegal drug is marijuana. Marijuana comes from *Cannabis sativa,* a species of hemp plant. Hashish, or hash, is a potent form of marijuana made from the flowering parts of the plant. The active ingredient in all forms of marijuana is tetrahydrocannabinol (THC). Smoking or ingesting THC can produce a temporary feeling of euphoria and disorientation. Smoking marijuana is bad for the lungs. In fact, smoking marijuana is even more destructive to the lungs than smoking tobacco. Long-term use of marijuana can also result in loss of memory; inability to concentrate; and, in males, reduced levels of the hormone testosterone.

What are the long-term effects of marijuana use?

Alcohol One of the most dangerous and abused legal drugs is alcohol. The most immediate effects of alcohol are on the central nervous system. **Alcohol is a depressant that slows down the rate at which the central nervous system functions.** Alcohol slows down reflexes, disrupts coordination, and impairs judgment. Heavy drinking fills the blood with so much alcohol that the central nervous system cannot function properly. People who have two or three drinks in the span of an hour may feel relaxed and confident, but their blood contains as much as 0.10 percent alcohol, making them legally drunk in most states. They usually cannot walk or talk properly, and they are certainly not able to safely control an automobile, as shown in **Figure 35–19.**

The abuse of alcohol has a frightening social price. About 40 percent of the 50,000 people who die on American highways in a typical year are victims of accidents in which at least one driver had been drinking. One third of all homicides can be attributed to the effects of alcohol. When health care, property damage, and lost productivity are considered, alcohol abuse costs the U.S. economy at least $150 billion per year.

▲ **Figure 35–19** **Alcohol slows down the rate at which the central nervous system functions.** It slows down reflexes, disrupts coordination, and impairs judgment. For this reason, you should never get into a car with a driver who has been drinking.

But the toll of alcohol abuse does not stop there. Women who are pregnant and drink on a regular basis run the risk of having a child with fetal alcohol syndrome. **Fetal alcohol syndrome** (FAS) is a group of birth defects caused by the effects of alcohol on the fetus. Babies born with FAS can suffer from heart defects, malformed faces, delayed growth, and poor motor development. In the United States alone, more than 50,000 babies are born every year with alcohol-related birth defects, many of which are irreversible.

Alcohol and Disease People who have become addicted to alcohol suffer from a disease called alcoholism. Some alcoholics feel the need to have a drink before work or school—every day. They may drink so heavily that they black out and cannot remember what they have done while drinking. Some alcoholics, however, do not drink to the point where it is obvious that they have an alcohol-abuse problem. If a person cannot function properly without satisfying the need or craving for alcohol, that person is considered to have an alcohol-abuse problem.

Long-term alcohol use destroys cells in the liver, where alcohol is broken down. As liver cells die, the liver becomes less able to handle large amounts of alcohol. The formation of scar tissue, known as cirrhosis of the liver, occurs next. The scar tissue blocks the flow of blood through the liver and interferes with its other important functions. Eventually, a heavy drinker may die from liver failure.

Analyzing Data

Blood Alcohol Concentration

Blood alcohol concentration (BAC) is a measure of the amount of alcohol in the bloodstream per 100 mL of blood. A BAC of 0.1 percent means that one tenth of 1.0 percent of the fluid in the blood is alcohol. In some states, if a driver has a BAC of 0.08 percent, he or she is considered legally drunk. In other states, drivers with a BAC of 0.10 percent are considered drunk. The graph shows the relative risk of being involved in a fatal accident as a result of the blood alcohol concentration of the driver.

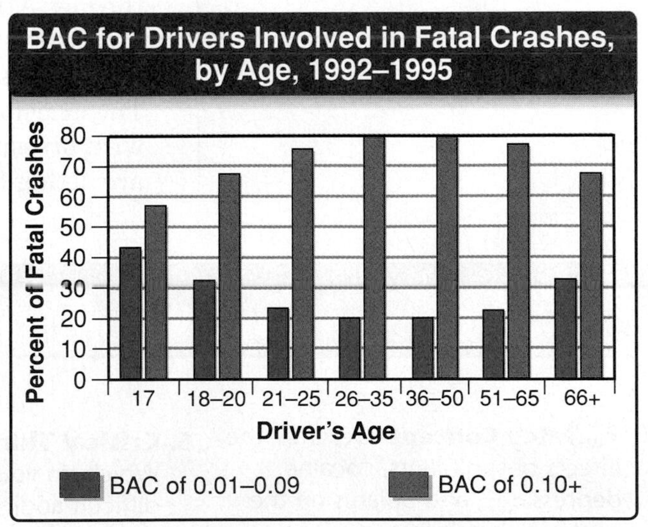

1. **Using Tables and Graphs** What trends do you see in the number of fatal crashes from age 17 to age 66+ based on the two ranges of BAC?
2. **Using Tables and Graphs** How does the consumption of alcohol affect driving risk for the average driver?
3. **Drawing Conclusions** Is the effect of alcohol consumption on driving independent of the age of the driver? Are young drivers more affected by alcohol or less affected by it than older drivers?
4. **Making Judgments** All levels of alcohol consumption affect driving skills, although the effect increases dramatically as more drinks are consumed. To minimize accidents and fatalities due to drunk driving, what should be the legal limit of blood alcohol for drivers?

For: Links on drugs and drug abuse
Visit: www.SciLinks.org
Web Code: cbn-0355

As with other drugs, dealing with alcohol abuse is not simply a matter of willpower. Alcoholics often need special help and support to quit their drinking habit. Organizations such as Alcoholics Anonymous are available in most communities to help individuals and families deal with the problems created by alcohol abuse.

Drug Abuse

Each of the drugs discussed so far presents a danger to users. The misuse of either a legal or an illegal drug is a serious problem in modern society. **Drug abuse** can be defined as the intentional misuse of any drug for nonmedical purposes. With some drugs, such as cocaine, drug abuse causes serious physical damage to the body. With other drugs, such as marijuana, drug abuse produces psychological dependence that can be strong enough to disrupt family life and schoolwork.

An uncontrollable dependence on a drug is known as a drug **addiction.** Some drugs cause a strong psychological dependence. People who are psychologically dependent on a drug have a mental craving, or need, for the drug. Other drugs cause a strong physical dependence. Physical dependence occurs when the body cannot function without a constant supply of the drug. Any attempt at withdrawal, or stopping the use of the drug, will cause pain, nausea, chills, and fever.

Because many users inject drugs for maximum effect, there is another important consequence of drug use—the increased transmission of human immunodeficiency virus (HIV), the virus that causes AIDS. The virus can be spread rapidly from person to person when drug users share contaminated needles. Many of the new AIDS cases reported in the United States can be traced back to the use of injected drugs.

The best way to avoid the effects of drugs is to avoid drugs. The decision not to use drugs can be difficult when you are faced with pressure to take them. By deciding not to take drugs, you are acting to take control of your life.

35–5 Section Assessment

1. **Key Concept** Describe the effects of stimulants, cocaine, depressants, and opiates on the central nervous system.
2. **Key Concept** Explain the effects of alcohol on the body.
3. What is a drug?
4. Why is drinking and driving an extremely dangerous behavior?
5. **Critical Thinking Inferring** Which do you think is a more difficult addiction to break: one in which a person is physically dependent on a drug, or one in which a person is psychologically dependent on a drug? Explain your answer.

Writing in Science

Persuasive Writing

Research one of the drugs mentioned in this section to find out more about the short- and long-term effects of the drug on the body. Then, develop an informational brochure trying to persuade someone not to take the drug. *Hint:* Be sure to include specific facts.

Real-World Lab

Modeling Corrective Lenses

The lenses of your eyes focus light on the retina. In people who are nearsighted, the lens focuses images in front of the retina, making distant objects appear blurry. In people who are farsighted, the lens focuses images behind the retina, making nearby objects difficult to see. To see more clearly, these people wear glasses or contact lenses. The shapes of these artificial lenses depend on the type of correction needed.

Problem **What types of corrective lenses are needed by near-sighted individuals and by farsighted individuals?**

Materials

- tape
- 2 cardboard photo easels
- black construction paper
- unruled white index card
- 6-V light bulb and socket
- 6-V battery and wires with alligator clips
- 2 convex lenses
- modeling clay
- meter stick
- concave lens

Skills Analyzing Data, Using Models

Procedure 

1. Set up your equipment as shown. Place the white index card about 50 to 60 cm in front of the bulb.
2. Place a convex lens in front of the bulb and move the lens until an image of the bulb focuses clearly on the index card. Secure the lens in this position with modeling clay or tape. The distance between the fixed lens and the index card is the focal length of the lens.
3. Move the index card about 5 to 8 cm away from the fixed lens to simulate the formation of an image in front of the retina. Observe the image and record your observations.
4. Hold the concave lens between the light bulb and the fixed lens. Try to focus the image by moving the concave lens between the light bulb and the fixed lens.
5. Repeat step 4, but this time use the second convex lens. Record your observations.
6. Move the index card about 10 to 16 cm closer to the fixed lens to simulate image formation behind the retina. Record your observations.
7. Repeat steps 4 and 5.

Analyze and Conclude

1. **Drawing Conclusions** Does the lens in your eye focus an image right side up or upside down on your retina? Why does an image appear right side up when you look at objects?
2. **Drawing Conclusions** Which lens sharpened the image that formed in front of the retina? Behind the retina?
3. **Using Models** Which condition—long-focal length or short-focal length—do you think models the problem of nearsightedness? Which condition models farsightedness? Explain your answers.

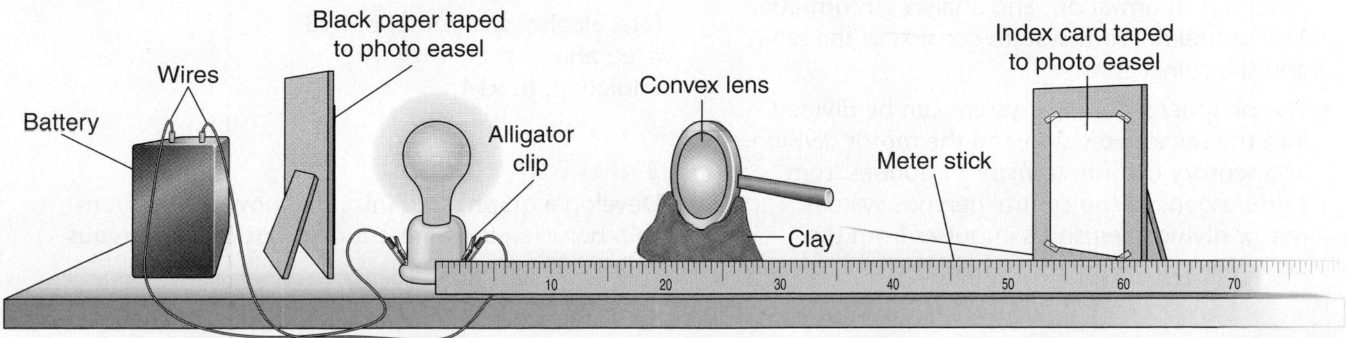

Chapter 35 Study Guide

35–1 Human Body Systems

Key Concepts

- The levels of organization in a multicellular organism include cells, tissues, organs, and organ systems.
- Homeostasis is the process by which organisms keep internal conditions relatively constant despite changes in external environments.

Vocabulary

specialized cell, p. 894
epithelial tissue, p. 894
connective tissue, p. 894
nervous tissue, p. 894
muscle tissue, p. 894
homeostasis, p. 895
feedback inhibition, p. 895

35–2 The Nervous System

Key Concepts

- The nervous system controls and coordinates functions throughout the body and responds to internal and external stimuli.
- The basic structural units of the nervous system are neurons.
- A nerve impulse begins when a neuron is stimulated by another neuron or by its environment.

Vocabulary

neuron, p. 897 • cell body, p. 897
dendrite, p. 898 • axon, p. 898
myelin sheath, p. 898
resting potential, p. 898
action potential, p. 899
threshold, p. 899 • synapse, p. 900
neurotransmitter, p. 900

35–3 Divisions of the Nervous System

Key Concepts

- The central nervous system relays messages, processes information, and analyzes information. The central nervous system consists of the brain and the spinal cord.
- The peripheral nervous system can be divided into the sensory division and the motor division. The sensory division transmits impulses from sense organs to the central nervous system. The motor division transmits impulses from the central nervous system to the muscles or glands.

Vocabulary

meninges, p. 901 • cerebrospinal fluid, p. 901
cerebrum, p. 902 • cerebellum, p. 902
brain stem, p. 902 • thalamus, p. 903
hypothalamus, p. 903 • reflex, p. 903
reflex arc, p. 904

35–4 The Senses

Key Concept

- There are five general categories of sensory receptors: pain receptors, thermoreceptors, mechanoreceptors, chemoreceptors, and photoreceptors.

Vocabulary

sensory receptor, p. 906 • pupil, p. 906
lens, p. 907 • retina, p. 907 • rod, p. 907
cone, p. 907 • cochlea, p. 908
semicircular canal, p. 908 • taste bud, p. 909

35–5 Drugs and the Nervous System

Key Concepts

- Stimulants increase heart rate, blood pressure, and breathing rate. In addition, stimulants increase the release of neurotransmitters at some synapses in the brain.
- Depressants slow down heart rate and breathing rate, lower blood pressure, relax muscles, and relieve tension.
- Cocaine causes the sudden release of a neurotransmitter in the brain called dopamine.
- Opiates mimic natural chemicals in the brain known as endorphins, which normally help to overcome sensations of pain.
- Alcohol is a depressant that slows down the rate at which the central nervous system functions.

Vocabulary

drug, p. 910
stimulant, p. 910
depressant, p. 911
fetal alcohol syndrome, p. 913
drug abuse, p. 914
addiction, p. 914

Thinking Visually

Develop a graphic organizer to show the relationship between the different divisions of the nervous system.

Preparing for the Living Environment Exam

NEW YORK LIVING ENVIRONMENT

Blue questions emphasize Regents Exam content

Chapter 35

Part A

Multiple Choice

For each statement or question, select the number of the word or expression that, of those given, best completes the statement or answers the question.

1 The type of tissue that covers the body, lines internal surfaces, and forms glands is
(1) muscle tissue
(2) connective tissue
(3) epithelial tissue
(4) nervous tissue

2 The process of maintaining a relatively constant internal environment despite changes in the external environment is called
(1) regulation (3) homeostasis
(2) synapse (4) stimulation

3 The basic units of structure and function of the nervous system are
(1) neurons
(2) axons
(3) neurotransmitters
(4) dendrites

4 The place where a nerve cell transfers an impulse to another cell is the
(1) synapse (3) axon
(2) sheath (4) receptor

5 Two organs are considered to be part of the same body system if the organs
(1) are located next to each other
(2) work independently of each other
(3) work together to carry out a life function
(4) are made up of cells with organelles

6 A hawk sees a field mouse and then captures it for food. In this activity, the eyes of the hawk function as
(1) dendrites
(2) receptors
(3) stimuli
(4) neurotransmitters

7 Which term is correctly paired with examples of that term?
(1) receptors: leg muscles and testes
(2) stimuli: temperature and light
(3) impulses: skin and eyes
(4) depressants: neurotransmitters and hormones

8 The central nervous system consists of
(1) sense organs
(2) reflexes
(3) brain and spinal cord
(4) sensory and motor neurons

9 Which division of the nervous system controls voluntary activities, such as walking the dog or singing a song?
(1) somatic (3) autonomic
(2) central (4) reflex

10 Which part of the brain controls conscious thought?
(1) medulla oblongata
(2) cerebellum
(3) cerebrum
(4) brain stem

11 The sympathetic nervous system and the parasympathetic nervous system are divisions of the
(1) peripheral nervous system
(2) central nervous system
(3) somatic nervous system
(4) autonomic nervous system

12 The semicircular canals and the two tiny sacs located behind them help the body to maintain
(1) vision
(2) respiratory rate
(3) equilibrium
(4) body temperature

13 The division of the nervous system that controls cardiac muscle is the
(1) autonomic
(2) somatic
(3) cerebellum
(4) hypothalamus

14 Drugs that increase heart rate, blood pressure, and breathing rate are called
(1) stimulants (3) depressants
(2) opiates (4) barbiturates

Test-Taking Tip Questions that begin with a list of lettered choices (A–E) followed by numbered statements are essentially multiple-choice questions. To solve these questions, use the same process that you use to solve standard multiple-choice questions.

Preparing for the Living Environment Exam

Part B

Multiple Choice and Extended Response
For those questions that ask you to select a response, choose the one that best completes the statement or answers the question. For all others follow the directions given.

Base your answers to questions 15 and 16 on the diagram below and on your knowledge of biology.

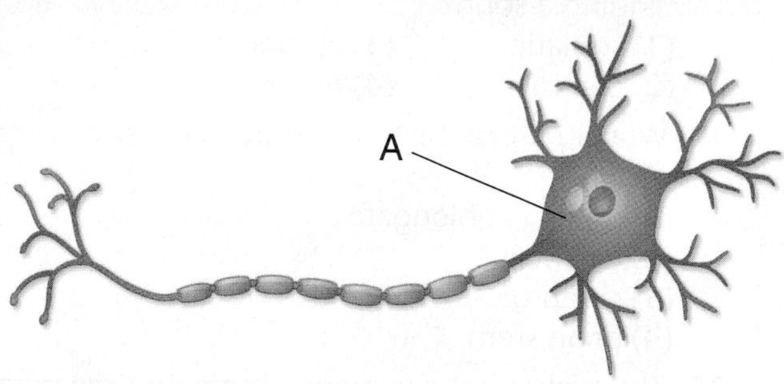

15 Letter A is pointing to the
(1) myelin sheath (3) axon
(2) dendrite (4) cell body

16 Copy the diagram on a sheet of paper. Then, circle the part of the cell that secretes a neuro-transmitter.

Base your answers to questions 17 through 19 on the information and graph below and on your knowledge of biology.

A student surveyed 200 students who each had an overall grade point average of A or B. The results of the survey are summarized in the graph.

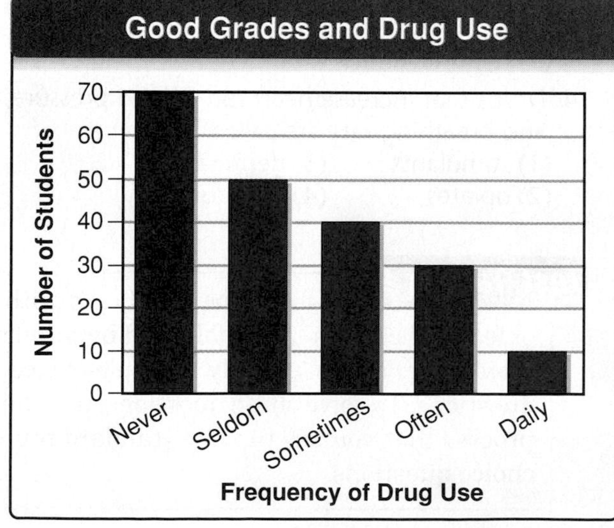

17 What is the manipulated (independent) variable in the study?
(1) good grades
(2) student age
(3) popularity at school
(4) frequency of drug use

18 What percentage of students with good grades say they never use drugs?
(1) 15% (3) 50%
(2) 35% (4) 70%

19 The student conducting the survey concluded that students with good grades use drugs less frequently than students with poor grades. Why might this conclusion not be valid?
(1) There are no data on students with poor grades.
(2) Students with good grades use drugs 70 percent of the time.
(3) The researcher did not survey enough students.
(4) Only students in one school were surveyed.

Base your answers to questions 20 through 23 on the reading passage below and on your knowledge of biology.

What Did You Say?

There are three types of hearing loss: conductive, sensorineural, and mixed. In conductive hearing loss, problems in the outer or middle ear block the transmission of vibrations to the inner ear. Conductive hearing loss can result from ear infections, excessive earwax, fluid in the middle ear, or a perforated eardrum. Sensorineural hearing loss, or "nerve deafness," is most often due to changes with aging or to long-term exposure to loud noises. For example, over a 6-year period a rock band player developed a 40 percent hearing loss because he did not use ear protection during performances. The use of personal listening devices, such as headphones, can also cause sensorineural hearing loss, as can high fevers, birth defects, and certain drugs. Mixed hearing loss is a combination of both other types.

Tests to determine the cause and extent of hearing loss include: tympanometry, which examines the middle ear, eardrum, and possible blockage of the ear canal; pure-tone and speech reception testing, which determines the lowest level at which tones and speech can be heard; and word discrimination testing, which measures the ability to distinguish words at a comfortable volume.

20 Which of the graphs below best represents a common relationship between age and nerve deafness?

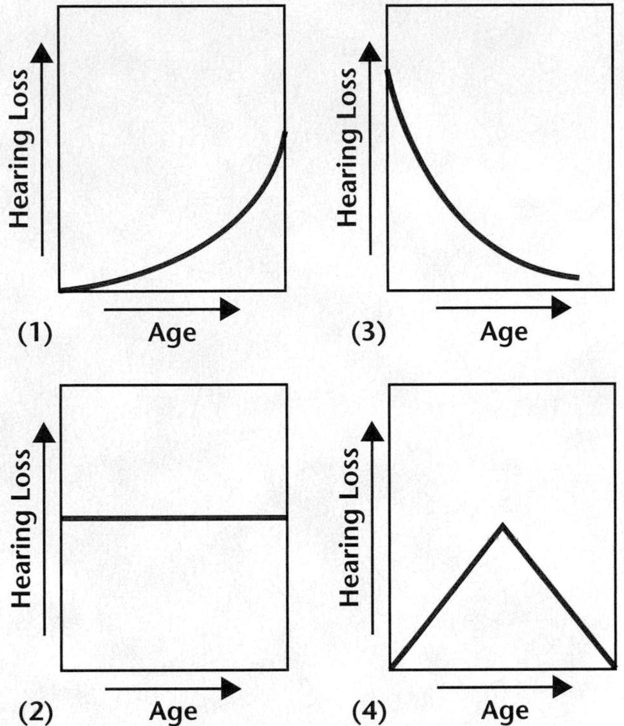

21 A prolonged body temperature of 105°F (40.4°C) may result in
(1) an inner ear infection
(2) conductive hearing loss
(3) sensorineural hearing loss
(4) a perforated eardrum

22 Which test is used to determine the presence of excessive wax in the ear canal?
(1) sensorineural assessment
(2) word discrimination testing
(3) pure-tone and speech reception testing
(4) tympanometry

23 State how a personal listening device can be controlled to decrease the risk of hearing damage.

24 Arrange the following terms in order from simplest to most complex: organ system, tissue, organ, organism, cell.

25 Explain why depressant drugs and alcohol are a life-threatening combination.

26 Explain why it is important for an organism to be able to maintain homeostasis.

27 Explain how the all-or-none principle relates to the transmission of a nerve impulse.

Part C

Extended Response

Answer the questions or follow the directions given.

28 A pregnant woman should avoid drinking alcohol. Explain why this statement is true. In your answer, be sure to:
- identify the specific part of pregnancy when this advice is most critical, supporting your answer with an explanation
- state one example of the possible short-term effects on the fetus if alcohol is consumed during the pregnancy
- state one example of possible long-term effects on the child if alcohol is consumed during pregnancy

29 The production of a nerve impulse depends on the movement of ions. Describe the changes that occur in a neuron as it responds to stimuli. In your answer, be sure to include the:
- changes that occur in a neuron during action potential
- changes that occur in a neuron during resting potential
- involvement of sodium and potassium ions
- role of the cell membrane

For: An interactive self-test
Visit: PHSchool.com
Web Code: cba-0350

CHAPTER 36

Skeletal, Muscular, and Integumentary Systems

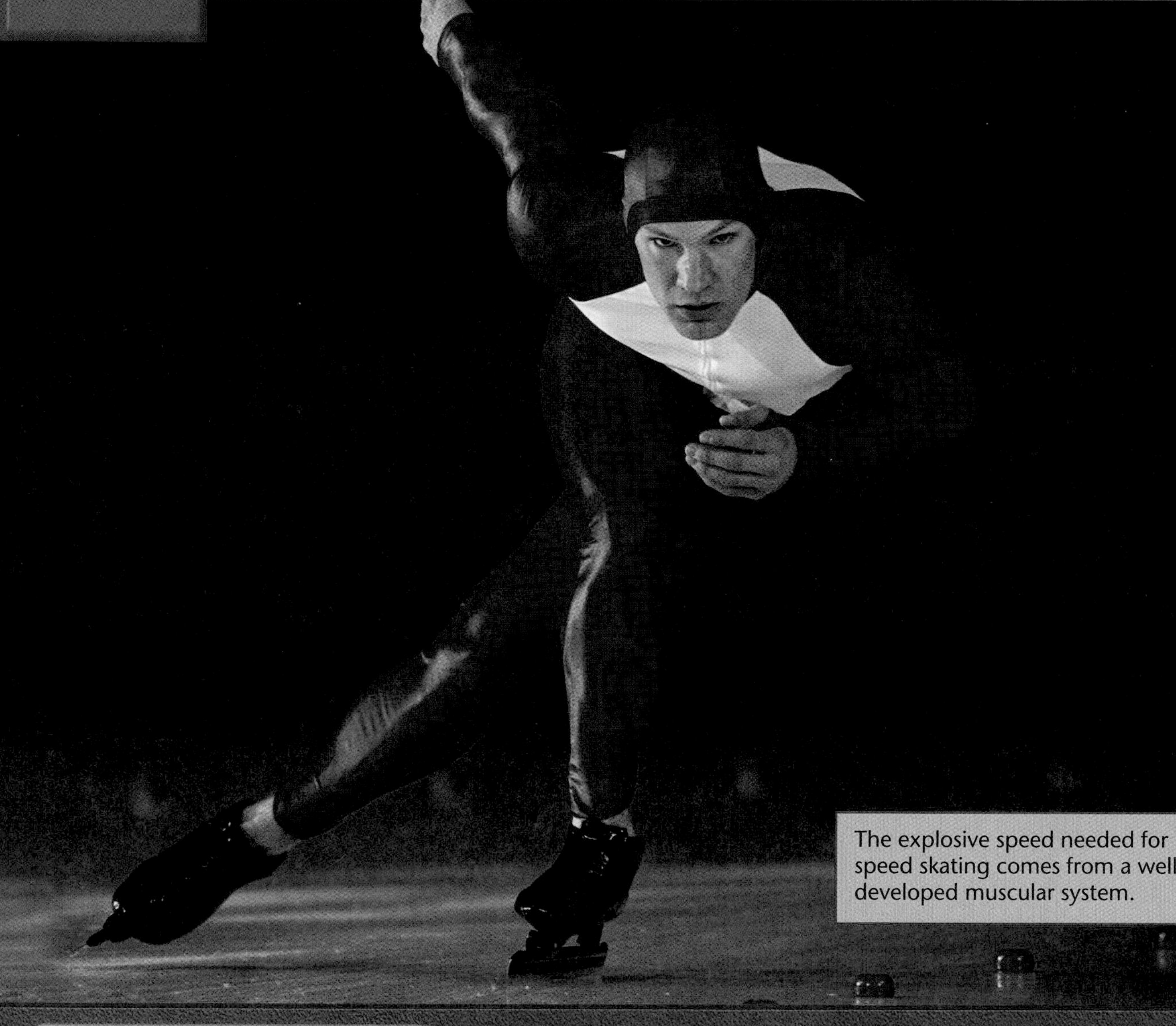

The explosive speed needed for speed skating comes from a well-developed muscular system.

Inquiry Activity

How do your joints move?

Procedure

1. Look at the examples of a hinge joint and a ball-and-socket joint provided by your teacher. Determine how each joint moves.
2. Based on your observations, identify joints in your body that are hinge joints and joints that are ball-and-socket joints.

Think About It

1. **Classifying** What type of movement does a hinge joint allow?
2. **Classifying** What type of movement does a ball-and-socket joint allow?
3. **Inferring** Your body also has joints called pivot joints and saddle joints. Based on their names, what type of movement might these joints allow? (*Hint:* Consider how a rider might move in a saddle.)

36–1 The Skeletal System

4-1.2 Humans have complex systems
4-1.2 Human systems detect changes
4-1.2 System disruptions affect homeostasis
4-1.2 Cells are grouped for efficiency
LS- Make observations

Guide for Reading

Key Concepts
- What are the functions of the skeletal system?
- What is the structure of a typical bone?
- What are the three different kinds of joints?

Vocabulary
periosteum
Haversian canal
bone marrow
cartilage
ossification
joint
ligament

Reading Strategy: Asking Questions Before you read, rewrite the headings in this section as *how, why,* or *what* questions about the skeletal system. As you read, write brief answers to those heading questions.

To retain their shapes, all organisms need some type of structural support. Single-celled organisms have a cytoskeleton that provides structural support. In multicellular animals, support is provided by some form of skeleton, including the external exoskeletons of arthropods and the internal endoskeletons of vertebrates. The human skeleton is composed of a type of connective tissue called bone. Bones and other connective tissues, such as cartilage and ligaments, form the skeletal system.

Scientists can infer a lot about the behavior of extinct species by studying fossil bones and reconstructing skeletons. The human skeleton also contains important clues. The shape of your hip bones shows that you walk upright on two legs. The structure of the bones in your hands, especially your opposable thumbs, indicates that you have the ability to grasp objects. The size and shape of your skull is a clue that you have a well-developed brain.

The Skeleton

The skeletal system has many important functions.  **The skeleton supports the body, protects internal organs, provides for movement, stores mineral reserves, and provides a site for blood cell formation.** The bones that make up the skeletal system support and shape the body much like an internal wooden frame supports a house. Just as a house could not stand without its wooden frame, the human body would collapse without its bony skeleton. Bones protect the delicate internal organs of the body. For example, the skull forms a protective shell around the brain, and the ribs form a basketlike cage that protects the heart and lungs.

Bones provide a system of levers on which muscles act to produce movement. Levers are rigid rods that can be moved about a fixed point. In addition, bones contain reserves of minerals, mainly calcium salts, that are important to many body processes. Finally, bones are the site of blood cell formation. Blood cells are produced in the soft marrow tissue that fills the internal cavities in some bones.

There are 206 bones in the adult human skeleton. As shown in **Figure 36–2** on page 922, these bones can be divided into two parts—the axial skeleton and the appendicular skeleton. The axial skeleton supports the central axis of the body. It consists of the skull, the vertebral column, and the rib cage. The bones of the arms and legs, along with the bones of the pelvis and shoulder area, form the appendicular skeleton.

▼ **Figure 36–1** **Bones provide a system of levers on which muscles act to produce movement.** Without this coordination, movement would not be possible.

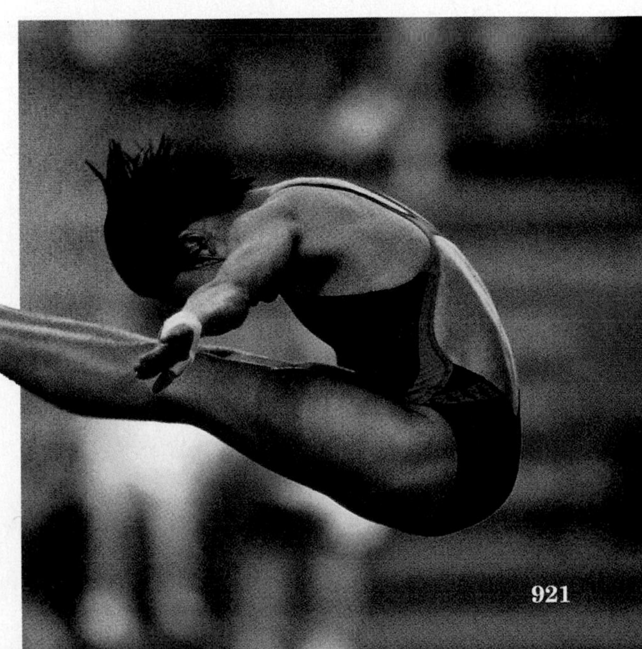

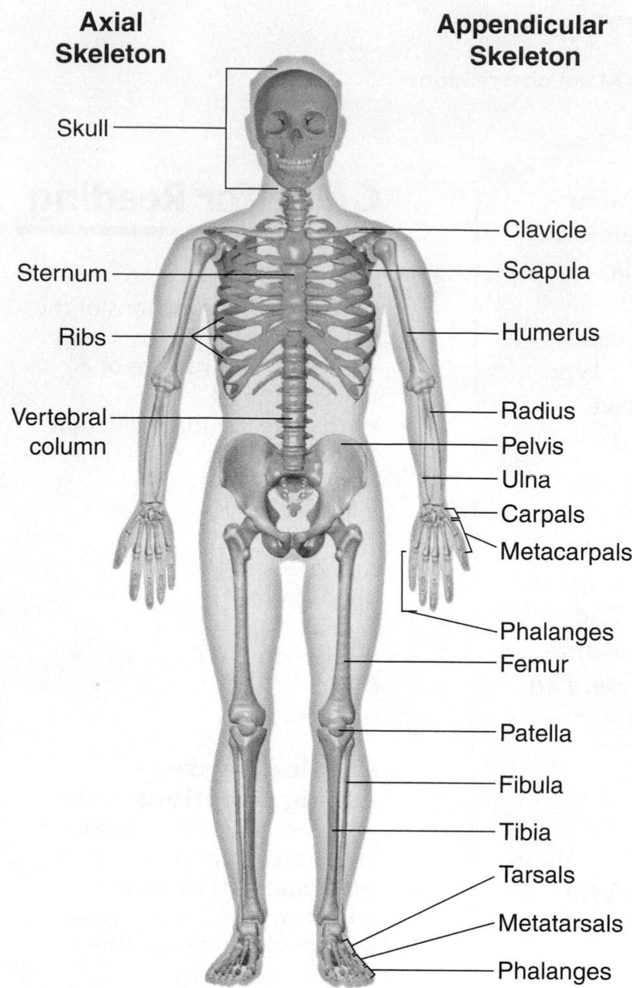

▲ **Figure 36–2** **The skeleton supports the body.** The human skeleton is divided into two parts: the axial skeleton and the appendicular skeleton.

Structure of Bones

It is easy to think of bones as nonliving. After all, most of the mass of bone is mineral salts—mainly calcium and phosphorus. However, bones are living tissue. **Bones are a solid network of living cells and protein fibers that are surrounded by deposits of calcium salts.**

Figure 36–3 shows the structure of a typical bone. The bone is surrounded by a tough layer of connective tissue called the **periosteum** (pehr-ee-AHS-tee-um). Blood vessels that pass through the periosteum carry oxygen and nutrients to the bone. Beneath the periosteum is a thick layer of compact bone. Although compact bone is dense, it is far from being solid. Running through compact bone is a network of tubes called **Haversian** (huh-VUR-zhun) **canals** that contain blood vessels and nerves.

A less dense tissue known as spongy bone is found inside the outer layer of compact bone. It is found in the ends of long bones and in the middle part of short, flat bones. Despite its name, spongy bone is not soft and spongy; it is actually quite strong. Near the ends of bones where force is applied, spongy bone is organized into structures that resemble the supporting girders in a bridge. This latticework structure of spongy bone helps to add strength to bone without adding mass.

Osteocytes, which are mature bone cells, are embedded in the bone matrix. Two other kinds of bone cells—osteoclasts (AHS-tee-oh-klasts) and osteoblasts line the Haversian canals and the surfaces of compact and spongy bone. Osteoclasts break down bone. Osteoblasts produce bone. Although we stop growing in our late teens, our bones are continuously remodeled through the activity of osteoclasts and osteoblasts.

Within bones are cavities that contain a soft tissue called **bone marrow.** There are two types of bone marrow: yellow and red. Yellow marrow is made up primarily of fat cells. Red marrow produces red blood cells, some kinds of white blood cells, and cell fragments called platelets.

Development of Bones

The skeleton of an embryo is composed almost entirely of a type of connective tissue called **cartilage.** The cells that make up cartilage are scattered in a network of protein fibers including both tough collagen and flexible elastin.

Figure 36–3 Structure of a Bone

Bones are a solid network of living cells and protein fibers that are supported by deposits of calcium salts. A typical long bone such as the femur contains spongy bone and compact bone. Within compact bone are Haversian canals, which contain blood vessels.

Haversian Canal
(magnification: 200×)

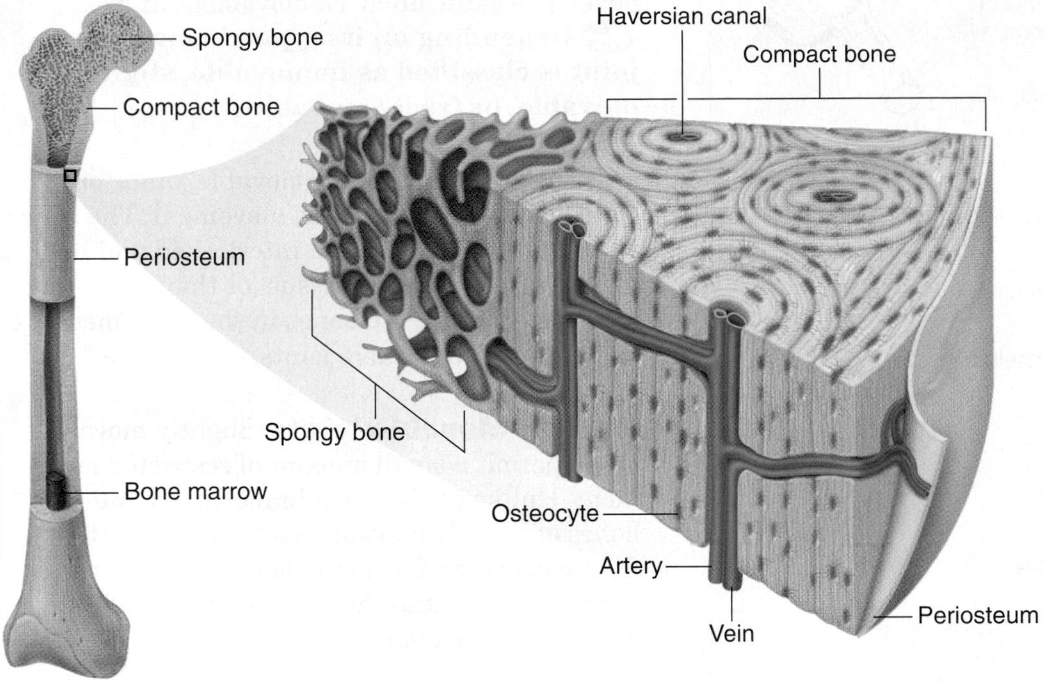

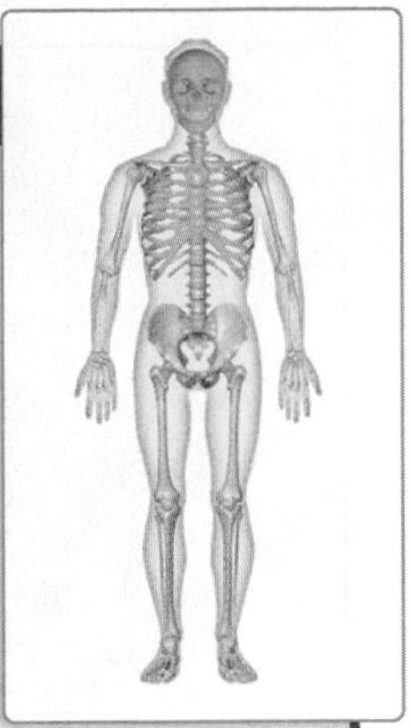

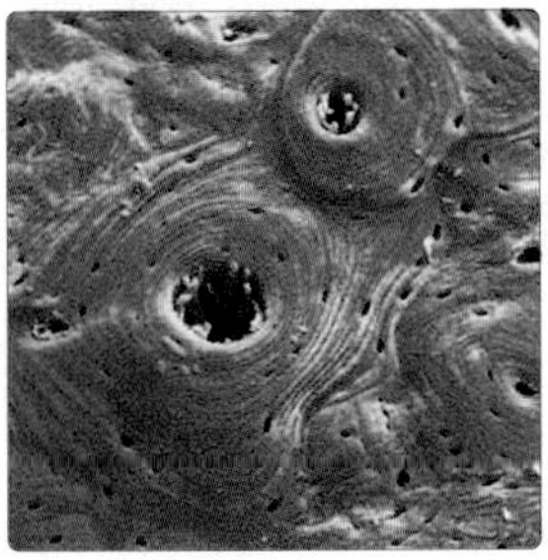

Unlike bone, cartilage does not contain blood vessels. Cartilage cells must rely on the diffusion of nutrients from the tiny blood vessels in surrounding tissues. Because cartilage is dense and fibrous, it can support weight, despite its extreme flexibility.

Cartilage is replaced by bone during the process of bone formation called **ossification** (ahs-uh-fih-KAY-shun). Ossification begins to take place up to seven months before birth. Bone tissue forms as osteoblasts secrete mineral deposits that replace the cartilage in developing bones. When the osteoblasts become surrounded by bone tissue, they mature into osteocytes.

Many long bones, including those of the arms and legs, have growth plates at either end. The growth of cartilage at these plates causes the bones to lengthen. Gradually, this new growth of cartilage is replaced by bone tissue, and the bones become larger and stronger. During late adolescence or early adulthood, the cartilage in the growth plates is replaced by bone, the bones become completely ossified, and the person "stops growing."

In adults, cartilage is found in those parts of the body that are flexible, such as the tip of the nose and the external ears. Cartilage also is found where the ribs are attached to the sternum, which allows the rib cage to move during breathing.

CHECKPOINT *What is ossification?*

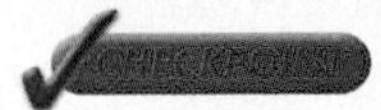

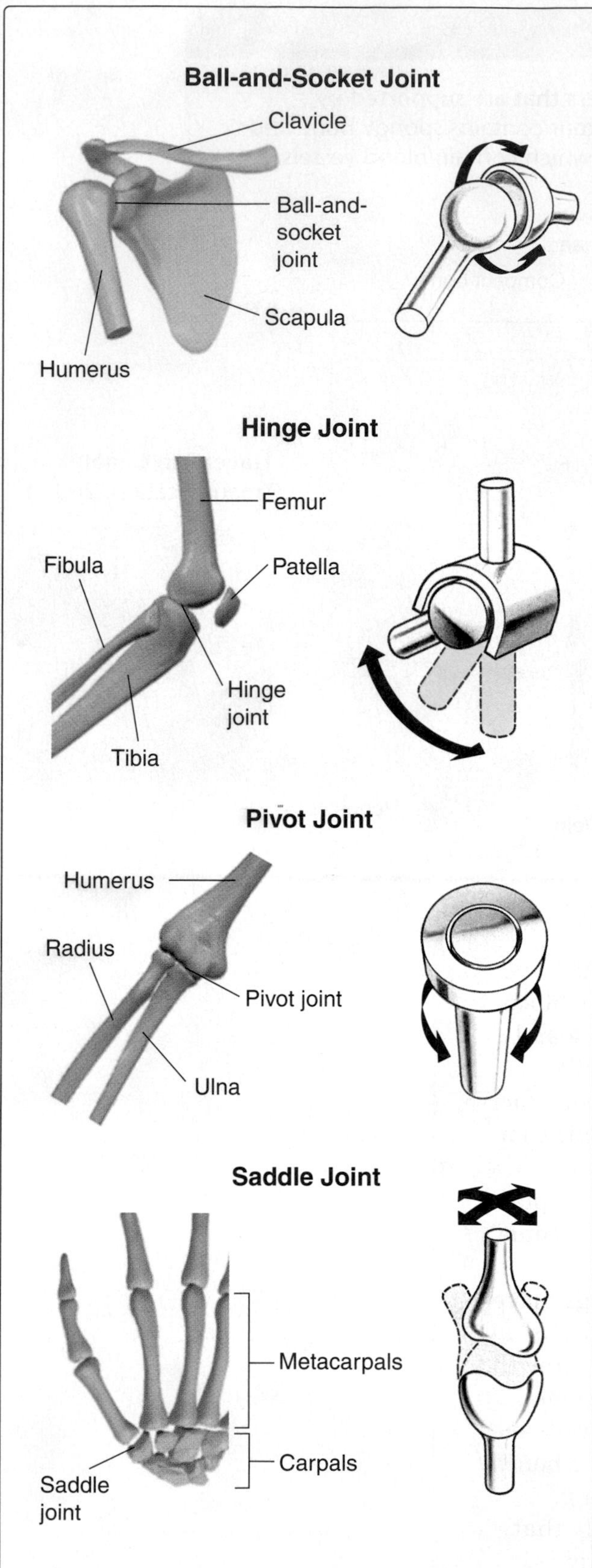

▲ **Figure 36–4** **Freely movable joints are classified by the type of movement they permit.** The joints illustrated are in the shoulder, knee, elbow, and hand.

Types of Joints

A place where one bone attaches to another bone is called a **joint.** Joints permit bones to move without damaging each other. Some joints, such as those of the shoulder, allow extensive movement. Others, like the joints of the fully developed skull, allow no movement at all. **Depending on its type of movement, a joint is classified as immovable, slightly movable, or freely movable.**

Immovable Joints Immovable joints, often called fixed joints, allow no movement. The bones at an immovable joint are interlocked and held together by connective tissue, or they are fused. The places where the bones in the skull meet are examples of immovable joints.

Slightly Movable Joints Slightly movable joints permit a small amount of restricted movement. Unlike the bones of immovable joints, the bones of slightly movable joints are separated from each other. The joints between the two bones of the lower leg and the joints between adjacent vertebrae are examples of slightly movable joints.

Freely Movable Joints Freely movable joints permit movement in one or more directions. Freely movable joints are grouped according to the shapes of the surfaces of the adjacent bones. The most common types of freely movable joints are shown in **Figure 36–4.**

Ball-and-socket joints permit movement in many directions. They allow the widest range of movement of any joint. Hinge joints permit back-and-forth motion, like the opening and closing of a door. Pivot joints allow one bone to rotate around another. Saddle joints permit one bone to slide in two directions.

CHECKPOINT *What are the four common types of freely movable joints?*

Structure of Joints

In freely movable joints, cartilage covers the surfaces where two bones come together. This protects the bones as they move against each other. The joints are also surrounded by a fibrous joint capsule that helps hold the bones together while still allowing them to move.

The joint capsule consists of two layers. One layer forms strips of tough connective tissue called **ligaments.** Ligaments, which hold bones together in a joint, are attached to the membranes that surround bones. Cells in the other layer of the joint capsule produce a substance called synovial (sin-OH-vee-ul) fluid. Synovial fluid enables the surfaces of the joint to slide over each other smoothly.

In some freely movable joints, such as the knee in **Figure 36–5,** small sacs of synovial fluid called bursae (BUR-see; singular: bursa) form. A bursa reduces the friction between the bones of a joint and also acts as a tiny shock absorber.

Skeletal System Disorders

Bones and joints can be damaged, just like any other tissue. Excessive strain on a joint may produce inflammation, a response in which excess fluid causes swelling, pain, heat, and redness. Inflammation of a bursa is called bursitis. A more serious disorder is arthritis, which involves inflammation of the joint itself.

In older people, especially women, loss of calcium in the bones can lead to a condition known as osteoporosis. Osteoporosis is a weakening of the bones that can cause serious fractures. Sound nutrition, including plenty of calcium in the diet, and weight-bearing exercise are among the best ways to prevent this serious problem.

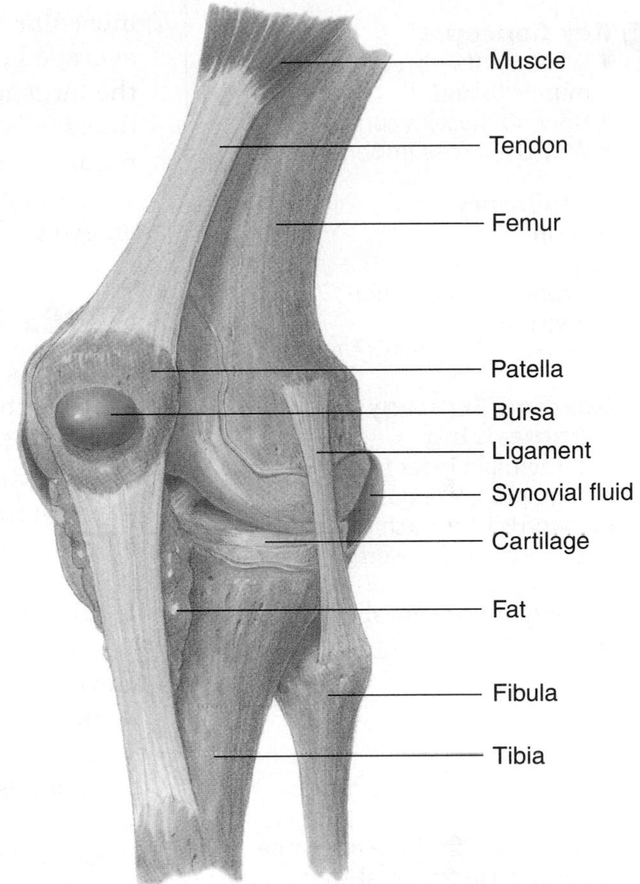

▲ **Figure 36–5** The knee joint is protected by cartilage and bursae. The ligaments hold the bones composing the knee joint—femur, patella, tibia, and fibula—together. **Inferring** ***How do the cartilage and bursae help reduce friction?***

36–1 Section Assessment

1. **Key Concept** List the different functions of the skeletal system.
2. **Key Concept** Describe the structure of a typical bone.
3. **Key Concept** What is a joint? List the three types of joints.
4. How does compact bone differ from spongy bone?
5. **Critical Thinking Inferring** Why do you think the amount of cartilage decreases and the amount of bone increases as a person develops?

Writing in Science

Creative Writing
Use library or Internet resources to find out more about osteoporosis. Then, develop an advertising campaign for the dairy industry based on the relationship between milk and healthy bone development.

36–2 The Muscular System

4-1.2 Humans have complex systems
4-1.2 Cells are grouped for efficiency
LS- Follow safety rules, make observations, analyze results
LS- Dissection of animal specimens

Guide for Reading

Key Concepts
- What are the three types of muscle tissue?
- How do muscles contract?
- Why is exercise important?

Vocabulary
myosin
actin
neuromuscular junction
acetylcholine
tendon

Reading Strategy: Summarizing As you read, find the main ideas for each paragraph. Write down a few key words from each main idea. Then, use the key words in your summary. Reread your summary, keeping only the most important ideas.

Despite the fantasies of Hollywood horror films, a skeleton cannot move by itself. Movement is the function of the muscular system. More than 40 percent of the mass of the average human body is muscle. The muscular system includes the large muscles displayed by some athletes. It also includes thousands of tiny muscles throughout the body that help to regulate blood pressure, move food through the digestive system, and power every movement of the body—from the blink of an eye to the hint of a smile.

Types of Muscle Tissue

Muscle tissue is found everywhere in the body—not only just beneath the skin but also deep within the body. **There are three different types of muscle tissue: skeletal, smooth, and cardiac.** Each type of muscle is specialized for a specific function in the body. Refer to **Figure 36–6** as you read about the different types of muscles.

Skeletal Muscles Skeletal muscles are usually attached to bones. Skeletal muscles are responsible for such voluntary movements as typing on a computer keyboard, dancing, or winking an eye. When viewed under a microscope at high magnification, skeletal muscle appears to have alternating light and dark bands called striations. For this reason, skeletal muscle is sometimes called striated muscle. Most skeletal muscles are consciously controlled by the central nervous system.

Skeletal muscle cells are large, have many nuclei, and vary in length from 1 millimeter to about 30 centimeters. Because skeletal muscle cells are long and slender, they are often called muscle fibers. Complete skeletal muscles consist of muscle fibers, connective tissues, blood vessels, and nerves. **Figure 36–7** shows the structure of a skeletal muscle in the leg.

Figure 36–6 There are three types of muscle tissue: skeletal, smooth, and cardiac. Skeletal muscle cells have striations, or stripes, and many nuclei. Smooth muscle cells are spindle-shaped and have one nucleus and no striations. Cardiac muscle cells have striations and usually only one nucleus.

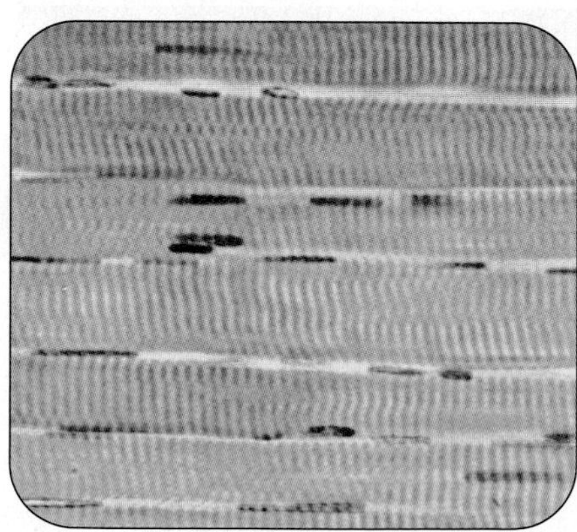

Skeletal Muscle (150×)

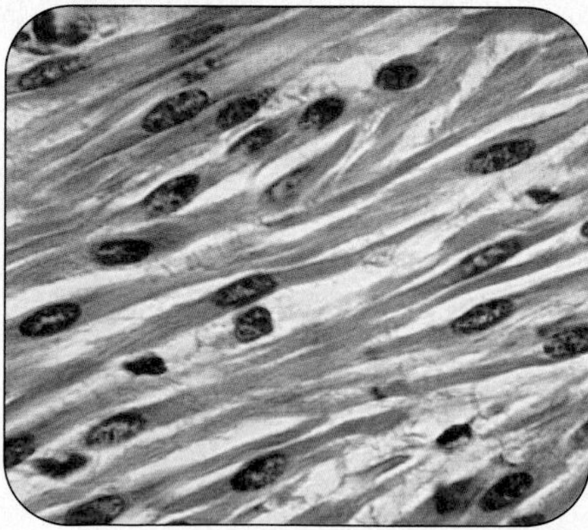

Smooth Muscle (400×)

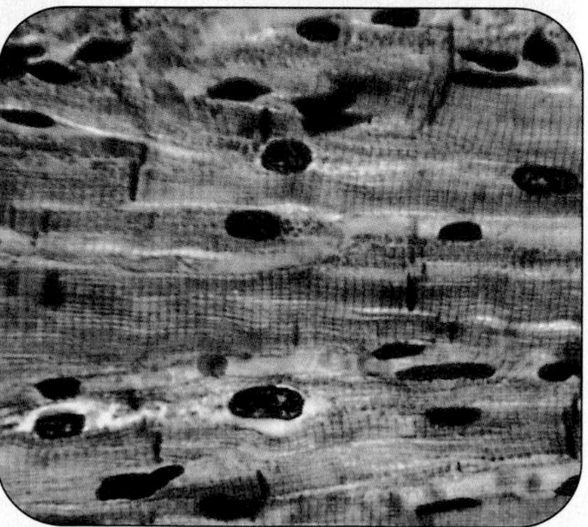

Cardiac Muscle (500×)

Figure 36–7 Skeletal Muscle Structure

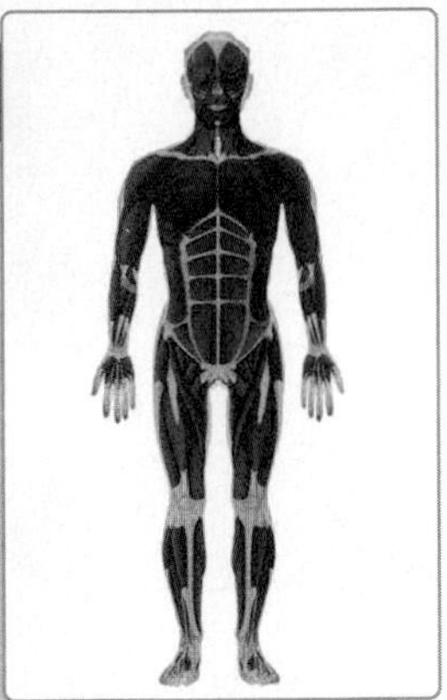

Skeletal muscles are made up of bundles of muscle fibers, which in turn are composed of myofibrils. Each myofibril contains thin filaments made of actin and thick filaments made of myosin. Muscle fibers are divided into functional units called sarcomeres. **Applying Concepts** ***What nervous system structures carry messages to skeletal muscles?***

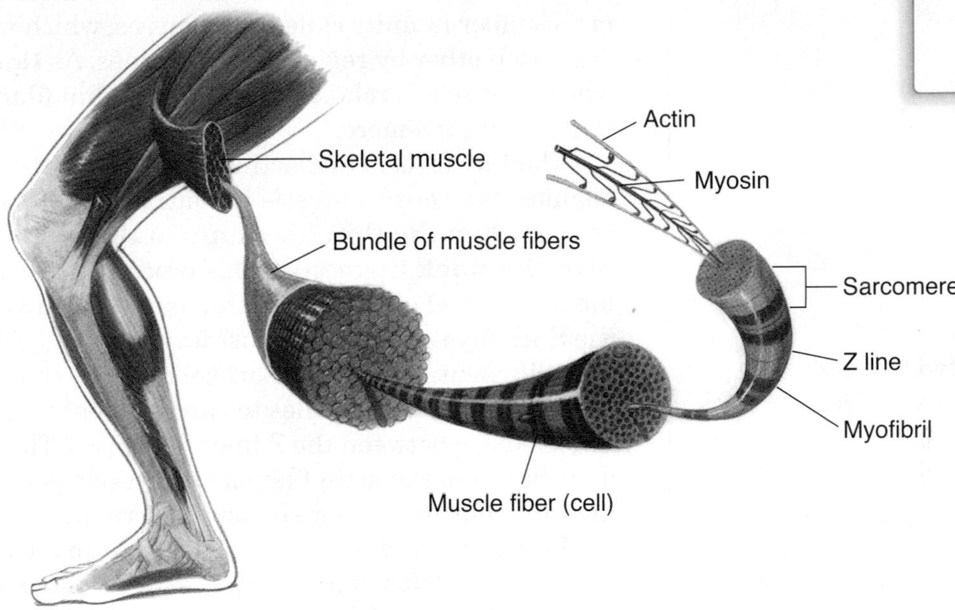

Actin
Skeletal muscle
Myosin
Bundle of muscle fibers
Sarcomere
Z line
Myofibril
Muscle fiber (cell)

Smooth Muscles Smooth muscles are usually not under voluntary control. A smooth muscle cell is spindle-shaped, has one nucleus, and is not striated. Smooth muscles are found in the walls of hollow structures such as the stomach, blood vessels, and intestines. Smooth muscles move food through your digestive tract, control the way blood flows through your circulatory system, and decrease the size of the pupils of your eyes in bright light. Most smooth muscle cells can function without nervous stimulation. They are connected to one another by gap junctions that allow electrical impulses to travel directly from one muscle cell to a neighboring muscle cell.

Cardiac Muscle Cardiac muscle is found in just one place in the body—the heart. The prefix *cardio* comes from a Greek word meaning "heart." Cardiac muscle shares features with both skeletal muscle and smooth muscle. Cardiac muscle is striated like skeletal muscle, although its cells are smaller. Cardiac muscle cells usually have one nucleus, but they may have two. Cardiac muscle is similar to smooth muscle because it is usually not under the direct control of the central nervous system and cardiac cells are connected to their neighbors by gap junctions. You will learn more about cardiac muscle in Chapter 37.

What kind of muscle tissue lines the blood vessels?

Muscle Contraction

The muscle fibers in skeletal muscles are composed of smaller structures called myofibrils. Each myofibril is made up of even smaller structures called filaments. The striations in skeletal muscle cells are formed by an alternating pattern of thick and thin filaments. The thick filaments contain a protein called **myosin** (MY-uh-sin). The thin filaments are made up mainly of a protein called **actin.** The filaments are arranged along the muscle fiber in units called sarcomeres, which are separated from each other by regions called Z lines. As **Figure 36–8** shows, when a muscle is relaxed, there are no thin filaments in the center of a sarcomere.

The tiny myosin and actin filaments are the force-producing engines that cause a muscle to contract. **A muscle contracts when the thin filaments in the muscle fiber slide over the thick filaments.** This process is called the sliding-filament model of muscle contraction. For a muscle to contract, the thick myosin filament must form a cross-bridge with the thin actin filament. As the cross-bridge changes shape, it pulls on the actin filament, which slides toward the center of the sarcomere. The distance between the Z lines decreases. The cross-bridge detaches from the actin filament. The cycle is repeated when the myosin binds to another site on the actin filament.

When hundreds of thousands of myosin cross-bridges change shape in a fraction of a second, the muscle fiber shortens with considerable force. The energy for muscle contraction is supplied by ATP. Because one molecule of ATP supplies the energy for one interaction between a myosin cross-bridge and an actin filament, the cell needs plenty of ATP molecules for a strong contraction. Recall that the cell can produce ATP in two ways—by cellular respiration and by fermentation.

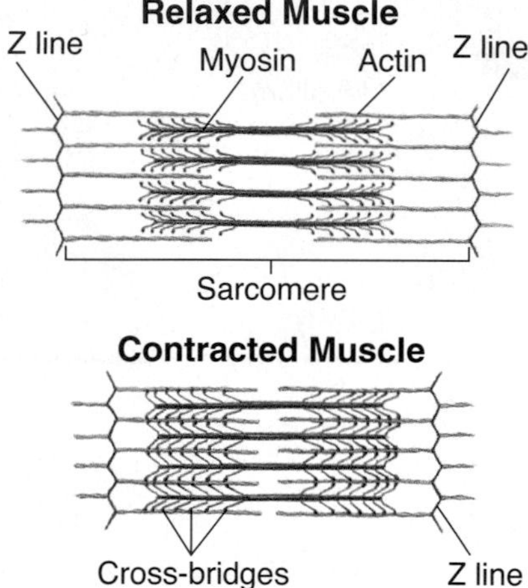

Figure 36–8 **During muscle contraction, the actin filaments slide over the myosin filaments, decreasing the distance between the Z lines.**

What is actin? What is myosin?

Actin

Binding sites

Cross-bridge

Myosin

During muscle contraction, the knoblike head of a myosin filament attaches to a binding site on actin, forming a cross-bridge.

Movement of Actin Filament

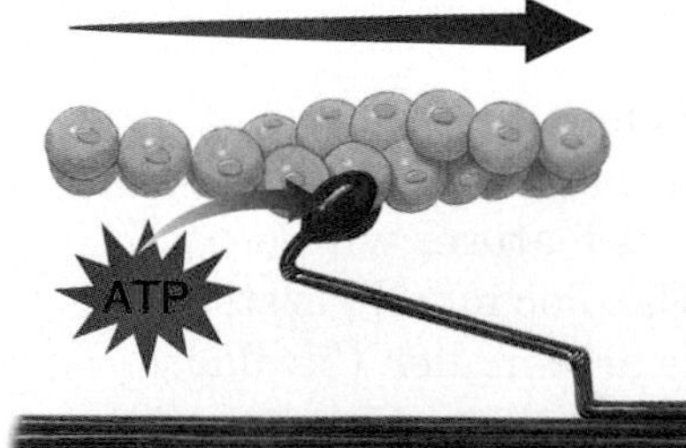

Powered by ATP, the myosin cross-bridge changes shape and pulls the actin filament toward the center of the sarcomere.

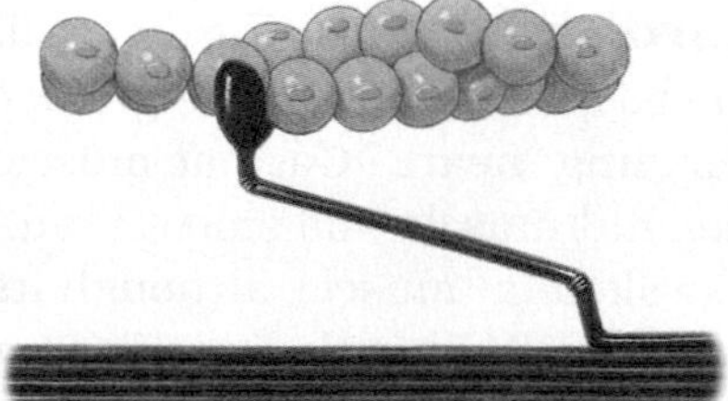

The cross-bridge is broken, the myosin binds to another site on the actin filament, and the cycle begins again.

Control of Muscle Contraction

Skeletal muscles are useful only if they contract in a controlled fashion. Remember that motor neurons connect the central nervous system to skeletal muscle cells. Impulses from motor neurons control the contraction of skeletal muscle fibers.

Figure 36–9 shows a **neuromuscular** (noo-roh-MUS-kyoo-lur) **junction,** which is the point of contact between a motor neuron and a skeletal muscle cell. Vesicles, or pockets, in the axon terminals of the motor neuron release a neurotransmitter called **acetylcholine** (as-ih-til-KOH-leen). Acetylcholine molecules diffuse across the synapse, producing an impulse in the cell membrane of the muscle fiber. The impulse causes the release of calcium ions (Ca^{2+}) within the fiber. The calcium ions affect regulatory proteins that allow actin and myosin filaments to interact. From the time a nerve impulse reaches a muscle cell, it is only a few milliseconds before these events occur and the muscle cell contracts.

A muscle cell remains contracted until the release of acetylcholine stops and an enzyme produced at the axon terminal destroys any remaining acetylcholine. Then, the cell pumps calcium ions back into storage, the cross-bridges stop forming, and contraction ends.

What is the difference between a strong contraction and a weak contraction? Each muscle contains hundreds of cells. When you lift something light, such as a sheet of paper, your brain stimulates only a few cells in your arm muscles to contract. However, as you exert maximum effort, as the rock climber in **Figure 36–10** is doing, almost all the muscle cells in your arm are stimulated to contract.

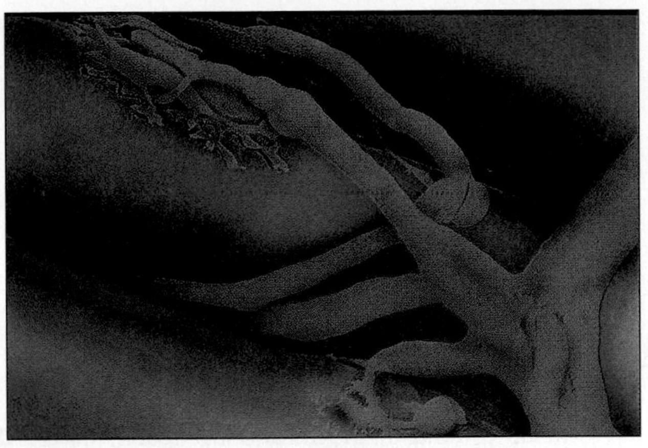

▲ **Figure 36–9** The long green axon of a motor neuron makes contact with a long pink muscle fiber at the neuromuscular junction. (Note that color has been added to this SEM.)

▼ **Figure 36–10** Because this rock climber exercises regularly, her muscles are firm and have increased in size. **Predicting** *What would happen to her muscles if she stopped exercising regularly?*

Quick Lab

What do tendons do?

Materials raw chicken wing treated with bleach, paper towels, forceps, scissors, scalpel

Procedure 

1. Put on the plastic gloves and lab apron. **CAUTION:** *Do not touch your face with your hands during the lab. Be careful with the scissors and scalpel.*
2. Put a chicken wing on a paper towel. Peel back or cut away the skin and fat of the largest wing segment to expose the large muscle. This muscle is called the biceps. Find the tendon that attaches the biceps to the bones of the middle segment of the wing. Tendons are the tough, shiny white cords that join the muscles to the bones.
3. Use forceps to pull on the tendon of the biceps and observe what happens to the chicken wing.

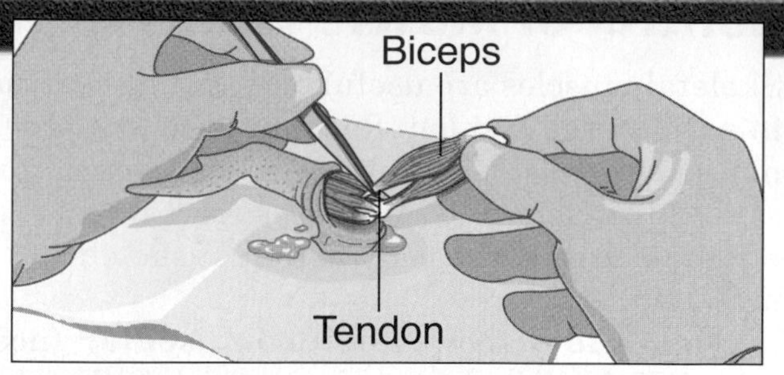

4. Clean your tools and dispose of the chicken wing and gloves according to your teacher's instructions. Wash your hands with soap and warm water.
5. Next, observe the back of your hand as you move each of your fingers in turn. Compare what you see to how the chicken wing moved.

Analyze and Conclude

1. **Applying Concepts** What happened when you pulled on the tendon? In a live chicken, what structure would pull on the tendon to move the wing?
2. **Comparing and Contrasting** How is the way the wing moves similar to the way your fingers move?

How Muscles and Bones Interact

Skeletal muscles generate force and produce movement by contracting, or pulling on body parts. Individual muscles can only pull in one direction. Yet, you know from experience that your legs bend when you sit and extend when you stand up. How is this possible?

Skeletal muscles are joined to bones by tough connective tissues called **tendons.** Tendons are attached in such a way that they pull on the bones and make them work like levers. The joint functions as a fulcrum—the fixed point around which the lever moves. The muscles provide the force to move the lever. Usually, there are several muscles surrounding each joint that pull in different directions.

Most skeletal muscles work in opposing pairs. When one muscle contracts, the other relaxes. The muscles of the upper arm shown in **Figure 36–11** are a good example of this dual action. When the biceps muscle contracts, it bends, or flexes, the elbow joint. When the triceps muscle contracts, it opens, or extends, the elbow joint. A controlled movement, however, requires contraction by both muscles. To hold a tennis racket or a violin, both the biceps and triceps must contract in balance. This is why the training of athletes and musicians is so difficult. The brain must learn how to work opposing muscle groups in just the right ways to make the joint move precisely.

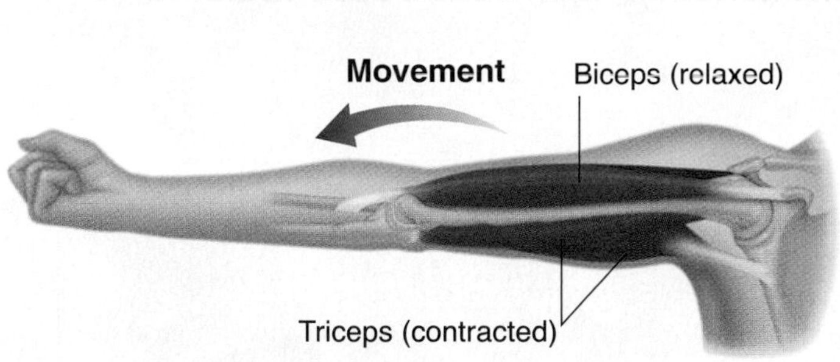

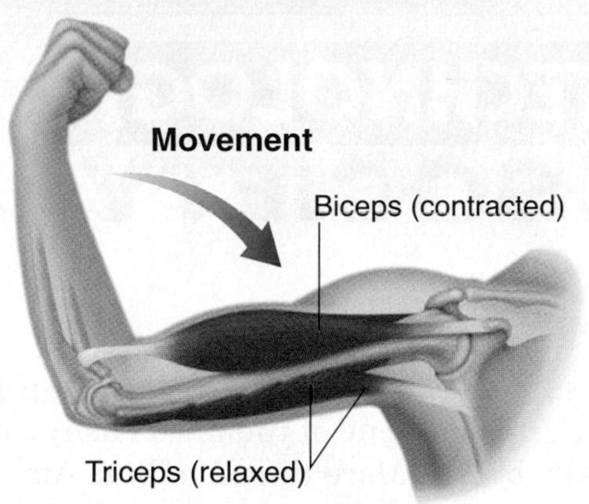

▲ **Figure 36–11** By contracting and relaxing, the triceps and biceps in the upper arm enable you to bend or straighten your elbow. **Applying Concepts** ***Which skeletal muscle must contract in order for you to straighten your elbow?***

Exercise and Health

Skeletal muscles generally remain in a state of partial contraction called resting muscle tone. Muscle tone is responsible for keeping the back and legs straight and the head upright, even when you are relaxed.

Regular exercise is important in maintaining muscular strength and flexibility. Muscles that are exercised regularly stay firm and increase in size and strength by adding actin and myosin filaments. Muscles that are not used become weak and can visibly decrease in size.

Aerobic exercises—such as running and swimming—cause the body's systems to become more efficient. For example, aerobic exercise helps your heart and lungs become more efficient. This, in turn, increases physical endurance—the ability to perform an activity without fatigue. Regular exercise also strengthens your bones, making them thicker and stronger. Strong bones and muscles are less likely to become injured.

Resistance exercises, such as weight lifting, increase muscle size and strength. Resistance exercises also decrease body fat and increase muscle mass. Over time, weight-training exercises will help to maintain coordination and flexibility.

36–2 Section Assessment

1. **Key Concept** List the three types of muscle tissue and explain the function of each.
2. **Key Concept** Explain how a muscle contracts.
3. **Key Concept** Describe the importance of regular exercise.
4. What is the function of the muscular system?
5. What is the role of acetylcholine in the process of muscle contraction?
6. **Critical Thinking Predicting** If a muscle cell receives a second stimulus while it is contracting, will it respond to the second stimulus? Explain.

Sharpen Your Skills

Using Models
Create your own model to show how actin filaments slide over myosin filaments during a muscle contraction. Include as much detail in your model as possible.

TECHNOLOGY & SOCIETY

Making Artificial Skin

The skin is not only the largest organ in the body, it is also one of the most easily injured, especially by fire. More than 2 million Americans suffer burn injuries every year, and more than 10,000 die from such injuries. The skin is the body's most important barrier against infection, but burns can destroy that barrier, leaving tissues exposed and vulnerable.

The best way to protect badly burned tissue is to cover it with a layer of fresh skin. If the burned region is small, this can be done with skin grafts taken from other parts of the body. For larger burns, however, this isn't possible. Scientists have developed a way to help many victims of serious burns—they have developed artificial skin.

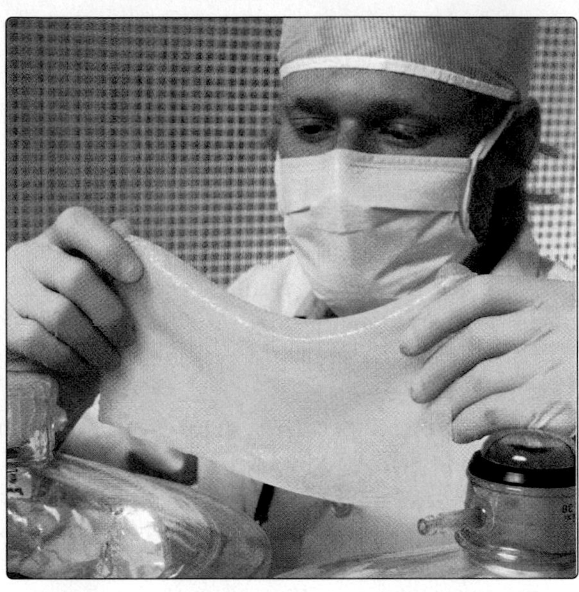

Constructing a Scaffold

Skin is a complex organ. For this reason, researchers realized that the best way to replace skin would be with an artificial skin that the body's own cells could grow into. After the outer layer of burned tissue is removed from a severely burned patient, surgeons can apply artificial skin made from a biodegradable meshwork of protein fibers similar to those in human skin. Cells from the dermis migrate upward and gradually "take over" the artificial layer, replacing the meshwork with human proteins. Thus, a new layer of dermis is produced. A very thin layer of the patient's own epidermal cells, grown in culture, is then applied to the surface of the artificial skin.

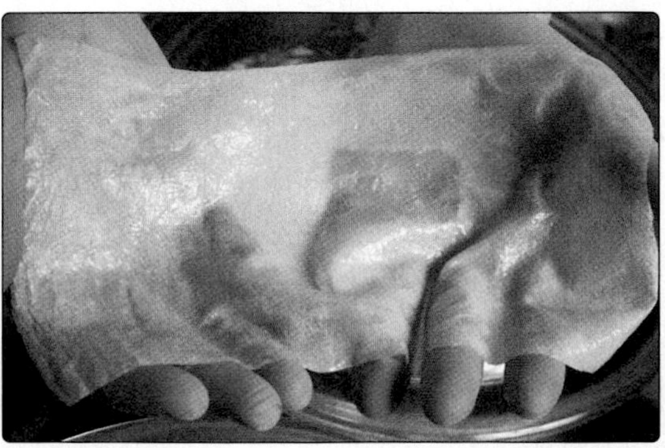

Perfecting the Technique

Artificial skin is used only in the treatment of burns so severe that normal healing is not possible. One of its main drawbacks is that the migration of cells into the artificial layer may take as long as three weeks, enough time for infection and other complications to develop. Researchers are trying to speed up the process by placing cell-growth signal chemicals in the artificial layer. If they succeed, the successful treatment of even serious burns may become routine.

Research and Decide

Use library or Internet references to learn more about artifical skin and how it is used for the treatment of serious burns. Design a brochure that explains and illustrates the steps in the treatment of third-degree burns.

For: Links from the authors
Visit: PHSchool.com
Web Code: cbe-0363

36–3 The Integumentary System

4-1.2 Humans have complex systems
4-1.2 Human systems detect changes
4-1.2 Cells are grouped for efficiency
LS- Analyze results
LS- Organize data in tables/graphs

"Good fences make good neighbors," wrote the American poet Robert Frost as he explained the importance of property boundaries. Living things have their own "fences," and none is as important as the skin—the boundary that separates the human body from the outside world.

The skin, the single largest organ of the body, is part of the integumentary (in-teg-yoo-MEN-tuh-ree) system. The word *integument* comes from a Latin word that means "to cover," reflecting the fact that the skin and its related structures form a covering over the entire body. Skin and its related structures—the hair, nails, and a variety of glands—make up the integumentary system.

Guide for Reading

Key Concept
- What are the functions of the integumentary system?

Vocabulary
epidermis
keratin
melanin
dermis
hair follicle

Reading Strategy: Building Vocabulary
Before you read, preview **Figure 36–13** to identify vocabulary with which you are unfamiliar. As you read, look for the meaning of these terms.

The Skin

The skin has many different functions, but its most important function is protection. **The integumentary system serves as a barrier against infection and injury, helps to regulate body temperature, removes waste products from the body, and provides protection against ultraviolet radiation from the sun.** Because the largest component of the integumentary system—the skin—contains several types of sensory receptors, it serves as the gateway through which sensations such as pressure, heat, cold, and pain are transmitted to the nervous system.

The skin is made up of two main layers—the epidermis and the dermis. Beneath the dermis is a subcutaneous layer of fat (the hypodermis) and loose connective tissue that help insulate the body.

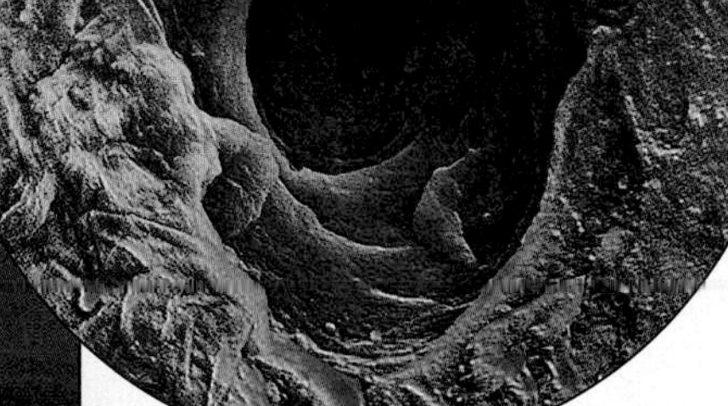

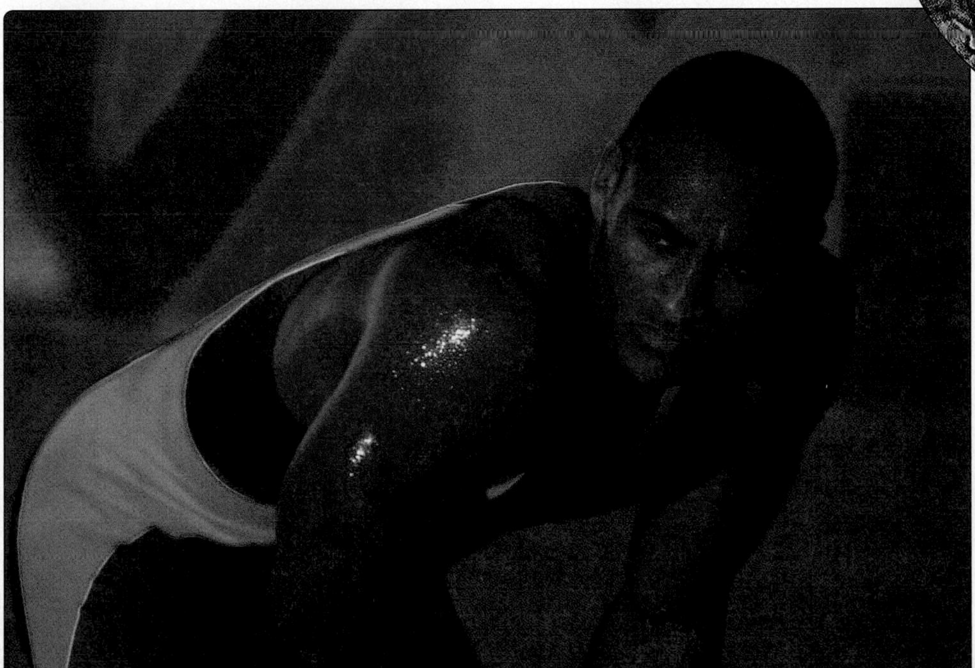

(magnification: 340×)

Figure 36–12 **After strenuous exercise, the skin produces sweat, which decreases the temperature of the body and rids the body of wastes.** Sweat is secreted by sweat glands and leaves the body through sweat pores.

FIGURE 36–13 STRUCTURE OF THE SKIN

The skin has an outer layer called the epidermis and an inner layer called the dermis. **Predicting** *What is the function of the dermis?*

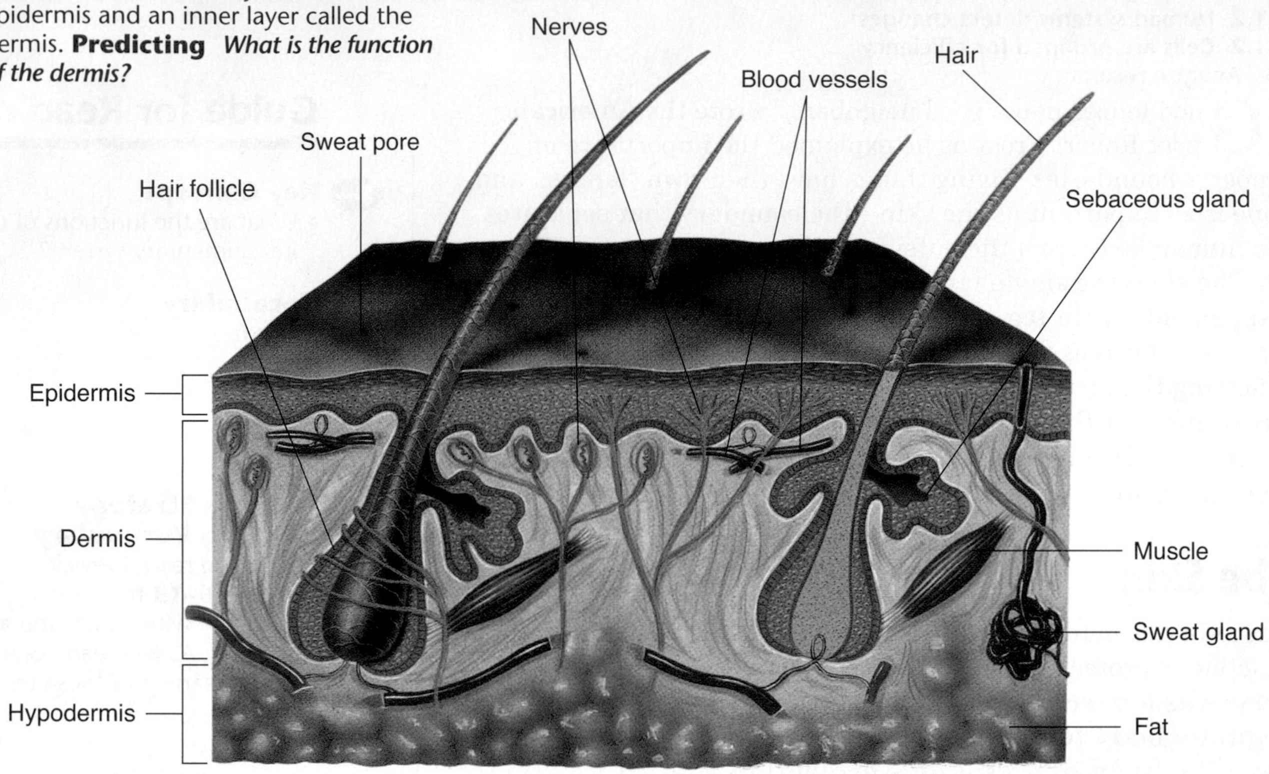

Nerves
Hair
Blood vessels
Sweat pore
Hair follicle
Sebaceous gland
Epidermis
Dermis
Hypodermis
Muscle
Sweat gland
Fat

Word Origins

Epidermis comes from two Greek words: *epi,* meaning "on the outside," and *derma,* meaning "skin." **If the Greek word *phyton* means "plant," what does the term *epiphyte* mean?**

Epidermis The outer layer of the skin is the **epidermis.** The epidermis has two layers. The outside of the epidermis—the part that comes in contact with the environment—is made up of dead cells. The inner layer of the epidermis is made up of living cells.

Cells in the inner layer of the epidermis undergo rapid cell division, producing new cells that push older cells to the surface of the skin. As they move upward, the older cells become flattened and their organelles disintegrate. They also begin making **keratin,** a tough, fibrous protein.

Eventually, the keratin-producing cells die and form a tough, flexible, waterproof covering on the surface of the skin. This outer layer of dead cells is shed or washed away at a surprising rate—once every four to five weeks.

The epidermis also contains melanocytes (MEL-uh-noh-syts). Melanocytes are cells that produce **melanin,** a dark brown pigment. Melanin helps protect the skin from damage by absorbing ultraviolet rays from the sun. Although most people have roughly the same number of melanocytes in their skin, differences in skin color are caused by the different amount of melanin the melanocytes produce and where these cells are distributed.

Look closely at **Figure 36–13** and you will see that there are no blood vessels in the epidermis. This explains why a slight scratch will not cause bleeding.

What is melanin?

Dermis The inner layer of the skin is the **dermis.** The dermis lies beneath the epidermis and contains collagen fibers, blood vessels, nerve endings, glands, sensory receptors, smooth muscles, and hair follicles.

The skin interacts with other body systems to maintain homeostasis by helping to regulate body temperature. When the body needs to conserve heat on a cold day, the blood vessels in the dermis narrow, helping to limit heat loss. On hot days, the blood vessels widen, bringing heat from the body's core to the skin and increasing heat loss.

The dermis contains two major types of glands: sweat glands and sebaceous (suh-BAY-shus), or oil, glands. If your body gets too hot, sweat glands produce perspiration, or sweat. Sweat contains water, salts, and other compounds. When sweat evaporates, it takes heat away from your body. Sweat also gets rid of wastes from the blood, along with water. In this way, the skin acts as an organ of excretion. Sebaceous glands produce an oily secretion called sebum. Sebum spreads out along the surface of the skin and helps to keep the keratin-rich epidermis flexible and waterproof.

What structures are found in the dermis?

Analyzing Data

The UV Index and Sunburn

Ultraviolet (UV) radiation is one type of energy from the sun. UV rays cause sunburn, some cataracts, and skin cancer. There are many factors that affect the amount of UV radiation to which you are exposed. These include the time of day, the season, the weather conditions, and your location. Recently, the National Weather Service, the Environmental Protection Agency, and the Centers for Disease Control agreed upon a national UV index. The UV index is issued daily to advise you of conditions in your region of the country. Use the information in the chart to answer the questions that follow.

Protection From Sunburn

UV Index Level	How to Protect Yourself	Minutes to Burn
Minimal (0–2)	Apply sunscreen Wear sunglasses near snow and water	60
Low (3–4)	Apply sunscreen Wear sunglasses and hat	45
Moderate (5–6)	Apply sunscreen Wear sunglasses and hat Apply lip balm	30
High (7–9)	Apply sunscreen Wear sunglasses and hat Seek shade from 10 AM to 4 PM	15
Very High (10+)	Apply sunscreen Wear sunglasses and hat Avoid sun from 10 AM to 4 PM	10

1. **Interpreting Graphics** Describe the trend in the amount of time it takes to sunburn, from a minimal UV index level to a very high UV index level.
2. **Applying Concepts** Why do you think applying sunscreen is always recommended?
3. **Drawing Conclusions** Why should a hat worn as protection against UV rays have a brim?
4. **Predicting** The minutes-to-burn data apply to most people. What variable could cause the time for a particular person to burn to be shorter or to be longer?
5. **Using Tables and Graphs** Use the data in the table to construct a bar graph. Place the UV index levels on the *x*-axis and the minutes to burn on the *y*-axis.

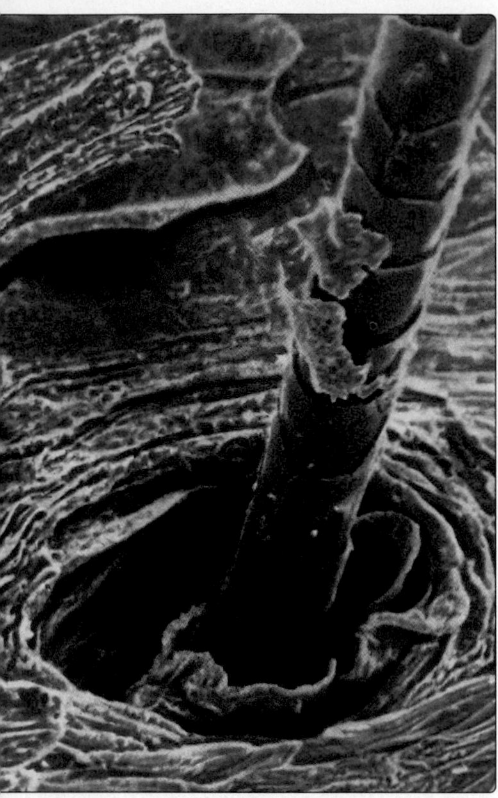

▲ **Figure 36–14** In this color-enhanced scanning electron micrograph of a hair shaft, the scalelike structures are layers of skin cells. The part of the hair that is above the skin is made up of dead cells that become filled with keratin. **Observing** *What layer of the skin contains the hair follicle?*

Skin Cancer Excessive exposure to the ultraviolet radiation in sunlight can produce skin cancer, an abnormal growth of cells in the skin. You can help protect yourself from this dangerous disease by wearing a hat, sunglasses, and protective clothing whenever you plan to spend time outside. In addition, you should always use a sunscreen with a sun protection factor (SPF) of at least 15.

Hair and Nails

The basic structure of human hair and nails is keratin. In other animals, keratin forms a variety of structures, including bull horns, reptile scales, bird feathers, and porcupine quills.

Hair Hair covers almost every exposed surface of the body and has important functions. Hair on the head protects the scalp from ultraviolet light from the sun and provides insulation from the cold. Hairs in the nostrils, external ear canals, and around the eyes (eyelashes) prevent dirt and other particles from entering the body.

Hair is produced by cells at the base of structures called hair follicles. **Hair follicles** are tubelike pockets of epidermal cells that extend into the dermis. The individual hair shown in **Figure 36–14** is actually a large column of cells that have filled with keratin and then died. Rapid cell growth at the base of the hair follicle causes the hair to grow longer. Hair follicles are in close contact with sebaceous glands. The oily secretions of these glands help maintain the condition of each individual hair.

Nails Nails grow from an area of rapidly dividing cells known as the nail root. The nail root is located near the tips of the fingers and toes. During cell division, the cells of the nail root fill with keratin and produce a tough, platelike nail that covers and protects the tips of the fingers and toes. Nails grow at an average rate of 3 millimeters per month, with fingernails growing more rapidly than toenails—about four times as fast.

36–3 Section Assessment

1. **Key Concept** List the functions of the integumentary system.
2. What organs and tissues make up the integumentary system?
3. Compare the structures of the epidermis and dermis.
4. How does the skin help maintain body temperature?
5. In what way is the growth of hair and nails similar?
6. **Critical Thinking Applying Concepts** Why does cutting your skin hurt, but cutting your hair or nails does not hurt?

Connecting Concepts

Plant Structure
Compare and contrast the structure and function of the dermal tissue in plants discussed in Chapter 23 with the structures in human skin. In what ways are they similar? *Hint:* You may wish to organize your ideas in a Venn diagram.

Making a Model of a Transdermal Patch

Some medications are introduced into the body using a patch attached to the skin, rather than by mouth or by injection. This is especially useful for medications that need to be continuously released in very small quantities over an extended period of time. In this investigation, you will model how these patches, called transdermal patches, work.

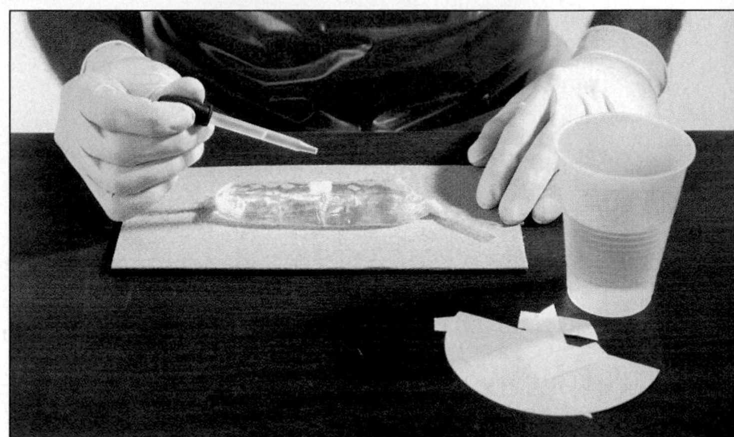

Problem

How can some medications be given through the skin?

Materials

- dialysis tubing
- plastic cup
- phenolphthalein solution
- 50-mL graduated cylinder
- paper towels
- scissors
- metric ruler
- filter paper
- dropper pipette
- sodium bicarbonate solution

Skills

Using Models, Observing

Procedure

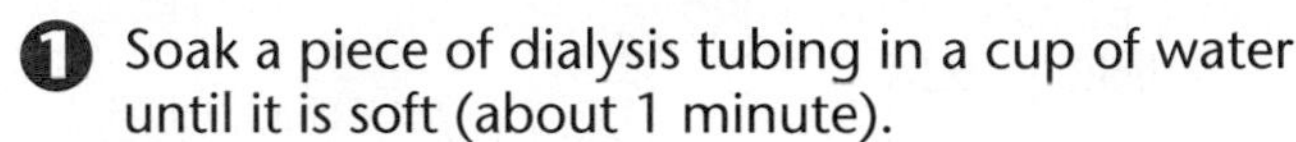

1. Soak a piece of dialysis tubing in a cup of water until it is soft (about 1 minute).
2. Put on your lab apron, goggles, and plastic gloves. Tie a knot in one end of the dialysis tubing. Use a graduated cylinder to fill the tubing with phenolphthalein solution. **CAUTION:** *Phenolphthalein is toxic. Do not rub your eyes during this investigation.*
3. Squeeze as much air out of the tubing as you can, then tie a knot in the open end of the tubing to seal it off. The tubing represents the cell membrane of a skin cell.
4. Lay the model skin cell down on a paper towel. Use another paper towel to wipe dry the outside of the tubing.
5. Use the scissors to carefully cut out four 1-cm squares of filter paper. **CAUTION:** *Scissors are sharp. Handle them carefully.* Stack the filter-paper squares on top of the model skin cell. The filter paper represents a patch that will be saturated with the medication to be delivered.
6. Using a dropper pipette, carefully soak the filter paper, 1 drop at a time, with sodium bicarbonate solution. Try not to let the solution run down the sides of the tubing. The sodium bicarbonate solution represents the medication.
7. Observe the model cell for 10 to 15 minutes and record your observations.

Analyze and Conclude

1. **Observing** What happened when you added the sodium bicarbonate solution to the filter paper?
2. **Evaluating** Do you consider this procedure an adequate model of a transdermal patch? If not, propose an alternative model. Explain your response by citing specific details.
3. **Drawing Conclusions** What kinds of substances would be absorbed most easily in this way? Explain your answer.
4. **SAFETY** Explain how you demonstrated safe practices as you carried out this investigation.

Go Further

Additional Research Research transdermal patches in the library or on the Internet. Write a brief report describing at least two uses of transdermal patches. Describe the advantages and disadvantages of transdermal patches compared with injections and oral medications.

Chapter 36 Study Guide

36–1 The Skeletal System

Key Concepts

- The human skeleton supports the body, protects internal organs, provides for movement, stores mineral reserves, and provides a site for blood cell formation.
- Bones are a solid network of living cells and protein fibers that are surrounded by deposits of calcium salts.
- Depending on its type of movement, a joint is classified as immovable, slightly movable, or freely movable.

Vocabulary

periosteum, p. 922
Haversian canal, p. 922
bone marrow, p. 922
cartilage, p. 922
ossification, p. 923
joint, p. 924
ligament, p. 925

36–2 The Muscular System

Key Concepts

- There are three different types of muscle tissue: skeletal, smooth, and cardiac.
- A muscle fiber contracts when the thin filaments in the muscle fiber slide over the thick filaments.
- Regular exercise is important in maintaining muscular strength and flexibility.

Vocabulary

myosin, p. 928
actin, p. 928
neuromuscular junction, p. 929
acetylcholine, p. 929
tendon, p. 930

36–3 The Integumentary System

Key Concept

- The integumentary system serves as a barrier against infection and injury, helps to regulate body temperature, removes waste products from the body, and provides protection against ultraviolet radiation from the sun.

Vocabulary

epidermis, p. 934
keratin, p. 934
melanin, p. 934
dermis, p. 935
hair follicle, p. 936

Thinking Visually

Using the information in this chapter, complete the following concept map:

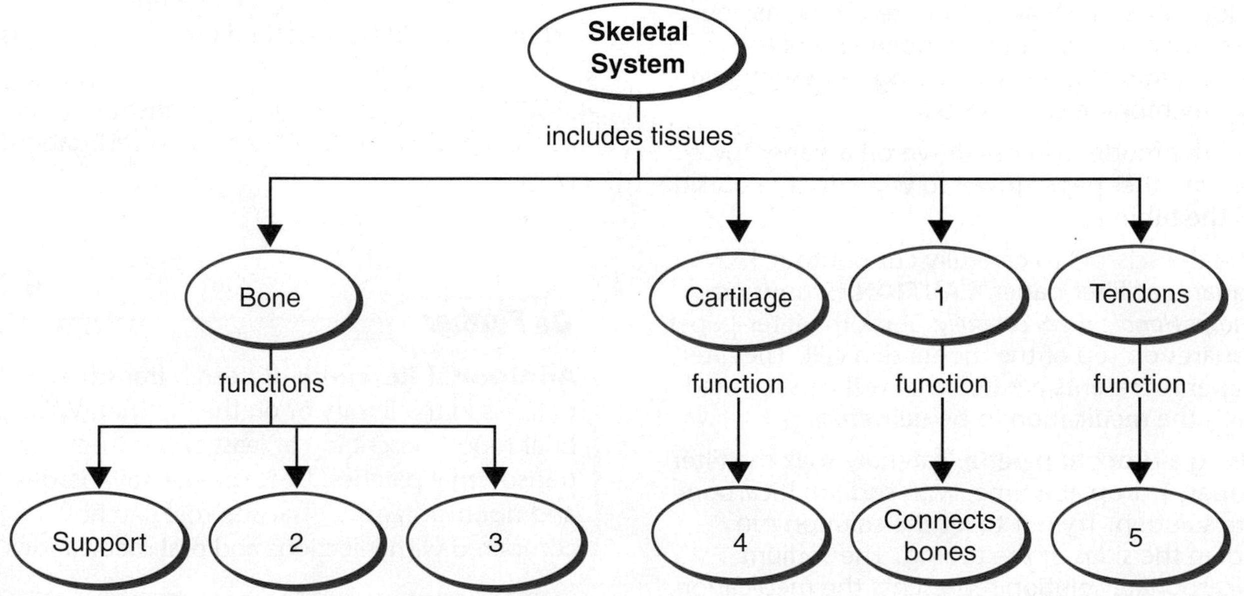

Preparing for the Living Environment Exam

Blue questions emphasize Regents Exam content

Chapter 36

Part A

Multiple Choice

For each statement or question, select the number of the word or expression that, of those given, best completes the statement or answers the question.

1 The tough connective tissue layer surrounding bone is called
(1) tendon
(2) ligament
(3) periosteum
(4) cartilage

2 Haversian canals are located
(1) in the periosteum
(2) in the cartilage
(3) running through compact bone
(4) running through spongy bone

3 Cartilage is replaced by bone during the process of
(1) ossification
(2) calcification
(3) ligamentation
(4) puberty

4 Strips of tough connective tissue that hold bones together are known as
(1) tendons
(2) smooth muscles
(3) striated muscles
(4) ligaments

5 Small sacs of synovial fluid that help reduce friction between the bones of a joint are called
(1) bursae
(2) ligaments
(3) tendons
(4) striations

6 Which figure shows smooth muscle tissue?

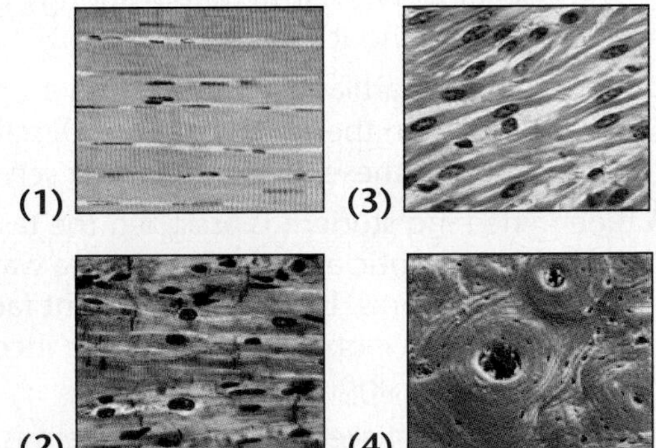

7 Joints that allow circular movement are referred to as
(1) gliding joints
(2) ball-and-socket joints
(3) hinge joints
(4) pivot joints

8 Two proteins that are involved in the contraction of muscle are
(1) sarcomere and myofibril
(2) actin and myosin
(3) periosteum and cartilage
(4) ATP and acetylcholine

9 The point of contact between a motor neuron and a skeletal muscle cell is called a
(1) cross-bridge site
(2) periosteum
(3) tendon
(4) neuromuscular junction

10 The outermost layer of skin is the
(1) dermis
(2) keratin
(3) epidermis
(4) melanin

11 Variations in human skin color are the result of differences in
(1) number of melanocytes in the skin
(2) amount of melanin produced by each melanocyte
(3) amount of keratin in the skin
(4) amount of sebum produced in the dermis

12 Smooth muscle is found in the
(1) walls of blood vessels
(2) heart
(3) skeletal muscles
(4) joints

13 All are important roles of the skeletal system *except*
(1) protection of internal organs
(2) movement of the body
(3) production of red blood cells
(4) regulation of body temperature

Test-Taking Tip When evaluating multiple-choice answers, be sure to read all the choices, even if the first choice seems to be correct. When you consider all the choices, you are more likely to choose the best one.

Preparing for the Living Environment Exam

Part B

Multiple Choice and Extended Response
For those questions that ask you to select a response, choose the one that best completes the statement or answers the question. For all others follow the directions given.

14 State *two* ways the circulatory system and skeletal system interact in the human body.

15 Explain how skeletal muscles work in opposing pairs, including one specific example.

Base your answers to questions 16 through 18 on the information and graphs below and on your knowledge of biology.

Osteoporosis is a disease characterized by the loss and weakening of bone tissue. One possible explanation for this condition is that, as people age, the calcium content of their bones decreases. To assess this hypothesis, the bone mineral content of 250 men and 250 women was measured. The data are shown in the graph below.

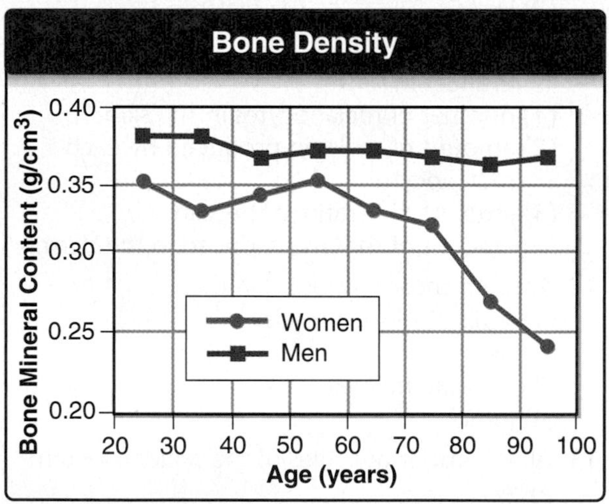

16 At which age range do women show the lowest bone mineral content?
(1) 60–69 years
(2) 70–79 years
(3) 80–89 years
(4) 90–95 years

17 A valid conclusion that can be drawn from this graph is that, on average,
(1) women lose more bone mineral content as they age than men do
(2) men lose more bone mineral content as they age than women do
(3) women gain bone mineral content as they age
(4) men gain bone mineral content as they age

18 A possible way of slowing osteoporosis is to
(1) add calcium to the diet
(2) strengthen the ligaments
(3) receive a bone marrow transplant
(4) reduce salt in the diet

Base your answer to question 19 on the information below. For each numbered space in the passage, record (on your own paper) the letter of the structure indicated on the section of long bone that most correctly completes the sentence. A choice may be used once, more than once, or not at all.

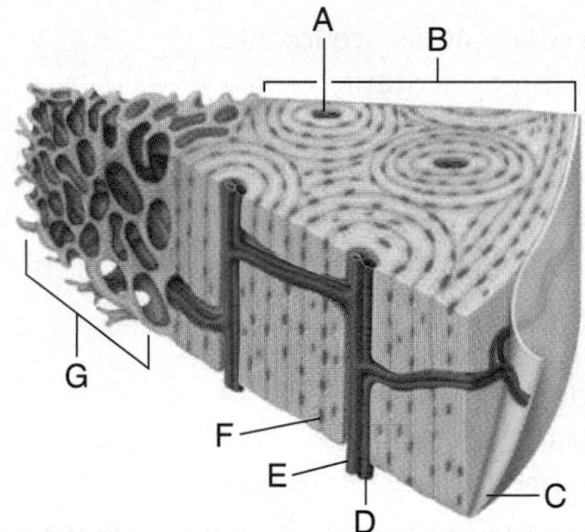

19 It is easy to think of bones as nonliving. However, a solid network of living cells such as **(1)** _______ forms bone tissue. A tough layer of connective tissue, the **(2)** _____, surrounds each bone. Even though it may appear to be, bone is far from being solid. Running through compact bone is a network of tubes, the **(3)** ______ that contain blood vessels and nerves. A less dense bone tissue, spongy bone, helps to add strength. Spongy bone is shown in region **(4)** ______. The latticework structure of spongy bone adds strength without adding mass.

20 Disks of rubbery cartilage are found between the individual bones in the spinal column. Describe the function that these disks of cartilage serve.

21 A bioengineering student is assigned the task of developing a robotic arm that works the way a human elbow works. List *three* important facts about the human elbow he will need to incorporate into his design.

22 A skin callus is a thickening of the epidermis caused by repeated rubbing. Explain why people often get calluses on their feet.

23 Cartilage does not appear on X-ray film. It is seen as a clear area between the shaft and the ends of the individual bones. Examine the X-rays below.

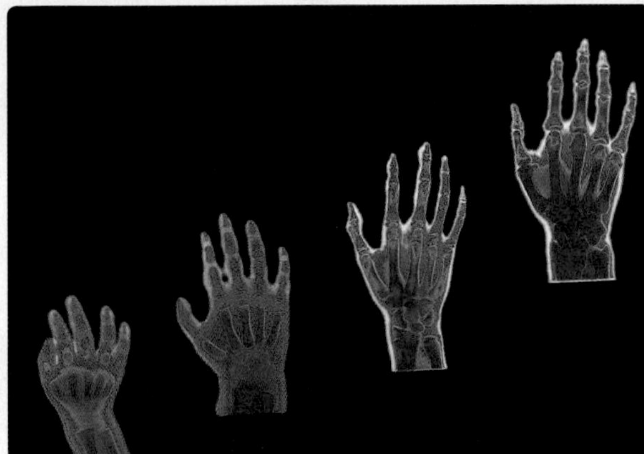

a Which *two* hands belong to the youngest individuals? Explain how you determined this.

b List *two* functions of cartilage in the human body.

24 Certain bacteria produce a toxin that prevents the release of acetylcholine from the motor neurons. Explain why this can result in a fatal loss of muscle movement.

25 Which of the joints shown below is a pivot joint?

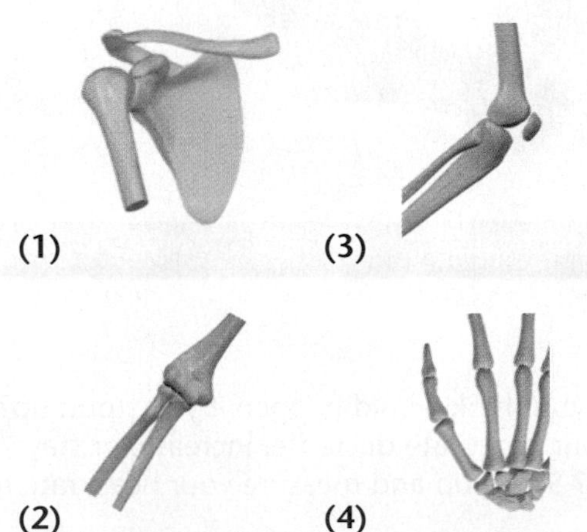

26 Explain why spongy bone tissue is found in the ends of long bones.

Part C

Extended Response

Answer the questions or follow the directions given.

Base your answers to questions 27 through 29 on the information below.

Ultraviolet rays from the sun can cause sunburn. Sunscreens have been advertised as effective protection against sunburns. A biology student wants to design an experiment to determine whether the advertising claims are accurate.

Provide the information requested below that should be included in a research plan to test the effectiveness of five different sunscreen products.

27 State a hypothesis.

28 Identify the manipulated (independent) variable.

29 State *two* factors that should be kept constant.

For: An interactive self-test
Visit: PHSchool.com
Web Code: cba-0360

CHAPTER 37

Circulatory and Respiratory Systems

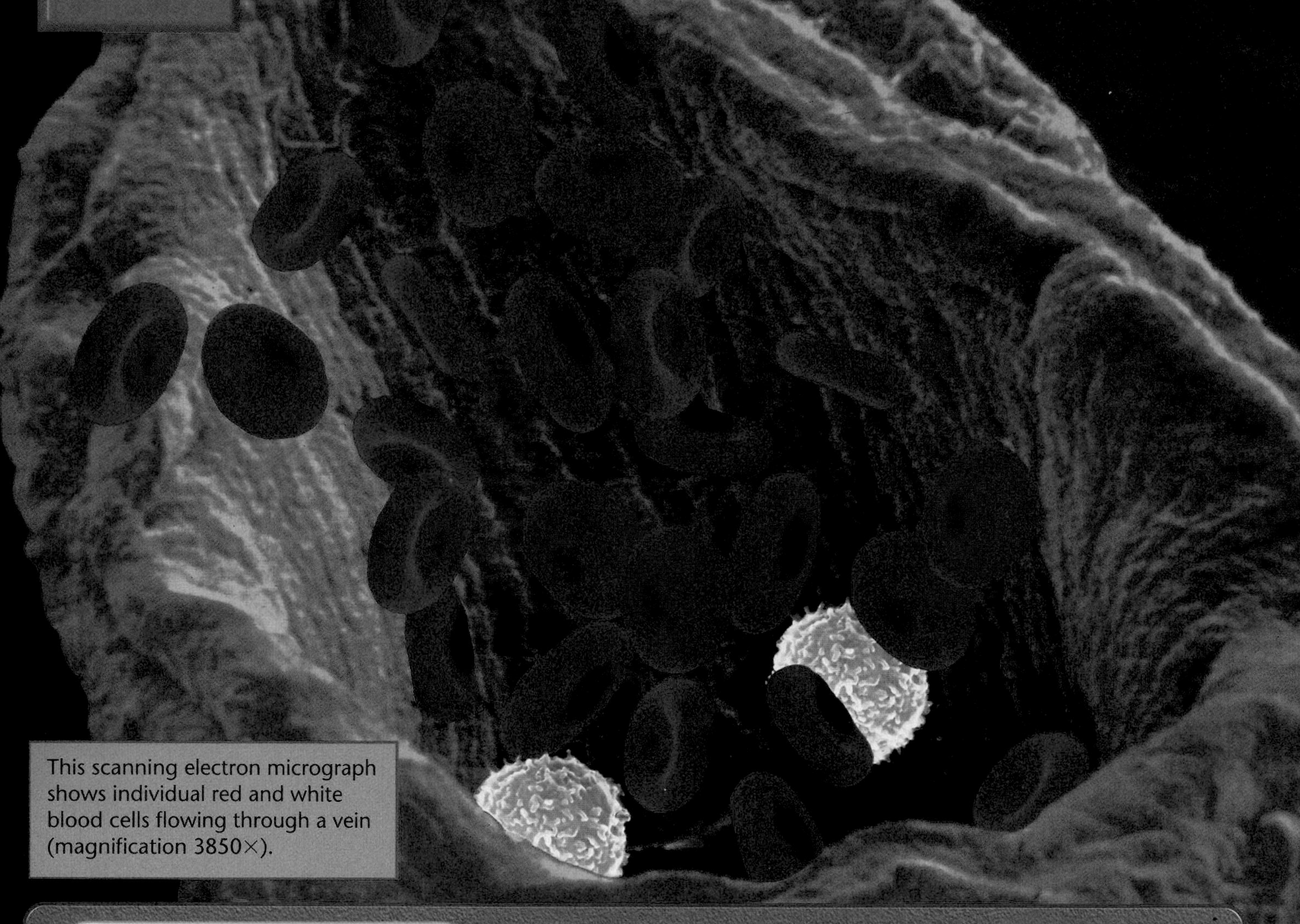

This scanning electron micrograph shows individual red and white blood cells flowing through a vein (magnification 3850×).

Inquiry Activity

What factors affect heart rate?

Procedure

1. If you are using a heart-rate sensor, see your teacher for instructions.
2. While sitting still, measure your heart rate. To do this, find the pulse in one of your wrists using the first two fingers of your other hand.
3. Count the number of beats you feel in 15 seconds and multiply this number by 4. This will give you the number of beats per minute.
4. What do you think would happen if you stood up? Would your heart rate decrease, increase, or stay the same? Stand up and measure your heart rate to find out.

Think About It

Formulating Hypotheses Propose an explanation for any difference between your sitting heart rate and your standing heart rate.

37–1 The Circulatory System

1-S1.1 Historical development of ideas in science
4-1.2 Humans have complex systems
4-5.2 Causes of disease
4-5.2 Biological research
LS- Make observations and state an appropriate hypothesis

Your heartbeat is a sign of life itself. Even when you drift off to sleep, your heart continues to beat at a steady rhythm. Why is this process so important that it must keep going even when you sleep?

Each breath you take brings air into your respiratory system. The oxygen in that air is needed by the trillions of cells in your body. Your heart is essential in delivering that oxygen. Its beating produces the force to move oxygen-rich blood through the circulatory system. Interrelationships between the circulatory and respiratory systems supply cells throughout the body with the nutrients and oxygen they need to stay alive.

Guide for Reading

Key Concepts
- What are the structures of the circulatory system?
- What are the three types of blood vessels in the circulatory system?

Vocabulary
myocardium
atrium
ventricle
pulmonary circulation
systemic circulation
valve
pacemaker
aorta
artery
capillary
vein
atherosclerosis

Reading Strategy: Using Visuals Before you read, preview **Figure 37–3.** Make a list of questions about the illustration. As you read, write down the answers to the questions.

Functions of the Circulatory System

Organisms composed of a small number of cells do not need a circulatory system. Most cells in such organisms are in direct contact with the environment. Oxygen, nutrients, and waste products can easily diffuse back and forth across cell membranes.

Larger organisms, however, cannot rely on diffusion. Most of their cells are not in direct contact with the environment, and substances made in one part of the organism may be needed in another part. In a way, this same problem is faced by the millions of people living in a large city. Cities have transportation systems that move people, goods, and waste material from one place to another. The transportation system of a city is its streets, highways, and rail lines. The transportation system of a living organism is its circulatory system.

Humans and other vertebrates have closed circulatory systems. This means that a circulating fluid called blood is contained within a system of vessels. **The human circulatory system consists of the heart, a series of blood vessels, and the blood that flows through them.**

◀ **Figure 37–1** These roads form a transportation system. **Using Analogies** *How is the human circulatory system like the streets and highways of a large city?*

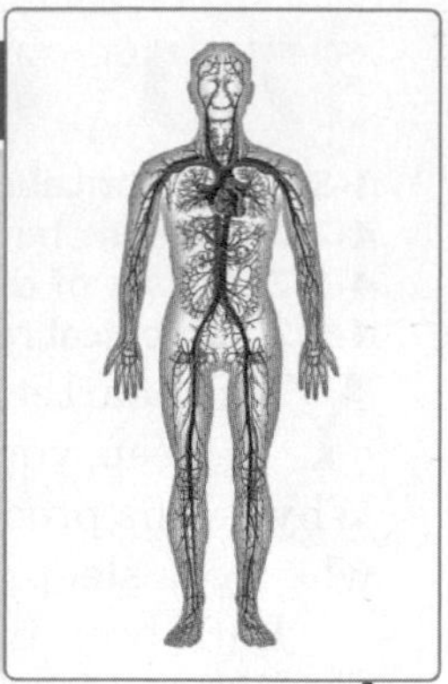

Figure 37–2 **The circulatory system consists of the heart, a series of blood vessels, and the blood.** Notice the valves between the atria and ventricles and those between the ventricles and the blood vessels leaving the heart. The valves prevent blood from flowing backward.

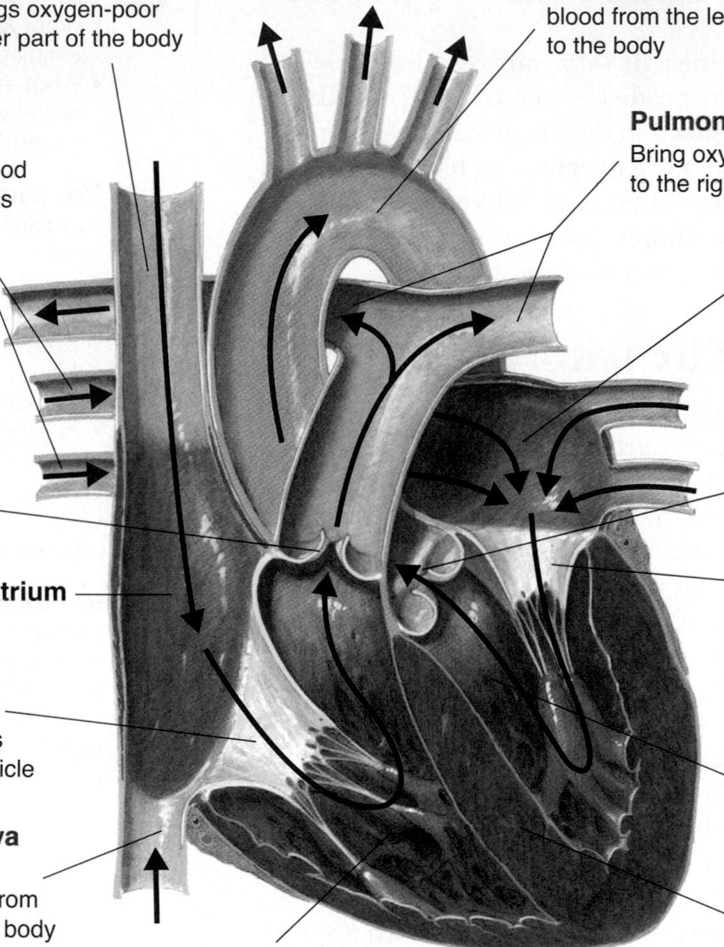

Superior Vena Cava
Large vein that brings oxygen-poor blood from the upper part of the body to the right atrium

Pulmonary Veins
Bring oxygen-rich blood from each of the lungs to the left atrium

Pulmonary Valve
Prevents blood from flowing back into the right ventricle after it has entered the pulmonary artery

Right Atrium

Tricuspid Valve
Prevents blood from flowing back into the right atrium after it has entered the right ventricle

Inferior Vena Cava
Vein that brings oxygen-poor blood from the lower part of the body to the right atrium

Right Ventricle

Aorta
Brings oxygen-rich blood from the left ventricle to the body

Pulmonary Arteries
Bring oxygen-poor blood to the right or left lung

Left Atrium

Aortic Valve
Prevents blood from flowing back into the left ventricle after it has entered the aorta

Mitral Valve
Prevents blood from flowing back into the left atrium after it has entered the left ventricle

Left Ventricle

Septum

Go Online
active art
For: The Heart activity
Visit: PHSchool.com
Web Code: cbp-0371

The Heart

As you can feel with your hand, your heart is located near the center of your chest. The heart, shown in **Figure 37–2,** which is composed almost entirely of muscle, is a hollow organ that is about the size of your clenched fist. The heart is enclosed in a protective sac of tissue called the pericardium (pehr-ih-KAHR-dee-um). In the walls of the heart, there are two thin layers of epithelial and connective tissue that form a sandwich around a thick layer of muscle called the **myocardium.** The powerful contractions of the myocardium pump blood through the circulatory system.

The heart muscle contracts on average 72 times a minute, pumping about 70 milliliters of blood with each contraction. This means that during one year, an average person's heart pumps more than enough blood to fill an Olympic-sized swimming pool. (An Olympic-sized swimming pool is about 2,000,000 liters: 0.07 liters × 4320 beats per hour × 24 hours × 365 days = 2,649,024 liters.)

Dividing the right side of the heart from the left side of the heart is the septum. The septum prevents the mixing of oxygen-poor and oxygen-rich blood. On each side of the septum are two chambers. The upper chamber, which receives the blood, is the **atrium** (plural: atria). The lower chamber, which pumps blood out of the heart, is the **ventricle.** The heart has four chambers in total—two atria and two ventricles.

Circulation Through the Body The heart functions as two separate pumps. **Figure 37–3** shows the circulation of blood through the body. The right side of the heart pumps blood from the heart to the lungs. This pathway is known as **pulmonary circulation.** In the lungs, carbon dioxide leaves the blood and oxygen is absorbed. The oxygen-rich blood then flows into the left side of the heart and is pumped to the rest of the body. This pathway is called **systemic circulation.** Blood that returns to the right side of the heart is oxygen-poor because cells have absorbed much of the oxygen and loaded the blood with carbon dioxide. At this point, it is ready for another trip to the lungs.

▼ **Figure 37–3** The circulatory system is divided into two pathways. Pulmonary circulation carries blood between the heart and the lungs. Systemic circulation carries blood between the heart and the rest of the body. **Observing** ***What kind of blood—oxygen-rich or oxygen-poor—leaves the lungs and returns to the heart?***

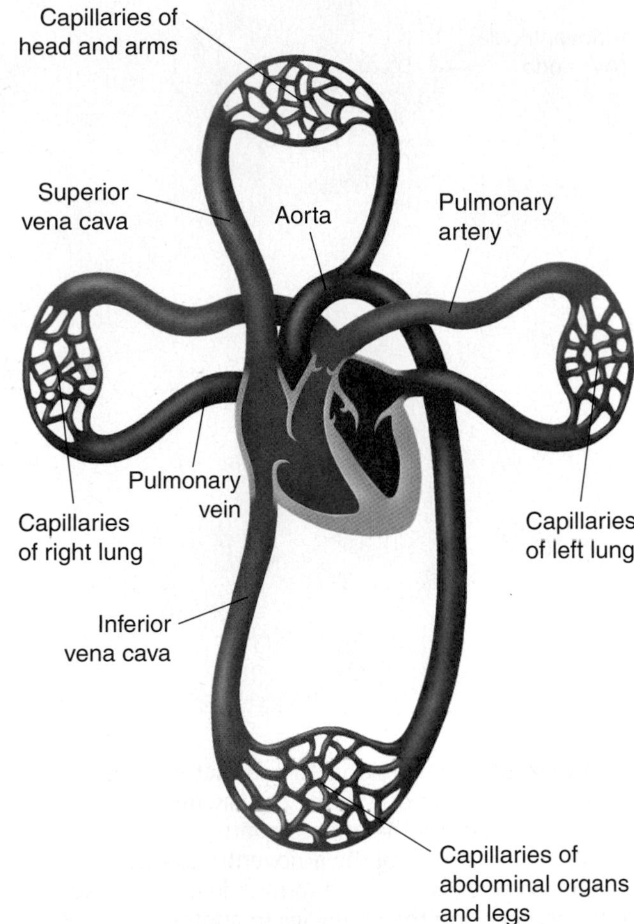

Circulation Through the Heart Blood enters the heart through the right and left atria. As the heart contracts, blood flows into the ventricles and then out from the ventricles to either the body or the lungs. There are flaps of connective tissue called **valves** between the atria and the ventricles. Blood moving from the atria holds the valves open. When the ventricles contract, the valves close, which prevents blood from flowing back into the atria.

At the exits from the right and left ventricles, there are valves that prevent blood that flows out of the heart from flowing back in. This system of valves keeps blood moving through the heart in one direction, like traffic on a one-way street. The one-way flow increases the pumping efficiency of the heart. The valves are so important to heart function that surgeons often attempt to repair or replace a valve that has been damaged due to disease.

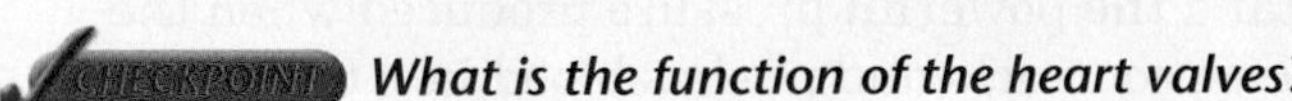
CHECKPOINT *What is the function of the heart valves?*

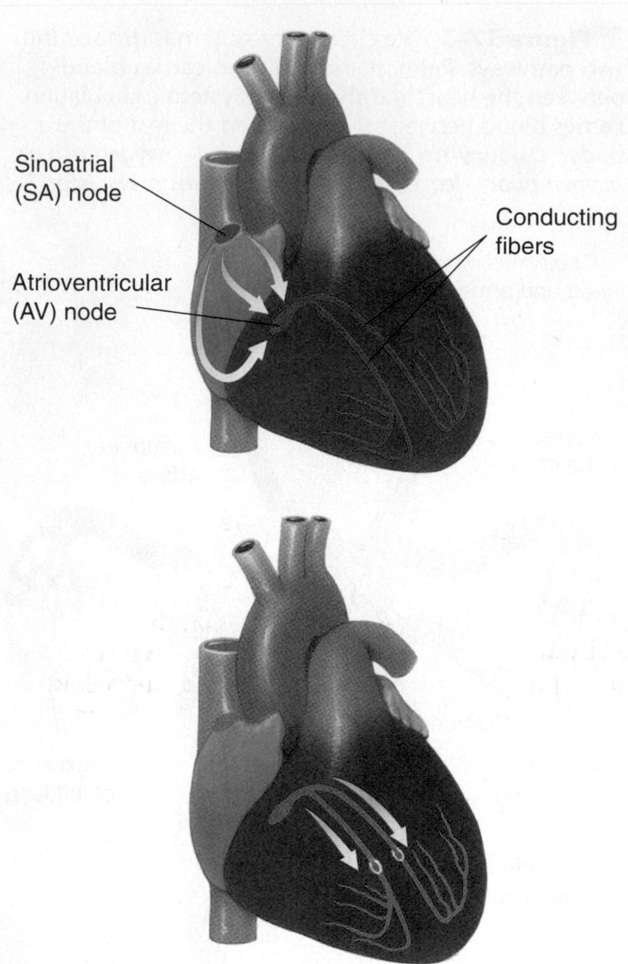

▲ **Figure 37–4** The signal to contract spreads from the sinoatrial node to the cardiac muscle cells of the atria, causing the atria to contract. The impulse is picked up by the atrioventricular node, which transmits the impulse to muscle fibers in the ventricles, causing the ventricles to contract. **Predicting** *In times of stress, does the heart beat faster or slower?*

Heartbeat There are two networks of muscle fibers in the heart, one in the atria and one in the ventricles. When a single fiber in either network is stimulated, all the fibers are stimulated and the network contracts as a unit. Each contraction begins in a small group of cardiac muscle cells—the sinoatrial node—located in the right atrium. Because these cells "set the pace" for the heart as a whole by starting the wave of muscle contraction through the heart, they are also called the **pacemaker.**

As shown in **Figure 37–4,** the impulse spreads from the pacemaker (SA node) to the network of fibers in the atria. It is picked up by a bundle of fibers called the atrioventricular node and carried to the network of fibers in the ventricles. When the network in the atria contracts, blood in the atria flows into the ventricles. When the muscles in the ventricles contract, blood flows out of the heart. This two-step pattern of contraction makes the heart a more efficient pump.

Your heart can beat faster or more slowly, depending on your body's need for oxygen-rich blood. During vigorous exercise, your heart rate may increase to about 200 beats per minute. Although the heartbeat is not directly controlled by the nervous system, the autonomic nervous system does influence heart rate. Neurotransmitters released by the sympathetic nervous system increase heart rate. Those released by the parasympathetic nervous system decrease heart rate.

Blood Vessels

Blood leaving the left side of the heart is loaded with oxygen from the lungs. When it leaves the left ventricle, the blood passes into a large blood vessel known as the **aorta.** The aorta is the first of a series of blood vessels that carry the blood on its round trip through the body and back to the heart. **As blood flows through the circulatory system, it moves through three types of blood vessels—arteries, capillaries, and veins.**

Arteries Large vessels that carry blood from the heart to the tissues of the body are called **arteries.** Arteries are the superhighways of the circulatory system. Except for the pulmonary arteries, all arteries carry oxygen-rich blood. Arteries have thick walls that help them withstand the powerful pressure produced when the heart contracts and pushes blood into the arteries.

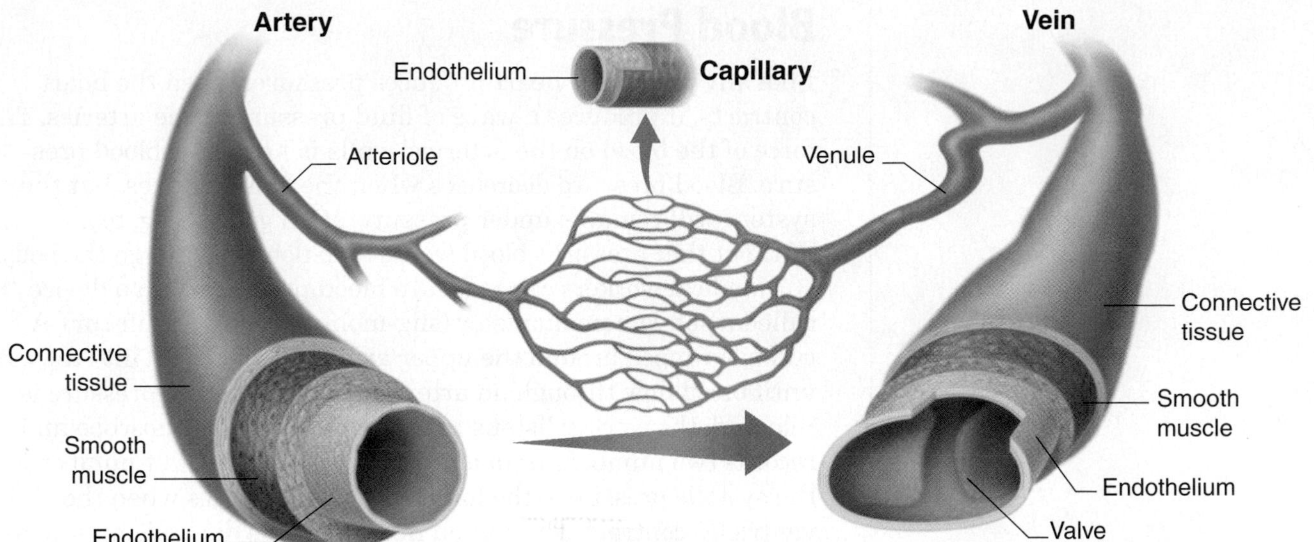

▲ **Figure 37–5** **In the circulatory system, there are three types of blood vessels—arteries, capillaries, and veins.** The walls of these vessels contain connective tissue, smooth muscle, and endothelium.

Figure 37–5 shows that the walls contain connective tissue, smooth muscle, and endothelium. The elastic connective tissue allows an artery to expand under pressure. Contractions of the smooth muscle regulate the diameter of an artery.

Capillaries The smallest of the blood vessels are the **capillaries.** Capillaries are the side streets and alleys of the circulatory system. The walls of capillaries are only one cell thick, and most are so narrow that blood cells must pass through them in single file. The real work of the circulatory system—bringing nutrients and oxygen to the tissues and absorbing carbon dioxide and other waste products from them—is done in the capillaries.

Veins Once blood has passed through the capillary system, it must be returned to the heart. This is the job of the **veins.** As with arteries, the walls of veins contain connective tissue and smooth muscle. Large veins, such as those shown in the leg in **Figure 37–6,** contain valves that keep blood moving toward the heart. Many veins are located near and between skeletal muscles. When you exercise, contracting these muscles helps force blood through the veins. Blood flow through the veins of the arms and legs often occurs against the force of gravity. Exercise helps to keep blood from accumulating in the limbs and stretching the veins out of shape. If the walls around the veins weaken from lack of activity, the valves can weaken. This causes blood to pool in the veins, producing a condition known as varicose veins.

CHECKPOINT *What happens in the capillaries?*

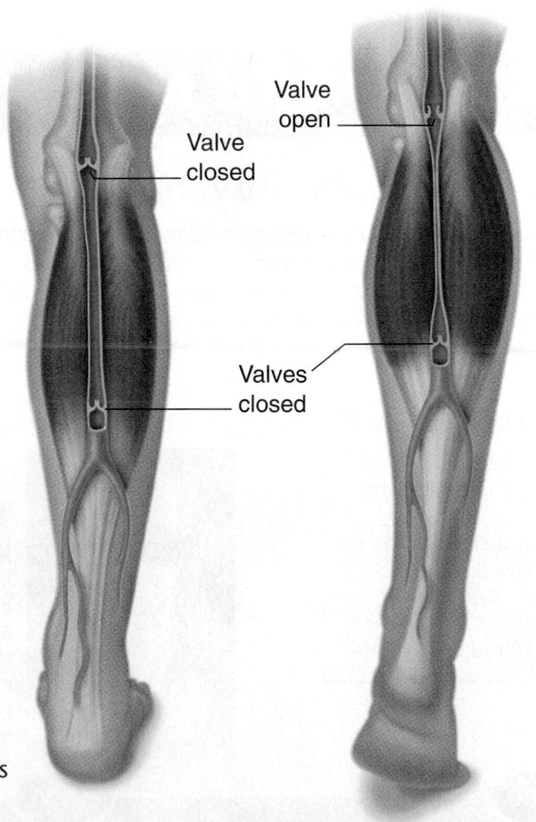

▶ **Figure 37–6** Contraction of skeletal muscles helps move blood in veins toward the heart. **Drawing Conclusions** *What role do valves play in large veins?*

Blood Pressure

Like any pump, the heart produces pressure. When the heart contracts, it produces a wave of fluid pressure in the arteries. The force of the blood on the arteries' walls is known as blood pressure. Blood pressure decreases when the heart relaxes, but the system still remains under pressure. It's a good thing, too. Without that pressure, blood would stop flowing through the body.

Medical workers can measure blood pressure with a device called a sphygmomanometer (sfig-moh-muh-NAHM-uh-tur). A cuff is wrapped around the upper arm. Air is pumped into the cuff until blood flow through an artery is blocked. As the pressure is released, the worker listens to the pulse with a stethoscope and records two numbers from a pressure gauge. The first number is the systolic pressure—the force felt in the arteries when the ventricles contract. The second number is the diastolic pressure—the force of the blood felt in the arteries when the ventricles relax. A typical blood pressure reading for a healthy person is 120/80.

The body normally regulates blood pressure in two ways. Sensory receptors at several places in the body detect the level of blood pressure, sending impulses to the medulla oblongata region of the brain stem. When blood pressure is too high, the autonomic nervous system releases neurotransmitters that cause the smooth muscles in blood vessel walls to relax, lowering blood pressure. When blood pressure is too low, neurotransmitters are released that elevate blood pressure by causing these smooth muscles to contract.

Biology and History

Cardiovascular Advances

William Harvey correctly described the role of the heart in the circulation of blood more than three centuries ago. Since then, advances in this area have improved the lives of many people with heart disease.

1939
Charles R. Drew
Drew develops a method to process and preserve blood plasma so that it can be stored and shipped.

1948
Dwight Harken
Charles Bailey
Harken and Bailey independently perform operations to open up closed heart valves in patients. Twelve years later, Harken replaces a heart valve with an artificial valve.

1902
Alexis Carrel
Carrel paves the way for organ transplantation by developing techniques for rejoining severed blood vessels.

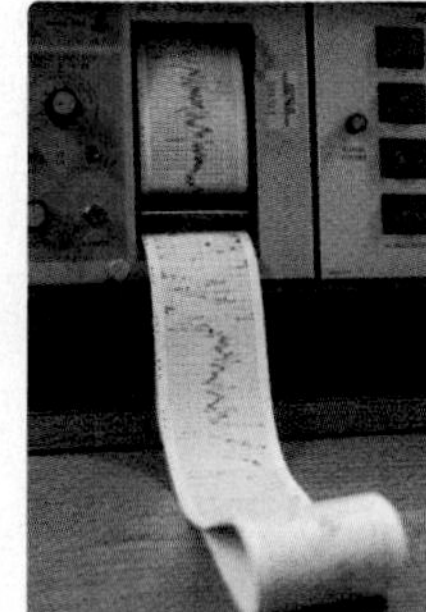

1924
Willem Einthoven
Einthoven wins a Nobel Prize for his invention of the electrocardiograph (EKG), a device used to measure tiny electric currents produced by the heart.

1900 1920 1940

The kidneys, which remove water from the blood, also help to regulate blood pressure. Hormones produced by the heart and other organs cause the kidneys to remove more water from the blood when blood pressure is high. This action reduces blood volume, thereby lowering the blood pressure.

What instrument measures blood pressure?

Diseases of the Circulatory System

Unfortunately, diseases of the circulatory system are all too common. Cardiovascular diseases—especially heart disease and stroke—are among the leading causes of death and disability in the United States. High blood pressure and a condition known as atherosclerosis (ath-ur-oh-skluh-ROH-sis) are two of the main causes of cardiovascular disease. **Atherosclerosis** is a condition in which fatty deposits called plaque build up on the inner walls of the arteries.

High Blood Pressure If blood pressure is too high, medical problems may result. High blood pressure, or hypertension, forces the heart to work harder, which may weaken or damage the heart muscle and blood vessels. People with high blood pressure are more likely to develop coronary heart disease and to suffer from other diseases of the circulatory system. Hypertension increases the risk of heart attack and stroke.

Writing in Science

Use the Internet or a library to find out more about the research conducted by one of these scientists. Then, write a summary of the contributions of the scientist to the field of medicine.

1958
Wilson Greatbatch
Greatbatch invents the implantable pacemaker. The mechanical device emits electrical signals that keep the heart beating normally.

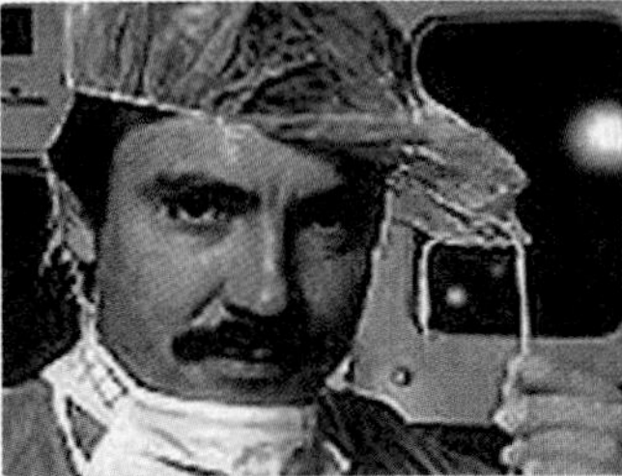

1977
Andreas Gruentzig
Gruentzig performs the first angioplasty by inserting a hollow tube containing a tiny uninflated balloon into a patient's coronary artery. The balloon is inflated, opening up the blocked area and restoring blood flow to the heart.

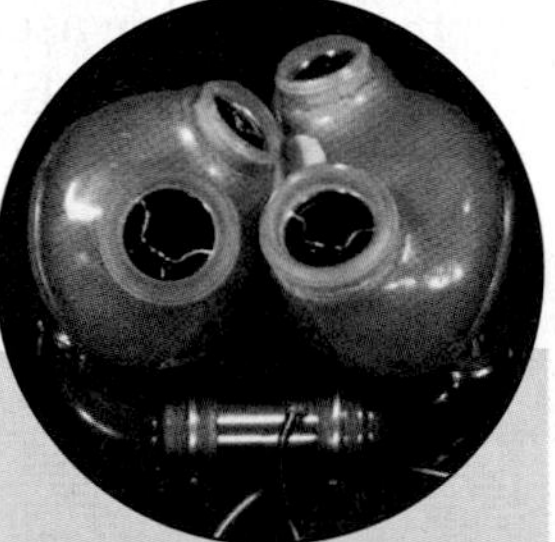

1982
William DeVries
DeVries leads a team of doctors to implant the Jarvik-7 artificial heart in a patient, who lives for 112 days.

2001
Laman Gray
Robert Dowling
Gray and Dowling implant the first completely self-contained artificial heart into a patient.

1960 1980 

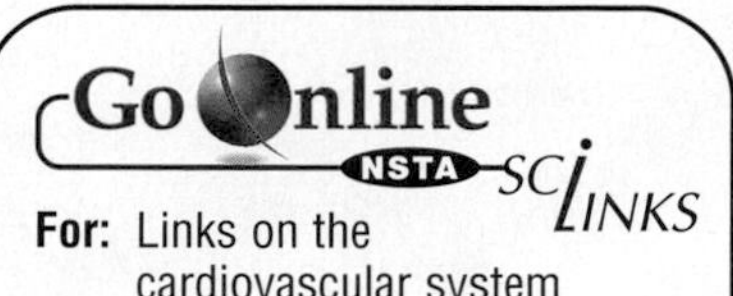

For: Links on the cardiovascular system
Visit: www.SciLinks.org
Web Code: cbn-0371

Consequences of Atherosclerosis Atherosclerosis is particularly dangerous in the coronary arteries, which bring oxygen and nutrients to the heart muscle itself. If one of these arteries becomes blocked, part of the heart muscle may begin to die from a lack of oxygen. If enough heart muscle is damaged, a condition known as a heart attack occurs.

The symptoms of a heart attack include nausea, shortness of breath, and severe, crushing chest pain. People who show these symptoms need immediate medical attention. New drugs are available that can increase blood flow enough to save the heart, but they must be given in the early stages of a heart attack to save the heart muscle and prevent death.

Blood clots that can form as a result of atherosclerosis may break free and get stuck in one of the blood vessels leading to a part of the brain. This condition is known as a stroke. Brain cells served by the particular blood vessel gradually die from a lack of oxygen, and brain function in that region may be lost. Depending on what part of the brain they affect, strokes may cause paralysis, loss of the ability to speak, and death.

Circulatory System Health Like other diseases, cardiovascular diseases are easier to prevent than to cure. Some of the ways of avoiding cardiovascular disease include getting regular exercise, eating a balanced diet, and avoiding smoking. Exercise makes your heart muscle stronger and more efficient. It also helps control your weight, reduces body fat, and reduces stress.

A diet low in saturated fat and cholesterol can reduce your risk of developing heart disease as well. High levels of fat and cholesterol in the blood increase the likelihood that it will be deposited onto the artery walls. This process begins in childhood and worsens as you get older. For this reason, you should limit your intake of foods with saturated fat. A low-fat diet will also help control your weight. Being overweight enlarges the circulatory system, causing the heart to pump harder to force blood through it. The cardiovascular system is also damaged by smoking. You will learn more about the effects of smoking later in this chapter.

37–1 Section Assessment

1. **Key Concept** List the structures of the circulatory system.
2. **Key Concept** Compare the functions of the three types of blood vessels in the circulatory system.
3. Describe the path of blood circulation through the body.
4. What is the role of the nervous system in heartbeat regulation?
5. **Critical Thinking Inferring** If you were standing, would you expect the blood pressure to be higher in your arm or in your leg? Explain your answer.

Writing in Science

Cause and Effect

Use library or Internet resources to research the connection between a high-fat diet and cardiovascular disease. Write a short commentary that could be used on a television news program that explains the connection. *Hint:* Prepare a cause-and-effect diagram to organize your ideas.

37–2 Blood and the Lymphatic System

4-1.2 Humans have complex systems
4-1.2e Cells are grouped for efficiency
4-5.2d White blood cells
LS- Analyze results and state an appropriate hypothesis

Guide for Reading

Key Concepts
- What is the function of each type of blood cell?
- What is the function of the lymphatic system?

Vocabulary
plasma
hemoglobin
lymphocyte
platelet
lymph

Reading Strategy: Asking Questions Before you read, rewrite the headings in the sections as *how, why,* or *what* questions about blood and the lymphatic system. As you read, write brief answers to the heading questions.

Just as a plumbing system carries water through a series of pipes to different parts of a house, the circulatory system carries blood through a series of blood vessels to different parts of the body. Blood is a type of connective tissue containing both dissolved substances and specialized cells. Blood collects oxygen from the lungs, nutrients from the digestive tract, and waste products from tissues. Blood helps to regulate factors in the body's internal environment, such as body temperature. In addition, components in blood help to fight infections. Blood can even form clots to repair damaged blood vessels.

Blood Plasma

The human body contains 4 to 6 liters of blood, which is about 8 percent of the total mass of the body. As **Figure 37–7** shows, about 45 percent of the volume of blood consists of cells, which are suspended in the other 55 percent—a straw-colored fluid called **plasma.** Plasma is about 90 percent water and 10 percent dissolved gases, salts, nutrients, enzymes, hormones, waste products, and proteins called plasma proteins.

Plasma proteins, which perform a variety of functions, are divided into three groups: albumins, globulins, and fibrinogen. Albumins and globulins transport substances such as fatty acids, hormones, and vitamins. Albumins also help to regulate osmotic pressure and blood volume. Some globulins fight viral and bacterial infections. Fibrinogen is the protein responsible for the ability of blood to clot.

▼ **Figure 37–7** Blood consists of plasma, blood cells, nutrients, hormones, waste products, and plasma proteins. **Interpreting Graphics** *When a whole blood sample is placed in a centrifuge, as shown below, what is the result?*

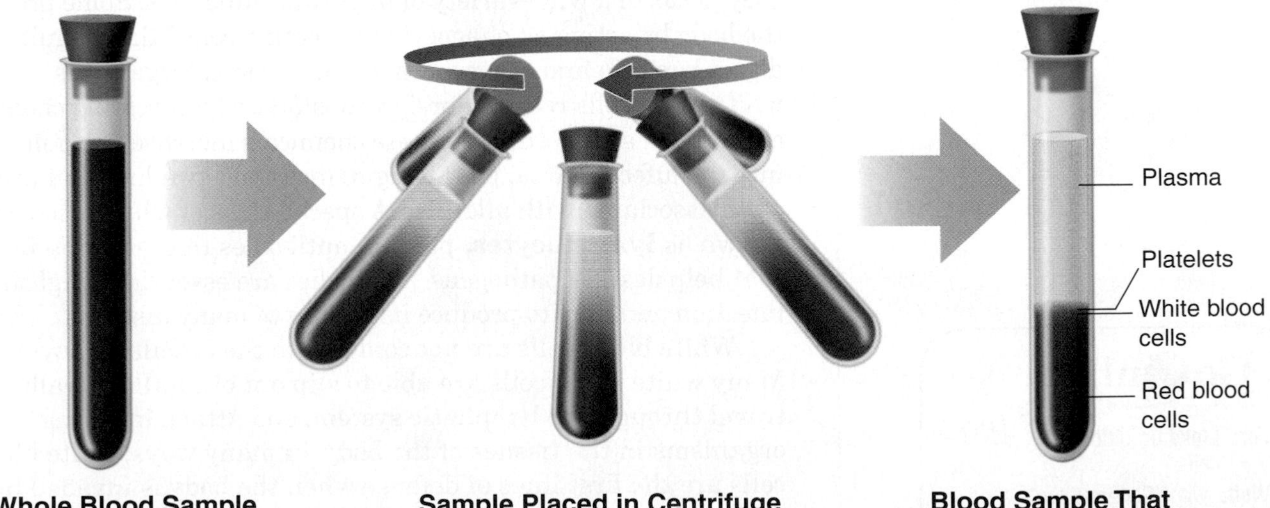

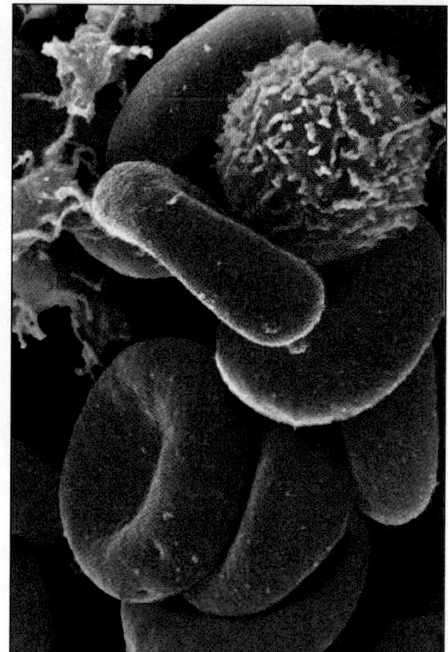

(magnification: 2342×)

▲ **Figure 37–8** **Red blood cells transport oxygen. White blood cells fight invasions of foreign substances, cells, and organisms.** Red blood cells and a single white blood cell are shown in this scanning electron micrograph.

Blood Cells

The cellular portion of blood consists of red blood cells, white blood cells, and platelets. Red blood cells transport oxygen, white blood cells perform a variety of protective functions, and platelets help in the clotting process. Platelets are actually fragments of cells derived from larger cells in bone marrow.

Red Blood Cells The most numerous cells in the blood are the red blood cells, or erythrocytes (eh-RITH-roh-syts). One milliliter of blood contains about 5 million red blood cells. **Red blood cells transport oxygen.** They get their color from hemoglobin. **Hemoglobin** is the iron-containing protein that binds to oxygen in the lungs and transports it to tissues throughout the body where the oxygen is released.

Red blood cells, like those shown in **Figure 37–8**, are shaped like disks that are thinner in the center than along the edges. These cells are produced from cells in red bone marrow. As these cells gradually become filled with hemoglobin, their nuclei and other organelles are forced out. Thus, mature red blood cells do not have nuclei. Red blood cells circulate for an average of 120 days before they are worn out from squeezing through narrow capillaries. Old red blood cells are destroyed in the liver and spleen.

White Blood Cells White blood cells, or leukocytes (LOO-koh-syts), do not contain hemoglobin. They are much less common than red cells, which outnumber them almost 1000 to 1. Both white and red blood cells are produced from the same population of blood-forming stem cells found in the bone marrow. Unlike red blood cells, however, white blood cells contain nuclei. They may live for days, months, or even years.

White blood cells are the "army" of the circulatory system—they guard against infection, fight parasites, and attack bacteria. There are many types of white blood cells, and they perform a wide variety of important functions. Some protect the body by acting as phagocytes, or "eating cells," that engulf and digest bacteria and other disease-causing microorganisms. Some white blood cells react to foreign substances by releasing chemicals known as histamines. These chemicals increase blood flow into the affected area, producing redness and swelling that are often associated with allergies. A special class of white blood cells, known as **lymphocytes,** produce antibodies that are proteins that help destroy pathogens. Antibodies are essential to fighting infection and help to produce immunity to many diseases.

White blood cells are not confined to the circulatory system. Many white blood cells are able to slip out of capillary walls, travel through the lymphatic system, and attack invading organisms in the tissues of the body. In many ways, white blood cells are the first lines of defense when the body is invaded by disease-causing organisms, making them part of the immune system as well.

Like an army with units in reserve, the body is able to increase the number of white blood cells dramatically when a "battle" is underway. A sudden increase in the white blood cell count is one of the ways in which physicians can tell that the body is fighting a serious infection.

Platelets and Blood Clotting Blood is essential to life. An injury can cause the body to lose this essential fluid. Fortunately, blood has an internal mechanism to slow bleeding and begin healing. A minor cut or scrape may bleed for a few seconds or minutes, but then it stops. Clean it up with soap and water, cover it with a bandage, and it begins to heal. Have you ever wondered why the bleeding stops?

The answer is that blood has the ability to form a clot. **Figure 37–9** summarizes the process. **Blood clotting is made possible by plasma proteins and cell fragments called platelets.** There are certain large cells in bone marrow that can break into thousands of small pieces. Each fragment of cytoplasm is enclosed in a piece of cell membrane and released into the bloodstream as a **platelet.**

When platelets come into contact with the edges of a broken blood vessel, their surfaces become very sticky, and a cluster of platelets develops around the wound. These platelets then release proteins called clotting factors. The clotting factors start a series of chemical reactions that are quite complicated. In one reaction, a clotting factor called thromboplastin (thrahm-boh-PLAS-tin) converts prothrombin, which is found in blood plasma, into thrombin. Thrombin is an enzyme that helps convert the soluble plasma protein fibrinogen into a sticky mesh of fibrin filaments. These filaments stop the bleeding by producing a clot. **Figure 37–10** shows the tangle of microscopic fibers in an actual blood clot.

What are platelets?

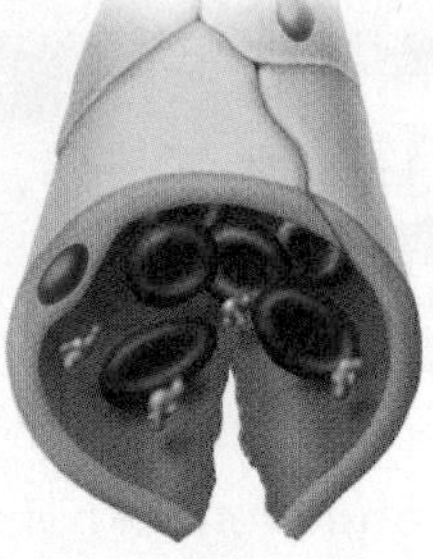

Break in Capillary Wall

Blood vessels injured.

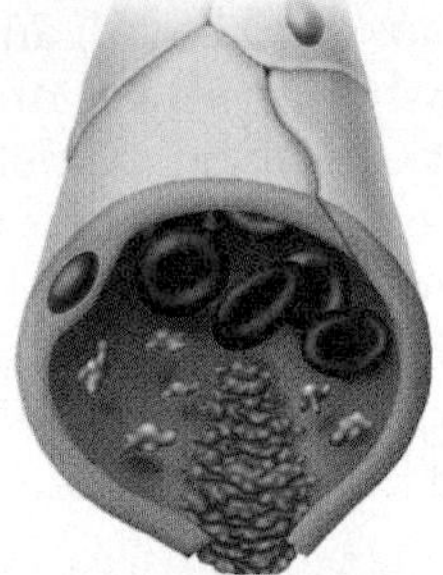

Clumping of Platelets

Platelets clump at the site and release thromboplastin. Thromboplastin converts prothrombin into thrombin.

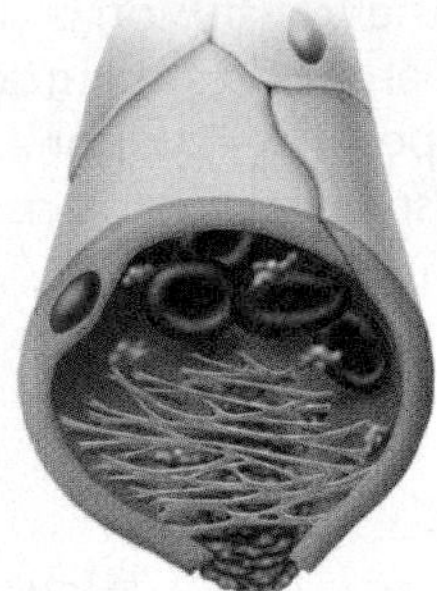

Clot Forms

Thrombin converts fibrinogen into fibrin, which causes a clot. The clot prevents further loss of blood.

▲ **Figure 37–9** **Blood clotting is made possible by a number of plasma proteins and cell fragments called platelets.** Calcium and vitamin K aid in converting prothrombin into thrombin.

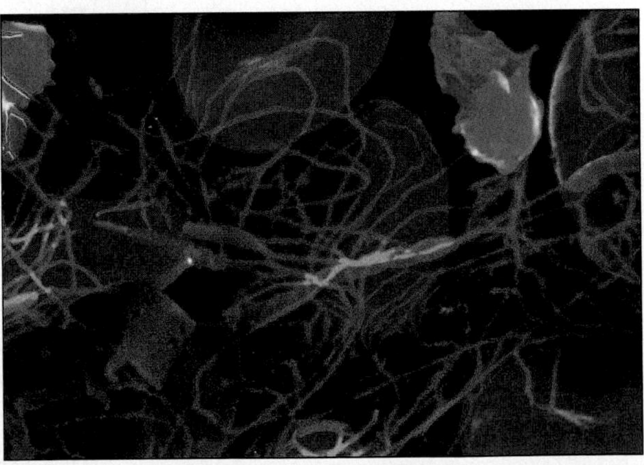

(magnification: 3000×)

▶ **Figure 37–10** Strands of fibrin trap blood cells, forming a net that prevents blood from leaving a damaged blood vessel. **Using Analogies** *How is a blood clot similar to a screened-in porch?*

Analyzing Data

Predicting the Success of Blood Transfusions

Although the first successful transfusions of human blood were carried out in the 1820s, many recipients had severe reactions to the transfused blood, and several died. Today we know why. We inherit one of four blood types—A, B, AB, or O—which are determined by antigens on our blood cells. Antigens are substances that trigger an immune response. People with blood type A have A antigens on their cells, those with type B have B antigens, those with AB blood have both A and B, and those with type O have neither A nor B antigens.

When blood types match, the transfusion is successful. However, transfusions are successful in some cases even when the blood types of the donor and the recipient do not match. Use the table to answer the questions that follow.

Blood Transfusions

Blood Type of Donor	Blood Type of Recipient			
	A	B	AB	O
A	✓	X	✓	X
B	X	✓	✓	X
AB	X	X	✓	X
O	✓	✓	✓	✓

X = Unsuccessful transfusion ✓ = Successful transfusion

1. **Drawing Conclusions** Which blood type is sometimes referred to as the "universal donor"? Which is known as the "universal recipient"?
2. **Drawing Conclusions** In a transfusion involving the A and O blood types, does it make a difference which blood type belongs to the recipient and which to the donor?
3. **Applying Concepts** Write a brief explanation for the results in the chart using information about phenotypes and genotypes in blood group genes. (*Hint:* Review Section 14–1 if needed.)

Blood Clotting Problems If the wound is small, within a few minutes the mesh of platelets and fibrin seals the wound, and bleeding stops. Most of the time, this clotting reaction works so well that we take it for granted. However, if one of the clotting factors is missing or defective, the clotting process does not work well. Hemophilia is a genetic disorder that results from a defective protein in the clotting pathway. People with hemophilia cannot produce blood clots that are firm enough to stop even minor bleeding. They must take great care to avoid injury. Fortunately, hemophilia can be treated by injecting extracts containing the missing clotting factor.

The Lymphatic System

As blood circulates, some fluid leaks from the blood into the surrounding tissues. This isn't an altogether bad thing. A steady flow of fluid helps to maintain an efficient movement of nutrients and salts from the blood into the tissues. However, more than 3 liters of fluid leak from the circulatory system into surrounding tissues every day! If this leakage continued unchecked, the body would begin to swell with fluid—not a very pleasant prospect.

Fortunately, the interrelationship between two body systems does not allow this to happen. **A network of vessels, nodes, and organs called the lymphatic system collects the fluid that is lost by the blood and returns it back to the circulatory system.** The fluid is known as **lymph** (LIMF).

Lymph collects in lymphatic capillaries and slowly flows into larger and larger lymph vessels. Like large veins, lymph vessels contain valves that prevent lymph from flowing backward. Ducts collect the lymph and return it to the circulatory system through two openings in the superior vena cava. The openings are under the left and right clavicle bones just below the shoulders. **Figure 37–11** shows the lymphatic system.

Along the length of the lymph vessels are small bean-shaped enlargements called lymph nodes. Lymph nodes act as filters, trapping bacteria and other microorganisms that cause disease. When large numbers of microorganisms are trapped in the lymph nodes, the nodes become enlarged. If you have ever had "swollen glands," you actually had swollen lymph nodes.

Lymph vessels do not merely return excess fluid to the circulation. They also play a very important role in nutrient absorption. Lymph vessels lie near the cells that line the intestines, where they absorb fats and fat-soluble vitamins from the digestive tract and carry them to the blood. Lymph moves through the lymphatic system under osmotic pressure from the blood and is pushed along by the contractions of nearby skeletal muscles. It is important that there is a steady flow of lymph. Edema, a swelling of the tissues due to the accumulation of excess fluid, can occur when lymphatic vessels are blocked due to injury or disease.

In addition to the lymph vessels and lymph nodes, the thymus and spleen also have important roles in the lymphatic system. The thymus is located beneath the sternum. Certain lymphocytes called T cells mature in the thymus before they can function in the immune system. T cells are the cells that recognize foreign "invaders" in the body. The spleen helps to cleanse the blood and removes damaged blood cells from the circulatory system. The spleen also harbors phagocytes that engulf and destroy bacteria and other microorganisms.

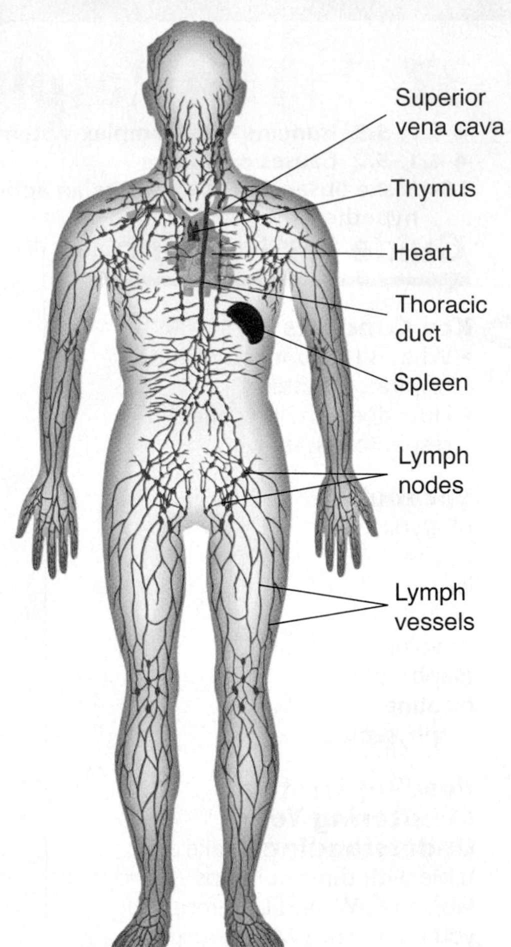

▲ **Figure 37–11** **The lymphatic system collects and returns fluid that leaks from blood vessels.** The spleen is an organ whose main function is to destroy damaged red blood cells and platelets. Certain white blood cells called T cells mature in the thymus gland, which produces hormones that promote their development.

37–2 Section Assessment

1. **Key Concept** List the main function of red blood cells, white blood cells, and platelets.
2. **Key Concept** Describe the role of the lymphatic system.
3. What types of materials are dissolved in plasma?
4. Explain how blood clots.
5. **Critical Thinking Inferring** Sometimes lymph nodes must be surgically removed. Although more lymph vessels eventually grow, what result would you expect to see immediately after surgery?

Thinking Visually

Constructing a Concept Map
Construct a concept map that shows the components of blood. Include information about the functions of the different components. (Be sure to include the different types of white blood cells.)

37–3 The Respiratory System

4-1.2, 5.3 Humans have complex systems
4-4.1, 5.2 Causes of disease
LS- Make observations and state an appropriate hypothesis

Guide for Reading

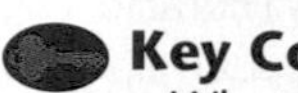

Key Concepts
- What is the function of the respiratory system?
- How does smoking affect the respiratory system?

Vocabulary
pharynx
trachea
larynx
bronchus
alveolus
diaphragm
nicotine
emphysema

Reading Strategy: Monitoring Your Understanding Make a table with three columns labeled K, W, and L. Before you read, write what you know about respiration in column K and what you want to learn in column W. After you read, write what you have learned in column L.

When paramedics rush to the aid of an injured person, they check to see if the person is breathing. If the person's chest is not rising and falling and they cannot feel or hear air being exhaled from the mouth or nose, it is likely that the person is not breathing. Paramedics will ignore broken bones or burns to focus on breathing because there is no time to lose! If breathing stops for more than a few minutes, a life may be lost.

Paramedics can do mouth-to-mouth rescue breathing to force air into the lungs. They can do chest compressions to keep the blood circulating. Cardiopulmonary resuscitation, or CPR, is rescue breathing combined with chest compressions.

What Is Respiration?

In biology, the word *respiration* is used in two slightly different ways. Cellular respiration, which takes place in mitochondria, is the release of energy from the breakdown of food molecules in the presence of oxygen. Without oxygen, cells lose much of their ability to produce ATP. Without ATP, cells cannot synthesize new molecules, pump ions, or carry nerve impulses.

The blood carries oxygen from the lungs to the body's tissues, and carries carbon dioxide—a waste product of cellular respiration—in the opposite direction. At the level of the organism, respiration means the process of gas exchange—the release of carbon dioxide and the uptake of oxygen between the lungs and the environment.

The Human Respiratory System

The basic function performed by the human respiratory system is remarkably simple—to bring about the exchange of oxygen and carbon dioxide between the blood, the air, and tissues. With each breath, air enters the body through the air passageways and fills the lungs, where gas exchange takes place. The respiratory system consists of the nose, pharynx, larynx, trachea, bronchi, and lungs.

Figure 37–13 shows the structures of the respiratory system. Air moves through the nose to a tube at the back of the mouth called the pharynx, or throat. The **pharynx** serves as a passageway for both air and food. Air moves from the pharynx into the **trachea,** or windpipe. A flap of tissue called the epiglottis covers the entrance to the trachea when you swallow.

(magnification: 5600×)

◀ **Figure 37–12** In this cross section of the trachea, the cilia have been colored green. **Inferring** *What is the role of cilia in the respiratory system?*

FIGURE 37–13 THE RESPIRATORY SYSTEM

The respiratory system is responsible for the exchange of oxygen and carbon dioxide. Air moves through the nose, pharynx, larynx, trachea, and lungs. After reaching the lungs, the trachea branches into smaller and smaller tubes called bronchioles, which end in alveoli, or air sacs.

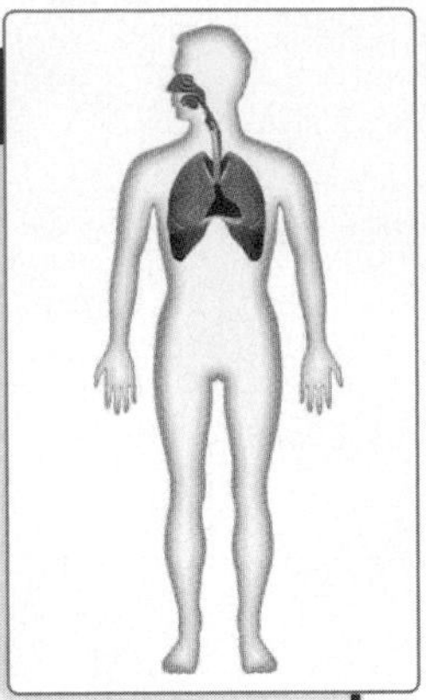

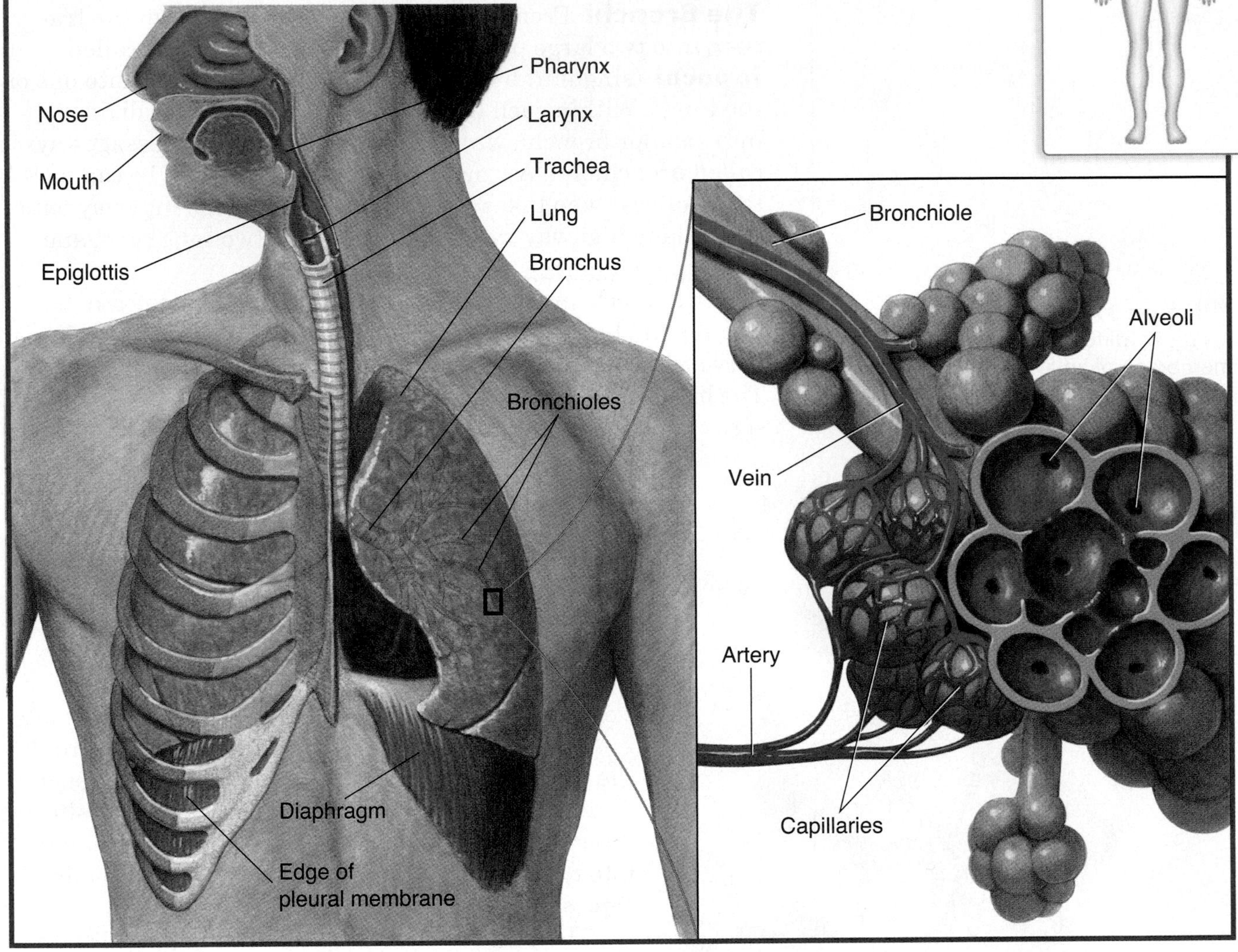

Nose
Mouth
Epiglottis
Pharynx
Larynx
Trachea
Lung
Bronchus
Bronchioles
Diaphragm
Edge of pleural membrane
Bronchiole
Alveoli
Vein
Artery
Capillaries

Cilia and Mucus The respiratory passageways allow air to pass directly into some of the most delicate tissues in the body. To keep the lung tissue healthy, air entering the respiratory system must be warmed, moistened, and filtered. Large dust particles get trapped by the hairs lining the entrance to the nasal cavity. Some of the cells that line the respiratory system produce a thin layer of mucus. The mucus moistens the air and traps inhaled particles of dust or smoke. Cilia sweep the trapped particles and mucus away from the lungs toward the pharynx. The mucus and trapped particles are either swallowed or spit out. These protective measures help keep the lungs clean and open for the important work of gas exchange.

What is the pharynx?

The Larynx At the top of the trachea is the larynx. The **larynx** contains two highly elastic folds of tissue known as the vocal cords. When muscles pull the vocal cords together, the air moving between them causes the cords to vibrate and produce sounds. Your ability to speak, shout, and sing comes from these tissues.

The Bronchi From the larynx, air passes through the trachea into two large passageways in the chest cavity called **bronchi** (singular: bronchus). Each bronchus leads into one of the lungs. Within each lung, the large bronchus subdivides into smaller bronchi, which lead to even smaller passageways called bronchioles. Air moving along this path can be compared to a motorist who takes an exit off an eight-lane highway onto a four-lane highway, makes a turn onto a two-lane road, and ends up on a narrow country lane.

The bronchi and bronchioles are surrounded by smooth muscle that helps to support them and enables the autonomic nervous system to regulate the size of the air passageways. The bronchioles continue to subdivide until they reach a series of dead ends—millions of tiny air sacs called **alveoli** (singular: alveolus). Alveoli are grouped in little clusters, like bunches of grapes. A delicate network of thin-walled capillaries surrounds each alveolus.

▼ **Figure 37–14** Gas exchange occurs by diffusion across the membrane of an alveolus and a capillary. **Drawing Conclusions** *Where is oxygen more concentrated, in an alveolus or in a capillary?*

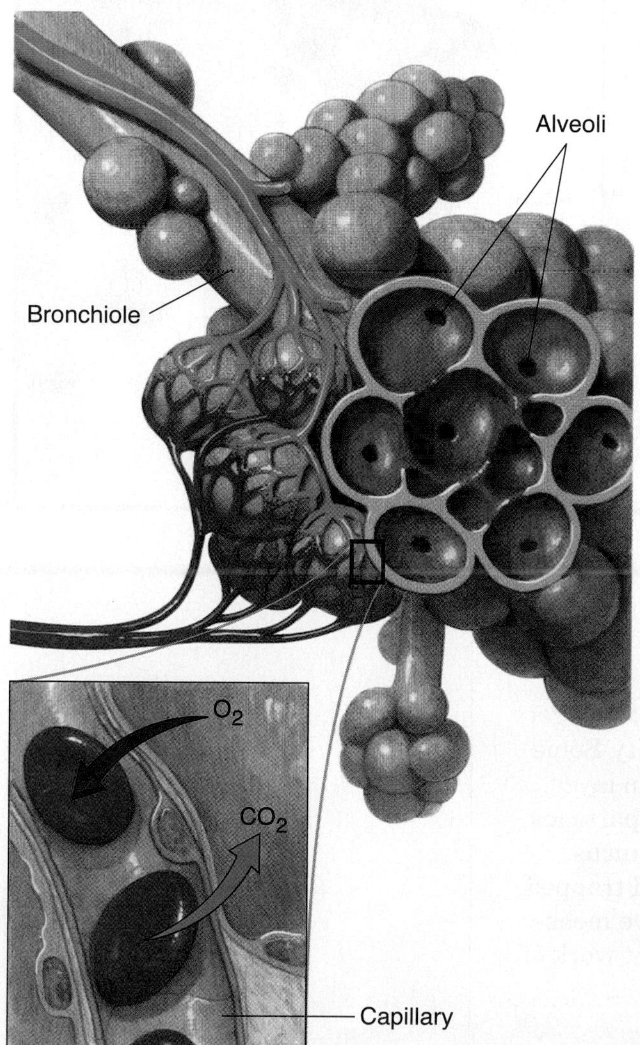

Gas Exchange

There are about 150 million alveoli in each healthy lung, providing an enormous surface area for gas exchange. Oxygen dissolves in the moisture on the inner surface of the alveoli and then diffuses across the thin-walled capillaries into the blood. Carbon dioxide in the bloodstream diffuses in the opposite direction, across the membrane of an alveolus and into the air within it. This process is illustrated in **Figure 37–14.**

The process of gas exchange in the lungs is very efficient. The air that you inhale usually contains 21 percent oxygen and 0.04 percent carbon dioxide. Exhaled air usually contains less than 15 percent oxygen and 4 percent carbon dioxide. The lungs remove about one fourth of the oxygen in the air that you inhale and increase the carbon dioxide content of that air by a factor of 100.

Because oxygen dissolves easily, you may wonder why hemoglobin, the oxygen-carrying protein in blood, is needed at all. The reason is efficiency. Hemoglobin binds with so much oxygen that it increases the oxygen-carrying capacity of the blood more than 60 times. Without hemoglobin to carry the oxygen that it uses, your body might need as much as 300 liters of blood to get the same result!

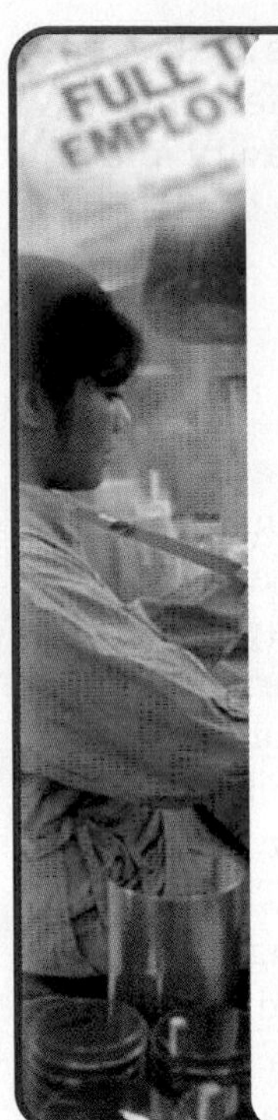

Careers in Biology

Respiratory Care Practitioner

Job Description: provide care for patients with respiratory problems in hospitals, clinics, nursing homes, schools, and at home

Education: a two-year or four-year training program; certification exams; individual states have additional licensing requirements

Skills: good communication skills; enjoy working with people; capable of working independently; good decision-making skills; knowledge of anatomy, physiology, microbiology

Highlights: You provide quick responses in emergency situations. You work as a member of a team.

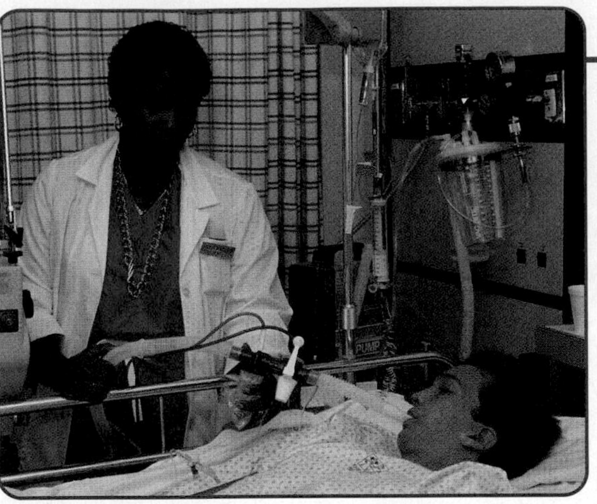

For: Career links
Visit: PHSchool.com
Web Code: cbb-0373

Breathing

Breathing is the movement of air into and out of the lungs. Surprisingly, there are no muscles connected to the lungs. The force that drives air into the lungs comes from ordinary air pressure. How does the body use this force to inflate the lungs? The lungs are sealed in two sacs, called the pleural membranes, inside the chest cavity. At the bottom of the cavity is a large, flat muscle known as the **diaphragm.**

As **Figure 37–15** shows, when you breathe in, or inhale, the diaphragm contracts and the rib cage rises up. This expands the volume of the chest cavity. Because the chest cavity is tightly sealed, this creates a partial vacuum inside the cavity. Atmospheric pressure does the rest, filling the lungs as air rushes into the breathing passages.

Most of the time, exhaling is a passive event. When the rib cage lowers and the diaphragm muscle relaxes, the pressure in the chest cavity becomes greater than atmospheric pressure. Air rushes back out of the lungs. To blow out a candle, you need a greater force. Muscles surrounding the chest cavity provide that extra force, contracting vigorously just as the diaphragm relaxes.

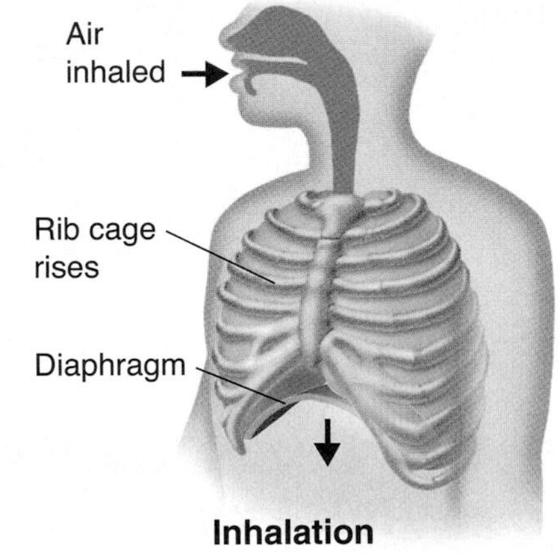

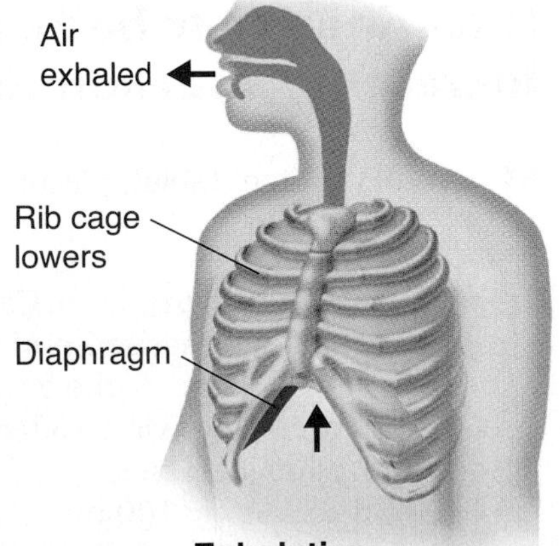

▶ **Figure 37–15** During inhalation the rib cage rises and the diaphragm contracts, increasing the size of the chest cavity. **Interpreting Graphics** ***What happens as the diaphragm relaxes?***

For: The Process of Breathing activity
Visit: PHSchool.com
Web Code: cbp-0373

The system works only because the chest cavity is sealed. A puncture wound to the chest—even if it does not affect the lungs directly—may allow air to leak into the chest cavity and make breathing impossible. This is one of the reasons chest wounds are always serious.

How Breathing Is Controlled

You can control your breathing almost anytime you want, whether it's to blow up a balloon or to play a musical instrument. But this doesn't mean that breathing is purely voluntary. If you hold your breath for a minute or so, you'll see what happens. Your chest begins to feel tight, your throat begins to burn, and the muscles in your mouth and throat struggle to keep from breathing. Eventually your body takes over. It "forces" you to breathe!

Breathing is such an important function that your nervous system will not let you have complete control over it. The part of the brain that controls breathing is the medulla oblongata. Autonomic nerves from the medulla oblongata to the diaphragm and chest muscles produce the cycles of contraction that bring air into the lungs. How does the medulla oblongata "know" when it's time to breathe? Cells in its breathing center monitor the amount of carbon dioxide in the blood. As the carbon dioxide level rises, nerve impulses from the breathing center cause the diaphragm to contract, bringing air into the lungs. The higher the carbon dioxide level, the stronger the impulses. If the carbon dioxide level reaches a critical point, the impulses become so powerful that you cannot keep from breathing.

Quick Lab

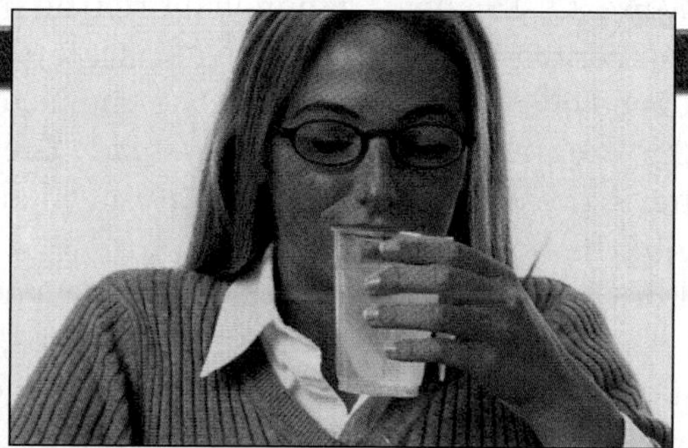

How does your body respond to increases in carbon dioxide?

Materials seltzer tablet, plastic cup

Procedure

1. **Formulating Hypotheses** Carbon dioxide is a waste material synthesized during the cellular process of respiration. Write a hypothesis about how your breathing will be affected if the level of carbon dioxide increases.
2. Place approximately 100 mL of water in the cup and add a seltzer tablet. The bubbles in the water are carbon dioxide. Bring the cup up to your face and inhale deeply.

Analyze and Conclude

1. **Observing** Describe what happened when you inhaled the carbon dioxide.
2. **Drawing Conclusions** Did your results support your hypothesis or not? Explain your answer.
3. **Inferring** Why is it important for your body to respond to the stimulus of increased carbon dioxide?

▲ **Figure 37–16** This pilot must use an oxygen mask because there is not enough oxygen available in the air at high altitudes. **Applying Concepts** *How would a mountain climber decide when to carry a supply of oxygen?*

That the breathing center responds primarily to carbon dioxide can have dangerous consequences. Consider a plane flying at high altitude. Although the amount of oxygen in the air decreases as the altitude increases, the passengers do not need oxygen masks because the cabin is pressurized. Oxygen is available for use in an emergency, but the passengers often have to be told to begin breathing the oxygen. Although their bodies may be starving for oxygen, they have no more carbon dioxide in their blood than usual, so the breathing center does not sense a problem. The pilot in **Figure 37–16** is not in a pressurized cabin and must use an oxygen mask at high altitudes.

What does the breathing center in the brain do?

Tobacco and the Respiratory System

The upper part of the respiratory system is generally able to filter out dust and foreign particles that could damage the lungs. Millions of people engage in an activity—smoking tobacco—that damages and eventually destroys this protective system.

Substances in Tobacco Tobacco smoke contains many substances that affect the body. Three of the most dangerous substances are nicotine, carbon monoxide, and tar. **Nicotine** is a stimulant drug that increases the heart rate and blood pressure. Carbon monoxide is a poisonous gas that blocks the transport of oxygen by hemoglobin in the blood. It decreases the blood's ability to supply oxygen to its tissues, depriving the heart and other organs of the oxygen they need to function. Tar contains a number of compounds that have been shown to cause cancer.

Effects on Respiratory System Smoking tobacco brings nicotine and carbon monoxide into the upper respiratory system. These compounds paralyze the cilia. With the cilia out of action, the inhaled particles stick to the walls of the respiratory tract or enter the lungs.

Without cilia to sweep it along, smoke-laden mucus becomes trapped along the airways. This explains why smokers often cough. Irritation from the accumulated mucus triggers a cough that helps to clear the airways. Smoking also causes the lining of the respiratory tract to swell, which reduces the air flow to the alveoli.

Diseases Caused by Smoking Only 30 percent of male smokers live to age 80, but 55 percent of male nonsmokers live to that age. Clearly, smoking reduces life expectancy. **Smoking can cause such respiratory diseases as chronic bronchitis, emphysema, and lung cancer.** In chronic bronchitis, the bronchi become swollen and clogged with mucus. Even smoking a moderate number of cigarettes on a regular basis can produce chronic bronchitis. Affected people often find simple activities, such as climbing stairs, difficult.

Long-term smoking can also cause a respiratory disease called emphysema (em-fuh-SEE-muh). **Emphysema** is the loss of elasticity in the tissues of the lungs. This condition makes breathing very difficult. People who have emphysema cannot get enough oxygen to the body tissues or rid the body of excess carbon dioxide.

Smoking is an important, but preventable, cause of lung cancer. **Figure 37–17** shows the effects of smoking on the lungs. Lung cancer is particularly deadly because its cells can spread to other locations. By the time lung cancer is detected, it usually has spread to dozens of other places. About 160,000 people in the United States are diagnosed with lung cancer each year. Few will survive for five years after the diagnosis.

▶ **Figure 37–17** **Smoking can cause respiratory diseases such as chronic bronchitis, emphysema, and lung cancer.** The lung on the left is from a smoker. The lung on the right is from a nonsmoker.

Smoking is also a major cause of heart disease. Smoking constricts, or narrows, the blood vessels. This causes blood pressure to rise and makes the heart work harder. The effects of smoking on the circulatory system can be seen in **Figure 37–18.** There is a drastic change in body temperature and in circulation immediately after smoking a cigarette. Smoking doubles the risk of death from heart disease for men between 45 and 65. Moreover, for men and women of all ages, the risk of death from heart disease is greater among smokers than among nonsmokers.

Smoking and the Nonsmoker In recent years, evidence has shown that tobacco smoke is damaging to anyone who inhales it, not just the smoker. For this reason, many states have restricted smoking in restaurants and other public places.

Passive smoking, or inhaling the smoke of others, is particularly damaging to young children because their lungs are still developing. Studies now indicate that the children of smokers are twice as likely as children of nonsmokers to develop respiratory problems, such as asthma.

Dealing With Tobacco Whatever the age of a smoker, and no matter how long that person has smoked, his or her health can be improved by quitting. Nicotine is a powerful drug with strong addictive qualities that make it very difficult to quit smoking. Thus, considering the cost, the medical dangers, and the powerful addiction, the best solution is not to begin smoking.

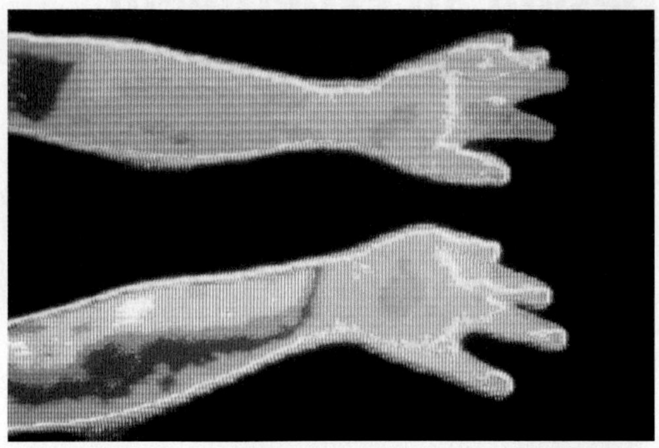

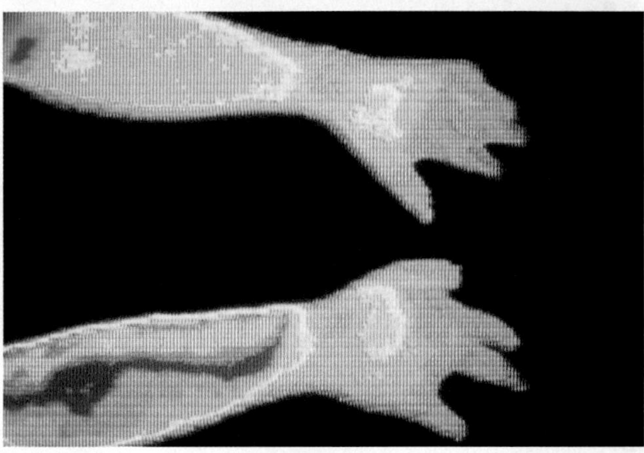

▲ **Figure 37–18** These thermograms provide a color-coded map of temperature distribution over the body surface (blue = cold; pink = hot). The top thermogram shows the forearm and hand area prior to smoking a cigarette. The bottom thermogram shows the same area after smoking. **Interpreting Graphics** ***Do you think circulation is increased or decreased after smoking?***

37–3 Section Assessment

1. **Key Concept** Interpret the function of the respiratory system by stating what it does.
2. **Key Concept** Describe some of the health problems caused by smoking tobacco.
3. Explain the process of gas exchange in the lungs.
4. Describe how breathing is controlled.
5. **Critical Thinking Inferring** As you have read, the breathing center in the brain responds to the level of carbon dioxide in the blood—not the level of oxygen. What consequences does this have for people at high altitudes?

Connecting Concepts

Comparative Anatomy
Compare what you learned in Units 8 and 9 about respiration in terrestrial arthropods, fish, and flatworms with human respiration. Relate the method of respiration to the type of environment the organism inhabits. What do these methods have in common? How do they differ?

Design an Experiment

Modeling Breathing

As you breathe, your body moves air into and out of your lungs. All body movements depend on muscles, which work only by contracting. How does your body use muscles to cause air to flow into and out of your lungs? In this investigation, you will make a working model of human lungs that will help you answer this question.

Problem **How do muscle contractions move air into and out of the lungs?**

Materials

- small, clear plastic bottle
- large round balloon
- small round balloon
- one-hole rubber stopper
- scissors

Skills Using Models

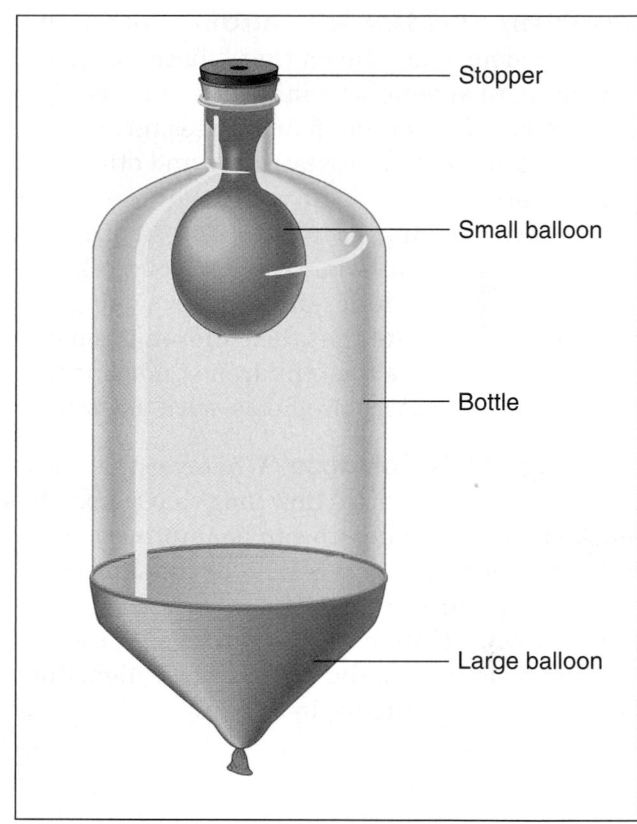

Design Your Experiment 

Part A: A Model of Normal Lungs

1. Place a clear plastic bottle on its side. Press one point of a pair of scissors through the side of the bottle about 1 cm from the bottom.
2. Using the scissors, cut off the bottom of the bottle by cutting all the way around. Trim off any rough spots from the edge.
3. Stretch a small balloon, and blow it up several times to make it pliable.
4. Pull the opening of the small balloon over the bottom of a one-hole rubber stopper.
5. Insert the balloon through the mouth of the bottle. Press the stopper tightly into the bottle so that it holds the lip of the balloon in place.

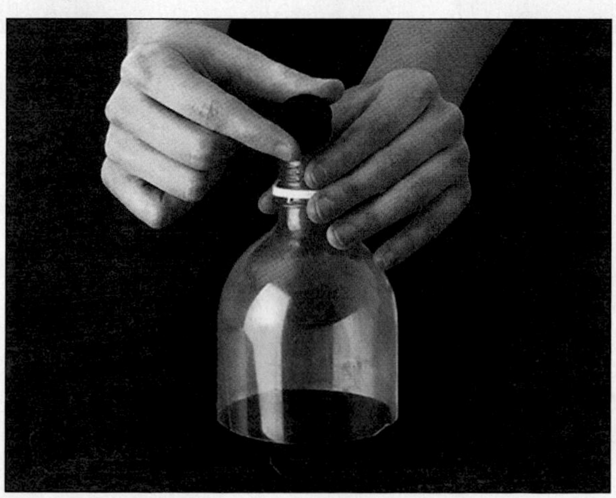

6. Stretch a large balloon, and blow it up several times to make it pliable.
7. Using the scissors, cut off about 1 cm from the rounded, closed end of the large balloon. Tie the other end closed.
8. Stretch the large balloon far enough over the cut end of the bottle to keep the balloon from slipping off, as shown in the diagram.
9. As you watch the small balloon, pull down on the knot of the large balloon. Then, still watching the small balloon, press up on the large balloon.

Part B: A Model of a Chest Injury

10. **Formulating Hypotheses** If a person receives an injury that punctures the skin and muscles of the chest, outside air can come into direct contact with the outer surfaces of the lungs. How would such an event affect a person's ability to breathe? Record your hypothesis.

11. Think of a way you could modify your model of human lungs to represent the lungs in a person with a punctured chest. Write a description of your plan, including your prediction of how the alternative model will behave and how the model will test your hypothesis.

12. Show your plan to your teacher. If your teacher approves, make a model of a punctured chest. Use your model to test your hypothesis.

Analyze and Conclude

1. **Observing** In Part A, what happened to the small balloon in your model when you pulled down on the large balloon?
2. **Observing** What happened to the small balloon when you pressed up on the large balloon?
3. **Inferring** What happened to the pressure inside the bottle when you moved the large balloon up and down?
4. **Formulating Hypotheses** What caused the small balloon in Part A to expand and contract?
5. **Using Models** Do you consider the model you made in Part A an adequate representation of the human respiratory system? Explain.
6. **Drawing Conclusions** In Part B, how did your alternative model represent a chest injury? What does that model show about the role of the chest wall in breathing?
7. **Evaluating** In Part B, was your prediction correct? Did the behavior of your second model support your hypothesis? Explain your answer.
8. **Drawing Conclusions** How do muscles cause air to flow into and out of human lungs?
9. **SAFETY** Explain how you demonstrated safe practices as you used sharp objects such as scissors.

Go Further

Making Models Obtain information from a hospital, doctor's office, or county health department about the mechanics of breathing and diseases such as asthma and emphysema that make breathing difficult. Find out what causes these diseases, how they affect breathing, and how they are prevented and treated. Then, make a new model that demonstrates the effects of one of these diseases. Be prepared to explain how well your model represents that disease.

Chapter 37 Study Guide

37–1 The Circulatory System

Key Concepts

- The human circulatory system consists of the heart, a series of blood vessels, and the blood that flows through them.
- As the blood flows through the circulatory system, it moves through three types of blood vessels—arteries, capillaries, and veins.

Vocabulary

myocardium, p. 944
atrium, p. 944
ventricle, p. 944
pulmonary circulation, p. 944
systemic circulation, p. 944
valve, p. 945
pacemaker, p. 946
aorta, p. 946
artery, p. 946
capillary, p. 947
vein, p. 947
atherosclerosis, p. 949

37–2 Blood and the Lymphatic System

Key Concepts

- Red blood cells transport oxygen.
- White blood cells guard against infection, fight parasites, and attack bacteria.
- Blood clotting is made possible by plasma proteins and cell fragments called platelets.
- A network of vessels, nodes, and organs called the lymphatic system collects the fluid that is lost by the blood and returns it to the circulatory system.

Vocabulary

plasma, p. 951
hemoglobin, p. 952
lymphocyte, p. 952
platelet, p. 953
lymph, p. 954

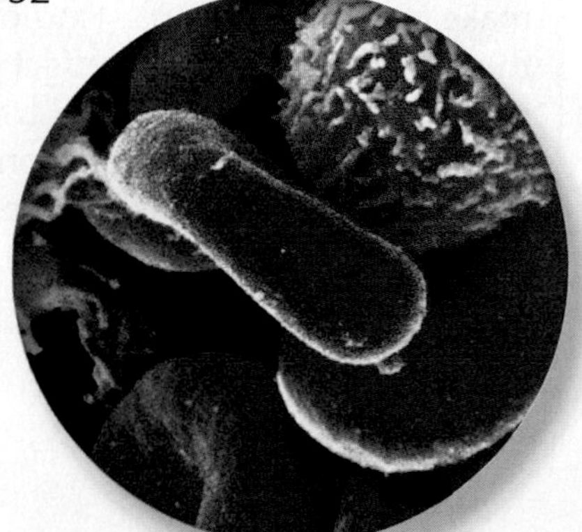

37–3 The Respiratory System

Key Concepts

- The basic function of the human respiratory system is to bring about the exchange of oxygen and carbon dioxide between the blood, the air, and tissues.
- Smoking can cause such respiratory diseases as chronic bronchitis, emphysema, and lung cancer.

Vocabulary

pharynx, p. 956
trachea, p. 956
larynx, p. 958
bronchus, p. 958
alveolus, p. 958
diaphragm, p. 959
nicotine, p. 961
emphysema, p. 962

Thinking Visually

On a separate sheet of paper, make a copy of the chart below. Then, fill in the missing structures and functions.

Structures and Functions of the Circulatory System

Structure	Function
1	Chamber where blood enters heart from the body
Right ventricle	2
3	Carry blood from the heart to the lungs
4	Carry blood back to the heart from the lungs
Left atrium	5
6	Chamber that pumps blood to the body
Aorta	7

Preparing for the Living Environment Exam

Blue questions emphasize Regents Exam content

Chapter 37

Part A

Multiple Choice

For each statement or question, select the number of the word or expression that, of those given, best completes the statement or answers the question.

1 Which group of structures best describes the circulatory system?
(1) arteries, veins, capillaries
(2) lungs, air passages, alveoli
(3) lungs, blood vessels, heart
(4) heart, blood, blood vessels

2 Blood leaving the heart for the body passes through a large blood vessel known as the
(1) aorta
(2) vena cava
(3) pulmonary vein
(4) pulmonary artery

3 Which cells are able to protect the body by engulfing foreign cells or producing antibodies?
(1) red blood cells
(2) plasma cells
(3) platelets
(4) white blood cells

4 Exchange of nutrients and wastes with the body cells takes place by diffusion through the walls of
(1) veins (3) arteries
(2) capillaries (4) atria

5 The process shown below is made possible by a number of plasma proteins and cell fragments called
(1) fibrinogens (3) platelets
(2) basophils (4) lymphocytes

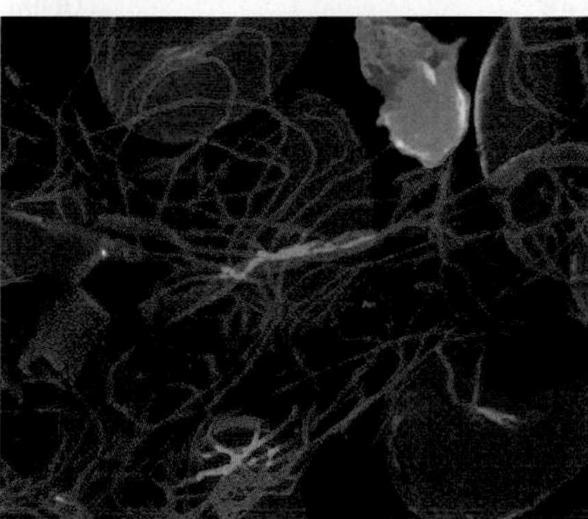

6 Which substance is the iron-containing protein found in red blood cells?
(1) hemoglobin
(2) fibrinogen
(3) prothrombin
(4) thrombin

7 To aid the process of breathing, the diaphragm
(1) increases blood flow from the heart to the lungs
(2) moves up and down to alter the volume of the chest cavity
(3) inflates and deflates to force air in and out of the lungs
(4) moves the rib cage in and out as air is inhaled

8 Which group consists entirely of materials found in human blood?
(1) plasma, alveoli, proteins
(2) platelets, mucus, red blood cells
(3) phagocytes, platelets, proteins
(4) hemoglobin, capillaries, white blood cells

9 Nicotine affects the body by
(1) paralyzing cilia
(2) decreasing blood pressure
(3) blocking transport of oxygen by hemoglobin
(4) decreasing heart rate

10 The upper chambers of the heart are the
(1) ventricles (3) myocardia
(2) vena cava (4) atria

For questions 11 and 12, complete each analogy by selecting the correct number. In analogies, A : B :: C : means "A is to B as C is to ?."

11 Platelets : clotting :: red blood cells :
(1) inhalation
(2) exhalation
(3) oxygen transport
(4) cellular respiration

12 Tree branch : bronchus :: leaf :
(1) pharynx (3) diaphragm
(2) alveolus (4) trachea

Test-Taking Tip When you are asked questions about structures in a diagram, first identify each structure. Then, try to answer the questions.

Preparing for the Living Environment Exam

Part B

Multiple Choice and Extended Response
For those questions that ask you to select a response, choose the one that best completes the statement or answers the question. For all others follow the directions given.

13 Explain how the circulatory system protects the human body against invading microorganisms.

14 Describe the process by which the human respiratory system provides oxygen to the body.

15 Identify the *three* most dangerous substances in tobacco smoke, and state how each substance affects the body.

Base your answers to questions 16 through 19 on the diagram and on your knowledge of biology.

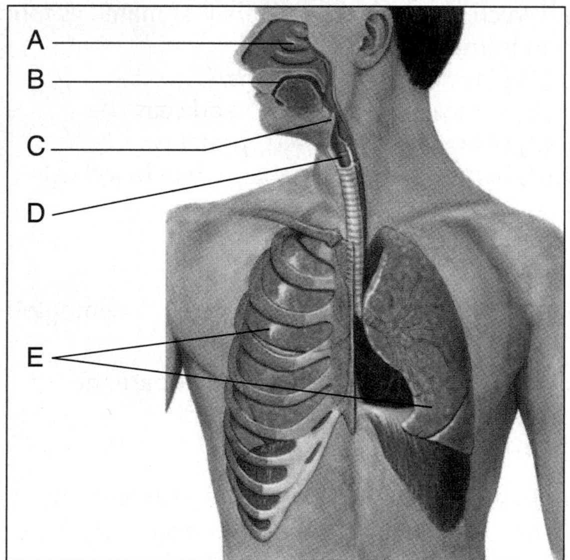

16 Which structure's primary function is to warm and moisten the air?
(1) A (3) C
(2) B (4) D

17 Which structure contains the vocal cords?
(1) A (3) C
(2) B (4) D

18 Which structure is altered by emphysema?
(1) E (3) C
(2) B (4) D

19 Which structure contains alveoli?
(1) E (3) C
(2) B (4) D

20 Explain how pulmonary circulation differs from systemic circulation.

21 Make a copy of the chart below. Then, fill in the missing structures and functions. (Do not write in this book.)

Structure	Function
	Chamber where blood enters heart from the body
Right ventricle	
	Carry blood from the heart to the lungs
	Carry blood back to the heart from the lungs
Left atrium	
	Chamber that pumps blood to the body
Aorta	

22 Distinguish between systolic pressure and diastolic pressure.

Base your answers to questions 23 and 24 on the table below and on your knowledge of biology.

Blood Flow Through Human Organs

Organ	Percentage of Total Flow
Brain	14%
Heart	5%
Kidneys	22%
Liver	13%
Lungs	100%
Skeletal muscles	18%
Skeletal muscles during exercise	75%

23 Identify the organ through which all the blood flows each time it passes through the body.

24 Explain the reason for the differences indicated in blood flow to skeletal muscles (normal vs. during exercise).

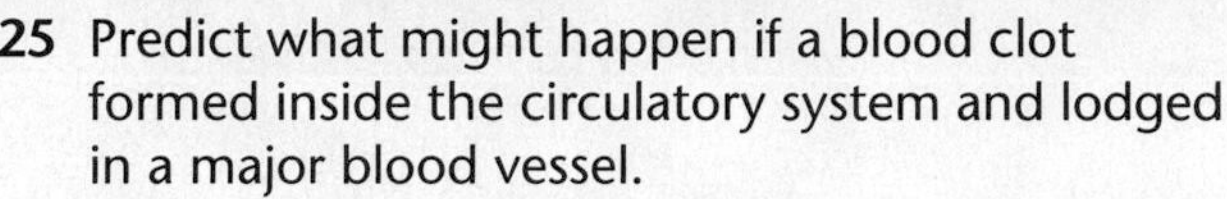

25 Predict what might happen if a blood clot formed inside the circulatory system and lodged in a major blood vessel.

26 Explain why a person with a low red blood cell count is likely to experience fatigue.

Part C

Extended Response

Answer the questions or follow the directions given.

27 Certain diseases may be a result of personal choices people make about their lifestyle. Some of these diseases affect the respiratory and circulatory systems. Discuss how certain specific personal choices can result in diseases of these two systems. In your answer, be sure to:

a Identify one specific personal choice that could lead to a respiratory system disease. Identify the disease, and then explain how this disease specifically affects the functioning of the respiratory system.

b Identify one specific personal choice that could lead to a circulatory system disease. Identify the disease, and then explain how this disease specifically affects the functioning of the circulatory system.

28 Explain the role of valves in the functioning of the circulatory system. In your explanation, be sure to

- identify the function of a valve in relation to the flow of blood
- identify *two* places in the circulatory system where valves are found
- identify one specific valve by name and describe its specific function

29 Describe the sequence of events that regulates the rate of the heartbeat. In your description, be sure to

- explain why the rate of heartbeat needs to be regulated
- name the specific group of cells that begins the process
- describe the specific pathway along which the impulses travel

30 Describe what happens in the body to result in "involuntary breathing" if you hold your breath for too long. In your answer, be sure to

- identify the region of the brain responsible for this action
- identify the substance that the body actually monitors to determine when this action is needed
- describe what actually happens in the respiratory system to start breathing again

31 A student undertook an investigation involving three subjects. The results of the investigation are shown in the table.

Person Tested	Resting Pulse Rate (beats per minute)	Time After Exercise for Pulse to Return to Resting Level
Subject A	75	8 minutes
Subject B	84	6 minutes
Subject C	67	2 minutes

Based on the information provided, discuss the purpose and usefulness of the investigation. In your answer, be sure to

- state what question the investigator was most likely attempting to answer
- state *two* reasons why a valid conclusion cannot be reached, based on the data provided
- state one way the investigation should be modified so a valid conclusion about the interaction between the variables could be reached

For: An interactive self-test
Visit: PHSchool.com
Web Code: cba-0370

CHAPTER 38

Digestive and Excretory Systems

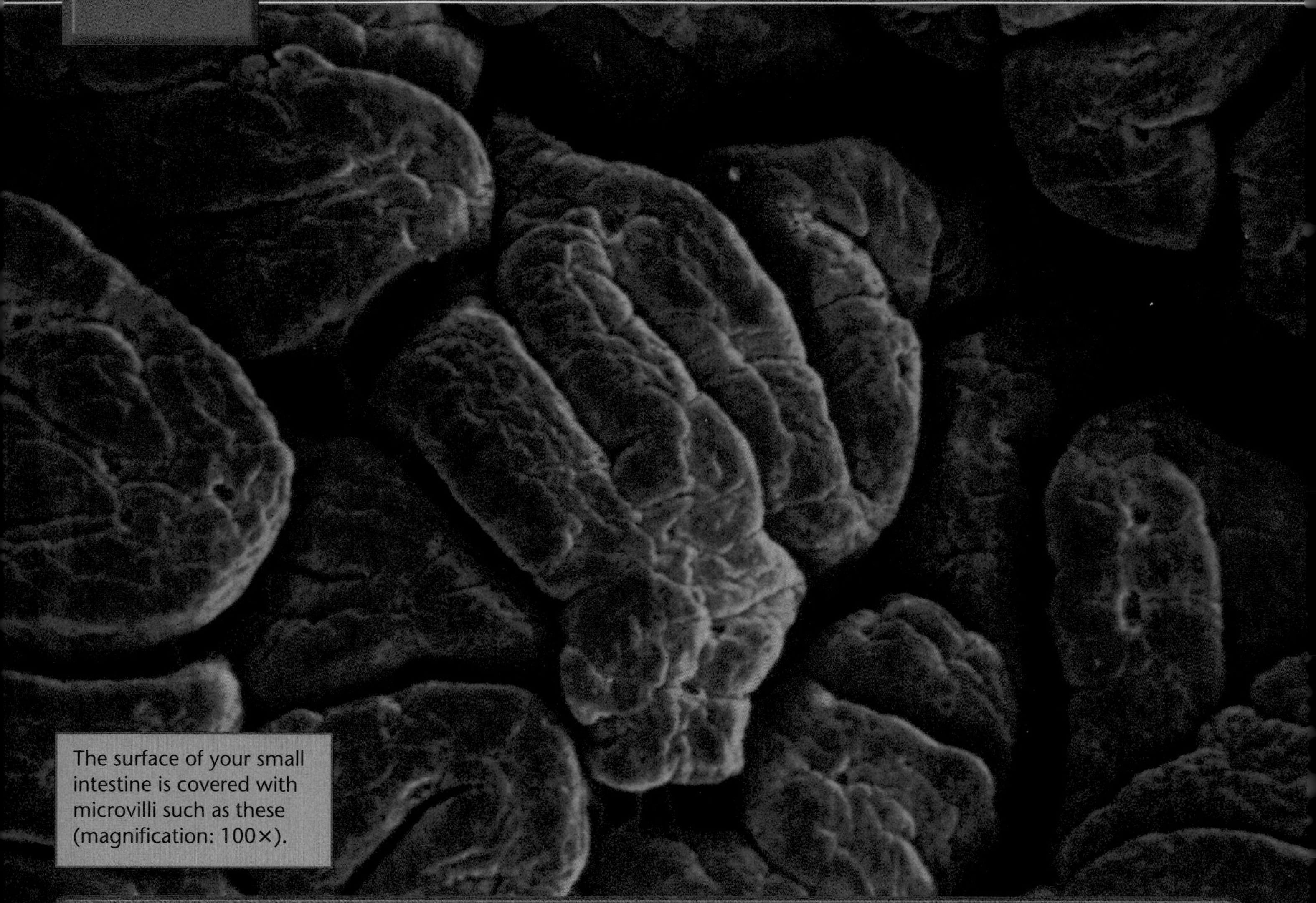

The surface of your small intestine is covered with microvilli such as these (magnification: 100×).

Inquiry Activity

What's in a chip?

Procedure 

1. Place an ordinary potato chip on a brown paper bag, and fold the bag over the chip. Repeat, using a similarly sized, baked potato chip and another paper bag. **CAUTION:** *Do not eat the potato chips.*
2. Press down on the bags for 1 minute, and then unfold them. Hold the bags up to the light. A bright spot indicates the presence of fat.
3. Observe as your teacher burns the potato chips.

Think About It

1. **Observing** Which type of potato chip contains more fat?
2. **Inferring** Which potato chip has more stored chemical energy?
3. **Drawing Conclusions** How are the results from burning the potato chips related to the fat and Calorie contents listed on their package labels?

38–1 Food and Nutrition

4-1.2 Cells digest large molecules
4-5.1 Organic compounds
LS- Analyze results, make observations, use indicators

How important is food in your life? Before you answer, think of two American holidays: Independence Day and Thanksgiving Day. What comes to mind? No matter where you live, chances are that meals are the centerpieces of those special days. To most of us, food is more than just nourishment—it is an important part of our culture. Human societies throughout the world organize meetings and family gatherings around food.

Guide for Reading

Key Concepts
- What are the nutrients your body needs?
- Why is water such an important nutrient?

Vocabulary
Calorie
carbohydrate
fat
protein
vitamin
mineral

Reading Strategy: Finding Main Ideas Before you read, skim the section to identify the key ideas. Then, carefully read the section, making a list of supporting details for each main idea.

Food and Energy

Have you ever wondered why you need to eat food? The most obvious answer is to obtain energy. You need energy to climb stairs, lift books, run, and even to think. Just as a car needs gasoline, your body needs fuel for all that work, and food is your fuel. Cells convert the chemical energy stored in the sugar glucose and other molecules into ATP.

The energy available in food can be measured in a surprisingly simple way—by burning the food! When food is burned, the energy content of the food is converted to heat, which is measured in terms of calories. The amount of heat needed to raise the temperature of 1 gram of water by 1 degree Celsius is 1 calorie. Scientists refer to the energy stored in food as dietary Calories with a capital *C*. One **Calorie** is equal to 1000 calories, or 1 kilocalorie (kcal).

The energy needs of an average-sized teenager are about 2200 Calories per day for females and about 2800 Calories per day for males. If you engage in vigorous physical activity, however, your energy needs may be higher.

Chemical pathways in your body's cells can extract energy from almost any type of food. Why then does it matter which foods you eat? Although most of the food you eat is used as fuel, a certain amount of the food you eat has other important functions. Food supplies the raw materials used to build and repair body tissues. Some of these raw materials are used to manufacture new biomolecules. These include the proteins that regulate cellular reactions, the phospholipids in cell membranes, and DNA—your genetic material. Food also contains at least 45 substances that the body needs but cannot manufacture.

The science of nutrition—the study of food and its effects on the body—tries to determine how food helps the body meet all of its various needs. Based on their research, nutritionists recommend balanced diets that include many different types of food. They also plan diets for people with particular needs, such as diabetics.

▼ **Figure 38–1** Holidays and other celebrations often center around food.

▲ **Figure 38–2** **Every cell in the body needs water because many of the body's processes take place in water.** On hot days or when you exercise, you need to drink more water to replace the water that is lost in sweat.

Nutrients

Nutrients are substances in food that supply the energy and raw materials your body uses for growth, repair, and maintenance. **The nutrients that the body needs are water, carbohydrates, fats, proteins, vitamins, and minerals.**

Water The most important nutrient is water. **Every cell in the human body needs water because many of the body's processes, including chemical reactions, take place in water.** Water makes up the bulk of blood, lymph, and other bodily fluids. On hot days or when you take part in strenuous exercise, sweat glands remove water from your tissues and release it as sweat on the surface of your body. As the water in sweat evaporates, it cools the body. In this way, sweating helps maintain homeostasis. Water vapor is also lost from the body with every breath you exhale and in urine.

Humans need to drink at least 1 liter of water each day. If enough water is not taken in to replace what is lost, dehydration can result. This condition leads to problems with the circulatory, respiratory, and nervous systems. Drinking plenty of clean water, as the woman is doing in **Figure 38–2,** is one of the best things you can do to help keep your body healthy.

CHECKPOINT *How does sweat help to maintain homeostasis?*

Carbohydrates Simple and complex **carbohydrates** are the main source of energy for the body. **Figure 38–3** shows some of the foods that contain carbohydrates. The sugars found in fruits, honey, and sugar cane are simple carbohydrates, or monosaccharides and disaccharides. The starches found in grains, potatoes, and vegetables are complex carbohydrates, or polysaccharides. Starches are broken down by the digestive system into simple sugars. These molecules are absorbed into the bloodstream and carried to cells throughout the body. Sugars that are not immediately used to supply energy are converted into the complex carbohydrate glycogen, which is stored in the liver and in skeletal muscles.

Many foods contain the complex carbohydrate cellulose, often called fiber. Although the human digestive system cannot break down cellulose, you need fiber in your diet. The bulk supplied by fiber helps muscles to keep food and wastes moving through your digestive and excretory systems. Foods such as whole-grain breads, bran, and many fruits and vegetables are rich in fiber.

▲ **Figure 38–3** Breads, pastas, and cereals are foods rich in carbohydrates. Simple carbohydrates do not have to be digested or broken down. Complex carbohydrates must be broken down before they can be used by the body. **Inferring** *Which type of carbohydrate—simple or complex—provides the body with quick energy?*

Fats Fats, or lipids, are an important part of a healthy diet. **Fats** are formed from fatty acids and glycerol. Your body needs certain fatty acids, called essential fatty acids, to produce cell membranes, myelin sheaths, and certain hormones. Fatty acids also help the body absorb fat-soluble vitamins. When a person eats more food than is needed, the body stores the extra energy as fat. Deposits of fat protect body organs and insulate the body.

Figure 38–4 Fats and proteins are two of the six nutrients the body needs. The foods on the left contain essential fatty acids. The foods below are good sources of proteins.

Based on the structure of their fatty acid chains, fats are classified as saturated or unsaturated. When there are only single bonds between the carbon atoms in the fatty acids, each carbon atom has the maximum number of hydrogen atoms and the fat is said to be saturated. Most saturated fats are solids at room temperature—including butter and other animal fats.

Unsaturated fats have at least one double bond in a fatty acid chain. Unsaturated fats are usually liquids at room temperature. Because many vegetable oils contain more than one double bond, they are called polyunsaturated. **Figure 38–4** shows foods containing both saturated and unsaturated fats.

People often consume more fat than they actually need. The American Heart Association recommends a diet with a maximum of 30 percent of Calories from fat, of which only 10 percent should be from saturated fats. The health consequences of a diet high in fat are serious. They include an increased risk of high blood pressure, heart disease, obesity, and diabetes.

Proteins Proteins have a wide variety of roles in the body. **Proteins** supply raw materials for growth and repair of structures such as skin and muscle. Proteins have regulatory and transport functions. For example, the hormone insulin is a protein that regulates the level of sugar in the blood. Hemoglobin, a protein found in red blood cells, helps the blood transport oxygen.

Proteins are polymers of amino acids. The body is able to synthesize only 12 of the 20 amino acids used to make proteins. The other 8, which are listed in **Figure 38–5,** are called essential amino acids. Essential amino acids must be obtained from the foods that you eat. Meat, fish, eggs, and milk generally contain all 8 essential amino acids. Foods derived from plants, such as grains and beans, do not. People who don't eat animal products must eat a combination of plant foods, such as beans and rice, to obtain all of the essential amino acids.

▼ **Figure 38–5** When plant foods are eaten in the right combination, they provide all of the essential amino acids. **Interpreting Graphics** ***Which amino acids are found in both grains and legumes?***

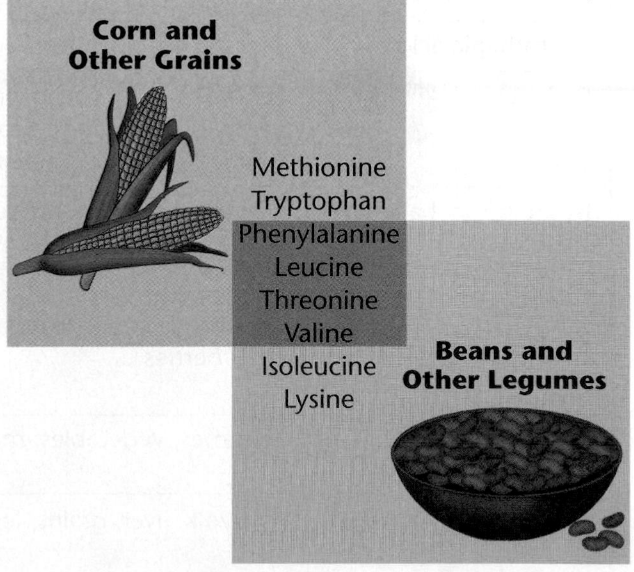

Vitamins If you think of carbohydrates, fats, and proteins as the fuel of an automobile, then vitamins are the ignition. **Vitamins** are organic molecules that help regulate body processes, often working with enzymes. As you can see in **Figure 38–6,** most vitamins must be obtained from food. However, the bacteria that live in the digestive tract are able to synthesize vitamin K. The skin is able to synthesize vitamin D when exposed to sunlight. A diet lacking certain vitamins can have serious, even fatal, consequences.

There are two types of vitamins: fat-soluble and water-soluble. The fat-soluble vitamins A, D, E, and K can be stored in the fatty tissues of the body. The body can build up small stores of these vitamins for future use.

▼ **Figure 38–6** This table lists the food sources and functions of 14 essential vitamins. The fat-soluble vitamins are listed in the blue rows, and the water-soluble vitamins in the white rows. **Using Tables and Graphs** *What is the function of vitamin K?*

Vitamins

Vitamin	Sources	Function
A (retinol)	Yellow, orange, and dark green vegetables; dairy products	Important for growth of skin cells; important for night vision
D (calciferol) 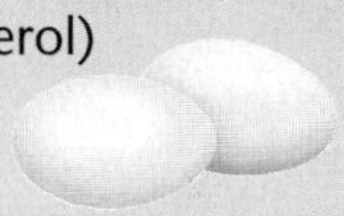	Fish oils, eggs; made by skin when exposed to sunlight; added to dairy products	Promotes bone growth; increases calcium and phosphorus absorption
E (tocopherol)	Green leafy vegetables, seeds, vegetable oils	Antioxidant; prevents cellular damage
K	Green leafy vegetables; made by bacteria that live in human intestine	Needed for normal blood clotting
B_1 (thiamine)	Whole grains, pork, legumes, milk	Normal metabolism of carbohydrates
B_2 (riboflavin) 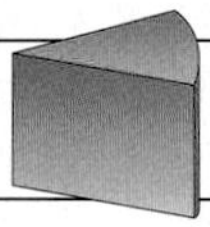	Dairy products, meats, vegetables, whole-grain cereal	Normal growth; part of electron transport chain; energy metabolism
Niacin	Liver, milk, whole grains, nuts, meats, legumes	Important in energy metabolism
B_6 (pyridoxine)	Whole grains, meats, vegetables	Important for amino acid metabolism
Pantothenic acid	Meats, dairy products, whole grains	Needed for energy metabolism
Folic acid 	Legumes, nuts, green leafy vegetables, oranges, broccoli, peas, fortified bread and cereal	Coenzyme involved in nucleic acid metabolism; prevents neural-tube defects in developing fetuses
B_{12} (cyanocobalamin)	Meats, eggs, dairy products, enriched cereals	Coenzyme in nucleic acid metabolism; maturation of red blood cells
C (ascorbic acid) 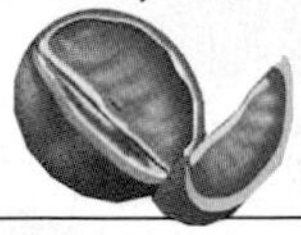	Citrus fruits, tomatoes, red or green peppers, broccoli, cabbage, strawberries	Maintenance of cartilage and bone; antioxidant; improves iron absorption; important for healthy gums, tissue repair, and wound healing
Biotin	Legumes, vegetables, meat	Coenzyme in synthesis of fat; glycogen formation; amino acid metabolism
Choline 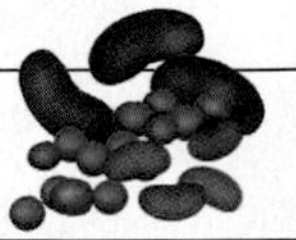	Egg yolk, liver, grains, legumes	Required for phospholipids and neurotransmitters

Important Minerals		
Mineral	**Sources**	**Function**
Calcium	Dairy products, salmon, sardines, kale, tofu, collard greens, legumes	Bone and tooth formation; blood clotting; nerve and muscle function
Phosphorus	Dairy products, meats, poultry, grains	Bone and tooth formation; acid-base balance
Potassium	Meats, dairy products, many fruits and vegetables, grains	Acid-base balance; body water balance; nerve function; muscle function
Chlorine	Table salt, processed foods	Acid-base balance; formation of gastric juice
Sodium	Table salt, processed foods	Acid-base balance; body water balance; nerve function; muscle function
Magnesium	Whole grains, green leafy vegetables	Activation of enzymes in protein synthesis
Iron	Meats, eggs, legumes, whole grains, green leafy vegetables, dried fruit	Component of hemoglobin and of electron carriers used in energy metabolism
Fluorine	Fluoridated drinking water, tea, seafood	Maintenance of tooth structure; maintenance of bone structure
Iodine	Seafood, dairy products, iodized salt	Component of thyroid hormones
Zinc	Meats, seafood, grains	Component of certain digestive enzymes

▲ **Figure 38–7** Minerals are sometimes called trace elements because they are needed by the body in such small amounts. **Inferring** *Why do you think some cities and towns add fluorlde to their water supplies?*

The water-soluble vitamins, which include vitamin C and the B vitamins, dissolve in water and cannot be stored in the body. Therefore, they should be included in the foods you eat each day. Eating a diet containing a variety of foods will supply the daily vitamin needs of nearly everyone.

Food stores and pharmacies sell vitamin supplements. Taking extra-large doses of vitamin supplements does not benefit the body; and, in some cases, it may cause real harm. Excessive amounts of vitamins A, D, E, and K can be toxic.

CHECKPOINT ***Why is it important not to take more than the recommended amount of certain vitamins?***

Minerals Inorganic nutrients that the body needs, usually in small amounts, are called **minerals.** Some examples of minerals are calcium, iron, and magnesium. Calcium is a major component of bones and teeth; and iron is needed to make hemoglobin, the oxygen-carrying protein in red blood cells. Calcium, sodium, and potassium are required for normal functioning of nerves. **Figure 38–7** lists some of the minerals needed by the body.

Although the body does not metabolize the minerals it takes in, it does lose many of them in sweat, urine, and other waste products. How are these important chemicals replaced? Many of these elements are found in the living tissues of plants and other animals. By eating a variety of foods, you can meet your daily requirement of minerals.

Nutrition and a Balanced Diet

It's no easy task to figure out the best balance of nutrients for the human diet, but nutritionists have tried to do exactly that. The result is the Food Guide Pyramid shown in **Figure 38–8.**

The Food Guide Pyramid classifies foods into six groups. It also indicates how many servings from each group should be eaten every day to maintain a healthy diet. Foods rich in complex carbohydrates are at the base of the pyramid. At the top of the pyramid are foods such as fats and sweets, which should be used sparingly. Some foods in the other groups also contain fats and sugars, so you should keep this in mind when choosing foods from these groups. The basic idea behind the pyramid is sound and simple—you should eat a variety of foods each day and limit your intake of fatty, sugary foods.

Food labels can also be used to choose healthful foods. A food label provides some general information about nutrition, listing the Daily Values and the Calories per gram for protein, carbohydrates, and fats. The daily value shows you how the particular food fits into the overall daily diet. Keep in mind that daily values are based on a 2000-Calorie diet. Nutrient needs are affected by age, gender, and lifestyle. Rapidly growing adolescents and other groups of people need more nutrients than the daily values indicate.

When choosing foods, you should use the information on food labels to compare similar foods on the basis of their proportion of nutrients to Calories. When you choose a food, it should be high in nutrition and low in Calories.

Go Online
active art
For: Food Guide Pyramid activity
Visit: PHSchool.com
Web Code: cbp-0381

▼ **Figure 38–8** The Food Guide Pyramid illustrates the main characteristics of a balanced diet. Foods at the base of the pyramid should make up the major portion of the diet, whereas foods containing fats and sugars should be eaten sparingly. **Interpreting Graphics** *Why do you think nutritionists recommend that you limit your intake of fats, oils, and sweets?*

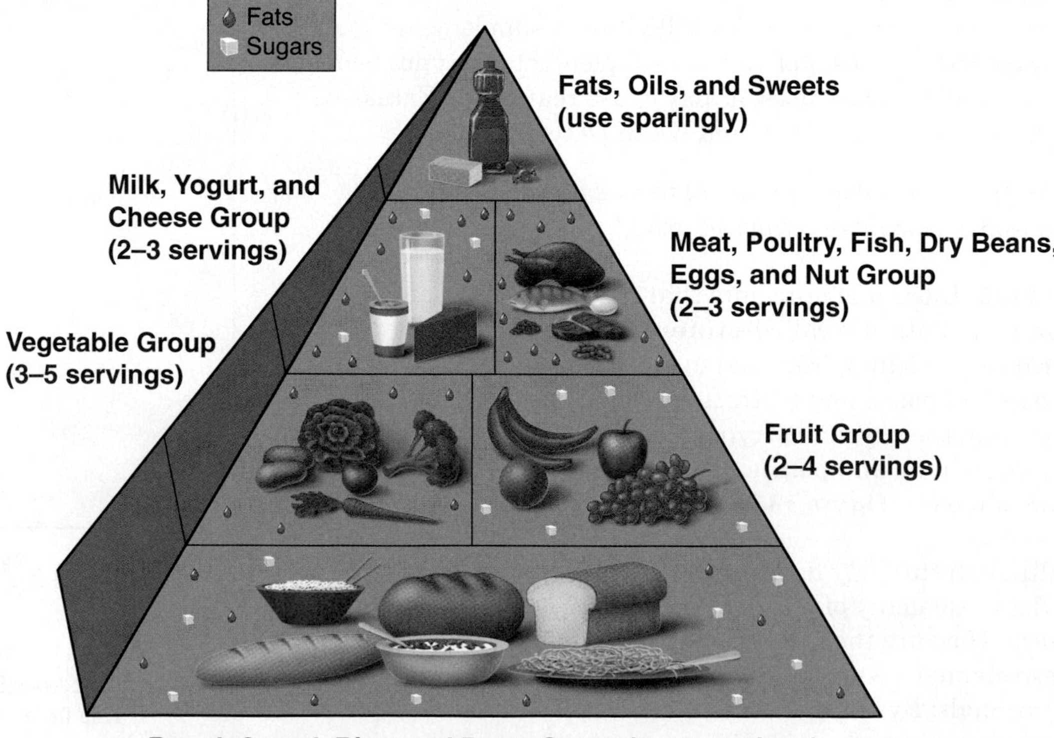

Analyzing Data

Evaluating Food Labels

Federal regulations require that labels on packaged foods display the nutrients each food contains and the percentage of daily value each nutrient represents for a person, as well as serving size, number of servings per container, and Calories per serving. Carefully examine the nutritional information on the cereal label shown. Based on the information on the label, answer the questions that follow.

1. **Calculating** If you ate 2 cups of this product, how many grams of fat would you eat? How many grams of protein?
2. **Interpreting Graphics** How many Calories are in a gram of fat? Of protein? Of carbohydrate?
3. **Interpreting Graphics** On a 2000-Calorie diet, what is the Daily Value for total fat? For sodium? For fiber?
4. **Evaluating** Advertising claims for this product say that it is a good source of iron. Is this promotional claim true?
5. **Going Further** People with hypertension, or high blood pressure, often are advised to restrict their intake of sodium. Visit a local food store and look at the labels on 5 types of packaged foods. From this information, recommend which of the foods would be healthful for people who have hypertension.

Nutrition Facts

Serving Size 1 cup (30g)
Servings Per Container About 10

Amount Per Serving

Calories 110 — Calories from Fat 15

	% Daily Value*
Total Fat 2g	**3%**
Saturated Fat 0g	**0%**
Cholesterol 0mg	**0%**
Sodium 280mg	**12%**
Total Carbohydrate 22g	**7%**
Dietary Fiber 3g	**12%**
Sugars 1g	
Protein 3g	

Vitamin A	10%	Vitamin C	20%
Calcium	4%	Iron	45%

* Percent Daily Values are based on a 2,000 Calorie diet. Your daily values may be higher or lower depending on your caloric needs:

	Calories	2,000	2,500
Total Fat	Less than	65g	80g
Sat. Fat	Less than	20g	25g
Cholesterol	Less than	300mg	300mg
Sodium	Less than	2,400mg	2,400mg
Total Carbohydrate		300g	375g
Fiber		25g	30g

Calories per gram:
Fat 9 • Carbohydrate 4 • Protein 4

Ingredients: Whole grain oats, sugar, salt, milled corn, oat fiber, dried whey, hon... almonds...

38–1 Section Assessment

1. **Key Concept** List the six nutrients needed by the body.
2. **Key Concept** What is the importance of water in the body?
3. Why is fiber an important part of your diet?
4. How are vitamins and minerals similar? How are they different?
5. **Critical Thinking Using Tables and Graphs** Which vitamins and minerals promote healthy bones? (*Hint*: See **Figure 38–6** and **Figure 38–7**.)

Writing in Science

Designing a Brochure

Design and create a brochure that explains how the body uses the six nutrients necessary for normal function. Use images from magazines or from the Internet to illustrate your brochure.

38–2 The Process of Digestion

4-1.2 Humans have complex systems
4-1.2 Cells are grouped for efficiency
4-5.1 Enzymes
LS- Follow safety rules, formulate conclusions
LS- Make observations, measure volume of liquids

Guide for Reading

Key Concepts

- What are the organs of the digestive system?
- What is the function of the digestive system?

Vocabulary

amylase
esophagus
peristalsis
stomach
chyme
small intestine
pancreas
liver
villus
large intestine

Reading Strategy: Asking Questions Before you read, rewrite the seven blue heads in the section as *how, why,* or *what* questions. As you read, write brief answers to your questions.

Food presents every chordate with at least two challenges. The first is how to obtain it. Once a chordate has caught, or gathered its food, it faces a new challenge—how to break that food down into small molecules that can be passed to the cells that need them. In humans and many other chordates, this is the job of the digestive system. As food passes through the digestive system, it gets disassembled, distributing its nutrient value to the body along the way.

The human digestive system, like those of other chordates, is built around an alimentary canal—a one-way tube that passes through the body. **The digestive system includes the mouth, pharynx, esophagus, stomach, small intestine, and large intestine. Several major accessory structures, including the salivary glands, the pancreas, and the liver, add secretions to the digestive system.**

The Mouth

As you take a forkful of food into your mouth, the work of the digestive system begins. The teeth, shown in **Figure 38–9,** tear and crush the food into a fine paste until it is ready to be swallowed. Chewing begins the process of mechanical digestion. Mechanical digestion is the physical breakdown of large pieces of food into smaller pieces. But there is a great deal more to it than that. As you chew your food, digestive enzymes begin the breakdown of carbohydrates into smaller molecules. This process is called chemical digestion. During chemical digestion, large food molecules are broken down into smaller food molecules. **The function of the digestive system is to help convert foods into simpler molecules that can be absorbed and used by the cells of the body.** The organs of the digestive system are shown in **Figure 38–10.**

Teeth The teeth are anchored in the bones of the jaw. The surfaces of the teeth are protected by a coating of mineralized enamel. Teeth do much of the mechanical work of digestion by cutting, tearing, and crushing food into small fragments.

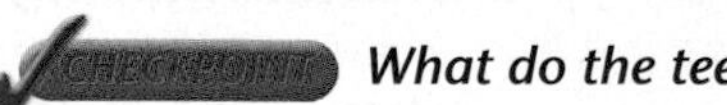

What do the teeth do?

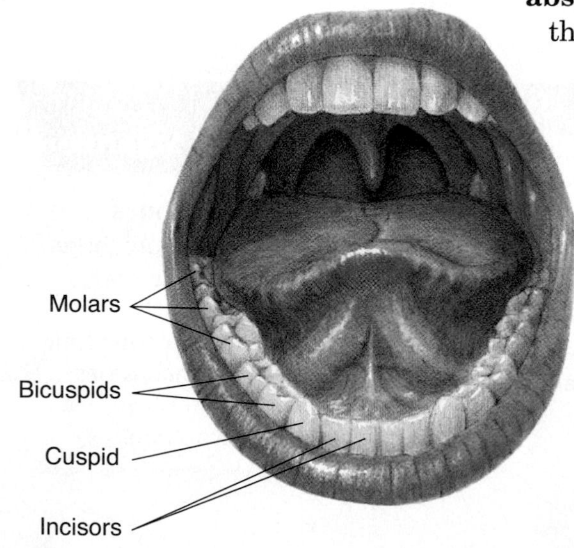

◀ **Figure 38–9** Human teeth include sharp incisors; cuspids and bicuspids, which grasp and tear food; and large, flat molars. **Inferring** *How do human teeth reflect an omnivorous diet?*

Figure 38–10 The Digestive System

The digestive system includes the mouth, pharynx, esophagus, stomach, small intestine, and large intestine. Because the pancreas and most of the gallbladder are behind other organs, their locations are indicated by dotted lines.

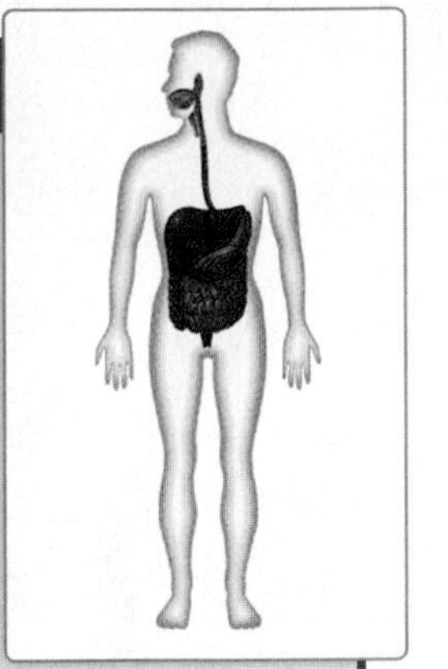

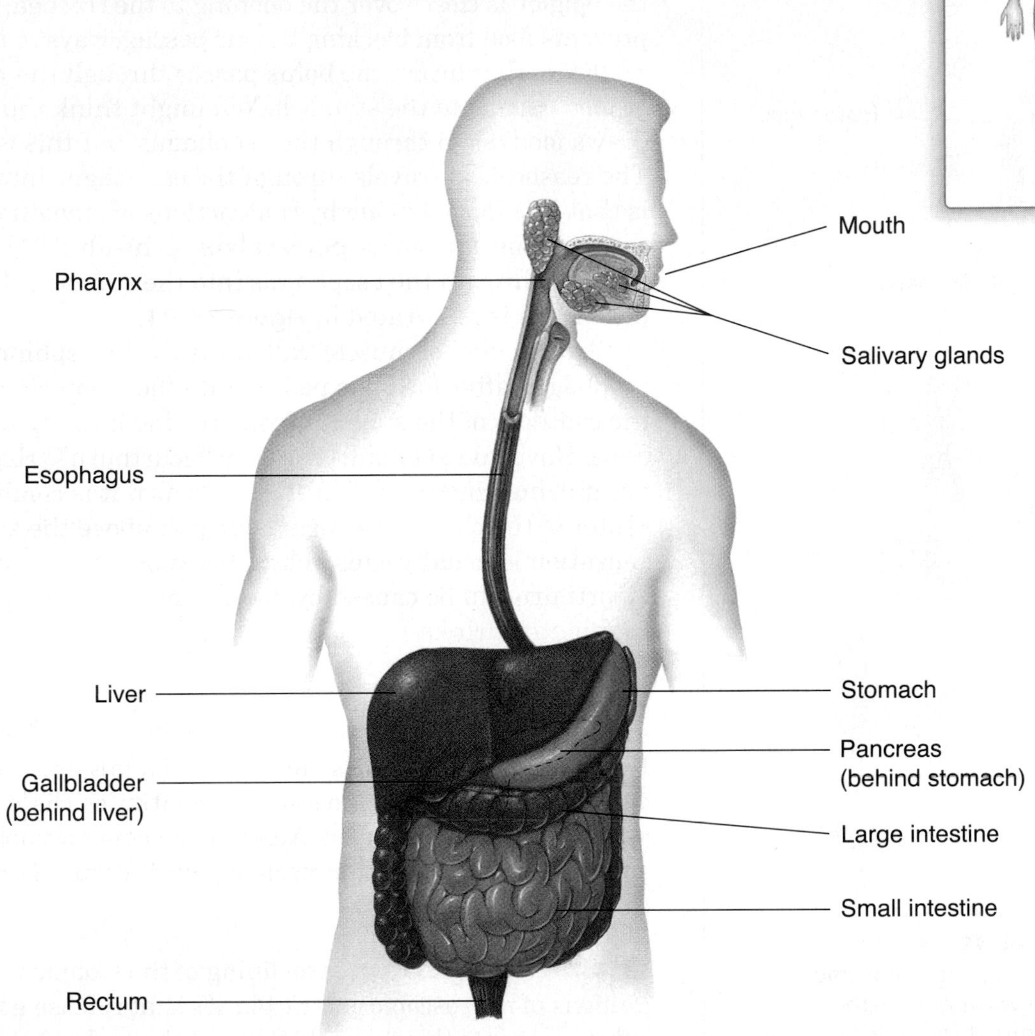

Mouth

Pharynx

Salivary glands

Esophagus

Liver

Stomach

Pancreas (behind stomach)

Gallbladder (behind liver)

Large intestine

Small intestine

Rectum

Saliva As the teeth cut and grind the food, the salivary glands secrete saliva, which helps to moisten the food and make it easier to chew. The release of saliva is under the control of the nervous system and can be triggered by the scent of food—especially when you are hungry!

Saliva not only helps ease the passage of food through the digestive system but also begins the process of chemical digestion. Saliva contains an enzyme called **amylase** that breaks the chemical bonds in starches and releases sugars. If you chew on a starchy food like a cracker long enough, it will begin to taste sweet. This sweet taste is a sign that sugar has been released from starch by the action of amylase. Saliva also contains lysozyme, an enzyme that fights infection by digesting the cell walls of many bacteria that may enter the mouth with food.

The Esophagus

During swallowing, the combined actions of the tongue and throat muscles push the chewed clump of food, called a bolus, down the throat. Recall that as you swallow, a flap of connective tissue called the epiglottis closes over the opening to the trachea. This action prevents food from blocking the air passageways to the lungs.

From the throat, the bolus passes through the **esophagus,** or food tube, into the stomach. You might think that gravity draws food down through the esophagus, but this is not correct. The reason food travels through the esophagus into the stomach is that it is moved along by contractions of smooth muscle. These contractions, known as **peristalsis** (pehr-uh-STAL-sis), squeeze the food through the esophagus into the stomach. The process of peristalsis is illustrated in **Figure 38–11.**

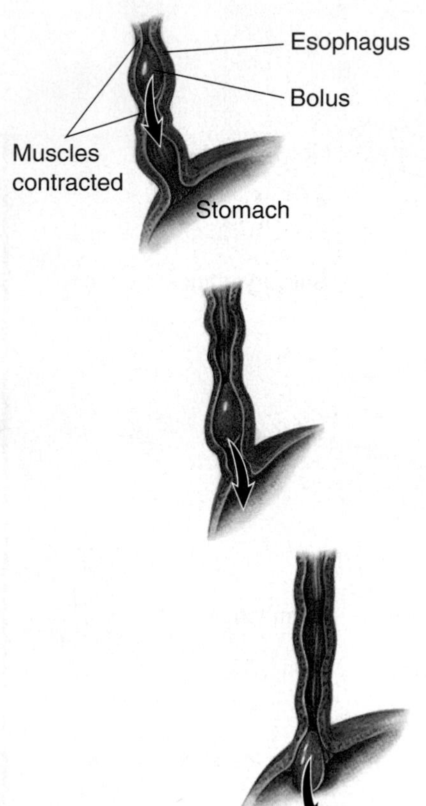

▲ **Figure 38–11** Muscles in the walls of the esophagus contract in waves. Each wave pushes the chewed clump of food, or bolus, in front of it. Eventually, the bolus is pushed into the stomach. **Applying Concepts** *What kind of muscle surrounds the esophagus?*

A thick ring of muscle, called the cardiac sphincter, closes the esophagus after food has passed into the stomach and prevents the contents of the stomach from moving back up into the esophagus. Have you ever suffered from "heartburn"? Heartburn is a painful, burning sensation that feels as if it is coming from the center of the chest (by your heart), just above the stomach. The sensation is usually caused by a backflow of stomach acid. Heartburn can be caused by overeating or drinking an excess of caffeinated drinks.

The Stomach

Food from the esophagus empties into a large muscular sac called the **stomach.** The stomach continues the mechanical and chemical digestion of food. Alternating contractions of the stomach's three smooth muscle layers thoroughly churn and mix the food you swallow.

Chemical Digestion The lining of the stomach contains millions of microscopic gastric glands that release a number of substances into the stomach. Some of these glands produce mucus, a fluid that lubricates and protects the stomach wall. Other glands produce hydrochloric acid, which makes the contents of the stomach very acidic. The acid activates pepsin, an enzyme that begins the digestion of protein and is secreted by a third set of stomach glands. Pepsin works best under the acidic conditions present in the stomach. The combination of pepsin and hydrochloric acid begins the complex process of protein digestion. Pepsin breaks proteins into smaller polypeptide fragments. While pepsin requires the acidic environment of the stomach in order to function, other enzymes such as amalyse are denatured by the stomach acid. As a result, chemical digestion of carbohydrates stops when food enters the stomach and does not resume until the food passes into the small intestine. Not all enzymes that aid in digestion are released by the stomach. Other enzymes that help in digestion are shown in **Figure 38–12.**

What is the role of pepsin?

Mechanical Digestion As digestion proceeds, stomach muscles contract to churn and mix stomach fluids and food, gradually producing a mixture known as **chyme** (KYM). After an hour or two, the pyloric valve, which is located between the stomach and small intestine, opens and chyme begins to flow into the small intestine.

Effects of Digestive Enzymes		
Active Site	**Enzyme**	**Effect on Food**
Mouth	Salivary amylase	Breaks down starches into disaccharides
Stomach	Pepsin	Breaks down proteins into large peptides
Small intestine (from pancreas)	Amylase	Continues the breakdown of starch
	Trypsin	Continues the breakdown of protein
	Lipase	Breaks down fat
Small intestine	Maltase, sucrase, lactase	Breaks down remaining disaccharides into monosaccharides
	Peptidase	Breaks down dipeptides into amino acids

▲ **Figure 38–12** Digestive enzymes break down foods and make nutrients available to the body. **Using Tables and Graphs** *Where in the body does the digestion of carbohydrates begin?*

The Small Intestine

As chyme is pushed through the pyloric valve, it enters the duodenum (doo-oh-DEE-num). The duodenum is the first of three parts of the **small intestine,** and it is where almost all of the digestive enzymes enter the intestine. Most of the chemical digestion and absorption of the food you eat occurs in the small intestine. As chyme enters the duodenum from the stomach, it mixes with enzymes and digestive fluids from the pancreas, the liver, and even the lining of the duodenum itself. The pancreas and liver are shown in **Figure 38–13.**

Accessory Structures of Digestion Just behind the stomach is the **pancreas.** The pancreas is a gland that serves three important functions. One function is to produce hormones that regulate blood sugar levels. Within the digestive system, the pancreas plays two key roles. It produces enzymes that break down carbohydrates, proteins, lipids, and nucleic acids. The pancreas also produces sodium bicarbonate, a base that neutralizes stomach acid so that these enzymes can be effective. Why is this neutralization necessary? Recall that enzymes are proteins. Stomach acid can change the shapes of protein molecules. If the shape of an enzyme's active site does not match the shape of its substrate, the enzyme will not be effective.

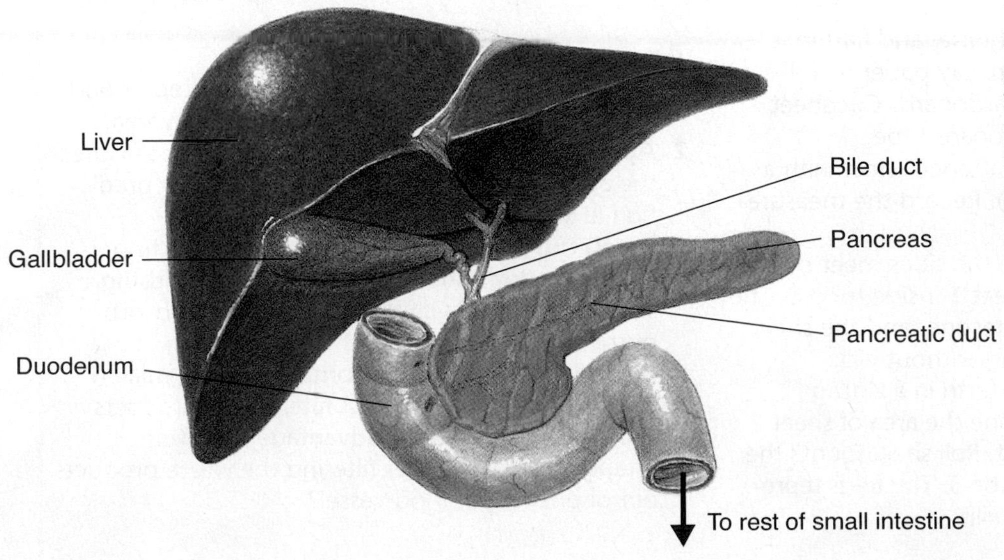

◀ **Figure 38–13** **Accessory structures, including the liver and pancreas, add secretions to the digestive system.** The pancreas secretes enzymes that help break down carbohydrates, proteins, and fats.

Assisting the pancreas is the **liver,** a large organ located just above and to the right of the stomach. The liver produces bile, a fluid loaded with lipids and salts. Bile acts like a detergent, dissolving and dispersing the droplets of fat found in fatty foods. This action makes it possible for enzymes to reach the smaller fat molecules and break them down. Bile is stored in a small, pouchlike organ called the gallbladder.

What is bile?

Absorption in the Small Intestine

The duodenum is much shorter than the remaining parts of the small intestine—the jejunum and the ileum, which together average about 6 meters long. By the time chyme enters these parts of the small intestine, much of the chemical digestion has been completed. The chyme is now a rich mixture of medium and small nutrient molecules.

The small intestine is specially adapted for the absorption of nutrients. The folded surfaces of the small intestine are covered with fingerlike projections called **villi** (VIL-eye; singular: villus).

Quick Lab

How do villi help the small intestine absorb nutrients?

Materials 2 paper towel sheets, scissors, 3 cardboard tubes, metric ruler, 30-mL graduated cylinder, 2 plastic cups

Procedure 

1. Cut cardboard tube 1 lengthwise, and flatten it. **CAUTION:** *Scissors are sharp.* Lay paper towel sheet 1 over the flattened cardboard. Cut sheet 1 to the same size as the cardboard tube.
2. Determine the area of the flattened sheet with a ruler (area = width x length). Record the measurements.
3. Roll sheet 1 lengthwise until the sides meet but do not overlap. Insert rolled sheet 1 inside tube 2. The tube represents the small intestine, and the sheet represents an intestinal lining without villi.
4. Fold uncut sheet 2 back and forth in a zigzag pattern, as for a fan. Determine the area of sheet 2 and record the measurement. Roll sheet 2 until the sides meet, and insert it in tube 3. The folds represent an intestinal lining with villi.
5. **Predicting** Predict which model will absorb more water.
6. Stand each tube in a plastic cup. Slowly pour 30 mL of water down the inside of each tube. Remove the tubes. Then, measure and record the quantity of water in each cup.

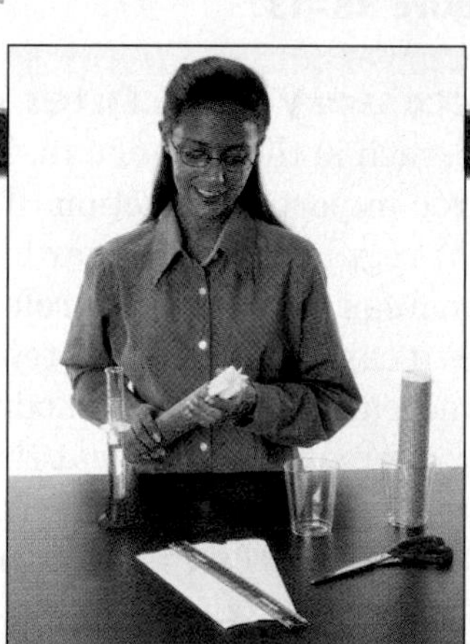

Analyze and Conclude

1. **Calculating** Use your calculations in steps 2 and 4 to show which model had more surface area.
2. **Applying Concepts** How does surface area affect the ability to absorb substances? Was your prediction in step 5 correct?
3. **Applying Concepts** How do folds and fingerlike projections affect the area of an absorbing surface? How do villi help the intestine absorb nutrients?
4. **Inferring** Your kidneys contain about 1 million microscopic structures that filter waste products from your blood. What advantage does this arrangement have over filtering the waste products out of one large blood vessel?

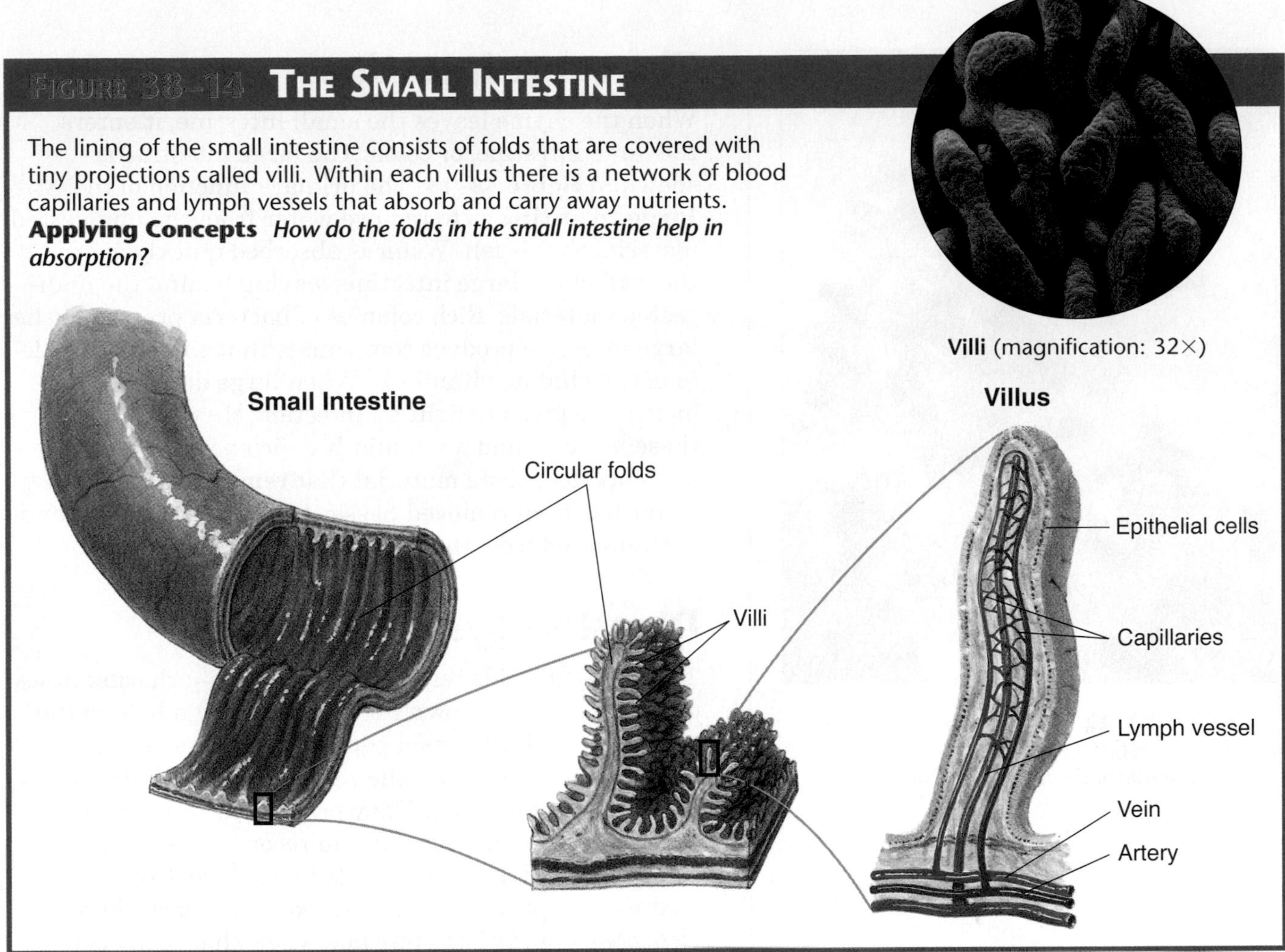

Figure 38–14 The Small Intestine

The lining of the small intestine consists of folds that are covered with tiny projections called villi. Within each villus there is a network of blood capillaries and lymph vessels that absorb and carry away nutrients. **Applying Concepts** *How do the folds in the small intestine help in absorption?*

The villi are illustrated in **Figure 38–14.** The surfaces of the cells of the villi are covered with thousands of fingerlike projections known as microvilli. These folds and projections provide an enormous surface area for the absorption of nutrient molecules. Slow, wavelike contractions of smooth muscles move the chyme along this surface.

Nutrient molecules are rapidly absorbed into the cells lining the small intestine. Most of the products of carbohydrate and protein digestion are absorbed into the capillaries in the villi. Molecules of undigested fat and some fatty acids are absorbed by lymph vessels.

By the time food is ready to leave the small intestine, it is basically nutrient-free. The complex organic molecules have been digested and absorbed, leaving only water, cellulose, and other undigestible substances behind.

As the water, cellulose, and other undigestible substances leave the small intestine and enter the large intestine, they pass by a small saclike organ called the appendix. In humans, the appendix appears to do little to promote digestion. In other mammals, the appendix is used to store cellulose and other materials that the digestive enzymes cannot break down. The only time you may pay attention to the appendix is when it becomes clogged and inflamed, causing appendicitis. The only remedy for appendicitis is to remove the infected organ by surgery—as quickly as possible.

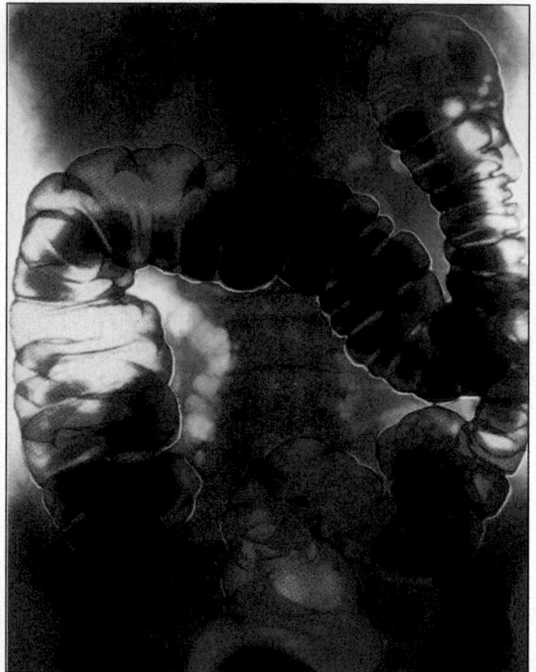

▲ **Figure 38–15** This barium X-ray shows the large intestine. **Applying Concepts** *What is the role of the large intestine?*

The Large Intestine

When the chyme leaves the small intestine, it enters the large intestine, or colon. The large intestine is shown in **Figure 38–15.** The primary function of the **large intestine** is to remove water from the undigested material that is left. Water is absorbed quickly across the wall of the large intestine, leaving behind the undigested materials. Rich colonies of bacteria present in the large intestine produce compounds that the body is able to use, including vitamin K. When large doses of antibiotics are given to fight an infection, they can destroy these bacteria and a vitamin K deficiency can occur. The concentrated waste material that remains after the water has been removed passes through the rectum and is eliminated from the body.

Digestive System Disorders

The powerful acids released into the stomach sometimes damage the organ's own lining, producing a hole in the stomach wall known as a peptic ulcer. For years, physicians hypothesized that the primary cause of ulcers was too much stomach acid. They prescribed drugs that suppressed acid production and recommended bland, easily digested diets. Scientists have since discovered that most peptic ulcers are caused by the bacterium *Helicobacter pylori*. Doctors now know that many peptic ulcers are caused by an infectious disease that can be cured. Thanks to powerful antibiotics, cure rates for peptic ulcers are as high as 90 percent.

Other digestive system disorders include diarrhea and constipation. When something happens that interferes with the removal of water by the large intestine, you usually become aware of it right away. If not enough water is absorbed, a condition known as diarrhea occurs. If too much water is absorbed from the undigested materials, a condition known as constipation occurs.

38–2 Section Assessment

1. **Key Concept** List the organs of the digestive system and give the function of each.
2. **Key Concept** Explain the function of the digestive system.
3. How do mechanical and chemical digestion work together to break down foods?
4. How does bile help in the digestion of fats?
5. **Critical Thinking Inferring** What can you infer about the diet of an animal that has a large appendix?

Connecting Concepts

Enzyme Action
How would the rate of digestion be affected if enzymes were not released by the various organs and glands? You may wish to refer to Chapter 2 for a review of enzyme action.

38–3 The Excretory System

4-1.2 Humans have complex systems
4-5.2 Maintaining homeostasis is critical to all organisms
4-5.2 Causes of disease
4-5.3 Dynamic equilibrium

Guide for Reading

Key Concepts
- What are the functions of the kidneys?
- How is blood filtered?

Vocabulary
kidney
ureter
urinary bladder
nephron
filtration
glomerulus
Bowman's capsule
reabsorption
loop of Henle
urethra

Reading Strategy: Building Vocabulary
Before you read, preview **Figure 38–17** to identify vocabulary with which you are unfamiliar. Look for the meanings of these terms as you read.

The chemistry of the human body is a marvelous thing. An intricate system of checks and balances controls everything from your blood pressure to your body temperature. Nutrients are absorbed, stored, and carefully released when they are needed. However, every living system, including the human body, produces chemical waste products that are not useful to the body. In fact, some waste products are so toxic that they will cause death if they are not eliminated.

Functions of the Excretory System

You might think that homeostasis involves the body's efforts to respond only to changes in the external environment. However, homeostasis also requires the body to deal with internal processes that might upset the internal cellular environment. For example, as a normal consequence of being alive, every cell in the body produces metabolic wastes, such as excess salts, carbon dioxide, and urea. Urea is a toxic compound that is produced when amino acids are used for energy. The process by which these metabolic wastes are eliminated is called excretion. Excretion is one part of the many processes that maintain homeostasis.

You have already learned about two organs of excretion—the skin and the lungs. The skin excretes excess water and salts, as well as a small amount of urea, in the form of sweat. The lungs excrete carbon dioxide, a gas produced when energy is captured from compounds in foods.

The liver, which we normally think of as a digestive organ, also plays a number of important roles in excretion. When cells of the body break down proteins, excess amino acids are released into the bloodstream. The liver takes up these amino acids and converts them into other useful compounds, producing nitrogen wastes in the process. The liver quickly converts these potentially poisonous nitrogen compounds into urea. Urea, in turn, is removed from the bloodstream along with other metabolic wastes by the body's principal organs of excretion, the kidneys. **The kidneys play an important role in maintaining homeostasis. They remove waste products from the blood; maintain blood pH; and regulate the water content of the blood and, therefore, blood volume.**

▶ **Figure 38–16** As part of the excretory system, the skin excretes water, salts, and urea in sweat.

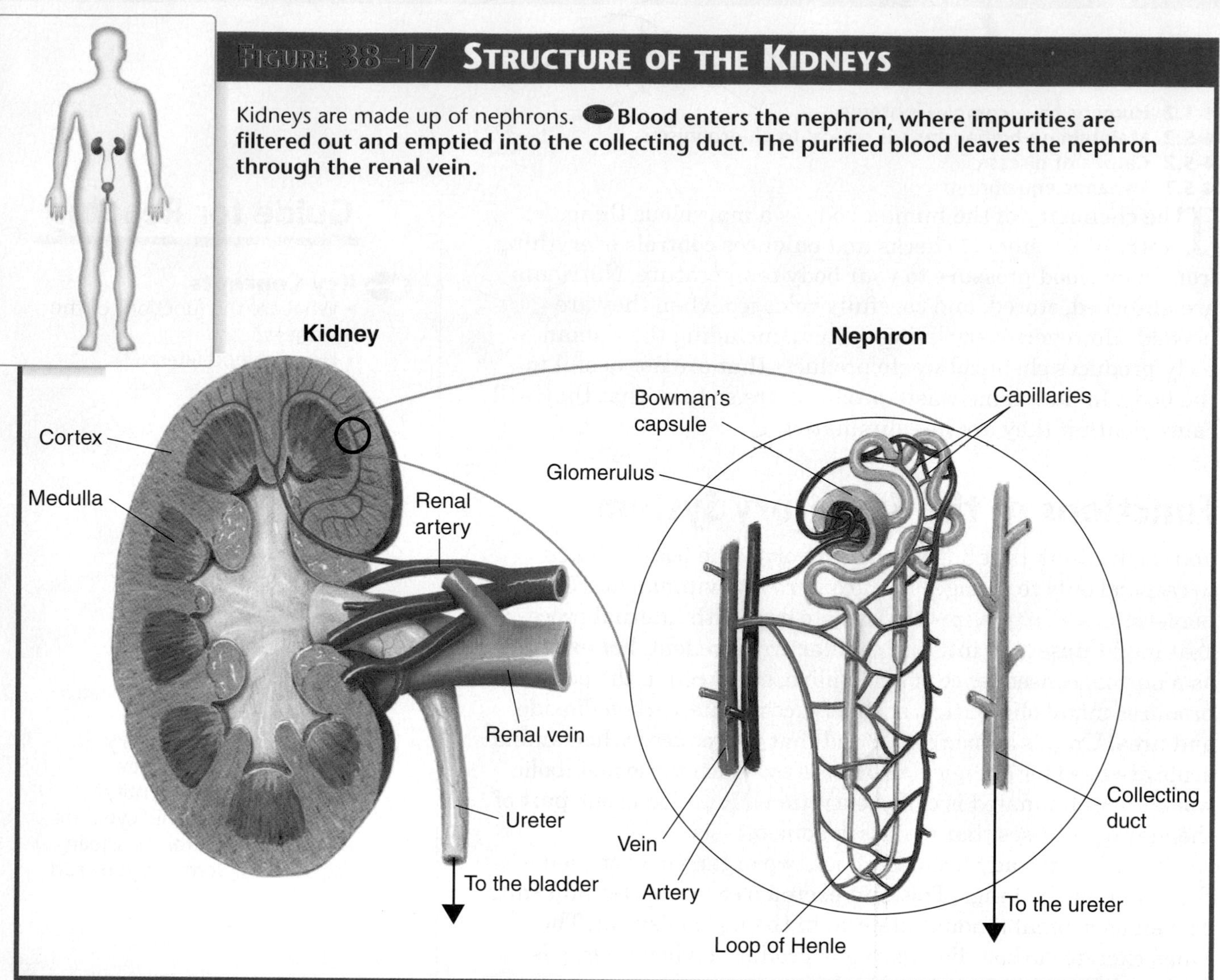

FIGURE 38–17 STRUCTURE OF THE KIDNEYS

Kidneys are made up of nephrons. **Blood enters the nephron, where impurities are filtered out and emptied into the collecting duct. The purified blood leaves the nephron through the renal vein.**

The Kidneys

The **kidneys** are located on either side of the spinal column near the lower back. A tube, called the **ureter** (yoo-REET-ur), leaves each kidney, carrying urine to the urinary bladder. The **urinary bladder** is a saclike organ where urine is stored before being excreted. The structures of the kidney are shown in **Figure 38–17.**

What does a kidney do? As waste-laden blood enters the kidney through the renal artery, the kidney removes urea, excess water, and other waste products and passes them to the ureter. The clean, filtered blood leaves the kidney through the renal vein and returns to circulation.

Kidney Structure If a kidney is cut in half, two distinct regions can be seen. The inner part is called the renal medulla. The outer part is called the renal cortex. The functional units of the kidney are called **nephrons** (NEF-rahnz). Each nephron is a small, independent processing unit. Nephrons are located in the renal cortex, except for their loops of Henle, which descend into the renal medulla.

Each nephron has its own blood supply: an arteriole, a venule, and a network of capillaries connecting them. In addition, each nephron releases fluids to a collecting duct, which leads to the ureter. **As blood enters a nephron through the arteriole, impurities are filtered out and emptied into the collecting duct. The purified blood exits the nephron through the venule.** The mechanism of blood purification involves two distinct processes: filtration and reabsorption.

CHECKPOINT *What are the two parts of a kidney?*

Filtration Passing a liquid or gas through a filter to remove wastes is called **filtration.** The filtration of blood mainly takes place in the glomerulus (gloh-MUR-yoo-lus). The **glomerulus** is a small network of capillaries encased in the upper end of the nephron by a hollow, cup-shaped structure called **Bowman's capsule.** A glomerulus is shown in **Figure 38–18.**

Because the blood is under pressure and the walls of the capillaries and Bowman's capsule are permeable, much of the fluid from the blood flows into Bowman's capsule. The materials that are filtered from the blood are collectively called the filtrate. The filtrate contains water, urea, glucose, salts, amino acids, and some vitamins. Because plasma proteins, cells, and platelets are too large to pass through the capillary walls, they remain in the blood.

Reabsorption The kidneys filter all the blood in the body approximately every 45 minutes. Needless to say, not all of the filtrate is excreted. Most of the material removed from the blood at Bowman's capsule makes its way back into the blood. The process in which liquid is taken back into a vessel is called **reabsorption.**

A number of materials, including amino acids, fats, and glucose, are removed from the filtrate by active transport and reabsorbed by the capillaries. Because water follows these materials by osmosis, almost 99 percent of the water that enters Bowman's capsule is reabsorbed into the blood. When the filtrate drains in the collecting ducts, most of the water and nutrients have been reabsorbed into the blood.

Urine Formation The material that remains, called urine, is emptied into a collecting duct. Urine, which contains urea, excess salts, and water, among other substances, is primarily concentrated in the loop of Henle. The **loop of Henle** is a section of the nephron tubule in which water is conserved and the volume of urine minimized.

As the kidney works, purified blood is returned to circulation while urine is collected in the urinary bladder. Urine is stored in the urinary bladder until it can be released from the body through a tube called the **urethra** (yoo-REE-thruh).

▼ **Figure 38–18** Blood enters each nephron through a ball of capillaries called a glomerulus. **The glomerulus is where filtration takes place.**

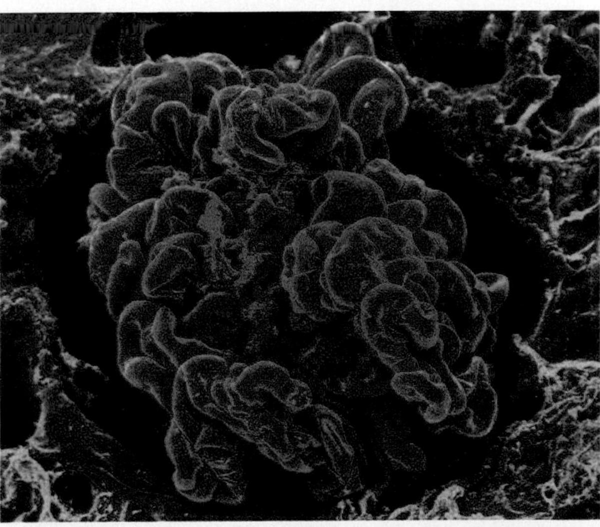

(magnification: 185×)

Urine Testing When blood is filtered through the kidneys, small molecules, including salts, amino acids, sugars, and many drugs, are removed from the circulation. Although many of these are reabsorbed into the bloodstream, drugs generally remain in the filtrate and are eliminated in the urine. This is one of the principal reasons why the effects of many drugs, including antibiotics, wear off over time. This also means that drugs, legal and illegal, become concentrated in the urine, providing a quick and easy way to test for their presence. Urine testing is now done routinely to check for the presence of prohibited drugs in athletes. It has also become common for employers to use such tests to screen job applicants for illegal drug use.

Kidney Stones Sometimes substances such as calcium, magnesium, or uric acid salts in the urine crystallize and form kidney stones. When kidney stones block the ureter, they cause great pain. Kidney stones are often treated using ultrasound waves. The sound waves pulverize the stones into smaller fragments, which are eliminated with the urine.

Control of Kidney Function

To a large extent, the activity of the kidneys is controlled by the composition of blood itself. In addition, regulatory hormones are released in response to the composition of blood. These mechanisms combine to ensure that the kidneys will maintain the proper composition of blood.

When you drink glass after glass of liquid, the liquid is quickly absorbed into the blood through the digestive system. As a result, the concentration of water in the blood increases. If it were not for your kidneys, this increased concentration of water in the blood would force water into cells and tissues by osmosis, causing your body to swell.

As the amount of water in the blood increases, the rate of water reabsorption in the kidneys decreases. Less water is returned to the blood, and the excess water is sent to the urinary bladder to be excreted as urine.

If you eat salty food, your kidneys will respond to the increased level of salt in your blood. When your kidneys detect an increase in salt, they respond by returning less salt to the blood by reabsorption. The excess salt the kidneys retain is excreted in urine, thus maintaining the composition of the blood.

Word Origins

Absorb comes from the Latin *ab-,* meaning "from" or "away," and *sorbere,* meaning "to draw in." **If the Latin word *radere* means "to scrape," what does the word *abrade* mean?**

Homeostasis by Machine

The kidneys are the master chemists of the blood supply. If anything goes wrong with the kidneys, serious medical problems soon follow. Fortunately, humans have two kidneys and can survive with only one. If both kidneys are damaged by disease or injury, however, there are only two ways to keep an individual alive. The first way is to transplant a healthy kidney from a compatible donor to the person in need of the kidney.

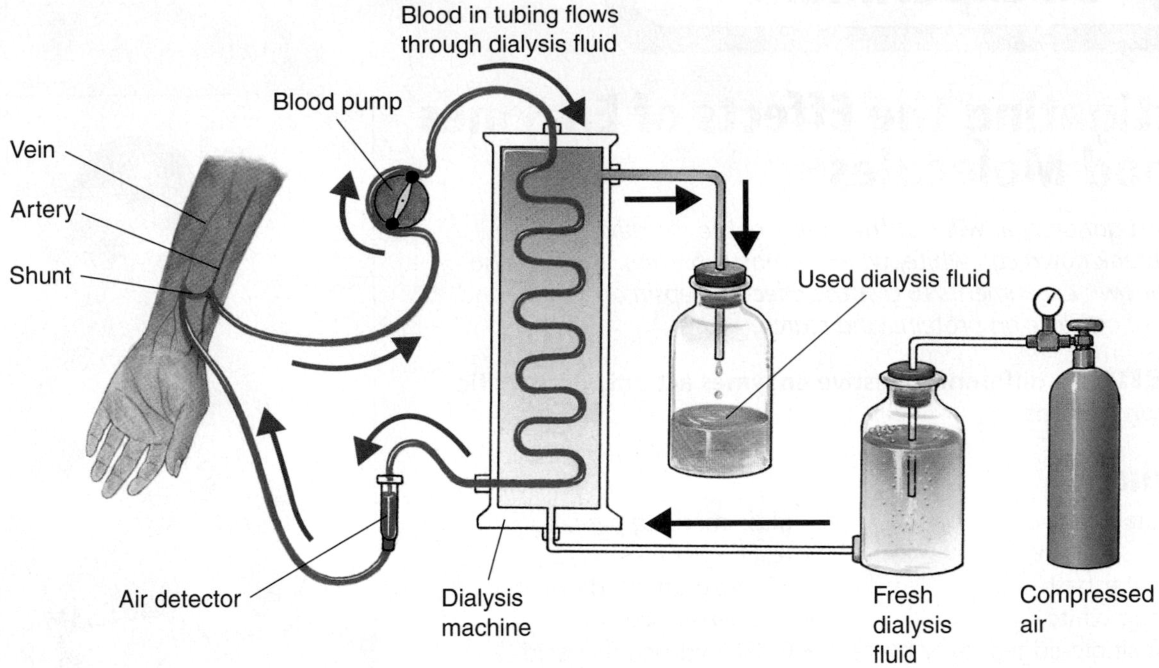

▲ **Figure 38–19** For people with damaged kidneys, dialysis machines can perform many of the functions of the kidneys. **Applying Concepts** *Why is dialysis such an important lifesaving technique?*

A second way is used when a donor is not available or surgery is not advisable. In these instances, a kidney dialysis machine becomes a lifesaver. In a common form of dialysis, blood is removed from the body through a tube inserted in the arm and pumped through special tubing that acts like nephrons. Tiny pores in the tubing allow salts and small molecules, including nitrogen wastes, to pass through. Wastes—urea and excess salts—diffuse out of the blood into the fluid-filled chamber, allowing purified blood to be returned to the body. This process of dialysis is shown in **Figure 38–19.** Dialysis is not only expensive, but it also is time-consuming, occupying several hours a day as often as three times a week. The ideal solution, assuming a kidney transplant is not possible, would be the implantation of an artificial kidney. Medical science is working toward developing such an artificial kidney.

38–3 Section Assessment

1. **Key Concept** What are the functions of the kidneys?
2. **Key Concept** Describe how blood is purified.
3. Describe the structures of a kidney.
4. What is the role of the skin in excretion?
5. **Critical Thinking Inferring** When there is too much fluid in the blood, the heart must pump harder. Diuretics are substances that stimulate the kidneys to remove more fluid from the body. Why do you think diuretics are often prescribed as a treatment for high blood pressure?

Thinking Visually

Constructing a Flowchart
Construct a flowchart that illustrates how wastes are removed by the kidneys. Be sure to include the terms *Bowman's capsule, loop of Henle, capillaries, collecting duct,* and *ureter.*

Design an Experiment

Investigating the Effects of Enzymes on Food Molecules

In this investigation, you will test the ability of the digestive enzyme pepsin to break down egg white, which is mostly protein. You will also design your own experiments to test the effect of pepsin on starch, and the effects of amylase on proteins and starch.

Problem **Do different digestive enzymes act only on specific types of compounds?**

Materials

- heat-resistant gloves
- Benedict's solution
- boiling water bath
- cooked egg white
- scalpel or single-edged razor blade
- metric ruler
- 6 large test tubes
- 6 stoppers for test tubes
- glass-marking pencil
- test-tube rack
- 10-mL graduated cylinder
- 1% pepsin solution
- 0.2% hydrochloric acid
- cooked potato
- 1% amylase solution
- test-tube holder

Skills Formulating Hypotheses, Controlling Variables, Forming Operational Definitions

Design Your Experiment     

Part A: The Basic Procedure

1. **Predicting** Predict whether pepsin can break down protein.
2. Put on an apron and safety goggles. Label three test tubes 1, 2, and 3; and put them in a test-tube rack. Cut three 5-mm cubes of cooked egg white and add one to each test tube.
3. Put on plastic gloves. Use a graduated cylinder to add 6 mL of water to test tube 1, and 3 mL of water and 3 mL 0.2% hydrochloric acid to test tube 2. **CAUTION:** *Hydrochloric acid can damage skin and clothing. If hydrochloric acid spills, notify your teacher at once. Wash the affected area with large amounts of cool water for 10 to 15 minutes.* Carefully rinse the graduated cylinder.
4. To test tube 3, add 3 mL 1% pepsin solution and 3 mL 0.2% hydrochloric acid. Carefully rinse the graduated cylinder.
5. Put a stopper in each test tube, and gently turn the tubes upside down several times to mix the contents. Put the tubes back in the test-tube rack. Set your test-tube rack where it will not be disturbed. Make a copy of the data table (on page 991).
6. After 2 days, examine the contents of each test tube. Record your observations in your copy of the data table.

Part B: Design Your Own Experiments

7. **Formulating Hypotheses** Do you think pepsin will digest potato, which is rich in starch? Use the observations you just made and your knowledge of enzymes to form a hypothesis about the way digestive enzymes work. Record your hypothesis.
8. Design an experiment to test your hypothesis. You can use the test for sugars described in Part C to determine whether starch has been broken down.
9. As you plan your investigative procedures, refer to the Lab Tips box on page 55 for information on demonstrating safe practices, making wise choices in the use of materials, selecting equipment and technology, and evaluating your experimental design.

Data Table			
Test Tube	**Compound Tested**	**Liquid(s) Added**	**Observations**
1	protein (egg white)	6 mL water	
2	protein (egg white)	3 mL water, 3 mL hydrochloric acid	
3	protein (egg white)	3 mL pepsin, 3 mL hydrochloric acid	

10. Write down your procedure. What is your manipulated variable? Your responding variable? Make sure to control all other variables. **CAUTION:** *Before you perform your experiment, have your teacher approve your procedure.*

11. Design two experiments to test whether amylase can digest protein or starch. Make sure to develop a hypothesis and to control your variables. Develop a data table similar to the one above. Record in your data table what you put in each test tube. **CAUTION:** *Before you perform your experiments, have your teacher approve your procedures.*

12. Set your test-tube rack aside where it will not be disturbed for 2 days.

13. After 2 days, examine each test tube. Record your observations in your data table.

Part C: Testing for Sugar

14. To test for the presence of sugar in the liquid in the tubes that contain potato: Put 1 mL of the liquid in a test tube. Add 2 mL of water and mix.

15. Add 3 mL Benedict's solution to the same tube.

16. Your teacher will provide a boiling water bath. Put on the heat-resistant gloves and use a test-tube holder to put the test tubes from step 14 in the boiling water bath. **CAUTION:** *Be careful when working with boiling water.* Observe the test tube for about 5 minutes. A change in color from blue to yellow (or green, or orange, or red) is a positive test for sugar. Record your observations in your data table.

Analyze and Conclude

1. **Applying Concepts** Why was hydrochloric acid included with the pepsin in step 4? Did you add hydrochloric acid to the amylase solution? Why or why not?
2. **Observing** What effect did pepsin have on the egg white? Was your prediction correct? Explain your answer.
3. **Observing** What effect did water, and water with hydrochloric acid, have on the egg white? What was the purpose of including these tests?
4. **Drawing Conclusions** Describe the results of the experiments you designed. Do the enzymes you tested act only on specific compounds? Explain your answer.
5. **SAFETY** Explain how you demonstrated safe practices when working with hydrochloric acid.

Go Further

Designing Experiments What factors affect the rates of the reactions you tested? How could you increase these rates? Design one or more experiments to test the effects of changing one of these factors. Remember to write a prediction and to control variables. After obtaining approval from your teacher, carry out your experiment(s).

Chapter 38 Study Guide

38–1 Food and Nutrition

Key Concepts

- The nutrients that the body needs are water, carbohydrates, fats, proteins, vitamins, and minerals.
- Every cell in the human body needs water because many of the body's processes, including chemical reactions, take place in water.

Vocabulary
Calorie, p. 971
carbohydrate, p. 972
fat, p. 972
protein, p. 973
vitamin, p. 974
mineral, p. 975

38–2 The Process of Digestion

Key Concepts

- The digestive system includes the mouth, pharynx, esophagus, stomach, small intestine, and large intestine. Several accessory structures, including the salivary glands, the pancreas, and the liver, add secretions to the digestive system.
- The function of the digestive system is to help convert foods into simpler molecules that can be absorbed and used by the cells of the body.

Vocabulary
amylase, p. 979
esophagus, p. 980
peristalsis, p. 980
stomach, p. 980
chyme, p. 981
small intestine, p. 981
pancreas, p. 981
liver, p. 982
villus, p. 982
large intestine, p. 984

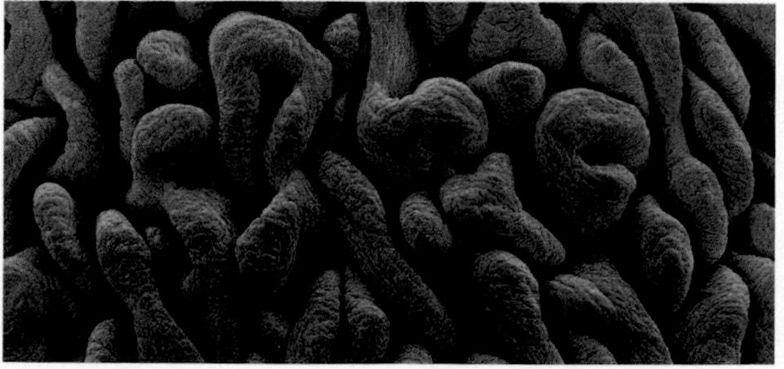

38–3 The Excretory System

Key Concepts

- The kidneys play an important role in maintaining homeostasis. They regulate the water content of the blood and, therefore, blood volume; maintain blood pH; and remove waste products from the blood.
- As blood enters a nephron through the arteriole, impurities are filtered out and emptied into the collecting duct. The purified blood exits the nephron through the venule.

Vocabulary
kidney, p. 986
ureter, p. 986
urinary bladder, p. 986
nephron, p. 986
filtration, p. 987
glomerulus, p. 987
Bowman's capsule, p. 987
reabsorption, p. 987
loop of Henle, p. 987
urethra, p. 987

Thinking Visually

Create a flowchart that shows the path of food through the organs of the digestive system.

Preparing for the Living Environment Exam

NEW YORK LIVING ENVIRONMENT

Blue questions emphasize Regents Exam content

Chapter 38

Part A

Multiple Choice

For each statement or question, select the number of the word or expression that, of those given, best completes the statement or answers the question.

1 If equal masses of nutrients are oxidized, the largest amount of energy will be released by
(1) fats (3) carbohydrates
(2) proteins (4) vitamins

2 Inorganic nutrients that your body needs, usually in small amounts, are called
(1) vitamins (3) proteins
(2) minerals (4) lipids

3 The mechanical breakdown of food
(1) occurs mainly in the large intestine
(2) exposes a larger surface area for chemical digestion
(3) produces the soluble end products of digestion
(4) is brought about by digestive enzymes

4 The diagram below represents a portion of the esophagus.

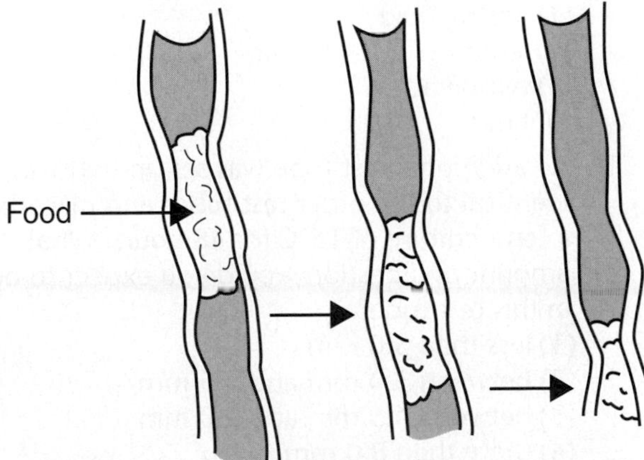

Which statement is correct about the process shown in the diagram?
(1) It transports food through the digestive tract.
(2) It must occur prior to the mechanical digestion of food in the oral cavity.
(3) It breaks down fats into fatty acids for digestion in the small intestine.
(4) It increases water absorption in the stomach.

5 An enzyme in saliva that breaks the chemical bonds in starch, releasing sugar, is
(1) pepsin (3) bile
(2) chyme (4) amylase

6 Most absorption of the end products of digestion into the circulatory system in humans occurs
(1) in the large intestine
(2) in the stomach
(3) through the lining of the esophagus
(4) through the villi of the small intestine

7 The main function of the human digestive system is to
(1) break down large, insoluble molecules into smaller, soluble molecules
(2) excrete oxygen and carbon dioxide
(3) synthesize minerals and vitamins needed for a healthy body
(4) add essential vitamins to blood

8 The basic functional unit of the kidney is the
(1) nephron (3) glomerulus
(2) loop of Henle (4) Bowman's capsule

9 Urine is excreted from the body through the
(1) ureter (3) urethra
(2) urinary bladder (4) renal vein

10 Which is *not* a function of the kidneys?
(1) maintenance of blood pH
(2) regulation of the water content of blood
(3) maintenance of homeostasis
(4) excretion of carbon dioxide

For questions 11 and 12, complete each analogy by selecting the correct number. In analogies, A : B :: C : means "A is to B as C is to ___?___."

11 Energy : carbohydrates :: structural material :
(1) proteins (3) water
(2) minerals (4) fat

12 Lung : carbon dioxide :: kidney :
(1) oxygen (3) urea
(2) nutrients (4) cellulose

Test-Taking Tip To complete an analogy, write a sentence that clearly describes the relationship between the first pair of terms. Then, rewrite the sentence with the third term and fill in the blank with the answer choice that best completes the analogy.

Preparing for the
Living Environment Exam

Part B

Multiple Choice and Extended Response

For those questions that ask you to select a response, choose the one that best completes the statement or answers the question. For all others follow the directions given.

13 Going without food affects the amount of urea in the urine, as shown in the graph of "Urea in Urine."

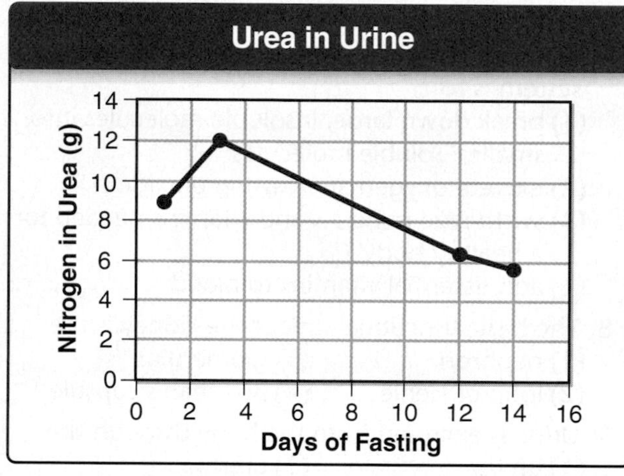

The graph shows that the amount of nitrogen in the urea excreted
(1) increases steadily during 14 days of fasting
(2) decreases steadily during 14 days of fasting
(3) increases for the first few days of fasting
(4) will be 6 grams after 16 days of fasting

Base your answers to questions 14 and 15 on the information below and on your knowledge of biology.

Your kidneys, along with your skin and lungs and their associated organs, make up your excretory system. All of these organs are vital in maintaining the chemical balance of your blood.

14 List *three* materials that healthy kidneys remove from the blood.

15 List *three* materials that remain in the blood as it passes through healthy kidneys.

---

16 Describe the function of enzymes during the process of digestion.

Base your answers to questions 17 through 20 on the information and table below and on your knowledge of biology.

A student is studying the effect of temperature on the action of a protein-digesting enzyme contained in stomach fluid. An investigation is set up using five identical test tubes, each containing 40 milliliters of stomach fluid and 20 millimeters of glass tubing filled with gelatin. After 48 hours, the amount of gelatin digested in each tube was measured. The data collected are shown in the data table below.

Test Tube	Temperature (°C)	Amount of Digestion After 48 Hours
1	2	0.0 mm
2	10	3.0 mm
3	22	4.5 mm
4	37	8.0 mm
5	100	0.0 mm

17 Which is the manipulated (independent) variable in this investigation?
(1) gastric fluid
(2) length of glass tubing
(3) temperature
(4) time

18 An additional test tube was set up that was identical to the other test tubes and placed at a temperature of 15°C for 48 hours. What amount of digestion would you expect to occur in this test tube?
(1) less than 3.0 mm
(2) between 3.0 mm and 4.5 mm
(3) between 4.5 mm and 8.0 mm
(4) more than 8.0 mm

19 The experiment was repeated a third time, using apple instead of gelatin. There was no evidence of any digestion after 48 hours at any temperature. Explain why no digestion occurred.

20 Which set of axes below should be used to plot the data?

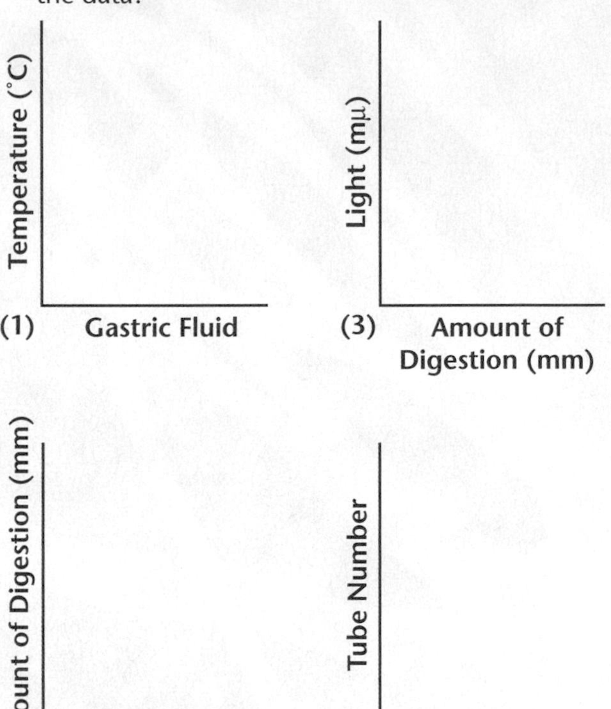

21 Fad diets that boast of rapid weight loss often become popular. Many of these diets involve eating only a limited variety of foods. Explain why these diets are an unhealthy way to lose weight.

Part C

Extended Response

Answer the questions or follow the directions given.

22 Explain what the effect on your digestive system would be if you took an antibiotic that killed all of the bacteria in your body.

23 Describe *three* ways proteins are important to the body.

24 Individuals who have had part, or even all, of their stomachs removed can survive if fed predigested food. Could individuals with a stomach survive without a small intestine if they were fed predigested food? Support your answer with an explanation.

Base your answers to questions 25 through 27 on the information and graph below and on your knowledge of biology.

Pancreatic juice contains sodium bicarbonate and digestive enzymes. The juice is secreted by the pancreas in response to the specific composition of chyme in the upper portion of the small intestine. The graph below shows secretions of the pancreas in response to the presence of three different substances.

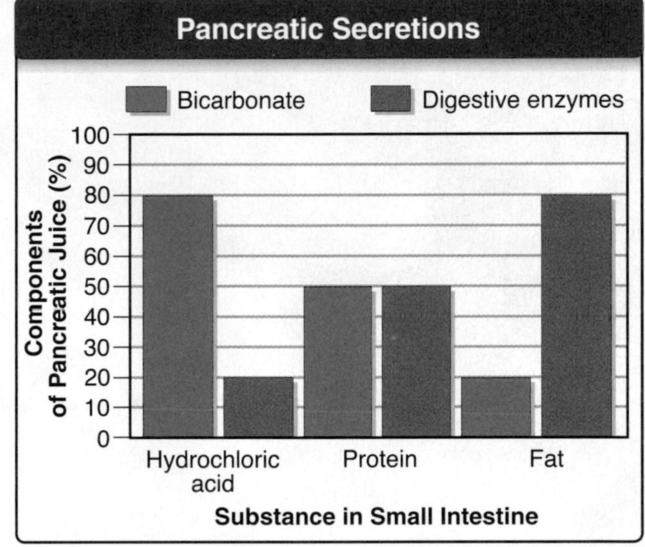

25 Each pair of bars on the graph represents the response of the pancreas to a different variable. What are the three variables?

26 Describe how the presence of protein affects the amounts of bicarbonate and digestive enzymes secreted.

27 How does the presence of fat affect the composition of pancreatic juice?

For: An interactive self-test
Visit: PHSchool.com
Web Code: cba-0380

CHAPTER 39

Endocrine and Reproductive Systems

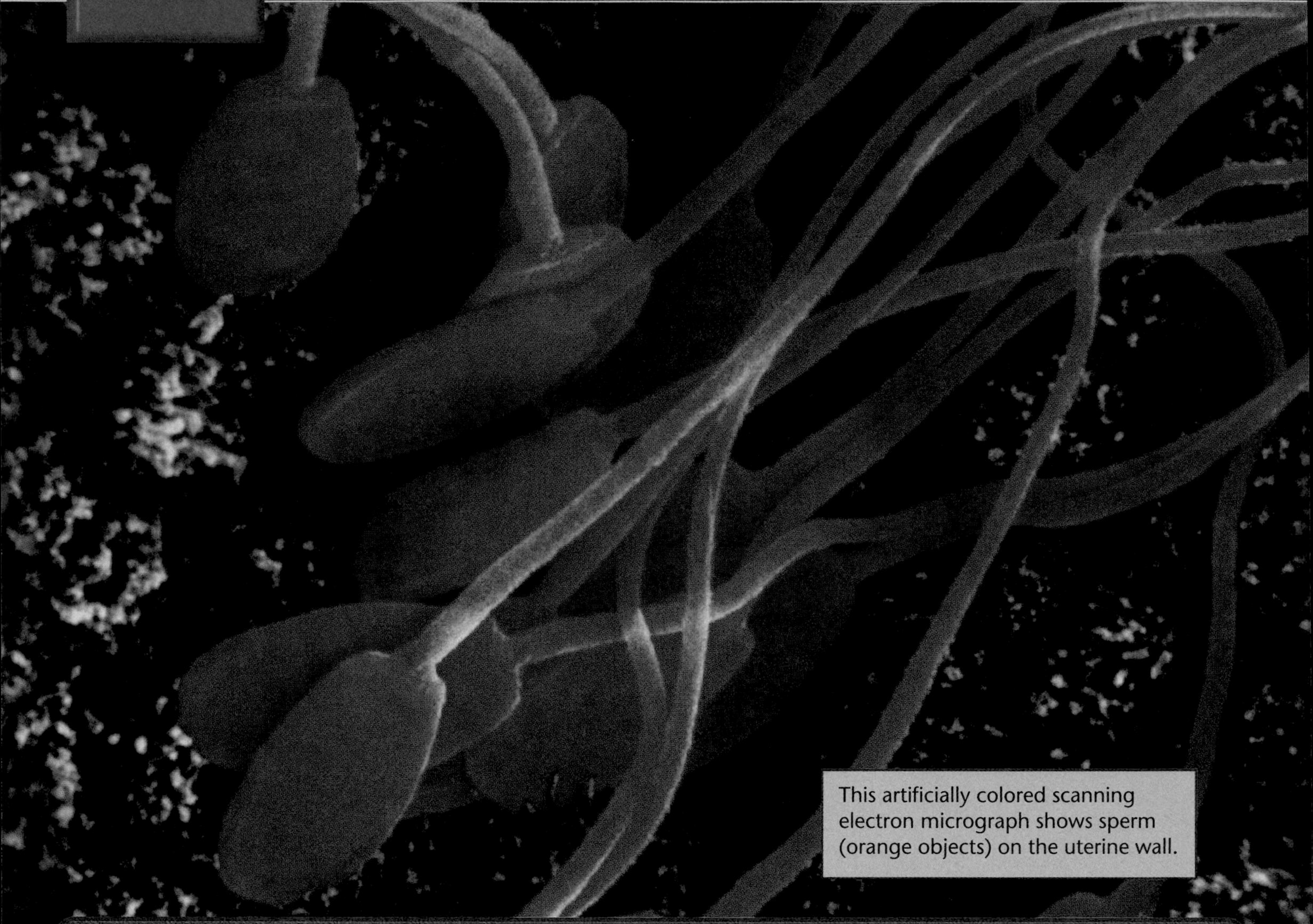

This artificially colored scanning electron micrograph shows sperm (orange objects) on the uterine wall.

Inquiry Activity

Where in cells do hormones go?

Procedure 

1. Fill 2 test tubes one third full of water. Add the same amount of vegetable oil (a lipid) to each test tube.
2. Add a few drops of food coloring to one of the test tubes. Stopper the test tube and turn it upside down to mix the contents.
3. Repeat step 2 using a drop of annatto coloring and the second test tube.

Think About It

1. **Observing** Did the food coloring dissolve in water or oil? Did the annatto coloring dissolve in water or oil?
2. **Inferring** Do you think food coloring can pass through cell membranes? (*Hint:* Cell membranes are composed of lipids.) Do you think annatto coloring can pass through cell membranes?

39–1 The Endocrine System

4-1.2 Humans have complex systems
4-1.2 Hormone signals and receptors
4-5.1 Hormones and receptor molecules have specific shapes
4-5.3 Feedback mechanisms maintain homeostasis
LS- Make observations

Guide for Reading

Key Concepts
- What is the function of the endocrine system?
- How does the endocrine system maintain homeostasis?

Vocabulary
hormone
target cell
exocrine gland
endocrine gland
prostaglandin

Reading Strategy: Making Comparisons
As you read, list the differences and similarities between types of glands, and between types of hormones.

If you had to get a message to just one or two of your friends, what would you do? You might use the telephone. Wires running from your house to theirs would carry the message almost instantaneously. The telephone is a good way to reach a small number of people, but what if you wanted to get that same message to thousands of people? You might decide to broadcast it on the radio, sending the message in a way that made it possible to contact thousands of people at once.

Your nervous system works much like the telephone: Many impulses move swiftly over a system of wirelike neurons that carry specific messages from one cell to another. But another system, the endocrine system, does what the nervous system generally cannot.  **The endocrine system is made up of glands that release their products into the bloodstream. These products deliver messages throughout the body.** In the same way that a radio broadcast can reach thousands or even millions of people in a large city, the chemicals released by the endocrine system can affect almost every cell in the body. In fact, the chemicals released by the endocrine system affect so many cells and tissues that the interrelationships of other organ systems to one another cannot be understood without taking the endocrine system into account.

Hormones

The chemicals that "broadcast" messages from the endocrine system are called hormones. **Hormones** are chemicals released in one part of the body that travel through the bloodstream and affect the activities of cells in other parts of the body. Hormones do this by binding to specific chemical receptors on those cells. Cells that have receptors for a particular hormone are called **target cells.** If a cell does not have receptors or the receptors do not respond to a particular hormone, the hormone has no effect on it.

In general, the body's responses to hormones are slower and longer-lasting than the responses to nerve impulses. It may take several minutes, several hours, or even several days for a hormone to have its full effect on its target cells. A nerve impulse, on the other hand, may take only a fraction of a second to reach and affect its target cells.

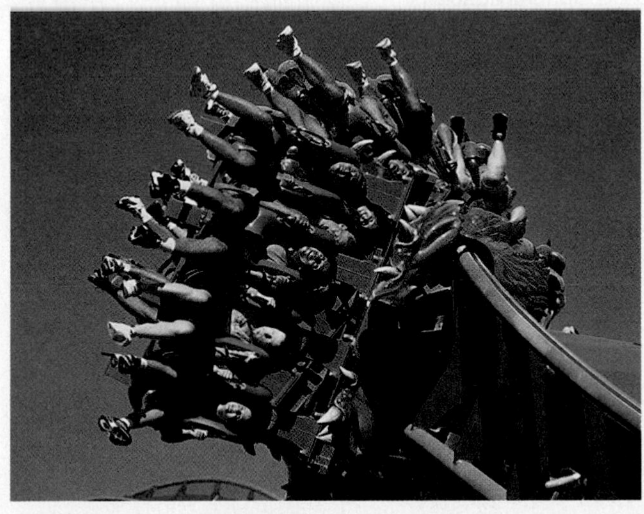

▶ **Figure 39–1** **The endocrine system releases hormones that affect the activities of other cells.** Much of the increase in heart rate and breathing that the people are experiencing on this ride is due to the actions of hormones.

Glands

A gland is an organ that produces and releases a substance, or secretion. **Exocrine glands** release their secretions, through tubelike structures called ducts, directly to the organs that use them. Exocrine glands include those that release sweat, tears, and digestive juices. Unlike exocrine glands, **endocrine glands** release their secretions (hormones) directly into the bloodstream. **Figure 39–2** shows the location of the major endocrine glands in the human body.

 *What are exocrine glands?*

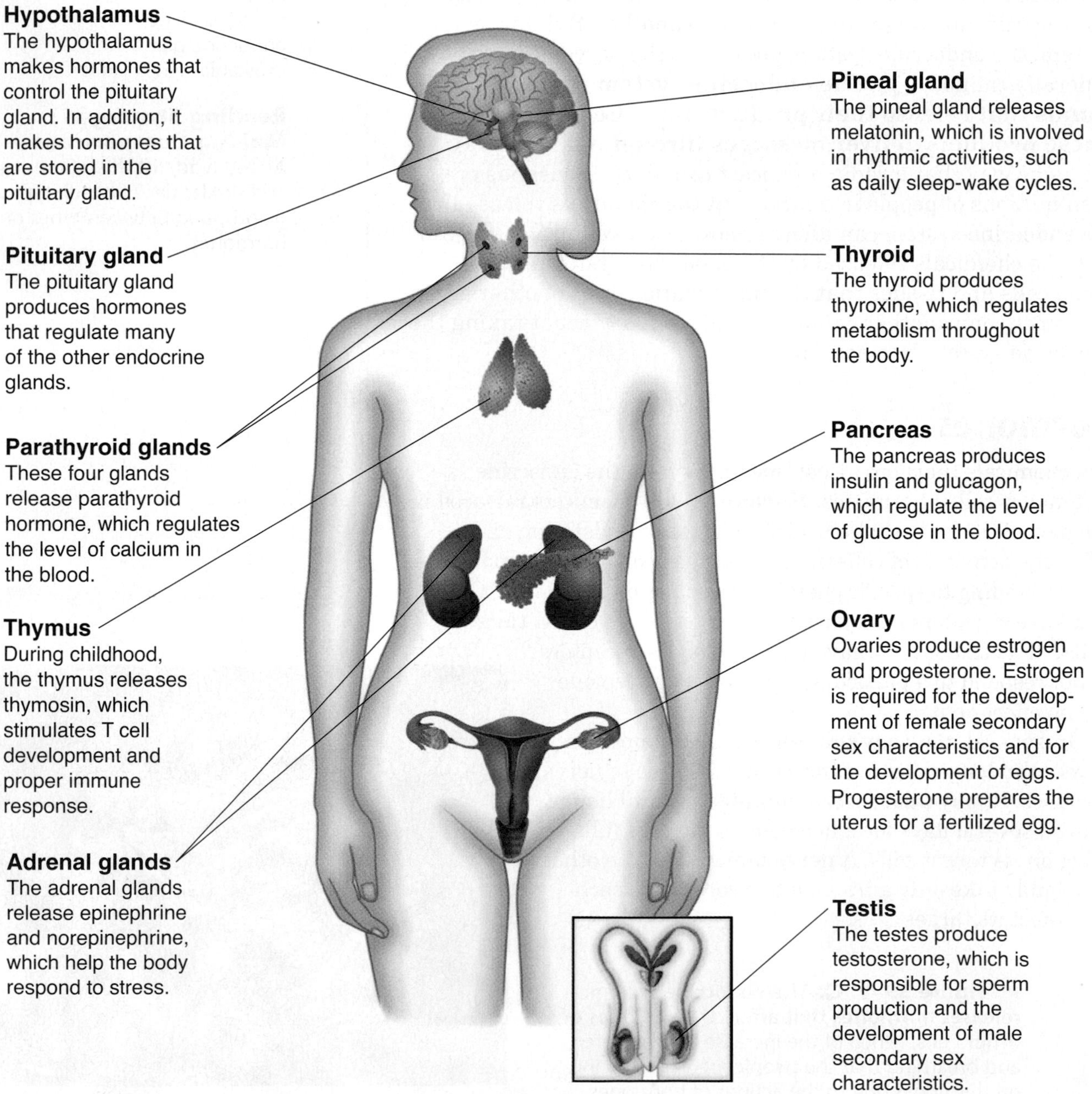

▼ **Figure 39–2** Endocrine glands produce hormones that affect many parts of the body. **Interpreting Graphics** *What is the function of the pituitary gland?*

Hypothalamus
The hypothalamus makes hormones that control the pituitary gland. In addition, it makes hormones that are stored in the pituitary gland.

Pituitary gland
The pituitary gland produces hormones that regulate many of the other endocrine glands.

Parathyroid glands
These four glands release parathyroid hormone, which regulates the level of calcium in the blood.

Thymus
During childhood, the thymus releases thymosin, which stimulates T cell development and proper immune response.

Adrenal glands
The adrenal glands release epinephrine and norepinephrine, which help the body respond to stress.

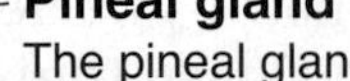

Pineal gland
The pineal gland releases melatonin, which is involved in rhythmic activities, such as daily sleep-wake cycles.

Thyroid
The thyroid produces thyroxine, which regulates metabolism throughout the body.

Pancreas
The pancreas produces insulin and glucagon, which regulate the level of glucose in the blood.

Ovary
Ovaries produce estrogen and progesterone. Estrogen is required for the development of female secondary sex characteristics and for the development of eggs. Progesterone prepares the uterus for a fertilized egg.

Testis
The testes produce testosterone, which is responsible for sperm production and the development of male secondary sex characteristics.

Hormone Action

Hormones may be classified as belonging to two general groups—steroid hormones and nonsteroid hormones. Steroid hormones are produced from a lipid called cholesterol. Nonsteroid hormones include proteins, small peptides, and modified amino acids. The two basic patterns of hormone action are shown in **Figure 39–3.**

Steroid Hormones Because they are lipids, steroid hormones can cross cell membranes easily, passing directly into the cytoplasm and even into the nuclei of target cells.

1. A steroid hormone enters a cell by passing directly across its cell membrane.
2. Once inside, it binds to a steroid receptor protein (found only in its target cells) to form a hormone-receptor complex.
3. The hormone-receptor complex enters the nucleus of the cell, where it binds to a DNA control sequence.
4. This binding initiates the transcription of specific genes to messenger RNA (mRNA).
5. The mRNA moves into the cytoplasm and directs protein synthesis.

Hormone-receptor complexes work as regulators of gene expression—they can turn on or turn off whole sets of genes. Because steroid hormones affect gene expression directly, they can produce dramatic changes in cell and organism activity.

Nonsteroid Hormones Nonsteroid hormones generally cannot pass through the cell membrane of their target cells.

1. A nonsteroid hormone binds to receptors on the cell membrane.
2. The binding of the hormone activates an enzyme on the inner surface of the cell membrane.
3. This enzyme activates secondary messengers that carry the message of the hormone inside the cell. Calcium ions, cAMP (cyclic adenosine monophosphate), nucleotides, and even fatty acids can serve as second messengers.
4. These second messengers can activate or inhibit a wide range of other cell activities.

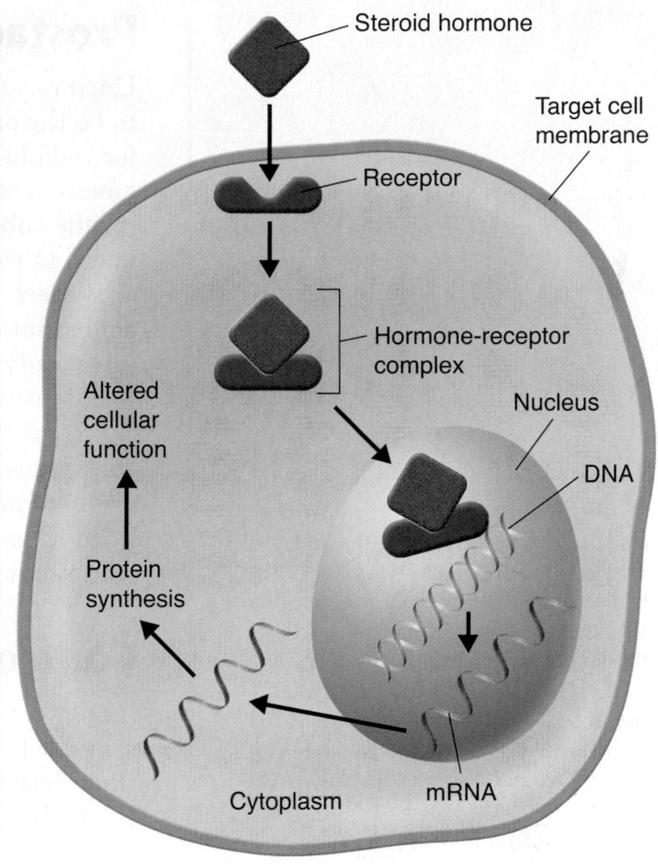

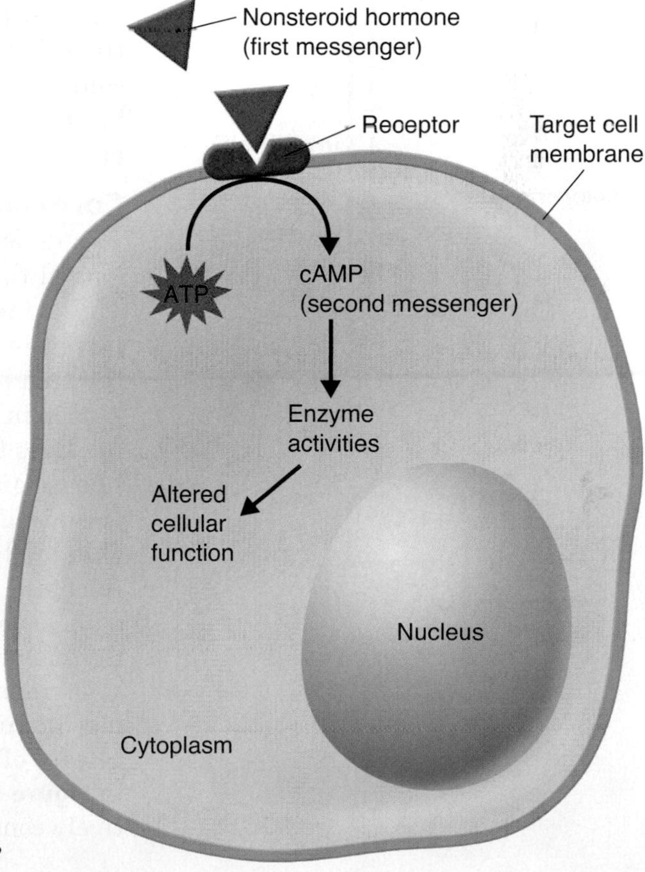

Figure 39–3 The two main types of hormones are steroid hormones (top) and nonsteroid hormones (bottom). **Comparing and Contrasting** *How are steroid hormones different from nonsteroid hormones?*

Prostaglandins

Until recently, the glands of the endocrine system were thought to be the only organs that produced hormones. However, except for red blood cells, all cells have been shown to produce small amounts of hormonelike substances called **prostaglandins** (prahs-tuh-GLAN-dinz). Prostaglandins get their name from a gland in the male reproductive system, the prostate, in which they were first discovered. Prostaglandins are modified fatty acids that are produced by a wide range of cells. They generally affect only nearby cells and tissues, and thus are known as "local hormones."

Some prostaglandins cause smooth muscles, such as those in the uterus, bronchioles, and blood vessels, to contract. One group of prostaglandins causes the sensation of pain in most headaches. Aspirin helps to stop the pain of a headache because it inhibits the synthesis of these prostaglandins.

Control of the Endocrine System

As powerful as they are, hormones are monitored by the body in order to keep the functions of different organs in balance. Even though the endocrine system is one of the master regulators of the body, it too must be controlled. **Like most systems of the body, the endocrine system is regulated by feedback mechanisms that function to maintain homeostasis.**

Recall that feedback inhibition occurs when an increase in any substance "feeds back" to inhibit the process that produced the substance in the first place. Heating and cooling systems, controlled by thermostats, are examples of mechanical feedback systems. The hormones of the endocrine system are biological examples of the same type of process.

Controlling Metabolism To see how an internal feedback mechanism regulates the activity of the endocrine system, let's look at the thyroid gland and its principal hormone, thyroxine. Thyroxine affects the activity of cells throughout the body, increasing their rate of metabolism. Recall that metabolism is the sum of all of the chemical reactions that occur in the body. A drop in thyroxine decreases the metabolic activity of cells.

Does the thyroid gland determine how much thyroxine to release on its own? No, instead the activity of the thyroid gland is controlled by the hypothalamus and the anterior pituitary gland. When the hypothalamus senses that the thyroxine level in the blood is low, it secretes thyrotropin-releasing hormone (TRH), a hormone that stimulates the anterior pituitary to secrete thyroid-stimulating hormone (TSH). TSH stimulates the release of thyroxine by the thyroid gland. High levels of thyroxine in the blood inhibit the secretion of TRH and TSH, which stops the release of additional thyroxine. This feedback mechanism, shown in **Figure 39–4,** keeps the level of thyroxine in the blood relatively constant.

▼ **Figure 39–4 One way the endocrine system is regulated by internal feedback mechanisms is by maintaining the rate of metabolism.** When the hypothalamus senses that the level of thyroxine in the blood is low, it secretes TRH. TRH stimulates the anterior pituitary to secrete TSH. TSH stimulates the thyroid to release thyroxine. Increased levels of TSH and thyroxine inhibit TRH secretion by the hypothalamus.

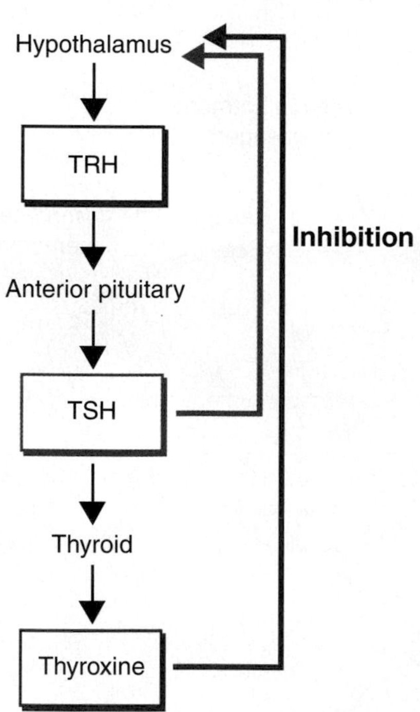

Recall that the hypothalamus is also sensitive to temperature. When the core body temperature begins to drop, even if the level of thyroxine is normal, the hypothalamus produces extra TRH. The release of TRH stimulates the release of TSH, which stimulates the release of additional thyroxine. Thyroxine increases oxygen consumption and cellular metabolism. The increase in metabolic activity that results helps the body maintain its core temperature despite lower temperatures.

CHECKPOINT *What process does thyroxine control?*

Maintaining Water Balance Homeostatic mechanisms regulate the levels of a wide variety of materials dissolved in the blood and in extracellular fluids. These include minerals such as sodium, potassium, and calcium, and soluble proteins such as serum albumin, which is found in blood plasma. Most of the time, homeostatic systems operate so smoothly that we are scarcely aware of their existence. However, that is not the case with one of the most important homeostatic processes, the one that regulates the amount of water in the body.

When you exercise strenuously, you lose water as you sweat. If this water loss continued, your body would soon become dehydrated. Generally, that doesn't happen because your body's homeostatic mechanisms swing into action.

The hypothalamus contains cells that are sensitive to the concentration of water in the blood. As you lose water, the concentration of dissolved materials in the blood rises. The hypothalamus responds in two ways. First, the hypothalamus signals the pituitary gland to release a hormone called antidiuretic hormone (ADH). ADH molecules are carried by the bloodstream to the kidneys, where the removal of water from the blood is quickly slowed down. Later, you experience a sensation of thirst, a signal that you should take a drink to restore lost water.

When you finally get around to taking that drink, you might take in as much as 1 or 2 liters of fluid. Most of that water is quickly absorbed into the bloodstream. But this volume of water added to the blood would dilute it so much that the equilibrium between the blood and the cells of the body would be disturbed. Large amounts of water would diffuse across blood vessel walls into the tissues. The cells of the body would swell with the excess water.

Needless to say, this doesn't happen, because the same homeostatic mechanism intervenes. When the water content of the blood rises, the pituitary releases less ADH. In response to lower ADH levels, the kidneys remove water from the bloodstream, restoring the blood to its original concentration. This homeostatic system sets both upper and lower limits for blood water content: A water deficit stimulates the release of ADH, causing the kidneys to conserve water; an oversupply of water causes the kidneys to eliminate the excess water as a component of urine.

▼ **Figure 39–5** When exercising on a hot day, it is important to replenish lost liquid. **Applying Concepts** *Explain why people who are exercising should drink fluids before they are thirsty.*

For: Links on the endocrine system
Visit: www.SciLinks.org
Web Code: cbn-0391

Complementary Hormone Action

Sometimes two hormones with opposite effects act to regulate part of the body's internal environment. One way to think about how the endocrine system functions is to think about driving a car. A good driver might be able to control a car on an open highway by using only the accelerator pedal. But driving around town, even a good driver would get into trouble using just the accelerator. There are too many situations in which the brake is needed to slow the car down.

In the same way, many endocrine functions depend on the complementary effects of two opposing hormones. Such a complementary system regulates the level of calcium ions in the bloodstream. The level of calcium dissolved in the bloodstream is kept within a narrow range. The two hormones that regulate calcium concentration are calcitonin, from the thyroid gland, and parathyroid hormone (PTH), from the parathyroid glands. Calcitonin decreases the level of calcium in the blood, while PTH increases it.

When blood calcium levels are too high, the thyroid secretes calcitonin. Calcitonin signals the kidneys to reabsorb less calcium as they form urine. Calcitonin also reduces the amount of calcium absorbed in the intestines and stimulates calcium deposition in the bones.

If calcium levels drop too low, PTH is released by the parathyroids. PTH, together with vitamin D, stimulates the intestine to absorb more calcium from food. PTH also causes the kidneys to retain more calcium, and it stimulates bone cells to release some of the calcium stored in bone tissue into the bloodstream.

You may be surprised that the body regulates calcium levels so carefully. This adaptation has evolved because calcium is one of the most important minerals in the body. If calcium levels drop below their normal range, blood cannot clot, muscles cannot contract, and the transport of materials across cell membranes may fail.

39–1 Section Assessment

1. **Key Concept** Describe the function of the endocrine system in the body.
2. **Key Concept** Explain how the endocrine system helps maintain homeostasis.
3. Compare endocrine glands and exocrine glands.
4. What are prostaglandins and why are they called "local hormones"?
5. **Critical Thinking Applying Concepts** What are the advantages of having both a nervous system and an endocrine system?

Connecting Concepts

Cell Structure
Use what you learned in Chapter 7 about diffusion and how materials cross cell membranes to explain the actions of steroid hormones and nonsteroid hormones.

39–2 Human Endocrine Glands

4-1.2 Humans have complex systems
4-5.2 Causes of disease
4-5.3 Feedback mechanisms maintain homeostasis

The endocrine glands are scattered throughout the body. Generally, they do not have direct connections to one another. Like signals that are beamed throughout the country from a broadcast station, the hormones released from the endocrine glands into the bloodstream travel throughout the body, reaching almost every cell.

The human endocrine system regulates a wide variety of activities. Any improper functioning of an endocrine gland may result in a disease or a disorder. The major glands of the endocrine system include the pituitary gland, the hypothalamus, the thyroid gland, the parathyroid glands, the adrenal glands, the pancreas, and the reproductive glands.

Guide for Reading

Key Concept
- What are the functions of the major endocrine glands?

Vocabulary
pituitary gland
diabetes mellitus
ovary
testis

Reading Strategy: Finding Main Ideas Before you read, skim the text paragraphs in this section to find the boldface key sentences. Copy each sentence onto a notecard. As you read, note supporting details on the cards.

Pituitary Gland

The **pituitary gland** is a bean-sized structure that dangles on a slender stalk of tissue at the base of the skull. As you can see in **Figure 39–6,** the gland is divided into two parts: the anterior pituitary and the posterior pituitary. **The pituitary gland secretes nine hormones that directly regulate many body functions and controls the actions of several other endocrine glands.**

Normal function of the pituitary gland is essential to good health. For example, if the pituitary gland produces too much growth hormone (GH) during childhood, the body grows too quickly and a condition called gigantism results. Too little GH during childhood causes a condition known as pituitary dwarfism, which can be treated by administering growth hormone. Growth hormone used to be in short supply. Today, however, genetically engineered bacteria are able to produce GH in large quantities.

▼ Figure 39–6 The pituitary gland, which controls many other endocrine glands, is located below the hypothalamus in the brain. The pituitary gland has two lobes: an anterior lobe and a posterior lobe.

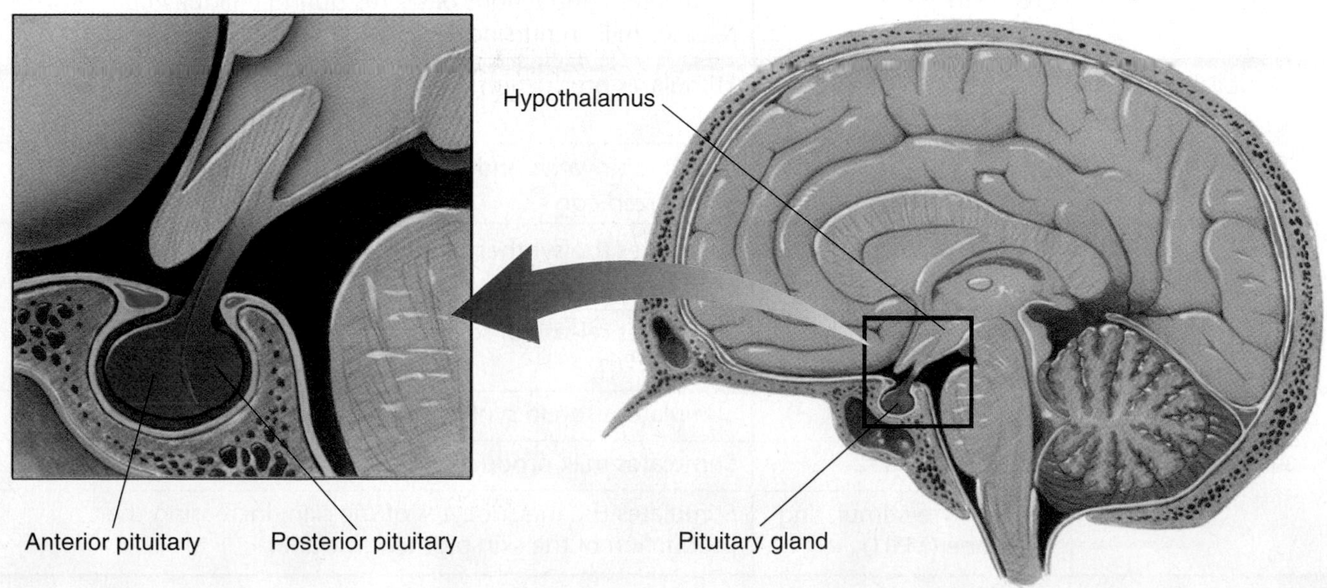

For: Links on glands
Visit: www.SciLinks.org
Web Code: cbn-0392

Hypothalamus

The hypothalamus is the part of the brain above and attached to the posterior pituitary. **The hypothalamus controls the secretions of the pituitary gland.** The activity of the hypothalamus is influenced by the levels of hormones in the blood and by sensory information collected by other parts of the central nervous system. Interactions between the nervous system and the endocrine system take place at the hypothalamus.

The posterior pituitary is made up of axons belonging to cells called neurosecretory cells, whose cell bodies are in the hypothalamus. When these cell bodies are stimulated, the axons in the posterior pituitary release their hormones into the bloodstream. In a way, the posterior pituitary is an extension of the hypothalamus.

In contrast, the hypothalamus has indirect control of the anterior pituitary. The hypothalamus produces small amounts of chemicals called releasing hormones, which are secreted directly into blood vessels. The releasing hormones are carried by the circulatory system to the anterior pituitary, where they control the production and release of hormones.

The close connection between the hypothalamus and the pituitary gland means that the nervous and endocrine systems can act together to help coordinate body activities. Hormones released by the pituitary gland are listed in **Figure 39–7.**

What is the role of releasing hormones?

▼ **Figure 39–7** **The hypothalamus controls the secretions of the pituitary gland.** Notice the effect that each hormone produced by the pituitary gland has on the body.

Pituitary Gland Hormones

Pituitary Gland	Hormone	Action
Posterior pituitary	Antidiuretic hormone (ADH)	Stimulates the kidneys to reabsorb water from the collecting tubules
	Oxytocin	Stimulates contractions of uterus during childbirth; releases milk in nursing mothers
Anterior pituitary	Follicle-stimulating hormone (FSH)	Stimulates production of mature eggs and sperm
	Luteinizing hormone (LH)	Stimulates ovaries and testes; prepares uterus for implantation of fertilized egg
	Thyroid-stimulating hormone (TSH)	Stimulates the synthesis and release of thyroxine from the thyroid gland
	Adreno-corticotropic hormone (ACTH)	Stimulates release of some hormones from the adrenal cortex
	Growth hormone (GH)	Stimulates protein synthesis and growth in cells
	Prolactin	Stimulates milk production in nursing mothers
	Melanocyte-stimulating hormone (MSH)	Stimulates the melanocytes of the skin, increasing their production of the skin pigment melanin

Thyroid Gland

If you look at **Figure 39–8,** you can see that the thyroid gland is located at the base of the neck and wraps around the upper part of the trachea. **The thyroid gland has the major role in regulating the body's metabolism.** Cells in the thyroid gland produce thyroxine, which is made up of the amino acid tyrosine and the mineral iodine. Remember that thyroxine affects nearly all of the cells of the body by regulating their metabolic rates. Thyroxine increases the rate of protein, carbohydrate, and fat metabolism as well as the rate of cellular respiration, which means that the cells release more heat and energy. Decreased levels of thyroxine can decrease the rate of cellular respiration and the amount of heat and energy released.

The homeostatic activities of the thyroid gland are so well controlled that you may never become aware of them. However, if the thyroid gland produces too much thyroxine, a condition called hyperthyroidism occurs. Hyperthyroidism results in nervousness, elevated body temperature, increased metabolic rate, increased blood pressure, and weight loss. Too little thyroxine causes a condition called hypothyroidism. Lower metabolic rates and body temperature, lack of energy, and weight gain are characteristics of this condition. In some cases, hypothyroidism can cause a goiter, an enlargement of the thyroid gland.

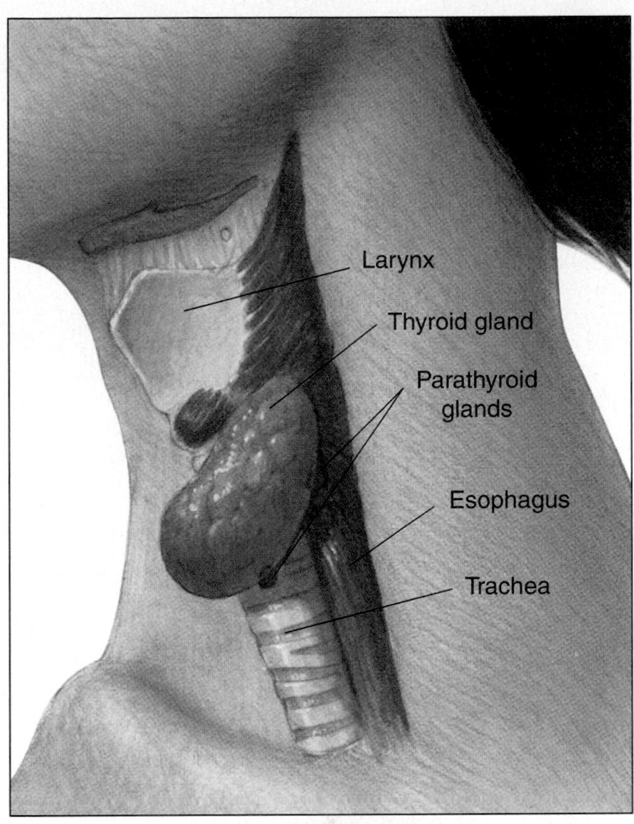

▲ **Figure 39–8 Hormones produced by the thyroid gland and the parathyroid glands maintain the level of calcium in the blood.** The thyroid gland wraps around the trachea.

The importance of proper thyroid activity can be seen in parts of the world where food lacks enough iodine for the thyroid to produce normal amounts of thyroxine. Unable to produce the thyroxine needed for normal development, iodine-deficient infants suffer from a condition called cretinism (KREE-tuh-niz-um), in which neither the skeletal system nor the nervous system develops properly. Two effects of cretinism are dwarfism and severe mental retardation. Cretinism usually can be prevented by the addition of small amounts of iodine to table salt or other items in the food supply.

Parathyroid Glands

The four parathyroid glands are found on the back surface of the thyroid gland. **Hormones from the thyroid gland and the parathyroid glands act to maintain homeostasis of calcium levels in the blood.** Parathyroid glands secrete parathyroid hormone (PTH). Recall that PTH and calcitonin have opposite effects on the body. PTH regulates the calcium levels in the blood by increasing the reabsorption of calcium in the kidneys and by increasing the uptake of calcium from the digestive system. Parathyroid hormone also affects other organ systems, promoting proper nerve and muscle function and bone structure.

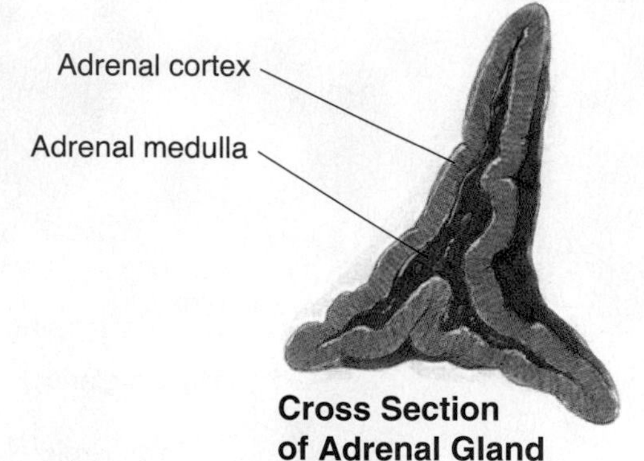

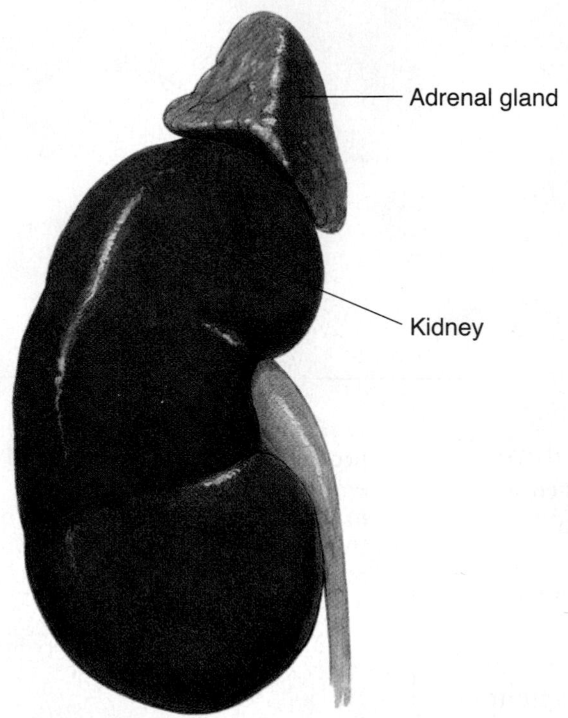

▲ **Figure 39–9** **The adrenal glands release hormones that help the body prepare for and deal with stress.** Each adrenal gland is divided into two structural parts: the adrenal cortex and the adrenal medulla.

Adrenal Glands

The adrenal glands are two pyramid-shaped structures that sit on top of the kidneys, one gland on each kidney, as shown in **Figure 39–9.** **The adrenal glands release hormones that help the body prepare for and deal with stress.** An adrenal gland has an outer part called the adrenal cortex and an inner part called the adrenal medulla. These parts contain different types of tissues.

Adrenal Cortex About 80 percent of an adrenal gland is its adrenal cortex. The adrenal cortex produces more than two dozen steriod hormones called corticosteroids (kawr-tih-koh-STEER-oydz). One of these hormones, aldosterone (al-DAHS-tuh-rohn), regulates the reabsorption of sodium ions and the excretion of potassium ions by the kidneys. Another hormone, called cortisol, helps control the rate of metabolism of carbohydrates, fats, and proteins.

Adrenal Medulla The release of hormones from the adrenal medulla is regulated by the sympathetic nervous system. The sympathetic nervous system prepares the body for energy-intense activities. The two hormones released by the adrenal medulla are epinephrine and norepinephrine. Epinephrine, which is more powerful than norepinephrine, makes up about 80 percent of the total secretions of the adrenal medulla.

The adrenal medulla produces the "fight or flight" response to stress. This response is the feeling you get when you are excited or frightened. Nerve impulses from the sympathetic nervous system stimulate cells of the adrenal medulla. This stimulation causes the cells to release large amounts of epinephrine and norepinephrine. These hormones increase heart rate, blood pressure, and blood flow to the muscles. They cause air passageways to open wider, allowing for an increase in the intake of oxygen. They also stimulate the release of extra glucose into the blood to help produce a sudden burst of energy. The result of all these actions is a general increase in body activity, which can serve as preparation for intense physical activity. If your heart rate speeds up and your hands begin to perspire when you take a test, you are feeling the effects of your adrenal medulla!

CHECKPOINT ***Which hormones are released from the adrenal cortex? From the adrenal medulla?***

Pancreas

The pancreas is an unusual gland that has both exocrine and endocrine functions. Recall that the pancreas is a digestive gland whose enzyme secretions help to break down food. These secretions are released into the pancreatic duct and flow into the small intestine. This makes the pancreas an exocrine gland. However, different cells in the pancreas release hormones into the blood, making the pancreas an endocrine gland as well.

The hormone-producing portion of the pancreas consists of clusters of cells that resemble islands. These clusters of cells are called islets of Langerhans after their discoverer, the German anatomist Paul Langerhans. Each islet includes beta cells, which secrete a hormone called insulin, and alpha cells, which secrete another hormone called glucagon. **Insulin and glucagon help to keep the level of glucose in the blood stable.** Insulin stimulates cells in the liver and muscles to remove sugar from the blood and store it as glycogen or fat. Glucagon stimulates the liver to break down glycogen and release glucose back into the blood. It also stimulates the release of fatty acids from stored fats.

Maintaining Blood Sugar Levels When blood glucose levels rise after eating, the pancreas releases insulin. Insulin stimulates cells throughout the body to take glucose out of the bloodstream. Insulin's major target cells are found in the liver, skeletal muscles, and fat (adipose) tissue. Glucose taken out of circulation is stored as glycogen in the liver and skeletal muscles. In fat tissue, glucose molecules are converted to lipids. Insulin prevents the level of glucose in the blood from rising too rapidly and ensures that excess glucose is stored for future use.

Within one or two hours after eating, when the level of blood glucose drops, glucagon is released from the pancreas. Glucagon stimulates the cells of the liver and skeletal muscles to break down glycogen and increase glucose levels in the blood. Glucagon also causes fat cells to break down fats so that they can be used for the production of carbohydrates. These actions make more chemical energy available to the body and help raise the blood glucose level back to normal.

Diabetes Mellitus When the pancreas fails to produce or properly use insulin, a condition known as **diabetes mellitus** occurs. In diabetes mellitus, the amount of glucose in the blood may rise so high that the kidneys actually excrete glucose in the urine. Very high blood glucose levels can damage almost every cell in the body, including the coronary artery, shown in **Figure 39–10.**

There are two types of diabetes mellitus. Type I diabetes is an autoimmune disorder that usually develops in people before the age of 15. In this type of diabetes, there is little or no secretion of insulin. People with this type of diabetes must follow a strict diet and get daily injections of insulin to keep their blood glucose levels under control.

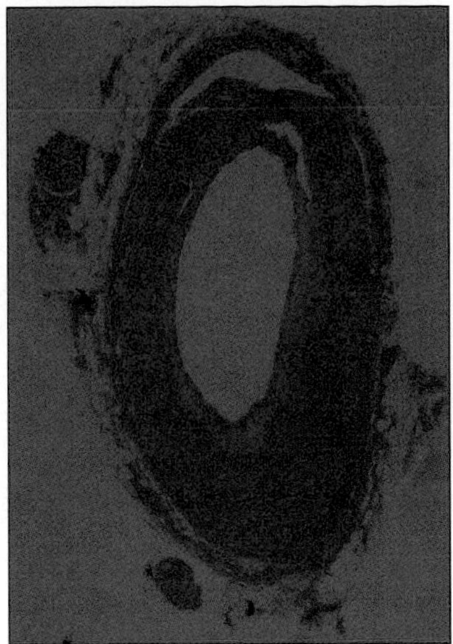

Normal Coronary Artery

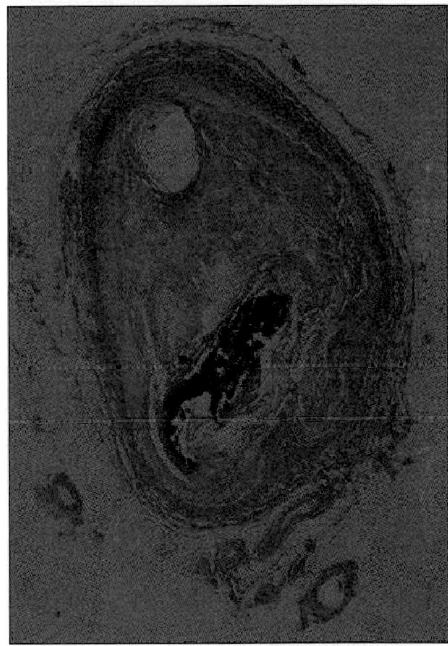

Coronary Artery Totally Blocked

▲ **Figure 39–10** Type II diabetes promotes atherosclerosis, which reduces the elasticity of arteries. **Applying Concepts** ***What effect do blocked arteries have on blood pressure?***

The second type of diabetes, Type II, most commonly develops in people after the age of 40. People with Type II diabetes produce low to normal amounts of insulin. However, their cells are unable to properly respond to the hormone because the interaction of the insulin receptors and the insulin is inefficient. In its early stages, Type II diabetes can often be controlled through diet and exercise. A diet high in complex carbohydrates and low in saturated fat and sugar can prevent blood sugar fluctuations.

Unfortunately, many people with Type II diabetes eventually require medication, as well. If the body stops producing insulin, the person will also need to have daily insulin injections.

Reproductive Glands

The gonads are the body's reproductive glands. **The gonads serve two important functions: the production of gametes and the secretion of sex hormones.** The female gonads—the **ovaries**—produce eggs (ova; singular: ovum). The male gonads—the **testes** (singular: testis)—produce sperm. The gonads also produce sex hormones.

The ovaries produce the female sex hormones, estrogen and progesterone. Estrogen is required for the development of eggs and for the formation of the physical characteristics associated with the female body. These characteristics include the development of the female reproductive system, widening of the hips, and development of the breasts. Progesterone prepares the uterus for the arrival of a developing embryo.

The testes produce testosterone (tes-TAHS-tuh-rohn). Testosterone is required for normal sperm production and the development of physical characteristics associated with the male body. These characteristics include the growth of facial hair, increase in body size, and deepening of the voice. You will read more about these hormones in the next section.

39–2 Section Assessment

1. **Key Concept** Describe the role of each major endocrine gland.
2. Why is the hypothalamus an important part of both the nervous system and the endocrine system?
3. What endocrine gland goes to work when you are surprised with a pop quiz?
4. What are the two types of diabetes mellitus?
5. **Critical Thinking Predicting** Suppose the secretion of a certain hormone causes an increase in the concentration of substance X in the blood. A low concentration of X causes the hormone to be released. What is the effect on the rate of hormone secretion if an abnormal condition causes the level of X in the blood to remain very low?

Writing in Science

Creating an Informational Brochure

Create a brochure that describes both types of diabetes. You may wish to include information on risk factors, treatment, and preventive measures that can be taken. Use images from magazines or the Internet to illustrate your brochure. *Hint:* Be sure to choose some high-interest images to make your brochure visually appealing.

39–3 The Reproductive System

4-4.1 Reproduction is necessary for species survival
4-4.1 The reproductive cycle in females is regulated by hormones
4-4.1 Human reproductive systems produce gametes

Reproduction is the formation of new individuals. This makes the reproductive system unique among the systems of the body. If any other body system, such as the nervous or circulatory system, failed to function, the result would be fatal in most animals. This is not the case for the reproductive system because an individual can lead a healthy life without reproducing. However, the reproductive system could be thought of as the single most important system for the continuation of a species—without it, no species could produce another generation.

In humans, as in other vertebrates, the reproductive system produces, stores, and releases specialized sex cells known as gametes. These cells are released in ways that make possible the fusion of sperm and egg to form a zygote, the single cell from which all cells of the human body develop.

Guide for Reading

Key Concepts

- What are the main functions of the male and female reproductive systems?
- What are the four phases of the menstrual cycle?

Vocabulary
puberty • scrotum
seminiferous tubule
epididymis • vas deferens
urethra • penis • follicle
ovulation • Fallopian tube
uterus • vagina
menstrual cycle
corpus luteum • menstruation
sexually transmitted disease

Reading Strategy: Outlining Before you read, use the headings in this section to make an outline about the reproductive system. As you read, fill in subtopics. Then, add phrases or a sentence after each subtopic to provide key information showing how the reproductive system is important.

Sexual Development

For the first six weeks of development, human male and female embryos are identical in appearance. Then, during the seventh week, major changes occur. The primary reproductive organs—the testes in males and the ovaries in females—begin to develop. The testes begin to produce testosterone. Tissues of the embryo respond to this hormone by developing into the male reproductive organs. If the embryo is female, the ovaries produce estrogen. In response to this hormone, the tissues of the embryo develop into the female reproductive organs. These hormones determine whether the embryo will develop physically into a male or female.

After birth, the gonads produce small amounts of sex hormones that continue to influence the development of the reproductive organs. However, neither the testes nor the ovaries are capable of producing active reproductive cells until puberty. **Puberty** is a period of rapid growth and sexual maturation during which the reproductive system becomes fully functional. At the completion of puberty, the male and female reproductive organs are fully developed. The onset of puberty varies considerably among individuals. It usually occurs any time between the ages of 9 and 15, and, on average, begins about one year earlier in females than in males.

Puberty begins when the hypothalamus signals the pituitary to produce increased levels of two hormones that affect the gonads. These hormones are follicle-stimulating hormone (FSH) and luteinizing hormone (LH).

▼ **Figure 39–11** Many changes in your life—both social and physical—are dependent on your age.

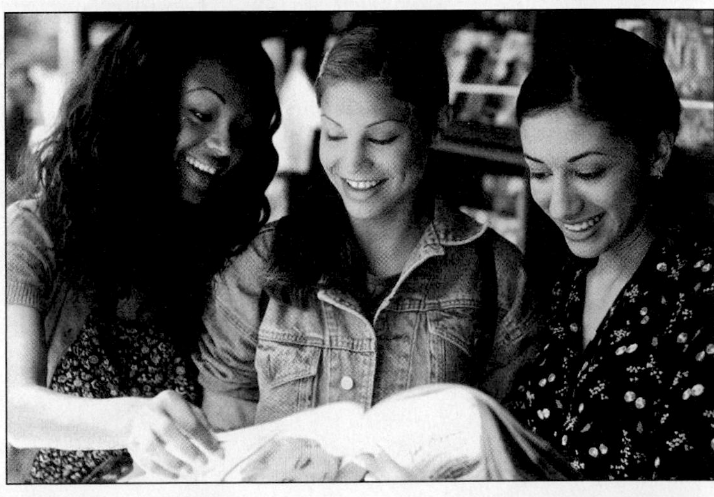

The Male Reproductive System

The release of FSH and LH stimulates cells in the testes to produce testosterone. FSH and testosterone stimulate the development of sperm. Once large numbers of sperm have been produced in the testes, the developmental process of puberty is completed. The reproductive system is now functional, meaning that the male can produce and release active sperm. **The main function of the male reproductive system is to produce and deliver sperm.**

Figure 39–12 shows the structures of the male reproductive system. The primary male reproductive organs, the testes, develop within the abdominal cavity. Just before birth (and sometimes just after) the testes descend through a canal into an external sac called the **scrotum.** The testes remain in the scrotum, outside the body cavity, where the temperature is about one to three degrees lower than the normal temperature of the body (37°C). The lower temperature is important for proper sperm development. Within each testis are clusters of hundreds of tiny tubules called **seminiferous** (sem-uh-NIF-ur-us) **tubules.** The seminiferous tubules are tightly coiled and twisted together. Sperm are produced in the seminiferous tubules.

What is the role of the seminiferous tubules?

▼ **Figure 39–12 The main structures of the male reproductive system produce and deliver sperm.** The main organs of the male reproductive system are the testes.

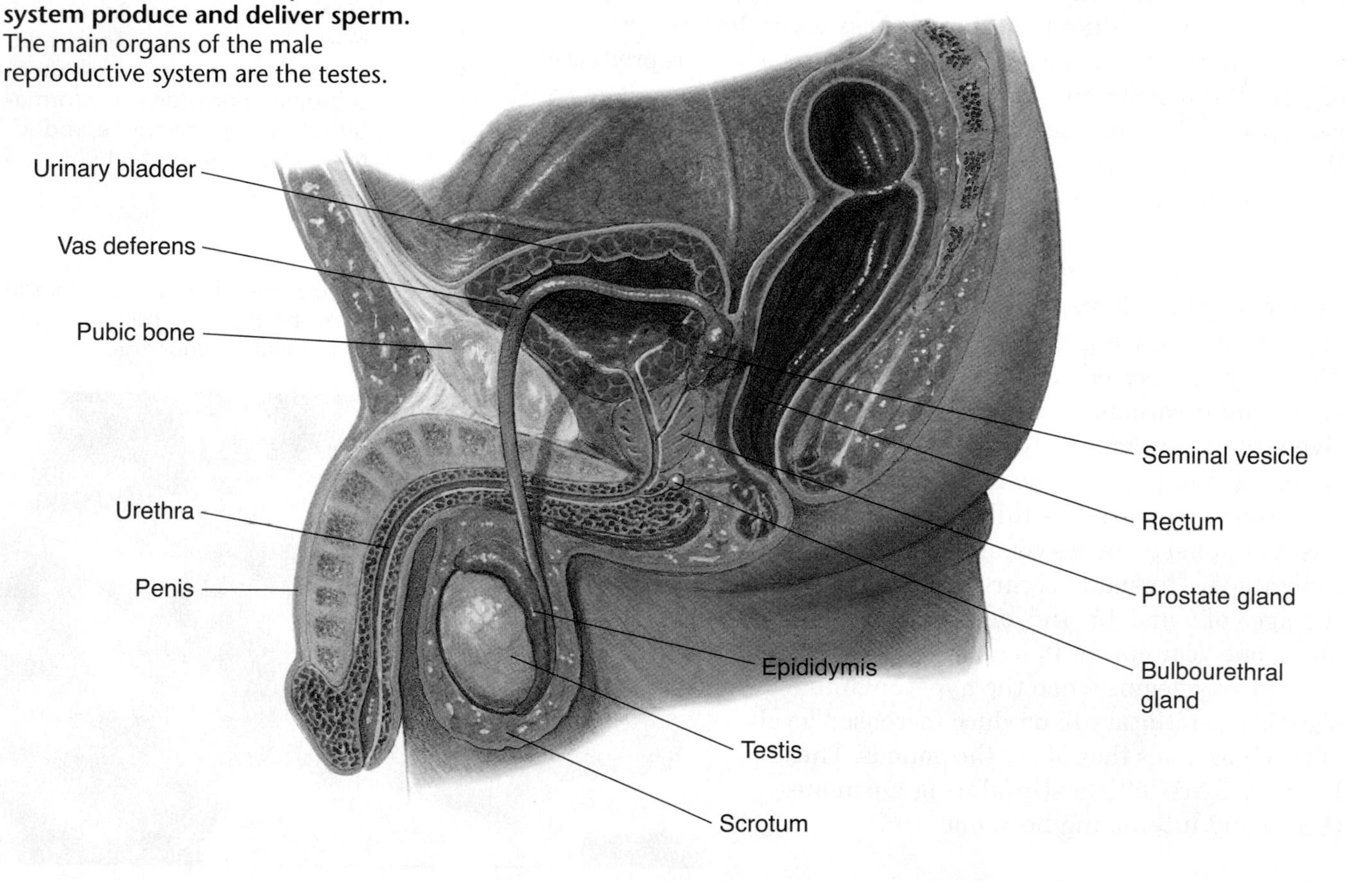

Sperm Development Sperm are derived from specialized cells in the testes that undergo the process of meiosis to form the haploid nuclei of mature sperm. Recall that a haploid cell contains only a single set of chromosomes.

A sperm cell is illustrated in **Figure 39–13.** A sperm cell consists of a head, which contains a highly condensed nucleus; a midpiece, which is packed with energy-releasing mitochondria; and a tail, or flagellum, which propels the cell forward. At the tip of the head is a small cap that contains an enzyme vital to the process of fertilization.

Sperm produced in the seminiferous tubules are moved into the **epididymis** (ep-uh-DID-ih-mis). This is the structure in which sperm fully mature and are stored. From the epididymis, some sperm are moved into a tube called the **vas deferens.** The vas deferens extends upward from the scrotum into the abdominal cavity. Eventually, the vas deferens merges with the **urethra,** the tube that leads to the outside of the body through the **penis.**

Glands lining the reproductive tract—including the seminal vesicles, the prostate, and the bulbourethral (bul-boh-yoo-REE-thrul) glands—produce a nutrient-rich fluid called seminal fluid. The seminal fluid nourishes the sperm and protects them from the acidity of the female reproductive tract. The combination of sperm and seminal fluid is known as semen. The number of sperm present in even a few drops of semen is astonishing. Between 50 and 130 million sperm are present in 1 milliliter of semen. That's about 2.5 million sperm per drop!

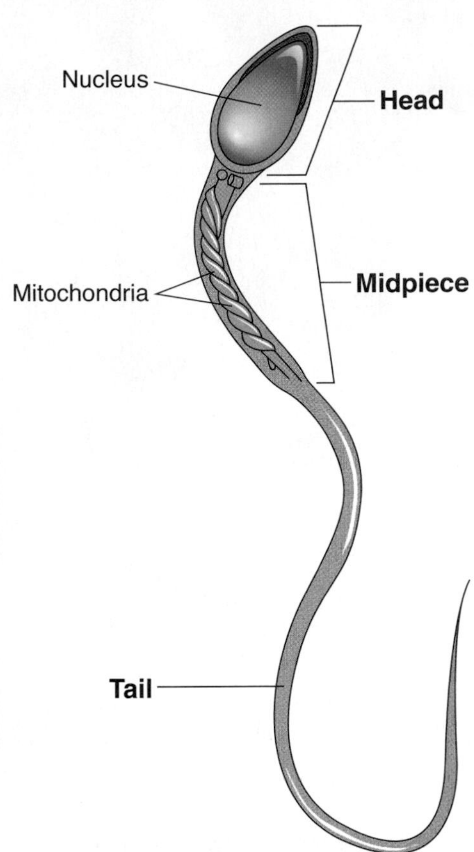

▲ **Figure 39–13** The sperm is the male gamete, or sex cell. **Interpreting Graphics** *What are the three sections of a sperm cell?*

Sperm Release When the male is sexually aroused, the autonomic nervous system prepares the male organs to deliver sperm. Sperm are ejected from the penis by the contractions of smooth muscles lining the glands in the reproductive tract. This process is called ejaculation. Because ejaculation is regulated by the autonomic nervous system, it is not completely voluntary. About 2 to 6 milliliters of semen are released in an average ejaculation. If these sperm are released in the reproductive tract of a female, the chances of a single sperm fertilizing an egg, if one is available, are quite good.

The Female Reproductive System

The primary reproductive organs in the female are the ovaries. The ovaries are located in the abdominal cavity. As in males, puberty in females starts when the hypothalamus signals the pituitary gland to release FSH and LH. FSH stimulates cells within the ovaries to produce estrogen.

The main function of the female reproductive system is to produce ova. In addition, the female reproductive system prepares the female's body to nourish a developing embryo. In contrast to the millions of sperm produced each day in the male reproductive system, the ovaries usually produce only one mature ovum (plural: ova), or egg, each month.

Egg Development Each ovary contains about 400,000 primary **follicles,** which are clusters of cells surrounding a single egg. The function of a follicle is to help an egg mature for release into the reproductive tract, where it can be fertilized. Eggs develop within their follicles.

Although a female is born with thousands of immature eggs (primary follicles), only about 400 eggs will actually be released. Approximately every 28 days, under the influence of FSH, a follicle gets larger and completes the first meiotic cell division. When meiosis is complete, a single large haploid egg and three smaller cells called polar bodies are produced. The polar bodies have very little cytoplasm and soon disintegrate.

Egg Release When a follicle has completely matured, its egg is released in a process called **ovulation.** The follicle breaks open, and the egg is swept from the surface of the ovary into the opening of one of the two **Fallopian tubes.** The egg moves through the fluid-filled Fallopian tube, pushed along by microscopic cilia lining the walls of the tube. During its journey through the Fallopian tube, an egg can be fertilized. After a few days, the egg passes from the Fallopian tube into the cavity of an organ known as the **uterus.** The lining of the uterus is ready to receive a fertilized egg, if fertilization has occurred. The outer end of the uterus is called the cervix. Beyond the cervix is a canal—the **vagina**—that leads to the outside of the body. The structures of the female reproductive system are shown in **Figure 39–14.**

▼ **Figure 39–14** **The main function of the female reproductive system is to produce ova.** The ovaries are the main organs of the female reproductive system.

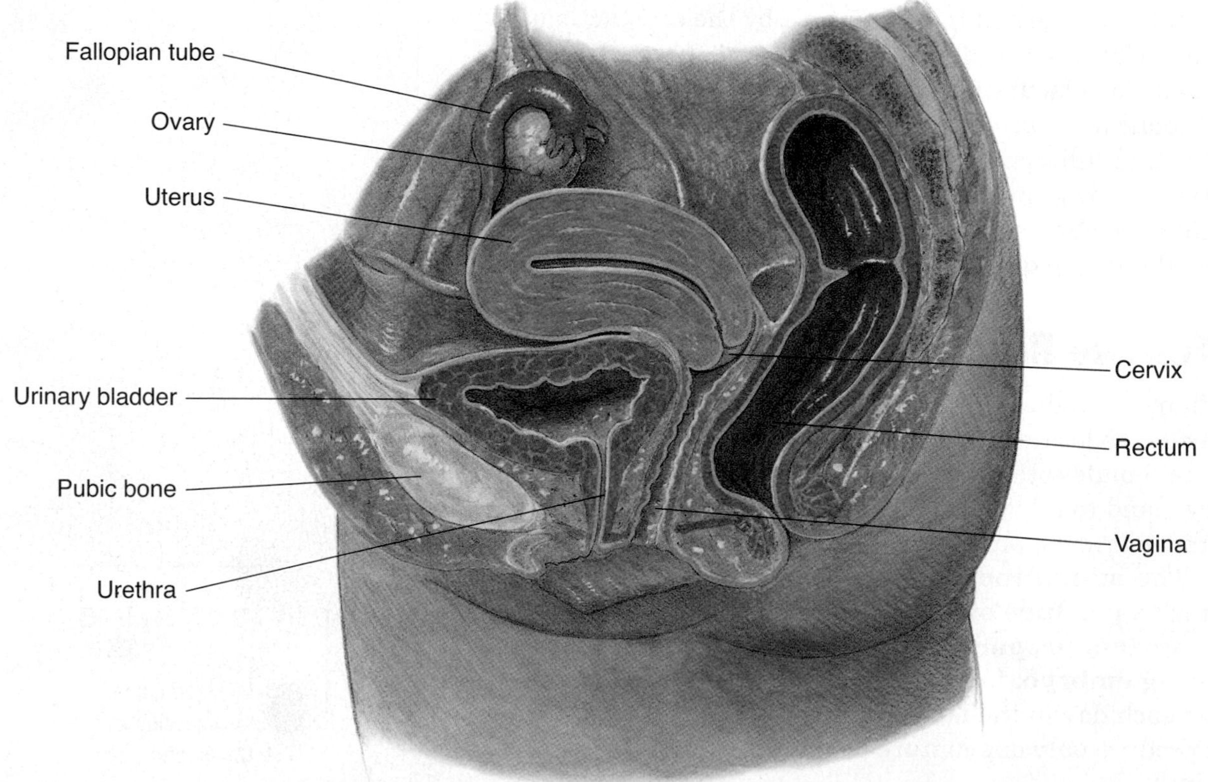

The Menstrual Cycle

After puberty, the interaction of the reproductive system and the endocrine system in females takes the form of a complex series of periodic events called the menstrual cycle. The cycle takes an average of about 28 days. The word *menstrual* comes from the Latin word *mensis,* meaning "month." The menstrual cycle is regulated by hormones made by the hypothalamus, pituitary gland, and ovaries; and it is controlled by internal feedback mechanisms.

The menstrual cycle begins at puberty and continues until a female is in her mid-forties. At this time, the production of estrogen declines, and ovulation and menstruation stop. The permanent stopping of the menstrual cycle is called menopause. The average age for menopause is about 51, but it can occur anytime between the late thirties and late fifties.

During the **menstrual cycle,** an egg develops and is released from an ovary. In addition, the uterus is prepared to receive a fertilized egg. If the egg is fertilized, it is implanted in the uterus and embryonic development begins. If an egg is not fertilized, it is discharged, along with the lining of the uterus. **The menstrual cycle has four phases: follicular phase, ovulation, luteal phase, and menstruation.** Refer to **Figure 39–16** on page 1014 as you read about what happens during each phase.

Follicular Phase The follicular phase begins when the level of estrogen in the blood is relatively low. The hypothalamus reacts to low estrogen levels by producing a releasing hormone that stimulates the anterior pituitary to secrete FSH and LH. These two hormones travel through the circulatory system to the ovaries, where they cause a follicle to develop to maturity. Generally, just a single follicle develops, but sometimes two or even three mature during the same cycle.

As the follicle develops, the cells surrounding the egg enlarge and begin to produce increased amounts of estrogen. As the follicle produces more and more of the hormone, the estrogen level in the blood rises dramatically. Estrogen causes the lining of the uterus to thicken in preparation for receiving a fertilized egg. The development of an egg in this stage of the cycle takes about 10 days.

CHECKPOINT *What happens during the follicular phase?*

Ovulation This phase is the shortest in the cycle. It occurs about midway through the cycle and lasts three to four days. During this phase, the hypothalamus sends a large amount of releasing hormone to the pituitary gland. This causes the pituitary gland to produce FSH and LH. The release of these hormones has a dramatic effect on the follicle: It ruptures, and a mature egg is released into one of the Fallopian tubes.

▼ **Figure 39–15** This photomicrograph shows an ovum (white object) being released from an ovary. **Applying Concepts** *What is this process called?*

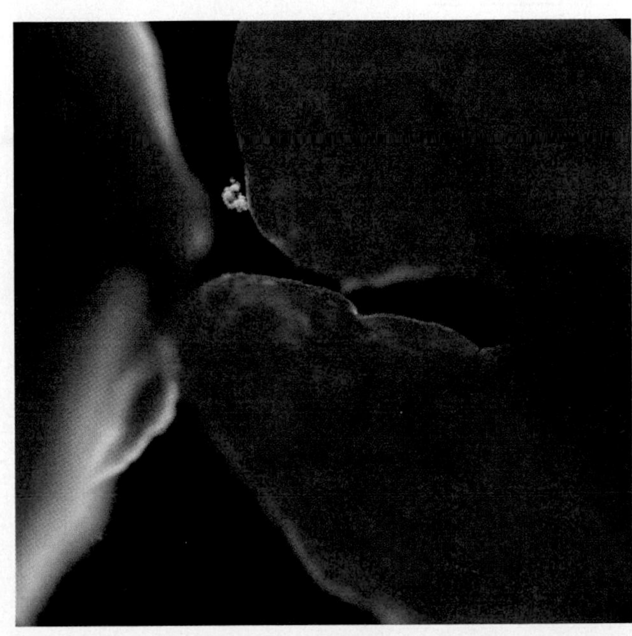

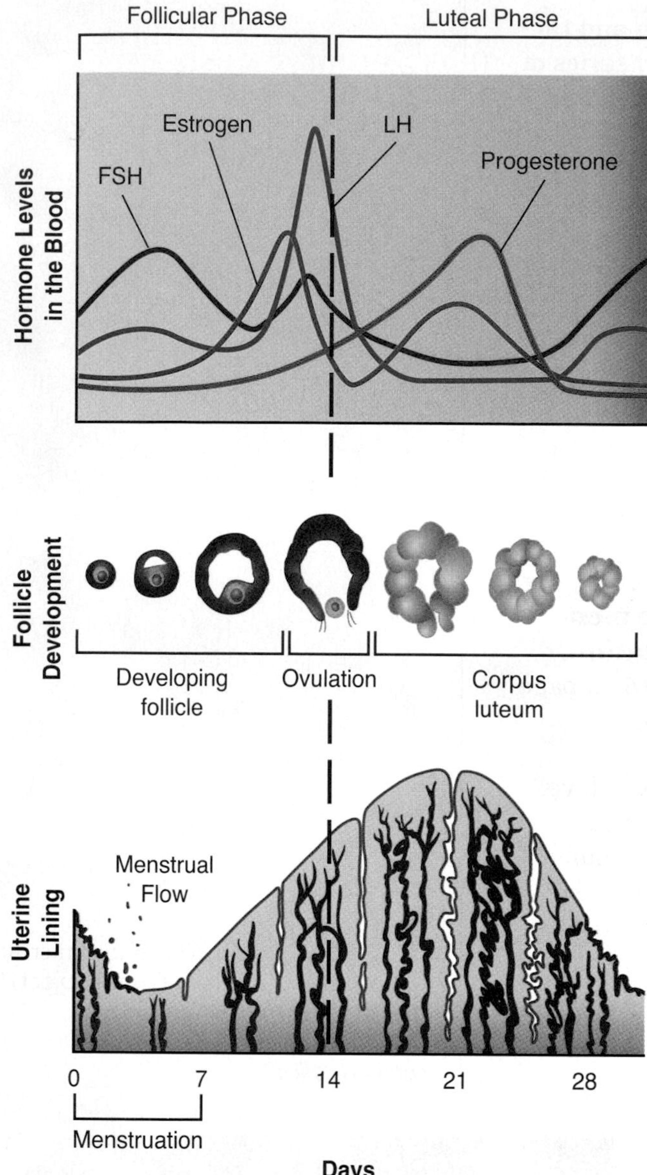

▲ **Figure 39–16** **The menstrual cycle is divided into four phases.** Notice the changes in hormone levels in the blood, the development of the follicle, and the changes in the uterine lining during the menstrual cycle.

Luteal Phase The luteal phase begins after the egg is released. As the egg moves through the Fallopian tube, the cells of the ruptured follicle undergo a change. The follicle turns yellow and is now known as the **corpus luteum** (KAWR-pus LOOT-ee-um), which means "yellow body" in Latin. The corpus luteum continues to release estrogen but also begins to release progesterone. During the first 14 days of the cycle, rising estrogen levels stimulate cell growth and tissue development in the lining of the uterus. Progesterone adds the finishing touches by stimulating the growth and development of the blood supply and surrounding tissue.

During the first two days of the luteal phase, immediately following ovulation, the chances that an egg will be fertilized are the greatest. This is usually from 10 to 14 days after the completion of the last menstrual cycle. If an egg is fertilized by a sperm, the fertilized egg will start to divide by the process of cell division known as mitosis. After several divisions, a ball of cells will form and implant itself in the lining of the uterus. The embryo continues to grow by repeated mitotic divisions. Within a few days of implantation, the uterus and the growing embryo will release hormones that keep the corpus luteum functioning for several weeks. This allows the lining of the uterus to nourish and protect the developing embryo.

Menstruation What happens if fertilization does not occur? Within two to three days of ovulation, the egg will pass through the uterus without implantation. The corpus luteum will begin to disintegrate. As the old follicle breaks down, it releases less estrogen and less progesterone. The result is a decrease in the level of these hormones in the blood.

When the level of estrogen falls below a certain point, the lining of the uterus begins to detach from the uterine wall. This tissue, along with blood and the unfertilized egg, are discharged through the vagina. This phase of the cycle is called **menstruation.** Menstruation lasts about three to seven days on average. A new cycle begins with the first day of menstruation.

A few days after menstruation ends, levels of estrogen in the blood are once again low enough to stimulate the hypothalamus. The hypothalamus produces a releasing hormone that acts on the pituitary gland, which then starts to secrete FSH and LH, and the menstrual cycle begins again.

Sexually Transmitted Diseases

Diseases that are spread from one person to another during sexual contact are known as **sexually transmitted diseases (STDs).** STDs are a serious health problem in the United States, infecting millions of people each year and accounting for thousands of deaths.

Unfortunately, public information about many STDs has not kept pace with the rate of infection. For example, one might think that the name of the most commonly reported infectious disease in the United States would be a household word, but it isn't. That disease is chlamydia. The Centers for Disease Control estimates that more than three million cases of chlamydia occur in the United States every year. Chlamydia is caused by a bacterium (shown in **Figure 39–17**) that is passed from person to person by sexual contact. Females between the ages of 15 and 19 show the highest incidence of chlamydia infection of any age group. Chlamydia puts them at risk of infertility due to the damage this disease can cause in the reproductive system.

Other STDs caused by bacteria include syphilis, which can be fatal, and gonorrhea, a serious infection that is easily spread during intercourse. Viruses can also cause STDs. Viral STDs include hepatitis B, genital herpes, genital warts, and AIDS. AIDS, a result of human immunodeficiency virus (HIV) infection, causes tens of thousands of deaths in the United States alone. Millions of deaths around the world can also be attributed to AIDS. Unlike the bacterial STDs, these viral infections cannot be treated with antibiotics.

Like other infectious diseases, STDs can be avoided. Any sexual contact carries with it the chance of infection. The safest course to follow is to abstain from sexual contact before marriage and for both partners in a committed relationship to remain faithful. The next safest course is to use a latex condom, but even a latex condom does not provide 100 percent protection.

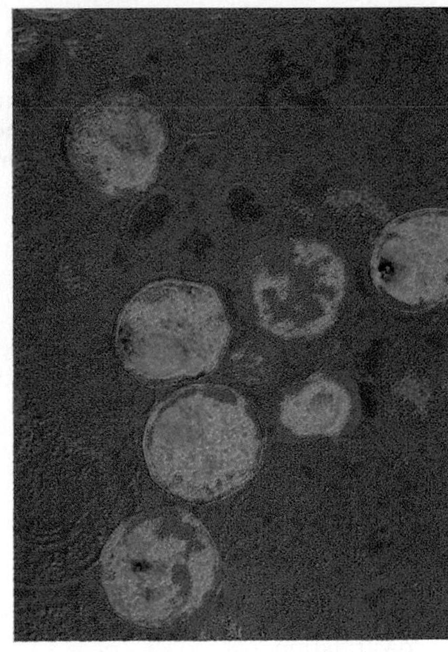

▲ **Figure 39–17** The red spherical objects in this micrograph show *Chlamydia trachomatis,* the bacterium that causes chlamydia.

39–3 Section Assessment

1. **Key Concept** Describe the functions of the male and female reproductive systems.
2. **Key Concept** What happens during each of the four phases of the menstrual cycle?
3. What is puberty?
4. Name two STDs caused by bacteria and two caused by viruses.
5. **Critical Thinking Using Tables and Graphs** Which hormone is at its peak during ovulation? (*Hint:* You may wish to refer to **Figure 39–16.**)

Connecting Concepts

Chromosomes

How many chromosomes are there in a human egg cell or in a sperm cell? How many are there in a fertilized egg? You may wish to refer back to Section 14–1.

39–4 Fertilization and Development

4-4.1 Specialized cells, tissues, and organs
4-4.1 The human female reproductive system
4-4.1 Development of essential organs

Guide for Reading

Key Concepts
- What is fertilization?
- What are the stages of early development?
- What is the function of the placenta?

Vocabulary
zygote
implantation
differentiation
gastrulation
neurulation
placenta
fetus

Reading Strategy: Using Graphic Organizers
As you read, draw a flowchart that shows the steps from fertilized egg to newborn baby.

When an egg is fertilized, the remarkable process of human development begins. In this process, a single cell no larger than the period at the end of this sentence undergoes a series of cell divisions that results in the formation of a new human being.

Fertilization

If an egg is to become fertilized, sperm must be present in the female reproductive tract—usually, in a Fallopian tube. During sexual intercourse, sperm are released when semen is ejaculated through the penis into the vagina. The penis generally enters the vagina to a point just below the cervix, which is the opening that connects the vagina to the uterus. Sperm swim actively through the uterus into the Fallopian tubes. Hundreds of millions of sperm are released during an ejaculation, so that if an egg is present in one of the Fallopian tubes, its chances of being fertilized are good.

The egg is surrounded by a protective layer that contains binding sites to which sperm can attach. When a sperm attaches to a binding site, a sac in the sperm head releases powerful enzymes that break down the protective layer of the egg. The sperm nucleus then enters the egg, and chromosomes from the sperm and egg are brought together. **The process of a sperm joining an egg is called fertilization.** After the two haploid (N) nuclei (one from the sperm and one from the egg) fuse, a single diploid (2N) nucleus is formed. A diploid cell contains a set of chromosomes from each parent cell. The fertilized egg is called a **zygote.**

Figure 39–18 **The process by which a sperm joins an egg is called fertilization.** Ernest Everett Just (left) discovered that once the sperm nucleus enters the egg, the egg's cell membrane changes, preventing other sperm from entering.

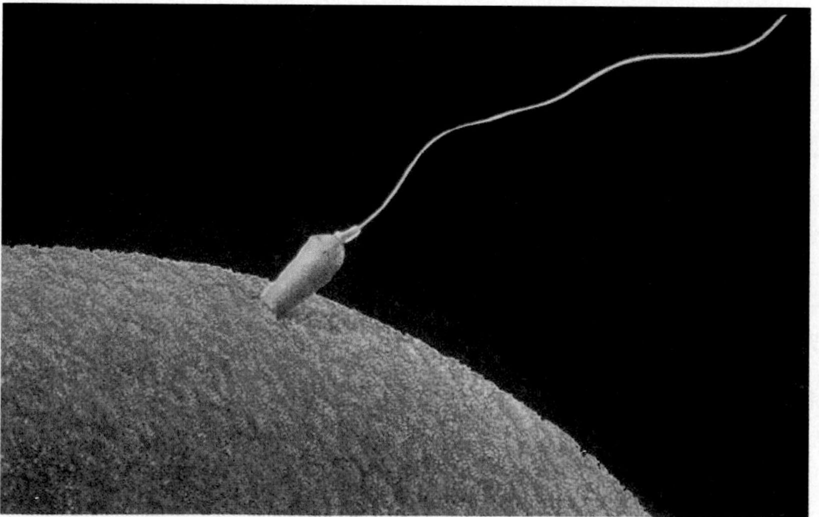

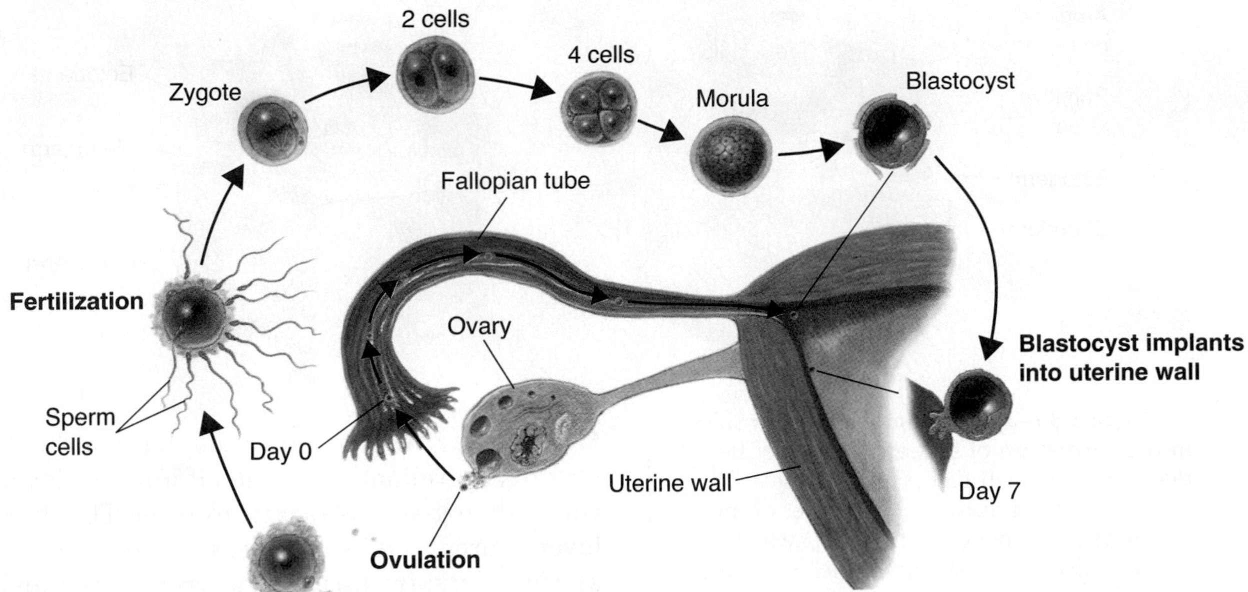

▲ **Figure 39–19** If an egg is fertilized, a zygote forms and begins to undergo cell division (mitosis) as it travels to the uterus. (The egg in this illustration has been greatly enlarged.) **Interpreting Graphics** ***How much time passes before the blastocyst is attached to the uterine wall?***

What prevents more than one sperm from fertilizing an egg? Early in the twentieth century, cell biologist Ernest Everett Just, shown in **Figure 39–18,** found the answer. The egg cell contains a series of granules just beneath its outer surface. When a single sperm enters the egg, the egg reacts by releasing the contents of these granules outside the cell. The material in the granules coats the surface of the egg, forming a barrier that prevents other sperm from attaching to and entering the egg.

Early Development

While still in the Fallopian tube, the zygote begins to undergo mitosis, as shown in **Figure 39–19.** Cell division continues. As each cell divides, the number of cells doubles. Four days after fertilization, the embryo is a solid ball of about 64 cells called a morula (MAWR-yoo-luh). **The stages of early development include implantation, gastrulation, and neurulation.**

Implantation As the morula grows, a cavity forms in the center. This transforms the morula into a hollow structure with an inner cavity called a blastocyst. About six or seven days after fertilization, the blastocyst attaches itself to the wall of the uterus. The embryo secretes enzymes that digest a path into the soft tissue. This process is known as **implantation.**

At this point, cells in the blastocyst begin to specialize as a result of the activation of genes. This specialization process, called **differentiation,** is responsible for the development of the various types of tissue in the body. A cluster of cells, known as the inner cell mass, develops within the inner cavity of the blastocyst. The embryo itself will develop from these cells, while the other cells of the blastocyst will differentiate into the tissues that surround the embryo.

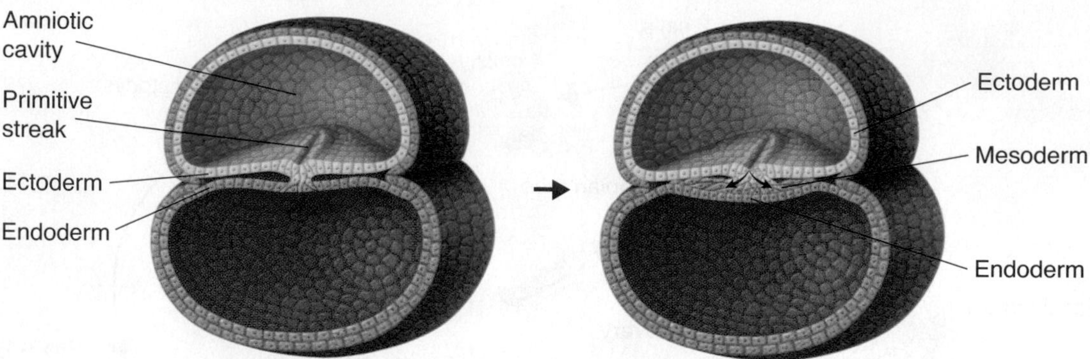

▲ **Figure 39–20** **Gastrulation results in the formation of three cell layers.** The diagram on the left shows the primitive streak, a line that forms in the center of the blastocyst. The movement of cells away from the primitive streak, shown in the diagram on the right, forms the mesoderm.

Gastrulation The inner cell mass of the blastocyst gradually sorts itself into two layers, which then give rise to a third layer. The third layer is produced by a process of cell migration known as **gastrulation** (gas-troo-LAY-shun), shown in **Figure 39–20.** The result of gastrulation is the formation of three cell layers: ectoderm, mesoderm, and endoderm. These three layers are referred to as the primary germ layers, because all of the organs and tissues of the embryo will be formed from them. The ectoderm will develop into the skin and the nervous system. The endoderm forms the lining of the digestive system and many of the digestive organs. Mesoderm cells differentiate to form many of the body's internal tissues and organs.

Neurulation Gastrulation is followed by an important step in human development, neurulation (NUR-uh-lay-shun). **Neurulation** is the development of the nervous system. Shortly after gastrulation is complete, a block of mesodermal tissue begins to differentiate into the notochord. Recall that all chordates possess a notochord at some stage of development. As the notochord develops, the neural groove changes shape, producing a pair of ridges, or neural folds, as shown in **Figure 39–21.** Gradually, these folds move together to create a neural tube from which the spinal cord and the rest of the nervous system, including the brain, develop.

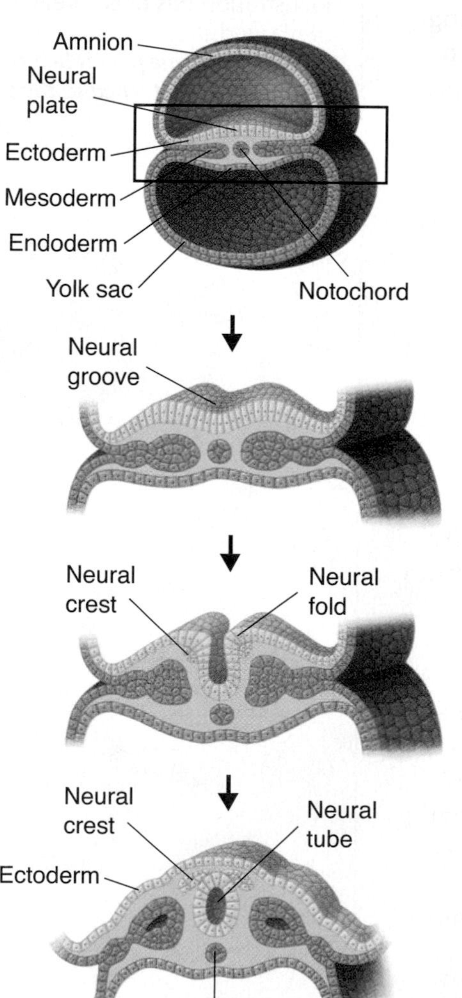

◀ **Figure 39–21** **Neurulation is the formation of the central nervous system.** The ectoderm near the notochord thickens and forms the neural plate. The raised edges of the neural plate form neural folds. The neural folds gradually move together and fuse to form the neural tube. One end of the neural tube will develop into the brain; the other end develops into the spinal cord. Cells of the neural crest migrate to other locations and develop into nerves.

Extraembryonic Membranes As the embryo develops, membranes form to protect and nourish the embryo. Two of these membranes are the amnion and the chorion. The amnion develops into a fluid-filled amniotic sac, which cushions and protects the developing embryo within the uterus. By the end of the third week of development, the chorion—the outermost of the extraembryonic membranes—has formed. Small, fingerlike projections called chorionic villi form on the outer surface of the chorion and extend into the uterine lining.

The chorionic villi and uterine lining form a vital organ called the **placenta.** The placenta is the connection between mother and developing embryo. The developing embryo needs a supply of nutrients and oxygen. It also needs a means of eliminating carbon dioxide and metabolic wastes. Nutrients and oxygen in the blood of the mother diffuse into the embryo's blood in the chorionic villi. Wastes diffuse from the embryo's blood into the mother's blood.

In actuality, the blood of the mother and that of the embryo flow past each other, but they do not mix. They are separated by the placenta. Across this thin barrier, gases exchange, and food and waste products diffuse. **The placenta is the embryo's organ of respiration, nourishment, and excretion.** The placenta allows the embryo to make use of the mother's organ systems while its own are developing. **Figure 39–22** shows a portion of the placenta.

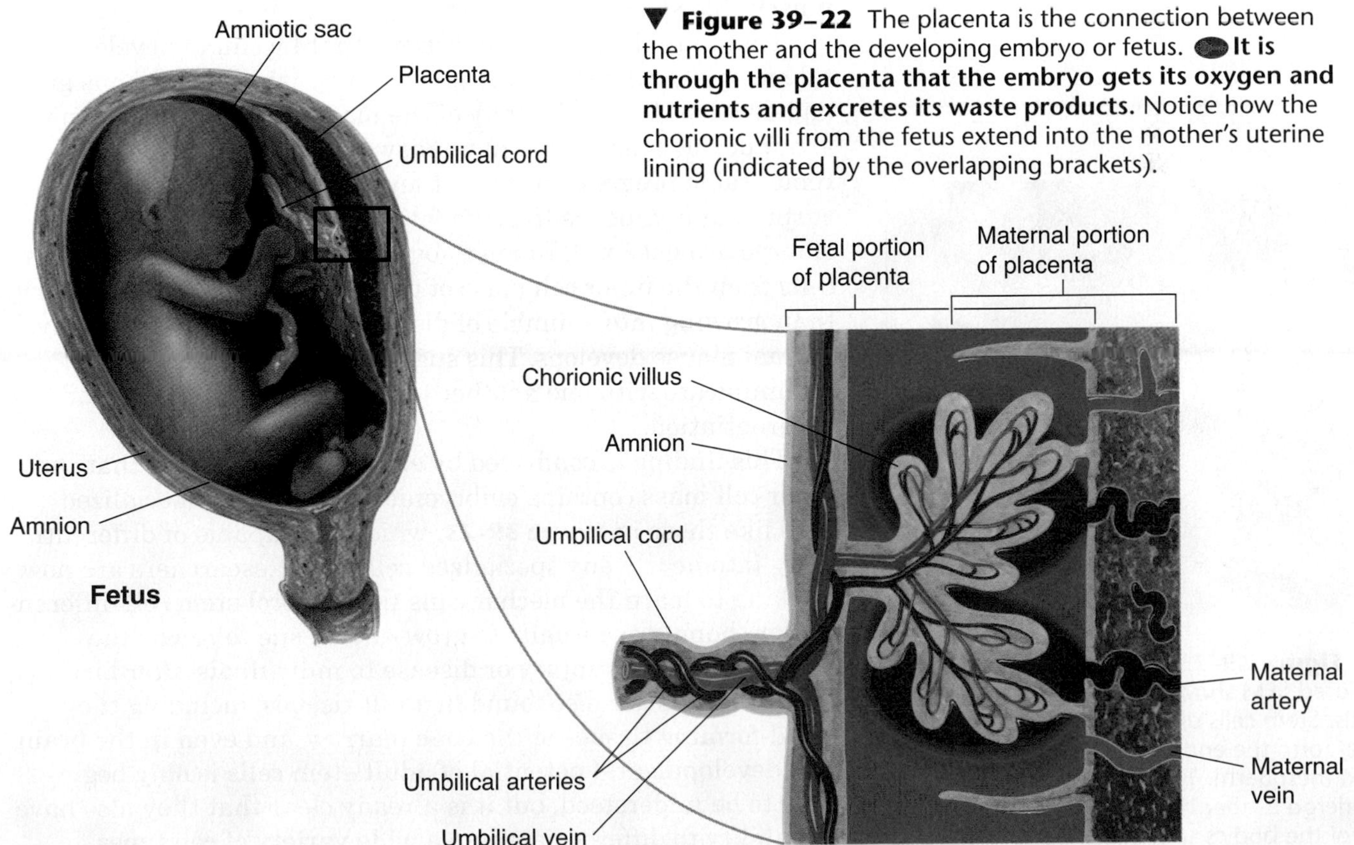

▼ **Figure 39–22** The placenta is the connection between the mother and the developing embryo or fetus. **It is through the placenta that the embryo gets its oxygen and nutrients and excretes its waste products.** Notice how the chorionic villi from the fetus extend into the mother's uterine lining (indicated by the overlapping brackets).

Importance of Development This early period of development is particularly important because a number of external factors can disrupt development at this time. The placenta acts as a barrier to some harmful or disease-causing agents. Other disease-causing agents, including the ones that cause AIDS and German measles, can penetrate the placenta and affect development. So can drugs—including alcohol, medications, and addictive substances.

After eight weeks of development, the embryo is called a **fetus.** By the end of three months of development, most of the major organs and tissues of the fetus are fully formed. During this time, the umbilical cord also forms. The umbilical cord, which contains two arteries and one vein, connects the fetus to the placenta. The muscular system of the fetus is by now well developed, and the fetus may begin to move and show signs of reflexes. The fetus is about 8 centimeters long and has a mass of about 28 grams.

CHECKPOINT *What is the function of the umbilical cord?*

Control of Development

As you have read, over just a few weeks of development, a single zygote cell differentiates into the many complex cells and tissues of a human fetus. How does this happen? Is the fate of each cell in the embryo predetermined? Is there a master control switch that decides whether a cell will become skin, muscle, blood, or bone?

These are the kinds of questions that fascinate developmental biologists, who study the processes by which organisms grow and develop. Although many of the most important questions about development are still unanswered, researchers have made remarkable progress in the last few years. One of their most surprising findings is that the fates of many cells in the early embryo are not fixed. In mice, for example, researchers can mix cells from the inner cell mass of two different embryos. Rather than growing into a jumble of disorganized tissues, a perfectly normal mouse develops. This suggests that embryonic cells communicate with one another to regulate development and differentiation.

This finding is confirmed by experiments showing that the inner cell mass contains embryonic stem cells, unspecialized cells like those in **Figure 39–23,** which are capable of differentiating into nearly any specialized cell type. Researchers are now working to learn the mechanisms that control stem cell differentiation, hoping eventually to grow new tissue to repair the damage caused by injury or disease to individuals after birth.

Stem cells are also found in adult tissues, including the blood-forming tissues of the bone marrow, and even in the brain. The developmental potential of adult stem cells is only beginning to be understood, but it is already clear that they also have the ability to differentiate into a wide variety of cell types.

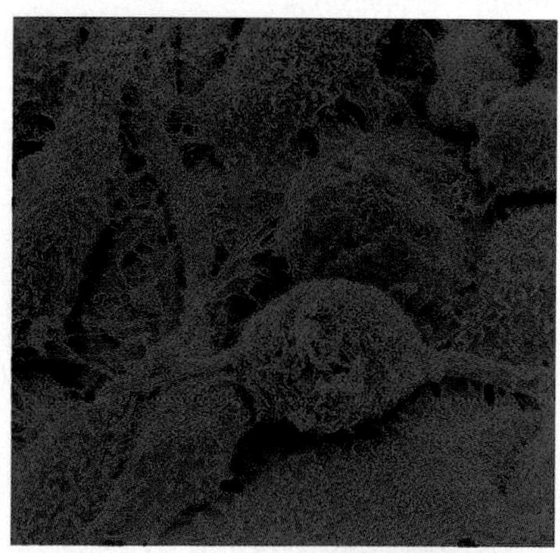

▲ **Figure 39–23** This artificially colored SEM shows embryonic stem cells. Stem cells differentiate into cells that form the endoderm, ectoderm, and mesoderm. These cells then undergo further differentiation to form all of the body's specialized cells.

Later Development

During the fourth, fifth, and sixth months after fertilization, the tissues of the fetus become more complex and specialized, and more tissues begin to function. The fetal heart becomes large enough so that it can be heard with a stethoscope. Bone continues to replace the cartilage that forms the early skeleton. A layer of soft hair grows over the fetus's skin. As the fetus increases in size, the mother's abdomen swells to accommodate it. The mother can begin to feel the fetus moving.

During the last three months, the organ systems mature, and the fetus grows in size and mass. The fetus doubles in mass, and the lungs and other organs undergo a series of changes that prepare them for life outside the uterus. The fetus is now able to regulate its body temperature. In addition, the central nervous system and lungs complete their development. **Figure 39–24** shows an embryo and a fetus at different stages of development.

On average, it takes nine months for a fetus to fully develop. Babies born before eight months of development, called premature babies, often have severe breathing problems because of incomplete lung development.

CHECKPOINT ***What happens in a fetus during the last three months of development?***

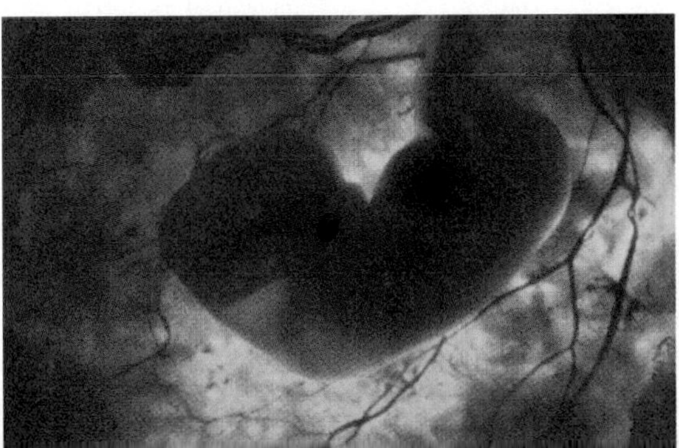

Embryo at 7 Weeks

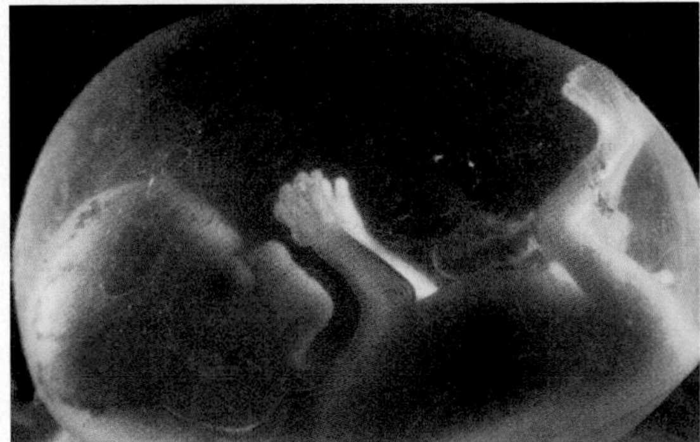

Fetus at 14 Weeks

Figure 39–24 At 7 weeks, most of the organs have begun to form. The heart—the large, dark rounded structure—is beating. By 14 weeks, the hands, feet, and legs have reached their birth proportions. The eyes, ears, and nose are well developed. When the fetus is full-term, it is fully developed and capable of living on its own. **Interpreting Graphics** ***What significant changes do you see from 7 weeks to 14 weeks?***

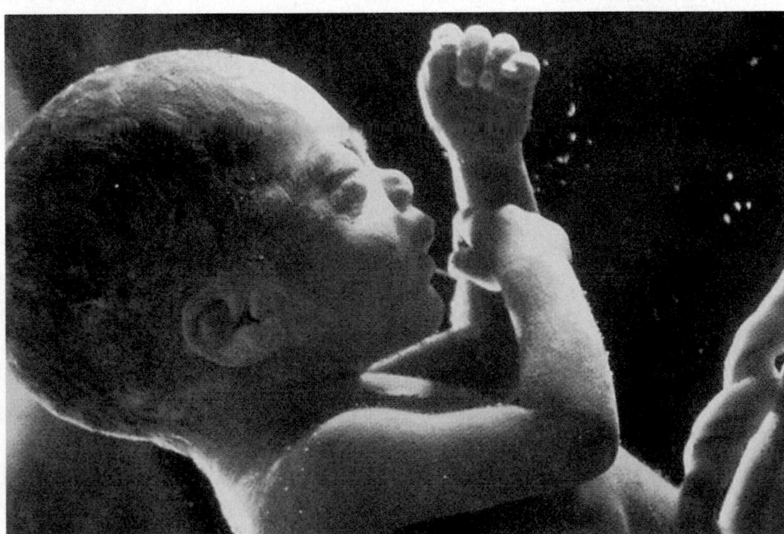

Fetus at Full Term

Quick Lab

How do embryos develop?

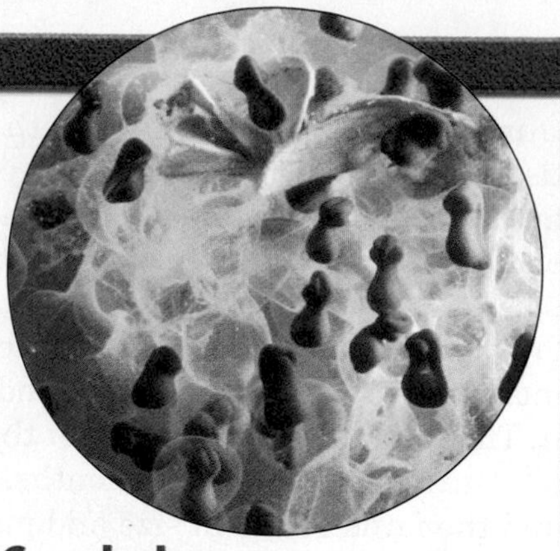
Frog Embryos

Materials dropper pipette, early-stage frog embryos, depression slide, dissecting microscope, prepared slides of frog embryos

Procedure  

1. Use a dropper pipette to transfer several early-stage frog embryos in water to a depression slide. **CAUTION:** *Microscopes and slides are fragile. Handle them carefully. Tell your teacher if you break any glass.*
2. Look at the embryos under the dissecting microscope at low power. Sketch what you see.
3. Look at prepared slides of the early embryonic stages of a frog. Make sketches of what you see.

Analyze and Conclude

1. **Observing** Describe any differences you saw among the cells. At what stage is cell differentiation visible?
2. **Observing** Were you able to see a distinct body plan? At what stage did the body plan become visible?
3. **Drawing Conclusions** Describe any organs you saw. At what stage did specific organs form?

▼ **Figure 39–25** A newborn baby takes its first breath of air.

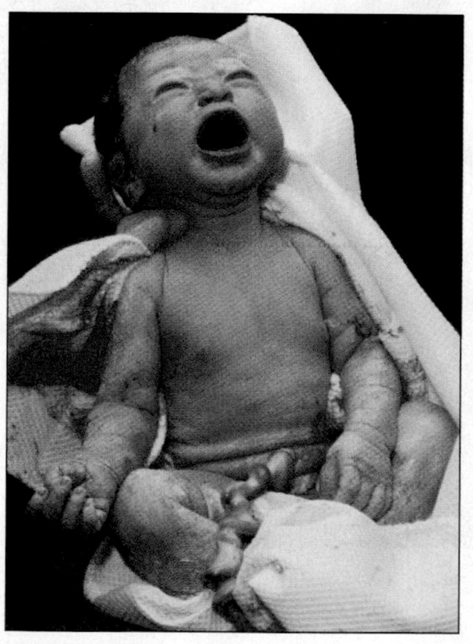

Childbirth

About nine months after fertilization, the fetus is ready for birth. A complex set of factors affects the onset of childbirth. One factor is the release of the hormone oxytocin from the mother's posterior pituitary gland. Oxytocin affects a group of large involuntary muscles in the uterine wall. As these muscles are stimulated, they begin a series of rhythmic contractions known as labor. The contractions become more frequent and more powerful. The opening of the cervix expands until it is large enough for the head of the baby to pass through it. At some point, the amniotic sac breaks, and the fluid it contains rushes out of the vagina. Contractions of the uterus force the baby, usually head first, out through the vagina.

As the baby meets the outside world, he or she may begin to cough or cry, a process that rids the lungs of fluid. Breathing starts almost immediately, and the blood supply to the placenta begins to dry up. The umbilical cord is clamped and cut, leaving a small piece attached to the baby. This piece will soon dry and fall off, leaving a scar known as the navel—or in its more familiar term, the belly button. In a final series of uterine contractions, the placenta itself and the now-empty amniotic sac are expelled from the uterus as the afterbirth.

The baby now begins an independent existence. Most newborn babies are remarkably hardy. Their systems quickly switch over to life outside the uterus, supplying their own oxygen, excreting wastes on their own, and maintaining their own body temperatures.

The interaction of the mother's reproductive and endocrine systems does not end at childbirth. Within a few hours after birth, the pituitary hormone prolactin stimulates the production of milk in the breast tissues of the mother. The nutrients present in that milk contain everything the baby needs for growth and development during the first few months of life.

Multiple Births

Sometimes more than one baby develops during a pregnancy. For example, if two eggs are released during the same cycle and fertilized by two different sperm, fraternal twins result. Fraternal twins are not identical in appearance because each has been formed by the fusion of a different sperm and egg cell. Fraternal twins may or may not be the same sex.

Sometimes a single zygote splits apart to produce two embryos. These two embryos are called identical twins. Identical siblings are formed by the fusion of the same sperm and egg cell; therefore, they are genetically identical. Identical twins are always the same sex.

CHECKPOINT ***What are the differences between identical twins and fraternal twins?***

Figure 39–26 During infancy, an infant learns to stand, walk, speak a few words, and imitate others. From ages 5 to 12, children grow to about 70 percent of their adult height and weight.

Early Years

Although the most spectacular changes of the human body occur before birth, development is a continuing process—it lasts throughout the life of an individual. In the first weeks of a baby's life, the systems that developed before birth now move into high gear, supporting rapid growth that generally triples a baby's birth weight within 12 months.

Infancy The first two years of life are known as infancy. Infancy is a period of rapid growth and development. The nervous system develops coordinated body movements as the infant begins to crawl and then to walk. A baby's first teeth appear, and the baby begins to understand and use language. Growth in the skeletal and muscular systems is especially rapid, demanding good nutrition to support proper development.

Childhood Childhood lasts from infancy until the onset of puberty, typically at an age of 12 or 13. Children become more active and independent. Language is acquired, motor coordination is perfected, permanent teeth begin to appear, and the long bones of the skeletal system reach 80 percent of their adult length. The key elements of personality and human social skills are developed, and reasoning skills are developed to a high level.

▲ **Figure 39–27** By maintaining a healthy lifestyle, you may be able to slow the aging process. **Applying Concepts** *What factors contribute to a healthy lifestyle?*

Adolescence Adolescence begins with puberty and ends with adulthood. The surge in sex hormones that starts at puberty produces a growth spurt that will conclude in mid-adolescence as the long bones of the arms and legs stop growing and complete their ossification. The continuing development of intellectual skills combines with personality changes that are associated with adult maturity.

Adulthood

Development continues during adulthood. By most measures, adults reach their highest levels of physical strength and development between the ages of 25 and 35. During these years most individuals assume the responsibilities of adulthood.

In most individuals, the first signs of physiological aging appear in their thirties. Joints begin to lose some of their flexibility, muscle strength starts to decrease, and several body systems show slight declines in efficiency. By age 50, these changes, although generally still minor, are apparent to most individuals. In women, menopause greatly reduces estrogen levels. After menopause, follicle development no longer occurs and ovulation stops. At around age 65, most systems of the body become less efficient, making homeostasis more difficult to maintain.

Although there are some changes in mental functioning during older adulthood, these changes usually have little effect on thinking, learning, or long-term memory. The brain remains open to change and to learning. In fact, evidence suggests that the aging process can be slowed by keeping the mind active and challenged. Most older adults are fully capable of continuing stimulating intellectual work. By practicing the habits of good health and regular exercise, as the woman in **Figure 39–27** is doing, every person can hope to be happy and productive at every stage of human development.

39–4 Section Assessment

1. **Key Concept** Describe the process of fertilization.
2. **Key Concept** Describe the role of the placenta.
3. **Key Concept** Describe the three stages of early development.
4. What are the three germ layers that result from gastrulation?
5. What is oxytocin, and what is its role in childbirth?
6. **Critical Thinking Applying Concepts** Why do you think doctors recommend that women avoid most medications and alcohol during pregnancy?

Thinking Visually

Creating a Time Line
Starting with your birth date, create a time line of physical and social developmental milestones. As resources, you can use interviews, photographs, and memories.

Exploration

Modeling Blood Glucose Regulation

Regulating the level of blood glucose is one of the body's most important jobs. Two hormones, insulin and glucagon, help to regulate the level of glucose in blood. Because these two hormones have opposite effects, it is important that a proper balance between them is maintained. In this investigation, you will simulate how this regulatory mechanism works.

Problem **How does the body regulate blood glucose levels?**

Materials

- 3 pieces of construction paper of different colors
- scissors

Skills Using Models, Asking Questions

Procedure 

1. Work in groups of three students. Give each member of the group a number from 1 to 3.
2. Cut 15 cards out of construction paper of one color. On each card, print "10 mg glucose/100 mL blood" on the front and "glycogen" on the back. These are your glucose cards. Turning over a glucose card represents converting glucose into glycogen, or vice versa.
3. Cut out 2 cards of a second color. On each of these cards print "insulin." Each of these insulin cards can convert 1 glucose card into glycogen.
4. Cut out 2 more cards of a third color. On each of these cards print "glucagon." One glucagon card can convert 1 glucose card from glycogen into glucose.
5. Place 9 glucose cards face up on the table. This represents the normal level of glucose in blood (90 mg glucose/100 mL blood). Student 1 should keep 2 more glucose cards face up.
6. Student 2 should keep the insulin and glucagon cards. Student 3 should keep the remaining 4 glucose cards face down, to represent stored glycogen.
7. To simulate the effect of a meal, student 1 should add a glucose card to the 9 on the table. Discuss how the body responds to this change.
8. Students 2 and 3 should use the cards to model how the body restores the normal blood glucose level after a meal.
9. To simulate the effect of exercise, student 1 should remove a glucose card from the 9 on the table. Repeat step 8.
10. To simulate what happens when a person has Type I diabetes, repeat steps 7 and 8 without using the insulin cards.

Analyze and Conclude

1. **Applying Concepts** What organ does student 2 represent? Explain your answer.
2. **Using Models** How did students 2 and 3 respond in step 8? In step 9? In step 10? Describe what happens in the body in each situation.
3. **Applying Concepts** How does this activity model homeostasis in the body?
4. **Predicting** What would happen if a person with Type I diabetes ate a large amount of sugar?

Go Further

Using Models What do you think would happen if the body did not produce enough glucagon? Use your cards to model what would happen in this situation.

Chapter 39 Study Guide

39–1 The Endocrine System

Key Concepts

- The endocrine system is made up of glands that release their products—hormones—into the bloodstream. Hormones travel through the bloodstream and affect the activities of other cells.
- The endocrine system is regulated by feedback mechanisms that function to maintain homeostasis.

Vocabulary

hormone, p. 997
target cell, p. 997
exocrine gland, p. 998
endocrine gland, p. 998
prostaglandin, p. 1000

39–2 Human Endocrine Glands

Key Concepts

- The pituitary gland secretes nine hormones that directly regulate many body functions and controls the actions of several other endocrine glands.
- The hypothalamus controls the secretions of the pituitary gland and helps coordinate the interactions of the nervous and endocrine systems.
- The thyroid gland secretes hormones that help to regulate the body's metabolism.
- Hormones from the thyroid gland and the parathyroid glands act to maintain homeostasis of calcium levels in the blood.
- The adrenal glands release hormones that help the body prepare for and deal with stress.
- The pancreas secretes insulin and glucagon, which help to keep the level of glucose in the blood stable.
- The gonads—the ovaries and testes—serve two important functions: the production of gametes and the secretion of sex hormones.

Vocabulary

pituitary gland, p. 1003
diabetes mellitus, p. 1007
ovary, p. 1008
testis, p. 1008

39–3 The Reproductive System

Key Concepts

- The main function of the male reproductive system is to produce and deliver sperm.
- The main function of the female reproductive system is to produce ova. In addition, the female reproductive system prepares the female's body to nourish a developing embryo.
- The menstrual cycle has four phases: follicular phase, ovulation, luteal phase, and menstruation.

Vocabulary

puberty, p. 1009 • scrotum, p. 1010
seminiferous tubule, p. 1010
epididymis, p. 1011 • vas deferens, p. 1011
urethra, p. 1011 • penis, p. 1011
follicle, p. 1012 • ovulation, p. 1012
Fallopian tube, p. 1012 • uterus, p. 1012
vagina, p. 1012 • menstrual cycle, p. 1013
corpus luteum, p. 1014 • menstruation, p. 1014
sexually transmitted disease, p. 1015

39–4 Fertilization and Development

Key Concepts

- The process of a sperm joining with an egg is called fertilization.
- The stages of early development include implantation, gastrulation, and neurulation.
- The placenta is the embryo's organ of respiration, nourishment, and excretion.

Vocabulary

zygote, p. 1016
implantation, p. 1017
differentiation, p. 1017
gastrulation, p. 1018
neurulation, p. 1018
placenta, p. 1019
fetus, p. 1020

Thinking Visually

Use the information in this chapter to construct a chart listing the actions of each hormone discussed. Your chart should include three headings: Endocrine Gland, Hormone, and Action of Hormone.

Preparing for the Living Environment Exam

NEW YORK LIVING ENVIRONMENT

Blue questions emphasize Regents Exam content

Chapter 39

Part A

Multiple Choice

For each statement or question, select the number of the word or expression that, of those given, best completes the statement or answers the question.

1 Glands that release hormones into the blood are part of the
(1) digestive system
(2) endocrine system
(3) circulatory system
(4) nervous system

2 Hormones produced from cholesterol are called
(1) protein hormones
(2) steroid hormones
(3) nonsteroid hormones
(4) peptide hormones

3 Hormonelike substances produced by nearly all cells are known as
(1) thyroxines
(2) steroids
(3) prostaglandins
(4) androgens

4 The hormone that helps regulate blood calcium levels is produced by the
(1) adrenal gland
(2) pancreas
(3) thymus gland
(4) parathyroid glands

5 The rate of body metabolism is regulated by
(1) PTH (3) aldosterone
(2) thyroxine (4) calcitonin

6 The diagram below shows the female reproductive system.

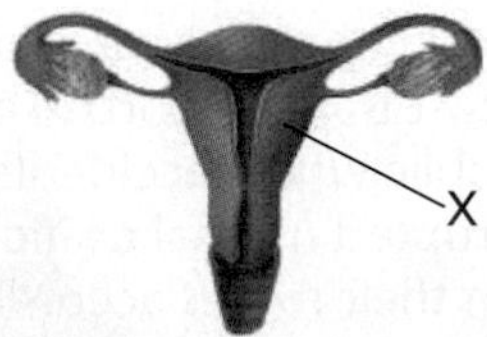

Which structure is indicated by the X?
(1) cervix (3) ovary
(2) Fallopian tube (4) uterus

7 The principal male sex hormone is
(1) FSH (3) insulin
(2) estrogen (4) testosterone

8 Fertilization usually occurs in the
(1) uterine wall (3) vagina
(2) Fallopian tube (4) ovary

9 After the eighth week of development, the human embryo is known as a(an)
(1) zygote (3) infant
(2) fetus (4) blastula

10 Which sequence correctly describes the route that sperm take through the male reproductive system?
(1) vas deferens, urethra, epididymis
(2) epididymis, vas deferens, urethra
(3) vas deferens, epididymis, urethra
(4) urethra, epididymis, vas deferens

11 Which term does *not* refer to a stage in the human menstrual cycle?
(1) ovulation
(2) follicular phase
(3) luteal phase
(4) corpus phase

12 Which gland is *not* part of the endocrine system?
(1) thyroid gland (3) pituitary gland
(2) sweat gland (4) adrenal gland

13 The part of the sperm that contains genetic information is the
(1) nucleus (3) mitochondria
(2) neck (4) tail

14 Development of sperm is stimulated by
(1) LH and estrogen
(2) FSH and testosterone
(3) the corpus luteum
(4) adrenalin

15 Structures that have receptors for a particular hormone are called
(1) target cells
(2) second messengers
(3) enzymes
(4) steroids

Test-Taking Tip For questions containing words like *not* or *except*, first rule out any choice that does fit the characteristic in question. Use this approach to eliminate three out of four choices. To check if your answer is correct, confirm that it does not fit the characteristic in question.

Preparing for the Living Environment Exam

Part B

Multiple Choice and Extended Response

For those questions that ask you to select a response, choose the one that best completes the statement or answers the question. For all others follow the directions given.

Base your answers to questions 16 through 19 on the diagram below and on your knowledge of biology.

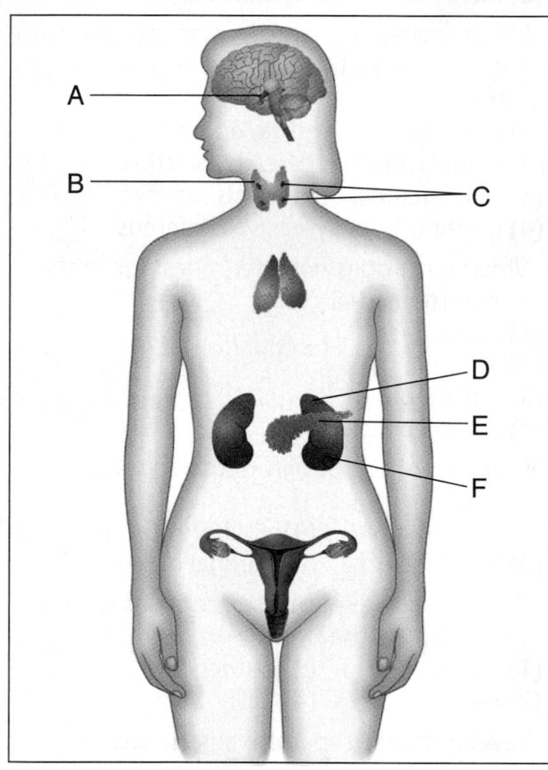

16 Which gland helps the body deal with stress?
(1) A (3) C
(2) B (4) D

17 Which gland is both an endocrine and an exocrine gland?
(1) E (3) C
(2) B (4) D

18 Which gland secretes growth hormone?
(1) A (3) E
(2) B (4) F

19 Which gland secretes thyroxine?
(1) A (3) D
(2) B (4) F

20 State *two* effects that insufficient amounts of FSH and LH will have on the menstrual cycle.

Base your answers to questions 21 and 22 on the information and graph below and on your knowledge of biology.

Levels of glucose in the blood of two people were measured repeatedly during a 5-hour period, immediately following the ingestion of a typical meal. One of the people has diabetes. The other one does not. The data are shown in the graph.

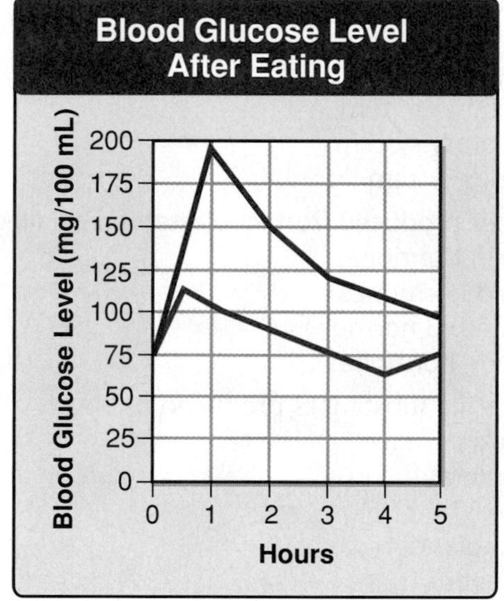

21 State which line represents a person with diabetes and which line represents a person without diabetes. Support your answer with an explanation.

22 Describe how the graph might be different if the person with diabetes had received insulin after the meal.

Base your answers to question 23 and 24 on the information below and on your knowledge of biology.

In many areas during rush hour, radio and television stations broadcast traffic reports. The reports inform the listening public where accidents and construction have interrupted normal traffic patterns so that drivers can plan their routes accordingly.

23 Explain how traffic reports are similar to hormones. What part of traffic reporting is similar to a target cell?

24 Explain how a traffic report acts as a feedback mechanism to control the flow of traffic.

25 Explain how the placenta prevents the mother's blood from mixing with the blood of the developing fetus.

26 Describe how insulin production and action differs between Type I and Type II diabetes.

27 Describe the structure of sperm.

28 Describe the path of an unfertilized egg from a follicle until it leaves the body.

29 Explain why the menstrual cycle is an example of a feedback mechanism.

30 Trace the development of a zygote from fertilization through implantation.

31 Describe gastrulation, and explain the importance of the primary germ layers.

32 Explain why some hormones can be taken orally, whereas others, such as insulin, are injected directly into the body.

Part C

Extended Response

Answer the questions or follow the directions given.

Base your answers to questions 33 through 35 on the information below and on your knowledge of biology.

Fetal Alcohol Syndrome

Pregnant women subject themselves to the same risks caused by alcohol use and abuse as the general population. In addition, they place their fetuses at risk of developing fetal alcohol syndrome, or FAS.

Although the placenta provides an effective barrier for most substances in the mother's blood, it does not keep out alcohol. Alcohol may damage the fetus and cause problems such as heart defects and facial abnormalities. Alcohol may also cause the fetus to grow and develop slowly, leading to low birth weight, small head circumference, delayed development, and mental retardation.

The fetus is particularly sensitive to the adverse effects of alcohol during the first three months of development because all the major organs and tissues are forming then. Alcohol may cause problems at other times as well. The only sure way to prevent the fetus from being harmed is to avoid alcohol throughout pregnancy.

33 Explain what causes fetal alcohol syndrome, and describe how it affects the fetus. How can it be prevented?

34 Explain why the fetus is especially sensitive to the adverse effects of alcohol during the first three months of development.

35 State one possible effect on the fetus from the use of other drugs, such as cocaine or heroine.

36 Describe the roles of the hormone FSH in changes that occur during human sexual development. In your answer, be sure to:
- identify, by name, the period of human development when sexual maturity develops
- state where FSH is produced in the body
- describe the effect of FSH on male steroid sex hormone production
- describe the effect of FSH on female steroid sex hormone production
- describe *two* specific effects of *each* of these steroid sex hormones on physical changes in sexually maturing individuals

37 There are a number of adaptations that enhance the chances of fertilization of an egg cell. Explain how each of these adaptations increase the likelihood of fertilization of an egg:
- seminal fluid production
- release of millions of sperm
- cilia lining the Fallopian tubes
- long flagella on sperm cells

For: An interactive self-test
Visit: PHSchool.com
Web Code: cba-0390

CHAPTER 40

The Immune System and Disease

White blood cells help protect the body from disease. Here, one type of white blood cell—a macrophage—engulfs a parasite (magnification: 1950×).

To find out more about the transmission of a virus, view the segment "Influenza: Tracking a Virus," on Videotape Three.

Inquiry Activity

How do diseases spread?

Procedure

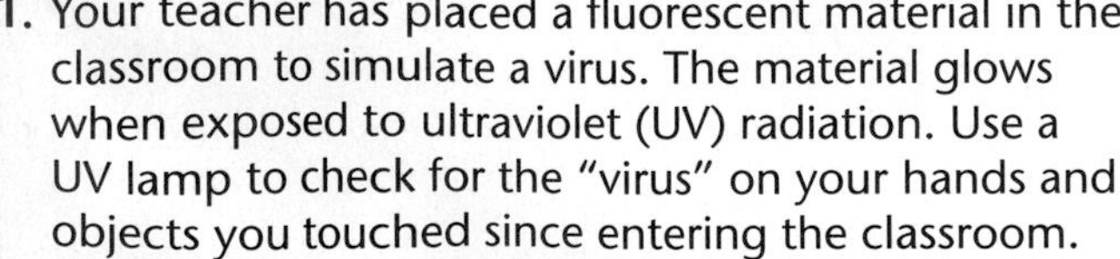

1. Your teacher has placed a fluorescent material in the classroom to simulate a virus. The material glows when exposed to ultraviolet (UV) radiation. Use a UV lamp to check for the "virus" on your hands and objects you touched since entering the classroom. **CAUTION:** *Ultraviolet light can harm your eyes. Do not look directly at the ultraviolet light.*
2. Exchange results with your classmates to determine how the "virus" spread through the classroom. Wash your hands with soap and warm water.

Think About It

1. **Inferring** What can you infer about how the "virus" spread through the classroom?
2. **Drawing Conclusions** How does thorough hand washing help prevent the spread of diseases?

40–1 Infectious Disease

4-5.2 Viruses, bacteria, fungi, and parasites
4-5.2 Causes of disease
4-5.2 Biological research of diseases
LS- Make observations; collect, organize and/or analyze data

Good health is something that you might take for granted—until you or someone close to you gets sick. Then, the value of good health becomes all too obvious. Why do you get sick? How do you get better? What is the best way for you to avoid getting sick in the first place? These are questions that people have been asking for centuries. Today, in most cases, these questions can be answered.

A **disease** is any change, other than an injury, that disrupts the normal functions of the body.  **Some diseases are produced by agents, such as bacteria, viruses, and fungi. Others are caused by materials in the environment, such as cigarette smoke. Still others, such as hemophilia, are inherited.** Disease-causing agents are called **pathogens,** which means "sickness-makers." Diseases caused by pathogens are generally called infectious diseases.

Guide for Reading

Key Concepts
- What causes disease?
- How are infectious diseases transmitted?

Vocabulary
disease
pathogen
germ theory of disease
Koch's postulates
vector
antibiotic

Reading Strategy: Using Prior Knowledge
Before you read, make a list of some of the diseases that you have had. As you read, determine which pathogen might have caused each disease.

The Germ Theory of Disease

For thousands of years, people believed that diseases were caused by curses, evil spirits, or night vapors. In the mid-nineteenth century, a new explanation was put forth based on the work of the French chemist Louis Pasteur and the German bacteriologist Robert Koch. The observations of Pasteur and Koch led them to conclude that infectious diseases were caused by microorganisms of different types, commonly called germs. This idea is now known as the **germ theory of disease.**

The world is filled with microorganisms of every shape and description. How can scientists be sure that a particular organism causes a certain disease? In 1975, Allen Steere of Yale University had a chance to ask that question. In a small area of Connecticut, Steere found 39 children and several adults suffering from pain and joint inflammation. Their symptoms looked like a rare form of childhood arthritis. However, Steere thought that there were far too many cases of arthritis for such a small population. He looked for another explanation. The rural location of the outbreak and the fact that most of the cases had started in summer or early fall made Steere suspect, at first, that this could be an infectious disease carried by an insect.

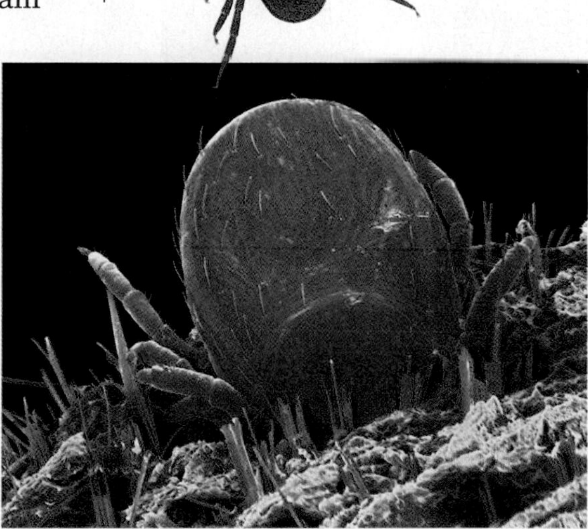

(magnification: about 30×)

Figure 40–1 **Diseases can be inherited, caused by materials in the environment, or produced by pathogens.** Certain species of ticks often carry bacteria or viruses, so their bites can transmit disease.

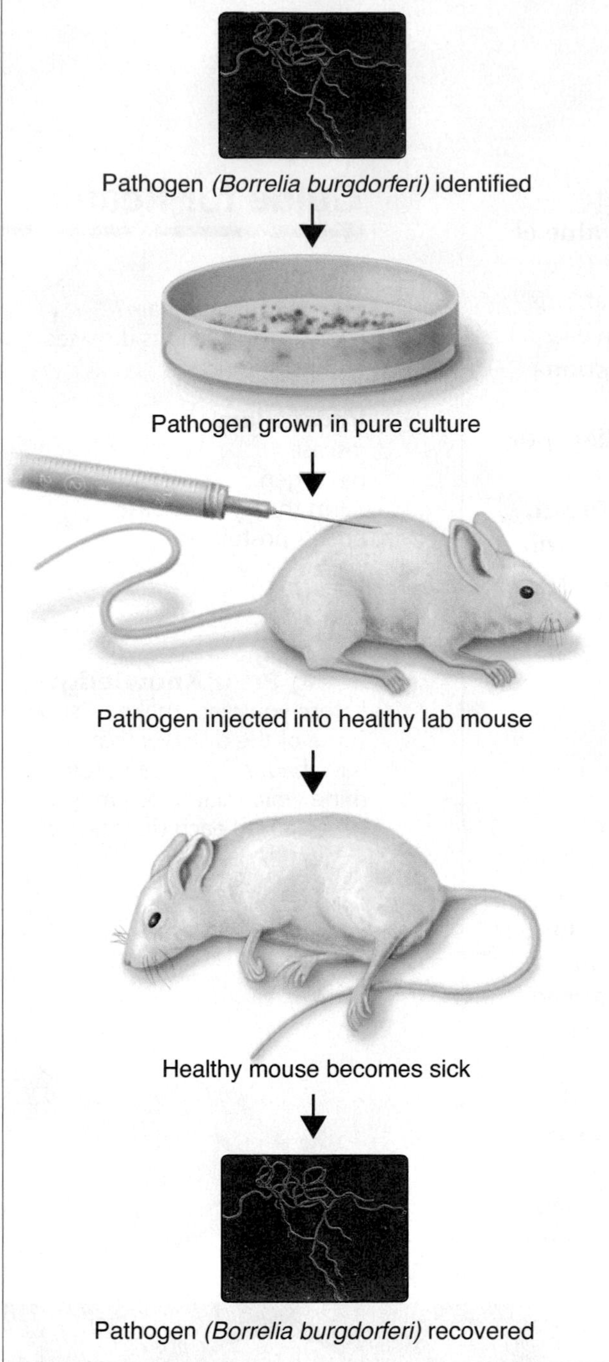
Pathogen (Borrelia burgdorferi) identified
Pathogen grown in pure culture
Pathogen injected into healthy lab mouse
Healthy mouse becomes sick
Pathogen (Borrelia burgdorferi) recovered

▲ **Figure 40–2** Allen Steere followed Koch's postulates to test his theory that the bacterium *Borrelia burgdorferi* caused Lyme disease. **Inferring** ***Why must the pathogen be grown in a pure culture?***

Sure enough, many of the children reported that their problems began with what they thought was an insect bite. The bite was followed by an expanding skin rash. Steere called the infection Lyme disease after the town of Lyme, Connecticut, where it was first discovered.

Steere and his colleagues were able to link the skin rash to the bite of the tiny deer tick *(Ixodes scapularis)*. One of Steere's colleagues, Dr. Willy Burgdorfer, found an unusual spiral-shaped bacterium *(Borrelia burgdorferi)* in the ticks. Steere found the same bacterium in patients with Lyme disease. Could this bacterium be the cause of Lyme disease?

For ethical reasons, Steere did not try to infect healthy children with the bacterium. However, when the bacterium was injected into laboratory mice, they developed arthritis and other symptoms, just as the children had. From the sick mice, Steere recovered the bacteria, which were then injected into healthy mice. The healthy mice then developed the disease. Steere and his colleagues had found the organism that caused Lyme disease. The process Steere used is shown in **Figure 40–2.**

Koch's Postulates

The groundwork for Allen Steere's work with Lyme disease was actually laid more than a hundred years earlier by Robert Koch. From his studies with various bacteria, Koch developed a series of rules still used today to identify the microorganism that causes a specific disease. These rules are known as **Koch's postulates.** Koch's postulates can be stated as follows:

1. The pathogen should always be found in the body of a sick organism and should not be found in a healthy one.
2. The pathogen must be isolated and grown in the laboratory in pure culture.
3. When the cultured pathogens are placed in a new host, they should cause the same disease that infected the original host.
4. The injected pathogen should be isolated from the second host. It should be identical to the original pathogen.

Why are these rules important? Because identifying pathogens that cause disease is the first step toward preventing or curing the ailments they produce.

Agents of Disease

For many pathogens, the human body provides just the right conditions for growth—a suitable body temperature, a watery environment, and an abundance of nutrients. The large intestine, for example, harbors dense colonies of bacteria that help in the process of digestion. Bacteria and yeast are also found in the mouth and throat. Fortunately, most of these organisms are harmless, and many are actually beneficial.

If this is true, then exactly how do pathogens cause disease? Some pathogens, including viruses and some bacteria, destroy cells as they grow. Other bacteria release toxins that harm an organism. Still others, especially parasitic worms, produce sickness when they block the flow of blood, remove nutrients from the digestive system, and disrupt other bodily functions. The *Ascaris* worm in **Figure 40–3** is a parasitic worm.

Viruses Viruses are tiny particles that invade and replicate within living cells. Viruses attach to the surface of a cell, insert their genetic material in the form of RNA or DNA, and take over many of the functions of the host cell. Viruses can infect nearly every type of organism—including plants, animals, and bacteria. Diseases caused by viruses include the common cold, influenza, smallpox, and warts.

Bacteria Most bacteria are harmless to humans. Unfortunately, the few that are pathogens cause serious diseases. Bacteria cause disease in one of two ways—either by breaking down the tissues of the infected organism for food or by releasing toxins that harm the body. Bacterial diseases include streptococcus infections, diphtheria, botulism, and anthrax.

Protists You may not associate protists with disease, but a protist causes what may be the single most damaging infectious disease afflicting humans—malaria. Malaria is caused by *Plasmodium*, a protist that is spread from person to person by mosquitoes. Insects also spread another protist known as *Trypanosoma*. *Trypanosoma* protists live in the bloodstreams of vertebrate animals. The protist feeds off the nutrients in the host organism's blood. *Trypanosoma* causes African sleeping sickness. Contaminated water supplies are responsible for amebic dysentery, a serious infection caused by the protist *Entamoeba*.

Worms Flatworms and roundworms are also responsible for a number of serious human diseases. People in many tropical regions of the world can become infected by a parasitic flatworm known as *Schistosoma*. These flatworms live part of their lives in snails and then leave the snails to enter the fresh water of streams and rice paddies. *Schistosoma* worms frequently infect people working in rice fields. Other parasitic worms that infect humans include tapeworms and hookworms.

What are three diseases caused by protists?

To see how scientists test a hypothesis about how a disease is caused and transmitted, view the segment "Hantavirus: A Tale of Mice and People," on Videotape Three.

Figure 40–3 Protists and worms often cause disease in humans and other animals. The protist *Trypanosoma* (purple objects) causes African sleeping sickness. The *Ascaris* worm matures in the intestine and causes severe malnutrition in its hosts.

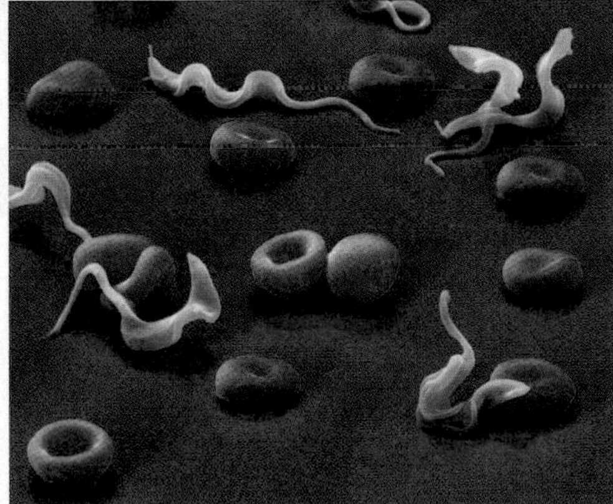

Trypanosoma Among Red Blood Cells

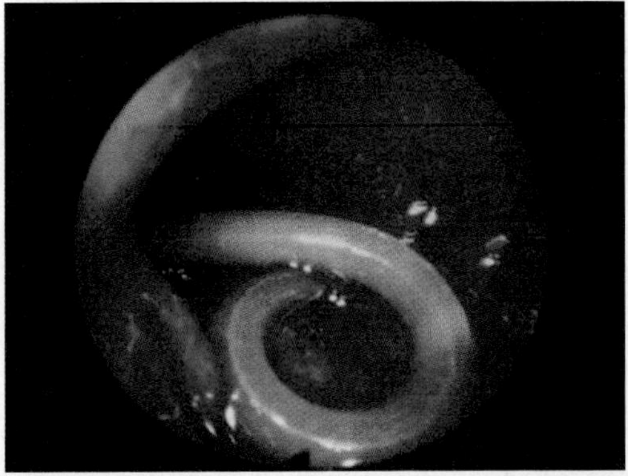

Ascaris Worm in Intestine

Fungi Most fungi are harmless, but a few are capable of causing serious problems. One genus of fungi, *Tinea,* is particularly adept at penetrating the outer layers of skin. When it attacks the skin between the toes it produces the infection known as athlete's foot. The same fungus can infect the scalp, where it results in rough, scaly patches known as ringworm. Other types of fungi infect the mouth, the throat, and even the fingernails and toenails.

How Diseases Are Spread

Infectious diseases can be transmitted in a number of ways. **Some infectious diseases are spread from one person to another through coughing, sneezing, or physical contact. Other infectious diseases are spread through contaminated water or food. Still others are spread by infected animals.**

Physical Contact Some infectious diseases can be spread by direct physical contact. For example, a disease may be transmitted when a healthy person touches a person with a disease. Some of the most dangerous pathogens are spread from one person to another by sexual contact.

Most diseases are spread by indirect contact. For example, some pathogens can be carried through the air. If a person with a cold or virus coughs or sneezes, thousands of droplets are released, as shown in **Figure 40–4.** The pathogens can also settle on objects. If you touch those objects, the pathogens can be transferred to your hands, and you can infect yourself by touching your mouth or nose.

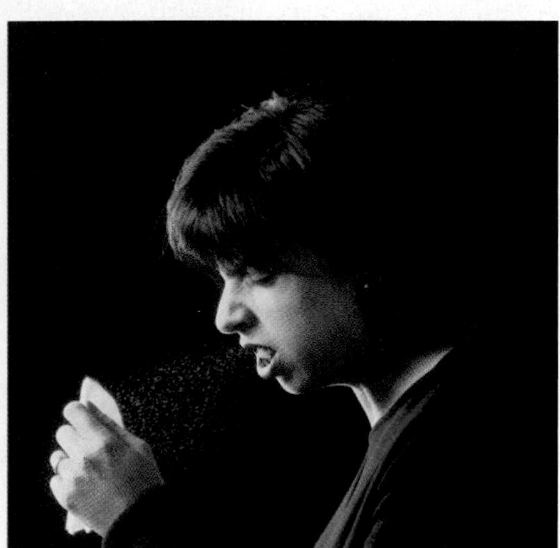

▲ **Figure 40–4** **Some infectious diseases are spread from person to person by sneezing.** Thousands of pathogen particles can be released by a sneeze.

Some behaviors can help to control transmission of diseases spread by physical contact. Simple measures, such as covering your mouth with a tissue when you cough, can limit the spread of infection. Washing your hands thoroughly and often also helps to prevent the spread of many pathogens.

Contaminated Food and Water Have you ever had food poisoning? Food poisoning is caused by eating food that contains pathogens. Bacteria are always present in uncooked meat. Bacteria also grow quickly in warm, partially cooked food. If food is cooked thoroughly, the risk of food poisoning due to contamination may be reduced. Contaminated water also causes disease, especially in parts of the world with poor sanitation and untreated sewage.

Infected Animals Animals, such as the mosquito shown in **Figure 40–5,** also spread infectious disease. Animals that carry pathogens from person to person are called **vectors.** Malaria, Lyme disease, West Nile virus, and rabies are diseases carried by vectors. Avoiding tall grass and wooded areas where deer and field mice dwell will limit your exposure to ticks that carry Lyme disease. Staying away from wild animals can reduce your risk of being bitten by a rabid animal.

Fighting Infectious Diseases

Because prevention isn't always possible, drugs have been developed for use against some types of pathogens. Antibiotics are perhaps the most useful single class of infection-fighting drugs. **Antibiotics** are compounds that kill bacteria without harming the cells of the human or animal hosts. Antibiotics work by interfering with the cellular processes of microorganisms.

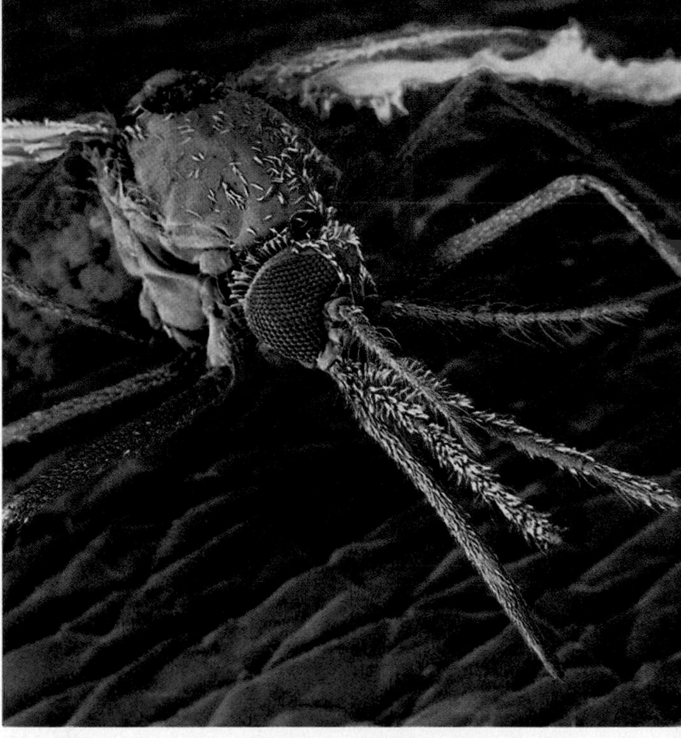

▲ **Figure 40–5** **Some infectious diseases are spread by insects.** This *Anopheles* mosquito may be a carrier of the protist that causes malaria.

Discovery of Antibiotics Many antibiotics are produced naturally by living organisms. Other antibiotics are synthetic. One antibiotic, penicillin, was discovered accidentally in 1928 by the Scottish bacteriologist Alexander Fleming. Fleming had been growing *Staphylococcus* bacteria in a culture dish. One day, he noticed that the culture of bacteria had been contaminated by a species of green mold called *Penicillium notatum.* On closer observation, Fleming saw something surprising. The bacteria were not growing near the mold. Something produced by the mold was apparently inhibiting their growth. Later, researchers discovered that penicillin—the name Fleming gave the antibiotic—interferes with the growth of bacteria.

Antibiotics have no effect on viruses. However, antiviral drugs have been developed to fight certain viral diseases. These drugs generally inhibit the ability of viruses to invade cells and to multiply once inside cells.

Over-the-Counter Drugs You probably know that you can buy many medicines without a prescription. These medicines, called over-the-counter drugs, treat only the symptoms of the disease—including cough, congestion, and fever. These medicines help you feel better, but they do not actually treat the cause of the infection. The best treatment for most infections includes rest, a well-balanced diet, and plenty of fluids.

40–1 Section Assessment

1. **Key Concept** Describe some of the causes of disease.
2. **Key Concept** What are the ways in which infectious diseases are spread?
3. How do vectors spread disease?
4. What are antibiotics?
5. **Critical Thinking Inferring** Why did Koch require all four steps in determining the cause of an infectious disease? Could you eliminate one of the steps? Explain your answer.

Writing in Science

Descriptive Writing
Describe how Allen Steere used Koch's postulates to discover the cause of Lyme disease. You may want to start by listing the postulates in one column of a table and, in another column, listing the steps used by Steere.

40–2 The Immune System

4-5.2 White blood cells
4-5.2 The immune system protects against antigens
4-5.2 Vaccinations stimulate the immune system

Guide for Reading

Key Concepts
- What is the function of the immune system?
- What are the body's nonspecific defenses against invading pathogens?

Vocabulary
immunity
inflammatory response
fever
interferon
immune response
antigen
humoral immunity
cell-mediated immunity
antibody
vaccination
active immunity
passive immunity

Reading Strategy: Finding Main Ideas Before you read, skim the section to identify the key ideas. Then, carefully read the section, making a list of supporting details for each main idea.

With pathogens all around us, it might seem like a miracle that you aren't sick all of the time. There's a reason, of course, why most of us enjoy good health. Our bodies have a protective system—a series of defenses that guard against disease.

The immune system is the body's main defense against pathogens. The immune system recognizes, attacks, destroys, and "remembers" each type of pathogen that enters the body. It does this by producing specialized cells that inactivate pathogens. For each kind of pathogen, the immune system produces cells that are specific to that pathogen. **The function of the immune system is to fight infection through the production of cells that inactivate foreign substances or cells.** This process is called **immunity.**

The immune system includes two general categories of defense mechanisms against infection: nonspecific defenses and specific defenses. Nonspecific defenses are like the fortress walls of the system. They guard against infections by keeping most things out of the body. Specific defenses work like security guards. They track down harmful pathogens that have managed to break through the body's nonspecific defenses.

Nonspecific Defenses

Nonspecific defenses do not discriminate between one threat and another. These defenses include physical and chemical barriers.

First Line of Defense The function of the first line of defense is to keep pathogens out of the body. This role is carried out by skin, mucus, sweat, and tears. **Your body's most important nonspecific defense is the skin.** Very few pathogens can penetrate the layers of dead cells at the skin's surface. The importance of the skin as a barrier against infection becomes obvious as soon as the skin is broken. When that happens, pathogens can enter your body and multiply. As they grow, they cause the symptoms of an infection, such as swelling, redness, and pain.

Many secretions of the body, including mucus, saliva, and tears, contain lysozyme, an enzyme that breaks down the cell walls of many bacteria. In addition, oil and sweat glands in the skin produce an acidic environment that kills many bacteria.

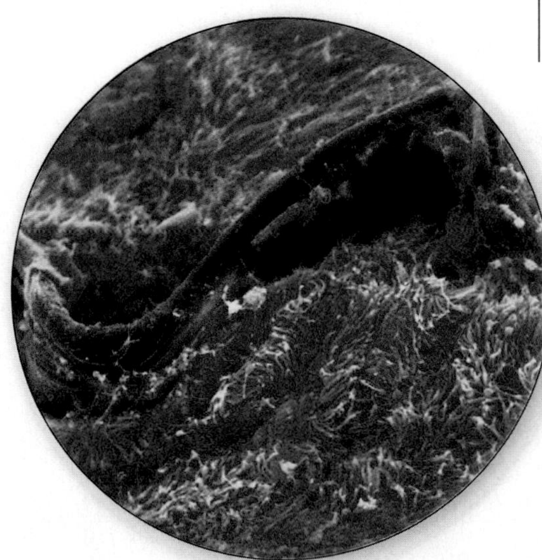

(magnification: 1100×)

Figure 40–6 **The immune system fights infection.** The production of mucus is one of your body's defenses. Pathogens can get trapped in mucus the way the long brown strand of dirt shown in the micrograph is trapped.

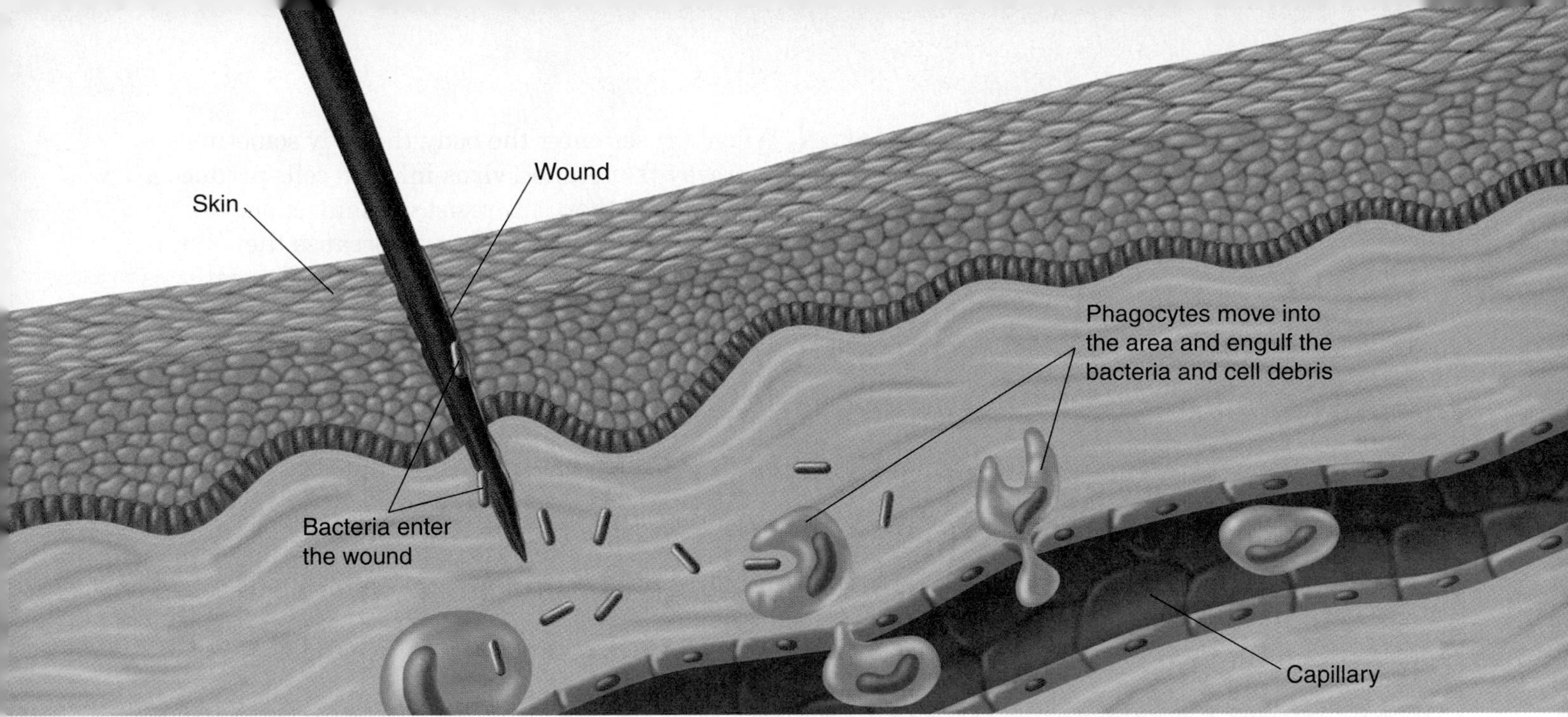
Skin
Wound
Phagocytes move into the area and engulf the bacteria and cell debris
Bacteria enter the wound
Capillary

▲ **Figure 40–7** **The inflammatory response is a nonspecific defense reaction to tissue damage caused by injury or infection.** When pathogens enter the body, phagocytes move into the area and engulf the pathogens. In addition, platelets and clotting factors leak from the capillaries.

Pathogens can also enter your body through other body openings, including your mouth and nose. Your body has other nonspecific defenses that protect these openings. Mucus in your nose and throat helps to trap pathogens. The cilia that line your nose and throat help to push pathogens away from your lungs. Stomach acid and digestive enzymes destroy many pathogens that make their way to your stomach.

Second Line of Defense If pathogens do manage to enter your body, they may multiply quickly, releasing toxins into your tissues. When this happens, the **inflammatory response**—a second line of defense—is activated. **The inflammatory response is a nonspecific defense reaction to tissue damage caused by injury or infection.** When pathogens are detected, the immune system produces millions of white blood cells, which fight the infection. Blood vessels near the wound expand, and white blood cells move from the vessels to enter the infected tissues. Many of these white blood cells are phagocytes, which engulf and destroy bacteria. The infected tissue may become swollen and painful. The inflammatory response is summarized in **Figure 40–7.**

The immune system also releases chemicals that increase the core body temperature. You may have experienced this elevated body temperature, called a **fever.** The increased body temperature is advantageous because many pathogens can survive only within a narrow temperature range. An elevated temperature slows down or stops the growth of such pathogens. The higher body temperature also increases the heart rate so that the white blood cells get to the site of infection faster. Physicians know that a fever and an increased number of white blood cells are two indications that the body is hard at work fighting infection.

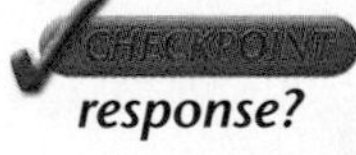
CHECKPOINT
What is the role of phagocytes in the inflammatory response?

Word Origins

Phagocyte comes from the Greek *phag,* meaning "eat," and *kutos,* meaning "cell." Thus, a phagocyte is a cell that eats or engulfs. **If the Greek prefix *macro-* means "large," what might the word *macrophage* mean?**

Interferon When viruses enter the body, the body sometimes reacts in a different way. Sometimes, virus-infected cells produce a group of proteins that help other cells resist viral infection. Scientists named these proteins **interferons** because they "interfere" with the growth of the virus. Interferons inhibit the synthesis of viral proteins in infected cells and help block viral replication. This process slows down the progress of infection and often gives the specific defenses of the immune system time to respond.

Specific Defenses

If a pathogen is able to get past the body's nonspecific defenses, the immune system reacts with a series of specific defenses that attack the particular disease-causing agent. These defenses are called the **immune response.** A substance that triggers this response is known as an **antigen.** Viruses, bacteria, and other pathogens may serve as antigens.

The cells of the immune system that recognize specific antigens are two types of lymphocytes: B lymphocytes (B cells) and T lymphocytes (T cells). B cells provide immunity against antigens and pathogens in the body fluids. This process is called **humoral immunity.** T cells provide a defense against abnormal cells and pathogens inside living cells. This process is called **cell-mediated immunity.**

Humoral Immunity When a pathogen invades the body, its antigens are recognized by a small fraction of the body's B cells. These B cells grow and divide rapidly, producing large numbers of plasma cells and memory B cells.

Plasma cells release antibodies. **Antibodies** are proteins that recognize and bind to antigens. The antibodies are carried in the bloodstream to attack the pathogen that is causing the infection. As the antibodies overcome the infection, the plasma cells die out and stop producing antibodies.

Once the body has been exposed to a pathogen, millions of memory B cells remain capable of producing antibodies specific to that pathogen. These memory B cells greatly reduce the chance that the disease could develop a second time. If the same antigen enters the body a second time, a secondary response occurs. The memory B cells divide rapidly, forming new plasma cells. The plasma cells produce the specific antibodies needed to destroy the pathogen.

▼ **Figure 40–8** An antibody molecule has two identical antigen-binding sites. It is at these sites that one or two specific antigens bind to the antibody. **Applying Concepts** *How do antibodies help in the immune response?*

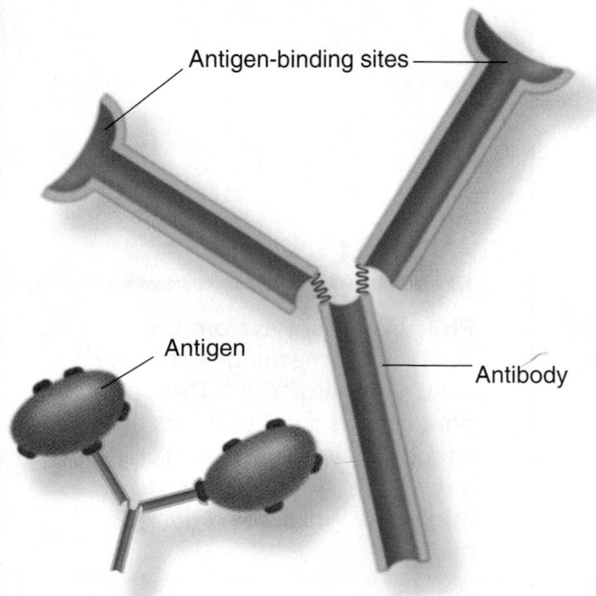

Antibody Structure As shown in **Figure 40–8,** an antibody is shaped like the letter Y and has two identical antigen-binding sites. Small differences in the amino acids affect the shapes of the binding sites. The shape of the binding site makes it possible for the antibody to recognize a specific antigen with a complementary shape. The different shapes give antibodies the ability to recognize a large variety of antigens. It is estimated that a healthy adult can produce about 100 million different types of antibodies.

FIGURE 40–9 HUMORAL IMMUNITY

Once the body has been exposed to a pathogen, it remains capable of producing specific antibodies to that pathogen. The reaction to a second infection by the same pathogen is much faster.

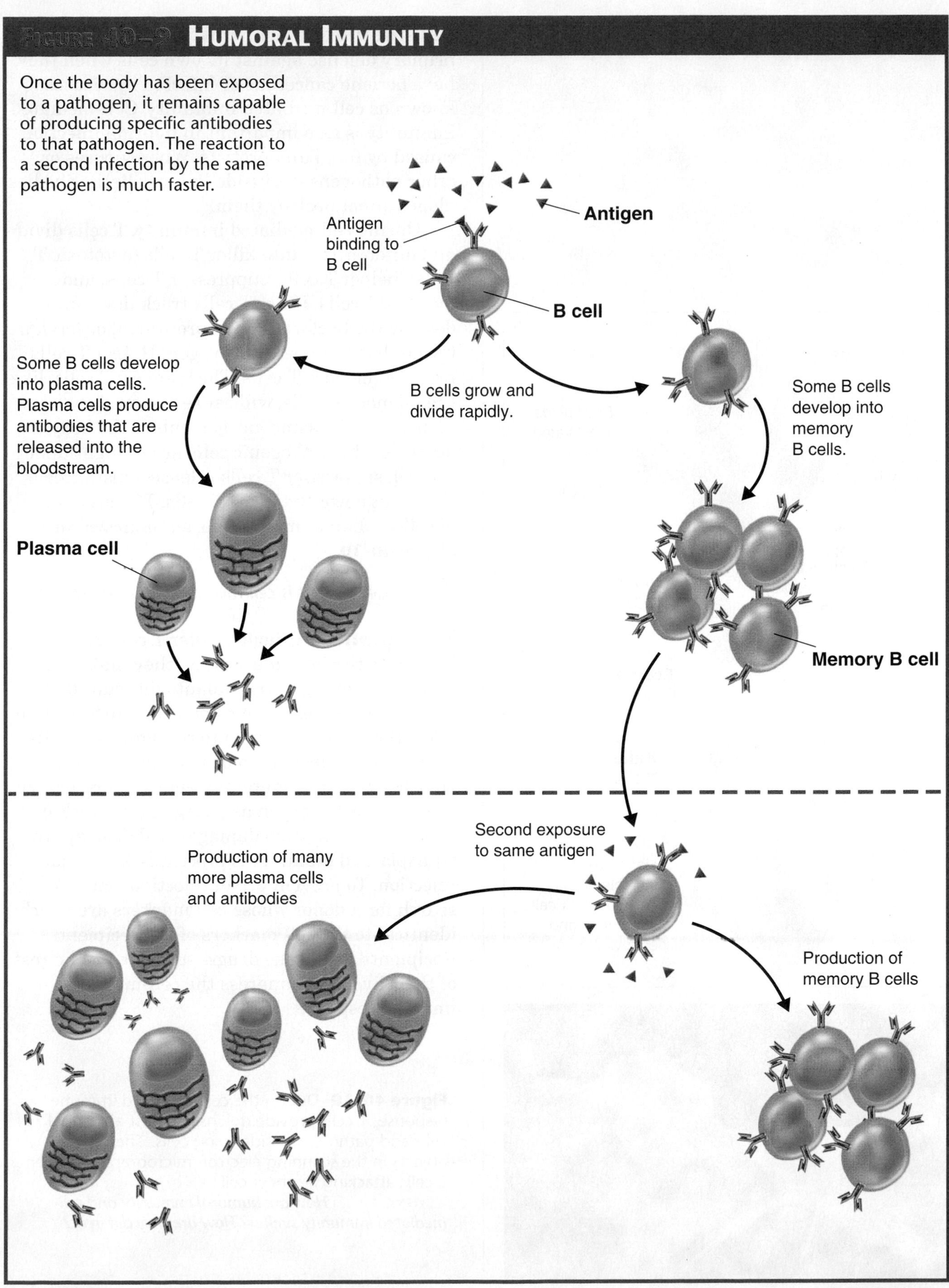

Antigen
Antigen binding to B cell
B cell
B cells grow and divide rapidly.
Some B cells develop into plasma cells. Plasma cells produce antibodies that are released into the bloodstream.
Some B cells develop into memory B cells.
Plasma cell
Memory B cell
Second exposure to same antigen
Production of many more plasma cells and antibodies
Production of memory B cells

Cell-Mediated Immunity

The body's primary defense against its own cells when they have become cancerous or infected by viruses is known as cell-mediated immunity. Cell-mediated immunity is also important in fighting infection caused by fungi and protists. When viruses or other pathogens get inside living cells, antibodies alone cannot destroy them.

During cell-mediated immunity, T cells divide and differentiate into killer T cells (cytotoxic T cells), helper T cells, suppressor T cells, and memory T cells. Killer T cells track down and destroy the bacteria, fungi, protozoan, or foreign tissue that contains the antigen. Helper T cells produce memory T cells. The memory T cells, like the memory B cells, will cause a secondary response if the same antigen enters the body again. As the pathogenic cells are brought under control, suppressor T cells release substances that shut down the killer T cells. The process of cell-mediated immunity is summarized in **Figure 40–10**.

CHECKPOINT *What is cell-mediated immunity?*

Transplants

Although killer T cells are helpful in the immune system, they make the acceptance of organ transplants difficult. Body cells have marker proteins on their surfaces that allow the immune system to recognize the cells. If an organ was going to be transplanted into your body, your immune system would recognize the transported organ as foreign and attack it. Your immune system damages and destroys the transplanted organ. This process is known as rejection. To prevent organ rejection, doctors search for a donor whose cell markers are nearly identical to the cell markers of the recipient. Recipients must take drugs—usually for the rest of their lives—to suppress the cell-mediated immune response.

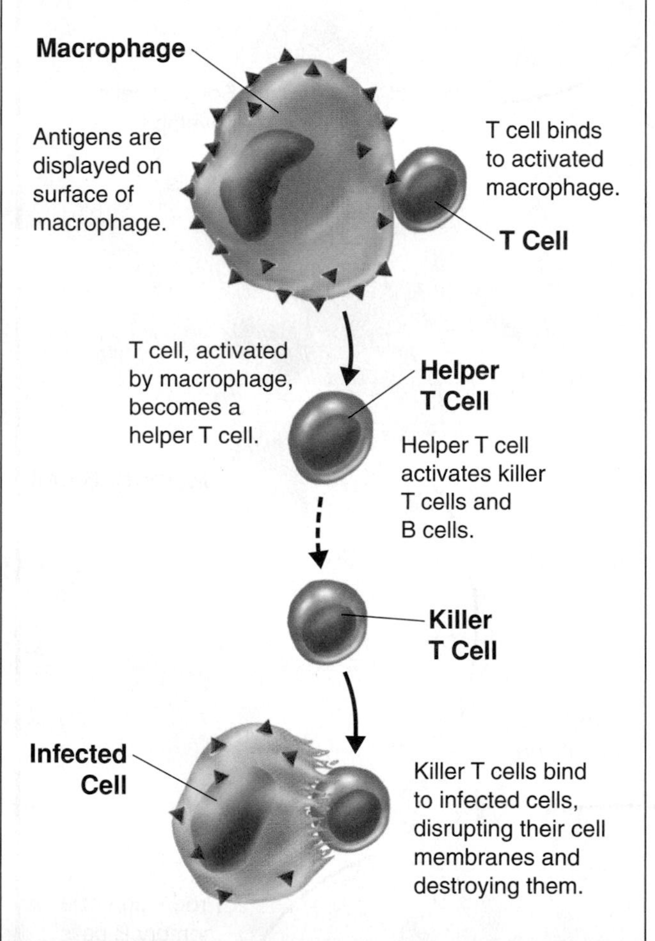
Macrophage
Antigens are displayed on surface of macrophage.
T cell binds to activated macrophage.
T Cell
T cell, activated by macrophage, becomes a helper T cell.
Helper T Cell
Helper T cell activates killer T cells and B cells.
Killer T Cell
Infected Cell
Killer T cells bind to infected cells, disrupting their cell membranes and destroying them.

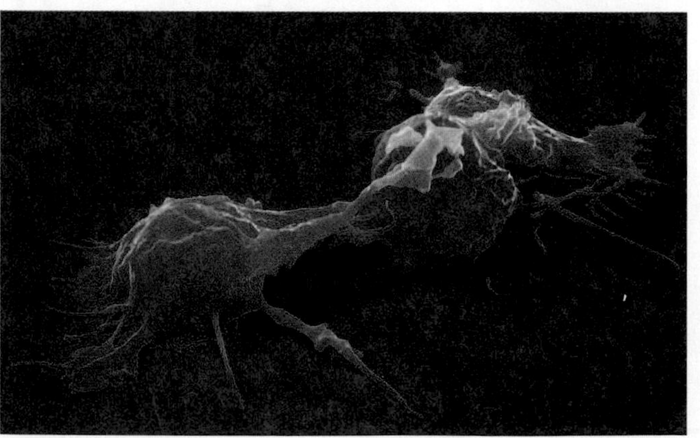

Figure 40–10 During the cell-mediated immune response, T cells provide defense against abnormal cells and pathogens inside living cells. The yellow objects in the scanning electron micrograph are killer T cells attacking a cancer cell. **Comparing and Contrasting** *How are humoral immunity and cell-mediated immunity similar? How are they different?*

Quick Lab

How does cell-mediated immunity work?

Materials 3 red balloons; 3 yellow balloons; 3 light-blue balloons; red, purple, and light-blue adhesive notes; toothpick

Procedure

1. Partially inflate and tie the balloons. The balloons represent pathogens. The different colors represent different surface antigens. Put the inflated balloons on the table.
2. The adhesive notes represent antibodies that can bind to antigens on the surface of a pathogen of the same color. Use the adhesive notes to model the binding of antibodies to antigens on pathogens.
3. The toothpick represents a killer T cell. Use the toothpick to burst any balloons marked by adhesive notes.

Analyze and Conclude

1. **Using Models** How did you model the binding of antibodies to matching antigens in step 2?
2. **Using Models** What signals a killer T cell to attack a pathogen?
3. **Using Models** What do the yellow balloons and purple adhesive notes represent in the model?

Acquired Immunity

More than 200 years ago, the English physician Edward Jenner wondered if it might be possible to produce immunity against one of the deadliest diseases of the day—smallpox. Jenner knew that a mild disease called cowpox was often contracted by milkmaids. Jenner observed that the milkmaids who contracted cowpox developed an immunity to smallpox. Was there a way, he wondered, to deliberately infect people with cowpox and thus protect them from getting the more serious disease of smallpox?

To answer this question, Jenner took fluid from one of the sores of a cowpox patient and put the fluid into a small cut that he made on the arm of a young farm boy named Jamie Phipps. As expected, Jamie developed a mild cowpox infection. Two months later, Jenner performed a daring experiment. He injected Jamie with fluid from a smallpox infection. Fortunately for Jamie, the experiment was a success—the boy did not develop smallpox. His cowpox infection had made him immune to smallpox.

Active Immunity The injection of a weakened form of a pathogen to produce immunity is known as a **vaccination.** *Vacca* is the Latin word for "cow," reflecting the history of Jenner's first vaccination experiment. Today, more than 20 serious human diseases can be prevented by vaccination. Like early vaccines, modern vaccines stimulate the immune system to create millions of plasma cells ready to produce specific types of antibodies.

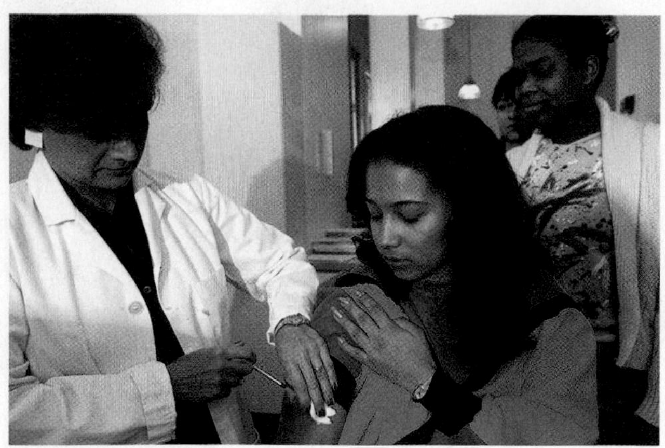

▲ **Figure 40–11** Vaccines stimulate the immune system to produce plasma cells. **Applying Concepts** *What type of immunity do vaccines produce?*

The type of immunity produced by the body's reaction to a vaccine is known as **active immunity.** Active immunity appears after exposure to an antigen, as a result of the immune response. Active immunity may develop as a result of natural exposure to an antigen (fighting an infection) or from deliberate exposure to the antigen (through a vaccine).

Passive Immunity In active immunity, the body makes its own antibodies in response to an antigen. The body can also be temporarily protected from disease in another way. If antibodies produced by other animals against a pathogen are injected into the bloodstream, the antibodies produce a **passive immunity** against the pathogen. Passive immunity lasts only a short time because eventually the body destroys the foreign antibodies.

Like active immunity, passive immunity can develop naturally or by deliberate exposure. One kind of natural immunity occurs when antibodies produced by the mother are passed to the fetus during development (across the placenta) or in early infancy through breast milk. This immunity protects a child against most infectious diseases for the first few months of its life, or longer if the infant is breast-fed.

Sometimes, antibodies are administered to fight infection or prevent disease. For example, travelers to certain regions of the world are given vaccines before leaving home. These vaccines may contain antibodies against tropical diseases, such as malaria. People who have been bitten by rabid animals are injected with antibodies that attack the rabies virus. This is another example of passive immunization.

40–2 Section Assessment

1. **Key Concept** Describe the body's nonspecific defenses against pathogens.
2. **Key Concept** Describe the function of the immune system.
3. How do interferons protect the body against viruses?
4. How are antigens related to antibodies?
5. **Critical Thinking Comparing and Contrasting** How are active and passive immunity similar? How are they different?

You & Your Community

Conducting a Debate
Getting vaccinated is much safer than getting the disease that the vaccine prevents. However, like any drug, vaccines are capable of causing serious problems. Interview five people about their thoughts on vaccinations. As a class, arrange a debate that addresses both the benefits and risks of vaccinations.

40–3 Immune System Disorders

4-1.2 Humans have complex systems
4-5.2 The AIDS virus damages the immune system
4-5.2 Allergic reactions

Although the immune system defends the body from a wide range of pathogens, sometimes disorders occur in the immune system itself. There are three different types of disorders. These disorders include allergies, autoimmune diseases, and immunodeficiency diseases.

Guide for Reading

Key Concepts
- What is an autoimmune disease?
- How can AIDS be prevented?

Vocabulary
allergy
histamine
asthma

Reading Strategy: Using Prior Knowledge Do you or someone you know have allergies? As you read this section, use what you learn to explain the causes and symptoms of allergies.

Allergies

The most common overreactions of the immune system to antigens are known as **allergies.** Common allergies include those to pollen, dust, mold, and bee stings. Antigens that cause allergic reactions are called allergens. Some common allergens are shown in **Figure 40–12.**

When allergy-causing antigens enter the body, they attach themselves to mast cells. Mast cells are specialized immune system cells that initiate the inflammatory response. The activated mast cells release chemicals known as **histamines.** Histamines increase the flow of blood and fluids to the surrounding area. They also increase mucus production in the respiratory system. The increased mucus production brings on the sneezing, watery eyes, runny nose, and other irritations that make a person with allergies so uncomfortable. If you have allergies, you may have taken *anti*histamines. Antihistamines are drugs that are used to counteract the effects of histamines.

Figure 40–12 Common allergens include ragweed pollen, dust, and dust mites. In the SEM of the dust ball, notice the insect parts, gray spider webbing, and other dirt. Dust mites live in furniture, mattresses, and even pillows. **Inferring** *Why do you think it is recommended that people wash their bed coverings in hot water?*

Ragweed Pollen (magnification: 770×)

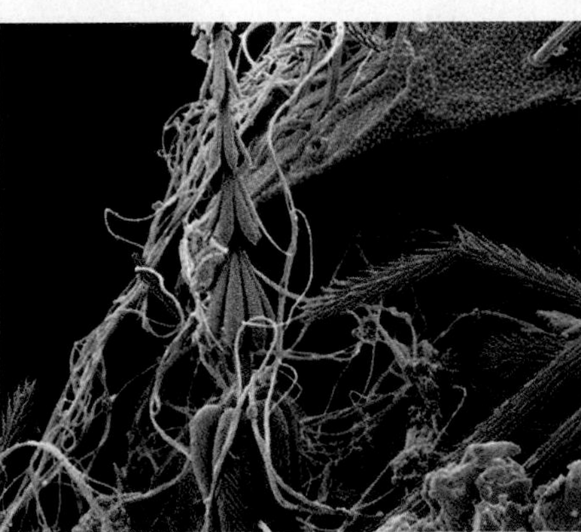

Dust Ball (magnification: 760×)

Dust Mite (magnification: 900×)

Asthma

Some allergic reactions can create a dangerous condition called asthma. **Asthma** is a chronic respiratory disease in which the air passages become narrower than normal. This narrowing of the air passages causes wheezing, coughing, and difficulty in breathing. Many factors, including both heredity and environment, play a role in the onset of the symptoms of asthma.

Asthma is a leading cause of serious illness among children, and can be a life-threatening disease. If treatment is not started early enough or if medications are not taken properly, asthma can lead to permanent damage or destruction of lung tissue.

Asthma attacks can be triggered by respiratory infections, exercise, emotional stress, and certain medications. Other triggers include cold air, pollen, dust, tobacco smoke, pollution, molds, and pet dander.

There is no cure for asthma; however, people who have asthma can sometimes control the condition. If the attacks are caused by an allergy, a series of tests can identify what substances cause the problem. Medications are sometimes used to relieve the symptoms of asthma. Often, these medications relax the smooth muscles around the airways, making breathing easier.

CHECKPOINT *What happens in the lungs during an asthma attack?*

Autoimmune Diseases

The immune system could not defend your body against a host of invading pathogens unless it was able to distinguish those pathogens from the cells and tissues that are part of your body. In other words, the immune system usually has the ability to distinguish "self" from "nonself." **When the immune system makes a mistake and attacks the body's own cells, it produces an autoimmune disease.** In an autoimmune disease, the immune system produces "antiself" antibodies.

Some examples of autoimmune diseases include Type I diabetes, rheumatoid arthritis, myasthenia gravis, and multiple sclerosis (MS). In Type I diabetes, antibodies attack the insulin-producing cells of the pancreas. In rheumatoid arthritis, antibodies attack connective tissues around the joints. In myasthenia gravis, antibodies attack neuromuscular junctions. Multiple sclerosis is an autoimmune disease in which antibodies destroy the functions of the neurons in the brain and spinal cord.

Some autoimmune diseases are treated with medications that alleviate specific symptoms. For example, people who have Type I diabetes can be given insulin injections. Other autoimmune diseases are treated with medications that suppress the immune response. However, these medications also affect the normal immune response against pathogens, so this type of therapy is not used often or is carefully monitored. As researchers find out more about autoimmune diseases, they hope to develop more effective treatments.

▼ **Figure 40–13 When the immune system makes a mistake and attacks the body's own cells, it produces an autoimmune disease.** Multiple sclerosis is one example of an autoimmune disease in which axons in the optic nerve, brain, or spinal cord are affected. Symptoms of multiple sclerosis include problems with balance and motor coordination.

AIDS, an Immunodeficiency Disease

Another type of immune system disorder is immunodeficiency disease. In one type of immunodeficiency disease, the immune system fails to develop normally. A second type of immunodeficiency disease is AIDS. AIDS results from a viral infection that destroys helper T cells. As the number of helper T cells declines, the normal immune response breaks down.

During the late 1970s, some physicians in Europe and the United States were bewildered. Some of their patients were dying from infections produced by microorganisms that didn't normally cause disease. Previously healthy people began to suffer from unusual illnesses such as *Pneumocystis carinii* (a kind of pneumonia), Kaposi's sarcoma (a rare form of skin cancer), and severe fungal infections of the mouth and throat. Normally, such infections are prevented by the immune system. Individual doctors realized that the symptoms were a signal that the immune systems of their patients had been weakened.

Some doctors recognized that these illnesses were actually symptoms of a new disease. Doctors in Los Angeles suggested the name AIDS—for acquired immune deficiency syndrome. As more cases appeared, researchers realized that this "syndrome" was actually an infectious disease caused by a pathogen that was unknown to the scientific community.

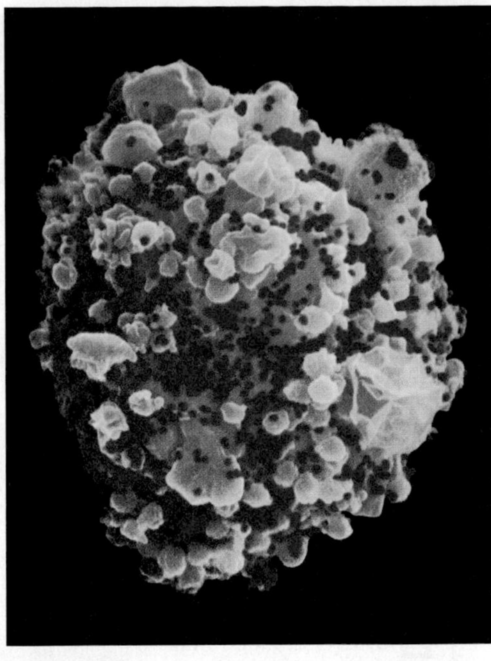

(magnification: about 5000×)

▲ **Figure 40–14** HIV is an example of a retrovirus, which contains RNA as its genetic material. Retroviruses get their name because their genetic information is first copied backward from RNA to DNA. **Interpreting Graphics** *In the micrograph, what type of blood cell are the red HIV particles attacking?*

The Virus That Causes AIDS In 1983, researchers identified the cause of AIDS—a virus that they named HIV for human immunodeficiency virus. HIV is a retrovirus—a virus that carries its genetic information in RNA, rather than DNA. HIV turned out to be a deadly and efficient virus for two reasons. First, HIV evades the defenses of the immune system. Second, HIV attacks key cells in the immune system, destroying the body's defenses and leaving the body with no protection against other pathogens.

Among HIV's main targets are the helper T cells. When the HIV virus attacks a helper T cell, it attaches to receptor molecules on the cell membrane. This allows the virus to enter the cell, as shown in **Figure 40–14.** Once the viral core is inside the cell, it forces the host cell to make DNA copies of the virus's RNA. Some of those copies insert themselves into host cell DNA and stay there permanently. Other copies remain in the cytoplasm. The viral DNA may remain inactive in the host cell for varying periods of time. When activated, it directs the production of viral RNA and proteins that are assembled into new virus particles. These viruses eventually leave the infected cell and infect new cells. The immune system produces antibodies for HIV. Unfortunately, these antibodies are not effective in stopping the progression of the disease.

Despite the production of antibodies, HIV destroys ever-increasing numbers of T cells, crippling the immune system. By counting the number of the helper T cells, the progression of HIV infection can be monitored. The fewer helper T cells, the more advanced the disease.

Figure 40–15 HIV Infection

HIV travels through the bloodstream, where it binds to receptors on helper T cells. Once inside the cell, the virus directs the cell to produce many new viruses. These new viruses are quickly released back into the bloodstream, where they travel to new cells and destroy them.

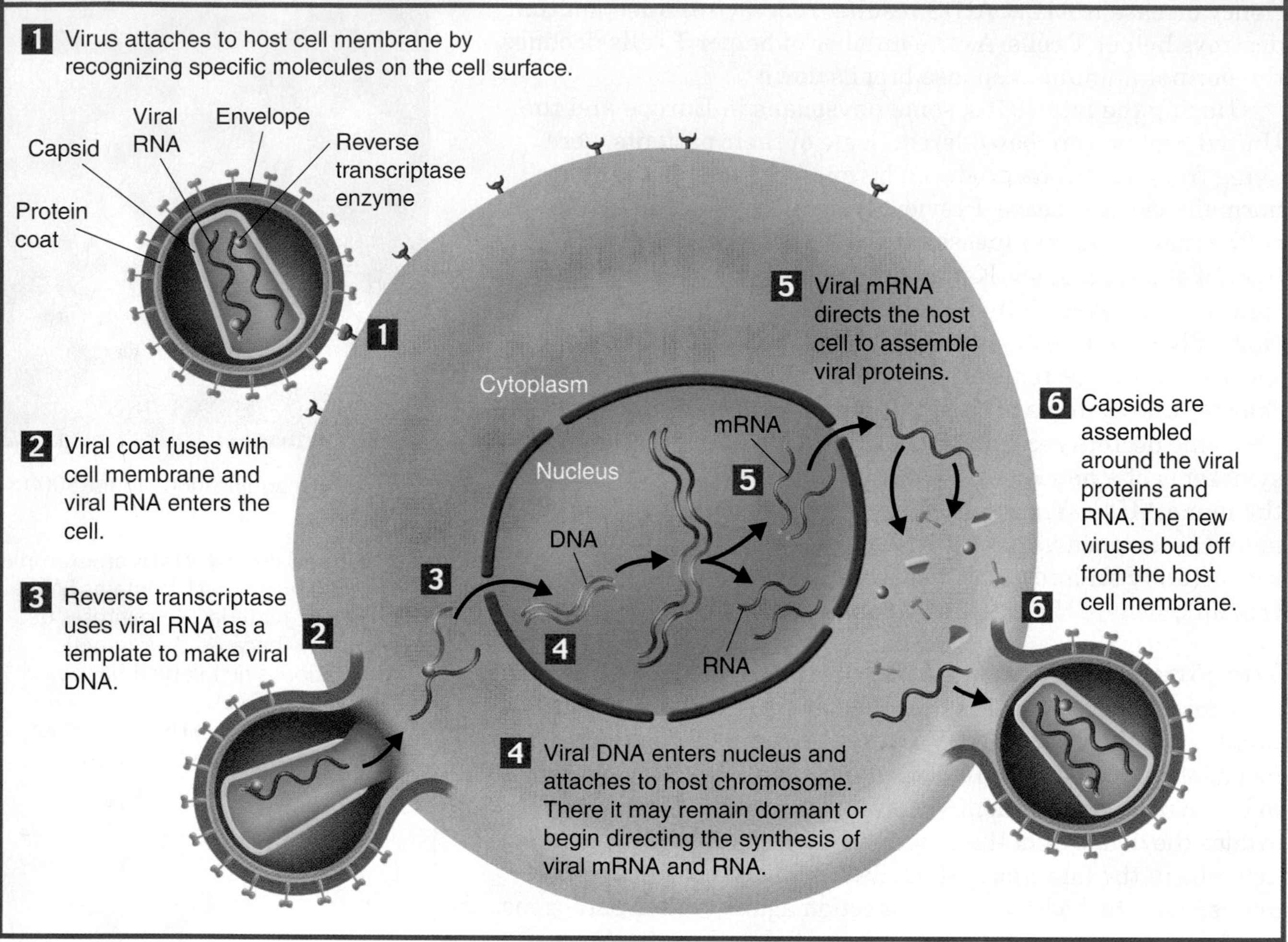

1 Virus attaches to host cell membrane by recognizing specific molecules on the cell surface.
Viral RNA
Envelope
Capsid
Reverse transcriptase enzyme
Protein coat
1
5 Viral mRNA directs the host cell to assemble viral proteins.
Cytoplasm
6 Capsids are assembled around the viral proteins and RNA. The new viruses bud off from the host cell membrane.
mRNA
2 Viral coat fuses with cell membrane and viral RNA enters the cell.
Nucleus
5
DNA
3 Reverse transcriptase uses viral RNA as a template to make viral DNA.
3
6
2
4
RNA
4 Viral DNA enters nucleus and attaches to host chromosome. There it may remain dormant or begin directing the synthesis of viral mRNA and RNA.

As the number of helper T cells decreases, the body becomes more and more susceptible to other diseases. The diseases that attack a person with a weakened immune system are called opportunistic diseases.

Transmission of HIV Although HIV is a deadly disease, it is not easily transmitted. It is not transmitted through casual contact. HIV can only be transmitted through the exchange of blood, semen, vaginal secretions, or breast milk.

There are four main ways that HIV can be transmitted:

- through any form of sexual intercourse with an infected person;
- through shared needles or syringes that are contaminated with the blood of an infected person;
- through contact with blood or blood products of an infected person; and
- from an infected mother to child, either during pregnancy, during birth, or during breast-feeding.

Preventing HIV Infection Fortunately you can choose behaviors that will help you reduce your risk of becoming infected with HIV. **The only no-risk behavior with respect to HIV and AIDS is abstinence.** Within a committed sexual relationship such as marriage, sexual fidelity between two uninfected partners presents the least risk of becoming infected with HIV.

Avoiding drug use is also important for reducing the risk of HIV infection. People who share contaminated needles to inject themselves with drugs are at a high risk for contracting HIV. People who have sex with drug abusers are also at high risk.

Before 1985, HIV was transmitted to some hemophiliacs and surgical patients through transfusions of infected blood or blood products. Such cases have been nearly eliminated by screening the blood supply for HIV antibodies and by discouraging potentially infected individuals from donating blood.

Can AIDS Be Cured? At present, there is no cure for AIDS. However, progress has been made in developing drugs that make it possible to survive HIV infection for years. Unfortunately, HIV mutates and evolves very rapidly. For this reason, the virus has been able to evolve into many different strains that are resistant to virtually all drugs used against them. Because HIV evolves so rapidly, no one has developed a vaccine that offers protection for any length of time.

At present, the only way to control the virus is to use expensive multidrug and multivitamin "cocktails" that fight the virus in several ways. Thanks to these drugs, more HIV-infected people are now living with HIV rather than dying from it.

Unfortunately, the knowledge that HIV can be treated (though not cured) has given people the idea that HIV infection is not as serious as it was a decade ago. In one year, more than 5 million people around the world became infected with HIV, including roughly 800,000 people under the age of 15. That same year, more than 3 million people around the world died of AIDS, bringing the total number of deaths worldwide to more than 20 million people.

Go Online
SCIENCE NEWS®
For: Articles on infectious diseases and the immune system
Visit: PHSchool.com
Web Code: cbe-0400

40–3 Section Assessment

1. **Key Concept** What happens in an autoimmune disease?
2. **Key Concept** Describe the various ways HIV is transmitted from person to person.
3. What are the two main types of immune system disorders?
4. Why is it difficult for a person with HIV to fight off infections?
5. **Critical Thinking Applying Concepts** In treating asthma, the first thing many physicians do is ask patients to list times and places they have experienced asthmatic reactions. Why do you think doctors do this?

Connecting Concepts

Viral Replication
Compare the process of HIV replication with that of other viruses. You may wish to review **Figure 40–14** as well as Chapter 19.

Slowing a Worldwide Epidemic

AIDS is a threat on every continent in the world, but nowhere has its effect been more devastating than in Africa. Thirty million of the world's 42 million people infected with HIV live in Africa. In some African countries, the HIV-infection rate is as high as one in three people. Leaders from around the world disagree on how the AIDS epidemic should be handled. Some argue that generic drugs should be made available. Others argue that the focus should be on AIDS prevention and education. Still others think that some money needs to be spent on the millions of AIDS orphans.

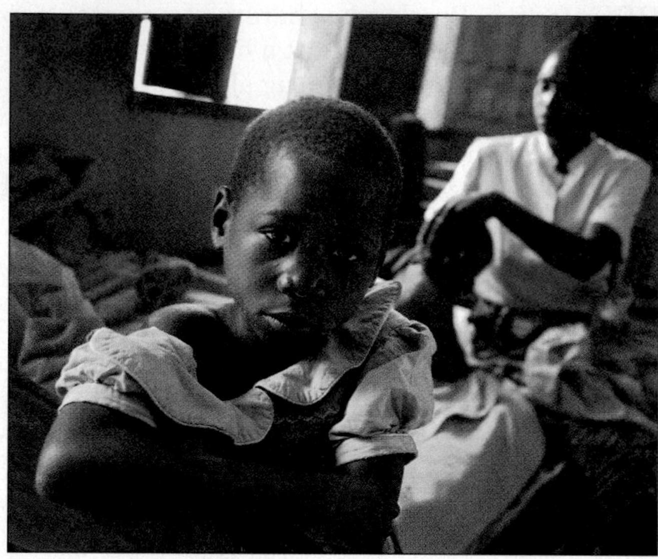

The Viewpoints

Make Drugs More Affordable

AIDS workers in Africa believe that more affordable drugs should be the top priority. HIV-infected people in Africa do not have access to the advanced medicines that people have in the United States. In Africa, the use of antiviral drugs is not common. Although the antiviral drugs do not cure AIDS, they help prolong life as long as they are taken on a regular basis. To increase access to these drugs, activists are looking for generic drugs, which would be lower in cost. Large pharmaceutical companies, however, don't like this idea because they say that generic drugs violate the companies' patents on such antiviral drugs.

Spend Money for Prevention

Many people in HIV-infected populations do not have basic knowledge about AIDS, including how HIV is spread. Thus, what is needed is an intensive program of public health education to stop the spread of the virus. If prevention programs including education and counseling were available, the incidence of new HIV infections could be reduced.

Spend Money on AIDS Orphans

More than 11 million children have lost parents to AIDS. Orphanages are overflowing with children who have no one to look after them. It is expected in Ethiopia—the country with the fastest-growing HIV-infection rate—that the number of orphans could increase about 150 percent over the next ten years. Because of this growing problem, a number of people feel that some of the money used to fight AIDS should be given to care for these orphans.

Research and Decide

1. **Analyzing the Viewpoints** To make an informed decision, learn more about this issue by consulting library or Internet resources. Then, list the key arguments for each of the viewpoints.
2. **Forming Your Opinion** Given limited resources to fight HIV, how would you decide the allocation of those resources? Would you spend all of the money on one area, or would you split it up among the different areas? What are the reasons for your decision?

For: Links from the authors
Visit: PHSchool.com
Web Code: cbe-0403

40–4 The Environment and Your Health

4-5.2 Homeostasis is constantly threatened
4-5.2 Viruses, bacteria, fungi, and other parasites infect plants and animals
4-5.2 Causes of disease
4-5.2 Factors that increase mutations
4-5.2 Gene mutations result in uncontrolled cell division
4-5.2 Biological research of diseases

Staying healthy involves more than the battles against pathogens. You interact constantly with both living and nonliving parts of your environment. Aspects of your environment that are important to health include the buildings in which you live, the people with whom you share those spaces, the air you breathe, the water you drink, and the food you eat.

Factors that have the potential to affect health in a negative way are called risk factors. A **risk factor** is anything that increases the chance of disease or injury. Both heredity (the genes you carry) and environmental factors can affect your health. **Environmental factors that can affect your health include air and water quality, poisonous wastes in landfills, and exposure to solar radiation.**

Guide for Reading

 **Key Concepts**
- What environmental factors affect your health?
- How can you maintain your health?

Vocabulary
risk factor
tumor
carcinogen

Reading Strategy: Hypothesizing Before you read, hypothesize about how the environment can affect your health. As you read, list evidence that supports or rejects your hypothesis.

Air Quality

The air you breathe comes into very close contact with your delicate lung tissue and blood. It shouldn't be surprising, therefore, that the quality of the air is very important to your health. But what is meant by "air quality"? Air quality refers to the number and concentrations of various gases present, as well as the nature and amount of tiny particles suspended in the air. Gases that are important to air quality include carbon monoxide and ozone. Particles in the air include dust, pollen, or particulates produced by cars and trucks or the burning of coal. If the concentration of these impurities gets too high, they can become risk factors for various health problems.

Carbon Monoxide Carbon monoxide (CO) is an odorless gas produced when certain compounds are burned. Carbon monoxide is found in automobile exhaust and cigarette smoke. Carbon monoxide also can be produced by the furnace of a heating system or by space heaters that burn fuel.

Recall that hemoglobin in red blood cells usually helps carry oxygen to the cells of your body. If you inhale carbon monoxide, that gas binds to hemoglobin, preventing it from carrying oxygen. As a result, the body does not receive the oxygen it needs. Overexposure to carbon monoxide can be fatal.

Ozone Ozone (O_3), a highly reactive form of oxygen, is another gas found in the air that is a potential risk factor when it occurs at ground level. Ozone is produced by vehicle exhaust and factory emissions. When the air is stagnant, ozone accumulates. When ozone levels are high, you should limit your time outdoors as much as possible, especially if you have a respiratory condition such as asthma, bronchitis, or emphysema.

▼**Figure 40–16** **Poor air quality can affect your health.** Smog is a mixture of chemicals that appears in the atmosphere as a gray-brown haze. Smog is particularly dangerous for people with respiratory conditions.

Airborne Particulates Airborne particulates of many different kinds can also be risk factors. Tiny dust mites, pollen, mold spores, and animal dander can trigger allergic reactions that can lead to respiratory problems or make existing health problems worse. Some potential sources of airborne particulates that can be found indoors are shown in **Figure 40–17.**

Another type of particulate that can cause serious harm is the metal lead. Lead can poison the liver, kidneys, and nervous system. Lead poisoning in babies and young children can also result in slow mental development.

Lead became a serious problem because for many years it was added to gasoline to improve the performance of engines. When that gas was burned, tiny particulates of lead were released into the air. People inhaled lead particulates as they breathed. Many more lead particulates were washed into rivers and streams. When research revealed the health problems that resulted, leaded gasoline was phased out and replaced with unleaded gasoline. Within a few years, levels of lead in surface waters dropped dramatically.

Another particulate that can be carried in air is asbestos, which was commonly used for insulation. Asbestos can fragment into tiny fibers that are small enough to remain suspended in air for some time. When inhaled repeatedly, asbestos fibers can cause lung cancer.

Water Quality

Water, like air, can carry biological and chemical pollution. Biological pollutants in water, such as human and animal wastes, can contain bacteria or viruses that can cause cramps, vomiting, diarrhea, or diseases such as hepatitis or cholera.

Some chemical pollutants can cause organ damage. Others interfere with the development of organs and tissues, causing birth defects. Still others can damage DNA, causing normal cells to become cancerous.

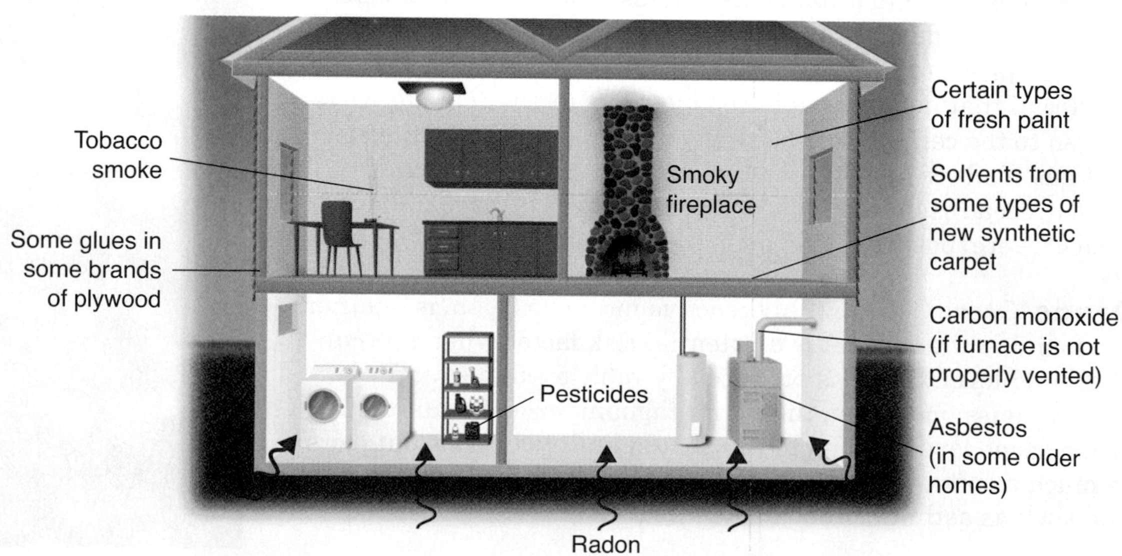

▼ **Figure 40–17** Air pollution can occur indoors as well as outdoors. Indoor air pollutants include fumes and vapors given off by carpets, paints, and household cleaning products.

Figure 40–18 Many cities and towns have sewage-treatment plants that process household waste water. In huge outdoor tanks, water is treated with chemicals and microorganisms and then aerated. **Applying Concepts** ***What is the role of microorganisms in treating waste water?***

Fortunately, regulations requiring proper treatment of residential and industrial sewage, for example, have led to significant decreases in the amount of sewage-related bacteria in drinking-water supplies across the nation. In the United States, for example, public water systems supply clean, safe drinking water to cities and many towns. Providing safe drinking water has probably been the single most important factor in nearly doubling human life expectancy over the last century or so.

Bioterrorism

In recent years, bioterrorism has become a new health threat. Bioterrorism is the intentional use of biological agents to disable or kill individuals. Bioterrorism can involve the intentional release of infectious agents—viruses (such as smallpox) or bacteria (such as anthrax)—or the spread of toxic compounds (such as botulinus toxin) extracted from living organisms.

Some forms of bioterrorism pose risks in part because research and public health measures have been so successful in the past. For example, worldwide vaccination programs eliminated smallpox around the world years ago. As a result, almost no one has been vaccinated against the virus for decades. Thus, the release of smallpox virus could cause serious problems.

Other forms of bioterrorism involve treating pathogens to maximize their ability to infect and cause disease. Anthrax is a disease that is common in cattle-ranching areas, but it is usually present in a form that either is not easily transmitted or is not life-threatening. The spores of anthrax bacteria, however, can be treated to make them light and fine enough to be spread through the air and inhaled—which produces a possibly fatal infection. Medical, research, and military establishments are still in the process of performing research and evaluating the best ways to minimize the risks of bioterrorism.

For: Links on cancer cells
Visit: www.SciLinks.org
Web Code: cbn-0404

Cancer

Cancer is a life-threatening disease in which cells multiply uncontrollably and destroy healthy tissue. Cancer is a unique disease because the cells that cause it are not foreign cells but rather the body's own cells. This fact has made cancer difficult to treat and to understand.

All forms of cancer are ultimately caused by harmful mutations in genes that control cell growth and development. Sometimes, cancer arises almost entirely because some factor in the environment damages DNA. An increased likelihood of developing some cancers can be inherited.

Cancers begin when something goes wrong with the controls that normally regulate cell growth and reproduction. A single cell or a group of cells begin to grow and divide uncontrollably, often resulting in the formation of a mass of growing tissue known as a **tumor.** However, not all tumors are cancerous. Some tumors are benign, or noncancerous. A benign tumor does not spread to surrounding healthy tissue or to other parts of the body. Cancerous tumors, on the other hand, are malignant, which means that they can invade and destroy surrounding healthy tissue.

As the cancer cells spread, they absorb the nutrients needed by other cells, block nerve connections, and prevent the organs they invade from functioning properly. Soon, the delicate balances that exist in the body are disrupted, and life-threatening illness results.

▼ **Figure 40–19** The body recognizes cancer cells as foreign and tries to destroy them. In this color-enhanced SEM, a killer T cell (orange) is attacking a cancer cell (purple).

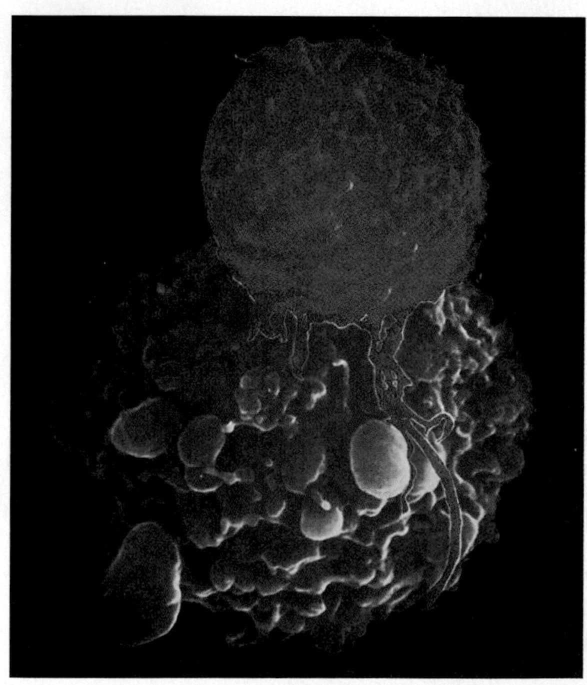

(magnification: about 3000×)

Causes of Cancer Cancers are caused by defects in the genes that regulate cell growth and division. There are several sources of such defects. They may be inherited, be caused by viruses, or may result from mutations in DNA that occur spontaneously or are produced by chemicals or radiation.

Chemical compounds cause cancer by triggering mutations in the DNA of normal cells. Chemical compounds that are known to cause cancer are called **carcinogens.** Some carcinogens are produced in nature. One of these, aflatoxin, is produced by molds that grow on peanuts. Others, such as chloroform and benzene, are synthetic compounds. Some of the most powerful chemical carcinogens are found in tobacco smoke. In the United States, cigarette smoking is responsible for nearly half the cancers that occur.

Most forms of radiation—including sunlight, X-rays, and nuclear radiation—cause cancer by producing mutations in DNA. If mutations occur in genes that control cell growth, a normal cell may be transformed into a cancer cell. Most cases of skin cancer, for example, are caused by the ultraviolet radiation in sunlight. For this reason, it is important to avoid prolonged exposure to the sun.

Analyzing Data

Cancer Mortality

Cancer is a disease that is easier to treat if it is detected early. There are also things you can do to decrease your risk of cancer, such as eating a diet high in fruits, vegetables, and fiber; staying out of the sun; and not smoking. The data in the table show the 5-year mortality rates of five different types of cancer since 1950. Use the data to answer the questions.

1. **Using Tables and Graphs** Construct a line graph of the data in the table.
2. **Using Tables and Graphs** Which type of cancer has shown the greatest increase in mortality rate?
3. **Inferring** What can you infer about the use of tobacco in men over the last 50 years? In women?
4. **Predicting** Given the trend in melanoma cancer deaths over the past 50 years, predict the incidence in 1995–1998 in both men and women.
5. **Inferring** Why do you think the incidence of death from breast cancer has stayed relatively stable over the last 50 years?

Cancer Mortality Rates (per 100,000 people)

Year	Lung		Colon		Melanoma		Breast	Prostate
	Male	Female	Male	Female	Male	Female	Female	Male
1950–54	25.51	4.98	16.94	18.49	1.20	0.92	26.42	20.85
1960–64	42.15	6.39	17.86	17.48	1.67	1.19	26.22	19.78
1970–74	60.79	12.80	19.49	16.43	2.18	1.40	26.92	20.05
1980–84	71.30	23.33	21.22	15.52	2.95	1.64	26.90	21.29
1990–94	71.71	33.43	18.79	12.85	3.49	1.69	26.19	24.37
1995–98	68.00	34.30	20.50	14.10	?	?	24.20	23.70

Radon is another source of radiation. Radon is a radioactive gas that is found naturally in some rocks and that sometimes leaks into the foundations of buildings. If your home is located in an area where radon is present, it can be tested for the presence of radon.

Treating Cancer As with other diseases, prevention is the best defense. The best way to fight cancer is by protecting your DNA from agents that cause cancer. For example, you can dramatically reduce your risk of developing lung cancer by not smoking. In addition, regular exercise and a balanced diet with plenty of fruits and vegetables can help to lower your cancer risk.

Physicians also stress that if a cancer is detected early the chances of treating it successfully may be as high as 90 percent. Regular checkups and tests are an important preventive measure. Recommended tests depend on a person's age, gender, and family history. Self-examinations for skin, breast, or testicular cancer are also helpful when combined with regular checkups. Your doctor can give you instructions for performing these self-examinations.

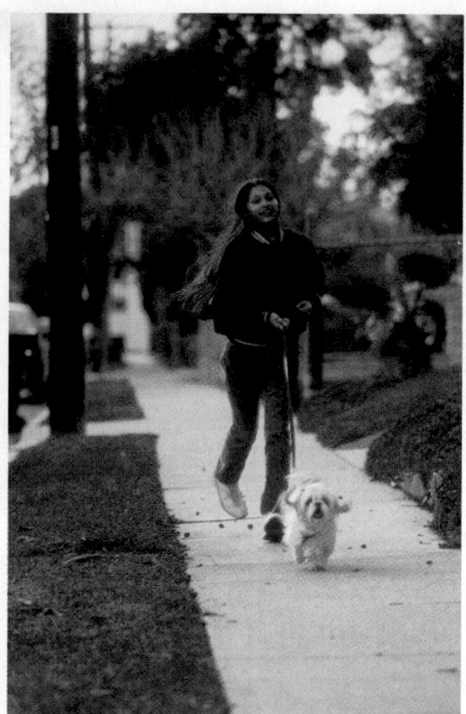

▲ **Figure 40–20** **Getting regular exercise is one way to maintain your health.** You should try to get a minimum of 30 minutes of aerobic exercise each day.

Maintaining Health

To keep your immune system working efficiently, you can practice behaviors that reduce your exposure to pathogens and maintain overall good health. **Healthful behaviors include eating a healthful diet, getting plenty of exercise and rest, abstaining from harmful activities, and having regular checkups.**

Healthful Diet Food provides the nutrients and energy your cells need to function properly. To help all your body systems work at their best, it is important to eat a balanced diet that provides essential nutrients. Eating foods that are low in saturated fat and cholesterol may help prevent obesity. Eating plenty of fruits, vegetables, and whole grains will also help protect you from certain cancers, especially colon and rectal cancers.

Exercise and Rest Regular exercise helps move blood throughout the body and maintains cardiovascular fitness. Exercise also helps maintain an appropriate body weight, which helps prevent certain kinds of heart disease. Adequate rest is important for keeping your body functioning well. For most people, adequate rest means getting about eight hours of sleep each night.

Abstaining From Harmful Activities Drugs, including alcohol and tobacco products, can have harmful effects on the body. Many types of drugs, including alcohol, can slow or suppress the immune system. Smoking and tobacco products also cause a variety of respiratory conditions as well as certain cancers, including cancers of the lung, mouth, and throat.

Some diseases can be spread through sexual contact with an infected person. These sexually transmitted diseases (STDs) include HIV, chlamydia, and gonorrhea. The only way to absolutely prevent exposure to sexually transmitted diseases is to abstain from all sexual activity.

Regular Checkups It usually is easier to treat a disease if it is discovered early. You can perform regular self-examinations for skin cancer, breast cancer, and testicular cancer. By getting regular checkups, you can help maintain your health.

40–4 Section Assessment

1. **Key Concept** Describe the environmental factors that affect your health.
2. **Key Concept** Name three things you can do to maintain your health.
3. List some of the causes of cancer.
4. Why are regular medical checkups and self-examinations important?
5. **Critical Thinking Classifying** Should cancer be considered an infectious disease? Explain your answer.

Connecting Concepts

The Cell Cycle
Recall the cell cycle from Section 10–2. In which phase do you think cells would be most vulnerable to damage from radiation? Explain your choice. What characteristic of cancer cells might make them especially vulnerable?

Testing the Specificity of Antibodies

Antibodies are very selective. They will bind only to specific antigens. An antibody that binds strongly to a certain protein or carbohydrate may not bind at all to another molecule that has a very similar structure. In this investigation, you will determine the specificity of an antibody.

Problem **How specific is the binding of antibodies to antigens?**

Materials

- Strep A diagnostic kits with control samples (materials for three tests)
- sterile water

Skills Predicting, Asking Questions

Procedure

1. Make a copy of the data table shown. To see how the antibody-based Strep A diagnostic kit reacts to an antigen found in the cell wall of *Streptococcus* group A (the bacterium that causes the infection known as "strep throat"), follow the instructions in the kit to test the positive control sample. Record the result of this test.
2. **Predicting** *Streptococcus* group C is closely related to *Streptococcus* group A but does not cause disease. Record your prediction of how the diagnostic kit will react to antigens from the cell wall of *Streptococcus* group C.
3. Test the *Streptococcus* group C sample as you did the *Streptococcus* group A sample in step 1. Record the result of this test.
4. **Predicting** Record your prediction of whether *Streptococcus* group A is present on the tabletops in your lab.
5. Use sterile water to moisten the tip of one of the test swabs supplied with your diagnostic kit and rub it on the tabletop. Then, test the sample on the swab and record your results.

Data Table

Sample	Result (Positive or Negative)
Streptococcus Group A	
Streptococcus Group C	
Tabletop Swab	

Analyze and Conclude

1. **Observing** Did the antibody-based test react to the antigen of *Streptococcus* group A? To the antigen of group C?
2. **Analyzing Data** Did your results support the idea that an antibody can be used to distinguish between two similar antigens, such as those of *Streptococcus* group A and group C?
3. **Evaluating** Assess the quality and appropriateness of the data from steps 1 through 3 by stating whether the results enable you to answer the Problem question. Did your data enable you to determine whether *Streptococcus* group A was present on the tabletop? Explain your reasoning.
4. **Drawing Conclusions** Use what you have learned about the specificity of antibodies to explain what happens in autoimmune diseases such as multiple sclerosis.

Go Further

Interviewing a Professional Interview a health professional to find out how antibody-based tests are used to determine blood types and to diagnose diseases.

Chapter 40 Study Guide

40–1 Infectious Disease

Key Concepts

- Some diseases are produced by pathogens. Others are caused by materials in the environment. Still others are inherited.
- Some infectious diseases are spread from one person to another through coughing, sneezing, or physical contact. Other infectious diseases are spread through contaminated water or food. Still others are spread by infected animals.

Vocabulary
disease, p. 1031 • pathogen, p. 1031
germ theory of disease, p. 1031
Koch's postulates, p. 1032
vector, p. 1034 • antibiotic, p. 1035

40–2 The Immune System

Key Concepts

- The function of the immune system is to fight infection through the activation of specific defenses.
- Your body's most important nonspecific defense is the skin.
- The inflammatory response is a nonspecific defense reaction to tissue damage caused by injury or infection.

Vocabulary
immunity, p. 1036
inflammatory response, p.1037 • fever, p. 1037
interferon, p. 1038 • immune response, p.1038
antigen, p. 1038 • humoral immunity, p. 1038
cell-mediated immunity, p. 1038
antibody, p. 1038 • vaccination, p. 1041
active immunity, p. 1042
passive immunity, p. 1042

40–3 Immune System Disorders

Key Concepts

- When the immune system makes a mistake and attacks the body's own cells, it produces an autoimmune disease.
- The only no-risk behavior with respect to HIV and AIDS is abstinence.

Vocabulary
allergy, p. 1043 • histamine, p. 1043
asthma, p. 1044

40–4 The Environment and Your Health

Key Concepts

- Environmental factors that can affect your health include air and water quality, poisonous wastes in landfills, and exposure to solar radiation.
- Healthful behaviors include eating a healthful diet, getting plenty of exercise and rest, abstaining from harmful activities, and having regular checkups.

Vocabulary
risk factor, p. 1049
tumor, p. 1052
carcinogen, p. 1052

Thinking Visually

Using the information in this chapter, complete the following concept map:

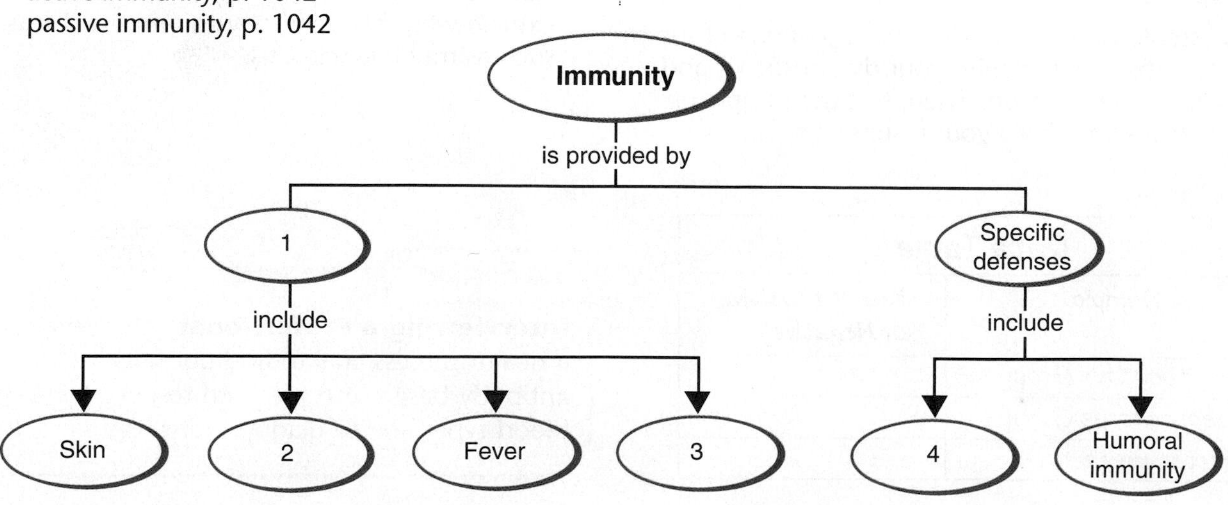

Preparing for the Living Environment Exam

NEW YORK LIVING ENVIRONMENT

Blue questions emphasize Regents Exam content

Chapter 40

Part A

Multiple Choice

For each statement or question, select the number of the word or expression that, of those given, best completes the statement or answers the question.

1 Any change, other than an injury, that disrupts the normal functions of the body is a(an)
(1) disease (3) allergy
(2) pathogen (4) vaccine

2 Which term best describes disease-causing organisms such as viruses, bacteria, and worms?
(1) antibodies (3) pathogens
(2) antigens (4) toxins

3 Which scientist's observations led to the germ theory of disease?
(1) Steere (3) Koch
(2) Hooke (4) Salk

4 The body's most important nonspecific defense against pathogens is
(1) tears (3) saliva
(2) mucus (4) skin

5 In the illustration below, the label X indicates the

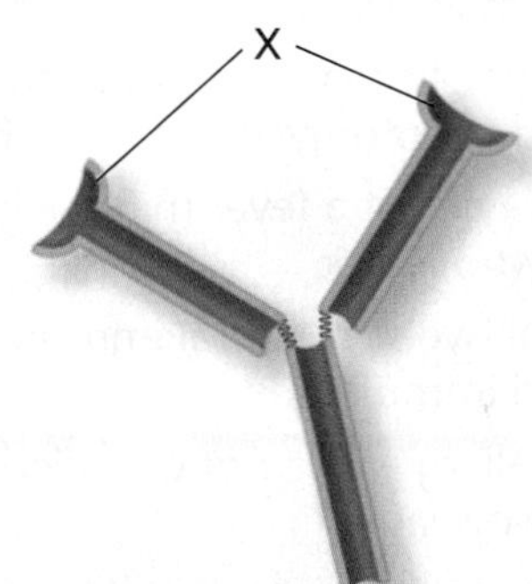

(1) antibodies (3) antigen-binding sites
(2) antigens (4) interferon parts

6 A substance that triggers an immune response is an
(1) antibody (3) allergy
(2) antigen (4) antibiotic

7 A nonspecific defense reaction to tissue damage caused by injury or infection is known as
(1) the inflammatory response
(2) active immunity
(3) cell-mediated immunity
(4) permanent immunity

8 A protein that helps cells resist viruses is
(1) interferon (3) plasma
(2) penicillin (4) histamine

9 Swelling and pain associated with inflammation are caused by the
(1) secretion of antibodies
(2) narrowing of local blood vessels
(3) secretion of antigens
(4) destruction of bacteria by white blood cells

10 Which activity is *not* a sign of an inflammatory response?
(1) white blood cells rushing to infected tissues
(2) blood vessels narrowing near a wound
(3) phagocytes engulfing pathogens
(4) infected tissues swelling

11 Which body defense does *not* prevent pathogens from entering the body?
(1) macrophages (3) mucus
(2) tears (4) skin

12 Mast cells release chemicals known as
(1) antibodies (3) histamines
(2) antigens (4) pathogens

13 Which statement describes one effect of a fever?
(1) It increases the growth of pathogens.
(2) It decreases the rate of chemical reactions.
(3) It increases the heart rate.
(4) It decreases the number of white blood cells.

14 White blood cells that can engulf pathogens are referred to as
(1) antibodies (3) B cells
(2) antigens (4) phagocytes

15 Proteins that bind to specific chemicals on the surface of foreign cells are called
(1) phagocytes (3) T cells
(2) antigens (4) antibodies

16 White blood cells that produce pathogen-destroying proteins are known as
(1) helper T cells (3) plasma cells
(2) antigens (4) phagocytes

Test-Taking Tip When evaluating multiple choice answers, be sure to read all of the answer choices, even if the first answer choice seems to be the correct one. By doing so, you can make sure that the answer you chose is the best one.

Preparing for the Living Environment Exam

Part B

Multiple Choice and Extended Response
For those questions that ask you to select a response, choose the one that best completes the statement or answers the question. For all others follow the directions given.

Base your answers to questions 17 through 20 on the information and graph below and on your knowledge of biology.

The graph shows concentrations of HIV and T cells in 120 HIV-infected patients over ten years.

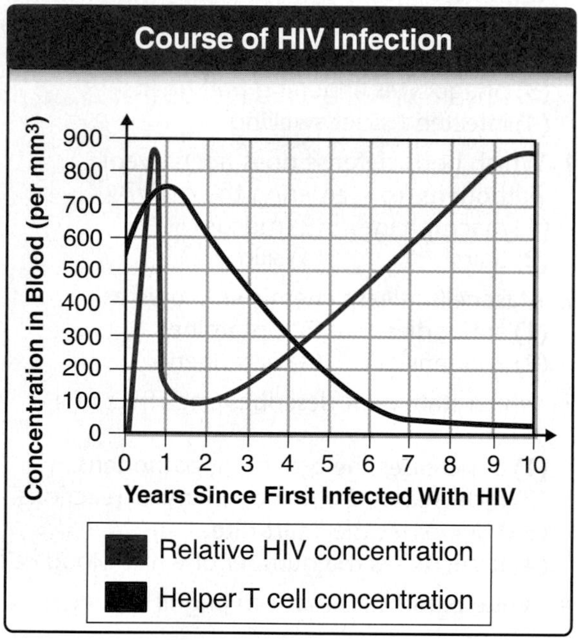

17 Which statement best explains why the T-cell concentration increases after two years?
(1) HIV dies off after two years.
(2) HIV attacks T-cells.
(3) T-cells produce toxins.
(4) B-cells increase.

18 Which statement best describes the change in the HIV concentration from years 2 through 10?
(1) It increased, then decreased, then gradually increased.
(2) It increased, then gradually decreased.
(3) It steadily increased, then began to level off.
(4) It steadily decreased, then began to level off.

19 What is most likely responsible for the change in HIV concentration during the first year?
(1) an immune response
(2) an inflammatory response
(3) an HIV vaccination
(4) HIV stopped replicating

20 What is the most likely result of the changes shown?
(1) The body will be unable to deal with infections caused by pathogens.
(2) Antibodies against the AIDS virus will eventually be released.
(3) Cancer cells in the body will be replaced by AIDS cells.
(4) The damage to the immune system will be repaired by vaccinations.

---

21 Explain why the fourth step of Koch's postulates is necessary to prove that a disease is caused by a specific pathogen.

22 List the five types of pathogens that are responsible for the spread of infectious disease. Give an example of a disease caused by each type of pathogen.

23 Explain what is meant by the term *vectors* in the statement: Mosquitoes and flies are often vectors of human disease.

24 Explain the specific way antibiotics such as penicillin and streptomycin work to kill bacteria.

25 State *three* ways that a fever may be beneficial to a person who is sick.

26 Distinguish between humoral immunity and cell-mediated immunity.

27 Explain why allergies are not classified as autoimmune diseases.

28 Describe how passive immunity to a disease is obtained, and explain why it does not last very long.

29 State the difference between a malignant tumor and a benign tumor.

Base your answers to questions 30 through 32 on the chart below, which shows the relative 5-year cancer survival rates in the United States, and on your knowledge of biology.

Relative 5-year Cancer Survival Rates (in %)

Site	1974–76	1980–82	1989–95
All sites	50	51	59
Brain	22	25	30
Breast (female)	75	76	85
Colon	50	55	62
Lung and bronchus	13	13	14
Leukemia	34	39	43
Prostate	67	73	92

30 Name the type of cancer that has the highest survival rate.

31 Name the type of cancer that has the lowest survival rate.

32 Describe the trend in survival rates that is evident from the data.

33 Humans have defenses against disease-causing agents. Describe the roles of B cells, helper T cells, and killer T cells in this process.

34 Explain why a second bee sting is more dangerous than the first for a person who is allergic to bee stings.

35 The virus that causes influenza mutates rapidly. Explain why this makes it necessary for people to receive flu shots repeatedly in order to remain immune to the disease.

Part C

Extended Response

Answer the questions or follow the directions given.

36 Antibodies and antibiotics are both useful in combating disease. Compare these two methods of attacking pathogens. In your answer, be sure to
- identify the source of both antibodies and antibiotics
- describe the way antibodies work to combat pathogens
- describe the way antibiotics combat pathogens
- compare the types of pathogens that antibodies and antibiotics can be used against successfully

37 Cancer results from errors in the genetic information that regulates cell division. Explain the connection between cancer and environmental conditions. In your answer be sure to
- identify *two* environmental conditions that can lead to cancer
- explain how such environmental conditions can specifically lead to unregulated cell division

38 Bone marrow transplants are a method of treatment being considered for some AIDS patients.
a State one way a bone marrow transplant would benefit an AIDS patient.
b State one possible problem that may result from this transplant procedure.

39 Immunity to a disease can be acquired either by getting the disease and recovering or by receiving a vaccination. Compare these two methods of becoming immune to a specific disease. In your answer, be sure to
- explain why getting a disease and recovering can leave a person immune to that disease for life
- explain how getting a vaccination results in the same type of immunity to the disease, but is safer

For: An interactive self-test
Visit: PHSchool.com
Web Code: cba-0400

Basic Process Skills

During a biology course, you often carry out short lab activities as well as lengthier experiments. Here are some skills that you will use.

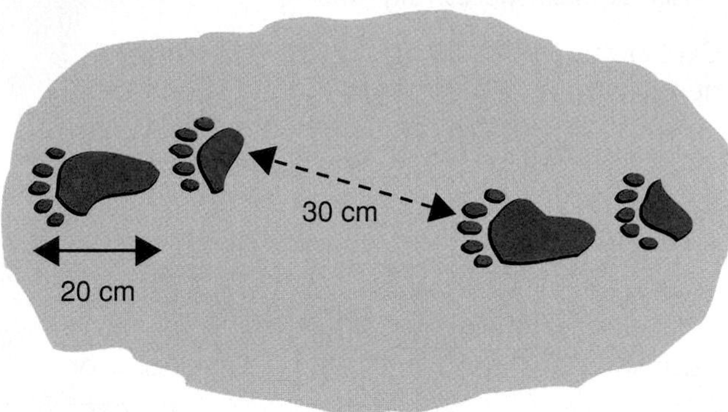

Observing

In every science activity, you make a variety of observations. Observing is using one or more of the five senses to gather information. Many observations involve the senses of sight, hearing, touch, and smell. On rare occasions in a lab—but only when explicitly directed by your teacher—you may use the sense of taste to make an observation.

Sometimes you will use tools that increase the power of your senses or make observations more precise. For example, hand lenses and microscopes enable you to see things in greater detail. Rulers, balances, and thermometers help you measure key variables. Besides expanding the senses or making observations more accurate, tools may help eliminate personal opinions or preferences.

In science, it is customary to record your observations at the time they are made, usually by writing or drawing in a notebook. You may also make records by using computers, cameras, videotapes, and other tools. As a rule, scientists keep complete accounts of their observations, often using tables to organize their observations.

Inferring

In science, as in daily life, observations are usually followed by inferences. Inferring is interpreting an observation or statement based on prior knowledge.

Comparing Observations and Inferences

Sample Observations	Sample Inferences
The footprints in the soil each have five toes.	An animal made the footprints.
The larger footprints are about 20 cm long.	A bear made the footprints.
The space between each pair of footprints is about 30 cm.	The animal was walking, not running.

For example, suppose you're on a mountain hike and you see footprints in wet soil. Based on their size and shape, you might infer that a large mammal had passed by. In making that inference, you would use your knowledge about the shape of animals' feet. Someone who knew much more about mammals might infer that a bear left the footprints. You can compare examples of observations and inferences in the table above.

Notice that an inference is an act of reasoning, not a fact. An inference may be logical but not true. It is often necessary to gather further information before you can be confident that an inference is correct. For scientists, that information may come from further observations or from research done by others.

As you study biology, you may make different types of inferences. For example, you may generalize about all cases based on information about some cases: *All the plant roots I've observed grow downward, so I infer that all roots grow downward.* You may determine that one factor or event was caused by another factor or event: *The bacteria died after I applied bleach, so I infer that bleach kills bacteria.* Predictions may be another type of inference.

Predicting

People often make predictions, but their statements about the future could be either guesses or inferences. In science, a prediction is an inference about a future event based on evidence, experience, or knowledge. For example, you can say, *On the first day next month, it will be sunny.* If your statement is based on evidence of weather patterns in the area, then the prediction is scientific. If the statement was made without considering any evidence, it's just a guess.

Predictions play a major role in science because they provide a way to test ideas. If scientists understand an event or the properties of a particular object, they should be able to make accurate predictions about that event or object. Some predictions can be tested simply by making observations. At other times, carefully designed experiments are needed. You'll read more about the relationship between predictions and experiments on the next two pages.

Classifying

If you have ever heard people debate whether a tomato is a fruit or a vegetable, you've heard an argument about classification. Classifying is the process of grouping items that are alike according to some organizing idea or system. Classifying occurs in every branch of science, but it is especially important in biology because living things are so numerous and diverse.

You may have the chance to practice classifying in different ways. Sometimes you will place objects into groups using an established system. At other times, you may create a system of your own by examining a variety of objects and identifying their properties.

Classification can have different purposes. Sometimes it's done just to keep things organized, for example, to make lab supplies easy to find. More likely, though, classification helps scientists understand living things better and discover relationships among them. For example, biologists classify certain animal parts as bone or muscle and investigate how they work together. One way biologists determine how groups of vertebrates are related is to compare their bones.

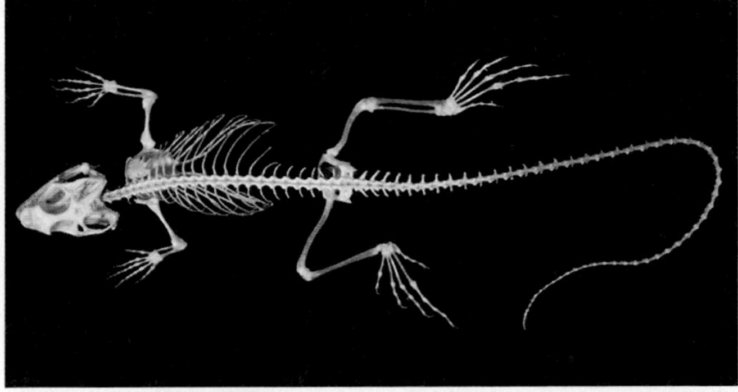

Using Models

Some cities refuse to approve any new buildings that could cast shadows on a popular park. As architects plan buildings in such locations, they use models that can show where a proposed building's shadow will fall at any time of day at any season of the year. A model is a mental or physical representation of an object, process, or event. In science, models are usually made to help people understand natural objects and processes.

Model of a Glucose Molecule

CH_2OH
C O
H OH
H
C C
OH H
HO H
C C
H OH

Models can be varied. Mental models, such as mathematical equations, can represent some kinds of ideas or processes. For example, the equation for the surface area of a sphere can model the surface of Earth, enabling scientists to determine its size. Physical models can be made of a huge variety of materials; they can be two-dimensional (flat) or three-dimensional (having depth). In biology, a drawing of a molecule or a cell is a typical two-dimensional model. Common three-dimensional models include a representation of a DNA molecule and a plastic skeleton of an animal.

Physical models can also be made "to scale," which means they are in proportion to the actual object. Something very large, such as an area of land being studied, can be shown at 1/100 of its actual size. A tiny organism can be shown at 100 times its size.

Conducting an Experiment

A science experiment is a procedure designed to test a prediction. Some types of experiments are fairly simple to design. Others may require ingenious problem solving.

Starting With Questions or Problems

A gardener collected seeds from a favorite plant at the end of the summer, stored them indoors for the winter, then planted them the following spring. None of the stored seeds developed into plants, yet uncollected seeds from the original plant germinated in the normal way. The gardener wondered: *Why didn't the collected seeds germinate?*

An experiment may have its beginning when someone asks a specific question or wants to solve a particular problem. Sometimes the original question leads directly to an experiment, but often researchers must restate the problem before they can design an appropriate experiment. The gardener's question about the seeds, for example, is too broad to be tested by an experiment, because there are so many possible answers. To narrow the topic, the gardener might think about related questions: *Were the seeds I collected different from the uncollected seeds? Did I try to germinate them in poor soil or with insufficient light or water? Did storing the seeds indoors ruin them in some way?*

Developing a Hypothesis

In science, a question about an object or event is answered by developing a possible explanation called a **hypothesis.** The hypothesis may be developed after long thought and research, or it may come to a scientist "in a flash." How a hypothesis is formed doesn't matter; it can be useful as long as it leads to predictions that can be tested.

The gardener decided to focus on the fact that the nongerminating seeds were stored in the warm conditions of a heated house. That led the person to propose this hypothesis: *Seeds require a period of low temperatures in order to germinate.* The next step is to make a prediction based on the hypothesis, for example: *If seeds are stored indoors in cold conditions, they will germinate in the same way as seeds left outdoors during the winter.* Notice that the prediction suggests the basic idea for an experiment.

Designing an Experiment

A carefully designed experiment can test a prediction in a reliable way, ruling out other possible explanations. As scientists plan their experimental procedures, they pay particular attention to the factors that must be controlled.

The gardener decided to study three groups of seeds: (1) some that would be left outdoors throughout the winter, (2) some that would be brought indoors and kept at room temperature, and (3) some that would be brought indoors and kept cold.

Controlling Variables

As researchers design an experiment, they identify the **variables,** factors that can change. Some common variables include mass, volume, time, temperature, light, and the presence or absence of specific materials. An experiment involves three categories of variables. The factor that scientists purposely change is called the **manipulated variable.** A manipulated variable is also known as an **independent variable.** The factor that may change because of the manipulated variable and that scientists want to observe is called the **responding variable.** A responding variable is also known as a **dependent variable.** Factors that scientists purposely keep the same are called **controlled variables.** Controlling variables enables researchers to conclude that the changes in the responding variable are due exclusively to changes in the manipulated variable.

What Is a Control Group?

When you read about certain experiments, you may come across references to a control group (or "a control") and the experimental groups. All the groups in an experiment are treated exactly the same except for the manipulated variable. In the experimental group, the manipulated variable is being changed. The control group is used as a standard of comparison. It may consist of objects that are not changed in any way or objects that are being treated in the usual way. For example, in the gardener's experiment, the seeds left outdoors would be the control group, because they reveal what happens under natural conditions.

For the gardener, the manipulated variable is whether the seeds were exposed to cold conditions. The responding variable is whether or not the seeds germinate. Among the variables that must be controlled are whether the seeds remain dry during storage, when the seeds are planted, the amount of water the seeds receive, and the type of soil used.

Forming Operational Definitions

In an experiment, it is often necessary to define one or more variables explicitly so that any researcher could measure or control the variable in exactly the same way. An **operational definition** describes how a particular variable is to be measured or how a term is to be defined. ("Operational" means "describing what to do.")

The gardener, for example, had to decide exactly what the indoor "cold" conditions of the experiment would involve. Since winter temperatures often fell below freezing, the gardener decided that "cold" would mean keeping the seeds in a freezer.

Interpreting Data

The observations and measurements that are made in an experiment are called **data.** Scientists usually record data in an orderly way. When an experiment is finished, the researcher analyzes the data for trends or patterns, often by doing calculations or making graphs, to determine whether the results support the hypothesis.

For example, after planting the seeds in the spring, the gardener counted the seeds that germinated and found these results: None of the seeds kept at room temperature germinated, 80 percent of the seeds kept in the freezer germinated, and 85 percent of the seeds left outdoors during the winter germinated. The trend was clear: The gardener's prediction appeared to be correct.

To be sure that the results of an experiment are correct, scientists review their data critically, looking for possible sources of error. Here, "error" refers to differences between the observed results and the true values. Experimental error can result from human mistakes or problems with equipment. It can also occur when the small group of objects studied does not accurately represent the whole group. For example, if some of the gardener's seeds had been exposed to a herbicide, the data might not reflect the true seed germination pattern.

Drawing Conclusions

If researchers are confident that their data are reliable, they make a final statement summarizing their results. That statement—called the conclusion of the experiment—indicates whether the data support or refute the hypothesis. The gardener's conclusion was: *Some seeds must undergo a period of freezing in order to germinate.* A conclusion is considered valid if it is a logical interpretation of reliable data.

Following Up an Experiment

When an experiment has been completed, one or more events often follow. Researchers may repeat the experiment to verify the results. They may publish the experiment so that others can evaluate and replicate their procedures. They may compare their conclusion with the discoveries made by other scientists. And they may raise new questions that lead to new experiments. For example, *Are the spores of fungi affected by temperature as these seeds were?*

Researching other discoveries about seeds would show that some other types of plants in temperate zones require periods of freezing before they germinate. Biologists infer that this pattern makes it less likely the seeds will germinate before winter, thus increasing the chances that the young plants will survive.

SCIENCE SKILLS

Organizing Information

When you study or want to communicate facts and ideas, you may find it helpful to organize information visually. Here are some common graphic organizers you can use. Notice that each type of organizer is useful for specific types of information.

Concept Maps

Concept maps can help you organize a broad topic having many subtopics. A concept map begins with a main idea and shows how it can be broken down into specific topics. It makes the ideas easier to understand by presenting their relationships visually.

You construct a concept map by placing the concept words (usually nouns) in ovals and connecting the ovals with linking words. The most general concept usually is placed at the top of the map or in the center. The content of the other ovals becomes more specific as you move away from the main concept. The linking words, which describe the relationship between the linked concepts, are written on a line between two ovals. If you follow any string of concepts and linking words down through a map, they should sound approximately like a sentence.

Some concept maps may also include linking words that connect a concept in one branch to another branch. Such connections, called cross-linkages, show more complex interrelationships.

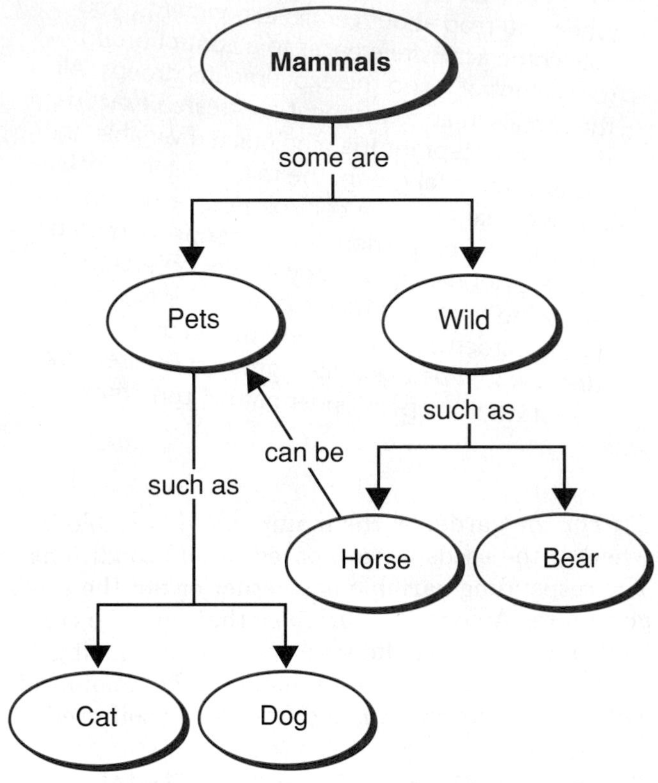

Compare-and-Contrast Tables

Compare-and-contrast tables are useful for showing the similarities and differences between two or more objects or processes. The table provides an organized framework for making comparisons based on specific characteristics.

To create a compare-and-contrast table, list the items to be compared across the top of the table. List the characteristics that will form the basis of your comparison in the column on the left. Complete the table by filling in information for each item.

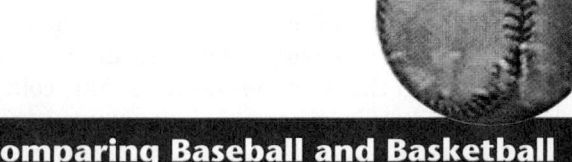

Comparing Baseball and Basketball

Characteristic	Baseball	Basketball
Number of Players	9	5
Playing Field	Baseball diamond	Basketball court
Equipment	Bat, baseball, mitts	Basket, basketball

Venn Diagrams

Another way to show similarities and differences between items is with a Venn diagram. A Venn diagram consists of two or more circles or ovals that partially overlap. Each circle or oval represents a particular object or idea. Characteristics that the objects share are written in the area of overlap. Differences or unique characteristics are written in the areas that do not overlap.

To create a Venn diagram, draw two overlapping circles or ovals. Label them with the names of the objects or the ideas they represent. Write the unique characteristics in the part of each circle or oval that does not overlap. Write the shared characteristics within the area of overlap.

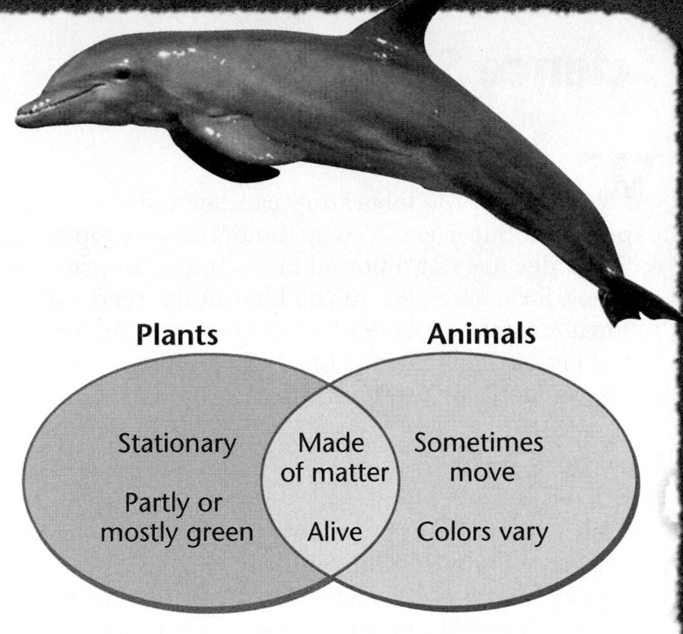

Flowcharts

A flowchart can help you represent the order in which a set of events has occurred or should occur. Flowcharts are useful for outlining the steps in a procedure or stages in a process with a definite beginning and end.

To make a flowchart, list the steps in the process you want to represent and count the steps. Then, create the appropriate number of boxes, starting at the top of a page or on the left. Write a brief description of the first event in the first box, then fill in the other steps, box by box. Link each box to the next event in the process with an arrow. Then, add a title to the flowchart.

Preparing Pasta

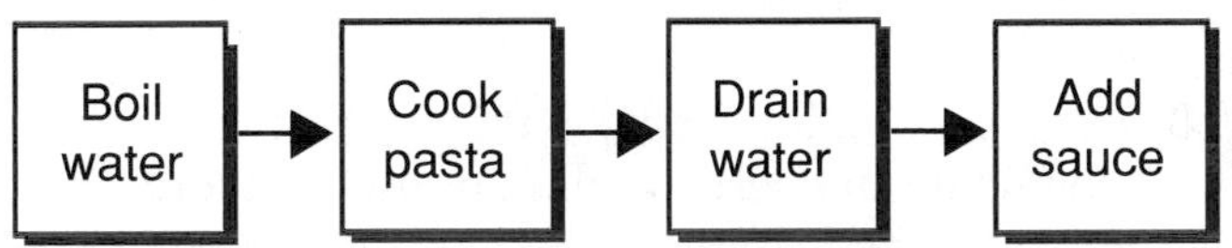

Cycle Diagrams

A cycle diagram shows a sequence of events that is continuous, or cyclical. A continuous sequence does not have a beginning or an end; instead, each event in the process leads to another event. The diagram shows the order of the events.

To create a cycle diagram, list the events in the process and count them. Draw one box for each event, placing the boxes around an imaginary circle. Write one of the events in a box, and then draw an arrow to the next box, moving clockwise. Continue to fill in the boxes and link them with arrows until the descriptions form a continuous circle. Then, add a title.

The Moon as Seen From Earth

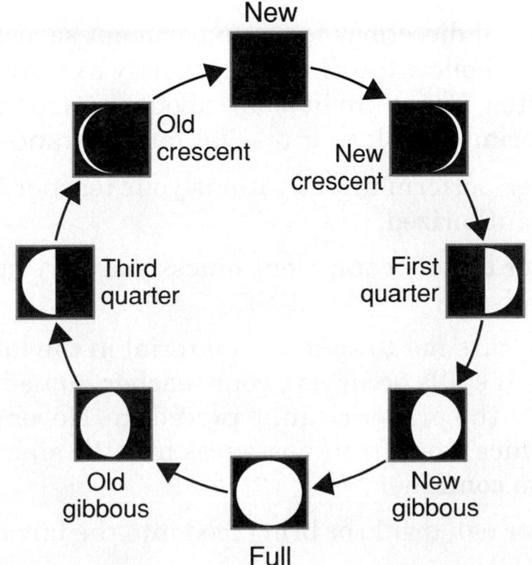

Science Safety Rules

Working in the laboratory can be an exciting experience, but it can also be dangerous if proper safety rules are not followed at all times. To prepare yourself for a safe year in the laboratory, read the following safety rules. Make sure that you understand each rule. Ask your teacher to explain any rules you don't understand.

Dress Code

1. Many materials in the laboratory can cause eye injury. To protect yourself from possible injury, wear safety goggles whenever you are working with chemicals, burners, or any substance that might get into your eyes. Avoid wearing contact lenses in the laboratory. Tell your teacher if you need to wear contact lenses to see clearly, and ask if there are any safety precautions you should observe.
2. Wear a laboratory apron or coat whenever you are working with chemicals or heated substances.
3. Tie back long hair to keep it away from any chemicals, burners, candles, or other laboratory equipment.
4. Before working in the laboratory, remove or tie back any article of clothing or jewelry that can hang down and touch chemicals and flames.

General Safety Rules and First Aid

5. Read all directions for an experiment several times. Follow the directions exactly as they are written. If you are in doubt about any part of the experiment, ask your teacher for assistance.
6. Never perform investigations your teacher has not authorized.
7. Never handle equipment unless you have specific permission.
8. Take care not to spill any material in the laboratory. If spills occur, ask your teacher immediately about the proper cleanup procedure. Never pour chemicals or other substances into the sink or trash container.
9. Never eat, drink, or bring food into the laboratory.
10. Immediately report all accidents, no matter how minor, to your teacher.
11. Learn what to do in case of specific accidents, such as getting acid in your eyes or on your skin. (Rinse acids off your body with lots of water.)
12. Be aware of the location of the first-aid kit. Your teacher should administer any required first aid due to injury. Your teacher may send you to the school nurse or call a physician.
13. Know where and how to report an accident or fire. Find out the location of the fire extinguisher, fire alarm, and phone. Report any fires to your teacher at once.

Heating and Fire Safety

14. Never use a heat source such as a candle or burner without wearing safety goggles.
15. Never heat a chemical you are not instructed to heat. A chemical that is harmless when cool can be dangerous when heated.
16. Maintain a clean work area and keep all materials away from flames. Be sure that there are no open containers of flammable liquids in the laboratory when flames are being used.
17. Never reach across a flame.
18. Make sure you know how to light a Bunsen burner. (Your teacher will demonstrate the proper procedure for lighting a burner.) If the flame leaps out of a burner toward you, turn the gas off immediately. Do not touch the burner. It may be hot. Never leave a lighted burner unattended!
19. When you are heating a test tube or bottle, point the opening away from yourself and others. Chemicals can splash or boil out of a heated test tube.
20. Never heat a closed container. The expanding hot air, vapors, or other gases inside may blow the container apart, causing it to injure you or others.
21. Never pick up a container that has been heated without first holding the back of your hand near it. If you can feel the heat on the back of your hand, the container may be too hot to handle. Use a clamp or tongs when handling hot containers.

Using Chemicals Safely

22. Never mix chemicals for "the fun of it." You might produce a dangerous, possibly explosive substance.

23. Many chemicals are poisonous. Never touch, taste, or smell a chemical that you do not know for certain is harmless. If you are instructed to smell fumes in an experiment, gently wave your hand over the opening of the container and direct the fumes toward your nose. Do not inhale the fumes directly from the container.

24. Use only those chemicals needed in the investigation. Keep all container lids closed when a chemical is not being used. Notify your teacher whenever chemicals are spilled.

25. Dispose of all chemicals as instructed by your teacher. To avoid contamination, never return chemicals to their original containers.

26. Be extra careful when working with acids or bases. Pour such chemicals from one container to another over the sink, not over your work area.

27. When diluting an acid, pour the acid into water. Never pour water into the acid.

28. If any acids or bases get on your skin or clothing, rinse them with water. Immediately notify your teacher of any acid or base spill.

Using Glassware Safely

29. Never heat glassware that is not thoroughly dry. Use a wire screen to protect glassware from any flame.

30. Keep in mind that hot glassware will not appear hot. Never pick up glassware without first checking to see if it is hot.

31. Never use broken or chipped glassware. If glassware breaks, notify your teacher and dispose of the glassware in the proper trash container.

32. Never eat or drink from laboratory glassware. Thoroughly clean glassware before putting it away.

Using Sharp Instruments

33. Handle scalpels or razor blades with extreme care. Never cut material toward you; cut away from you.

34. Notify your teacher immediately if you cut yourself when in the laboratory.

Working With Live Organisms

35. No experiments that will cause pain, discomfort, or harm to animals should be done in the classroom or at home.

36. Your teacher will instruct you how to handle each species that is brought into the classroom. Animals should be handled only if necessary. Special handling is required if an animal is excited or frightened, pregnant, feeding, or with its young.

37. Clean your hands thoroughly after handling any organisms or materials, including animals or cages containing animals.

End-of-Experiment Rules

38. When an experiment is completed, clean up your work area and return all equipment to its proper place.

39. Wash your hands before and after every experiment.

40. Turn off all burners before leaving the laboratory. Check that the gas line leading to the burner is off as well.

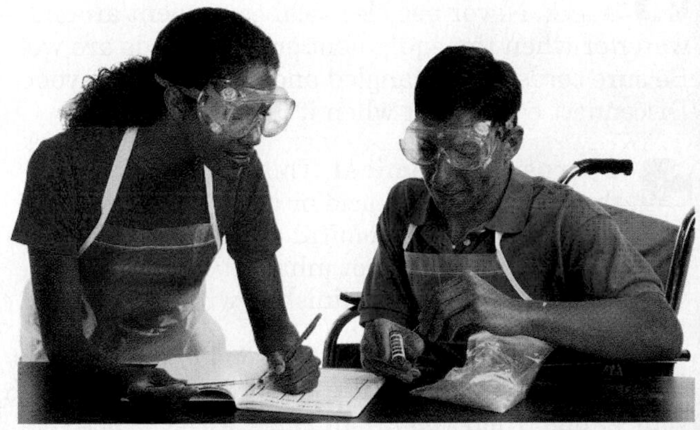

Safety Symbols

These symbols appear in laboratory activities to alert you to possible dangers and to remind you to work carefully.

Safety Goggles Always wear safety goggles to protect your eyes during any activity involving chemicals, flames or heating, or the possibility of flying objects, particles, or substances.

Lab Apron Wear a laboratory apron to protect your skin and clothing from injury.

Breakage Handle breakable materials such as thermometers and glassware with care. Do not touch broken glass.

Heat-Resistant Gloves Use an oven mitt or other hand protection when handling hot materials. Heating plates, hot water, and glassware can cause burns. Never touch hot objects with your bare hands.

Plastic Gloves Wear disposable plastic gloves to protect yourself from contact with chemicals or organisms that could be harmful. Keep your hands away from your face, and dispose of the gloves according to your teacher's instructions at the end of the activity.

Heating Use a clamp or tongs to hold hot objects. Do not touch hot objects with your bare hands.

Sharp Object Scissors, scalpels, pins, and knives are sharp. They can cut or puncture your skin. Always direct sharp edges and points away from yourself and others. Use sharp instruments only as directed.

Electric Shock Avoid the possibility of electric shock. Never use electrical equipment around water or when the equipment or your hands are wet. Be sure cords are untangled and cannot trip anyone. Disconnect equipment when it is not in use.

Corrosive Chemical This symbol indicates the presence of an acid or other corrosive chemical. Avoid getting the chemical on your skin or clothing, or in your eyes. Do not inhale the vapors. Wash your hands when you are finished with the activity.

Poison Do not let any poisonous chemical get on your skin, and do not inhale its vapor. Wash your hands when you are finished with the activity.

Physical Safety This activity involves physical movement. Use caution to avoid injuring yourself or others. Follow instructions from your teacher. Alert your teacher if there is any reason that you should not participate in the activity.

Animal Safety Treat live animals with care to avoid injuring the animals or yourself. Working with animal parts or preserved animals may also require caution. Wash your hands when you are finished with the activity.

Plant Safety Handle plants only as your teacher directs. If you are allergic to any plants used in an activity, tell your teacher before the activity begins. Avoid touching poisonous plants and plants with thorns.

Flames Tie back loose hair and clothing, and put on safety goggles before working with fire. Follow instructions from your teacher about lighting and extinguishing flames.

No Flames Flammable materials may be present. Make sure there are no flames, sparks, or exposed sources of heat present.

Fumes Poisonous or unpleasant vapors may be produced. Work in a ventilated area. Avoid inhaling a vapor directly. Test an odor only when directed to do so by your teacher, using a wafting motion to direct the vapor toward your nose.

Disposal Chemicals and other materials used in the activity must be disposed of safely. Follow the instructions from your teacher.

Hand Washing Wash your hands thoroughly when finished with the activity. Use antibacterial soap and warm water. Lather both sides of your hands and between your fingers. Rinse well.

General Safety Awareness You may see this symbol when none of the symbols described earlier applies. In this case, follow the specific instructions provided. You may also see this symbol when you are asked to design your own experiment. Do not start your experiment until your teacher has approved your plan.

The Metric System

The metric system of measurement is used by scientists throughout the world. It is based on units of ten. Each unit is ten times larger or ten times smaller than the next unit. The most commonly used units of the metric system are given below. After you have finished reading about the metric system, try to put it to use. How tall are you in meters? What is your mass? What is your normal body temperature in degrees Celsius?

Commonly Used Metric Units

Length The distance from one point to another

meter (m)	A meter is slightly longer than a yard.
	1 meter = 1000 millimeters (mm)
	1 meter = 100 centimeters (cm)
	1000 meters = 1 kilometer (km)

Volume The amount of space an object takes up

liter (L)	A liter is slightly more than a quart.
	1 liter = 1000 milliliters (mL)

Mass The amount of matter in an object

gram (g)	A paper clip has a mass equal to about one gram.
	1000 grams = 1 kilogram (kg)

Temperature The measure of hotness or coldness

degrees Celsius (°C)	0°C = freezing point of water
	100°C = boiling point of water

Metric–English Equivalents

2.54 centimeters (cm) = 1 inch (in.)
1 meter (m) = 39.37 inches (in.)
1 kilometer (km) = 0.62 miles (mi)
1 liter (L) = 1.06 quarts (qt)
236 milliliters (mL) = 1 cup (c)
1 kilogram (kg) = 2.2 pounds (lb)
28.3 grams (g) = 1 ounce (oz)
$°C = 5/9 \times (°F-32)$

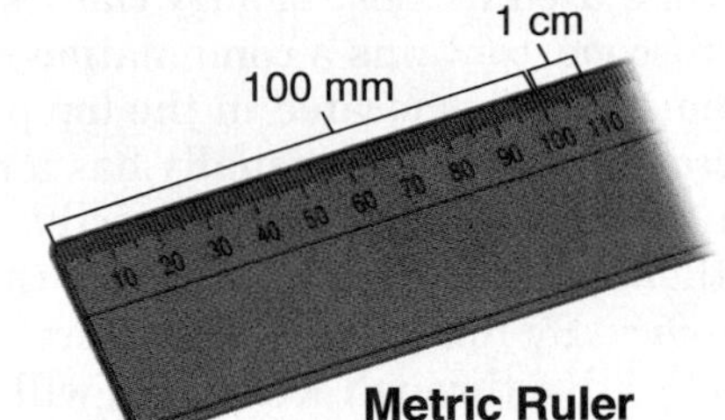

Metric Ruler

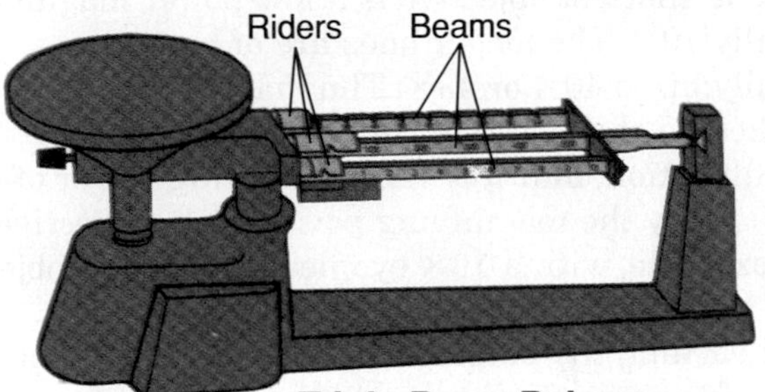

Triple-Beam Balance

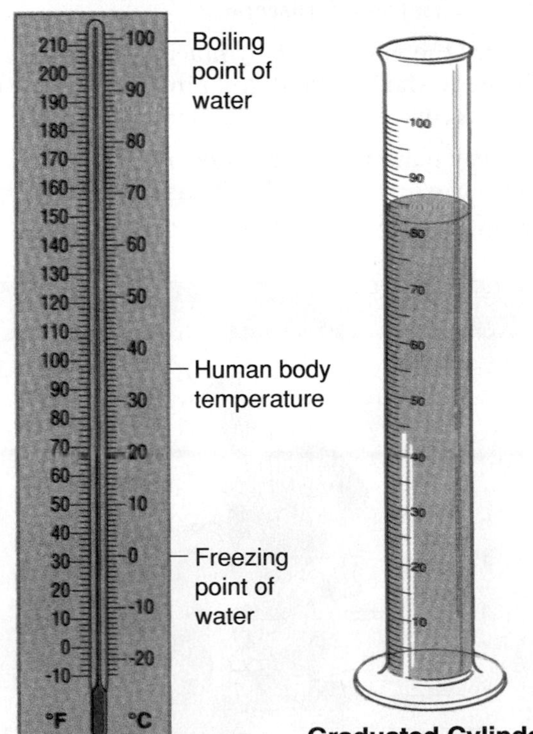

Thermometer

Graduated Cylinder

Appendix D Use of the Microscope

The Compound Microscope

The microscope used in most biology classes, the compound microscope, contains a combination of lenses. The eyepiece lens is located in the top portion of the microscope. This lens usually has a magnification of 10×. Other lenses, called objective lenses, are at the bottom of the body tube on the revolving nosepiece. By rotating the nosepiece, you can select the objective through which you will view your specimen.

The shortest objective is a low-power magnifier, usually 10×. The longer ones are of high power, usually up to 40× or 43×. The magnification is marked on the objective. To determine the total magnification, multiply the magnifying power of the eyepiece by the magnifying power of the objective. For example, with a 10× eyepiece and a 40× objective, the total magnification is $10 \times 40 = 400\times$.

Learning the name, function, and location of each of the microscope's parts is necessary for proper use. Use the following procedures when working with the microscope.

1. Carry the microscope by placing one hand beneath the base and grasping the arm of the microscope with the other hand.
2. Gently place the microscope on the lab table with the arm facing you. The microscope's base should be resting evenly on the table, approximately 10 cm from the table's edge.
3. Raise the body tube by turning the coarse adjustment knob until the objective lens is about 2 cm above the opening of the stage.
4. Rotate the nosepiece so that the low-power objective (10×) is directly in line with the body tube. A click indicates that the lens is in line with the opening of the stage.
5. Look through the eyepiece and switch on the lamp or adjust the mirror so that a circle of light can be seen. This is the field of view. Moving the lever of the diaphragm permits a greater or smaller amount of light to come through the opening of the stage.
6. Place a prepared slide on the stage so that the specimen is over the center of the opening. Use the stage clips to hold the slide in place.
7. Look at the microscope from the side. Carefully turn the coarse adjustment knob to lower the body tube until the low-power objective almost touches the slide or until the body tube can no longer be moved. Do not allow the objective to touch the slide.

Parts of the Microscope and Their Function

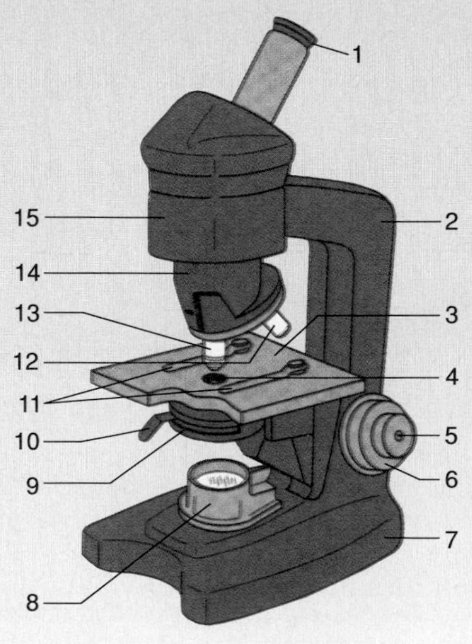

1. **Eyepiece** Contains a magnifying lens
2. **Arm** Supports the body tube
3. **Stage** Supports the slide being observed
4. **Opening of the stage** Permits light to pass up to the eyepiece
5. **Fine adjustment knob** Moves the body tube slightly to sharpen the image
6. **Coarse adjustment knob** Moves the body tube to focus the image
7. **Base** Supports the microscope
8. **Illuminator** Produces light or reflects light up toward the eyepiece
9. **Diaphragm** Regulates the amount of light passing up toward the eyepiece
10. **Diaphragm lever** Opens and closes the diaphragm
11. **Stage clips** Hold the slide in place
12. **Low-power objective** Provides a magnification of 10× and is the shortest objective
13. **High-power objective** Provides a magnification of 40× and is the longest objective
14. **Nosepiece** Holds the objectives and can be rotated to change the magnification
15. **Body tube** Maintains the proper distance between the eyepiece and the objectives

8. Look through the eyepiece and observe the specimen. If the field of view is out of focus, use the coarse adjustment knob to raise the body tube while looking through the eyepiece. **CAUTION:** *To prevent damage to the slide and the objective, do not lower the body tube using the coarse adjustment while looking through the eyepiece.* Focus the image as best you can with the coarse adjustment knob. Then, use the fine adjustment knob to focus the image more sharply. Keep both eyes open when viewing a specimen. This helps prevent eyestrain.
9. Adjust the lever of the diaphragm to allow the right amount of light to enter.
10. To change the magnification, rotate the nosepiece until the desired objective is in line with the body tube and clicks into place.
11. Look through the eyepiece and use the fine adjustment knob to bring the image into focus.
12. After every use, remove the slide. Return the low-power objective into place in line with the body tube. Clean the stage of the microscope and the lenses with lens paper. Do not use other types of paper to clean the lenses; they may scratch the lenses.

Preparing a Wet-Mount Slide

1. Obtain a clean microscope slide and a coverslip. A coverslip is very thin, permitting the objective lens to be lowered very close to the specimen.
2. Place the specimen in the middle of the microscope slide. The specimen must be thin enough for light to pass through it.

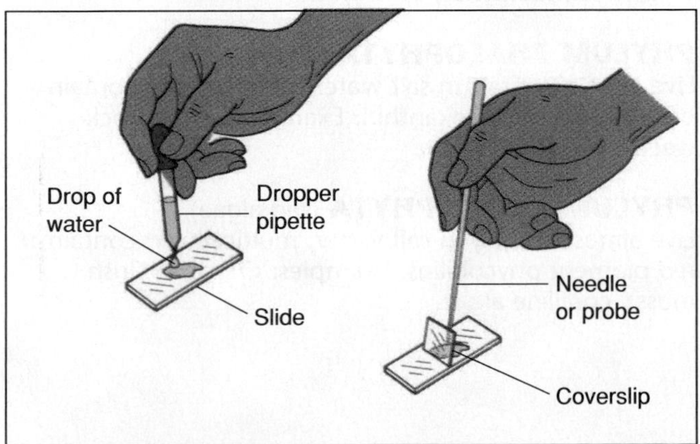

3. Using a dropper pipette, place a drop of water on the specimen.
4. Lower one edge of the coverslip so that it touches the side of the drop of water at about a 45° angle. The water will spread evenly along the edge of the coverslip. Using a dissecting needle or probe, slowly lower the coverslip over the specimen and water as shown in the drawing. Try not to trap any air bubbles under the coverslip. If air bubbles are present, gently tap the surface of the coverslip over the air bubble with a pencil eraser.
5. Remove any excess water at the edge of the coverslip with a paper towel. If the specimen begins to dry out, add a drop of water at the edge of the coverslip.

Staining Techniques

1. Obtain a clean microscope slide and coverslip.
2. Place the specimen in the middle of the microscope slide.
3. Using a dropper pipette, place a drop of water on the specimen. Place the coverslip so that its edge touches the drop of water at a 45° angle. After the water spreads along the edge of the coverslip, use a dissecting needle or probe to lower the coverslip over the specimen.

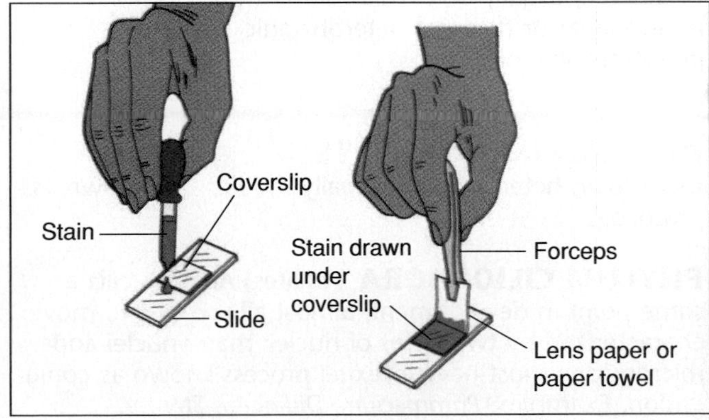

4. Add a drop of stain at the edge of the coverslip. Using forceps, touch a small piece of lens paper or paper towel to the opposite edge of the coverslip, as shown in the drawing. The paper causes the stain to be drawn under the coverslip and to stain the cells in the specimen.

Classification

DOMAIN ARCHAEA
Kingdom Archaebacteria

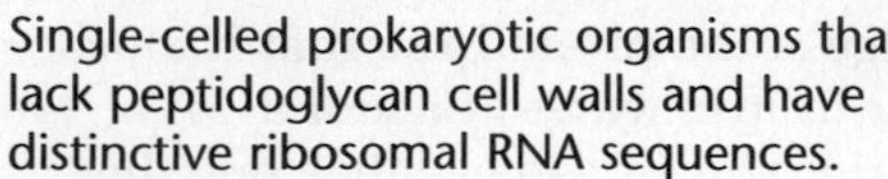

Single-celled prokaryotic organisms that lack peptidoglycan cell walls and have distinctive ribosomal RNA sequences.

The Archaebacteria include methanogens (organisms that produce methane gas, such as *Methanobacterium*), salt-loving bacteria (*Halococcus*), and thermoacidophilic bacteria (*Thermoplasma*), which grow in extremely high temperatures.

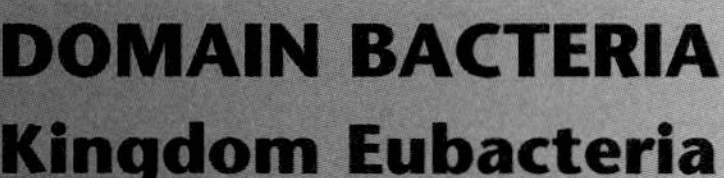

DOMAIN BACTERIA
Kingdom Eubacteria

Single-celled prokaryotic organisms; most have peptidoglycan cell walls. Sometimes form colonies of clumps or filaments.

The Eubacteria include the blue-green bacteria (cyanobacteria such as *Anabaena*), chemoautotrophs (*Nitrobacter*), spirochetes (*Treponema*), prochlorobacteria (*Prochloron*), spore-forming bacteria (*Bacillus*), and obligate internal parasites, such as the rickettsiae (*Rickettsia*).

DOMAIN EUKARYA
Kingdom Protista

Eukaryotic; usually unicellular; some multicellular or colonial; heterotrophic or autotrophic organisms.

ANIMALLIKE PROTISTS
Unicellular; heterotrophic; usually motile; also known as protozoa.

PHYLUM CILIOPHORA (ciliates) All have cilia at some point in development; almost all use cilia to move; characterized by two types of nuclei: macronuclei and micronuclei; most have a sexual process known as conjugation. Examples: *Paramecium, Didinium, Stentor.*

PHYLUM ZOOMASTIGINA (zooflagellates)
Possess one or more flagella (some have thousands). Examples: *Trichomonas, Trichonympha.*

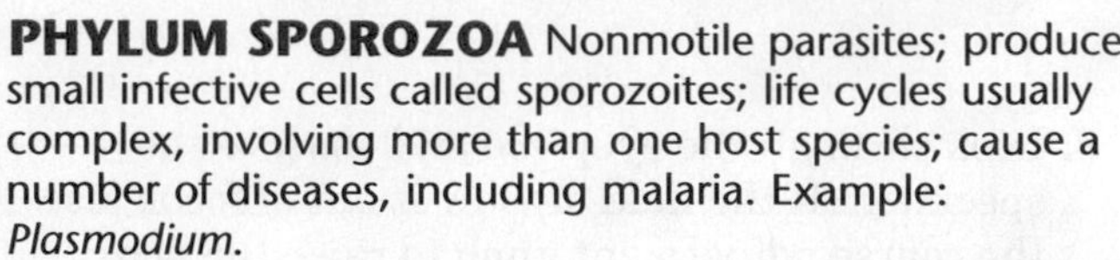

PHYLUM SPOROZOA Nonmotile parasites; produce small infective cells called sporozoites; life cycles usually complex, involving more than one host species; cause a number of diseases, including malaria. Example: *Plasmodium.*

PHYLUM SARCODINA Sarcodines use pseudopods for feeding and movement; some produce elaborate shells that contain silica or calcium carbonate; most free-living; a few parasitic; some involved in formation of sedimentary rock. Examples: *Amoeba*, foraminiferans.

PLANTLIKE PROTISTS
Mostly unicellular photosynthetic autotrophs that have characteristics similar to those of plants. A few species are multicellular or heterotrophic.

PHYLUM EUGLENOPHYTA (euglenophytes)
Primarily photosynthetic; most live in fresh water; possess two unequal flagella; lack cell walls. Example: *Euglena.*

PHYLUM PYRROPHYTA (dinoflagellates) Two flagella; most live in salt water, are photosynthetic, and have rigid cell walls that contain cellulose; some are luminescent; many are symbiotic. Examples: *Gonyaulux, Noctilucans scintillans.*

PHYLUM CHRYSOPHYTA (chrysophytes)
Mostly photosynthetic; aquatic; mostly unicellular; contain yellow-brown pigments. Example: *Thallasiosira.*

PHYLUM BACILLARIOPHYTA (diatoms)
Photosynthetic; live in fresh and salt water; have unique glasslike cell walls; among the most abundant organisms on Earth. Example: *Navicula.*

PHYLUM CHLOROPHYTA (green algae)
Live in fresh water and salt water; unicellular or multicellular; chlorophylls and accessory pigments similar to those in vascular plants; food stored as starch. Examples: *Ulva, Chlamydomonas, Spirogyra.*

PHYLUM PHAEOPHYTA (brown algae)
Live almost entirely in salt water; multicellular; contain brown pigment fucoxanthin. Examples: *Fucus* (rockweed), kelp, *Sargassum.*

PHYLUM RHODOPHYTA (red algae)
Live almost entirely in salt water; multicellular; contain red pigment phycobilins. Examples: *Chondrus* (Irish moss), coralline algae.

FUNGUSLIKE PROTISTS

Heterotrophs that have some characteristics similar to those of fungi, though they have centrioles and lack cell walls of chitin.

PHYLUM ACRASIOMYCOTA (cellular slime molds) Spores develop into independent free-living amoeba-like cells that may come together to form a multicellular structure; this structure forms a fruiting body that produces spores. Example: *Dictyostelium*.

PHYLUM MYXOMYCOTA (acellular slime molds) Spores develop into haploid cells that can switch between flagellated and amoeba-like forms; these haploid cells fuse to form a zygote that grows into a plasmodium, which ultimately forms spore-producing fruiting bodies. Example: *Physarum*.

PHYLUM OOMYCOTA (water molds) Unicellular or multicellular; mostly aquatic; cell walls contain cellulose. Example: *Phytophthora infestans*.

Kingdom Fungi

Eukaryotic; heterotrophic; unicellular or multicellular; cell walls typically contain chitin; mostly decomposers; some parasites; some commensal or mutualistic symbionts; asexual reproduction by spore formation, budding, or fragmentation; sexual reproduction involving mating types; classified according to structure and method of reproduction.

PHYLUM ZYGOMYCOTA (common molds) Cell walls of chitin; hyphae generally lack cross walls; sexual reproduction by conjugation produces diploid zygospores; asexual reproduction produces haploid spores; most parasites; some decomposers. Example: *Rhizopus stolonifer* (black bread mold).

PHYLUM ASCOMYCOTA (sac fungi) Cell walls of chitin; hyphae have perforated cross walls; most multicellular; yeasts unicellular; sexual reproduction produces ascospores; asexual reproduction by spore formation or budding; some cause plant diseases such as chestnut blight and Dutch elm disease. Examples: *Neurospora* (red bread mold), baker's yeast, morels, truffles.

PHYLUM BASIDIOMYCOTA (club fungi) Cell walls of chitin; hyphae have cross walls; sexual reproduction involves basidiospores, which are borne on club-shaped basidia; asexual reproduction by spore formation. Examples: mushrooms, puffballs, shelf fungi, rusts.

PHYLUM DEUTEROMYCOTA (imperfect fungi) Cell walls of chitin; sexual reproduction never observed; members resemble ascomycetes, basidiomycetes, or zygomycetes. Example: *Penicillium*.

Kingdom Plantae

Eukaryotic; multicellular and nonmotile; photosynthetic autotrophs; possess chlorophylls *a* and *b* and other pigments in organelles called chloroplasts; cell walls contain cellulose; food stored as starch; reproduce sexually; alternate haploid (gametophyte) and diploid (sporophyte) generations.

PHYLUM BRYOPHYTA (mosses) Generally small; multicellular plants; live on land in moist habitats; lack vascular tissue; lack true roots, leaves, and stems; gametophyte dominant; water required for reproduction.

PHYLUM HEPATICOPHYTA (liverworts) Generally small, flat, lobe-shaped; multicellular plants; live on land in moist habitats; lack vascular tissue and true roots, leaves, and stems; gametophyte dominant; water required for reproduction.

PHYLUM ANTHCEROPHYTA (hornworts) Generally small; multicellular plants; live on land in moist habitats; lack vascular tissue and true roots, leaves, and stems; gametophyte dominant; named for horn-shaped sporophyte; water required for reproduction.

PHYLUM LYCOPHYTA (club mosses) Primitive vascular plants; usually small; sporophyte dominant; possess roots, stems, and leaves; water required for reproduction. Examples: club moss, quillwort.

PHYLUM ARTHROPHYTA (horsetails) Primitive vascular plants; stems comprise most of mature plants and contain silica; produce only one kind of spore; motile sperm must swim in water. Only one living genus. Example: *Equisetum*.

PHYLUM PTEROPHYTA (ferns) Vascular plants well adapted to live in predominantly damp or seasonally wet environments; sporophyte dominant and well adapted to terrestrial life; gametophyte inconspicuous; reproduction still dependent on water for free-swimming gametes. Examples: cinnamon fern, Boston fern, tree fern, maidenhair fern.

PHYLUM CYCADOPHYTA (cycads) Evergreen, slow-growing, tropical and subtropical shrubs; many resemble small palm trees; palmlike or fernlike compound leaves; sexes are separate—individuals have either male pollen-producing cones or female seed-producing cones.

PHYLUM GINKGOPHYTA (ginkgoes) Deciduous trees with fan-shaped leaves; sexes separate; outer skin of ovule develops into a fleshy, fruitlike covering. Only one living species: *Ginkgo biloba* (ginkgo).

PHYLUM GNETOPHYTA (gnetophytes) Few species; mostly desert-living. Examples: *Welwitschia*, Mormon tea (*Ephedra*).

PHYLUM CONIFEROPHYTA (conifers) Seeds born on cones; predominantly wind-pollinated; most are evergreen; most are temperate and subarctic shrubs and trees; many have needlelike leaves; in most species, sexes are not separate. Examples: pine, spruce, cedar, cypress, yew, fir, larch, sequoia.

PHYLUM ANTHOPHYTA (angiosperms: flowering plants) Seeds develop enclosed within ovaries; leaves modified into flowers; flowers pollinated by wind or by animals, including insects, birds, and bats; occur in many different forms; found in most land and freshwater habitats; a few species found in shallow saltwater and estuarine areas.

CLASS MONOCOTYLEDONAE (monocots) Embryo with a single cotyledon; leaves with predominantly parallel venation; flower parts in multiples of three; vascular bundles scattered throughout stem. Examples: lily, corn, grasses, iris, palm, tulip.

CLASS DICOTYLEDONAE (dicots) Embryo with two cotyledons; leaves with venation in netlike patterns; flower parts in multiples of fours or fives; vascular bundles arranged in rings in stem. Examples: rose, maple, oak, daisy, apple.

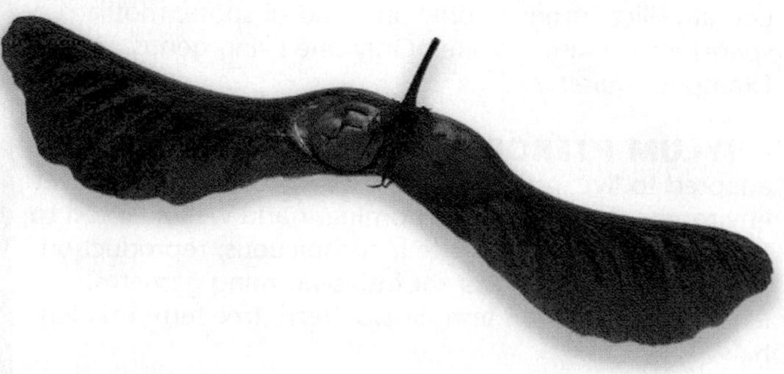

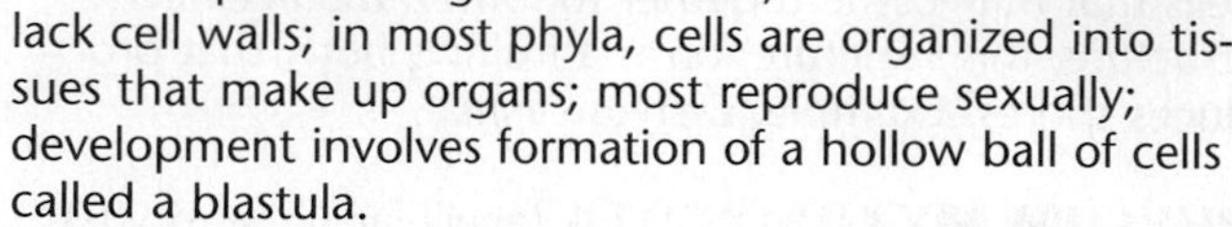

Kingdom Animalia

Multicellular; eukaryotic; typical heterotrophs that ingest their food; lack cell walls; in most phyla, cells are organized into tissues that make up organs; most reproduce sexually; development involves formation of a hollow ball of cells called a blastula.

PHYLUM PORIFERA (sponges) Aquatic; lack true tissues and organs; motile larvae and sessile adults; filter feeders; internal skeleton made up of spongin and/or spicules of calcium carbonate or silica. Examples: Venus' flower basket, bath sponge, tube sponge.

PHYLUM CNIDARIA (cnidarians) Previously known as coelenterates; aquatic; mostly carnivorous; two layers of true tissues; radial symmetry; tentacles bear stinging nematocysts; many alternate between polyp and medusa body forms; gastrovascular cavity.

CLASS HYDROZOA Spend most of their time as polyps; colonial or solitary; life cycle typically includes a medusa generation that reproduces sexually and a polyp generation that reproduces asexually. Examples: hydra, Portuguese man-of-war.

CLASS SCYPHOZOA Spend most of their time as medusas; some species bypass polyp stage. Examples: lion's mane jellyfish, moon jelly, sea wasp.

CLASS ANTHOZOA Colonial or solitary polyps; no medusa stage. Examples: reef coral, sea anemone, sea pen, sea fan.

PHYLUM PLATYHELMINTHES (flatworms) Three layers of tissues (endoderm, mesoderm, ectoderm); bilateral symmetry; some cephalization; acoelomate; free-living or parasitic.

CLASS TURBELLARIA (turbellarians) Free-living carnivores and scavengers; live in fresh water, in salt water, or on land; move with cilia. Example: planarians.

CLASS TREMATODA (flukes) Parasites; life cycle typically involves more than one host. Examples: *Schistosoma*, liver fluke.

CLASS CESTODA (tapeworms) Internal parasites; lack digestive tract; body composed of many repeating sections (proglottids). Example: tapeworms.

PHYLUM NEMATODA (roundworms)
Digestive system has two openings—a mouth and an anus; pseudocoelomates. Examples: *Ascaris lumbricoides*, hookworms, *Trichinella*.

PHYLUM ANNELIDA (segmented worms) Body composed of segments separated by internal partitions; digestive system has two openings; coelomate; closed circulatory system.

CLASS POLYCHAETA (polychaetes) Live in salt water; pair of bristly, fleshy appendages on each segment; some live in tubes. Examples: sandworm, fanworm, feather-duster worm.

CLASS OLIGOCHAETA (oligochaetes) Lack appendages; few bristles; terrestrial or fresh water. Examples: *Tubifex*, earthworm.

CLASS HIRUDINEA (leeches) Lack appendages; carnivores or blood-sucking external parasites; most live in fresh water. Example: medicinal leech (*Hirudo medicinalis*).

PHYLUM MOLLUSCA (mollusks) Soft-bodied; often possess a hard, calcified shell secreted by a mantle; muscular foot; digestive system with two openings; coelomates.

CLASS BIVALVIA (bivalves) Two-part hinged shell; wedge-shaped foot; typically sessile as adults; primarily aquatic; some burrow in mud or sand. Examples: clam, oyster, scallop, mussel.

CLASS GASTROPODA (gastropods) Use broad, muscular foot in movement; most have spiral, chambered shell; some lack shell; distinct head; some terrestrial, others aquatic; many are cross-fertilizing hermaphrodites. Examples: snail, slug, nudibranch, sea hare, sea butterfly.

CLASS CEPHALOPODA (cephalopods) Foot is divided into tentacles; live in salt water; closed circulatory system. Examples: octopus, squid, nautilus, cuttlefish.

PHYLUM ARTHROPODA (arthropods) Exoskeleton of chitin; jointed appendages; segmented body; many undergo metamorphosis during development; open circulatory system; largest animal phylum.

Subphylum Trilobita (trilobites) Two furrows running from head to tail divide body into three lobes; one pair of unspecialized appendages on each body segment; each appendage divided into two branches—a gill and a walking leg; all extinct.

Subphylum Chelicerata (chelicerates) First pair of appendages specialized as feeding structures called chelicerae; body composed of two parts—cephalothorax and abdomen; lack antennae; most terrestrial. Examples: horseshoe crab, tick, mite, spider, scorpion.

Subphylum Crustacea (crustaceans) Most aquatic; most live in salt water; two pairs of antennae; mouthparts called mandibles; appendages consist of two branches; many have a carapace that covers part or all of the body. Examples: crab, crayfish, pill bug, water flea, barnacle.

Subphylum Uniramia Almost all terrestrial; one pair of antennae; mandibles; unbranched appendages.

CLASS CHILOPODA (centipedes) Long body consisting of many segments; one pair of legs per segment; poison claws for feeding; carnivorous.

CLASS DIPLOPODA (millipedes) Long body consisting of many segments; two pairs of legs per segment; mostly herbivorous.

CLASS INSECTA (insects) Body divided into three parts—head, thorax, and abdomen; three pairs of legs and usually one or two pairs of wings attached to thorax; some undergo complete metamorphosis. Examples: termite, ant, beetle, dragonfly, fly, moth, grasshopper.

PHYLUM ECHINODERMATA (echinoderms)
Live in salt water; larvae have bilateral symmetry; adults typically have radial symmetry; endoskeleton; tube feet; water vascular system used in respiration, excretion, feeding, and locomotion; deuterostomes.

CLASS CRINOIDEA (crinoids) Filter feeders; feathery arms; mouth and anus on upper surface of body disk; some sessile. Examples: sea lily, feather star.

CLASS ASTEROIDEA (sea stars) Star-shaped; carnivorous; bottom dwellers; mouth on lower surface. Examples: crown-of-thorns sea star, sunstar.

CLASS OPHIUROIDEA Small body disk; long armored arms; most have only five arms; lack an anus; most are filter feeders or detritus feeders. Examples: brittle star, basket star.

CLASS ECHINOIDEA Lack arms; body encased in rigid, box-like covering; covered with spines; most grazing herbivores or detritus feeders. Examples: sea urchin, sand dollar, sea biscuit.

CLASS HOLOTHUROIDEA (sea cucumbers) Cylindrical body with feeding tentacles on one end; lie on their side; mostly detritus or filter feeders; endoskeleton greatly reduced.

PHYLUM CHORDATA (chordates) Dorsal hollow nerve cord, notochord, pharyngeal pouches, and a muscular tail during at least part of development.

Subphylum Urochordata (tunicates) Live in salt water; tough outer covering; display chordate features during larval stages; many adults sessile, some free-swimming. Examples: sea squirt, sea peach, salp.

Subphylum Cephalochordata (lancelets) Fishlike; live in salt water; filter feeders; no internal skeleton. Example: Branchiostoma.

Subphylum Vertebrata Most possess a vertebral column (backbone) that supports and protects dorsal nerve chord; endoskeleton; distinct head with a skull and brain.

CLASS MYXINI (hagfishes) Mostly scavengers; live in salt water; short tentacles around mouth; rasping tongue; extremely slimy; open circulatory system.

CLASS CEPHALASPIDOMORPHI (lampreys) Larvae filter feeders; adults are parasites whose circular mouth is lined with rasping toothlike structures; many live in both salt water and fresh water during the course of their lives.

CLASS CHONDRICHTHYES (cartilaginous fishes) Have jaws, fins, and endoskeleton of cartilage; most live in salt water; typically several gill slits; tough small scales with spines; ectothermic; two-chambered heart; males possess structures for internal fertilization. Examples: shark, ray, skate, chimaera, sawfish.

CLASS OSTEICHTHYES (bony fishes) Bony endoskeleton; aquatic; ectothermic; well-developed respiratory system, usually involving gills; possess swim bladder; paired fins; divided into two groups—ray-finned fishes, which include most living species, and lobe-finned fishes, which include lungfishes and the coelacanth. Examples: salmon, perch, sturgeon, tuna, goldfish, eel.

CLASS AMPHIBIA (amphibians) Adapted primarily to life in wet places; ectothermic; most carnivorous; smooth, moist skin; typically lay eggs that develop in water; usually have gilled larvae; most have three-chambered heart; adults either aquatic or terrestrial; terrestrial forms respire using lungs, skin, and/or lining of the mouth.

Order Urodela (salamanders) Possess tail as adults; carnivorous; usually have four legs; usually aquatic as larvae and terrestrial as adults.

Order Anura (frogs and toads) Adults in almost all species lack tail; aquatic larvae called tadpoles; well-developed hind legs adapted for jumping.

Order Apoda (legless amphibians) Wormlike; lack legs; carnivorous; terrestrial burrowers; some undergo direct development; some viviparous. Example: caecilians.

CLASS REPTILIA (reptiles) As a group, adapted to fully terrestrial life, some live in water; dry, scale-covered skin; ectothermic; most have three-chambered hearts; internal fertilization; amniotic eggs typically laid on land; extinct forms include dinosaurs and flying reptiles.

Order Sphenodonta (tuataras) Lack internal ears; primitive scales; found only in New Zealand; carnivorous. One species: *Sphenodon punctatus.*

Order Squamata (lizards and snakes) Most carnivorous; majority terrestrial; lizards typically have legs; snakes lack legs. Examples: iguana, gecko, skink, cobra, python, boa.

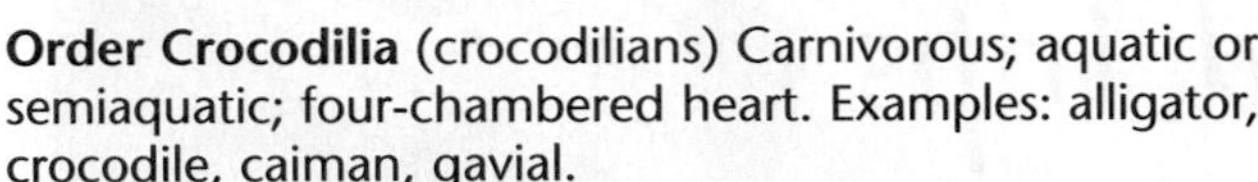

Order Crocodilia (crocodilians) Carnivorous; aquatic or semiaquatic; four-chambered heart. Examples: alligator, crocodile, caiman, gavial.

Order Testudines (turtles and tortoises) Bony shell; ribs and vertebrae fused to upper part of shell; some terrestrial, others semiaquatic or aquatic; all lay eggs on land. Examples: snapping turtle, tortoise, hawksbill turtle, box turtle.

CLASS AVES (birds) Endothermic; feathered over much of body surface; scales on legs and feet; bones hollow and lightweight in flying species; four-chambered heart; well-developed lungs and air sacs for efficient air exchange. Examples: owl, eagle, duck, chicken, pigeon, penguin, sparrow, stork.

CLASS MAMMALIA (mammals) Endothermic; subcutaneous fat; hair; most viviparous; suckle young with milk produced in mammary glands; four-chambered heart; most have four legs; use lungs for respiration.

Order Monotremata (monotremes) Exhibit features of both mammals and reptiles; possess a cloaca; lay eggs that hatch externally; produce milk from primitive nipple-like structures. Examples: duckbill platypus, short-beaked echidna.

Order Marsupialia (marsupials) Young develop in the female's uterus but emerge at very early state of development; development completed in mother's pouch. Examples: opossum, kangaroo, koala.

Order Insectivora (insectivores) Have long, narrow snouts and sharp claws for digging. Examples: shrew, mole, hedgehog.

Order Chiroptera (bats) Flying mammals, with forelimbs adapted for flight; most nocturnal; most navigate by echolocation; most species feed on insects, nectar, or fruits; some species feed on blood. Examples: fruit bat, flying fox, vampire bat.

Order Primates (primates) Highly developed brain and complex social behavior; excellent binocular vision; quadrupedal or bipedal locomotion; five digits on hands and feet. Examples: lemur, monkey, chimpanzee, human.

Order Xenarthra (xenarthrans) Teeth reduced or absent; feed primarily on social insects, such as termites and ants. Examples: anteater, armadillo.

Order Lagomorpha (lagomorphs) Small herbivores with chisel-shaped front teeth; generally adapted to running and jumping. Examples: rabbit, pika, hare.

Order Rodentia (rodents) Mostly herbivorous but some omnivorous; sharp front teeth. Examples: rat, beaver, guinea pig, hamster, gerbil, squirrel.

Order Cetacea (cetaceans) Fully adapted to aquatic existence; feed, breed, and give birth in water; forelimbs specialized as flippers; external hindlimbs absent; many species capable of long, deep dives; some use echolocation to navigate; communicate using complex auditory signals. Examples: whale, porpoise, dolphin.

Order Carnivora (carnivores) Mostly carnivorous; live in salt water or on land; aquatic species must return to land to breed. Examples: seal, bear, raccoon, weasel, skunk.

Order Proboscidea (elephants) Herbivorous; have trunks; largest land animal. Examples: Asian elephant, African elephant.

Order Sirenia (sirenians) Aquatic herbivores; slow-moving; forelimbs modified as flippers; hindlimbs absent; little body hair. Examples: manatee, sea cow.

Order Perissodactyla (odd-toed ungulates) Hoofed herbivores; odd number of digits on each foot; teeth, jaw, and digestive system adapted to plant material. Examples: horse, donkey, rhinoceros, tapir.

Order Artiodactyla (even-toed ungulates) Hoofed herbivores; hoofs derived from two digits on each foot; digestive system adapted to thoroughly process tough plant material. Examples: sheep, cow, hippopotamus, antelope, camel, giraffe, pig.

Tips for Successful Field Trips

Biology field trips can have different purposes and take place in a variety of environments. The steps you take and the observations you make can vary greatly. However, field trips often involve common elements, such as the way you plan the event and what you do at the site. If you plan well and organize your activities thoughtfully, your field trips will be more productive and enjoyable. Here are some suggestions to consider.

Planning the Trip

1. Discuss with your teacher and classmates the type of area you will visit and decide what you are likely to gather. This will help determine the materials needed to collect specimens.
2. When you go on a field trip, you will encounter some living things you can collect and some you cannot.
   - For things you can't collect, such as most animals and large plants or plants on other people's property, take a photograph or make a sketch.
   - For things you can collect, such as water samples, soil samples, small plants, flowers, pine cones, fungi, and insects, take containers such as prelabeled plastic bags and jars with lids. Some jar lids should contain air holes. You may also need tools for collecting, such as a small trowel or garden spade for soil and an aquarium net for small water organisms.
3. List the materials you will need, including the following items:
   - data table and blank sheets of paper in a firm notebook or on a clipboard
   - a camera
   - marking pens and writing utensils
   - a magnifying glass
4. Write the steps in your plan. Have your teacher check it for practicality and safety.

During the Trip

1. Before leaving for the site, make sure you have all the materials listed in your plan.
2. Wear sturdy shoes, long sleeves, and long pants. Depending upon the time of year and the site itself, you should also consider wearing insect repellent and sunscreen.
3. Work in the groups that your teacher has assigned.
4. When you collect samples to bring back to the classroom, make sure you follow these rules:
   - Observe all local laws, and respect other people's property.
   - Avoid contact with poisonous plants and animals. Bright colors and highly contrasting colors may indicate that an animal is dangerous.
   - When turning over logs and stones, use a long stick in case stinging insects or snakes are underneath.
   - Do not collect any animals without the permission of your teacher.
   - Remember that all animals must be treated humanely. All vertebrates collected for study, such as small fish or tadpoles, must be returned to their environment unharmed.
   - As soon as possible after you have finished, wash your hands thoroughly with soap and warm water.

After the Trip

Make sure that the samples you bring back to the classroom for observation are stored under the appropriate conditions. Generally, samples should have access to air (either put holes in the lids of the containers or keep them loosely covered). Do not leave any samples completely uncovered, because they might dry out. Keep the samples cool and *do not* store in direct sunlight.

How Do Living Things Interact?

Living things spend a lot of time obtaining nutrients. How they do this influences their relationships with other organisms. In this activity, you will discover those relationships.

Problem

What interactions exist among organisms in an ecosystem?

Materials

- containers (plastic bags and jars with lids)
- camera (optional)
- magnifying glass
- microscope
- glass slides
- coverslips
- dropper pipette
- field guides

Skills

Observing, Inferring, Analyzing Data, Drawing Conclusions

Procedure

Part A: Preparing for the Field Trip

1. Your goal is to observe and identify as many organisms as you can in the area you are visiting so that you can construct an accurate picture of the food webs in that ecosystem. During the field trip itself, you will identify each organism or trace of an organism you observe by name or with a description and a picture.
2. Discuss with your teacher and classmates the type of area you will visit to help you plan for what you might observe.
3. Review classification at the kingdom level on pages 457–461, if necessary. Identifying the kingdom is a useful step in determining how an organism gets food.
4. Gather enough descriptive information about the organisms you expect to observe so that you can identify them with a field guide. This will enable you to research which step in the food chain the organism occupies.
5. Just because you don't see an organism doesn't mean it leaves no traces of its existence and interactions with its surroundings. Spider webs, for example, mean there are spiders eating insects. This kind of indirect evidence enables you to identify a consumer and infer where it is in the food chain. Other indirect evidence can include nests, burrows, and paw prints. Plan to sketch or photograph these traces.
6. Familiarize yourself with the biomes and ecosystems described on pages 99–112. Different plants grow in different biomes. The types of plants in an area determine the type of community.
7. Physical characteristics of an area determine the kinds of producers and ultimately the type of ecosystem. Find out as much as you can about the biome and ecosystem you will be visiting.
8. Some of your observations will be made in the field, and some will be made in the classroom. Prepare a data table similar to the one on the next page to record your observations.
9. Have your teacher check your written plan and review all safety considerations.

Part B: Working at the Site

10. On the day of your trip, bring along all the materials listed in your plan.
11. Describe the location in which you are making observations. Observe a sufficient number of plants to help determine the nature of the ecosystem. If it is a land ecosystem, examine the soil for moisture and texture.
12. If you are visiting an aquatic ecosystem, collect some water samples. The organisms at or near the bottom of the water food chains are often microscopic.
13. Describe, sketch, and photograph any organisms or traces of organisms (tracks, nests, burrows, for example) that you see.
14. The best way to get close to larger animals is to wait patiently and quietly, hiding where you will not be seen. While you are waiting you can observe the surrounding plants and the behavior of smaller animals. Use a magnifying glass. Watch the skies for birds as well.

How Do Living Things Interact? (continued)

Data Table						
Number	Location	Organism or Trace	Feeding Behavior (Producer, herbivore, carnivore, decomposer)	Other Behavior	Other	Identity of Organism
1						
2						
3						

15 When you see an animal, pay careful attention to the placement of the eyes. Predators often have their eyes in the front of their heads. Animals that are preyed upon often have eyes at the sides of their heads.

16 Watch for behavior. Observe what an animal eats and how it eats. This tells you something about where it is on the food chain. Describe any other animal behavior you observe, such as hiding, burrowing, or nesting.

17 Record any other observations that you think might help to identify the role of the organism in its community. As soon as possible after you have finished, wash your hands with soap and warm water.

Part C: Following the Field Trip

18 If you collected any water samples, prepare wet mounts of samples from the top, middle, and bottom of the container. Examine the slides for the presence of organisms. Fill in the required observations on the data table. Note whether the organisms have chlorophyll or not. Watch for feeding behavior. Wash your hands with soap and warm water when you have finished.

19 Try to identify the organisms you have observed and the organisms that produced the traces you have observed, using field guides or the Internet. It is not necessary to know the species of each organism. You need to know only enough to learn how the organism obtains nutrients and what its predators are. For example, identifying a bird as an owl, a hawk, or a pigeon is sufficient for finding out what it eats. Write your conclusion in your data table.

20 If necessary, after you identify the organisms you observed, research in the library or on the Internet how the organisms obtain nutrients and which other organisms interact with them.

Analyze and Conclude

1. **Classifying** What were some of the interactions you observed between organisms? Describe at least one example of predation.
2. **Analyzing Data** Based on your observations and research, draw one or more food chains from the organisms in the community you visited. Identify the trophic levels in each food chain (producer, primary consumer, secondary consumer, decomposer).
3. **Analyzing Data** Based on the food chains you drew, draw a food web for the community you visited.
4. **Drawing Conclusions** Give one or more examples of symbiosis that you observed. Explain whether each relationship is based on food-getting or on other factors, such as living space.
5. **Drawing Conclusions** Based on the climate and types of organisms found in the community you observed, in what biome is it found? Support your conclusion with evidence and reasoning.
6. **SAFETY** How did you demonstrate safe practices during this investigation?

Go Further

Comparing and Contrasting Select a biome different from the one you visited. Do research to determine what organisms are present in a community located in that biome and what ecological relationships exist among them. Write a plan describing how you would gather data in that biome and what you might observe. Describe some possible food chains and food webs in that biome. How is it different from the one you observed? How is it similar?

Which Kingdoms Live in Your Neighborhood?

Much of the life around you goes unnoticed because it is either hidden or so familiar that you take it for granted. In this activity, you will observe the life forms in your neighborhood in sufficient detail to classify them into their proper kingdoms.

Problem
How can you collect and classify organisms at the kingdom level?

Materials
- camera (optional)
- containers (plastic bags and jars with lids)
- small trowel or garden spade
- aquarium net
- unrefrigerated food
- large plastic cup
- marking pens
- rubber tubing
- large funnel
- hose clamp
- iron ring and ring stand
- cheesecloth
- white paper
- dissecting tray
- magnifying glass
- coverslips
- petroleum jelly
- dropper pipette
- depression slides
- microscope
- glass slides

Skills
Observing, Classifying, Comparing and Contrasting

Procedure     

Part A: Preparing for the Field Trip

1. As you plan for your trip, follow the guidelines in the Lab Tips box on page 55 and the field trip tips on page 1078.
2. You will make observations in the field and in the classroom. Prepare a data table similar to the one below to record observations.
3. Make sure you are familiar with the six-kingdom classification system explained in Section 18–3.
4. Write a plan that describes a procedure for your field trip. Have your teacher review the plan for practicality and safety.
5. At home, select some food items to bring to class just before your field trip. These will be left unrefrigerated to speed growth of microorganisms.
6. Before going on the trip, set aside the food items you brought in a place designated by your teacher. Dry foods such as beans or bread should be placed in a container with some moisture. Also, set aside a large plastic cup of water.

Part B: Working at the Site

7. At the site, look in a variety of places with different characteristics to find the largest variety of organisms. Look in sunny areas, in the shade, in the water, in the air, behind plants, between the blades of grass, within a forest, at the edge of a forest, and so on. When you locate an organism, record your observations in your data table.

Data Table

Number	Size (microscopic or macroscopic)	Movement (yes or no)	Color	Description	Kingdom
1					
2					
3					

Which Kingdoms Live in Your Neighborhood? (continued)

8 Supplement your observations with drawings or photographs. Keep in mind that when you take photographs outside, using a flash may sometimes be necessary. Place the row number from your data table on each drawing, photograph, or container to help keep your observations organized.

9 Here are some hints for filling in your data table:

- The organisms you see in the field will all be macroscopic (able to be seen without a microscope). This usually tells you that the organism is multicellular.
- When you look for locomotion, you are looking for movement by an animal, not motion because of wind or other objects.
- As you examine an organism's color, look for signs of the green pigment chlorophyll and note if it is present. The presence of chlorophyll is typical of plants and some protists.
- In your description, include information such as where the organism is found. If the organism is found on another living thing, for example, it may be using it for food, as fungi do.
- Indicate whether the organism has appendages. Animals may remain still when you look at them, but the presence of wings or legs is a sign they can move.
- Note if the organism is anchored. Plants and fungi are generally anchored, but some animals such as sponges or barnacles are anchored, too. Look for an opening it uses for taking in food.

10 Try to collect the following samples to bring back to the classroom: water from ponds, lakes, streams, oceans, or puddles; soil and sand; natural mulch or leaves; and small plants or parts of plants. Wash your hands with soap and warm water.

Part C: Following the Field Trip, Day 1

11 If you collected moist soil, set up the apparatus shown above, right, to collect roundworms and other tiny animals. Put a piece of rubber tubing on the end of a large funnel. Place a hose clamp on the rubber tubing. Hang the funnel through an iron ring on a ring stand.

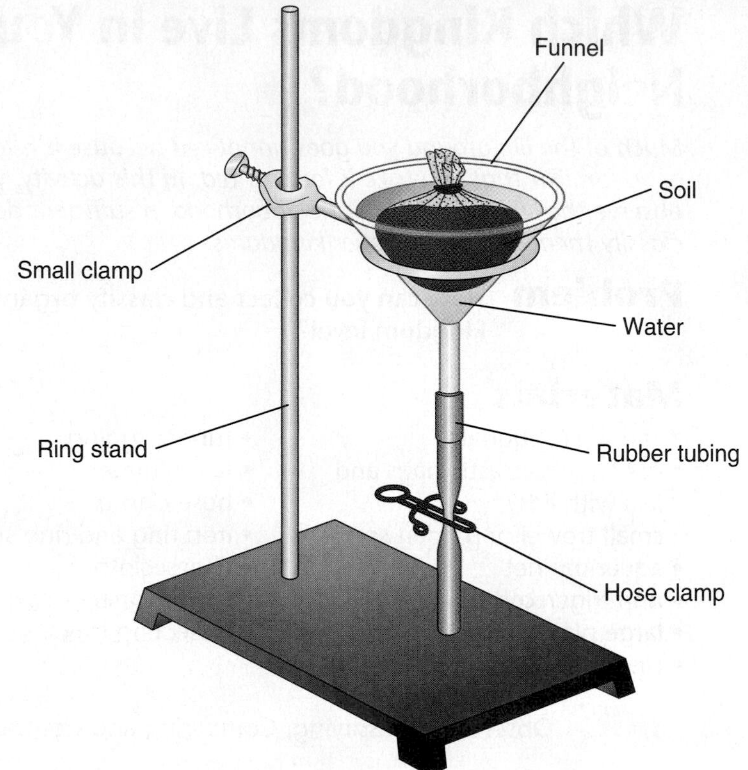

12 Double a piece of cheesecloth and place a sample of soil in the middle. Then, tie it closed to make a small sack. Put the sack in the funnel. Then, pour enough water into the funnel to fill it almost to the top. Leave the sack in the water for 24 hours.

13 If you collected sand or dry soil, place a sheet of white paper in a dissecting tray and spread a thin layer of the sand or soil on the paper. Examine the thin layer of soil with a magnifying glass. Look for signs of life. If you find any organisms, record your observations in your data table and draw diagrams or take a photograph of what you find.

14 If you collected mulch or leaves, place a clean piece of white paper in a dissecting tray and repeat the procedure you used in step 13 with a portion of the leaves or mulch.

15 Fallen leaves and mulch often contain microorganisms that can be rinsed off for study. Take some moist leaves or mulch from the bottom of the pile and place them in the cup of water you set aside in step 6. Leave them overnight.

16. To examine water samples you collected, prepare a slide as follows: Using a dropper pipette, withdraw water from the top of the water sample. Place a drop in the center of a clean slide. Then, cover the drop with a coverslip. If you pick up any macroscopic organisms with your dropper pipette, use a depression slide rather than a plain glass slide.
17. Prepare two more slides with water from the middle and bottom of the sample.
18. Examine the slides under low power. If necessary, switch to higher power for a closer look. Record your observations in your data table and draw diagrams of what you find. Wash your hands with soap and warm water.

Part D: Following the Field Trip, Day 2

19. Examine the food substances from step 5 for the presence of organisms. Look for fuzzy growth on the surface of the food. Examine the fluid surrounding the food using the process in steps 16–18. Record your observations in your data table and draw diagrams of what you find.
20. Examine the water in the funnel you set up in steps 11 and 12. Look for the presence of soil organisms as follows. Place a beaker under the rubber tubing and open the hose clamp for an instant to release some water.
21. Using a dropper pipette, put a few drops of the water onto a depression slide. Cover the slide with a coverslip. Locate some organisms under low power. Then, switch to high power. Record your observations in your data table and draw diagrams of what you find.
22. Prepare a slide from the beaker of water containing leaves or mulch from step 15. Using a dropper pipette, put a drop of the water onto a glass slide. Cover the slide with a coverslip.
23. Locate some organisms under low power with a microscope. Then, switch to higher power. If you don't find any organisms, make new slides each day for a week. As the organisms reproduce, your chance of finding them will improve. Record your observations in your data table and draw diagrams of what you find. Wash your hands with soap and warm water.
24. Classify each kind of organism you observed, using the dichotomous key above, right. Note any problems with the key as you work. Record the kingdom in your data table.

Dichotomous Key for Kingdoms

1. Microscopic or macroscopic
   1a) Microscopic (often unicellular) ....go to step 2
   1b) Macroscopic (multicellular) ....go to step 4
2. Presence or absence of nucleus
   2a) No nucleus (cell is also very small) ....Eubacteria or Archaebacteria
   2b) Nucleus (organelles will also be visible) ....go to step 3
3. Presence or absence of cell walls
   3a) Cell walls but no chloroplasts ....Fungi
   3b) May have or lack cell walls; may have chloroplasts............Protista
4. Presence or absence of chloroplasts
   4a) Chloroplasts (some green color) ....Plantae
   4b) No chloroplasts (lack of green color) ....go to step 5
5. Mobile or anchored
   5a) Anchored to food source; absorbs food ....Fungi
   5b) Moves (or has appendages) and/or eats food ....Animalia

Analyze and Conclude

1. **Classifying** How did you determine the kingdoms of the various organisms?
2. **Evaluating and Revising** Did you detect any problems with the dichotomous key you used? How could you improve it? What difficulties might arise as you try to improve it?
3. **Inferring** Modern classification is based on evolutionary relationships. Does the dichotomous key you used reflect those relationships? Explain your answer.
4. **SAFETY** How did you demonstrate safe practices during this investigation?

Go Further

Classifying Select one kingdom you just investigated. Develop a dichotomous key to group those organisms into phyla. Review your key with classmates to see if it is workable. Then, classify the organisms.

How Do Plant Adaptations Compare?

Plants have adaptations that enable them to survive in their specific environments. In this activity, you will observe the plants in your neighborhood and describe their adaptations.

Problem

What are some methods of plant reproduction, growth and development, and adaptations to the environment?

Materials

- camera (optional)
- containers (plastic bags and jars with lids)
- small trowel or spade
- magnifying glass
- glass slides
- microscope
- coverslips
- dropper pipette

Skills

Observing, Measuring, Inferring

Procedure   

Part A: Preparing for the Field Trip

1. Read the guidelines in the Lab Tips box on page 55 and in Planning the Trip on page 1078.
2. Prepare a data table similar to the one below so that you can record your observations.
3. Review Sections 22–1, 24–1, and 24–2. Gather information on each consideration below.
   - Plants need light in order to make food, and they compete to obtain sunlight. Think of possible adaptations for this competition.
   - Plants have adaptations that enable them to obtain and retain water.
   - Plants depend upon mechanisms of seed dispersal and vegetative propagation to find new, suitable places to grow.
   - Plants have adaptations that enable them to reproduce sexually, such as flower structure and ways of enabling pollen to reach flowers.
4. Write a plan for the field trip. Have your teacher review the plan.

Part B: Working at the Site

5. On the day of your trip, read and follow the guidelines in During the Trip on page 1078.
6. When you locate an interesting plant, record your observations in your data table. Number that plant and record its number in the table. Then, as you supplement your observations with drawings or photographs, place that number on each image.
7. For each plant, make the following kinds of observations:
   - Where is the plant found? Is its location sunny or shady, moist or dry? Is the soil sand, clay, or humus? What plants or other organisms are on or near it?
   - Observe the amount and source of water in the environment. Is the soil moist or dry? Is there a body of water nearby?
   - What kind of leaves does the plant have? Are they broad or narrow, large or small? What color are they?

Data Table

Plant Number	Location (soil, humidity, sunlight)	Leaves (shape, color)	Stem (support structures, tendrils, vines)	Roots (tap root, fibrous root, adventitious root)	Reproductive structures (flowers, cones, fruits, vegetative structures)	Other
1						
2						
3						

- How does the plant compete for sunlight? Is it tall? Does it have a thick stem or trunk to support its height? Does it climb on other plants? If so, how? Does it float on the surface of the water?
- How does it get water? Does it have a long taproot or fibrous branching roots? You may need to dig to observe this.
- Is there evidence of vegetative propagation? Look for runners (overground stems with new plants at the end), rhizomes (underground stems that sprout new leaves along the length), bulbs that form clusters, and so on.
- Is there evidence of sexual reproduction? Are there cones, flowers, seeds, or fruits?
- Most seed plants absorb all their minerals from the soil and produce their food by photosynthesis. Some seed plants are parasitic, however. Others that live in nitrogen-poor soil may supplement their diets by eating insects. What evidence is there for the manner in which your plants get food?

8. Collect the following samples to bring back to the classroom, if they are available:
   - leaves, pine cones, seeds, and fruits from various plants (make sure you know which plants they came from)
   - small plants or parts of plants that you may wish to press or otherwise preserve
9. Wash your hands with soap and warm water.

Part C: Following the Field Trip

10. Examine the size and shape of the leaves you collected. In general, the larger the leaf, the more rapidly it loses water.
11. Examine the flowers you collected. Look for adaptations to prevent self-pollination. Some adaptations that are easy to see are separate male flowers (stamens only), female flowers (pistils only), and flowers in which the pistil extends significantly beyond the anthers.
12. Look for adaptations to aid pollination. Are the petals large or small, brightly colored or greenish? Are the flowers odorless or do they have strong odors? Are the pollen grains small and powdery or large and sticky? Prepare a wet mount of the pollen grains and examine them with a microscope. Always keep track of which plant specimen you are examining.
13. Examine the fruits and seeds you collected to identify adaptations that aid dispersal by either animals or wind. Are the fruits fleshy or dry? Do they smell like food? Are they brightly colored or basically green or brown? Do the dry fruits have structures that look like parachutes, feathers, or wings? Do they have spines or hooks like burrs?
14. Wash your hands with soap and warm water when you have finished.

Analyze and Conclude

1. **Comparing and Contrasting** Describe the most unusual plant adaptations you observed. How do they compare with the more common plant structures you examined?
2. **Observing** Describe ways that the plants you observed are adapted to obtain light.
3. **Analyzing Data** Examine your observations to determine the relationship between availability of water and the size and shape of the leaf. Explain how this relationship contributes to the plant's survival.
4. **Analyzing Data** What relationship is there between a particular plant's reproductive structures, such as flowers and pollen? How do the structures contribute to the plant's reproductive success?
5. **Inferring** How do the structures you observed on seeds or fruits aid in the dispersal of plants?
6. **Drawing Conclusions** What overall patterns did you observe in the number, size, and type of plants? How are those patterns related to the environment's physical factors, such as amount of sunlight, availability of water, and type of soil?
7. **SAFETY** How did you demonstrate safe practices during this investigation?

Go Further

Plants have adaptations that take advantage of animals in their surroundings. For example, some plants have flowers with ultraviolet markings and trap doors that capture pollinators, and some flowers sound like bees when the wind blows. Using the Internet or library, research ways in which plants take advantage of animals. Find a particularly exotic example and report on it to the class.

Periodic Table of the Elements

	Nonmetals	Metals	Metalloids
Solid	C	Li	B
Liquid	Br	Hg	
Gas	H		
Not found in nature		Tc	

Atomic number — 6
Element symbol — C
Element name — Carbon
Atomic mass — 12.011

1 1A	2 2A	3 3B	4 4B	5 5B	6 6B	7 7B	8 8B	9 8B	10 8B	11 1B	12 2B	13 3A	14 4A	15 5A	16 6A	17 7A	18 8A
1 H Hydrogen 1.0079																	2 He Helium 4.0026
3 Li Lithium 6.941	4 Be Beryllium 9.0122											5 B Boron 10.81	6 C Carbon 12.011	7 N Nitrogen 14.007	8 O Oxygen 15.999	9 F Fluorine 18.998	10 Ne Neon 20.179
11 Na Sodium 22.990	12 Mg Magnesium 24.305											13 Al Aluminum 26.982	14 Si Silicon 28.086	15 P Phosphorus 30.974	16 S Sulfur 32.06	17 Cl Chlorine 35.453	18 Ar Argon 39.948
19 K Potassium 39.098	20 Ca Calcium 40.08	21 Sc Scandium 44.956	22 Ti Titanium 47.90	23 V Vanadium 50.941	24 Cr Chromium 51.996	25 Mn Manganese 54.938	26 Fe Iron 55.847	27 Co Cobalt 58.933	28 Ni Nickel 58.71	29 Cu Copper 63.546	30 Zn Zinc 65.38	31 Ga Gallium 69.72	32 Ge Germanium 72.59	33 As Arsenic 74.922	34 Se Selenium 78.96	35 Br Bromine 79.904	36 Kr Krypton 83.80
37 Rb Rubidium 85.468	38 Sr Strontium 87.62	39 Y Yttrium 88.906	40 Zr Zirconium 91.22	41 Nb Niobium 92.906	42 Mo Molybdenum 95.94	43 Tc Technetium (98)	44 Ru Ruthenium 101.07	45 Rh Rhodium 102.91	46 Pd Palladium 106.4	47 Ag Silver 107.87	48 Cd Cadmium 112.41	49 In Indium 114.82	50 Sn Tin 118.69	51 Sb Antimony 121.75	52 Te Tellurium 127.60	53 I Iodine 126.90	54 Xe Xenon 131.30
55 Cs Cesium 132.91	56 Ba Barium 137.33	71 Lu Lutetium 174.97	72 Hf Hafnium 178.49	73 Ta Tantalum 180.95	74 W Tungsten 183.85	75 Re Rhenium 186.21	76 Os Osmium 190.2	77 Ir Iridium 192.22	78 Pt Platinum 195.09	79 Au Gold 196.97	80 Hg Mercury 200.59	81 Tl Thallium 204.37	82 Pb Lead 207.2	83 Bi Bismuth 208.98	84 Po Polonium (209)	85 At Astatine (210)	86 Rn Radon (222)
87 Fr Francium (223)	88 Ra Radium (226)	103 Lr Lawrencium (262)	104 Rf Rutherfordium (261)	105 Db Dubnium (262)	106 Sg Seaborgium (263)	107 Bh Bohrium (264)	108 Hs Hassium (265)	109 Mt Meitnerium (268)	110 *Uun Ununnilium (269)	111 *Uuu Unununium (272)	112 *Uub Ununbium (277)		114 *Uuq Ununquadium				

*Name not officially assigned.

Lanthanide Series

57 La Lanthanum 138.91	58 Ce Cerium 140.12	59 Pr Praseodymium 140.91	60 Nd Neodymium 144.24	61 Pm Promethium (145)	62 Sm Samarium 150.4	63 Eu Europium 151.96	64 Gd Gadolinium 157.25	65 Tb Terbium 158.93	66 Dy Dysprosium 162.50	67 Ho Holmium 164.93	68 Er Erbium 167.26	69 Tm Thulium 168.93	70 Yb Ytterbium 173.04

Actinide Series

89 Ac Actinium (227)	90 Th Thorium 232.04	91 Pa Protactinium 231.04	92 U Uranium 238.03	93 Np Neptunium (237)	94 Pu Plutonium (244)	95 Am Americium (243)	96 Cm Curium (247)	97 Bk Berkelium (247)	98 Cf Californium (251)	99 Es Einsteinium (252)	100 Fm Fermium (257)	101 Md Mendelevium (258)	102 No Nobelium (259)

abdomen posterior part of an arthropod's body (p. 721)
abiotic factor physical, or nonliving, factor that shapes an ecosystem (p. 90)
abscission layer layer of cells at the petiole that seals off a leaf from the vascular system (p. 642)
accessory pigment compound other than chlorophyll that absorbs light at different wavelengths than chlorophyll (p. 506)
acellular slime mold slime mold that passes through a stage in which its cells fuse to form large cells with many nuclei (p. 516)
acetylcholine neurotransmitter that diffuses across a synapse and produces an impulse in the cell membrane of a muscle cell (p. 929)
acid compound that forms hydrogen ions (H^+) in solution (p. 43)
acid rain rain containing nitric and sulfuric acids (p. 148)
acoelomate animal lacking a coelom, or body cavity (p. 683)
actin protein that mainly makes up the thin filaments in striations in skeletal muscle cells (p. 928)
action potential reversal of charges across the cell membrane of a neuron; also called a nerve impulse (p. 899)
activation energy energy needed to get a reaction started (p. 50)
active immunity immunity produced by exposure to an antigen, as a result of the immune response (p. 1042)
active transport energy-requiring process that moves material across a cell membrane against a concentration difference (p. 188)
adaptation inherited characteristic that increases an organism's chance of survival (p. 380)
adaptive radiation process by which a single species or small group of species evolves into several different forms that live in different ways; rapid growth in the diversity of a group of organisms (pp. 436, 851)
addiction uncontrollable dependence on a drug (p. 914)
adenosine triphosphate (ATP) one of the principal chemical compounds that living things use to store and release energy (p. 202)
adhesion attraction between molecules of different substances; in plants, attraction between unlike molecules (pp. 41, 599)
aerobic process that requires oxygen (p. 226)
age-structure diagram graph of the numbers of males and females within different age groups of a population (p. 131)
aggression threatening behavior that one animal uses to gain control over another (p. 881)
agriculture the practice of farming (p. 141)
air sac one of several sacs attached to a bird's lungs into which air moves when a bird inhales; allows for the one-way flow of air through the respiratory system (p. 810)
algal bloom an immediate increase in the amount of algae and other producers that results from a large input of a limiting nutrient (p. 80)
allele one of a number of different forms of a gene (p. 265)
allergy overreaction of the immune system to antigens (p. 1043)
alternation of generations process in which many algae switch back and forth between haploid and diploid stages of their life cycles (p. 512)
alveolus tiny air sac at the end of a bronchiole in the lungs that provides surface area for gas exchange to occur (pp. 859, 958)
amino acid compound with an amino group ($—NH_2$) on one end and a carboxyl group ($—COOH$) on the other end (p. 47)
amniotic egg egg composed of shell and membranes that create a protected environment in which the embryo can develop out of the water (p. 802)
amoeboid movement type of locomotion used by amoebas (p. 500)
amphibian vertebrate that, with some exceptions, lives in water as a larva and on land as an adult, breathes with lungs as an adult, has moist skin that contains mucous glands, and lacks scales and claws (p. 782)
amylase enzyme in saliva that breaks the chemical bonds in starches (p. 979)
anaerobic process that does not require oxygen (p. 224)
anal pore region of the cell membrane of a ciliate where waste-containing food vacuoles fuse and are then emptied into the environment (p. 502)
anaphase the third phase of mitosis, during which the chromosome pairs separate and move toward opposite poles (p. 248)
angiosperm flowering plant; bears its seeds within a layer of tissue that protects the seed (p. 564)
Animalia kingdom of multicellular eukaryotic heterotrophs whose cells do not have cell walls (p. 461)
annual flowering plant that completes a life cycle within one growing season (p. 572)
anther flower structure in which haploid male gametophytes are produced (p. 612)
antheridium male reproductive structure in some algae and plants (pp. 519, 559)
anthropoid primate group made up of humans, apes, and most monkeys (p. 835)
antibiotic compound that blocks the growth and reproduction of bacteria (pp. 486, 1035)
antibody protein that helps destroy pathogens (p. 1038)
anticodon group of three bases on a tRNA molecule that are complementary to an mRNA codon (p. 304)
antigen substance that triggers an immune response (p. 1038)
anus opening through which wastes leave the digestive tract (pp. 661, 689)
aorta large blood vessel in mammals through which blood travels after it leaves the left ventricle (p. 946)

aphotic zone permanently dark layer of the oceans below the photic zone (p. 109)

apical dominance phenomenon in which the closer a bud is to the stem's tip, the more its growth is inhibited (p. 636)

apical meristem group of undifferentiated cells that divide to produce increased length of stems and roots (p. 582)

appendage structure, such as a leg or antenna, that extends from the body wall (p. 715)

aquaculture the raising of aquatic organisms for human consumption (p. 147)

Archaea domain of unicellular prokaryotes that have cell walls that do not contain peptidoglycan (p. 459)

Archaebacteria kingdom of unicellular prokaryotes whose cell walls do not contain peptidoglycan (p. 459)

archaeocyte specialized cell in a sponge that makes spicules (p. 665)

archegonium female reproductive structure in some plants, including mosses and liverworts (p. 559)

artery large blood vessel that carries blood from the heart to the tissues of the body (p. 946)

artificial selection selection by humans for breeding of useful traits from the natural variation among different organisms (p. 379)

ascospore haploid spore produced within the ascus of ascomycetes (p. 532)

ascus structure within the fruiting body of an ascomycete in which two nuclei of different mating types fuse (p. 532)

asexual reproduction process by which a single parent reproduces by itself (p. 17)

asthma chronic respiratory disease in which the air passageways become narrower than normal (p. 1044)

atherosclerosis condition in which fatty deposits called plaque build up on the inner walls of the arteries (p. 949)

atom basic unit of matter (p. 35)

ATP synthase large protein that uses energy from H^+ ions to bind ADP and a phosphate group together to produce ATP (p. 210)

atrium upper chamber of the heart that receives and holds blood that is about to enter the ventricle (pp. 776, 944)

autosome chromosome that is not a sex chromosome (p. 341)

autotroph organism that can capture energy from sunlight or chemicals and use it to produce its own food from inorganic compounds; also called a producer (pp. 67, 201)

auxin substance produced in the tip of a seedling that stimulates cell elongation (p. 635)

axon long fiber that carries impulses away from the cell body of a neuron (p. 898)

bacillus rod-shaped prokaryote (p. 473)

Bacteria domain of unicellular prokaryotes that have cell walls containing peptidoglycan (p. 459)

bacteriophage virus that infects bacteria (pp. 289, 479)

bark tree structure that includes all tissues outside the vascular cambium, including phloem, the cork cambium, and cork (p. 593)

base compound that produces hydroxide ions (OH^+) in solution (p. 43)

base pairing principle that bonds in DNA can form only between adenine and thymine and between guanine and cytosine (p. 294)

basidiospore spore in basidiomycetes that germinates to produce haploid primary mycelia (p. 535)

basidium spore-bearing structure of a basidiomycete (p. 534)

behavior the way an organism reacts to changes in its internal condition or external environment (p. 871)

behavioral isolation form of reproductive isolation in which two populations have differences in courtship rituals or other types of behavior that prevent them from interbreeding (p. 404)

benthos organisms that live attached to or near the ocean floor (p. 112)

biennial flowering plant that completes its life cycle in two years (p. 572)

bilateral symmetry body plan in which only a single, imaginary line can divide the body into two equal halves; characteristic of worms, arthropods, and chordates (pp. 662, 748)

binary fission type of asexual reproduction in which an organism replicates its DNA and divides in half, producing two identical daughter cells (p. 475)

binocular vision ability to merge visual images from both eyes, which provides depth perception and a three-dimensional view of the world (p. 834)

binomial nomenclature classification system in which each species is assigned a two-part scientific name (p. 448)

biodiversity biological diversity; the sum total of the variety of organisms in the biosphere (p. 150)

biogeochemical cycle process in which elements, chemical compounds, and other forms of matter are passed from one organism to another and from one part of the biosphere to another (p. 74)

biological magnification increasing concentration of a harmful substance in organisms at higher trophic levels in a food chain or food web (p. 152)

biology science that seeks to understand the living world (p. 16)

biomass total amount of living tissue within a given trophic level (p. 72)

biome group of ecosystems that have the same climate and dominant communities (pp. 64, 98)

biosphere part of Earth in which life exists including land, water, and air or atmosphere (p. 63)

biotic factor biological influence on organisms within an ecosystem (p. 90)

bipedal term used to refer to two-footed locomotion (p. 835)

bird endothermic animal that has an outer covering of feathers, two legs covered with scales that are used for walking or perching, and front limbs modified into wings (p. 806)

blade thin, flattened section of a plant leaf that collects sunlight (p. 595)

blastula hollow ball of cells formed when a zygote undergoes a series of divisions (p. 661)

bone marrow soft tissue inside the cavities within bones (p. 922)

book lung organ that has layers of respiratory tissue that is used by some terrestrial arthropods for the exchange of gases (p. 717)

Bowman's capsule cup-shaped structure in the upper end of a nephron that encases the glomerulus (p. 987)

brain stem structure that connects the brain and spinal cord; includes the medulla oblongata and the pons (p. 902)

bronchus passageway leading from the trachea to a lung (p. 958)

bryophyte nonvascular plant; examples are mosses and their relatives (p. 556)

bud plant structure containing undeveloped tissue that can produce new stems and leaves (p. 589)

budding asexual process by which yeasts increase in number; process of attaching a bud to a plant to produce a new branch (pp. 533, 623)

buffer weak acid or base that can react with strong acids or bases to help prevent sharp, sudden changes in pH (p. 43)

calorie amount of energy needed to raise the temperature of 1 gram of water by 1 degree Celsius (p. 221)

Calorie term used by scientists to measure the energy stored in foods; 1000 calories (p. 971)

Calvin cycle reactions of photosynthesis in which energy from ATP and NADPH is used to build high-energy compounds such as sugars (p. 212)

cancer disorder in which some of the body's own cells lose the ability to control growth (p. 252)

canopy dense covering formed by the leafy tops of tall rain forest trees (p. 100)

capillary smallest blood vessel; brings nutrients and oxygen to the tissues and absorbs carbon dioxide and waste products (p. 947)

capillary action tendency of water to rise in a thin tube (p. 599)

capsid outer protein coat of a virus (p. 479)

carapace in crustaceans, the part of the exoskeleton that covers the cephalothorax; in turtles and tortoises, the dorsal part of the shell (pp. 721, 805)

carbohydrate compound made up of carbon, hydrogen, and oxygen atoms; major source of energy for the human body (pp. 45, 972)

carcinogen chemical compound known to cause cancer (p. 1052)

carnivore organism that obtains energy by eating animals (p. 69)

carpel innermost part of a flower that produces the female gametophytes (p. 612)

carrying capacity largest number of individuals of a population that a given environment can support (p. 122)

cartilage strong connective tissue that supports the body and is softer and more flexible than bone (pp. 773, 922)

Casparian strip waterproof strip that surrounds plant endodermis cells (p. 587)

caste group of individual insects specialized to perform particular tasks, or roles (p. 732)

catalyst substance that speeds up the rate of a chemical reaction (p. 51)

cell collection of living matter enclosed by a barrier that separates the cell from its surroundings; basic unit of all forms of life (pp. 17, 170)

cell body largest part of a typical neuron; contains the nucleus and much of the cytoplasm (p. 897)

cell culture group of cells grown in a nutrient solution from a single original cell (p. 27)

cell cycle series of events that cells go through as they grow and divide (p. 245)

cell division process by which a cell divides into two new daughter cells (p. 243)

cell fractionation technique in which cells are broken into pieces and the different cell parts are separated (p. 27)

cell-mediated immunity immunity against abnormal cells and pathogens inside living cells (p. 1038)

cell membrane thin, flexible barrier around a cell; regulates what enters and leaves the cell (p. 182)

cell specialization the process in which cells develop in different ways to perform different tasks (p. 190)

cell theory idea that all living things are composed of cells, cells are the basic units of structure and function in living things, and new cells are produced from existing cells (p. 170)

cell wall strong supporting layer around the cell membrane in plants, algae, and some bacteria (p. 182)

cellular respiration process that releases energy by breaking down glucose and other food molecules in the presence of oxygen (p. 222)

cellular slime mold slime mold whose individual cells remain separated during every phase of the mold's life cycle (p. 516)

centriole one of two tiny structures located in the cytoplasm of animal cells near the nuclear envelope (pp. 181, 246)

centromere area where the chromatids of a chromosome are attached (p. 245)

cephalization concentration of sense organs and nerve cells at the front of an animal's body (pp. 663, 748)

cephalothorax region of a crustacean formed by the fusion of the head with the thorax (p. 721)

cerebellum region of the brain that coordinates body movements (pp. 777, 902)

cerebral cortex outer layer of the cerebrum of a mammal's brain; center of thinking and other complex behaviors (p. 825)

cerebrospinal fluid fluid in the space between the meninges that acts as a shock absorber that protects the central nervous system (p. 901)

cerebrum area of the brain responsible for all voluntary activities of the body (pp. 777, 902)

chelicerae pair of mouthparts in chelicerates that contain fangs and are used to stab and paralyze prey (p. 722)

cheliped one of the first pair of legs of decapods (p. 721)

chemical reaction process that changes one set of chemicals into another set of chemicals (p. 49)

chemoautotroph organism that makes organic carbon molecules from carbon dioxide using energy from chemical reactions (p. 474)

chemoheterotroph organism that must take in organic molecules for both energy and carbon (p. 473)

chemosynthesis process by which some organisms, such as certain bacteria, use chemical energy to produce carbohydrates (p. 68)

chitin complex carbohydrate that makes up the cell walls of fungi; also found in the external skeletons of arthropods (pp. 527, 715)

chlorophyll principal pigment of plants and other photosynthetic organisms; captures light energy (p. 207)

chloroplast organelle found in cells of plants and some other organisms that captures the energy from sunlight and converts it into chemical energy (p. 180)

choanocyte specialized cell in sponges that uses a flagellum to move a steady current of water through the sponge (p. 665)

chordate member of the phylum Chordata; animal that has, for at least some stage of its life, a dorsal hollow nerve cord, a notochord, pharyngeal pouches, and a muscular tail (p. 767)

chromatid one of two identical "sister" parts of a duplicated chromosome (p. 244)

chromatin granular material visible within the nucleus; consists of DNA tightly coiled around proteins (pp. 176, 296)

chromosome threadlike structure within the nucleus containing the genetic information that is passed from one generation of cells to the next (p. 176)

chyme mixture of stomach fluids and food produced in the stomach by contracting stomach muscles (p. 981)

cilium short hairlike projection similar to a flagellum; produces movement in many cells (p. 501)

circadian rhythm behavioral cycle that occurs in a daily pattern (p. 878)

cladogram diagram that shows the evolutionary relationships among a group of organisms (p. 453)

class group of similar orders (p. 449)

classical conditioning learning process in which an animal makes a mental connection between a stimulus and some kind of reward or punishment (p. 874)

climate average, year-after-year conditions of temperature and precipitation in a particular region (p. 87)

clitellum band of thickened, specialized segments in annelids that secretes a mucus ring into which eggs and sperm are released (p. 696)

cloaca a muscular cavity at the end of the large intestine through which digestive wastes, urine, and eggs or sperm leave the body (p. 748)

clone member of a population of genetically identical cells produced from a single cell (p. 333)

closed circulatory system system in which blood is contained within a network of blood vessels (pp. 695, 754)

cnidocyte stinging cell of cnidarians; used for defense and to capture prey (p. 669)

coastal ocean marine zone that extends from the low-tide mark to the end of the continental shelf (p. 110)

coccus spherical prokaryote (p. 473)

cochlea fluid-filled part of the inner ear; sends nerve impulses to the brain through the cochlear nerve (p. 908)

codominance situation in which both alleles of a gene contribute to the phenotype of the organism (p. 272)

codon three-nucleotide sequence on messenger RNA that codes for a single amino acid (p. 302)

coelom fluid-filled body cavity lined with mesoderm (pp. 683, 749)

coevolution process by which two species evolve in response to changes in each other (p. 437)

cohesion attraction between molecules of the same substance (p. 41)

collenchyma type of ground tissue cell with a strong, flexible cell wall; helps support larger plants (p. 582)

commensalism symbiotic relationship in which one member of the association benefits and the other is neither helped nor harmed (p. 93)

common descent principle that all living things were derived from common ancestors (p. 382)

communication passing of information from one organism to another (p. 881)

community assemblage of different populations that live together in a defined area (p. 64)

companion cell phloem cell that surrounds sieve tube elements (p. 581)

competitive exclusion principle ecological rule that states that no two species can occupy the same exact niche in the same habitat at the same time (p. 92)

complete metamorphosis type of insect development in which the larvae look and act nothing like their parents and also feed in completely different ways (p. 729)

compound substance formed by the chemical combination of two or more elements in definite proportions (p. 37)

compound light microscope microscope that allows light to pass through a specimen and uses two lenses to form an image (p. 26)

concentration the mass of solute in a given volume of solution, or mass/volume (p. 183)

cone in gymnosperms, a seed-bearing structure; in the retina of the eye, a photoreceptor that responds to light of different colors, producing color vision (pp. 564, 907)

conidium tiny fungal spore that forms at the tips of specialized hyphae in ascomycetes (p. 532)

coniferous term used to refer to trees that produce seed-bearing cones and have thin leaves shaped like needles (p. 103)

conjugation form of sexual reproduction in which paramecia and some prokaryotes exchange genetic information (pp. 475, 502)

connective tissue tissue that holds organs in place and binds different parts of the body together (p. 894)

conservation wise management of natural resources, including the preservation of habitats and wildlife (p. 154)

consumer organism that relies on other organisms for its energy and food supply; also called a heterotroph (p. 68)

contractile vacuole cavity in the cytoplasm of some protists that collects water and discharges it from the cell (p. 502)

controlled experiment a test of the effect of a single variable by changing it while keeping all other variables the same (p. 9)

controlled variable factor in an experiment that a scientist purposely keeps the same (p. 1062)

convergent evolution process by which unrelated organisms independently evolve similarities when adapting to similar environments (p. 437)

coral reef diverse and productive environment named for the coral animals that make up its primary structure (p. 111)

cork cambium lateral meristematic tissue that produces the outer covering of stems (p. 591)

corpus luteum name given to a follicle after ovulation because of its yellow color (p. 1014)

cortex spongy layer of ground tissue just inside the epidermis of a root (p. 585)

cotyledon first leaf or first pair of leaves produced by the embryo of a seed plant (p. 570)

courtship type of behavior in which an animal sends out stimuli in order to attract a member of the opposite sex (p. 879)

covalent bond bond formed by the sharing of electrons between atoms (p. 38)

crop in earthworms, part of the digestive system in which food can be stored; in birds, structure at the lower end of the esophagus in which food is stored and moistened (pp. 695, 809)

crossing-over process in which homologous chromosomes exchange portions of their chromatids during meiosis (p. 277)

cyclin one of a family of closely related proteins that regulate the cell cycle in eukaryotic cells (p. 251)

cytokinesis division of the cytoplasm during cell division (p. 244)

cytokinin plant hormone produced in growing roots and in developing fruits and seeds (p. 636)

cytoplasm material inside the cell membrane—not including the nucleus (p. 174)

cytoskeleton network of protein filaments within some cells that helps the cell maintain its shape and is involved in many forms of cell movement (p. 181)

data evidence; information gathered from observations (pp. 4, 1057)

deciduous term used to refer to a tree that sheds its leaves during a particular season each year (p. 100)

decomposer organism that breaks down and obtains energy from dead organic matter (p. 69)

deforestation destruction of forests (p. 146)

demographic transition change in a population from high birth and death rates to low birth and death rates (p. 130)

demography scientific study of human populations (p. 130)

dendrite extension of the cell body of a neuron that carries impulses from the environment or from other neurons toward the cell body (p. 898)

denitrification conversion of nitrates into nitrogen gas (p. 78)

density-dependent limiting factor limiting factor that depends on population size (p. 125)

density-independent limiting factor limiting factor that affects all populations in similar ways, regardless of population size (p. 127)

deoxyribonucleic acid (DNA) nucleic acid that contains the sugar deoxyribose (p. 47)

dependent variable factor in an experiment that a scientist wants to observe, which may change because of the manipulated variable; also known as a responding variable (p. 1062)

depressant drug that decreases the rate of functions regulated by the brain (p. 911)

derived character characteristic that appears in recent parts of a lineage, but not in its older members (p. 453)

dermis inner layer of the skin (p. 935)

descent with modification principle that each living species has descended, with changes, from other species over time (p. 381)

desertification in areas with dry climates, a process caused by a combination of poor farming practices, overgrazing, and drought that turns productive land into desert (p. 145)

detritivore organism that feeds on plant and animal remains and other dead matter (p. 69)

detritus particles of organic material that provide food for organisms at the base of an estuary's food web (p. 108)

deuterostome animal whose anus is formed from the blastopore of a blastula (p. 661)

diabetes mellitus condition that occurs when the pancreas produces too little insulin, resulting in an increase in the level of blood glucose (p. 1007)

diaphragm large, flat muscle at the bottom of the chest cavity that helps with breathing (pp. 824, 959)

dicot angiosperm whose seeds have two cotyledons (p. 570)

differentiation process in which cells become specialized in structure and function (pp. 312, 583, 1017)

diffusion process by which molecules tend to move from an area where they are more concentrated to an area where they are less concentrated (p. 184)

diploid term used to refer to a cell that contains both sets of homologous chromosomes (p. 275)

directional selection form of natural selection in which the entire curve moves; occurs when individuals at one end of a distribution curve have higher fitness than individuals in the middle or at the other end of the curve (p. 398)

disease any change, other than an injury, that disrupts the normal functions of the body (p. 1031)

disruptive selection form of natural selection in which a single curve splits into two; occurs when individuals at the upper and lower ends of a distribution curve have higher fitness than individuals near the middle (p. 399)

DNA fingerprinting analysis of sections of DNA that have little or no known function, but vary widely from one individual to another, in order to identify individuals (p. 357)

DNA polymerase enzyme involved in DNA replication that joins individual nucleotides to produce a DNA molecule (p. 299)

domain most inclusive taxonomic category; larger than a kingdom (p. 458)

dormancy period of time during which a plant embryo is alive but not growing (pp. 620, 641)

double fertilization fertilization in angiosperms, in which two distinct fertilization events take place between the male and female gametophytes (p. 616)

drug any substance, other than food, that causes a change in the structure or function of the body (p. 910)

drug abuse intentional misuse of any drug for nonmedical purposes (p. 914)

ecological pyramid diagram that shows the relative amounts of energy or matter within each trophic level in a food chain or food web (p. 72)

ecological succession gradual change in living communities that follows a disturbance (p. 94)

ecology scientific study of interactions among organisms and between organisms and their environment (p. 63)

ecosystem collection of all the organisms that live in a particular place, together with their nonliving environment (p. 64)

ecosystem diversity variety of habitats, living communities, and ecological processes in the living world (p. 150)

ectoderm outermost germ layer of most animals; gives rise to outer layer of the skin, sense organs, and nerves (p. 661)

ectotherm animal that relies on interactions with the environment to help it control body temperature (pp. 800, 855)

electron negatively charged particle; located outside the atomic nucleus (p. 35)

electron microscope microscope that forms an image by focusing beams of electrons onto a specimen (p. 26)

electron transport chain a series of proteins in which the high-energy electrons from the Krebs cycle are used to convert ADP into ATP (p. 228)

element substance consisting entirely of one type of atom (p. 36)

embryo organism in its early stage of development (p. 565)

embryo sac female gametophyte within the ovule of a flowering plant (p. 615)

emigration movement of individuals out of an area (p. 120)

emphysema disease in which the tissues of the lungs lose elasticity, making breathing very difficult (p. 962)

endangered species species whose population size is rapidly declining and will become extinct if the trend continues (p. 151)

endocrine gland gland that releases its secretions directly into the bloodstream (p. 998)

endocytosis process by which a cell takes material into the cell by infolding of the cell membrane (p. 189)

endoderm innermost germ layer of most animals; develops into the linings of the digestive tract and much of the respiratory system (p. 661)

endodermis layer of cells that completely encloses vascular tissue (p. 585)

endoplasmic reticulum internal membrane system in cells in which lipid components of the cell membrane are assembled and some proteins are modified (p. 177)

endoskeleton structural support located inside the body of an animal (pp. 734, 757)

endosperm food-rich tissue that nourishes a seedling as it grows (p. 616)

endospore type of spore formed when a bacterium produces a thick internal wall that encloses its DNA and a portion of its cytoplasm (p. 475)

endosymbiotic theory theory that eukaryotic cells formed from a symbiosis among several different prokaryotic organisms (p. 427)

endotherm animal that generates its own body heat and controls its body temperature from within (pp. 808, 855)

enzyme protein that acts as a biological catalyst (p. 51)

epidermal cell cell that makes up the dermal tissue, which is the outer covering of a plant (p. 580)

epidermis outer layer of the skin (p. 934)

epididymis structure in the male reproductive system in which sperm fully mature and are stored (p. 1011)

epiphyte plant that is not rooted in soil but instead grows directly on the body of another plant (p. 645)

epithelial tissue tissue that covers the surface of the body and lines internal organs (p. 894)

equilibrium when the concentration of a solute is the same throughout a solution (p. 184)

era one of several subdivisions of the time between the Precambrian and the present (p. 421)

esophagus food tube connecting the mouth to the stomach (p. 980)

estuary wetlands formed where rivers meet the ocean (p. 108)

ethylene plant hormone that stimulates fruits to ripen (p. 638)

Eubacteria kingdom of unicellular prokaryotes whose cell walls are made up of peptidoglycan (p. 459)

Eukarya domain of all organisms whose cells have nuclei, including protists, plants, fungi, and animals (p. 460)

eukaryote organism whose cells contain nuclei (p. 173)

evaporation process by which water changes from a liquid into an atmospheric gas (p. 75)

evolution change in a kind of organism over time; process by which modern organisms have descended from ancient organisms (pp. 20, 369)

evolutionary classification method of grouping organisms together according to their evolutionary history (p. 452)

exocrine gland gland that releases its secretions through tubelike structures called ducts (p. 998)

exocytosis process by which a cell releases large amounts of material (p. 189)

exon expressed sequence of DNA; codes for a protein (p. 302)

exoskeleton external skeleton; tough external covering that protects and supports the body of many invertebrates (pp. 715, 757)

exponential growth growth pattern in which the individuals in a population reproduce at a constant rate (p. 121)

external fertilization process in which eggs are fertilized outside the female's body (pp. 672, 758)

extinct term used to refer to a species that has died out (p. 417)

extinction disappearance of a species from all parts of its geographical range (p. 151)

extracellular digestion process in which food is broken down outside the cells in a digestive tract (p. 751)

eyespot group of cells that can detect changes in the amount of light in the environment (pp. 507, 685)

facilitated diffusion movement of specific molecules across cell membranes through protein channels (p. 187)

facultative anaerobe organism that can survive with or without oxygen (p. 474)

Fallopian tube one of two fluid-filled tubes in human females through which an egg passes after its release from an ovary (p. 1012)

family group of genera that share many characteristics (p. 449)

fat lipid; made up of fatty acids and glycerol; protects body organs, insulates body, and stores energy in the body (p. 972)

feather structure made mostly of protein that develops from a pit in a bird's skin (p. 806)

feedback inhibition process in which the product or result stops or limits the process (pp. 658, 895)

fermentation process by which cells release energy in the absence of oxygen (p. 224)

fertilization process in sexual reproduction in which male and female reproductive cells join to form a new cell (p. 263)

fetal alcohol syndrome group of birth defects caused by the effects of alcohol on a fetus (p. 913)

fetus name given to a human embryo after eight weeks of development (p. 1020)

fever elevated body temperature that occurs in response to infection (p. 1037)

fibrous root part of a root system in which roots branch to such an extent that no single root grows larger than the rest (p. 584)

filament in algae, a long threadlike colony formed by many green algae; in plants, a long, thin structure that supports an anther (pp. 512, 612)

filtration process by which a liquid or gas passes through a filter to remove wastes (p. 987)

fish aquatic vertebrate characterized by paired fins, scales, and gills (p. 771)

fission form of asexual reproduction in which an organism splits into two, and each half grows new parts to become a complete organism (p. 686)

fitness ability of an organism to survive and reproduce in its environment (p. 380)

flame cell specialized cell that filters and removes excess water from the body of a flatworm (p. 684)

flower seed-bearing structure of an angiosperm (p. 564)

follicle cluster of cells surrounding a single egg in the human female reproductive system (p. 1012)

food chain series of steps in an ecosystem in which organisms transfer energy by eating and being eaten (p. 69)

food vacuole small cavity in the cytoplasm of protists that temporarily stores food (p. 500)

food web network of complex interactions formed by the feeding relationships among the various organisms in an ecosystem (p. 70)

foot muscular part of a mollusk (p. 702)

fossil preserved remains or evidence of an ancient organism (p. 371)

fossil record information about past life, including the structure of organisms, what they ate, what ate them, in what environment they lived, and the order in which they lived (p. 417)

founder effect change in allele frequencies as a result of the migration of a small subgroup of a population (p. 400)

frameshift mutation mutation that shifts the "reading" frame of the genetic message by inserting or deleting a nucleotide (p. 307)

frond large leaf of a fern (p. 562)

fruit wall of tissue surrounding an angiosperm seed (p. 569)

fruiting body slender reproductive structure that produces spores and is found in some funguslike protists; reproductive structure of fungus that develops from a mycelium (pp. 516, 528)

Fungi kingdom composed of heterotrophs; many obtain energy and nutrients from dead organic matter (p. 460)

gametangium gamete-producing structure found in mold (p. 530)

gamete specialized cell involved in sexual reproduction (p. 266)

gametophyte haploid, or gamete-producing, phase of an organism (pp. 514, 552)

ganglion group of nerve cells (p. 685)

gastrovascular cavity digestive chamber with a single opening, in which cnidarians, flatworms, and echinoderms digest food (p. 671)

gastrulation process of cell migration by which a third layer of cells is formed within the cavity of a blastocyst (p. 1018)

gel electrophoresis procedure used to separate and analyze DNA fragments by placing a mixture of DNA fragments at one end of a porous gel and applying an electrical voltage to the gel (p. 323)

gemma small cup-shaped structure in liverworts that contains many haploid cells; used for asexual reproduction (p. 557)

gemmule group of archaeocytes surrounded by a tough layer of spicules; produced by some sponges (p. 667)

gene sequence of DNA that codes for a protein and thus determines a trait (pp. 265, 300)

gene map diagram showing the relative locations of each known gene on a particular chromosome (p. 280)

gene pool combined genetic information of all the members of a particular population (p. 394)

genetic diversity sum total of all the different forms of genetic information carried by all organisms living on Earth today (p. 150)

genetic drift random change in allele frequencies that occurs in small populations (p. 400)

genetic engineering process of making changes in the DNA code of living organisms (p. 322)

genetic equilibrium situation in which allele frequencies remain constant (p. 401)

genetic marker gene that makes it possible to distinguish bacteria that carry a plasmid with foreign DNA from those that don't (p. 328)

genetics scientific study of heredity (p. 263)

genotype genetic makeup of an organism (p. 268)

genus group of closely related species, and the first part of the scientific name in binomial nomenclature (p. 448)

geographic isolation form of reproductive isolation in which two populations are separated physically by geographic barriers such as rivers, mountains, or stretches of water (p. 405)

geologic time scale scale used by paleontologists to represent evolutionary time (p. 421)

germ theory of disease idea that infectious diseases are caused by microorganisms, or germs (p. 1031)

germination early growth stage of a plant embryo (p. 621)

gibberellin growth-promoting substance produced by plants (p. 637)

gill filamentous organ in aquatic animals specialized for the exchange of gases with water (p. 696)

gizzard in earthworms, part of the digestive system in which food is ground into smaller pieces; in birds, a muscular organ that helps in the mechanical break-down of food (pp. 695, 809)

global warming increase in the average temperatures on Earth (p. 159)

glomerulus small network of capillaries encased in the upper end of a nephron; where the filtration of blood takes place (p. 987)

glycolysis first step in releasing the energy of glucose, in which a molecule of glucose is broken into two molecules of pyruvic acid (p. 221)

Golgi apparatus stack of membranes in the cell that modifies, sorts, and packages proteins from the endoplasmic reticulum (p. 178)

grafting use of a stem as a scion (p. 623)

gravitropism response of a plant to the force of gravity (p. 635)

greenhouse effect natural situation in which heat is retained in Earth's atmosphere by carbon dioxide, methane, water vapor, and other gases (p. 87)

green revolution the development of highly productive crop strains and the use of modern agricultural techniques to increase yields of food crops (p. 142)

guard cell specialized cell in the epidermis of plants that controls the opening and closing of stomata by responding to changes in water pressure (p. 596)

gullet indentation in one side of a ciliate that allows food to enter the cell (p. 502)

gymnosperm seed plant that bears its seeds directly on the surfaces of cones (p. 564)

habitat the area where an organism lives, including the biotic and abiotic factors that affect it (p. 90)

habitat fragmentation splitting of ecosystems into small fragments (p. 151)

habituation learning process by which an animal decreases or stops its response to a repetitive stimulus that neither rewards nor harms it (p. 874)

hair follicle tubelike pocket of epidermal cells that extends into the dermis; cells at the base of hair follicles produce hair (p. 936)

half-life length of time required for half of the radioactive atoms in a sample to decay (p. 420)

haploid term used to refer to a cell that contains only a single set of chromosomes and therefore only a single set of genes (p. 275)

Hardy-Weinberg principle principle that allele frequencies in a population will remain constant unless one or more factors cause the frequencies to change (p. 401)

Haversian canal one of a network of tubes running through compact bone that contains blood vessels and nerves (p. 922)

heartwood older xylem near the center of a woody stem that no longer conducts water (p. 592)

hemoglobin iron-containing protein in red blood cells that transports oxygen from the lungs to the tissues of the body (p. 952)

herbicide compound that is toxic to plants (p. 636)

herbivore organism that obtains energy by eating only plants (p. 69)

hermaphrodite individual that has both male and female reproductive organs (p. 686)

heterotroph organism that obtains energy from the foods it consumes; also called a consumer (pp. 68, 201)

heterozygous term used to refer to an organism that has two different alleles for the same trait (p. 268)

histamine chemical released by activated mast cells that increases the flow of blood and fluids to the surrounding area (p. 1043)

histone protein molecule around which DNA is tightly coiled in chromatin (p. 296)

homeostasis process by which organisms maintain a relatively stable internal environment (pp. 19, 895)

hominid primate that walks upright, has opposable thumbs, and possesses a large brain; only living members are humans (p. 835)

hominoid anthropoid group that includes apes and humans (p. 835)

homologous term used to refer to chromosomes that each have a corresponding chromosome from the opposite-sex parent (p. 275)

homologous structures structures that have different mature forms in different organisms but develop from the same embryonic tissues (p. 384)

homozygous term used to refer to an organism that has two identical alleles for a particular trait (p. 268)

hormone substance produced in one part of an organism that affects another part of the same organism (pp. 634, 997)

hox genes series of genes that controls the differentiation of cells and tissues in an embryo (p. 312)

humoral immunity immunity against antigens and pathogens in the body fluids (p. 1038)

humus material formed from decaying leaves and other organic matter (p. 103)

hybrid offspring of crosses between parents with different traits (p. 264)

hybridization breeding technique that involves crossing dissimilar individuals to bring together the best traits of both organisms (p. 319)

hydrostatic skeleton layers of circular and longitudinal muscles, together with the water in the gastrovascular cavity, that enable movement (pp. 671, 756)

hypertonic when comparing two solutions, the solution with the greater concentration of solutes (p. 185)

hypha tiny filament that makes up a multicellular fungus or a water mold (pp. 518, 527)

hypothalamus brain structure that acts as a control center for recognition and analysis of hunger, thirst, fatigue, anger, and body temperature (p. 903)

hypothesis possible explanation for a set of observations or possible answer to a scientific question (pp. 5, 1062)

hypotonic when comparing two solutions, the solution with the lesser concentration of solutes (p. 185)

immigration movement of individuals into an area occupied by an existing population (p. 120)

immune response the body's specific defenses that attack a disease-causing agent (p. 1038)

immunity ability of the body to resist a specific pathogen (p. 1036)

implantation process in which a blastocyst attaches itself to the wall of the uterus (p. 1017)

imprinting learning based on early experience; once imprinting has occurred, the behavior cannot be changed (p. 876)

inbreeding continued breeding of individuals with similar characteristics to maintain the desired characteristics of a line of organisms (p. 320)

incomplete dominance situation in which one allele is not completely dominant over another (p. 272)

incomplete metamorphosis type of insect development characterized by a similar appearance throughout all stages of the life cycle (p. 729)

independent assortment independent segregation of genes during the formation of gametes (p. 271)

independent variable factor in an experiment that a scientist purposely changes; also known as a responding variable (p. 1062)

index fossil distinctive fossil used to compare the relative ages of fossils (p. 419)

inference logical interpretation based on prior knowledge and experience (p. 4)

inflammatory response nonspecific defense reaction to tissue damage caused by injury or infection (p. 1037)

innate behavior instinct, or inborn behavior; behavior that appears in a fully functional form the first time it is performed (p. 873)

insight learning also called reasoning; learning process in which an animal applies something it has already learned to a new situation without a period of trial and error (p. 875)

interferon one of a group of proteins that help cells resist viral infection (p. 1038)

internal fertilization process in which eggs are fertilized inside the female's body (pp. 666, 758)

internode region between nodes on plant stems (p. 589)

interphase period of the cell cycle between cell divisions (p. 245)

intracellular digestion process in which food is digested inside cells (p. 751)

intron sequence of DNA that is not involved in coding for a protein (p. 302)

invasive species plants and animals that have migrated to places where they are not native (p. 153)

invertebrate animal that does not have a backbone, or vertebral column (p. 657)

ion atom that has a positive or negative charge (p. 38)

ionic bond bond formed when one or more electrons are transferred from one atom to another (p. 38)

isotonic when the concentration of two solutions is the same (p. 185)

isotope atom of an element that has a number of neutrons different from that of other atoms of the same element (p. 36)

joint place where one bone attaches to another (p. 924)

karyotype photograph of chromosomes grouped in order in pairs (p. 341)

kelp forest coastal ocean community named for its dominant organism—kelp, a giant brown alga (p. 110)

keratin tough, fibrous protein found in skin (p. 934)

kidney organ that removes urea, excess water, and other waste products from the blood (p. 986)

kingdom large taxonomic group, consisting of closely related phyla (p. 449)

Koch's postulates series of guidelines used to identify the microorganism that causes a specific disease (p. 1032)

Krebs cycle second stage of cellular respiration, in which pyruvic acid is broken down into carbon dioxide in a series of energy-extracting reactions (p. 226)

language system of communication that combines sounds, symbols, or gestures according to a set of rules about word order and meaning (p. 882)

large intestine colon; organ that removes water from the undigested materials that pass through it (p. 984)

larva immature stage of an organism that looks different from the adult form (p. 666)

larynx structure in the throat containing the vocal cords (p. 958)

lateral bud meristematic area on the side of a stem that gives rise to side branches (p. 636)

lateral line system sensitive receptor system that enables fish to detect gentle currents and vibrations in the water (p. 777)

leaf photosynthetic organ that contains one or more bundles of vascular tissue (p. 561)

learning alterations in behavior as a result of experience; also called acquired behavior (p. 873)

lens transparent object behind the iris that changes shape to help adjust the eye's focus to see near or distant objects (p. 907)

lichen symbiotic association between a fungus and a photosynthetic organism (p. 540)

ligament strip of tough connective tissue that holds bones together at a joint (p. 925)

light-dependent reactions reactions of photosynthesis that use energy from light to produce ATP and NADPH (p. 210)

lignin substance in vascular plants that makes cell walls rigid (p. 560)

limiting factor factor that causes the growth of a population to decrease (p. 124)

limiting nutrient single nutrient that either is scarce or cycles very slowly, limiting the growth of organisms in an ecosystem (p. 80)

lipid macromolecule made mainly from carbon and hydrogen atoms; includes fats, oils, and waxes (p. 46)

lipid bilayer double-layered sheet that forms the core of nearly all cell membranes (p. 182)

liver large organ just above the stomach that produces bile (p. 982)

logistic growth growth pattern in which a population's growth rate slows or stops following a period of exponential growth (p. 122)

long-day plant plant that flowers when days are long (p. 641)

loop of Henle section of the nephron tubule that conserves water and minimizes the volume of urine (p. 987)

lymph fluid lost by the blood into surrounding tissue (p. 954)

lymphocyte type of white blood cell that produces antibodies that help destroy pathogens (p. 952)

lysogenic infection process by which a virus embeds its DNA into the DNA of the host cell and is replicated along with the host cell's DNA (p. 480)

lysosome cell organelle filled with enzymes needed to break down certain materials in the cell (p. 179)

lytic infection process in which a virus enters a cell, makes a copy of itself, and causes the cell to burst (p. 480)

macroevolution large-scale evolutionary changes that take place over long periods of time (p. 435)

macronucleus the larger of a ciliate's two nuclei, contains multiple copies of most of the genes that the cell needs in its day-to-day existence (p. 501)

madreporite sievelike structure through which the water vascular system of an echinoderm opens to the outside (p. 735)

Malpighian tubule saclike organ in most terrestrial arthropods that extracts wastes from the blood, adding them to feces that move through the gut (p. 717)

mammary gland gland in mammals that produces milk to nourish the young (p. 821)

mandible mouthpart adapted for biting and grinding food (p. 721)

mangrove swamp coastal wetland dominated by mangroves, salt-tolerant woody plants (p. 108)

manipulated variable factor in an experiment that a scientist purposely changes; also known as independent variable (pp. 9, 1062)

mantle thin layer of tissue that covers most of a mollusk's body (p. 702)

marsupial mammal which bears live young that complete their development in an external pouch (p. 829)

mass extinction event in which many types of living things become extinct at the same time (p. 431)

medulla oblongata area of the brain that controls the functioning of many internal organs (p. 777)

medusa motile stage of the life cycle of a cnidarian that has a bell-shaped body (p. 670)

meiosis process by which the number of chromosomes per cell is cut in half through the separation of homologous chromosomes in a diploid cell (p. 276)

melanin dark-brown pigment found in skin (p. 934)

meninges three layers of connective tissue in which the brain and spinal cord are wrapped (p. 901)

menstrual cycle cycle during which an egg develops and is released from an ovary and the uterus is prepared to receive a fertilized egg (p. 1013)

menstruation phase of the menstrual cycle during which the lining of the uterus, along with blood and the unfertilized egg, is discharged through the vagina (p. 1014)

meristem cluster of tissue that is responsible for continuing growth throughout a plant's lifetime (p. 582)

meristematic tissue plant tissue found only in the tips of shoots and roots; responsible for plant growth (p. 582)

mesoderm middle germ layer of most animals; gives rise to muscles and much of the circulatory, reproductive, and excretory systems (p. 661)

mesophyll specialized ground tissue that makes up the bulk of most leaves; performs most of a plant's photosynthesis (p. 596)

messenger RNA (mRNA) RNA molecule that carries copies of instructions for the assembly of amino acids into proteins from DNA to the rest of the cell (p. 301)

metabolism set of chemical reactions through which an organism builds up or breaks down materials as it carries out its life processes (p. 18)

metaphase second phase of mitosis, during which the chromosomes line up across the center of the cell (p. 248)

metric system decimal system of measurement based on certain physical standards and scaled on multiples of 10 (p. 24)

microclimate climate within a small area that differs significantly from the climate of the surrounding area (p. 98)

microfossil microscopic fossil (p. 426)

micronucleus the smaller of a ciliate's two nuclei; contains a "reserve copy" of all of the cell's genes (p. 501)

microscope device that produces magnified images of structures that are too small to see with the unaided eye (p. 25)

migration periodic movement and return of animals from one place to another (p. 878)

mineral inorganic nutrient the body needs, usually in small amounts (p. 975)

mitochondrion cell organelle that converts the chemical energy stored in food into compounds that are more convenient for the cell to use (p. 179)

mitosis part of eukaryotic cell division during which the cell nucleus divides (p. 244)

mixture material composed of two or more elements or compounds that are physically mixed together but not chemically combined (p. 41)

molecular clock model that uses DNA comparisons to estimate the length of time that two species have been evolving independently (p. 455)

molecule smallest unit of most compounds (p. 38)

molting process in which an arthropod sheds its exoskeleton and manufactures a larger one to take its place (p. 719)

monocot angiosperm whose seeds have one cotyledon (p. 569)

monoculture farming strategy in which large fields are planted with a single crop, year after year (p. 141)

monomer small unit that can join together with other small units to form polymers (p. 45)

monosaccharide single sugar molecule (p. 46)

monotreme egg-laying mammal (p. 828)

multiple alleles three or more alleles of the same gene (p. 273)

muscle tissue tissue that controls the internal movement of materials in the body, as well as external movement (p. 894)

mutation change in a DNA sequence that affects genetic information (p. 307)

mutualism symbiotic relationship in which both species benefit from the relationship (p. 93)

mycelium many hyphae tangled together into a thick mass; comprises the bodies of multicellular fungi (p. 528)

mycorrhiza symbiotic association of plant roots and fungi (p. 541)

myelin sheath insulating membrane surrounding the axon in some neurons (p. 898)

myocardium thick middle muscle layer of the heart; pumps blood through the circulatory system (p. 944)

myosin protein that makes up the thick filaments in striations in skeletal muscle cells (p. 928)

NAD⁺ (nicotinamide adenine dinucleotide) electron carrier involved in glycolysis (p. 223)

NADP⁺ (nicotinamide adenine dinucleotide phosphate) one of the carrier molecules that transfers high-energy electrons from chlorophyll to other molecules (p. 209)

natural selection process by which individuals that are better suited to their environment survive and reproduce most successfully; also called survival of the fittest (p. 381)

nematocyst stinging structure within each cnidocyte of a cnidarian that is used to poison or kill prey (p. 669)

nephridium excretory organ of an annelid that filters fluid in the coelom (p. 696)

nephron blood-filtering unit in the renal cortex of the kidney (p. 986)

nerve net loosely organized network of nerve cells that together allow cnidarians to detect stimuli (p. 671)

nervous tissue tissue that receives messages from the body's external and internal environment, analyzes the data, and directs the response (p. 894)

neuromuscular junction point of contact between a motor neuron and a skeletal muscle cell (p. 929)

neuron cell that carries messages throughout the nervous system (p. 897)

neurotransmitter chemical used by a neuron to transmit an impulse across a synapse to another cell (p. 900)

neurulation development of the nervous system (p. 1018)

niche full range of physical and biological conditions in which an organism lives and the way in which the organism uses those conditions (p. 91)

nicotine stimulant drug in tobacco that increases heart rate and blood pressure (p. 961)

nictitating membrane movable transparent membrane in amphibians located inside the regular eyelid; protects the surface of the eye from damage under water and keeps it moist on land (p. 787)

nitrogen fixation process of converting nitrogen gas into ammonia (pp. 78, 477)

node point on a stem where a leaf is attached (p. 589)

nondisjunction error in meiosis in which homologous chromosomes fail to separate (p. 352)

nonrenewable resource resource that cannot be replenished by natural processes (p. 144)

notochord long supporting rod that runs through a chordate's body just below the nerve cord (pp. 767, 849)

nuclear envelope layer of two membranes that surrounds the nucleus of a cell (p. 176)

nucleic acid macromolecule containing hydrogen, oxygen, nitrogen, carbon, and phosphorus (p. 47)

nucleolus small, dense region within most nuclei in which the assembly of proteins begins (p. 176)

nucleotide monomer of nucleic acids made up of a 5-carbon sugar, a phosphate group, and a nitrogenous base (pp. 47, 291)

nucleus the center of the atom which contains the protons and neutrons; in cells, structure that contains the cell's genetic material (DNA) and controls the cell's activities (pp. 35, 173)

nutrient chemical substance that an organism requires to live (p. 76)

nymph immature form that lacks functional sex organs and other adult structures (p. 729)

obligate aerobe organism that requires a constant supply of oxygen in order to live (p. 474)

obligate anaerobe organism that cannot live in the presence of oxygen (p. 474)

observation use of one or more of the senses—sight, hearing, touch, smell, and sometimes taste—to gather information (p. 4)

omnivore organism that obtains energy by eating both plants and animals (p. 69)

oogonium specialized structure formed by hyphae that produces female nuclei (p. 519)

open circulatory system system in which blood is not always contained within a network of blood vessels (pp. 703, 754)

operant conditioning learning process in which an animal learns to behave in a certain way through repeated practice, in order to receive a reward or avoid punishment; also called trial-and-error learning (p. 875)

operational definition description of how a particular variable is to be measured or how a term is to be defined (p. 1063)

operator region of chromosome in an operon to which the repressor binds when the operon is "turned off" (p. 310)

operon group of genes operating together (p. 309)

opposable thumb thumb that enables grasping objects and using tools (p. 835)

order group of similar families (p. 449)

organ group of tissues that work together to perform closely related functions (p. 193)

organ system group of organs that work together to perform a specific function (p. 193)

organelle specialized structure that performs important cellular functions within a eukaryotic cell (p. 174)

osculum large hole at the top of the sponge through which water leaves the sponge (p. 665)

osmosis diffusion of water through a selectively permeable membrane (p. 185)

ossification process of bone formation, during which cartilage is replaced by bone (p. 923)

ovary in plants, a flower structure that contains one or more ovules from which female gametophytes are produced; in animals, the female gonad that produces eggs (pp. 612, 1008)

oviparous term used to refer to animals whose eggs hatch outside the mother's body (p. 778)

ovoviviparous term used to refer to animals whose young are born alive after developing in eggs inside the mother's body (p. 778)

ovulation process in which an egg is released from the ovary (p. 1012)

ovule structure in seed cones in which female gametophytes develop (p. 610)

ozone layer atmospheric layer in which ozone gas is relatively concentrated (p. 157)

pacemaker small group of cardiac muscle cells in the right atrium that "set the pace" for the heart as a whole; also known as the sinoatrial node (p. 946)

paleontologist scientist who studies fossils (p. 417)

palisade mesophyll layer of tall, column-shaped mesophyll cells just under the upper epidermis of a leaf (p. 596)

pancreas gland that produces hormones that regulate blood sugar; produces enzymes that break down carbohydrates, proteins, lipids, and nucleic acids; and produces sodium bicarbonate, a base that neutralizes stomach acid (p. 981)

parasitism symbiotic relationship in which one organism lives in or on another organism (the host) and consequently harms it (p. 93)

parenchyma type of ground-tissue cell with a thin cell wall and large central vacuole (p. 582)

passive immunity short-term immunity caused when antibodies produced by other animals for a pathogen are injected into the body (p. 1042)

pathogen disease-causing agent (pp. 485, 1031)

pedigree chart that shows the relationships within a family (p. 342)

pedipalps pair of mouthparts in chelicerates that are usually modified to grab prey (p. 722)

pellicle cell membrane in euglenas (p. 507)

penis external male reproductive organ (p. 1011)

perennial flowering plant that lives for more than two years (p. 572)

period unit of time into which eras are subdivided (p. 422)

periosteum tough layer of connective tissue surrounding a bone (p. 922)

peristalsis rhythmic muscular contractions that squeeze food through the esophagus into the stomach (p. 980)

permafrost layer of permanently frozen subsoil in the tundra (p. 104)

petal brightly colored structure just inside the sepals; attracts insects and other pollinators to a flower (p. 612)

petiole thin stalk by which a leaf blade is attached to a stem (p. 595)

pH scale measurement system used to indicate the concentration of hydrogen ions (H^+) in solution; ranges from 0 to 14 (p. 43)

phagocytosis process in which extensions of cytoplasm surround and engulf large particles and take them into the cell (p. 189)

pharyngeal pouch one of a pair of structures in the throat (pharynx) region of a chordate (p. 767)

pharynx muscular tube at the end of the gastrovascular cavity, or throat, that connects the mouth with the rest of the digestive tract and serves as a passageway for air and food (pp. 684, 956)

phenotype physical characteristics of an organism (p. 268)

pheromone specific chemical messenger that affects the behavior or development of other individuals of the same species (p. 731)

phloem vascular tissue responsible for the transport of nutrients and the carbohydrates produced by photosynthesis (p. 560)

photic zone well-lit upper layer of the oceans (p. 109)

photoautotroph organism that uses energy from sunlight to convert carbon dioxide and water to carbon compounds (p. 474)

photoheterotroph organism that is photosynthetic but needs organic compounds as a carbon source (p. 473)

photoperiodism response of plants to periods of light and darkness (p. 641)

photosynthesis process by which plants and some other organisms use light energy to convert water and carbon dioxide into oxygen and high-energy carbohydrates such as sugars and starches (pp. 68, 204)

photosystem light-collecting units of the chloroplast (p. 208)

phototropism tendency of plants to grow toward a source of light (p. 634)

phycobilin accessory pigment found in red algae that is especially good at absorbing blue light (p. 510)

phylogeny the study of evolutionary relationships among organisms (p. 452)

phylum group of closely related classes (p. 449)

phytochrome plant pigment responsible for photoperiodism (p. 641)

phytoplankton population of algae and other small, photosynthetic organisms found near the surface of the ocean and forming part of plankton (pp. 107, 509)

pigment light-absorbing molecule (p. 207)

pinocytosis process by which a cell takes in liquid from the surrounding environment (p. 189)

pioneer species first species to populate an area during primary succession (p. 94)

pith parenchyma cells inside the ring of vascular tissue in dicot stems (p. 590)

pituitary gland gland in the base of the skull that secretes nine hormones that directly regulate many body functions and control the actions of several other endocrine glands (p. 1003)

placenta organ in placental mammals through which nutrients, oxygen, carbon dioxide, and wastes are exchanged between embryo and mother (pp. 829, 1019)

plankton tiny, free-floating organisms that occur in aquatic environments (p. 107)

Plantae kingdom of multicellular photosynthetic autotrophs that have cell walls containing cellulose (p. 461)

plasma straw-colored fluid that makes up about 55 percent of blood (p. 951)

plasmid small circular piece of DNA (p. 327)

plasmodium structure with many nuclei formed by acellular slime molds (p. 518)

plastron ventral part of a turtle's or tortoise's shell (p. 805)

platelet cell fragment released by bone marrow that helps in blood clotting (p. 953)

point mutation gene mutation involving changes in one or a few nucleotides (p. 307)

polar zone cold climate zone where the sun's rays strike Earth at a very low angle (p. 88)

pollen cone cone in gymnosperms that produces male gametophytes in the form of pollen grains (p. 610)

pollen grain male gametophyte in seed plants (p. 565)

pollen tube structure grown by a pollen grain; contains two haploid sperm nuclei (p. 611)

pollination transfer of pollen from the male reproductive structure to the female reproductive structure (p. 565)

pollutant harmful material that can enter the biosphere through the land, air, or water (p. 148)

polygenic trait trait controlled by two or more genes (pp. 273, 396)

polymer large compound formed from combinations of many monomers (p. 45)

polymerase chain reaction (PCR) technique that allows molecular biologists to make many copies of a particular gene (p. 325)

polyp usually sessile stage of the life cycle of a cnidarian that has a cylindrical body with armlike tentacles (p. 670)

polyploidy condition in which an organism has extra sets of chromosomes (p. 308)

polysaccharide large macromolecule formed from monosaccharides (p. 46)

population group of individuals of the same species that live in the same area (p. 64)

population density number of individuals per unit of area (p. 119)

predation interaction in which one organism captures and feeds on another organism (p. 93)

predator-prey relationship mechanism of population control in which a population is regulated by predation (p. 126)

prehensile term used to refer to a long tail that can grasp branches (p. 835)

pressure-flow hypothesis hypothesis that considers plants in terms of where they produce and use materials from photosynthesis (p. 602)

primary growth type of plant growth that occurs at the tips of roots and shoots (p. 590)

primary productivity rate at which organic matter is created by producers in an ecosystem (p. 80)

primary succession succession that occurs on surfaces where no soil exists (p. 94)

prion infectious particle made up of protein rather than RNA or DNA (p. 490)

probability likelihood that a particular event will occur (p. 267)

producer organism that can capture energy from sunlight or chemicals and use it to produce food from inorganic compounds; also called an autotroph (p. 67)

product element or compound produced by a chemical reaction (p. 49)

proglottid one of the segments that make up most of a tapeworm's body (p. 688)

prokaryote unicellular organism lacking a nucleus (pp. 173, 471)

promoter region of DNA that indicates to an enzyme where to bind to make RNA (p. 301)

prophage the viral DNA that is embedded in the host cell's DNA (p. 480)

prophase first and longest phase of mitosis, during which the chromosomes become visible and the centrioles separate and take up positions on the opposite sides of the nucleus (p. 246)

prosimian small, nocturnal primate that has large eyes for seeing in the dark (p. 834)

prostaglandin hormonelike modified fatty acid produced by a wide range of cells; generally affects only nearby cells and tissues (p. 1000)

protein macromolecule that contains carbon, hydrogen, oxygen, and nitrogen; needed by the body for growth and repair and to make up enzymes (pp. 47, 973)

proteinoid microsphere tiny bubble, formed of large organic molecules, that has some characteristics of a cell (p. 425)

protist any eukaryote that is not a plant, an animal, or a fungus (p. 497)

Protista kingdom composed of eukaryotes that are not classified as plants, animals, or fungi (p. 460)

protonema mass of tangled green filaments in mosses that forms during germination (p. 558)

protostome animal whose mouth is formed from its blastopore (p. 661)

pseudocoelom body cavity between the endoderm and mesoderm tissues that is partially lined with mesoderm tissue (p. 689)

pseudopod temporary projection of cytoplasm, or a "false foot," used by some protists for feeding or movement (p. 500)

puberty period of rapid growth and sexual maturation during which the reproductive system becomes fully functional (p. 1009)

pulmonary circulation pathway of circulation between the heart and the lungs (p. 944)

punctuated equilibrium pattern of evolution in which long stable periods are interrupted by brief periods of more rapid change (p. 439)

Punnett square diagram showing the gene combinations that might result from a genetic cross (p. 268)

pupa stage of metamorphosis in which an insect changes from a larva into an adult (p. 729)

pupil small opening in the middle of the iris through which light enters the eye (p. 906)

radial symmetry body plan in which body parts repeat around the center of the body; characteristic of sea anemones and sea stars (pp. 662, 748)

radioactive dating technique in which scientists calculate the age of a sample based on the amount of remaining radioactive isotopes it contains (p. 420)

radula tongue-shaped structure used for feeding by snails and slugs (p. 702)

reabsorption process in which liquid is taken back into a vessel (p. 987)

reactant element or compound that enters into a chemical reaction (p. 49)

recombinant DNA DNA produced by combining DNA from different sources (p. 324)

reflex quick automatic response to a stimulus (p. 903)

reflex arc sensory receptor, sensory neuron, motor neuron, and effector that are involved in a quick response to a stimulus (p. 904)

relative dating method of determining the age of a fossil by comparing its placement with that of fossils in other layers of rock (p. 419)

relative frequency number of times an allele occurs in a gene pool compared with the number of times other alleles occur (p. 394)

renewable resource resource that can regenerate quickly and that is replaceable (p. 144)

replication copying process by which a cell duplicates its DNA (p. 299)

reproductive isolation separation of species or populations so that they cannot interbreed and produce fertile offspring (p. 404)

reptile any vertebrate that has dry scaly skin, lungs, and terrestrial eggs with several protective membranes (p. 797)

resource any necessity of life, such as water, nutrients, light, food, or space (p. 92)

responding variable factor in an experiment that a scientist wants to observe, which may change in response to the manipulated variable; also known as a dependent variable (pp. 9, 1062)

response single, specific reaction to a stimulus (p. 871)

resting potential electrical charge across the cell membrane of a resting neuron (p. 898)

restriction enzyme enzyme that cuts DNA at a specific sequence of nucleotides (p. 323)

retina innermost layer of the eye; contains photoreceptors (p. 907)

retrovirus virus that contains RNA as its genetic information (p. 482)

rhizoid in fungi, a rootlike hypha that penetrates the surface of an object; in mosses, a long, thin cell that anchors the moss to the ground and absorbs water and minerals from the surrounding soil (pp. 530, 557)

rhizome creeping or underground stem in ferns (p. 562)

ribonucleic acid (RNA) single-stranded nucleic acid that contains the sugar ribose (p. 47)

ribosomal RNA (rRNA) type of RNA that makes up the major part of ribosomes (p. 301)

ribosome small particle in the cell on which proteins are assembled; made of RNA and protein (p. 177)

risk factor anything that increases the chance of disease or injury (p. 1049)

RNA polymerase enzyme similar to DNA polymerase that binds to DNA and separates the DNA strands during transcription (p. 301)

rod photoreceptor in eye that is sensitive to light but not to colors (p. 907)

root underground organ in plants that absorbs water and minerals (p. 561)

root cap tough structure that protects a root as it forces its way through the soil (p. 585)

root hair tiny projection from the outer surface, or epidermis, of a root (p. 585)

rumen stomach chamber in cows and related animals in which newly swallowed plant food is stored and processed (p. 823)

salt marsh temperate-zone estuary dominated by salt-tolerant grasses above the low-tide line and by seagrasses under water (p. 108)

saprobe organism that obtains food from decaying organic matter (p. 537)

sapwood area in plants that surrounds heartwood and is active in fluid transport (p. 592)

science organized way of using evidence to learn about the natural world; also, the body of knowledge that scientists have built up after years of using this process (p. 3)

sclerenchyma type of ground-tissue cell with an extremely thick, rigid cell wall that makes ground tissue tough and strong (p. 582)

scolex head of an adult tapeworm; can contain suckers or hooks (p. 688)

scrotum external sac containing the testes (p. 1010)

secondary growth pattern of plant growth in which stems increase in width (p. 591)

secondary succession succession following a disturbance that destroys a community without destroying the soil (p. 95)

seed embryo of a living plant that is encased in a protective covering and surrounded by a food supply (p. 565)

seed coat structure that surrounds and protects a plant embryo and keeps it from drying out (p. 565)

seed cone cone that produces female gametophytes (p. 610)

segregation separation of alleles during gamete formation (p. 266)

selective breeding method of breeding that allows only those individual organisms with desired characteristics to produce the next generation (p. 319)

semicircular canal one of three structures within the inner ear that help monitor the position of the body (p. 908)

seminiferous tubule one of hundreds of tiny tubules in the testes in which sperm are produced (p. 1010)

sensory receptor neuron that reacts to a specific stimulus, such as light or sound, by sending impulses to other neurons and eventually to the central nervous system (p. 906)

sepal outermost circle of flower parts that encloses a bud before it opens and protects the flower while it is developing (p. 612)

septum internal wall between the segments of an annelid's body (p. 694)

seta bristle attached to the segments of many annelids (p. 694)

sex chromosome one of two chromosomes that determine an individual's sex (p. 341)

sex-linked gene gene located on the X or Y chromosome (p. 350)

sexual reproduction process by which cells from two different parents unite to produce the first cell of a new organism (p. 17)

sexually transmitted disease (STD) disease spread from one person to another during sexual contact (p. 1015)

shell structure in mollusks made by glands in the mantle that secrete calcium carbonate (p. 702)

short-day plant plant that flowers when daylight is short (p. 641)

sieve tube element phloem cell that is joined end-to-end to similar cells to form sieve tubes (p. 581)

single-gene trait trait controlled by a single gene that has two alleles (p. 395)

siphon tubelike structure through which water enters and leaves a mollusk's body (p. 703)

small intestine digestive organ in which most chemical digestion takes place (p. 981)

smog mixture of chemicals that occurs as a gray-brown haze in the atmosphere (p. 148)

society group of closely related animals of the same species that work together for the benefit of the group (p. 732)

soil erosion wearing away of surface soil by water and wind (p. 145)

solute substance that is dissolved in a solvent to make a solution (p. 42)

solution mixture of two or more substances in which the molecules of the substances are evenly distributed (p. 42)

solvent substance in which a solute is dissolved to form a solution (p. 42)

sorus cluster of sporangia on the underside of a fern frond (p. 562)

specialized cell cell that is uniquely suited to performing a particular function (p. 894)

speciation formation of new species (p. 404)

species group of similar organisms that can breed and produce fertile offspring (p. 64)

species diversity number of different species in the biosphere (p. 150)

spicule spike-shaped structure that makes up the skeletons of harder sponges; made of either calcium carbonate or silica (p. 665)

spindle fanlike microtubule structure that helps separate the chromosomes during mitosis (p. 247)

spinneret organ in spiders that contains silk glands (p. 723)

spiracle small opening located along the side of the body through which air enters and leaves the body of many terrestrial arthropods (p. 717)

spirillum spiral or corkscrew-shaped prokaryote (p. 473)

spongy mesophyll loose tissue beneath the palisade layer of a leaf (p. 596)

spontaneous generation hypothesis (disproven) stating that life could arise from nonliving matter (p. 8)

sporangiophore specialized hyphae where sporangia are found (p. 528)

sporangium structure in ferns and some fungi that contains spores (pp. 528, 562)

spore haploid reproductive cell (p. 514)

sporophyte diploid, or spore-producing, phase of an organism (pp. 514, 552)

stabilizing selection form of natural selection by which the center of the curve remains in its current position; occurs when individuals near the center of a distribution curve have higher fitness than individuals at either end (p. 399)

stamen male part of the flower; made up of an anther and a filament (p. 612)

stem supporting structure that connects roots and leaves and carries water and nutrients between them (p. 561)

stigma sticky portion at the top of the style where pollen grains frequently land (p. 612)

stimulant drug that increases the actions regulated by the nervous system (p. 910)

stimulus a signal to which an organism responds (pp. 19, 871)

stolon in fungi, a stemlike hypha that runs along the surface of an object; in plants, a long, trailing stem that produces roots when it touches the ground (pp. 530, 622)

stoma opening in the underside of a leaf that allows carbon dioxide and oxygen to diffuse into and out of the leaf (p. 596)

stomach large muscular sac that continues the mechanical and chemical digestion of food (p. 980)

stroma region outside the thylakoid membranes in chloroplasts (p. 208)

struggle for existence competition among members of a species for food, living space, and the other necessities of life (p. 380)

style narrow stalk of the carpel in a flower (p. 612)

subcutaneous fat layer of fat cells beneath the skin that helps conserve body heat (p. 822)

substrate reactant of an enzyme-catalyzed reaction (p. 52)

survival of the fittest process by which individuals that are better suited to their environment survive and reproduce most successfully; also called natural selection (p. 381)

suspension mixture of water and nondissolved materials (p. 42)

sustainable development using natural resources at a rate that does not deplete them (p. 145)

swim bladder internal gas-filled organ in many bony fishes that adjusts their buoyancy (p. 777)

swimmerets flipperlike appendages used by decapods for swimming (p. 721)

symbiosis relationship in which two species live closely together (p. 93)

synapse location at which a neuron can transfer an impulse to another cell (p. 900)

systemic circulation pathway of circulation between the heart and the rest of the body except the lungs (p. 944)

taiga biome in which the winters are cold but summers are mild enough to allow the ground to thaw (p. 104)

taproot primary root found in some plants that grows longer and thicker than other roots (p. 584)

target cell cell that has a receptor for a particular hormone (pp. 634, 997)

taste bud sense organ that detects the flavor of a substance (p. 909)

taxon group or level of organization into which organisms are classified (p. 449)

taxonomy discipline of classifying organisms and assigning each organism a universally accepted name (p. 447)

telophase fourth and final phase of mitosis, during which the chromosomes begin to disperse into a tangle of dense material (p. 248)

temperate zone moderate climate zone between the polar zones and the tropics (p. 88)

temporal isolation form of reproductive isolation in which two populations reproduce at different times (p. 405)

tendon tough connective tissue that joins skeletal muscles to bones (p. 930)

territory specific area occupied and protected by an animal or group of animals (p. 881)

testis male reproductive organ that produces sperm (pp. 688, 1008)

tetrad structure containing 4 chromatids that forms during meiosis (p. 276)

thalamus brain structure that receives messages from the sense organs and relays the information to the proper region of the cerebrum for further processing (p. 903)

theory well-tested explanation that unifies a broad range of observations (pp. 14, 369)

thigmotropism response of plants to touch (p. 639)

thorax body part of a crustacean that lies just behind the head and houses most of the internal organs (p. 721)

threshold minimum level of a stimulus required to activate a neuron (p. 899)

thylakoid saclike photosynthetic membrane found in chloroplasts (p. 208)

tissue group of similar cells that perform a particular function (p. 192)

tolerance organism's capacity to grow or thrive when subjected to an unfavorable environmental factor (p. 98)

trachea windpipe; tube through which air moves (p. 956)

tracheal tube one of many branching, air-filled tubes that extend throughout the bodies of many terrestrial arthropods (p. 717)

tracheid hollow plant cell in xylem tissue with thick cell walls that resist pressure (p. 560)

trait specific characteristic that varies from one individual to another (p. 264)

transcription process in which part of the nucleotide sequence of DNA is copied into a complementary sequence in RNA (p. 301)

transfer RNA (tRNA) type of RNA molecule that transfers amino acids to ribosomes during protein synthesis (p. 301)

transformation process in which one strain of bacteria is changed by a gene or genes from another strain of bacteria (p. 288)

transgenic term used to refer to an organism that contains genes from other organisms (p. 331)

translation decoding of a mRNA message into a polypeptide chain (p. 304)

transpiration loss of water from a plant through its leaves (pp. 75, 596)

trichocyst small, bottle-shaped structure used for defense by paramecia (p. 501)

trochophore free-swimming larval stage of an aquatic mollusk (p. 701)

trophic level step in a food chain or food web (p. 70)

tropical zone warm climate zone that receives direct or nearly direct sunlight year round (p. 88)

tropism response of a plant to an external stimulus (p. 639)

true-breeding term used to describe organisms that produce offspring identical to themselves if allowed to self-pollinate (p. 263)

tube foot suction-cuplike structure attached to radial canals of echinoderms; used to walk and to open shells (p. 735)

tumor mass of growing tissue (p. 1052)

tympanic membrane eardrum of amphibians inside the skull; vibrates in response to sound, allowing hearing (p. 787)

understory layer in a rain forest formed by shorter trees and vines (p. 100)

ureter tube that carries urine from the kidney to the urinary bladder (p. 986)

urethra tube that carries urine from the bladder and releases it from the body; in males, tube through which semen is released from the body (pp. 987, 1011)

urinary bladder saclike organ in which urine is stored before being excreted (p. 986)

uterus organ of the female reproductive system in which a fertilized egg can develop (p. 1012)

vaccination injection of a weakened or mild form of a pathogen to produce immunity (p. 1041)

vaccine a preparation of weakened or killed pathogens (p. 486)

vacuole cell organelle that stores materials such as water, salts, proteins, and carbohydrates (p. 179)

vagina in the human female reproductive system, a canal that leads from the uterus to the outside of the body (p. 1012)

valve flap of connective tissue between an atrium and a ventricle, or in a vein, that prevents backflow of blood (p. 945)

van der Waals forces a slight attraction that develops between the oppositely charged regions of nearby molecules (p. 39)

variable factor in an experiment that can change (p. 1062)

vas deferens tube that carries sperm from the epididymis to the urethra (p. 1011)

vascular bundle plant stem structure that contains xylem and phloem tissue (p. 590)

vascular cambium lateral meristematic tissue that produces vascular tissues and increases the thickness of the stem over time (p. 591)

vascular cylinder central region of a root that includes the vascular tissue—xylem and phloem (p. 585)

vascular tissue type of plant tissue specialized to conduct water and nutrients throughout a plant (p. 560)

vector animal that carries pathogens from person to person (p. 1034)

vegetative reproduction method of asexual reproduction used by many flowering plants (p. 622)

vein in plants, a cluster of vascular tissue in leaves; in animals, a blood vessel that returns blood to the heart (pp. 561, 947)

ventricle lower chamber of the heart that pumps blood out of the heart (pp. 776, 944)

vertebra individual segment of the backbone; encloses and protects the spinal cord (p. 768)

vertebrate animal that has a vertebral column, or backbone (p. 657)

vessel element in angiosperms, xylem cell that forms part of a continuous tube through which water can move (p. 581)

vestigial organ organ that serves no useful function in an organism (p. 384)

villus folded projection that increases the surface area of the walls of the small intestine (p. 982)

viroid single-stranded RNA molecule that has no surrounding capsids (p. 490)

virus particle made up of nucleic acid, protein, and in some cases lipids that can replicate only by infecting living cells (p. 478)

visceral mass area beneath the mantle of a mollusk that contains the internal organs (p. 702)

vitamin organic molecule that helps regulate body processes (p. 974)

viviparous term used to refer to animals that bear live young that are nourished directly by the mother's body as they develop (p. 778)

water vascular system system of internal tubes in echinoderms that carries out essential functions such as feeding, respiration, circulation, and movement (p. 735)

weather condition of Earth's atmosphere at a particular time and place (p. 87)

wetland ecosystem in which water either covers the soil or is present at or near the surface of the soil for at least part of the year (p. 107)

xerophyte plant that lives in the desert biome (p. 644)

xylem vascular tissue that carries water upward from the roots to every part of a plant (p. 560)

zonation prominent horizontal banding of organisms that live in a particular habitat (p. 110)

zooplankton tiny animals that form part of the plankton (p. 107)

zoosporangium spore case (p. 518)

zygospore resting spore that contains zygotes formed during the sexual phase of a mold's life cycle (p. 530)

zygote fertilized egg (p. 1016)

abdomen/abdomen parte posterior del cuerpo de un artrópodo (pág. 721)

abiotic factor/factor abiótico factor físico, o sin vida, que da forma a un ecosistema (pág. 90)

abscission layer/capa de absición capa de células en el pecíolo que separa una hoja del sistema vascular (pág. 642)

accessory pigment/pigmento accesorio compuesto diferente a la clorofila que absorbe luz de diferentes longitudes de onda que la clorofila (pág. 506)

acellular slime mold/moho mucilaginoso acelular moho mucilaginoso que pasa por una etapa en la que sus células se unen para formar células más grandes con muchos núcleos (pág. 516)

acetylcholine/acetilcolina neurotransmisor que se difunde a través de una sinapsis y produce un impulso en la membrana celular de una célula muscular (pág. 929)

acid/ácido compuesto que forma iones de hidrógeno (H^+) en una solución (pág. 43)

acid rain/lluvia ácida lluvia que contiene ácidos nítrico y sulfúrico (pág. 148)

acoelomate/acelomado animal que carece de celoma o cavidad corporal (pág. 683)

actin/actina proteína que compone principalmente los finos filamentos en las estrías de células musculares esqueléticas (pág. 928)

action potential/potencial de acción inversión de cargas a través de la membrana celular de una neurona; también llamada impulso nervioso (pág. 899)

activation energy/energía de activación energía que se necesita para conseguir que comience una reacción (pág. 50)

active immunity/inmunidad activa inmunidad producida por la exposición a un antígeno, como resultado de una respuesta inmune (pág. 1042)

active transport/transporte activo proceso que necesita energía para mover material a través de una membrana celular contra una diferencia en concentración (pág. 188)

adaptation/adaptación característica heredada que aumenta la probabilidad de supervivencia de un organismo (pág. 380)

adaptive radiation/radiación adaptiva proceso en el cual una especie única o un grupo pequeño de especies evoluciona y cambia a varias formas diferentes que viven de diferentes maneras; crecimiento rápido en la diversidad de un grupo de organismos (págs. 436, 851)

addiction/adicción dependencia incontrolable de una droga (pág. 914)

adenosine triphosphate (ATP)/trifosfato de adenosina (ATP) uno de los principales compuestos químicos que los seres vivos usan para almacenar y desprender energía (pág. 202)

adhesion/adhesión atracción entre moléculas de diferentes sustancias; en plantas: atracción entre moléculas diferentes (págs. 41, 599)

aerobic/aeróbico proceso que requiere oxígeno (pág. 226)

age-structure diagram/diagrama de estructura por edades gráfica del número de hombres y mujeres en diferentes grupos de edades de una población (pág. 131)

aggression/agresión comportamiento amenazador que un animal usa para ejercer control sobre otro (pág. 881)

agriculture/agricultura práctica del cultivo (pág. 141)

air sac/saco aéreo uno de muchos sacos que se encuentran en los pulmones de las aves en los que fluye el aire cuando el ave aspira; permite el flujo de aire en una dirección a través del sistema respiratorio (pág. 810)

algal bloom/floración de algas un aumento inmediato en la cantidad de algas y otros productores que resulta de un aporte significativo de un nutriente limitante (pág. 80)

allele/alelo una de las diferentes formas de un gen (pág. 265)

allergy/alergia reacción exagerada del sistema inmune a los antígenos (pág. 103)

alternation of generations/alternación de generaciones proceso en el cual muchas algas alternan entre las etapas de haploide y diploide en sus ciclos de vida (pág. 512)

alveolus/alvéolo saco de aire diminuto al final de un bronquiolo en los pulmones que provee área de superficie para que ocurra el intercambio de gases (págs. 859, 958)

amino acid/aminoácido compuesto con un grupo de aminos ($-NH_2$) en un extremo y un grupo de carboxilo ($-COOH$) en el otro (pág. 47)

amniotic egg/huevo amniótico huevo compuesto de una cáscara y membranas que crean un ambiente protegido en el cual el embrión puede desarrollarse fuera del agua (pág. 802)

amoeboid movement/movimiento ameboide tipo de movimiento que usan las amebas (pág. 500)

amphibian/anfibio vertebrado que, con algunas excepciones, vive en el agua de larva y en la tierra de adulto, respira con pulmones de adulto, tiene piel húmeda que contiene glándulas mucosas, y no tiene escamas ni garras (pág. 782)

amylase/amilasa enzima de la saliva que rompe los enlaces químicos de los almidones (pág. 979)

anaerobic/anaeróbico proceso que no necesita oxígeno (pág. 224)

anal pore/poro anal región de la membrana celular de un ciliado donde se fusionan las vacuolas alimentarias que contienen desechos de alimentos y se vacían al exterior (pág. 502)

anaphase/anafase tercera fase de la mitosis durante la cual las parejas de cromosomas se separan y se mueven hacia polos opuestos (pág. 248)

angiosperm/angiosperma planta con flores; porta sus semillas dentro de una capa de tejido que las protege (pág. 564)

Animalia/*Animalia* reino de eucariotas heterótrofos multicelulares cuyas células no tienen pared celular (pág. 461)

annual/anual planta con flores que completa un ciclo de vida durante una estación de crecimiento (pág. 572)

anther/antera estructura de la flor en la que se producen gametofitos haploides masculinos (pág. 612)

antheridium/anteridio estructura reproductora masculina de algunas plantas y algas (págs. 519, 559)

anthropoid/antropoideo grupo de primates compuesto por humanos y la mayoría de los monos (pág. 835)

antibiotic/antibiótico compuesto que bloquea el crecimiento y la reproducción de una bacteria (págs. 486, 1035)

antibody/anticuerpo proteína que ayuda a destruir a los patógenos (pág. 1038)

anticodon/anticodón grupo de tres bases en una molécula de tARN que son complementarias a un codón de mARN (pág. 304)

antigen/antígeno sustancia que provoca una respuesta inmunológica (pág. 1038)

anus/ano orificio por donde las sustancias de desecho salen del tracto digestivo (págs. 661, 689)

aorta/aorta arteria de los mamíferos a través de la cual viaja la sangre después de salir del ventrículo izquierdo (pág. 946)

aphotic zone/zona afótica capa permanentemente oscura de los océanos que se encuentra debajo de la zona fótica (pág. 109)

apical dominance/dominancia apical fenómeno en el cual cuanto más cerca está una yema de la punta del tallo, más inhibido es su crecimiento (pág. 636)

apical meristem/meristemo apical grupo de células no diferenciadas que se dividen para producir mayor longitud en tallos y raíces (pág. 582)

appendage/apéndice estructura, como una pata o una antena, que se extiende desde la cubierta del cuerpo (pág. 715)

aquaculture/acuicultura cría de organismos acuáticos para el consumo humano (pág. 147)

Archaea/*Archaea* dominio de procariotas unicelulares cuyas paredes celulares que no contienen peptidoglicano (pág. 459)

Archaebacteria/*Archaebacteria* reino de procariotas unicelulares cuyas paredes celulares no contienen peptidoglicano (pág. 459)

archaeocyte/arqueocito célula especializada en una esponja que crea espículas (pág. 665)

archegonium/arquegonio estructura reproductora femenina en algunas plantas, incluidas musgos y hepáticas (pág. 559)

artery/arteria vaso sanguíneo grande que lleva la sangre desde el corazón a los tejidos del cuerpo (pág. 946)

artificial selection/selección artificial selección por parte de los humanos para reproducir rasgos útiles provenientes de la variación natural en diferentes organismos (pág. 379)

ascospore/ascospora espora haploide producida en el asca de los ascomicetos (pág. 532)

ascus/asca estructura dentro de un cuerpo frutal de un ascomiceto en el cual se unen dos núcleos de diferentes tipos de reproducción (pág. 532)

asexual reproduction/reproducción asexual proceso por el cual un solo individuo se reproduce por sí mismo (pág. 17)

asthma/asma enfermedad respiratoria crónica en la cual se reduce el tamaño de las vías respiratorias más de lo normal (pág. 1044)

atherosclerosis/arteriosclerosis condición en la que depósitos de grasa, llamados placas, se forman en las paredes interiores de las arterias (pág. 949)

atom/átomo unidad básica de la materia (pág. 35)

ATP synthase/ATP sintetasa proteína grande que usa energía de los iones H^+ para unirse al ADP y a un grupo fosfato para producir ATP (pág. 210)

atrium/atrio cámara superior del corazón que recibe y mantiene la sangre que está a punto de entrar al ventrículo (págs. 776, 944)

autosome/autosoma cromosoma que no es un cromosoma sexual (pág. 341)

autotroph/autótrofo organismo que capta energía de la luz solar o de sustancias químicas y la usa para producir su propia alimentación de compuestos inorgánicos; también se le llama productor (págs. 67, 201)

auxin/auxina sustancia producida en la punta de una plántula que estimula la elongación celular (pág. 635)

axon/axón fibra larga que lleva los impulsos del cuerpo celular de una neurona (pág. 898)

bacillus/bacilo procariota con forma de bastoncillo (pág. 473)

Bacteria/Bacteria dominio de procariotas unicelulares cuyas paredes celulares contienen peptidoglicano (pág. 459)

bacteriophage/bacteriófago virus que infecta a una bacteria (págs. 289, 479)

bark/corteza estructura del árbol que incluye todos los tejidos fuera del cámbium vascular, incluido el floema, el felógeno y el corcho (pág. 593)

base/base compuesto que produce iones de hidróxido (OH^+) en una solución (pág. 43)

base pairing/pares de bases principio que dice que los enlaces del ADN pueden formarse sólo entre adenina y tiamina y entre guanina y citosina (pág. 294)

basidiospore/basidiospora espora en los basidiomicetos que germina para producir un micelio primario haploide (pág. 535)

basidium/basidio estructura que contiene las esporas de un basidiomiceto (pág. 534)

behavior/comportamiento manera en que un organismo reacciona a los cambios en sus condiciones internas o en el ambiente exterior (pág. 871)

behavioral isolation/aislamiento de comportamiento forma de aislamiento reproductivo en la cual dos poblaciones tienen diferencias en rituales de cortejo u otros tipos de comportamiento que previene su apareamiento (pág. 404)

benthos/bentos organismos que viven pegados o cerca del suelo oceánico (pág. 112)

biennal/bienal planta con flores que completa su ciclo de vida en dos años (pág. 572)

bilateral symmetry/simetría bilateral conformación corporal en el cual una sola línea imaginaria puede dividir el cuerpo en dos mitades exactas; característica de gusanos, artrópodos y cordados (págs. 662, 748)

binary fission/fisión binaria tipo de reproducción asexual en la cual un organismo replica su ADN y se divide por la mitad, produciendo dos células hijas idénticas (pág. 475)

binocular vision/visión binocular capacidad de fusionar imágenes visuales de los dos ojos, que provee una percepción profunda y tridimensional del mundo (pág. 834)

binomial nomenclature/nomenclatura binaria sistema de clasificación en el que se le asigna a cada especie un nombre científico de dos partes (pág. 448)

biodiversity/biodiversidad diversidad biológica; la suma total de la variedad de organismos en la biosfera (pág. 150)

biogeochemical cycle/ciclo biogeoquímico proceso en el cual elementos, compuestos químicos y otras formas de materia pasan de un organismo a otro y de una parte de la biosfera a otra (pág. 74)

biological magnification/magnificación biológica incremento en la concentración de una sustancia dañina en organismos a niveles tróficos más altos en una cadena o trama alimentaria (pág. 152)

biology/biología ciencia que busca entender el mundo de los seres vivos (pág. 16)

biomass/biomasa cantidad total de tejido vivo en un nivel trófico dado (pág. 72)

biome/bioma grupo de ecosistemas que tienen el mismo clima y comunidades dominantes semejantes (págs. 64, 98)

biosphere/biosfera parte de la tierra en la que la vida existe y que incluye la tierra, el agua y el aire o la atmósfera (pág. 63)

biotic factor/factor biótico influencia biológica en organismos de un ecosistema (pág. 90)

bipedal/bípedo término usado para referirse a la locomoción en dos extremidades (pág. 835)

bird/ave animal endotérmico que tiene una cubierta externa de plumas, dos patas cubiertas con escamas que usa para caminar o posarse y extremidades delanteras transformadas en alas (pág. 806)

blade/limbo sección delgada y plana de la hoja de una planta que recoge la luz solar (pág. 595)

blastula/blástula esfera hueca de células formada cuando el cigoto sufre una serie de divisiones (pág. 661)

bone marrow/médula ósea tejido suave dentro de las cavidades de los huesos (pág. 922)

book lung/pulmón laminar órgano que tiene capas de tejido respiratorio usadas por algunos artrópodos terrestres para intercambiar gases (pág. 717)

Bowman's capsule/cápsula de Bowman estructura en forma de taza en la parte superior de una nefrona que encierra al glomérulo (pág. 987)

brain stem/tronco cerebral estructura que conecta el cerebro y la espina dorsal; incluye el bulbo raquídeo y la protuberancia anular (pág. 902)

bronchus/bronquio vía que conecta la tráquea con los pulmones (pág. 958)

bryophyte/briofita planta no vascular; por ejemplo el musgo y sus parientes (pág. 556)

bud/yema estructura de la planta que contiene tejidos no desarrollados que pueden producir nuevos tallos y hojas (pág. 589)

budding/gemación proceso asexual por el cual las levaduras aumentan en número; proceso de unir una yema a una planta para producir nuevas ramas (pág. 533, 623)

buffer/disolución amortiguadora ácido o base débil que puede reaccionar con ácidos o bases fuertes para ayudar a prevenir cambios fuertes y repentinos en el pH (pág. 43)

calorie/caloría cantidad de energía necesaria para elevar la temperatura de 1 gramo de agua 1 grado Celsius (pág. 221)

Calorie/Caloría término usado por los científicos para medir la energía almacenada en los alimentos; 1000 calorías (pág. 971)

Calvin cycle/ciclo de Calvin reacciones de fotosíntesis en las cuales la energía de ATP y NADPH se usa para crear componentes de alta energía, como los azúcares (pág. 212)

cancer/cáncer desorden por el que algunas de las células del cuerpo pierden la capacidad de controlar su crecimiento (pág. 252)

canopy/bóveda arbórea cubierta densa formada por las cimas hojeadas de los árboles altos en los bosques lluviosos (pág. 100)

capillary/capilar el vaso sanguíneo más pequeño; trae nutrientes y oxígeno a los tejidos y absorbe el dióxido de carbono y los productos de desecho (pág. 947)

capillary action/acción capilar tendencia del agua a subir por un tubo delgado (pág. 599)

capsid/cápside cubierta externa de proteína de un virus (pág. 479)

carapace/caparazón en los crustáceos, la parte del exoesqueleto que cubre el cefalotórax; en las tortugas, la parte dorsal de la coraza (pág. 721)

carapace/carapacho parte dorsal del caparazón (pág. 805)

carbohydrate/carbohidrato compuesto formado por carbono, hidrógeno y átomos de oxígeno; fuente principal de energía para el cuerpo humano (págs. 45, 972)

carcinogen/carcinógeno compuesto químico que causa cáncer (pág. 1052)

carnivore/carnívoro organismo que obtiene energía de comer otros animales (pág. 69)

carpel/carpelo parte más interna de una flor que produce los gametofitos femeninos (pág. 612)

carrying capacity/capacidad de carga mayor número de individuos que puede sustentar un medio ambiente dado (pág. 122)

cartilage/cartílago tejido de conexión fuerte que sostiene el cuerpo y es más suave y más flexible que el hueso (págs. 773, 922)

Casparian strip/banda de Caspary banda a prueba de agua que rodea las células de la endodermis de las plantas (pág. 587)

caste/casta grupo de insectos especializados para realizar tareas o asumir papeles particulares (pág. 732)

catalyst/catalizador sustancia que acelera la velocidad de una reacción química (pág. 51)

cell/célula colección de materia viva rodeada por una barrera que separa la célula de su alrededor; unidad básica en todas las formas de vida (págs. 17, 170)

cell body/cuerpo celular parte más grande de una neurona típica; contiene el núcleo y la mayoría del citoplasma (pág. 897)

cell culture/cultivo celular grupo de células que crecen en una solución de nutrientes a partir de una célula única (pág. 27)

cell cycle/ciclo celular serie de sucesos que sufren las células a medida que crecen y se dividen (pág. 245)

cell division/división celular proceso por el cual una célula se divide en dos células hijas nuevas (pág. 243)

cell fractionation/fraccionamiento celular técnica en la cual se rompen las células en pedazos y se separan las diferentes partes de las células (pág. 27)

cell-mediated immunity/inmunidad celular inmunidad contra células anormales y patógenos dentro de células vivas (pág. 1038)

cell membrane/membrana celular barrera delgada y flexible alrededor de la célula; regula lo que entra y sale de la célula (pág. 182)

cell specialization/especialización celular proceso por el que se desarrollan las células de diferentes maneras para realizar tareas distintas (pág. 190)

cell theory/teoría celular idea que propone que todos los seres vivos están compuestos de células, las células son la unidad básica de la estructura y función en los seres vivos y las células existentes producen nuevas células (pág. 170)

cell wall/pared celular capa fuerte de apoyo alrededor de la membrana celular en plantas, algas y algunas bacterias (pág. 182)

cellular respiration/respiración celular proceso que libera energía al romper glucosa y otras moléculas de alimentos en presencia de oxígeno (pág. 222)

cellular slime mold/moho mucilaginoso celular moho mucilaginoso cuyas células permanecen separadas durante todas las fases del ciclo de vida del moho (pág. 516)

centriole/centriolo una de dos estructuras diminutas localizadas en el citoplasma de las células animales cerca de la membrana nuclear (págs. 181, 246)

centromere/centrómero área donde se unen las cromátidas de un cromosoma (pág. 245)

cephalization/cefalización concentración de los órganos de los sentidos y las células nerviosas en la parte frontal del cuerpo de un animal (págs. 663, 748)

cephalothorax/cefalotórax región de un crustáceo formado por la fusión de la cabeza con el tórax (pág. 721)

cerebellum/cerebelo región del cerebro que coordina los movimientos del cuerpo (págs. 777, 902)

cerebral cortex/corteza cerebral capa externa del cerebro de un mamífero; centro de pensamiento y otros comportamientos complejos (pág. 825)

cerebrospinal fluid/líquido cefalorraquídeo líquido en el espacio entre las meninges que actúa como un absorbente de golpes que protege el sistema nervioso central (pág. 901)

cerebrum/cerebro área responsable de las actividades voluntarias del cuerpo (págs. 777, 902)

chelicerae/quelíceros par de colmillos en la boca de los quelicerados que usan para clavar y paralizar a la presa (pág. 722)

cheliped/quelipedo cada una del par de patas anteriores de los decápodos (pág. 721)

chemical reaction/reacción química proceso que transforma un conjunto de sustancias químicas en otro conjunto de sustancias químicas (pág. 49)

chemoautotroph/quimioautótrofo organismo que fabrica moléculas de carbono orgánico a partir del dióxido de carbono usando la energía de una reacción química (pág. 474)

chemoheterotroph/quimioheterótrofo organismo que debe consumir moléculas orgánicas tanto para la energía como para el carbono (pág. 473)

chemosynthesis/quimiosíntesis proceso por el cual algunos organismos usan la energía química para producir carbohidratos (pág. 68)

chitin/quitina carbohidrato complejo que conforma la pared celular de los hongos; también se encuentra en el esqueleto externo de los artrópodos (págs. 527, 715)

chlorophyll/clorofila pigmento principal de las plantas y otros organismos fotosintetizadores; absorbe energía de la luz (pág. 207)

chloroplast/cloroplasto organelo que se encuentra en las células de las plantas y otros organismos que capta la energía de la luz solar y la convierte en energía química (pág. 180)

choanocyte/coanocito célula especializada de las esponjas que usa un flagelo para mover una corriente de agua continua a través de la esponja (pág. 665)

chordate/cordado miembro del fílum Chordata; animal que tiene, durante al menos algunas etapas de su vida, un cordón nervioso hueco, notocordio, sacos faríngeos y una cola musculosa (pág. 767)

chromatid/cromátida una de dos partes "hermanas" idénticas de un cromosoma duplicado (pág. 244)

chromatin/cromatina material granular visible del núcleo; consiste de ADN enrollado fuertemente alrededor de las proteínas (págs. 176, 296)

chromosome/cromosoma estructura filamentosa en el núcleo que contiene la información genética que se pasa de una generación de células a la siguiente (pág. 176)

chyme/quimo mezcla de líquidos y alimento producida en el estómago al contraerse los músculos estomacales (pág. 981)

cilium/cilio estructura parecida a un pelo y similar a un flagelo, que muchas células usan para moverse (pág. 501)

circadian rhythm/ritmo circadiano ciclo de comportamiento que ocurre en un patrón diario (pág. 878)

cladogram/cladograma diagrama que muestra las relaciones evolutivas entre un grupo de organismos (pág. 453)

class/clase grupo de órdenes similares (pág. 449)

classical conditioning/condicionamiento clásico proceso de aprendizaje en el cual un animal hace una conexión mental entre un estímulo y algún tipo de recompensa o castigo (pág. 874)

climate/clima media de las condiciones de temperatura y precipitación año tras año en una región particular (pág. 87)

clitellum/clitelio en los anélidos, banda de segmentos especializados y gruesos que secreta un anillo mucoso en el que se liberan los huevos y el esperma (pág. 696)

cloaca/cloaca cavidad muscular al final del intestino grueso a través de la cual los desechos de la digestión, la orina, los huevos o el esperma abandonan el cuerpo (pág. 784)

clone/clon miembro de una población de células genéticamente idénticas producidas por una única célula (pág. 333)

closed circulatory system/sistema circulatorio cerrado sistema en el cual la sangre se mueve por una red de vasos sanguíneos (págs. 695, 754)

cnidocyte/cnidocito célula urticante de los cnidarios; la usan para defenderse y para capturar a la presa (pág. 669)

coastal ocean/océano continental zona marina que se extiende desde la marea baja hasta el final de la costa continental (pág. 110)

coccus/coco procariota esférico (pág. 473)

cochlea/caracol parte del oído interno lleno de fluido; envía impulsos nerviosos al cerebro mediante el nervio acústico (pág. 908)

codominance/codominancia situación en la que ambos alelos de un gen contribuyen al fenotipo de un organismo (pág. 272)

codon/codón secuencia triple de nucleótidos en el ARN mensajero que codifica un aminoácido específico (pág. 302)

coelom/celoma cavidad corporal llena de fluidos envuelta con mesodermo (págs. 683, 749)

coevolution/coevolución proceso por el cual dos especies evolucionan en respuesta a cambios en uno o en el otro (pág. 437)

cohesion/cohesión atracción entre moléculas de la misma sustancia (pág. 41)

collenchyma/colénquima tipo de célula de tejido fundamental con una pared celular fuerte y flexible; ayuda al soporte de plantas grandes (pág. 582)

commensalism/comensalismo relación simbiótica en la cual un miembro de la asociación se beneficia y al otro ni se le ayuda ni se le perjudica (pág. 93)

common descent/descendencia común principio que enuncia que todos los seres vivos vienen de antepasados comunes (pág. 382)

communication/comunicación pasar información de un organismo a otro (pág. 881)

community/comunidad ensamblaje de diferentes poblaciones que viven juntas en un área específica (pág. 64)

companion cell/célula acompañante célula floema que rodea el tubo criboso (pág. 581)

competitive exclusion principle/principio de la exclusión competitiva norma ecológica que enuncia que dos especies no pueden ocupar el mismo nicho ecológico en el mismo hábitat al mismo tiempo (pág. 92)

complete metamorphosis/metamorfosis completa tipo de desarrollo en los insectos en el que la larva no se parece ni actúa como sus padres y también se alimenta de forma diferente (pág. 729)

compound/compuesto sustancia formada por una combinación química de dos o más elementos en proporciones definidas (pág. 37)

compound light microscope/microscopio óptico compuesto microscopio que permite que la luz pase a través de un espécimen y usa dos lentes para formar una imagen (pág. 26)

concentration/concentración masa de un soluto en un volumen dado de solución; o masa/volumen (pág. 183)

cone/cono en las gimnospermas, estructura que porta las semillas; en la retina del ojo, un fotoreceptor que responde a la luz de diferentes colores produciendo visión de color (págs. 564, 907)

conidium/conidio espora diminuta de un hongo que se forma en la punta de una hifa especializada en los ascomicetos (pág. 532)

coniferous/conifera término usado para referirse a los árboles que producen conos que portan semillas y tienen hojas delgadas en forma de agujas (pág. 103)

conjugation/conjugación forma de reproducción sexual en la cual los paramecios y algunos procariotes intercambian información genética (págs. 475, 502)

connective tissue/tejido conectivo tejido que mantiene los órganos en su lugar y une diferentes partes del cuerpo (pág. 894)

conservation/conservación administración sensata de los recursos naturales, que incluye la preservación de hábitats y de la vida silvestre (pág. 154)

consumer/consumidor organismo que depende de otros organismos para energía y alimentación; también se le conoce como heterótrofo (pág. 68)

contractile vacuole/vacuola contráctil cavidad en el citoplasma de algunos protistas que recoge el agua de la célula y la elimina (pág. 502)

controlled experiment/experimento controlado prueba del efecto de una variable única al cambiarla, mientras el resto de las variables se mantienen fijas (pág. 9)

controlled variable/variable controlada factor en un experimento que un científico mantiene fijo a propósito (pág. 1062)

convergent evolution/evolución convergente proceso por el cual organismos no relacionados que evolucionan independientemente desarrollan semejanzas cuando se adaptan a medio ambientes similares (pág. 437)

coral reef/arrecife de coral medio ambiente diverso y productivo, nombrado así por los corales que forman su estructura primaria (pág. 111)

cork cambium/felógeno tejido merismático lateral que produce la cubierta externa de los tallos (pág. 591)

corpus luteum/cuerpo luteal nombre dado a un folículo después de la ovulación debido a su color amarillo (pág. 1014)

cortex/parénquima cortical capa esponjosa de tejido fundamental que se encuentra dentro de la epidermis de una raíz (pág. 585)

cotyledon/cotiledón primera hoja o par de hojas producidas por el embrión de una plántula (pág. 570)

courtship/cortejo tipo de comportamiento en el cual un animal produce estímulos para atraer a un miembro del sexo opuesto (pág. 879)

covalent bond/enlace covalente enlace formado entre átomos al compartir electrones (pág. 38)

crop/buche en los gusanos, parte del sistema digestivo en el que se almacena la comida; en los pájaros, estructura en la parte inferior del esófago en que la comida se almacena y se humedece (págs. 595, 809)

crossing-over/cruzamiento proceso en el cual los cromosomas homólogos intercambian porciones de cromátidas durante la meiosis (pág. 277)

cyclin/ciclina de una familia de proteínas muy relacionadas que regula el ciclo celular en las células eucarióticas (pág. 581)

cytokinesis/citocinesis división del citoplasma durante la división de la célula (pág. 244)

cytokinin/citocinina hormonas vegetales que se producen en las raíces, frutos y semillas en desarrollo (pág. 636)

cytoplasm/citoplasma material dentro de la membrana celular, sin incluir el núcleo (pág. 174)

cytoskeleton/citoesqueleto red de filamentos de proteína dentro de algunas células que ayuda a que la célula mantenga su forma y que participa en muchas formas del movimiento de la célula (pág. 181)

data/datos evidencia; información reunida a partir de observaciones (págs. 4, 1057)

deciduous/caducifolio término usado para referirse a un árbol que muda sus hojas durante una estación específica cada año (pág. 100)

decomposer/descomponedor organismo que deshace y obtiene energía de materia orgánica muerta (pág. 69)

deforestation/deforestación destrucción de bosques (pág. 146)

demographic transition/transición demográfica cambio en una población de altos a bajos índices de natalidad y mortandad (pág. 130)

demography/demografía estudio científico de poblaciones humanas (pág. 130)

dendrite/dendrita extensión de la célula de una neurona que lleva impulsos desde el medio ambiente o desde otras neuronas hacia el cuerpo celular (pág. 898)

denitrification/desnitrificación conversión de nitratos en gas nitrógeno (pág. 78)

density-dependent limiting factor/factor limitante dependiente de la densidad factor limitante que depende del tamaño de la población (pág. 125)

density-independent limiting factor/factor limitante independiente de la densidad factor limitante que afecta todas las poblaciones de manera similar, sin importar el tamaño de la población (pág. 127)

deoxyribonucleic acid (DNA)/ácido desoxirribonucleico (ADN) ácido nucleico que contiene el azúcar desoxirribosa (pág. 47)

dependent variable/variable dependiente factor en un experimento que un científico quiere observar, el cual puede cambiar debido a la variable manipulada; también conocido como variable respuesta (pág. 1062)

depressant/depresivo droga que reduce la velocidad de las funciones reguladas por el cerebro (pág. 911)

derived character/rasgo derivado característica que aparece en partes recientes de un linaje, pero que no tienen los miembros más viejos (pág. 453)

dermis/dermis capa interna de la piel (pág. 935)

descent with modification/descendencia con modificación principio que dice que todos los seres vivos han descendido, con cambios, de otras especies con el tiempo (pág. 381)

desertification/desertificación en áreas con clima seco, proceso causado por la combinación de prácticas inadecuadas de agricultura, pastoreo excesivo y sequía que convierte la tierra productiva en desértica (pág. 145)

detritivore/detritívoro organismo que se alimenta de restos de animales y plantas y otra materia muerta (pág. 69)

detritus/detrito partículas de material orgánico que proveen alimento para los organismos en la base de una trama alimentaria de un estuario (pág. 108)

deuterosome/deuterostomo animal cuyo ano se forma a partir de la blastopora de una blástula (pág. 661)

diabetes mellitus/diabetes mellitus condición que ocurre cuando el páncreas produce muy poca insulina, resultando en un aumento en la cantidad de glucosa en la sangre (pág. 1007)

diaphragm/diafragma músculo plano y grande bajo la cavidad pectoral que ayuda a la respiración (págs. 824, 959)

dicot/dicotiledónea angiosperma cuyas semillas tienen dos cotiledóneas (pág. 570)

differentiation/diferenciación proceso en el cual las células se especializan en estructura y función (págs. 312, 583, 1017)

diffusion/difusión proceso por el cual las moléculas tienden a moverse desde un área donde están más concentradas a un área donde están menos concentradas (pág. 184)

diploid/diploide término usado para referirse a una célula que contiene los dos conjuntos de cromosomas homólogos (pág. 275)

directional selection/selección direccional forma de selección natural en la cual se mueve la curva completa; ocurre cuando los individuos a un extremo de una curva de distribución son más aptos que los individuos en el medio o en el otro extremo de la curva (pág. 398)

disease/enfermedad cualquier cambio, diferente a una herida, que interrumpe las funciones normales del cuerpo (pág. 1031)

disruptive selection/selección disruptiva forma de selección natural en la cual una única curva se divide en dos; ocurre cuando los individuos en los extremos más alto y más bajo de una curva de distribución son más aptos que los individuos en el medio (pág. 399)

DNA fingerprinting/huellas de ADN análisis de secciones de ADN que tienen una función poco o nada conocida, pero que varía notablemente de un individuo a otro; se usa para identificar individuos (pág. 357)

DNA polymerase/polimerasa de ADN enzima que participa en la replicación del ADN al unir nucleótidos individuales para producir una molécula de ADN (pág. 299)

domain/dominio categoría taxonómica más inclusiva; más grande que un reino (pág. 458)

dormancy/dormición periodo durante el cual el embrión de una planta está vivo pero no crece (págs. 620, 641)

double fertilization/doble fertilización fertilización de angiospermas, en la que dos sucesos distintivos de fertilización tienen lugar entre los gametofitos masculino y femenino (pág. 616)

drug/droga cualquier sustancia, diferente a los alimentos, que causa un cambio en la estructura o función del cuerpo (pág. 910)

drug abuse/toxicomanía mal uso intencionado de cualquier droga para propósitos no médicos (pág. 914)

ecological pyramid/pirámide ecológica diagrama que muestra las cantidades de energía o materia relativas en cada nivel trófico en la cadena o trama alimentaria (pág. 72)

ecological succession/sucesión ecológica cambio gradual en comunidades vivas que sigue a una alteración (pág. 94)

ecology/ecología estudio científico de interacciones entre organismos y entre organismos y su medio ambiente (pág. 63)

ecosystem/ecosistema colección de todos los organismos que viven en un lugar particular, junto con su medio ambiente no vivo (pág. 64)

ecosystem diversity/diversidad de ecosistemas variedad de hábitats, comunidades vivas y procesos ecológicos en el mundo vivo (pág. 150)

ectoderm/ectodermo capa embrionaria más externa de la mayoría de los animales; origina la capa externa de la piel, órganos sensoriales y nervios (pág. 661)

ectotherm/ectotérmico animal que depende de las interacciones con el medio ambiente para ayudarse a controlar la temperatura del cuerpo (págs. 800, 855)

electron/electrón partícula cargada negativamente; localizado fuera del núcleo del átomo (pág. 35)

electron microscope/microscopio electrónico microscopio que forma una imagen al centrar un haz de electrones en un espécimen (pág. 26)

electron transport chain/cadena de transporte de electrones serie de proteínas en las que se usan los electrones de alta energía del ciclo de Krebs para convertir ADP en ATP (pág. 228)

element/elemento sustancia que consiste enteramente de un tipo de átomo (pág. 36)

embryo/embrión organismo en su primera etapa de desarrollo (pág. 565)

embryo sac/saco embrionario gametofito femenino en el óvulo de una planta con flores (pág. 615)

emigration/emigración movimiento de individuos fuera de un área (pág. 120)

emphysema/enfisema enfermedad en la cual los tejidos de los pulmones pierden elasticidad, lo que dificulta la respiración (pág. 962)

endangered species/especies en vías de extinción especies cuyo tamaño poblacional está disminuyendo rápidamente y se extinguiría si continúa la tendencia (pág. 151)

endocrine gland/glándula endocrina glándula que libera sus secreciones directamente en la corriente sanguínea (pág. 998)

endocytosis/endocitosis proceso por el cual una célula introduce material en la célula por doblamiento de la membrana celular (pág. 189)

endoderm/endodermo capa embrionaria más interna de la mayoría de los animales; se convierte en las paredes del tracto digestivo y de la mayoría del sistema respiratorio (pág. 661)

endodermis/endodermis capa de células que encierra completamente el tejido vascular (pág. 585)

endoplasmic reticulum/retículo endoplasmático sistema de membranas internas en las células en la que se forman los componentes lípidos de la membrana celular y se modifican algunas proteínas (págs. 177)

endoskeleton/endoesqueleto soporte estructural localizado dentro del cuerpo de un animal (págs. 734, 757)

endosperm/endosperma tejido rico en alimento que nutre a la semilla mientras crece (pág. 616)

endospore/endospora tipo de espora formada cuando una bacteria produce una pared interna gruesa que encierra su ADN y una porción de su citoplasma (pág. 475)

endosymbiotic theory/teoría endosimbiótica teoría que enuncia que las células eucarióticas se formaron por una simbiosis entre varios organismos procarióticos diferentes (pág. 427)

endotherm/endotérmico animal que genera su propio calor y controla la temperatura de su cuerpo internamente (págs. 808, 855)

enzyme/enzima proteína que actúa como catalizador biológico (pág. 51)

epidermal cell/célula epidérmica célula que crea el tejido dermal, que es la cubierta externa de la planta (pág. 580)

epidermis/epidermis capa externa de la piel (pág. 934)

epididymis/epididimio estructura del sistema reproductor masculino en donde el esperma madura completamente y es almacenado (pág. 1011)

epiphyte/epífito planta que no está arraigada al suelo, sino que crece directamente en el cuerpo de otra planta (pág. 645)

epithelial tissue/tejido epitelial tejido que cubre la superficie del cuerpo y las paredes de los órganos internos (pág. 894)

equilibrium/equilibrio cuando la concentración de un soluto es igual en toda la solución (pág. 184)

era/era una de las muchas subdivisiones temporales entre el Precámbrico y el presente (pág. 421)

esophagus/esófago tubo para el alimento que conecta la boca con el estómago (pág. 980)

estuary/estuario humedal formado donde los ríos se encuentran con el océano (pág. 108)

ethylene/etileno hormona de la planta que estimula la maduración de los frutos (pág. 638)

Eubacteria/*Eubacteria* reino de procariotas unicelulares cuyas paredes celulares están hechas de peptidoglicano (pág. 459)

Eukarya/*Eukarya* dominio de todos los organismos cuyas células tienen núcleo, incluyen los protistas, plantas, hongos y animales (pág. 460)

eukaryote/eucariota organismo cuyas células contienen núcleo (pág. 173)

evaporation/evaporación proceso en el cual el agua cambia de líquido a gas atmosférico (pág. 75)

evolution/evolución cambio de una clase de organismo con el tiempo; proceso por el cual los organismos modernos descienden de organismos antiguos (pág. 369)

evolutionary classification/clasificación evolutiva método de agrupación de organismos según su historia evolutiva (pág. 452)

evolve/evolucionar cambiar con el paso del tiempo (pág. 20)

exocrine gland/glándula exocrina glándula que libera sus secreciones a través de estructuras tubulares llamadas conductos (pág. 998)

exocytosis/exocitosis proceso en el cual una célula libera grandes cantidades de material (pág. 189)

exon/exón secuencia expresada de ADN; codifica una proteína (pág. 302)

exoskeleton/exoesqueleto esqueleto externo; cubierta externa resistente que protege y soporta el cuerpo de muchos invertebrados (págs. 715, 757)

exponential growth/crecimiento exponencial patrón de crecimiento en el que los individuos en una población se reproducen a una razón constante (pág. 121)

external fertilization/fertilización externa proceso en el cual los huevos se fertilizan fuera del cuerpo femenino (págs. 672, 758)

extinct/extinto término usado para referirse a una especie que ha desaparecido (pág. 417)

extinction/extinción desaparición de una especie de toda su zona de distribución geográfica (pág. 151)

extracellular digestion/digestión extracelular proceso en el que los alimentos se descomponen fuera de las células del tracto digestivo (pág. 751)

eyespot/mancha ocular grupo de células que pueden detectar cambios en la cantidad de luz en el ambiente (págs. 509, 685)

facilitated diffusion/difusión facilitada movimiento de moléculas específicas a lo largo de las membranas celulares a través de canales de proteínas (pág. 187)

facultative anaerobe/anaerobio facultativo organismo que puede sobrevivir con o sin oxígeno (pág. 474)

Fallopian tube/trompa de falopio uno de dos tubos llenos de fluido en las mujeres a través de los que pasa un óvulo después de su liberación del ovario (pág. 1012)

family/familia grupo de géneros que tienen muchas características en común (pág. 449)

fat/grasa lípido; formada por ácidos grasos y glicerina; protege los órganos corporales, aisla el cuerpo y almacena energía para el cuerpo (pág. 972)

feather/pluma estructura compuesta principalmente de proteína que se desarrolla en la superficie de la piel del pájaro (pág. 806)

feedback inhibition/retroinhibición proceso por el cual el producto o resultado para o limita el proceso (pág. 658, 895)

fermentation/fermentación proceso por el cual las células liberan energía en la ausencia de oxígeno (pág. 224)

fertilization/fertilización proceso en la reproducción sexual en el cual células reproductoras masculinas y femeninas se unen para formar una nueva célula (pág. 263)

fetal alcohol syndrome/síndrome alcohólico fetal grupo de defectos de nacimiento causados por los efectos del alcohol en un feto (pág. 913)

fetus/feto nombre dado al embrión humano después de ocho semanas de desarrollo (pág. 1020)

fever/fiebre temperatura corporal elevada que ocurre como respuesta a una infección (pág. 1037)

fibrous root/raíz fibrosa parte de un sistema de raíces en la cual las raíces se ramifican a tal grado que ninguna raíz crece más que el resto (pág. 584)

filament/filamento en las algas, na colonia larga en forma de hilos formada por muchas algas verdes; en las plantas, estructura larga y fina que soporta una antera (págs. 512, 612)

filtration/filtración proceso por el cual un líquido o gas pasa a través de un filtro para eliminar desperdicios (pág. 987)

fish/pez vertebrado acuático caracterizado por tener un par de aletas, escamas y branquias (pág. 771)

fission/fisión forma de reproducción asexual en la que un organismo se divide en dos, y cada mitad genera nuevas partes hasta convertirse en un organismo completo (pág. 686)

fitness/eficacia biológica capacidad de un organismo de sobrevivir y reproducirse en su medio ambiente (pág. 380)

flame cell/célula flamígera célula especializada que filtra y elimina el exceso de agua del cuerpo de un gusano plano (pág. 684)

flower/flor estructura portadora de semillas de una angiosperma (pág. 564)

follicle/folículo grupo de células que rodean a un solo óvulo en el sistema reproductor de la mujer (pág. 1012)

food chain/cadena alimentaria serie de pasos en el ecosistema en el que los organismos transfieren energía al comer y ser comidos (pág. 69)

food vacuole/vacuola alimentaria cavidad pequeña en el citoplasma de los protistas que almacena comida temporalmente (pág. 500)

food web/trama alimentaria red de interacciones complejas formada por las relaciones de alimentación entre varios organismos en un ecosistema (pág. 70)

foot/pie parte muscular de un molusco (pág. 702)

fossil/fósil restos o evidencias preservadas de un organismo antiguo (pág. 371)

fossil record/registro fósil información sobre la vida del pasado que incluye la estructura de organismos, lo que comían, sus predadores, el ambiente en que vivían y el orden en el que vivieron (pág. 417)

founder effect/efecto fundador cambio en las frecuencias alélicas como resultado de la migración de un pequeño subgrupo de una población (pág. 400)

frameshift mutation/cambio de pauta mutación que cambia el marco de lectura del mensaje genético al insertar o borrar un nucleótido (pág. 307)

frond/fronda hoja grande de un helecho (pág. 562)

fruit/fruto pared de tejido que rodea a la semilla de una angiosperma (pág. 569)

fruiting body/cuerpo fructífero estructura reproductora fina que produce esporas y que se halla en algunos protistas de tipo hongo; estructura reproductora de un hongo que se desarrolla de un micelio (págs. 516, 528)

Fungi/*Fungi* reino compuesto de heterótrofos; muchos obtienen la energía y los nutrientes de materia orgánica muerta (pág. 460)

gametangium/gametangio estructura productora de gametos, que se halla en el moho (pág. 529)

gamete/gameto célula especializada que participa en la reproducción sexual (pág. 266)

gametophyte/gametofito fase haploide o productora de gametos de un organismo (págs. 514, 552)

ganglion/ganglio grupo de células nerviosas (pág. 685)

gastrovascular cavity/cavidad gastrovascular espacio hueco digestivo con una abertura única, en la que los cnidarios, gusanos y equinodermos digieren la comida (pág. 671)

gastrulation/gastrulación proceso de migración celular por el cual una tercera capa de células se forma en la cavidad de un blastocisto (pág. 1018)

gel electrophoresis/electroforesis de gel procedimiento usado para separar y analizar fragmentos de ADN, colocando una mezcla de los fragmentos de ADN en un extremo de un gel poroso y aplicando un voltaje eléctrico al gel (pág. 323)

gemma/cápsula estructura pequeña en forma de taza en las hepáticas que contiene muchas células haploides; se usa en la reproducción asexual (pág. 557)

gemmule/gémula grupo de arqueocitos rodeados por una capa resistente de espículas; producida por algunas esponjas (pág. 667)

gene/gen secuencia de ADN que codifica una proteína y por ende determina un rasgo (pág. 265, 300)

gene map/mapa génico diagrama que muestra las ubicaciones relativas de cada gen conocido en un cromosoma particular (pág. 280)

gene pool/reservorio génico información genética combinada de todos los miembros de una población en particular (pág. 394)

genetic diversity/diversidad genética suma total de todas las diferentes formas de información genética llevada por todos los organismos que viven en la Tierra en la actualidad (pág. 150)

genetic drift/deriva genética cambio aleatorio en frecuencias alélicas que ocurre en poblaciones pequeñas (pág. 400)

genetic engineering/ingeniería genética proceso que consiste en hacer cambios en el código de ADN de organismos vivos (pág. 322)

genetic equilibrium/equilibrio genético situación en la que las frecuencias alélicas se mantienen constantes (pág. 401)

genetic marker/marcador genético gene que hace posible distinguir la bacteria que lleva un plásmido con un ADN extraño de las que no lo llevan (pág. 328)

genetics/genética estudio científico de la herencia (pág. 263)

genotype/genotipo formación genética de un organismo (pág. 268)

genus/género grupo de especies muy relacionadas, primera parte del nombre científico en la nomenclatura binomial (pág. 448)

geographic isolation/aislamiento geográfico forma de aislamiento reproductivo en la cual dos poblaciones están separadas físicamente por barreras geográficas como ríos, montañas o extensiones de agua (pág. 405)

geologic time scale/escala de cronología geológica escala usada por los paleontólogos para representar el tiempo evolutivo (pág. 421)

germ theory of disease/teoría germinal de las enfermedades idea de que las enfermedades infecciosas son causadas por microorganismos o gérmenes (pág. 1031)

germination/germinación etapa del crecimiento temprano del embrión de una planta (pág. 621)

gibberellin/giberelina sustancia producida por las plantas que ayuda al crecimiento (pág. 637)

gill/branquia órgano filamentoso en animales acuáticos especializado en el intercambio de gases en el agua (pág. 696)

gizzard/molleja en lombrices de tierra, parte del sistema digestivo en el que el alimento es despedazado en pedazos más pequeños; en pájaros, un órgano muscular que ayuda a la descomposición mecánica del alimento (págs. 695, 809)

global warming/calentamiento global aumento del promedio de temperatura en la tierra (pág. 159)

glomerulus/glomérulo pequeña red de capilares encerrados en el extremo superior de una nefrona; donde ocurre la filtración de la sangre (pág. 987)

glycolysis/glucólisis primer paso en la liberación de energía de la glucosa, en el cual una molécula de glucosa se divide en dos moléculas de ácido pirúvico (pág. 221)

Golgi apparatus/aparato de Golgi pila de membranas en la célula que modifica, clasifica y empaqueta proteínas del retículo endoplasmático (pág. 178)

grafting/injerto uso de un tallo como esqueje (pág. 623)

gravitropism/gravitropismo respuesta de una planta a la fuerza de la gravedad (pág. 635)

greenhouse effect/efecto invernadero ocurrencia natural en la que el calor es retenido en la atmósfera de la Tierra por el dióxido de carbono, el metano, el vapor de agua y otros gases (pág. 87)

green revolution/revolución verde desarrollo de variedades de cultivo altamente productivas y la introducción de técnicas de agricultura modernas para aumentar el rendimiento de los cultivos alimenticios (pág. 142)

guard cell/célula oclusiva célula especializada en la epidermis de las plantas que controla la apertura y cierre de los estomas como respuesta a cambios en la presión del agua (pág. 596)

gullet/cavidad bucal abertura en un lado de un ciliado que permite la entrada de alimento a la célula (pág. 502)

gymnosperm/gimnosperma planta con semillas que porta sus semillas directamente en la superficie de sus conos (pág. 564)

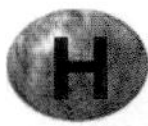

habitat/hábitat área donde vive un organismo, incluyendo los factores bióticos y abióticos que afectan al organismo (pág. 90)

habitat fragmentation/fragmentación del hábitat segmentación de ecosistemas en pequeños fragmentos (pág. 151)

habituation/habituación proceso de aprendizaje mediante el cual un animal disminuye o detiene su respuesta a un estímulo repetitivo que ni lo premia ni lo castiga (pág. 874)

hair follicle/folículo piloso saco en forma de tubo de las células de la epidermis que se extiende hasta la dermis; células en la base de los folículos pilosos que producen pelo (pág. 936)

half-life/vida media periodo requerido para que la mitad de los átomos radioactivos de una muestra se descompongan (pág. 420)

haploid/haploide término usado para referirse a una célula que contiene un único juego de cromosomas y, por lo tanto, un único juego de genes (pág. 275)

Hardy-Weinberg principle/principio de Hardy-Weinberg principio que enuncia que las frecuencias de los alelos en una población se mantendrán constantes, a menos que uno o más factores causen cambios en las frecuencias (pág. 401)

Haversian canal/conducto de Havers tubo perteneciente a una red de tubos que recorren el hueso compacto y que contienen vasos sanguíneos y nervios (pág. 922)

heartwood/duramen xilema más viejo situado cerca del centro de un tallo leñoso que ya no conduce agua (pág. 592)

hemoglobin/hemoglobina proteína en los glóbulos rojos que contiene hierro y que transporta el oxígeno de los pulmones a los tejidos del cuerpo (pág. 952)

herbicide/herbicida compuesto que es tóxico para las plantas (pág. 636)

herbivore/herbívoro organismo que obtiene energía alimentándose únicamente de plantas (pág. 69)

hermaphrodite/hermafrodita organismo que tiene órganos reproductores masculinos y femeninos (pág. 686)

heterotroph/heterótrofo organismo que obtiene energía de los alimentos que consume; también se le llama consumidor (págs. 68, 201)

heterozygous/heterocigoto término usado para referirse a un organismo que tiene dos alelos diferentes para el mismo rasgo (pág. 268)

histamine/histamina sustancia química liberada por las células madre activas, que incrementa el flujo de la sangre y los fluidos a la zona circundante (pág. 1043)

histone/histona proteína globular alrededor de la cual el ADN se enrolla estrechamente en la cromatina (pág. 296)

homeostasis/homeostasis proceso por el cual los organismos mantienen un ambiente interno relativamente estable (págs. 19, 895)

hominid/homínido primate que camina en dos patas, tiene pulgares oponibles y posee un cerebro grande; los humanos son los únicos miembros sobrevivientes (pág. 835)

hominoid/hominoideo grupo de antropoides que incluye los monos y los humanos (pág. 835)

homologous/homólogo término usado para referirse a los cromosomas que tienen por cada cromosoma correspondiente al progenitor de un sexo, otro correspondiente al progenitor del otro sexo (pág. 275)

homologous structures/estructuras homólogas estructuras que tienen diferentes formas en diferentes organismos pero que se desarrollan a partir de los mismos tejidos embriónicos (pág. 384)

homozygous/homocigoto término usado para referirse a un organismo que tiene dos alelos idénticos para un rasgo particular (pág. 268)

hormone/hormona sustancia producida en una parte de un organismo que afecta otra parte del mismo organismo (págs. 634, 997)

hox genes/genes HOX serie de genes que controla la diferenciación de células y tejido en un embrión (pág. 312)

humoral immunity/inmunidad humoral inmunidad contra patógenos en los fluidos del cuerpo (pág. 1038)

humus/humus material formado por hojas en descomposición y otra materia orgánica (pág. 103)

hybrid/híbrido descendencia de cruzamientos entre padres con diferentes rasgos (pág. 264)

hybridization/hibridación técnica de crianza que incluye el cruce de individuos distintos para reunir los mejores rasgos de ambos organismos (pág. 319)

hydrostatic skeleton/esqueleto hidrostático capas de músculos circulares y longitudinales que junto con el agua de la cavidad gastrovascular, permiten el movimiento (pág. 671, 756)

hypertonic/hipertónico cuando se comparan dos soluciones, la solución que tiene la mayor concentración de solutos (pág. 185)

hypha/hifa filamento diminuto que conforma un hongo multicelular o un moho de agua (págs. 518, 527)

hypothalamus/hipotálamo estructura del cerebro que actúa como un centro de control para el reconocimiento y el análisis del hambre, la sed, la fatiga, el enojo y la temperatura del cuerpo (pág. 903)

hypothesis/hipótesis explicación posible a un grupo de observaciones o respuesta posible a una pregunta científica (págs. 5, 1062)

hypotonic/hipotónico cuando se comparan dos soluciones, la solucion con la menor concentración de solutos (pag. 185)

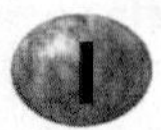

immigration/inmigración movimiento de individuos hacia un área que ya tiene población (pág. 120)

immune response/respuesta inmunológica defensas específicas del cuerpo que atacan al agente causante de una enfermedad (pág. 1038)

immunity/inmunidad capacidad del cuerpo de resistir un patógeno específico (pág. 1036)

implantation/implantación proceso en el cual un blastocisto se pega a la pared del útero (pág. 1017)

imprinting/impronta aprendizaje basado en la experiencia temprana; una vez que sucede la impronta, no se puede cambiar el comportamiento (pág. 876)

inbreeding/endogamia reproducción continua de individuos con características similares para mantener las características deseadas en una generación de organismos (pág. 320)

incomplete dominance/dominancia incompleta situación en la cual un alelo no es completamente dominante sobre el otro (pág. 272)

incomplete metamorphosis/metamorfosis incompleta tipo de desarrollo en los insectos caracterizado por una apariencia similar a través de todas las etapas del ciclo de vida (pág. 729)

independent assortment/transmisión independiente segregación independiente de genes durante la formación de gametos (pág. 271)

independent variable/variable independiente factor en un experimento que un científico cambia a propósito; también conocida como variable respuesta (pág. 1062)

index fossil/fósil índice fósil distintivo usado para comparar las edades relativas de los fósiles (pág. 419)

inference/inferencia interpretación lógica basada en conocimiento previo y en experiencia (pág. 4)

inflammatory response/respuesta inflamatoria reacción de defensa no específica a un daño de los tejidos causada por una lesión o infección (pág. 1037)

innate behavior/comportamiento innato comportamiento instintivo o de nacimiento; comportamiento que aparece de forma completamente funcional la primera vez que se realiza (pág. 873)

insight learning/aprendizaje por discernimiento también se llama razonamiento; proceso de aprendizaje en el cual un animal aplica algo que ya ha aprendido a una nueva situación sin un periodo de ensayo y error (pág. 875)

interferon/interferón una de un grupo de proteínas que ayuda a las células a resistir las infecciones virales (pág. 1038)

internal fertilization/fertilización interna proceso en el cual los huevos son fertilizados dentro del cuerpo de la madre (págs. 666, 758)

internode/entrenudo región entre los nudos en el tallo de una planta (pág. 589)

interphase/interfase periodo en el ciclo de una célula entre las divisiones celulares (pág. 245)

intracellular digestion/digestión intracelular proceso en el cual el alimento se digiere dentro de las células (pág. 751)

intron/intrón secuencia de ADN que no participa en la codificación de una proteína (pág. 302)

invasive species/especie invasora plantas y animales que han emigrado a lugares de donde no son nativas (pág. 153)

invertebrate/invertebrado animal que no tiene columna vertebral o espina dorsal (pág. 657)

ion/ion átomo que tiene una carga positiva o negativa (pág. 38)

ionic bond/enlace iónico enlace formado cuando uno o más electrones se transfieren de un átomo a otro (pág. 38)

isotonic/isotónico cuando la concentración de dos soluciones es igual (pág. 185)

isotope/isótopo átomo de un elemento que tiene un número de neutrones diferente a los otros átomos del mismo elemento (pág. 36)

joint/articulación lugar donde un hueso se une a otro (pág. 924)

karyotype/cariotipo fotografía de cromosomas agrupados en orden en pares (pág. 341)

kelp forest/bosque de laminarias comunidad del litoral marítimo nombrada así por su comunidad dominante, el quelpo, un alga marrón gigante (pág. 110)

keratin/queratina proteína resistente y fibrosa que se encuentra en la piel (pág. 934)

kidney/riñón órgano que remueve la urea, el exceso de agua y otros productos de desecho de la sangre (pág. 986)

kingdom/reino grupo taxonómico grande que consiste de los fílums cercanos (pág. 449)

Koch's postulates/postulados de Koch serie de directrices usadas para identificar el microorganismo que causa una enfermedad específica (pág. 1032)

Krebs cycle/ciclo de Krebs segunda etapa de la respiración celular en la cual el ácido pirúvico es descompuesto en dióxido de carbono en una serie de reacciones de extracción de energía (pág. 226)

language/lenguaje sistema de comunicación que combina sonidos, símbolos o gestos según un conjunto de reglas sobre el orden y significado de las palabras (pág. 882)

large intestine/intestino grueso colon, órgano que remueve el agua de los materiales no digeridos que pasan a través de él (pág. 984)

larva/larva etapa inmadura de un organismo que tienen una apariencia diferente a la forma adulta (pág. 666)

larynx/laringe estructura en la garganta que contiene las cuerdas vocales (pág. 958)

lateral bud/brote lateral área meristemática en el lado de un tallo que origina las ramas laterales (pág. 636)

lateral line system/sistema lineal lateral sistema receptor sensible que permite a un pez detectar corrientes suaves y vibraciones en el agua (pág. 777)

leaf/hoja órgano fotosintetizador que contiene uno o más fajos de tejido vascular (pág. 561)

learning/aprendizaje alteraciones en el comportamiento como resultado de la experiencia; también se llama comportamiento aprendido (pág. 873)

lens/cristalino objeto transparente detrás del iris que cambia de forma para que el ojo enfoque y pueda ver objetos cercanos y lejanos (pág. 907)

lichen/liquen asociación simbiótica entre un hongo y un organismo fotosintetizador (pág. 540)

ligament/ligamento tira de tejido conectivo resistente que mantiene los huesos unidos en una articulación (pág. 925)

light-dependent reactions/reacciones dependientes de la luz reacciones de fotosíntesis que usan la energía de la luz para producir ATP y NADPH (pág. 210)

lignin/lignina sustancia en las plantas vasculares que hace que las paredes celulares sean rígidas (pág. 560)

limiting factor/factor limitante factor que causa la disminución del crecimiento de una población (pág. 124)

limiting nutrient/nutriente limitante nutriente único que es escaso o tienen un ciclo muy lento, limitando así el crecimiento de organismos en un ecosistema (pág. 80)

lipid/lípido macromolécula formada principalmente por átomos de carbono e hidrógeno; incluye las grasas, los aceites y las ceras (pág. 46)

lipid bilayer/bicapa lípida lámina de doble capa que forma la base de casi todas las membranas celulares (pág. 182)

liver/hígado órgano grande justo encima del estómago que produce bilis (pág. 982)

logistic growth/crecimiento logístico patrón de crecimiento en el cual la tasa de crecimiento de una población baja o se detiene después de un periodo de crecimiento exponencial (pág. 122)

long-day plant/planta de día largo planta que florece cuando los días son largos (pág. 641)

loop of Henle/asa de Henle sección del túbulo de la nefrona que conserva agua y minimiza el volumen de orina (pág. 987)

lymph/linfa fluido perdido por la sangre al tejido circundante (pág. 954)

lymphocyte/linfocito tipo de célula blanca que produce anticuerpos que ayudan a destruir los patógenos (pág. 952)

lysogenic infection/infección lisogénica proceso en el cual un virus introduce su ADN en el ADN de una célula huésped y es replicado junto con el ADN de la célula huésped (pág. 480)

lysosome/lisosoma organelo de la célula lleno de enzimas necesarias para descomponer ciertos materiales de la célula (pág. 179)

lytic infection/infección lítica proceso en el cual un virus entra una célula, hace una copia de sí mismo y causa que la célula se reviente (pág. 480)

macroevolution/macroevolución cambios evolutivos a gran escala que tienen lugar durante largos periodos (pág. 435)

macronucleus/macronúcleo el núcleo más grande de los dos núcleos de un ciliado, contiene copias múltiples de la mayoría de los genes que la célula necesita para su existencia diaria (pág. 501)

madreporite/madreporita estructura parecida a un colador a través de la cual el sistema vascular acuoso de un equinodermo se abre al exterior (pág. 735)

Malpighian tubule/túbulo de Malpigio órgano en forma de saco que tienen la mayoría de los artrópodos terrestres, que extrae los desechos de la sangre y los añade a las heces que pasan por la tripa (pág. 717)

mammary gland/glándula mamaria glándula en los mamíferos que produce leche para alimentar a las crías (pág. 821)

mandible/mandíbula parte de la boca adaptada para morder y triturar alimentos (pág. 721)

mangrove swamp/manglar humedal costero dominado por mangles, plantas leñosas que toleran la sal (pág. 108)

manipulated variable/variable manipulada factor en un experimento que un científico cambia a propósito; también conocida como variable independiente (págs. 9, 1062)

mantle/manto capa fina de tejido que cubre la mayor parte del cuerpo de un molusco (pág. 702)

marsupial/marsupial mamífero que engendra crías vivas que completan su desarrollo en una bolsa externa (pág. 829)

mass extinction/extinción masiva suceso en el cual muchos tipos de seres vivos se extinguen al mismo tiempo (pág. 431)

medulla oblongata/bulbo raquídeo área del cerebro que controla el funcionamiento de muchos órganos internos (pág. 777)

medusa/medusa etapa móvil del ciclo de vida de un cnidario en que el cuerpo tiene forma de campana (pág. 670)

meiosis/meiosis en una célula diploide, proceso por el cual el número de cromosomas por célula se corta a la mitad a través de la separación de cromosomas homólogos (pág. 276)

melanin/melanina pigmento marrón oscuro que se encuentra en la piel (pág. 934)

meninges/meninges tres capas de tejido conectivo que envuelven el cerebro y la espina dorsal (pág. 901)

menstrual cycle/ciclo menstrual ciclo durante el cual un óvulo se desarrolla y sale del ovario y el útero se prepara para recibir el óvulo fertilizado (pág. 1013)

menstruation/menstruación fase del ciclo menstrual durante la cual el revestimiento del útero, junto con sangre y el óvulo sin fertilizar, salen por la vagina (pág. 1014)

meristem/meristemo grupo de tejido que es responsable del crecimiento continuo de una planta a lo largo de su vida (pág. 582)

meristematic tissue/tejido meristemático tejido de las plantas que se encuentra sólo en la punta de los brotes y de las raíces; es responsable del crecimiento de las plantas (pág. 582)

mesoderm/mesodermo capa embrionaria media de la mayoría de los animales; da origen a los músculos y una gran parte de los sistemas circulatorio, reproductor y excretor (pág. 661)

mesophyll/mesofilo tejido fundamental especializado que forma la mayor parte de casi todas las hojas; realiza la mayoría de la fotosíntesis de la planta (pág. 596)

messenger RNA (mRNA)/ARN mensajero (mARN) molécula de ARN que lleva copias de instrucciones para la transformación de aminoácidos a proteínas, del ADN al resto de la célula (pág. 301)

metabolism/metabolismo conjunto de reacciones químicas mediante las cuales un organismo construye o descompone materia mientras realiza sus procesos vitales (pág. 18)

metaphase/metafase segunda fase de la mitosis durante la cual los cromosomas se alinean a través del centro de la célula (pág. 248)

metric system/sistema métrico sistema decimal de medida basado en ciertos estándares físicos y que mide en múltiplos de 10 (pág. 24)

microclimate/microclima clima dentro de un área pequeña que difiere significativamente del clima del área de alrededor (pág. 98)

microfossil/microfósil fósil microscópico (pág. 426)

micronucleus/micronúcleo el núcleo más pequeño de los dos núcleos de un ciliado; contiene una "copia de reserva" de todos los genes de la célula (pág. 501)

microscope/microscopio aparato que produce imágenes ampliadas de estructuras que son demasiado pequeñas para verlas a simple vista (pág. 25)

migration/migración desplazamiento periódico y regreso de animales de un lugar a otro (pág. 878)

mineral/mineral nutriente inorgánico que el cuerpo necesita, normalmente en pequeñas cantidades (pág. 975)

mitochondrion/mitocondria organelo de la célula que convierte la energía química almacenada en el alimento en compuestos que la célula puede usar más cómodamente (pág. 179)

mitosis/mitosis parte de la división celular eucariota durante la cual se divide el núcleo (pág. 245)

mixture/mezcla material compuesto por dos o más elementos o compuestos que están mezclados físicamente pero no están combinados químicamente (pág. 41)

molecular clock/reloj molecular modelo que usa comparaciones de ADN para estimar el tiempo que dos especies han evolucionado independientemente (pág. 455)

molecule/molécula unidad más pequeña de la mayoría de los compuestos (pág. 38)

molting/mudar cubierta proceso en el cual un artrópodo pierde el exoesqueleto y fabrica uno más grande que ocupa su lugar (pág. 719)

monocot/monocotiledónea angiosperma cuyas semillas tienen un cotiledón (pág. 569)

monoculture/monocultivo estrategia de cultivo en la cual campos grandes se siembran con un solo cultivo (pág. 141)

monomer/monómero unidad pequeña que se puede unir a otras unidades pequeñas para formar polímeros (pág. 45)

monosaccharide/monosacárido molécula de azúcar única (pág. 46)

monotreme/monotrema mamífero que pone huevos (pág. 828)

multiple alleles/alelos múltiples tres o más alelos del mismo gen (pág. 273)

muscle tissue/tejido muscular tejido que controla el movimiento interno de materiales en el cuerpo, y el movimiento externo (pág. 894)

mutation/mutación cambio en una secuencia del ADN que afecta la información genética (pág. 307)

mutualism/mutualismo relación simbiótica en la que dos especies se benefician de la relación (pág. 93)

mycelium/micelio muchas hifas unidas juntas que forman una masa gruesa; comprende los cuerpos de los hongos multicelulares (pág. 528)

mycorrhiza/micorriza asociación simbiótica de raíces de plantas y hongos (pág. 541)

myelin sheath/vaina de mielina membrana aislante que rodea el axón de algunas neuronas (pág. 898)

myocardium/miocardio capa media de músculo grueso del corazón; bombea la sangre a través del sistema circulatorio (pág. 944)

myosin/miosina proteína que forma los filamentos gruesos en las estriaciones de las células del músculo esquelético (pág. 928)

NAD$^+$ (nicotinamide adenine dinucleotide)/NAD$^+$ (dinucleótido de adenina y nicotinamida) portador de electrones que participa en la glucólisis (pág. 223)

NADP$^+$ (nicotinamide adenine dinucleotide phosphate)/NADP$^+$ (fosfato de dinucleótido de adenina y nicotinamida) una de las moléculas portadoras que transfiere los electrones de alta energía de la clorofila a las otras moléculas (pág. 209)

natural selection/selección natural proceso por el cual los individuos que se adaptan mejor a su medio ambiente sobreviven y se reproducen con más éxito; también se le llama supervivencia del más apto (pág. 381)

nematocyst/nematocisto estructura urticante en cada cnidocito de un cnidario que usa para envenenar o matar a la presa (pág. 669)

nephridium/nefridio órgano excretor de un anélido que filtra fluido en el celoma (pág. 696)

nephron/nefrona unidad de filtración de sangre en la corteza renal de un riñón (pág. 986)

nerve net/plexo nervioso red de células nerviosas vagamente organizadas que juntas permiten a los cnidarios detectar estímulos (pág. 671)

nervous tissue/tejido nervioso tejido que recibe mensajes del medio ambiente interno y externo del cuerpo, analiza la información y dirige la respuesta (pág. 894)

neuromuscular junction/unión neuromuscular punto de contacto entre una neurona motora y una célula muscular esquelética (pág. 929)

neuron/neurona célula que lleva mensajes a través del sistema nervioso (pág. 897)

neurotransmitter/neurotransmisor sustancia química usada por una neurona para transmitir un impulso a otra célula mediante una sinapsis (pág. 900)

neurulation/neurulación desarrollo del sistema nervioso (pág. 1018)

niche/nicho gama completa de todas las condiciones físicas y biológicas en las que un organismo vive y la que manera en la que el organismo usa esas condiciones (pág. 91)

nicotine/nicotina droga estimulante en el tabaco que acelera el pulso y aumenta la presión sanguínea (pág. 961)

nictitating membrane/membrana nictitante en los anfibios, membrana transparente movible localizada dentro del párpado regular; protege la superficie del ojo de daños bajo el agua y lo mantiene húmedo en la tierra (pág. 787)

nitrogen fixation/fijación del nitrógeno proceso de conversión del gas nitrógeno en amoniaco (págs. 78, 477)

node/nudo punto de un tallo donde una hoja se une al tallo (pág. 589)

nondisjunction/no disyunción error en la meiosis en la que los cromosomas homólogos no se separan (pág. 352)

nonrenewable resource/recurso no renovable recurso que no puede ser reemplazado por procesos naturales (pág. 144)

notochord/notocordio varilla larga de sostén que atraviesa el cuerpo de un cordado justo debajo del cordón nervioso (pág. 849)

nuclear envelope/membrana nuclear capa de dos membranas que rodea el núcleo de una célula (pág. 176)

nucleic acid/ácido nucleico macromolécula que contiene hidrógeno, oxígeno, nitrógeno, carbono y fósforo (pág. 47)

nucleolus/nucléolo región pequeña y densa dentro de la mayoría de los núcleos en la que empieza la formación de los proteínas (pág. 176)

nucleotide/nucleótido monómero de ácidos nucleicos formado por un azúcar de 5 carbonos, un grupo fosfato y una base nitrogenada (págs. 47, 291)

nucleus/núcleo centro de un átomo que contiene los protones y neutrones; en las células, estructura que contiene el material genético (ADN) y controla las actividades de la célula (págs. 35, 173)

nutrient/nutriente sustancia química que necesita un organismo para vivir (pág. 76)

nymph/ninfa forma inmadura que no tiene órganos sexuales funcionales ni ninguna otra estructura adulta (pág. 729)

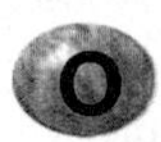

obligate aerobe/aerobio obligado organismo que requiere suministro constante de oxígeno para vivir (pág. 474)

obligate anaerobe/anaerobio obligado organismo que no puede vivir en presencia de oxígeno (pág. 474)

observation/observación uso de uno o más de los sentidos (vista, oído, tacto, olfato y, a veces, gusto) para reunir información (pág. 4)

omnivore/omnívoro organismo que obtiene energía al comer tanto animales como plantas (pág. 69)

oogonium/oogonio estructura especializada formada por hifas que produce núcleos femeninos (pág. 519)

open circulatory system/sistema circulatorio abierto sistema en el cual la sangre no está siempre contenida en una red de vasos sanguíneos (págs. 703, 754)

operant conditioning/condicionamiento operante proceso de aprendizaje en el cual un animal aprende a comportarse de una cierta manera por medio de una práctica repetida, para recibir un premio o evitar un castigo; también se le llama aprendizaje de ensayo y error (pág. 875)

operational definition/definición operacional descripción de cómo una variable particular se puede medir o de cómo un término se puede definir (pág. 1063)

operator/operador región del cromosoma en un operón en el que el represor se une cuando el operón es desactivado (pág. 310)

operon/operón grupo de genes que operan juntos (pág. 309)

opposable thumb/pulgar oponible pulgar que permite agarrar objetos y usar herramientas (pág. 835)

order/orden grupo de familias similares (pág. 449)

organ/órgano grupo de tejidos que trabajan juntos para realizar funciones que están muy relacionadas (pág. 193)

organ system/sistema de órganos grupo de órganos que trabajan juntos para realizar una función específica (pág. 193)

organelle/organelo estructura especializada que realiza importantes funciones celulares dentro de una célula eucariótica (pág. 174)

osculum/ósculo gran orifico en la parte superior de la esponja a través del cual la esponja expulsa el agua (pág. 665)

osmosis/osmosis difusión de agua a través de una membrana permeable selectiva (pág. 185)

ossification/osificación proceso de formación de huesos, durante el cual el cartílago es reemplazado por hueso (pág. 923)

ovary/ovario en las plantas, una estructura de la flor que contiene uno o más óvulos en los que se producen los gametofitos femeninos; en los animales, la gónada femenina que produce los óvulos (págs. 612, 1008)

oviparous/ovíparo término usado para referirse a los animales cuyos huevos se desarrollan fuera del cuerpo de la madre (pág. 778)

ovoviviparous/ovovivíparo término usado para referirse a los animales cuyas crías nacen vivas después de desarrollarse en huevos dentro del cuerpo de la madre (pág. 778)

ovulation/ovulación proceso en el cual el óvulo es liberado por el ovario (pág. 1012)

ovule/óvulo estructura en conos de semillas en el que se desarrollan los gametofitos femeninos (pág. 610)

ozone layer/capa de ozono capa en la atmósfera en la que el gas ozono está relativamente concentrado (pág. 157)

pacemaker/marcapasos grupo pequeño de células musculares cardiacas en el atrio derecho que "marcan el paso" para el corazón como un todo; también conocido como nodo sinoatrial (pág. 946)

paleontologist/paleontólogo científico que estudia los fósiles (pág. 417)

palisade mesophyll/mesofilo en empalizada capa de células mesófilas en forma de columna altas justo debajo de la epidermis superior de una hoja (pág. 596)

pancreas/páncreas glándula que produce hormonas que regulan el azúcar de la sangre; produce enzimas que descomponen carbohidratos, proteínas, lípidos y ácidos nucleicos; y produce bicarbonato sódico, una base que neutraliza el ácido del estómago (pág. 982)

parasitism/parasitismo relación simbiótica en la cual un organismo vive dentro o sobre otro organismo (el anfitrión) y como consecuencia lo daña (pág. 93)

parenchyma/parénquima tipo de célula de tejido fundamental con una pared celular fina y una vacuola central grande (pág. 582)

passive immunity/inmunidad pasiva inmunidad de corto plazo causada cuando los anticuerpos de otros animales producidos para un patógeno, son inyectados en el cuerpo (pág. 1042)

pathogen/patógeno agente causante de enfermedades (págs. 485, 1031)

pedigree/genealogía gráfica que muestra las relaciones en una familia (pág. 342)

pedipalps/pedipalpo en los quelicerados, par de partes de la boca que generalmente están adaptadas para atrapar a las presas (pág. 722)

pellicle/cutícula membrana celular en las euglenas (pág. 507)

penis/pene órgano reproductor masculino externo (pág. 1011)

perennial/perenne planta con flores que vive durante más de dos años (pág. 572)

period/periodo unidad de tiempo en las que están subdivididas las eras (pág. 422)

periosteum/periostio capa resistente de tejido conectivo que cubre hueso (pág. 922)

peristalsis/peristaltismo contracciones musculares rítmicas que hacen pasar el alimento del esófago al estómago (pág. 980)

permafrost/permagélido capa de subsuelo permanentemente congelada en la tundra (pág. 104)

petal/pétalo estructura de color reluciente que se encuentra justo dentro de los sépalos; atrae insectos y otros polinizadores a la flor (pág. 612)

petiole/pecíolo estructura fina que une la hoja al tallo (pág. 595)

pH scale/escala pH sistema de medida usado para indicar la concentración de iones de hidrógeno (H^+) en una solución; el rango va del 0 al 14 (pág. 43)

phagocytosis/fagocitosis proceso en el cual extensiones del citoplasma rodean y atrapan partículas grandes y las llevan a la célula (pág. 189)

pharyngeal pouch/saco faríngeo una de las dos estructuras en la región de la garganta (faringe) de un cordado (pág. 767)

pharynx/faringe tubo muscular al final de la cavidad gastrovascular, o garganta, que une la boca con el resto del tracto digestivo y que sirve como vía para el aire y el alimento (págs. 684, 956)

phenotype/fenotipo características físicas de un organismo (pág. 268)

pheromone/feromona mensajero químico específico que afecta el comportamiento o el desarrollo de otros individuos de la misma especie (pág. 731)

phloem/floema tejido vascular responsable del transporte de los nutrientes y carbohidratos producidos por la fotosíntesis (pág. 560)

photic zone/zona fótica capa superior bien iluminada de los océanos (pág. 109)

photoautotroph/fotoautótrofo organismo que usa la energía del sol para convertir dióxido de carbono y agua en componentes de carbono (pág. 474)

photoheterotroph/fotoheterótrofo organismo que es fotosintetizador pero que también necesita compuestos orgánicos como fuente de carbono (pág. 474)

photoperiodism/fotoperiodicidad respuesta de las plantas a los periodos de luz y oscuridad (pág. 641)

photosynthesis/fotosíntesis proceso por el cual las plantas y algunos otros organismos usan la energía de la luz para convertir el agua y el dióxido de carbono en oxígeno y en carbohidratos de alta energía, como azúcares y almidones (págs. 68, 204)

photosystem/fotosistema unidades recolectoras de luz del cloroplasto (pág. 208)

phototropism/fototropismo tendencia de las plantas a crecer hacia una fuente de luz (pág. 634)

phycobilin/ficobilina pigmento accesorio que se encuentra en las algas rojas y que es especialmente bueno en la absorción de luz azul (pág. 510)

phylogeny/filogenia el estudio de las relaciones evolutivas entre organismos (pág. 452)

phylum/fílum grupo de clases muy relacionadas (pág. 449)

phytochrome/fitocromo pigmento de la planta responsable de la fotoperiodicidad (pág. 641)

phytoplankton/fitoplancton población de algas y otros pequeños organismos fotosintetizadores que se encuentran cerca de la superficie del mar y que forman parte del plancton (págs. 107, 509)

pigment/pigmento molécula que absorbe la luz (pág. 207)

pinocytosis/pinocitosis proceso por el cual una célula absorbe líquido del ambiente que la rodea (pág. 189)

pioneer species/especie pionera primera especie que puebla un área durante la sucesión primaria (pág. 94)

pith/médula conjunto de células parénquimas dentro del anillo de tejido vascular en el tallo de las dicotiledóneas (pág. 590)

pituitary gland/glándula pituitaria glándula en la base del cráneo que secreta nueve hormonas que regulan directamente muchas funciones del cuerpo y controlan las acciones de otras glándulas endocrinas (pág. 1003)

placenta/placenta órgano en los mamíferos placentarios a través del cual nutrientes, oxígeno, dióxido de carbono y desechos son intercambiados entre el embrión y la madre (págs. 829, 1019)

plankton/plancton organismos diminutos de flotación libre que viven en medios acuáticos (pág. 107)

Plantae/*Plantae* reino de autótrofos multicelulares fotosintetizadores que tienen pared celular que contiene celulosa (pág. 461)

plasma/plasma fluido de color amarillo claro que compone el 55 por ciento de la sangre (pág. 951)

plasmid/plásmido pequeña pieza circular de ADN (pág. 327)

plasmodium/plasmodio estructura con muchos núcleos formada por mohos mucilagenosos acelulares (pág. 518)

plastron/plastrón parte ventral de la coraza de una tortuga (pág. 805)

platelet/plaqueta fragmento celular liberado por la médula ósea que ayuda a la coagulación de la sangre (pág. 953)

point mutation/mutación puntual mutación genética que provoca cambios en uno o pocos nucleótidos (pág. 307)

polar zone/zona polar zona de clima frío donde los rayos de sol llegan a la Tierra a un ángulo muy bajo (pág. 88)

pollen cone/cono de polen cono en las gimnospermas que produce gametofitos masculinos en forma de granos de polen (pág. 610)

pollen grain/grano de polen gametofito masculino en las plantas con semillas (pág. 565)

pollen tube/tubo polínico estructura que crece en el grano de polen; contiene dos núcleos espermáticos haploides (pág. 611)

pollination/polinización transporte del polen de la estructura reproductora masculina a la estructura reproductora femenina (pág. 565)

pollutant/contaminante sustancia dañina que puede entrar en la biosfera a través de la tierra, aire o agua (pág. 148)

polygenic trait/rasgo poligénico rasgo controlado por dos o más genes (págs. 273, 396)

polymer/polímero compuesto grande formado por combinaciones de muchos monómeros (pág. 45)

polymerase chain reaction (PCR)/reacción en cadena de la polimerasa (PCR) técnica que permite a los biólogos moleculares hacer muchas copias de un gen en particular (pág. 325)

polyp/pólipo etapa normalmente sésil del ciclo de vida de un cnidario en la que tiene el cuerpo cilíndrico y tentáculos que parecen brazos (pág. 670)

polyploidy/poliploidía condición en la que un organismo tiene grupos extra de cromosomas (pág. 308)

polysaccharide/polisacárido macromolécula grande formada por monosacáridos (pág. 46)

population/población grupo de individuos de la misma especie que vive en la misma área (pág. 64)

population density/densidad de población número de individuos por unidad de área (pág. 119)

predation/depredación interacción en la cual un organismo captura a otro organismo y se alimenta de él (pág. 93)

predator-prey relationship/relación entre depredador-y presa mecanismo de control de población en la cual una población es regulada por la depredación (pág. 126)

prehensile/prensil término usado para referirse a una cola larga que puede agarrarse de las ramas (pág. 835)

pressure-flow hyphothesis/hipótesis de flujo por presión hipótesis que considera las plantas en términos de dónde producen y usan los materiales de la fotosíntesis (pág. 602)

primary growth/crecimiento primario en las plantas, tipo de crecimiento que ocurre en las puntas de las raíces y brotes (pág. 590)

primary productivity/productividad primaria tasa a la que la materia orgánica es producida por los productores en un ecosistema (pág. 80)

primary succession/sucesión primaria sucesión que ocurre en las superficies donde no existe el suelo (pág. 94)

prion/prión partícula infecciosa compuesta de proteína en vez de ARN o ADN (pág. 490)

probability/probabilidad posibilidad de que ocurra un suceso en particular (pág. 267)

producer/productor organismo que puede captar la energía de la luz solar o de las sustancias químicas y usarla para producir alimento de compuestos inorgánicos; también se le llama autótrofo (pág. 67)

product/producto elemento o compuesto producido por una reacción química (pág. 49)

proglottid/proglótide uno de los segmentos que forman la mayoría del cuerpo de la tenia (pág. 688)

prokaryote/procariota organismos unicelulares que carecen de núcleo (págs. 173, 471)

promoter/promotor región del ADN que le indica a una enzima adónde debe enlazarse para formar ARN (pág. 301)

prophage/prófago el ADN vírico que está incrustado en el ADN de la célula anfitriona (pág. 480)

prophase/profase fase primera y más larga de la mitosis, durante la cual los cromosomas se hacen visibles y los centríolos se separan y toman posiciones en lados opuestos del núcleo (pág. 246)

prosimian/prosimio primate pequeño y nocturno que tiene ojos grandes que le permiten ver en la oscuridad (pág. 834)

prostaglandin/prostaglandina ácido graso modificado parecido a una hormona y producido por una gran variedad de células; generalmente afecta sólo células y tejidos cercanos (pág. 1000)

protein/proteína macromolécula que contiene carbono, hidrógeno, oxígeno y nitrógeno; necesitada por el cuerpo para el crecimiento y la reparación y para fabricar enzimas (págs. 47, 973)

proteinoid microsphere/microsfera proteinoide burbuja diminuta formada por grandes moléculas orgánicas, que tiene algunas de las mismas características de la célula (pág. 425)

protist/protista cualquier eucariota que no es una planta, un animal o un hongo (pág. 497)

Protista/*Protista* reino compuesto de eucariotas que no están clasificados como plantas, animales u hongos (pág. 460)

protonema/protonema masa de filamentos verdes entrelazados en los musgos, que se forma durante la germinación (pág. 558)

protostome/protostomo animal cuya boca se forma de su blastoporo (pág. 661)

pseudocoelom/seudoceloma cavidad corporal entre los tejidos endodermo y mesodermo que está parcialmente recubierta de mesodermo (pág. 689)

pseudopod/seudópodo proyección temporal del citoplasma, o un "pie falso", que usan algunos protistas para alimentarse o moverse (pág. 500)

puberty/pubertad periodo de crecimiento rápido y maduración sexual durante el cual el sistema reproductor se hace totalmente funcional (pág. 1009)

pulmonary circulation/circulación pulmonar vía circulatoria entre el corazón y los pulmones (pág. 944)

punctuated equilibrium/equilibrio puntual patrón de evolución en el cual los periodos estables largos son interrumpidos por breves periodos de cambio rápido (pág. 439)

Punnett square/cuadro de Punnett diagrama que muestra las combinaciones de genes que podría resultar de un cruce genético (pág. 268)

pupa/pupa etapa de la metamorfosis en la cual un insecto cambia de larva a adulto (pág. 729)

pupil/pupila pequeña abertura en el centro del iris a través de la cual entra la luz al ojo (pág. 906)

radial symmetry/simetría radial conformación corporal en la cual las partes del cuerpo se repiten alrededor del centro del cuerpo; característica de las anémonas y las estrellas de mar (págs. 662, 748)

radioactive dating/datación radioactiva técnica en la que los científicos calculan la edad de una muestra basándose en la cantidad residual de isótopos radiactivos que contiene (pág. 420)

radula/rádula estructura en forma de lengua usada por los caracoles y babosas para alimentarse (pág. 702)

reabsorption/reabsorción proceso en el cual se recupera el líquido en un vaso (pág. 987)

reactant/reaccionante elemento o compuesto que entra en una reacción química (pág. 49)

recombinant DNA/ADN recombinante ADN producido por la combinación de ADN de diferentes fuentes (pág. 324)

reflex/reflejo respuesta rápida y automática a un estímulo (pág. 903)

reflex arc/arco reflejo receptor sensorial, neurona sensorial, neurona motriz y catalizador que están involucrados en una respuesta rápida a un estímulo (pág. 904)

relative dating/datación relativa método para determinar la edad de un fósil al comparar su ubicación con los fósiles que están en otras capas de la roca (pág. 419)

relative frequency/frecuencia relativa número de veces que ocurre un alelo en un reservorio génico comparado con el número de veces que ocurren otros alelos (pág. 394)

renewable resource/recurso renovable recurso que se puede regenerar rápidamente y que es reemplazable (pág. 144)

replication/replicación proceso de copia por el cual una célula duplica su ADN (pág. 299)

reproductive isolation/aislamiento reproductivo separación de especies o poblaciones tal que no pueden cruzarse ni tener descendencia fértil (pág. 404)

reptile/reptil cualquier vertebrado que tiene piel seca escamada, pulmones y se reproduce en tierra por huevos que tienen varias membranas protectoras (pág. 797)

resource/recurso cualquier necesidad vital, como el agua, nutrientes, luz, alimento o espacio (pág. 92)

responding variable/variable respuesta factor en un experimento que un científico quiere observar, el cual puede cambiar en respuesta a una variable manipulada; también se conoce como variable dependiente (págs. 9, 1062)

response/respuesta reacción única y específica a un estímulo (pág. 871)

resting potential/potencial de reposo carga eléctrica en toda la membrana celular de una neurona en reposo (pág. 898)

restriction enzyme/enzima de restricción enzima que corta el ADN en una secuencia específica de nucleótidos (pág. 323)

retina/retina capa más interna del ojo; contiene fotoreceptores (pág. 907)

retrovirus/retrovirus virus que contiene ARN como su información genética (pág. 482)

rhizoid/rizoide en los hongos, una hifa parecida a una raíz que penetra la superficie de un objeto; en los musgos, una célula larga y delgada que sujeta el musgo a la tierra y absorbe el agua y los minerales del suelo que le rodea (págs. 530, 557)

rhizome/rizoma tallo trepador o subterráneo de los helechos (pág. 562)

ribonucleic acid (RNA)/ácido ribonucleico (ARN) hebra única de ácido nucleico que contiene el azúcar ribosa (pág. 47)

ribosomal RNA (rRNA)/ARN ribosómico (rARN) tipo de ARN que conforma principalmente a los ribosomas (pág. 301)

ribosome/ribosoma partícula pequeña en la célula en la que se fabrican las proteínas; está hecho de ARN y proteína (pág. 177)

risk factor/factor de riesgo cualquier elemento que aumenta las posibilidades de enfermedad o lesión (pág. 1049)

RNA polymerase/polimerasa de ARN enzima similar al ADN polimerasa que se une al ADN y separa las hebras de ADN durante la transcripción (pág. 301)

rod/bastoncillo fotoreceptor en el ojo que es sensible a la luz, pero no a los colores (pág. 907)

root/raíz órgano subterráneo en las plantas que absorbe agua y minerales (pág. 561)

root cap/caliptra estructura resistente que protege la raíz a medida que ésta penetra en la tierra (pág. 585)

root hair/pelos radicales proyecciones diminutas de la superficie externa, o epidermis, de una raíz (pág. 585)

rumen/rumen cavidad estomacal en los vacunos y animales relacionados en la que se almacenan y procesan las plantas recién tragadas (pág. 823)

salt marsh/marisma estuario de zona templada dominado por pastos que toleran la sal, por encima del nivel de la marea baja, y por algas, bajo el agua (pág. 108)

saprobe/saprófito organismo que obtiene los alimentos de materia orgánica en descomposición (pág. 537)

sapwood/albura área en las plantas que rodea el duramen y es activa en el transporte de fluidos (pág. 592)

science/ciencia manera organizada de usar la evidencia para aprender sobre el mundo natural; también el conjunto de conocimientos que los científicos han desarrollado después de años de usar este proceso (pág. 3)

sclerenchyma/esclerénquima tipo de célula del tejido fundamental con una pared celular extremadamente rígida y gruesa que hace que el tejido fundamental sea resistente y fuerte (pág. 582)

scolex/escólex cabeza de un tenia adulta; puede tener ventosas o ganchos (pág. 688)

scrotum/escroto saco externo que contiene los testículos (pág. 1010)

secondary growth/crecimiento secundario patrón del crecimiento de una planta en la cual el tallo aumenta su grosor (pág. 591)

secondary succession/sucesión secundaria sucesión que sigue a una alteración que destruye una comunidad sin destruir el suelo (pág. 95)

seed/semilla embrión de una planta viva que está en una cápsula protectora y rodeado de su fuente de alimento (pág. 565)

seed coat/tegumento seminal estructura que rodea y protege el embrión de una planta y evita que se seque (pág. 565)

seed cone/cono de semillas cono que produce gametofitos femeninos (pág. 610)

segregation/segregación separación de alelos durante la formación de gametos (pág. 266)

selective breeding/cruzamiento dirigido método de cruzamiento que permite que sólo aquellos organismos con las características deseadas produzcan la siguiente generación (pág. 319)

semicircular canal/conducto semicircular una de las tres estructuras en el oído interno que ayudan a mantener la posición del cuerpo (pág. 908)

seminiferous tubule/tubo seminífero uno de los cientos de túbulos diminutos en los testículos en donde se produce el semen (pág. 1010)

sensory receptor/receptor sensorial neurona que reacciona a un estímulo concreto, como la luz o el sonido, enviando impulsos a otras neuronas y con el tiempo al sistema nervioso central (pág. 906)

sepal/sépalo círculo externo de las flores que encierra un brote antes de que se abra y que protege la flor mientras se desarrolla (pág. 612)

septum/septo pared interna entre los segmentos del cuerpo de un anélido (pág. 694)

seta/queta cilio pegado a los segmentos de muchos anélidos (pág. 694)

sex chromosome/cromosoma sexual uno de los dos cromosomas que determinan el sexo de un individuo (pág. 341)

sex-linked gene/gen ligado al sexo gen localizado en el cromosoma X o Y (pág. 350)

sexual reproduction/reproducción sexual proceso por el cual células de dos diferentes padres se unen para producir la primera célula de un nuevo organismo (pág. 17)

sexually transmitted disease (STD)/enfermedad de transmisión sexual (ETS) enfermedad que se propaga de una persona a otra durante el contacto sexual (pág. 1015)

shell/concha en los moluscos, estructura producida por glándulas del manto que secretan carbonato de calcio (pág. 702)

short-day plant/planta de día corto planta que da flores cuando la luz del día dura poco (pág. 641)

sieve tube element/tubo criboso célula floema que se une en los extremos a células similares para formar tubos cribosos (pág. 581)

single-gene trait/rasgo de gen único rasgo controlado por un sólo gene que tiene dos alelos (pág. 395)

siphon/sifón estructura en forma de tubo a través del que entra y sale el agua en el cuerpo de un molusco (pág. 703)

small intestine/intestino delgado órgano digestivo en el cual se realiza la mayoría de la digestión química (pág. 981)

smog/niebla tóxica mezcla de sustancias químicas que ocurre como bruma marrón grisácea en la atmósfera (pág. 148)

society/sociedad grupo de animales de la misma especie, estrechamente relacionados, que trabajan juntos en beneficio del grupo (pág. 732)

soil erosion/erosión del suelo desgaste de la superficie de la tierra causado por el agua y el viento (pág. 145)

solute/soluto sustancia que se disuelve en un solvente para hacer una solución (pág. 42)

solution/solución mezcla de dos o más sustancias en las que las moléculas de las sustancias están distribuidas por igual (pág. 42)

solvent/solvente sustancia en la que un soluto se disuelve para formar una solución (pág. 42)

sorus/soro racimo de esporangios en la parte inferior de la hoja de un helecho (pág. 562)

specialized cell/célula especializada célula que está únicamente capacitada para realizar una función particular (pág. 894)

speciation/especiación formación de una nueva especie (pág. 404)

species/especie grupo de organismos similares que pueden cruzarse y producir descendencia fértil (pág. 64)

species diversity/diversidad de especies número de diferentes especies en la biosfera (pág. 150)

spicule/espícula estructura con forma de espina que forma el esqueleto de las esponjas más duras; está compuesto por carbonato de calcio o por silicio (pág. 665)

spindle/huso estructura microtubular con forma de abanico que ayuda a separar los cromosomas durante la mitosis (pág. 247)

spinneret/hilera órgano en las arañas que contiene las glándulas que fabrican seda (pág. 723)

spiracle/espiráculo abertura pequeña localizada en la parte lateral del cuerpo de muchos artrópodos terrestres, mediante la cual entra y sale el aire (pág. 717)

spirillum/espirilo procariota con forma de espiral o sacacorchos (pág. 473)

spongy mesophyll/mesofilo lacunoso tejido suelto bajo el mesofilo en empalizada de una hoja (pág. 596)

spontaneous generation/generación espontánea hipótesis (no probada) que enuncia que la vida podría nacer de la materia no viva (pág. 8)

sporangiophore/esporangióforo hifa especializada donde se encuentran los esporangios (pág. 528)

sporangium/esporangio estructura en los helechos y algunos hongos que contiene esporas (págs. 528, 562)

spore/espora célula reproductiva haploide (pág. 514)

sporophyte/esporofito fase diploide o productora de esporas de un organismo (págs. 514, 552)

stabilizing selection/selección estabilizante forma de selección natural en la que el centro de la curva mantiene su posición actual; ocurre cuando los individuos cerca del centro de una curva de distribución son más aptos que los individuos en los extremos (pág. 399)

stamen/estambre parte masculina de una flor; está compuesto por una antera y un filamento (pág. 612)

stem/tallo estructura de soporte que une las raíces y las hojas y que transporta el agua y los nutrientes ente ellas (pág. 561)

stigma/estigma porción pegajosa en la parte superior del estilo donde caen frecuentemente los granos de polen (pág. 612)

stimulant/estimulante droga que aumenta las acciones reguladas por el sistema nervioso (pág. 910)

stimulus/estímulo señal a la que responde un organismo (págs. 19, 871)

stolon/estolón en los hongos, una hifa con forma de tallo que va por la superficie de un objeto; en las plantas, un tallo largo rastrero que forma raíces cuando toca el suelo (págs. 530, 622)

stoma/estoma abertura en la parte inferior de la hoja que permite la difusión del dióxido de carbono y del oxígeno hacia dentro y hacia fuera de la hoja (pág. 596)

stomach/estómago cavidad grande muscular que continúa la digestión mecánica y química de los alimentos (pág. 980)

stroma/estroma región fuera de las membranas tilacoides en los cloroplastos (pág. 208)

struggle for existence/lucha por la existencia competición entre los miembros de una especie por comida, espacio para vivir y las otras necesidades vitales (pág. 380)

style/estilo tallo estrecho en el carpelo de una flor (pág. 612)

subcutaneous fat/grasa subcutánea capa de células de grasa bajo la piel que ayuda a conservar el calor del cuerpo (pág. 822)

substrate/sustrato reaccionante de una reacción catalizada por una enzima (pág. 52)

survival of the fittest/supervivencia del más apto proceso por el cual los individuos que están mejor acondicionados para su medio ambiente sobreviven y se reproducen con más éxito; también se le llama selección natural (pág. 381)

suspension/suspensión mezcla de agua y materiales no disueltos (pág. 42)

sustainable use/desarrollo sostenible uso de recursos naturales a un ritmo que no los agota (pág. 145)

swim bladder/vejiga natatoria órgano interno lleno de gas en muchos peces óseos con la que ajustan su flotabilidad (pág. 777)

swimmerets/pleópodos apéndices como aletas usadas por los decápodos para nadar (pág. 721)

symbiosis/simbiosis relación en la que dos especies viven cercanamente (pág. 93)

synapse/sinapsis ubicación en la que una neurona puede transferir un impulso a otra célula (pág. 900)

systemic circulation/circulación sistémica vía circulatoria entre el corazón y el resto del cuerpo, excepto los pulmones (pág. 944)

taiga/taiga bioma en el que los inviernos son fríos, y los veranos templados y duran lo suficiente para que el suelo se descongele (pág. 104)

taproot/raíz axonomorfa raíz primaria hallada en algunas plantas, que crece más larga y gruesa que las otras raíces (pág. 584)

target cell/célula blanco célula que tiene un receptor para una hormona específica (págs. 634, 997)

taste bud/papila gustativa órgano sensorial que detecta el sabor de una sustancia (pág. 909)

taxon/taxón grupo o nivel de organización en el cual se clasifican los organismos (pág. 449)

taxonomy/taxonomía disciplina que clasifica organismos y asigna a cada organismo un nombre aceptado universalmente (pág. 447)

telophase/telofase fase cuarta y final de la mitosis, durante la cual los cromosomas comienzan a dispersarse en una maraña de materiales densos (pág. 248)

temperate zone/zona templada zona de clima moderado entre las zonas polares y los trópicos (pág. 88)

temporal isolation/aislamiento temporal forma de aislamiento reproductivo en la cual dos poblaciones se reproducen en momentos diferentes (pág. 405)

tendon/tendón tejido conectivo resistente que une los músculos esqueléticos a los huesos (pág. 930)

territory/territorio área específica ocupada y protegida por un animal o grupo de animales (pág. 881)

testis/testículo órgano reproductor masculino que produce semen (págs. 688, 1008)

tetrad/tétrada estructura que contiene cuatro cromátidas y que se forma durante la meiosis (pág. 276)

thalamus/tálamo estructura cerebral que recibe mensajes de los órganos de los sentidos y transmite la información a la región adecuada del cerebro para que sea procesada (pág. 903)

theory/teoría explicación probada concienzudamente que unifica un amplio rango de observaciones (págs. 14, 369)

thigmotropism/tigmotropismo respuesta de las plantas al tacto (pág. 639)

thorax/tórax parte del cuerpo de un crustáceo que se sitúa justo detrás de la cabeza y que alberga la mayoría de órganos internos (pág. 721)

threshold/umbral nivel mínimo de un estímulo que se requiere para activar una neurona (pág. 899)

thylakoid/tilacoide membrana fotosintética en forma de saco que se halla en los cloroplastos (pág. 208)

tissue/tejido grupo de células similares que realizan una función específica (pág. 192)

tolerance/tolerancia capacidad de los organismos de crecer y desarrollarse cuando están sujetos a un factor medioambiental desfavorable (pág. 98)

trachea/tráquea conducto de aire; tubo por el que se mueve el aire (pág. 956)

tracheal tube/tráquea uno de los muchos tubos llenos de aire, ramificados, que se extienden por todo el cuerpo de muchos artrópodos terrestres (pág. 717)

tracheid/traqueída célula hueca de una planta en el tejido de xilema con paredes celulares gruesas que resisten la presión (pág. 560)

trait/rasgo característica específica que varía de un individuo a otro (pág. 264)

transcription/transcripción proceso en el cual parte de la secuencia de nucleótidos de ADN se copia a una secuencia complementaria de ARN (pág. 301)

transfer RNA (tRNA)/ARN de transferencia tipo de molécula de ARN que transfiere aminoácidos a los ribosomas durante la síntesis de proteínas (pág. 301)

transformation/transformación proceso en el cual una cepa de bacterias es cambiada por un gen o genes de otra cepa de bacterias (pág. 288)

transgenic/transgénico término empleado para referirse aun organismo que contiene genes de otros organismos (pág. 331)

translation/traducción decodificación de un mensaje de mARN a una cadena polipéptida (pág. 304)

transpiration/transpiración pérdida de agua de una planta a través de sus hojas (págs. 75, 596)

trichocyst/tricocisto pequeña estructura en forma de botella que los paramecios usan para defenderse (pág. 501)

trochophore/trocófora etapa de natación libre de la larva de un molusco acuático (pág. 701)

trophic level/nivel trófico etapa en una cadena o trama alimenticia (pág. 70)

tropical zone/zona tropical zona de clima cálido que recibe luz solar directa o casi directa durante todo el año (pág. 88)

tropism/tropismo respuesta de una planta a un estímulo externo (pág. 639)

true-breeding/raza pura término usado para describir organismos que producen crías idénticas a sí mismos si se les permite autopolinizarse (pág. 263)

tube foot/ventosa estructura en forma de taza adherida a los canales radiales de los equinodermos; las usan para caminar y para abrir conchas (pág. 735)

tumor/tumor masa de tejido que crece (pág. 1052)

tympanic membrane/membrana timpánica tambor del oído de los anfibios dentro del cráneo; vibra en respuesta a un sonido, permitiendo la audición (pág. 787)

understory/sotobosque capa de un bosque tropical lluvioso formada por árboles más bajos y plantas trepadoras (pág. 100)

ureter/uréter tubo que lleva la orina del riñón a la vejiga urinaria (pág. 986)

urethra/uretra tubo que lleva la orina desde la vejiga y la expulsa del cuerpo; en los machos, tubo a través del cual el semen es expulsado del cuerpo (págs. 986, 1011)

urinary bladder/vejiga urinaria órgano en forma de saco en el que la orina se almacena antes de ser desechada (pág. 986)

uterus/útero órgano del sistema reproductivo femenino en el que un óvulo fertilizado se puede desarrollar (pág. 1012)

vaccination/vacunación inyección de una forma debilitada o suave de un patógeno para producir inmunidad (pág. 1041)

vaccine/vacuna un preparado de patógenos debilitados o muertos (pág. 486)

vacuole/vacuola organelo de una célula que almacena materiales como agua, sales, proteínas y carbohidratos (pág. 179)

vagina/vagina en el sistema reproductivo de la mujer, un canal que va del útero al exterior del cuerpo (pág. 1012)

valve/válvula tapa de tejido conectivo entre el atrio y el ventrículo, o en una vena, que previene que la sangre retroceda (pág. 945)

van der Waals forces/fuerzas de van der Waals ligera atracción que se desarrolla entre las regiones cargadas de forma opuesta en moléculas próximas (pág. 39)

variable/variable factor de un experimento que puede cambiar (pág. 1062)

vas deferens/conducto deferente tubo que transporta el semen del epidídimio a la uretra (pág. 1011)

vascular bundle/haces vasculares estructura del tallo de las plantas que contiene tejido de xilema y floema (pág. 590)

vascular cambium/cámbium tejido lateral meristemático que produce tejidos vasculares y aumenta el grosor del tallo a lo largo del tiempo (pág. 591)

vascular cylinder/cilindro vascular región central de una raíz que incluye el tejido vascular: xilema y floema (pág. 585)

vascular tissue/tejido vascular tipo de tejido en las plantas, especializado en el transporte de agua y nutrientes por toda la planta (pág. 560)

vector/vector animal que porta patogénos de persona a persona (pág. 1034)

vegetative reproduction/reproducción vegetativa método de reproducción asexual común en muchas plantas con flores (pág. 622)

vein/vena en las plantas, un grupo de tejido vascular en las hojas; en los animales, vaso sanguíneo que devuelve la sangre al corazón (págs. 561, 947)

ventricle/ventrículo cámara baja del corazón que bombea la sangre hacia fuera del corazón (pág. 776, 944)

vertebra/vértebra segmento individual de la espina dorsal; rodea y protege la médula espinal (pág. 768)

vertebrate/vertebrado animal que tiene columna vertebral o espina dorsal (pág. 657)

vessel element/tráquea en las angioespermas, célula de xilema que forma parte de un tubo continuo a través del cual se mueve el agua (pág. 581)

vestigial organ/órgano vestigial órgano que no tiene una función útil en un organismo (pág. 384)

villus/vellosidad proyección doblada que aumenta el área total de las paredes del intestino delgado (pág. 982)

viroid/viroide molécula de ARN de una sola cadena que no tiene cápsides que la recubran (pág. 490)

virus/virus partícula formada a partir de ácido nucleico, proteína y en algunos casos lípidos que se puede replicar sólo infectando células vivas (pág. 478)

visceral mass/masa visceral área bajo el manto de un molusco que contiene los órganos internos (pág. 702)

vitamin/vitamina molécula orgánica que ayuda a regular los procesos corporales (pág. 974)

viviparous/vivíparo término usado para referirse a los animales que dan a luz crías vivas que se nutren directamente del cuerpo de la madre a medida que se desarrollan (pág. 778)

water vascular system/aparato vascular acuífero sistema de tubos internos en los equinodermos que desempeña funciones esenciales, tales como la alimentación, la respiración, la circulación y el movimiento (pág. 735)

weather/tiempo atmosférico condición de la atmósfera terrestre en un tiempo y lugar concreto (pág. 87)

wetland/humedal ecosistema en el que el agua cubre el suelo o está presente en o cerca de la superficie del suelo al menos parte del año (pág. 107)

xerophyte/xerofito planta que vive en el bioma desértico (pág. 644)

xylem/xilema tejido vascular que lleva agua hacia arriba de las raíces a cada parte de la planta (pág. 560)

zonation/zonación franja horizontal prominente de organismos que viven en un hábitat específico (pág. 110)

zooplankton/zooplancton animales diminutos que forman parte del plancton (pág. 107)

zoosporangium/zoosporangio cápsula de la espora (pág. 518)

zygospore/cigospora espora en reposo que contiene cigotos formados durante la fase sexual del ciclo de vida del moho (pág. 530)

zygote/cigoto óvulo fertilizado (pág. 1016)

Index

H

I

N

O

P

T

Credits

Staff Credits

The people who made up the ***Prentice Hall Biology*** team—representing design services, editorial, editorial services, electronic publishing technology, manufacturing & inventory planning, market research, marketing services, online services & multimedia development, planning & budgeting, product planning, production services, project office, publishing processes, and rights & permissions—are listed below. Bold type denotes the core team members.

Dori Amtmann, Rachel Avenia-Prol, **Laura Baselice**, **Neil Benjamin**, Peggy Bliss, Kristen Cetrulo Braghi, Patricia M. Dambry, Robert Danielenko, Lisa Del Gatto, Irene Ehrmann, **Joe Galka**, Holly Gordon, Maureen Grassi, Jon Greenberg, **Diana Hahn**, **Monduane Harris**, Kristan Hoskins, Anne G. Jones, **Ellen Levinger**, Jennifer Keezer, Constance McCarty, **Sandra McGloster**, Carrie O'Connor, **Maureen Raymond**, **Robert Siek**, Jerry Thorne

Additional Credits

Greg Abrom, Ernest Albanese, Robert Aleman, Diane Alimena, Penny Baker, Claudio Barriga, John Carle, Rui Camarinha, Martha Conway, Paul DelSignore, Lisa Ferrari, Angelo Focaccia, Elizabeth Forsyth, Florrie Gadson, Kathy Gavilanes, Michael Ginsberg, Evan Holstrom, Beth Hyslip, Vicki Lamb, Kathleen Mercandetti, Art Mkrtchyan, Kenneth Myett, Raymond Parenteau, Lesley Pierson, Linda Punskovsky, Candy Rodó, Bruce Rolff, Fred Romanucci, Laura Ross, Rachel Ross, Gerry Schrenk, Mildred Schulte, Debi Taffet, Jeff Zoda

t. = Top, b. = Bottom; l. = Left; r. = Right; m. = Middle

Art Credits

Charts and Graphs: Ernest Albanese and Studio A

Aleman, Rob **400, 440, 460** (fungi icons), **461, 610, 612, 630** Art and Science **767, 769, 770, 795** Articulate Graphics **71, 72, 73, 85, 109, 115, 187, 243** (cubes; with E. Albanese), **245, 246–247, 248, 250, 251, 257, 258, 259, 266, 268** t., **269, 270, 271, 272, 276, 277, 278, 283, 284, 285, 290, 291, 294, 295, 298, 300, 301, 302, 303, 304, 305, 306, 307, 308, 309, 310, 311, 312, 315, 316–317, 322, 323, 324, 325, 326, 327, 328, 329, 332, 337, 338–339, 342, 343, 347, 349, 350, 352, 356, 358, 360, 361, 363, 365, 391, 472, 483, 484, 485, 498, 499, 500, 506, 523, 524, 661, 679, 680–681, 718, 763, 847, 852, 941, 944, 953, 959, 999, 1018, 1035, 1037, 1038, 1044** Bechtold, Glory **264** (from Biology, The Living Science), **265** (from Biology, The Living Science), **379** (from Science Explorer), Cavallo, Tamara **514, 517, 518, 519, 527, 528, 531, 533, 534, 540, 545, 547, 973, 974, 975** Cummings, Sally **193** r., **979, 980, 995** Dorling Kindersley Publishers **892–893, 903, 922, 933** t.r., **924, 927** t.r., **945** t.r., **955** Duray-Bito, Cecile **414, 436, 450, 465, 467** Edwards, John **175–177** Gagliano, Tom **35, 36, 38, 39, 40, 41, 42, 44, 45, 46, 47, 48, 52, 57, 92, 153, 163, 184, 185, 186, 188, 189, 193** l. (from Science Explorer), **198, 202, 203, 206, 209** t., **211, 212, 217, 219, 222, 223, 225, 227, 228, 230, 599, 652, 653, 701, 878** (turtles in map), **892–893, 897–900, 902, 907, 908, 917, 998, 1025, 1027** Imagineering **9, 11, 12, 21, 24, 25, 64, 68, 75, 77, 78, 79, 85, 87, 88, 148, 152, 159, 160, 237, 297**(with Articulate Graphics), **299** (with Articulate Graphics), **312, 369, 389, 418, 419, 422, 424, 425, 443, 566, 580** (with Patrice Rossi Calkin), **586** (leaf art), **588, 591, 597, 599, 602, 607, 683, 763, 777, 793, 810** t.l., **811, 817, 825, 858, 859** b., **862** Iverson, Carlyn **69, 384, 501, 513, 517, 518, 523, 525, 685, 687, 688, 689, 694, 697, 702, 703, 711, 713, 772, 773, 774, 776, 782, 783, 786, 803, 823, 826–827, 837, 838, 845, 859** t., **867, 868, 934** Levine, Andy **182, 209** b. Mapping Specialists **89, 91, 99, 101, 148, 153, 156, 159, 165, 348, 371, 383** (with Wendy Smith), **405, 410** (with Ernest Albanese), **700, 724, 832** (with Wendy Smith), **878, 1045** McGregor, Malcolm **423** Miller, Mark **923, 931, 947, 951, 1030, 1036, 1051** Mkrtchyan, Art **195, 460, 461, 807** (icons), **836, 869** Morales, Elizabeth **904, 1011, 1014, 1017** (from Biology, The Living Science) Oh, Steve **169, 172, 174, 180, 181, 208, 427, 551** O'Keefe, Laurie **376, 382, 391, 406, 439** (modern horse), **452, 552, 557, 558, 609, 611, 612, 634, 635, 636, 641, 662, 665, 666, 669, 670, 672, 717, 718, 721, 722, 728, 729, 732, 733, 735, 741, 784, 785, 798, 799, 801, 806, 809, 810** b., **812, 824, 849, 860, 862, 874, 885** Phippin, Spencer **901, 902, 925, 927, 928, 945, 946, 957, 958, 969, 978, 981, 983, 986, 987, 989, 995, 1003, 1005, 1006, 1010, 1012,** Precision Graphics **111, 280, 288, 290, 334, 461, 554** b., **555, 625, 627, 640, 649, 660, 726, 747, 768, 790, 807** (icons), **850** (icons), **905, 915, 930, 964** Rossi-Calkin, Patrice **280, 511, 554** t., **563, 565, 570, 575, 576, 580** (with Imagineering, Inc.), **581, 582, 584, 585, 587, 589, 590, 593, 595, 596, 600, 602** (with Imagineering, Inc.), **616, 621, 629, 642, 651, 671, 745, 746, 752, 753, 754, 755, 756, 757** Rothman, Michael **96, 97** Smith, Wendy **64, 68, 69, 83, 84, 85, 383** (animals), **692, 832** Woolsey Associates, J/B **41, 209, 226, 259** Adapted from Neil A. Campbell, Jane B. Reece, and Lawrence G. Mitchell, Biology: Concepts and Connections, 3rd ed. (Menlo Park, CA: Benjamin/Cummings, 2000) **973**

Photo Credits

Photo Research: Slip Jig

Cover & title page: ©Tim Fitzharris 1996/Minden Pictures, Inc. **ii** F. Rauschenbach/Natural Selection Stock Photography, Inc. **iii** b. Russ Lappa/PH School **iii** t. Courtesy of Ken Miller **vi** ©Gregory Ochocki/Photo Researchers, Inc. **vii** b. ©XX NCI/CNRI/Phototake NYC/Phototake **vii** t. Joseph Van Os/The Image Bank **viii** ©Oliver Meckes/Photo Researchers, Inc. **ix** Lee Rentz/Bruce Coleman, Inc. **x** b. ©Kjell B. Sandved/Visuals Unlimited **x** t. ©Dorling Kindersley **xi** b. ©Wayne Lankinen/DRK Photo **xi** t. Courtesy of Wolfgang Kaehler **xiii** b. ©Michael Fogden/DRK Photo **xiii** t. Manny Millan/Sports Illustrated **xiv** b.l. Pearson Education/PH School **xiv** b.r. ©William Leonard/DRK Photo **xiv** t. Pearson Education/PH School **xv** b. Pearson Education/PH School **xv** t. Pearson Education/PH School **xvi** Runk/Schoenberger/Grant Heilman Photography **xvii** b.l. ©Dan McCoy/Rainbow **xvii** b.r. Richard Anderson/PH School **xvii** t.l. ©Andy Rouse/DRK Photo **xviii** Courtesy of Ken Miller **xix** Russ Lappa/PH School **xxi** l. ©Harold Hoffman/Photo Researchers, Inc. **xxi** r. ©Steve Kaufman/DRK Photo **xxii–1** ©Steve Wolper/DRK Photo **1** inset Russ Lappa/PH School **2** ©Andrew Syred/Science Photo Library/Photo Researchers, Inc. **3** ©Peter Scoones/Pictor International, Ltd./PictureQuest **4** b. ©The Stock Market/John Zoiner **4** t. ©The Stock Market/Douglas Faulkner **5** ©Jim Sugar Photography/CORBIS **6** ©CORBIS Sygma **7** Mark Ostrow **10** ©James L. Amos/CORBIS **12** b.l. ©CORBIS **12** b.r. Courtesy of the National Portrait Gallery, London **12** t. ©Bettmann/CORBIS **13** b.l. ©Julia Cameron/CORBIS **13** b.r. ©A. Barrington Brown/Science Source/Photo Researchers, Inc. **13** t. ©CORBIS **14** ©Frans Lanting/Minden Pictures, Inc. **15** l. ©Eric and David Hosking/CORBIS **15** r. ©Tom McHugh/Photo Researchers, Inc. **16** b. ©Marty Cordano/DRK Photo **16** t. ©Chris Bjornberg/Photo Researchers, Inc. **17** b. ©Biophoto Associates/Photo Researchers, Inc. **17** m. ©Dwight R. Kuhn/DRK Photo **17** t. Animals Animals/©Robert Maier **18** b. Animals Animals/©Bruce Davidson **18** b. Animals Animals/©Bruce Davidson **18** l-r1 Animals Animals/©E.R. Degginger **18** l-r2 Animals Animals/©Jennifer Loomis **18** l-r3 Animals Animals/©Patti Murray **18** l-r4 Animals Animals/©Patti Murray **19** ©Ron Spomer/Visuals Unlimited **20** ©Michael Fogden/DRK Photo **22** ©Zigy Kaluzny/Stone **23** Stephff/Cartoonists & Writers Syndicate **25** ©Kevin and Betty Collins/Visuals Unlimited **25** Jacob Halaska/Index Stock Photography, Inc. **26** b.l. ©Biodisc/Visuals Unlimited **26** b.r. ©David M. Phillips/ Visuals Unlimited **26** m.b. ©David M. Phillips/Visuals Unlimited **26** t. ©Doug Martin/ Photo Researchers, Inc. **27** ©The Stock Market/Charles Gupton **28** ©Paul Chesley/Stone **31** Anthony Bannister/Gallo Images/CORBIS **34** ©John Conrad/CORBIS **37** t.l. ©PhotoDisc, Inc., 2001 **37** t.r. Richard Anderson/Pearson Education/PH School **39** b. ©Mark Moffett/Minden Pictures, Inc. **39** t. Kellar Autumn & Ed Florance **40** Wood Sabold/Index Stock Photography, Inc. **41** ©Mark Moffett/Minden Pictures, Inc. **45** ©Bill Bachmann/Photo Network/PictureQuest **46** ©Ricardo Arias, Latin Stock/Science Photo Library/Photo Researchers, Inc. **49** Richard Megna/Fundamental Photographs **53** Thomas Steitz, Yale University **54** Richard Haynes Photography/Pearson Education/PH School **56** Wood Sabold/Index Stock Photography, Inc. **60-61** Corel Professional Photos CD-ROM™ **61** b. Russ Lappa/PH School **62** ©Bruce Coleman, Ltd./Natural Selection **63** ©Gerry Ellis/Minden Pictures, Inc. **65** ©Mark Moffett/Minden Pictures, Inc. **66** b. Provided by the SeaWiFS Project, NASA/Goddard Space Flight Center, and ORBIMAGE **66** t. U.S. Department of the Interior/U.S. Geological Survey **67** ©Gregory Ochocki/Photo Researchers, Inc. **69** ©Rod Planck/Photo Researchers, Inc. **70** Pearson Education/PH School **74** b. ©Ron Sanford & Mike Agliolo/Photo Researchers, Inc. **74** l. ©Bill Frymire/ Masterfile Stock Image Library **76** Rod Wiliams/Bruce Coleman, Inc. **80** ©Larry Ulrich/DRK Photo **81** Pearson Education/PH School **82** ©Richard Matthews/Masterfile Stock Image Library **86** ©Michael Fogden/DRK PHOTO **90** ©Kenneth H. Thomas/Photo Researchers, Inc. **91** ©Ray Ellis/Photo Researchers, Inc. **93** b. ©CORBIS **93** m. ©Kenneth Fink/Photo Researchers, Inc. **93** t. ©Nuridseny et Perennou/Photo Researchers, Inc. **95** b.l. ©PhotoDisc, Inc., 2001 **95** b.r. Michael Schuessler/Tribal Liaison Forester, Wisc. Dept. of Natural Resources **95** t. ©M. P. Kahl/DRK Photo **97** University of Hawaii at Manoa School of Ocean and Earth Science and Technology **100** b. ©E. Hanumantha Rao/Photo Researchers, Inc. **100** inset: b.l. ©Belinda Wright 1984/DRK Photo **100** inset: b.r. ©1994 Chamberlain, MC/DRK Photo **100** inset: t.l. ©Tom & Pat Leeson/Photo Researchers, Inc. **100** inset: t.r. ©Wayne Lynch/DRK Photo **100** t. ©Luiz C. Marigo/Peter Arnold, Inc. **101** b. ©Larry Ulrich/DRK Photo **101** b.l. ©Marty Cordano/DRK Photo **101** b.r. ©Stephen J. Krasemann/DRK Photo **101** t. Courtesy of Wolfgang Kaehler **101** t.l. ©Barbara Gerlach/DRK Photo **101** t.r. ©Stephen J. Krasemann/DRK Photo **102** b. ©Walter H. Hodge/Peter Arnold, Inc. **102** b.l. ©Gary R. Zahm/DRK Photo **102** b.r. ©Mark Smith/Photo Researchers, Inc. **102** t. Courtesy of David Lemke **102** t.l. ©Wayne Lankinen/DRK Photo **102** t.r. ©Tom & Pat Leeson/DRK Photo **103** b. ©Gerry Ellis/Minden Pictures, Inc. **103** b.l. ©Stephen Dalton/Photo Researchers, Inc. **103** b.r. Animals Animals/©Leo Keeler **103** t. ©Michael P. Gadomski/Photo Researchers, Inc. **103** t.l. ©Noble Proctor/Photo Researchers, Inc. **103** t.r. ©Stephen J. Krasemann/DRK Photo **104** b. ©Kim Heacox Photography/DRK Photo **104** b.l. Daniel J. Cox/naturalexposures.com **104** b.r. ©Steve Kaufman 1991/DRK Photo **104** t. ©Tom Bean/CORBIS **104** t.l. ©Lynn M. Stone 1997/DRK Photo **104** t.r. Daniel J. Cox/naturalexposures.com **105** ©Dennis Flaherty/Photo Researchers, Inc. **106** Animals Animals/©Richard & Susan Day **107** b. ©Clint Farlinger/Natural Selection **107** t. ©Roland Birke/Peter Arnold, Inc. **108** l. Animals Animals/©Fred Whitehead **108** r. ©Belinda Wright/DRK Photo **110** b. ©Flip Nicklin/Minden Pictures, Inc. **110** t. ©Frans Lanting/Photo Researchers, Inc. **111** ©Fred Bavendam/Minden Pictures, Inc. **112** b. ©Norbert Wu/DRK Photo **112** t. ©Dough Perrine 1990/DRK Photo **113** ©Spike Walker/Stone **118** ©Frans Lanting/Minden Pictures, Inc. **119** ©Terry Donnelly **120** Joseph Van Os/The Image Bank **121** b. ©Frans Lanting/Minden Pictures, Inc. **121** t. ©CNRI/Phototake **123** Bernard W. Knott, Ed. D. **124** l-r #1 ©Lee F. Snyder/Photo Researchers, Inc. **124** l-r #2 ©Stephen J. Krasemann/DRK Photo **124** l-r #3 John Gerlach/Tom Stack & Associates **124** l-r #4 ©Ford Kristo/Masterfile Stock Image Library **124** l-r #5 ©Gerry Ellis/Minden Pictures, Inc. **125** Keren Su/Getty Images, Inc. **126** b. John Gerlach/Tom Stack & Associates **126** t.l. ©Patrick J. Endres/Visuals Unlimited **126** t.r. ©Andy Rouse/DRK Photo **127** ©Ford Kristo/Masterfile Stock Image Library **128** ©Roy Corral/Stone **130** t.l. Robin Nelson **130** t.r. Bett Press/Woodfin Camp & Associates **133** ©M. Abbey/Photo Researchers, Inc. **138** ©Sun Star/Stock Photos Hawaii **139** ©Frans Lanting/Minden Pictures, Inc. **140** b. ©BIOS (A. Compost)/Peter Arnold, Inc. **140** t. Gallery of Prehistoric Art **141** University of Reading ©Rural History Centre **142** ©Mitch Kezar/Stone **143** b. ©Murray & Associates, Inc./Picturesque/PictureQuest **143** t. ©Jake Rajs/Stone **144** ©Holt Studios International (Miss P. Peacock)/Photo Researchers, Inc. **145** b. ©Mark Edwards/Still Pictures/Peter Arnold, Inc. **145** t. Animals Animals/©James H. Robinson **146** b. ©Peter Christopher/Masterfile Stock Image Library **148** ©Gary Milburn/Tom Stack & Associates **149** ©John Sohlden/Visuals Unlimited **150** ©Scott Camazine/Photo Researchers, Inc. **151** ©Academy of Natural Sciences of Philadelphia/CORBIS **153** ©Tom Vezo/Peter Arnold, Inc. **154** b.l. Bobbe' Z. Christopherson **154** b.r. ©Doug Armand/Stone **154** t.r. Portrait of Mrs. Augustus Hemenway, John Singer Sargent, Private Collection; Photo courtesy Adelson Galleries, Inc., New York **155** b.l. NASA **155** b.r. Graeme Ellis-Ursus/Ursus Photography, Vancouver **155** t. Kjell Sandved/Bruce Coleman, Inc. **156** cw 1 ©Joe McDonald/DRK Photo **156** cw 2 ©Doug Cheeseman/Peter Arnold, Inc. **156** cw 3 ©Simon D. Pollard/Photo Researchers, Inc. **156** cw 4 ©E. Hanumantha Rao/Photo Researchers, Inc. **156** cw 5 Kjell B. Sandved/Butterfly Alphabet, Inc. **156** cw 6 ©R. Ian Lloyd/Masterfile Stock Image Library **156** cw 7 ©Ted Schiffman/Peter Arnold, Inc. **156** cw 8 Animals Animals/©Fabio Colombini **157** NASA **158** AP/Wide World Photos **161** ©Impact Visuals/Phototake **162** ©Joe McDonald/DRK Photo **166–167** ©Dr. Brian Eyden/Science Photo Library/Photo Researchers, Inc. **167** b. Courtesy of Ken Miller **168** ©Quest/Science Photo Library/Photo Researchers, Inc. **169** ©Peter Arnold, Inc. **170** b. Bausch & Lomb Incorporated **170** m. ©Spike Walker/Stone **170** t. ©Martha J. Powell/Visuals Unlimited **171** b. ©Biophoto Associates/Photo Researchers, Inc. **171** t.l. Courtesy National Archives **171** t.r. Jerry Bauer **172** b.l. ©K.G. Murti/Visuals Unlimited **172** t.l. ©Dr. Dennis Kunkel/Phototake **172** t.r. Dr. Jan Hoh of Johns Hopkins University, School of Medicine. **173** b. ©Gopal Murti/Phototake **173** t. ©Ralph A. Slepecky/Visuals Unlimited **174** ©Dr. Dennis Kunkel/Phototake **176** ©Don W. Fawcett/Visuals Unlimited **177** b. ©Don W. Fawcett/Visuals Unlimited **177** l. ©Science Source/Photo Researchers, Inc. **178** ©R. Bolender-D. Fawcett/Visuals Unlimited **179** b. ©Mike Abbey/Visuals Unlimited **179** t. ©Newcomb & Wergin/BPS/Stone **180** Pearson Education/PH School **181** ©Albert Tousson/Phototake **183** PhotoDisc/Getty Images **188** ©Mike Abbey/Visuals Unlimited **190** l. ©David M. Phillips/Visuals Unlimited **190** m. ©Cabisco/Visuals Unlimited **190** r. ©CNRI/Science Photo Library/Photo Researchers, Inc. **191** b.l. ©Don Fawcett/Photo Researchers, Inc. **191** b.r. Ron Boardman/Getty Images Inc-Stone **191** m.b. ©Manfred Kage/Peter Arnold, Inc. **191** t. ©Dr. Dennis Kunkel/Phototake **192** l. ©PhotoDisc, Inc.,

2001 **192** r. ©Robert Rathe/Folio, Inc. **194** Pearson Education/PH School **197** b.l. ©Manfred Kage/Peter Arnold, Inc. **197** b.r. Ron Boardman/Getty Images Inc-Stone **197** t.l. ©CNRI/ Science Photo Library/Photo Researchers, Inc. **197** t.r. ©Stan Flegler/Visuals Unlimited **200** ©Stone **201** l. Pearson Education Corporate Digital Archive **201** r. A. Shah/ABPL Anthony Bannister's Photo Library **202** David Young-Wolff/PhotoEdit **204** The Granger Collection, New York **205** b. Lawrence Berkley Nat'l Lab **205** t.l. Dwight Kuhn Photography **205** t.r. ©Bettmann/CORBIS **208** b.l. ©John Durham/Science Photo Library/ Photo Researchers, Inc. **208** b.r. ©Newcomb & Wegin/Stone **208** t.l. ©Clyde H. Smith/ Peter Arnold, Inc. **210** ©David Muench 2000 **214** b. ©PhotoDisc, Inc., 2001 **214** t. ©Larry Brownstein/Rainbow/PictureQuest **215** Pearson Education/PH School **216** ©David Muench 2000 **218** ©Ken Wagner/Phototake/PictureQuest **220** Duomo Photography, Inc. **221** l. ©Bob Gurr/DRK Photo **221** m.b. ©John Durham/Science Photo Library/Photo Researchers, Inc. **221** m.t. ©Ron Boardman/Stone **221** r. ©Keith Porter/Photo Researchers, Inc. **224** ©Becky Luigart-Stayner/CORBIS **226** ©Science Photo Library/Photo Researchers, Inc. **230** ©Allsport/Ross Kinnaird **231** Pearson Education/PH School **233** l. ©Najlah Feanny/CORBIS **233** r. Getty Images-Photodisc **234** Pearson Education/PH School **235** Pearson Education/PH School **236** ©Allsport/Ross Kinnaird **236** b. ©Bob Gurr/ DRK Photo **240** ©CAMR/A.B. Dowsett/Science Photo Library/Photo Researchers, Inc. **241** ©Kevin Summers/Stone **242** Pearson Education/PH School **244** ©Gunther F. Bahr/ AFIP/Stone **246** b. ©Ed Reschke/Peter Arnold, Inc. **246** m. ©Ed Reschke/Peter Arnold, Inc. **246** t. ©Ed Reschke/Peter Arnold, Inc. **247** b.l. ©Ed Reschke/Peter Arnold, Inc. **247** b.r. ©Ed Reschke/Peter Arnold, Inc. **247** t. ©Ed Reschke/Peter Arnold, Inc. **248** ©R. Calentine/ Visuals Unlimited **252** ©Dr. Gopal Murti/Science Photo Library/Photo Researchers, Inc. **253** b.l. ©Stan Flegler/Visuals Unlimited **253** b.r. ©Professor P.M. Motta & E. Vizza/ Science Photo Library/Photo Researchers, Inc. **253** t.l. ©CAMR/A.B. Dowsett/Science Photo Library/Photo Researchers, Inc. **253** t.r. ©Dr. Dennis Kunkel/Phototake **254** ©Ed Reschke/Peter Arnold, Inc. **255** Pearson Education/PH School **256** ©Dr. Gopal Murti/ Science Photo Library/Photo Researchers, Inc. **166-167** ©Dr. Brian Eyden/Science Photo Library/Photo Researchers, Inc. **260-261** ©Tom & Pat Leeson **261** b. Courtesy of Ken Miller **262** W. Perry Conway/CORBIS **263** ©CORBIS **267** ©Al Francekevich/The Stock Market **270** ©James W. Richardson/Visuals Unlimited **271** Runk/Schoenberger/Grant Heilman Photography **273** b.l. ©Jane Burton/Bruce Coleman, Inc. **273** b.r. ©Hans Reinhard/Bruce Coleman, Inc. **273** t.l. ©John Gerlach/Visuals Unlimited **273** t.r. Animals Animals/©Richard Kolar **274** Kim Taylor/Bruce Coleman, Inc. **279** Animals Animals/ ©George Bernard **281** Pearson Education/PH School **284** ©S. Nielsen/DRK Photo **286** Jacob Halaska/Index Stock Imagery, Inc. **287** ©Klaus Guldbrandsen/Science Photo Library/Photo Researchers, Inc. **289** ©Lee D. Simon/Science Source/Photo Researchers, Inc. **292** b. ©Bettmann/CORBIS **292** t.l. ©Science Source/Photo Researchers, Inc. **292** t.r. ©Cold Spring Harbor Laboratory Archives/Peter Arnold, Inc. **293** b.l. ©A. Barrington/ Photo Researchers, Inc. **293** b.r. Jane Reed/Harvard University **293** t. ©2000 Kay Chernush/Howard Hughes Medical Institute **294** Jacob Halaska/Index Stock Imagery, Inc. **296** Science Photo Library/Custom Medical Stock Photo, Inc. **298** ©Dr. Gopal Murti/ Science Photo Library/Photo Researchers, Inc. **301** From J. Frank, American Scientist 86 (2000), 428–439, Courtesy of Joachim Frank, All Rights Reserved. **313** Pearson Education/ PH School **318** ©Anup Shah/Dembinsky Photo Associates **319** ©Darrell Gulin/DRK Photo **320** b. ©Manfred Kage/Peter Arnold, Inc. **320** t. ©Mitsuaki Iwago/Minden Pictures, Inc. **321** Runk/Schoenberger/Grant Heilman Photography **326** Pearson Education/PH School **330** N. Cobbing. ©Still Pictures/Peter Arnold, Inc. **331** ©Keith V. Wood/Visuals Unlimited **333** "PA" News **335** Pearson Education/PH School **336** "PA" News **340** Richard Hutchings/ Photo Researchers, Inc. **341** ©CNRI/Science Photo Library/Photo Researchers, Inc. **343** ©Craig Farraway **344** ©The Stock Market/Charles Gupton **346** ©Simon Fraser/RVI, Newcastle-Upon Tyne/Science Photo Library/Photo Researchers, Inc. **347** ©Omikron/ Photo Researchers, Inc. **352** ©PhotoDisc, Inc., 2001 **353** t.l. ©Lawrence Migdale **353** t.r. ©Dr. Dennis Kunkel/CNRI/Phototake **354** AP/Wide World Photos **355** b. AP/Wide World Photos **355** t. ©James King-Holmes/Science Photo Library/Photo Researchers, Inc. **356** l. ©Leonard Lessin/Peter Arnold, Inc. **356** r. ©D. VoTrung/Phototake **357** Paul Hosefros/NYT Permissions **359** t.l. ©PhotoDisc, Inc., 2001 **359** t.r. ©Peter Hvizdak/The Image Works **362** ©CNRI/Science Photo Library/Photo Researchers, Inc. **364** ©ISM/Phototake **366–367** ©1996 Jack S. Grove c/o Mira **367** b. Russ Lappa/PH School **368** Art Wolfe Incorporated **370** l. Syndics of Cambridge University Library **370** r. ©Joe McDonald/Bruce Coleman, Inc./PictureQuest **371** b. ©D. Cavagnaro/DRK Photo **371** m. ©David Cavagnaro/DRK Photo **371** t. ©D. Cavagnaro/DRK Photo **372** ©Frans Lanting/Photo Researchers, Inc. **373** Bibliotheque des Arts Decoratifs, Paris, France/Archives Charmet/Bridgeman Art Library **374** b. Stock Montage, Inc. **374** m. The Granger Collection, New York **374** t. ©Tom and Susan Bean/DRK Photo **375** b. ©2000 North Wind Picture Archives **375** t.l. The Granger Collection, New York **375** t.r. Brown Brothers **377** Archiv für Kunst und Geschichte, Berlin **378** Mark Downey/Index Stock Photography, Inc. **380** ©J. Sneesby/B. Wilkins/Stone **381** ©Ron Austing/Photo Researchers, Inc. **382** Neil Fletcher/©Dorling Kindersley **385** b. Prof. Dr. Michael K. Richardson **385** b.l. ©George Whiteley/Photo Researchers, Inc. **385** b.r. ©David Spears/Science Photo Library/Photo Researchers, Inc. **385** m.b. Animals Animals/©Keith Gillett **385** m.b. Ann Campbell Burke/Wesleyan University/Journal of Morphology, **385** t. Harry Taylor/©Dorling Kindersley **386** ©ARCHIV/Photo Researchers, Inc. **390** b. ©D. Cavagnaro/DRK Photo **390** t. ©David Cavagnaro/DRK Photo **392** ©MURRAY, PATTI/Animals Animals Enterprises **393** ©Melanie Carr/Zephyr Photos **395** ©David Young-Wolff/PhotoEdit/PictureQuest **396** New York Public Library, (Rare Book Division or Print Collection. Miriam and Ira D. Wallach Division of Art, Prints and Photographs); Astor, Lenox and Tilden Foundations **397** ©Charlie Ott/Photo Researchers, Inc. **399** ©Melanie Carr/Zephyr Photos **401** Pearson Education/PH School **402** ©Lee F. Snyder/Photo Researchers, Inc. **403** ©David R. Frazier/ Photo Researchers, Inc. **404** l. ©Harold Hoffman/Photo Researchers, Inc. **404** r. ©Steve Kaufman/DRK Photo **405** inset: l. Animals Animals/©Breck P. Kent **405** inset: r. ©Tom & Pat Leeson/DRK Photo **405** t. ©Danny Lehman/CORBIS **407** b. Photograph by P.R. Grant **407** t. Photograph by B.R. Grant **410** David Sanders/DS Photography **411** Pearson Education/PH School **416** Jackie Beckett/American Museum of Natural History **417** Ira Block/National Geographic Society **419** l. ©David Hanson/Stone **419** r. ©CORBIS **425** ©Sidney Fox/Visuals Unlimited **426** ©Fred Bavendam/Peter Arnold, Inc. **428** British Museum of Natural History, London **429** ©D.W. Miller **430** British Museum of Natural History, London/J. Sibbick **431** b. Grant Heilman Photography **431** t. Field Museum of Natural History **432** 1989 Mark Hallett **433** b.l. ©PhotoDisc, Inc., 2001 **433** b.r. Ira Block **433** t. The Natural History Museum London/M. Long **434** ©Douglas Henderson **435** ©D. Van Ravenswaay/Science Photo Library/Photo Researchers, Inc. **437** b. Mike Bacon/Tom Stack & Associates **437** m. ©Wayne Lynch/DRK Photo **437** t. ©PhotoDisc, Inc., 2001 **438** b. ©Charles Marden Fitch **438** t. The Natural History Museum, London **439** Sean Milne/ ©Dorling Kindersley **441** Pearson Education/PH School **446** ©Gary Randall/Visuals Unlimited **447** ©Jeff Lepore/Photo Researchers, Inc. **448** ©Kenneth W. Fink/Photo Researchers, Inc. **449** b.r. Daniel J. Cox/naturalexposures.com **449** m.b. Animals Animals/ ©Norbert Rosing **449** m.l. ©Art Wolfe/Photo Researchers, Inc. **449** t. ©Bettmann/CORBIS **451** b.l. ©Peter Howorth/Mo Yung Productions/www.norbertwu.com **451** b.r. ©Nancy Sefton/Photo Researchers, Inc. **451** t.l. Animals Animals/©Rudolf Ingo Riepl **454** b. ©D. Parer & E. Parer-Cook/Auscape International Photo Library **454** m. ©PhotoDisc, Inc., 2001 **454** t. ©Barbara Gerlach/DRK Photo **456** ©Marie Selby Botanical Gardens **457** l. ©Michael Abbey/Photo Researchers, Inc. **457** r. ©CNRI/Phototake **463** Matthew Ward/ ©Dorling Kindersley **463** cw-1 Matthew Ward/©Dorling Kindersley **463** cw-2 ©Dorling Kindersley **463** cw-3 ©Dorling Kindersley **463** cw-4 ©Dorling Kindersley **463** cw-6 Matthew Ward/©Dorling Kindersley **463** m. Matthew Ward/©Dorling Kindersley **468–469** ©David M. Dennis **469** b. Courtesy of Ken Miller **470** Michael T. Sedam/CORBIS **471** Esther R. Angert, Harvard University **472** ©M. Wurtz/Biozentrum, University of Basel/Science Photo Library/Photo Researchers, Inc. **473** b. ©Scott Camazine/Photo Researchers, Inc. **473** m. ©David M. Phillips/Visuals Unlimited **473** t. ©David Scharf/ Peter Arnold, Inc. **474** ©Fred McConnaughey/Science Source/Photo Researchers, Inc. **475** l. ©Dr. Dennis Kunkel/Phototake **475** m. ©Dr. Dennis Kunkel/Phototake **475** r. ©A. B. Dowsett/Science Photo Library/Photo Researchers, Inc. **476** ©Michael P. Gadomski/Photo Researchers, Inc. **477** ©Richard L. Carlton/Visuals Unlimited **478** ©Norm Thomas/Photo Researchers, Inc. **479** l. ©M. Wurtz/Biozentrum, University of Basel/Science Photo Library/Photo Researchers, Inc. **479** m. ©Dr. O. Bradfute/Peter Arnold, Inc. **479** r. ©National Institute for Biological Standards and Control, England/Photo Researchers, Inc. **482** Pearson Education/PH School **484** ©Kim Kulish/CORBIS **485** ©A. Wolf/Explorer/Photo Researchers, Inc. **487** l. ©PhotoDisc, Inc., 2001 **487** t.r. CDC/PHIL/CORBIS **490** Sinclair Stammers/Science Photo Library/Photo Researchers, Inc. **492** t. ©M. Wurtz/Biozentrum, University of Basel/Science Photo Library/Photo Researchers, Inc. **493** b.l. ©David Scharf/Peter Arnold, Inc. **493** b.r. ©Scott Camazine/Photo Researchers, Inc. **493** t.l. ©M. Wurtz/Biozentrum, University of Basel/ Science Photo Library/Photo Researchers, Inc. **493** t.r. ©David M. Phillips/Visuals Unlimited **496** Andrew Syred/Science Photo Library/Photo Researchers, Inc. **497** l. ©Manfred Kage/Peter Arnold, Inc. **497** m. ©Manfred Kage/Peter Arnold, Inc. **497** r. ©M.I. Walker/Photo Researchers, Inc. **498** ©T.E. Adams/Visuals Unlimited **499** l. ©Michael Abbey/Photo Researchers, Inc. **499** r. ©Oliver Meckes/Photo Researchers, Inc. **500** Runk/ Schoenberger/Grant Heilman Photography **501** ©Eric V. Grave/Photo Researchers, Inc. **503** ©Oliver Meckes/Photo Researchers, Inc. **504** ©Robert Brons/Biological Photo Service **505** l. ©Dr. Dennis Kunkel/Phototake **505** r. ©Eric Grave/Science Source/Photo Researchers, Inc. **506** ©A. Flowers & L. Newman/Photo Researchers, Inc. **507** b. ©Dr. Dennis Kunkel/Phototake **508** ©Dr. Dennis Kunkel/Phototake **509** inset ©David M. Phillips/Visuals Unlimited **509** t. ©Bill Bachman/Photo Researchers, Inc. **510** ©G. Robinson/Visuals Unlimited **512** b. ©Laurie Campbell/NHPA **512** m. ©James W. Richardson/Visuals Unlimited **512** t. Biophoto Assoc./Photo Researchers, Inc. **515** b. DeSanto/StockFood **515** t. Eising/StockFood **516** ©L. West/Photo Researchers, Inc. **517** ©Matt Meadows/Peter Arnold, Inc. **518** ©Dr. Dennis Kunkel/Phototake **520** b.l. ©E. Webber/Visuals Unlimited **520** b.r. ©Holt Studios Int./Photo Researchers, Inc. **520** t. The Granger Collection, New York **521** Pearson Education/PH School **526** ©D. Cavagnaro/ DRK Photo **528** b. Robert & Linda Mitchell Photography **528** t. ©Sarah J. Frankling/ Stone **529** ©Jeff Lepore/Photo Researchers, Inc. **532** Lee Rentz/Bruce Coleman, Inc. **535** b.l. ©Michael Fogden/DRK Photo **535** b.r. ©Ed Reschke/Peter Arnold, Inc. **535** m.b. ©Michael Fogden/DRK Photo **535** m.t. ©Robert W. Domm/Visuals Unlimited **535** t.l. ©Jeff Lepore/Photo Researchers, Inc. **535** t.r. ©Laurie Campbell/Stone **536** b. ©David Scharf/Peter Arnold, Inc. **536** t. ©Jack M. Bostrack/Visuals Unlimited **537** D. Redecker (B-E), R. Kodner (A); ©Science, 2000 **538** ©Stephen G. Maka/DRK Photo **539** b. ©Michael Fogden/DRK Photo **539** m.t. ©Holt Studios International/Nigel Cattlin/Photo Researchers, Inc. **539** t.l. ©Astrid & Hanns-Frieder Michler/Science Photo Library/Photo Researchers, Inc. **539** t.r. ©Dr. P. Marazzi/Photo Researchers, Inc. **540** b. ©L. West/Photo Researchers, Inc. **540** m. ©Jack Dermid **540** t. ©Courtney Milne **541** Mark Richards/PhotoEdit **542** b. Runk/Schoenberger/Grant Heilman Photography **542** t. ©John D. Cunningham/Visuals Unlimited **543** Richard Haynes Photography/Pearson Education/PH School **548–549** ©Clyde H. Smith/Peter Arnold, Inc. **549** b. Courtesy of Ken Miller **550** Terry Donnelly/ Dembinsky Photo Associates **551** Runk/Schoenberger/Grant Heilman Photography **552** ©Russell D. Curtis/Photo Researchers, Inc. **553** b. Animals Animals/©Joyce & Frank Burek **553** t. Jane Grushow/Grant Heilman Photography **554** Hans Steur, The Netherlands **555** cw: 1 ©Dorling Kindersley **555** cw: 2 ©Ed Reschke/Peter Arnold, Inc. **555** cw: 3 ©Ed Reschke/Peter Arnold, Inc. **555** cw: 4 ©Pat Lynch/Photo Researchers, Inc. **556** ©Terry Donnelly/Stone **557** l. ©Alvin E. Staffan/National Audubon Society/Photo Researchers, Inc. **557** r. Robert & Linda Mitchell Photography **559** ©Farrell Greham/ Photo Researchers, Inc. **560** b. ©Brad Mogen/Visuals Unlimited **560** t. ©Dorling Kindersley **561** l. ©Gary W. Carter/Visuals Unlimited **561** r. ©Ed Reschke/Peter Arnold, Inc. **562** b.l. ©Biophoto Associates/Photo Researchers, Inc. **562** b.r. ©Ed Reschke/Peter Arnold, Inc. **562** t. ©Peter Chadwick/Dorling Kindersley **564** Animals Animals/©Erwin & Peggy Bauer **565** b. CORBIS Digital Stock **566** b. Peter Chadwick/©Dorling Kindersley **566** t. Dr. E.R. Degginger **567** b. ©Walter H. Hodge/Peter Arnold, Inc. **567** t.l. ©Biophoto Associates/Photo Researchers, Inc. **567** t.r. ©Gerald & Buff Corsi/Visuals Unlimited **568** l. ©Stephen G. Maka/DRK Photo **568** r. Larry Lefever/Grant Heilman Photography **569** l. Hans Reinhard/Bruce Coleman, Inc. **569** r. ©PhotoDisc, Inc., 2001 **571** r. Alana Van Rensselaer **571** l. ©PhotoDisc, Inc., 2001 **572** l. Joy Spurr/Bruce Coleman, Inc. **572** m. Jonathan Buckley/©Dorling Kindersley **572** r. Larry Lefever/Grant Heilman Photography **573** ©Fritz Polking/Visuals Unlimited **574** ©Dorling Kindersley **576** Brian Parker/Tom Stack & Associates **578** Getty Images **580** b. ©Andrew Syred/Science Photo Library/Photo Researchers, Inc. **581** Ray F. Evert, University of Wisconsin **582** l. ©Ed Reschke/Peter Arnold, Inc. **582** m. ©Ed Reschke/Peter Arnold, Inc. **582** r. ©George Wilder/Visuals Unlimited **583** Ray F. Evert, University of Wisconsin **590** ©Ed Reschke/Peter Arnold, Inc. **592** ©Manfred Kage/Peter Arnold, Inc. **594** b.l. ©Geoff Dann/ Dorling Kindersley **594** b.r. ©Dorling Kindersley **594** t.l. Barry L. Runk/Grant Heilman Photography **594** t.r. ©Dorling Kindersley **597** ©Dr. Jeremy Burgess/Science Photo Library/Photo Researchers, Inc. **598** b.r. ©Kjell B. Sandved/Visuals Unlimited **598** l. ©Kjell B. Sandved/Visuals Unlimited **598** m. ©Doug Sokell/Visuals Unlimited **598** t.r. ©Brian P. Foss/Visuals Unlimited **600** ©Jack M. Bostrack/Visuals Unlimited **601** Richard Haynes Photography/Pearson Education/PH School **608** ©Carl R. Sams II/Peter Arnold, Inc. **610** b.l. ©Martha Cooper/Peter Arnold, Inc. **610** b.r. ©Manfred Kage/Peter Arnold, Inc. **610** t. ©Walter H. Hodge/Peter Arnold, Inc. **612** l. ©Nigel Cattlin/H.S.I./Photo Researchers, Inc. **612** r. ©Rod Planck/Photo Researchers, Inc. **613** b.l. Geoff Dann©Dorling Kindersley **613** t. Pearson Education/PH School **615** b.l. Animals Animals/©Carroll W. Perkins **615** b.r. ©M. H. Sharp/Photo Researchers, Inc. **615** t.r. ©Geoff Bryant/Photo Researchers, Inc. **617** Florigene Limited **618** ©Dorling Kindersley **619** b. ©Stephen J. Krasemann/Photo Researchers, Inc. **619** t. ©Gregory K. Scott/Photo Researchers, Inc. **620** ©L. Linkhart/ Visuals Unlimited **622** Runk/Schoenberger/Grant Heilman Photography **623** b. ©Holt Studios Int./Photo Researchers, Inc. **623** t. ©Michael P. Gadomski/Photo Researchers, Inc. **624** b.l. ©Werner H. Muller/Peter Arnold, Inc. **624** b.r. ©Keren Su/CORBIS **624** m.l. ©PhotoDisc, Inc., 2001 **624** m.r. SBG **624** t. ©Wolfgang Kaehler/CORBIS **625** b. ©PhotoDisc, Inc., 2001 **625** t.l. ©Holt Studios Int./Nigel Cattlin/Photo Researchers, Inc. **625** t.r. ©David Cavagnaro/Peter Arnold, Inc. **626** ©Michael P. Gadomski/Photo Researchers, Inc. **632** ©Dr. Paul A. Zahl/Photo Researchers, Inc. **633** Animals Animals/©Dani/Jeske **635** Dr. E.R. Degginger **637** ©Sylvan Wittwer/Visuals Unlimited **638** Courtesy of Stephen Gladfelter, Stanford University **639** ©Charles D. Winters/Photo Researchers, Inc. **640** ©Ed. Reschke/Peter Arnold, Inc. **642** ©Ed. Reschke/Peter Arnold, Inc. **643** ©Paul A. Souders/CORBIS **644** ©Doug Sokell/Visuals Unlimited **645** b. ©Ray Pfortner/ Peter Arnold, Inc. **645** t. Sean Morris/©Oxford Scientific Films **646** l. ©Bill Ivy/Stone **646** r.

Credits

©Rod Planck/Photo Researchers, Inc. 647 Richard Haynes Photography/Pearson Education/PH School 648 ©Jack Bostrack/Visuals Unlimited 654-655 ©Wayne Lynch/DRK Photo 655 b. Russ Lappa/PH School 656 Fred McConnaughey/Photo Researchers, Inc. 657 ©Ken Highfill/Photo Researchers, Inc. 658 b.l. ©BIOS (F. Marquez)/Peter Arnold, Inc. 658 b.r. ©Roger Eriksson 658 m.l. Francisco Cruz/SuperStock 658 t.l. ©John Cancalosi/DRK Photo 659 b. ©Tom & Pat Leeson/Photo Researchers, Inc. 659 l. ©Anthony Bannister/Photo Researchers, Inc. 659 r. ©Kevin Schafer/Stone 661 ©Carolina Biological Supply/Phototake 663 F. Rauschenbach/Natural Selection Stock Photography, Inc. 664 l. ©Mary Beth Angelo/Photo Researchers, Inc. 664 r. ©Charles V. Angelo/Photo Researchers, Inc. 667 ©Fred McConnaughey/Photo Researchers, Inc. 668 ©Larry Dunmire/Photo Network/PictureQuest 671 l. Jeffrey L. Rotman 671 r. ©Mary Beth Angelo/Photo Researchers, Inc. 673 b. ©2001 Norbert Wu/www.norbertwu.com 673 t.l. Copyright ©2000 Harbor Branch Oceanographic/E. Widder 673 t.r. Copyright ©2000 Harbor Branch Oceanographic 674 ©Doug Perrine/Innerspace Visions 675 ©2001 Norbert Wu/www.norbertwu.com 677 Pearson Education/PH School 682 ©Jeffrey L. Rotman 683 ©Fred McConnaughey/Photo Researchers, Inc. 684 ©Drs. Kessel and Shih/Peter Arnold, Inc. 685 ©Carolina Biological Supply Company/Phototake 686 l. ©Jeffrey L. Rotman/Peter Arnold, Inc. 686 r. ©Brian Rogers/Visuals Unlimited 688 ©Oliver Meckes/Photo Researchers, Inc. 689 ©Cabisco/Visuals Unlimited 690 b. ©David Scharf/Peter Arnold, Inc. 690 t. ©Oliver Meckes/Photo Researchers, Inc. 691 b. ©R. Umesh Chandran, TDR, WHO/Science Photo Library/Photo Researchers, Inc. 691 t.l. ©PhotoDisc, Inc., 2001 691 t.r. Jim Foster/Pearson Education/PH School 692 ©C. James Webb/Phototake NYC 693 l. ©Sinclair Stammers/Science Photo Library/Photo Researchers, Inc. 693 r. ©Fernand Ivaldi/Stone 694 ©Kjell B. Sandved/Visuals Unlimited 695 b. Animals Animals/©Raymond A. Mendez 695 t. Pearson Education/PH School 696 b. Bruce Coleman, Ltd. 696 t. ©Aldo Brando/Peter Arnold, Inc. 698 b. ©Hal Beral/Visuals Unlimited 698 t.l. ©C.P. Hickman/Visuals Unlimited 698 t.r. National Archives 699 ©Robert Pickett/CORBIS 700 James F. Lubner, University of Wisconsin Sea Grant Institute 701 ©Kelvin Aitken/Peter Arnold, Inc. 704 b. ©Fred Bavendam/Peter Arnold, Inc. 704 ©Jane Burton/Dorling Kindersley 705 b.r. ©Alexandra Edwards/Peter Arnold, Inc. 705 t.l. ©A. Flowers and L. Newman/Photo Researchers, Inc. 705 t.r. ©William J. Weber/Visuals Unlimited 706 b. ©Dave B. Fleetham/Visuals Unlimited 706 t. ©Fred Bavendam/Peter Arnold, Inc. 707 ©Frank Greenway/Dorling Kindersley 708 ©Heather R. Davidson 710 ©Jeffrey L. Rotman/Peter Arnold, Inc. 712 ©Marty Snyderman/Visuals Unlimited 713 ©T.E. Adams/Visuals Unlimited 714 ©Skip Moody/Dembinsky Photo Associates 715 ©Carolina Biological Supply/Phototake 716 b. ©Dorling Kindersley 716 t. ©John Cancalosi/DRK Photo 719 Barry L. Runk/Grant Heilman Photography 720 ©Rod Planck/Photo Researchers, Inc. 723 b. ©Dorling Kindersley 723 t. ©Franz Lanting/Minden Pictures, Inc. 724 b. ©BIOS (X. Eichaker)/Peter Arnold, Inc. 724 t. ©R. Calentine/Visuals Unlimited 725 b. ©Michael & Patricia Fogden/DRK Photo 725 t. ©Tom McHugh/Photo Researchers, Inc. 726 b.l. ©Dorling Kindersley 726 b.r. ©M.C. Chamberlain/DRK Photo 726 t. Wolfgang Kaehler Photography 727 ©Dorling Kindersley 728 ©Stephen Dalton/Photo Researchers, Inc. 730 b.l. ©David Scharf/Peter Arnold, Inc. 730 b.r. ©Galen Rowell/CORBIS 730 t. ©Martin Dohrn/Science Photo Library/Photo Researchers, Inc. 731 b. AP/Wide World Photos/David Jennings 731 t. ©E. R. Degginger/Photo Researchers, Inc. 734 ©Glenn M. Oliver/Visuals Unlimited 736 ©Dorling Kindersley 737 b.l. ©Fred Bavendam/Peter Arnold, Inc. 737 b.r. ©Andrew J. Martinez/Photo Researchers, Inc. 737 m. Animals Animals/©Clay Wiseman 737 t. ©Charles V. Angelo/Photo Researchers, Inc. 738 b. ©James Amos/Photo Researchers, Inc. 738 t. ©M.C. Chamberlain/DRK Photo 739 Raymond A Mendez/Animals Animals 744 ©Brandon Cole/Visuals Unlimited 746 Chip Clark/National Museum of Natural History, Smithsonian 750 Runk/Schoenberger/Grant Heilman Photography 751 ©Ray Coleman/Photo Researchers, Inc. 753 Pearson Education/PH School 757 ©Lawrence Naylor/Photo Researchers, Inc. 758 b. ©Kelvin Aitken/Peter Arnold, Inc. 758 t. ©Brandon D. Cole 759 Pearson Education/PH School 764–765 ©Merlin D. Tuttle/Bat Conservation International 765 b. Russ Lappa/PH School 766 ©Art Wolfe/Stone 769 Animals Animals/©W. Gregory Brown 770 Runk/Schoenberger/Grant Heilman Photography 771 ©Labat-Lanceau/AUSCAPE International 773 Dr. Michael E. Williams/Cleveland Museum of Natural History 774 ©Peter David/Masterfile Stock Image Library 775 b. Animals Animals/©A. Root 775 t. Pearson Education/PH School 777 ©Richard T. Nowitz/Photo Researchers, Inc. 778 b. ©Brian Parker/Tom Stack & Associates 778 m. Animals Animals/©Zig Leszczynski 778 t. ©Natalie Fobes/Stone 779 b. ©Stephen Frink/Stone 779 m. Animals Animals/©Herb Segars 779 t. Howard Hall Productions 780 m.l. ©2001 Stephen Frink/Waterhouse Stock 780 m.r. Howard Hall Productions 780 m.t. ©Fred Bavendam/Minden Pictures, Inc. 780 t.l. ©Fred Bavendam/Minden Pictures, Inc. 780 t.r. ©Norbert Wu/DRK Photo 781 ©Ralph A. Clevenger/CORBIS 787 Animals Animals/©Bill Beatty 788 b.l. Animals Animals/©Juan Manuel Renjifo 788 b.r. ©Dorling Kindersley 788 t.l. ©William Leonard/DRK Photo 789 Animals Animals/©Stephen Dalton 791 Pearson Education/PH School 792 b. ©Labat-Lanceau/AUSCAPE International 792 t. ©William Leonard/DRK Photo 796 ©Bruce Coleman, Ltd./Natural Selection 797 ©David A. Northcott/CORBIS 800 ©Joe McDonald/Natural Selection 801 ©Michael Fogden/DRK Photo 802 b. ©E.R. Degginger/Photo Researchers, Inc. 802 t.l. ©Michael Fogden/DRK Photo 802 t.r. ©Michael Fogden/DRK Photo 804 b.l. ©John Cancalosi/Peter Arnold, Inc. 804 b.r. ©Gary Retherford/Photo Researchers, Inc. 804 m. Michael & Patricia Fogden/CORBIS 804 t.l. ©Dorling Kindersley 804 t.r. ©Anup & Manoj Shah/DRK Photo 805 ©Gerry Ellis/gerryellis.com 806 AP/Wide World Photos 807 ©Sinclair Stammers/Science Photo Library/Photo Researchers, Inc. 808 t-b:1 ©Steve Gettle/gerryellis.com 808 t-b:2 ©Joe McDonald/DRK Photo 808 t-b:3 ©Gerry Ellis/gerryellis.com 808 t-b:4 ©Michael Fogden/DRK Photo 808 t-b:5 © McDonald Wildlife Photo., Inc./DRK Photo 808 t-b:6 ©Frans Lanting/Minden Pictures, Inc. 813 cw: 1 ©Stephen J. Krasemann/DRK Photo 813 cw: 2 Michael Gore/Frank Lane Picture Agency/CORBIS 813 cw: 3 ©Tim Davis/Photo Researchers, Inc. 813 cw: 4 ©M.H. Sharp/Photo Researchers, Inc. 813 cw: 5 ©PhotoDisc, Inc., 2001 813 cw: 6 Seldon Jr., W. Lynn/Omni-Photo Communications, Inc. 813 m.l. ©2000, Gail Shumway/FPG International LLC 814 ©Wayne Lankinen/DRK Photo 815 AP/Wide World Photos 816 ©Dorling Kindersley 820 ©Zefa (RM)/M. Botzek/Masterfile 821 ©Frans Lanting/Minden Pictures, Inc. 822 b. ©Flip Nicklin/Minden Pictures, Inc. 822 t. Daniel J. Cox/naturalexposures.com 824 ©The Stock Market/Keenan Ward 826 b. ©Thomas Mangelsen/Minden Pictures, Inc. 826 t.l. ©Jany Sauvanet/Photo Researchers, Inc. 826 t.r. ©Mitsuaki Iwago/Minden Pictures, Inc. 827 l. ©Manfred Danegger/OKAPIA/Photo Researchers, Inc. 827 m. ©Stephen Dalton/Photo Researchers, Inc. 827 r. ©Gregory Ochocki/Photo Researchers, Inc. 828 ©Tom McHugh/Photo Researchers, Inc. 829 b. Nicole Galeazzi/Omni-Photo Communications, Inc. 829 m. ©D. Parer and E. Parer-Cook/Stone 829 t.r. ©Art Wolfe/Stone 830 cw: 1 ©Merlin D. Tuttle/Bat Conservation International/Photo Researchers, Inc. 830 cw: 2 ©Wayne Lawler/Photo Researchers, Inc. 830 cw: 3 ©Stone 830 cw: 4 Graeme Ellis-Ursus/Ursus Photography, Vancouver 830 cw: 5 ©Doug Perrine/Innerspace Visions 830 cw: 6 ©Anthony Mercieca/Photo Researchers, Inc. 831 b.l. ©Thomas Kitchin/Natural Selection 831 b.r. ©Frans Lanting/Minden Pictures, Inc. 831 m.l. Animals Animals/©Michael Dick 831 m.r. Daniel J. Cox/naturalexposures.com 831 t.l. ©Tui De Roy/Minden Pictures, Inc. 831 t.r. Daniel J. Cox/naturalexposures.com 833 ©Gerry Ellis/Minden Pictures, Inc. 834 l-r #1 ©Mitsuaki Iwago/Minden Pictures, Inc. 834 l-r #2 ©Frans Lanting/Minden Pictures, Inc. 834 l-r #3 ©Tom McHugh/Photo Researchers, Inc. 834 l-r #4 Kevin Schafer 834 l-r #5 Daniel J. Cox/naturalexposures.com 834 l-r #6 ©Tim Davis/Photo Researchers, Inc. 834 l-r #7 ©Mark Newman/Photo Researchers, Inc. 834 l-r #8 ©Frans Lanting/Minden Pictures, Inc. 834 l-r #9 ©Tim Davis/Photo Researchers, Inc. 834 l-r #10 ©PhotoDisc, Inc., 2001 836 b. ©Science Photo Library/Photo Researchers, Inc. 836 m. ©Archivo Iconograpico, S.A./CORBIS 836 t. ©John Reader/Science Photo Library/Photo Researchers, Inc. 837 b.l. ©David L. Brill Photography 837 b.r. ©John Reader/Photo Researchers, Inc. 837 t. Institute of Human Origins 838 b. Animals Animals/©E. R. Degginger 838 m. Fred Spoor, copyright National Museums of Kenya 838 t. copyright M.P.F.T 840 Laurie Grace & Janna Brenning/Scientific American Magazine 841 ©De Sazo/Photo Researchers, Inc. 843 l. Runk/Schoenberger/Grant Heilman Photography 843 m. Dwight Kuhn Photography, ©1986 843 r. Runk/Schoenberger/Grant Heilman Photography 844 ©The Stock Market/Keenan Ward 848 Nigel J. Dennis/Photo Researchers, Inc. 849 S. Conway Morris, University of Cambridge 851 ©Dorling Kindersley 852 CW 1 ©Hal Beral/Visuals Unlimited 852 CW 2 ©Tom & Pat Leeson/Photo Researchers, Inc. 852 CW 3 ©Roger Treadwell/Visuals Unlimited 852 CW 4 Nicole Galeazzi/Omni-Photo Communications, Inc. 852 CW 5 ©Stephen J. Krasemann/DRK Photo 852 CW 6 ©Tom McHugh/Photo Researchers, Inc. 853 ©CORBIS 854 ©Frans Lanting/Minden Pictures, Inc. 856 Animals Animals/©Marian Bacon 857 ©Art Wolfe/Photo Researchers, Inc. 863 The Zoological Society of San Diego 863 b. ©E.R. Degginger/Photo Researchers, Inc. 863 t.l. ©PhotoDisc, Inc., 2001 864 t.l. ©Fred Bavendam/Minden Pictures, Inc. 864 t.m. ©Stephen J. Krasemann/Photo Researchers, Inc. 864 t.r. Daniel J. Cox/naturalexposures.com 866 b. Daniel J. Cox/naturalexposures.com 866 t. Animals Animals/©Marian Bacon 870 ©OSF/LILLIE, PETER/Animals Animals Enterprises 871 ©Heather Angel/Biofotos 872 b.l. ©Rod Planck/Photo Researchers, Inc. 872 t. ©Joe McDonald/DRK Photo 873 Courtesy of Wolfgang Kaehler 876 William Lishman & Associates Limited 877 ©Flip Nicklin/Minden Pictures, Inc. 879 Courtesy of Wolfgang Kaehler 880 Michael K. Nichols/National Geographic Society 881 b. ©Fred McConnaughey/Photo Researchers, Inc. 881 t. ©Gregory Dimijian/Photo Researchers, Inc. 882 ©Francois Gohier/Photo Researchers, Inc. 882 Philip Gould/CORBIS 883 Anne et Jacques Six 884 ©Francois Gohier/Photo Researchers, Inc. 888–889 ©Orion Press/Black Sheep 889 b. Courtesy of Ken Miller 891 l. Corel Professional Photos CD-ROM™ 891 r. ©Jim Cummins/FPG International LLC 894 b.l. ©Dr. Dennis Kunkel/Phototake 894 b.r. Quest/Science Photo Library/Photo Researchers, Inc. 894 t.l. ©David M. Phillips/Visuals Unlimited 894 t.r. ©Michael Abbey/Photo Researchers, Inc. 895 David Mager/Pearson Learning Group 906 Quest/Science Photo Library/Photo Researchers, Inc. 908 ©Prof. P. Motta, Dept. of Anatomy, University La Sapienza, Rome/Science Photo Library/Photo Researchers, Inc. 909 ©Prof. P. Motta/Dept. of Anatomy, University La Sapienza, Rome/Science Photo Library/Photo Researchers, Inc. 910 l. Pearson Education Corporate Digital Archive 910 r. ©PhotoDisc, Inc., 2001 911 b. Dr. E.R. Degginger 911 t. ©Dr. Morley Read/Science Photo Library/Photo Researchers, Inc. 912 ©David Young-Wolff/PhotoEdit/PictureQuest 920 ©Getty Images 921 Manny Millan/Sports Illustrated 923 t. ©Andrew Syred/Science Photo Library/Photo Researchers, Inc. 926 l. ©Eric Graves/Phototake 926 m. ©Biophoto Associates/Photo Researchers, Inc. 926 r. ©John D. Cunningham/Visuals Unlimited 929 b. ©James Balog/Stone 929 t. Don W. Fawcett/Photo Researchers, Inc. 932 ©Dan McCoy/Rainbow 933 b. ©1996 Jim Cummins/FPG International LLC 933 t. ©Dr. Jeremy Burgess/Science Photo Library/Photo Researchers, Inc. 936 ©Quest/Science Photo Library/Photo Researchers, Inc. 937 Pearson Education/PH School 939 b.l. ©John D. Cunningham/Visuals Unlimited 939 b.r. ©Andrew Syred/Science Photo Library/Photo Researchers, Inc. 939 t.l. ©Eric Graves/Phototake 939 t.r. ©Biophoto Associates/Photo Researchers, Inc. 940 ©Salisbury District Hospital/Science Photo Library/Photo Researchers, Inc. 942 ©Image Shop/Phototake 943 ©Will & Deni McIntyre/Photo Researchers, Inc. 948 b. ©Joseph Nettis/Photo Researchers, Inc. 948 t. The Granger Collection, New York 949 b.r. ©Hank Morgan/Science Source/Photo Researchers, Inc. 949 l. AP/Wide World Photos 949 t.r. ABIOMED, Inc 952 ©Yorgos Nikas/Stone 953 ©Dr. Dennis Kunkel/Phototake 956 ©Prof. Motta, Correr & Nottola/University La Sapienza, Rome/Science Photo Library/Photo Researchers, Inc. 959 l. ©PhotoDisc, Inc., 2001 959 r. Custom Medical Stock Photo 960 Pearson Education/PH School 961 ©George Hall/Check Six/PictureQuest 962 ©A. Glauberman/Photo Researchers, Inc. 963 b. ©Science Photo Library/Photo Researchers, Inc. 963 t. ©Science Photo Library/Photo Researchers, Inc. 965 Pearson Education/PH School 966 ©Yorgos Nikas/Stone 967 ©Dr. Dennis Kunkel/Phototake 970 ©Fred Hossler/Visuals Unlimited 971 b. Bob Daemmrich/Stock, Boston 972 b. ©Don & Pat Valenti/DRK Photo 972 t. ©Chris Harvey/Stone 973 t.l. Grant Heilman Photography 973 t.r. United States Department of Agriculture 982 b. Pearson Education/PH School 983 t.r. ©David Scharf/Peter Arnold, Inc. 984 ©Sovereign/Phototake 985 John McDonough/Sports Illustrated 987 ©Lennart Nilsson/The Incredible Machine, Albert Bonniers Forlag AB 990 Pearson Education/PH School 992 b. ©David Scharf/Peter Arnold, Inc. 992 t. Bob Daemmrich/Stock, Boston 996 ©David M. Phillips/Photo Researchers, Inc. 997 ©Jeff Greenberg/Visuals Unlimited 1001 David Young-Wolff/PhotoEdit 1007 ©Sloop-Ober/Visuals Unlimited 1009 Florian Franke/SuperStock 1013 Lennart Nilsson/Albert Bonnier Förlag AB, A CHILD IS BORN, Dell Publishing Company 1015 ©CNRI/Photo Researchers, Inc. 1016 l. The Granger Collection, New York 1016 r. ©Leroy Francis/Photo Researchers, Inc. 1020 ©Dr. Yorgas Nikas/Photo Researchers, Inc. 1021 ©Petit Format/Nestle/Science Source/Photo Researchers, Inc. 1022 b. Keith/Custom Medical Stock Photo 1022 t. ©T. Wiewandt/DRK Photo 1023 b. ©William Campbell/DRK Photo 1023 t. ©Jose Luis Pelaez, Inc./The Stock Market 1024 ©Bob Daemmrich/Stock, Boston/PictureQuest 1025 Pearson Education/PH School 1030 © Juergen Berger/Max-Plank Institute/Science Photo Library/Photo Researchers, Inc. 1031 b. ©Volker Steger/Science Photo Library/Photo Researchers, Inc. 1031 t. ©Carolina Biological Supply/Phototake 1032 ©Microworks/Phototake 1033 b. Fuessl, NEJM.331:301, (1994) 1033 t. ©Oliver Meckes/Photo Researchers, Inc. 1034 ©Mednet/Phototake 1035 ©Oliver Meckes/Photo Researchers, Inc. 1036 Lennart Nilsson/Albert Bonniers Forlag 1040 ©Eye of Science/Photo Researchers, Inc. 1041 Richard Haynes Photography/Pearson Education/PH School 1042 ©Zeva Oelbaum/Peter Arnold, Inc. 1043 l. ©David Scharf/Peter Arnold, Inc. 1043 m. ©David Scharf/Peter Arnold, Inc. 1043 r. ©Oliver Meckes/Ottawa/Photo Researchers, Inc. 1044 ©Rodolfo Gonzalez/Denver Rocky Mountain News/CORBIS Sygma 1045 ©National Institute for Biological Standards and Control, England/Science Photo Library/Photo Researchers, Inc. 1048 Andy Nelson/The Christian Science Monitor 1049 Getty Images, Inc./Liaison Agency 1051 ©David Smart/DRK Photo 1052 ©Dr. Andrejs Liepins/Science Photo Library/Photo Researchers, Inc. 1054 ©Michael Newman/PhotoEdit 1055 Pearson Education/PH School 1061 ©E.R. Degginger/Photo Researchers, Inc. 1062 ©Mark Moffett/Minden Pictures, Inc. 1063 t. ©Nigel Cattlin/Holt Studios Int'l/Photo Researchers, Inc. 1064 l. ©Dan Smith/Stone 1064 r. ©PhotoDisc, Inc., 2001 1065 ©Francois Gohier/Photo Researchers, Inc. 1067 Pearson Education/PH School 1072 b. ©Manfred Kage/Peter Arnold, Inc. 1072 m. ©David Scharf/Peter Arnold, Inc. 1072 t. ©Fr. Westall/Eurelios/Phototake 1073 l. Lee Rentz/Bruce Coleman, Inc. 1073 r. ©Ed Reschke/Peter Arnold, Inc. 1074 l. Geoff Dann/©Dorling Kindersley 1074 r. ©Charles V. Angelo/Photo Researchers, Inc. 1075 l. ©R. Calentine/Visuals Unlimited 1075 r. ©John Cancalosi/DRK Photo 1076 b.l. Animals Animals/©Marian Bacon 1076 b.r. ©William Leonard/DRK Photo 1076 t. ©Labat/Jacana/Photo Researchers, Inc. 1077 b Kevin Schafer 1077 t. Merlin D. Tuttle/Bat Conservation International 1078 Animals Animals/©Jennifer Loomis 1079 ©Sarah J. Frankling/Stone 1081 ©Gerry Ellis/Minden Pictures, Inc. 1084 Animals Animals/©Carroll W. Perkins

Periodic Table of the Elements

	Nonmetals	Metals	Metalloids	
	C	Li	B	Solid
	Br	Hg		Liquid
	H			Gas
		Tc		Not found in nature

1 1A	2 2A	3 3B	4 4B	5 5B	6 6B	7 7B	8 8B	9 8B
1 H Hydrogen 1.0079								
3 Li Lithium 6.941	4 Be Beryllium 9.0122							
11 Na Sodium 22.990	12 Mg Magnesium 24.305							
19 K Potassium 39.098	20 Ca Calcium 40.08	21 Sc Scandium 44.956	22 Ti Titanium 47.90	23 V Vanadium 50.941	24 Cr Chromium 51.996	25 Mn Manganese 54.938	26 Fe Iron 55.847	27 Co Cobalt 58.933
37 Rb Rubidium 85.468	38 Sr Strontium 87.62	39 Y Yttrium 88.906	40 Zr Zirconium 91.22	41 Nb Niobium 92.906	42 Mo Molybdenum 95.94	43 Tc Technetium (98)	44 Ru Ruthenium 101.07	45 Rh Rhodium 102.91
55 Cs Cesium 132.91	56 Ba Barium 137.33	71 Lu Lutetium 174.97	72 Hf Hafnium 178.49	73 Ta Tantalum 180.95	74 W Tungsten 183.85	75 Re Rhenium 186.21	76 Os Osmium 190.2	77 Ir Iridium 192.22
87 Fr Francium (223)	88 Ra Radium (226)	103 Lr Lawrencium (262)	104 Rf Rutherfordium (261)	105 Db Dubnium (262)	106 Sg Seaborgium (263)	107 Bh Bohrium (264)	108 Hs Hassium (265)	109 Mt Meitnerium (268)

Lanthanide Series

57 La Lanthanum 138.91	58 Ce Cerium 140.12	59 Pr Praseodymium 140.91	60 Nd Neodymium 144.24	61 Pm Promethium (145)	62 Sm Samarium 150.4

Actinide Series

89 Ac Actinium (227)	90 Th Thorium 232.04	91 Pa Protactinium 231.04	92 U Uranium 238.03	93 Np Neptunium (237)	94 Pu Plutonium (244)